COLUMBIAN

STAMP COMPANY INC

BUILDING AND BUYING GREAT STAMP COLLECTIONS

HARRY HAGENDORF

DEALER IN RARE STAMPS

700 WHITE PLAINS ROAD SCARSDALE NY 10583 TELEPHONE 914 725 2290 FAX 914 725 2576
E-MAIL: harryhagendorf@aol.com

album accessories

ADVANTAGE STOCK SHEETS

Advantage stock sheets fit directly in your 2-post or 3-ring National or Specialty album. Available with 1 to 8 pockets.

Sheets are sold in packages of 10.

- Stock sheets match album pages in every respect, including size, border, and color.
- Punched to fit perfectly in binder.
- Ideal for storing minor varieties and collateral material. A great place to keep new issues until the next supplement is available.
- Provides the protection of clear acetate pockets on heavyweight pages.

NATIONAL BORDER

Item			Retail	AA*
AD11	1 Pocket	242mm	$19.99	$17.99
AD12	2 Pockets	119mm	$19.99	$17.99
AD13	3 Pockets	79mm	$19.99	$17.99
AD14	4 Pockets	58mm	$19.99	$17.99
AD15	5 Pockets	45mm	$19.99	$17.99
AD16	6 Pockets	37mm	$19.99	$17.99
AD17	7 Pockets	34mm	$19.99	$17.99
AD18	8 Pockets	31mm	$19.99	$17.99

SPECIALTY BORDER

Item			Retail	AA*
AD21	1 Pocket	242mm	$19.99	$17.99
AD22	2 Pockets	119mm	$19.99	$17.99
AD23	3 Pockets	79mm	$19.99	$17.99
AD24	4 Pockets	58mm	$19.99	$17.99
AD25	5 Pockets	45mm	$19.99	$17.99
AD26	6 Pockets	37mm	$19.99	$17.99
AD27	7 Pockets	34mm	$19.99	$17.99
AD28	8 Pockets	31mm	$19.99	$17.99

BLANK PAGES

Ideal for developing your own album pages to be integrated with your album.

SPECIALTY SERIES PAGES (BORDER A)
(20 per pack)

Item		Retail	AA*
ACC110		$7.74	$5.99
ACC111	Quadrille*	$7.74	$5.99

* Graph pattern printed on page.

SPECIALTY/NATIONAL SERIES BINDERS

National series pages are punched for 3-ring and 2-post binders. The 3-ring binder is available in two sizes. The 2-post binder comes in one size. All Scott binders are covered with a tough green leatherette material that is washable and reinforced at stress points for long wear.

3-RING BINDERS & SLIPCASES

With the three ring binder, pages lay flat and the rings make turning the pages easy. The locking mechanism insure that the rings won't pop open even when the binder is full.

Item			Retail	AA*
ACBR01	Small 3-Ring Binder	Holds up to 100 pages	$36.74	$29.99
ACBR03	Large 3-Ring Binder	Holds up to 250 pages	$36.74	$29.99
ACSR01	Small 3-Ring Slipcase.		$29.99	$24.99
ACSR03	Large 3-Ring Slipcase.		$29.99	$24.99

LARGE 2-POST BINDER & SLIPCASE

For the traditional Scott collector, we offer the standard hinge post binder. Scott album pages are punched with rectangular holes that fit on rectangular posts. The posts and pages are held by a rod that slides down from the top. With the post binder pages do not lie flat. However, filler strips are available for a minimal cost.

Item			Retail	AA*
ACBS03	Large 2-Post Binder	Holds up to 250 pages	$52.99	$45.99
ACSS03	Large 2-Post Slipcase		$29.99	$24.99

ALBUM PAGE DIVIDERS

Postage, air post, semi-postals; they're all right at your fingertips with Specialty Album Page Dividers. The dividers are a great way to keep your albums organized and save wear and tear on your pages.

Item		Retail	AA*
ACC145	Package of 10	$4.49	$3.49

NATIONAL SERIES PAGES (BORDER B)
(20 per pack)

Item		Retail	AA*
ACC120		$7.74	$5.99
ACC121	Quadrille*	$7.74	$5.99

PAGE PROTECTORS

Protect your stamps and album pages with clear archival quality plastic sleeve. Sleeves fit over the entire page and protects pages from creasing fingerprints and tears. Scott Page protectors pvc free and thin enough that they won't make your binder bulge. Page Protectors are available two sizes. Sold in packages of 25.

2-Post Minuteman/International Pg Protors

Item	Retail	AA*
ACC165	$13.99	$11.7

National/Specialty Series Pg Protectors*

Item	Retail	AA*
ACC166	$13.99	$11.7

*Punched to fit 2-post and 3-ring binder.

AMOS ADVANTAGE

To Order Call 1-800-572-6885
www.amosadvantage.com

1. AA* prices apply to paid subscribers of *Scott Stamp Monthly* and *Linns*.
2. Prices, terms and product availability subject to change.
3. **Shipping & Handling:**
   United States: 10% of order total. Minimum charge $5.99 Maximum charge $40.00.
   Canada: 15% of order total. Minimum charge $14.99 Maximum charge $45.00.
   Foreign orders are shipped via DHL and billed actual freight. Credit cards only.

SCOTT

2010
Specialized Catalogue of United States Stamps & Covers

EIGHTY-EIGHTH EDITION

CONFEDERATE STATES • CANAL ZONE • DANISH WEST INDIES
GUAM • HAWAII • UNITED NATIONS

UNITED STATES ADMINISTRATION:
Cuba • Puerto Rico • Philippines • Ryukyu Islands

EDITOR	James E. Kloetzel
ASSOCIATE EDITOR	William A. Jones
ASSISTANT EDITOR /NEW ISSUES & VALUING	Martin J. Frankevicz
ASSISTANT EDITOR	Charles Snee
VALUING ANALYST	Steven R. Myers
ADMINISTRATIVE ASSISTANT/IMAGE COORDINATOR	Beth L. Brown
DESIGN MANAGER	Teresa M. Wenrick
ADVERTISING	Angela Nolte
CIRCULATION/PRODUCT PROMOTION MANAGER	Tim Wagner
VICE PRESIDENT/EDITORIAL AND PRODUCTION	Steve Collins
PRESIDENT	William Fay

Released October 2009
Includes New Stamp Listings through the October 2009 *Scott Stamp Monthly* Catalogue Update

Copyright© 2009 by

Scott Publishing Co.

911 Vandemark Road, Sidney, OH 45365-0828
A division of AMOS PRESS, INC., publishers of *Linn's Stamp News, Coin World* and *Scott Stamp Monthly* magazine.

Scott Publishing Mission Statement

The Scott Publishing Team exists to serve the recreational,
educational and commercial hobby needs of stamp collectors and dealers.

We strive to set the industry standard for philatelic information and products by developing and providing goods that help collectors identify, value, organize and present their collections.

Quality customer service is, and will continue to be, our highest priority.
We aspire toward achieving total customer satisfaction.

Scott Publishing Co.

SCOTT
911 VANDEMARK ROAD, SIDNEY, OHIO 45365   937-498-0802

Dear Scott Catalogue User:

Another noteworthy year for value and editorial changes in the Scott Specialized Catalogue of United States Stamps and Covers.

More than 11,000 value changes have been made in the 2010 edition of the U.S. Specialized Catalogue, with 5,800 of these changes being in the Postage section and more than 1,500 in the Revenue sections. Other changes are spread throughout the catalogue, with significant numbers of changes appearing in the First Day Covers, Booklet Panes, Envelopes and Postal Cards, Locals and Carriers, Proofs, Canal Zone, Hawaii, Philippines and United Nations sections.

Unlike many recent years, in which values tended to creep higher throughout the listings, the trends for 2010 are decidedly mixed. This no doubt is the result of the current state of the economy, plus slight changes in collecting habits of philatelists. In general terms, we can say that the trend for unused classic and semi-classic stamps, especially the more common varieties, is slightly down. This is not the case for the true rarities, which continue to trend higher. In the used column of the catalogue, values are trending higher, as more collectors seem to be taking up collecting used stamps rather than further pursuing the often more expensive unused examples.

Not all used stamps move up in value. The 1847 5¢ red brown and 10¢ black first issue, Scott 1-2, drop in value by about ten percent. Scott 1 has moved to $550 used from $600 in the 2009 U.S. Specialized and 2010 Volume 1, while Scott 2 slides to $1,250 used from $1,400. The unused values remain unchanged. More typical of the trends is the 1851 3¢ orange brown, Scott 10, which drops slightly unused to $3,750 from $4,000, but increases in value used to $200 from $160.

One big winner this year in both unused and used conditions is the 1857 3¢ perforated type II stamp, Scott 25A. Try finding one of these unused in dealer stocks or auctions. We tried, and we found just one offered in the last year plus. In unused condition, Scott 25A increases in value to $5,250 from $4,750, and in used condition there is an increase to $550 from $450.

The values for many classic rarities have increased, in many cases substantially. The more important A, B and Z grills increased in value in the 2010 Volume 1 catalogue, and those increases are joined in the U.S. Specialized by such stamps as Scott 28 unused, the 1857 5¢ red brown, type I, which takes an incredible jump to $60,000, from just $10,000 last year. Scott 28b, the bright red brown shade, jumps to $70,000 from just $12,500. The extreme rarity of these stamps in decent condition and with original gum has only recently become apparent in the marketplace.

The trend of lower values for unused stamps becomes quite evident starting with the 1870 Banknote issues and continuing into the 20th century. The weakness is especially noticeable in the early commemorative sets such as the 1893 Columbians, the 1898 Trans-Mississippis and others. Decreases in unused values of 20 percent are not unusual in these sets. That is not true of the used values, however, where increases commonly are seen.

In the modern era, values are fairly steady, with occasional advances seen. Many plate blocks rise in value, and very modern plate blocks from panes of 100 with water activated gum often have increased in value considerably. Examples here are Scott 3616, the 2002 23¢ Washington stamp; Scott 4000, the 2006 24¢ Butterfly stamp; and Scott 4129, the 2007 non-denominated (41¢) Flag stamp. The 2006 Champlain souvenir sheet, Scott 4074, sails to $8.00 from $4.25.

In the back of the book, used values are up in the Offices in China section, and unused values are down in the Parcel Post, Parcel Post Postage Due and Special Handling sections.

What about editorial changes?

Nearly 2,500 illustrations have been replaced by new color scans in this year's volume, more than 1,600 of them in the postage section alone. This includes new scans of images not previously shown, replacements of black-and-white images, and improvements to existing color images that were not up to acceptable quality standards. This was a huge effort involving editorial, scanning and design staff.

New earliest documented uses are noted for Scott 85, 206, 250, 276, 301, 320, 425e and 536. New varieties are listed in the 1943-44 Overrun Countries issues for reverse and partial reverse printings on the 5¢ Belgium stamp, Scott 914, plus double impressions of the black color on the Netherlands stamp, Scott 913, and on the Austria stamp, Scott 919.

A very big change has been put into effect in the way modern tagging varieties are listed. Scott has always listed tagging types separately, and we will continue to do so. Variations such as block tagging, overall tagging, tagging on uncoated paper (embedded tagging) and tagging on coated paper (surface tagging) will still be listed separately. Unfortunately, the look of tagging on very modern coated papers sometimes varies, sometimes giving the appearance of solid tagging, sometimes grainy solid, and sometimes uneven tagging. The problem is that very modern tagging on coated paper that looks uneven has a similar look to the mottled appearance of embedded tagging on uncoated paper, and it has even been called "mottled" until the present change was put into place. From this point forward, any tagged new printing of an issue on coated paper that shows a different appearance will be handled in footnotes rather than as separate lettered listings, and the term "mottled" will be reserved for embedded tagging on uncoated paper. The editors have gone back into previous listings to bring them into conformity with the new style, and this has involved changing some terminology, removing some minor listings, and adding new footnotes where necessary.

Many new error listings appear in 2010, including such interesting types as a new imperforate 1¼¢ turquoise Palace of Governors coil that showed up for the first time at the recent American Philatelic Society Stampshow in Pittsburgh, fully 49 years after the stamp was issued. Another striking new error is the 58¢ Senator Margaret Chase Smith sheet stamp, Scott 3427, with the black omitted (which removes everything but the red "Margaret Chase Smith" from the stamp).

Several important additions have been made the Essays and Proofs sections. In an exciting new find, a new essay has been listed for the almost complete engraving of the 1847 10¢ Washington, a die impression on proof paper with a new major number, Scott 2-E1.

Two completely new sections have been added in the Essays. The first is for the 1864 Henry Lowenberg Decalcomania essays of the 1861-63 2¢-90¢ definitives on goldbeater's skin, now Scott 79-E65P5 to 79-E73P5. Also new is the section of 1867 "Z" grill experimental essays, now Scott 85E-E1a to 85E-E1h. Expect the 3¢ "Z" grill experimentals to appear next year.

In Die and Plate Proofs, interesting progressive proofs of the $3.20 Space Shuttle stamp in magenta only, paired with the $11.75 Piggyback Space Shuttle in cyan only, on both coated and uncoated papers, take their place as Scott 3261P-3262P and varieties. Also in the Proofs section, new listings appear for plate proofs of Duck stamps, Nos. RW26P3-RW30P3 and RW32P3-RW50P3, all on gummed stamp paper, and each the only recorded example. In addition, new small die proofs have been added as Nos. RW13P2-RW23P2, also not previously recorded.

In Confederate States, eight new listings for Postmasters' Provisionals have been added, a large number for one catalogue season.

For these and other catalogue changes for 2010, see the 2010 U.S. Specialized additions, deletions & number changes list on page 85A.

A hobby is a great gift. Enjoy.

James E Kloetzel

James E. Kloetzel/Catalogue Editor

Table of contents

Entries in this subsection are arranged alphabetically to facilitate use. Where applicable, the Scott number prefix or consistent suffix for a section is included in parentheses.

Acknowledgments

Our appreciation and gratitude go to the following individuals and organizations who have assisted us in preparing information included in this year's edition of the Scott Specialized Catalogue of U.S. Stamps and Covers. Some helpers prefer anonymity. Those individuals have generously shared their stamp knowledge with others through the medium of the Scott Catalogue.

Those who follow provided information that is in addition to the hundreds of dealer price lists and advertisements and scores of auction catalogues and realizations which were used in producing the Catalogue Values provided herein. It is from those noted here that we have been able to obtain information on items not normally seen in published lists and advertisements. Support from these people of course goes beyond data leading to Catalogue Values, for they also are key to editorial changes.

Michael E. Aldrich (Michael E. Aldrich, Inc.)
Roland Austin
Steven R. Belasco
Alan Berkun
John Birkinbine II
Charles R. Biro
Brian M. Bleckwenn
Victor Bove (AVB Stamps)
John D. Bowman (Carriers and Locals Society)
Lawrence A. Bustillo (Suburban Stamp Inc.)
James R. Callis, Jr. (Precancel Stamp Society)
A. Bryan Camarda (University Stamp Co.)
Alan C. Campbell
Gil Celli (Gold Mine Cover Co.)
Richard A. Champagne (Richard A. Champagne, Ltd.)
Leroy P. Collins III (United Postal Stationery Society)
Harry Corrigan
Francis J. Crown, Jr.
Tony L. Crumbley (Carolina Coin & Stamp, Inc.)
Stephen R. Datz
Charles Deaton
Kenneth E. Diehl
Bob Dumaine (Sam Houston Philatelics)
Mark Eastzer (Markest Stamp Co.)

Jeremiah Farrington
Henry Fisher
Jeffrey M. Forster
Robert S. Freeman
Marvin Frey
Richard Friedberg
Melvin Getlan
Stan Goldfarb
Marty Graff
Bruce Hecht (Bruce L. Hecht Co.)
Robert R. Hegland
Steven Hines
Peter Hoffman
Doug Iams
Tom Jacks (Mountainside Stamps)
Eric Jackson
Allan Katz (Ventura Stamp Co.)
Lewis Kaufman (The Philatelic Foundation)
Patricia A. Kaufmann (Confederate Stamp Alliance)
Jim Kotanchik
Maurice J. Landry (Maurice J. Landry Covers)
Lester C. Lanphear III
John L. Larson
Richard L. Lazorow (The Plate Block Stamp Co.)
James E. Lee
John R. Lewis (The William Henry Stamp Co.)
William A. Litle

Larry Lyons
Robert L. Markovits (Quality Investors, Ltd.)
Frank Marrelli (F & M Stamps)
Peter Martin
William K. McDaniel
Timothy M. McRee
Allen Mintz
Gary Morris (Pacific Midwest Co.)
Peter Mosiondz, Jr.
Bruce M. Moyer (Moyer Stamps & Collectibles)
Joseph M. Napp
James Natale
Gerald Nylander
Michael O. Perry
Stanley M. Piller (Stanley M. Piller & Associates)
Peter W. W. Powell
Louis E. Repeta
Martin D. Richardson
Peter A. Robertson
Peter Robin
Robert G. Rufe
Richard H. Salz
Byron Sandfield (Park Cities Stamps)
Alex Schauss (Schauss Philatelics)
Jacques C. Schiff, Jr. (Jacques C. Schiff, Jr., Inc.)
Terry R. Scott

Charles F. Shreve (Spink Shreves Galleries)
Merle Spencer (The Stamp Gallery)
Frank J. Stanley, III
Philip & Henry Stevens (postalstationery.com)
Gordon Stimmell
Stephen L. Suffet
Jerry Summers
Alan Thomson (Plate Number Coil Collectors Club)
David R. Torre
Scott R. Trepel (Robert A. Siegel Auction Galleries, Inc.)
Steven R. Unkrich
George P. Wagner
Philip T. Wall
Larry S. Weiss
William R. Weiss, Jr. (Weiss Philatelics)
Robert Wurdeman
Robert F. Yacano (K-Line Philippines)
Dr. Clarke Yarbrough
John P. Zuckerman (Robert A. Siegel Auction Galleries, Inc.)

Expertizing Services

The following organizations will, for a fee, provide expert opinions about stamps submitted to them. Collectors should contact these organizations to find out about their fees and requirements before submitting philatelic material to them. The listing of these groups here is not intended as an endorsement by Scott Publishing Co.

General Expertizing Services

American Philatelic Expertizing Service (a service of the American Philatelic Society)
100 Match Factory Place
Bellefonte PA 16823-1367
Ph: (814) 933-3803
Fax: (814) 933-6128
www.stamps.org
E-mail: apsinfo@stamps.org

Philatelic Foundation
70 West 40th St., 15th Floor
New York NY 10018
Ph: (212) 221-6555
Fax: (212) 221-6208
www.philatelicfoundation.org
E-mail:
philatelicfoundation@verizon.net

Philatelic Stamp Authentication and Grading, Inc.
PO Box 56-2111
Miami FL 33256-2111
Customer Service: (305) 345-9864
www.stampauthentication.com
E-mail:
info@stampauthentication.com

Professional Stamp Experts
PO Box 6170
Newport Beach CA 92658
Ph: (877) STAMP-88
Fax: (949) 833-7955
www.psestamp.com
E-mail: pseinfo@collectors.com

Expertizing Services Covering Specific Fields Or Countries

American First Day Cover Society Expertizing Committee
P.O. Box 141379
Columbus, OH 43214

Confederate Stamp Alliance Authentication Service
Gen. Frank Crown, Jr.
PO Box 278
Capshaw AL 35742-0396
Ph: (302) 422-2656
Fax: (302) 424-1990
www.csalliance.org
E-mail: csaas@knology.net

Errors, Freaks and Oddities Collectors Club Expertizing Service
138 East Lakemont Dr.
Kingsland GA 31548
Ph: (912) 729-1573

Hawaiian Philatelic Society Expertizing Service
PO Box 10115
Honolulu HI 96816-0115

Addresses, Telephone Numbers & E-Mail Addresses of General & Specialized Philatelic Societies

Collectors can contact the following groups for information about the philately of the areas within the scope of these societies, or inquire about membership in these groups. Many more specialized philatelic societies exist than those listed below. Aside from the general societies, we limit this list to groups which specialize in areas covered by the Scott U.S. Specialized Catalogue. These addresses were compiled two months prior to publication, and are, to the best of our knowledge, correct and current. Groups should inform the editors of address changes whenever they occur. The editors also want to hear from other such specialized groups not listed.

American Air Mail Society
Stephen Reinhard
P.O. Box 110
Mineola NY 11501
www.americanairmailsociety.org
E-mail: sreinhard1@optonline.net

American First Day Cover Society
Douglas Kelsey
P.O. Box 16277
Tucson AZ 85732-6277
Ph: (520) 321-0880
http://www.afdcs.org
E-mail: afdcs@aol.com

American Philatelic Society
100 Match Factory Place
Bellefonte PA 16823-1367
Ph: (814) 933-3803
http://www.stamps.org
E-mail: apsinfo@stamps.org

American Revenue Association
Eric Jackson
P.O. Box 728
Leesport PA 19533-0728
Ph: (610) 926-6200
http://www.revenuer.org
E-mail: eric@revenuer.com

American Society for Philatelic
Pages and Panels
Gerald N. Blankenship
539 North Gum Gully
Crosby TX 77532
Ph: (281) 324-2709
www.asppp.org
E-mail: membership@asppp.org

American Stamp Dealers
Association
Joe Savarese
3 School St., Suite #205
Glen Cove NY 11542
Ph: (516) 759-7000
http://www.asdaonline.com
E-mail: asda@erols.com

American Topical Association
Ray E. Cartier
P.O. Box 57
Arlington TX 76004-0057
Ph: (817) 274-1181
http://americantopicalassn.org
E-mail: americantopical@msn.com

Canal Zone Study Group
Richard H. Salz
60 27th Ave.
San Francisco CA 94121

Carriers and Locals Society
John D. Bowman
PO Box 74
Grosse Ile. MI 48138
http://www.pennypost.org
E-mail: jbowman@stx.rr.net

Christmas Seal & Charity Stamp
Society
John Denune
234 East Broadway
Granville OH 43023
Ph: (740) 587-0276
http://cscss.home.att.net
E-mail: jdenune@roadrunner.com

Confederate Stamp Alliance
Gen. Francis J. Crown
PO Box 278
Capshaw AL 35742-0278
www.csalliance.org
E-mail: csaas@knology.org

Errors, Freaks, and Oddities
Collectors Club
Stan Raugh
4217 8th Avenue
Temple PA 19560
Ph: (610) 921-5717
www.efocc.org
E-mail: trex@bigplanet.com

Hawaiian Philatelic Society
Kay H. Hoke
P.O. Box 10115
Honolulu HI 96816-0115
Ph: (808) 521-5721
E-mail: bannan@pixi.com

International Philippine Philatelic
Society
Robert F. Yacano
P.O. Box 100
Toast NC 27049
Ph: (336) 783-0768
E-mail: ryacano@triad.rr.com

International Society of Reply
Coupon Collectors
Peter Robin
P.O. Box 353
Bala Cynwyd PA 19004
E-mail: peterrobin@att.net

National Duck Stamp Collectors
Society
Anthony J. Monico
P.O. Box 43
Harleysville PA 19438-0043
http://www.ndscs.org
E-mail: ndscs@hwcn.org

National Stamp Dealers
Association
Dick Keiser, President
2916 NW Bucklin Hill Rd., #136
Silverdale WA 98383-8514
Ph: (800) 875-6633
www.nsdainc.org
E-mail: gail@nsdainc.org

Perfins Club
Jerry Hejduk
PO Box 490450
Leesburg FL 34749-0450
Ph: (352) 326-2117
E-mail: flprepers@comcast.net

Plate Number Coil Collectors
Club
Ronald E. Maifeld
P.O. Box 54622
Cincinnati OH 45254-0622
http://www.pnc3.org
E-mail: ron.maifeld@pnc3.org

Post Mark Collectors Club
Dave Proulx
7629 Homestead Dr.
Baldwinsville NY 13207
www.postmarks.org
E-mail: stampdance@yahoo.com

Postal History Society
Kalman V. Illyefalvi
869 Bridgewater Dr.
New Oxford PA 17350-8206
Ph: (717) 624-5941
www.stampclubs.com
E-mail: kalphyl@uno.com

Precancel Stamp Society
Arthur Damm
176 Bent Pine Hill
North Wales PA 19454
Ph: (215) 368-6082
E-mail: psspromosec@comcast.net

Ryukyu Philatelic Specialists
Society
Laura Edmonds, Sec'y
P.O. Box 240177
Charlotte NC 28224-0177
Ph: (704) 519-5157
www.ryukyustamps.org
E-mail:
secretary@ryukyustamps.org

Souvenir Card Collectors Society
Dana Marr
P.O. Box 4155
Tulsa OK 74159-0155
Ph: (918) 585-9199
E-mail: dmarr5569@aol.com

State Revenue Society
Harold Effner, Jr.
27 Pine St.
Lincroft NJ 07738
www.staterevenue.org
E-mail: staterevs@comcast.net

United Nations Philatelists
Blanton Clement, Jr.
P. O. Box 146
Morrisville PA 19067-0146
http://www.unpi.com
E-mail: bclemjr@yahoo.com

United Postal Stationery Society
Stuart Leven
1445-50 Foxworthy Ave., #187
San Jose CA 95118-1119
http://www.upss.org
E-mail: postat@gmail.com

U.S. Cancellation Club
Roger Rhoads
6160 Brownstone Ct.
Mentor OH 44060
http://www.geocities.com/athens/2088/uscchome.html
E-mail: rrrhoads@aol.com

U.S. Philatelic Classics Society
Rob Lund
2913 Fulton
Everett WA 98201-3733
http://www.uspcs.org
E-mail:
membershipchairman@uspcs.org

U.S. Possessions Philatelic Society
Geoffrey Brewster
6453 East Stallion Rd.
Paradise Valley AZ 85253-3151
Ph: (480) 607-7184

United States Stamp Society
Executive Secretary
P.O. Box 6634
Katy TX 77491-6634
http://www.usstamps.org
E-mail: webmaster@usstamps.org

Information on Catalogue Values, Grade and Condition

Catalogue Value

The Scott Catalogue value is a retail value; that is, an amount you could expect to pay for a stamp in the grade of Very Fine with no faults. Any exceptions to the grade valued will be noted in the text. The general introduction on the following pages and the individual section introductions further explain the type of material that is valued. The value listed for any given stamp is a reference that reflects recent actual dealer selling prices for that item.

Dealer retail price lists, public auction results, published prices in advertising and individual solicitation of retail prices from dealers, collectors and specialty organizations have been used in establishing the values found in this catalogue. Scott Publishing Co. values stamps, but Scott is not a company engaged in the business of buying and selling stamps as a dealer.

Use this catalogue as a guide for buying and selling. The actual price you pay for a stamp may be higher or lower than the catalogue value because of many different factors, including the amount of personal service a dealer offers, or increased or decreased interest in the country or topic represented by a stamp or set. An item may occasionally be offered at a lower price as a "loss leader," or as part of a special sale. You also may obtain an item inexpensively at public auction because of little interest at that time or as part of a large lot.

Stamps that are of a lesser grade than Very Fine, or those with condition problems, generally trade at lower prices than the values shown in this catalogue. Stamps of exceptional quality in both grade and condition often command higher prices than the values listed.

Values for pre-1900 unused issues are for stamps with approximately half or more of their original gum. Stamps with most or all of their original gum may be expected to sell for more, and stamps with less than half of their original gum may be expected to sell for somewhat less than the values listed. On rarer stamps, it may be expected that the original gum will be somewhat more disturbed than it will be on more common issues. Post-1900 unused issues are assumed to have full original gum. From breakpoints in most countries' listings, stamps are valued as never hinged, due to the wide availability of stamps in that condition. These notations are prominently placed in the listings and in the country information preceding the listings. Some countries also feature listings with dual values for hinged and never-hinged stamps.

Grade

A stamp's grade and condition are crucial to its value. The accompanying illustrations show examples of Very Fine stamps from different time periods, along with examples of stamps in Fine to Very Fine and Extremely Fine grades as points of reference. When a stamp seller offers a stamp in any grade from fine to superb without further qualifying statements, that stamp should not only have the centering grade as defined, but it also should be free of faults or other condition problems.

FINE stamps (illustrations not shown) have designs that are noticeably off center on two sides. Imperforate stamps may have small margins, and earlier issues may show the design touching one edge of the stamp design. For perforated stamps, perfs may barely clear the design on one side, and very early issues normally will have the perforations slightly cutting into the design. Used stamps may have heavier than usual cancellations.

FINE-VERY FINE stamps may be somewhat off center on one side, or slightly off center on two sides. Imperforate stamps will have two margins of at least normal size, and the design will not touch any edge. For perforated stamps, the perfs are well clear of the design, but are still noticeably off center. *However, early issues of a country may be printed in such a way that the design naturally is very close to the edges. In these cases, the perforations may cut into the design very slightly.* Used stamps will not have a cancellation that detracts from the design.

VERY FINE stamps may be slightly off center on one or two sides, but the design will be well clear of the edge. The stamp will present a nice, balanced appearance. Imperforate stamps will have three normal-sized margins. *However, early issues of many countries may be printed in such a way that the perforations may touch the design on one or more sides. Where this is the case, a boxed note will be found defining the centering and margins of the stamps being valued.* Used stamps will have light or otherwise neat cancellations. This is the grade used to establish Scott Catalogue values.

EXTREMELY FINE stamps are close to being perfectly centered. Imperforate stamps will have even margins that are larger than normal. Even the earliest perforated issues will have perforations clear of the design on all sides.

Scott Publishing Co. recognizes that there is no formally enforced grading scheme for postage stamps, and that the final price you pay or obtain for a stamp will be determined by individual agreement at the time of transaction.

Condition

Grade addresses only centering and (for used stamps) cancellation. *Condition* refers to factors other than grade that affect a stamp's desirability.

Factors that can increase the value of a stamp include exceptionally wide margins, particularly fresh color, the presence of selvage, and plate or die varieties. Unusual cancels on used stamps (particularly those of the 19th century) can greatly enhance their value as well.

Factors other than faults that decrease the value of a stamp include loss of original gum, regumming, a hinge remnant or foreign object adhering to the gum, natural inclusions, straight edges, and markings or notations applied by collectors or dealers.

Faults include missing pieces, tears, pin or other holes, surface scuffs, thin spots, creases, toning, short or pulled perforations, clipped perforations, oxidation or other forms of color changelings, soiling, stains, and such man-made changes as reperforations or the chemical removal or lightening of a cancellation.

Grading Illustrations

On the following page are illustrations of 11 different representative stamps from various time periods, 1847 to the modern era. Beginning with the 1847 10¢ Washington, examples are shown from the 1851-57 imperforates, two examples from the difficult 1857-61 perforated issues, a Black Jack representative of the 1861-67 issues, a Franklin stamp from the 1869 issue, a Bank Note stamp representative of the 1870-88 issues, an 1898 commemorative, a stamp from the 1902-03 issue, a representative 1908-22 Washington-Franklin design, and a 20th century definitive from the 1922 issue.

The editors believe these illustrations will prove useful in showing the margin size and centering that will be seen in the different time periods of U.S. stamp production.

In addition to the matters of margin size and centering, collectors are reminded that the very fine stamps valued in the Scott catalogues also will possess fresh color and intact perforations, and they will be free from defects.

Examples shown are computer-manipulated images made from single digitized master illustrations.

Stamp Illustrations Used in the Catalogue

It is important to note that the stamp images used for identification purposes in this catalogue may not be indicative of the grade of stamp being valued. Refer to the written discussion of grades on this page and to the grading illustrations on the following two pages for grading information.

	1847 ISSUE	1851-57 ISSUES	1857-61 ISSUES	1857-61 ISSUES	1861-67 ISSUES	1869 ISSUE
Fine-Very Fine →						
SCOTT CATALOGUES VALUE STAMPS IN THIS GRADE **Very Fine** →						
Extremely Fine →						

	1870-88 ISSUES	1898 TRANS-MISSISSIPPIS	1902-03 ISSUES	1908-20 WASHINGTON-FRANKLIN ISSUES	1922-25 ISSUES
Fine-Very Fine →					
SCOTT CATALOGUES VALUE STAMPS IN THIS GRADE **Very Fine** →					
Extremely Fine →					

For purposes of helping to determine the gum condition and value of an unused stamp, Scott Publishing Co. presents the following chart which details different gum conditions and indicates how the conditions correlate with the Scott values for unused stamps. Used together, the Illustrated Grading Chart on the previous page and this Illustrated Gum Chart should allow catalogue users to better understand the grade and gum condition of stamps valued in the *Scott U.S. Specialized Catalogue.*

Gum Categories:	MINT N.H.	ORIGINAL GUM (O.G.)				NO GUM
	Mint Never Hinged *Free from any disturbance*	**Lightly Hinged** *Faint impression of a removed hinge over a small area*	**Hinge Mark or Remnant** *Prominent hinged spot with part or all of the hinge remaining*	**Large part o.g.** *Approximately half or more of the gum intact*	**Small part o.g.** *Approximately less than half of the gum intact*	**No gum** *Only if issued with gum*
Commonly Used Symbol:	★★	★	★	★	★	(★)
PRE-1879 ISSUES	*Very fine pre-1890 stamps in these categories trade at a premium over Scott value*			Scott Value for "Unused"		Scott "No Gum" Values thru No. 218
1879-1935 ISSUES	Scott "Never Hinged" Values for Nos. 182-771	Scott Value for "Unused" (Actual value will be affected by the degree of hinging of the full o.g.)				
1935 TO DATE	Scott Value for "Unused"					

Never Hinged (NH; ★★): A never-hinged stamp will have full original gum that will have no hinge mark or disturbance. The presence of an expertizer's mark does not disqualify a stamp from this designation.

Original Gum (OG; ★): Pre-1890 stamps should have approximately half or more of their original gum. On rarer stamps, it may be expected that the original gum will be somewhat more disturbed than it will be on more common issues. Stamps issued in 1890 or later should have full original gum. Original gum will show some disturbance caused by a previous hinge(s) which may be present or entirely removed. The actual value of an 1890 or later stamp will be affected by the degree of hinging of the full original gum.

Disturbed Original Gum: Gum showing noticeable effects of humidity, climate or hinging over more than half of the gum. The significance of gum disturbance in valuing a stamp in any of the Original Gum categories depends on the degree of disturbance, the rarity and normal gum condition of the issue and other variables affecting quality.

Regummed (RG; (★)): A regummed stamp is a stamp without gum that has had some type of gum privately applied at a time after it was issued. This normally is done to deceive collectors and/or dealers into thinking that the stamp has original gum and therefore has a higher value. A regummed stamp is considered the same as a stamp with none of its original gum for purposes of grading.

IMPORTANT INFORMATION REGARDING VALUES FOR NEVER-HINGED STAMPS

Collectors should be aware that the values given for never-hinged stamps from No. 182 on are for stamps in the grade of very fine. The never-hinged premium as a percentage of value will be larger for stamps in extremely fine or superb grades, and the premium will be smaller for fine-very-fine, fine or poor examples. This is particularly true of the issues of the late-19th and early 20th centuries. For example, in the grade of very fine, an unused stamp from this time period may be valued at $100 hinged and $200 never hinged. The never-hinged premium is thus 100%. But in a grade of extremely fine, this same stamp will not only sell for more hinged, but the never-hinged premium will increase, perhaps to 200%-400% or more over the higher extremely fine value. In a grade of superb, a hinged copy will sell for much more than a very fine copy, and additionally the never-hinged premium will be much larger, perhaps as large as 500%-1,000%. On the other hand, the same stamp in a grade of fine or fine-very-fine not only will sell for less than a very fine stamp in hinged condition, but additionally the never-hinged premium will be smaller than the never-hinged premium on a very fine stamp, perhaps as small as 15%-30%.

Please note that the above statements and percentages are NOT a formula for arriving at the values of stamps in hinged or never-hinged condition in the grades of very good, fine, fine to very fine, extremely fine or superb. The percentages given apply only to the size of the premium for never-hinged condition that might be added to the stamp value for hinged condition. Further, the percentages given are only generalized estimates. Some stamps or grades may have percentages for never-hinged condition that are higher or lower than the ranges given. For values of the most popular U.S. stamps in the grades of very good, fine, fine to very fine, very fine to extremely fine, extremely fine, extremely fine to superb and superb, see the *Scott United States Specialized Valuing Supplement,* updated and issued twice each year in April and October.

Never-Hinged Plate Blocks

Values given for never-hinged plate blocks are for blocks in which all stamps have original gum that has never been hinged and has no disturbances, and all selvage, whether gummed or ungummed, has never been hinged.

Catalogue Values for Stamps on Covers

Definition of a Cover

Covers are philatelically defined as folded letters, folded covers or envelopes, with or without postage stamps, that have passed through the mail and bear postal or other markings of philatelic interest. Before the introduction of envelopes about 1840, people folded letters and wrote the address on the outside. Used stamped envelopes and wrappers and other items of postal stationery also are considered covers, as is a postage stamp used on a post card.

Catalogue Value

The Scott Catalogue value for a stamp on cover, as for a stamp off cover, is a retail value; that is, an amount you could expect to pay for that cover in a grade of Very Fine, as defined below. Folded letters, folded covers, envelopes, stationery entires and newspapers are valued as whole and complete, not as fronts of letter sheets or envelopes or as fragments of newspapers or circulars. Values given are for covers bearing stamps that are "tied on" by the cancellation. A stamp is said to be "tied" to a cover when the cancellation or postmark falls on both the stamp and the cover. Exceptions always will be noted. Values for bisected stamps on cover are for items on which the cancellation ties the stamp across the cut. Values for U.S. patriotic covers of the Civil War period (bearing pictorial designs of a patriotic nature) are for the most common designs.

It should be noted that conventions observed for calculating the catalogue value of a cover with several different stamps vary somewhat between types of covers. In a general way, however, the most common procedure may be summarized as follows: the stamp which has the highest "value on cover" is counted with its on-cover value, while the other stamps are added on to the total with their normal value as used stamps "off cover."

The value generally is given for the stamps as they are most commonly found on a cover. In some cases a stamp is most commonly found alone, paying a specified rate for the envelope, given its weight, destination and method of intended delivery. For instance, beginning July 1, 1863, and continuing through September 30, 1883, a one-half ounce letter sent domestically by ordinary first-class mail required three cents postage. Because such letters were very common, it follows that stamps with denominations of three cents are most often found on envelopes paying that one-half ounce domestic rate. Three-cent stamps also are found on letters together with other stamps making up different rates. A pair of three-cent stamps paid for a one-ounce domestic letter, four three-cent stamps paid for a one-ounce letter addressed to England (rate effective January 1, 1870, through June 30, 1875), and so forth. Because letters addressed abroad are less common than letters addressed domestically, the on-cover value of the three-cent stamps refers to the single usage. That is not true in all instances, because there are some stamps issued during the 19th century that are more scarce used singly than in combination with other stamps. In all these other cases, the value given is for the least scarce of the combinations. For most stamps issued during 1922-31, the value is for a specific use. For example, the value for the 1922 15-cent Statue of Liberty stamp (Scott 566) is for that stamp on a registered cover with a two-cent stamp, to pay the two-cent domestic first-class letter rate and 15-cent registry fee.

If the value of a single stamp on a cover is of particular philatelic importance, as in the case of certain stamps used to pay for reduced rates for the delivery of newspapers or other printed matter, then their different value for this use may be indicated in footnotes or as a separate listing. For example, the 3-cent George Washington stamp of 1851 (Scott 10) is specifically valued paying the 3-cent rate for a circular mailed a distance of 1,000 miles to 1,500 miles from the point of mailing. It clearly is impossible to add to a specialized catalogue of U.S. stamps the detailed information regarding the relative scarcity and value of all rates and combinations. We have limited ourselves to some of the more noteworthy and important cases.

In the majority of cases, the value of a cover assumes that the stamps on it have been used in the period contemporaneous with their issuance. Late uses are sometimes considered premium items, but in most cases late and very late uses are of no significance and detract from the value of the cover.

Condition

When evaluating a cover, care must be given to the factors that determine the overall condition of the item. It is generally more difficult to grade and evaluate a cover than a stamp. The condition of the stamps affixed to the cover must be taken into account — always in relation to the criteria for the particular issue. The Scott Catalogue does specify the grade and condition of the stamps for which a value is given, so it is important to consult this information. In addition, the condition of the cover must be taken into account. Values are for covers that are reasonably well preserved given the period of usage and the country of origin. A tiny nick or tear, or slight reduction from opening, are normal for 19th century covers. Folded letters may be expected to have tears on the reverse from opening, and often they will have file folds. Unless these factors affect the stamps or postal markings, they should not detract from the on-cover values given in the catalogue.

Just as with stamps, various factors can lower the value of a cover. Missing pieces, serious tears, holes, creases, toning, stains and alterations of postal markings are examples of factors that lower the value of a cover. The necessity of considering these factors for the cover, as well as having to consider the condition of the stamps on the cover, helps to explain why it is more difficult to determine the value of a cover than a stamp off cover.

Factors Enhancing the Value of a Cover

A further difficulty in the valuation of covers is the necessity of considering factors other than the stamps used on a cover and the condition of the stamps and the cover. As stated previously, catalogue values listed herein generally reflect the most common uses of stamps on covers that are reasonably well preserved given the period of usage. Consideration of factors that may enhance the value of covers for the most part is beyond the scope of the Scott Catalogue. However, it is critical to understand that there are many such factors. Following is a list of many of the factors that often will increase the value of a cover.

- postal markings indicating origin, transit and arrival;
- postal markings indicating rates paid, which include postage, registration, acknowledgment of receipt, express charges, insurance, postage due, forwarding and many others;
- postal markings indicating carriers such as stagecoaches, trains, ships, aircraft, etc.;
- markings applied by censors, other civilian or military authorities, and others;
- scarce or rare destinations and routings;
- interruptions in the delivery system due to accidents, wars, natural calamities, etc.;
- unusual combinations of stamps;
- printed or hand-drawn pictorial, advertising or patriotic cover designs;
- unusual quality of stamps, postal markings or cover;
- and, outside of postal history, particularly noteworthy addressee, sender or contents.

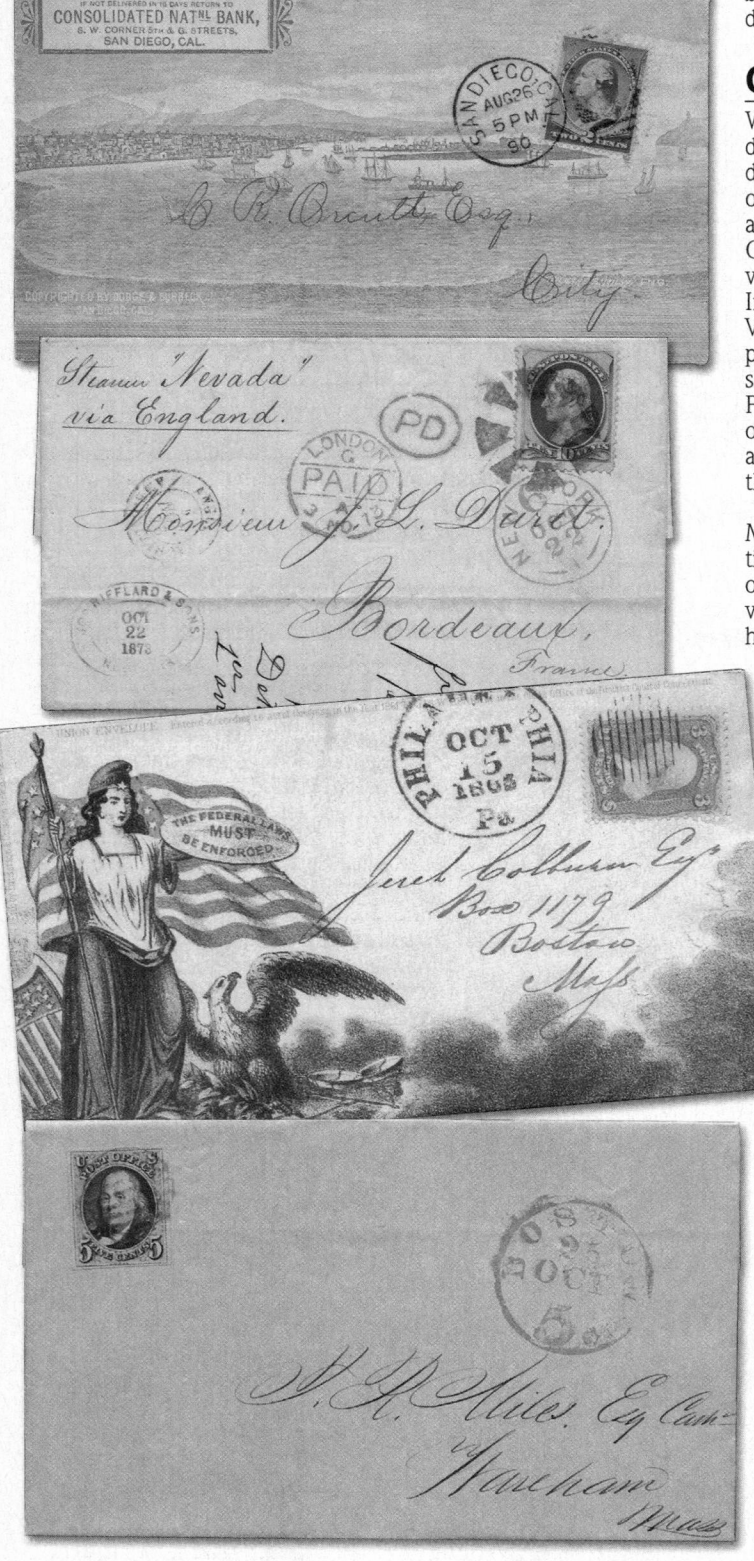

Catalogue Listing Policy

It is the intent of Scott Publishing Co. to list all postage stamps of the world in the *Scott Standard Postage Stamp Catalogue*. The only strict criteria for listing is that stamps be decreed legal for postage by the issuing country and that the issuing country actually have an operating postal system. Whether the primary intent of issuing a given stamp or set was for sale to postal patrons or to stamp collectors is not part of our listing criteria. Scott's role is to provide basic comprehensive postage stamp information. It is up to each stamp collector to choose which items to include in a collection.

It is Scott's objective to seek reasons why a stamp should be listed, rather than why it should not. Nevertheless, there are certain types of items that will not be listed. These include the following:

1. Unissued items that are not officially distributed or released by the issuing postal authority. If such items are officially issued at a later date by the country, they will be listed. Unissued items consist of those that have been printed and then held from sale for reasons such as change in government, errors found on stamps or something deemed objectionable about a stamp subject or design.

2. Stamps "issued" by non-existent postal entities or fantasy countries, such as Nagaland, Occusi-Ambeno, Staffa, Sedang, Torres Straits and others. Also, stamps "issued" in the names of legitimate, stamp-issuing countries that are not authorized by those countries.

3. Semi-official or unofficial items not required for postage. Examples include items issued by private agencies for their own express services. When such items are required for delivery, or are valid as prepayment of postage, they are listed.

4. Local stamps issued for local use only. Postage stamps issued by governments specifically for "domestic" use, such as Haiti Scott 219-228, or the United States non-denominated stamps, are not considered to be locals, since they are valid for postage throughout the country of origin.

5. Items not valid for postal use. For example, a few countries have issued souvenir sheets that are not valid for postage. This area also includes a number of worldwide charity labels (some denominated) that do not pay postage.

6. Intentional varieties, such as imperforate stamps that look like their perforated counterparts and are usually issued in very small quantities. Also, other egregiously exploitative issues such as stamps sold for far more than face value, stamps purposefully issued in artificially small quantities or only against advance orders, stamps awarded only to a selected audience such as a philatelic bureau's standing order customers, or stamps sold only in conjunction with other products. All of these kinds of items are usually controlled issues and/or are intended for speculation. These items normally will be included in footnotes.

7. Items distributed by the issuing government only to a limited group, such as a stamp club, philatelic exhibition or a single stamp dealer, or other private company. These items normally will be included in a footnote.

The fact that a stamp has been used successfully as postage, even on international mail, is not in itself sufficient proof that it was legitimately issued. Numerous examples of so-called stamps from non-existent countries are known to have been used to post letters that have successfully passed through the international mail system.

There are certain items that are subject to interpretation. When a stamp falls outside our specifications, it may be listed along with a cautionary footnote.

A number of factors are considered in our approach to analyzing how a stamp is listed. The following list of factors is presented to share with you, the catalogue user, the complexity of the listing process.

Additional printings — "Additional printings" of a previously issued stamp may range from an item that is totally different to cases where it is impossible to differentiate from the original. At least a minor number (a small-letter suffix) is assigned if there is a distinct change in stamp shade, noticeably redrawn design, or a significantly different perforation measurement. A major number (numeral or numeral and capital-letter combination) is assigned if the editors feel the "additional printing" is sufficiently different from the original that it constitutes a different issue.

Commemoratives — Where practical, commemoratives with the same theme are placed in a set. For example, the U.S. Civil War Centennial set of 1961-65 and the Constitution Bicentennial series of 1989-90 appear as sets. Countries such as Japan and Korea issue such material on a regular basis, with an announced, or at least predictable, number of stamps known in advance. Occasionally, however, stamp sets that were released over a period of years have been separated. Appropriately placed footnotes will guide you to each set's continuation.

Definitive sets — Blocks of numbers generally have been reserved for definitive sets, based on previous experience with any given country. If a few more stamps were issued in a set than originally expected, they often have been inserted into the original set with a capital-letter suffix, such as U.S. Scott 1059A. If it appears that many more stamps than the originally allotted block will be released before the set is completed, a new block of numbers will be reserved, with the original one being closed off. In some cases, such as the U.S. Transportation and Great Americans series, several blocks of numbers exist. Appropriately placed footnotes will guide you to each set's continuation.

New country — Membership in the Universal Postal Union is not a consideration for listing status or order of placement within the catalogue. The index will tell you in what volume or page number the listings begin.

"No release date" items — The amount of information available for any given stamp issue varies greatly from country to country and even from time to time. Extremely comprehensive information about new stamps is available from some countries well before the stamps are released. By contrast some countries do not provide information about stamps or release dates. Most countries, however, fall between these extremes. A country may provide denominations or subjects of stamps from upcoming issues that are not issued as planned. Sometimes, philatelic agencies, those private firms hired to represent countries, add these later-issued items to sets well after the formal release date. This time period can range from weeks to years. If these items were officially released by the country, they will be added to the appropriate spot in the set. In many cases, the specific release date of a stamp or set of stamps may never be known.

Overprints — The color of an overprint is always noted if it is other than black. Where more than one color of ink has been used on overprints of a single set, the color used is noted. Early overprint and surcharge illustrations were altered to prevent their use by forgers.

Se-tenants — Connected stamps of differing features (se-tenants) will be listed in the format most commonly collected. This includes pairs, blocks or larger multiples. Se-tenant units are not always symmetrical. An example is Australia Scott 508, which is a block of seven stamps. If the stamps are primarily collected as a unit, the major number may be assigned to the multiple, with minors going to each component stamp. In cases where continuous-design or other unit se-tenants will receive significant postal use, each stamp is given a major Scott number listing. This includes issues from the United States, Canada, Germany and Great Britain, for example.

Understanding the Listings

On the opposite page is an enlarged "typical" listing from this cata-logue. Following are detailed explanations of each of the highlighted parts of the listing.

1 **Scott number** — Stamp collectors use Scott numbers to identify specific stamps when buying, selling, or trading stamps, and for ease in organizing their collections. Each stamp issued by a country has a unique number. Therefore, U.S. Scott 219 can only refer to a single stamp. Although the Scott Catalogue usually lists stamps in chronological order by date of issue, when a country issues a set of stamps over a period of time the stamps within that set are kept together without regard to date of issue. This follows the normal collecting approach of keeping stamps in their natural sets.

When a country is known to be issuing a set of stamps over a period of time, a group of consecutive catalogue numbers is reserved for the stamps in that set, as issued. If that group of numbers proves to be too few, capital-letter suffixes are added to numbers to create enough catalogue numbers to cover all items in the set. Scott uses a suffix letter, e.g., "A," "b," etc., only once. If there is a Scott 296B in a set, there will not be a Scott 296b also.

There are times when the block of numbers is too large for the set, leaving some numbers unused. Such gaps in the sequence also occur when the editors move an item elsewhere in the catalogue or remove it from the listings entirely. Scott does not attempt to account for every possible number, but rather it does attempt to assure that each stamp is assigned its own number.

Scott numbers designating regular postage normally are only numerals. Scott numbers for other types of stamps, e.g., air post, special delivery, and so on, will have a prefix of either a capital letter or a combination of numerals and capital letters.

2 **Illustration number** — used to identify each illustration. Where more than one stamp in a set uses the same illustration number, that number needs to be used with the description line (noted below) to be certain of the exact variety of the stamp within the set. Illustrations normally are 75, 100, or 150 percent of the original size of the stamp. An effort has been made to note all illustrations not at those percentages. Overprints are shown at 100 percent of the original, unless otherwise noted. Letters *in parentheses* which follow an illustration number refer to illustrations of overprints or surcharges.

3 **Listing styles** — there are two principal types of catalogue listings: major and minor.

Majors may be distinguished by having as their catalogue number a numeral with or without a capital-letter suffix and with or without a prefix.

Minors have a small-letter suffix (or, only have the small letter itself shown if the listing is immediately beneath its major list-ing). These listings show a variety of the "normal," or major item. Examples include color variation or a different watermark used for that stamp only.

Examples of major numbers are 9X1, 16, 28A, 6LB1, C13, RW1, and TS1. Examples of minor numbers are 22b, 279Bc and C3a.

4 **Denomination** — normally value printed on the stamp (generally known as the *face value*), which is — unless other-wise stated — the cost of the stamp at the time of issue.

5 **Basic information on stamp or set** — introducing each stamp issue, this section normally includes the date of issue, method of printing, perforation, watermark, and sometimes addi-tional information. New information on method of printing, water-mark or perforation measurement will appear when that information changes. Dates of issue are as precise as Scott is able to confirm, either year only, month and year, or month, day and year.

In stamp sets issued over more than one date, the year or span of years will be in bold type above the first catalogue number. Individual stamps in the set will have a date-of-issue appearing in italics. Stamps without a year listed appeared during the first year of the span. Dates are not always given for minor varieties.

6 **Color or other description** — this line provides informa-tion to solidify identification of the stamp. Historically, when stamps normally were printed in a single color, only the color appeared here. With modern printing techniques, which include multicolor presses which mix inks on the paper, earlier methods of color identification are no longer applicable. When space permits, a description of the stamp design will replace the terms "multi" or "multicolored." The color of the paper is noted in italic type when the paper used is not white.

7 **Date of issue** — As precisely as Scott is able to confirm, either year only; month and year, or month, day and year. In some cases, the earliest known use (eku) is given. All dates, espe-cially where no official date of issue has been given, are subject to change as new information is obtained. Many cases are known of inadvertent sale and use of stamps prior to dates of issue announced by postal officials. These are not listed here.

8 **Value unused** and **Value used** — the catalogue values are in U. S. dollars and are based on stamps that are in a grade of Very Fine unless stated otherwise. Unused values refer to items that have not seen postal or other duty for which they were intended. For pre-1890 issues, unused stamps must have at least most of their original gum; for later issues, complete gum is expected. Stamps issued without gum are noted. Unused values are for never-hinged stamps beginning at the point immediately following a prominent notice in the actual listing. Scott values for used self-adhesive stamps are for examples either on piece or off piece.

Some sections in this book have more than two columns for values. Check section introductions and watch for value column headers. See the sections "Catalogue Values" and "Understanding Valuing Notations" for an explanation of the meaning of these values.

9 **Changes in basic set information** — bold or other type is used to show any change in the basic data between stamps within a set of stamps, e.g., perforation from one stamp to the next or a different paper or printing method or watermark.

10 **Other varieties** — these include additional shades, plate varieties, multiples, used on cover, plate number blocks. coil line pairs, coil plate number strips of three or five, ZIP blocks, etc.

On early issues, there may be a "Cancellation" section. Values in this section refer to single stamps off cover, unless otherwise noted. Values with a "+" are added to the basic used value. See "Basic Stamp Information" for more details on stamp and cancellation varieties.

11 **Footnote** — Where other important details about the stamps can be found.

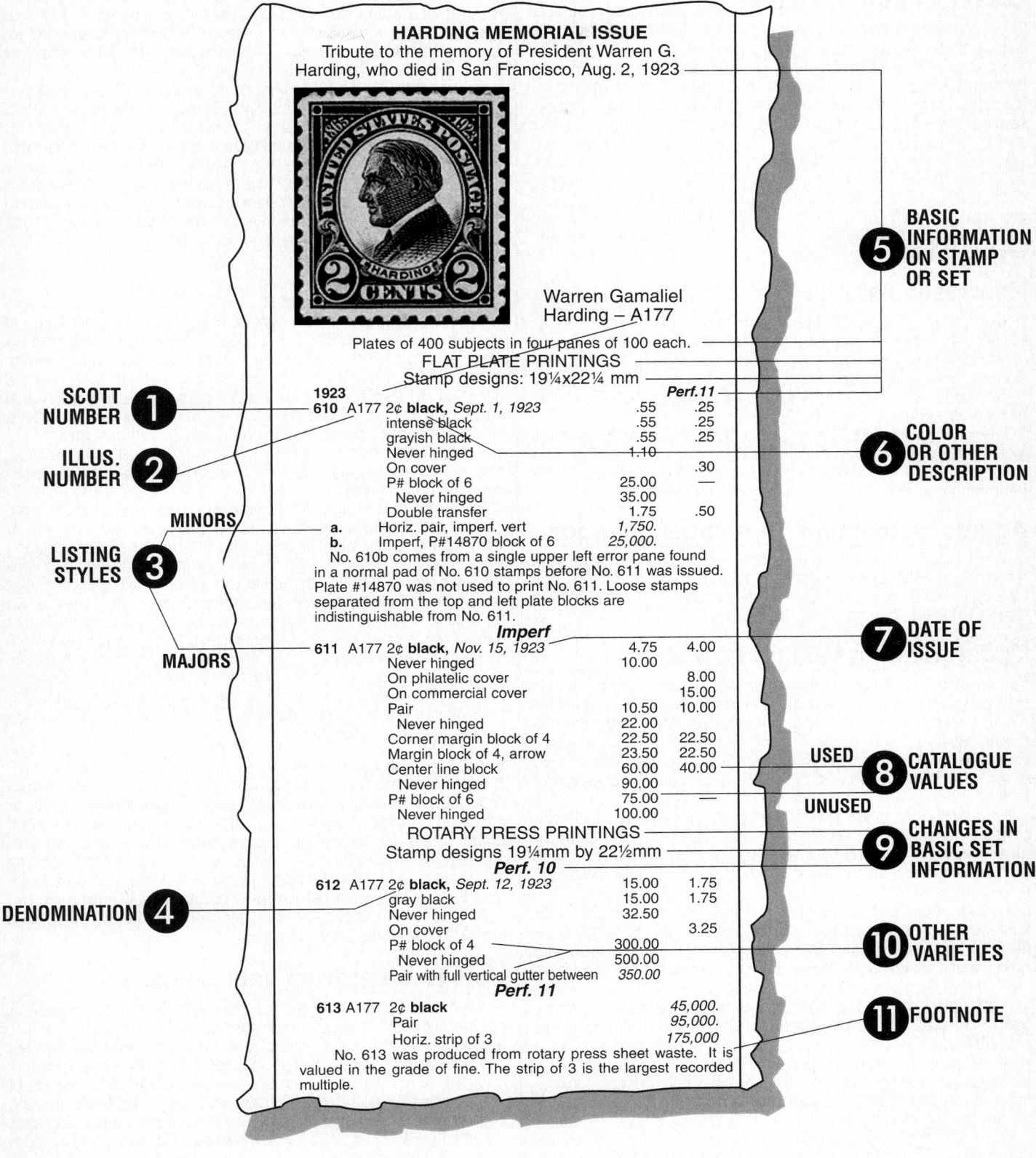

HARDING MEMORIAL ISSUE
Tribute to the memory of President Warren G.
Harding, who died in San Francisco, Aug. 2, 1923

Warren Gamaliel
Harding – A177

Plates of 400 subjects in four panes of 100 each.

FLAT PLATE PRINTINGS
Stamp designs: 19¼x22¼ mm

5 BASIC INFORMATION ON STAMP OR SET

SCOTT NUMBER 1

1923   *Perf.11*

610	A177	2¢ **black,** *Sept. 1, 1923*	.55	.25
		intense black	.55	.25
		grayish black	.55	.25
		Never hinged	1.10	
		On cover		.30
		P# block of 6	25.00	—
		Never hinged	35.00	
		Double transfer	1.75	.50
a.		Horiz. pair, imperf. vert	*1,750.*	
b.		Imperf, P#14870 block of 6	*25,000.*	

ILLUS. NUMBER 2

6 COLOR OR OTHER DESCRIPTION

LISTING STYLES 3   MINORS / MAJORS

No. 610b comes from a single upper left error pane found
in a normal pad of No. 610 stamps before No. 611 was issued.
Plate #14870 was not used to print No. 611. Loose stamps
separated from the top and left plate blocks are
indistinguishable from No. 611.

Imperf

611	A177	2¢ **black,** *Nov. 15, 1923*	4.75	4.00
		Never hinged	10.00	
		On philatelic cover		8.00
		On commercial cover		15.00
		Pair	10.50	10.00
		Never hinged	22.00	
		Corner margin block of 4	22.50	22.50
		Margin block of 4, arrow	23.50	22.50
		Center line block	60.00	40.00
		Never hinged	90.00	
		P# block of 6	75.00	—
		Never hinged	100.00	

7 DATE OF ISSUE

USED / UNUSED

8 CATALOGUE VALUES

ROTARY PRESS PRINTINGS
Stamp designs 19¼mm by 22½mm

Perf. 10

612	A177	2¢ **black,** *Sept. 12, 1923*	15.00	1.75
		gray black	15.00	1.75
		Never hinged	32.50	
		On cover		3.25
		P# block of 4	300.00	
		Never hinged	500.00	
		Pair with full vertical gutter between	*350.00*	

9 CHANGES IN BASIC SET INFORMATION

DENOMINATION 4

10 OTHER VARIETIES

Perf. 11

613	A177	2¢ **black**		*45,000.*
		Pair		*95,000.*
		Horiz. strip of 3		*175,000*

11 FOOTNOTE

No. 613 was produced from rotary press sheet waste. It is
valued in the grade of fine. The strip of 3 is the largest recorded
multiple.

Scott Numbering Practices and Special Notices

Classification of stamps

The *Scott Specialized Catalogue of United States Stamps* lists the stamps of the United States and its possessions and territories and the stamps of the United Nations. The next level is a listing by section on the basis of the function of the stamps or postal stationery. In each case, the items are listed in specialized detail. The principal sections cover regular postage stamps; air post stamps; postage due stamps, special delivery, and so on. Except for regular postage, catalogue numbers for most sections include a prefix letter (or number-letter combination) denoting the class to which the stamp belongs.

The Table of Contents, on page 4A, notes each section and, where pertinent, the prefix used. Some, such as souvenir cards and encased postage, do not have prefixes. Some sections, such as specimens and private perforations, have suffixes only.

New issue listings

Updates to this catalogue appear each month in the *Scott Stamp Monthly.* Included are corrections and updates to the current edition of this catalogue.

From time to time there will be changes in the listings from the *Scott Stamp Monthly* to the next edition of the catalogue, as additional information becomes available.

The catalogue update section of the *Scott Stamp Monthly* is the most timely presentation of this material available. For current subscription rates, see advertisements in this catalogue or write Scott Publishing Co., P.O. Box 828, Sidney, OH 45365-0828.

Additions, deletions & number changes

A list of catalogue additions, deletions, and number changes from the previous edition of the catalogue appears in each volume. See Catalogue Additions, Deletions & Number Changes in the Table of Contents for the location of this list.

Understanding valuing notations

The *absence of a value* does not necessarily suggest that a stamp is scarce or rare. In the U.S. listings, a dash in the value column means that the stamp is known in a stated form or variety, but information is lacking or insufficient for purposes of establishing a usable catalogue value. These could include rarities, such as Scott 3X4 on cover, or items that have a limited market, such as used plate blocks of Scott 1097.

Stamp values in *italics* generally refer to items which are difficult to value accurately. For expensive items, e.g., value at $1,000 or more, a value in italics represents an item which trades very seldom, such as a unique item. For inexpensive items, a value in italics represents a warning.

The Scott Catalogue values for used stamps reflect canceled-to-order material when such are found to predominate in the marketplace for the issue involved. Frequently notes appear in the stamp listings to specify items which are valued as canceled-to-order (Canal Zone Scott O1-O8) or if there is a premium for postally used examples.

Scott values for used stamps are not for precanceled examples, unless so stated. Precanceled copies must not have additional postal cancellations.

An example of a warning to collectors is a stamp that used has a value considerably higher than the unused version. Here, the collector is cautioned to be certain the used version has a readable, contemporaneous cancellation.

The *minimum catalogue value* of a stamp is 20 cents, to cover a dealer's costs of purchase and preparation for resale. The minimum catalogue value of a first day cover is one dollar. As noted, the sum of these values does not properly represent the "value" of a packet of unsorted or unmounted stamps sold in bulk. Such large collections, mixtures or packets generally consist of the lower-valued stamps.

There are examples where the catalogue value of a block of stamps is less than the sum of the values of the individual stamps. This situation is caused by the overhead involved in handling single stamps, and should not be considered a suggestion that all blocks be separated into individual stamps to achieve a higher market value.

Values in the "unused" column are for stamps with original gum, if issued with gum. The stamp is valued as hinged if the listing appears *before* the point at which stamps are valued as never hinged. This point is marked by prominent notes in many sections. A similar note will appear at the beginning of the section's listing, noting exactly where the dividing point between hinged and never hinged is for each section of the listings. Where a value for a used stamp is considerably higher than for the unused stamp, the value applies to a stamp showing a distinct contemporaneous cancellation.

Cancellations

A complete treatment of this subject is impossible in a catalogue of this limited size. Only postal markings of meaning — those which were necessary to the proper function of the postal service — are recorded here, while those of value owing to their fanciness only are disregarded. The latter are the results of the whim of some postal official. Many of these odd designs, however, command high prices, based on their popularity, scarcity and clearness of impression.

Although there are many types of most of the cancellations listed, only one of each is illustrated. The values quoted are for the most common type of each.

Values for cancellation varieties are for stamp specimens off cover. Some cancellation varieties (e.g., pen, precancel, cut) are valued individually. Other varieties on pre-1900 stamps (e.g., less common colors, specific dates, foreign usages) are valued using premiums (denoted by "+") which are added to the stated value for the used stamp. When listed on cover, the distinctive cancellation must be on the stamp in order to merit catalogue valuation. Postal markings that denote origin or a service (as distinguished from canceling a stamp) merit catalogue valuation when on a cover apart from the stamp, provided the stamp is otherwise tied to the cover by a cancellation.

One type of "Paid" cancellation used in Boston, and shown in this introduction under "Postal Markings," is common and values given are for types other than this.

Examination

Scott Publishing Co. will not pass upon the genuineness, grade or condition of stamps, because of the time and responsibility involved. Rather, there are several expertizing groups which undertake this work for both collectors and dealers. Neither will Scott Publishing Co. appraise or identify philatelic material. The Company cannot take responsibility for unsolicited stamps or covers sent by individuals.

All letters, E-mails, etc. are read attentively, but they are not always answered due to time considerations

How to order from your dealer

It is not necessary to write the full description of a stamp as listed in this catalogue. All that you need is the name of the country or *U.S. Specialized* section, the Scott Catalogue number and whether the item is unused or used. For example, "U.S. Scott 833" is sufficient to identify the stamp of the United States listed as the 2-dollar value of a set of stamps issued between 1938-43. This stamp was issued September 29, 1938. It is yellow green and black in color, has a perforation of 11, and is printed on paper without a watermark by a flat plate press. Sections without a prefix or suffix must be mentioned by name.

Abbreviations

Scott Publishing Co. uses a consistent set of abbreviations throughout this catalogue and the *Standard Postage Stamp Catalogue* to conserve space while still providing necessary information. The first block shown here refers to color names only:

COLOR ABBREVIATIONS

amb	amber	ind	indigo
anil	aniline	int	intense
ap	apple	lav	lavender
aqua	aquamarine	lem	lemon
az	azure	lil	lilac
bis	bister	lt	light
bl	blue	mag	magenta
bld	blood	man	manila
blk	black	mar	maroon
bril	brilliant	mv	mauve
brn	brown	multi	multicolored
brnsh	brownish	mlky	milky
brnz	bronze	myr	myrtle
brt	bright	ol	olive
brnt	burnt	olvn	olivine
car	carmine	org	orange
cer	cerise	pck	peacock
chlky	chalky	pnksh	pinkish
cham	chamois	Prus	Prussian
chnt	chestnut	pur	purple
choc	chocolate	redsh	reddish
chr	chrome	res	reseda
cit	citron	ros	rosine
cl	claret	ryl	royal
cob	cobalt	sal	salmon
cop	copper	saph	sapphire
crim	crimson	scar	scarlet
cr	cream	sep	sepia
dk	dark	sien	sienna
dl	dull	sil	silver
dp	deep	sl	slate
db	drab	stl	steel
emer	emerald	turq	turquoise
gldn	golden	ultra	ultramarine
grysh	grayish	ven	venetian
grn	green	ver	vermilion
grnsh	greenish	vio	violet
hel	heliotrope	yel	yellow
hn	henna	yelsh	yellowish

When no color is given for an overprint or surcharge, black is the color used. Abbreviations for colors used for overprints and surcharges are: "(B)" or "(Blk)," black; "(Bl)," blue; "(R)," red; "(G)," green; etc.

Additional abbreviations used in this catalogue are shown below:

Adm.	Administration
AFL	American Federation of Labor
Anniv.	Anniversary
APU	Arab Postal Union
APS	American Philatelic Society
ASEAN	Association of South East Asian Nations
ASPCA	American Society for the Prevention of Cruelty to Animals
Assoc.	Association
b.	Born
BEP	Bureau of Engraving and Printing
Bicent.	Bicentennial
Bklt.	Booklet
Brit.	British
btwn.	Between
Bur.	Bureau
c. or ca.	Circa
CAR	Central African Republic
Cat.	Catalogue
Cent.	Centennial, century, centenary
CEPT	Conference Europeenne des Administrations des Postes et des Telecommunications
CIO	Congress of Industrial Organizations
Conf.	Conference
Cong.	Congress
Cpl.	Corporal
CTO	Canceled to order
d.	Died
Dbl.	Double
DDR	German Democratic Republic (East Germany)
EC	European Community
ECU	European currency unit
EEC	European Economic Community
EKU	Earliest known use
Engr.	Engraved
Exhib.	Exhibition
Expo.	Exposition
FAO	Food and Agricultural Organization of the United Nations
Fed.	Federation
FIP	Federation International de Philatelie
GB	Great Britain
Gen.	General
GPO	General post office
Horiz.	Horizontal
ICAO	International Civil Aviation Organization
ICY	International Cooperation Year
ILO	International Labor Organization
Imperf.	Imperforate
Impt.	Imprint
Intl.	International
Invtd.	Inverted
IQSY	International Quiet Sun Year
ITU	International Telecommunications Union
ITY	International Tourism Year
IWY	International Women's Year
IYC	International Year of the Child
IYD	International Year of the Disabled
IYSH	International Year of Shelter for the Homeless
IYY	International Youth Year
L.	Left
Lieut.	Lieutenant
Litho.	Lithographed

LL .... Lower left
LR .... Lower right

mm .... Millimeter
Ms .... Manuscript

NASA .... National Aeronautics and Space Administration
Natl. .... National
NATO .... North Atlantic Treaty Organization
No. .... Number
NY .... New York
NYC .... New York City

OAU .... Organization of African Unity
OPEC .... Organization of Petroleum Exporting Countries
Ovpt. .... Overprint
Ovptd. .... Overprinted

P# .... Plate number
Perf .... Perforated, perforation
Phil .... Philatelic
Photo .... Photogravure
PO .... Post office
Pr. .... Pair
P.R. .... Puerto Rico
PRC .... People's Republic of China (Mainland China)
Prec. .... Precancel, precanceled
Pres. .... President

R .... Right
Rio .... Rio de Janeiro
ROC .... Republic of China (Taiwan)

SEATO .... South East Asia Treaty Organization
Sgt. .... Sergeant
Soc. .... Society
Souv. .... Souvenir
SSR .... Soviet Socialist Republic
St. .... Saint, street
Surch .... Surcharge

Typo. .... Typographed
UAE .... United Arab Emirate
UAMPT ...... Union of African and Malagasy Posts and Telecommunications
UL .... Upper left
UN .... United Nations
UNESCO .... United Nations Educational, Scientific and Cultural Organization
UNICEF ...... United Nations Children's Fund
Univ .... University
UNPA .... United Nations Postal Administration
Unwmkd .... Unwatermarked
UPU .... Universal Postal Union
UR .... Upper Right
US .... United States
USPO .... United States Post Office Department
USPS .... United States Postal Service (also "U.S. Postage Stamp" when referring to the watermark)
USSR .... Union of Soviet Socialist Republics

Vert .... Vertical
VP .... Vice president

WCY .... World Communications Year
WFUNA ...... World Federation of United Nations Associations
WHO .... World Health Organization
Wmk .... Watermark
Wmkd .... Watermarked
WMO .... World Meteorological Organization
WRY .... World Refugee Year
WWF .... World Wildlife Fund
WWI .... World War I
WWII .... World War II

YAR .... Yemen Arab Republic
Yemen PDR . Yemen People's Democratic Republic

Postmasters General of the United States

1775 Benjamin Franklin, July 26.	**1869** John A.J. Creswell, Mar. 6.	**1923** Harry S. New, Mar. 4.
1776 Richard Bache, Nov. 7.	**1874** Jas. W. Marshall, July 7.	**1929** Walter F. Brown, Mar. 6.
1782 Ebenezer Hazard, Jan. 28.	**1874** Marshall Jewell, Sept. 1.	**1933** James A. Farley, Mar. 4.
1789 Samuel Osgood, Sept. 26.	**1876** James N. Tyner, July 13.	**1940** Frank C. Walker, Sept. 11.
1791 Timothy Pickering, Aug. 12.	**1877** David McK. Key, Mar. 13.	**1945** Robert E. Hannegan, July 1.
1795 Joseph Habersham, Feb. 25.	**1880** Horace Maynard, Aug. 25.	**1947** Jesse M. Donaldson, Dec. 16.
1801 Gideon Granger, Nov. 28.	**1881** Thomas L. James, Mar. 8.	**1953** Arthur E. Summerfield, Jan. 21.
1814 Return J. Meigs, Jr., Apr. 11.	**1882** Timothy O. Howe, Jan. 5.	**1961** J. Edward Day, Jan. 21.
1823 John McLean, July 1.	**1883** Walter Q. Gresham, Apr. 11.	**1963** John A. Gronouski, Sept. 30.
1829 William T. Barry, Apr. 6.	**1884** Frank Hatton, Oct. 14.	**1965** Lawrence F. O'Brien, Nov. 3.
1835 Amos Kendall, May 1.	**1885** Wm. F. Vilas, Mar. 7.	**1968** W. Marvin Watson, Apr. 26.
1840 John M. Niles, May 26.	**1888** Don M. Dickinson, Jan. 17.	**1969** Winton M. Blount, Jan. 22.
1841 Francis Granger, Mar. 8.	**1889** John Wanamaker, Mar. 6.	**U.S. POSTAL SERVICE**
1841 Charles A. Wickliffe, Oct. 13.	**1893** Wilson S. Bissell, Mar. 7.	**1971** Elmer T. Klassen, Dec. 7.
1845 Cave Johnson, Mar. 7.	**1895** William L. Wilson, Apr. 4.	**1975** Benjamin Bailar, Feb. 15.
1849 Jacob Collamer, Mar. 8.	**1897** James A. Gary, Mar. 6.	**1978** William F. Bolger, Mar. 1.
1850 Nathan K. Hall, July 23.	**1898** Charles Emory Smith, Apr. 22.	**1985** Paul N. Carlin, Jan. 1.
1852 Samuel D. Hubbard, Sept. 14.	**1902** Henry C. Payne, Jan. 15.	**1986** Albert V. Casey, Jan. 6.
1853 James Campbell, Mar. 8.	**1904** Robert J. Wynne, Oct. 10.	**1986** Preston R. Tisch, Aug. 17.
1857 Aaron V. Brown, Mar. 7.	**1905** Geo. B. Cortelyou, Mar. 7.	**1988** Anthony M. Frank, Mar. 1.
1859 Joseph Holt, Mar. 14.	**1907** Geo. von L. Meyer, Mar. 4.	**1992** Marvin T. Runyon, Jr., July 6.
1861 Horatio King, Feb. 12.	**1909** Frank H. Hitchcock, Mar. 6.	**1998** William J. Henderson, May 16.
1861 Montgomery Blair, Mar. 9.	**1913** Albert S. Burleson, Mar. 5.	**2001** John E. Potter, June 1
1864 William Dennison, Oct. 1.	**1921** Will H. Hays, Mar. 5.	
1866 Alexander W. Randall, July 25.	**1922** Hubert Work, Mar. 4.	

Basic Stamp Information

A stamp collector's knowledge of the combined elements that make a given issue of a stamp unique determines his or her ability to identify stamps. These elements include paper, watermark, method of separation, printing, design and gum. On the following pages these important areas are described in detail.

The guide below will direct you to those philatelic terms which are not major headings in the following introductory material. The major headings are:

Plate	Paper	Gum	Postal Markings
Printing	Separation	Luminescence	General Glossary

Subheadings are shown in parentheses after the major heading for a given term.

Guide to Subjects

Arrows	See Plate (Sheet Stamps)
Bisect	See General Glossary
Blind Perforations	See General Glossary
Blocks	See Plate (Sheet Stamps)
Booklet Panes	See Plate (Sheet Stamps)
Booklets	See Plate (Sheet Stamps), General Glossary
Booklets A.E.F.	See Plate (Sheet Stamps)
Bureau Precancels	See Postal Markings
Cancellations	See Postal Markings, General Glossary
Carrier Postmarks	See Postal Markings
Coarse Perforation	See Separation (Perforations)
Coils	See Plate (Coil Stamps)
Coil Waste	See Plate (Coil Stamps)
Color Changeling	See Printing (Additional Terms)
Color Registration Markings	See Plate (Sheet Stamps)
Color Trials	See Printing (Additional Terms)
Commemorative Stamps	See General Glossary
Compound Perforation	See Separation (Perforations)
Covers	See General Glossary
Cracked Plate	See Printing (Common Flaws)
Die	See Plate (Line Engraving)
Die Cutting	See Separation
Double Impression	See Printing (Additional Terms)
Double Paper	See Paper
Double Perforation	See Separation (Perforations)
Double Transfer	See Plate (Line Engraving)
Dry Printings	See note after Scott 1029
Electric Eye	See Separation (Perforations)
Embossed Printing	See Printing
End Roller Grills	See Paper (Grills)
Engraved	See Printing
Error	See General Glossary
Essay	See Printing (Additional Terms)
Fine Perforation	See Separation (Perforations)
First Day Cover	See General Glossary
Flat Plate Printing	See Printing (Additional Terms)
Fluorescent Papers	See Luminescence
Foil Application	See Printing
Foreign Entry	See Plate
Giori Press	See Printing
Gridiron Cancellation	See Postal Markings
Grills	See Paper
Gripper Cracks	See Printing (Common Flaws)
Gouge	See Printing (Additional Terms)
Guide Lines	See Plate (Sheet Stamps)
Gum Breaker Ridges	See General Glossary
Gutter	See Plate (Sheet Stamps)
Hidden Plate Number	See Plate (Coil Stamps)
Holograms	See Printing
Imperforate	See General Glossary
Imprint	See Plate (Sheet Stamps)
India Paper	See Paper
Intaglio	See Plate (Line Engraving), Printing
Inverted Center	See Printing (Additional Terms)
Joint Line	See Plate (Coil Stamps)
Laid Paper	See Paper
Line Engraved	See Printing
Line Pair	See Plate (Coil Stamps)
Lithography	See Printing
Manila Paper	See Paper
Margin	See Plate (Sheet Stamps)
Military Postmarks	See Postal Markings
Multicolored Stamps	See Printing (Additional Terms)
New York City Foreign Mail	See Postal Markings
Offset Lithography	See Printing
Original Gum	See General Glossary
Overprint	See Printing (Additional Terms), General Glossary
Pair Imperf. Between	See General Glossary
Pane	See Plate (Plate Arrangement)
Part-Perforate	See General Glossary
Paste-up	See Plate (Coil Stamps)
Paste-up Pair	See Plate (Coil Stamps)
Patent Cancellations	See Postal Markings
Pelure Paper	See Paper
Perforation Gauge	See Separation (Perforations)
Phosphor Tagged	See Luminescence
Photogravure	See Printing
Plate Flaws	See Printing (Common Flaws)
Plate Markings	See Plate (Sheet Stamps)
Plate Numbers	See Plate (Sheet Stamps)
Postmarks	See Postal Markings
Precancels	See Postal Markings
Printed on Both Sides	See Printing (Additional Terms)
Proofs	See Printing (Additional Terms)
Railroad Postmarks	See Postal Markings
Receiving Mark	See Postal Markings
Re-cut	See Plate (Line Engraving)
Re-engraved	See Plate (Line Engraving)
Re-entry	See Plate (Line Engraving)
Reissue	See Printing (Additional Terms)
Relief	See Plate (Line Engraving)
Reprint	See Printing (Additional Terms)
Retouch	See Plate (Line Engraving)
Ribbed Paper	See Paper
Rosette Crack	See Printing (Common Flaws)
Rotary Press Printing	See Printing (Additional Terms)
Rough Perforation	See Separation (Perforations)
Rouletting	See Separation
Se-Tenant	See General Glossary
Service Indicators	See Postal Markings
Sheet	See Plate (Plate Arrangement)
Shifted Transfer	See Plate (Line Engraving)
Ship Postmarks	See Postal Markings
Short Transfer	See Plate (Line Engraving)
Silk Paper	See Paper
Specimens	See General Glossary
Splice	See General Glossary
Split Grill	See Paper (Grills)
Stitch Watermark	See Paper
Supplementary Mail	See Postal Markings
Surcharge	See Printing (Additional Terms), General Glossary

PLATE

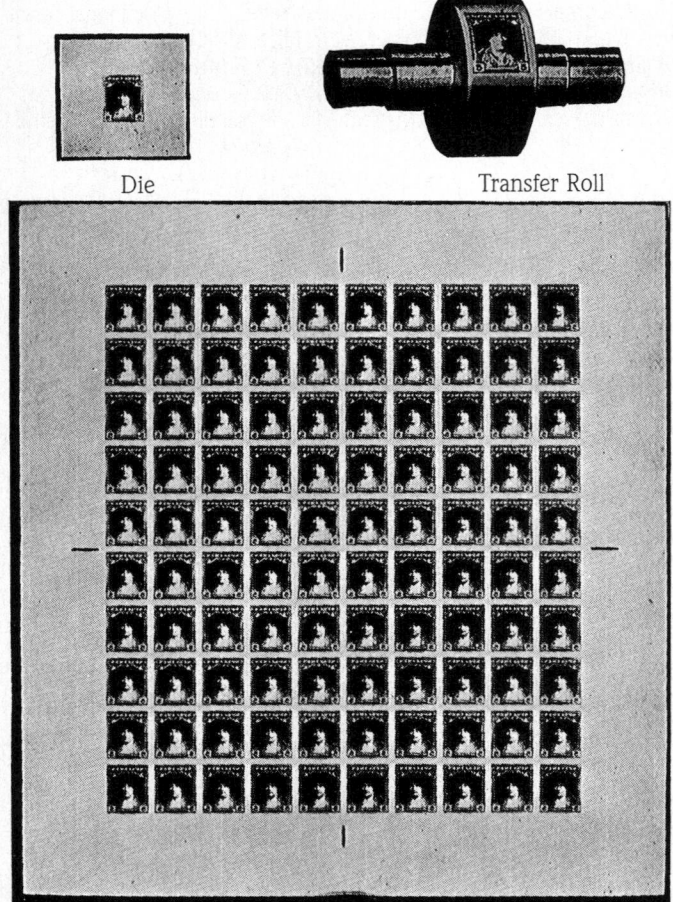

Die   Transfer Roll

Plate

Line Engraving (Intaglio)

Die — Making the die is the initial operation in developing the inta-glio plate. The die is a small flat piece of soft steel on which the sub-ject (design) is recess-engraved in reverse. Dies are usually of a single-subject type, but dies exist with multiple subjects of the same design, or even different designs. After the engraving is completed, the die is hardened to withstand the stress of subsequent operations.

Transfer Roll — The next operation is making the transfer roll, which is the medium used to transfer the subject from the die to the plate. A blank roll of soft steel, mounted on a mandrel, is placed under the bearers of a transfer press. The hardened die is placed on the bed of the press and the face of the roll is brought to bear on the die. The bed is then rocked backed and forth under increasing pres-sure until the soft steel of the roll is forced into every line of the die.

The resulting impression on the roll is known as a "relief" or "relief transfer." Several reliefs usually are rocked in on each roll. After the required reliefs are completed, the roll is hardened.

Relief — A relief is the normal reproduction of the design on the die, in reverse. A defective relief, caused by a minute piece of foreign material lodging on the die, may occur during the rocking-in process, or from other causes. Imperfections in the steel of the transfer roll may also result in a breaking away of parts of the design. If the dam-aged relief is continued in use, it will transfer a repeating defect to the plate. Also, reliefs sometimes are deliberately altered. "Broken relief" and "altered relief" are terms used to designate these changed conditions.

Plate — A flat piece of soft steel replaces the die on the bed of the transfer press and one of the reliefs on the transfer roll is brought to bear on this soft steel. The position of the plate is determined by guide dots, which have been lightly marked on the plate in advance. After the position of the relief is determined, pressure is brought to bear and, by following the same method used in the making of the transfer roll, a transfer is entered. This transfer reproduces, in reverse, every detail of the design of the relief. As many transfers are entered on the plate as there are to be subjects printed at one time.

After the required transfers have been entered, the guide dots, lay-outs and lines, scratches, etc., are burnished out. Also, any required guide lines, plate numbers, or other marginal markings are added. A proof impression is then taken and if certified (approved), the plate is machined for fitting to the press, hardened and sent to the plate vault until used.

Rotary press plates, after being certified, require additional machining. They are curved to fit the press cylinder and gripper slots are cut into the back of each plate to receive the grippers, which hold the plate securely to the press. The rotary press plate is not hardened until these additional processes are completed.

Transfer — An impression entered on the plate by the transfer roll. A relief transfer is made when entering the design of the die onto the transfer roll.

Double Transfer — The condition of a transfer on a plate that shows evidence of a duplication of all or a portion of the design. A double transfer usually is the result of the changing of the registra-tion between the relief and the plate during the rolling of the original entry.

Occasionally it is necessary to remove the original transfer from a plate and enter the relief a second time. When the finished re-trans-fer shows indications of the original transfer, because of incomplete erasure, the result is known as a double transfer.

Triple Transfer — Similar to a double transfer, this situation shows evidence of a third entry or two duplications.

Foreign Entry — When original transfers are erased incompletely from a plate, they can appear with new transfers of a different design which are entered subsequently on the plate.

Re-entry — When executing a re-entry, the transfer roll is reap-plied to the plate at some time after the latter has been put to press. Thus, worn-out designs may be resharpened by carefully re-entering the transfer roll. If the transfer roll is not carefully entered, the reg-istration will not be true and a double transfer will result. With the protective qualities of chromium plating, it is no longer necessary to resharpen the plate. In fact, after a plate has been curved for the rotary press, it is impossible to make a re-entry.

Shifted Transfer (Shift) — In transferring, the metal displaced on the plate by the entry of the ridges, constituting the design on the transfer roll, is forced ahead of the roll as well as pressed out at the sides. The amount of displaced metal increases with the depth of the entry. When the depth is increased evenly, the design will be uniformly entered. Most of the displaced metal is pressed ahead of the roll. If too much pressure is exerted on any pass (rocking), the impression on the previous partial entry may be floated (pushed) ahead of the roll and cause a duplication of the final design. The duplication appears as an increased width of frame lines or a doubling of the lines.

The ridges of the displaced metal are flattened out by the hammering or rolling back of the plate along the space occupied by the subject margins.

Short Transfer — Occasionally the transfer roll is not rocked its entire length in the entering of a transfer onto a plate, with the result that the finished transfer fails to show the complete design. This is known as a short transfer.

Short transfers are known to have been made deliberately, as in the Type III of the 1-cent issue of 1851-60 (Scott 8, 21), or accidentally, as in the 10-cent 1847 (Scott 2).

Re-engraved — Either the die that has been used to make a plate or the plate itself may have its temper drawn (softened) and be recut. The resulting impressions for such re-engraved die or plate may differ very slightly from the original issue and are given the label "re-engraved."

Re-cut — A re-cut is the strengthening or altering of a line by use of an engraving tool on unhardened plates.

Retouch — A retouch is the strengthening or altering of a line by means of etching.

Plate Arrangement

Arrangement — The first engraved plates used to produce U.S. postage stamps in 1847 contained 200 subjects. The number of subjects to a plate varied between 100 and 300 until the issue of 1890, when the 400-subject plate was first laid down. Since that time, this size of plate has been used for a majority of the regular postal issues (those other than commemoratives). Exceptions to this practice exist, particularly among the more recent issues, and are listed under the headings of the appropriate issues in the catalogue.

Sheet — In single-color printings, the complete impression from a plate is termed a sheet. A sheet of multicolored stamps (two or more colors) may come from a single impression of a plate, i.e., many Giori-type press printings from 1957, or from as many impressions from separate plates as there are inks used for the particular stamp. Combination process printings may use both methods of multicolor production: Giori-type intaglio with offset lithography or with photogravure.

The Huck multicolor press used plates of different format (40, 72 or 80 subjects). The sheet it produced had 200 subjects for normal-sized commemoratives or 400 subjects for regular-issue stamps, similar to the regular products of other presses.

See the note on the Combination Press following the listing for Scott 1703 in this catalogue.

In casual usage, a "pane" often is referred to as a "sheet."

Pane — A pane is the part of the original sheet that is issued for sale at post offices. A pane may be the same as an entire sheet, where the plate is small, or it may be a half, quarter, or some other fraction of a sheet where the plate is large.

The illustration shown later under the subtopic "Sheet Stamps" shows the layout of a 400-subject sheet from a flat plate, which for issuance would have been divided along the intersecting guide lines into four panes of 100.

Panes are classified into normal reading position according to their location on the printed sheet: U.L., upper left; U.R., upper right; L.L., lower left; and L.R., lower right. Where only two panes appear on a sheet, they are designed "R" (right) and "L" (left) or "T" (top) and "B" (bottom), on the basis of the division of the sheet vertically or horizontally.

To fix the location of a particular stamp on any pane, except for those printed on the Combination press, the pane is held with the subjects in the normal position, and a position number is given to each stamp starting with the first stamp in the upper left corner and proceeding horizontally to the right, then staring on the second row at the left and counting across to the right, and so on to the last stamp in the lower right corner.

In describing the location of a stamp on a sheet of stamps issued prior to 1894, the practice is to give the stamp position number first, then the pane position and finally the plate number, i.e., "1R22." Beginning with the 1894 issue and on all later issues the method used is to give the plate number first, then the position of the pane, and finally the position number of the stamp, i.e., "16807LL48" to identify an example of Scott 619 or "2138L2" to refer to an example of Scott 323.

Booklet Stamps

Plates for Stamp Booklets — These are illustrated and described preceding the listing of booklet panes and covers in this catalogue.

Booklet Panes — Panes specially printed and cut to be sold in booklets which are a convenient way to purchase and store stamps. U.S. Booklet panes are straight-edged on three sides, but perforated between the stamps. Die cut, ATM and other panes will vary from this. Except for BK64 and BK65, the A.E.F. booklets, booklets were sold by the Post Office Department for a one-cent premium until 1962. Other sections of this catalogue with listings for booklet panes include Savings stamps, Telegraph stamps and Canal Zone.

A.E.F. Booklets — These were special booklets prepared principally for use by the U.S. Army Post Office in France during World War I. They were issued in 1-cent and 2-cent denominations with 30 stamps to a pane (10 x 3), bound at right or left. As soon as Gen. John J. Pershing's organization reached France, soldiers' mail was sent free by means of franked envelopes.

Stamps were required during the war for the civilian personnel, as well as for registered mail, parcel post and other types of postal service. See the individual listings for Scott 498f and 499f and booklets BK64 and BK65.

Coil Stamps

First issued in 1908-09, coil stamps originally were produced in two roll sizes, 500 and 1,000 stamps, with the individual stamps arranged endways or sideways and with or without perforations between.

Rolls of stamps for use in affixing or vending machines were first constructed by private companies and later by the Bureau of Engraving and Printing. Originally, it was customary for the Post Office Department to sell to the private vending companies and others imperforate sheets of stamps printed from the ordinary 400-subject flat plates. These sheets were then pasted together end-to-end or side-to-side by the purchaser and cut into rolls as desired, with the perforations being applied to suit the requirements of the individual machines. Such stamps with private perforations are listed in this catalogue under "Vending and Affixing Machine Perforations."

Later the Bureau produced coils by the same method, also in rolls of 500 and 1,000. These coils were arranged endways or sideways and were issued with or without perforations.

With the introduction of the Stickney rotary press, curved plates made for use on these presses were put into use at the Bureau of Engraving and Printing, and the sale of imperforate sheets was discontinued. This move marked the end of the private perforation. Rotary press coils have been printed on a number of presses over the years and have been made in roll sizes of 100, 500, 1,000, 3,000 and 10,000 stamps, etc.

Paste-up — The junction of two flat-plate printings joined by pasting the edge of one sheet onto the edge of another sheet to make coils. A two-stamp example of this joining is a "paste-up pair." See Splice.

Guide Line Pair — Attached pair of flat-plate-printed coil stamps with printed line between. This line is identical with the guide line (See listing under (Sheet Stamps) found in sheets.

Joint Line — The edges of two curved plates do not meet exactly on the press and the small space between the plates takes ink and prints a line. A pair of rotary-press-printed stamps with such a line is called a "joint line pair."

Coil stamps printed on the Multicolor Huck Press do not consistently produce such lines. Occasionally accumulated ink will print partial lines in one or more colors, and very occasionally complete lines will be printed. Stamps resulting from such situations are not listed in this catalogue. The "B" and "C" presses do not print joint lines at all.

Plate Number — for U.S. coil stamps prior to Scott 1891, Scott 1947, War Savings coils and Canal Zone:

On a rotary-press horizontal coil the top or bottom part of a plate number may show. On a vertical coil, the left or right part of a plate number may show. The number was entered on the plate to be cut off when the web was sliced into coils and is found only when the web was sliced off center. Every rotary press coil plate number was adjacent to a joint line, so both features could occur together in one strip.

For U.S. coil stamps from Scott 1891 onward (excluding Scott 1947) and Official coils:

The plate number is placed in the design area of the stamp, so it will not be trimmed off. Such items are normally collected unused with the stamp containing the plate number in the center of a strip of three or five stamps. They normally are collected used as singles. The line, if any, will be at the right of the plate-number stamp. On the Bureau's Cottrell press, the number occurs every 24th stamp, on the "B" press every 52nd stamp, on the "C," "D" and "F" presses every 48th stamp. On modern private contractor presses, the number occurs in a range from every 5th stamp to every 31st stamp, depending on the press used.

Unused plate-number strips of three and five are valued in this catalogue.

Hidden Plate Number — A plate number may be found entirely on a coil made from flat plates, but usually is hidden by a part of the next sheet which has been lapped over it.

Coil Waste — an occurrence brought about by stamps issued in perforated sheets from a printing intended for coils. These stamps came from short lengths of paper at the end of the coil run. Sometimes the salvaged sections were those which had been laid aside for mutilation because of some defect. Because the paper had been moistened during printing, it sometimes stretched slightly and provided added printing area. Sheets of 70, 100, and 170 are known. See Scott 538-541, 545-546, 578-579, and 594-595.

"T" — Letter which appears in the lower design area of Scott 2115b, which was printed on an experimental pre-phosphored paper. The stamp with the plate number is inscribed "T1."

Sheet Stamps

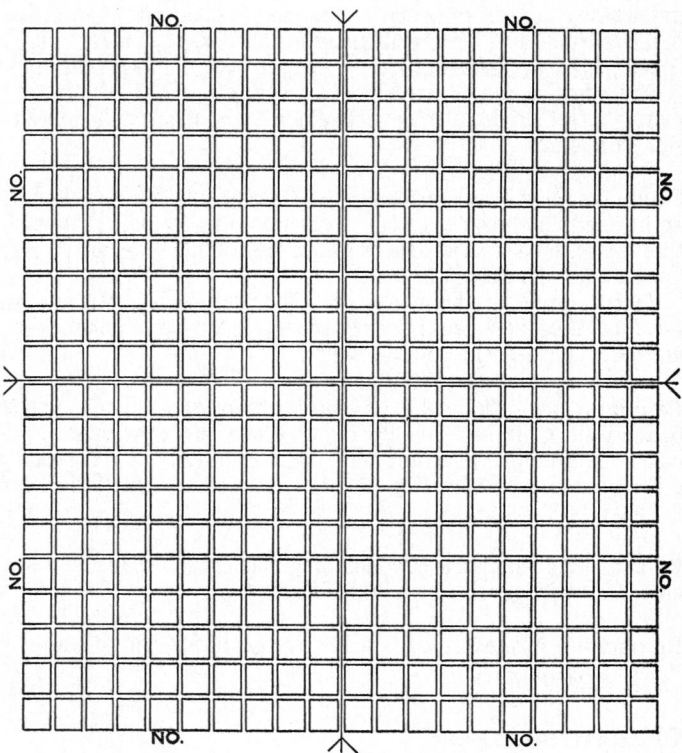

A typical 400-subject plate of 1922

Plate Markings — The illustration above shows a typical 400-subject plate of the 1922 issue, with markings as found on this type of plate. Other layouts and markings are found further in the catalogue text.

Guide Lines — Horizontal or vertical colored lines between the stamps, extending wholly or partially across the sheet. They serve as guides for the operators of perforating machines or to indicate the point of separation of the sheet into panes.

A block of stamps divided by any of the guide lines is known as a "line block" or "guide line block." The block of stamps from the exact center of the sheet, showing the crossed guide lines, is a "center line block."

Gutter — When guide lines are used to mark the division of the sheet into panes, the space between the stamps at the edge of the pane is no different than the space between any other stamps on the sheet. Some plates provide a wide space, or gutter, between the panes. These plates do not produce guide lines.

A pair of stamps with the wide space between is known as a "gutter pair," and blocks with that feature are "gutter blocks." A block of stamps from the exact center of the sheet, showing the two wide spaces crossing, is a "center gutter block" or "cross gutter block."

Gutter pairs or gutter blocks must contain complete stamps on both sides of the gutter, intact including perforation teeth unless imperforate. The stamps on either side of the gutter may or may not be creased; either way they qualify as the listed variety.

Arrows — Arrow-shaped markings were used in the margins of stamp sheets, in place of guide lines, on the issues of 1870 through 1894. Since 1894, guide lines with arrows at both ends have been the standard practice on flat-plate printings.

A margin block of at least four stamps, showing the arrow centered at one edge, is known as a "margin block with arrow."

Color Registration Markings — marks of different sizes and shapes, used as an aid in properly registering the colors in producing a bicolored or multicolored stamp.

Imprint — design containing the name of the producer of the stamps, which appears on the sheet margin usually near the plate number.

A block of stamps with the sheet margin attached, bearing the imprint, is known as an "imprint block." Imprints and plate numbers usually are collected in blocks of six, or of sufficient length to include the entire marking. From 1894 until about 1907, one fashion was to collect the imprints in strips of three, and these are listed in this catalogue.

The imprint and plate number combination are found in eight types I-VIII, which are illustrated at Scott 245 and Scott E3. Example: "T V" refers to Type V.

Plate Numbers — Serial numbers assigned to plates, appearing on one or more margins of the sheet or pane to identify the plate.

Flat Press Plate Numbers — usually collected in a margin block of six stamps with the plate number centered in the margin.

Rotary Press Plate Numbers — usually collected in a corner margin block large enough to show the plate number(s) and position along the margin and complete selvage on two sides. For issues with a single plate number at the corner of the pane, a block of four normally suffices.

During 1933-39, some plates had the number opposite the third stamp (up or down) from the corner of the sheet and for these the number is customarily collected in a corner block of no less than eight stamps. Multicolored stamps may have more than one plate number in the margin and the "plate block" may then be expanded to suit the collector's desire.

The catalogue listing for plate blocks includes enough stamps to accommodate all numbers on the plate. Plate block listings for se-tenant issues include all the designs as part of the block. When a continuous design is involved, such as Scott 1629-31, the complete design will be included in the plate number block. The entire pane constitutes the plate number block for issues such as the State Birds and Flowers (Scott 1953-2002, 1953A-2002A).

Plate numbers take a further designation from the position on the sheet on which they appear, e.g. U.L. refers to upper left pane, etc.

See note following Scott 1703 for description of combination press markings.

Private Contractor Marks — On rotary plates from Scott 1789 onward: "A" denotes issues produced by private contractor American Bank Note Co., "B" by Banknote Corp of America, "D" by Dittler Brothers, "G" by Guilford Gravure, "K" by KCS Industries, "M" by 3M Corp., "P" by Ashton-Potter (USA) Ltd., "S" by Stamp Venturers, Inc. (now Sennett Security Products), "U" by U.S. Bank Note Co., "V" by Avery Dennison.

Stars — used on the flat plates to indicate a change from the previous spacing of the stamps. They also were used as a check on the assignment of the printed sheets to a perforating machine of the proper setting. Stars appear on certain rotary plates used for printing stamps for coils, appearing adjacent to the plate joint line and above stamp No. 1 on the 170-subject plates, and to the left of stamp No. 141 on the 150-subject plates.

"A" — on flat plates; used on plates having uniform vertical spacing between rows of subjects, but wider than those with the star marking.

"C.S." and "C" — plate has been chromium plated.

"E.I." — abbreviation for Electrolytic Iron. The designation is for plates made by the electrolytic process.

"F" — used to indicate the plate is ready for hardening. This appears only on flat plates and generally precedes the upper right plate number.

"O" — plate has undergone an experimental oil-hardening process during manufacture.

"Top" — marking on the top sheet margin of printings from both plates of some bicolored issues. This marking is used to check printings for "inverts." Beginning with the 6-cent bicolored airpost issue of 1938 (Scott C23), bicolored crosses also were used as an additional check.

"Coil Stamps" — appearing on the side sheet margins, designates plates used in the production of endwise coils.

"S 20," "S 30," "S 40" — marginal markings appearing on certain 150- and 170-subject rotary press plates to designate experimental variations in the depth and character of the frame line to over-come excess inking. "S 30" was adopted as the standard. Blocks showing these markings are listed as "Margin Block with S 20," etc., in this catalogue.

Initials — used in sheet margins to identify individuals in the Bureau of Engraving and Printing who participated in the production or use of the plates.

Gutter Dashes — on the first 400-subject rotary plates, 3/16-inch horizontal dashes appear in the gutter between the 10th and 11th vertical rows of stamps. This arrangement was superseded by dashes 3/16-inch at the extreme ends of the vertical and horizontal gutters, and a 1/4-inch cross at the central gutter intersection. This latter arrangement continued until replaced by the scanning marks on the Electric Eye plates. See Electric Eye.

Margin — border outside the printed design or perforated area of a stamp, also known as selvage, or the similar border of a sheet of stamps. A block of stamps from the top, side or bottom of a sheet or pane to which is attached the selvage (margin) is known as a "margin block." A block of stamps from the corner of a sheet with full selvage attached to two adjoining sides is known as a "corner block."

NOTE: The descriptions and definitions above indicate that a certain number of stamps make up an arrow or plate number block. Any block of stamps, no matter how large or small, which had an arrow or plate number on its margin would be considered by that name. The usual practice is to collect flat-plate numbers in margin blocks of six and arrow blocks in margin blocks of four. Plate number blocks from rotary press printings generally are collected in blocks of 4 when the plate number appears beside the stamp at any of the four corners of the sheet. Particularly relative to bi-colored stamps, an arrow block is now separated from a plate number block. Thus, in those situations, the two individual types of blocks might form a block of eight or 10, as the situation dictates.

PRINTING

Methods Used — all four basic forms of printing have been used in producing U.S. stamps, engraved, photogravure, lithography, and typography. Holography has been used on some stamps and stamped envelopes.

Engraved (Recess or Intaglio) — process where ink is received and held in lines depressed below the surface of the plate. Initially, in printing from such plates, damp paper was forced into the depressed lines and therefore picked up ink. Consequently, ink lines on the stamp are slightly raised. This also is noted from the back of the stamp, where depressions mark where ink is placed on the front.

When the ornamental work for a stamp is engraved by a machine, the process is called "engine turned" or lathe-work engraving. An example of such lathe-work background is the 3-cent stamp of 1861 (Scott Illustration No. A25).

Engraved stamps were printed only with flat plates until 1914, when rotary press printing was introduced. "Wet" and "dry" printings are explained in the note in the text of the catalogue following Scott 1029. The various Giori presses, used to print some U.S. stamps from 1957 (see Scott 1094, 4-cent Flag issue until the early 1990s), applied two or three different colored inks simultaneously.

The Huck Multicolor press, put into service at the Bureau of

Engraving and Printing in 1968, was first used to produce the 1969 Christmas stamp (Scott 1363) and the 6-cent Flag coil of 1969 (Scott 1338A). Developed by the Bureau's technical staff and the firm of graphic arts engineers whose name it bears, the Huck press printed, tagged with phosphor ink, gummed and perforated stamps in a continuous operation. Printing was accomplished in as many as nine colors. Fed by paper from a roll, the Huck Multicolor used many recess-engraved plates of smaller size than any used previously for U.S. stamp printing. Its product has certain characteristics which other U.S. stamps do not have. Post office panes of the 1969 Christmas stamp, for example, show seven or eight plate numbers in the margins. Joint lines appear after every two or four stamps. Other presses providing multiple plate numbers are the Andreotti, Champlain, Combination, Miller Offset, A Press, D Press and more.

Photogravure — the design of a stamp to be printed by photogravure usually is photographed through an extremely fine screen, lined in minute quadrille. The screen breaks up the reproduction into tiny dots, which are etched onto the plate and the depressions formed hold the ink. Somewhat similarly to engraved printing, the ink is lifted out of the recesses by the paper, which is pressed against the plate. Unlike engraved printing, however, the ink does not appear to be raised relative to the surface of the paper.

Gravure is most often used for multicolored stamps, generally using the three primary colors (red, yellow and blue) and black. By varying the dot matrix pattern and density of these colors, virtually any color can be reproduced. A typical full-color gravure stamp will be created from four printing cylinders (one for each color). The original multicolored image will have been photographically separated into its component colors.

For U.S. stamps, photogravure first appeared in 1967, with the Thomas Eakins issue (Scott 1335). The early photogravure stamps were printed by outside contractors until the Bureau obtained the multicolor Andreotti press in 1971. The earliest stamp printed on that press was the 8-cent Missouri Statehood issue of 1971 (Scott 1426).

Color control bars, dashes or dots are printed in the margin of one pane in each "Andreotti" sheet of 200, 160 or 128 stamps. These markings generally are collected in blocks of 20 or 16 (two full rows of one pane), which include the full complement of plate numbers, Mr. Zip and the Zip and Mail Early slogans.

Details on the Combination Press follow the listing for Scott 1703.

Modern gravure printing may use computer-generated dot-matrix screens, and modern plates may be of various types including metal-coated plastic. The catalogue designation of Photogravure (or "Photo") covers any of these older and more modern gravure methods of printing.

Lithography — this is the most common and least expensive process for printing stamps. In this method, the design is drawn by hand or transferred in greasy ink from an original engraving to the surface of a lithographic stone or metal plate. The stone or plate is wet with an acid fluid, which causes it to repel the printing ink except at the greasy lines of the design. A fine lithographic print closely resembles an engraving, but the lines are not raised on the face or depressed on the back. Thus there usually is a more dull appearance to the lithograph than to the engraving.

Offset Lithography (Offset Printing) — a modern development of the lithographic process. Anything that will print — type, woodcuts, photoengravings, plates engraved or etched in intaglio, half-tone plates, linoleum blocks, lithographic stones or plates, photogravure plates, rubber stamps, etc. — may be used. Greasy ink is applied to the dampened plate or form and an impression made on a rubber blanket. Paper immediately is pressed against the blanket, which transfers the ink. Because of its greater flexibility, offset printing has largely displaced lithography.

Because the processes and results obtained are similar, stamps printed by either of these two methods normally are considered to be "lithographed."

The first application of lithographic printing for any U.S. items listed in this catalogue was for Post Office seals, probably using stone printing bases. See also some Confederates States general issues. Offset lithography was used for the 1914 documentary revenues (Scott R195-R216). Postage stamps followed in 1918-20 (Scott 525-536) because of war-time shortages of ink, plates and manpower relative to the regular intaglio production.

The next use of offset lithography for postage stamps was in 1964 with the Homemakers issue (Scott 1253), in combination with intaglio printing. Many similar issues followed, all of which were produced by the combination of offset lithography and intaglio. The combination process serves best for soft backgrounds and tonal effects.

Typography — an exact reverse of engraved-plate printing, this process provides for the parts of the design which are to show in color to be left at the original level of the plate and the spaces between cut away. Ink is applied to the raised lines, and the pressure of the printing forces these lines more or less into the paper. The process impresses the lines on the face of the stamp and slightly raises them on the back. Normally, a large number of electrotypes of the original are made and assembled into a plate with the requisite number of designs for printing a sheet of stamps. Stamps printed by this process show greater uniformity, and the stamps are less expensive to print than with intaglio printing.

The first U.S. postal usage of an item printed by typography, or letterpress, under national authority was the 1846 "2" surcharge on the United States City Despatch Post 3-cent carrier stamp (Scott 6LB7). The next usage was the 1865 newspaper and periodical stamp issue, which for security reasons combined the techniques of machine engraving, colorless embossing and typography. This created an unusual first.

Most U.S. stamp typography consists of overprints, such as those for the Canal Zone, the Molly Pitcher and Hawaii Sesquicentennial stamps of 1928 (Scott 646-648), the Kansas-Nebraska control markings (Scott 658-679), Bureau-printed precancels, and "specimen" markings.

Embossed (relief) Printing — method in which the design is sunk in the metal of the die and the printing is done against a platen that is forced into the depression, thus forming the design on the paper in relief. Embossing may be done without ink (blind embossing), totally with ink, or a combination thereof. The U.S. stamped envelopes are an example of this form of printing.

Typeset — made from movable type.

Typeset Stamps — printed from ordinary printer's type. Sometimes electrotype or stereotype plates are made, but because such stamps usually are printed only in small quantities for temporary use, movable type often is used for the purpose. This method of printing is apt to show broken type and lack of uniformity. See Hawaii Scott 1-4 and 12-26.

Holograms — for objects to appear as holograms on stamps, a model exactly the same size as it is to appear on the hologram must be created. Rather than using photographic film to capture the image, holography records an image on a photoresist material. In processing, chemicals eat away at certain exposed areas, leaving a pattern of constructive and destructive interference. When the photoresist is developed, the result is a pattern of uneven ridges that acts as a mold. This mold is then coated with metal, and the resulting form is used to press copies in much the same way phonograph records are produced.

A typical reflective hologram used for stamps consists of a reproduction of the uneven patterns on a plastic film that is applied to a reflective background, ususally a silver or gold foil. Light is reflected off the background through the film, making the pattern present on the film visible. Because of the uneven pattern of the film, the viewer will perceive the objects in their proper three-dimensional relationships with appropriate brightness.

The first hologram on a stamp was produced by Austria in 1988 (Scott 1441).

Foil Application — A modern technique of applying color to stamps involves the application of metallic foil to the stamp paper. A pattern of foil is applied to the stamp paper by use of a stamping die. The foil usually is flat, but it may be textured. Canada Scott 1735 has three different foil applications in pearl, bronze, and gold. The gold foil was texured using a chemical-etch copper embossing die. The printing of this stamp also involved two-colored offset lithography plus embossing.

Additional Terms

Multicolored Stamps — Until 1957 when the Giori press was introduced, bicolored stamps were printed on a flat-bed press in two runs, one for each color (example: Norse-American Issue of 1925, Scott 620-621). In the flat-press bicolors, if the sheet were fed to the press on the second run in reversed position, the part printed in the second color would be upside down, producing an "invert" such as the famed Scott C3a.

With the Giori press and subsequent presses, stamps could be printed in more than one color at the same time.

Many bicolored and multicolored stamps show varying degrees of poor color registration (alignment). Such varieties are not listed in this catalogue.

Color Changeling — a stamp which, because of exposure to the environment, has naturally undergone a change of ink colors. Orange U.S. stamps of the early 1900's are notorious for turning brown as the ink reacts with oxygen. Exposure to light can cause some inks to fade. These are not considered color-omitted errors. Exposure to other chemicals can cause ink colors to change. These stamps are merely altered stamps, and their value to collectors is greatly diminished.

Color Trials — printings in various colors, made to facilitate selection of color for the issued stamp.

Double Impression — a second impression of a stamp over the original impression.

This is not to be confused with a "double transfer," which is a plate imperfection and does not show a doubling of the entire design. A double impression shows every line clearly doubled. See also "Printed on Both Sides."

Essay — a proposed design, a designer's model or an incomplete engraving. Its design differs in some way — great or small — from the issued item.

Inverted Center — bicolored or multicolored stamp with the center printed upside down relative to the remainder of the design. A stamp may be described as having an inverted center even if the center is printed first. See "Multicolored Stamps."

Flat Plate Printing — stamp printed on a flat-bed press, rather than on a rotary press. See "Plate."

Overprint — any word, inscription or image printed across the face of a stamp to alter its use or locality or otherwise to serve a special purpose. An example is U.S. Scott 646, the "Molly Pitcher" overprint, which is Scott 634 with a black overprinted inscription as a memorial to the Revolutionary War heroine. See "Surcharge."

Printed on Both Sides — Occasionally a sheet of stamps already printed will, through error, be turned over and passed through the press a second time, creating the rare "printed on both sides" variety.

On one side the impression is almost always poor or incomplete. This often is confused with an "offset," which occurs when sheets of stamps are stacked while the ink is still wet.

The "printed on both sides" variety will show the design as a positive (all inscriptions reading correctly) and the offset shows a reverse impression. See "Double Impression."

Progressive Proof — a type of essay that is an incomplete engraving of the finished, accepted die.

Proofs — trial printings of a stamp made from the original die or the finished plate.

Reprints and Reissues — are impressions of stamps (usually obsolete) made from the original plates or stones. If they are valid for postage and reproduce obsolete issues (such as U.S. Scott 102-111), the stamps are *reissues*. If they are from current issues, they are designated as *second, third,* etc., *printing*. If designated for a particular purpose, they are called *special printings*.

When special printings are not valid for postage, but are made from original dies and plates by authorized persons, they are *official reprints*. *Private reprints* are made from the original plates and dies by private hands. An example of a private reprint is that of the 1871-1932 reprints made from the original die of the 1845 New Haven, Conn., postmaster's provisional. *Official reproductions* or imitations are made from new dies and plates by government authorization. Scott will list those reissues that are valid for postage if they differ significantly from the original printing.

The U.S. government made special printings of its first postage stamps in 1875. Produced were official imitations of the first two stamps (listed as Scott 3-4), reprints of the demonetized pre-1861 issues (Scott 40-47) and reissues of the 1861 stamps, the 1869 stamps and the then-current 1875 denominations. Even though the official imitations and the reprints were not valid for postage, Scott lists all of these U.S. special printings.

Most reprints or reissues differ slightly from the original stamp in some characteristic, such as gum, paper, perforation, color or watermark. Sometimes the details are followed so meticulously that only a student of that specific stamp is able to distinguish the reprint or reissue from the original.

Rotary Press Printing — stamps which have been printed on a rotary-type press from curved plates. Rotary press-printed stamps are longer or wider than stamps of the same design printed from flat plates. All rotary press printings through 1953, except coil waste (such as Scott 538), exist with horizontal "gum breaker ridges" varying from one to four per stamp. See: "Plate."

Surcharge — overprint which alters or restates the face value or denomination of the stamp to which it is applied. An example is Scott K1-K18, U.S. stamps that were surcharged for use by U.S. offices in China. Many surcharges are typeset. See: "Overprint" and "Typeset."

Common Flaws

Cracked Plate — A term to describe stamps that show evidence that the plate from which they were printed was cracked.

Plate cracks have various causes, each which may result in a different formation and intensity of the crack. Cracks similar to the above illustration are quite common in older issues and are largely due to the plate being too quickly immersed in the cooling bath when being tempered. These cracks are known as *crystallization cracks*. A jagged line running generally in one direction and most often in the gutter between stamps is due to the stress of the steel during the rolling in or transferring process.

In curved (rotary) plates, there are two types of cracks. Once is the bending or curving crack, which is quite marked and always runs in the direction in which the plate is curved.

The accompanying illustration shows the second type, the *gripper crack*. This type is caused by the cracking of the plate over the slots cut in the underside of the plate, which receive the "grippers" that fasten the plate to the press. These occur only on curved plates and are to be found in the row of stamps adjoining the plate joint. These appear on the printed impression as light, irregularly colored lines, usually parallel to the plate joint line.

Rosette Crack — cluster of fine cracks radiating from a central point in irregular lines. These usually are caused by the plate receiving a blow.

Scratched Plate — caused by foreign matter scratching the plate, these usually are too minor to mention. See: "Gouge."

Gouge — exceptionally heavy and usually short scratches, these may be caused by a tool falling onto the plate.

Surface Stains — irregular surface marks resembling the outline of a point on a map. Experts differ on the cause. These are too minor to list.

PAPER

Paper falls broadly into two types: wove and laid. The difference in the appearance is caused by the wire cloth upon which the pulp is first formed.

Paper also is distinguished as thick or thin, hard or soft, and by its color (such as bluish, yellowish, greenish, etc.).

Wove — where the wire cloth is of even and closely woven nature, producing a sheet of uniform texture throughout. This type shows no light or dark figures when held to the light.

Laid — where the wire cloth is formed of closely spaced parallel wires crossed at much wider intervals by cross wires. The resultant paper shows alternate light and dark lines. The distances between the widely spaced lines and the thickness of these lines may vary, but on any one piece of paper they will be the same.

Pelure — type of paper which is very thin and semi-transparent. It may be either wove or laid.

Bluish — The 1909 so-called "bluish" paper was made with 35 percent rag stock instead of all wood pulp. The bluish (actually grayish-blue) color goes through the paper, showing clearly on back and face. See the note with Scott 331.

Manila — a coarse paper formerly made of Manila hemp fiber. Since about 1890, so-called "manila" paper has been manufactured entirely from wood fiber. It is used for cheaper grades of envelopes and newspaper wrappers and normally is a natural light brown. Sometimes color is added, such as in the U.S. "amber manila" envelopes. It may be either wove or laid.

Silk — refers to two kinds of paper found by stamp collectors.

One type has one or more threads of silk embedded in the substance of the paper, extending across the stamp. In the catalogues, this type of paper usually is designated as "with silk threads."

The other type, used to print many U.S. revenue stamps, has short silk fibers strewn over it and impressed into it during manufacture. This is simply called "silk paper."

Ribbed — paper which shows fine parallel ridges on one or both sides of a stamp.

India — a soft, silky appearing wove paper, usually used for proof impressions.

Double Paper — as patented by Charles F. Steel, this style of paper consists of two layers, a thin surface paper and a thicker backing paper. Double paper was supposed to be an absolute safeguard against cleaning cancellations off stamps to permit reuse, for any attempt to remove the cancellation would result in the destruction of the upper layer. The Continental Bank Note Co. experimented with this paper in the course of printing Scott 156-165. See "Rotary Press Double Paper."

China Clay Paper — See note preceding Scott 331.

Fluorescent or Bright Paper — See "Luminescence."

Rotary Press Double Paper — Rotary press printings occasionally are found on a double sheet of paper. The web (roll) of paper used on the press must be continuous. Therefore, any break in the web during the process of manufacture must be lapped and pasted. The overlapping portion, when printed upon, is known as a "double paper" variety. In some cases, the lapped ends are joined with colored or transparent adhesive tape.

Such results of splicing normally are removed from the final printed material, although some slip through quality control efforts.

In one instance known, two splices have been made, thus leaving three thicknesses of paper. All rotary press stamps may exist on double paper.

Watermarks — Closely allied to the study of paper, watermarks normally are formed in the process of paper manufacture. Watermarks used on U.S. items consist of the letters "USPS" (found on postage stamps). "USPOD" (found on postal cards), the Seal of the United States (found on official seals), "USIR" (found on revenue items), and various monograms of letters, numbers, and so on, found on stamped envelopes.

The letters may be single- or double-lined and are formed from dies made of wire or cut from metal and soldered to the frame on which the pulp is caught or to a roll under which it is passed. The action of these dies is similar to the wires causing the prominent lines of laid paper, with the designs making thin places in the paper which show by more easily transmitting light.

The best method of detecting watermarks is to lay the stamp face down on a dark tray and immerse the stamp in a commercial brand of watermark fluid, which brings up the watermark in dark lines against a lighter background. When collectors discuss watermarks, they refer to their appearance as viewed from the back of the stamp.

Note: This method of detecting watermarks may damage certain stamps printed with inks that run when immersed (such as U.S. Scott 1260 and 1832). It is advisable to first test a damaged stamp of the same type, if possible.

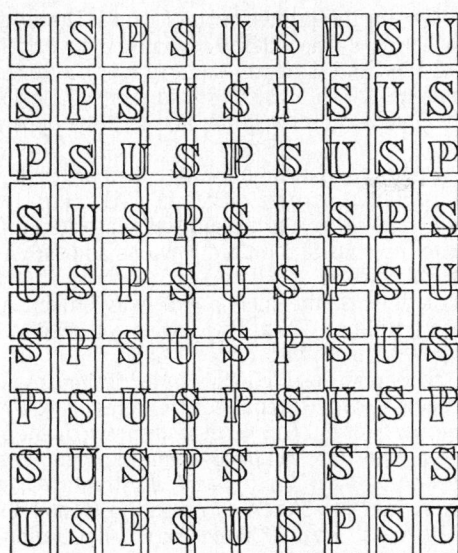

Wmk. 191
PERIOD OF USE
Postage: 1895-1910   Revenue: none

In the 1895-1903 U.S. issues, the paper was fed through the press so that the watermark letters read horizontally on 400 subject sheets and vertically on 200 subject sheets.

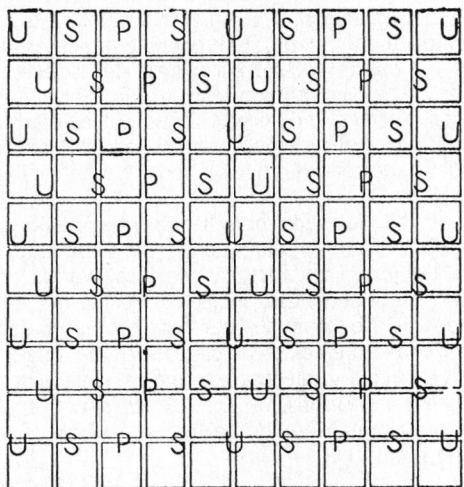

Wmk. 190
PERIOD OF USE
Postage: 1910-1916   Revenue: 1914

USIR
Wmk. 191R
PERIOD OF USE
Postage (unintentionally): 1895   Revenue: 1878-1958
(Scott 271a, 272a), 1951 (832b)

Paper watermarked "USPOD" was used for postal cards from 1873 to 1875. For watermarks used on stamped envelopes, see Stamped Envelopes & Wrappers section in this catalogue.

Watermarks may be found normal, reversed, inverted, inverted reversed and sideways, as seen from the back of the stamp.

Stitch Watermark — a type of watermark consisting of a row of short parallel lines. This is caused by the stitches which join the ends of the band on which the paper pulp is first formed. Stitch watermarks have been found on a great many issues, and may exist on all.

Grills

The grill consists of small square pyramids in parallel rows, impressed or embossed on the stamp. The object of the process is to break the fibers of the paper so that the ink from the cancellation would soak into the paper and make washing for reuse impossible. Grill impressions, when viewed from the face of the stamp, may be either "points up" or "points down." This process was used on U.S. Scott 79-101, 112-122 and 134-144, as well as some examples of 156-165 and 178-179.

Regular   Continuous   Split Grill
Grill   Marginal Grill

Continuous Marginal Grill — includes continuous rows of grill points impressed by the untrimmed parts of the ends of the grill rollers, noted as "end roller grill" on the 1870 and 1873 issues, and those grills which came from a continuous band lengthwise of the roller.

Split Grill — situation on a stamp showing parts of two or more grills, caused by a sheet being fed under the grill roller off center.

Double (or Triple) Grill — stamp showing two or more separate grill impressions. This is not to be confused with a split grill, which shows two or four partial impressions from a single grill impression.

Rotary Grills — grilled appearance occasionally found on rotary press printings that was produced unintentionally by a knurled roller during the perforating process.

Similarly, grill-like impressions can be left on stamps dispensed from vending machines.

SEPARATION

"Separation" is the general term used to describe methods used to separate stamps. The standard forms currently in use in the United States are perforating and die-cutting. These methods are done during the stamp production process, after printing. Sometimes these methods are done on-press or sometimes as a separate step. The earliest issues, such as the 1847 5¢ Franklin (Scott 1), did not have any means provided for separation. It was expected the stamps would be cut apart with scissors or folded and torn. These are examples of imperforate stamps. Many stamps were first issued in imperforate formats and were later issued with perforations. Therefore, care must be observed in buying single imperforate stamps, to be certain they were issued imperforate and are not perforated examples that have been altered by having the perforations trimmed away. Stamps issued imperforate usually are valued as singles. However, imperforate varieties of normally perforated stamps should be collected in pairs or larger multiples as indisputable evidence of their imperforate character.

Perforations

The chief style of separation of U.S. stamps has been perforating. This is produced by cutting away the paper between the stamps in a line of holes (usually round) and leaving little bridges of paper between the stamps. These little bridges are the "teeth" of the perforation and, of course, project from the stamp when it is torn from the pane.

Because the gauge of the perforation often is the distinguishing difference among stamps, it is necessary to measure and describe perforations by a gauge number. The standard for this measurement is the number of such teeth within two centimeters. Thus, we say that a stamp is perforated 12 or 10½ to note that there are either 12 or 10½ teeth counted within two centimeters.

Some later U.S. stamps are "stroke" perforated rather than "line" perforated. While it is difficult to tell the difference on a single stamp, with a block of four or more stamps the difference is more easily seen where the horizontal and vertical perforations cross. On the stroke-perforated items, the crossing point is clean and no holes are out of line. On the line-perforated stamps, the crossing point only rarely is perfect and generally there is a roughness.

Perforation Gauge — tool for measuring perforation, as described above.

Fine Perforation — perforation with small holes and teeth close together.

Coarse Perforation — perforation with large holes and teeth far apart, frequently irregularly spaced.

Rough Perforation — holes not clean cut, but jagged.

Compound Perforation — normally where perforations at the top and bottom differ from the perforations at the sides of the stamp. In describing compound perforations, the gauge of the top is given first, then the sides.

Some stamps are found where one side will differ from the other three, and in this case the reading will be the top first, then the right side, then the bottom, then the left side.

Double Perforation — often found on early U.S. revenue stamps and occasionally on postage issues, double perforations are applied in error. They do not generally command a premium over catalogue values of properly perforated stamps and are not to be confused with a variety found on occasional rotary press printings, where stamps adjacent to the center gutters will show the entire width of the gutter and a line of perforations on the far end of the gutter. These are caused by the sheet having been cut off center and are called "gutter snipes." They command a small premium.

Many double perforations were privately made to increase the value of the stamp, and are to be considered damaged stamps.

Electric Eye — an electronically controlled mechanical device acting as a guide in the operation of the perforating machine. Positive identification of stamps perforated by the electric eye process may be made by means of the distinctive marks in the gutters and margins of the full sheets on the printed web of paper. The original marks consisted of a series of heavy dashes dividing the vertical sheet gutter between the left and right panes (illustration A), together with a single line (margin line, illustration B), in the right sheet margin at the end of the horizontal sheet gutter between the upper and lower panes.

They first were used in 1933 on 400-subject plates for Scott 634, which was distributed to post offices in 1935 (used were plates 21149-50 and 21367-68). On these plates the plate numbers were placed opposite the ends of the third row of stamps from the top or bottom of the full sheet.

In later experiments, the margin line was broken into closely spaced thin vertical lines. Then it was again returned to its original form, but somewhat narrower.

In 1939, the Bureau of Engraving and Printing installed a new perforating machine which required a different layout to operate the centering mechanism. The vertical dashes remained the same, but the margin line was removed from the right sheet margin and a corresponding line ("gutter bar," illustration C) was placed in the left sheet margin at the end of the horizontal sheet gutter. Additional horizontal lines ("frame bars," illustration D) were added in the left sheet margin opposite the top frame line of the adjacent stamp design of all horizontal rows except the upper horizontal row of each left pane, where the frame bar is omitted. The plate numbers were moved back to their normal positions adjoining the corner stamps. Plates for the two types of machines could not be interchanged.

Later in 1939, a "convertible" plate was employed, consisting of a combination of the two previous layouts, the current one with the addition of a margin line (B) in its former position in the right sheet margin, thus making the perforation possible on either machine.

Originally laid out as 400-subject plates, electric-eye plates were later used for 200-subject horizontal or vertical format (commemorative, special delivery and airpost issues), 280-subject (Famous Americans and those with similar formats) and 180- and 360-subject plates (booklet panes of definitives, airpost, postal savings and war savings issues).

In laying out the plates for the 400-subject and 200-subject horizontal format issues, the marks retained the same relative position to the stamp designs. This was changed, however, in entering the design for the stamps of the 200-subject vertical format and 280-subject issues because the stamp designs were turned 90 degrees. That is, the designs were entered on the plates with the longer dimension horizontal. Although the electric eye marks were entered on the plates in the usual positions, on the printed sheet they appear as though shifted 90 degrees when the stamps are held in the customary upright position.

Thus a "horizontal" mark on a 400-subject or 200-subject horizontal format sheet would become a "vertical" mark on a 200-subject vertical format or 280-subject sheet. This situation has caused confusion among collectors and dealers in determining a definite description of the various marks. The designation of the position of the plate numbers also has not been uniform for the "turned" designs.

To solve this confusion, the United States Stamp Society (formerly the Bureau Issues Association) adopted a standard terminology for all the marks appearing on the electric eye sheets. Dashes (A), Margin Line (B), Gutter Bar (C) and Frame Bars (D), whereby each type of mark may be identified readily without referring to its plate-number position. The plate-number designation of the panes will continue to be established by holding the pane of stamps with the designs in an upright position; the corner of the pane on which the plate number appears will determine whether the pane is upper left, upper right, lower left, or lower right.

Die Cutting

The other major form of U.S. stamp separation is die-cutting. This is a method where a die in the pattern of separation is created that later cuts the stamp paper in a stroke motion. This process is used for self-adhesive postage stamps. Die-cutting can appear in straight lines, such as U.S. Scott 2522; shapes, such as U.S. Scott 1552; or imitating the appearance of perforations, such as U.S. Scott 2920.

On stamps where the die cutting is unintentionally omitted, the terms "die cutting omitted" or "imperforate" may be used interchangeably.

Rouletting

A third type of separation is seen on a few revenue stamps. In rouletting, the stamp paper is cut partly or wholly through in a series of short consecutive cuts, with no paper removed. The number of cuts made in a two-centimeter space determines the gauge of the rouletting, just as the number of perforations in two centimeters determines the gauge of the perforation.

GUM

The Illustrated Gum Chart in the first part of this introduction shows and defines various types of gum condition. Because gum condition has an important impact on the value of unused stamps, we recommend studying this chart and the accompanying text carefully.

The gum on the back of a stamp may be shiny, dull, smooth, rough, dark, white, colored or tinted. Most stamp gumming adhesives use gum arabic or dextrine as a base. Certain polymers such as polyvinyl alcohol (PVA) have been used extensively since World War II.

The *Scott Standard Postage Stamp Catalogue* does not list items by types of gum. The *Scott Specialized Catalogue of United States Stamps and Covers* does differentiate among some types of gum for certain issues.

Because collectors generally prefer unused stamps with original gum, many unused stamps with no gum have been regummed to make them more desirable (and costly) to collectors who want stamps with full original gum. Some used stamps with faint cancels have had these cancels chemically removed and have been regummed. Skillful regumming can be difficult to detect, particularly on imperforate stamps. Certification of such stamps by competent authorities is suggested.

Reprints of stamps may have gum differing from the original issues. In addition, some countries have used different gum formulas for different seasons. These adhesives have different properties that may become more apparent over time.

Many stamps have been issued without gum, and this catalogue will note this fact. See United States Scott PR33-PR56.

LUMINESCENCE

Kinds of Luminescence — Fluorescence and phosphorescence, two different luminescent qualities, are found in U.S. postage stamps and postal stationery. While all luminescent stamps glow when exposed to short-wave ultraviolet (UV) light, only those with phosphorescent properties display brief afterglow when the UV light source is extinguished.

Fluorescent or "Hi-Bright" Papers — The Bureau of Engraving and Printing, at one point accepting paper for the printing of stamps without regard to fluorescent properties, unknowingly used a mix of paper with infinitely varying amounts of fluorescent optical brighteners added during the papermaking process. In March 1964, to preserve uniformity of product and as a safeguard for an emerging but still incomplete plan for nationwide use of luminescent stamps, BEP purchasing specifications were amended to limit the use of fluorescent paper brighteners. The amended specification permitted paper with some brightener content, but excluded brilliantly glowing papers known in the printing trade as "hi-bright."

Stamps printed on such papers emit a distinctive, intense whitish-violet glow when viewed with either long or short-wave UV. In following years, stamps were produced on papers with lower levels of fluorescence permitted by amended specifications.

Tagged Stamps — The Post Office Department (now the U.S. Postal Service) field-tested automated mail-handling equipment to face, cancel and sort mail at rates up to 30,000 pieces an hour, by sensing UV-light-activated afterglow from phosphorescent substances. For the first tests at Dayton, Ohio, started after August 1, 1963, the 8-cent carmine airpost stamp (Scott C64a) was overprinted (tagged) with a so-called "nearly-invisible" calcium silicate compound which phosphoresces orange-red when exposed to short-wave UV. A facer-canceler, with modifications that included a rapidly cycling on-off UV light, activated the phosphor-tagged airpost stamps and extracted envelopes bearing them from the regular flow of mail.

While the airpost extraction test was still in progress, the entire printing of the City Mail Delivery commemorative (Scott 1238) was ordered tagged with a yellow-green glowing zinc orthosilicate compound intended for use with the automated recognition circuits to be tested with surface-transported letter mail.

After the first-day ceremonies October 26, 1963, at Washington, D.C., it was learned the stamps had been tagged to publicize the innovative test by coupling tagging with stamps memorializing "100 years of postal progress" and to provide the first national distribution of tagged stamps for collectors. Between October 28 and November 2, to broaden the scope of the test in the Dayton area, the 4-cent and 5-cent denominations of the regular issue then in use were issued with the same yellow-green glowing compound applied in an experimental tagging format (Scott 1036b, 1213b, 1213c, and 1229a).

By June 1964, testing had proven sufficiently effective for the Post Office Department to order all 8-cent airpost adhesive stamps phosphor-tagged for general distribution. By January 1966, all airpost stamps, regardless of denomination, were ordered tagged. Meanwhile, from 1963 through 1965, limited quantities of the Christmas issues were tagged for use in the continuing test in the Dayton area on the use of tagging to automatically position (face) and cancel mail. (Scott 1240a, 1254a-1257a, and 1276a).

On May 19, 1966, the use of phosphor-tagged stamps was expanded to the Cincinnati Postal Region, which then included offices in Ohio, Kentucky and Indiana. During the last half of 1966, primarily to meet postal needs of that region, phosphor-tagged issues were authorized to include additional denominations of regular issues, some postal stationery, and about 12 percent of each commemorative issue, starting with the National Park Service 5-cent issue (Scott 1314a) and continuing through the Mary Cassatt 5-cent commemorative (Scott 1322a). After January 1, 1967, most regular values through the 16-cent, all commemoratives, and additional items of postal stationery were ordered tagged.

Adhesive stamps precanceled by the Bureau of Engraving and Printing (Bureau precancels), however, were not tagged, with the exception of Scott 1394, 1596, 1608, and 1610. Because there was no need to cancel mail with these stamps and since precancel permit holders post such mail already faced, postal officials bypassed facer-canceler operations and avoided the cost of tagging.

Overall phosphorescent overprints, when newly issued, are practically invisible in ordinary light. After aging three to five years, the tagging can discolor and become more easily visible. When viewed with UV light, there is little change in the hue of either orange-red or yellow-green emitted light. Even though observable discoloration exists, the presence or absence of tagging is best determined by examination with UV light.

Bar, or block, tagging, instead of the usual overall phosphorescent overprint, was used for some stamps beginning with the Andreotti-printed Mail Order Business commemorative (Scott 1468). These are much easier to identify than the overall overprint, often without need for a UV light.

Band tagging, a bar extending across two or more stamps, was first used with Scott 1489-1498.

Beginning in the 1990s, many stamps are printed on prephosphored paper. Unlike overall tagging, in which the tagging substance is applied to the entire stamp after it is printed, prephosphored paper has the tagging substance added to the surface of the paper during the paper-making process, before printing occurs.

In the late 1990s, some stamps appeared with the tagging formed in the shape of the stamp design elements.

Most of the luminescent issues exist with the luminescent coating unintentionally omitted. Such stamps are termed "tagging omitted" errors and should not be confused with stamps printed intentionally without tagging, which are termed "untagged."

In some postal stationery, such as Scott U551, UC40, UX48a and UX55, the luminescent element is in the ink with which the stamp design is printed. The luminescent varieties of Scott U550 and UC37 were made by adding a vertical phosphorescent bar or panel to the left of the stamp imprint. On Scott UC42, this "glow-bar" passes through the tri-globe design.

The *Scott Specialized Catalogue of U.S. Stamps and Covers* lists different tagging types when more than one type is known on a stamp. Currently, these types can be large or small block tagging, overall tagging and prephosphored paper. Prephosphored paper is further broken down into two types, each listed separately. In the first case, the tagging compound is applied to uncoated paper, seeping into its fibers and creating a highly mottled, or blotchy, appearance under short-wave UV light. This type is designated in the catalogue listings as "prephosphored uncoated paper with embedded tagging showing a mottled appearance." Some specialists shorten this to "embedded phosphor paper (EP)." In the second case, the tagging compound is mixed with the substance used to coat the surface when making coated paper. The taggant lies on top of the paper and can be removed if the coating is scraped off. This surface phosphor can have a number of different appearances, including solid (or smooth), grainy solid, uneven or randomly wavy. These variations should not be confused with the heavy and irregular mottled appearance of embedded tagging. This second type of prephosphored paper is designated in the catalogue listings as "prephosphored coated paper with surface tagging showing a solid [or grainy solid, or uneven, etc.] appearance." Some specialists shorten this to "surface phosphor paper (SP)." In instances where different prephosphored coated papers are used in the printing or printings of a single stamp, giving rise to surface phosphor paper with different appearances as noted above, such differences are mentioned in footnotes.

NOTE: Users of UV light should avoid prolonged exposure, which can burn the eyes. Sunglasses (particularly those that feature a "UV block") or prescription eyeglasses, tinted or plain, screen the rays and provide protection.

POSTAL MARKINGS

Postal markings are those marks placed by postal employees of this and other countries on the stamp or cover or both. These marks may indicate the mailing place of a letter, date, rate, route, accounting between post offices, and so on.

In addition to the basic town designations, there are many varieties of supplemental markings. Among these are rate marks, route marks, obliterators, special dating markings usually found on advertised or dead-letter covers, transportation markings (rail, steam, ship, airpost, etc.), and service markings (advertised, forwarded, missent, second delivery, mail route, too late, charged, paid box, due, returned for postage, soldier's letter, held for postage, short paid, unpaid, not paid, paid, free, dead letter office, etc.).

These markings originated, for material mailed in what is now the United States, in the Colonial period when manuscript postal markings were first introduced under the Ordinance of December 10, 1672, of New York, which established an inland postal system between the colonies. A "Post Payd" is found on the first letter ever sent under the system, on January 22, 1673. Manuscript postal markings continued in use right through the pre-stamp period and even can be found on some letters today.

The earliest handstamp associated with American service is a "NEW/YORK" blank handstamp found on letters conveyed via the Bristol Packet line in 1710-12 between New York and England. Following the demise of this operation, the first regular handstamp postal markings were introduced at New York in 1756, when a post office packet service was established between Falmouth, England, and New York. The marking merely was "NEW YORK" on two lines of type. The marking (see illustration), with each word of the city name on a separate line, is represented in presentations such as this as "NEW/YORK." Similar markings were later introduced at other towns, such as ANNA/POLIS, by 1766; CHARLES/TOWN, by 1770; PHILA/DELPHIA, by 1766; HART/FORD, by 1766; while other offices received a single-line marking: BOSTON, by 1769; ALBANY, by 1773; PENSACOLA, by 1772; SAVANNA, by 1765; BALTIMORE, by 1772; and WMSBURG, by 1770.

Some of these early letters also bear a circular datestamp containing the month in abbreviated form, i.e., "IV" for June and "IY" for July, and the date in a 14-17mm circle (see illustration). Known from at least nine towns, these are called "Franklin marks" after Benjamin Franklin, then deputy postmaster general for the English crown. The marks also are known as "American Bishopmarks," to distinguish them from the Bishopmark used in England, which has a center line.

First U.S. Handstamp

Franklin Mark

During 1774-75, an American provisional postal system was established in opposition to that of the English crown. Both manuscript and handstamp markings have been attributed to it. This system was taken over by Congress on July 26, 1775, and the same markings were continued in use. The earliest reported Congressional marks are a manuscript "Camb Au 8" and a blue-green straightline "NEW*YORK*AU*24." Postal markings are known throughout Revolution, including English occupation markings. Most are manuscript.

In the post-war Confederation period, handstamped circular markings were introduced at Charleston, South Carolina, in 1778-1780, and later at New London, Connecticut. Straightlines and manuscripts continued to dominate until the use of oval markings became widespread about 1800, with circles becoming the predominant markings shortly thereafter.

Handstamp rate markings are known as early as the 1789 pennyweight markings of Albany. Such types of markings became more common in the 1830's and almost the standard by the "5"-and-"10"-cent rate period which began on July 1, 1845. This period also is when envelopes began to replace folded letter sheets. Before that date, envelopes were charged with an extra rate of postage. These "5," "10," and succeeding "3," "6," "5," and "10" rates of 1851-56 were common on domestic mail until prepayment became compulsory April 1, 1855, on all but drop or local letters domestically. The markings were common on foreign mail through about 1875.

Only 1.3 percent of all letters posted between 1847 and 1852 bore stamps. This proportion increased to 25 percent in 1852, 32 percent in 1853, 34 percent in 1854, 40 percent in 1855, and 64 percent in 1856. Stampless covers are commonplace, although there are some that are highly prized on the basis of their markings. Most are more common than stamped covers of the same period.

While the government began issuing handstamps as early as 1799 and obliterators in 1847, many postmasters were required, or at least permitted, to purchase their own canceling devices or to use pen strokes. Pen cancellations continued to be common in the smaller offices into the 1880's. Because of collector prejudice against pen-canceled stamps, many have ended up being "cleaned" (having the pen cancel removed). These are sold either as unused or with a different, faked cancellation to cover the evidence of cleaning. Ultraviolet light (long-wave) usually will reveal traces of the original pen markings.

From around 1850 until 1900, many postmasters used obliterators cut from wood or cork. Many bear fanciful designs, such as bees, bears, chickens, locks, eagles, Masonic symbols, flags, numerals and so on. Some of the designs symbolized the town of origin. These are not listed in this catalogue, for they owe their origin to the whim of some individual rather than a requirement of the postal regulations. Many command high prices and are eagerly sought by collectors. This has led to extensive forgery of such markings so that collectors are advised to check them carefully.

Rapid machine cancellations were introduced at Boston in 1880-90 and later spread across the country. Each of the various canceling machine types had identifiable characteristics, and collectors form collections based on type. One sub-specialty is that of flag cancellations. While handstamp flag designs are known earlier, the first machine flag cancellation was that of Boston in November-December 1894.

Specialists have noted that different canceling inks are used at different times, depending partly on the type of canceling device used. Rubber handstamps, prohibited in 1893 although used for parcel post and precanceling after that date, require a different type of ink from the boxwood or type-metal cancelers of the classic period, while a still different ink is used for the steel devices of the machine cancels.

Registry of letters was first authorized in this country in the Dutch colony of New Netherlands on overseas mail. Records of valuable letters were kept by postmasters throughout the stampless period while an "R" marking was introduced at Philadelphia in 1845 for registered mail. Cincinnati also had such a registry system. The first appearance of the word "registered" is on mail in November 1847, in manuscript, and in handstamp in May 1850. The official registration for U.S. mail, however, did not begin until July 1, 1855.

In recent years, the handstamped and machine types of cancellations have been standardized by the U.S. Postal Service and supplied to the various post offices.

Postmarks — markings to indicate the office of origin or manner of postal conveyance. In general terms, the postmark refers to the post office of origin, but sometimes there also are receiving postmarks of the post office of destination or of transit. Other post office markings include: advertised, forwarded, mail route, missent, paid, not paid, second delivery, too late, etc. Postmarks often serve to cancel postage stamps with or without additional obliterating cancels.

Cancellations — postal markings that make further use of stamps impossible. As used in the listings in this catalogue, cancellations include both postmarks used as cancellations and obliterations intended primarily to cancel (or "kill") the stamp.

Carrier Postmarks — usually show the words "Carrier" "City Delivery," or "U.S.P.O. Dispatch." They were applied to letters to indicate the delivery of mail by U.S. Government carriers. These markings should not be confused with those of local posts or other private mail services that used postmarks of their own. Free delivery of city mail by carriers was begun on July 1, 1863.

Free — handstamp generally used on free, franked mail. The marking occasionally is seen on early adhesives of the United States, used as a canceling device.

Railroad Postmarks — usually handstamps, the markings were used to postmark unpouched mail received by route agents of the Post Office Department traveling on trains on railway mail route. The route name in an agent's postmark often was similar to the name of the railroad or included the terminals of the route. The earliest known use of the word "Railroad" as a postmark is 1838. Route agents gradually became R.P.O. clerks, and some continued to use their handstamps after the route-agent service ceased June 30, 1882. The railroad postmarks of the 1850 period and later usually carried the name of the railroad.

A sub-group of railroad postmarks is made up of those applied in the early days by railroad station agents, using the railroad's ticket dating handstamp as a postmark. Sometimes the station agent was also the postmaster.

In 1864, the Post Office Department equipped cars for the general distribution of mails between Chicago and Clinton, Iowa.

Modern railroad marks, such as "R.P.O.," indicate transportation by railroad, and include Railway Post Office, Terminal Railway Post Office, Transfer Office, Closed Mail Service, Air Mail Field, and Highway Post Office.

Effective November 1, 1949, the Railway Mail Service was merged with others of like nature under the consolidated title Postal Transportation Service (PTS). The service was discontinued June 30, 1977.

The modern "railway marks" are quite common and are not the types referred to under cancellations as listed in this catalogue.

Way Markings — Way letters are those received by a mail carrier on his way between post offices and delivered at the first post office he reached. The postmaster ascertained where the carrier received them and charged, in his postbills, the postage from those places to destination. He wrote "Way" against those charges in his bills and also wrote or stamped "Way" on each letter. If the letter was exempt from postage, it should have been marked "Free."

The term "mail carrier" above refers to any carrier under contract to carry U.S. mail: a stage line, a horseback rider, or a steamboat or railroad that did not have a route agent on board. Only unpouched mail (not previously placed in a post office) was eligible for a Way fee of one cent. The postmaster paid this fee to the carrier, if demanded, for the carrier's extra work of bringing the letter individually to the post office. For a limited time at certain post offices, the Way fee was added to the regular postage. This explains the use of a numeral with the "Way" marking.

Packet Markings — Packet markings listed in this catalogue are those applied on a boat traveling on inland or coastal waterways. This group does not include mail to foreign countries that contains the words "British Packet," "American Packet," etc, or their abbreviations. These are U.S. foreign-mail exchange-office markings.

Listed packet markings are in two groups: 1) waterways route-agent markings that denote service exactly the same as that of the railroad route-agent markings, except that the route agent traveled on a boat instead of a train; 2) name-of-boat markings placed on the cover to advertise the boat or, as some believe, to expedite payment of Way and Steam fees at the post office where such letters entered the U.S. mails.

Occasionally waterways route-agent markings included the name of a boat, "S.B.," "STEAMBOAT," or merely a route number. Such supplemental designations do not alter the character of the markings as those of a route-agent.

19th Century U.S. Express Mail Postmarks — In pre-stamp days these represented either an extra-fast mail service or mail under the care of an express-mail messenger who also carried out-of-mail express packages. The service was permitted as a practical means of competing with package express companies that also carried mail in competition with the U.S. Mail. Several of these early postmarks were later used by U.S. Mail route agents on the New York-Boston and New York-Albany runs, or by U.S. steamboat letter carriers on the coastal run between Boston and St. John, New Brunswick.

Steamboat or **Steam Markings** — Except for the circular markings "Maysville Ky. Steam" and "Terre Haute Stb." and the rectangular "Troy & New York Steam Boat," these markings contain only the word "STEAMBOAT" or "STEAM," with or without a rating numeral. They represent the same service as that of Way markings, except that the carrier was an inland or coastal steamer that had no contract to carry U.S. mails. Such boats, however, were required by law to carry to the nearest post office any mail given them at landings. The boat owner was paid a two-cent fee for each letter so delivered, except on Lake Erie where the fee was one-cent. At some post offices, the Steamboat fee was added to regular postage. In 1861, the two-cent fee was again added to the postage, and in 1863 double postage was charged.

Ship Postmarks — postal markings indicating arrival on a private ship (one not under contract to carry mail). This marking was applied to letters delivered by such ships to the post office at their port of entry as required by law, for which they received a fee and the letters were taxed with a specified fee for the service in place of the ordinary open postage.

The use of U.S. postage stamps on ship letters is unusual, except for letters from Hawaii, because the U.S. inland postage on ship letters from a foreign point did not need to be prepaid. "U.S. SHIP" is a special marking applied to mail posted on naval vessels, especially during the Civil War period.

Steamship Postmarks — akin to Ship postmarks, but they appear to have been used mostly on mail from Caribbean or Pacific ports to New Orleans or Atlantic ports carried on steamships having a U.S. mail contract. An associated numeral usually designates the through rate from where the letter was received by the ship to its inland destination.

Receiving Mark — postal marking placed on the back of envelopes by the receiving post office to indicate the name of the office and date of arrival. It also is known as a "backstamp." Generally discontinued about 1913, the marking was employed for a time on airmail service until it was found the practice slowed the service. Receiving markings now are used on regisered and special-delivery mail.

Miscellaneous Route Markings — wordings associated with the previously described markings include "Bay Route," "River Mail," "Steamer," "Mail Route," etc. Classification of the marking ordinarily is evident from the use, or it can be identified from publications on postal markings.

U.S. Foreign-Mail Exchange-Office Markings — These served to meet the accounting requirements of the various mail treaties before the Universal Postal Union was established. The markings usually designate the exchange office or the carrier (British Packet, Bremen Packet, American Packet, etc.). Sometimes these markings are a restatement of the through rate, or a numeral designating the amount credited or debited to the foreign country as a means of allocating the respective parts of the total postage, according to conditions of route, method of transit, weight, etc.

Gridiron Cancellation — most common type of cancellation on early U.S. stamps. The marking consists of a circle enclosing parallel lines. There are many varieties of grid cancellations.

Paid Markings — generally consist of the word "PAID," sometimes within a frame, indicating regular postage prepaid by the sender of a letter. They are found as separate handstamps, within town or city postmarks, and as a part of obliterating cancels. In each case, the "paid" marking may be used with or without an accompanying or combined rate numeral indication.

Precancels — stamps having the cancellation applied before the article is presented for mailing. The purpose is to reduce handling and speed up the mails. A permit is required for use by the public, except for special cases, such as the experiments using Scott 1384a, 1414a-1418a, or 1552 for Christmas mail. Normally the precanceling is done with devices not used for ordinary postal service. Most precancellations consist of the city and state names between two lines or bars.

Precancels are divided into two groups: locals and Bureaus. Locals were printed, usually from 100-subject plates, or handstamped, usually by means of a 10- or 25-subject device having a rubber, metal or vinyl surface, at the town using the stamps. Most locals were made with devices furnished by the Post Office Department and the Postal Service, but a number were made with devices created in the city using them. Early locals include the printed "PAID" or "paid" on Scott 7 and 9, "CUMBERLAND, ME." on Scott 24-26 and the Glen Allen, Virginia stars. The U.S. Postal Service discontinued the practice of local precanceling as of July 5, 2007.

Many styles of precancellation are known. More than 600,000 different precancels exist from more than 20,000 post offices in the United States.

The Bureaus, or Bureau Prints, were precancels furnished to the post offices by the Post Office Department in Washington. For 75 years these were printed by the Bureau of Engraving and Printing, hence the name "Bureaus."

In late 1991, the American Bank Note Co. and J.W. Fergusson and Sons for Stamp Venturers also began producing precanceled stamps under contract with the Postal Service. Other companies have followed. Because the stamps go to the local post office from the same source, the Postal Service, and the method of production is essentially the same as used by the BEP, the term "Bureau precancel" has been retained in this catalogue. The cancellations consist of the name of the city and state where the stamps are to be used, lines or the class of mail. They originated in 1916, when postal officials were seeking ways to reduce costs as well as increase the legibility of the overprint. The BEP was low bidder in three cities,

which resulted in the "experimentals." These 16 denominations, including two postage dues, were issued for Augusta, Maine (one value); Springfield, Massachusetts (14 values); and New Orleans (six values) in quanities ranging from 4,000,000 down to 10,000. Electrotype plates mounted on a flat-bed press were used to print the precancellations.

Regular production of Bureau precancels began on May 2, 1923, with Scott 581 precanceled "New York, N.Y." All regular Bureaus until 1954 were produced by the Stickney rotary press, whereby the stamps, immediately after printing, pass under the precanceling plates. Then the roll is gummed, perforated and cut into sheets or coils. Since 1954, a variety of printing methods have been used.

Precancels are listed in this catalogue only if the precanceled stamp is different from the nonprecanceled version (untagged stamps such as Scott 1582a); or, if the stamp only exists precanceled (Scott 2265). Classic locals and experimental Bureaus also are included as cancellations. See Service Indicator.

Service Indicator — inscription included in the design of the stamp to indicate the category of postal service to be rendered. The first regular postage stamp to include a service indicator was the 1976 7.9-cent Drum coil stamp of the Americana series (Scott 1615), which was for bulk rate mailings. This stamp was issued with Bureau precancels for proper usage from 107 cities. Examples without the Bureau precancellation were for philatelic purposes.

A second category of service indicator came about when the USPS began to include the service inscription between the lines of the Bureau precancellation. Examples of this group are "Bulk Rate" and "Nonprofit Organization."

Finally, with the 16.7-cent Transportation coil (Scott 2261), issued July 7, 1988, the USPS went back to including the service indicator in the design, with the indicator serving as the cancellation. With the precancellation now part of the design, the USPS stopped offering tagged versions of the stamps for collectors. The only so-called precancels currently in use are the service class/rate inscribed coils, and mailers' postmarks. This change was announced in *Postal Bulletin* 22210, dated July 5, 2007.

In all cases, the "service indicator" stamp does not normally receive an additional cancellation when used for the indicated service. For examples see Postal Markings - Bureau Precancels.

Tied On — when the cancellation (or postmark) extends from the stamp to the envelope.

Postal Markings - Cancellation Examples

Numerals
Values are for rating marks such as those illustrated. Later types of numerals in grids targets, etc., are common.

PAID ALL
PAID

The common Boston Paid cancellation
(Values are for types other than this)

STEAMBOAT
SHIP STEAM
FREE

Steamship

Steamboat
(Route agent marking)

RAILROAD LINE STEAMER
St. Louis, Cairo and New Orleans
CHAMPION
Leaves New Orleans for Cairo and St. Louis. MAR 25
Packet Boat
(Name-of-boat marking)

Packet Boat
(Name-of-boat marking)

Packet Boat
(Name-of-boat marking)

Railroad
(Route agent marking)

U.S. Express Mail
(Route agent marking)

(In red on letter to Germany via Prussian Closed Mail, via British Packet. Credits 7 cents to Prussia.)

Carrier

Canadian

Express Company

Army Field Post

Town

Year dated

U.S. Postmark used in China

Vera Cruz, Mexico 1914

Exposition Station
Used while exposition is open. Many styles.

Exposition advertising
Used before exposition opens. Many styles.

U.S. Postmark used in Japan

New York City Foreign Mail — A group of design cancellations used between 1871 and 1877 in New York City on outgoing foreign mail only. This group of handstamps totals about 200 different fancy stars, geometric designs, wheels conventionalized flowers, etc., the majority within a circle 26-29 mm in diameter.

Patent Defacing Cancellations — When adhesive stamps came into general use, the Post Office Department made constant efforts to find a type of cancellation which would make the reuse of the stamp impossible. Many patents were granted to inventors, and some of the cancellations (killers) came into more or less general use. Some of them appear in combination with the town postmarks.

About 125 different types are known on the stamps issued up to about 1887. Their principal use and greatest variety occur on Scott 65, 147, 158, 183 and 184.

Patent cancellations generally fall into three groups:

1) Small pins or punches which pierce the paper or depress it sufficiently to break the fiber.

2) Sharp blades or other devices for cutting the paper.

3) Rotation of a portion of the canceler so that part of the paper is scraped away.

1. Dot punches through paper   2. Blades cut the paper

2. Small circle cuts the paper   3. Scraped in the shaded circle

Supplementary Mail — markings which designate the special post office service of dispatching mail after the regular mail closed. Two kinds of supplementary mail were available:

1. Foreign mail. For New York, the postmaster general established in 1853 a fee of double the regular rate. This paid to get the mail aboard ship after the regular mail closing and before sailing time. The service continued until 1939. Postmark Types A, D, E, F, and G were used.

2. Domestic mail. For Chicago, at no extra fee, supplementary mail entitled a letter to catch the last eastbound train. Postmark Types B and C were used. No foreign destination was implied.

Similar service with "Supplementary" in the postmark apparently was available in Philadelphia and possibly elsewhere.

Type A   Type D   Type E

Type F
Combination Handstamp
(Also comes with numeral "1")
(Stamps with numeral cancel alone do not qualify for Supplementary Mail cancel premiums.)

Type G (also with other numerals)

Type B   Type C

Military Postmarks – Although mail from soldiers and sailors exists for all of the wars back to the American Revolution, such early letters were ordinarily sent through nearby civilian post offices. In fact, the first postal stations specifically for the handling of military mail were opened during the Spanish-American War in 1898. They were initially set up at training camps in the U.S. However, as the actual conflict took place in the Spanish colonies in the Caribbean and the Pacific, 77 special post offices were opened to handle military mail in Cuba, Puerto Rico, Guam and the Philippines. Most of these offices were issued cancels inscribed "Military Postal Station No. __" with the name of the town and territory in which they were located.

For many years, the warships of the U.S. Navy did not have post offices, so sailors' mail was simply deposited at the next convenient port. However, in 1908 the creation of on-board postal facilities was authorized, resulting in new postmarks showing the name of each vessel, thus creating a vast new collecting field. During both World Wars, these were replaced with generic cancels reading simply "U.S. Navy" so that they would not provide any information about ships' names or locations to enemy agents.

When the United States entered World War I on April 6, 1917, a vast expansion of U.S. military forces was required. This had to be met with an equally large expansion of postal facilities. Many post offices were opened at training camps in the U.S. In addition, an entirely new system of Army Post Offices (APOs) was created overseas, with the first being opened at St. Nazaire, France, on July 10, 1917. This system eventually involved about 200 different military stations. Most were located in France, but some were in Italy. Following the Armistice on November 11, 1918, other offices were opened in Belgium, Germany, Luxembourg and The Netherlands.

Elsewhere, American forces were involved in military interventions in China, the Caribbean and Latin America (Cuba, Dominican Republic, Haiti, Mexico and Nicaragua). In each case, U.S. military postal facilities were opened to serve the troops, thus creating new postal markings that are collected by specialists.

During World War II, the first new U.S. military post offices were opened in connection with the bases acquired from Great Britain in exchange for a fleet of old destroyers. The first of these offices was opened on January 15, 1941, using a postmark inscribed "American Forces in Newfoundland." When other offices opened, the inscription was changed to "American Base Forces" and an APO number added. After the U.S. entered the war on December 7, 1941, there was a vast expansion of the system, and the postmarks were changed to "U.S. Army Postal Service" with an APO number.

At first, members of the AEF were allowed to send mail from the APOs to the U.S., its territories and possessions at domestic postage rates, which were 1¢ for postcards and 2¢ for letters. However, from October 4, 1917, the troops were granted free postage for such items, although they were still required to pay at domestic rates for special services such as registration, special delivery and parcel post.

Civilians serving with the army, war correspondents and workers with welfare organizations, including the American Red Cross, YMCA, Knights of Columbus and Salvation Army, were permitted to use the APOs but had to pay domestic postage, including the war tax of 1¢ per piece that was in effect from November 2, 1917, until June 30, 1919.

Some American units participated in the Allied intervention in Russia in 1918-1920, including Siberia and North Russia. A U.S. postal agency was opened in Vladivostok, Siberia, to handle mail from the AEF-Siberia, but the troops in North Russia used the British postal facilities (with their so-called "Polar Bear" markings).

During the course of the war and its aftermath, more than 1,000 APOs were created, serving Army and Air Force personnel around the world. Some of these were open for very short periods, and their postmarks are scarce. As in World War I, the troops were granted free franking for surface cards and letters from April 1, 1942, to December 31, 1947, but postage was required for special services, including airmail, at normal domestic rates.

More recently, of course, there is military mail from the conflicts in Korea, Vietnam, Kuwait, Afghanistan and Iraq, not to mention smaller events in places like Grenada, Panama and Kosovo. It should be noted that the APO numbering system was switched over to five digits in 1965, to bring it in line with the civilian zip code designations.

In looking at covers, collectors will find that most military mail from World War I on bears evidence of military and/or civilian censorship, after which the letters were permitted to be forwarded.

Readers desiring more information on military postal markings, censorship and the handling of military mail, or a list of available publications on these and related subjects, are invited to visit www.MilitaryPHS.org, the website of the Military Postal History Society.

Postal Markings - Bureau Precancels

AUGUSTA MAINE

NEW ORLEANS LA.

SPRINGFIELD MASS.

Experimentals

PERU IND.

LANSING MICH.

SAINT LOUIS MO.

New Orleans La.

San Francisco Calif.

PORTLAND ME.

LAKEWOOD N. J.

KANSAS CITY MO.

POUGHKEEPSIE N. Y.

LONG ISLAND CITY, N. Y.

CORPUS CHRISTI TEXAS

ATLANTA GEORGIA

ATLANTA GA.

PEORIA IL

CINCINNATI OH

Postal Markings - Service Indicators

Blk. Rt. CAR-RT SORT

Bulk Rate

Nonprofit Org.

Nonprofit Org.

PRESORTED FIRST-CLASS

ZIP+4

Postal Markings - Local Precancels

QUINCY ILLINOIS

FITCHBURG MASS.

LOS ANGELES CALIF.

Fergus Falls Minn.

COVINGTON KY.

REDWOOD CITY CALIF.

BELMONT CALIF.

ELGIN ILLINOIS

Electroplates

Ashland Wis.

PALMYRA N. Y.

Northhampton MASS.

DES PLAINES ILL.

RICHMOND VA.

BROOKFIELD ILLINOIS

PAONIA COLO.

GOSHEN IND

TOWER CITY N. DAK.

NEW BRUNSWICK N. J.

ORLANDO, FLA.

RICHTON PARK ILL.

MULINO, OREG.

PINE HILL N.Y.

FARRELL, PA

SACRAMENTO CA

Handstamps

GENERAL GLOSSARY

Scott Publishing Co. uses the following terms in its catalogues, as appropriate. Definitions follow each term.

Imperforate — stamps without perforations, rouletting, or other form of separation. Some self-adhesive stamps are die cut with straight lines. They look imperforate, but they are not.

Type A   Type B

Part-Perforate — Stamps with perforations on the two opposite sides, the other two sides remaining imperforate. See Coil Stamps.

Vertical Pair, Imperforate Horizontally — (Type A illustrated) indicating that a pair of stamps is fully perforated vertically, but has no horizontal perforations.

Horizontal Pair, Imperforate Vertically — (Type A) indicating that a pair of stamps is fully perforated horizontally but has no vertical perforations.

Vertical Pair, Imperforate Between — (Type B illustrated) indicating that the vertical pair is fully perforated at the top, sides and bottom, but has no perforations between the stamps.

Horizontal Pair, Imperforate Between — (Type B) indicating that the horizontal pair is fully perforated at the top, sides and bottom, but has no perforations between the stamps.

Note: Of the above two types (A and B), Type A is the more common.

Blind Perforations — the slight impressions left by the perforating pins if they fail to puncture the paper. While multiples of stamps showing blind perforations may command a slight premium over normally perforated stamps, they are not imperforate errors. Fakers have removed gum from stamps to make blind perforations less evident.

Diagonal   *Horizontal*   *Vertical*

Bisect — Stamps cut in half so that each part prepaid postage. These items were used in emergencies where no stamps of the lower denomination were available. These may be diagonal, horizontal or vertical, as shown. Listings are for bisects on full covers with the bisected stamp tied to the cover on the cut side. Those on piece or part of a cover sell for considerably less. "Half-stamps" that receive a surcharge or overprint are not considered bisects.

This catalogue does not list unofficial bisects after the 1880's.

Block of Four, Imperforate Within — Examples exist of blocks of four stamps that are perforated on all four outside edges, but lack both horizontal and vertical perforations within the block. Scott 2096c, the Smokey the Bear commemorative, is an accidental example of this phenomenon. Scott RS173j and RS174j are examples of a situation where internal perforations were omitted intentionally to create 4-cent "stamps" from four 1-cent stamps.

Rouletting — short consecutive cuts in the paper to facilitate separation of the stamps, made with a toothed wheel or disc.

Booklets — Many countries have issued stamps in booklets for the convenience of users. This idea is becoming increasingly popular today in many countries. Booklets have been issued in all sizes and forms, often with advertising on the covers, on the panes of stamps or on the interleaving.

The panes may be printed from special plates or made from regular sheets. All panes from booklets issued by the United States and many from those of other countries are imperforate on three sides, but perforated between the stamps. Any stamplike unit in the pane, either printed or blank, which is not a postage stamp, is considered a *label* in the catalogue listings. The part of the pane through which stitches or staples bind the booklet together, or which affixes the pane to the booklet cover, is considered to be a *binding stub* or *tab*.

Scott lists and values booklets in this volume. Except for panes from Canal Zone, handmade booklet panes are not listed when they are fashioned from existing sheet stamps and, therefore, are not distinguishable from the sheet-stamp foreign counterparts.

Panes usually do not have a "used" value because there is little market activity in used panes, even though many exist used.

Cancellations — the marks or obliterations put on a stamp by the authorities to show that it has done service and is no longer valid for use. If made with a pen, it is a "pen cancellation." When the location of the post office appears in the cancellation, it is a "town cancellation." When calling attention to a cause or celebration, it is a "slogan cancellation." Many other types and styles of cancellations exist, such as duplex, numerals, targets, etc.

Coil Stamps — stamps issued in rolls for use in dispensers, affixing and vending machines. Those of the United States and its territories are perforated horizontally or vertically only, with the outer edges imperforate. Coil stamps of some countries, such as Great Britain, are perforated on all four sides.

Commemorative Stamps — Special issues that commemorate some anniversary or event or person. Usually such stamps are available for a limited period concurrently with the regular issue of stamps. Examples of commemorative issues are Scott 230-245, 620-621, 946, 1266, C68, and U218-U221.

Covers — envelopes, with or without adhesive postage stamps, which have passed through the mail and bear postal or other markings of philatelic interest. Before the introduction of envelopes in about 1840, people folded letters and wrote the address on the outside. Many people covered their letters with an extra sheet of paper on the outside for the address, producing the term "cover." Used air letter sheets and stamped envelopes also are considered covers. Stamps on paper used to cover parcels are said to be "on wrapper." ("Wrapper" also is the term used for postal stationery items that were open at both sides and wrapped around newspapers or pamphlets.) Often stamps with high face values are rare on cover, but more common on wrapper. Some stamps and postal stationery items are difficult to find used in the manner for which they were intended, but quite common when used to make philatelic items such as flight or first day covers. High face-value stamps also may be more common on package address tags. See Postal Cards.

Earliest Documented Use (EDU) — For stamps that do not have a designated first day of issue, the earliest documented use is the date when a stamp was first used in the U.S. mails. These dates are listed in the U.S. Specialized catalogue, and new dates must be documented with recognized certificates from leading expertizing committees.

Error — stamps having some unintentional major deviation from the normal. Errors include, but are not limited to, mistakes in color, paper, or watermark; inverted centers or frames on multicolor printing; missing color;inverted or double surcharges or overprints; imperforates and part-perforates; unintentionally omitted tagging; and double impressions. A factually wrong or misspelled inscription, if it appears on all examples of a stamp, even if corrected later, is not classified as a philatelic error.

Color-Omitted Errors — This term refers to stamps where a missing color is caused by the complete failure of the printing plate to deliver ink to the stamp paper or any other paper. Generally, this is caused by the printing plate not being engaged on the press or by the ink station running dry of ink during printing.

Color-Missing Errors — This term refers to stamps where a color or colors were printed somewhere but do not appear on the finished stamp. There are four different classes of color-missing errors, and this catalogue indicates with a two-letter code appended to each such listing what caused the color to be missing:

FO = A *foldover* of the stamp sheet during printing may block ink from appearing on a stamp. Instead, the color will appear on the back of the foldover (where it might fall on the back of the selvage or perhaps on the back of another stamp). FO also will be used in the case of foldunders, where the paper may fold underneath the other stamp paper and the color will print on the platen.

EP = A piece of *extraneous paper* falling across the plate or stamp paper will receive the printed ink. When the extraneous paper is removed, an unprinted area of stamp paper remains and shows partially or totally missing colors.

CM = A misregistration of the printing plates during printing will result in a *color misregistration*, and such a misregistration may result in a color not appearing on the finished stamp.

PS = A *perforation shift* after printing may remove a color from the finished stamp. Normally, this will occur on a row of stamps at the edge of the stamp pane.

First Day Cover — A philatelic term to designate the use of a certain stamp (on cover) or postal stationery item on the first day of issue at a place officially designated for such issue or so postmarked. Current U.S. stamps may have such a postal marking applied considerably after the actual issue date.

Gum Breaker Ridges — Colorless marks across the backs of some rotary press stamps, impressed during manufacture to prevent curling. Many varieties of "gum breaks" exist.

Measurements — When measurements are given in the Scott catalogues for stamp size, grill size or any other reason, the first measurement given is always for the top and bottom dimension, while the second measurement will be for the sides (just as perforation gauges are measured). Thus, a stamp size of 15mm x 21mm will indicate a vertically oriented stamp 15mm wide at top and bottom, and 21mm tall at the sides. The same principle holds for measuring or counting items such as U.S. grills. A grill count of 22x18 points (B grill) indicates that there are 22 grill points across by 18 grill points down.

Original Gum — A stamp is described as "O.G." if it has the original gum as applied when printed. Some are issued without gum, such as Scott 730, 731, 735, 752, etc; government reproductions, such as Scott 3 and 4; and official reprints.

Overprinted and Surcharged Stamps — Overprinting is a wording or design placed on stamps to alter the place of use (e.g., "Canal Zone" on U.S. stamps), to adapt them for a special purpose ("I.R." on 1-cent and 2-cent U.S. stamps of the 1897-1903 regular issue for use as revenue stamps. Scott R153-R155A), or for a special occasion

(U.S. Scott 647-648).

Surcharge is an overprint that changes or restates the face value of the item.

Surcharges and overprints may be handstamped, typeset or, occasionally, lithographed or engraved. A few handwritten overprints and surcharges are known. The world's first surcharge was a handstamped "2" on the United States City Despatch Post stamps of 1846.

Postal Cards — cards that have postage printed on them. Ones without printed stamps are referred to as "postcards."

Proofs and Essays — *Proofs* are impressions taken from an approved die, plate or stone in which the design and color are the same as the stamp issued to the public. *Trial color proofs* are impressions taken from approved dies, plates or stones in varying colors. An *essay* is the impression of a design that differs in some way from the stamp as issued.

Provisionals — stamps issued on short notice and intended for temporary use pending the arrival of regular (definitive) issues. They usually are issued to meet such contingencies as changes in government or currency, shortage of necessary denominations, or military occupation.

In the 1840's, postmasters in certain American cities issued stamps that were valid only at specific post offices. Postmasters of the Confederate States also issued stamps with limited validity. These are known as "postmaster's provisionals." See U.S. Scott 9X1-9X3 and Confederate States Scott 51X1.

Se-Tenant — joined, referring to an unsevered pair, strip or block of stamps differing in design, denomination or overprint. See U.S. Scott 2158a. Unless the se-tenant item has a continuous design (see U.S. Scott 1451a, 1694a), the stamps do not have to be in the same order as shown in the catalogue (see U.S. Scott 2158a).

Tete Beche — A pair of stamps in which one is upside down in relation to the other. Some of these are the result of intentional sheet arrangements, i.e. Morocco Scott B10-B11. Others occurred when one or more electrotypes accidentally were placed upside down on the plate. See Hawaii Scott 21a and 22a. Separation of the stamps, of course, destroys the tete beche variety.

Specimens — One of the regulations of the Universal Postal Union requires member nations to send samples of all stamps they put into service to the International Bureau in Switzerland. Member nations of the UPU receive these specimens as samples of what stamps are valid for postage. Many are overprinted, handstamped or initial-perforated "Specimen," "Canceled" or "Muestra."Stamps distributed to government officials or for publicity purposes, and stamps submitted by private security printers for official approval also may receive such defacements.

These markings prevent postal use, and all such items generally are known as "specimens." There is a section in this catalogue devoted to this type of material. U.S. officials with "specimen" overprints and printings are listed in the Special Printings section.

Splice — The junction of two rotary-press printings by butting the ends of the web (roll) of paper together and pasting a strip of perforated translucent paper on the back of the junction. The two-stamp specimen to show this situation is a "spliced pair."

Splices occur when a web breaks and is repaired or when one web is finished and another begins.

Territorial and Statehood Dates

	Territorial Date	**Statehood Date**	
Alabama	Sept. 25, 1817	Dec. 14, 1819	Territory by enabling act of March 3, 1817, effective Sept. 25, 1817. Created out of part of existing Mississippi Territory.
Alaska	Oct. 18, 1867	Jan. 3, 1959	A district from Oct. 18, 1867, until it became an organized territory Aug. 24, 1912.
Arizona	Feb. 24, 1863	Feb. 14, 1912	This region was sometimes called Arizona before 1863 though still in the Territory of New Mexico.
Arkansas	July 5, 1819*	June 15, 1836	The territory was larger than the state. After statehood, the left-over area to the west had post offices that continued for some years to use an Arkansas abbreviation in the postmarks although really they were in the "Indian Country."
California		Sept. 9, 1850	Ceded by Mexico by the Treaty of Guadalupe-Hidalgo, concluded Feb. 2, 1848, and proclaimed July 4, 1848. From then until statehood, California had first a military government until Dec. 20, 1849, and then a local civil government. It never had a territorial form of government.
Colorado	Feb. 28, 1861	Aug. 1, 1876	
Connecticut		Jan. 9, 1788	The fifth of the original 13 colonies.
Delaware		Dec. 7, 1787	The first of the original 13 colonies.
Dakota	March 2, 1861	Nov. 2, 1889	Became two states: North and South Dakota.
Deseret	March 5, 1849		Brigham Young created the unofficial territory of Deseret. In spite of the fact that Utah Territory was created Sept. 9, 1850, Deseret continued to exist unofficially, in what is now Utah, at least as late as 1862.
Frankland or Franklin			This unofficial state was formed in Aug. 1784, in the northeast corner of what is now Tennessee, and the government existed until 1788. In reality it was part of North Carolina.
Florida	March 30, 1822	March 3, 1845	
Georgia		Jan. 2, 1788	The fourth of the original 13 colonies.
Hawaii	Aug. 12, 1898	Aug. 21, 1959	The territorial date given is that of the formal transfer to the United States, with Sanford B. Dole as first Governor.
Idaho	March 3, 1863	July 3, 1890	
Illinois	March 2, 1809*	Dec. 3, 1818	
Indiana	July 5, 1800*	Dec. 11, 1816	There was a residue of Indiana Territory which continued to exist under that name from Dec. 11, 1816 until Dec. 3, 1818, when it was attached to Michigan Territory.
Indian Territory		Nov. 16, 1907	In the region first called the "Indian Country," established June 30, 1834. It never had a territorial form of government. Finally, with Oklahoma Territory, it became the State of Oklahoma on Nov. 16, 1907.
Iowa	July 4, 1838	Dec. 28, 1846	
Jefferson	Oct. 24, 1859		An unofficial territory from Oct. 24, 1859, to Feb. 28, 1861. In reality it included parts of Kansas, Nebraska, Utah and New Mexico Territories, about 30% being in each of the first three and 10% in New Mexico. The settled portion was mostly in Kansas Territory until Jan. 29, 1861, when the State of Kansas was formed from the eastern part of Kansas Territory. From this date the heart of "Jefferson" was in unorganized territory until Feb. 28, 1861, when it became the Territory of Colorado.
Kansas	May 30, 1854	Jan. 29, 1861	
Kentucky		June 1, 1792	Never a territory, it was part of Virginia until statehood.
District of Louisiana	Oct. 1, 1804		An enormous region, it encompassed all of the Louisiana Purchase except the Territory of Orleans. Created by Act of March 26, 1804, effective Oct. 1, 1804, and attached for administrative purposes to the Territory of Indiana.
Territory of Louisiana	July 4, 1805		By Act of March 3, 1805, effective July 4, 1805, the District of Louisiana became the Territory of Louisiana.
Louisiana		April 30, 1812	With certain boundary changes, had been the Territory of Orleans.
District of Maine		March 16, 1820	Before statehood, what is now the State of Maine was called the District of Maine and belonged to Massachusetts.
Maryland		April 28, 1788	The seventh of the original 13 colonies.

	Territorial Date	Statehood Date	
Massachusetts		Feb. 6, 1788	The sixth of the original 13 colonies.
Michigan	July 1, 1805	Jan. 26, 1837	
Minnesota	March 3, 1849	May 11, 1858	
Mississippi	May 7, 1798	Dec. 10, 1817	Territory by Act of April 7, 1798, effective May 7, 1798.
Missouri	Dec. 7, 1812	Aug. 10, 1821	The state was much smaller than the territory. The area to the west and northwest of the state, which had been in the territory, was commonly known as the "Missouri Country" until May 30, 1854, and certain of the post offices in this area show a Missouri abbreviation in the postmark.
Montana	May 26, 1864	Nov. 8, 1889	
Nebraska	May 30, 1854	March 1, 1867	
Nevada	March 2, 1861	Oct. 31, 1864	
New Hampshire		June 21, 1788	The ninth of the original 13 colonies.
New Jersey		Dec. 18, 1787	The third of the original 13 colonies.
New Mexico	Dec. 13, 1850	Jan. 6, 1912	
New York		July 26, 1788	The 11th of the original 13 colonies.
North Carolina		Nov. 21, 1789	The 12th of the original 13 colonies.
North Dakota		Nov. 2, 1889	Had been part of the Territory of Dakota.
Northwest Territory	July 13, 1787		Ceased to exist March 1, 1803, when Ohio became a state. The date given is in dispute, Nov. 29, 1802 often being accepted.
Ohio		March 1, 1803	Had been part of Northwest Territory until statehood.
Oklahoma	May 2, 1890	Nov. 16, 1907	The state was formed from Oklahoma Territory and Indian Territory.
Oregon	Aug. 14, 1848	Feb. 14, 1859	
Orleans	Oct. 1, 1804		A territory by Act of March 26, 1804, effective Oct. 1, 1804. With certain boundary changes, it became the State of Louisiana, April 30, 1812.
Pennsylvania		Dec. 12, 1787	The second of the original 13 colonies.
Rhode Island		May 29, 1790	The 13th of the original 13 colonies.
South Carloina		May 23, 1788	The eighth of the original 13 colonies.
South Dakota		Nov. 2, 1889	Had been part of Dakota Territory.
Southwest Territory			Became the State of Tennessee, with minor boundary changes, June 1, 1796.
Tennessee		June 1, 1796	Had been Southwest Territory before statehood.
Texas		Dec. 29, 1845	Had been an independent Republic before statehood.
Utah	Sept. 9, 1850	Jan. 4, 1896	
Vermont		March 4, 1791	Until statehood, had been a region claimed by both New York and New Hampshire.
Virginia		June 25, 1788	The 10th of the original 13 colonies.
Washington	March 2, 1853	Nov. 11, 1889	
West Virginia		June 20, 1863	Had been part of Virginia until statehood.
Wisconsin	July 4, 1836	May 29, 1848	The state was smaller than the territory, and the left-over area continued to be called the Territory of Wisconsin until March 3, 1849.
Wyoming	July 29, 1868	July 10, 1890	

* The dates followed by an asterisk are one day later than those generally accepted. The reason is that the Act states, with Arkansas for example, "from and after July 4." While it was undoubtedly the intention of Congress to create Arkansas as a Territory on July 4, the U.S. Supreme Court decided that "from and after July 4," for instance, meant "July 5."

Territorial and statehood data compiled by Dr. Carroll Chase and Richard McP. Cabeen.

Domestic Letter Rates

Effective Date	Prepaid	Collect
1845, July 1		
Reduction from 6¢ to 25¢ range on single-sheet letters		
Under 300 miles, per ½ oz	5¢	5¢
Over 300 miles, per ½ oz	10¢	10¢
Drop letters	2¢	
1847-1848		
East, to or from Havana (Cuba) per ½ oz	12½¢	12½¢
East, to or from Chagres (Panama) per ½ oz	20¢	20¢
East, to or from Panama, across Isthmus, per ½ oz.	30¢	30¢
To or from Astoria (Ore.) or Pacific Coast, per ½ oz	40¢	40¢
Along Pacific Coast, per ½ oz	12½¢	12½¢
1847, July 1		
Unsealed circulars		
1 oz. or less	3¢	
1851, July 1		
Elimination of rates of 1847-1848 listed above		
Up to 3,000 miles, per ½ oz.	3¢	5¢
Over 3,000 miles, per ½ oz	6¢	10¢
Drop letters	1¢	
Unsealed circular		
1 oz. or less up to 500 miles	1¢	
Over 500 miles to 1,500 miles	2¢	
Over 1,500 miles to 2,500 miles	3¢	
Over 2,500 miles to 3,500 miles	4¢	
Over 3,500 miles	5¢	
1852, September 30		
Unsealed circulars		
3 oz. or less anywhere in U.S.	1¢	
Each additional ounce	1¢	
(Double charge if collect)		
1855, April 1		
Prepayment made compulsory		
Not over 3,000 miles, per ½ oz.	3¢	
Over 3,000 miles, per ½ oz.	10¢	
Drop letters	1¢	
1863, July 1		
Distance differential eliminated		
All parts of United States, per ½ oz.	3¢	
1883, October 1		
Letter rate reduced one-third		
All parts of United States, per ½ oz.	2¢	
1885, July 1		
Weight increased to 1 oz.		
All parts of United States, per 1 oz.	2¢	
1896, October 1		
Rural Free Delivery started		

Effective Date	Prepaid
1917, November 2	
War emergency	
All parts of United States, per 1 oz.	3¢
1919, July 1	
Restoration of pre-war rate	
All parts of United States, per 1 oz.	2¢
1932, July 6	
Rise due to depression	
All parts of United States, per 1 oz.	3¢
1958, August 1	
All parts of United States, per 1 oz.	4¢
1963, January 7	
All parts of United States, per 1 oz.	5¢
1968, January 7	
All parts of United States, per 1 oz.	6¢
1971, May 16	
All parts of United States, per 1 oz.	8¢
1974, March 2	
All parts of United States, per 1 oz.	10¢
1975, December 31	
All parts of United States, 1st oz.	13¢
1978, May 29	
All parts of United States, 1st oz.	15¢
1981, March 22	
All parts of United States, 1st oz.	18¢
1981, November 1	
All parts of United States, 1st oz.	20¢
1985, February 17	
All parts of United States, 1st oz.	22¢
1988, April 3	
All parts of United States, 1st oz.	25¢
1991, February 3	
All parts of United States, 1st oz.	29¢
1995, January 1	
All parts of United States, 1st oz.	32¢
1999, January 10	
All parts of United States, 1st oz.	33¢
2001, January 7	
All parts of United States, 1st oz.	34¢
2002, June 30	
All parts of United States, 1st oz.	37¢
2006, January 8	
All parts of United States, 1st oz.	39¢
2007, May 14	
All parts of United States, 1st oz.	41¢
2008, May 12	
All parts of United States, 1st oz.	42¢
2009, May 11	
All parts of United States, 1st oz.	44¢

Domestic Air Mail Rates

Effective Date	Prepaid
1911-1916 – The Pioneer Period	
Special official Post Office Flights at Fairs, aviation meets, etc., per 1 oz.	2¢
Postal cards and postcards	1¢
(Regulations prohibited an additional charge for air service on Post Office authorized flights.)	
1918, May 15 - July 13, 1918	
Service between Washington, DC, New York and Philadelphia (including 10¢ special delivery fee), per 1 oz.	24¢
1918, July 15-Dec. 14, 1918	
Service between Washington, DC, New York and Philadelphia (including 10¢ special delivery fee), per 1 oz.	16¢
Additional ounces	6¢
1918, Dec. 15-July 17, 1919	
Service between selected cities (other cities added later, special delivery no longer included), per 1 oz.	6¢
1919, July 18-June 29, 1924	
No specific airmail rate: mail carried by airplane on space available basis but airmail service not guaranteed, per 1 oz.	2¢
Postal cards and postcards, per 1 oz.	1¢
1924, June 30-Jan. 31, 1927	
Airmail service per zone (New York-Chicago; Chicago-Cheyenne, Wyo.; Cheyenne-San Francisco), per 1 oz. (each zone or portion thereof)	8¢
1925, July 1-Jan. 31, 1927	
Special overnight service New York-Chicago (with three intermediate stops), per 1 oz.	10¢
1926, Feb. 15-Jan. 31, 1927	
Contract routes not exceeding 1,000 miles (first flight Feb. 15) per 1 oz. (each route or portion thereof)	10¢
Contract routes between 1,000 and 1,500 miles (Seattle-Los Angeles, first flight Sept. 15) per 1 oz.	15¢
Mail traveling less than entire Seattle-Los Angeles route per 1 oz.	10¢
Contract routes exceeding 1,500 miles (none established during this rate period) per 1 oz.	20¢
Additional service on govt. route, per 1 oz. (each route or portion thereof)	5¢
1927, Feb. 1-July 31, 1928	
All contract routes or govt. zones, or combinations thereof, per ½ oz.	10¢
1928, Aug. 1-July 5, 1932	
All routes, 1st oz.	5¢
Each additional ounce or fraction thereof	10¢

Effective Date	Prepaid
1932, July 6-June 30, 1934	
All routes, 1st oz.	8¢
Each additional ounce or fraction thereof	13¢
1934, July 1-Mar. 25, 1944	
All routes, per oz.	6¢
1944, Mar. 26-Sept. 30, 1946	
All routes, per oz.	8¢
1946, Oct. 1-Dec. 31, 1948	
All routes, per oz.	5¢
1949, Jan. 1-July 31, 1958	
All routes, per oz.	6¢
Postal cards and postcards, per oz.	4¢
1958, Aug. 1-Jan. 6, 1963	
All routes, per oz.	7¢
Postal cards and postcards, per oz.	5¢
1963, Jan. 7-Jan. 6, 1968	
All routes, per oz.	8¢
Postal cards and postcards, per oz.	6¢
1968, Jan. 7-May 15, 1971	
All routes, per oz.	10¢
Postal cards and postcards, per oz.	8¢
1971, May 16-Mar. 1, 1974	
All routes, per oz.	11¢
Postal cards and postcards, per oz.	9¢
1974, Mar. 2-Oct. 10, 1975	
All routes, per oz.	13¢
Postal cards and postcards, per oz.	11¢

As of Oct. 11, 1975, separate domestic airmail service was abolished, although at least one more airmail rate was published; effective Dec. 28, 1975, 17¢ per 1st oz., 15¢ each additional oz., 14¢ for postal cards and postcards. It lasted until May 1, 1977.

Many thanks to the American Air Mail Society for sharing information on airmail rates. For further study, we highly recommend the society's book, *Via Airmail, An Aerophilatelic Survey of Events, Routes, and Rates;* Simine Short, editor; James R. Adams, author (available from the American Airmail Society, P.O. Box 110, Mineola, NY 11501. Price: $20, plus $2.50 postage to U.S. addresses; $3.50 to addresses outside the U.S.).

IDENTIFIER OF DEFINITIVE ISSUES — ARRANGED BY TYPE NUMBERS

This section covers only listed postage stamps. See the Proofs section for imperforate items in the stamp colors mentioned which are not listed here and the Trial Color Proofs section for items in other colors.

ISSUES OF 1847-75

Benjamin Franklin — A1

Reproduction — A3

5¢ On the originals the left side of the white shirt frill touches the oval on a level with the top of the "F" of "Five." On the reproductions it touches the oval about on a level with the top of the figure "5."

George Washington A2

Reproduction A4

Top image original, bottom image reproduction

10¢ On the originals line of coat (A) points to "T" of TEN and (B) it points between "T" and "S" of CENTS.

On the reproductions line of coat (A) points to right tip of "X" and line of coat (B) points to center of "S."

On the reproductions the eyes have a sleepy look, the line of the mouth is straighter, and in the curl of the hair near the left cheek is a strong black dot, while the originals have only a faint one.

Imperforate and Unwatermarked

Design Number		*Scott Number*
A1	5¢ red brown	1
A1	5¢ blue (reproduction)	948a
A3	5¢ red brown (reproduction, Special Printing)	3
A2	10¢ black	2
A2	10¢ brown orange (reproduction)	948b
A4	10¢ black (reproduction, Special Printing)	4

ISSUE OF 1851-75

Franklin — A5

A5

Type I Has a curved line outside the labels with "U.S. Postage" and "One Cent." The scrolls below the lower label are turned under, forming little balls. The scrolls and outer line at top are complete.

A6

Type Ia Same as I at bottom but top ornaments and outer line at top are partly cut away.

Type Ib Same as I but balls below the bottom label are not so clear. The plume-like scrolls at bottom are not complete.

Type Ic Same as type Ia, but bottom right plume and ball ornament is incomplete. The bottom left plume is complete or almost complete.

A7

Type II The little balls of the bottom scrolls and the bottoms of the lower plume ornaments are missing. The side ornaments are complete.

A8

Type III The top and bottom curved lines outside the labels are broken in the middle. The side ornaments are complete.

Type IIIa Similar to III with the outer line broken at top or bottom but not both. Type IIIa from Plate IV generally shows signs of plate erasure between the horizontal rows. Those from Plate IE show only a slight break in the line at top or bottom.

A9 Type IV

A20 Type V

Type IV Similar to II, but with the curved lines outside the labels recut at top or bottom or both.

The seven types listed account for most of the varieties of recutting.

Type V Similar to type III of 1851-56 but with side ornaments partly cut away.

A5	1¢ blue, type I, imperf.	5
A5	1¢ blue, type Ib, imperf.	5A
A5	1¢ blue, type I, perf. 15½	18
A5	1¢ bright blue, perf. 12 (Special Printing)	40
A6	1¢ blue, type Ia, imperf.	6
A6	1¢ blue, type Ic, imperf.	6b
A6	1¢ blue, type Ia, perf. 15½	19
A6	1¢ blue, type Ic, perf. 15½	19b
A7	1¢ blue, type II, imperf.	7
A7	1¢ blue, type II, perf. 15½	20
A8	1¢ blue, type III, imperf.	8
A8	1¢ blue, type IIIa, imperf.	8A
A8	1¢ blue, type III, perf. 15½	21
A8	1¢ blue, type IIIa, perf. 15½	22
A9	1¢ blue, type IV, imperf.	9
A9	1¢ blue, type IV, perf. 15½	23
A20	1¢ blue, type V, perf. 15½	24
A20	1¢ blue, type V, perf. 15½, laid paper	24b

Washington, Type I — A10

Type I

Type I. There is an outer frame line on all four sides. The outer frame lines at the sides are always recut, but the inner lines at the sides are not.

Type II

Type II. As type I, but with the inner lines at the sides also recut.

Washington (Type III) — A21

Type III. There are no outer frame lines at top and bottom. The side frame lines were recut so as to be continuous from the top to the bottom of the plate.

Washington (Type IV) — A21a

Type IV — As type III, but the side frame lines extend only to the top and bottom of the stamp design. All Type IV stamps are from plates 10 and 11 (each of which exists in three states), and these plates produced only Type IV. The side frame lines were recut individually for each stamp, thus being broken between the stamps vertically.

Beware of type III stamps with frame lines that stop at the top of the design (from top row of plate) or bottom of the design (from bottom row of plate). These are often mistakenly offered as No. 26A.

Jefferson, Type I
There are projections on all four sides. — A11

Type II, The projections at top and bottom are partly cut away. Several minor types could be made according to the extent of cutting of the projections. — A22

Nos. 40-47 are reprints produced by the Continental Bank Note Co. The stamps are on white paper without gum, perf. 12. They were not good for postal use. They also exist imperforate.

A10	3¢ orange brown, type I, imperf.	10
A10	3¢ orange brown, type II, imperf.	10A
A10	3¢ dull red, type I, imperf.	11
A10	3¢ dull red, type II, imperf.	11A
A10	3¢ rose, type I, perf. 15½	25
A10	3¢ rose, type II, perf. 15½	25A
A10	3¢ scarlet, perf. 12 (Special Printing)	41
A10	3¢ dull red, type III, perf. 15½	26
A10	3¢ dull red, type IV, perf. 15½	26A
A11	5¢ red brown, type I, imperf.	12
A11	5¢ brick red, type I, perf. 15½	27
A11	5¢ red brown, type I, perf. 15½	28
A11	5¢ Indian red, type I, perf. 15½	28A
A11	5¢ brown, type I, perf. 15½	29
A22	5¢ orange brown, type II, perf. 15½	30
A22	5¢ brown, type II, perf. 15½	30A
A22	5¢ orange brown, type II, perf. 12 (Special Printing)	42

Washington, Type I — A12

Washington — A16

A12 Type I The shells at the lower corners are practically complete. The outer line below the label is very nearly complete. The outer lines are broken above the middle of the top label and the "X" in each upper corner.

A13 Type II The design is complete at the top. The outer line at the bottom is broken in the middle. The shells are partly cut away.

A14 Type III The outer lines are broken above the top label and the "X" numerals. The outer line at the bottom and the shells are partly cut away as in Type II.

A15 Type IV The outer lines have been recut at top or bottom or both.

A23 Type V The side ornaments are slightly cut away. Usually only one pearl remains at each end of the lower label but some copies show two or three pearls at the right side. At the bottom, the outer line is complete and the shells nearly so. The outer lines at top are complete except over the right "X."

A16 Plate 1 Outer frame lines recut on plate and complete.
Plate 3 Outer frame lines not recut and light, uneven and/or broken.

A12	10¢ green, type I, imperf.	13
A12	10¢ green, type I, perf. 15½	31
A12	10¢ blue green, perf. 12 (Special Printing)	43
A13	10¢ green, type II, imperf.	14
A13	10¢ green, type II, perf. 15½	32
A14	10¢ green, type III, imperf.	15
A14	10¢ green, type III, perf. 15½	33
A15	10¢ green, type IV, imperf.	16
A15	10¢ green, type IV, perf. 15½	34
A23	10¢ green, type V, perf. 15½	35
A16	12¢ black, imperf.	17
A16	12¢ black, plate 1, perf. 15½	36
A16	12¢ black, plate 3	36B
A16	12¢ greenish black, perf. 12	44

Washington — A17

Franklin — A18

Washington — A19

A17	24¢ gray lilac, perf. 15½	37
A17	24¢ blackish violet, perf. 12 (Special Printing)	45
A18	30¢ orange, perf. 15½	38
A18	30¢ yellow orange, perf. 12 (Special Printing)	46
A19	90¢ blue, perf. 15½	39
A19	90¢ deep blue, perf. 12 (Special Printing)	47

ISSUES OF 1861-75

Franklin — A24

A24 See the essay section for type A24 in indigo on perf. 12 thin, semi-transparent paper without the dash under the tip of the ornament at the right of the numeral in the upper left corner.

A24	1¢ blue, perf. 12	63
A24	1¢ blue, same, laid paper	63c
A24	1¢ blue, grill 11x14mm	85A
A24	1¢ blue, grill 11x13mm	86
A24	1¢ blue, grill 9x13mm	92
A24	1¢ blue, no grill, hard white paper (Special Printing)	102

Washington — A25

A25 See the essay section for type A25 in brown rose on perf. 12 thin, semi-transparent paper with smaller ornaments in the corners which do not end in a small ball.

A25	3¢ pink, no grill, perf. 12	64
A25	3¢ lake, same (Special Printing)	66
A25	3¢ scarlet, same (Special Printing)	74
A25	3¢ rose, same	65
A25	3¢ rose, same, laid paper	65b
A25	3¢ rose, grilled all over	79
A25	3¢ rose, grill 18x15mm	82
A25	3¢ rose, grill 13x16mm	83
A25	3¢ rose, grill 12x14mm	85
A25	3¢ rose, grill 11x14mm	85C
A25	3¢ rose, grill 11x13mm	88
A25	3¢ red, grill 9x13mm	94
A25	3¢ brown red, no grill, hard white paper (Special Printing)	104

Jefferson — A26

A26 See the essay section for type A26 in brown on perf. 12 thin, semi-transparent paper without the leaflet in the foliated ornament at each corner.

A26	5¢ buff, no grill	67
A26	5¢ red brown, no grill	75
A26	5¢ brown, no grill	76
A26	5¢ brown, laid paper	76b
A26	5¢ brown, grilled all over	80
A26	5¢ brown, grill 9x13mm	95
A26	5¢ brown, no grill, hard white paper	105

A27a

Washington — A27

A27 A heavy curved line has been cut below the stars and an outer line added to the ornaments above them.

A27a	10¢ dark green, thin paper	62B
A27	10¢ green, see illustration A27	68
A27	10¢ green, grill 11x14mm	85D
A27	10¢ green, grill 11x13mm	89
A27	10¢ yellow green, grill 9x13mm	96
A27	10¢ green, no grill, hard white paper (Special Printing)	106

Washington — A28

A28 See the essay section for type A28 in black on perf. 12 thin, semi-transparent paper without corner ornaments.

A28	12¢ black, no grill	69
A28	12¢ black, grill 11x14mm	85E
A28	12¢ black, grill 11x13mm	90
A28	12¢ black, grill 9x13mm	97
A28	12¢ black, no grill, hard white paper, (Special Printing)	107

Washington — A29

Franklin — A30

See the Trial Color proof section for type A29 in dark violet on perf. 12 thin paper without grill and type A30 in red orange on perf. 12 thin paper without grill.

A29	24¢ red lilac, no grill	70

A29	24¢ violet, no grill, thin, transparent paper	70c
A29	24¢ lilac, no grill	78
A29	24¢ gray lilac, grill 9x13mm	99
A29	24¢ deep violet, no grill, hard white paper, (Special Printing)	109
A30	30¢ orange, no grill	71
A30	30¢ orange, grilled all over	81
A30	30¢ orange, grill 9x13mm	100
A30	30¢ brownish orange, no grill, hard white paper, (Special Printing)	110

Washington — A31

A31 See the essay section for type A31 in dull blue on perf. 12 thin semi-transparent paper without dashes between the parallel lines which form the angle above the ribbon with "U.S. Postage," and without the point of color at the apex of the lower line.

A31	90¢ blue, no grill	72
A31	90¢ blue, grill 9x13mm	101
A31	90¢ blue, no grill, hard white paper, (Special Printing)	111

ISSUES OF 1861-75

Jackson — A32

Lincoln — A33

Perf. 12, Unwmkd.

A32	2¢ black, no grill	73
A32	2¢ black, laid paper	73d
A32	2¢ black, grill 12x14mm	84
A32	2¢ black, grill 11x14mm	85B
A32	2¢ black, grill 11x13mm	87
A32	2¢ black, grill 9x13mm	93
A32	2¢ black, no grill, hard white paper, (Special Printing)	103
A33	15¢ black, no grill	77
A33	15¢ black, grill 11x14mm	85F
A33	15¢ black, grill 11x13mm	91
A33	15¢ black, grill 9x13mm	98
A33	15¢ black, no grill, hard white paper, (Special Printing)	108

ISSUES OF 1869-80

Franklin — A34

A34	1¢ buff, grill 9½x9mm	112
A34	1¢ buff, no grill	112b
A34	1¢ buff, no grill, hard white paper (Special Printing)	123
A34	1¢ buff, no grill, soft porous paper (Special Printing)	133
A34	1¢ brown orange, same without gum (Special Printing)	133a

Pony Express — A35

Baldwin 4-4-0
Locomotive, c.
1857 — A36

A35	2¢ brown, grill 9½x9mm	113
A35	2¢ brown, no grill	113b
A35	2¢ brown, no grill, hard white paper (Special Printing)	124
A36	3¢ ultramarine, grill 9½x9mm	114
A36	3¢ ultramarine, no grill	114a
A36	3¢ blue, no grill, hard white paper (Special Printing)	125

Washington — A37

Shield and
Eagle — A38

S.S. Adriatic — A39

A37	6¢ ultramarine, grill 9½x9mm	115
A37	6¢ blue, no grill, hard white paper (Special Printing)	126
A38	10¢ yellow, grill 9½x9mm	116
A38	10¢ yellow, no grill, hard white paper (Special Printing)	127
A39	12¢ green, grill 9½x9mm	117
A39	12¢ green, no grill, hard white paper (Special Printing)	128

Landing of Columbus — A40

A40 Type I
Picture
unframed

A40a Type II
Picture
framed

Type III same as Type I but without the fringe of brown shading lines around central vignette.

A40	15¢ brown & blue, type I, grill 9½x9mm	118
A40	15¢ brown & blue, type I, no grill	118a
A40	15¢ brown & blue, type III, no grill, hard white paper (Special Printing)	129
A40a	15¢ brown & blue, type II, grill 9½x9mm	119

The Declaration of
Independence — A41

Shield, Eagle and
Flags — A42

Lincoln — A43

A41	24¢ green & violet, grill 9½x9mm	120
A41	24¢ green & violet, no grill	120a
A41	24¢ green & violet, no grill, hard white paper (Special Printing)	130
A42	30¢ ultramarine & carmine, grill 9½x9mm	121
A42	30¢ ultramarine & carmine, no grill	121a
A42	30¢ ultramarine & carmine, no grill, hard white paper (Special Printing)	131
A43	90¢ carmine & black, grill 9½x9mm	122
A43	90¢ carmine & black, no grill	122a
A43	90¢ carmine & black, no grill, hard white paper (Special Printing)	132
A43	90¢ carmine & black, 28x28mm, imperf., litho. & engraved	2433a
A43	90¢ blue & brown, 28x28mm, imperf., litho. & engraved	2433b
A43	90¢ green & blue, 28x28mm, imperf., litho. & engraved	2433c
A43	90¢ scarlet & blue, 28x28mm, imperf., litho. & engraved	2433d

ISSUES OF 1870-88

The secret mark shown in the detail of A45a is seldom found on the actual stamps. Stamps Nos. 146 and 157 are best identified by color which is red brown for No. 146 and brown for No. 157.

Note I: Special printings of 1880-83 — All denominations of this series were printed on special order from the Post Office Department during the period the stamps were current. The paper being the same as used on current issue, the special printings are extremely difficult to identify. The 2¢ brown, 7¢ scarlet vermilion, 12¢ blackish purple and 24¢ dark violet are easily distinguished by the soft porous paper as these denominations were never previously printed on soft paper. The other denominations can be distinguished by shades only, those of the special printings being slightly deeper and richer than the regular issue. The special printings except No. 211B were issued without gum. The only certain way to identify them is by comparison with stamps previously established as special printings.

Franklin — A44

A44

A44a With secret mark. In the pearl at the left of the numeral "1" there is a small dash.

A44b Re-engraved. The vertical lines in the upper part of the stamp have been so deepened that the background often appears to be solid. Lines of shading have been added to the upper arabesques.

A44	1¢ ultramarine, with grill	134
A44	1¢ ultramarine, no grill	145
A44a	1¢ ultramarine, white wove paper no grill	156
A44a	1¢ ultramarine, with grill	156e
A44a	1¢ ultramarine, hard white paper, without gum (Special Printing)	167
A44a	1¢ dark ultra, soft porous paper	182
A44a	1¢ dark ultra, soft porous paper, without gum (Special Printing, see note I)	192
A44b	1¢ gray blue	206

Jackson — A45

A45

A45a Under the scroll at the left of "U.S." there is a small diagonal line.

A45	2¢ red brown, with grill	135
A45	2¢ red brown, no grill	146
A45a	2¢ brown, white wove paper no grill	157
A45a	2¢ brown, with grill	157c
A45a	2¢ dark brown, hard white paper, without gum (Special Printing)	168
A45a	2¢ black brown, soft porous paper, without gum (Special Printing)	193
A45a	2¢ vermilion, yellowish paper	178
A45a	2¢ vermilion, same, with grill	178c
A45a	2¢ vermilion, soft porous paper	183
A45a	2¢ carmine vermilion, hard white paper, without gum (Special Printing)	180
A45a	2¢ scarlet vermilion, soft porous paper, without gum (Special Printing, see note I)	203

Washington — A46

A46

A46a With secret mark. The under part of the tail of the left ribbon is heavily shaded.

A46b Re-engraved. The shading at the sides of the central oval appears only about one half the previous width. A short horizontal dash has been cut about 1mm. below the "TS" of "CENTS."

A46	3¢ green, with grill	136
A46	3¢ green, no grill	147
A46a	3¢ green, white wove paper, no grill	158
A46a	3¢ green, same, with grill	158e
A46a	3¢ blue green, hard white paper, without gum (Special Printing)	169
A46a	3¢ green, soft porous paper	184
A46a	3¢ blue green, soft porous paper, without gum (Special Printing see note I)	194
A46b	3¢ blue green, re-engraved	207
A46b	3¢ vermilion re-engraved	214

Lincoln — A47

A47

A47a With secret mark. The first four vertical lines of the shading in the lower part of the left ribbon have been strengthened.

A47b Re-engraved. On the original stamps four vertical lines can be counted from the edge of the panel to the outside of the stamp. On the re-engraved stamps there are three lines in the same place.

A47	6¢ carmine, with grill	137
A47	6¢ carmine, no grill	148
A47a	6¢ dull pink, no grill, white wove paper	159
A47a	6¢ dull pink, with grill	159b
A47a	6¢ dull rose, hard white paper, without gum (Special Printing)	170
A47a	6¢ pink, soft porous paper	186
A47a	6¢ dull rose, soft porous paper, without gum (Special Printing see note I)	195
A47b	6¢ rose, re-engraved	208

Edwin McMasters Stanton — A48

Thomas Jefferson — A49

A48

A48a With secret mark. Two small semi-circles are drawn around the ends of the lines which outline the ball in the lower right hand corner.

A49

A49a With secret mark. A small semi-circle in the scroll at the right end of the upper label.

A49b Re-engraved. On the original stamps there are five vertical lines between the left side of the oval and the edge of the shield. There are only four lines on the re-engraved stamps. In the lower part of the re-engraved stamps the horizontal lines of the background have been strengthened.

Henry Clay — A50

A50

A50a With secret mark. The balls of the figure "2" are crescent shaped.

A48	7¢ vermilion, with grill	138
A48	7¢ vermilion, no grill	149
A48a	7¢ orange verm., white wove paper no grill	160
A48a	7¢ orange verm., same, with grill	160a
A48a	7¢ reddish verm., hard white paper, without gum (Special Printing)	171
A48a	7¢ scarlet verm., soft porous paper, without gum (Special Printing)	196
A49	10¢ brown, with grill	139
A49	10¢ brown, no grill	150
A49	10¢ brown, soft porous paper	187
A49a	10¢ brown, white wove paper no grill	161
A49a	10¢ brown, with grill	161c
A49a	10¢ pale brown, hard white paper, without gum (Special Printing)	172
A49a	10¢ brown, soft porous paper	188
A49a	10¢ deep brown, soft porous paper, without gum (Special Printing, see note I)	197
A49b	10¢ brown, re-engraved	209
A50	12¢ dull violet, with grill	140
A50	12¢ dull violet, no grill	151
A50a	12¢ blackish violet, white wove paper no grill	162
A50a	12¢ blackish violet, with grill	162a
A50a	12¢ dark violet, hard white paper, without gum (Special Printing)	173
A50a	12¢ blackish purple, soft porous paper, without gum (Special Printing)	198

Webster — A51

A51

A51a With secret mark. In the lower part of the triangle in the upper left corner two lines have been made heavier forming a "V." This mark can be found on some of the Continental and American (1879) printings, but not all stamps show it.

A51	15¢ orange, with grill	141
A51	15¢ bright orange, no grill	152
A51a	15¢ yellow orange, white wove paper, no grill	163
A51a	15¢ yellow orange, with grill	163a
A51a	15¢ bright orange, hard white paper, without gum (Special Printing)	174
A51a	15¢ red orange, soft porous paper	189
A51a	15¢ orange, soft porous paper, without gum (Special Printing, see note I)	199

General Winfield Scott — A52

Hamilton — A53

Perry — A54

Secret marks were added to the dies of the 24¢, 30¢ and 90¢ but new plates were not made from them. The various printings of these stamps can be distinguished only by the shades and paper.

A52	24¢ purple, with grill	142
A52	24¢ purple, no grill	153
A52	24¢ purple, vertically ribbed white wove paper, no grill	164
A52	24¢ dull purple, hard white paper, without gum (Special Printing)	175
A52	24¢ dark violet, soft porous paper, without gum (Special Printing)	200
A53	30¢ black, with grill	143
A53	30¢ black, no grill	154
A53	30¢ full black, soft porous paper	190
A53	30¢ gray black, white wove paper, no grill	165
A53	30¢ greenish black, with grill	165c
A53	30¢ greenish black, hard white paper, without gum (Special Printing)	176
A53	30¢ greenish black, soft porous paper, without gum (Special Printing, see note I)	201
A53	30¢ orange brown	217
A54	90¢ carmine, with grill	144
A54	90¢ carmine, no grill	155
A54	90¢ carmine, soft porous paper	191
A54	90¢ rose carmine, white wove paper	166
A54	90¢ violet carmine, hard white paper, without gum (Special Printing)	177
A54	90¢ dull carmine, soft porous paper, without gum (Special Printing, see note I)	202

A54   90¢ purple **218**

ISSUES OF 1875-88

Taylor — A55

Garfield — A56

Perf. 12, Unwmkd.

A55 5¢ blue, yellowish wove paper, no grill **179**
A55 5¢ blue, with grill **179c**
A55 5¢ bright blue, hard, white wove paper,
       without gum (Special Printing) **181**
A55 5¢ blue, soft porous paper **185**
A55 5¢ deep blue, soft porous paper, without gum
       (Special Printing, see note I).....................**204**
A56 5¢ yellow brown..**205**
A56 5¢ gray brown, soft porous paper, without gum
       (Special Printing, see note I)..................**205C**
A56 5¢ indigo **216**

Washington — A57

Jackson — A58

A57 2¢ red brown **210**
A57 2¢ pale red brown, soft porous paper (Special
      Printing, see note I) **211B**
A57 2¢ green **213**
A58 4¢ blue green **211**
A58 4¢ deep blue green, soft porous paper,
      without gum (Special Printing, see note I)......
      ....**211D**
A58 4¢ carmine..**215**

Franklin — A59

A59 1¢ ultramarine...**212**

ISSUES OF 1890-93

Franklin — A60

Washington — A61

Jackson — A62

Lincoln — A63

Grant — A64

William T.
Sherman — A66

Henry Clay — A68

Garfield — A65

Daniel
Webster — A67

Jefferson — A69

Perry — A70

A60	1¢ dull blue	**219**
A61	2¢ lake	**219D**
A61	2¢ carmine	**220**
A62	3¢ purple	**221**
A63	4¢ dark brown	**222**
A64	5¢ chocolate	**223**
A65	6¢ brown red	**224**
A66	8c lilac	**225**
A67	10¢ green	**226**
A68	15¢ indigo	**227**
A69	30¢ black	**228**
A70	90¢ orange	**229**

ISSUES OF 1894-1903

This series, the first to be printed by the Bureau of Engraving and Printing, closely resembles the 1890 series but is identified by the triangles which have been added to the upper corners of the designs.

The Catalogue divides this group into three separate series, the first of which was issued in 1894 and is unwatermarked. In 1895 the paper used was watermarked with the double line letters USPS (United States Postage Stamp). The stamps show one complete letter of the watermark or parts of two or more letters.

This watermark appears on all United States stamps issued from 1895 until 1910.

In 1898 the colors of some of the denominations were changed, which created the third series noted in the Catalogue.

Other than the watermark, or lack of it, there are three styles of the corner triangles used on the 2 cent stamps and two variations of designs are noted on the 10 cent and $1 denomination. In the following list all of these variations are illustrated and described immediately preceding the denominations on which they appear.

USPS

Wmkd. (191) Horizontally

or Vertically

USPS

(Actual size of letter)

Franklin — A87

Washington — A88

Jackson — A89

Lincoln — A90

Grant — A91

Garfield — A92

Sherman — A93

Webster — A94

Clay — A95

Jefferson — A96

Perry — A97

James
Madison — A98

John Marshall — A99

A87 1¢ ultramarine, unwmkd.............................**246**

A87	1¢ blue, unwmkd.	247
A87	1¢ blue, wmkd.	264
A87	1¢ deep green, wmkd.	279
A87	1¢ on 1¢ yellow green, "CUBA"	Cuba 221
A87	1¢ deep green, "GUAM"	Guam 1
A87	1¢ yellow green, "PHILIPPINES"	Phil. 213
A87	1¢ yellow green, "PORTO RICO"	P.R. 210
A87	1¢ yellow green, "PUERTO RICO"	P.R. 215

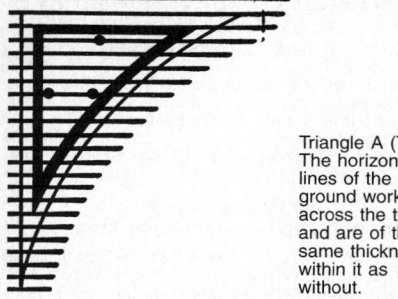

Triangle A (Type I) The horizontal lines of the ground work run across the triangle and are of the same thickness within it as without.

Triangle B (Type II) The horiztonal lines cross the triangle but are thinner within it than without. Other minor differences exist, but the change to Triangle B is a sufficient determinant.

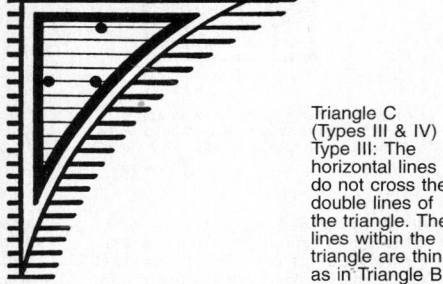

Triangle C (Types III & IV) Type III: The horizontal lines do not cross the double lines of the triangle. The lines within the triangle are thin, as in Triangle B.

The rest of the design is the same as Type II, except that most of the designs had the dot in the "S" of "CENTS" removed. Stamps with this dot are listed; some specialists refer to them as "Type IIIa" varieties.

Type IV: Same triangle C as type III, but other design differences including (1) recutting and lengthening of hairline, (2) shaded toga button, (3) strengthening of lines on sleeve, (4) additional dots on ear, (5) "T" of "TWO" straight at right, (6) background lines extend into white oval opposite "U" of "UNITED." Many other differences exist.

A88	2¢ pink, type I, unwmkd.	248
A88	2¢ carmine lake, type I, unwmkd.	249
A88	2¢ carmine, type I, unwmkd.	250
A88	2¢ carmine, type I, wmkd.	265
A88	2¢ carmine, type II, unwmkd.	251

A88	2¢ carmine, type II, wmkd.	266
A88	2¢ carmine, type III, unwmkd.	252
A88	2¢ carmine, type III, wmkd.	267
A88	2¢ red, type IV, wmkd.	279B
A88	2¢ booklet pane of 6, wmkd., single stamps with 1 or 2 straight edges	279Bj
A88	2c on 2¢ reddish carmine, type III "CUBA"	Cuba 222
A88	2c on 2¢ reddish carmine, type IV, "CUBA"	Cuba 222A
A88	2 ½c on 2¢ reddish carmine, type III, "CUBA"	Cuba 223
A88	2½c on 2¢ reddish carmine, type IV, "CUBA"	Cuba 223A
A88	2¢ red, type IV, "GUAM"	Guam 2
A88	2¢ red, type IV, "PHILIPPINES"	Phil. 214
A88	Same, booklet pane of 6	Phil. 214b
A88	2¢ reddish carmine, type IV, "PORTO RICO"	P.R. 211
A88	Same, "PUERTO RICO"	P.R. 216
A89	3¢ purple, unwmkd.	253
A89	3¢ purple, wmkd.	268
A89	3¢ on 3¢ purple, "CUBA"	Cuba 224
A89	3¢ purple, "GUAM"	Guam 3
A89	3¢ purple "PHILIPPINES"	Phil. 215
A90	4¢ dark brown, unwmkd.	254
A90	4¢ dark brown, wmkd.	269
A90	4¢ rose brown, wmkd.	280
A90	4¢ lilac brown, "GUAM"	Guam 4
A90	4¢ orange brown, "PHILIPPINES"	Phil. 220
A91	5¢ chocolate, unwmkd.	255
A91	5¢ chocolate, wmkd.	270
A91	5¢ dark blue, wmkd.	281
A91	5¢ on 5¢ blue, "CUBA"	Cuba 225
A91	5¢ blue, "GUAM"	Guam 5
A91	5¢ blue, "PHILIPPINES"	Phil. 216
A91	5¢ blue, "PORTO RICO"	P.R. 212
A92	6¢ dull brown, unwmkd.	256
A92	6¢ dull brown, wmkd. USPS	271
A92	6¢ dull brown, wmkd. USIR	271a
A92	6¢ lake, wmkd.	282
A92	6¢ lake, "GUAM"	Guam 6
A92	6¢ lake, "PHILIPPINES"	Phil. 221
A93	8¢ violet brown, unwmkd.	257
A93	8¢ violet brown, wmkd. USPS	272
A93	8¢ violet brown, wmkd. USIR	272a
A93	8¢ violet brown, "GUAM"	Guam 7
A93	8¢ violet brown, "PHILIPPINES"	Phil. 222
A93	8¢ violet brown, "PORTO RICO"	P.R. 213

Type I The tips of the foliate ornaments do not impinge on the white curved line below "ten cents."

Type II The tips of the ornaments break the curved line below the "e" of "ten" and the "t" of "cents."

A94	10¢ dark green, unwmkd.	258
A94	10¢ dark green, wmkd.	273
A94	10¢ brown, type I, wmkd.	282C
A94	10¢ orange brown, type II, wmkd.	283
A94	10¢ on 10¢ brown, type I, "CUBA"	Cuba 226
A94	Same, type II, "CUBA"	Cuba 226A
A94	10¢ brown, type I, "GUAM"	Guam 8
A94	10¢ brown, type II, "GUAM"	Guam 9
A94	10¢ brown, type I, "PHILIPPINES"	Phil. 217
A94	10¢ orange brown, type II, "PHILIPPINES"	Phil. 217A
A94	10¢ brown, type I, "PORTO RICO"	P.R. 214
A95	15¢ dark blue, unwmkd.	259
A95	15¢ dark blue, wmkd.	274
A95	15¢ olive green, wmkd.	284
A95	15¢ olive green, "GUAM"	Guam 10
A95	15¢ olive green, "PHILIPPINES"	Phil. 218
A96	50¢ orange, unwmkd.	260
A96	50¢ orange, wmkd.	275
A96	50¢ orange, "GUAM"	Guam 11
A96	50¢ orange, unwmkd., "PHILIPPINES"	Phil. 212
A96	50¢ orange, wmkd., "PHILIPPINES"	Phil. 219

A97 Type I The circles enclosing "$1" are broken where they meet the curved line below "One Dollar."

A97 Type II The circles are complete.

A97	$1 black, type I, unwmkd.	261
A97	$1 black, type I, wmkd.	276
A97	$1 black, type II, unwmkd.	261A
A97	$1 black, type II, wmkd.	276A
A97	$1 black, type I, "GUAM"	Guam 12
A97	$1 black, type II, "GUAM"	Guam 13
A97	$1 black, type I, "PHILIPPINES"	Phil. 223
A97	$1 black, type II, "PHILIPPINES"	Phil. 223A
A98	$2 bright blue, unwmkd.	262
A98	$2 blue, perf. 11, tagged	2875a
A98	$2 bright blue, wmkd.	277
A98	$2 dark blue, "PHILIPPINES"	Phil. 224
A99	$5 dark green, unwmkd.	263
A99	$5 dark green, wmkd.	278
A99	$5 dark green, "PHILIPPINES"	Phil. 225

ISSUES OF 1902-17

Franklin — A115

Washington — A116

Jackson — A117

Grant — A118

Lincoln — A119

Garfield — A120

Martha Washington — A121

Daniel Webster — A122

Benjamin Harrison — A123

Henry Clay — A124

Jefferson — A125

David G. Farragut — A126

Madison — A127

Marshall — A128

Unless otherwise noted all stamps are Perf. 12 and Wmkd. (191)

Single stamps from booklet panes show 1 or 2 straight edges.

A115 1¢ blue green 300
A115 1¢ booklet pane of 6 .... 300b
A115 1¢ blue green, imperf. 314
A115 1¢ blue green, perf. 12 horiz., pair 316
A115 1¢ blue green, perf. 12 vert., pair 318
A115 1¢ blue green, "CANAL ZONE PANAMA" .... C.Z. 4
A115 1¢ blue green, "PHILIPPINES" .... Phil. 226
A116 2¢ carmine 301
A116 2¢ booklet pane of 6 .... 301c
A116 2¢ carmine, "PHILIPPINES" .... Phil. 227
A117 3¢ bright violet 302
A117 3¢ bright violet, "PHILIPPINES" .... Phil. 228
A118 4¢ brown 303
A118 4¢ brown, imperf. 314A
A118 4¢ brown, "PHILIPPINES" .... Phil. 229
A119 5¢ blue 304
A119 5¢ blue, imperf. 315
A119 5¢ blue, perf. 12 horiz. pair 317
A119 5¢ blue, "CANAL ZONE PANAMA" .... C.Z. 6
A119 5¢ blue, "PHILIPPINES" .... Phil. 230
A120 6¢ claret 305
A120 6¢ brownish lake, "PHILIPPINES" ...... Phil. 231
A121 8¢ violet black 306
A121 8¢ violet black, "CANAL ZONE PANAMA" ......
.... C.Z. 7
A121 8¢ violet black, "PHILIPPINES" .... Phil. 232
A122 10¢ pale red brown 307
A122 10¢ pale red brown, "CANAL ZONE PANAMA"
.... C.Z. 8
A122 10¢ pale red brown, "PHILIPPINES" ....
.... Phil. 233
A123 13¢ purple black 308
A123 13¢ purple black, "PHILIPPINES" ...... Phil. 234
A124 15¢ olive green 309
A124 15¢ olive green, "PHILIPPINES" .... Phil. 235
A125 50¢ orange 310
A125 50¢ orange, "PHILIPPINES" .... Phil. 236
A126 $1 black 311
A126 $1 black, "PHILIPPINES" .... Phil. 237
A127 $2 dark blue 312
A127 $2 dark blue, unwmkd., perf. 10 479
A127 $2 dark blue, "PHILIPPINES" .... Phil. 238
A128 $5 dark green 313
A128 $5 light green, unwmkd., perf. 10 480
A128 $5 dark green, "PHILIPPINES" .... Phil. 239

ISSUES OF 1903

Washington — A129

Type I

Type II

Specialists recognize over a hundred shades of this stamp in various hues of vermilion, red, carmine and lake. The Scott Catalogue lists only the most striking differences.

The Government coil stamp, No. 322 should not be confused with the scarlet vermilion coil of the International Vending Machine Co., which is perforated 12½ to 13.

A129 2¢ carmine, type I, wmkd. 319
A129 2¢ lake, type II 319f
A129 2¢ carmine, type I, booklet pane of 6 .... 319g
A129 Same, type II 319h
A129 2¢ carmine, type I, imperf. 320
A129 2¢ lake, type II, imperf. 320a
A129 2¢ carmine, perf. 12 horiz. pair 321
A129 2¢ carmine, perf. 12 vert. pair 322
A129 2¢ carmine, "CANAL ZONE PANAMA" ... C.Z. 5
A129 2¢ carmine, "PHILIPPINES" .... Phil. 240
A129 2¢ carmine, same, booklet pane of 6 ....
.... Phil. 240a

ISSUES OF 1908-09

This series introduces for the first time the single line watermark USPS. Only a small portion of several letters is often all that can be seen on a single stamp.

Franklin — A138

Washington — A139

Wmk. 190

A138 1¢ green, perf. 12, double line wmk. 331
A138 1¢ green, perf. 12, single line wmk. 374
A138 1¢ green, perf. 12, bluish paper 357
A138 1¢ green, imperf., double line wmk. 343
A138 1¢ green, imperf., single line wmk. 383
A138 1¢ green, perf. 12 horiz., double line wmk. .....
.... 348
A138 1¢ green, perf. 12 horiz., single line wmk. ....
.... 385
A138 1¢ green, perf. 12 vert., double line wmk. ......
.... 352
A138 1¢ green, perf. 12 vert., single line wmk. ... 387
A138 1¢ green, perf. 8½ horiz., single line wmk. .....
.... 390
A138 1¢ green, perf. 8½ vert., single line wmk. .. 392
A139 2¢ carmine, perf. 12, double line wmk. 332
A139 2¢ carmine, perf. 12, single line wmk. 375
A139 2¢ carmine, perf. 12, bluish paper 358
A139 2¢ carmine, perf. 11, double line wmk. 519
A139 2¢ carmine, imperf., double line wmk. 344
A139 2¢ carmine, imperf., single line wmk. 384
A139 2¢ carmine, perf. 12 horiz., double line wmk.
.... 349
A139 2¢ carmine, perf. 12 horiz., single line wmk. .....
.... 386
A139 2¢ carmine, perf. 12 vert., double line wmk.
.... 353

A139 2¢ carmine, perf. 12 vert., single line wmk.
.... 388
A139 2¢ carmine, perf. 8½ horiz. single line wmk. ....
.... 391
A139 2¢ carmine, perf. 8½ vert., single line wmk. ....
.... 393

Single stamps from booklet panes show 1 or 2 straight edges.

A138 1¢ green, perf. 12, double line wmk., booklet pane of 6 .... 331a
A138 1¢ green, perf.12, single line wmk., booklet pane of 6 .... 374a
A139 2¢ carmine, perf. 12, double line wmk., booklet pane of 6 .... 332a
A139 2¢ carmine, perf. 12, single line wmk., booklet pane of 6 .... 375a

ISSUES OF 1908-21
FLAT BED AND ROTARY PRESS STAMPS

The Rotary Press Stamps are printed from plates that are curved to fit around a cylinder. This curvature produces stamps that are slightly larger, either horizontally or vertically, than those printed from flat plates. Designs of stamps from flat plates measure about 18½-19mm. wide by 22mm. high. When the impressions are placed sidewise on the curved plates the designs are 19½-20mm. wide; when they are placed vertically the designs are 22½ to 22¾mm. high. A line of color (not a guide line) shows where the curved plates meet or join on the press.

Rotary Press Coil Stamps were printed from plates of 170 subjects for stamps coiled sidewise, and from plates of 150 subjects for stamps coiled endwise.

Washington — A140

1¢ A138 Portrait of Franklin, value in words.
2¢ A139 Portrait of Washington, value in words.
A140 Portrait of Washington, value in numerals.

A140 1¢ green, perf. 12, single line wmk. 405
A140 1¢ green, same, booklet pane of 6 .... 405b
A140 1¢ green, perf. 11, flat plate, unwmkd. 498
A140 1¢ green, same, booklet pane of 6 .... 498e
A140 1¢ green, same, booklet pane of 30 .... 498f
A140 1¢ green, perf. 11, rotary press measuring
19mmx22½mm, unwmkd. 544
A140 1¢ green, same, measuring 19½ to
20mmx22mm 545
A140 1¢ gray green, perf. 11, offset, unwmkd. 525
A140 1¢ gray green, perf. 12½ 536
A140 1¢ green, perf. 11x10 538
A140 1¢ green, perf. 10x11 542
A140 1¢ green, perf. 10, single line wmk. 424
A140 1¢ green, same, perf. 12x10 .... 423A
A140 1¢ green, same, perf. 10x12 .... 423D
A140 1¢ green, perf.10, single line wmk., booklet
pane of 6 .... 424d
A140 1¢ green, perf. 10, flat plate, unwmkd. 462
A140 1¢ green, same, booklet pane of 6 .... 462a
A140 1¢ green, perf. 10, rotary press, unwmkd.
.... 543
A140 1¢ green, imperf., single line wmk. 408
A140 1¢ green, imperf., unwmkd. 481
A140 1¢ green, imperf., offset 531
A140 1¢ green, perf. 10 horiz., flat plate, single line
wmk. 441
A140 1¢ green, same, rotary press 448
A140 1¢ green, perf. 10 horiz., rotary press,
unwmkd. 486
A140 1¢ green, perf. 10 vert., flat plate, single line
wmk. 443
A140 1¢ green, same, rotary press 452
A140 1¢ green, perf. 10 vert., rotary press, unwmkd.
.... 490
A140 1¢ green, perf. 8½ horiz. single line wmk. ......
.... 410
A140 1¢ green, perf. 8½ vert., same 412

TYPES OF TWO CENTS

TYPE I

TYPE IA

Type Ia *The design characteristics are similar to type I except that all of the lines of the design are stronger.*
The toga button, toga rope and rope shading lines are heavy.
The latter characteristics are those of type II, which, however, occur only on impressions from rotary plates.
Used only on flat plates 10208 and 10209.

TYPE II

Type II *Shading lines in ribbons as on type I.*
The toga button, rope and rope shading lines are heavy.
The shading lines of the face at the lock of hair end in a strong, vertical curved line.
Used on rotary press printings only.

TYPE III

Type III

Type III *Two lines of shading in the curves of the ribbons.*
Other characteristics similar to type II.
Used on rotary press printings only.

TYPE IV

Type IV *Top line of the toga rope is broken.*
The shading lines in the toga button are so arranged that the curving of the first and last form "ID."
The line of color in the left "2" is very thin and usually broken.
Used on offset printings only.

TYPE V

Type V *Top line of the toga is complete.*
There are five vertical shading lines in the toga button.
The line of color in the left "2" is very thin and usually broken.
The shading dots on the nose are as shown on the diagram.
Used on offset printings only.

TYPE VA

Type Va *Characteristics are the same as type V except in the shading dots of the nose. The third row of dots from the bottom has four dots instead of six. The overall height is ⅓mm shorter than type V.*
Used on offset printings only.

TYPE VI

Type VI *General characteristics the same as type V except that the line of color in the left "2" is very heavy. Used on offset printings only.*

TYPE VII

Type VII *The line of color in the left "2" is invariably continuous, clearly defined and heavier than in type V or Va but not as heavy as type VI.*
An additional vertical row of dots has been added to the upper lip.
Numerous additional dots have been added to the hair on top of the head.
Used on offset printings only.

A140 2¢ carmine, perf. 12, type I, single line wmk. **406**
A140 2¢ carmine, same, booklet pane of 6 .... **406a**
A140 2¢ pale car. red, perf. 11, single line wmk., type I **461**
A140 2¢ rose, perf. 11, flat plate, unwmkd., type I **499**
A140 2¢ rose, same, booklet pane of 6 .... **499e**
A140 2¢ rose, same, booklet pane of 30 .... **499f**
A140 2¢ deep rose, perf. 11, unwmkd., type Ia... **500**
A140 2¢ carmine rose, perf. 11, rotary press, unwmkd., type III **546**
A140 2¢ carmine, perf. 11, offset, unwmkd., type IV **526**
A140 2¢ carmine, same, type V **527**
A140 2¢ carmine, same, type Va **528**
A140 2¢ carmine, same, type VI **528A**
A140 2¢ carmine, same, type VII **528B**
A140 2¢ carmine rose, perf. 11x10, type II.......... **539**
A140 2¢ carmine rose, same, type III **540**
A140 2¢ rose red, perf. 10x12, single line wmk., type I **423B**
A140 2¢ rose red, perf. 12x10, single line wmk., type I **423E**
A140 2¢ rose red, perf. 10, single line wmk., type I **425**
A140 2¢ rose red, same, perf. 10, booklet pane of 6 .... **425e**
A140 2¢ carmine, perf. 10, unwmkd., type I **463**
A140 2¢ carmine, same, booklet pane of 6 .... **463a**
A140 2¢ carmine, imperf., flat plate, single line wmk., type I **409**
A140 2¢ carmine, imperf., rotary press, single line wmk., type I **459**
A140 2¢ carmine, imperf., flat plate, unwmkd., type I **482**
A140 2¢ deep rose, same, type Ia **482A**
A140 2¢ carmine rose, imperf., offset, unwmkd., type IV **532**
A140 2¢ carmine rose, same, type V **533**
A140 2¢ carmine, same, type Va **534**
A140 2¢ carmine, same, type VI **534A**
A140 2¢ carmine, same, type VII **534B**
A140 2¢ carmine, perf. 10 horiz., flat plate, single line wmk., type I **442**
A140 2¢ red, same, rotary press **449**
A140 2¢ carmine, same, type III **450**
A140 2¢ carmine, perf. 10 horiz., rotary press unwmkd., type II **487**
A140 2¢ carmine, same, type III **488**
A140 2¢ carmine, perf. 10 vert., flat plate, single line wmk., type I **444**
A140 2¢ carmine rose, same, rotary press **453**
A140 2¢ red, same, type II **454**
A140 2¢ carmine, same, type III **455**
A140 2¢ carmine, perf. 10 vert., rotary press, unwmkd., type II **491**
A140 2¢ carmine, same, type III **492**
A140 2¢ carmine, perf. 8½ horiz., type I **411**
A140 2¢ carmine, perf. 8½ vert., type I **413**

TYPES OF THREE CENTS

TYPE I

Type I *The top line of the toga rope is weak and the rope shading lines are thin. The 5th line from the left is missing. The line between the lips is thin.*

TYPE II

Type II *The top line of the toga rope is strong and the rope shading lines are heavy and complete.*
The line between the lips is heavy.
Used on both flat plate and rotary press printings.

TYPE III

Type III *The top line of the toga rope is strong but the 5th shading line is missing as in type I.*
Center shading line of the toga button consists of two dashes with a central dot.
The "P" and "O" of "POSTAGE" are separated by a line of color.
The frame line at the bottom of the vignette is complete.
Used on offset printings only.

TYPE IV

Type IV *The shading lines of the toga rope are complete.*
The second and fourth shading lines in the toga button are broken in the middle and the third line is continuous with a dot in the center.
The "P" and "O" of "POSTAGE" are joined.

The frame line at the bottom of the vignette is broken.
Used on offset printings only.

A140 3¢ deep violet, perf. 12, double line wmk., type I 333
A140 3¢ deep violet, perf. 12, single line wmk., type I 376
A140 3¢ deep violet, perf. 12, bluish paper, type I.... 359
A140 3¢ light violet, perf. 11, unwmkd., type I..... 501
A140 3¢ light violet, same, booklet pane of 6 ...501b
A140 3¢ dark violet, perf. 11, unwmkd., type I ... 502
A140 3¢ dark violet, same, booklet pane of 6 ...502b
A140 3¢ violet, perf. 11, offset, type III 529
A140 3¢ purple, same, type IV 530
A140 3¢ violet, perf. 11x10, type II 541
A140 3¢ deep violet, perf. 10, single line wmk., type I 426
A140 3¢ violet, perf. 10, unwmkd., type I 464
A140 3¢ deep violet, imperf., double line wmk., type I 345
A140 3¢ violet, imperf., unwmkd., type I............ 483
A140 3¢ violet, same, type II........................... 484
A140 3¢ violet, imperf., offset, type IV 535
A140 3¢ deep violet, perf. 12 vert., single line wmk., type I 389
A140 3¢ violet, perf. 10 vert., flat plate, single line wmk., type I 445
A140 3¢ violet, perf. 10 vert., rotary press, single line wmk., type I 456
A140 3¢ violet, perf. 10 vert., rotary press, unwmkd., type I 493
A140 3¢ violet, same, type II........................... 494
A140 3¢ violet, perf. 10 horiz., type I 489
A140 3¢ deep violet, perf. 8½ vert., type I........... 394
A140 4¢ orange brown, perf. 12, double line wmk. ... 334
A140 4¢ orange brown, perf. 12, bluish paper..... 360
A140 4¢ brown, perf. 12, single line wmk. 377
A140 4¢ brown, perf. 11, unwmkd. 503
A140 4¢ brown, perf. 10, single line wmk. 427
A140 4¢ orange brown, perf. 10, unwmkd. 465
A140 4¢ orange brown, imperf. 346
A140 4¢ orange brown, perf. 12 horiz. 350
A140 4¢ orange brown, perf. 12 vert. 354
A140 4¢ brown, perf. 10 vert., flat plate, single line wmk....................................... 446
A140 4¢ brown, same, rotary press 457
A140 4¢ orange brown, perf. 10 vert., rotary press, unwmkd.. 495
A140 4¢ brown, perf. 8½ vert., single line wmk........ 395
A140 5¢ blue, perf. 12, double line wmk............. 335
A140 5¢ blue, perf. 12 bluish paper 361
A140 5¢ blue, perf. 12, single line wmk. 378
A140 5¢ blue, perf. 11, unwmkd. 504
A140 5¢ rose (error), same 505
A140 5¢ carmine (error), perf. 10, unwmkd. 467
A140 5¢ blue, perf. 10, single line wmk. 428
A140 5¢ blue, perf. 12x10 .... 423C
A140 5¢ blue, perf. 10, unwmkd. 466
A140 5¢ blue, imperf. 347
A140 5¢ carmine (error), imperf. 485
A140 5¢ blue, perf. 12 horiz. 351
A140 5¢ blue, perf. 12 vert. 355
A140 5¢ blue, perf. 10 vert., flat plate, single line wmk.. 447
A140 5¢ blue, same, rotary press 458
A140 5¢ blue, perf. 10 vert., rotary press, unwmkd. 496
A140 5¢ blue, perf. 8½ vert............................ 396
A140 6¢ red orange, perf. 12, double line wmk........ 336
A140 6¢ red orange, perf. 12, bluish paper 362
A140 6¢ red orange, perf. 12, single line wmk. ... 379
A140 6¢ red orange, perf. 11, unwmkd. 506
A140 6¢ red orange, perf. 10, single line wmk. ... 429
A140 6¢ red orange, perf. 10, unwmkd. 468
A140 7¢ black, perf. 12, single line wmk. 407
A140 7¢ black, perf. 11, unwmkd. 507
A140 7¢ black, perf. 10, single line wmk. 430
A140 7¢ black, perf. 10, unwmkd. 469
A140 8¢ olive green, perf. 12, double line wmk........ 337
A140 8¢ olive green, perf. 12, bluish paper 363
A140 8¢ olive green, perf. 12, single line wmk. ... 380
A140 10¢ yellow, perf. 12, double line wmk. 338
A140 10¢ yellow, perf. 12, bluish paper 364
A140 10¢ yellow, perf. 12, single line wmk. 381
A140 10¢ yellow, perf. 12 vert. 356
A140 13¢ blue green, perf. 12, double line wmk. ... 339
A140 13¢ blue green, perf. 12, bluish paper......... 365
A140 15¢ pale ultra, perf. 12, double line wmk. 340
A140 15¢ pale ultra, perf. 12, bluish paper......... 366
A140 15¢ pale ultra, perf. 12, single line wmk..... 382
A140 50¢ violet 341
A140 $1 violet brown 342

ISSUES OF 1912-19

A148

Franklin — A149

Designs of 8¢ to $1 denominations differ only in figures of value.

A148 8¢ pale olive green, perf. 12, single line wmk. 414
A148 8¢ olive bister, perf. 11, unwmkd.............. 508
A148 8¢ pale olive grn., perf. 10, single line wmk..... 431
A148 8¢ olive green, perf. 10, unwmkd. 470
A148 9¢ salmon red, perf. 12, single line wmk.... 415
A148 9¢ salmon red, perf. 11, unwmkd. 509
A148 9¢ salmon red, perf. 10, single line wmk. ... 432
A148 9¢ salmon red, perf. 10, unwmkd. 471
A148 10¢ orange yellow, perf. 12, single line wmk. 416
A148 10¢ orange yellow, perf. 11, unwmkd. 510
A148 10¢ orange yellow, perf. 10, single line wmk. 433
A148 10¢ orange yellow, perf. 10, unwmkd. 472
A148 10¢ orange yellow, perf. 10 vert., same 497
A148 11¢ light green, perf. 11, unwmkd. 511
A148 11¢ dark green, perf. 10, single line wmk. 434
A148 11¢ dark green, perf. 10, unwmkd. 473
A148 12¢ claret brown, perf. 12, single line wmk..... 417
A148 12¢ claret brown, perf. 11, unwmkd. 512
A148 12¢ claret brown, perf. 10, single line wmk. 435
A148 12¢ claret brown, perf. 10, unwmkd. 474
A148 13¢ apple green, perf. 11, unwmkd............. 513
A148 15¢ gray, perf. 12, single line wmk. 418
A148 15¢ gray, perf. 11, unwmkd. 514
A148 15¢ gray, perf. 10, single line wmk. 437
A148 15¢ gray, perf. 10, unwmkd. 475
A148 20¢ ultramarine, perf. 12, single line wmk....... 419
A148 20¢ light ultra., perf. 11, unwmkd. 515
A148 20¢ ultramarine, perf. 10, single line wmk....... 438
A148 20¢ light ultra. perf. 10, unwmkd. 476
A148 30¢ orange red, perf. 12, single line wmk....... 420
A148 30¢ orange red, perf. 11, unwmkd. 516
A148 30¢ orange red, perf. 10, single line wmk....... 439
A148 30¢ orange red, perf. 10, unwmkd............. 476A
A148 50¢ violet, perf. 12, single line wmk. 421
A148 50¢ violet, perf. 12, double line wmk. 422
A148 50¢ red violet, perf. 11, unwmkd. 517
A148 50¢ violet, perf. 10, single line wmk. 440
A148 50¢ light violet, perf. 10, unwmkd. 477
A148 $1 violet brown, perf. 12, double line wmk. 423
A148 $1 violet brown, perf. 11, unwmkd............. 518
A148 $1 violet black, perf. 10, double line wmk. 460
A148 $1 violet black, perf. 10, unwmkd. 478

ISSUES OF 1918-20
Perf. 11 Unwmkd.

A149 $2 orange red & black............................. 523
A149 $2 carmine & black 547
A149 $5 deep green & black 524

ISSUES OF 1922-32

Nathan Hale — A154

Franklin — A155

Warren G. Harding — A156

Washington — A157

Lincoln — A158

Martha Washington — A159

Theodore Roosevelt — A160

Garfield — A161

McKinley — A162

Grant — A163

Jefferson — A164

Monroe — A165

Hayes — A166

Cleveland — A167

American Indian — A168

Statue of Liberty — A169

Golden Gate — A170

Niagara Falls — A171

Buffalo — A172

Arlington Amphitheater and Tomb of the Unknown Soldier — A173

Lincoln Memorial — A174

United States Capitol — A175

"America" — A176

Canal Zone Overprints:
Type A has flat-topped "A's" in "CANAL."
Type B has sharp-pointed "A's" in "CANAL."

Unwmkd.

A154 ½¢ olive brown, perf. 11 551
A154 ½¢ olive brown, perf. 11x10½ 653
A154 ½¢ olive brown, "CANAL ZONE" .... C.Z. 70
A155 1¢ deep green, perf. 11, flat plate 552
A155 1¢ deep green, booklet pane of 6 ....552a
A155 1¢ green, perf. 11, rotary press 19¾x22¼mm
.... 594
A155 1¢ green, same, 191/4x22½mm (used) 596
A155 1¢ green, perf. 11x10, rotary press 578
A155 1¢ green, perf. 10 581
A155 1¢ green, perf. 11x10½ 632
A155 1¢ green, same, booklet pane of 6 ....632a
A155 1¢ green, ovpt. Kans. 658
A155 1¢ green, ovpt. Nebr. 669
A155 1¢ green, imperf. 575
A155 1¢ green, perf. 10 vert. 597
A155 1¢ yellow green, perf. 10 horiz. 604
A155 1¢ deep green, "CANAL ZONE" type A, perf.
    11 .... C.Z. 71
A155 1¢ deep green, same, booklet pane of 6 ....
    .... C.Z. 71e
A155 1¢ green, "CANAL ZONE" type B, perf.
    11x10½ .... C.Z. 100
A156 1½¢ yellow brown, perf. 11 553
A156 1½¢ yellow brown, perf. 11x10½ 633
A156 1½¢ brown, ovpt. Kans. 659
A156 1½¢ brown, ovpt. Nebr. 670
A156 1½¢ brown, perf. 10 582
A156 1½¢ brown, perf. 10 vert. 598
A156 1½¢ yellow brown, perf. 10 horiz. 605
A156 1½¢ yellow brown, imperf., flat plate 576
A156 1½¢ yellow brown, imperf., rotary press,
    19¼x22½mm 631
A156 1½¢ yellow brown "CANAL ZONE" .... C.Z. 72

Type I

No heavy hair lines at top center of head. Outline of left acanthus scroll generally faint at top and toward base at left side.

Type II

Three heavy hair lines at top center of head; two being outstanding in the white area. Outline of left acanthus scroll very strong and clearly defined at top (under left edge of lettered panel) and at lower curve (above and to left of numeral oval).

A157 2¢ carmine, perf. 11, flat plate 554
A157 2¢ carmine, same, booklet pane of 6 ....554c
A157 2¢ carmine, perf. 11, rotary press,
    19¾x22¼mm 595
A157 2¢ carmine, perf. 11x10 579
A157 2¢ carmine, perf. 11x10½, type I 634
A157 2¢ carmine, perf. 11x10½, type II 634A
A157 2¢ carmine lake, same, type I 634b
A157 2¢ carmine lake, same, booklet pane of 6 ....
    .... 634d
A157 2¢ carmine, overprt. Molly Pitcher 646
A157 2¢ carmine, overprt. Hawaii 1778-1928 647
A157 2¢ carmine, overprt. Kans. 660
A157 2¢ carmine, overprt. Nebr. 671
A157 2¢ carmine, perf. 10 583
A157 2¢ carmine, same, booklet pane of 6 ......583a
A157 2¢ carmine, imperf. 577
A157 2¢ carmine, perf. 10 vert., type I 599
A157 2¢ carmine, same, type II 599A
A157 2¢ carmine, perf. 10 horiz. 606
A157 2¢ carmine, "CANAL ZONE" type A, perf. 11
    .... C.Z. 73
A157 2¢ carmine, same, booklet pane of 6 ....
    .... C.Z. 73a
A157 2¢ carmine, "CANAL ZONE" type B, perf. 11
    .... C.Z. 84
A157 2¢ carmine, same, booklet pane of 6 ....
    .... C.Z. 84d
A157 2¢ carmine, "CANAL ZONE" type B, perf. 10
    .... C.Z. 97
A157 2¢ carmine, same, booklet pane of 6 ....
    .... C.Z. 97b
A157 2¢ carmine, "CANAL ZONE" type B, perf.
    11x10½ .... C.Z. 101
A157 2¢ carmine, same, booklet pane of 6 ....
    .... C.Z. 101a
A158 3¢ violet, perf. 11 555
A158 3¢ violet, perf. 11x10½ 635
A158 3¢ violet, overprt. Kans. 661
A158 3¢ violet, overprt. Nebr. 672
A158 3¢ violet, perf. 10 584
A158 3¢ violet, perf. 10 vert. 600
A158 3¢ violet, "CANAL ZONE" perf. 11 .... C.Z. 85
A158 3¢ violet, "CANAL ZONE" perf. 10 .... C.Z. 98
A158 3¢ violet, "CANAL ZONE" perf. 11x10½ ....
    .... C.Z. 102
A159 4¢ yellow brown, perf. 11 556
A159 4¢ yellow brown, perf. 11x10½ 636
A159 4¢ yellow brown, ovrpt. Kans. 662
A159 4¢ yellow brown, ovrpt. Nebr. 673
A159 4¢ yellow brown, perf. 10 585
A159 4¢ yellow brown, perf. 10 vert. 601

A160 5¢ dark blue, perf. 11.....................557
A160 5¢ dark blue, perf. 11x10½.............637
A160 5¢ dark blue, ovpt. Hawaii 1778-1928.......648
A160 5¢ deep blue, ovpt. Kans...............663
A160 5¢ deep blue, ovpt. Nebr..............674
A160 5¢ blue, perf. 10.......................586
A160 5¢ dark blue, perf. 10 vert............602
A160 5¢ dark blue, "CANAL ZONE" type A, perf. 11
....C.Z. 74
A160 5¢ dark blue, same, type B.............C.Z. 86
A160 5¢ dark blue, same, perf. 11x10½......C.Z. 103
A161 6¢ red orange, perf. 11................558
A161 6¢ red orange, perf. 11x10½...........638
A161 6¢ red orange, ovrpt. Kans............664
A161 6¢ red orange, ovrpt. Nebr............675
A161 6¢ red orange, perf. 10...............587
A161 6¢ deep orange, perf. 10 vert.........723
A162 7¢ black, perf. 11.....................559
A162 7¢ black, perf. 11x10½................639
A162 7¢ black, ovrpt. Kans.................665
A162 7¢ black, ovrpt. Nebr.................676
A162 7¢ black, perf. 10.....................588
A163 8¢ olive green, perf. 11..............560
A163 8¢ olive green, perf. 11x10½..........640
A163 8¢ olive green, ovrpt. Kans...........666
A163 8¢ olive green, ovrpt. Nebr...........677
A163 8¢ olive green, perf. 10..............589
A164 9¢ rose, perf. 11......................561
A164 9¢ orange red, perf. 11x10½...........641
A164 9¢ light rose, ovrpt. Kans............667
A164 9¢ light rose, ovrpt. Nebr............678
A164 9¢ rose, perf. 10......................590
A165 10¢ orange, perf. 11..................562
A165 10¢ orange, perf. 11x10½.............642
A165 10¢ orange yellow, ovrpt. Kans.........668
A165 10¢ orange yellow, ovrpt. Nebr........679
A165 10¢ orange, perf. 10..................591
A165 10¢ orange, perf. 10 vert............603
A165 10¢ orange, "CANAL ZONE" type A, perf. 11
....C.Z. 75
A165 10¢ orange, same, type B.............C.Z. 87
A165 10¢ orange, same, perf. 10...........C.Z. 99
A165 10¢ orange, same, perf. 11x10½.......C.Z. 104
A166 11¢ light blue, perf. 11..............563
A166 11¢ light blue, perf. 11x10½..........692
A167 12¢ brown violet, perf. 11............564
A167 12¢ brown violet, perf. 11x10½........693
A167 12¢ brown violet, "CANAL ZONE" type A
....C.Z. 76
A167 12¢ brown violet, same, type B.........C.Z. 88
A168 14¢ blue, perf. 11.....................565
A168 14¢ dark blue, perf. 11x10½...........695
A168 14¢ dark blue, "CANAL ZONE" type A, perf.
11..C.Z. 77
A168 14¢ dark blue, same, type B...........C.Z. 89
A168 14¢ dark blue, same, perf. 11x10½....C.Z. 116
A169 15¢ gray, perf. 11.....................566
A169 15¢ gray, perf. 11x10½................696
A169 15¢ gray, "CANAL ZONE" type A.........C.Z. 78
A169 15¢ gray, "CANAL ZONE" type B.........C.Z. 90
A170 20¢ carmine rose, perf. 11............567
A170 20¢ carmine rose, perf. 10½x11........698
A170 20¢ carmine rose, "CANAL ZONE".........C.Z. 92
A171 25¢ yellow green, perf. 11............568
A171 25¢ blue green, perf. 10½x11..........699
A172 30¢ olive brown, perf. 11.............569
A172 30¢ brown, perf. 10½x11..............700
A172 30¢ olive brown, "CANAL ZONE" type A.........
....C.Z. 79
A172 30¢ olive brown, "CANAL ZONE" type B.........
....C.Z. 93
A173 50¢ lilac, perf. 11....................570
A173 50¢ lilac, perf. 10½x11..............701
A173 50¢ lilac, "CANAL ZONE" type A.........C.Z. 80
A173 50¢ lilac, "CANAL ZONE" type B.........C.Z. 94
A174 $1 violet brown, perf. 11.............571
A174 $1 violet brown, perf. 10¾x10½.......4075a
A174 $1 violet brown, "CANAL ZONE" type A.........
....C.Z. 81
A174 $1 violet brown, "CANAL ZONE" type B.........
....C.Z. 95
A175 $2 deep blue, perf. 11................572
A175 $2 deep blue, perf. 10¾x10½..........4075b
A176 $5 carmine & blue, perf. 11...........573
A176 $5 carmine & blue, perf. 10¾x10½......4075c

REGULAR ISSUES OF 1925-26, 1930 and 1932

Harrison — A186   Wilson — A187

A186 13¢ green, perf. 11....................622

A186 13¢ yellow green, perf. 11x10½.........694
A187 17¢ black, perf. 11....................623
A187 17¢ black, perf. 10½x11..............697
A187 17¢ black, "CANAL ZONE"...............C.Z. 91

Harding — A203   Taft — A204

A203 1½¢ brown, perf. 11x10½...............684
A203 1½¢ brown, perf. 10 vert.............686
A204 4¢ brown, perf. 11x10½...............685
A204 4¢ brown, perf. 10 vert..............687

Washington — A226

A226 3¢ deep violet, perf. 11x10½.........720
A226 3¢ deep violet, same, booklet pane of 6   720b
A226 3¢ deep violet, perf. 10 vert.........721
A226 3¢ deep violet, perf. 10 horiz........722
A226 3¢ deep violet, "CANAL ZONE".........C.Z. 115

PRESIDENTIAL ISSUE OF 1938

Benjamin   George
Franklin — A275   Washington — A276

Martha   John
Washington — A277   Adams — A278

Thomas   James
Jefferson — A279   Madison — A280

The White   James
House — A281   Monroe — A282

John Quincy   Andrew
Adams — A283   Jackson — A284

Martin Van   William H.
Buren — A285   Harrison — A286

John Tyler — A287   James K.
                      Polk — A288

Zachary   Millard
Taylor — A289   Fillmore — A290

Franklin   James
Pierce — A291   Buchanan — A292

Abraham   Andrew
Lincoln — A293   Johnson — A294

Ulysses S.   Rutherford B.
Grant — A295   Hayes — A296

James A.
Garfield — A297

Chester A.
Arthur — A298

Grover
Cleveland — A299

Benjamin
Harrison — A300

William
McKinley — A301

Theodore
Roosevelt — A302

William Howard
Taft — A303

Woodrow
Wilson — A304

Warren G.
Harding — A305

Calvin
Coolidge — A306

Rotary Press Printing
Unwmkd.

A275	½¢ deep orange, perf. 11x10½	803
A275	½¢ red orange, "CANAL ZONE"	C.Z. 118
A276	1¢ green, perf. 11x10½	804
A276	1¢ green, booklet pane of 6	804b
A276	1¢ green, perf. 10 vert.	839
A276	1¢ green, perf. 10 horiz.	848
A277	1½¢ bister brown, perf. 11x10½	805
A277	1½¢ bister brown, perf. 10 vert.	840
A277	1½¢ bister brown, perf. 10 horiz.	849
A277	1½¢ bister brown, "CANAL ZONE"	C.Z. 119
A278	2¢ rose carmine, perf. 11x10½	806
A278	2¢ booklet pane of 6	806b
A278	2¢ rose carmine, perf. 10 vert.	841
A278	2¢ rose carmine, perf. 10 horiz.	850
A279	3¢ deep violet, perf. 11x10½	807
A279	3¢ deep violet, booklet pane of 6	807a
A279	3¢ deep violet, perf. 10 vert.	842
A279	3¢ deep violet, perf. 10 horiz.	851
A280	4¢ red violet, perf. 11x10½	808
A280	4¢ red violet, perf. 10 vert.	843
A281	4½¢ dark gray, perf. 11x10½	809
A281	4½¢ dark gray, perf. 10 vert.	844
A282	5¢ bright blue, perf. 11x10½	810
A282	5¢ bright blue, perf. 10 vert.	845
A283	6¢ red orange, perf. 11x10½	811
A283	6¢ red orange, perf. 10 vert.	846
A284	7¢ sepia, perf. 11x10½	812
A285	8¢ olive green, perf. 11x10½	813
A286	9¢ rose pink, perf. 11x10½	814
A287	10¢ brown red, perf. 11x10½	815

A287	10¢ brown red, perf. 10 vert.	847
A288	11¢ ultramarine, perf. 11x10½	816
A289	12¢ bright violet, perf. 11x10½	817
A290	13¢ blue green, perf. 11x10½	818
A291	14¢ blue, perf. 11x10½	819
A292	15¢ blue gray, perf. 11x10½	820
A293	16¢ black, perf. 11x10½	821
A294	17¢ rose red, perf. 11x10½	822
A295	18¢ brn. carmine, perf. 11x10½	823
A296	19¢ bright violet, perf. 11x10½	824
A297	20¢ bright blue green, perf. 11x10½	825
A298	21¢ dull blue, perf. 11x10½	826
A299	22¢ vermilion, perf. 11x10½	827
A300	24¢ gray black, perf. 11x10½	828
A301	25¢ dp. red lilac, perf. 11x10½	829
A302	30¢ deep ultra, perf. 11x10½	830
A303	50¢ lt. red violet, perf. 11x10½	831

Flat Plate Printing
Perf. 11

A304	$1 pur. & blk., unwmkd.	832
A304	$1 pur. & blk., wmkd. USIR	832b
A304	$1 red vio. & blk., thick white paper, smooth colorless gum	832c
A305	$2 yellow green & black	833
A306	$5 carmine & black	834

LIBERTY ISSUE 1954-73

Benjamin
Franklin — A477

George
Washington — A478

Palace of the
Governors, Santa Fe —
A478a

Mount Vernon — A479

Thomas
Jefferson — A480

Bunker Hill
Monument and
Massachusetts Flag
1776 — A481

Statue of
Liberty — A482

Abraham
Lincoln — A483

The Hermitage — A484

James
Monroe — A485

Theodore
Roosevelt — A486

Woodrow
Wilson — A487

Statue of Liberty
(Rotary and flat plate
printing) — A488

Design slightly
altered; see position
of torch (Giorgi
press
printing) — A489

John J. Pershing —
A489a

The Alamo — A490

Independence
Hall — A491

Statue of Liberty —
A491a

Benjamin
Harrison — A492

John Jay — A493

Monticello — A494

Paul Revere — A495

Robert E.
Lee — A496

John
Marshall — A497

Susan B.
Anthony — A498

Patrick
Henry — A499

Alexander Hamilton — A500

Unwmkd.

A477	½¢ red orange, perf. 11x10½	....	**1030**
A478	1¢ dark green, perf. 11x10½	....	**1031**
A478	1¢ dark green, perf. 10 vert.	....	**1054**
A478a	1¼¢ turquoise, perf. 10½x11	....	**1031A**
A478a	1¼¢ turquoise, perf. 10 horiz.	....	**1054A**
A479	1½¢ brown carmine, perf. 10½x11	....	**1032**
A480	2¢ carmine rose, perf. 11x10	....	**1033**
A480	2¢ carmine rose, perf. 10 vert.	....	**1055**
A481	2½¢ gray blue, perf. 11x10½	....	**1034**
A481	2½¢ gray blue, perf. 10 vert.	....	**1056**
A482	3¢ deep violet, perf. 11x10½	....	**1035**
A482	3¢ deep violet, perf. 10 vert.	....	**1057**
A482	3¢ deep violet, imperf., size: 24x28mm.		**1075a**
A483	4¢ red violet, perf. 11x10½	....	**1036**
A483	4¢ red violet, perf. 10 vert.	....	**1058**
A484	4½¢ blue green, perf. 10½x11	....	**1037**
A484	4½¢ blue green, perf. 10 horiz.	....	**1059**
A485	5¢ deep blue, perf. 11x10½	....	**1038**
A486	6¢ carmine, perf. 11x10½	....	**1039**
A487	7¢ rose carmine, same	....	**1040**
A488	8¢ dark violet blue & carmine, flat plate printing, perf. 11, mapprox. 22.7mm high		**1041**
A488	8¢ dark violet blue & carmine, rotary press printing, perf. 11, appprox. 22.9mm high		**1041B**
A488	8¢ dark violet blue & carmine, imperf., size: 24x28mm		**1075b**
A489	8¢ dark violet blue & carmine, perf. 11	...	**1042**
A489a	8¢ brown, perf. 11x10½	....	**1042A**
A490	9¢ rose lilac, perf. 10½x11	....	**1043**
A491	10¢ rose lake, same	....	**1044**
A491a	11¢ carmine & dark violet blue, perf. 11		**1044A**
A492	12¢ red, perf. 11x10½	....	**1045**
A493	15¢ rose lake, perf. 11x10½	....	**1046**
A494	20¢ ultramarine, perf. 10½x11	....	**1047**
A495	25¢ green, perf. 11x10½	....	**1048**
A495	25¢ green, perf. 10 vert.	....	**1059A**
A496	30¢ black, perf. 11x10½	....	**1049**
A497	40¢ brown red, perf. 11x10½	....	**1050**
A498	50¢ bright purple, perf. 11x10½	....	**1051**
A499	$1 purple, perf. 11x10½	....	**1052**
A500	$5 black, perf. 11	....	**1053**

ISSUE OF 1962-66

Andrew
Jackson — A646

George
Washington — A650

A646	1¢ green, perf. 11x10½	....	**1209**
A646	1¢ green, perf. 10 vert.	....	**1225**
A650	5¢ dk. bl. gray, perf. 11x10½	....	**1213**
A650	5¢ dk. bl. gray, perf. 10 vert.	....	**1229**

PROMINENT AMERICANS ISSUE 1965-81

Thomas
Jefferson — A710

Frank Lloyd Wright
and Guggenheim
Museum, New
York — A712

Abraham
Lincoln — A714

Re-engraved —
A715a

Franklin D.
Roosevelt (vertical
coil) — A727a

Albert
Einstein — A717

Henry Ford and 1909
Model I — A718a

Albert
Gallatin — A711

Francis
Parkman — A713

George
Washington — A715

Franklin D.
Roosevelt — A716

Benjamin Franklin and
his signature — A816

Andrew
Jackson — A718

John F.
Kennedy — A719

Fiorello H.
LaGuardia and New
York skyline —
A817a

Ernest (Ernie) Taylor
Pyle — A818

George C.
Marshall — A721

Frederick
Douglass — A722

Thomas
Paine — A724

Eugene
O'Neill — A726

Oliver Wendell
Holmes — A720

Dr. Elizabeth
Blackwell — A818a

Amadeo P. Giannini
— A818b

John Dewey — A723

Lucy Stone — A725

John Bassett
Moore — A727

Types of 15¢:

I — Necktie barely touches coat at bottom; cross-hatching of tie strong and complete. Flag of "5" is true horizontal. Crosshatching of "15" is colorless when visible.

II — Necktie does not touch coat at bottom; LL to UR crosshatching lines strong, UL to LR lines very faint. Flag of "5" slants down slightly at right. Crosshatching of "15" is colored and visible when magnified.

A third type, used only for No. 1288B, is smaller in overall size, and "15¢" is ¾mm closer to head.

Unwmkd.
Rotary Press Printing

A710	1¢ green, perf. 11x10½	....	**1278**
A710	1¢ green, perf. 10, vert., tagged	....	**1299**

A711   1 1/4¢ light green, perf. 11x10½ 1279
A712   2¢ dk. bl. gray, perf. 11x10½ 1280
A713   3¢ violet, perf. 10½x11 1281
A713   3¢ violet, perf. 10 horiz. 1297
A714   4¢ black, perf. 11x10½ 1282
A714   4¢ black, perf. 10, vert. 1303
A715   5¢ blue, perf. 11x10½ 1283
A715   5¢ blue, perf. 10 vert. 1304
A715a 5¢ blue, perf. 11x10½ 1283B
A715a 5¢ blue, perf. 10 vert. 1304C
A716   6¢ gray brown, perf. 10½x11 1284
A716   6¢ gray brown, perf. 10 horiz., tagged 1298
A727a 6¢ gray brown, perf. 10 vert., tagged 1305
A816   7¢ bright blue, perf. 10½x11 .... 1393D
A717   8¢ violet, perf. 11x10½ 1285
A718   10¢ lilac, perf. 11x10½ 1286
A718a 12¢ black, perf. 10½x11 .... 1286A
A719   13¢ brown, perf. 11x10½ 1287
A817a 14¢ gray brown, perf. 11x10½ 1397
A720   15¢ magenta, perf. 11x10½ 1288
A720   15¢ magenta, perf. 10 (booklet panes only) ...
       .... 1288B
A720   15¢ magenta, perf. 10 vert. 1305E
A818   16¢ brown 1398
A818a 18¢ violet, perf. 11x10½ 1399
A721   20¢ deep olive, perf. 11x10½ 1289
A818b 21¢ green, perf. 11x10½ 1400
A722   25¢ rose lake, perf. 11x10½ 1290
A723   30¢ red lilac, perf. 10½x11 1291
A724   40¢ blue black, perf. 11x10½ 1292
A725   50¢ rose magenta, perf. 11x10½ 1293
A726 $1 dull purple, perf. 11x10½ 1294
A726 $1 dull purple, perf. 10 vert, tagged 1305C
A727 $5 gray black, perf 11x10½ 1295

Dwight D.
Eisenhower — A815

A815a

A815   6¢ dark blue gray, perf. 11x10½ 1393
A815   6¢ dk. bl. gray, perf. 10, vert. 1401
A815   8¢ deep claret, perf. 11x10½ (Booklet panes
       only) 1395
A815   8¢ deep claret, perf. 10 vert 1402
A815a 8¢ blk., red & bl. gray, perf. 11 1394

FLAG ISSUE 1968-71

Flag and White House — A760

A760   6¢ dark blue, red & green, perf. 11, size:
       19x22mm 1338
A760   6¢ dark blue, red & green, perf. 11x10½,
       size: 18¼x21mm 1338D
A760   6¢ dark blue, red & green, perf. 10 vert.,
       size: 18¼x21mm 1338A
A760   8¢ multicolored, perf. 11x10½ 1338F
A760   8¢ multicolored, perf. 10 vert. 1338G

REGULAR ISSUE 1971-74

U.S. Postal Service
Emblem — A817

50-Star and 13-Star
Flags — A923

Jefferson Memorial
and quotation from
Declaration of
Independence
A924

Liberty Bell — A926

A817   8¢ multicolored, perf. 11x10½ 1396
A923   10¢ red & blue, perf 11x10½ 1509
A923   10¢ red & blue, perf. 10 vert. 1519
A924   10¢ blue, perf. 11x10½ 1510
A924   10¢ blue, perf. 10 vert. 1520
A925   10¢ multicolored, perf. 11x10½ 1511
A926   6.3¢ brick red, perf. 10 vert. 1518

AMERICANA ISSUE 1975-81

Inkwell and
Quill — A984

Speaker's
Stand — A985

Early Ballot
Box — A987

Books, Bookmark,
Eyeglasses — A988

Dome of
Capitol — A994

Contemplation of
Justice — A995

Early American
Printing
Press — A996

Torch Statue of
Liberty — A997

Mail Transport and
"Zip Code"
A925

Liberty Bell — A998

Eagle and
Shield — A999

Ft. McHenry
Flag — A1001

Head Statue of
Liberty — A1002

Old North
Church — A1003

Ft.
Nisqually — A1004

Sandy Hook
Lighthouse
A1005

Morris Township
School No. 2,
Devil's Lake
A1006

Iron "Betty" Lamp
Plymouth Colony,
17th-18th
Centuries — A1007

Rush Lamp and
Candle
Holder — A1008

Kerosene Table
Lamp — A1009

Railroad Conductors
Lantern, c.
1850 — A1010

COIL STAMPS

Six-string
guitar — A1011

Weaver
violins — A1199

Saxhorns — A1012

Drum — A1013

Steinway Grand Piano, 1857 — A1014

A984   1¢ dark blue, greenish, perf. 11x10½...... **1581**
A984   1¢ dark blue, greenish, perf. 10 vert. **1811**
A985   2¢ red brown, greenish, perf. 11x10½ **1582**
A987   3¢ olive, greenish, perf 11x10½ **1584**
A988   4¢ rose magenta, cream, perf. 11x10½ .. **1585**
A994   9¢ slate green, gray, perf. 11x10½ (booklet
     panes only)...................................... **1590**
A994   9¢ slate green, gray, perf. 10x9¾ (booklet
     panes only)..................................... **1590A**
A994   9¢ slate green, gray, perf. 11x10½........ **1591**
A994   9¢ slate green, gray, perf. 10 vert. **1616**
A995   10¢ violet, gray, perf. 10 vert. **1617**
A995   10¢ violet, gray, perf. 11x10½ **1592**
A996   11¢ orange, gray, perf. 11x10½ **1593**
A997   12¢ red brown, beige, perf. 11x10½ **1594**
A997   12¢ red brown, beige, perf. 10 vert. **1816**
A998   13¢ brown, perf. 11x10½........................ **1595**
A998   13¢ brown, perf. 10 vert. **1618**
A999   13¢ multicolored............................... **1596**
A1001 15¢ gray, dark blue & red, perf. 11 .... **1597**
A1001 15¢ gray, dark blue & red, perf. 11x10½
     (booklet panes only)...................... **1598**
A1001 15¢ gray, dark blue & red, perf. 10 vert. ...
     .... **1618C**
A1002 16¢ blue, perf. 11x10½......................... **1599**
A1002 16¢ blue, perf. 10 vert. **1619**
A1003 24¢ red, blue, perf. 11x10½................. **1603**
A1004 28¢ brown, blue, perf. 11x10½ **1604**
A1005 29¢ blue, blue, perf. 11x10½ **1605**
A1006 30¢ green, perf. 11x10½...................... **1606**
A1007 50¢ black & orange, perf. 11 .... **1608**
A1008 $1 brown, orange & yellow, tan, perf. 11 ...
     .... **1610**
A1009 $2 dark green & red, tan, perf. 11.......... **1611**
A1010 $5 red brown, yellow & orange, tan, perf. 11
     .... **1612**
A1011 3.1¢ brown, yellow, perf. 10 vert. **1613**
A1199 3.5¢ purple, yellow, perf. 10 vert. **1813**
A1012 7.7¢ brown, bright yellow, perf. 10 vert. ....
     .... **1614**
A1013 7.9¢ carmine, yellow, perf. 10 vert. **1615**
A1014 8.4¢ dark blue, yellow, perf. 10 vert. **1615C**

FLAG ISSUE 1975-77

13-star Flag over
Independence
Hall — A1015

Flag over
Capitol — A1016

A1015 13¢ dark blue & red, perf. 11x10¾ **1622**
A1015 13¢ dark blue & red, perf. 11¼ **1622C**
A1015 13¢ dark blue & red, perf. 10 vert. **1625**
A1016 13¢ blue & red, perf. 11x10½ (booklet panes
     only).. **1623**
A1016 13¢ blue & red, perf. 10x9¾ (booklet panes
     only).. **1623B**

REGULAR ISSUE 1978

Indian Head,
Penny, 1877
A1123

Red Masterpiece and
Medallion Roses — A1126

A1123 13¢ brown & blue, green, bister, perf. 11........
     .... **1734**
A1126 15¢ multicolored, perf 10 (booklet panes
     only).. **1737**
A1209 15¢ red brown & sepia, perf. 11............. **1822**

REGULAR ISSUE 1978-85

"A" Eagle — A1124

"B" Eagle — A1207

"C" Eagle
A1332

"C" Eagle
(Booklet)
A1333

"D" Eagle
A1496

"D" Eagle
(Booklet)
A1497

A1124 (15¢) orange, perf. 11 .... **1735**
A1124 (15¢) orange, perf. 11x10½ (booklet panes
     only).. **1736**
A1124 (15¢) orange, perf. 10 vert...................... **1743**
A1207 (18¢) violet, perf. 11x10½...................... **1818**
A1207 (18¢) violet, perf. 10 (booklet panes only) ......
     .... **1819**
A1207 (18¢) violet, perf. 10 vert........................ **1820**
A1332 (20¢) brown, perf. 11x10½...................... **1946**
A1332 (20¢) brown, perf. 10 vert....................... **1947**
A1333 (20¢) brown, perf. 11x10½ (booklet panes
     only).. **1948**
A1496 (22¢) green, perf. 11 .... **2111**
A1496 (22¢) green, perf. 10 vert....................... **2112**
A1497 (22¢) green, perf. 11 (booklet panes only)......
     .... **2113**

Dolley Madison
A1209

GREAT AMERICANS ISSUE 1980-99

A1231

A1551

A1232

A1552

A1233

A1553

A1234

A1554

A1235

A1555

A1556

A1236

A1237

A1238

Sylvanus Thayer — USA 9 — A1239
Richard Russell — USA 10c — A1240
Chester Carlson — USA 21 — A1562
John J. Audubon — USA 22 — A1250
Lillian M. Gilbreth — USA 40c — A1255
Claire Chennault — USA 40 Flying Tigers, 1940s — A1569

Red Cloud — 10 USA — A1557
Alden Partridge — USA 11 — A1241
Mary Cassatt — USA 23 — A1563
Jack London — USA 25 — A1564
Harvey Cushing MD — USA 45 — A1570
Ruth Benedict — USA 46 ANTHROPOLOGIST — A2253

Crazy Horse — USA 13c — A1242
Sinclair Lewis — USA 14 — A1243
Sitting Bull — USA 28 — A1565
Earl Warren — 1891–1974 Chief Justice of the US — 29 — A1566
Chester W. Nimitz — USA 50 — A1256
Hubert H. Humphrey — VICE PRESIDENT USA 52 — A1571

Julia Ward Howe — 14 USA — A1558
Buffalo Bill Cody — USA 15 — A1559
Thomas Jefferson — USA 29 — A1567
Frank C. Laubach — USA 30c — A1251
Alice Hamilton, MD — SOCIAL REFORMER USA 55 — A2255
Justin S. Morrill — LAND GRANT COLLEGES USA 55 — A2256

Rachel Carson — USA 17c — A1244
Belva Ann Lockwood — USA 17 — A1560
Milton S. Hershey — PHILANTHROPIST USA 32 — A2248
Cal Farley — HUMANITARIAN USA 32 — A2249
John Harvard — USA 56 — A1572
H.H. 'Hap' Arnold — USA 65 — A1573

George Mason — USA 18c — A1245
Sequoyah — USA 19c — A1246
Henry R. Luce — EDITOR USA 32 — A2250
Lila and DeWitt Wallace — PHILANTHROPISTS USA 32 — A2251
Wendell Willkie — 1892–1944 Statesman 75 USA — A1574
Mary Breckinridge — Frontier Nursing Service USA 77 — A2257

Ralph Bunche — USA 20c — A1247
Thomas H. Gallaudet — USA 20c — A1248
Charles R Drew MD — USA 35c — A1252
Dennis Chavez — United States Senator USA 35 — A1568
Alice Paul — SUFFRAGIST USA 78 — A2258
Bernard Revel — USA $1 — A1575

Harry S Truman — USA 2Oc — A1249
Virginia Apgar — Physician 1909–1974 USA 20 — A1561
Robert Millikan — 37c USA — A1253
Grenville Clark — USA 39 — A1254
Johns Hopkins — USA $1 — A1576
Bryan — $2 USA William Jennings — A1577

A1578

Brown
bear — A1271

Elk
(wapiti) — A1273

White-tailed
deer — A1275

Polar bear — A1272

Moose — A1274

Pronghorn — A1276

Rocky Mountain
Bighorn — A1334

Of the
People, By
the People,
For the
People
A1499

A1231	1¢ black, perf. 11		1844
A1551	1¢ brownish vermilion, perf. 11		2168
A1232	2¢ brown black, perf. 11x10½		1845
A1552	2¢ bright blue, perf. 11		2169
A1233	3¢ olive green, perf. 11x10½		1846
A1553	3¢ bright blue, perf. 11		2170
A1234	4¢ violet, perf. 11x10½		1847
A1554	4¢ blue violet, perf. 11		2171
A1235	5¢ henna brown, perf. 11x10½		1848
A1555	5¢ dark olive green, perf. 11		2172
A1556	5¢ carmine, perf. 11		2173
A1236	6¢ orange vermilion, perf. 11		1849
A1237	7¢ bright carmine, perf. 11		1850
A1238	8¢ olive black, perf. 11		1851
A1239	9¢ dark green, perf. 11		1852
A1240	10¢ Prussian blue, perf. 11		1853
A1557	10¢ lake, perf. 11		2175
A1241	11¢ dark blue, perf. 11		1854
A1242	13¢ light maroon, perf. 11x10½		1855
A1243	14¢ slate green, perf. 11		1856
A1558	14¢ crimson, perf. 11		2176
A1559	15¢ claret, perf. 11		2177
A1244	17¢ green, perf. 11x10½		1857
A1560	17¢ dull blue green, perf. 11		2178
A1245	18¢ dark blue, perf. 11x10½		1858
A1246	19¢ brown, perf. 11x10½		1859
A1247	20¢ claret, perf. 11x10½		1860
A1248	20¢ green, perf. 11x10½		1861
A1249	20¢ black, perf. 11		1862
A1561	20¢ red brown, perf. 11		2179
A1562	21¢ blue violet, perf. 11		2180
A1250	22¢ dark chalky blue, perf. 11		1863
A1563	23¢ purple, perf. 11		2181
A1564	25¢ blue, perf. 11		2182
A1564	25¢ blue, perf. 10		2197
A1565	28¢ myrtle green, perf. 11		2183
A1566	29¢ blue, perf. 11		2184
A1567	29¢ indigo, perf. 11½x11		2185
A1251	30¢ olive gray, perf. 11		1864
A2248	32¢ brown, perf.11.1		2933
A2249	32¢ green, perf. 11.2		2934
A2250	32¢ lake, perf. 11.2		2935
A2251	32¢ blue, perf. 11.2x11.1		2936
A1252	35¢ gray, perf. 11x10½		1865
A1568	35¢ black, perf. 11		2186
A1253	37¢ blue, perf. 11x10½		1866
A1254	39¢ rose lilac, perf. 11		1867
A1255	40¢ dark green, perf. 11		1868
A1569	40¢ dark blue, perf. 11		2187
A1570	45¢ bright blue, perf. 11		2188
A2253	46¢ carmine, perf. 11.1		2938
A1256	50¢ brown, perf. 11		1869
A1571	52¢ purple, perf. 11		2189
A2255	55¢ green, perf. 11		2940
A2256	55¢ black, serpentine die cut 11½, self-adhesive		2941
A1572	56¢ scarlet, perf. 11		2190
A1573	65¢ dark blue, perf. 11		2191
A1574	75¢ deep magenta, perf. 11		2192
A2257	77¢ blue, perf.11.8x11.6		2942
A2258	78¢ purple, perf. 11.2		2943
A1575	$1 dark Prussian green, perf. 11		2193
A1576	$1 dark blue, perf. 11		2194
A1577	$2 bright violet, perf. 11		2195
A1578	$5 copper red, perf. 11		2196

WILDLIFE ISSUES 1981-82

Bighorn — A1267

Puma — A1268

Harbor
Seal — A1269

Bison — A1270

FROM BOOKLET PANES

A1267	18¢ dark brown, perf. 11		1880
A1268	18¢ dark brown, perf. 11		1881
A1269	18¢ dark brown, perf. 11		1882
A1270	18¢ dark brown, perf. 11		1883
A1271	18¢ dark brown, perf. 11		1884
A1272	18¢ dark brown, perf. 11		1885
A1273	18¢ dark brown, perf. 11		1886
A1274	18¢ dark brown, perf. 11		1887
A1275	18¢ dark brown, perf. 11		1888
A1276	18¢ dark brown, perf. 11		1889
A1334	20¢ dark blue, perf. 11		1949

FLAG ISSUES 1981-85

A1277

A1278

Field of 1777
flag — A1279

A1280

A1281

A1498

A1277	18¢ multicolored, perf. 11		1890
A1278	18¢ multicolored, perf. 10 vert.		1891
A1279	6¢ perf. 11 (booklet panes only)		1892
A1280	18¢ perf. 11 (booklet panes only)		1893
A1281	20¢ black, dark blue & red, perf. 11		1894
A1281	20¢ black, dark blue & red, perf. 10 vert.		1895
A1281	20¢ black, dark blue & red, perf. 11x10½ (booklet panes only)		1896
A1498	22¢ blue, red & black, perf. 11		2114
A1498	22¢ blue, red & black, perf. 10 vert.		2115
A1499	22¢ blue, red & black, perf. 10 horiz. (booklet panes only)		2116

TRANSPORTATION ISSUE 1981-95

A1283

A1604a

A1284

A1604b

A1284a

A1622

A1506

A1285

A1810

A1507

A1283	1¢ violet	1897
A1604a	1¢ violet	2225
A1284	2¢ black	1897A
A1604b	2¢ black	2226
A1284a	3¢ dark green	1898
A1622	3¢ claret	2252
A1506	3.4¢ dark bluish green	2123
A1285	4¢ reddish brown, inscription 19 ½mm long	1898A
A1285	4¢ reddish brown, inscription 17mm long	2228
A1810	4¢ claret	2451
A1507	4.9¢ brown black	2124
A1286	5¢ gray green	1899
A1623	5¢ black	2253
A1811	5¢ carmine, engraved	2452
A1811	5¢ carmine, photogravure	2452B
A1811a	5¢ carmine	2452D
A1812	5¢ brown, engraved (Bureau precanceled)	2453
A1812	5¢ red, photogravure (Bureau precanceled)	2454
A1287	5.2¢ carmine	1900
A1624	5.3¢ black (Bureau precanceled)	2254
A1508	5.5¢ deep magenta	2125
A1288	5.9¢ blue	1901
A1509	6¢ red brown	2126

A1510	7.1¢ lake	2127
A1289	7.4¢ brown	1902
A1625	7.6¢ brown (Bureau precanceled)	2255
A1511	8.3¢ green, inscription 18½mm long	2128
A1511	8.3¢ green, same, untagged (Bureau precanceled)	2128a
A1511	8.3¢ green, inscription 18mm long, untagged (Bureau precanceled)	2231
A1626	8.4¢ deep claret, (Bureau precanceled)	2256
A1512	8.5¢ dark Prussian green	2129
A1290	9.3¢ carmine rose	1903
A1627	10¢ sky blue	2257
A1816	10¢ green, engraved (Bureau precanceled)	2457
A1816	10¢ green, photogravure (Bureau precanceled)	2458
A1513	10.1¢ slate blue	2130
A1291	10.9¢ purple	1904
A1292	11¢ red	1905
A1514	11¢ dark green	2131
A1515	12¢ dark blue	2132
A1516	12.5¢ olive green	2133
A1628	13¢ black, (Bureau precanceled)	2258
A1629	13.2¢ slate green, (Bureau precanceled)	2259
A1517	14¢ sky blue	2134
A1630	15¢ violet	2260
A1631	16.7¢ rose, (Bureau precanceled)	2261
A1293	17¢ ultramarine	1906
A1518	17¢ sky blue	2135
A1632	17.5¢ dark violet	2262
A1294	18¢ dark brown	1907
A1295	20¢ vermilion	1908
A1633	20¢ blue violet	2263
A1822	20¢ green	2463
A1634	20.5¢ rose, (Bureau precanceled)	2264
A1635	21¢ olive green, (Bureau precanceled)	2265
A1823	23¢ dark blue	2464
A1636	24.1¢ deep ultramarine, (Bureau precanceled)	2266
A1519	25¢ orange brown	2136
A1825	32¢ blue	2466
A1827	$1 dark blue & scarlet	2468

REGULAR ISSUE 1983-99

A1894

A1897

A1898

A2532

A1758

Eagle and Moon A1296

A1895

Eagle and Half Moon — A1505

A1898a

A2533

A1896

A1894	$2.90 multicolored, perf. 11	2540
A1897	$2.90 multicolored, perf. 11x10½	2543
A1898	$3 multicolored, perf. 11	2544
A2532	$3.20 multicolored, serpentine die cut 11.5	3261
A1758	$8.75 multicolored, perf. 11	2394
A1296	$9.35 multicolored, perf. 10 vert. (booklet panes only)	1909
A1296	$9.35 multicolored, booklet pane of 3	1909a
A1895	$9.95 multicolored, perf. 11	2541
A1505	$10.75 multicolored, perf. 10 vert. (booklet panes only)	2122
A1898a	$10.75 multicolored, perf. 11	2544A
A2533	$11.75 multicolored, serpentine die cut 11.5	3262
A1896	$14 multicolored, perf. 11	2542

REGULAR ISSUE 1982-85

George Washington Washington Monument — A1532

Consumer Education — A1390

Sealed Envelopes — A1533

A1532	18¢ multicolored, perf. 10 vert.	2149
A1532	18¢ multicolored, same, untagged (Bureau precanceled)	2149a
A1390	20¢ sky blue, perf. 10 vert.	2005
A1533	21.1¢ multicolored, perf. 10 vert.	2150
A1533	21.1¢ multicolored, same, untagged (Bureau precanceled)	2150a

REGULAR ISSUE 1987-88

A1646

A1647

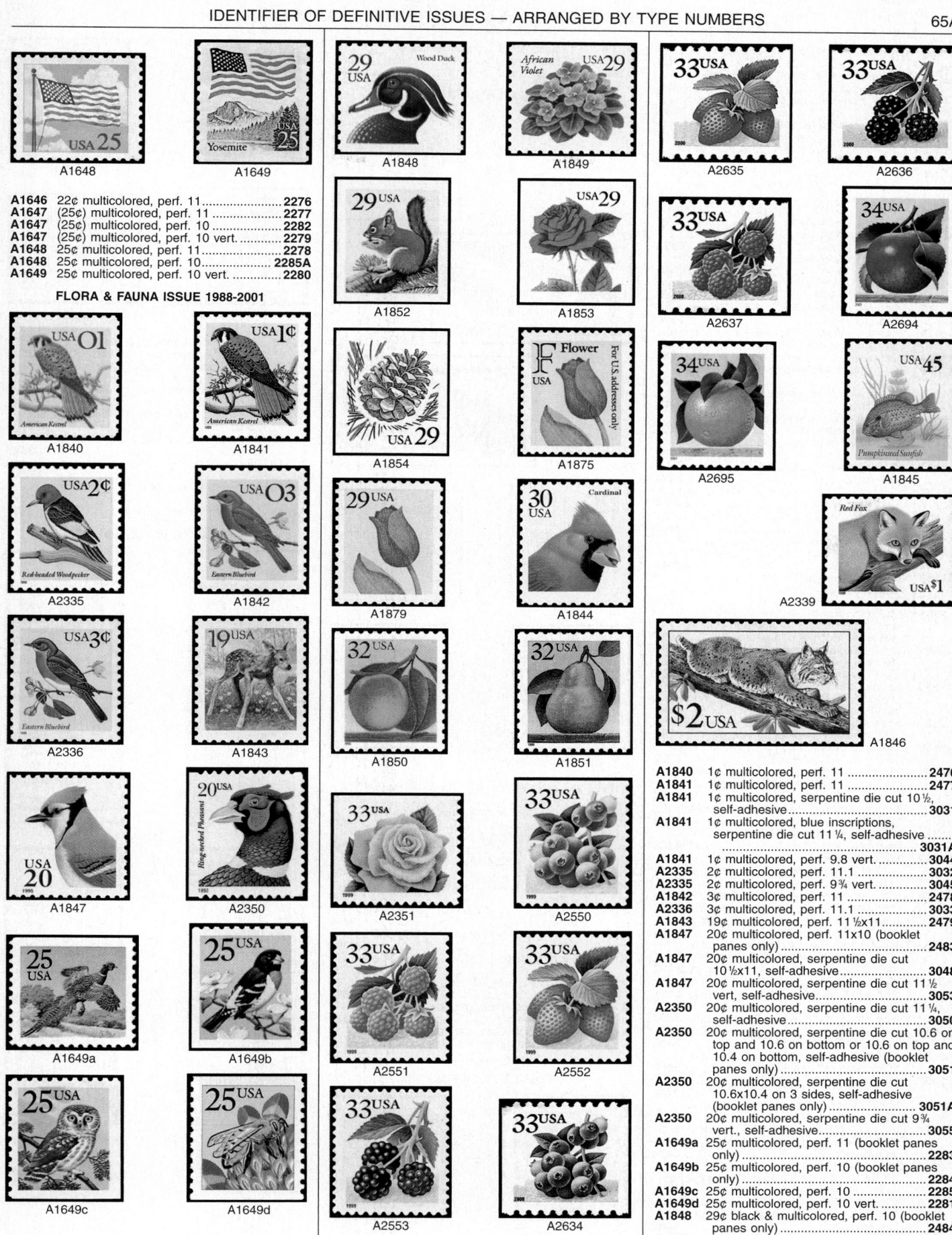

A1648

A1649

A1646 22¢ multicolored, perf. 11 ....**2276**
A1647 (25¢) multicolored, perf. 11 ....**2277**
A1647 (25¢) multicolored, perf. 10 ....**2282**
A1647 (25¢) multicolored, perf. 10 vert. **2279**
A1648 25¢ multicolored, perf. 11 ....**2278**
A1648 25¢ multicolored, perf. 10 ....**2285A**
A1649 25¢ multicolored, perf. 10 vert. **2280**

FLORA & FAUNA ISSUE 1988-2001

A1840

A1841

A2335

A1842

A2336

A1843

A1847

A2350

A1649a

A1649b

A1649c

A1649d

A1848

A1849

A1852

A1853

A1854

A1875

A1879

A1844

A1850

A1851

A2351

A2550

A2551

A2552

A2553

A2634

A2635

A2636

A2637

A2694

A2695

A1845

A2339

A1846

A1840 1¢ multicolored, perf. 11 ....**2476**
A1841 1¢ multicolored, perf. 11 ....**2477**
A1841 1¢ multicolored, serpentine die cut 10½,
self-adhesive..............................**3031**
A1841 1¢ multicolored, blue inscriptions,
serpentine die cut 11¼, self-adhesive ....
....**3031A**
A1841 1¢ multicolored, perf. 9.8 vert. **3044**
A2335 2¢ multicolored, perf. 11.1 ....**3032**
A2335 2¢ multicolored, perf. 9¾ vert. **3045**
A1842 3¢ multicolored, perf. 11 ....**2478**
A2336 3¢ multicolored, perf. 11.1 ....**3033**
A1843 19¢ multicolored, perf. 11½x11............**2479**
A1847 20¢ multicolored, perf. 11x10 (booklet
panes only) **2483**
A1847 20¢ multicolored, serpentine die cut
10½x11, self-adhesive.......................**3048**
A1847 20¢ multicolored, serpentine die cut 11½
vert., self-adhesive.........................**3053**
A2350 20¢ multicolored, serpentine die cut 11¼,
self-adhesive..............................**3050**
A2350 20¢ multicolored, serpentine die cut 10.6 on
top and 10.6 on bottom or 10.6 on top and
10.4 on bottom, self-adhesive (booklet
panes only) **3051**
A2350 20¢ multicolored, serpentine die cut
10.6x10.4 on 3 sides, self-adhesive
(booklet panes only) **3051A**
A2350 20¢ multicolored, serpentine die cut 9¾
vert., self-adhesive..........................**3055**
A1649a 25¢ multicolored, perf. 11 (booklet panes
only) **2283**
A1649b 25¢ multicolored, perf. 10 (booklet panes
only) **2284**
A1649c 25¢ multicolored, perf. 10 ....**2285**
A1649d 25¢ multicolored, perf. 10 vert. **2281**
A1848 29¢ black & multicolored, perf. 10 (booklet
panes only) **2484**
A1848 29¢ red & multicolored, perf. 11 (booklet
panes only) **2485**
A1849 29¢ multicolored, perf. 10x11 (booklet
panes only) **2486**

A1852 29¢ multicolored, die cut, self-adhesive........
....**2489**
A1853 29¢ red, green & black, die cut, self-
adhesive...**2490**
A1854 29¢ multicolored, die cut, self-adhesive........
....**2491**
A1875 (29¢) yellow, black, red & yellow green,
perf. 13 ....**2517**
A1875 (29¢) yellow, black, dull red & dark yellow
green, perf. 10 vert. **2518**
A1875 (29¢) yellow, black, dull red & dark green,
bullseye perf. 11.2 (booklet panes only) .....
....**2519**
A1875 (29¢) pale yellow, black, red & brightgreen,
perf. 11 (booklet panes only) **2520**
A1879 29¢ dull yellow, black, red & yellow green,
perf. 11 ....**2524**
A1879 29¢ dull yellow, black, red & yellow green,
perf. 13x12¾...**2524A**
A1879 29¢ pale yellow, black, red & yellow green,
roulette 10 vert. **2525**
A1879 29¢ pale yellow, black, red & yellow green,
perf. 10 vert. **2526**
A1879 29¢ pale yellow, black, red & bright green,
perf. 11 (booklet panes only) **2527**
A1844 30¢ multicolored, perf. 11 ½x11............**2480**
A1850 32¢ multicolored, perf. 11x10 (booklet
panes only) **2487**
A1850 32¢ multicolored, serpentine die cut, self-
adhesive...**2493**
A1850 32¢ multicolored, serpentine die cut vert.,
self-adhesive...**2495**
A1851 32¢ multicolored, perf. 11x10 (booklet
panes only) **2488**
A1851 32¢ multicolored, serpentine die cut, self-
adhesive...**2494**
A1851 32¢ multicolored, serpentine die cut vert.,
self-adhesive...**2495A**
A1853 32¢ pink, green & black, serpentine die cut,
self-adhesive...**2492**
A1853 32¢ yellow, orange, green & black,
serpentine die cut 11.3x11.7, self-adhesive
....**3049**
A1853 32¢ yellow, orange, green & black,
serpentine die cut 9.8 vert., self-adhesive
....**3054**
A2351 33¢ multicolored, serpentine die cut
11½x11¼ on 2, 3, or 4 sides, self-
adhesive (booklet panes only) **3052**
A2351 33¢ multicolored, serpentine die cut
10¾x10½ on 2 or 3 sides, self-adhesive
(booklet panes only) **3052E**
A2550 33¢ multicolored, serpentine die cut
11.2x11.7, self-adhesive (booklet panes
only) **3294**
A2550 33¢ multicolored, serpentine die cut 9.5x10,
self-adhesive (booklet panes only)......**3298**
A2550 33¢ multicolored, serpentine die cut 8.5
vert., self-adhesive..............................**3302**
A2551 33¢ multicolored, serpentine die cut
11.2x11.7, self-adhesive (booklet panes
only) **3295**
A2551 33¢ multicolored, serpentine die cut 9.5x10,
self-adhesive (booklet panes only)......**3300**
A2551 33¢ multicolored, serpentine die cut 8.5
vert., self-adhesive..............................**3303**
A2552 33¢ multicolored, serpentine die cut
11.2x11.7, self-adhesive (booklet panes
only) **3296**
A2552 33¢ multicolored, serpentine die cut 9.5x10,
self-adhesive (booklet panes only)......**3299**
A2552 33¢ multicolored, serpentine die cut 8.5
vert., self-adhesive..............................**3305**
A2553 33¢ multicolored, serpentine die cut
11.2x11.7, self-adhesive (booklet panes
only) **3297**
A2553 33¢ multicolored, serpentine die cut 9.5x10,
self-adhesive (booklet panes only)......**3301**
A2553 33¢ multicolored, serpentine die cut 8.5
vert., self-adhesive..............................**3304**
A2634 33¢ multicolored, serpentine die cut 8½
horiz., self-adhesive............................**3404**
A2635 33¢ multicolored, serpentine die cut 8½
horiz., self-adhesive............................**3405**
A2636 33¢ multicolored, serpentine die cut 8½
horiz., self-adhesive............................**3406**
A2637 33¢ multicolored, serpentine die cut 8½
horiz., self-adhesive............................**3407**
A2694 34¢ multicolored, serpentine die cut 11¼ on
2, 3 or 4 sides (booklet panes only), self-
adhesive...**3491**
A2694 34¢ multicolored, serpentine die cut
11½x10¾ on 2 or 3 sides (booklet panes
only), self-adhesive..............................**3493**
A2695 34¢ multicolored, serpentine die cut 11¼ on
2, 3 or 4 sides (booklet panes only), self-
adhesive...**3492**
A2695 34¢ multicolored, serpentine die cut
11½x10¾ on 2 or 3 sides (booklet panes
only), self-adhesive..............................**3494**
A1845 45¢ multicolored, perf. 11 ....**2481**

A2339 $1 multicolored, serpentine die cut
11½x11¼, self-adhesive.....................**3036**
A1846 $2 multicolored, perf. 11 ....**2482**

REGULAR ISSUE 1989-98

A1793

A1834

A1877

A1884

A1947

A1950   A1951

A1793 25¢ multicolored, die cut, self-adhesive........
....**2431**
A1834 25¢ dark red & dark blue, die cut, self-
adhesive...**2475**
A1877 (29¢) black, blue & dark red, die cut, self-
adhesive...**2522**
A1884 29¢ black, gold & green, die cut, self-
adhesive **2531A**
A1947 29¢ brown & multicolored, die cut, self-
adhesive...**2595**
A1947 29¢ green & multicolored, die cut, self-
adhesive...**2596**
A1947 29¢ red & multicolored, die cut, self-
adhesive...**2597**
A1950 29¢ red, cream & blue, die cut, self-adhesive
....**2598**
A1951 29¢ multicolored, die cut, self-adhesive........
....**2599**
A1951 32¢ red, light blue, dark blue & yellow,
serpentine die cut 11, self-adhesive.....**3122**
A1951 32¢ red, light blue, dark blue & yellow,
serpentine die cut 11.5x11.8, self-adhesive
....**3122E**

REGULAR ISSUE 1991-94

A1876

A1881

A1882

A1878

A1880

A1883

A1876 (4¢) bister & carmine, perf. 11 ....**2521**
A1881 19¢ multicolored, perf. 10 vert. **2529**
A1881 19¢ multicolored, perf. 10 vert., two rope
loops on piling...**2529**
A1881 19¢ multicolored, perf. 10 vert., one rope
loop on piling..**2529C**
A1882 19¢ multicolored, perf. 10 (booklet panes
only) **2530**
A1878 29¢ multicolored, engraved, perf. 10 vert. .....
....**2523**
A1878 29¢ multicolored, photogravure, perf. 10 vert.
....**2523A**
A1880 29¢ multicolored, perf. 11 (booklet panes
only) **2528**
A1883 29¢ multicolored, perf. 11.....................**2531**

REGULAR ISSUE 1991-98

A1956

A1957

A2534

A1959

A1960

A1946

A1961

A1939

A1942

A1944

A1956 (10¢) multicolored, perf. 10 vert. (Bureau
precanceled) **2602**
A1957 (10¢) orange yellow & multicolored, perf. 10
vert. (Bureau precanceled) **2603**
A1957 (10¢) gold & multicolored, perf. 10 vert.
(Bureau precanceled) **2604**
A1957 (10¢) gold & multicolored, serpentine die cut
11.5 vert., self-adhesive **2907**
A2534 (10¢) multicolored, perf. 9.9 vert. (Bureau
precanceled) **3270**
A2534 (10¢) multicolored, serpentine die cut 9.9
vert., self-adhesive (Bureau precanceled) **3271**
A1959 (23¢) multicolored, perf. 10 vert. (Bureau
precanceled) **2605**
A1960 23¢ multicolored, perf. 10 vert. (Bureau
precanceled) **2606**
A1960 23¢ multicolored, perf. 10 vert., "23" 7mm
long (Bureau precanceled) **2607**
A1960 23¢ violet blue, red & black, perf. 10 vert.,
"First Class" 8½mm long (Bureau
precanceled) **2608**
A1946 29¢ black & multicolored, perf. 10 (booklet
panes only) **2593**
A1946 29¢ black & multicolored, perf. 11x10
(booklet panes only) **2593B**
A1946 29¢ red & multicolored, perf. 11x10 (booklet
panes only) **2594**
A1961 29¢ blue & red, perf. 10 vert. **2609**
A1939 32¢ red brown, perf. 11.2 .... **2587**
A1942 $1 blue, perf. 11½ **2590**
A1944 $5 slate green, perf. 11½ **2592**

G RATE ISSUE 1994-95

A2206

A2210

A2207

A2209

A2208

A2206 (3¢) tan, bright blue & red, perf. 11x10.8 ......
.... **2877**
A2206 (3¢) tan, dark blue & red, perf. 10.8x10.9 .....
.... **2878**
A2210 (5¢) green & multicolored, perf. 9.8 vert.
(Bureau precanceled) **2893**
A2207 (20¢) black "G," yellow & multicolored, perf.
11.2x11.1 .... **2879**
A2207 (20¢) red "G," yellow & multicolored, perf.
11x10.9 .... **2880**
A2209 (25¢) black "G," blue & multicolored, perf.
9.8 vert.(Bureau precanceled) **2888**
A2208 (32¢) black "G" & multicolored, perf.
11.2x11.1 .... **2881**
A2208 (32¢) black "G" & multicolored, perf. 10x9.9
(booklet panes only) **2883**
A2208 (32¢) black "G" & multicolored, die cut, self-
adhesive, small number of blue shading
dots in white stripes below blue field ... **2886**
A2208 (32¢) black "G" & multicolored, die cut, self-
adhesive, thin translucent paper, more blue
shading dots in white stripes below blue
field... **2887**
A2208 (32¢) black "G" & multicolored, perf. 9.8 vert.
.... **2889**
A2208 (32¢) red "G" & multicolored, perf. 11x10.9,
distance from bottom of "G" to top of flag is
13¾mm **2882**
A2208 (32¢) red "G" & multicolored, perf. 11x10.9
on 2 or 3 sides (booklet panes only),
distance from bottom of "G" to top of flag is
13½mm **2885**
A2208 (32¢) red "G" & multicolored, perf. 9.8 vert.
.... **2891**
A2208 (32¢) red "G" & multicolored, rouletted. 9.8
vert. **2892**
A2208 (32¢) blue "G" & multicolored, perf. 10.9
(booklet panes only) **2884**
A2208 (32¢) blue "G" & multicolored, perf. 9.8 vert.
.... **2890**

REGULAR ISSUE 1995-2008

A2217

A2218

A2489

A2853

A2220

A2509

A2223

A2724

A2225

A2490

A2212

A2230

A2217 (5¢) yellow, red & blue, perf. 9.8 vert.
(Bureau precanceled) **2902**
A2217 (5¢) yellow, red & blue, serpentine die cut
11.5 vert., self-adhesive (Bureau
precanceled) **2902B**
A2218 (5¢) purple & multicolored, perf. 9.9 vert.
(Bureau precanceled) **2903**
A2218 (5¢) purple & multicolored, serpentine die
cut 11.2 vert., self-adhesive (Bureau
precanceled) **2904A**
A2218 (5¢) purple & multicolored, serpentine die
cut 9.8 vert., self-adhesive (Bureau
precanceled) **2904B**
A2218 (5¢) blue & multicolored, perf. 9.9 vert.
(Bureau precanceled) **2904**
A2489 (5¢) multicolored, perf. 10 vert. (Bureau
precanceled) **3207**
A2489 (5¢) multicolored, serpentine die cut 9.7
vert., self-adhesive (Bureau precanceled) ....
.... **3207A**
A2853 (5¢) multicolored, serpentine die cut 8½
vert., self-adhesive (Bureau precanceled) ....
.... **3693**
A2853 (5¢) multicolored, perf. 9¾ vert., "2003" date
in blue, unclear dots in surf (Bureau
precanceled) **3775**
A2853 (5¢) multicolored, serpentine die cut 9½x10
(coil stamp), self-adhesive (Bureau
precanceled) **3785**
A2853 (5¢) multicolored, perf. 9¾ vert., "2004" date
in black, rows of dots in surf (Bureau
precanceled) **3864**
A2853 (5¢) multicolored, serpentine die cut 10 vert.,
"2003" date in black, self-adhesive (Bureau
precanceled) **3874**
A2853 (5¢) multicolored, serpentine die cut 11½
vert., "2004" date in black, self-adhesive
(Bureau precanceled) **3875**
A2853 (5¢) multicolored, perf. 9¾ vert., "2008" date
in black, with microprinted "USPS" (Bureau
precanceled) **4348**
A2220 (10¢) black, red brown & brown, perf. 9.8
vert. (Bureau precanceled) **2905**
A2220 (10¢) black, red brown & brown, serpentine
die cut 11.5 vert., self-adhesive (Bureau
precanceled) **2906**
A2509 (10¢) multicolored, serpentine die cut 9.8
vert., self-adhesive (Bureau precanceled) ....
.... **3228**
A2509 (10¢) multicolored, perf 9.9 vert. (Bureau
precanceled) **3229**
A2223 (15¢) dark orange, yellow & multicolored
(dark, bold colors, heavy shading lines,
heavily shaded chrome), perf. 9.8 vert.........
.... **2908**
A2223 (15¢) buff & multicolored (more subdued
colors, finer details, shinier chrome), perf.
9.8 vert. **2909**
A2223 (15¢) buff & multicolored, serpentine die cut
11.5 vert., self-adhesive....................... **2910**
A2724 (15¢) multicolored, serpentine die cut 11½
vert., self-adhesive (Bureau precanceled) .....
.... **3522**

A2225 (25¢) dark red, dark yellow green & multicolored (dark, saturated colors, dark blue lines in music selection board), perf.9.8 vert. **2911**

A2225 (25¢) dark red, yellow green & multicolored, serpentine die cut 9.8 vert, self-adhesive **2912B**

A2225 (25¢) bright orange red, bright yellow green & multicolored (bright colors, less shading and light blue lines in music selection board), perf. 9.8 vert. **2912**

A2225 (25¢) bright orange red, bright yellow green & multicolored, serpentine die cut 11.5 vert., self-adhesive **2912A**

A2225 (25¢) bright orange red, bright yellow green & multicolored, imperf, with simulated perforations, self-adhesive **3132**

A2490 (25¢) multicolored, perf. 10 .... **3208**

A2490 (25¢) multicolored, serpentine die cut 9.7 vert., self-adhesive (Bureau precanceled).... **3208A**

A2212 32¢ multicolored, perf. 10.4 .... **2897**

A2212 32¢ blue, tan, brown, red & light blue, perf. 10.8x9.8 (booklet panes only) **2916**

A2212 32¢ blue, tan, brown, red & light blue (pronounced blue shading in flag and red "1995"), perf. 9.8 vert. **2913**

A2212 32¢ blue, yellow brown, red & gray (gray shading in flag and blue "1995"), perf. 9.8 vert. **2914**

A2212 32¢ multicolored, serpentine die cut 8.7 vert., self-adhesive **2915**

A2212 32¢ dark blue, tan, brown, red & light blue, red "1996," serpentine die cut 9.8 vert., self-adhesive **2915A**

A2212 32¢ dark blue, tan, brown, red & light blue, red "1997," serpentine die cut 9.8 vert., straight cut at bottom and top with 9 teeth between, self-adhesive **2915D**

A2212 32¢ dark blue, tan, brown, red & light blue (sky shows color graduation at lower right, blue "1996"), serpentine die cut 9.9 vert., self-adhesive **3133**

A2212 32¢ dark blue, tan, brown, red & light blue, serpentine die cut 10.9 vert, self-adhesive **2915C**

A2212 32¢ dark blue, tan, brown, red & light blue, serpentine die cut 11.5 vert, self-adhesive **2915B**

A2212 32¢ multicolored, serpentine die cut 8.8 on 2, 3 or 4 adjacent sides, dated "1995" in blue, self-adhesive (booklet panes only) **2920**

A2212 32¢ multicolored, serpentine die cut 11.3 on 2, 3 or 4 adjacent sides, dated "1996" in blue, self-adhesive (booklet panes only) **2920D**

A2212 32¢ dark blue, tan, brown, red & light blue, serpentine die cut 9.8 on 2 or 3 adjacent sides, dated "1996" in red, self-adhesive (booklet panes only) **2921**

A2212 32¢ dark blue, tan, brown, red & light blue, serpentine die cut 9.8 on 2 or 3 adjacent sides, dated "1997" in red, self-adhesive (booklet panes only) **2921b**

A2230 32¢ multicolored, die cut, self-adhesive. **2919**

H RATE ISSUE 1999

A2529

A2530

A2531

A2529 (1¢) multicolored, white USA, black "1998," perf. 11.2 .... **3257**

A2529 (1¢) multicolored, pale blue USA, blue "1998," perf. 11.2 .... **3258**

A2530 22¢ multicolored, serpentine die cut 10.8, self-adhesive **3259**

A2530 22¢ multicolored, serpentine die cut 9.9 vert, self-adhesive **3263**

A2530 22¢ multicolored, perf. 9¾ vert. **3353**

A2531 (33¢) multicolored, perf. 11.2 .... **3260**

A2531 (33¢) multicolored, perf. 9.8 vert. **3264**

A2531 (33¢) multicolored, serpentine die cut 9.9 vert., stamp corners at right angles, backing paper same size as stamp, self-adhesive **3265**

A2531 (33¢) multicolored, serpentine die cut 9.9 vert., stamp corners rounded, backing paper larger than stamp, self-adhesive **3266**

A2531 (33¢) multicolored, serpentine die cut 9.9, (booklet panes only), self-adhesive **3267**

A2531 (33¢) multicolored, serpentine die cut 11.2x11.1 (booklet panes only), self-adhesive **3268**

A2531 (33¢) multicolored, die cut 8 (booklet panes only), self-adhesive **3269**

REGULAR ISSUE 1999

A2540

A2541

A2540 33¢ multicolored, perf. 11.2 .... **3277**

A2540 33¢ multicolored, serpentine die cut 11.1, self-adhesive **3278**

A2540 33¢ multicolored, serpentine die cut 11 ½x11 ¾, self-adhesive **3278F**

A2540 33¢ multicolored, serpentine die cut 9.8 (booklet panes only), self-adhesive **3279**

A2540 33¢ multicolored, perf. 9.9 vert. **3280**

A2540 33¢ multicolored, serpentine die cut 9.8 vert., stamp corners at right angles, backing paper same size as stamp, self-adhesive **3281**

A2540 33¢ multicolored, serpentine die cut 9.8 vert., stamp corners rounded, backing paper same larger than stamp, self-adhesive **3282**

A2541 33¢ multicolored, serpentine die cut 7.9 (booklet panes only), self-adhesive **3283**

DISTINGUISHED AMERICANS ISSUE 2000-09

A2650

A2652

A2656

A2657

A2657a

A2658

A2660

A2661

A2661a

A2661b

A2662

A2663

A2664

A2650 10¢ red & black, perf 11 .... **3420**

A2652 23¢ red & black, litho. & engr., serpentine die cut 11 ¼x10 ¾, self-adhesive **3422**

A2652 23¢ red & black, litho., serpentine die cut 11 ¼x10 ¾ on 3 sides, self-adhesive (booklet panes only) **3436**

A2656 33¢ red & black, perf 11 .... **3426**

A2657 58¢ red & black, serpentine die cut 11, self-adhesive **3427**

A2657a 59¢ multicolored, serpentine die cut 11 ¼x10 ¾, self-adhesive **3427A**

A2658 63¢ red & black, serpentine die cut 11 ¼x11, self-adhesive **3428**

A2660 75¢ red & black, serpentine die cut 11 ¼x10 ¾, self-adhesive **3430**

A2661 76¢ red & black, serpentine die cut 11, self-adhesive **3431**

A2661 76¢ red & black, serpentine die cut 11 ½x11, self-adhesive **3432**

A2661a 76¢ multicolored, serpentine die cut 11 ¼x10 ¾, self-adhesive **3432A**

A2661b 78¢ multicolored, serpentine die cut 11 ¼x10 ¾, self-adhesive **3432B**

A2662 83¢ red & black, serpentine die cut 11x11 ¾, self-adhesive **3433**

A2663 83¢ red & black, serpentine die cut 11 ¼, self-adhesive **3434**

A2664 87¢ red & black, serpentine die cut 11 ¼x11, self-adhesive **3435**

AMERICAN CULTURE ISSUE 2000-03

A2677

A2722

A2875

A2677 (10¢) multicolored, serpentine die cut 11½ vert., self adhesive (Bureau precanceled)....
....**3447**
A2677 (10¢) multicolored, perf. 10 vert. (Bureau precanceled) **3769**
A2722 (10¢) multicolored, serpentine die cut 8½ vert., self-adhesive (Bureau precanceled)....
....**3520**
A2722 (10¢) multicolored, serpentine die cut 11 vert., self-adhesive (Bureau precanceled)....
....**3770**
A2875 $1 multicolored, serpentine die cut 11¼x11 vert., self-adhesive...............................**3766**

REGULAR ISSUE 2000-03

A2686

A2687

A2678

A2679

A2680

A2681

A2682

A2683

A2684

A2685

A2688

A2689

A2690

A2691

A2692

A2693

A2696

A2686 20¢ dark carmine, serpentine die cut 11¼x11 on 3 sides (booklet panes only), self-adhesive **3482**
A2686 20¢ dark carmine, serpentine die cut 10½x11 on 3 sides (booklet panes only), self-adhesive **3483**
A2687 21¢ multicolored, perf. 11¼ **3467**
A2687 21¢ multicolored, serpentine die cut 11¼ on 3 sides, self-adhesive (booklet panes only) **3484**
A2687 21¢ multicolored, serpentine die cut 10½x11¼ on 3 sides, self-adhesive (booklet panes only **3484A**
A2687 21¢ multicolored, serpentine die cut 11, self-adhesive.......................................**3468**
A2687 21¢ multicolored, serpentine die cut 8½ vert., self-adhesive.............................**3475**
A2686 23¢ green, perf. 11¼ **3616**
A2686 23¢ green, serpentine die cut 11¼x11¾, self-adhesive **3468A**
A2686 23¢ green, serpentine die cut 8½ vert., self-adhesive (Banknote Corp. Printing) **3475A**
A2686 23¢ gray green, serpentine die cut 8½ vert., self-adhesive (Avery Printing).......**3617**
A2686 23¢ green, serpentine die cut 11¼ on 3 sides, self-adhesive (booklet panes only......
....**3618**
A2686 23¢ green, serpentine die cut 10½x11¼ on 3 sides, self-adhesive (booklet panes only)
....**3619**
A2686 23¢ gray green, serpentine die cut 11, self-adhesive (Avery Printing)...................**3819**
A2678 (34¢) multicolored, perf. 111/4..................**3448**
A2678 (34¢) multicolored, serpentine die cut 11¼, self-adhesive **3449**
A2678 (34¢) multicolored, serpentine die cut 8 on 2, 3 or 4 sides (booklet panes only), self-adhesive......................................**3450**
A2679 (34¢) multicolored, serpentine die cut 11 on 2, 3 or 4 sides (booklet panes only), self-adhesive......................................**3451**
A2680 (34¢) multicolored, perf. 9¾ vert. **3452**
A2680 (34¢) multicolored, serpentine die cut 10 vert., self-adhesive **3453**
A2681 (34¢) purple & multicolored, serpentine die cut 10½x10¾ on 2 or 3 sides (booklet panes only), self-adhesive **3454**
A2681 (34¢) purple & multicolored, serpentine die cut 11½x11¾ on 2 or 3 sides (booklet panes only), self-adhesive **3458**

A2681 (34¢) purple & multicolored, serpentine die cut 8½ vert., self-adhesive...................**3465**
A2682 (34¢) tan & multicolored, serpentine die cut 10½x10¾ on 2 or 3 sides (booklet panes only), self-adhesive **3455**
A2682 (34¢) tan & multicolored, serpentine die cut 11½x11¾ on 2 or 3 sides (booklet panes only), self-adhesive **3459**
A2682 (34¢) tan & multicolored, serpentine die cut 8½ vert., self-adhesive.........................**3464**
A2683 (34¢) green & multicolored, serpentine die cut 10½x10¾ on 2 or 3 sides (booklet panes only), self-adhesive **3456**
A2683 (34¢) green & multicolored, serpentine die cut 11½x11¾ on 2 or 3 sides (booklet panes only), self-adhesive **3460**
A2683 (34¢) green & multicolored, serpentine die cut 8½ vert., self-adhesive.................**3462**
A2684 (34¢) red & multicolored, serpentine die cut 10½x10¾ on 2 or 3 sides (booklet panes only), self-adhesive **3457**
A2684 (34¢) red & multicolored, serpentine die cut 11½x11¾ on 2 or 3 sides (booklet panes only), self-adhesive **3461**
A2684 (34¢) red & multicolored, serpentine die cut 8½ vert., self-adhesive.........................**3463**
A2685 34¢ multicolored, serpentine die cut 9¾ vert., stamp corners rounded, backing paper larger than stamp, self-adhesive........
....**3466**
A2685 34¢ multicolored, perf. 9¾ vert. **3476**
A2685 34¢ multicolored, serpentine die cut 9¾ vert., stamp corners at right angles, backing paper same size as stamp, self-adhesive..**3477**
A2688 34¢ multicolored, perf. 11¼..................**3469**
A2688 34¢ multicolored, serpentine die cut 11¼, self-adhesive **3470**
A2688 34¢ multicolored, serpentine die cut 8 on 2, 3 or 4 sides, self-adhesive (booklet panes only **3495**
A2689 34¢ multicolored, serpentine die cut 11 on 2, 3 or 4 sides (booklet panes only), self-adhesive..**3485**
A2690 34¢ green & multicolored, serpentine die cut 8½ vert., self-adhesive.........................**3478**
A2690 34¢ green & multicolored, serpentine die cut 10½x10¾ on 2 or 3 sides (booklet panes only), self-adhesive **3489**
A2691 34¢ red & multicolored, serpentine die cut 8½ vert., self-adhesive.........................**3479**
A2691 34¢ red & multicolored, serpentine die cut 10½x10¾ on 2 or 3 sides (booklet panes only), self-adhesive **3490**
A2692 34¢ tan & multicolored, serpentine die cut 8½ vert., self-adhesive.........................**3480**
A2692 34¢ tan & multicolored, serpentine die cut 10½x10¾ on 2 or 3 sides (booklet panes only), self-adhesive **3488**
A2693 34¢ purple & multicolored, serpentine die cut 8½ vert., self-adhesive...................**3481**
A2693 34¢ purple & multicolored, serpentine die cut 10½x10¾ on 2 or 3 sides (booklet panes only), self-adhesive **3487**
A2696 55¢ multicolored, serpentine die cut 10¾, self-adhesive **3471**
A2696 57¢ multicolored, serpentine die cut 10¾, self-adhesive **3471A**

WASHINGTON VIEWS ISSUE 2001-03

A2697

A2818

A2698

A2819

A2697 $3.50 multicolored, serpentine die cut
11¼x11½, self-adhesive 3472
A2818 $3.85 multicolored, serpentine die cut 11¼,
self-adhesive 3647
A2818 $3.85 multicolored, serpentine die cut
11x10¾, self-adhesive 3647A
A2698 $12.25 multicolored, serpentine die cut
11¼x11½, self-adhesive 3473
A2819 $13.65 multicolored, serpentine die cut 11¼,
self-adhesive 3648

UNITED WE STAND ISSUE 2001-02

A2744

A2744 34¢ multicolored, serpentine die cut 11¼ on
2, 3 or 4 sides, self-adhesive (booklet
panes only) 3549
A2744 34¢ multicolored, serpentine die cut
10½x10¾ on 2 or 3 sides, self-adhesive
(booklet panes only) 3549B
A2744 34¢ multicolored, serpentine die cut 9¾
vert., stamp corners at right angles,
backing paper same size as stamp, self-
adhesive 3550
A2744 34¢ multicolored, serpentine die cut 9¾
vert., stamp corners rounded, backing
paper larger than stamp, self-adhesive........
....3550A

AMERICAN DESIGN ISSUE 2002-08

A2866

A2858

A2868

A2805

A2859

A2860

A2866 1¢ multicolored, serpentine die cut 11¼x11,
self-adhesive 3749
A2866 1¢ multicolored, serpentine die cut 11, self-
adhesive 3749A
A2866 1¢ multicolored, perf. 9¾ vert., photo.,
without microprinting, dated "2003"......3758
A2866 1¢ multicolored, perf. 9¾ vert., litho., with
microprinting, dated "2008".............3758A
A2858 2¢ multicolored, serpentine die cut 11,
without microprinting,self-adhesive, dated
"2004"......................................3750
A2858 2¢ multicolored, without microprinting,
serpentine die cut 11¼x11½, self-adhesive,
dated "2006"...............................3751
A2858 2¢ multicolored, with microprinting at right,
serpentine die cut 11¼x11, self-adhesive,
dated "2006".................................3752
A2858 2¢ multicolored, with microprinting at left,
serpentine die cut 11¼x10¾, self-adhesive,
date "2007".................................3753
A2868 3¢ multicolored, serpentine die cut 11¼x11,
self-adhesive 3754
A2868 3¢ multicolored, perf. 9¾ vert. 3759
A2859 4¢ multicolored, serpentine die cut
10¾x10¼, self-adhesive 3755
A2859 4¢ multicolored, perf. 9¾ vert. 3761
A2805 5¢ multicolored, serpentine die cut
11¼x11¾, photo., without microprinting,
self-adhesive 3756
A2805 5¢ multicolored, serpentine die cut
11¼x11¾, photo., with microprinting, self-
adhesive 3756A
A2805 5¢ multicolored, perf. 9¾ vert. 3612
A2860 10¢ multicolored, serpentine die cut 11¼x11,
self-adhesive 3757
A2860 10¢ multicolored, perf. 9¾ vert., photo.,
without microprinting.........................3762
A2860 10¢ multicolored, perf. 9¾ vert., litho., with
microprinting.................................3763

REGULAR ISSUE 2002-05

A2806

A2807

A2808

A2810

A2809

A2809

A2811

A2813

A2814

A2815

A2816

A2812

A2817

A2806 3¢ red, blue & black, serpentine die cut 11,
self-adhesive, lithographed, year at lower
left 3613
A2806 3¢ red, blue & black, serpentine die cut 10,
self-adhesive, photogravure, year at lower
right 3614
A2806 3¢ red, blue & black, perf. 10 vert.,
photogravure, year at lower left...........3615
A2807 (37¢) multicolored, perf. 11¼x11 3620
A2807 (37¢) multicolored, serpentine die cut
11¼x11, self-adhesive 3621
A2807 (37¢) multicolored, serpentine die cut 10
vert., self-adhesive..........................3622
A2807 (37¢) multicolored, serpentine die cut 11¼
on 2, 3 or 4 sides, self-adhesive (booklet
panes only) 3623
A2807 (37¢) multicolored, serpentine die cut
10½x10¾ on 2 or 3 sides, self-adhesive
(booklet panes only) 3624
A2807 (37¢) multicolored, serpentine die cut 8 on
2, 3 or 4 sides, self-adhesive (booklet
panes only) 3625
A2808 (37¢) multicolored, serpentine die cut 11 on
2, 3 or 4 sides, self-adhesive (booklet
panes only) 3626
A2809 (37¢) multicolored, serpentine die cut 11 on
2, 3 or 4 sides, self-adhesive (booklet
panes only) 3627
A2810 (37¢) multicolored, serpentine die cut 11 on
2, 3 or 4 sides, self-adhesive (booklet
panes only) 3628
A2811 (37¢) multicolored, serpentine die cut 11 on
2, 3 or 4 sides, self-adhesive (booklet
panes only) 3629
A2812 37¢ multicolored, perf. 11¼................3629F
A2812 37¢ multicolored, serpentine die cut 11¼x11,
self-adhesive 3630
A2812 37¢ multicolored, perf. 10 vert. 3631
A2812 37¢ multicolored, serpentine die cut 9¾
vert., self-adhesive..........................3632
A2812 37¢ multicolored, serpentine die cut 10¼
vert., self-adhesive, lacking points of stars
at upper left.................................3632A
A2812 37¢ multicolored, serpentine die cut 11¾
vert., self-adhesive............................3632C
A2812 37¢ multicolored, serpentine die cut 8½
vert., rounded corners, self-adhesive ...3633
A2812 37¢ multicolored, serpentine die cut 8½
vert., right angle corners, self-adhesive......
....3633A
A2812 37¢ multicolored, serpentine die cut 9½
vert., with microprinted "USA" in top red
stripe, self-adhesive 3633B
A2812 37¢ multicolored, serpentine die cut 11 on 3
sides, self-adhesive (booklet panes only) ....
....3634
A2812 37¢ multicolored, serpentine die cut 11¼ on
2 or 3 sides, self-adhesive (booklet panes
only) 3635
A2812 37¢ multicolored, serpentine die cut
10½x10¾ on 2 or 3 sides, self-adhesive
(booklet panes only) 3636
A2812 37¢ multicolored, serpentine die cut 11¼x11
on 2 or 3 sides, self-adhesive (booklet
panes only) 3636D

A2812 37¢ multicolored, serpentine die cut 8 on 2, 3 or 4 sides, self-adhesive (booklet panes only) 3637
A2813 37¢ multicolored, serpentine die cut 8½ horiz., self-adhesive 3638
A2813 37¢ multicolored, serpentine die cut 11 on 2, 3 or 4 sides, self-adhesive (booklet panes only) 3643
A2814 37¢ multicolored, serpentine die cut 8½ horiz., self-adhesive 3639
A2814 37¢ multicolored, serpentine die cut 11 on 2, 3 or 4 sides, self-adhesive (booklet panes only) 3642
A2815 37¢ multicolored, serpentine die cut 8½ horiz., self-adhesive 3640
A2815 37¢ multicolored, serpentine die cut 11 on 2, 3 or 4 sides, self-adhesive (booklet panes only) 3645
A2816 37¢ multicolored, serpentine die cut 8½ horiz., self-adhesive 3641
A2816 37¢ multicolored, serpentine die cut 11 on 2, 3 or 4 sides, self-adhesive (booklet panes only) 3644
A2817 60¢ multicolored, serpentine die cut 11x11¼ self-adhesive 3646

PURPLE HEART ISSUE 2003-09

A2891

A2891 37¢ multicolored, serpentine die cut 11¼x10¾, self-adhesive 3784
A2891 37¢ multicolored, serpentine die cut 10¾x10¼, self-adhesive 3784A
A2891 39¢ multicolored, serpentine die cut 11¼x11, self-adhesive 4032
A2891 41¢ multicolored, serpentine die cut 11¼x10¾, self-adhesive 4164
A2891 42¢ multicolored, perf. 11¼ 4263
A2891 42¢ multicolored, serpentine die cut 11¼x10¾, self-adhesive 4264
A2891 44¢ multicolored, serpentine die cut 11¼x10¾, self-adhesive 4390

EAGLE ISSUE 2003-04

A2898

A2899

A2898 (25¢) gray & gold, serpentine die 11¾ vert. 3792
A2898 (25¢) gray & gold, perf. 9¾ vert. 3844
A2898 (25¢) dull blue & gold, serpentine die 11¾ vert. 3794
A2898 (25¢) dull blue & gold, perf. 9¾ vert. 3852
A2898 (25¢) green & gold, serpentine die 11¾ vert. 3796
A2898 (25¢) green & gold, perf. 9¾ vert. 3850
A2898 (25¢) Prussian blue & gold, serpentine die 11¾ vert. 3798
A2898 (25¢) Prussian blue & gold, perf. 9¾ vert. 3848
A2898 (25¢) red & gold, serpentine die cut 11¾ vert. 3800
A2898 (25¢) red & gold, perf. 9¾ vert. 3846
A2899 (25¢) gold & red, serpentine die cut 11¾ vert. 3793
A2899 (25¢) gold & red, perf. 9¾ vert. 3853
A2899 (25¢) gold & Prussian blue, serpentine die cut 11¾ vert. 3795
A2899 (25¢) gold & Prussian blue, perf. 9¾ vert. 3851
A2899 (25¢) gold & gray, serpentine die cut 11¾ vert. 3797
A2899 (25¢) gold & gray, perf. 9¾ vert. 3849
A2899 (25¢) gold & dull blue, serpentine die cut 11¾ vert. 3799
A2899 (25¢) gold & dull blue, perf. 9¾ vert. 3847
A2899 (25¢) gold & green, serpentine die cut 11¾ vert. 3801
A2899 (25¢) gold & green, perf. 9¾ vert. 3845

WILDLIFE ISSUE 2003-09

A3151

A3152

A3340

A2925

A3230

A3341

A3151 17¢ multicolored, without microprinting, serpentine die cut 11, self-adhesive 4138
A3151 17¢ multicolored, without microprinting, serpentine die cut 11 vert., self-adhesive 4140
A3152 26¢ multicolored, with microprinting, perf. 11¼x11 4137
A3152 26¢ multicolored, with microprinting, serpentine die cut 11¼x11 4139
A3152 26¢ multicolored, with microprinting, serpentine die cut 11 vert. 4141
A3152 26¢ multicolored, without microprinting, serpentine die cut 11¼x11 on 3 sides (booklet panes only) 4142
A3340 28¢ multicolored, serpentine die cut 11¼x11 self-adhesive 4387
A3340 28¢ multicolored, serpentine die cut 8½ vert., self-adhesive 4389
A2925 37¢ multicolored, serpentine die cut 8½ vert., self-adhesive 3829
A2925 37¢ multicolored, serpentine die cut 9½ vert., self-adhesive 3829A
A2925 37¢ multicolored, without microprinting, serpentine die cut 11½x11 on 2, 3 or 4 sides, self-adhesive (booklet panes only) 3830
A2925 37¢ multicolored, with microprinting, serpentine die cut 11½x11 on 2, 3 or 4 sides, self-adhesive (booklet panes only) 3830D
A3230 62¢ multicolored, serpentine die cut 11¼x11, self-adhesive 4267
A3341 64¢ multicolored, serpentine die cut 11, self-adhesive 4388

FLAG AND STATUE OF LIBERTY ISSUE 2005-06

A3038

A3040

A3038 (39¢) multicolored, with microprinting, perf. 11¼ 3965
A3038 (39¢) multicolored, with microprinting, serpentine die cut 11¼x11, self-adhesive 3966
A3038 (39¢) multicolored, without microprinting, perf. 9¾ vert. 3967
A3038 (39¢) multicolored, without microprinting, serpentine die cut 8½ vert., self-adhesive 3968

A3038 (39¢) multicolored, without microprinting, serpentine die cut 10¼ vert., self-adhesive 3969
A3038 (39¢) multicolored, with microprinting, serpentine die cut 9½ vert., self-adhesive 3970
A3038 (39¢) multicolored, lithographed, without microprinting, serpentine die cut 11¼x10¾ on 2 or 3 sides, self-adhesive (booklet panes only) 3972
A3038 (39¢) multicolored, without microprinting, serpentine die cut 10¼x10¾ on 2 or 3 sides, self-adhesive (booklet panes only) 3973
A3038 (39¢) multicolored, photogravure, without microprinting, serpentine die cut 11¼x11 on 2 or 3 sides, self-adhesive (booklet panes only) 3974
A3038 (39¢) multicolored, without microprinting, serpentine die cut 8 on 2, 3 or 4 sides, self-adhesive (booklet panes only) 3975
A3040 39¢ multicolored, with microprinting, serpentine die cut 11¼x10¾, self-adhesive 3978
A3040 39¢ multicolored, without microprinting, perf. 10 vert. 3979
A3040 39¢ multicolored, with microprinting, serpentine die cut 11 vert., self-adhesive 3980
A3040 39¢ multicolored, with microprinting, serpentine die cut 9½ vert., self-adhesive 3981
A3040 39¢ multicolored, without microprinting, serpentine die cut 10¼ vert., self-adhesive 3982
A3040 39¢ multicolored, without microprinting, serpentine die cut 8½ vert., self-adhesive 3983
A3040 39¢ multicolored, without microprinting, serpentine die cut 11¼x10¾ on 2 or 3 sides, self-adhesive (booklet panes only) 3985

REGULAR ISSUE 2006

A3053

A3054

A3055

A3056

A3057

A3058

A3053 24¢ multicolored, perf. 11¼ 4000
A3053 24¢ multicolored, serpentine die cut 11, self-adhesive 4001
A3053 24¢ multicolored, serpentine die cut 8½ horiz., self-adhesive 4002
A3054 39¢ multicolored, serpentine die cut 10¼ horiz., self-adhesive 4003
A3054 39¢ multicolored, serpentine die cut 10¾x10½ on 2 or 3 sides, self-adhesive (booklet panes only) 4012
A3054 39¢ multicolored, serpentine die cut 10¾x11¼ on 2 or 3 sides, self-adhesive (booklet panes only) 4013
A3055 39¢ multicolored, serpentine die cut 10¼ horiz., self-adhesive 4004
A3055 39¢ multicolored, serpentine die cut 10¾x10½ on 2 or 3 sides, self-adhesive (booklet panes only) 4011
A3055 39¢ multicolored, serpentine die cut 10¾x11¼ on 2 or 3 sides, self-adhesive (booklet panes only) 4017

A3056 39¢ multicolored, serpentine die cut 10¼ horiz., self-adhesive **4005**
A3056 39¢ multicolored, serpentine die cut 10¾x10½ on 2 or 3 sides, self-adhesive (booklet panes only) **4010**
A3056 39¢ multicolored, serpentine die cut 10¾x11¼ on 2 or 3 sides, self-adhesive (booklet panes only) **4016**
A3057 39¢ multicolored, serpentine die cut 10¼ horiz., self-adhesive **4006**
A3057 39¢ multicolored, serpentine die cut 10¾x10½ on 2 or 3 sides, self-adhesive (booklet panes only) **4009**
A3057 39¢ multicolored, serpentine die cut 10¾x11¼ on 2 or 3 sides, self-adhesive (booklet panes only) **4015**
A3058 39¢ multicolored, serpentine die cut 10¼ horiz., self-adhesive **4007**
A3058 39¢ multicolored, serpentine die cut 10¾x10½ on 2 or 3 sides, self-adhesive (booklet panes only) **4008**
A3058 39¢ multicolored, serpentine die cut 10¾x11¼ on 2 or 3 sides, self-adhesive (booklet panes only) **4014**

X-PLANES ISSUE 2006

A3059

A3060

A3059 $4.05 multicolored, serpentine die cut 10¾x10½, self-adhesive **4018**
A3060 $14.40 multicolored, serpentine die cut 10¾x10½, self-adhesive **4019**

LIBERTY BELL (FOREVER) ISSUE 2007

A3148

Large

Small   Medium

A3148 (41¢) multicolored, large microprinting, bell 16mm wide, serpentine die cut 11¼x10¾ on 2 or 3 sides, self-adhesive (booklet panes only) **4125**
A3148 (41¢) multicolored, large microprinting, bell 16mm wide, serpentine die cut 8 on 2, 3 or 4 sides, self-adhesive (booklet panes only) **4128**
A3148 (41¢) multicolored, small microprinting, bell 16mm wide, serpentine die cut 11¼x10¾ on 2 or 3 sides, self-adhesive (booklet panes only) **4126**
A3148 (41¢) multicolored, medium microprinting, bell 15mm wide, serpentine die cut 11¼x10¾ on 2 or 3 sides, self-adhesive (booklet panes only) **4127**

FLAG ISSUE 2007

A3149   A3184

A3149 (41¢) multicolored, perf. 11¼ **4129**
A3149 (41¢) multicolored, serpentine die cut 11¼x10¾, self-adhesive **4130**
A3149 (41¢) multicolored, perf. 9¾ vert. **4131**
A3149 (41¢) multicolored, serpentine die cut 9½ vert., with perpendicular corners, self-adhesive **4132**
A3149 (41¢) multicolored, serpentine die cut 11 vert., with perpendicular corners, self-adhesive **4133**
A3149 (41¢) multicolored, serpentine die cut 8½ vert., with perpendicular corners, self-adhesive **4134**
A3149 (41¢) multicolored, serpentine die cut 11 vert., with rounded corners, self-adhesive **4135**
A3184 41¢ multicolored, serpentine die cut 9½ vert., with "USPS" microprinted on right side of flagpole, self-adhesive **4186**
A3184 41¢ multicolored, serpentine die cut 11 vert., with "USPS" microprinted on left side of flagpole, self-adhesive, with perpendicular corners **4187**
A3184 41¢ multicolored, serpentine die cut 8½ vert., with "USPS" microprinted on flagpole, self-adhesive, with perpendicular corners **4188**
A3184 41¢ multicolored, serpentine die cut 11 vert., with "USPS" microprinted on flagpole, self-adhesive, with rounded corners **4189**
A3184 41¢ multicolored, serpentine die cut 11¼x10¾ on 3 sides, with "USPS" microprinted on right side of flagpole, self-adhesive (booklet panes only) **4190**
A3184 41¢ multicolored, serpentine die cut 11¼x10¾ on 2 or 3 sides, with "USPS" microprinted on leftt side of flagpole, self-adhesive (booklet panes only) **4191**

PRESIDENTIAL AIRCRAFT ISSUE 2007

A3154

A3155

A3154 $4.60 multicolored, serpentine die cut 10¾, self-adhesive **4144**
A3155 $16.25 multicolored, serpentine die cut 10¾, self-adhesive **4145**

PATRIOTIC BANNER ISSUE 2007-09

Patriotic Banner — A3167

A3167 (10¢) multicolored, serpentine die cut 11 vert., photo., self-adhesive **4157**
A3167 (10¢) multicolored, serpentine die cut 11¾ vert., litho., self-adhesive **4158**
A3167 (10¢) multicolored, perf. 9¾ vert. **4385**

FLOWERS ISSUE 2007

Iris — A3174

Dahlia — A3175

Magnolia — A3176

Red Gerbera Daisy — A3177

Coneflower — A3178

Tulip — A3179

Water Lily — A3180

Poppy — A3181

Chrysanthemum A3182

Orange Gerbera Daisy A3183

A3174 41¢ multicolored, serpentine die cut 9½ vert., self-adhesive **4166**
A3174 41¢ multicolored, serpentine die cut 11¼x11½ on 2 or 3 sides, self-adhesive (booklet pane only) **4178**
A3175 41¢ multicolored, serpentine die cut 9½ vert., self-adhesive **4167**
A3174 41¢ multicolored, serpentine die cut 11¼x11½ on 2 or 3 sides, self-adhesive (booklet pane only) **4179**
A3176 41¢ multicolored, serpentine die cut 9½ vert., self-adhesive **4168**
A3176 41¢ multicolored, serpentine die cut 11¼x11½ on 2 or 3 sides, self-adhesive (booklet pane only) **4180**
A3177 41¢ multicolored, serpentine die cut 9½ vert., self-adhesive **4169**
A3177 41¢ multicolored, serpentine die cut 11¼x11½ on 2 or 3 sides, self-adhesive (booklet pane only) **4181**
A3178 41¢ multicolored, serpentine die cut 9½ vert., self-adhesive **4170**
A3178 41¢ multicolored, serpentine die cut 11¼x11½ on 2 or 3 sides, self-adhesive (booklet pane only) **4184**
A3179 41¢ multicolored, serpentine die cut 9½ vert., self-adhesive **4171**

A3179 41¢ multicolored, serpentine die cut 11¼x11½ on 2 or 3 sides, self-adhesive (booklet pane only) **4185**

A3180 41¢ multicolored, serpentine die cut 9½ vert., self-adhesive **4172**

A3180 41¢ multicolored, serpentine die cut 11¼x11½ on 2 or 3 sides, self-adhesive (booklet pane only) **4182**

A3181 41¢ multicolored, serpentine die cut 9½ vert., self-adhesive **4173**

A3181 41¢ multicolored, serpentine die cut 11¼x11½ on 2 or 3 sides, self-adhesive (booklet pane only) **4183**

A3182 41¢ multicolored, serpentine die cut 9½ vert., self-adhesive **4174**

A3182 41¢ multicolored, serpentine die cut 11¼x11½ on 2 or 3 sides, self-adhesive (booklet pane only) **4176**

A3183 41¢ multicolored, serpentine die cut 9½ vert., self-adhesive **4175**

A3183 41¢ multicolored, serpentine die cut 11¼x11½ on 2 or 3 sides, self-adhesive (booklet pane only) **4177**

FLAG ISSUE 2008

Flag at Dusk — A3214

Flag at Night — A3215

Flag at Dawn — A3216

Flag at Midday — A3217

A3214 42¢ multicolored, perf. 10 vert., without microprinting.. **4228**

A3214 42¢ multicolored, serpentine die cut 9½ vert., with microprinting, self-adhesive, with perpendicular corners **4232**

A3214 42¢ multicolored, perf. 11 vert., without microprinting, self-adhesive, with perpendicular corners **4236**

A3214 42¢ multicolored, serpentine die cut 8½ vert., without microprinting, self-adhesive, with perpendicular corners **4240**

A3214 42¢ multicolored, serpentine die cut 11 vert., without microprinting, self-adhesive, with rounded corners..................................... **4244**

A3215 42¢ multicolored, perf. 10 vert., without microprinting.. **4229**

A3215 42¢ multicolored, serpentine die cut 9½ vert., with microprinting, self-adhesive, with perpendicular corners **4233**

A3215 42¢ multicolored, perf. 11 vert., without microprinting, self-adhesive, with perpendicular corners **4237**

A3215 42¢ multicolored, serpentine die cut 8½ vert., without microprinting, self-adhesive, with perpendicular corners **4241**

A3215 42¢ multicolored, serpentine die cut 11 vert., without microprinting, self-adhesive, with rounded corners.................................... **4245**

A3216 42¢ multicolored, perf. 10 vert., without microprinting.. **4230**

A3216 42¢ multicolored, serpentine die cut 9½ vert., with microprinting, self-adhesive, with perpendicular corners **4234**

A3216 42¢ multicolored, perf. 11 vert., without microprinting, self-adhesive, with perpendicular corners **4238**

A3216 42¢ multicolored, serpentine die cut 8½ vert., without microprinting, self-adhesive, with perpendicular corners **4242**

A3216 42¢ multicolored, serpentine die cut 11 vert., without microprinting, self-adhesive, with rounded corners.................................... **4246**

A3217 42¢ multicolored, perf. 10 vert., without microprinting.. **4231**

A3217 42¢ multicolored, serpentine die cut 9½ vert., with microprinting, self-adhesive, with perpendicular corners **4235**

A3217 42¢ multicolored, perf. 11 vert., without microprinting, self-adhesive, with perpendicular corners **4239**

A3217 42¢ multicolored, serpentine die cut 8½ vert., without microprinting, self-adhesive, with perpendicular corners **4243**

A3217 42¢ multicolored, serpentine die cut 11 vert., without microprinting, self-adhesive, with rounded corners.................................. **4247**

TROPICAL FRUIT ISSUE 2008

Pomegranate A3223

Star Fruit A3224

Kiwi — A3225

Papaya — A3226

Guava — A3227

A3223 27¢ multicolored, serpentine die cut 11¼x10¾, self-adhesive **4253**

A3223 42¢ multicolored, serpentine die cut 8½ vert., self-adhesive................................. **4260**

A3224 27¢ multicolored, serpentine die cut 11¼x10¾, self-adhesive **4254**

A3224 42¢ multicolored, serpentine die cut 8½ vert., self-adhesive................................. **4261**

A3225 27¢ multicolored, serpentine die cut 11¼x10¾, self-adhesive **4255**

A3225 42¢ multicolored, serpentine die cut 8½ vert., self-adhesive................................. **4262**

A3226 27¢ multicolored, serpentine die cut 11¼x10¾, self-adhesive **4256**

A3226 42¢ multicolored, serpentine die cut 8½ vert., self-adhesive................................. **4258**

A3227 27¢ multicolored, serpentine die cut 11¼x10¾, self-adhesive **4257**

A3227 42¢ multicolored, serpentine die cut 8½ vert., self-adhesive................................. **4259**

AMERICAN LANDMARKS ISSUE 2008-09

Mount Rushmore A3231

Redwood Forest A3332

Hoover Dam — A3232

Old Faithful A3333

A3231 $4.80 multicolored, serpentine die cut 10¾x10½, self-adhesive **4268**

A3332 $4.95 multicolored, serpentine die cut 10¾x10½, self-adhesive **4378**

A3232 $16.50 multicolored, serpentine die cut 10¾x10½, self-adhesive **4269**

A3333 $17.50 multicolored, serpentine die cut 10¾x10½, self-adhesive **4379**

SUNFLOWER ISSUE 2008

Sunflower — A3309

A3309 42¢ multicolored, serpentine die cut 11¼x10¾ on 2 or 3 sides, self-adhesive (booklet panes only) **4259**

FLAG ISSUE 2009

Flag — A3342

A3342 44¢ multicolored, perf 9¾ vert. **4391**

A3342 44¢ multicolored, serpentine die cut 11 vert., with pointed corners, litho., self-adhesive **4392**

A3342 44¢ multicolored, serpentine die cut 9½ vert., with pointed corners, litho., self-adhesive **4393**

A3342 44¢ multicolored, serpentine die cut 8½ vert., with pointed corners, litho., self-adhesive **4394**

A3342 44¢ multicolored, serpentine die cut 11 vert., with rounded corners, photo., self-adhesive **4395**

A3342 44¢ multicolored, serpentine die cut 11¼x10¾ on 3 sides, photo., self-adhesive (booklet panes only) **4396**

scott**mounts**

For stamp presentation unequaled in beauty and clarity, insist on ScottMounts. Made of 100% inert polystyrol foil, ScottMounts protect your stamps from the harmful effects of dust and moisture. Available in your choice of clear or black backs, ScottMounts are center-split across the back for easy insertion of stamps and feature crystal clear mount faces. Double layers of gum assure stay-put bonding on the album page. Discover the quality and value ScottMounts have to offer. ScottMounts are available from your favorite stamp dealer or direct from:

Discover the quality and value ScottMounts have to offer.
For a complete list of ScottMount sizes visit www.amosadvantage.com

SCOTT.

Scott Publishing Co.
1-800-572-6885
P.O. Box 828 Sidney OH 45365-0828
www.amosadvantage.com

AMOS PUBLISHING

Publishers of:
Coin World, Linn's Stamp News and Scott Publishing Co.

SUBJECT INDEX OF REGULAR, COMMEMORATIVE & AIR POST ISSUES

Additions, Deletions & Number Changes

Number in 2009 Catalogue	Number in 2010 Catalogue
new	114d
new	148c
new	153a
new	156a
new	157a
new	158a
new	159a
new	160b
new	161a
new	163b
new	165a
new	178a
new	179a
new	187a
new	191a
new	329a
new	332b
new	577a
new	654a
new	913c
new	914b
new	914c
new	919d
new	1054Ac
new	1059Ac
1059Ac	1059Ad
new	1240c
new	1384j
new	1384k
new	1529c
new	1595h
new	1618j
new	1686r
new	1890c
new	1919c
1919c	1919d
new	2124b
new	2126c
new	2276c
new	2354c
2359c	deleted
new	2423a
new	2424a
new	2425a
2425a	2425b
2425b	2425c
new	2520d
new	2527e
new	2538a
new	2538b
new	3007e
new	3030g
new	3082e
new	3422a
new	3427b
new	3492f
new	3629Fg
new	3635b
new	3636f
new	3649u
new	3657b
new	3829f
new	3830Dg
new	3980a
new	4125d
new	4125e
4127g	deleted
new	4127g
4127h	deleted
new	4127h
4127i	deleted
new	4127i
new	4127j
4207a	deleted
4208a	deleted
4209a	deleted
4210a	deleted
4210b	4210a
4210c	deleted

Number in 2009 Catalogue	Number in 2010 Catalogue
4210d	4210b
new	4359b

Computer Vended Postage Stamps

CVP79a (Mar '09 Update)	CVP79e
CVP38	1CVP1

Personal Computer Postage

1CVP2a-1CVP2e	deleted
1CVP1	1CVP2A

Carrier's Stamps

new	4LB2A
new	4LB10

Locals

new	163L1b
new	15LU7b

Stamped Envelopes & Wrappers

new	U201a
new	U411k
new	U436k
new	U446b
new	U471A
new	UC13B
new	UC16e
new	UC21a

Postal Cards

new	UX8g
new	UX63d
new	UX65b
new	UY19s
new	UXC3b
new	UXC21a

Post Office Seals

new	OX40c
new	OXSP1
LOX13a	LOX13A
LOX17b	LOX18A

Revenue Stamps

new	R11a
new	R15b
new	R23e
REA99a	REA99A
REA100a	REA100A
REA100b	REA100Ab
REA140a	REA140A
RG77a	deleted
RG78a	deleted
RG79a	deleted
RG80a	deleted
RG81a	deleted
RG82a	deleted
new	RJA103db

Essays

new	2-E1
new	67-E2d
new	79-E65P5
new	79-E65P5a
new	79-E65P5b
new	79-E66P5
new	79-E66P5a
new	79-E66P5b
new	79-E67P5
new	79-E68P5
new	79-E68P5a
new	79-E68P5b
new	79-E69P5
new	79-E70P5
new	79-E70P5a
new	79-E70P5b
new	79-E71P5
new	79-E71P5a
new	79-E71P5b

Number in 2009 Catalogue	Number in 2010 Catalogue
Essays	
new	79-E72P5
new	79-E73P5
new	79-E73P5a
new	79-E73P5b
new	79-E7A
79-E15r	85C-E1
79-E15q	85C-E2
new	85E-E1
new	85E-E1a
new	85E-E1b
new	85E-E1c
new	85E-E1d
new	85E-E1e
new	85E-E1f
new	85E-E1g
new	85E-E1h
new	116-E1
116-E1	116-E1D
new	129-E2
new	129-E8
new	147-E12A
new	219-E4
new	922-E1
new	922-E2
new	922-E3
new	922-E4
02-E1	02-E2
145-E10	01-E1
146-E10	02-E1
147-E10	03-E1
148-E13	04-E1
151-E10	06-E1
152-E4	07-E1
154-E6	09-E1
149-E5	039-E1

Die and Plate Proofs

new	41Pa
new	43Pa
new	44Pa
new	193P
new	3261P
new	3261Pa
new	3261Pb
new	3262P
new	3262Pa
new	3262Pb
new	3262Pc
new	3262Pd
new	PR1P
new	RW16P
new	RW17P
new	RW18P
new	RW19P
new	RW20P
new	RW21P
new	RW22P
new	RW24P
new	RW25P
new	RW26P
new	RW27P
new	RW28P
new	RW29P
new	RW30P
new	RW32P
new	RW33P
new	RW34P
new	RW35P
new	RW36P
new	RW37P
new	RW38P
new	RW39P
new	RW40P
new	RW41P
new	RW42P
new	RW43P
new	RW44P
new	RW45P

Number in 2009 Catalogue	Number in 2010 Catalogue
Die and Plate Proofs	
new	RW46P
new	RW47P
new	RW48P
new	RW49P
new	RW50P

Trial Color Proofs

new	260TC
new	826TC

Number in 2009 Catalogue	Number in 2010 Catalogue
Souvenir Cards	
new	SC3a
new	SC132A
new	SC160A

Test Stamps

new	TD127C

Confederate States Postmasters' Provisionals

new	4XU3
new	146XU1
18XU3	18XU1a
new	20XU1c
new	145XU1
new	25XU2
new	98XU5
new	144XU1
new	102XU2
new	78XU1
new	94XU1a
94XU2a	deleted

Canal Zone

new	14h
new	OX5b
new	OX5c
OX6b	OX6a

Cuba

new	U3b

Hawaii

new	33b

Philippines

new	411b
new	UY1s

Cover Supplies

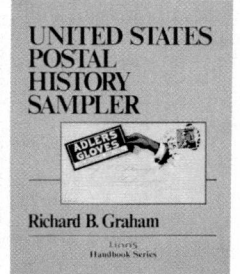

POSTMASTERS' PROVISIONALS

The Act of Congress of March 3, 1845, effective July 1, 1845, established rates of postage as follows:

"For every single letter in manuscript or paper of any kind by or upon which information shall be asked or communicated in writing or by marks designs, conveyed in the mail, for any distance under 300 miles, five cents; and for any distance over 300 miles, ten cents; and for a double letter there shall be charged double these rates; and for a treble letter, treble these rates; and for a quadruple letter, quadruple these rates; and every letter or parcel not exceeding half an ounce in weight shall be deemed a single letter, and every additional weight of half an ounce, shall be charged with an additional single postage. All drop letters, or letters placed in any post office, not for transmission through the mail but for delivery only, shall be charged with postage at the rate of two cents each."

Circulars were charged 2 cents, magazines and pamphlets 2 ½ cents; newspapers according to size.

Between the time of the Act of 1845, effecting uniform postage rates, and the Act of Congress of March 3, 1847, authorizing the postmaster-general to issue stamps, postmasters in various cities issued provisional stamps.

Before adhesive stamps were introduced, prepaid mail was marked "Paid" either with pen and ink or handstamps of various designs. Unpaid mail occasionally was marked "Due." Most often, however, unpaid mail did not have a "Due" marking, only the amount of postage to be collected from the recipient, e.g. "5," "10," "18¾," etc. Thus, if a letter was not marked "Paid," it was assumed to be unpaid. These "stampless covers" are found in numerous types and usually carry the town postmark.

New York Postmaster Robert H. Morris issued the first postmaster provisional in July 1845. Other postmasters soon followed. The provisionals served until superseded by the federal government's 5c and 10c stamps issued July 1, 1847.

Postmasters recognized the provisionals as indicating postage prepaid. On several provisionals, the signature of initials of the postmaster vouched for their legitimate use.

On July 12, 1845, Postmaster Morris sent examples of his new stamp to the postmasters of Boston, Philadelphia, Albany and Washington, asking that they be treated as unpaid until they reached the New York office. Starting in that year, the New York stamps were distributed to other offices. Postmaster General Cave Johnson reportedly authorized this practice with the understanding that these stamps were to be sold for letters directed to or passing through New York. This was an experiment to test the practicality of the use of adhesive postage stamps.

ALEXANDRIA, VA.

Daniel Bryan, Postmaster

A1

All known examples are cut to shape.
Type I — 40 asterisks in circle.
Type II — 39 asterisks in circle.

1846		Typeset		Imperf.
1X1	A1	5c black, *buff*, type I		
a.		5c black, *buff*, type II	100,000.	
		On cover (I or II)		200,000.
1X2	A1	5c black, *blue*, type I, on cover		

Cancellations

Red circular town
Black "PAID"
Black ms. accounting number ("No. 45," "No. 70")

The approximately 6 examples of Nos. 1X1 and 1X1a known on cover or cover front are generally not tied by postmark and some are uncanceled. The value for "on cover" is for a stamp obviously belonging on a cover which bears the proper circular dated town, boxed "5" and straight line "PAID" markings.

No. 1X2 is unique. It is canceled with a black straight line "PAID" marking which is repeated on the cover. The cover also bears a black circular "Alexandria Nov. 25" postmark.

ANNAPOLIS, MD.

Martin F. Revell, Postmaster
ENVELOPE

E1

1846	Printed in upper right corner of envelope	
2XU1	E1 5c carmine red, *white*	300,000.

No. 2XU1 exists in two sizes of envelope.
Envelopes and letter sheets are known showing the circular design and figure "2" handstamped in blue or red. They were used locally. Value, blue $7,500, red $11,000.

Letter sheets are known showing the circular design and figure "5" handstamped in blue or red. Value, blue $3,500, red $5,000.

Similar circular design in blue without numeral or "PAID" is known to have been used as a postmark.

BALTIMORE, MD.

James Madison Buchanan, Postmaster

Signature of Postmaster — A1

Printed from a plate of 12 (2x6) containing nine 5c stamps (Pos. 1-6, 8, 10, 12) and three 10c (Pos. 7, 9, 11).

1845		Engr.		Imperf.
3X1	A1	5c black		6,000.
		On cover		13,500.
		Vertical pair on cover		35,000.
3X2	A1	10c black, on cover		70,000.
3X3	A1	5c black, *bluish*	65,000.	6,000.
		On cover		13,500.
3X4	A1	10c black, *bluish*		60,000.
		On cover		

Nos. 3X3-3X4 preceded Nos. 3X1-3X2 in use.
No. 3X3 unused is unique. Value is based on 1997 auction sale.

Cancellations

Blue circular town
Blue straight line "PAID"
Blue "5" in oval
Blue "10" in oval
Black pen

Off cover values are for stamps canceled by either pen or handstamp. Stamps on cover tied by handstamps command premiums.

BALTIMORE, MD. Envelopes

E1

Three Separate Handstamps

The "PAID" and "5" in oval were handstamped in blue or red, always both in the same color on the same entire. "James M. Buchanan" was handstamped in black, blue or red. Blue town and rate with black signature was issued first and sells for more.

The paper is manila, buff, white, salmon or grayish. Manila is by far the most frequently found 5c envelope. All 10c envelopes are rare, with manila or buff the more frequent. Of the 10c on salmon, only one example is known.

The general attractiveness of the envelope and the clarity of the handstamps primarily determine the value.
The color listed is that of the "PAID" and "5" in oval.

1845	Various Papers		Handstamped
3XU1	E1	5c blue	6,500.
3XU2	E1	5c red	10,000.
3XU3	E1	10c blue	16,000.
3XU4	E1	10c red	20,000.

Earliest documented uses: Sept. 7, 1845 (No. 3UX1); Apr. 27, 1846 (No. 3XU2); Nov. 16, 1845 (No. 3UX3); June 12, 1846 (No. 3XU4).

Cancellations

Blue circular town
Blue "5" in oval

The second "5" in oval on the unlisted "5 + 5" envelopes is believed not to be part of the basic prepaid marking, but envelopes bearing this marking merit a premium over the values for Nos. 3XU1-3XU2.

BOSCAWEN, NH.

Worcester Webster, Postmaster

A1

1846 (?)   **Typeset**   *Imperf.*
4X1 A1 5c dull blue, *yellowish,* on cover   *300,000.*

One example known, uncanceled on cover with ms. postal markings.

BRATTLEBORO, VT.

Frederick N. Palmer, Postmaster

Initials of Postmaster (FNP) — A1

Printed from plate of 10 (5x2) separately engraved subjects with imprint "Eng'd by Thos. Chubbuck, Bratto." below the middle stamp of the lower row (Pos. 8).

1846   *Imperf.*
Thick Softwove Paper Colored Through

5X1 A1 5c **black,** *buff*   11,000.
          On cover   35,000.
          Two singles on cover   230,000.

Earliest documented use: Aug. 28, 1846.

Cancellations

Red straight line "PAID"
Red pen
Blue "5"

The red pen-marks are small and lightly applied. They were used to invalidate a single sample sheet. One example of each plate position is known so canceled.
The No. 5X1 cover with two singles is unique. Value represents 2007 auction sale price.

LOCKPORT, N.Y.

Hezekiah W. Scovell, Postmaster

A1

"Lockport, N.Y." oval and "PAID" separately handstamped in red, "5" in black ms.

1846   *Imperf.*
6X1 A1 5c **red,** *buff,* on cover   300,000.

Cancellation

Black ms. "X"

One example of No. 6X1 is known. Small fragments of two other copies adhering to one cover also exist.

MILLBURY, MASS.

Asa H. Waters, Postmaster

George Washington — A1

Printed from a woodcut, singly, on a hand press.

1846   *Imperf.*
7X1 A1 5c **black,** *bluish*   130,000. 50,000.
          On cover   125,000.

Earliest documented use: Aug. 21, 1846.

Cancellations

Red straight line "PAID"
Red circular "MILBURY, MS.,"
  date in center

NEW HAVEN, CONN.

Edward A. Mitchell, Postmaster
ENVELOPES

E1

Impressed from a brass handstamp at upper right of envelope.
Signed in blue, black or magenta ms., as indicated in parenthesis.

1845
8XU1 E1 5c **red** (Bl or M)   100,000.
          Cut square   40,000.
          Cut to shape   15,000.
8XU2 E1 5c **red,** *light bluish* (Bk)   125,000.
8XU3 E1 5c **dull blue,** *buff* (Bl)   125,000.
          Cut to shape (Bk)   55,000.
8XU4 E1 5c **dull blue** (Bl)   125,000.

Values of Nos. 8XU1-8XU4 are a guide to value. They are based on auction realizations and take condition into consideration. All New Haven envelopes are of almost equal rarity. An entire of No. 8XU2 is the finest example known. The other envelopes and cut squares are valued according to condition as much as rarity.

REPRINTS

Twenty reprints in dull blue on white paper, signed by E. A. Mitchell in lilac rose ink, were made in 1871 for W. P. Brown and others, value $1,500. Thirty reprints in carmine on hard white paper, signed in dark blue or red, were made in 1874 for Cyrus B. Peets, Chief Clerk for Mitchell, value $1,200. Unsigned reprints in dull red on soft yellowish white paper were made for N. F. Seebeck and others about 1872, value $400.
Edward A. Mitchell, grandson of the Postmaster, in 1923 delivered reprints in lilac on soft white wove paper, dated "1923" in place of the signature, value $400.
In 1932, the New Haven Philatelic Society bought the original handstamp and gave it to the New Haven Colony Historical Society. To make the purchase possible (at the $1000 price) it was decided to print 260 stamps from the original handstamp. Of these, 130 were in red and 130 in dull blue, all on hard, white wove paper, value approximately $250 each.
According to Carroll Alton Means' booklet on the New Haven Provisional Envelope, after this last reprinting the brass handstamp was so treated that further reprints cannot be made. The reprints were sold originally at $5 each. A facsimile signature of the postmaster, "E. A. Mitchell," (blue on the red reprints, black on the blue) was applied with a rubber handstamp. These 260 reprints are all numbered to correspond with the number of the booklet issued then.

NEW YORK, N.Y.

Robert H. Morris, Postmaster

George Washington — A1

Printed by Rawdon, Wright & Hatch from a plate of 40 (5x8). The die for Washington's head on the contemporary bank notes was used for the vignette. It had a small flaw—a line extending from the corner of the mouth down the chin—which is quite visible on the paper money. This was corrected for the stamp.
The stamps were usually initialed "ACM" (Alonzo Castle Monson) in magenta ink as a control before being sold or passed through the mails. There are four or five styles of these initials. The most common is "ACM" without periods. The scarcest is "A.C.M.", believed written by Marcena Monson. The rare initials

"RHM" (Robert H. Morris, the postmaster) and "MMJr" (Marcena Monson) are listed separately.
The stamps were printed on a variety of wove papers varying in thickness from pelure to thick, and in color from gray to bluish and blue. A thick brown gum was used first, succeeded by a thin whitish transparent gum. Some stamps appear to have a slight ribbing or mesh effect. A few also show letters of a double-line papermaker's watermark, a scarce variety. All used true blue copies carry "ACM" without periods; of the three unused copies, two lack initials.

Nos. 9X1-9X3 and varieties unused are valued without gum. Examples with original gum are extremely scarce and will command higher prices.

Earliest documented use: July 15, 1845 (No. 9X1e).

1845-46   Engr.   Bluish Wove Paper   *Imperf.*
9X1 A1 5c **black,** signed ACM, connected,
                  1846   1,500. 500.
          On cover   625.
          On cover to France or England   2,250.
          On cover to other European
            countries   5,500.
          Pair   5,750. 1,300.
          Pair on cover   2,000.
          Pair on cover to England   4,500.
          Pair on cover to Canada   5,500.
          Strip of 3   5,000.
          Strip of 3 on cover   9,000.
          Strip of 4   12,500.
          Strip of 4 on cover   20,000.
          Block of 4   50,000.
          Double transfer at bottom (Pos.
            2)
          Double transfer at top (Pos. 7) 1,700. 575.
          Bottom frame line double (Pos.
            31)   1,700. 575.
          Top frame line double (Pos. 36) 1,700. 575.

The only blocks currently known are a used block of 4 off cover (faulty) and a block of 9 on cover.

Cancellations

Blue pen   525.
Black pen   +25.
Magenta pen   +100.
Red square grid (New York)   +50.
Black circular date stamp
Red round grid (Boston)   +350.
Blue numeral (Philadelphia)   +750.
Red "U.S" in octagon frame
  (carrier)   +1,200.
Red "PAID"   +50.
Red N.Y. circular date stamp   +100.
Large red N.Y. circular date
  stamp containing "5"
Small red "5"   +125.

a.   Signed ACM, AC connected   1,750. 575.
          On cover   725.
          On cover to France or England   2,250.
          On cover to other European
            countries   6,000.
          Pair   5,750. 1,600.
              Pair, on cover   2,100.
          Pair, Nos. 9X1, 9X1a   — 4,500.
          Pair, Nos. 9X1 and 9X1a, on
            cover   10,000.
          Double transfer at bottom (Pos.
            2)
          Double transfer at top (Pos. 7) 1,800. 700.
          Bottom frame line double (Pos.
            31)   1,800. 700.
          Top frame line double (Pos. 36) 1,800. 700.

Cancellations

Blue pen   575.
Black pen   +25.
Magenta pen   +100.
Red N.Y. circular date stamp   +125.
Large red N.Y. circular date
  stamp with "5"   +150.
Red square grid   +100.
Red "PAID"   +50.

b.   Signed A.C.M.   3,750. 700.
          On cover   850.
          On cover to France or England   2,750.
          On cover to other European
            countries   6,000.
          Pair   2,400.
          Pair on cover   3,250.
          Double transfer at bottom (Pos.
            2)   — 950.
          Double transfer at top (Pos. 7)   950.
          Bottom frame line double (Pos.
            31)   950.
          Top frame line double (Pos. 36)   950.

Cancellations

Blue pen   700.
Black pen   +25.
Red square grid   +100.
Red N.Y. circular date stamp   +100.
Large red N.Y. circular date
  stamp containing "5"   +150.
Red "PAID"   +50.

c.   Signed MMJr   10,000.
          On cover   —
          Pair on cover front   26,500.
d.   Signed RHM   13,000. 3,500.
          Pair   12,000.
          On cover   5,500.
          On cover from New Hamburgh,
            N.Y.   12,500.

Cancellations

Blue pen	3,250.
Black pen	+150.
Red square grid	+250.
Red N.Y. circular date stamp	+400.
Red "PAID"	+300.

Earliest documented use: July 17, 1845.

e.	Without signature	4,000.	900.
	On cover		1,350.
	On cover to France or England		2,400.
	On cover to other European countries		6,000.
	On cover, July 15, 1845		30,000.
	Pair		2,500.
	Pair on cover		2,750.
	Double transfer at bottom (Pos. 2)	4,250.	1,000.
	Double transfer at top (Pos. 7)	4,250.	1,000.
	Bottom frame line double (Pos. 31)	4,250.	1,000.
	Top frame line double (Pos. 36)	4,250.	1,000.
	Ribbed paper		—

Cancellations

Blue pen	900.
Black pen	+25.
Red square grid	+100.
Red N.Y. circular date stamp	+100.
Large red N.Y. circular date stamp containing "5"	+150.
Red "PAID"	+100.

Known used from Albany, Boston, Jersey City, N.J., New Hamburgh, N.Y., Philadelphia, Sing Sing, N.Y., Washington, D.C., and Hamilton, Canada, as well as by route agents on the Baltimore R.R. Covers originating in New Hamburgh are known only with No. 9X1d (one also bearing the U.S. City Despatch Post carrier); one also known used to Holland.

1847	Engr.	**Blue Wove Paper**	*Imperf.*
9X2	A1 5c	**black,** signed ACM connected	6,500.	3,500.

	On cover	5,750.
	Pair	13,000.
	Pair on cover	
	Double transfer at bottom (Pos. 2)	4,000.
	Double transfer at top (Pos. 7)	4,000.
	Bottom frame line double (Pos. 31)	4,000.
	Top frame line double (Pos. 36)	—
a.	Signed RHM	5,000.
b.	Signed ACM, AC connected	
d.	Without signature	11,000.	7,250.

Earliest documented use: Mar. 4, 1847.

Cancellations

Red square grid	3,500.
Red "PAID"	+100.
Red N.Y. circular date stamp	+650.

On the only example known of No. 9X2a the "R" is illegible and does not match those of the other "RHM" signatures.

1847	Engr.	**Gray Wove Paper**	*Imperf.*
9X3	A1 5c	**black,** signed ACM connected	5,250.	2,250.

	On cover	5,250.
	On cover to Europe	8,500.
	Pair	7,750.
	Pair on cover	8,750.
	Double transfer at bottom (Pos. 2)	2,600.
	Double transfer at top (Pos. 7)	2,600.
	Bottom frame line double (Pos. 31)	2,600.
	Top frame line double (Pos. 36)	2,600.
a.	Signed RHM	7,000.
b.	Without signature	13,000.

Earliest documented use: Feb. 8, 1847.

Cancellations

Red square grid	2,250.
Red N.Y. circular date stamp	2,250.
Red "PAID"	+100.

All known used examples of No. 9X3a have red square grid or red "PAID" in arc cancel.

The first plate was of nine subjects (3x3). Each subject differs slightly from the others, with Position 8 showing the white stock shaded by crossed diagonal lines. At some point prints were struck from this plate in black on deep blue and white bond paper, as well as in blue, green, scarlet and brown on white bond paper. These are listed in the Proof and Trial Color Proof sections. Stamps from this plate were not issued, and it is possible that it is an essay, as the design differs slightly from the issued stamps from the sheet of 40. No examples from the plate of nine are known used.

ENVELOPES

Postmaster Morris, according to newspaper reports of July 2 and 7, 1845, issued envelopes. The design was not stated and no example has been seen. It is possible that these items were envelopes to which stamps had been affixed.

PROVIDENCE, R.I.

Welcome B. Sayles, Postmaster

A1 & A2

Engraved on copper plate containing 12 stamps (3x4). Upper right corner stamp (Pos. 3) "TEN"; all others "FIVE." The stamps were engraved directly on the plate, each differing from the other. The "TEN" and Pos. 4, 5, 6, 9, 11 and 12 have no period after "CENTS."

Yellowish White Handmade Paper
Earliest documented use: Aug. 25, 1846 (No. 10X1).

1846, Aug. 24			*Imperf.*	
10X1	A1 5c	**gray black**	350.	1,750.
	No gum	225.	
	On cover, tied by postmark		20,000.
	On cover, pen canceled		6,000.
	Two on cover		—
	Pair	725.	
	Block of four	1,450.	
10X2	A2 10c	**gray black**	1,150.	15,000.
	No gum	725.	
	On cover, pen canceled		35,000.
a.	Se-tenant with 5c	2,000.	
	Complete sheet	5,500.	
	No gum	3,500.	

Cancellations

Black pen check mark	
Red circular town	
Red straight line "PAID" (2 types)	
Red "5"	

All canceled examples of Nos. 10X1-10X2, whether or not bearing an additional handstamped cancellation, are obliterated with a black pen check mark. There is only one known certified used example off cover of No. 10X2, and it has a minor fault. Value represents a 1997 sale. All genuine covers must bear the red straight line "PAID," the red circular town postmark, and the red numeral "5" or "10" rating mark.

Reprints were made in 1898. In general, each stamp bears one of the following letters on the back: B. O. G. E. R. T. D. U. R. B. I. N. However, some reprint sheets received no such printing on the reverse. All reprints are without gum. Value for 5c, $50; for 10c, $125; for sheet, $725. Reprints without the printing on the reverse sell for more.

ST. LOUIS, MO.

John M. Wimer, Postmaster

A1   A2

A3

Missouri Coat of Arms

Printed from a copper plate of 6 (2x3) subjects separately engraved by J. M. Kershaw.

The plate in its first state, referred to as Plate 1, comprised: three 5c stamps in the left vertical row and three 10c in the right vertical row. The stamps vary slightly in size, measuring from 17¾ to 18¼ by 22 to 22½mm.

Later a 20c denomination was believed necessary. So two of the 5c stamps, types I (pos. 1) and II (pos. 3) were changed to 20c by placing the plate face down on a hard surface and hammering on the back of the parts to be altered until the face was driven flush at those points. The new numerals were then engraved. Both 20c stamps show broken frame lines and the paw of the right bear on type II (pos. 3) is missing. The 20c type I (pos. 1) reengraved, the "5" (pos. 3) also shows retouching in the dashes under "SAINT" and "LOUIS." The characteristics of types I and II of the 20c also serve to distinguish the two types of the 20c. This altered, second state of the plate is referred to as Plate 2. It is the only state to contain the 20c.

The demand for the 20c apparently proved inadequate, and the plate was altered again. The "20" was erased and "5" engraved in its place, resulting in noticeable differences from the 5c stamps from Plate 1. In type I (pos. 1) reengraved, the "5"

---

is twice as far from the top frame line as in the original state, and the four dashes under "SAINT" and "LOUIS" have disappeared except for about half of the upper dash under each word. In type II (pos. 3) reengraved, the ornament in the flag of the "5" is a diamond instead of a triangle; the diamond in the bow is much longer than in the first state, and at right of the "5," originally blank, contains a large dot. At right of the shading of the "5" is a short curved line which is evidently a remnant of the "0" of "20." Type III (pos. 5) of the 5c was slightly retouched. This second alteration of the plate is referred to as Plate 3.

Type characteristics common to Plates 1, 2 and 3:

5 Cent. Type I (pos. 1). Haunches of both bears almost touch frame lines.

Type II (pos. 3). Bear at right almost touches frame line, but left bear is about ¼mm from it.

Type III (pos. 5). Haunches of both bears about ½mm from frame lines. Small spur on "S" of "POST."

10 Cent. Type I (pos. 2). Three dashes below "POST OFFICE."

Type II (pos. 4). Three pairs of dashes.

Type III (pos. 6). Pairs of dashes (with rows of dots between) at left and right. Dash in center with row of dots above it.

20 Cent. Type I. See 5c Type I.

Type II. See 5c Type II.

Nos. 11X1-11X8 unused are valued without gum.

Wove Paper Colored Through

1845, Nov.-1846				*Imperf.*	
11X1	A1 5c	**black,** *greenish*	50,000.	8,000.
	On cover		17,500.
	Pair	—	18,000.
	Two on cover		25,000.
	Strip of 3		35,000.
	Strip of 3 plus single on cover		45,000.
11X2	A2 10c	**black,** *greenish*	50,000.	8,000.
	On cover		14,000.
	Pair		18,000.
	Pair on cover		22,500.
	Strip of 3		32,500.
	Strip of 3 on cover		40,000.
	Five on cover		225,000.
	On cover, #11X2, 11X6		75,000.
11X3	A3 20c	**black,** *greenish*		160,000.
	On cover, #11X5, two #11X3		325,000.

Printed from Plate 1 (3 varieties each of the 5c and 10c) and Plate 2 (1 variety of the 5c, 3 of the 10c, 2 of the 20c).

1846					
11X4	A1 5c	**black,** (III), *gray lilac*	—	55,000.
	On cover		—
11X5	A2 10c	**black,** *gray lilac*	50,000.	8,000.
	On cover		12,000.
	Pair		19,000.
	Pair, 10c (III), 5c (III)		90,000.
	Strip of 3		40,000.
	Strip of 3 on cover		160,000.
	Pair 10c (II), 10c (III) se-tenant with 5c (III)		70,000.
	Strip of 3 10c (I, II, III) se-tenant with 5c (III)		300,000.
11X6	A3 20c	**black,** *gray lilac*	100,000.	50,000.
	On cover		60,000.
	Pair		110,000.
	Pair on cover		125,000.
	On cover, #11X6 and #11X5		62,500.
	Pair, #11X6 and #11X5		125,000.
	Pair, #11X6 and #11X5, on cover		210,000.
	Strip of 3, 2#11X6 and #11X4		175,000.

Printed from Plate 2 (1 variety of the 5c, 3 of the 10c, 2 of the 20c).

No. 11X6 unused is unique. It is in the grade of fine and is valued thus.

The used pair of No. 11X6 is unique. The left margin cuts into the frameline, and it is valued thus.

1846				**Pelure Paper**	
11X7	A1 5c	**black,** *bluish*	—	11,000.
	On cover		16,000.
	Pair		40,000.
	Two on cover		37,500.
11X8	A2 10c	**black,** *bluish*		13,000.
	On cover		18,500.
a.	Impression of 5c on back		—

Printed from Plate 3 (3 varieties each of the 5c, 10c).
Earliest documented use: Nov. 25, 1846 (#11X8).

Cancellations, Nos. 11X1-11X8

Black pen	
Ms. initials of postmaster (#11X2, type I)	
Red circular town	
Red straight line "PAID"	
Red grid (#11X7)	

Values of Nos. 11X1-11X8, on and off cover, reflect the usual poor condition of these stamps, which were printed on fragile pelure paper. Attractive examples with minor defects sell for considerably more.

Values for used off-cover stamps are for pen-canceled examples. Handstamp-canceled stamps sell for much more. Values for stamps on cover are for examples with pen cancels. Covers with the stamps tied by handstamp sell at considerable premiums depending upon the condition of the stamps and the general attractiveness of the cover. In general, covers with multiple frankings (unless separately valued) are valued at the "on cover" value of the highest item, plus the "off cover" value of the other stamps.

POSTAGE

GENERAL ISSUES

Please Note:

Stamps are valued in the grade of very fine unless otherwise indicated.

Values for early and valuable stamps are for examples with certificates of authenticity from acknowledged expert committees, or examples sold with the buyer having the right of certification. This applies to examples with original gum as well as examples without gum. Beware of stamps offered "as is," as the gum on some unused stamps offered with "original gum" may be fraudulent, and stamps offered as unused without gum may in some cases be altered or faintly canceled used stamps.

Color Cancellations

Additional values for color cancellations listed in the "cancellations" section after stamps from No. 1 through No. 218 are for full or nearly full unfaded strikes on very fine stamps. Premiums for such strikes on extremely fine or superb stamps often are much larger, and premiums for strikes on stamps in grades lower than very fine are smaller.

Issues from 1847 through 1894 are unwatermarked.

Benjamin Franklin — A1

Double transfer of top frame line — (A) position 80R1

Double transfer of top and bottom frame lines — (B) position 90R1

Double transfer of bottom frame line and lower part of left frame line — (C)

Double transfer of top, bottom and left frame lines, also numerals — (D)

Double transfer of "U," "POST OFFICE" and left numeral — (E)

Double transfer of top frame line, upper part of side frame lines, "U," and "POST OFFICE" — (F)

This issue was authorized by an Act of Congress, approved March 3, 1847, to take effect July 1, 1847, from which date the use of Postmasters' Stamps or any which were not authorized by the Postmaster General became illegal.

This issue was declared invalid as of July 1, 1851.

Produced by Rawdon, Wright, Hatch & Edson.

Plates of 200 subjects in two panes of 100 each.

1847, July 1			Engr.	Imperf.

Thin Bluish Wove Paper

				Engr.	Imperf.
1	A1	5c	**red brown**	6,750.	550.
			pale brown	6,750.	550.
			brown	7,000.	575.
			No gum	2,400.	
			On cover		625.
			On cover to England or France		2,750.
			On cover to other European countries		3,250.
			Pair	16,000.	1,200.
			Pair on cover		1,400.
			Strip of 3	26,000.	2,300.
			Strip of 4		5,000.
			Block of 4	50,000.	27,500.
			Block of 4 on cover		240,000.
			Dot in "S" in upper right corner	7,000.	600.
			Cracked plate (69R1)		—
a.		5c	**dark brown**	8,750.	775.
			No gum	3,250.	
			Pair	21,000.	2,000.
			Block of 4	55,000.	
			grayish brown	9,000.	850.
			No gum	3,500.	
			Pair		2,100.
			blackish brown	10,000.	1,100.
			No gum	3,750.	
			Pair	25,000.	2,750.
b.		5c	**orange brown**	10,000.	1,100.
			No gum	3,500.	
			Pair		2,750.
			Block of 4 on cover		—
c.		5c	**red orange**	25,000.	9,500.
			No gum	9,500.	
			Pair		35,000.
d.		5c	**brown orange**		1,300.
			No gum	4,500.	
			Pair on cover		—
e.			Double impression		—
(A)			Double transfer of top frame line (80R1)		675.
(B)			Double transfer of top and bottom frame lines (90R1)	—	675.
(C)			Double transfer of bottom frame line and lower part of left frame line		3,250.
(D)			Double transfer of top, bottom and left frame lines, also numerals		3,250.
(E)			Double transfer of "U," "POST OFFICE" and left numeral		1,500.
(F)			Double transfer of top frame line, upper part of side frame lines, "U," and "POST OFFICE"		—

The only known double impression shows part of the design doubled.

Some students believe that the "E double transfer" actually shows plate scratches instead.

Earliest documented use: July 7, 1847.

Cancellations

Red	550.
Red town	+200.
Orange red	+15.
Orange red town	+220.
Blue	+35.
Blue town	+125.
Black	+100.
Black town	+400.
Magenta	+250.
Orange	+750.
Ultramarine	+1,000.
Violet	+900.
Violet town	
Green	+1,250.
"Paid"	+50.
"Paid" in grid (demonetized usage)	+300.
"Free"	+400.

Railroad	+200.
U. S. Express Mail (on the cover)	+100.
U. S. Express Mail (on stamp)	—
U. S. Express Mail in black (on stamp) (demonetized usage)	+12,500.
"Way"	+250.
"Way" with numeral	+500.
"Steamboat"	+350.
"Steam"	+200.
"Steamship"	+300.
Philadelphia RR	—
Hotel (on the cover)	+2,000.
Numeral	+100.
Canada	+3,000.
Wheeling, Va., grid	+6,000.
Pen	275.

George Washington — A2

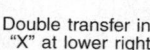

Double transfer in "X" at lower right

Double transfer in "Post Office"

Double transfer in "X" at lower right

Double transfer of left and bottom frame line

2	A2 10c	**black**	35,000.	1,250.
		gray black	35,000.	1,250.
		No gum	15,000.	—
		greenish black	—	—
		On cover		1,600.
		On cover to Canada		2,000.
		On cover to Great Britain		3,250.
		On cover to France		5,250.
		On cover with 5c No. 1		50,000.
		Pair	80,000.	3,000.
		Pair on cover		3,500.
		Strip of 3	125,000.	10,500.
		Block of 4	200,000.	75,000.
		Short transfer at top	37,500.	1,400.
		Vertical line through second "F" of "OFFICE" (68R1)	—	2,000.
		With "Stick Pin" in tie (52L1)	—	3,000.
		With "harelip" (57L1)	—	3,000.
a.		Diagonal half used as 5c on cover		13,000.
b.		Vertical half used as 5c on cover		35,000.
c.		Horizontal half used as 5c on cover		—
(A)		Double transfer in "X" at lower right (1R1)	70,000.	2,250.
(B)		Double transfer in "Post Office" (31R1)	—	2,250.
(C)		Double transfer in "X" at lower right (2R1)	—	3,350.
(D)		Double transfer of left and bottom frame line (41R1)	—	2,250.

Earliest documented use: July 2, 1847.

Two examples of the unused block are recorded, only one of which is available to collectors.
The value for the used block of 4 represents a block with manuscript cancel. One block is recorded with a handstamp cancellation and it is worth significantly more.

Cancellations

Red	1,250.
Orange red	+25.
Blue	+50.
Orange	+500.
Black	+350.
Magenta	+650.
Violet	+950.
Green	+2,000.
Ultramarine	+1,100.
"Paid"	+100.
"Free"	+900.
Railroad	+1,000.
Philadelphia RR straightline	+500.
U.S. Express Mail (on the cover)	+500.
"Way"	+550.
Numeral	+250.
"Steam"	+350.
"Steamship"	+400.
"Steamboat"	+650.
"Steamer 10"	+1,000.
Canada	+3,000.
Panama	—
Wheeling, Va., grid	+5,500.
Pen	700.

A3

A4

REPRODUCTIONS of 1847 ISSUE

Actually, official imitations made from new plates of 50 subjects made by the Bureau of Engraving and Printing by order of the Post Office Department. These were not valid for postal use.

Reproductions. The letters R. W. H. & E. at the bottom of each stamp are less distinct on the reproductions than on the originals.

5c. On the originals the left side of the white shirt frill touches the oval on a level with the top of the "F" of "Five." On the reproductions it touches the oval about on a level with the top of the figure "5." On the originals, the bottom of the right leg of the "N" in "CENTS" is blunt. On the reproductions, the "N" comes to a point at the bottom.

10c. On the originals line of coat (A) points to "T" of TEN and (B) it points between "T" and "S" of "CENTS." On the reproductions line of coat (A) points to right tip of "X" and line of coat (B) points to center of "S."

The bottom of the right leg of the "N" of "CENTS" shows the same difference as on the 5c originals and reproductions.

On the reproductions the eyes have a sleepy look, the line of the mouth is straighter, and in the curl of the hair near the left cheek is a strong black dot, while the originals have only a faint one.

(See Nos. 948a and 948b for 1947 reproductions — 5c blue and 10c brown orange in larger size.)

			Imperf.
1875		**Bluish paper, without gum**	
3	A3 5c	**red brown** (4779)	750.
		brown	750.
		dark brown	750.
		Pair	1,650.
		Block of 4	5,250.
4	A4 10c	**black** (3883)	900.
		gray black	900.
		Pair	1,950.
		Block of 4	6,500.

Numbers in parentheses are quantities sold.

Produced by Toppan, Carpenter, Casilear & Co.

Stamps of the 1851-57 series were printed from plates consisting of 200 subjects and the sheets were divided into two panes of 100 each. Stamps printed from different positions on the plate often have characteristics which make them more valuable than the basic listing. It is, therefore, necessary to be able to clearly identify each position on the plates used to print these stamps. In order that each stamp in the sheet and within each pane could be identified easily in regard to its relative position it was devised that the stamps in each pane be numbered from one to one hundred, starting with the top horizontal row and numbering consecutively from left to right. Thus the first stamp at the upper left corner would be 1 and the last stamp at the bottom right corner, would be 100. The left and right panes are indicated by the letters "L" or "R." The number of the plate is given last. As an example, the best-known of the scarce type III, one cent 1851 being the 99th stamp in the right pane of Plate No. 2 is listed as (99R2), *i.e.* 99th stamp, right pane, Plate No. 2.

One plate of the one cent and several plates of the three cents were reentered after they had been in use. The original state of the plate is called "Early" and the reentered state is termed "Late." If the plate was reentered twice, the inbetween state is called "Intermediate." Identification of "Early," "Intermediate" or "Late" state is explained by the addition of the letters "E," "i" or "L" after the plate numbers. The sixth stamp of the right pane of Plate No. 1 from the "Early" state would be 6R1E. The same plate position from the "Late" state would be 6R1L. Many varieties occur on the same position in each of the states of the plate. The state of the plate is mentioned only if that variety does not show on the other states.

One plate of the three cent stamp never had a plate number and is referred to by specialists as "Plate O."

The position of the stamp in the sheet is placed within parentheses, for example: (99R2).

The different values of this issue were intended primarily for the payment of specific rates, though any value might be used in making up a rate. The one cent stamp was to pay the postage on newspapers, drop letters and circulars, and the one cent carrier fee in some cities from 1856. The three cent stamp represented the rate on ordinary letters and two of them made up the rate for distances over 3000 miles prior to April 1, 1855. The five cent stamp was originally for the registration fee but the fee was usually paid in cash. Occasionally two of them were used to pay the rate over 3000 miles, after it was changed in April, 1855. Singles paid the "Shore to ship" rate to certain foreign countries and, from 1857, triples paid the fifteen-cent rate to France. Ten cents was the rate to California and points distant more than 3000 miles. The twelve cent stamp was for quadruple the ordinary rate. Twenty-four cents represented the single letter rate to Great Britain. Thirty cents was the rate to Germany. The ninety cent stamp was apparently intended to facilitate the payment of large amounts of postage.

Act of Congress, March 3, 1851. "From and after June 30, 1851, there shall be charged the following rates: Every single letter not exceeding 3000 miles, prepaid postage, 3 cents; not prepaid, 5 cents; for any greater distance, double these rates. Every single letter or paper conveyed wholly or in part by sea, and to or from a foreign country over 2500 miles, 20 cents;

under 2500 miles, 10 cents. Drop or local letters, 1 cent each. Letters uncalled for and advertised, to be charged 1 cent in addition to the regular postage."

Act of Congress, March 3, 1855. "For every single letter, in manuscript or paper of any kind, in writing, marks or signs, conveyed in the mail between places in the United States not exceeding 3000 miles, 3 cents; and for any greater distance, 10 cents. Drop or local letters, 1 cent."

The Act of March 3, 1855, made the prepayment of postage on domestic letters compulsory April 1, 1855, and prepayment of postage on domestic letters compulsory by stamps effective January 1, 1856.

The Act authorized the Postmaster to establish a system for the registration of valuable letters, and to require prepayment of postage on such letters as well as registration fee of five cents. Stamps to prepay the registry fee were not required until June 1, 1867.

In Nos. 5-17 the 1c, 3c and 12c have very small margins between the stamps. The 5c and 10c have moderate size margins. The values of these stamps take the margin size into consideration.

Franklin — A5

ONE CENT. Issued July 1, 1851.
Type I. Has complete curved lines outside the labels with "U. S. Postage" and "One Cent." The scrolls below the lower label are turned under, forming little balls. The ornaments at top are substantially complete.
Type Ib. As type I, but balls below bottom label are not so clear. Plume-like scrolls at bottom are incomplete.

1851-57			*Imperf.*
5 A5 1c **blue**, type I (7R1E)		225,000.	85,000.
dark blue			95,000.
On cover			150,000.
Pair, types I, Ib			
On cover, pair, one stamp type I			—
Strip of 3, one stamp type I			210,000.
On cover, strip of 3, one stamp type I			220,000.

Only one example of No. 5 in the dark blue shade is recorded.

Earliest documented use: July 5, 1851.

Cancellations

Blue	+1,000.
Blue town	—
Red grid	+3,000.
Red town	—
Red "Paid"	—

Values for No. 5 are for examples with margins touching or cutting slightly into the design, or for examples with four margins and minor faults. Very few sound examples with the design untouched exist, and these sell for much more than the values shown.

Value for No. 5 unused is for a stamp with no gum. Only one example unused with original gum is recorded. It is in a multiple and is creased.

5A A5 1c **blue**, type Ib, July 1, 1851			
(Less distinct examples 3-5, 9R1E)		32,500.	10,000.
No gum		12,000.	
Pair		70,000.	21,000.
On cover			10,500.
blue, type Ib (Best examples 6, 8R1E)		45,000.	16,000.
No gum		18,000.	
On cover			19,000.
Pair, type Ib, II			14,000.
Block of 4, pair type Ib, pair type IIIa (8-9, 18-19R1E)			—

Earliest documented use: July 1, 1851 (FDC).

Cancellations

Blue town	+300.
Red town	—
Red Carrier	—

Red "Paid"	+550.
Pen (3, 4, 5 or 9R1E)	4,500.
Pen (6 or 8R1E)	7,500.

A6

Type Ia. Same as type I at bottom, but top ornaments and outer line at top are partly cut away. Type Ia comes only from the bottom row of both panes of Plate 4. All type Ia stamps have the flaw below "U" of "U.S.," but this flaw also appears on some stamps of types Ic, III and IIIa of Plate 4.
Type Ic. Same as type Ia, but bottom right plume and ball ornament incomplete. Bottom left plume complete or nearly complete. Best examples are from bottom row, "F" relief, positions 91 and 96R4. Less distinct examples are "E" reliefs from 5th and 9th rows, positions 47L, 49L, 83L, 49R, 81R, 82R, and 89R, Plate 4, and early impressions of 41R4.

6 A6 1c **blue**, type Ia, 1857		45,000.	13,000.
No gum		20,000.	
On cover			17,500.
Pair		—	30,000.
Strip of 3 on cover			75,000.
Pair, types Ia, Ic			26,000.
Horizontal strip of 3, (95-97R4) types Ia, Ic			37,500.
Vertical pair, types Ia, III		75,000.	18,000.
Vertical pair, types Ia, IIIa		55,000.	17,000.
Block of 4, types Ia, IIIa		110,000.	
"Curl on shoulder" (97L4)		47,500.	14,000.
"Curl in C" (97R4)		47,500.	14,000.

The horizontal strip of 3 represents positions 95-97R4, position 96R4 being type 1c.

Earliest documented use: Apr. 19, 1857.

Cancellations

Blue	+100.
Black Carrier	+350.
Red Carrier	+350.
Pen	6,250.

6b A6 1c **blue**, type Ic ("E" relief, less distinct examples)		7,000.	3,000.
No gum		3,000.	
On cover			4,500.
Horizontal pair (81-82R4)			—
Pair, types Ic, III			—
Pair, types Ic, IIIa			—
blue, type Ic ("F" relief, best examples, 91, 96R4)		27,500.	10,000.
No gum		12,500.	
On cover			11,000.
Vertical pair (81-91R4)			—

Earliest documented use: May 20, 1857 (dated cancel on off-cover stamp); June 6, 1857 (on cover).

Cancellations

Blue ("E" relief)	—
Red ("E" relief)	—
Blue town ("F" relief)	—
Red("F" relief)	—
Pen ("E" relief)	1,600.
Pen ("F" relief)	5,000.

A7

Type II — Same as Type I at top, but the little balls of the bottom scrolls and the bottoms of the lower plume ornaments are missing. The side ornaments are substantially complete.

7 A7 1c **blue**, type II, (Plates 1E, 2);			
July 1, 1851 (Plate 1E)		1,100.	170.
No gum		425.	
On cover			200.
Pair		2,500.	375.
Strip of 3		3,800.	575.
Block of 4 (Plate 1E)		—	—
Block of 4 (Plate 2)		5,500.	1,150.
P# block of 8, Impt. (Plate 2)		37,500.	
Design complete at top (10R1E only)			2,000.
Pair, types II, IIIa (Plate 1E)		7,500.	1,350.
Double transfer (Plate 1E or 2)		1,200.	180.
Double transfer (89R2)		1,250.	220.
Double transfer, one inverted (71L1E)		1,550.	390.
Triple transfer, one inverted (91L1E)		1,550.	410.
Cracked Plate (2L, 12L, 13L, 23L and 33L, Plate 2)		1,400.	390.
Plate 1L (4R1L only, double transfer), June 1852		2,000.	360.
Pair, types II (4R1L), IV		3,900.	650.
Plate 3, May, 1856		9,000.	600.

Visualize selling.

Lilly 1967

Kapiloff 1992

Honolulu Advertiser 1995

Zoellner 1998

Golden 1999

Hall 2001

LeBow 2004

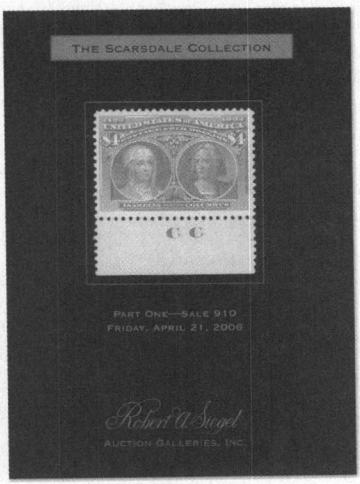

Scarsdale 2006

**The next great
Siegel sale could have
your name on it.**

Robert A. Siegel

AUCTION GALLERIES, INC.

**60 EAST 56th STREET, 4th FLOOR
NEW YORK, N.Y. 10022**
Ph. (212) 753-6421 Fax (212) 753-6429
E-mail: stamps@siegelauctions.com

www.siegelauctions.com

On cover	—	850.
Pair	—	1,500.
Strip of 3	—	—
Block of 4	—	—
Double transfer		700.
Major plate crack (22L, 24L,		
31L, 33L, 34L, 8R, Plate 3)		950.
Plate 4, *April, 1857*	3,500.	1,100.
On cover		1,350.
Pair	—	2,300.
Pair (vert.), types II, IIIa	—	—
Vertical strip of 3 (9L, 19L,		
29L; Plate 4), types II, III, III,		
on cover		—
Block of 4, type II and types		
III, IIIa	—	—
"Curl in hair" (3R, 4R4)	—	1,200.
Double transfer (10R4)	—	—
Perf. 12½, unofficial	22,500.	8,500.
On cover		35,000.

See note concerning unofficial perfs following listings for No. 11.

Earliest documented uses: July 1, 1851 (Plate 1E) (FDC); Dec. 5, 1855 (Plate 2); May 6, 1856 (Plate 3).

Cancellations

Blue	+7.50
Red	+20.00
Magenta	+80.00
Ultramarine	+175.00
Green	+400.00
Orange	—
1855 year date	+10.00
1856 year date	+5.00
1857 year date	+2.50
1858 year date	+5.00
"Paid"	+5.00
"Way"	+35.00
Red "Too Late"	+200.00
Numeral	+25.00
Railroad	+50.00
"Steam"	+60.00
"Steamboat"	+80.00
Red Carrier	+45.00
Black Carrier	+25.00
U. S. Express Mail	+25.00
Territorial	+200.00
Printed precancel "PAID"	+2,500.
Printed precancel "paid"	+2,500.
Pen	80.00

A8

Type III — The top and bottom curved lines outside the labels are broken in the middle. The side ornaments are substantially complete.

The most desirable examples of type III are those showing the widest breaks in the top and bottom framelines.

A special example is 99R2. All other stamps come from plate 4 and almost all show the breaks in the lines less clearly defined. Some of these breaks, especially of the bottom line, are very small.

Type IIIa — Similar to III with the outer line broken at top or, rarely, at bottom but not both. The side ornaments are substantially complete.

8 A8 1c **blue,** type III (Plate 4) see
below for 99R2.

	25,000.	3,500.
No gum	9,500.	
On cover		3,750.
Pair	55,000.	7,250.
Pair, types III, IIIa	35,000.	5,250.
Strip of 3		11,500.
Block of 4, types III, IIIa	—	—

Earliest documented use: July 7, 1857 (on off-cover stamp); July 9, 1857 (on cover).

Cancellations

Blue	+75.
Red	+200.
Red Carrier	+250.
Black Carrier	+250.
Pen	1,750.

Values for type III are for at least a 2mm break in each outer line. Examples of type III with wider breaks in outer lines command higher prices; those with smaller breaks sell for much less.

(8) A8 1c **blue,** type III (99R2)

	35,000.	12,500.
No gum	13,000.	
Pair, types III (99R2), II		13,500.
Pair, types III (99R2), IIIa	45,000.	—
Block of 4, type III (99R2), 3		
type II	47,500.	—
On cover (99R2)		18,000.

Cancellations

Blue	+150.00
Green	—
"Paid"	—
Red Carrier	+500.00

8A A8 1c **blue,** type IIIa (Plate 1E) *July 1, 1851*

	6,000.	1,200.
No gum	2,250.	
On cover		1,300.
Pair	12,500.	2,900.
Double transfer, one inverted		
(81L1E)	6,500.	1,450.
Plate 1E (100R), break in		
lower line	—	—
Plate 2 (100R), break in low-		
er line	—	—
Plate 4, *April, 1857*	6,250.	1,250.
No gum	2,350.	
On cover		1,400.
Pair	13,500.	2,600.
Block of 4		9,500.

Earliest documented uses: July 3, 1851 (Plate 1E); Apr. 4, 1857 (Plate 4).

Cancellations

Blue	+50.00
Red	+125.00
"Paid"	+90.00
Black Carrier	+175.00
Red Carrier	+175.00
Pen	600.00

Values are for stamps with at least a 2mm break in the top outer line. Examples with a wider break or a break in the lower line command higher prices, those with a smaller break sell for less.

"Paid" Cancellations
Values for "Paid" cancellations are for those OTHER than the common Boston type. See Postal Markings in the Introduction for illustrations.

A9

Type IV. Similar to type II, but with the curved lines outside the labels recut at top or bottom or both.

9 A9 1c **blue,** type IV, *1852*

	800.00	130.00
No gum	275.00	
On cover		150.00
Pair	1,750.	275.00
Strip of 3	2,650.	450.00
Block of 4	4,000.	2,000.
P# block of 8, Impt. (Plate 1)	—	—
Double transfer	900.00	140.00
Triple transfer, one inverted		
(71L, 81L and 91L Plate 1L)	950.00	180.00
Cracked plate	950.00	180.00
Bottom frameline broken (30L,		
50L, 67R, 89R, 90R, 99R		
Plate 1L), late printings	—	275.00
Perf. 12½, unofficial	12,500.	
Strip of 3		—
a. Printed on both sides, reverse inverted		—

See note concerning unofficial perfs following listings for No. 11.

VARIETIES OF RECUTTING

Stamps of this type were printed from Plate 1 after it had been reentered and recut in 1852. All but one stamp (4R, see No. 7 for listings) were recut and all varieties of recutting are listed below:

Recut once at top and once at bottom, (113 on plate)	800.00	130.00
Recut once at top, (40 on plate)	825.00	135.00
Recut once at top and twice at bottom, (21 on plate)	850.00	140.00
Recut twice at bottom, (11 on plate)	875.00	150.00
Recut once at bottom, (8 on plate)	900.00	160.00
Recut once at bottom and twice at top, (4 on plate)	950.00	170.00
Recut twice at bottom and twice at top, (2 on plate)	1,000.	225.00

Earliest documented use: June 5, 1852.

Cancellations

Blue	+5.00
Red	+30.00
Ultramarine	+150.00
Brown	+150.00
Green	+400.00
Violet	+350.00
1853 year date	+250.00
1855 year date	+10.00
1856 year date	+7.50
1857 year date	+10.00
"Paid"	+10.00
"U. S. PAID"	+50.00
"Way"	+50.00
"Free"	+75.00
Railroad	+75.00
"Steam"	+60.00
Numeral	+10.00

"Steamboat"	+90.00
"Steamship"	+60.00
Red Carrier	+15.00
Black Carrier	+25.00
U. S. Express Mail	+60.00
Express Company	—
Packet boat	—
Printed precancel "PAID"	+2,500.
Printed precancel "paid"	+2,500.
Pen	65.00

These 1c stamps were often cut apart carelessly, destroying part or all of the top and bottom lines. When this is so, it makes it difficult to determine whether a stamp is type II, III, IIIa or IV without identifying the position. Such mutilated examples sell for much less.

PLEASE NOTE:
Stamps are valued in the grade of very fine unless otherwise indicated.

Values for early and valuable stamps are for examples with certificates of authenticity from acknowledged expert committees, or examples sold with the buyer having the right of certification. This applies to examples with original gum as well as examples without gum. Beware of stamps offered "as is," as the gum on some unused stamps offered with "original gum" may be fraudulent, and stamps offered as unused without gum may in some cases be altered or faintly canceled used stamps.

VALUES FOR NEVER-HINGED STAMPS PRIOR TO SCOTT NO. 182
This catalogue does not value pre-1879 stamps in never-hinged condition. Premiums for never-hinged condition in the classic era invariably are even larger than those premiums listed for the 1879 and later issues. Generally speaking, the earlier the stamp is listed in the catalogue, the larger will be the never-hinged premium. On some early classics, the premium will be several multiples of the unused, hinged values given in the catalogue.

Washington — A10

All of the 3c stamps of the 1851 and 1857 issues were recut at least to the extent of the outer frame lines and often other lines in triangles, diamond blocks, label blocks and/or top/bottom frame lines. Some of the most prominent varieties are listed below each major listing (others are described in "The 3c Stamp of U.S. 1851-57 Issue," by Carroll Chase).

OUTER FRAME LINE

Type I

THREE CENTS. Issued July 1, 1851 (Plate 1E).
Type I — There is an outer frame line on all four sides. The outer frame lines at the sides are always recut, but the inner lines at the sides are not recut.

10 A10 3c **orange brown,** type I

(Plates 1E, 1i)	3,750.	200.00
No gum	1,400.	
deep orange brown	4,000.	240.00
No gum	1,550.	
On cover, orange brown		275.00
On cover (3c circular rate		
- 1000-1500 miles)		1,000.
Pair	8,500.	650.00
Pair on cover (double rate)		750.00
Pair on cover (6c West		
Coast rate)		850.00
Strip of 3	14,000.	1,400.

Block of 4	*22,000.*	—
Pair, types I, II	*12,000.*	900.00
Double transfer		225.00
Gash on shoulder		220.00

VARIETIES OF RECUTTING

1 line recut in upper left triangle	4,000.	220.00
2 lines recut at top of upper right diamond block		290.00

Earliest documented uses: July 1, 1851 (Plate 1E) (FDC); July 12, 1851 (Plate 1i).

Cancellations

Blue	+3.00
Red	+5.00
Orange red	+10.00
Brown	+40.00
Ultramarine	+25.00
Green	+225.00
Violet	+250.00
1851 year date	*+1,500.*
1852 year date	+750.00
"Paid"	+5.00
"Way"	+40.00
"Way" with numeral	+150.00
"Free"	+50.00
Numeral	+15.00
Railroad	+50.00
U. S. Express Mail	+20.00
"Steam"	+35.00
"Steamship"	+60.00
"Steamboat"	+70.00
Packet Boat	+300.00
Black Carrier (circular)	+400.00
Blue Carrier (circular)	+600.00
Blue Carrier (New Orleans "snowshovel")	+400.00
Green Carrier (New Orleans "snowshovel")	+500.00
Canadian	—
Territorial	+200.00
Pen	75.00

OUTER FRAME LINE

INNER LINE

Type II

Type II — As type I, but with the inner lines at the sides also recut.

10A A10 3c **orange brown,** type II

(Plates 1E, 1i, 2E, 5E, 0)	3,500.	150.00
No gum	1,325.	
deep orange brown	3,750.	190.00
No gum	1,400.	
copper brown	*4,500.*	1,250.
No gum	*1,700.*	
On cover, orange brown		210.00
On cover (3c circular rate - 1000-1500 miles)		1,000.
Pair	8,000.	550.00
Pair on cover (double rate)		600.00
Pair on cover (6c West Coast rate)		700.00
Strip of 3	12,500.	1,250.
Block of 4	20,000.	—
Double transfer		180.00
Triple transfer		450.00
Gash on shoulder		170.00
Dot in lower right diamond block (69L5E)		325.00
On part-India paper		*1,250.*
b. Printed on both sides		20,000.

Only one example of No. 10Ab is recorded.

VARIETIES OF RECUTTING

All of these stamps also were recut at least to the extent of the outer frame lines at the sides and the inner lines at the sides (the basic type II criteria).

Left inner line only recut		200.00
Right inner line only recut		160.00
1 line recut in upper left triangle	4,250.	160.00
2 lines recut in upper left triangle		160.00
3 lines recut in upper left triangle		180.00
5 lines recut in upper left triangle (47L0)		1,000.
1 line recut in lower left triangle		160.00
1 line recut in lower right triangle		160.00
2 lines recut in lower left triangle (57L0)		1,000.
2 lines recut in upper left triangle and 1 line recut in lower right triangle		225.00

---

1 line recut in upper right triangle		170.00
Upper part of top label and diamond block recut	4,000.	150.00
Top label and right diamond block joined		160.00
Top label and left diamond block joined at top (6R2E, 100R2E)		300.00
Lower label and right diamond block joined		210.00
1 line recut at bottom of lower left diamond block (34R2E)		1,000.
Vertical line ties upper left corner of upper left diamond block to top frame line (45R2E)		1,000.

Earliest documented uses: July 1, 1851 (Plate 1E) (FDC); July 12, 1851 (Plate 1i); July 23, 1851 (Plate 2E); July 19, 1851 (Plate 5E); Sept. 6, 1851 (Plate 0).

Cancellations

Blue	+3.00
Red	+5.00
Orange red	+10.00
Orange	—
Brown	+40.00
Ultramarine	+25.00
Green	+225.00
Violet	+250.00
1851 year date	*+1,000.*
1852 year date	+750.00
"Paid"	+5.00
"Way"	+40.00
"Way" with numeral	+150.00
"Free"	+100.00
Numeral	+15.00
Railroad	+50.00
U. S. Express Mail	+20.00
"Steam"	+35.00
"Steamship"	+60.00
"Steamboat"	+70.00
Packet Boat	+300.00
Black Carrier (circular)	+400.00
Blue Carrier (circular)	+600.00
Blue Carrier (New Orleans "snowshovel")	+400.00
Green Carrier (New Orleans "snowshovel")	+500.00
Canadian	—
Territorial	+200.00
Pen	70.00

11 A10 3c **dull red** (1855), type I

(Plates 4, 6, 7, 8)	275.00	15.00
orange red (1855)	275.00	15.00
rose red (1855)	275.00	15.00
No gum	85.00	
brownish carmine (1856)	300.00	18.00
No gum	95.00	
claret (1857)	325.00	21.00
No gum	120.00	
deep claret (1857)	350.00	25.00
No gum	125.00	
plum (1857)	—	*2,000.*
No gum	—	
pinkish		—
On cover, dull red		17.50
On cover, orange red		19.00
On cover, brownish carmine		24.00
On cover, claret		26.00
On cover, plum		—
On propaganda cover, dull red		400.00
Pair	650.00	62.50
Pair on cover (double rate)		70.00
Pair on cover (6c West Coast rate)		—
Strip of 3	1,100.	140.00
Block of 4	2,100.	1,000.
P# block of 8, Impt.	*4,500.*	
Double transfer	300.00	18.00
Gash on shoulder	300.00	17.00
Worn plate	275.00	13.00
Perf. 12½, unofficial		*6,000.*
On cover		*9,000.*

The unofficial perf varieties listed under Nos. 7, 11 and 11A represent the first perforated stamps in the U. S. made using a true perforating machine. Known as the "Chicago perfs," both the perf. 11 and perf. 12½ stamps were made by Dr. Elijah W. Hadley, using a machine of his construction. None of the perf 11 stamps are believed to have been used.

VARIETIES OF RECUTTING

All of these stamps were recut at least to the extent of three outer frame lines (including both sides) and often other lines in triangles, diamond blocks, label blocks and/or top/bottom frame lines. Some of the most prominent varieties are listed below.

Lines on bust and bottom of medallion circle recut (47R6)	*1,175.*	500.00
Top label and right diamond block joined	300.00	16.00
Top label and right diamond block joined at top and bottom (68R4)	325.00	17.50
Lower label and right diamond block joined	325.00	17.50
Extra line at right	325.00	17.50

Earliest documented uses: Mar. 28, 1855 (Plate 4); Feb. 18, 1856 (Plate 6); Feb. 9, 1856 (Plate 7); Apr. 14, 1856 (Plate 8).

Cancellations

Blue	+1.00
Red	+7.50
Orange red	+5.00
Orange	+250.00
Brown	+75.00

Magenta	+50.00
Ultramarine	+40.00
Green	+125.00
Violet	+250.00
Purple	+250.00
Olive	+200.00
1855 year date	+50.00
1856 year date	+12.50
1857 year date	+12.50
1858 year date	+1.00
1859 year date	+25.00
"Paid"	+1.50
"Way"	+10.00
"Free"	+25.00
Numeral	+25.00
Railroad	+20.00
Supplemental Mail Type A	*+2,500.*
"Steam"	+25.00
"Ship"	+25.00
"New York Ship"	+35.00
"Steamboat"	+45.00
"Steamship"	+45.00
Packet boat	+120.00
Express Company	+120.00
Black Carrier	+60.00
Red Carrier (New York)	+100.00
Blue Carrier (New Orleans)	+300.00
Green Carrier (New Orleans)	+500.00
Canada	—
Territorial	+200.00
Pen	8.00

11A A10 3c **dull red** (1853-54-55), type II (Plates 1L, 2L, 3, 5L)

	275.00	15.00
orange red (1855)	275.00	15.00
rose red (1854-55)	275.00	15.00
No gum	85.00	
brownish carmine (1851-52)	300.00	18.00
No gum	95.00	
claret (1852)	325.00	21.00
No gum	120.00	
experimental orange brown (1851-52, Plate 1L))		400.00
plum (1852)		*2,000.*
On cover, dull red		17.50
On cover, orange red		19.00
On cover, brownish carmine		24.00
On cover, claret		26.00
On cover, experimental orange brown (Plate 1L)		900.00
On propaganda cover, dull red		400.00
On cover (3c circular rate - 1000-1500 miles)		850.00
Pair	650.00	62.50
Pair on cover (double rate)		70.00
Pair on cover (6c West Coast rate)		100.00
Strip of 3	1,100.	140.00
Block of 4	2,100.	1,000.
P# block of 8, Impt.	*4,500.*	
Double transfer in "Three Cents"	300.00	18.00
Double transfer line through "Three Cents" and rosettes double (92L1L)	425.00	70.00
Double transfer, "Gents" instead of "Cents" (66R2L)	425.00	55.00
Triple transfer (92L2L)	425.00	55.00
Gash on shoulder	300.00	17.00
Dot in lower right diamond block (69L5L)	375.00	45.00
Major cracked plate (84L, 94L, 9R, Plate 5L)	*800.00*	160.00
Intermediate cracked plate (80L, 96L, 71R, Plate 5L)	525.00	80.00
Minor cracked plate (8L, 27L, 31L, 44L, 45L, 51L, 55L, 65L, 71L, 72L, 74L, 78L, 79L, 7R, Plate 5L)	400.00	60.00
Worn plate	275.00	13.00
Perf. about 11, unofficial	*6,500.*	
Block of 4	*27,500.*	
Perf. 12½, unofficial		*6,000.*
On cover		*9,000.*
Pair on cover		—
c. Vertical half used as 1c on cover		*5,000.*
Strip of 4 No. 11Ac used as 6c on cover		*15,000.*
d. Diagonal half used as 1c on cover		*5,000.*
e. Double impression		*5,000.*

The unofficial perf varieties listed represent the first perforated stamps in the U. S. made using a true perforating machine. Known as the "Chicago perfs," both were made by Dr. Elijah W. Hadley, using a machine of his construction. None of the perf 11 stamps are believed to have been used.

The strip of 4 No. 11Ac on cover is the only recorded multiple of a bisected stamp in United States philately.

VARIETIES OF RECUTTING

All of these stamps also were recut at least to the extent of the outer lines at the sides and the inner frame lines at the sides (the basic type II criteria).

Right inner line only recut	300.00	17.50
1 line recut in upper left triangle	300.00	16.00
2 lines recut in upper left triangle	300.00	16.00
3 lines recut in upper left triangle	325.00	16.00
5 lines recut in upper left triangle (95L1L)	650.00	200.00

CHOOSING THE RIGHT AUCTION HOUSE
MAY MEAN MORE THAN YOU REALIZE

When you're ready to sell your treasures, let us help you make sure you get the highest possible price. For individual rarities or entire collections, Rumsey Auctions earns its reputation for quality, honesty and integrity with every sale.

Please visit our website at:

www.rumseyauctions.com

email: srumsey@rumseyauctions.com

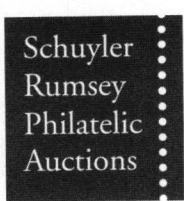

1 line recut in lower left triangle	325.00	16.00
1 line recut in lower right triangle	300.00	16.00
1 line recut in upper right triangle	425.00	18.00
1 line recut in UL, LL and LR triangles (49L1L, 95R3)	475.00	32.50
2 lines recut in UL triangle, 1 line recut in LL triangle (9L1L)	475.00	32.50
Recut button on shoulder (10R2L)	475.00	100.00
Upper part of top label and diamond block recut	275.00	16.00
Top label and left diamond block joined	300.00	16.00
Top label and left diamond block joined	325.00	17.50
Lower label and right diamond block joined	325.00	17.50
1 extra vertical line outside of left frame line (29L, 39L, 49L, 59L, 69L, 79L, Plate 3)	300.00	17.50
2 extra vertical lines outside of left frame line (89L, 99L, Plate 3)	375.00	32.50
1 extra vertical line outside of right frame line (58L, 68L, 78L, 88L, 98L, Plate 3)	425.00	20.00
No inner line and frame line close to design at right (9L, 19L, Plate 3)	375.00	32.50
No inner line and frame line close to design at left (70, 80, 90, 100L, Plate 3)	325.00	19.00

Earliest documented uses: Oct. 6, 1851 (Plate 1L); Jan. 7, 1852 (Plate 2L); Jan. 15, 1852 (Plate 3); July 13, 1855 (Plate 5L).

Cancellations

Blue	+1.00
Red	+7.50
Orange red	+5.00
Orange	+250.00
Brown	+75.00
Magenta	+50.00
Ultramarine	+40.00
Green	+175.00
Violet	+250.00
Purple	+250.00
Olive	+200.00
Yellow	+7,500.
Yellow, on cover	15,000.
1852 year date	+300.00
1852 year date, on cover	1,000.
1853 year date	+100.00
1854 year date	—
1855 year date	+50.00
1856 year date	+12.50
"Paid"	+1.50
"Way"	+10.00
"Way" with numeral	+60.00
"Free"	+25.00
Numeral	+7.50
Railroad	+20.00
U. S. Express Mail	+5.00
Supplemental Mail Type A	+2,500.
"Steam"	+15.00
"Ship"	+20.00
"New York Ship"	+35.00
"Steamboat"	+45.00
"Steamship"	+45.00
Packet boat	+120.00
Express Company	+120.00
Black Carrier	+60.00
Red Carrier (New York)	+50.00
Blue Carrier (New Orleans)	—
Green Carrier (New Orleans)	+200.00
Canada	+350.00
Territorial	—
Pen	+100.00
	8.00

Thomas Jefferson — A11

FIVE CENTS.
Type I — Projections on all four sides.

12	A11 5c **red brown,** type I, *1856*	30,000.	825.
	dark red brown	30,000.	825.
	No gum	11,000.	
	On domestic cover		1,300.
	Single on cover to France		1,700.
	Strip of 3 on cover to France		5,750.
	Pair	67,500.	1,900.
	Strip of 3	100,000.	4,500.

Block of 4	200,000.	45,000.
Double transfer (40R1)		1,150.
Defective transfer (23R1)		1,300.

Earliest documented use: Mar. 24, 1856.

Cancellations

Red	+150.
Magenta	+200.
Blue	+125.
Green	+900.
1856 year date	+25.
1857 year date	+25.
1858 year date	—
"Paid"	+200.
"Steamship"	+200.
U.S. Express Mail	+200.
Express Company	+400.
"Steamboat"	+350.
Railroad	+400.
Numeral	+1,000.
Pen	400.

Washington — A12

TEN CENTS

Type I — The "shells" at the lower corners are practically complete. The outer line below the label is very nearly complete. The outer lines are broken above the middle of the top label and the "X" in each upper corner. Beware of type V perforated (No. 35) trimmed to resemble type I imperforate (No. 13). Note that the pearls on No. 35 normally will be missing from each end of the lower label.

Types I, II, III and IV have complete ornaments at the sides of the stamps, and three pearls at each outer edge of the bottom panel.

Type I comes only from the bottom row of both panes of Plate 1.

13	A12 10c **green,** type I, *1855*	18,000.	950.
	dark green	18,000.	950.
	yellowish green	18,000.	950.
	No gum	7,000.	
	On domestic cover		1,050.
	Pair	40,000.	2,200.
	Strip of 3		3,250.
	Vert. pair, types III, I	25,000.	1,550.
	Vert. pair, types IV, I (86, 96L1)		5,250.
	Vertical strip of 3, types II, III, I		4,250.
	Block of 4, types III, I	55,000.	10,500.
	Block of 4, types III, IV, I		16,000.
	Double transfer (100R1)	19,000.	1,050.
	"Curl" in left "X" (99R1)	19,000.	1,050.

Earliest documented use: July 11, 1855.

Cancellations

Blue	+50.
Red	+100.
Magenta	+200.
Orange	—
1855 year date	+25.
1856 year date	+25.
1857 year date	+25.
"Paid"	+50.
"Steamship"	+150.
Railroad	+175.
Territorial	+400.
Numeral	+50.
U.S. Express Mail	—
Pen	500.

A13

Type II — The design is complete at the top. The outer line at the bottom is broken in the middle. The shells are partly cut away.

14	A13 10c **green,** type II, *1855*	5,000.	200.
	dark green	5,000.	200.
	yellowish green	5,000.	200.

No gum	1,800.	
On domestic cover		260.
Pair	11,000.	450.
Strip of 3	17,000.	775.
Block of 4	25,000.	4,000.
Pair, types II, III	11,000.	450.
Pair, types II, IV	42,500.	2,200.
Vertical strip of 3, types II, III, IV		2,600.
Block of 4, types II, III	—	3,500.
Block of 4, types II, IV		
Block of 4, types II, III, IV		10,000.
Double transfer (31L, 51L, and 20R, Plate 1)	5,500.	280.
"Curl" opposite "X" (10R1)	5,500.	300.

Earliest documented use: May 12, 1855.

Cancellations

Blue	+10.
Red	+25.
Brown	+75.
Ultramarine	+100.
Magenta	+100.
Green	+200.
Violet	+150.
1855 year date	+100.
1856 year date	+50.
1857 year date	+10.
1858 year date	+10.
"Paid"	+25.
"Way"	+75.
"Free"	+75.
Railroad	+75.
Steamship	+75.
Steamboat	+100.
Numeral	+50.
Territorial	+150.
Express Company	+200.
U. S. Express Mail	+75.
Pen	90.

A14

Type III — The outer lines are broken above the top label and the "X" numerals. The outer line at the bottom and the shells are partly cut away similar to type II.

15	A14 10c **green,** type III, *1855*	5,000.	200.
	dark green	5,000.	200.
	yellowish green	5,000.	200.
	No gum	1,800.	
	On domestic cover		260.
	Pair	11,000.	450.
	Strip of 3	17,000.	775.
	Pair, types III, IV	40,000.	2,200.
	Double transfer at top and at bottom		—
	"Curl" on forehead (85L1)	5,500.	300.
	"Curl" to right of left "X" (87R1)	5,500.	300.

Earliest documented use: May 19, 1855.

Cancellations

Blue	+10.
Red	+25.
Orange red	+35.
Magenta	+100.
Violet	+150.
Brown	+75.
Orange	+100.
Green	+200.
1855 year date	—
1856 year date	+50.
1857 year date	+10.
1858 year date	+10.
"Paid"	+25.
Steamship	+75.
U. S. Express Mail	+75.
Express Company	+200.
Packet boat	—
Canada (on cover)	+1000.
Territorial	+150.
Railroad	+75.
Numeral	+50.
Pen	90.

A15

Type IV — The outer lines have been recut at top or bottom or both.

16	A15 10c **green,** type IV, *1855*	35,000.	1,700.
	dark green	35,000.	1,700.
	yellowish green	35,000.	1,700.

No gum	*15,000.*	
On domestic cover	—	2,000.
Pair	—	4,500.
Block of 4 (54-55, 64-65L)	—	—

VARIETIES OF RECUTTING

Eight stamps on Plate 1 were recut. All are listed below.

Outer line recut at top (65L, 74L, 86L, and 3R, Plate 1)	35,000.	1,700.
Outer line recut at bottom (54L, 55L, 76L, Plate 1)	36,500.	1,800.
Outer line recut at top and bottom (64L1)	42,500.	2,250.

Positions 65L1 and 86L1 have both "X" ovals recut at top, as well as the outer line.

Earliest documented use: June 4, 1855.

Cancellations

Blue	+90.
Red	+185.
Brown	+250.
1857 year date	—
1859 year date	—
"Paid"	+150.
Steamship	+300.
Territorial	+500.
Express Company	+750.
Numeral	+150.
Pen	900.

Types I, II, III and IV occur on the same sheet, so it is possible to obtain pairs and blocks showing combinations of types. For listings of type combinations in pairs and blocks, see Nos. 13-15.

Washington — A16

17	A16 12c	**black,** *July 1, 1851*	6,250.	300.
		gray black	6,250.	300.
		intense black	6,250.	300.
		No gum	2,200.	
		Single, on cover		1,450.
		Single on cover with No. 11 to France		1,100.
		Pair	14,500.	650.
		Pair, on cover to England		750.
		Block of 4	35,000.	5,500.
		Double transfer	6,500.	325.
		Triple transfer (5R1 & 49R1)	6,750.	450.
		Not recut in lower right corner	6,500.	325.
		Recut in lower left corner (43L, 53L, 63L, 73L and 100L, Plate 1)	6,500.	375.
		Cracked plate (32R1)	—	—
		On part-India paper		1,100.
		No gum	*5,000.*	
a.		Diagonal half used as 6c on cover		2,750.
		Diagonal half used as 6c on "Via Nicaragua" cover		5,750.
b.		Vertical half used as 6c on cover		8,500.
c.		Printed on both sides		30,000.

Earliest documented use: Aug. 4, 1851.

Cancellations

Red	+30.
Orange red	+55.
Blue	+15.
Brown	+60.
Magenta	+75.
Orange	+150.
Green	+600.
"Paid"	+25.
"Way"	+75.
Steamship	+100.
Steamboat	+125.
Supplementary Mail Type A	+125.
Railroad	+100.
"Honolulu" in red (on cover)	+400.
U. S. Express Mail	+125.
Pen	175.

Please Note:

Stamps are valued in the grade of very fine unless otherwise indicated.

Values for early and valuable stamps are for examples with certificates of authenticity from acknowledged expert committees, or examples sold with the buyer having the right of certification. This applies to examples with original gum as well as examples without gum. Beware of stamps offered "as is," as the gum on some unused stamps offered with "original gum" may be fraudulent, and stamps offered as unused without gum may in some cases be altered or faintly canceled used stamps.

SAME DESIGNS AS 1851-57 ISSUES
Printed by Toppan, Carpenter & Co.

Nos. 18-39 have small or very small margins. The values take into account the margin size.

1857-61				*Perf. 15½*
18	A5 1c	blue, type I (Plate 12), *1861*	2,250.	700.
		No gum	850.	
		On cover		850.
		On patriotic cover		1,400.
		Pair	5,000.	1,500.
		Strip of 3	7,500.	2,600.
		Block of 4	14,000.	
		Pair, types I, II	3,750.	1,100.
		Pair, types I, IIIa	5,000.	1,350.
		Block of 4, types I, II	9,500.	5,250.
		Block of 4, types I, II, IIIa	11,000.	6,500.
		Double transfer	2,750.	750.
		Cracked plate (91R12)	—	950.

Plate 12 consists of types I & II. A few positions are type IIIa. Late printings of position 46L12 are type III.

Earliest documented use: Jan. 25, 1861.

Cancellations

Blue	+20.
Red	+50.
Violet	+125.
Steamboat	+100.
"Paid"	+25.
"Free"	+750.
Black Carrier	+85.
Red Carrier	+85.
Pen	350.

19	A6 1c	**blue,** type Ia (Plate 4)	40,000.	11,500.
		No gum	18,000.	
		On cover		14,000.
		Pair	90,000.	26,000.
		Strip of 3	135,000.	41,500.
		Vertical pair, types Ia, III	62,500.	15,000.
		Vertical pair, types Ia, IIIa	47,500.	13,000.
		Pair, types Ia, Ic	—	—
		Strip of 3, types Ia, Ia, Ic (94-96R4 or 96-98R4)	—	—
		Block of 4, types Ia, Ic, and IIIa	100,000.	
		Block of 4, pair type Ia and types III or IIIa	—	—
		"Curl on shoulder" (97L4)	42,500.	12,000.

Examples of this stamp exist with perforations not touching the design at any point. Such examples command very high prices.

Type Ia comes only from the bottom row of both panes of Plate 4. Two strips of three, types Ia, Ia, Ic ("F" relief) are recorded.

Earliest documented use: Sept. 9, 1857. No. 19 is known on a folded circular with Aug. 1 postmark, but the year of use has not been certified.

Cancellations

Red Carrier	+200.
Green	+1,750.
Pen	5,000.

19b	A6 1c	**blue,** type Ic ("E" relief, less distinct examples)	4,500.	2,250.
		No gum	1,900.	
		On cover		3,000.
		Horizontal pair (81-82R4)	—	—
		Pair, types Ic, III	—	—
		Pair, types Ic, IIIa	—	—
		blue, type Ic ("F" relief, best examples, 91, 96R4)	20,000.	8,000.
		No gum	9,000.	
		On cover		9,000.

Type Ic — Same as Ia, but bottom right plume and ball ornament incomplete. Bottom left plume complete or nearly complete. Best examples are from bottom row, "F" relief, positions 91 and 96R4. Less distinct examples are "E" reliefs from 5th and 9th rows, positions 47L, 49L, 83L, 49R, 81R, 82R, and 89R, Plate 4, and early impressions of 41R4. Several combination type multiples can be found in the unused complete left pane of 100 from Plate 4.

Examples of the "F" relief type Ic stamps exist with perforations not touching the design at any point. Such examples command a substantial premium.

Cancellations

Pen ("E" relief)		*1,000.*
Blue ("F" relief)	—	—
Red ("F" relief)	—	—
Pen ("F" relief)		3,000.

20	A7 1c	**blue,** type II (Plate 2)	1,100.	300.
		No gum	425.	
		On cover		350.
		Pair	2,300.	675.
		Strip of 3	3,600.	1,050.
		Block of 4	6,000.	2,500.
		Double transfer (Plate 2)	1,150.	325.
		Double transfer (89R2)	2,400.	1,000.
		Cracked plate (2L, 12L, 13L, 23L & 33L, Plate 2)	2,900.	800.
		Plate 1L (4R1L only, double transfer), *July 1857*		1,000.
		Pair, types II (4R1L), IV		2,500.
		Plate 4	3,500.	1,250.
		On cover		1,500.
		Pair	7,500.	2,750.
		Vertical pair, types II, III	—	—
		Strip of 3	—	—
		Double transfer (10R4)	3,750.	1,800.
		"Curl in hair" (3R, 4R4)	—	1,350.
		Plate 11	1,750.	750.
		On cover		1,000.
		On patriotic cover		—
		Pair	3,000.	1,650.

	Strip of 3	—	—
	Double transfer	—	—
	Plate 12	1,100.	300.
	On cover		350.
	On patriotic cover		700.
	Pair	2,300.	650.
	Strip of 3	3,600.	1,050.
	Block of 4	6,000.	2,500.
	Double transfer	—	—

Earliest documented uses: July 26, 1857 (Plate 2), July 26, 1857 (Plate 4), Jan. 12, 1861 (Plate 11), Jan. 21, 1861 (Plate 12).

No. 20, plate 2, is also known on two folded circulars dated July 24 and July 25, respectively, but no postal year date or docketing verifies the actual day of mailing.

Cancellations

Blue	+10.
Red	+30.
Green	+200.
1857 year date	+10.
1858 year date	+5.
1861 year date	+5.
"FREE"	+200.
1863 year date	+15.
"Paid"	+60.
Railroad	+75.
"Way"	+75.
Steamboat	+35.
Red Carrier	+50.
Pen	150.

21	A8 1c	**blue,** type III (Plate 4), see below for 99R2	17,500.	2,750.
		No gum	7,000.	
		On cover		3,250.
		Pair	40,000.	6,250.
		Strip of 3		9,500.
		Block of 4	—	—
		Pair, types III, IIIa	22,500.	3,500.
		Block of 4, types III, IIIa	—	—
		Plate 12 (46L12)	—	—
a.		Horiz. pair, imperf between		23,000.

Earliest documented use: Sept. 18, 1857.

Cancellations

Blue	+50.
Red	+90.
Green	+750.
1858 year date	+35.
"Paid"	+60.
Black Carrier	+175.
Red Carrier	+200.
Pen	1,350.

Values for type III are for at least a 2mm break in each outer line. Examples of type III with wider breaks in outer lines command higher prices; those with smaller breaks sell for less.

No. 21a is unique and is contained in a strip of three. Value reflects auction sale in 1999.

(21)	A8 1c	**blue,** type III (99R2)	—	20,000.
		On cover	—	—
		Pair, types III (99R2), II	—	—
		Pair, types III (99R2), IIIa	—	—
		Strip of 3, types III (99R2), II, IIIa	—	—
		Block of 9, one type III (99R2), others type II	110,000.	

The only recorded unused example is the one in the block of 9. Only two covers are recorded bearing No. 21 (99R2).

Earliest documented use: Oct. 27, 1857.

22	A8 1c	**blue,** type IIIa (Plate 4)	2,600.	550.
		No gum	1,000.	
		On cover		600.
		On patriotic cover		900.
		Pair	5,750.	1,200.
		Vertical pair, types IIIa, II	—	*1,900.*
		Strip of 3	8,500.	1,900.
		Block of 4	13,000.	5,500.
		Block of 4, types IIIa, II	—	—
		Double transfer	2,750.	600.
		Plate 2 (100R)	—	—
		Plate 11 and Plate 12	2,750.	575.
		On cover		625.
		On patriotic cover		1,050.
		Pair	6,000.	1,250.
		Vert. pair, types IIIa, II (Plate 11)	*5,250.*	*1,250.*
		Strip of 3	9,000.	1,800.
		Strip of 3, types IIIa, II, I (46-48L12)	—	—
		Block of 4	13,000.	
		Block of 4, types IIIa, II (Plate 11)	12,500.	4,250.
		Double transfer (Plate 11)	2,900.	600.
		Triple transfer (Plate 11)	—	—
		Bottom line broken (46L12)	—	2,000.
b.		Horizontal pair, imperf. between		5,000.

One pair of No. 22b is reported. Beware of numerous pairs that have blind perforations. These are not to be confused with No. 22b.

Earliest documented uses: July 26, 1857 (Plate 4), Dec. 1860 (day unknown) (dated cancel on off-cover stamp) (Plate 11), Dec. 31, 1860, (on cover) (Plate 11), Jan. 25, 1861 (Plate 12).

Cancellations

Blue	+10.
Red	+50.
Green	+275.
1857 year date	—
1858 year date	—
1861 year date	—
1863 year date	—

"Paid"			+50.
"Steamboat"			—
Red Carrier			+50.
Black Carrier			+60.
Blue Carrier			+100.
Pen			325.

23	A9	1c **blue**, type IV	10,000.	950.
		No gum	4,000.	
		On cover		1,150.
		Pair	22,500.	2,100.
		Strip of 3	35,000.	3,250.
		Block of 4		25,000.
		Double transfer	11,000.	1,000.
		Triple transfer, one inverted (71L1L, 81L1L and 91L1L)	17,500.	4,000.
		Cracked plate	10,500.	1,025.
		Bottom line broken (89R1L)	—	2,000.

Three or four used blocks of No. 23 are presently known. Value of used block of four is based on 1998 auction sale of the well-centered block of 5 sold at auction in 1998. Other blocks are poorly centered and will sell for much less.

VARIETIES OF RECUTTING

Recut once at top and once at bottom (113 on plate)	10,000.	950.
Recut once at top, (40 on plate)	10,250.	975.
Recut once at top and twice at bottom, (21 on plate)	10,500.	975.
Recut twice at bottom, (11 on plate)	10,250.	1,000.
Recut once at bottom, (8 on plate)	10,500.	1,025.
Recut twice at top and once at bottom, (4 on plate)	11,000.	1,050.
Recut twice at top and twice at bottom, (2 on plate)	11,500.	1,050.

One example of the "recut twice at top and once at bottom" variety is pos. 71L1L, valued separately under the main listing.

Earliest documented use: July 25, 1857.

Cancellations

Blue	+20.
Red	+75.
1857 year date	+50.
"Paid"	+25.
Red Carrier	+80.
Black Carrier	+100.
Railroad	+100.
"Way"	+120.
"Steamboat"	+135.
"Steam"	+100.
Pen	475.

Franklin — A20

Type V — Similar to type III of 1851-57 but with side ornaments partly cut away. About one-half of all positions have side scratches. Wide breaks in top and bottom framelines.

Type Va — Stamps from Plate 5 with almost complete ornaments at right side and no side scratches. Many, but not all, stamps from Plate 5 are Type Va, the remainder being Type V.

24	A20	1c **blue**, type V (Plates 5, 7, 8, 9, 10) *1857*	150.00	45.00
		No gum	60.00	
		On cover		52.50
		On patriotic cover		300.00
		Pair	325.00	97.50
		Strip of 3	500.00	160.00
		Block of 4	800.00	425.00
		P# strip of 4, Impt.	1,400.	
		P# block of 8, Impt.	3,500.	—
		Double transfer at top (8R and 10R, Plate 8)	210.00	90.00
		Double transfer at bottom (52R9)	270.00	100.00
		Curl on shoulder, (57R, 58R, 59R, 98R, 99R, Plate 7)	210.00	72.50
		With "Earring" below ear (10L9)	575.00	100.00
		"Curl" over "C" of "Cent"	220.00	72.50
		"Curl" over "E" of "Cent" (41R and 81R8)	240.00	87.50
		"Curl in hair," 23L7; 39, 69L8; 34, 74R9	210.00	62.50
		"Curl" in "O" of "ONE" (62L5)	—	—
		Horizontal dash in hair (24L7)	325.00	90.00
		Horizontal dash in hair (36L8)	325.00	90.00
		Long double "curl" in hair (52, 92R8)	270.00	85.00
		Type Va	500.00	250.00
		On cover (Type Va)		350.00

		Pair (Type Va)	—	—
		Strip of 3 (Type Va)	—	—
		Block of 4 (Type Va)	—	—
		"Curl" on shoulder (48L5)	—	—
b.		Laid paper		2,500.

Earliest documented uses: Dec. 2, 1857 (Plate 5); Dec. 31, 1857 (Plate 7); Nov. 17, 1857 (Plate 8); Aug. 2, 1859 (Plate 9); June 14, 1860 (Plate 10).

Cancellations

Blue	+2.50
Red	+15.00
Green	+250.00
Brown	+150.00
Magenta	+150.00
Ultramarine	+100.00
1857 year date	+70.00
1858 year date	+2.50
1859 year date	+2.50
1860 year date	+2.50
1861 year date	+2.50
1862 year date	—
1863 year date	+250.00
Printed Precancel "CUMBER-LAND, ME." (on cover)	
"Paid"	+5.00
"Free"	+25.00
Railroad	+50.00
Numeral	+12.50
Express Company	+90.00
Steamboat	+55.00
"Steam"	+30.00
Steamship	+40.00
Packet boat	—
Supp. Mail Type A, B, or C	+55.00
"Way"	+30.00
Red Carrier	+20.00
Black Carrier	+12.50
Blue Carrier	+50.00
"Old Stamps-Not Recognized"	+1,500.
Territorial	+80.00
Pen	20.00

25	A10	3c **rose**, type I (Plates 4, 6, 7, 8)	2,750.	125.00
		rose red	2,750.	125.00
		dull red	2,750.	125.00
		No gum	1,050.	
		On cover		140.00
		claret	3,000.	140.00
		No gum	1,100.	
		On patriotic cover		500.00
		Pair	6,000.	300.00
		Strip of 3	9,500.	475.00
		Block of 4	16,000.	7,000.
		Double transfer	3,000.	160.00
		Worn plate	2,750.	125.00
		Major cracked plate (47R, 48R, Plate 7)	4,750.	750.00
		Gash on shoulder	3,000.	140.00
b.		Vert. pair, imperf. horizontally		10,000.

All type I perforated stamps were printed from 4 of the plates used for the imperfs., so many varieties exist both imperf. and perf.

VARIETIES OF RECUTTING

Lines on bust and bottom of medallion circle recut (47R6)	—	1,500.
Top label and right diamond block joined		600.00
Top label and right diamond block joined at top and bottom (68R4)	—	600.00
Lower label and right diamond block joined	—	600.00
Extra line at right	—	750.00

All varieties of recutting listed under No. 11 are found on No. 25.

Earliest documented use: May 9, 1857 (Plate 4); April 30, 1857 (Plate 6); Feb. 28, 1857 (Plate 7); April 15, 1857 (Plate 8).

Cancellations

Blue	+7.50
Red	+20.00
Orange red	+30.00
Orange	+175.00
Brown	+100.00
Ultramarine	+125.00
Green	+250.00
1857 year date	+10.00
1858 year date	+10.00
1859 year date	+10.00
"Paid"	+5.00
"Way"	+20.00
Numeral	+10.00
Railroad	+25.00
"Steam"	+20.00
Steamship	+35.00
Steamboat	+45.00
Packet Boat	+50.00
Supplementary Mail Type A	+40.00
U. S. Express Mail	+7.50
Express Company	+65.00
Black Carrier	+30.00
"Old Stamps-Not Recognized"	+1,000.
Territorial	+50.00
Printed precancel "Cumberland, Me." (on cover)	—
Pen	55.00

25A	A10	3c **rose**, type II, (Plates 2L, 3, 5L)	5,250.	550.00
		rose red	5,250.	550.00
		dull red	5,250.	550.00
		No gum	2,100.	
		On cover		625.00

claret	5,500.	625.00
No gum	2,500.	
Pair	11,500.	1,300.
Strip of 3	18,500.	2,200.
Block of 4	24,000.	10,000.
Double transfer "Gents" instead of "Cents" (66R2L)	—	1,350.
Triple transfer	—	1,350.
Dot in lower right diamond block (69L5L)	—	625.00
Major cracked plate (84L, 94L, 9R, Plate 5L)	6,250.	1,100.
Intermediate cracked plate (80L, 96L, 71R, Plate 5L)	5,750.	850.00
Minor cracked plate (8L, 27L, 31L, 44L, 45L, 51L, 55L, 65L, 71L and 72L, 74L, 78L, 79L, 7R, Plate 5L)	5,500.	600.00
Gash on shoulder	5,500.	600.00
Worn plate	5,250.	550.00

All type II perforated stamps were printed from 3 of the plates used for the imperfs., so most varieties exist both imperf. and perf. See "Varieties of Recutting" under No. 11A — All these varieties also exist on No. 25A except the "5 lines recut in upper left triangle" variety.

VARIETIES OF RECUTTING

Recut inner line only at right		675.00
1 extra vertical line outside of left frame line (29L, 39L, 49L, 59L, 69L, 79L, Plate 3)	—	700.00
2 extra vertical lines outside of left frame line (89L, 99L, Plate 3)		725.00
1 extra vertical line outside of right frame line (58L, 68L, 78L, 88L, 98L, Plate 3)	—	700.00
No inner line and frame line close to design at right (9L, 19L, Plate 3)		725.00
No inner line and frame line close to design at left (70L, 80L, 90L, 100L, Plate 3)	—	700.00
Recut button (10R2L)		1,850.

Except for "5 lines recut in upper left triangle," all varieties of recutting listed under No. 11A are found on No. 25A.

Earliest documented use: July 16, 1857 (Plate 2L); July 16, 1857 (Plate 3); April 15, 1857 (Plate 5L).

Cancellations

Blue	+10.00
Red	+20.00
Orange red	+40.00
Orange	+175.00
Brown	+100.00
Ultramarine	+125.00
Green	+250.00
1857 year date	+5.00
1858 year date	+5.00
1859 year date	+5.00
"Paid"	+5.00
"Way"	+20.00
Numeral	+10.00
Railroad	+25.00
"Steam"	+20.00
Steamship	+35.00
Steamboat	+45.00
Packet Boat	+50.00
Supplementary Mail Type A	+40.00
Express Company	+65.00
Black Carrier	+30.00
Green Carrier (New Orleans "snow shovel")	—
Territorial	+50.00
Pen	250.00

Washington (Type III) — A21

Type III — There are no outer frame lines at top and bottom. The side frame lines were recut so as to be continuous from the top to the bottom of the plate. Stamps from the top or bottom rows show the ends of the side frame lines and may be mistaken for Type IV.

Beware of type III stamps with frame lines that stop at the top of the design (from top row of plate) or bottom of the design (from bottom row of plate). These are often mistakenly offered as No. 26A.

26	A21	3c **dull red**, type III (Plates 9, 12-28)	65.00	9.00
		red	65.00	9.00
		rose	65.00	9.00
		No gum	22.50	
		brownish carmine	140.00	20.00
		No gum	47.50	
		claret	160.00	25.00
		No gum	55.00	
		orange brown	—	—
		plum	—	—
		On cover, dull red		10.50
		On cover, orange brown		950.00
		On patriotic cover		125.00

On Confederate patriotic cover		2,000.
On Pony express cover		
Pair	150.00	21.00
Strip of 3	220.00	42.50
Block of 4	375.00	175.00
P# block of 8, Impt.	3,250.	
Double transfer	100.00	20.00
Double transfer, rosettes double and line through "Postage" and "Three Cents" (87R15)	—	2,500.
Left frame line double	100.00	20.00
Right frame line double	100.00	20.00
Cracked plate (71L18)	1,000.	400.00
Cracked plate (62L, 72L, Plate 18)	750.00	250.00
Damaged transfer above lower left rosette	75.00	11.00
Same, retouched	95.00	12.00
Same, retouched with 2 vertical lines	130.00	13.00
Same, both damaged areas retouched	310.00	100.00
"Quadruple" plate flaw (18L28)	—	1,750.
1 line recut in upper left triangle	—	30.00
5 lines recut in upper left triangle (52L25)		500.00
Inner line recut at left	—	500.00
Inner line recut at right	—	350.00
Worn plate	65.00	8.50
b. Horiz. pair, imperf. vertically	4,000.	
c. Vert. pair, imperf. horizontally		13,000.
d. Horizontal pair, imperf. between		2,500.
e. Double impression		

Frame line double varieties are separate and distinct for virtually the entire length of the stamp. Examples with partly split lines are worth considerably less.

Earliest documented use: Sept. 14, 1857.

Cancellations

Blue	+.25
Red	+1.50
Orange red	+2.50
Orange	+150.00
Brown	+100.00
Ultramarine	+100.00
Violet	+100.00
Green	+150.00
1857 year date	+3.00
1858-1861 year date	+1.00
Printed Circular Precancel "Cumberland, Me." (on cover)	—
"Paid"	+.50
"Paid All"	+15.00
"Free"	+20.00
"Collect"	+40.00
Numeral	+2.50
"Steam"	+12.50
Steamer	
Steamboat	+22.50
Steamship	+22.50
"Way"	+12.50
Railroad	+15.00
U. S. Express Mail	+20.00
Express Company	+65.00
Packet boat	+65.00
Supp. Mail Type A, B or C	+500.00
Black Carrier	+30.00
Red Carrier	+25.00
"Southn. Letter Unpaid"	+750.00
Territorial	+20.00
"Old Stamps-Not Recognized"	+500.00
On cover	7,500.
Pen	3.25

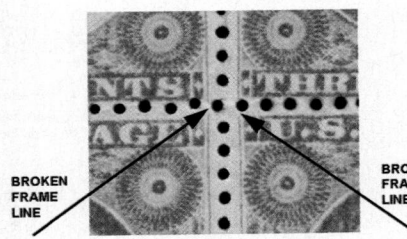

BROKEN FRAME LINE   **BROKEN FRAME LINE**

Washington (Type IV) — A21a

Type IV — As type III, but the side frame lines extend only to the top and bottom of the stamp design. All Type IV stamps are from plates 10 and 11 (each of which exists in three states), and these plates produced only Type IV. The side frame lines were recut individually for each stamp, thus being broken between the stamps vertically.

Beware of type III stamps with frame lines that stop at the top of the design (from top row of plate) or bottom of the design (from bottom row of plate). These are often mistakenly offered as No. 26A.

26A A21a 3c **dull red,** type IV (Plates 10-11)	550.00	125.00
brownish carmine	550.00	125.00
rose	550.00	125.00
No gum	190.00	
claret	575.00	140.00
No gum	200.00	
On cover		170.00
On patriotic cover		425.00

Pair	1,150.	300.00
Strip of 3	1,800.	500.00
Block of 4	5,000.	2,250.
P# block of 8, Impt.	12,500.	
Double transfer	625.00	200.00
Double transfer, line through rosettes (61R10i, 61R10L, 98R10i, 98R10L)	—	925.00
Double transfer of rosettes and lower part of stamp (91R11L)	—	260.00
Triple transfer	—	475.00
Damaged transfer above lower left rosette	600.00	150.00
Same, retouched	575.00	145.00
Same, both damaged areas retouched (10R11)	—	325.00
Inner line recut at right	—	325.00
Inner line recut at left (79L10)	—	525.00
Left frame line double (70, 80, 90, 100R11)	—	225.00
Worn plate	550.00	125.00
f. Horiz. strip of 3, imperf. vert., on cover		14,500.

No. 26Af is unique.

Earliest documented use: July 11, 1857.

Cancellations

Blue	+2.50
Red	+10.00
Orange red	+15.00
Orange	+150.00
Brown	+100.00
Ultramarine	+100.00
Violet	+150.00
Green	+175.00
1857 year date	+2.50
1858 or 1859 year date	+1.50
"Paid"	+2.50
"Paid All"	+15.00
"Free"	+20.00
"Collect"	+40.00
Numeral	+2.50
"Steam"	+15.00
Steamer	
Steamboat	+25.00
Steamship	+25.00
"Way"	+15.00
Railroad	+17.50
U. S. Express Mail	+17.50
Express Company	+65.00
Packet boat	+65.00
Black Carrier	+30.00
Red Carrier	+20.00
Territorial	+30.00
Pen	32.50

27 A11 5c **brick red,** type I, *1858*	80,000.	1,800.
No gum	20,000.	
On cover		2,200.
On patriotic cover		5,000.
Pair	175,000.	4,250.
Strip of 3		6,500.
Block of 4	800,000.	40,000.
Defective transfer (23R1)	—	—

The unused block of 4 is unique. Value reflects 2009 auction sale price.

Earliest documented use: Oct. 6, 1858.

Cancellations

Blue	+175.
Red	+200.
Ultramarine	+450.
1859 year date	+50.
1860 year date	+50.
"Paid"	+50.
Supplementary Mail Type A	+150.
"Steamship"	+150.
Pen	950.

28 A11 5c **red brown,** type I	60,000.	1,300.
pale red brown	60,000.	1,300.
No gum	15,000.	
On cover		1,500.
Pair	125,000.	3,000.
Strip of 3		4,750.
Block of 4	90,000.	8,500.
Defective transfer (23R1)		—
b. **Bright red brown**	70,000.	2,000.
No gum	20,000.	

The value of the block of 4 of No. 28 is based on the 2009 auction sale of the finest original-gum block, which grades Average-Fine.

Earliest documented use: Aug. 23, 1857 (No. 28).

Cancellations

Blue	+40.
Ultramarine	
Red	+75.
1857 year date	+20.
1858 year date	+15.
"Paid"	+35.
Railroad	+75.
"Short Paid"	
Pen	625.

28A A11 5c **Indian red,** type I, *1858*	175,000.	3,750.
No gum	40,000.	
On cover		5,250.

Pair	8,000.
Strip of 3	13,500.
Block of 4	

There are only four recorded examples of No. 28A with any amount of original gum. Value is for a fine stamp, the highest recorded grade (two thus).

Earliest documented use: Mar. 31, 1858.

Cancellations

Red	+250.
Blue	+350.
1858 year date	+50.
1859 year date	+25.
Pen	1,800.

29 A11 5c **brown,** type I, *1859*	5,000.	425.
pale brown	5,000.	425.
deep brown	5,000.	425.
yellowish brown	5,000.	425.
No gum	1,750.	
On cover		550.
Pair	11,000.	900.
Strip of 3	17,500.	1,400.
Block of 4	90,000.	5,000.
Defective transfer (23R1)	—	—

Earliest documented use: Mar. 21, 1859.

Cancellations

Blue	+15.
Ultramarine	150.
Red	+50.
Brown	+75.
Magenta	+125.
Green	+400.
1859 year date	+10.
1860 year date	+10.
"Paid"	+15.
"Steam"	+75.
Steamship	+100.
Numeral	+80.
Pen	175.

Jefferson — A22

FIVE CENTS.

Type II — The projections at top and bottom are partly cut away. Several minor types could be made according to the extent of cutting of the projections.

30 A22 5c **orange brown,** Type II, *1861*	1,350.	1,400.
deep orange brown	1,350.	1,400.
No gum	500.	
On cover		2,400.
On patriotic cover		
Pair	2,900.	3,500.
Strip of 3	4,500.	
Block of 4	7,000.	—

Earliest documented use: May 8, 1861.

Cancellations

Blue	+30.
Red	+75.
Green	
"Paid"	+75.
Steamship	+110.
Supplementary Mail Type A	+150.
Railroad	
Pen	700.

30A A22 5c **brown,** type II, *1860*	2,200.	300.
dark brown	2,200.	300.
yellowish brown	2,200.	300.
No gum	825.	
On cover		350.
On patriotic cover		
Pair	4,750.	625.
Strip of 3	7,500.	1,000.
Block of 4	25,000.	3,250.
Cracked plate		
b. Printed on both sides		55,000.

Earliest documented use: May 4, 1860.

Cancellations

Blue	+5.
Red	+20.
Magenta	+75.
Green	+350.
"Paid"	+20.
Supplementary Mail Type A	+50.
"Steamship"	+50.
"Steam"	+50.
Express Company	+250.
Railroad	
Packet boat	
Pen	160.

31   A12   **10c green,** type I

	30,000.	1,350.
dark green	30,000.	1,350.
bluish green	30,000.	1,350.
yellowish green	30,000.	1,350.
No gum	10,000.	
On domestic cover		1,550.
On patriotic cover		3,500.
Pair	65,000.	2,900.
Vertical pair, types III, I	40,000.	1,750.
Vertical pair, types IV, I (86, 96 L 1)		—
Strip of 3		—
Vertical strip of 3, types II, III, I		—
Block of 4, types III, I	75,000.	—
Block of 4, types III, IV, I		9,750.
Vertical block of 6, 2 each types II, III, I	90,000.	
Double transfer (100R1)	32,500.	1,450.
"Curl" in left "X" (99R1)	32,500.	1,450.

Type I comes only from the bottom row of both panes of Plate 1.

Earliest documented use: Aug. 25, 1857.

Cancellations

Blue	+30.
Red	+90.
Green	+600.
Supplementary Mail Type A	
"Steamship"	+100.
Canadian	
Pen	675.

Act of February 27, 1861. Ten cent rate of postage to be prepaid on letters conveyed in the mail from any point in the United States east of the Rocky Mountains to any State or Territory on the Pacific Coast and vice versa, for each half-ounce.

32   A13   **10c green,** type II

	6,250.	275.
dark green	6,250.	275.
bluish green	6,250.	275.
yellowish green	6,250.	275.
No gum	2,250.	
On domestic cover		325.
On pony express cover		8,500.
Pair	13,000.	575.
Strip of 3	—	875.
Block of 4	30,000.	4,500.
Pair, types II, III	13,000.	650.
Pair, types II, IV	60,000.	2,700.
Vertical strip of 3, types II, III, IV		—
Block of 4, types II, III	30,000.	3,500.
Block of 4, types II, IV		—
Block of 4, types II, III, IV	95,000.	18,000.
Double transfer (31L, 51L and 20R, Plate 1)	6,500.	300.
"Curl opposite left X" (10R1)		350.

Earliest documented use: July 27, 1857 (dated cancel on off-cover stamp), Aug. 8, 1857 (on cover).

Cancellations

Blue	+15.
Red	+35.
Brown	+125.
Green	+300.
"Paid"	+20.
1857 year date	+10.
Supplementary Mail Type A	
Steamship	+50.
Packet boat	
Railroad	
Express Company	
Pen	150.

33   A14   **10c green,** type III

	6,250.	275.
dark green	6,250.	275.
bluish green	6,250.	275.
yellowish green	6,250.	275.
No gum	2,250.	
On domestic cover		325.
Pair	13,000.	575.
Strip of 3		875.
Pair, types III, IV		2,700.
"Curl" on forehead (85L1)	—	350.
"Curl in left X" (87R1)		350.

Earliest documented use: Aug. 8, 1857.

Cancellations

Blue	+15.
Red	+35.
Brown	+125.
Ultramarine	+125.
1857 year date	+10.
"Paid"	+20.
"Steam"	+45.
Steamboat	
Steamship	+50.
Numeral	+20.
Packet boat	
Pen	150.

34   A15   **10c green,** type IV

	50,000.	2,500.
dark green	50,000.	2,500.
bluish green	50,000.	2,500.
yellowish green	50,000.	2,500.
No gum	20,000.	
On domestic cover		2,900.
Pair		6,250.
Block of 4 (54-55, 64-65L)		

VARIETIES OF RECUTTING

Eight stamps on Plate I were recut. All are listed below.

Outer line recut at top (65L, 74L, 86L and 3R, Plate I)	50,000.	2,500.
Outer line recut at bottom (54L, 55L, 76L, Plate 1)	52,500.	2,600.
Outer line recut at top and bottom (64L1)	55,000.	3,000.

Earliest documented use: Oct. 5, 1857.

Cancellations

Blue	+100.
Red	+175.
Steamship	+200.
Packet boat	
Pen	1,250.

Types I, II, III and IV occur on the same sheet, so it is possible to obtain pairs and blocks showing combinations of types. For listings of type combinations in pairs and blocks, see Nos. 31-33.

Washington (Two typical examples) — A23

Type V — The side ornaments are slightly cut away. Usually only one pearl remains at each end of the lower label, but some copies show two or three pearls at the right side. At the bottom the outer line is complete and the shells nearly so. The outer lines at top are complete except over the right "X."

35   A23   **10c green,** type V, (Plate 2),

1859	250.00	65.00
dark green	250.00	65.00
yellowish green	250.00	65.00
No gum	95.00	
On domestic cover		77.50
On patriotic cover		625.00
On pony express cover		—
On cover to Canada		125.00
Pair	525.00	140.00
Block of 4	1,200.	650.00
P# block of 8, Impt.	*17,500.*	
Double transfer at bottom (47R2)	325.00	90.00
Small "Curl" on forehead (37, 78L2)	290.00	77.50
Curl in "e" of "cents" (93L2)	340.00	90.00
Curl in "t" of "cents" (73R2)	340.00	90.00
Cracked plate		—

Earliest documented use: Apr. 29, 1859.

Cancellations

Red	+7.50
Orange red	+12.50
Brown	+100.00
Blue	+5.00
Orange	+150.00
Magenta	+100.00
Green	+250.00
1859 year date	+5.00
"Paid"	+5.00
"Paid All"	
Red carrier	
Railroad	+40.00
Steamship	+35.00
"Steam"	+30.00
Numerals	+15.00
Supp. Mail Type A or C	+60.00
Express Company	+135.00
"Southn Letter Unpaid"	
Territorial	
Pen	30.00

TWELVE CENTS. Printed from two plates.
Plate 1 (No. 36) — Outer frame lines were recut on the plate and are complete. Very narrow spacing of stamps on the plate.

No. 36 outer frame lines recut on plate

36   A16   **12c black** (Plate 1)

	1,900.	375.
gray black	1,900.	375.
No gum	600.	
Single on cover		800.
Single on cover with No. 26 to France		525.
Pair on cover to England		950.
Pair on patriotic cover		—
Pair	4,250.	800.
Block of 4	10,500.	2,750.
Not recut in lower right corner	2,100.	400.
Recut in lower left corner (43, 53, 63, 73, 100L)	2,100.	400.
Double transfer	2,100.	400.
Triple transfer	2,300.	
a. Diagonal half used as 6c on cover		17,500.
c. Horizontal pair, imperf. between		12,500.

Earliest documented use: July 30, 1857.

Cancellations

Blue	+10.
Red	+20.
Brown	+75.
Magenta	+75.
Green	+300.
1857 year date	+100.
"Paid"	+10.
Supplementary Mail Type A	+60.
Express Company	
Railroad	+60.
Numeral	+20.
"Southn Letter Unpaid"	
Pen	150.

Typical No. 36B, outer frame lines not recut

Plate 3 (No. 36B) — Weak outer frame lines from the die were not recut on the plate and are noticeably uneven or broken, sometimes partly missing. Somewhat wider spacing of stamps on the plate.

36B   A16   **12c black** (Plate 3)

	825.	350.
intense black	825.	350.
No gum	400.	
Single on cover		1,250.
Single on cover with No. 26 to France		475.
Pair on cover to England		850.
Pair	1,700.	775.
Block of 4	5,000.	3,250.
Double frame line at right	875.	375.
Double frame line at left	875.	375.
Vertical line through rosette (95R3)	1,000.	425.

Earliest documented use: June 1, 1860. (The previously listed Dec. 3, 1859, cover requires expertization in order to be considered.)

Cancellations

Blue	+10.
Red	+20.
Brown	+85.
Magenta	+60.
Green	+275.
1860 year date	+100.
1861 year date	+50.
"Paid"	+12.
Supplementary Mail Type A	+300.
Express Company	
Railroad	+65.
Numeral	+25.
"Southn Letter Unpaid"	
Pen	175.

A31

1c — There is a dash under the tip of the ornament at right of the numeral in upper left corner.

3c — Ornaments at corners end in a small ball.

5c — There is a leaflet in the foliated ornaments at each corner.

10c (A27) — A heavy curved line has been cut below the stars and an outer line added to the ornaments above them.

12c — There are corner ornaments consisting of ovals and scrolls.

90c — Parallel lines form an angle above the ribbon with "U. S. Postage"; between these lines there is a row of dashes and a point of color at the apex of the lower line.

Patriotic Covers covering a wide range of historical interest were used during the Civil War period, in the North as well as the South, and are collected by manufacturer and topic as well as generally, both used and unused. There are believed to be as many as 12,000 varieties.

During the war, these stamps were used as small change until Postage Currency was issued.

The Act of Congress of March 3, 1863, effective July 1, 1863, created a rate of three cents for each half ounce, first class domestic mail. This Act was the first law which established uniform rate of postage regardless of the distance. This rate remained in effect until Oct. 1, 1883.

Plates of 200 subjects in two panes of 100 each.

The following items, formerly listed here as Nos. 55-62, are considered to be essays or trial color proofs. They will be found in their respective sections as follows. Previous No. 58 has been combined with No. 62B.

Formerly	Currently	Formerly	Currently
55	63-E11e	59	69-E6e
56	65-E15h	60	70eTC
57	67-E9e	61	71bTC
58	62B	62	72-E7h

The paper of Nos. 62B-72 is thicker and more opaque than the essays and trial color proofs, except Nos. 62B, 70c, and 70d.

1861 **Perf. 12**

62B	A27a	10c	dark green	8,000.	1,600.
			dark yellow green	8,000.	1,600.
			No gum	3,250.	
			On cover		2,100.
			On patriotic cover		3,000.
			Pair	17,500.	3,750.
			Block of 4	37,500.	13,500.
			Foreign entry 94R4	9,250.	
			Block of 4, one stamp 94R4	—	

The foreign entry is of the 90c 1861.

Earliest documented use: Sept. 17, 1861.

Cancellations

Red	+110.
Blue	+70.
"Paid"	+60.
Steamship	+100.
Express Company	+200.
Supplementary Mail Type A	+125.

1861-62 **Perf. 12**

63	A24	1c	blue, Aug. 17, 1861	325.00	50.00
			pale blue	325.00	50.00
			bright blue	325.00	50.00
			No gum	115.00	
			On cover (single)		57.50
			On prisoner's letter		
			On patriotic cover		225.00
			Pair	700.00	105.00
			Block of 4	1,750.	500.00
			P# block of 8, Impt.	6,500.	
			Double transfer		62.50
			Dot in "U"	350.00	55.00
a.		1c	ultramarine	2,500.	650.00
			No gum	1,000.	
			dark ultramarine	5,000.	1,500.
			No gum	2,250.	
b.		1c	dark blue	800.00	400.00
			No gum	300.00	
c.			Laid paper, horiz. or vert.	10,000.	7,500.
d.			Vertical pair, imperf. horiz.		
e.			Printed on both sides, reverse inverted	—	65,000.

Earliest documented use: Aug. 17, 1861 (dated cancel on off-cover stamp); Aug. 21, 1861 (on cover).

Cancellations

Blue	+5.00
Red	+15.00
Magenta	+50.00
Green	+250.00
Violet	+50.00
1861 year date	+7.50
1865 year date	+2.00
1866 year date	+2.00
"Free"	+40.00
"Paid"	+2.50
"Paid All"	+15.00
Supp. Mail Type A or B	+30.00

Steamship	+35.00
Steam	+30.00
Express Company	+175.00
Red Carrier	+20.00
Black Carrier	+15.00
Railroad	+40.00
Numeral	+10.00
"Steamboat"	+50.00
Printed Precancel "CUMBERLAND, ME."	—

64	A25	3c	pink, Aug. 17, 1861	14,000.	1,000.
			No gum	5,000.	
			On cover		1,100.
			On patriotic cover		1,300.
			Pair	30,000.	2,500.
			Block of 4	65,000.	—

Earliest documented use: Aug. 17, 1861 (FDC).

Cancellations

Blue	+50.00
Red	+150.00
Green	+500.00
1861 date	+25.00
"Paid"	+175.00
"Free"	+85.00
"Ship"	+150.00
Supplementary Mail Type B	+125.00
Railroad	+175.00
Steamboat	

a.		3c	pigeon blood pink	50,000.	5,000.
			No gum	15,000.	
			On cover		5,750.
			On patriotic cover		7,750.

Earliest documented use: Aug. 21, 1861.

b.		3c	rose pink, Aug. 17, 1861	600.00	160.00
			No gum	230.00	
			On cover		190.00
			On patriotic cover		250.00
			Pair	1,350.	350.00
			Block of 4	3,250.	875.00

Earliest documented use: Aug. 17, 1861 (FDC).

Cancellations

Blue	+15.00
Red	+30.00
Orange red	+40.00
Green	+180.00
Orange	
"Paid"	+10.00
"Free"	+75.00
Supplementary Mail Type C	
"Ship"	+30.00
Railroad	+60.00
Steamboat	+90.00

65	A25	3c	rose	125.00	3.00
			bright rose	125.00	3.00
			dull red	125.00	3.00

	rose red	125.00	3.00
	No gum	40.00	
	On cover		3.50
	On patriotic cover		40.00
	On prisoner's letter		150.00
	On pony express cover		
	Pair	270.00	6.75
	Block of 4	700.00	42.50
	P# block of 8, Impt.	4,250.	
	Double transfer	160.00	6.00
	Cracked plate		
	brown red	275.00	5.50
	No gum	100.00	
	pale brown red	210.00	5.50
	No gum	70.00	
	dull brown red	250.00	5.50
	No gum	90.00	
	Block of 4	1,250.	
	deep pinkish rose	290.00	25.00
	On cover		
b.	Laid paper, horiz. or vert.	—	750.00
d.	Vertical pair, imperf. horiz.	15,000.	1,500.
e.	Printed on both sides, reverse inverted	40,000.	5,000.
	Pair	82,500.	
f.	Double impression		7,500.

See Die and Plate Proofs for imperfs. on stamp paper.

Earliest documented use: Aug. 19, 1861.

Cancellations

Blue	+1.00
Ultramarine	+2.75
Brown	+50.00
Red	+3.00
Orange red	+3.50
Violet	+75.00
Magenta	+8.00
Green	+100.00
Olive	+100.00
Orange	+150.00
Yellow	+3,500.
1861 year date	+2.00
1867 or 1868 year date	+1.00
"Paid"	+.35
"Paid All"	+7.50
"Mails Suspended"	
Railroad	+12.50
"Way"	+20.00
"Free"	+20.00
"Collect"	+35.00
"Ship"	+15.00
"U. S. Ship"	+35.00
"Steam"	+12.00
Steamship	+15.00
Steamboat	+20.00
"Ship Letter"	+35.00

Red Carrier	+15.00
Blue Carrier	+25.00
Black Carrier	+20.00
Supplementary Mail Type A, B or C	+15.00
Numeral	+3.00
Express Company	+90.00
Army Field Post	+60.00
Packet Boat	+40.00
"Registered"	+30.00
"Postage Due"	+25.00
"Advertised"	+15.00
"U.STATES"	+300.00
Territorial	+25.00
St. Thomas	—
China	—

The 3c lake can be found under No. 66 in the Trial Color Proofs section.

67	A26	5c **buff**		27,500.	1,200.
		No gum		10,500.	
		On cover			1,450.
		On patriotic cover			4,000.
		Pair		60,000.	2,750.
		Block of 4		11,500.	13,000.
a.		5c **brown yellow**		30,000.	1,300.
		No gum		11,500.	
b.		5c **olive yellow**		—	3,500.

The unused block of 4 is unique but very faulty. Value is based on actual 1993 sale.

Earliest documented uses: Aug. 19, 1861 (No. 67); Aug. 21, 1861 (No. 67a).

Cancellations

Red	+60.00
Blue	+30.00
Magenta	+125.00
Green	+750.00
1861 year date	+10.00
"Paid"	+25.00
Supplementary Mail Type A	+100.00
Express Company	+250.00
Numeral	+50.00
"Steamship"	+100.00

Values of Nos. 67, 67a, 67b reflect the normal small margins.

68	A27	10c **green**		1,200.	62.50
		yellow green		1,150.	62.50
		No gum		450.	
		On cover			75.00
		On patriotic cover			375.00
		On cover to Canada			100.00
		Pair		2,500.	130.00
		Block of 4		5,750.	650.00
		P# block of 8, Impt.		13,000.	
		Double transfer		1,300.	65.00
		deep yellow green on thin paper		1,400.	70.00
a.		10c **dark green**		1,450.	85.00
		blue green		1,450.	85.00
		No gum		550.	
b.		Vertical pair, imperf. horiz.			3,500.

Earliest documented use: Aug. 20, 1861.

Cancellations

Blue	+5.00
Red	+10.00
Purple	+50.00
Magenta	+50.00
Brown	+50.00
Green	+250.00
1865 year date	+3.50
"Paid"	+2.50
"Collect"	+32.50
"Short Paid"	+50.00
"P.D." in circle	+30.00
"Free"	+50.00
Numeral	+7.50
Red Carrier	+65.00
Railroad	+20.00
Steamship	+15.00
"Steamboat"	+35.00
Supplementary Mail Type A	+30.00
Red Supp. Mail Type D	—
Express Company	+70.00
China	—
Japan	+200.00
St. Thomas	—

Please Note:

Values for early and valuable stamps are for examples with certificates of authenticity from acknowledged expert committees, or examples sold with the buyer having the right of certification.

This applies to examples with original gum as well as examples without gum.

Beware of stamps offered "as is," as the gum on some unused stamps offered with "original gum" may be fraudulent, and stamps offered as unused without gum may in some cases be altered or faintly canceled used stamps.

69	A28	12c **black**		2,000.	120.00
		gray black		2,000.	130.00
		No gum		800.	
		intense black		2,100.	135.00
		No gum		825.	

	On domestic cover				160.00
	On patriotic cover				900.00
	On cover to France or Germany with #65				180.00
	Pair			4,500.	280.00
	Block of 4			10,500.	1,150.
	Double transfer of top frame line			2,100.	150.00
	Double transfer of bottom frame line			2,100.	150.00
	Double transfer of top and bottom frame lines			2,200.	155.00

Earliest documented use: Aug. 30, 1861.

Cancellations

Blue	+5.00
Ultramarine	—
Red	+25.00
Purple	+70.00
Magenta	+100.00
Green	+550.00
1861 year date	+5.00
"Paid"	+5.00
"Registered"	+35.00
Supp. Mail Type A, B or C	+45.00
Express Company	+175.00
Railroad	+50.00
Numeral	+15.00

70	A29	24c **red lilac**		3,000.	300.00
		No gum		1,150.	
		On cover			350.00
		On patriotic cover			3,000.
		Pair		6,500.	625.00
		Block of 4		15,000.	3,000.
		Scratch under "A" of "Postage"			—
a.		24c **brown lilac**		3,250.	300.00
		No gum		1,250.	
		Block of 4		17,000.	3,500.
b.		24c **steel blue** ('61)		16,500.	900.00
		No gum		6,250.	
		On cover			1,350.
		Block of 4		75,000.	
c.		24c **violet,** thin paper, *Aug. 20, 1861*		35,000.	2,200.
		No gum		13,500.	
d.		24c **pale gray violet,** thin paper		25,000.	2,400.
		No gum		6,000.	

There are numerous shades of the 24c stamp in this and the following issue.

Color changelings, especially of No. 78, are frequently offered as No. 70b. Obtaining a certificate from an acknowledged expert committee is strongly advised.

Nos. 70c and 70d are on a thinner, harder and more transparent paper than Nos. 70, 70a, 70b or the latter Nos. 78, 78a, 78b and 78c. No. 70eTC (formerly No. 60, see Trial Color Proofs section) is distinguished by its distinctive dark color.

Earliest documented uses: Jan. 7, 1862 (No. 70); Feb. 5, 1862 (No. 70a); Sept. 21, 1861 (No. 70b); Aug. 20, 1861 (No. 70c); Sept. 10, 1861 (No. 70d).

Cancellations, No. 70

Blue	+25.00
Red	+40.00
Magenta	+200.00
Brown	+125.00
Green	+350.00
1865 year date	+5.00
"Paid"	+15.00
Supp. Mail Types A or B	+75.00
Express Company	+350.00

71	A30	30c **orange**		2,600.	200.
		deep orange		2,600.	225.
		No gum		1,000.	
		On cover to France or Germany			400.
		On patriotic cover			3,500.
		Pair		5,500.	450.
		Block of 4		17,500.	2,500.
		P# strip of 4, Impt.		—	
a.		Printed on both sides			—

Values for No. 71 are for examples with small margins, especially at sides. Large-margined examples sell for much more.

Earliest documented use: Aug. 20, 1861.

Cancellations

Blue	+15.00
Magenta	+100.00
Brown	+100.00
Red	+35.00
"Paid"	+20.00
"Paid All"	+50.00
"Registered"	—
Railroad	—
Packet Boat	—
"Steamship"	+75.00
Supplementary Mail Type A	+75.00
Red Supp. Mail Type D	—
Express Company	+350.00
Japan	—

72	A31	90c **blue**		3,250.	600.
		dull blue		3,250.	600.
		No gum		1,300.	
		On cover			25,000.
		Pair		7,000.	1,300.
		Block of 4		32,500.	5,000.
		P# strip of 4, Impt.		25,000.	
a.		90c **pale blue**		3,250.	650.
		No gum		1,300.	
b.		90c **dark blue**		4,000.	800.
		No gum		1,600.	

The unique plate number and imprint strip of 4 of No. 72 has no gum and is valued thus.

Earliest documented use: Nov. 27, 1861.

Cancellations

Blue	+40
Red	+100
Green	+750
1865 year date	+35
"Paid"	+25
"Registered"	+75
Express Company	+500
Supplementary Mail Type A	+100

Nos. 68a, 69, 71 and 72 exist as imperforate sheet-margin singles with pen cancel. They were not regularly issued.

The 90c was distributed to several post offices in the last two weeks of August, 1861.

Owing to the Civil War, stamps and stamped envelopes in current use or available for postage in 1860, were demonetized by various post office orders, beginning in August, 1861, and extending to early January, 1862.

P. O. Department Bulletin.

"A reasonable time after hostilities began in 1861 was given for the return to the Department of all these (1851-56) stamps in the hands of postmasters, and as early as 1863 the Department issued an order declining to longer redeem them."

The Act of Congress, approved March 3, 1863, abolished carriers' fees and established a prepaid rate of two cents for drop letters, making necessary the 2-cent Jackson (No. 73).

Free City Delivery was authorized by the Act of Congress of March 3, 1863, effective in 49 cities with 449 carriers, beginning July 1, 1863.

Produced by the National Bank Note Co.
DESIGNS AS 1861 ISSUE

Andrew Jackson — A32   Abraham Lincoln — A33

1861-66   **Perf. 12**

73	A32	2c **black,** *1863*		375.00	70.00
		gray black		375.00	70.00
		intense black		375.00	75.00
		No gum		140.00	
		On cover			90.00
		On prisoner's letter			—
		On patriotic cover			2,000.
		Pair		800.00	150.00
		Block of 4		4,000.	1,350.
		P# strip of 4, Impt.		4,500.	
		P# block of 8, Impt.		15,000.	
		Double transfer		425.00	75.00
		Major double transfer of top left corner and "Postage" ("Atherton shift")			15,000.
		Major double transfer of right side, pos. 81, right pane ("Preston shift")		5,000.	4,500.
		Major double transfer of frame in all corners plus hair and chin ("Metzger shift")			—
		Triple transfer			—
		Short transfer		400.00	75.00
		Cracked plate			—
a.		Diagonal half used as 1c as part of 3c rate on cover			1,500.
b.		Diagonal half used alone as 1c on cover			3,000.
c.		Horiz. half used as 1c as part of 3c rate on cover			3,500.
d.		Vert. half used as 1c as part of 3c rate on cover			2,000.
e.		Vert. half used alone as 1c on cover			4,000.
f.		Printed on both sides, reverse inverted		—	18,500.
g.		Laid paper		—	12,500.

Earliest documented use: July 1, 1863 (dated cancel on off-cover stamp); July 6, 1863 (on cover).

Cancellations

Blue	+15.00
Brown	+75.00
Red	+50.00
Orange red	+70.00
Magenta	+200.00
Ultramarine	+150.00
Orange	+200.00
Green	+700.00
1863 year date	+5.00
Printed Precancel "Jefferson, Ohio"	—
"PAID ALL"	+40.00
"Paid"	+10.00
Numeral	+15.00
"Way"	+150.00
Railroad	+300.00
"Steam"	+40.00
Steamship	+100.00
"Steamboat"	+65.00
"Ship Letter"	+150.00
Black Carrier	+20.00
Blue Carrier	+35.00
Supp. Mail Type A or B	+100.00
Express Company	+300.00

"Short Paid"			+250.00
Territorial			+100.00
China			+100.00

The 3c scarlet, design A25, can be found under No. 74 in the Trial Color Proofs section.

75	A26 5c **red brown**	5,750.	600.
	dark red brown	5,750.	600.
	No gum	2,200.	
	On cover		900.
	On patriotic cover		4,000.
	Pair	12,000.	1,500.
	Block of 4	62,500.	7,750.
	Double transfer	6,000.	650.

Values for No. 75 reflect the normal small margins.

Earliest documented use: Jan. 2, 1862.

Cancellations

Blue	+30.
Red	+60.
Magenta	+90.
Green	+1,000.
"Paid"	+25.
Supplementary Mail Type A	+50.
Express Company	+300.

76	A26 5c **brown**, *1863*	1,600.	150.
	pale brown	1,650.	150.
	dark brown	1,650.	150.
	No gum	600.	
	On cover		200.
	On patriotic cover		2,000.
	Pair	3,750.	325.
	Block of 4	8,500.	1,200.
	P# strip of 4, Impt.	15,000.	
	Double transfer of top frame line	1,700.	160.
	Double transfer of bottom frame line	1,700.	160.
	Double transfer of top and bottom frame lines	1,750.	175.
a.	**5c black brown**	2,250.	350.
	No gum	850.	
	Block of 4	9,000.	2,000.
b.	Laid paper		

Values of Nos. 76, 76a reflect the normal small margins. The plate no. strip of 4 with imprint of No. 76 is unique.

Earliest documented use: Feb. 3, 1863.

Cancellations

Blue	+15.00
Magenta	+75.00
Red	+45.00
Brown	+150.00
Green	+750.00
1865 year date	+10.00
"Paid"	+15.00
"Short Paid"	+75.00
Supp. Mail Type A or F	+55.00
Express Company	+175.00
"Steamship"	+65.00
Packet boat	

77	A33 15c **black**, *April 1866*	4,500.	225.
	full black	4,500.	225.
	No gum	1,750.	
	On cover to France or Germany		300.
	Pair	9,500.	500.
	Block of 4	32,500.	1,150.
	P# block of 8, Impt.		
	Double transfer	4,750.	250.
	Cracked plate		

Earliest documented use: April 21, 1866.

Cancellations

Blue	+10.
Indigo	+25.
Purple	+90.
Lavender	+150.
Violet	+100.
Magenta	+100.
Red	+45.
Brown	+125.
Green	+400.
Ultramarine	+75.
"Paid"	+15.
"Short Paid"	+85.
"Insufficiently Paid" or "Insufficiently Prepaid"	+150.
"Ship"	+50.
Steamship	+50.
Supplementary Mail Type A	+70.

78	A29 24c **lilac**, *1862*	2,750.	350.
	dark lilac	2,750.	400.
	No gum	950.	
	On cover		325.
	Pair	5,750.	525.
	Block of 4	18,000.	1,850.

	Scratch under "A" of "Postage"	—	—
a.	24c grayish lilac	2,900.	300.
b.	24c gray	2,900.	300.
c.	24c blackish violet	100,000.	17,500.
	No gum	30,000.	
	On cover		22,500.

Only three examples are recorded of No. 78c unused with original gum. No. 78c unused with and without gum are valued in the grade of fine-very fine.

d.	Printed on both sides, reverse inverted		50,000.
	On cover		55,000.

No. 78d off cover and on cover are each unique.

Earliest documented uses: Oct. 23, 1862 (No. 78a); May 1, 1863 (No. 78c).

Cancellations

Blue	+12.50
Red	+25.00
Magenta	+90.00
Green	+400.00
"Paid"	+15.00
Numeral	+20.00
Supplementary Mail Type A	+50.00
"Free"	+100.00

Nos. 73, 76-78 exist as imperforate sheet-margin singles, all with pen cancel except No. 76 which is uncanceled. They were not regularly issued.

SAME DESIGNS AS 1861-66 ISSUES
Printed by the National Bank Note Co.

Grill

Embossed with grills of various sizes. Some authorities believe that more than one size of grill probably existed on one of the grill rolls.

A peculiarity of the United States issues from 1867 to 1870 is the grill or embossing. The object was to break the fiber of the paper so that the ink of the canceling stamp would soak in and make washing for a second using impossible. The exact date at which grilled stamps came into use is unsettled. Luff's "Postage Stamps of the United States" places the date as probably August 8, 1867.

Horizontal measurements are given first.

GRILL WITH POINTS UP

Grills A and C were made by a roller covered with ridges shaped like an inverted V. Pressing the ridges into the stamp paper forced the paper into the pyramidal pits between the ridges, causing irregular breaks in the paper. Grill B was made by a roller with raised bosses.

A. GRILL COVERING THE ENTIRE STAMP.

1867			**Perf. 12**
79	A25 3c **rose**	8,500.	1,750.
	No gum	2,750.	
	On cover		2,250.
	Pair	18,000.	4,000.
	Block of 4	55,000.	
b.	Printed on both sides		—

Earliest documented use: Aug. 13, 1867.

Cancellations

Blue	+125.
Ultramarine	+325.
Railroad	

Values for No. 79 are for fine-very fine examples with minor perf. faults. Examples with complete or virtually complete perforations sell for much more.

An essay (#79-E15) which is often mistaken for No. 79 shows the points of the grill as small squares faintly impressed in the paper but not cutting through it. On the issued stamp the grill generally breaks through the paper. Examples without defects are rare.

See Die and Plate Proofs for imperf. on stamp paper.

80	A26 5c **brown**		250,000.
a.	5c dark brown		250,000.
81	A30 30c **orange**		200,000.

Four examples of Nos. 80 and 80a (two of each shade), and eight examples of No. 81 (one in the New York Public Library Miller collection and not available to collectors) are known. All are more or less faulty and/or off center. Values are for off-center examples with small perforation faults.

B. GRILL ABOUT 18x15mm
(22x18 POINTS)

82	A25 3c **rose**		1,000,000.

The four known examples of No. 82 are valued in the grade of fine.

Earliest documented use: Feb. 1?, 1869 (dated cancel on off-cover stamp).

C. GRILL ABOUT 13x16mm
(16 TO 17 BY 18 TO 21 POINTS)

The grilled area on each of four C grills in the sheet may total about 18x15mm when a normal C grill adjoins a fainter grill extending to the right or left edge of the stamp. This is caused by a partial erasure on the grill roller when it was changed to produce C grills instead of the all-over A grill. Do not mistake these for the B grill. Unused exists and is very rare, value unused $7,500; value used $2,750; on cover $4,500.

83	A25 3c **rose**	6,250.	1,200.
	No gum	2,250.	
	On cover		1,400.
	Pair	13,500.	3,500.
	Block of 4	30,000.	—
	Double grill	7,500.	2,500.
	Grill with points down	7,000.	1,500.

Earliest documented use: Nov. 16, 1867.

Cancellation

Blue	+50.

See Die and Plate Proofs for imperf. on stamp paper.

The 1c, 3c, 5c, 10c, 12c, 30c of 1861 are known with experimental C grills. They are listed in the Essays section. The 3c differs slightly from No. 83.

GRILL WITH POINTS DOWN

The grills were produced by rollers with the surface covered, or partly covered, by pyramidal bosses. On the D, E and F grills the tips of the pyramids are vertical ridges. On the Z grill the ridges are horizontal.

D. GRILL ABOUT 12x14mm
(15 BY 17 TO 18 POINTS)

84	A32 2c **black**	16,000.	4,500.
	No gum	6,500.	
	On cover		5,000.
	Pair	35,000.	9,250.
	Block of 4	80,000.	—
	Double transfer	—	
	Split grill		4,750.

No. 84 is valued in the grade of fine.

Earliest documented use: Feb. 15, 1868.

Cancellations

Red	+400.
Blue	+750.
"Paid All"	+100.

85	A25 3c **rose**	6,500.	1,250.
	No gum	2,600.	
	On cover		1,400.
	Pair	13,750.	2,850.
	Block of 4	35,000.	—
	Double grill	—	
	Split grill		1,350.

Earliest documented use: Feb. 1, 1868 (on cover front); Feb. 2, 1868 (on full cover.

Cancellations

Blue	+50.
Green	+450.
"Paid"	+50.

Z. GRILL ABOUT 11x14mm
(13 TO 14 BY 18 POINTS)

85A	A24 1c **blue**		3,000,000.

Two examples of No. 85A are known. One is contained in the New York Public Library collection.

85B	A32 2c **black**	17,500.	1,500.
	No gum	6,750.	
	On cover		1,650.
	Pair	32,500.	3,400.
	Block of 4	75,000.	—
	Double transfer	19,000.	1,600.
	Double grill	—	
	Split grill	—	

Earliest documented use: Jan. 17, 1868 (on piece); Feb. 11, 1868 (on cover).

Cancellations

Blue	+100.
Red	+200.
Black Carrier	+75.
"Paid All"	+75.

85C	A25 3c **rose**	25,000.	3,750.
	No gum	9,000.	
	On cover		4,250.
	Pair	—	
	Block of 4	120,000.	
	Double grill	27,000.	

Earliest documented use: Feb. 12, 1868.

Cancellations

Green	+400.
Blue	+50.
Red	+200.
"Paid"	+50.

85D	A27 10c **green**		650,000.

Six examples of No. 85D are known. One is contained in the New York Public Library collection. Value is for a well-centered example with small faults.

85E	A28 12c **intense black**	17,500.	2,500.
	black	17,500.	2,500.
	No gum	6,500.	
	On cover		—
	Strip of 3		3,000.

	Block of 4	—	—
	Double transfer of top frame line		2,600.

Earliest documented use: Feb. 12, 1868.

85F A33 15c **black** — 2,000,000.

Two examples of No. 85F are documented, one in the grade of very good, the other extremely fine. Value is for the extremely fine example.

E. GRILL ABOUT 11x13mm
(14 BY 15 TO 17 POINTS)

86	A24	1c **blue**	3,500.	575.
		No gum	1,350.	
a.		1c **dull blue**	3,500.	550.
		No gum	1,350.	
		On cover		675.
		Pair	7,500.	1,200.
		Block of 4	20,000.	3,500.
		Double grill	—	700.
		Split grill	3,750.	675.
		Very thin paper	—	

Earliest documented use: Mar. 9, 1868.

Cancellations

Blue	+25.
Red	+80.
Green	+450.
"Paid"	+25.
Steamboat	+90.
Red Carrier	+110.

87	A32	2c **black**	1,750.	225.
		gray black	1,750.	225.
		No gum	675.	
		intense black	1,850.	250.
		No gum	700.	
		On cover		325.
		Pair	3,750.	475.
		Block of 4	8,750.	6,250.
		P# strip of 4, Impt.	9,750.	
		Double grill	—	—
		Double grill, one split	—	—
		Triple grill	—	—
		Split grill	2,000.	240.
		Grill with points up	—	
		Double transfer	1,900.	240.
a.		Diagonal half used as 1c on cover		2,000.
b.		Vertical half used as 1c on cover		2,000.

Earliest documented use: Mar. 7, 1868.

Cancellations

Blue	+10.00
Purple	+50.00
Brown	+40.00
Red	+65.00
Green	+1,000.
"Paid"	+10.00
Steamship	+60.00
Black Carrier	+35.00
"Paid All"	+20.00
"Short Paid"	+65.00
Japan	

88	A25	3c **rose**	1,000.	30.00
		pale rose	1,000.	30.00
		rose red	1,000.	30.00
		No gum	375.	
		On cover		35.00
		Pair	2,100.	65.00
		Block of 4	6,000.	360.
		P# block of 8, Impt.	13,000.	
		Double grill	—	—
		Double grill, one split	—	—
		Triple grill	—	—
		Split grill	1,100.	35.00
		Very thin paper	1,050.	35.00
a.		3c **lake red**	1,250.	60.
		No gum	475.	
b.		Two diagonal halves from different stamps used as 3c stamp (fraudulent use), one half having grill with points up, on cover		—

Earliest documented use: Feb. 12, 1868.

Cancellations

Blue	+5.00
Red	+10.00
Ultramarine	+40.00
Green	+110.00
"Paid"	+5.00
"Way"	+30.00
Numeral	+5.00
Steamboat	+35.00
Railroad	+25.00
Express Company	+80.00

89	A27	10c **green**	5,500.	350.
		dark green	5,500.	350.
		blue green	5,500.	350.
		No gum	2,200.	
		On cover		450.
		Pair	11,500.	750.
		Block of 4	26,000.	3,500.
		Double grill	7,000.	525.
		Split grill	5,750.	375.
		Double transfer	—	375.
		Very thin paper	5,750.	375.

Earliest documented use: Feb. 21, 1868.

Cancellations

Blue	+30.
Red	+75.
"Paid"	+15.
Steamship	+50.
Japan	+225.

90	A28	12c **black**	5,000.	425.
		gray black	5,000.	425.

---

		intense black	5,000.	425.
		No gum	2,000.	
		On cover		575.
		Pair	10,500.	900.
		Block of 4	32,500.	2,850.
		Double transfer of top frame line	5,250.	450.
		Double transfer of bottom frame line	5,250.	450.
		Double transfer of top and bottom frame lines	5,500.	500.
		Double grill	5,750.	750.
		Split grill	5,250.	450.

Earliest documented use: Mar. 3, 1868.

Cancellations

Blue	+25.
Red	+75.
Purple	—
Green	+275.
Railroad	+60.
"Paid"	+20.

91	A33	15c **black**	13,500.	750.
		gray black	13,500.	750.
		No gum	5,250.	
		On cover		975.
		Pair	30,000.	1,550.
		Block of 4	72,500.	12,500.
		Double grill	—	1,050.
		Split grill	—	775.

Earliest documented use: May 2, 1868.

Cancellations

Blue	+30.
Magenta	+150.
Red	+150.
"Paid"	+30.
Supplementary Mail Type A	+100.

F. GRILL ABOUT 9x13mm
(11 TO 12 BY 15 TO 17 POINTS)

92	A24	1c **blue**	3,250.	575.
		dark blue	3,250.	575.
		No gum	1,075.	
a.		1c **pale blue**	2,750.	525.
		No gum	825.	
		On cover		625.
		Pair	7,000.	1,200.
		Block of 4	16,500.	3,250.
		Double transfer	3,500.	625.
		Double grill	—	950.
		Split grill	3,500.	625.
		Double grill, one split	—	—
		Very thin paper	3,500.	600.

Earliest documented use: Aug. 11 1868.

Cancellations

Blue	+20.00
Red	+50.00
Green	+350.00
"Paid"	+10.00
Red Carrier	+60.00
"Paid All"	+15.00

93	A32	2c **black**	500.	60.00
		gray black	500.	60.00
		No gum	190.	
		On cover		75.00
		Pair	1,050.	130.00
		Block of 4	2,750.	525.00
		P# strip of 4, Impt.	6,500.	
		P# block of 8, Impt.	—	
		Double transfer	550.	67.50
		Double grill	—	180.00
		Split grill	550.	65.00
		Double grill, one split	—	—
		Double grill, one quadruple split	1,100.	—
		Very thin paper	550.	65.00
a.		Vertical half used as 1c as part of 3c rate on cover		1,250.
b.		Diagonal half used as 1c as part of 3c rate on cover		1,250.
c.		Horizontal half used alone as 1c on cover		2,500.
d.		Diagonal half used alone as 1c on cover		2,500.

Earliest documented use: Mar. 27, 1868.

Cancellations

Blue	+8.00
Red	+20.00
Green	+250.00
"Paid"	+5.00
"Paid All"	+15.00
Black Carrier	+20.00
Red Carrier	+30.00
Japan	+350.00

94	A25	3c **red**	375.	10.00
		rose red	375.	10.00
a.		3c **rose**	375.	10.00
		No gum	150.	
		On cover		11.00
		Pair	800.	21.00
		Block of 4	3,000.	135.00
		P# block of 8, Impt.	8,750.	
		Double transfer	425.	25.00
		Double grill	—	—
		Double grill, one normal, one partial with points up		—
		Triple grill	—	250.00
		End roller grill		450.00
		Split grill	400.	15.00
		Quadruple split grill	700.	175.00
		Double grill, one quadruple split		—
		Grill with points up		—

		On cover		7,500.
		Very thin paper	400.	10.50
c.		Vertical pair, imperf. horiz.	15,000.	
		Block of 4	40,000.	
d.		Printed on both sides	9,000.	

Seven examples of No. 94d are recorded. Six are in the top row of an unused top margin imprint block of 18 (6x3).

Earliest documented use: Mar. 21, 1868.

Cancellations

Blue	+.25
Ultramarine	+3.00
Red	+3.50
Violet	+5.50
Green	+70.00
Numeral	+3.00
"Paid"	+2.25
"Paid All"	+12.50
"Free"	+20.00
Railroad	+30.00
Steamboat	+40.00
Packet boat	+80.00
Express Company	+50.00

See Die and Plate Proofs for imperf. on stamp paper.

95	A26	5c **brown**	3,750.	1,000.
		No gum	1,400.	
		dark brown	3,900.	1,100.
		No gum	1,450.	
		On cover		1,050.
		Pair	7,750.	2,100.
		Block of 4	17,500.	9,000.
		Double transfer of top frame line	—	—
		Double transfer of bottom frame line		
		Double grill	—	—
		Split grill	4,250.	1,025.
		Very thin paper	4,000.	1,000.
a.		5c **black brown**	4,750.	1,400.
		No gum	1,800.	

Earliest documented use: Aug. 19, 1868.

Cancellations

Blue	+25.
Magenta	+90.
Violet	+90.
Red	+80.
Green	+300.
"Paid"	+25.
"Free"	+75.
"Steamship"	+100.

Values of Nos. 95, 95a reflect the normal small margins.

96	A27	10c **yellow green**	3,000.	290.
		green	3,000.	290.
		blue green	3,000.	290.
		dark green	3,000.	375.
		No gum	1,000.	
		On cover		340.
		Pair	6,250.	600.
		Block of 4	26,500.	3,500.
		P# strip of 4, Impt.	29,000.	
		Double transfer	—	—
		Double grill	—	450.
		Split grill	3,250.	325.
		Quadruple split grill		725.
		Very thin paper	3,250.	325.

Earliest documented use: May 28, 1868.

Cancellations

Blue	+10.00
Red	+35.00
Magenta	+40.00
Green	+250.00
"Paid"	+10.00
"Free"	+50.00
Supplementary Mail Type A	
Steamship	+75.00
Japan	+200.00
China	

97	A28	12c **black**	3,250.	325.
		gray black	3,250.	325.
		No gum	1,200.	
		On cover		375.
		Pair	6,750.	675.
		Block of 4	50,000.	2,500.
		P# strip of 4, Impt.	50,000.	
		Double transfer of top frame line	3,750.	350.
		Double transfer of bottom frame line	3,750.	350.
		Double transfer of top and bottom frame lines		375.
		Double grill	—	550.
		Triple grill	—	—
		Split grill	3,750.	350.
		End roller grill	—	—
		Very thin paper	3,750.	350.

Earliest documented use: May 27, 1868.

Cancellations

Blue	+10.00
Red	+50.00
Magenta	+50.00
Brown	+50.00
Green	+250.00
Purple	+150.00
"Paid"	+20.00
"Insufficiently Prepaid"	+100.00
"Paid All"	+25.00
Supplementary Mail Type A	+50.00

98	A33	15c **black**	4,500.	400.
		gray black	4,500.	400.
		No gum	1,700.	
		On cover		450.

Pair			9,500.	825.
Block of 4			35,000.	6,000.
P# block of 8, Impt.			47,500.	
Double transfer of upper right corner			—	—
Double grill			—	550.
Split grill			4,750.	425.
Quadruple split grill			5,250.	750.
Very thin paper			4,750.	425.

Value for the plate block is for an example in fine condition.
Earliest documented use: May 4, 1868.

Cancellations

Blue	+20.00
Magenta	+75.00
Red	+150.00
Orange red	+40.00
Green	+300.00
Orange	+175.00
Purple	+100.00
Lavender	+150.00
"Paid"	+20.00
"Insufficiently Prepaid"	+135.00
"Insufficiently Paid"	+135.00
Japan	+300.00
Supplementary Mail Type A	+80.00

99	A29	24c	gray lilac	9,000.	1,500.
			gray	9,000.	1,500.
			No gum	3,500.	
			On cover		2,500.
			Pair	19,000.	3,250.
			Block of 4	45,000.	10,000.
			P# block of 8, Impt.	90,000.	
			Double grill	10,000.	2,300.
			Split grill	9,250.	1,600.
			Scratch under "A" of "Postage"	—	

Earliest documented use: Jan. 5, 1869.

Cancellations

Blue	+50.
Red	+150.
"Paid"	+50.

100	A30	30c	orange	8,500.	1,000.
			deep orange	8,500.	1,000.
			No gum	3,250.	
			On cover		2,000.
			Pair	18,000.	2,100.
			Block of 4	42,500.	10,000.
			Double grill	11,000.	1,800.
			Split grill	8,750.	1,050.
			Double grill, one split	—	
			Triple grill, two split	—	

Values for No. 100 are for examples with small margins, especially at sides. Large-margined examples sell for much more.

Earliest documented use: Nov. 10, 1868.

Cancellations

Blue	+25.
Red	+75.
Magenta	+100.
Green	+500.
"Paid"	+50.
Supplementary Mail Type A	+100.
Japan	+400.

101	A31	90c	blue	14,500.	2,400.
			dark blue	14,500.	2,400.
			No gum	5,500.	
			On cover		100,000.
			Pair	31,500.	5,000.
			Block of 4	75,000.	25,000.
			Double grill	19,000.	
			Split grill	15,000.	2,500.

Two usages on cover are recorded (one being a cover front). Value is for use on full cover to Peru.

Earliest documented use: May 8, 1869.

Cancellations

Blue	+100.
Red	+250.
Japan	+600.
"Paid"	+50.

RE-ISSUE OF 1861-66 ISSUES
Produced by the National Bank Note Co.
Without grill, hard white paper, with white crackly gum.

The 1, 2, 5, 10 and 12c were printed from new plates of 100 subjects each.

1875				Perf. 12	
102	A24	1c	blue (3195)	900.	1,250.
			No gum	400.	
			On cover		—
			Block of 4	60,000.	
103	A32	2c	black (979)	4,250.	10,000.
			No gum	2,000.	
			Block of 4	90,000.	
104	A25	3c	brown red (465)	4,750.	15,000.
			No gum	2,250.	
			Block of 4	100,000.	
105	A26	5c	brown (672)	3,250.	7,500.
			No gum	1,600.	
			Block of 4	100,000.	
106	A27	10c	green (451)	4,000.	25,000.
			No gum	1,900.	
			Block of 4	100,000.	
107	A28	12c	black (389)	4,750.	12,500.
			No gum	2,350.	
			Block of 4	125,000.	
108	A33	15c	black (397)	5,250.	19,000.
			No gum	2,600.	

109	A29	24c	deep violet (346)	6,500.	19,000.
			No gum	3,000.	
			Block of 4	125,000.	
110	A30	30c	brownish orange (346)	6,750.	22,500.
			No gum	3,250.	
			Pair	16,500.	
			Block of 4	125,000.	
111	A31	90c	blue (317)	7,250.	225,000.
			No gum	3,500.	

Earliest documented uses: No. 102, July 25, 1881; No. 104, July ?, 1883 (dated cancel on off-cover stamp); No. 111, Nov. 30, 1888 (dated cancel on off-cover stamp).

These stamps can be distinguished from the 1861-66 issue by the brighter colors, the sharper proof-like impressions and the paper which is very white instead of yellowish. The gum is almost always somewhat yellowed with age, and unused stamps with original gum are valued with such gum.

Numbers in parentheses are quantities sold.

Five examples are recorded of No. 111 used, one of which has a non-contemporaneous cancel. Value is for centered and sound example (two are known thus).

PLEASE NOTE:
Stamps are valued in the grade of very fine unless otherwise indicated.

Values for early and valuable stamps are for examples with certificates of authenticity from acknowledged expert committees, or examples sold with the buyer having the right of certification. This applies to examples with original gum as well as examples without gum. Beware of stamps offered "as is," as the gum on some unused stamps offered with "original gum" may be fraudulent, and unused stamps offered without may in some cases be altered or faintly canceled used stamps.

VALUES FOR NEVER-HINGED STAMPS PRIOR TO SCOTT No. 182
This catalogue does not value pre-1879 stamps in never-hinged condition. Premiums for never-hinged condition in the classic era invariably are even larger than those premiums listed for the 1879 and later issues. Generally speaking, the earlier the stamp is listed in the catalogue, the larger will be the never-hinged premium. On some early classics, the premium will be several multiples of the unused, hinged values given in the catalogue.

Produced by the National Bank Note Co.

Plates for the 1c, 2c, 3c, 6c, 10c and 12c consisted of 300 subjects in two panes of 150 each. For the 15c, 24c, 30c and 90c plates of 100 subjects each.

NOTE: Stamps of the 1869 issue without grill cannot be guaranteed except when unused and with the original gum or traces of the original gum.

Franklin — A34

Post Horse and Rider — A35

G. Grill measuring 9 ½x9mm
(12 by 11 to 11 ½ points)

1869			Hard Wove Paper		Perf. 12
112	A34	1c	buff	750.	175.
			brown orange	750.	175.
			dark brown orange	800.	200.
			No gum	275.	
			On cover, single		300.
			Pair	1,550.	400.
			Block of 4	6,000.	2,250.
			Margin block of 4, arrow	6,250.	
			P# block of 10, Impt.	—	—
			Double transfer	—	
			Double grill	1,150.	350.
			Split grill	850.	225.
			Double grill, one split		
			Double grill, one quadruple split		—
b.	Without grill, original gum			20,000.	

Earliest documented use: Apr. 1, 1869.

Cancellations

Blue	+25.
Ultramarine	+700.
Magenta	+75.
Purple	+100.
Red	+65.
Green	+800.
"Paid"	+50.
Numeral	+100.
Steamship	+110.
Black town	+30.

Red town		+90.
Black Carrier		+80.
Blue Carrier		+100.
Japan		+675.
113 A35 2c **brown**	700.	100.
pale brown	700.	100.
dark brown	700.	100.
yellow brown	700.	100.
No gum	250.	
On cover, single		140.
Pair	1,500.	250.
Block of 4	3,750.	1,350.
Margin block of 4, arrow	3,850.	
P# block of 10, Impt.	—	
Double grill	—	325.
Split grill	850.	125.
Quadruple split grill	—	450.
End roller grill	1,150.	
Double transfer		120.
b. Without grill, original gum	*7,500.*	
c. Half used as 1c on cover, diagonal, vertical or horizontal		*6,000.*
d. Printed on both sides		*9,000.*

Earliest documented use: Mar. 20, 1869.

Cancellations

Blue	+20.
Red	+40.
Orange red	+45.
Orange	+100.
Magenta	+40.
Purple	+50.
Ultramarine	+80.
Green	+500.
Brown	+150.
"Paid"	+15.
"Paid All"	+25.
Steamship	+75.
Black town	+10.
Blue town	+30.
Japan	+250.
Blue Carrier	+90.
Black Carrier	+80.
China	—
Printed Precancellation "Jefferson, Ohio"	+6,500.

Locomotive — A36

Washington — A37

114 A36 3c **ultramarine**	275.	20.00
pale ultramarine	275.	20.00
dark ultramarine	275.	20.00
No gum	90.	
blue	625.	100.00
No gum	225.	
violet blue		—
On cover		25.00
Pair	600.	45.00
Block of 4	1,500.	450.00
Margin block of 4, arrow	1,700.	
P# block of 10, Impt.	*7,500.*	
Double transfer	350.	37.50
Double grill	575.	110.00
Triple grill	—	—
Sextuple grill	—	*7,000.*
Split grill	325.	40.00
Quadruple split grill	625.	150.00
Double grill, one split		—
Double grill, one quadruple split		—
End roller grill	—	—
Grill with points up	—	—
Gray paper	—	100.00
On cover		850.00
Without grill		—
Cracked plate	—	160.00
a. Without grill, original gum	*12,500.*	
b. Vert. one-third used as 1c on cover		—
c. Vert. two-thirds used as 2c on cover		*5,000.*
d. Double impression		*11,000.*
e. Printed on both sides, reverse inverted		*55,000.*

The grill-with-points-up variety is found on a unique margin "pair" of stamps where the paper was folded over prior to perforating and grilling. The stamps have drastic freak perfs.

The existence of the violet blue shade has been questioned by specialists. The editors would like to receive authenticated evidence of its existence.

Nos. 114d and 114e each are unique. No. 114d has a pre-printing paper fold.

Earliest documented use: Mar. 27, 1869.

Cancellations

Blue	+5.
Ultramarine	+25.
Magenta	+35.
Purple	+75.
Violet	+65.
Red	+15.
Orange red	+20.
Brown	+200.
Green	+400.
Orange	—
Yellow	—
Black town	+3.
Blue town	+7.
Red town	+30.
Numeral	+15.
"Paid"	+20.
"Paid All"	+15.
"Steamboat"	—
"Steamship"	+50.
Ship	+35.
"U. S. Ship"	+450.
Railroad	+30.
Packet Boat	+100.
Black Carrier	+30.
Blue Carrier	+40.
Express Company	+250.
"Way"	—
"Free"	+150.
Alaska	—
Japan	+600.

The authenticity of the yellow cancel has been questioned by some specialists. The editors would like to see an expertizing certificate for this stamp and cancel.

115 A37 6c **ultramarine**	2,750.	250.
pale ultramarine	2,750.	250.
No gum	1,000.	
On cover		450.
Pair	5,750.	600.
Block of 4	16,500.	9,000.
Margin block of 4, arrow	*17,500.*	
Double grill		675.
Split grill	3,000.	325.
Quadruple split grill	—	850.
Double transfer		290.
b. Vertical half used as 3c on cover		*50,000.*

Earliest documented use: Apr. 26, 1869.
No. 115b is unique.

Cancellations

Blue	+25.
Brown	+125.
Magenta	+50.
Purple	+85.
Red	+75.
Green	+1,000.
"Paid"	+15.
"Paid All"	+25.
Black town	+30.
"Short Paid"	+75.
"Insufficiently Paid"	+75.
Steamship	+45.
Railroad	+50.
Japan	+1,500.

Shield and Eagle — A38

S.S. "Adriatic" — A39

116 A38 10c **yellow**	2,250.	150.
yellowish orange	2,250.	150.
No gum	875.	
On cover		425.
Pair	4,750.	350.
Block of 4	14,000.	8,000.
Margin block of 4, arrow	*14,000.*	
Double grill		425.
Split grill	2,500.	175.
End roller grill	—	

Earliest documented use: Apr. 1, 1869.

Cancellations

Blue	+35.
Magenta	+80.
Purple	+250.
Red	+40.
Ultramarine	+200.
Green	+5,000.
Black town	+20.
Numeral	—
Steamship	+35.
Railroad	+45.
"Paid"	+15.
"Paid All"	+30.
"Insufficiently Paid"	+50.
Supplementary Mail Type A	+150.
Express Company	—
Alaska	+5,000.
St. Thomas	—
Hawaii	—
Japan	+150.
China	—

117 A39 12c **green**	2,250.	160.
yellowish green	2,250.	160.
bluish green	2,500.	200.
No gum	825.	
On cover		500.
Pair	4,750.	340.
Block of 4	14,000.	1,800.
Margin block of 4, arrow	*14,500.*	
Double grill		425.
Split grill	2,750.	190.
Double grill, one quadruple split		—
End roller grill		600.

Earliest documented use: Apr. 1, 1869.

Cancellations

Blue	+150.
Magenta	+125.
Purple	+250.
Brown	+250.
Red	+150.
Green	+3,500.
Numeral	+125.
"Paid"	+25.
"Paid All"	+40.
"Too Late"	+100.
"Insufficiently Paid"	+125.
Black town	+35.
Red town	+250.
Japan	+500.

Landing of Columbus — A40

No. 118 has horizontal shading lines at the left and right sides of the vignette.

118 A40 15c **brown & blue,** type I, Picture unframed	10,000.	750.
dark brown & blue	10,000.	750.
No gum	3,750.	
On cover		1,900.
Pair	22,500.	1,750.
Block of 4	*60,000.*	30,000.
Double grill	18,000.	950.
Split grill	10,500.	800.
a. Without grill, original gum	*13,000.*	

Earliest documented use: Mar. 31, 1869 (dated cancel on off-cover stamp); Apr. 2, 1869 (on cover).

Cancellations

Blue	+75.
Red	+135.
Brown	+150.
"Paid"	+50.
"Paid All"	+100.
"Insufficiently Paid"	+150.
Black town	+50.
Blue town	+150.
Steamship	+100.

A40a

No. 119 has diagonal shading lines at the left and right sides of the vignette.

119 A40a 15c **brown & blue,** type II, Picture framed	3,500.	275.
dark brown & blue	3,500.	275.
No gum	1,300.	
On cover		900.
Pair	7,500.	600.
Block of 4	*18,500.*	9,000.
P# block of 8, Impt.	*45,000.*	
Double transfer		—
Double grill	5,750.	525.
Split grill	3,750.	350.
b. Center inverted	1,250,000.	20,000.
No gum	750,000.	
c. Center double, one inverted		*80,000.*

Earliest documented use: Apr. 5, 1869.

Cancellations

Blue	+60.
Purple	+135.
Magenta	+135.
Red	+150.
Brown	+200.
Green	+1,500.
Numeral	+75.
"Paid"	+20.
"Paid All"	+35.
Black town	+30.
Blue town	+75.
Red town	+200.
"Steamship"	+75.
Supp. Mail Type A or F	+40.
Japan	+500.

Most examples of No. 119b are faulty. Values are for fine centered examples with only minimal faults. Three examples of No. 119b unused are recorded; only one has original gum.

Three examples of No. 119c are recorded. Value is for the finer of the two sound examples.

The Declaration of
Independence — A41

120 A41 24c **green & violet**   9,000.   775.
        bluish green & violet   9,000.   775.
        No gum   3,500.
        On cover, domestic usage   12,500.
        On cover, foreign usage   24,000.
        Pair   20,000.   1,650.
        Block of 4   52,500. 25,000.
        Double grill   2,250.
        Split grill   9,500.   900.
  a. Without grill, original gum   15,000.
  b. Center inverted   750,000. 32,500.
        On cover   105,000.
        Pair   110,000.
        Block of 4   600,000.

Earliest documented use: Apr. 7, 1869 (No. 120); Mar. 1874
(No. 120b).

Cancellations

Blue   +250.
Red   +300.
Black town   +100.
Red town   +400.
"Paid All"   +150.
"Steamship"   +250.
Supp. Mail Type A   +200.
China   +750.

Most examples of No. 120b are faulty. Values are for fine
centered examples with only minimal faults. No. 120b unused is
valued without gum, as all of the three examples available to
collectors are without gum.

Shield, Eagle and   Lincoln — A43
Flags — A42

121 A42 30c **ultramarine & carmine**   7,000.   550.
        ultramarine & dark car-
        mine   7,000.   550.
        No gum   2,750.
        On cover, domestic us-
        age   17,500.
        On cover, foreign usage   32,500.
        Pair   15,500.   1,250.
        Block of 4   40,000.   3,750.
        Double grill   1,500.
        Split grill   7,500.   600.
        Double paper (without
        grill), original gum   7,750.
  a. Without grill, original gum   12,000.
        Block of 4   50,000.
        P# block of 8, Impt.
  b. Flags inverted   1,000,000. 110,000.
        No gum   250,000.

Seven examples of No. 121b unused are recorded. Only one
has part of its original gum.

Earliest documented use: May 22, 1869.

Cancellations

Blue   +250.
Red   +250.
Brown   +600.
Purple   +1,000.
Green   +7,500.
"Paid"   +50.
"Paid All"   +250.
Black town   +100.
Steamship   +85.
"Steam"   +70.
Supp. Mail Type A   +75.
Japan   +600.
China

122 A43 90c **carmine & black**   13,000.   2,500.
        carmine rose & black   13,000.   2,500.
        No gum   5,000.
        On cover   430,000.
        Pair   32,500.   9,000.
        Block of 4   115,000. 55,000.
        Split grill
  a. Without grill, original gum   25,000.

Cancellations

Blue   +1,500.
Red   +700.
Orange red   +750.
Brown   +2,000.
Purple   +3,000.
Ultramarine   +1,750.
Black town   +1,500.
Red town   +1,750.
Magenta town   +2,500.

"Paid"   —
"Paid All"   —
N.Y. steamship   +1,000.

Nos. 112, 114, 117, 118, 120b, 121, 122 exist as imperf.
singles. They were not regularly issued.
No. 122 on cover is unique. Value reflects 2009 auction sale
price.

CANCELLATIONS

The common type of cancellation on the 1869 issue is the
block or cork similar to illustrations above. Japanese cancellations seen on this issue (not illustrated) resulted from the sale of
U.S. stamps in Japanese cities where post offices were main-
tained for mail going from Japan to the United States.

RE-ISSUE OF 1869 ISSUE
Produced by the National Bank Note Co.
**Without grill, hard white paper, with white crackly
gum.**

The gum is almost always somewhat yellowed with age, and
unused stamps with original gum are valued with such gum.
A new plate of 150 subjects was made for the 1c and for the
frame of the 15c. The frame on the 15c is the same as type I but
without the fringe of brown shading lines around central
vignette.

1875   *Perf. 12*
123 A34 1c **buff** *(10,000)*   600.   400.
        No gum   250.
        Block of 4   3,500.
        On cover   3,000.
124 A35 2c **brown** *(4755)*   700.   875.
        No gum   275.
        Block of 4   4,500.
        On cover   12,500.
125 A36 3c **blue** *(1406)*   5,500. 27,500.
        No gum   2,750.
        On cover   —

Cancellation
Supplementary Mail Type F   —

Very few authenticated sound used examples of No. 125 are
recorded. The used value is for an attractive fine to very fine
example with minimal faults. Examples of No. 114 with faint or
pressed-out grill are frequently offered as No. 125. Expertization by competent authorities is required.

126 A37 6c **blue** *(2226)*   2,000.   2,750.
        No gum   900.
        Block of 4   24,000.
        On cover   —
127 A38 10c **yellow** *(1947)*   2,000.   2,000.
        No gum   900.
        Block of 4   25,000.
        On cover   22,500.
128 A39 12c **green** *(1584)*   2,750.   3,250.
        No gum   1,250.
        Block of 4   30,000.
        On cover   —
129 A40 15c **brown & blue**, Type III,
        (1981)   1,650.   1,300.
        No gum   750.
        Pair   6,000.
        Block of 4   29,000.
        On cover   22,500.
  a. Imperf. horizontally, single   6,250.   7,000.
        No gum   4,000.
130 A41 24c **green & violet** *(2091)* 2,500.   1,750.
        Pair   1,100.
        On cover   10,000.
                                     27,500.
131 A42 30c **ultra & carmine** *(1535)* 3,000.   3,000.
        No gum   1,450.
        Pair   28,000.
132 A43 90c **carmine & black** *(1356)* 4,500.   6,500.
        No gum   1,900.
        Pair   32,500.
        Block of 4   35,000.
        P# block of 10, Impt. 325,000.

Numbers in parentheses are quantities sold.
Two used examples of No. 129a are recorded. Both are faulty
and are valued thus.

Earliest documented uses:
No. 123, Dec. 9, 1877;
No. 124, Mar. 20, 1880;
No. 127, Nov. 11, 1880;
No. 128, Mar. 20, 1880.
No. 129, Mar. 20, 1880;
No. 130, Mar. 27, 1880.

RE-ISSUE OF 1869 ISSUE
Produced by the American Bank Note Co.
Without grill, soft porous paper.
1880-82
133 A34 1c **buff**, issued with gum (5,000)   350.   *400.*
        No gum   150.
        Block of 4, with gum   1,750.
        Margin block of 10, Impt. & P# 22,500.
        On cover   1,900.
  a.   1c **brown orange**, issued without gum,
        1881-82 (18,252)   225.   *350.*
        Block of 4, without gum   1,050.
        Margin block of 10, Impt. & P#,
        without gum   22,500.

Earliest documented use: Oct. 5, 1880 (No. 133).

PRODUCED BY THE NATIONAL BANK NOTE COMPANY
Plates of 200 subjects in two panes of 100 each.

Franklin

A44

Jackson

A45

Washington

A46

Lincoln

A47

The World's Great Rarities Benefit from Philatelic Foundation Certificates
Your Stamps and Covers Will, Too

The unique Ice House cover has been shrouded in secrecy for over 80 years – yet it was no mystery to the experts of The Philatelic Foundation. Recently our experts examined this legendary cover and we issued our Expert Opinion declaring it to be a genuine usage of the 1869 90¢ Lincoln Pictorial – the only known example on cover.

Why do savvy collectors and knowledgeable dealers turn to The Philatelic Foundation for their opinions? Because PF opinions are respected and add additional value to genuine stamps and covers. Simply put, many stamps and covers are worth more with a PF Certificate than without one.

Submit Your Stamps and Covers Today for a PF Certificate

The same experts who worked on the unique Ice House cover will examine your stamps and covers. These experts will access the same multimillion-dollar reference collection, apply decades of scholarship and issue an opinion you can trust.

Call 1-212-221-6555 or visit www.PhilatelicFoundation.org today to download a submission form. Fill out the one-page form and send it to us with your stamp or cover. Our experts will study your stamp or cover and return it to you (typically within 30 business days, often less) along with your certificate.

Reward yourself with the security of a Philatelic Foundation Certificate – the gold standard of philatelic certificates for over 60 years.

The Philatelic Foundation
70 West 40th Street, 15th Floor
New York, NY 10018
(212) 221-6555
www.PhilatelicFoundation.org

Edwin M. Stanton

A48

Jefferson

A49

Henry Clay

A50

Daniel Webster

A51

Two varieties of grill are known on this issue.
H. Grill about 10x12mm (11 to 13 by 14 to 16 points.) On all values 1c to 90c.
I. Grill about 8½x10mm (10 to 11 by 10 to 13 points.) On 1, 2, 3, 6, 7, 10 and 15c.
On the 1870-71 stamps the grill impressions are usually faint or incomplete. This is especially true of the H grill, which often shows only a few points.
Values for 1c-7c are for stamps showing well-defined grills.
Killer cancellation of the oval grid type with letters or numeral centers was first used in 1876 Bank Note issues. By order of the Postmaster-General (July 23, 1860) it was prohibited to use the town mark as a canceling instrument, and a joined town and killer cancellation was developed.
Numeral cancellations—see "Postal Markings-Examples."

White Wove Paper, Thin to Medium Thick.

1870-71   **Perf. 12**
134 A44   1c **ultramarine**, *Apr. 1870*   2,250.   210.00
              pale ultramarine   2,250.   210.00
              dark ultramarine   2,250.   210.00
              No gum   800.
              On cover   240.00
              Pair   4,750.   450.00

Block of 4		12,500.	1,150.
Double transfer		2,500.	230.00
Double grill			350.00
Split grill		2,750.	230.00
Quadruple split grill		—	550.00
End roller grill			725.00

Earliest documented use: Apr. 9, 1870.

Cancellations
Blue	+25.00
Red	+50.00
Green	+150.00
"Paid"	+10.00
"Paid All"	+20.00
"Steamship"	+45.00

135 A45   2c **red brown**, *Apr. 1870*   1,100.   90.00
              pale red brown   1,100.   90.00
              dark red brown   1,100.   90.00
              No gum   400.
              On cover   115.00
              Pair   2,300.   190.00
              Block of 4   6,000.   525.00
              Double grill   1,500.   160.00
              Split grill   1,150.   105.00
              Quadruple split grill   2,400.   250.00
              End roller grill   1,900.   400.00
              Grill with points up   500.00
  a.   Diagonal half used as 1c on cover   —
  b.   Vertical half used as 1c on cover   —

Earliest documented use: July 14, 1870.

Cancellations
Blue	+10.00
Red	+20.00
Brown	+15.00
Green	+100.00
"Paid"	+5.00
"Paid All"	+10.00
Numeral	+5.00
China	

136 A46   3c **green**, *Mar. 1870*   675.   32.50
              pale green   675.   32.50
              yellow green   675.   32.50
              deep green   675.   32.50
              No gum   225.
              On cover   37.50
              Pair   1,400.   67.50
              Block of 4   3,500.   240.00
              P# block of 10, Impt.   9,000.
              P# block of 12, Impt.   11,000.
              Printed on both sides   —
              Double transfer   —   37.50
              Double grill   1,100.   90.00
              Split grill   725.   37.50
              Quadruple split grill   —   150.00
              End roller grill   —   275.00
              Cracked plate   —   100.00
  a.   Pair, one without grill, on cover   —

Earliest documented use: Mar. 24, 1870.

Cancellations
Blue	+5.00
Purple	+10.00
Magenta	+10.00
Red	+10.00
Orange red	+10.00
Orange	+25.00
Brown	+2.50
Green	+60.00
"Paid"	+2.50
Railroad	+10.00
"Steamship"	+20.00
"Paid All"	+15.00
Numeral	+4.00
"Free"	+25.00

See Die and Plate Proofs for imperf. on stamp paper.

137 A47   6c **carmine**, *Apr. 1870*   5,250.   575.00
              pale carmine   5,250.   575.00
              carmine rose   5,250.   575.00
              No gum   1,850.
              On cover   800.00
              Pair   11,000. 1,200.
              Block of 4   28,500.
              Double grill   —   950.00
              Split grill   5,500.   600.00
              Quadruple split grill   —   1,000.
              End roller grill   6,750. 1,150.
  a.   Pair, one without grill   —
              Strip of 4 + single, one in
              strip without grill, on cover   —

Earliest documented use: Apr. 11, 1870.

Cancellations
Blue	+50.
Red	+75.
"Paid"	+35.

138 A48   7c **vermilion**, *1871*   4,500.   575.
              deep vermilion   4,500.   575.
              No gum   1,650.
              On cover   750.
              Pair   9,500. 1,200.
              Block of 4   25,000.
              Double grill   —   875.
              Split grill   4,750.   600.
              Quadruple split grill   — 1,000.
              End roller grill   — 1,050.

Earliest documented use: Feb. 12, 1871.

Cancellations
Blue	+25.00
Purple	+35.00
Red	+50.00
Green	+250.00
"Paid"	+25.00

The 7c stamps, Nos. 138 and 149, were issued for a 7c rate of July 1, 1870, to Prussia, German States and Austria, including Hungary, via Hamburg (on the Hamburg-American Line steamers), or Bremen (on North German Lloyd ships), but issue was delayed by the Franco-Prussian War.
The rate for this service was reduced to 6c in 1871.
For several months there was no 7c rate, but late in 1871 the Prussian closed mail rate via England was reduced to 7c which revived an important use for the 7c stamps.
The rate to Denmark direct via Baltic Lloyd ships, or via Bremen and Hamburg as above, was 7c from Jan. 1, 1872.

139 A49   10c **brown**, *Apr. 1870*   7,000.   850.
              yellow brown   7,000.   850.
              dark brown   7,000.   850.
              No gum   2,550.
              On cover   1,050.
              Pair   14,500. 1,750.
              Block of 4   35,000.   —
              Double grill   —   1,400.
              Split grill   7,250.   875.
              End roller grill   —   1,750.

Earliest documented use: May 6, 1870.

Cancellations
Blue	+50.
Red	+100.
"Steamship"	+50.
"Honolulu Paid All"	

140 A50   12c **dull violet**, *Apr. 1870*   27,500.   3,750.
              No gum   13,000.
              On cover   7,000.
              Pair   60,000.   8,500.
              Strip of 3   16,000.
              Strip of 4   20,000.
              Block of 4   130,000.
              Split grill   4,000.
              End roller grill   7,250.

Earliest documented use: June 17, 1870.

Cancellations
Blue	+100.
Red	+250.
"Paid all"	—

141 A51   15c **orange**, *Apr. 1870*   8,000.   1,500.
              bright orange   8,000.   1,500.
              deep orange   8,000.   1,500.
              No gum   2,750.
              On cover   2,200.
              Pair   17,000. 3,250.
              Block of 4   45,000.
              Double grill   4,000.
              Split grill   8,250. 1,600.
              Quadruple split grill

Earliest documented use: June 2, 1870.

Cancellations
Blue	+50.
Purple	+100.
Red	+150.
Green	+400.

General Winfield Scott — A52

Alexander Hamilton — A53

142 A52   24c **purple**   —   7,500.
              On cover   —
              Pair, double grill   —
              Split grill   —
              End roller grill   —
              Grill with points up   —

Earliest documented use: July 11, 1872.

Cancellations
Red	+750.
Blue	+1,000.
Purple	

The pair of No. 142 is the unique multiple of this stamp.

143 A53   30c **black**, *Apr. 1870*   20,000.   4,000.
              full black   20,000.   4,000.
              No gum   7,500.
              On cover   5,000.
              Pair   42,500.   8,500.
              Block of 4   100,000.
              Double grill   —
              End roller grill   —   5,500.

Earliest documented use: Aug. 18, 1870.

Cancellations
Blue	+75.
Red	+125.

Commodore Oliver Hazard Perry — A54

144 A54 90c **carmine,** *Apr. 12, 1870*	25,000.	2,750.
dark carmine	25,000.	2,750.
No gum	10,000.	
On cover		—
Pair	*55,000.*	6,000.
Block of 4	*125,000.*	*13,500.*
Double grill		—
Split grill		2,900.

Cancellations

Blue	+80.
Red	+140.

PRODUCED BY THE NATIONAL BANK NOTE COMPANY.

White Wove Paper, Thin to Medium Thick.
Issued (except 3c, 6c and 7c) in April, 1870.
Without Grill.

1870-71 ***Perf. 12***

145 A44 1c **ultramarine**	750.	25.00
pale ultramarine	750.	25.00
dark ultramarine	750.	25.00
gray blue	750.	25.00
No gum	275.	
On cover		27.50
Pair	1,550.	52.50
Block of 4	3,750.	150.00
P# block of 12, Impt.	*4,500.*	
Double transfer	—	30.00
Worn plate	750.	25.00

Only one plate block of No. 145 is known in private hands. It is of average condition and is without gum. Value is based on 1998 auction sale.

Earliest documented use: May 7, 1870.

Cancellations

Blue	+1.50
Ultramarine	+2.50
Magenta	+2.00
Purple	+2.00
Brown	+2.00
Red	+5.00
Green	+55.00
"Paid"	+3.00
"Paid All"	+15.00
"Steamship"	+25.00
Railroad	+20.00
Numeral	+2.00

146 A45 2c **red brown**	350.	20.00
pale red brown	350.	20.00
dark red brown	350.	20.00
No gum	125.	
orange brown	375.	21.50
No gum	135.	
On cover		22.50
Pair	725.	42.50
Block of 4	1,750.	130.00
P# block of 10, Impt.	*7,000.*	
Double transfer	—	22.50
a. Diagonal half used as 1c on cover		*700.00*
b. Vertical half used as 1c on cover		*800.00*
c. Horiz. half used as 1c on cover		*800.00*
d. Double impression	*9,000.*	

The No. 146 plate block is unique. Value is 1998 auction realization. No. 146d is also unique. It has VG-Fine centering and faults and is valued thus.

Earliest documented use: May 7, 1870.

Cancellations

Blue	+1.00
Purple	+1.25
Red	+3.00
Green	+55.00
Brown	+1.25
"Paid"	+2.00
"Paid All"	+10.00
Numeral	+2.00
"Steamship"	+22.50
Black Carrier	+12.50
Japan	—
China	—
Curacao	—

Major Plate Crack At Bottom

147 A46 3c **green**	275.	2.00
pale green	275.	2.00
dark green	275.	2.00
No gum	95.	
yellow green	300.	2.10
No gum	105.	
On cover		2.40
Pair	575.	4.25
Block of 4	1,400.	25.00
P# block of 10, Impt.	*3,750.*	
Double transfer	—	12.00
Short transfer at bottom	300.	20.00
Cracked plate	—	55.00
Major plate crack at bottom (91L, plate ?)		*400.00*
On cover		*800.00*
Worn plate	275.	2.00
a. Printed on both sides		*15,000.*
b. Double impression		*40,000.*
On cover		—

See Die and Plate Proofs for imperf. on stamp paper.

Earliest documented use: Mar. 1, 1870.

Cancellations

Blue	+.25
Purple	+.50
Magenta	+.50
Brown	+1.50
Red	+2.50
Ultramarine	+2.00
Green	+55.00
Orange	+750.00
"Paid"	+2.00
"Paid All"	+10.00
"Free"	+15.00
Numeral	+2.00
Railroad	+10.00
Express Company	—
"Steamboat"	+20.00
"Steamship"	+17.50
Ship	+15.00
Japan	+75.00

148 A47 6c **carmine**	1,100.	37.50
dark carmine	1,100.	37.50
rose	1,100.	37.50
No gum	350.	
On cover		52.50
Pair	2,300.	80.00
Block of 4	5,500.	360.00
Double transfer		47.50
brown carmine	1,150.	67.50
No gum	425.	
violet carmine	1,300.	95.00
No gum	500.	
a. Vertical half used as 3c on cover		*3,500.*
b. Double impression		*1,500.*
On cover		*3,000.*
c. Double paper	—	*100.00*

Earliest documented use: Mar. 28, 1870.

Cancellations

Blue	+1.50
Purple	+2.00
Violet	+2.00
Ultramarine	+3.00
Brown	+2.00
Red	+5.00
Claret	+10.00
Orange red	+7.00
Orange	+10.00
Green	+115.00
"Paid"	+3.00
"Steamship"	+25.00
"Paid All"	+15.00
Numeral	—
Supp. Mail Type A or D	+25.00
China	+75.00
Japan	+150.00

149 A48 7c **vermilion,** *Mar. 1871*	1,100.	100.00
deep vermilion	1,100.	100.00
No gum	375.	
On cover		160.00
Pair	2,300.	220.00
Block of 4	6,250.	*775.00*
Cracked plate		—

Earliest documented use: May 11, 1871.

Cancellations

Blue	+2.50
Purple	+7.50
Ultramarine	+12.50
Red	+10.00
Green	+450.00
Japan	+150.00

150 A49 10c **brown**	2,000.	35.00
dark brown	2,000.	35.00
yellow brown	2,000.	35.00
No gum	750.	
On cover		50.00
Pair	4,250.	72.50
Block of 4	9,250.	*275.00*
P# block of 10, Impt.	—	
Double transfer	—	90.00

Earliest documented use: May 14, 1870 (stamp on piece); May 19, 1870 (on cover).

Cancellations

Blue	+1.00
Purple	+2.00
Magenta	+2.00
Ultramarine	+4.00
Red	+4.00
Orange red	+5.00
Orange	+10.00
Green	+120.00
Brown	+3.00
"Paid All"	+20.00
"Steamship"	+20.00
Supp. Mail Type A or D	+25.00
Japan	+120.00
China	—
St. Thomas	—

151 A50 12c **dull violet**	2,750.	220.00
violet	2,750.	220.00
dark violet	2,750.	220.00
No gum	1,000.	
On cover		475.00
Pair	5,750.	475.00
Block of 4	*14,000.*	*2,250.*

Earliest documented use: July 9, 1870.

Cancellations

Blue	+25.00
Ultramarine	+1,000.
Magenta	+10.00
Red	+15.00
Orange	—
Green	+150.00
"Paid All"	+25.00
"Steamship"	+50.00
Supp. Mail Type A or D	+40.00
Japan	—

152 A51 15c **bright orange**	3,000.	220.00
deep orange	3,000.	220.00
No gum	1,100.	
On cover		375.00
Pair	6,250.	475.00
Block of 4	*15,000.*	*1,850.*
a. Double impression		*6,000.*

Earliest documented use: June 24, 1870.

Cancellations

Blue	+7.50
Magenta	+7.50
Ultramarine	+10.00
Red	+15.00
Purple	+750.00
"Paid"	+12.50
"Steamship"	+40.00
Supp. Mail Type A or F	+30.00
China	—

153 A52 24c **purple**	2,000.	230.00
bright purple	2,000.	230.00
No gum	700.	
On cover		*1,500.*
Pair	4,250.	500.00
Block of 4	*14,000.*	*3,500.*
a. Double paper	—	—

Earliest documented use: Nov. 18, 1870.

Cancellations

Red	+15.00
Blue	+5.00
Purple	+7.50
China	—
"Paid"	+25.00
Town	+15.00
"Steamship"	—
Supp. Mail Type A, D or F	+30.00

154	A53	30c **black**	7,500.	300.00
		full black	7,500.	325.00
		No gum	2,750.	
		On cover		900.00
		Pair	*16,000.*	625.00
		Block of 4	*38,500.*	

Earliest documented use: July 13, 1870.

Cancellations

Blue	+5.00
Brown	+50.00
Magenta	+15.00
Red	+50.00
"Steamship"	+55.00
Supplementary Mail Type A	+40.00

155	A54	90c **carmine**	5,500.	350.00
		dark carmine	5,500.	350.00
		No gum	2,100.	
		On cover		—
		Pair	*11,500.*	725.00
		Block of 4	*26,000.*	2,250.
		P# strip of 5, Impt.	*36,000.*	

Earliest documented use: Sept. 1, 1872.

Cancellations

Blue	+10.00
Purple	+15.00
Magenta	+15.00
Green	+275.00
Red	+50.00
Town	+20.00
Supp. Mail Type A or F	+40.00
Japan	—

PLEASE NOTE:

Stamps are valued in the grade of very fine unless otherwise indicated.

Values for early and valuable stamps are for examples with certificates of authenticity from acknowledged expert committees, or examples sold with the buyer having the right of certification. This applies to examples with original gum as well as examples without gum. Beware of stamps offered "as is," as the gum on some unused stamps offered with "original gum" may be fraudulent, and stamps offered as unused without gum may in some cases be altered or faintly canceled used stamps.

VALUES FOR NEVER-HINGED STAMPS PRIOR TO SCOTT No. 182

This catalogue does not value pre-1879 stamps in never-hinged condition. Premiums for never-hinged condition in the classic era invariably are even larger than those premiums listed for the 1879 and later issues. Generally speaking, the earlier the stamp is listed in the catalogue, the larger will be the never-hinged premium. On some early classics, the premium will be several multiples of the unused, hinged values given in the catalogue.

PRINTED BY THE CONTINENTAL BANK NOTE COMPANY

Plates of 200 subjects in two panes of 100 each.

Designs of the 1870-71 Issue with secret marks on the values from 1c to 15c, as described and illustrated:

The object of secret marks was to provide a simple and positive proof that these stamps were produced by the Continental Bank Note Company and not by their predecessors.

Franklin — A44a

1c. In the pearl at the left of the numeral "1" there is a small crescent.

Jackson — A45a

2c. Under the scroll at the left of "U. S." there is a small diagonal line. This mark seldom shows clearly. The stamp, No. 157, can be distinguished by its color.

Washington — A46a

3c. The under part of the upper tail of the left ribbon is heavily shaded.

Lincoln — A47a

6c. The first four vertical lines of the shading in the lower part of the left ribbon have been strengthened.

Stanton — A48a

7c. Two small semi-circles are drawn around the ends of the lines that outline the ball in the lower right hand corner.

Jefferson — A49a

10c. There is a small semi-circle in the scroll at the right end of the upper label.

Clay — A50a

12c. The balls of the figure "2" are crescent shaped.

Webster — A51a

15c. In the lower part of the triangle in the upper left corner two lines have been made heavier forming a "V." This mark can be found on some of the Continental and American (1879) printings, but not all stamps show it.

Secret marks were added to the dies of the 24c, 30c and 90c but new plates were not made from them. The various printings of the 30c and 90c can be distinguished only by the shades and paper.

J. Grill about 7x9½mm exists on all values except 24c and 90c. Grill was composed of truncated pyramids and was so strongly impressed that some points often broke through the paper.

White Wove Paper, Thin to Thick

1873, July (?)				**Perf. 12**
156	A44a	1c **ultramarine**	275.	6.00
		pale ultramarine	275.	6.00
		gray blue	275.	6.00
		blue	275.	6.00
		No gum	95.	
		dark ultramarine	300.	6.00
		No gum	105.	
		On cover		7.50
		Pair	575.	12.50
		Block of 4	1,250.	50.00
		P# block of 12, Impt.	*6,250.*	
		Double transfer	350.	10.00
		Ribbed paper	400.	25.00
		Paper with silk fibers	—	35.00
		Cracked plate		
		Paper cut with "cogwheel" punch	*450.*	
a.		Double paper	*2,000.*	500.00
e.		With grill	*2,000.*	
f.		Imperf., pair		*1,500.*

The No. 156 plate block is unique. Value is 1998 auction sale. No. 156f may not have been regularly issued.

Earliest documented use: Aug. 22, 1873.

Cancellations

Blue	+.25
Purple	+.35
Magenta	+.35
Ultramarine	+1.00
Red	+3.50
Orange red	+4.00
Orange	+5.00
Brown	+20.00
Green	+60.00
"Paid All"	+7.00
"Paid"	+1.00
Railroad	+12.00
"Free"	+12.00
Black carrier	+15.00
Numeral	+2.50
Alaska	—
Japan	—
Printed "G." Precancel (Glastonbury, Conn.)	+200.00
Printed Star Precancel (Glen Allen, Va.)	+100.00

157	A45a	2c **brown**	400.	25.00

		dark brown	400.	25.00
		dark reddish brown	400.	25.00
		yellowish brown	400.	25.00
		No gum	145.	
		With secret mark	425.	27.50
		No gum	155.	
		On cover		30.00
		Pair	825.	52.50
		Block of 4	1,900.	180.00
		P# block of 12, Impt.	*6,250.*	
		P# block of 14, Impt.	*10,000.*	
		Ribbed paper	550.	60.00
		Double transfer	—	30.00
		Cracked plate		
a.		Double paper	*1,500.*	200.00
c.		With grill	*1,850.*	750.00
d.		Double impression	—	*5,000.*
e.		Vertical half used as 1c on cover		

Earliest documented use: July 12, 1873.

Cancellations

Blue	+.75
Magenta	+1.00
Purple	+1.00
Red	+5.00
Orange red	+5.50
Orange	+7.50
Green	+100.00
"Paid"	+2.50
"Insufficiently Paid"	—
"Paid All"	+13.50
"P. D." in circle	+15.00
Town	+2.00
Numeral	+1.50
Black Carrier	+8.50
"Steamship"	+15.00
Supplementary Mail Type F	+5.00
China	—
Japan	+100.00
Printed Star Precancellation (Glen Allen, Va.)	—

158	A46a	3c **green**	130.	1.00
		bluish green	130.	1.00
		yellow green	130.	1.00
		dark yellow green	130.	1.00
		dark green	130.	1.00
		No gum	40.	
		olive green, ribbed paper	*375.*	15.00
		No gum	*140.*	
		On cover		1.20
		Pair	275.	2.10
		Block of 4	600.	14.50
		P# strip of 5, Impt.	775.	
		P# strip of 6, Impt.	925.	
		P# block of 10, Impt.	2,750.	
		P# block of 12, Impt.	3,750.	
		P# block of 14, Impt.	4,750.	
		Paper cut with "cogwheel" punch	300.	250.
		Ribbed paper	300.	10.00
		Paper with silk fibers	—	10.00
		Cracked plate	—	32.50
		Double transfer		6.00
		Short transfer at bottom		15.00
a.		Double paper	600.	100.00
e.		With grill	500.	
		End roller grill	*950.*	*425.*
h.		Horizontal pair, imperf. vert.		
i.		Horizontal pair, imperf. between		*1,300.*
j.		Double impression		*10,000.*
k.		Printed on both sides		*15,000.*

See Die and Plate Proofs for imperfs. on stamp paper, with and without grill.

Earliest documented use: July 17, 1873.

Cancellations

Blue	+.10
Magenta	+.20
Purple	+.20
Ultramarine	+1.25
Red	+2.50
Orange red	+2.75
Orange	+3.50
Green	+25.00
Town	+.05
"Paid"	+2.50
"Paid All"	+20.00
"Free"	+15.00
Numeral	+1.00
China	—
Railroad	+7.00
"R. P. O."	+1.50
"P. D." in circle	—
"Steamboat"	—
"Steamship"	—
Supplementary Mail Type D	+11.00
Supplementary Mail Type F	+8.50
Express Company	—
Black Carrier	+8.00
Red Carrier	+25.00
Japan	+65.00
Alaska	—

159	A47a	6c **dull pink**	425.	20.00
		brown rose	425.	20.00
		No gum	140.	
		On cover		47.50
		Pair	900.	42.50
		Block of 4	2,250.	150.00
		P# block of 12, Impt.	*16,000.*	
		Ribbed paper		65.00

	Paper with silk fibers	—	70.00
a.	Diagonal half used as 3c on cover		4,000.
b.	With grill	1,800.	
	End roller grill	2,400.	
c.	Double paper	—	—

Earliest documented use: June 8, 1873.
No. 159a is unique.
No. 159b is valued in the grade of fine.

Cancellations

Blue	+1.00
Indigo	+2.50
Magenta	+1.50
Purple	+1.50
Violet	+3.00
Ultramarine	+2.50
Red	+7.50
Orange red	+9.00
Green	+100.00
Numeral	+1.50
"Paid"	+10.00
"Paid All"	+15.00
Supp. Mail Type D, E or F	+15.00
Japan	+100.00
China	+125.00
Railroad	+6.00
"R. P. O."	+3.00

160 A48a	**7c orange vermilion**	1,400.	90.00
	vermilion	1,400.	90.00
	No gum	500.	
	On cover		175.00
	Pair	3,000.	190.00
	Block of 4	6,500.	
	P# block of 12, Impt.	14,500.	
	Double transfer of "7 cents" (1R22)	—	210.00
	Double transfer in lower left corner	—	160.00
	Ribbed paper	—	150.00
	Paper with silk fibers	2,000.	200.00
a.	With grill	3,500.	
b.	Double paper	—	—

The plate block of 12 is in fine condition. It is unique.

Earliest documented use: Sept. 10, 1873.

Cancellations

Blue	+4.00
Red	+10.00
Purple	+10.00
Brown	+5.00
"Paid"	+15.00

161 A49a	**10c brown**	1,150.	25.00
	dark brown	1,150.	25.00
	yellow brown	1,150.	25.00
	No gum	350.	
	On cover		40.00
	Pair	2,500.	52.50
	Block of 4	6,000.	200.00
	P# block of 10, Impt.	16,500.	
	P# block of 12, Impt.	21,500.	
	Ribbed paper	—	100.00
	Paper with silk fibers	1,750.	100.00
	Double transfer	—	55.00
a.	Double paper		
c.	With grill	3,750.	
d.	Horizontal pair, imperf. between		2,750.

Earliest documented use: Aug. 2, 1873.

Cancellations

Blue	+1.50
Ultramarine	+2.00
Purple	+6.00
Red	+7.00
Orange red	+10.00
Orange	
Magenta	+2.00
Brown	+20.00
Green	+100.00
"Paid"	+4.00
"P. D." in circle	+20.00
"Steamship"	+15.00
Supplementary Mail Type E	+7.00
Supplementary Mail Type F	+2.50
Japan	+100.00
China	
Alaska	—

162 A50a	**12c blackish violet**	2,500.	140.00
	No gum	850.	
	On cover		325.00
	Pair	5,250.	300.00
	Block of 4	12,500.	1,000.
	Ribbed paper		350.00
a.	With grill	5,500.	

Earliest documented use: Jan. 3, 1874.

Cancellations

Blue	+2.50
Ultramarine	+15.00
Brown	+5.00
Red	+15.00
Purple	+500.00
Supplementary Mail Type D	+15.00
Japan	+200.00

163 A51a	**15c yellow orange**	2,750.	160.00
	pale orange	2,750.	160.00
	reddish orange	2,750.	160.00
	No gum	900.	
	On cover		350.00
	Pair	5,750.	350.00
	Block of 4	14,000.	1,150.
	Paper with silk fibers	3,150.	250.00

	Vertical ribbed paper	3,150.	250.00
a.	With grill		5,750.
b.	Double paper		—

Earliest documented use: July 22, 1873.

Cancellations

Blue	+5.00
Purple	+10.00
Red	+20.00
Green	+350.00
Brown	
Supplementary Mail Type E	—
Supplementary Mail Type F	+10.00
"Steamship"	
Numeral	+7.50
Puerto Rico	
China	

164 A52	**24c purple**		357,500.

The Philatelic Foundation has certified as genuine a 24c on vertically ribbed paper, and that is the unique stamp listed as No. 164. Specialists believe that only Continental used ribbed paper. It is not known for sure whether or not Continental also printed the 24c value on regular paper; if it did, specialists currently are not able to distinguish these from No. 153. The catalogue value represents a 2004 auction sale price realized.

165 A53	**30c gray black**	3,250.	140.
	greenish black	3,250.	140.
	No gum	1,100.	
	On cover		725.
	Pair	7,000.	300.
	Block of 4	17,500.	1,200.
	Double transfer		160.
	Ribbed paper	3,750.	150.
	Paper with silk fibers	—	
a.	Double paper	—	
c.	With grill	22,500.	

Earliest documented use: Oct. 14, 1874.

Cancellations

Purple	+10.00
Blue	+5.00
Red	+25.00
Brown	+30.00
Magenta	+10.00
"Steamship"	
Supplementary Mail Type E	+10.00
Supplementary Mail Type F	+5.00
Japan	+200.00

166 A54	**90c rose carmine**	2,400.	300.00
	pale rose carmine	2,400.	300.00
	No gum	800.	
	On cover		7,500.
	Pair	5,000.	625.00
	Block of 4	14,000.	2,500.
	P# strip of 5, Impt.	14,500.	

Earliest documented use: June 25, 1875.

Cancellations

Blue	+10.
Purple	+40.
Red	+40.
Supplementary Mail Type F	+30.

SPECIAL PRINTING OF 1873 ISSUE
Produced by the Continental Bank Note Co.

1875   **Perf. 12**

Hard, white wove paper, without gum

167 A44a	**1c ultramarine**	20,000.
168 A45a	**2c dark brown**	10,000.
169 A46a	**3c blue green**	25,000.
	On cover	—
170 A47a	**6c dull rose**	24,000.
171 A48a	**7c reddish vermilion**	6,250.
172 A49a	**10c pale brown**	23,000.
173 A50a	**12c dark violet**	8,000.
	Horizontal pair	
174 A51a	**15c bright orange**	23,000.
175 A52	**24c dull purple**	5,500. 22,500.
	Horizontal pair	
176 A53	**30c greenish black**	19,000.
177 A54	**90c violet carmine**	30,000.

Although perforated, these stamps were usually cut apart with scissors. As a result, the perforations are often much mutilated and the design is frequently damaged.

These can be distinguished from the 1873 issue by the shades; also by the paper, which is very white instead of yellowish.

These and the subsequent issues listed under the heading of "Special Printings" are special printings of stamps then in current use which, together with the reprints and re-issues, were made for sale to collectors. They were available for postage except for the Officials, Newspaper and Periodical, and demonetized issues.

Only No. 169 is documented on cover (unique; postmarked Mar. 5, 1876).

Only one example of No. 175 used has been certified. It is off-center and creased, and it is valued thus.

PRINTED BY THE CONTINENTAL BANK NOTE COMPANY
REGULAR ISSUE
Yellowish Wove Paper

1875   **Perf. 12**

178 A45a	**2c vermilion**, *June 1875*	390.	15.00
	No gum	120.	
	On cover		17.50
	Pair	825.	32.50

	Block of 4	1,900.	130.00
	P# strip of 6, Impt.	3,000.	
	P# block of 12, Impt.		
	P# block of 14, Impt.	7,000.	
	Double transfer		
	Ribbed paper		
	Paper with silk fibers	450.	30.00
a.	Double paper	—	—
b.	Half used as 1c on cover		750.00
c.	With grill	900.	2,750.

See Die and Plate Proofs for imperf. on stamp paper.

Earliest documented use: July 15, 1875.

Cancellations

Blue	+.50
Purple	+.75
Magenta	+.75
Red	+6.00
"Paid"	+8.00
"Steamship"	
Supplementary Mail Type F	+5.50
Black Carrier	+15.00
Railroad	+12.50

Zachary Taylor — A55

179 A55	**5c blue**, *June 1875*	750.	25.00
	dark blue	750.	25.00
	bright blue	750.	25.00
	light blue	750.	25.00
	No gum	240.	
	greenish blue	775.	30.00
	No gum	250.	
	On cover		37.50
	Pair	1,600.	52.50
	Block of 4	4,000.	375.00
	Cracked plate	—	170.00
	Double transfer	—	37.50
	Ribbed paper	—	
	Paper with silk fibers		50.00
a.	Double paper	950.	
c.	With grill	4,500.	
	End roller grill	—	

Earliest documented use: July 10, 1875.

Cancellations

Blue	+1.00
Ultramarine	+3.00
Purple	+2.00
Magenta	+2.00
Red	+10.00
Green	+70.00
Numeral	+5.00
Railroad	+17.50
"Steamship"	+12.50
Ship	+12.50
Supplementary Mail Type E	+5.00
Supplementary Mail Type F	+2.00
China	
Japan	+100.00
Peru	—

The five cent rate to foreign countries in the Universal Postal Union began on July 1, 1875. No. 179 was issued for that purpose.

SPECIAL PRINTING OF 1875 ISSUE
Produced by the Continental Bank Note Co.
Hard, White Wove Paper, without gum

1875

180 A45a	**2c carmine vermilion**	85,000.
181 A55	**5c bright blue**	500,000.

Unlike Nos. 167-177, Nos. 180-181 were not cut apart with scissors.

Numbers sold: No. 180, 917; No. 181, 317. However, fewer than 25 No. 180 and fewer than 10 No. 181 have been expertized and are available to collectors.

IMPORTANT INFORMATION REGARDING VALUES FOR NEVER-HINGED STAMPS

Collectors should be aware that the values given for never-hinged stamps from No. 182 on are for stamps in the grade of very fine, just as the values for all stamps in the catalogue are for very fine stamps unless indicated otherwise. The never-hinged premium as a percentage of value will be larger for stamps in extremely fine or superb grades, and the premium will be smaller for fine-very fine, fine or poor examples. This is particularly true of the issues of the late-19th and early-20th centuries. For example, in the grade of very fine, an unused stamp from this time period may be valued at $100 hinged and $200 never hinged. The never-hinged premium is thus 100%. But in a grade of extremely fine, this same stamp will not only sell for more hinged, but the never-hinged premium will increase, perhaps to 200%-400% or more over the higher extremely fine value. In the grade of superb, a hinged stamp will sell for much more than a very fine stamp, and additionally the never-hinged premium will be much larger, perhaps as large as 500%-1,000%. On the other hand, the same stamp in a grade of fine or fine-very fine not only will sell for less than a very fine stamp in hinged condition, but additionally the never-hinged premium will be smaller than the never-hinged premium on a very fine stamp, perhaps as small as 40%-60%.

Please note that the above statements and percentages are NOT a formula for arriving at the values of stamps in hinged or never-hinged condition in the grades of very good, fine, fine to very fine, extremely fine or superb. The percentages given apply only to the size of the premium for never-hinged condition that might be added to the stamp value for hinged condition. Further, the percentages given are only generalized estimates. Some stamps or grades may have percentages for never-hinged condition that are higher or lower than the ranges given. For values of the most popular U.S. stamps in the grades of very good, fine, fine to very fine, very fine, very fine to extremely fine, extremely fine and superb, see the *Scott Stamp Values: U.S. Specialized by Grade*, updated and issued twice each year in April and October.

VALUES FOR NEVER-HINGED STAMPS PRIOR TO SCOTT 182

This catalogue does not value pre-1879 stamps in never-hinged condition. Premiums for never-hinged condition in the classic era invariably are even larger than those premiums listed for the 1879 and later issues. Generally speaking, the earlier the stamp is listed in the catalogue, the larger will be the never-hinged premium. On some early classics, the premium will be several multiples of the unused, hinged values given in the catalogue.

NEVER-HINGED PLATE BLOCKS

Values given for never-hinged plate blocks are for blocks in which all stamps have original gum that has never been hinged and has no disturbances, and all selvage, whether gummed or ungummed, has never been hinged.

PRINTED BY THE AMERICAN BANK NOTE COMPANY

The Continental Bank Note Co. was consolidated with the American Bank Note Co. on February 4, 1879. The American Bank Note Company used many plates of the Continental Bank Note Company to print the ordinary postage, Departmental and Newspaper stamps. Therefore, stamps bearing the Continental Company's imprint were not always its product.

The A. B. N. Co. also used the 30c and 90c plates of the N. B. N. Co. Some of No. 190 and all of No. 217 were from A. B. N. Co. plate 405.

Early printings of No. 188 were from Continental plates 302 and 303 which contained the normal secret mark of 1873. After those plates were re-entered by the A. B. N. Co. in 1880, pairs or multiple pieces contained combinations of normal, hairline or missing marks. The pairs or other multiples usually found contain at least one hairline mark which tended to disappear as the plate wore.

A. B. N. Co. plates 377 and 378 were made in 1881 from the National transfer roll of 1870. No. 187 from these plates has no secret mark.

Identification by Paper Type:

Collectors traditionally have identified American Bank Note Co. issues by the soft, porous paper on which they were printed. However, the Continental Bank Note Co. used soft paper from August 1878 through early 1879, before the consolidation of the companies. When the consolidation occurred in the late afternoon of Feb. 4, 1879, American Bank Note Co. took over the presses, plates, paper, ink, and the employees of Continental. Undoubtedly they also acquired panes of finished stamps and sheets of printed stamps that had not yet been gummed and/or perforated. Since the soft paper that was in use at the time of the consolidation and after is approximately the same texture and thickness as the soft paper that American Bank Note Co. began using regularly in June or July of 1879, all undated soft paper stamps have traditionally been classified as American Bank Note Co. printings.

However, if a stamp bears a dated cancellation or is on a dated cover from Feb. 4, 1879 or earlier, collectors (especially specialist collectors) must consider the stamp to be a Continental Bank Note Co. printing. Undated stamps off cover, and stamps and covers dated Feb. 5 or later, traditionally have been considered to be American Bank Note Co. printings since that company held the contract to print U.S. postage stamps beginning on that date. The most dedicated and serious specialist students sometimes attempt to determine the stamp printer of the issues on soft, porous paper in an absolute manner (by scientifically testing the paper and/or comparing printing records).

Earliest documented uses for American Bank Note Co. issues are given for stamps on the soft, porous paper that has been traditionally associated with that company. But, for reasons given above, sometimes that date will precede the Feb. 4, 1879 consolidation date.

SAME AS 1870-75 ISSUES
Soft Porous Paper

1879					*Perf. 12*
182	A44a	1c	**dark ultramarine**	300.	6.00
			blue	300.	6.00
			gray blue	300.	6.00
			Never hinged	1,000.	
			No gum	95.	
			On cover		6.50
			Pair	625.	12.50
			Block of 4	1,500.	67.50
			P# block of 10, Impt.	4,750.	
			Double transfer		12.50

Earliest documented use: Jan. 3, 1879.

Cancellations

Blue	+.20
Magenta	+.30
Purple	+.30
Red	+7.00
Printed Star Precancellation (Glen Allen, Va.)	+75.00
Green	+35.00
"Paid"	+4.00
Supplementary Mail Type F	+10.00
Railroad	+12.50
Printed "G." Precancellation (Glastonbury, Conn.)	+100.00

183	A45a	2c	**vermilion**	110.	5.00
			orange vermilion	110.	5.00
			Never hinged	400.	
			No gum	37.50	
			On cover		5.50
			Pair	230.	11.00
			Block of 4	575.	55.00
			P# block of 10, Impt.	2,000.	
			P# block of 12, Impt.	2,500.	
			Double transfer		—
a.			Double impression	—	5,500.
b.			Half used as 1c on cover	750.00	

Earliest documented use: Aug. 19, 1878.

Cancellations

Blue	+.25
Purple	+.40
Magenta	+.40
Red	+6.00
Green	+175.00
"Paid"	+5.00
"Paid All"	—
"Ship"	—
Numeral	+4.00
Railroad	+15.00
Supplementary Mail Type F	+8.00
China	—
Printed Star Precancellation in black (Glen Allen, Va.)	+350.00
Printed Star Precancellation in red (Glen Allen, Va.)	+1,750.

184	A46a	3c	**green**	95.	1.00
			light green	95.	1.00
			dark green	95.	1.00
			Never hinged	350.	
			No gum	30.	
			On cover		1.10
			Pair	200.	2.10
			Block of 4	475.	12.50
			P# block of 10, Impt.	1,350.	
			P# block of 12, Impt.	1,600.	
			P# block of 14, Impt.	2,000.	
			Double transfer		—
			Short transfer		7.00
b.			Double impression	5,500.	

See Die and Plate Proofs for imperf. on stamp paper.

Earliest documented use: July 2, 1878.

Cancellations

Blue	+.10
Magenta	+.15
Purple	+.15
Violet	+.15
Brown	+1.00
Red	+7.50
Green	+25.00
"Paid"	+3.00
"Free"	+15.00
Numeral	+2.00
Railroad	+12.50
"Steamboat"	
Supplementary Mail Type F	+8.00
Printed Star Precancel (Glen Allen, Va.)	
China	+60.00
Alaska	—

185	A55	5c	**blue**	475.	17.50
			light blue	475.	17.50
			bright blue	475.	17.50
			dark blue	475.	17.50
			Never hinged	1,600.	
			No gum	150.	
			On cover		27.50
			Pair	1,000.	37.50
			Block of 4	2,400.	190.00
			P# block of 12, Impt.	12,500.	
			Double transfer		—

Earliest documented use: Jan. 16, 1879.

Cancellations

Blue	+.25
Purple	+1.00
Magenta	+1.00
Ultramarine	+3.50
Red	+7.50
Railroad	+20.00
Numeral	+2.00
Supplementary Mail Type F	+1.50
"Steamship"	+35.00
China	+60.00
Peru	—
Panama	—

186	A47a	6c	**pink**	950.	32.50
			dull pink	950.	32.50
			brown rose	950.	32.50
			Never hinged	3,250.	
			No gum	310.	
			On cover		50.00
			Pair	2,100.	67.50
			Block of 4	4,750.	650.00

Earliest documented use: April 18, 1879.

Cancellations

Blue	+.50
Ultramarine	+3.00
Purple	+1.00
Magenta	+1.00
Red	+12.00
Supplementary Mail Type F	+4.00
Railroad	+22.50
Numeral	+4.00
China	+70.00

187	A49	10c	**brown,** without secret mark	3,500.	37.50
			yellow brown	3,500.	37.50
			Never hinged	12,000.	
			No gum	1,200.	
			On cover		55.00
			Pair	7,250.	80.00
			Block of 4	16,000.	—
			Double transfer		57.50
a.			Double paper	6,000.	—

Earliest documented use: Sept. 5, 1879.

Cancellations

Blue	+.50
Magenta	+1.50
Red	+10.00
"Paid"	+3.50
Supplementary Mail Type F	+3.00
China	+70.00

188	A49a	10c	**brown,** with secret mark	2,000.	32.50
			yellow brown	2,000.	32.50
			Never hinged	7,000.	
			No gum	700.	
			black brown	2,250.	45.00
			Never hinged	7,500.	
			No gum	800.	
			On cover		47.50
			Pair	4,250.	67.50
			Block of 4	11,000.	325.00
			Pair, one stamp No. 187	10,000.	725.00
			Double transfer		52.50
			Cracked plate		—

Earliest documented use: Oct. 5, 1878.

Cancellations

Blue	+.50
Ultramarine	+3.00
Purple	+2.00
Magenta	+2.00
Red	+10.00
Green	+70.00
"Paid"	+7.50
Supplementary Mail Type F	+5.00
Numeral	+3.00
Printed Star Precancel (Glen Allen, Va.)	—

189	A51a	15c	**red orange**	275.	27.50
			orange	275.	27.50
			yellow orange	275.	27.50
			Never hinged	925.	
			No gum	105.	
			On cover		90.00
			Pair	575.	57.50

Block of 4 ... 1,600. 240.00
P# block of 12, Impt. ... *7,250.*
Double transfer

Earliest documented use: Jan. 20, 1879.

Cancellations

Blue	+1.50
Purple	+3.00
Magenta	+3.00
Ultramarine	+5.00
Red	+12.00
"Steamship"	+22.50
Supplementary Mail Type E	—
Supplementary Mail Type F	+5.00
Japan	+120.00
China	

190 A53 30c full black 950. 100.00
  greenish black 950. 100.00
  Never hinged *3,250.*
  No gum 350.
  On cover *450.00*
  Pair 2,000. 220.00
  Block of 4 4,750. 600.00
  P# block of 10, Impt. *15,000.*

Earliest documented use: April 5, 1881.

Cancellations

Blue	+1.50
Purple	+3.00
Magenta	+3.00
Red	+20.00
Supplementary Mail Type F	+6.00
"Steamship"	+35.00
Tahiti	—
Samoa	

191 A54 90c carmine 2,250. 375.00
  rose 2,250. 375.00
  carmine rose 2,250. 375.00
  Never hinged *7,750.*
  No gum 750.
  On cover *5,000.*
  Pair 5,000. 775.00
  Block of 4 12,500. 2,000.
a. Double paper

See Die and Plate Proofs for imperf. on stamp paper.

Earliest documented use: May 27, 1882 (dated cancel on off-cover stamp), June 24, 1882 (on cover).

Cancellations

Blue	+15.00
Purple	+20.00
Red	+45.00
Supplementary Mail Type F	+20.00

SPECIAL PRINTING OF 1879 ISSUE
Produced by the American Bank Note Co.

1880   **Perf. 12**
Soft porous paper, without gum

192 A44a 1c **dark ultramarine** *75,000.*
193 A45a 2c **black brown** *27,500.*
194 A46a 3c **blue green** *125,000.*
195 A47a 6c **dull rose** *100,000.*
196 A48a 7c **scarlet vermilion** *10,000.*
197 A49a 10c **deep brown** *55,000.*
198 A50a 12c **blackish purple** *15,000.*
199 A51a 15c **orange** *50,000.*
200 A52 24c **dark violet** *14,000.*
201 A53 30c **greenish black** *35,000.*
202 A54 90c **dull carmine** *45,000.*
203 A45a 2c **scarlet vermilion** *140,000.*
204 A55 5c **deep blue** *350,000.*

Nos. 192 and 194 are valued in the grade of fine.
No. 197 was printed from Continental plate 302 (or 303) after plate was re-entered. Therefore, the stamp may show normal, hairline or missing secret mark.
The Post Office Department did not keep separate records of the 1875 and 1880 Special Printings of the 1873 and 1879 issues, but the total quantity sold of both is recorded.
Unlike the 1875 hard-paper Special Printings (Nos. 167-177), the 1880 soft-paper Special Printings were never cut apart with scissors.

Numbers Sold of 1875 and 1880 Special Printings.

1c ultramarine & dark ultramarine *(388)*
2c dark brown & black brown *(416)*
2c carmine vermilion & scarlet vermilion *(917)*
3c blue green *(267)*
5c bright blue & deep blue *(317)*
6c dull rose *(185)*
7c reddish vermilion & scarlet vermilion *(473)*
10c pale brown & deep brown *(180)*
12c dark violet & blackish purple *(282)*
15c bright orange & orange *(169)*
24c dull purple & dark violet *(286)*
30c greenish black *(179)*
90c violet carmine & dull carmine *(170)*

REGULAR ISSUE
Printed by the American Bank Note Co.

James A. Garfield — A56

1882
205 A56 5c yellow brown 275. 12.00
  brown 275. 12.00
  gray brown 275. 12.00
  Never hinged 900.
  No gum 90.
  On cover 20.00
  Pair 575. 25.00
  Block of 4 1,300. 125.00
  P# strip of 5, Impt. *1,900.*
  P# strip of 6, Impt. *2,250.*
  P# block of 10, Impt. *5,750.*
  P# block of 12, Impt. *6,500.*

Earliest documented use: Feb. 18, 1882.

Cancellations

Blue	+.75
Purple	+1.00
Magenta	+1.00
Red	+7.00
"Ship"	
Numeral	+2.00
Supplementary Mail Type F	+2.50
Red Express Co.	
China	+125.00
Japan	+125.00
Samoa	+150.00
Puerto Rico	

SPECIAL PRINTING
Printed by the American Bank Note Co.

1882   **Perf. 12**
Soft porous paper, without gum

205C A56 5c gray brown *85,000.*

Although Post Office records indicate that 2,463 examples of the 5c Garfield Special Printing were sold, almost all of these stamps appear to have been from supplies of the regular issue No. 205. The actual Special Printings, No. 205C, came from a small supply sent to the Third Assistant Post Master General before the regular issue was available. Only 22 examples have been certified as genuine Special Printings.

DESIGNS OF 1873 RE-ENGRAVED

Franklin — A44b

1c — The vertical lines in the upper part of the stamp have been so deepened that the background often appears to be solid. Lines of shading have been added to the upper arabesques.

1881-82
206 A44b 1c gray blue, *Aug. 1881* 80.00 1.00
  ultramarine 80.00 1.25
  dull blue 80.00 1.00
  slate blue 80.00 1.25
  Never hinged 260.00
  No gum 25.00
  On cover 1.75
  Pair 190.00 2.60
  Block of 4 425.00 17.50
  P# strip of 5, Impt. 550.00
  P# strip of 6, Impt. 650.00
  P# block of 10, Impt. *1,900.*
  P# block of 12, Impt. *2,100.*
  Double transfer 115.00 6.00
  Punched with 8 small holes in a circle 200.00
  P# block of 10, Impt. (8-hole punch) *2,750.*

Earliest documented use: Oct. 11, 1881.

Cancellations

Purple	+.10
Magenta	+.10
Blue	+.20
Red	+3.00
Orange red	+3.50
Orange	+5.00
Green	+50.00
"Paid"	+4.75
"Paid All"	+12.00
Numeral	+3.50
Supplementary Mail Type F	+5.00
Railroad	+10.00
Printed Star Precancel (Glen Allen, Va.)	+55.00
China	—

Washington — A46b

3c. The shading at the sides of the central oval appears only about one-half the previous width. A short horizontal dash has been cut about 1mm below the "TS" of "CENTS."

207 A46b 3c blue green, *July 16, 1881* 85.00 .80
  green 85.00 .80
  yellow green 85.00 .80
  Never hinged 275.00
  No gum 27.50
  On cover .95
  Pair 180.00 1.70
  Block of 4 425.00 30.00
  P# strip of 5, Impt. 550.00
  P# block of 10, Impt. *1,900.*
  Double transfer 12.00
  Cracked plate —
  Punched with 8 small holes in a circle *220.00*
  P# block of 10, Impt. (8-hole punch) *3,000.*
c. Double impression —

Earliest documented use: Aug. 7, 1881.

Cancellations

Purple	+.10
Magenta	+.10
Blue	+.25
Brown	+1.50
Red	+2.50
"Paid"	+3.00
"Paid All"	
Numeral	+2.50
"Ship"	
Railroad	+5.00
Supplementary Mail Type F	+8.00
Printed Star Precancellation (Glen Allen, Va.)	

Lincoln — A47b

6c. On the original stamps four vertical lines can be counted from the edge of the panel to the outside of the stamp. On the re-engraved stamps there are but three lines in the same place.

208 A47b 6c rose 800. 110.00
  dull rose 800. 110.00
  Never hinged 2,500.
  No gum 240.
  On cover (rose) 190.00
  Pair (rose) 1,700. 230.00
  Block of 4 (rose) 4,250. 900.00
  P# block of 10, Impt. *11,500.*
  Double transfer 850. 130.00
a. 6c **deep brown red** 600. 175.00
  Never hinged 1,850.
  No gum 180.
  pale brown red 525. 125.00
  Never hinged 1,600.
  No gum 160.
  On cover (deep brown red) *425.00*
  Pair (deep brown red) 1,250. 360.00
  Block of 4 (deep brown red) 3,000. 1,250.
  P# strip of 5, Impt. 3,750.
  P# strip of 6, Impt. *4,500.*
  P# block of 10, Impt. *9,500.*
  P# block of 12, Impt.

Earliest documented use: June 1, 1882.

Cancellations

Magenta	+3.00
Purple	+3.00
Blue	+5.00
Red	+15.00
Supplementary Mail Type F	+10.00

Jefferson — A49b

10c. On the original stamps there are five vertical lines between the left side of the oval and the edge of the shield. There are only four lines on the re-engraved stamps. In the lower part of the latter, also, the horizontal lines of the background have been strengthened.

209 A49b 10c brown, *Apr. 1882* 175. 6.00
  yellow brown 175. 6.00
  orange brown 175. 6.00
  Never hinged 525.
  No gum 55.
  dark brown 190. 10.00
  purple brown 210. 15.00
  olive brown 210. 15.00
  Never hinged 600.
  No gum 60.
  On cover 11.00
  Pair 375. 12.50

Block of 4	950.	40.00
P# strip of 5, Impt.	1,275.	
P# strip of 6, Impt.	1,500.	
P# block of 10, Impt.	3,750.	
P# block of 12, Impt.	4,500.	
Never hinged	8,750.	

b. 10c **black brown** — 3,000. / 350.00
Never hinged — 6,000.
No gum — 950.
On cover — 550.00
Pair — — / 725.00
Block of 4 — —
c. Double impression — —

Specimen stamps (usually overprinted "Sample") without overprint exist in a brown shade that differs from No. 209. The unoverprinted brown specimen is cheaper than No. 209. Expertization is recommended.

Earliest documented use: May 4, 1882.

Cancellations
Purple	+.50
Magenta	+.50
Blue	+1.00
Red	+4.00
Green	+35.00
Numeral	+2.00
"Paid"	+2.50
Supplementary Mail Type F	+3.00
Express Company	—
Japan	+75.00
China	—
Samoa	—

Printed by the American Bank Note Company.

Washington — A57 | Jackson — A58

Nos. 210-211 were issued to meet the reduced first class rate of 2 cents for each half ounce, and the double rate, which Congress approved Mar. 3, 1883, effective Oct. 1, 1883.

1883, Oct. 1 — Perf. 12

210 A57 2c **red brown** — 42.50 / .75
dark red brown — 42.50 / .75
orange brown — 42.50 / .75
Never hinged — 130.00
No gum — 12.50
On cover — .85
Pair — 90.00 / 1.60
Block of 4 — 220.00 / 12.50
P# strip of 5, Impt. — 260.00
P# strip of 6, Impt. — 325.00
P# block of 10, Impt. — 1,050.
P# block of 12, Impt. — 1,300.
Double transfer — 47.50 / 2.25

See Die and Plate Proofs for imperf. on stamp paper.

Earliest documented use: Oct. 1, 1883 (FDC).

Cancellations
Purple	+.10
Margenta	+.10
Blue	+.20
Violet	+.30
Brown	+.30
Red	+3.50
Green	+25.00
Numeral	+2.50
"Paid"	+3.00
Railroad	+5.00
Express Company	—
Supplementary Mail Type F	+5.00
"Ship"	—
"Steamboat"	—
China	—

211 A58 4c **blue green** — 300. / 27.50
deep blue green — 300. / 27.50
Never hinged — 1,050.
No gum — 100.
On cover — 55.00
Pair — 625. / 57.50
Block of 4 — 1,400. / 130.00
P# strip of 5, Impt. — 1,950.
P# strip of 6, Impt. — 2,250.
P# block of 10, Impt. — 5,250.
P# block of 12, Impt. — 6,250.
Never hinged — 8,500.
Double transfer — —
Cracked plate — —

See Die and Plate Proofs for imperf. on stamp paper.

Earliest documented use: Oct. 1, 1883 (FDC).

Cancellations
Purple	+1.00
Magenta	+1.00
Green	+50.00

Blue	+1.00
Numeral	+2.00
Supplementary Mail Type F	+5.00

SPECIAL PRINTING
Printed by the American Bank Note Company.

1883-85 — **Soft porous paper** — *Perf. 12*

211B A57 2c **pale red brown**, with gum ('85) — 375. / —
Never hinged — 850.
No gum — 130.
Block of 4 — 1,650.
c. Horizontal pair, imperf. between — 2,000.
Never hinged — 3,000.
Top margin strip of 6, "Steamer-American Bank Note Co." imprint — 35,000.

Earliest documented use: May 23, 1885 (dated cancel on off-cover stamp).

211D A58 4c **deep blue green**, without gum — 80,000.

Postal records indicate that 26 examples of No. 211D were sold. Records also indicate an 1883 delivery and sales of 55 examples of the 2c red brown stamp, but there is no clear evidence that these can be differentiated from no gum examples of No. 210.

No. 211B is from a special trial printing by a new steampowered American Bank Note Company press. Approximately 1,000 of these stamps (in sheets of 200 with an imperf gutter between the panes of 100) were delivered as samples to the Third Assistant Postmaster General and subsequently made their way to the public market.

REGULAR ISSUE
Printed by the American Bank Note Company.

Franklin — A59

1887 — *Perf. 12*

212 A59 1c **ultramarine**, *June* — 100.00 / 2.50
bright ultramarine — 100.00 / 2.50
Never hinged — 310.00
No gum — 32.50
On cover — 3.25
Pair — 210.00 / 5.25
Block of 4 — 475.00 / 37.50
P# strip of 5, Impt. — 625.00
P# strip of 6, Impt. — 750.00
P# block of 10, Impt. — 1,600.
P# block of 12, Impt. — 2,000.
Double transfer — —

See Die and Plate Proofs for imperf. on stamp paper.

Earliest documented use: July 15, 1887. The previously listed July 7, 1887, cover has not been adequately documented. The editors would like to see authenticated evidence of its existence.

Cancellations
Purple	+.10
Magenta	+.10
Blue	+.10
Red	+5.50
Numeral	+2.00
Railroad	+10.00
Supplementary Mail Type F	+5.00
China	—

213 A57 2c **green**, *Sept. 10* — 45.00 / .60
bright green — 45.00 / .60
dark green — 45.00 / .60
Never hinged — 130.00
No gum — 14.00
On cover — .75
Pair — 95.00 / 1.30
Block of 4 — 210.00 / 10.50
P# strip of 5, Impt. — 275.00
P# strip of 6, Impt. — 340.00
P# block of 10, Impt. — 1,250.
Never hinged — 2,250.
P# block of 12, Impt. — 1,500.
Double transfer — 3.25
b. Printed on both sides — —

See Die and Plate Proofs for imperf. on stamp paper.

Earliest documented use: Sept. 20, 1887 (dated cancel on off-cover stamp); Sept. 21, 1887 (on cover).

Cancellations
Purple	+.10
Magenta	+.10
Blue	+.90
Red	+5.00
Green	+25.00
"Paid"	+5.00
Railroad	+12.00
Numeral	+2.00
"Steam"	—
"Steamboat"	—
Supplementary Mail Type F	+7.50
China	—

Japan	—	
214 A46b 3c **vermilion**, *Sept.*	65.00	67.50
Never hinged	200.00	
No gum	21.00	
On cover (single)		110.00
Pair	140.00	140.00
Block of 4	325.00	375.00
P# strip of 5, Impt.	400.00	
P# strip of 6, Impt.	475.00	
P# block of 10, Impt.	1,300.	
Never hinged	3,000.	
P# block of 12, Impt.	1,500.	

Earliest documented use: Sept. 23, 1887.

Cancellations
Purple	+5.00
Magenta	+5.00
Green	+150.00
Blue	+10.00
Supplementary Mail Type F	+15.00
Railroad	+30.00

Printed by the American Bank Note Company.
SAME AS 1870-83 ISSUES

1888 — *Perf. 12*

215 A58 4c **carmine**, *Nov.* — 225. / 27.50
rose carmine — 225. / 27.50
pale rose — 225. / 27.50
Never hinged — 675.
No gum — 70.
On cover — 50.00
Pair — 475. / 57.50
Block of 4 — 1,050. / 175.00
P# strip of 5, Impt. — 1,525.
Never hinged — 4,000.
P# strip of 6, Impt. — 1,750.
P# block of 10, Impt. — 4,500.
P# block of 12, Impt. — 5,300.

Earliest documented use: Dec. 26, 1888.

Cancellations
Blue	+1.00
Red	+5.00
Purple	+2.00
Magenta	+2.00
Supplementary Mail Type F	+5.00

216 A56 5c **indigo**, *Feb.* — 250. / 17.50
deep blue — 250. / 17.50
Never hinged — 775.
No gum — 80.
On cover — 30.00
Pair — 525. / 37.50
Block of 4 — 1,150. / 140.00
P# strip of 5, Impt. — 1,500.
P# strip of 6, Impt. — 2,000.
P# block of 10, Impt. — 7,250.
P# block of 12, Impt. — 8,750.

Earliest documented use: Mar. 15, 1888.

Cancellations
Purple	+1.00
Magenta	+1.00
Blue	+1.00
Supplementary Mail Type F	+3.00
China	+85.00
Japan	+85.00
Puerto Rico	+75.00
Samoa	—

217 A53 30c **orange brown**, *Jan.* — 375. / 130.00
deep orange brown — 375. / 130.00
Never hinged — 1,100.
No gum — 110.
On cover — 1,400.
Pair — 850. / 275.00
Block of 4 — 1,900. / 700.00
P# strip of 5, Impt. — 2,500.
P# block of 10, Impt. — 7,000.

Earliest documented use: Aug. 18, 1888 (dated cancel on off-cover stamp); Sept. 7, 1888 (on cover).

Cancellations
Blue	+5.00
Magenta	+10.00
Supplementary Mail Type F	+10.00
"Paid All"	+25.00
"Paid"	+15.00

218 A54 90c **purple**, *Feb.* — 1,000. / 275.00
bright purple — 1,000. / 275.00
Never hinged — 3,000.
No gum — 300.
On cover — 10,000.
Pair — 2,100. / 600.00
Block of 4 — 5,250. / 1,500.
P# strip of 5, Impt. — 6,250.
P# block of 10, Impt. — 22,500.
P# block of 12, Impt. — —

Earliest documented use: Sept. (day ?), 1888 (dated cancel on off-cover stamp); Oct. 29, 1888 (on cover).

Cancellations
Blue	+80.00
Purple	+100.00
Supplementary Mail Type F	+25.00

See Die and Plate Proofs for imperfs. on stamp paper.

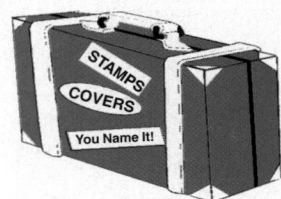

Printed by the American Bank Note Company. Plates for the 1c and 2c were of 400 subjects in 4 panes of 100 each. All other values were from plates of 200 subjects in two panes of 100 each.

Franklin — A60

Washington — A61

Jackson — A62

Lincoln — A63

Ulysses S. Grant — A64

Garfield — A65

William T. Sherman — A66

Daniel Webster — A67

Henry Clay — A68

Jefferson — A69

Perry — A70

1890-93 — Perf. 12

219	A60	1c **dull blue,** Feb. 22, 1890	25.	.75
		deep blue	25.	.75
		ultramarine	25.	.75
		Never hinged	80.	
		On cover		.80
		Block of 4	110.	5.25
		P# strip of 5, Impt. & letter	150.	
		P# strip of 6, Impt. & letter	180.	
		P# strip of 7, Impt. & letter	220.	
		P# block of 10, Impt. & letter	775.	
		P# block of 12, Impt. & letter	1,075.	
		P# block of 14, Impt. & letter	1,450.	
		Never hinged	*3,400.*	
		Double transfer	—	—

Earliest documented use: Feb 27, 1890.

Cancellations

		Samoa	—	
		China	—	
219D	A61	2c **lake,** Feb. 22, 1890	220.	5.50
		Never hinged	700.	
		On cover		7.50
		Block of 4	900.	47.50

		P# strip of 5, Impt.	1,200.	
		P# block of 10, Impt.	3,750.	
		Double transfer	—	—

Earliest documented use: Feb. 22, 1890 (FDC).

Cancellation

		Supplementary Mail Type F		+3.00
220	A61	2c **carmine,** 1890	22.50	.70
		dark carmine	22.50	.70
		carmine rose	22.50	.70
		rose	22.50	.70
		Never hinged	70.00	
		On cover		.75
		Block of 4	100.00	2.75
		P# strip of 5, Impt. & letter	145.00	
		P# strip of 6, Impt. & letter	190.00	
		Never hinged	360.00	
		P# strip of 7, Impt. & letter	200.00	
		P# block of 10, Impt. & letter	575.00	
		P# block of 12, Impt. & letter	800.00	
		P# block of 14, Impt. & letter	1,050.	
		Never hinged	—	
		Double transfer	—	3.25
a.		Cap on left "2" (Plates 235-236, 246-247-248)	140.00	11.00
		Never hinged	400.00	
		Block of 4	625.00	*150.00*
		Pair, Nos. 220, 220a	—	
		Never hinged	—	
c.		Cap on both "2's" (Plates 245, 246)	625.00	32.50
		Never hinged	1,800.	
		Pair, Nos. 220a, 220c	—	
		Never hinged	—	

Earliest documented uses: Mar. 11, 1890 (No. 220); Sept. 9, 1892 (No. 220a); July 7, 1892 (No. 220c).

Cancellations

		Blue		+.05
		Purple		+.05
		Supp. Mail Types F or G		+3.00
		China		+20.00
221	A62	3c **purple,** Feb. 22, 1890	75.00	9.00
		bright purple	75.00	9.00
		dark purple	75.00	9.00
		Never hinged	230.00	
		On cover		17.50
		Block of 4	350.00	55.00
		P# strip of 5, Impt.	475.00	
		P# block of 10, Impt.	2,800.	
		Never hinged	—	

Earliest documented use: Feb. 28, 1890.

Cancellation

		Samoa	—	
222	A63	4c **dark brown,** June 2, 1890	100.00	4.50
		blackish brown	100.00	4.50
		Never hinged	310.00	
		On cover		15.00
		Block of 4	450.00	32.50
		P# strip of 5, Impt.	575.00	
		P# block of 10, Impt.	3,400.	
		Never hinged	*5,300.*	
		Double transfer	115.00	—

Earliest documented use: July 16, 1890.

Cancellation

		China		+40.00
223	A64	5c **chocolate,** June 2, 1890	80.00	4.50
		yellow brown	80.00	4.50
		Never hinged	250.00	
		On cover		14.00
		Block of 4	350.00	27.50
		P# strip of 5, Impt.	450.00	
		P# block of 10, Impt.	2,900.	
		Never hinged	—	
		Double transfer	105.00	3.75

Earliest documented use: June 14, 1890.

Cancellations

		China		+35.00
		Samoa	—	
		Supp. Mail Types F or G		+3.00
224	A65	6c **brown red,** Feb. 22, 1890	75.00	25.00
		dark brown red	75.00	25.00
		Never hinged	230.00	
		On cover		40.00
		Block of 4	325.00	130.00
		P# strip of 5, Impt.	450.00	
		P# block of 10, Impt.	2,850.	
		Never hinged	*4,500.*	

Earliest documented use: May 8, 1890.

Cancellation

		Supplementary Mail Type F		+3.00
225	A66	8c **lilac,** Mar. 21, 1893	60.00	17.00
		grayish lilac	60.00	17.00
		magenta	60.00	17.00
		Never hinged	180.00	
		On cover		32.50
		Block of 4	260.00	100.00
		P# strip of 5, Impt.	350.00	
		P# block of 10, Impt.	1,900.	
		Never hinged	3,250.	

The 8c was issued because the registry fee was reduced from 10 to 8 cents effective Jan. 1, 1893.

Earliest documented use: May 4, 1893.

226	A67	10c **green,** Feb. 22, 1890	190.00	4.25
		bluish green	190.00	4.25
		dark green	190.00	4.25
		Never hinged	575.00	
		On cover		10.00
		Block of 4	825.00	40.00
		P# strip of 5, Impt.	1,050.	

		P# block of 10, Impt.	4,000.	
		Never hinged	*6,500.*	
		Double transfer	—	—

Earliest documented use: Mar. 5, 1890.

Cancellations

		Samoa	—	
		Supp. Mail Type F or G		+2.50
227	A68	15c **indigo,** Feb. 22, 1890	250.00	27.50
		deep indigo	250.00	27.50
		Never hinged	750.00	
		On cover		65.00
		Block of 4	1,100.	135.00
		P# strip of 5, Impt.	1,600.	
		P# block of 10, Impt.	*8,750.*	
		Never hinged	—	
		Double transfer	—	—
		Triple transfer	—	—

Earliest documented use: May 16, 1890.

Cancellation

		Supplementary Mail Type F		+3.00
228	A69	30c **black,** Feb. 22, 1890	400.00	42.50
		gray black	400.00	42.50
		full black	400.00	42.50
		Never hinged	1,200.	
		On cover		*600.00*
		Block of 4	1,700.	225.00
		P# strip of 5, Impt.	2,250.	
		P# block of 10, Impt.	13,000.	
		Never hinged	—	
		Double transfer	—	—

Earliest documented use: April 14, 1890.

Cancellation

		Supplementary Mail Type F		+5.00
229	A70	90c **orange,** Feb. 22, 1890	550.00	160.00
		yellow orange	550.00	160.00
		red orange	550.00	160.00
		Never hinged	1,650.	
		On cover		—
		Block of 4	2,500.	800.00
		P# strip of 5, Impt.	3,250.	
		P# block of 10, Impt.	27,500.	
		Never hinged	*42,500.*	
		Short transfer at bottom	—	—

The No. 220 with "cap on right 2" variety is due to imperfect inking, not a plate defect.

Earliest documented use: (?) 16, 1890 (dated cancel on off-cover stamp); Feb. 7, 1892 (on cover).

Cancellation

		Supp. Mail Type F or G		+10.00
		Nos. 219-229 (12)	2,047.	301.20

VALUES FOR VERY FINE STAMPS
Please note: Stamps are valued in the grade of Very Fine unless otherwise indicated.

COLUMBIAN EXPOSITION ISSUE
World's Columbian Exposition, Chicago, Ill., May 1 - Oct. 30, 1893, celebrating the 400th anniv. of the discovery of America by Christopher Columbus.
See Nos. 2624-2629 for souvenir sheets containing stamps of designs A71-A86 but with "1992" at upper right.

Columbus in Sight of Land — A71

Landing of Columbus — A72

"Santa Maria," Flagship of Columbus — A73

Fleet of Columbus — A74

Columbus Soliciting Aid from Queen Isabella — A75

Columbus Welcomed at Barcelona — A76

Columbus Restored to Favor — A77

Columbus Presenting Natives — A78

Columbus Announcing His Discovery — A79

Columbus at La Rábida — A80

Recall of Columbus — A81

Queen Isabella Pledging Her Jewels — A82

Columbus in Chains — A83

Columbus Describing His Third Voyage — A84

Queen Isabella and Columbus — A85

Columbus — A86

No. 57

Type of imprint and plate number

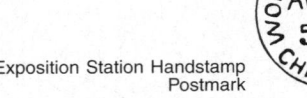

Exposition Station Handstamp Postmark

Printed by the American Bank Note Company.
Plates of 200 subjects in two panes of 100 each (1c, 2c).
Plates of 100 subjects in two panes of 50 each (2c-$5).
Issued (except 8c) Jan. 1 (a Sunday) and Jan. 2 (Monday), 1893. Jan. 1 and Jan. 2 first day covers are documented for the 1c, 2c, 3c, 4c, 5c and 10c. Jan. 2-only first day covers exist for the 6c and $2. See the First Day Cover section for values.

1893				Perf. 12	
230	A71	1c	**deep blue**	16.00	.40
			blue	16.00	.40
			pale blue	16.00	.40
			Never hinged	47.50	
			On cover		.90
			Pair on cover, Expo. station machine canc.		100.00
			Pair on cover, Expo. station duplex handstamp canc.		175.00
			Block of 4	70.00	7.00
			P# strip of 3, Impt.	70.00	
			P# strip of 4, Impt. & letter	105.00	
			P# block of 6, Impt.	450.00	
			Never hinged	625.00	
			P# block of 8, Impt. & letter	725.00	
			Never hinged	1,050.	
			Double transfer	21.00	.75
			Cracked plate	85.00	

Earliest documented use: Jan. 1, 1893 (FDC).

Cancellation

China		—
Philippines		—

"Broken hat" variety

231	A72	2c	**brown violet**	16.00	.30
			deep brown violet	16.00	.30
			gray violet	16.00	.30
			Never hinged	47.50	
			On cover		.35
			On cover or card, Expo. station machine cancel		55.00
			On cover or card, Expo. station duplex handstamp cancel		110.00
			Block of 4	70.00	4.50
			P# strip of 3, Impt.	70.00	
			P# strip of 4, Impt. & letter	105.00	
			Never Hinged	260.00	
			P# block of 6, Impt.	550.00	
			Never hinged	750.00	
			P# block of 8, Impt. & letter	850.00	
			Never hinged	1,200.	
			Double transfer	21.00	.35
			Triple transfer	52.50	—
			Quadruple transfer	85.00	
			Broken hat on third figure to left of Columbus	50.00	3.50
			Never hinged	150.00	
			Broken frame line	18.50	.45
			Recut frame lines	18.50	—
			Cracked plate	75.00	—

There are a number of different versions of the broken hat variety, some of which may be progressive.
Earliest documented use: Jan. 1, 1893 (FDC).

Cancellations

China		—
Supplementary Mail Type G		+3.50

See Die and Plate Proofs for the 2c, imperf. on stamp paper.

232	A73	3c	**green**	45.00	17.50
			dull green	45.00	17.50
			dark green	45.00	17.50
			Never hinged	135.00	
			On cover		35.00
			On cover, Expo. station machine canc.		225.00
			On cover, Expo. station duplex handstamp cancel		325.00
			Block of 4	200.00	140.00
			P# strip of 3, Impt.	190.00	
			Never hinged	375.00	
			P# strip of 4, Impt. & letter	275.00	
			Never hinged	575.00	
			P# block of 6, Impt.	750.00	
			Never hinged	1,300.	
			P# block of 8, Impt. & letter	1,175.	
			Never hinged	2,100.	
			Double transfer	65.00	—

Earliest documented use: Jan. 1, 1893 (FDC).

Cancellations

	China			—	
	Supp. Mail Type F or G				+7.50
233	A74	4c **ultramarine**	65.00		9.00
		dull ultramarine	65.00		9.00
		deep ultramarine	65.00		9.00
		Never hinged	200.00		
		On cover			24.00
		On cover, Expo. station machine canc.			275.00
		On cover, Expo. station duplex handstamp cancel			400.00
		Block of 4	290.00		75.00
		P# strip of 3, Impt.	275.00		
		P# strip of 4, Impt. & letter	425.00		
		P# block of 6, Impt.	1,000.		
		Never hinged	1,650.		
		P# block of 8, Impt. & letter	2,100.		
		Never hinged	3,500.		
		Double transfer	100.00		—
a.		4c **blue** (error)	19,000.		16,500.
		Never hinged	35,000.		
		Block of 4	95,000.		—
		Never hinged	160,000.		
		P# strip of 4, Impt., letter	200,000.		

No. 233a exists in two shades. No. 233a used is valued with small faults, as almost all examples come thus.

Earliest documented use: Jan. 1, 1893 (FDC).

Cancellation

	Supplementary Mail Type G				+3.00
234	A75	5c **chocolate**	70.00		9.50
		pale brown	70.00		9.50
		yellow brown	70.00		9.50
		dark chocolate	70.00		9.50
		Never hinged	210.00		
		On cover			24.00
		On cover, Expo. station machine canc.			275.00
		On cover, Expo. station duplex handstamp cancel			400.00
		Block of 4	300.00		85.00
		P# strip of 3, Impt.	300.00		
		P# strip of 4, Impt. & letter	500.00		
		P# block of 6, Impt.	1,300.		
		Never hinged	2,250.		
		P# block of 8, Impt. & letter	2,650.		
		Never hinged	4,500.		
		Double transfer	130.00		—

Earliest documented use: Jan. 1, 1893 (FDC).

Cancellations

	China			—	
	Philippines			—	
	Supplementary Mail Type F				+3.00
235	A76	6c **purple**	65.00		25.00
		dull purple	65.00		25.00
		Never hinged	200.00		
a.		6c **red violet**	65.00		25.00
		Never hinged	200.00		
		On cover			50.00
		On cover, Expo. station machine canc.			300.00
		On cover, Expo. station duplex handstamp cancel			450.00
		Block of 4	290.00		165.00
		P# strip of 3, Impt.	270.00		
		P# strip of 4, Impt. & letter	425.00		
		P# block of 6, Impt.	1,150.		
		Never hinged	2,000.		
		P# block of 8, Impt. & letter	2,150.		
		Never hinged	3,600.		
		Double transfer	90.00		32.50

Earliest documented use: Jan. 2, 1893 (FDC).

Cancellations

	China			—	
	Supplementary Mail Type F				+5.00
236	A77	8c **magenta**, *Mar. 1893*	60.00		12.00
		light magenta	60.00		12.00
		dark magenta	60.00		12.00
		Never hinged	180.00		
		On cover			24.00
		On cover, Expo. station machine canc.			300.00
		On cover, Expo. station duplex handstamp cancel			475.00
		Block of 4	270.00		95.00
		P# strip of 3, Impt.	240.00		
		P# strip of 4, Impt. & letter	375.00		
		P# block of 6, Impt.	1,025.		
		Never hinged	1,650.		
		P# block of 8, Impt. & letter	1,550.		
		Never hinged	2,600.		
		Double transfer	67.50		

Earliest documented use: Mar. 18, 1893.

Cancellations

	China			—	
	Supplementary Mail Type F				+4.50
237	A78	10c **black brown**	110.00		9.00
		dark brown	110.00		9.00
		gray black	110.00		9.00
		Never hinged	325.00		
		On cover			32.50
		On cover, Expo. station machine canc.			400.00
		On cover, Expo. station duplex handstamp cancel			550.00
		Block of 4	475.00		85.00
		P# strip of 3, Impt.	475.00		
		P# strip of 4, Impt. & letter	675.00		
		Never hinged	1,500.		
		P# block of 6, Impt.	3,500.		
		Never hinged	6,000.		

	P# block of 8, Impt. & letter	6,250.			
	Never hinged	10,500.			
	Double transfer	135.00		13.50	
	Triple transfer	—			

Earliest documented use: Jan. 1, 1893 (FDC).

Cancellations

	Philippines			—	
	Supp. Mail Types F or G				+4.00
238	A79	15c **dark green**	225.00		82.50
		green	225.00		82.50
		dull green	225.00		82.50
		Never hinged	675.00		
		On cover			230.00
		On cover, Expo. station machine canc.			700.00
		On cover, Expo. station duplex handstamp cancel			1,000.
		Block of 4	950.		625.00
		P# strip of 3, Impt.	925.		
		P# strip of 4, Impt. & letter	1,450.		
		P# block of 6, Impt.	4,000.		
		Never hinged	6,750.		
		P# block of 8, Impt. & letter	7,250.		
		Never hinged	12,500.		
		Double transfer	—		

Earliest documented use: Jan. 26, 1893.

Cancellations

	China				+75.00
	Supp. Mail Type F or G				+10.00
239	A80	30c **orange brown**	240.00		100.00
		bright orange brown	240.00		100.00
		Never hinged	750.00		
		On cover			400.00
		On cover, Expo. station machine canc.			1,250.
		On cover, Expo. station duplex handstamp cancel			1,750.
		Block of 4	1,150.		850.00
		P# strip of 3, Impt.	1,050.		
		P# strip of 4, Impt. & letter	1,550.		—
		P# block of 6, Impt.	8,750.		
		Never hinged	14,500.		
		P# block of 8, Impt. & letter	15,500.		
		Never hinged	24,000.		

Earliest documented use: Jan. 10, 1893 (dated cancel on off-cover stamp); Feb. 8, 1893 (cover).

Cancellations

	Supp. Mail Types F or G				+25.00
240	A81	50c **slate blue**	500.00		200.00
		dull slate blue	500.00		200.00
		Never hinged	1,500.		
		On cover			625.00
		On cover, Expo. station machine canc.			1,750.
		On cover, Expo. station duplex handstamp cancel			2,250.
		Block of 4	2,250.		2,000.
		P# strip of 3, Impt.	2,250.		
		P# strip of 4, Impt. & letter	3,500.		—
		Never hinged	7,250.		
		P# block of 6, Impt.	14,500.		
		Never hinged	24,000.		
		P# block of 8, Impt. & letter	30,000.		
		Never hinged	50,000.		
		Double transfer	—		—
		Triple transfer	—		—

Earliest documented use: Feb. 8, 1893.

Cancellation

	Supp. Mail Types F or G				+30.00
241	A82	$1 **salmon**	1,100.		700.
		dark salmon	1,100.		700.
		Never hinged	3,850.		
		No gum	525.		
		On cover			2,000.
		On cover, Expo. station machine canc.			3,500.
		On cover, Expo. station duplex handstamp cancel			4,500.
		Block of 4	5,000.		5,000.
		P# strip of 3, Impt.	5,250.		
		P# strip of 4, Impt. & letter	8,000.		
		P# block of 6, Impt.	47,500.		
		P# block of 8, Impt. & letter	85,000.		
		Never hinged	130,000.		
		Double transfer	—		—

Earliest documented use: Jan. 11, 1893 (dated cancel on off-cover stamp); Jan. 21, 1893 (on cover).

Cancellations

	Supp. Mail Types F or G				+50.
242	A83	$2 **brown red**	1,150.		700.
		deep brown red	1,150.		700.
		Never hinged	4,000.		
		No gum	550.		
		On cover			2,100.
		On cover, Expo. station machine canc.			3,500.
		On cover, Expo. station duplex handstamp cancel			4,500.
		Block of 4	5,000.		5,500.
		P# strip of 3, Impt.	5,500.		
		P# strip of 4, Impt. & letter	8,500.		
		P# block of 6, Impt.	125,000.		
		P# block of 8, Impt. & letter	225,000.		

Earliest documented use: Jan. 2, 1893 (FDC).

Cancellations

	Supplementary Mail Type G				+50.

The No. 242 plate block of 8 is believed to be unique.

243	A84	$3 **yellow green**	1,600.		1,000.
		pale yellow green	1,600.		1,000.

	Never hinged	5,250.			
	No gum	850.			
a.	$3 **olive green**	1,600.		1,000.	
	Never hinged	5,250.			
	No gum	850.			
	On cover			2,600.	
	On cover, Expo. station machine canc.			5,000.	
	On cover, Expo. station duplex handstamp cancel			7,000.	
	Block of 4	8,250.		10,000.	
	P# strip of 3, Impt.	7,500.			
	P# strip of 4, Impt. & letter	11,000.			
	P# block of 6, Impt.	95,000.			

Earliest documented use: Mar. 24, 1893.

244	A85	$4 **crimson lake**	2,250.		1,300.
		Never hinged	7,250.		
		No gum	1,150.		
a.		$4 **rose carmine**	2,250.		1,300.
		pale aniline rose	2,250.		1,300.
		Never hinged	7,250.		
		No gum	1,150.		
		On cover			4,000.
		On cover, Expo. station machine canc.			6,500.
		On cover, Expo. station duplex handstamp cancel			9,000.
		Block of 4	11,000.		15,000.
		P# strip of 3, Impt.	11,000.		
		P# strip of 4, Impt. & letter	15,000.		
		P# block of 6, Impt.	300,000.		
		P# block of 8, Impt. & letter	400,000.		

The No. 244 plate block of 8 is unique; it has full original gum with light hinge marks.

Earliest documented use: Mar. 24, 1893.

245	A86	$5 **black**	2,700.		1,500.
		grayish black	2,700.		1,500.
		Never hinged	10,500.		
		No gum	1,350.		
		On cover			4,750.
		On cover, Expo. station machine canc.			15,000.
		On cover, Expo. station duplex handstamp cancel			17,500.
		Block of 4	13,500.		15,000.
		P# strip of 3, Impt.	15,000.		
		P# strip of 4, Impt. & letter	62,500.		
		Never hinged	175,000.		
		P# block of 6, Impt.	225,000.		
		Never hinged	290,000.		
		P# block of 8, Impt. & letter	250,000.		

Earliest documented use: Jan. 6, 1893.

The No. 245 plate block of 8 is unique; it has traces of original gum.

See Nos. 2624-2629 for souvenir sheets containing stamps of designs A71-A86 but with "1992" at upper right.

Nos. 230-245 exist imperforate; not issued. See Die and Plate proofs for the 2c.

Never-Hinged Stamps

See note before No. 182 regarding premiums for never-hinged stamps.

BUREAU ISSUES

In the following listings of postal issues mostly printed by the Bureau of Engraving and Printing at Washington, D.C., the editors acknowledge with thanks the use of material prepared by the Catalogue Listing Committee of the Bureau Issues Association.

The Bureau-printed stamps until 1965 were engraved except the Offset Issues of 1918-19 (Nos. 525-536). Engraving and lithography were combined for the first time for the Homemakers 5c (No. 1253). The Bureau used photogravure first in 1971 on the Missouri 8c (No. 1426).

Stamps in this section that were not printed by the Bureau begin with Nos. 909-921 and are so noted.

"On cover" listings carry through No. 701. Beyond this point a few covers of special significance are listed. Many Bureau Issue stamps are undoubtedly scarce properly used on cover. Most higher denominations exist almost exclusively on pieces of package wrapping and usually in combination with other values. Collector interest in covers is generally limited to fancy cancellations, attractive corner cards, uses abroad and other special usages.

Plate number blocks are valued unused. Although many exist used, and are scarcer in that condition, they tend to sell for less than the value of the unused examples because they are less sought after.

IMPRINTS AND PLATE NUMBERS

In listing the Bureau of Engraving & Printing Imprints, the editors have followed the classification of types adopted by the Bureau Issues Association. Types I, II, IV, V and VIII occur on postage issues and are illustrated below. Types III, VI and VII occur only on Special Delivery plates, so are illustrated with the listings of those stamps; other types are illustrated with the listings of the issues on which they occur.

Type I   II   IV   V   VIII

In listing Imprint blocks and strips, the editors have designated for each stamp the various types known to exist. If, however, the Catalogue listing sufficiently describes the Imprint, no type number is given. Thus a listing reading: "P# block of 6, Impt. (Imprint) & A" in the 1912-14 series would not be followed by a type number as the description is self-explanatory. Values are for the commonest types.

PLATE POSITIONS

At the suggestion of the Catalogue Listing Committee of the Bureau Issues Association (now the United States Stamp Society), all plate positions of these issues are indicated by giving the plate number first, next the pane position, and finally the stamp position. For example: 20234 L.L. 58.

Franklin — A87

Washington — A88

Jackson — A89

Lincoln — A90

Grant — A91

Garfield — A92

Sherman — A93

Webster — A94

Clay — A95

Jefferson — A96

Perry — A97

James Madison — A98

John Marshall — A99

Designed by Thomas F. Morris.

REGULAR ISSUE

Plates for the issue of 1894 were of two sizes: 400 subjects for all 1c, 2c and 10c denominations; 200 subjects for all 6c, 8c, 15c, 50c, $1.00, $2.00 and $5.00, and both 400 and 200 subjects for the 3c, 4c and 5c denominations; all issued in panes of 100 each.

1894		Unwmk.		Perf. 12
246	A87	1c **ultramarine,** *Oct. 1894*	30.00	7.00
		bright ultramarine	30.00	7.00
		dark ultramarine	30.00	7.00
		Never hinged	90.00	
		On cover		22.50
		Block of 4	130.00	45.00
		P# strip of 3, Impt., T I	135.00	
		Never hinged	300.00	
		P# block of 6, Impt., T I	425.00	
		Never hinged	925.00	
		Double transfer	37.50	8.00

Earliest documented use: Oct. 17, 1894.

Cancellation

		China		—
247	A87	1c **blue**	65.00	4.00
		bright blue	65.00	4.00
		dark blue	65.00	4.00
		Never hinged	190.00	
		On cover		18.50
		Block of 4	290.00	27.50
		P# strip of 3, Impt., T I or II	290.00	
		Never hinged	600.00	
		P# block of 6, Impt., T I or II	850.00	
		Never hinged	1,600.	
		Double transfer	—	5.00

Earliest documented use: Nov. 5, 1894.

TWO CENTS:

Triangle A (Type I)

Type I (Triangle A). The horizontal lines of the ground work run across the triangle and are of the same thickness within it as without.

Triangle B (Type II)

Type II (Triangle B). The horizontal lines cross the triangle but are thinner within it than without. Other minor design differences exist, but the change to Triangle B is a sufficient determinant.

Triangle C (Types III and IV)

Type III (Triangle C). The horizontal lines do not cross the double lines of the triangle. The lines within the triangle are thin, as in Type II. The rest of the design is the same as Type II, except that most of the designs had the dot in the "S" of "CENTS" removed. Stamps with this dot present are listed; some specialists refer to them as "Type IIIa" varieties.

Type IV (Triangle C). See No. 279B and its varieties. Type IV is from a new die with many major and minor design variations including, (1) re-cutting and lengthening of hairline, (2) shaded toga button, (3) strengthening of lines on sleeve, (4) additional dots on ear, (5) "T" of "TWO" straight at right, (6) background lines extend into white oval opposite "U" of "UNITED." Many other differences exist.

For further information concerning type IV, see also George Brett's article in the Sept. 1993 issue of the "The United States Specialist" and the 23-part article by Kenneth Diehl in the Dec. 1994 through Aug. 1997 issues of the "The United States Specialist."

248	A88	2c **pink,** type I, *Oct. 1894*	27.50	9.00
		pale pink	27.50	9.00
		Never hinged	82.50	
		On cover		16.00
		Block of 4	120.00	47.50
		P# strip of 3, Impt., T I or II	115.00	
		Never hinged	260.00	
		P# block of 6, Impt., T I or II	300.00	
		Never hinged	675.00	
		Double transfer	—	—
a.		Vert. pair, imperf horiz.	*5,500.*	

Earliest documented use: Oct. 16, 1894.

249	A88	2c **carmine lake,** type I, *Oct. 1894*	150.00	7.00
		dark carmine lake	150.00	7.00
		Never hinged	450.00	
		On cover		12.50
		Block of 4	650.00	45.00
		P# strip of 3, Impt., T I or II	625.00	
		Never hinged	1,450.	

	P# block of 6, Impt., T I or				
	II	2,400.			
	Never hinged	5,000.			
	Double transfer	—	8.00		
a.	Double impression		—		
250 A88	2c **carmine**, type I, *Oct. 1894*	27.50	3.00		
	dark carmine	30.00	5.00		
	Never hinged	82.50			
	On cover		4.00		
	Block of 4	120.00	20.00		
a.	2c **rose**, type I, *Oct. 1894*	27.50	5.25		
	Never hinged	82.50			
	On cover		6.50		
	Block of 4	120.00	22.50		
b.	2c **scarlet**, type I, *Jan. 1895*	27.50	3.00		
	Never hinged	82.50			
	On cover		4.00		
	Block of 4	120.00	20.00		
	P# strip of 3, Impt., T I or				
	II	115.00			
	Never hinged	275.00			
	P# block of 6, Impt., T I or				
	II	350.00			
	Never hinged	750.00			
	Double transfer		5.50		
d.	Horizontal pair, imperf. between	*2,000.*			

Earliest documented uses: Oct. 11, 1894 (No. 250), Oct. 13, 1894 (No. 250a), Jan. 17, 1895 (No. 250b).

251 A88	2c **carmine**, type II, *Feb.*				
	1895	350.00	14.00		
	dark carmine	350.00	14.00		
	Never hinged	1,100.			
	On cover		22.50		
	Block of 4	1,250.	110.00		
a.	2c **scarlet**, type II, *Feb. 1895*	350.00	11.00		
	Never hinged	1,100.			
	On cover		17.50		
	Block of 4	1,250.	80.00		
	P# strip of 3, Impt., T II	1,200.			
	Never hinged	3,500.			
	P# block of 6, Impt., T II	3,250.			
	Never hinged	7,000.			

Earliest documented uses: Feb. 12, 1895 (No. 251, dated cancel on off-cover stamp); Feb. 16, 1895 (No. 251, on cover); Feb. 19, 1895 (No. 251a).

252 A88	2c **carmine**, type III, *Mar.*				
	1895	120.00	14.00		
	pale carmine	120.00	14.00		
	Never hinged	360.00			
a.	2c **scarlet**, type III, *Mar. 1895*	120.00	14.00		
	Never hinged	360.00			
	On cover		18.00		
	Block of 4	500.00	110.00		
	P# strip of 3, Impt., T II or				
	IV	500.00			
	Never hinged	1,200.			

	P# block of 6, Impt., T II or				
	IV	1,850.			
	Never hinged	4,000.			
	Dot in "S" of "CENTS"				
	(carmine)	140.00	14.00		
	Never hinged	390.00			
b.	Horiz. pair, imperf. vert.	*5,000.*			
c.	Horiz. pair, imperf. between	*5,500.*			

Former Nos. 252a, 252b are now Nos. 252b, 252c.

Earliest documented uses: Apr. 2, 1895 (dated cancel tying No. 252 dot in "S" variety on piece); Apr. 5, 1895 (No. 252); Apr. 17, 1895 (No. 252a).

253 A89	3c **purple**, *Sept. 1894*	110.00	13.00		
	dark purple	110.00	13.00		
	Never hinged	325.00			
	On cover		27.50		
	Block of 4	500.00	87.50		
	Margin block of 4, arrow, R				
	or L	525.00			
	P# strip of 3, Impt., T I or				
	II	450.00			
	Never hinged	1,150.			
	P# block of 6, Impt., T I or				
	II	1,450.			
	Never hinged	3,250.			

Earliest documented use: Oct. 20, 1894 (dated cancel on off-cover stamp); Nov. 15, 1894 (on cover).

See Die and Plate Proofs for imperf. on stamp paper.

254 A90	4c **dark brown**, *Sept. 1894*	175.00	9.00		
	brown	175.00	9.00		
	Never hinged	525.00			
	On cover		22.50		
	Block of 4	750.00	47.50		
	Margin block of 4, arrow, R				
	or L	775.00			
	P# strip of 3, Impt., T I or				
	II	725.00			
	Never hinged	1,750.			
	P# block of 6, Impt., T I or				
	II	2,000.			
	Never hinged	4,250.			

Earliest documented use: Oct. 16, 1894 (dated cancel on off-cover stamp); Nov. 21, 1894 (on cover).

See Die and Plate Proofs for imperf. on stamp paper.

Cancellations
Supplementary Mail Type

	F		+2.00		
255 A91	5c **chocolate**, *Sept. 1894*	110.00	9.00		
	deep chocolate	110.00	9.00		
	yellow brown	110.00	9.00		

	Never hinged	325.00			
	On cover		22.50		
	Block of 4	500.00	57.50		
	Margin block of 4, arrow, R				
	or L	525.00			
	P# strip of 3, Impt., T I, II				
	or IV	500.00			
	Never hinged	1,200.			
	P# block of 6, Impt., T I, II				
	or IV	1,300.			
	Never hinged	2,750.			
	Double transfer	140.00	10.00		
	Worn plate, diagonal lines				
	missing in oval back-				
	ground	135.00	10.00		
c.	Vert. pair, imperf. horiz.	*4,000.*			
	P# block of 6, Impt., T IV	—			

See Die and Plate Proofs for imperf. on stamp paper.

Earliest documented use: Oct. 23, 1894.

Cancellations
Supplementary Mail Type

	G		+2.00		
	China		—		
256 A92	6c **dull brown**, *July 1894*	160.00	30.00		
	Never hinged	500.00			
	On cover		50.00		
	Block of 4	700.00	190.00		
	Margin block of 4, arrow, R				
	or L	725.00			
	P# strip of 3, Impt., T I	675.00			
	Never hinged	1,650.			
	P# block of 6, Impt., T I	2,750.	—		
	Never hinged	*5,750.*			
a.	Vert. pair, imperf. horiz.	*3,000.*			
	P# block of 6, Impt., T I	*21,500.*			

Earliest documented use: Aug. 11, 1894.

257 A93	8c **violet brown**, *Mar. 1895*	175.00	22.50		
	bright violet brown	175.00	22.50		
	Never hinged	525.00			
	On cover		50.00		
	Block of 4	750.00	140.00		
	Margin block of 4, arrow, R				
	or L	775.00			
	P# strip of 3, Impt., T I	725.00			
	Never hinged	1,750.			
	P# block of 6, Impt., T I	2,500.			
	Never hinged	5,500.			

Earliest documented use: May 8, 1895.

258 A94	10c **dark green**, *Sept. 1894*	325.00	19.00		
	green	325.00	19.00		
	dull green	325.00	19.00		
	Never hinged	1,000.			
	On cover		37.50		

Block of 4		1,350.	100.00
P# strip of 3, Impt., T I		1,450.	
Never hinged		3,250.	
P# block of 6, Impt., T I		3,500.	
Never hinged		7,250.	
Double transfer		375.00	19.00

See Die and Plate Proofs for imperf. on stamp paper.

Earliest documented use: Nov. 2, 1894.

Cancellations

China			—
Supp. Mail Types F, G			+2.00
259 A95 15c **dark blue**, *Oct. 1894*		325.00	70.00
indigo		325.00	70.00
Never hinged		1,000.	
On cover			125.00
Block of 4		1,350.	450.00
Margin block of 4, arrow, R or L		1,400.	
P# strip of 3, Impt., T I		1,500.	
Never hinged		3,250.	
P# block of 6, Impt., T I		5,000.	
Never hinged		10,000.	

Earliest documented use: Dec. 6, 1894.

Cancellation

China			—
260 A96 50c **orange**, *Nov. 1894*		525.	160.
deep orange		525.	160.
Never hinged		1,600.	
On cover			1,000.
Block of 4		2,500.	1,200.
Margin block of 4, arrow, R or L		2,600.	
P# strip of 3, Impt., T I		2,400.	
Never hinged		5,250.	
P# block of 6, Impt., T I		20,000.	
Never hinged		32,500.	

Earliest documented use: Dec. 12, 1894 (dated cancel on off-cover stamp); Jan. 15, 1895 (on cover).

Cancellations

Supp. Mail Type F or G			—
China			—

Type I

Type II

ONE DOLLAR
Type I. The circles enclosing "$1" are broken where they meet the curved line below "One Dollar."
Type II. The circles are complete.
The fifteen left columns of impressions from the plate of 200 subjects are Type I, the other five columns being Type II.

261 A97 $1 **black**, type I, *Nov. 1894*		1,050.	375.
grayish black		1,050.	375.
Never hinged		3,250.	
No gum		350.	
On cover			2,750.
Block of 4		4,750.	2,200.
Margin block of 4, arrow, L		5,000.	
P# strip of 3, Impt., T V		4,500.	
P# block of 6, Impt., T V		20,000.	

Earliest documented use: Jan. 18, 1895.

261A A97 $1 **black**, type II, *Nov. 1894*		2,200.	850.
Never hinged		6,750.	
No gum		725.	
On cover			4,500.
Block of 4		9,500.	5,000.
Margin block of 4, arrow, R		10,000.	
Horizontal pair, types I and II		4,000.	1,450.
Block of 4, two each of types I and II		9,500.	—
P# strip of 3, Impt., T V, one stamp No. 261		10,000.	
P# block of 6, Impt., T V, two stamps No. 261		75,000.	

Earliest documented use: Mar. 22, 1895. A Mar. 11, 1895, cover has been reported. The editors would like to see evidence of certification of this date.

262 A98 $2 **bright blue**, *Dec. 1894*		2,750.	1,300.
Never hinged		8,750.	
No gum		1,100.	
dark blue		2,900.	1,350.
Never hinged		9,250.	
On cover			5,000.
Block of 4		12,500.	9,500.
Margin block of 4, arrow, R or L		13,000.	
P# strip of 3, Impt., T V		13,500.	
P# block of 6, Impt., T V		45,000.	

The only recorded plate block of 6 of No. 262 has average centering and is valued as such.
Earliest documented use: July 6, 1895 (dated cancel on off-cover stamp); July 15, 1895 (on cover).

263 A99 $5 **dark green**, *Dec. 1894*		4,500.	2,900.
Never hinged		15,000.	
No gum		2,400.	
On cover			—

Block of 4		22,000.	16,000.
Margin block of 4, arrow, R or L		22,500.	
P# strip of 3, Impt., T V		25,000.	

Earliest documented use: July 6, 1896 (dated cancel on off-cover stamp).

REGULAR ISSUE

Designed by Thomas F. Morris.

(Actual size of letter)

repeated in rows, thus

HORIZONTAL WATERMARK ORIENTATIONS

Normal	Reversed
Inverted	Inverted Reversed

VERTICAL WATERMARK ORIENTATIONS

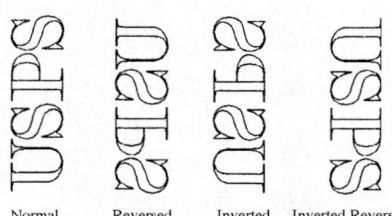

Normal	Reversed	Inverted	Inverted Reversed

Watermark 191
The letters stand for "United States Postage Stamp."

Plates for the 1895 issue were of two sizes:
400 subjects for all 1c, 2c and 10c denominations; 200 subjects for all 3c, 4c, 5c, 6c, 8c, 15c, 50c, $1, $2 and $5; all issued in panes of 100 each.
Printings from the 400 subject plates show the watermark reading horizontally, on the 200 subject printings the watermark reads vertically. Watermarks are viewed from the back of the stamp.

Wmk. 191 Horizontally or Vertically

1895					*Perf. 12*
264 A87 1c	**blue**, *Apr. 1895*		6.00	.60
	dark blue		6.00	.60
	pale blue		6.00	.60
	Never hinged		17.50	
	On cover			1.25
	Block of 4		26.00	5.00
	P# strip of 3, Impt., T I, II, IV or V		26.00	
	Never hinged		65.00	
	P# block of 6, Impt., T I, II, IV or V		240.00	
	Never hinged		450.00	
	Double transfer			1.10

Earliest documented use: May 16, 1895.

Cancellations

China			—
Philippines			—
Samoa			—

265 A88 2c	**carmine**, type I, *May 1895*	27.50	3.50
	deep carmine	27.50	3.50
	Never hinged	82.50	
	On cover		5.50
	Block of 4	120.00	18.00
	P# strip of 3, Impt., T II	110.00	
	Never hinged	275.00	
	P# block of 6, Impt., T II	400.00	
	Never hinged	800.00	
	Double transfer		7.25

Earliest documented use: May 2, 1895.

266 A88 2c	**carmine**, type II, *May 1895*	32.50	5.50
	Never hinged	100.00	
	On cover		8.50
	Block of 4	200.00	40.00
	Horizontal pair, types II and III	175.00	17.50
	Never hinged	500.00	
	P# strip of 3, Impt., T II or IV	135.00	
	Never hinged	340.00	
	P# block of 6, Impt., T II or IV	475.00	
	Never hinged	1,000.	

Earliest documented use: May 27, 1895.

267 A88 2c	**carmine**, type III *May 1895*	5.50	.50
	deep carmine	5.50	.50
	reddish carmine	5.50	.50
	Never hinged	16.00	
	On cover		.65
	Block of 4	24.00	3.50
	P# strip of 3, Impt., T II, IV or V	22.50	
	Never hinged	57.50	
	P# block of 6, Impt., T II, IV or V	190.00	
	Never hinged	325.00	
	Dot in "S" of "CENTS"	7.50	.60
	Never hinged	22.50	
	Double transfer	16.50	1.30
a. 2c	**pink**, type III, *Nov. 1897*	20.00	2.25
	Never hinged	60.00	
	bright pink	25.00	5.50
	Never hinged	75.00	
	On cover		3.00
	Block of 4	90.00	15.00
	P# strip of 3, Impt., T II, IV or V	75.00	
	Never hinged	200.00	
	P# block of 6, Impt., T II, IV or V	425.00	
	Never hinged	825.00	
	Dot in "S" of "CENTS"	35.00	2.75
	Never hinged	110.00	
b. 2c	**vermilion**, type III, *early 1899*	50.00	10.00
c. 2c	**rose carmine**, type III, *Mar. 1899*	—	—

Earliest documented uses:
No. 267, May 28, 1895;
No. 267 with dot in "S", July 15, 1895;
No. 267a, Dec. 8, 1897;
No. 267a with dot in "S", Mar. 18, 1898.

Cancellations

Green			—
China			—
Hawaii			—
Philippines			—
Samoa			—

The three left vertical rows of impressions from plate 170 are Type II, the balance being Type III.

268 A89 3c	**purple**, *Oct. 1895*	37.50	2.25
	dark purple	37.50	2.25
	Never hinged	115.00	
	On cover		8.00
	Block of 4	160.00	21.00
	Margin block of 4, arrow, R or L	175.00	
	P# strip of 3, Impt., T II or V	150.00	
	Never hinged	400.00	
	P# block of 6, Impt., T II or IV	725.00	
	Never hinged	1,300.	
	Double transfer	45.00	4.75

Earliest documented use: Dec. 1, 1895.

Cancellations

Guam			—
China			—
Philippines			—

269 A90 4c	**dark brown**, *June, 1895*	45.00	3.50
	dark yellow brown	45.00	3.50

			Never hinged	135.00	
			On cover		11.00
			Block of 4	190.00	29.00
			Margin block of 4, arrow, R or L	210.00	
			P# strip of 3, Impt., T I, II, IV or V	190.00	
			Never hinged	475.00	
			P# block of 6, Impt., T I, II, IV or V	800.00	
			Never hinged	1,650.	
			Double transfer	50.00	5.50

Earliest documented use: July 22, 1895.

Cancellations

			Philippines		—
			China		—
			Samoa		—
270	A91	5c	**chocolate,** *June, 1895*	35.00	3.50
			deep brown	35.00	3.50
			chestnut	35.00	3.50
			Never hinged	105.00	
			On cover		8.00
			Block of 4	150.00	30.00
			Margin block of 4, arrow, R or L	160.00	
			P# strip of 3, Impt., T I, II, IV or V	145.00	
			Never hinged	375.00	
			P# block of 6, Impt., T I, II, IV or V	675.00	
			Never hinged	1,300.	
			Double transfer	42.50	5.00
			Worn plate, diagonal lines missing in oval background	37.50	3.75

Earliest documented use: Sept. 12, 1895.

Cancellations

			China		—
			Supplementary Mail G		+2.50
271	A92	6c	**dull brown,** *Aug. 1895*	120.00	8.50
			claret brown	120.00	8.50
			Never hinged	360.00	
			On cover		27.50
			Block of 4	550.00	70.00
			Margin block of 4, arrow, R or L	575.00	
			P# strip of 3, Impt., T I, IV or V	500.00	
			Never hinged	1,250.	
			P# block of 6, Impt., T I, IV or V	2,900.	
			Never hinged	5,500.	
			Very thin paper	140.00	9.50
a.			Wmkd. USIR	15,000.	12,500.
			Pair		
			P# strip of 3, Impt.	—	

Earliest documented use: Sept. 14, 1895.

Cancellation

			Philippines		—

No. 271a is valued in the grade of fine.

Nos. 271a, 272a must have an identifiable portion of the letters "I" or "R." Single stamps from the same sheets, but showing the "U" or "S" are considered to be Nos. 271 and 272.

272	A93	8c	**violet brown,** *July 1895*	70.00	2.75
			dark violet brown	70.00	2.75
			Never hinged	210.00	
			On cover		14.00
			Block of 4	300.00	17.50
			Margin block of 4, arrow, R or L	310.00	
			P# strip of 3, Impt., T I, IV or V	300.00	
			Never hinged	750.00	
			P# block of 6, Impt., T I, IV or V	975.00	
			Never hinged	2,100.	
			Double transfer	85.00	4.25
a.			Wmkd. USIR	6,000.	1,000.
			Block of 4		5,500.
			P# strip of 3 Impt., T I	20,000.	

Earliest documented use: Sept. 11, 1895.

Cancellations

			China		—
			Guam		—
			Philippines		—
			Puerto Rico, 1898		—
			Samoa		—
			Supplementary Mail Type G		+2.50
273	A94	10c	**dark green,** *June 1895*	95.00	2.25
			green	95.00	2.25
			Never hinged	290.00	
			On cover		15.00
			Block of 4	400.00	21.00
			P# strip of 3, Impt., T I or IV	410.00	
			Never hinged	1,000.	
			P# block of 6, Impt., T I or IV	1,750.	
			Never hinged	3,500.	
			Double transfer	120.00	4.75

Earliest documented use: July 25, 1895.

Cancellations

			Green		—
			China		—
			Cuba		—
			Philippines		—
			Supp. Mail Types F, G		+2.00

274	A95	15c	**dark blue,** *Sept. 1895*	225.00	17.50
			indigo	225.00	17.50
			Never hinged	675.00	
			On cover		55.00
			Block of 4	950.00	105.00
			Margin block of 4, arrow, R or L	975.00	
			P# strip of 3, Impt., T I or IV	900.00	
			Never hinged	2,250.	
			P# block of 6, Impt., T I or IV	3,750.	
			Never hinged	10,000.	

Earliest documented use: May 5, 1896.

Cancellations

			China		—
			Philippines		—
			Supplementary Mail Type G		+3.00
275	A96	50c	**orange,** *Nov. 1895*	275.	40.00
			Never hinged	850.	
			On cover		400.00
			Block of 4	1,200.	225.00
			Margin block of 4, arrow, R or L	1,250.	
			P# strip of 3, Impt., T I	1,125.	
			P# block of 6, Impt., T I	6,000.	
			Never hinged	12,500.	
a.		50c	**red orange**	325.	47.50
			Never hinged	1,000.	
			On cover		425.00
			Block of 4	1,400.	275.00
			Margin block of 4, arrow, R or L	1,450.	
			P# strip of 3, Impt., T I	1,350.	
			P# block of 6, Impt., T I	6,500.	

Earliest documented use: May 5, 1896.

Cancellations

			China		—
			Philippines		—
			Supp. Mail Types F, G		+5.
276	A97	$1	**black,** type I, *Aug. 1895*	650.	110.
			greenish black	650.	110.
			Never hinged	2,000.	
			No gum	180.	
			On cover		2,250.
			Block of 4	2,800.	800.
			Margin block of 4, arrow, L	2,900.	
			P# strip of 3, Impt., T V	2,750.	
			Never hinged	6,500.	
			P# block of 6, Impt., T V	40,000.	

Earliest documented use: April 9, 1897.

Cancellation

			Philippines		—
276A	A97	$1	**black,** type II, *Aug. 1895*	1,350.	225.
			greenish black	1,350.	225.
			Never hinged	4,250.	
			No gum	400.	
			On cover		3,750.
			Block of 4	6,000.	1,550.
			Margin block of 4, arrow, R	6,250.	
			Horizontal pair, types I and II	2,400.	2,600.
			Block of 4, two each of types I and II	6,250.	6,500.
			P# strip of 3, Impt., T V, one stamp No. 276	5,000.	
			P# block of 6, Impt., T V, two stamps No. 276	125,000.	

Earliest documented use: Apr. 6, 1896.

Cancellation

			China		—
			Philippines		—

The fifteen left columns of impressions from the plate of 200 subjects are Type I, the other five columns being Type II.

277	A98	$2	**bright blue**	1,000.	450.
			Never hinged	3,250.	
			No gum	300.	
a.		$2	**dark blue**	1,000.	450.
			Never hinged	3,250.	
			No gum	300.	
			On cover		3,500.
			Block of 4	4,500.	3,000.
			Margin block of 4, arrow, R or L	4,750.	
			P# strip of 3, Impt., T V	4,250.	—
			P# block of 6, Impt., T V	85,000.	

Earliest documented use: July 18, 1895.

Cancellation

			Supplementary Mail Type G		—
278	A99	$5	**dark green,** *Aug. 1895*	2,250.	650.
			Never hinged	7,000.	
			No gum	700.	
			On cover		10,000.
			Block of 4	10,000.	4,000.
			Margin block of 4, arrow, R or L	10,500.	
			P# strip of 3, Impt., T V	9,500.	
			P# block of 6, Impt., T V	200,000.	

Earliest documented use: Nov. 3, 1896.

See Die and Plate Proofs for imperf. or horiz. pair, imperf. vert. (1c) on stamp paper.

REGULAR ISSUE
Designed by Thomas F. Morris.

Wmk. 191 Horizontally or Vertically
1897-1903   *Perf. 12*

Plates for the sheet stamps for the 1897-1903 issue were of two sizes:

400 subjects for the 1c and 2c denominations; 200 subjects for all 4c, 5c, 6c and 15c denominations; and both 400 and 200 for the 10c denomination; all issued in panes of 100 each.

Printings from the 400 subject plates show the watermark reading horizontally. On the 200 subject plate printings the watermark reads vertically.

Plates for booklet panes for the 1897-1903 issue were of two sizes: 360 subjects and 180 subjects. Printings from the 360-subject plates show the watermark reading horizontally, while printings from the 180-subject plates show the watermark reading vertically.

In January, 1898, the color of the 1-cent stamp was changed to green and in March, 1898, that of the 5-cents to dark blue in order to conform to the colors assigned these values by the Universal Postal Union. These changes necessitated changing the colors of the 10c and 15c denominations in order to avoid confusion.

279	A87	1c	**deep green,** horizontal watermark, *Jan. 1898*	9.00	.50
			green	9.00	.50
			yellow green	9.00	.50
			dark yellow green	9.00	.50
			Never hinged	25.00	
			On cover		.60
			Block of 4	37.50	5.00
			P# strip of 3, Impt., T V	37.50	—
			Never hinged	85.00	
			P# block of 6, Impt., T V	185.00	
			Never hinged	350.00	
			Double transfer	12.00	1.10
a.		1c	deep green, vertical watermark (error), *May 1902*	40.00	7.50
			Never hinged	120.00	
			On cover		22.50
			Block of 4	200.00	
			P# strip of 3, Impt., T V	250.00	
			Never hinged	650.00	

Earliest documented use: Jan. 31, 1898

Cancellations

			China		—
			Guam		—
			Puerto Rico, 1898		—
			Philippines		—
279B	A88	2c	**red,** type IV *May 1899*	9.00	.40
			light red, *May 1899*	9.00	.40
			Never hinged	25.00	
			deep red, *Sept. 1901*	13.50	1.25
			Never hinged	32.50	

On cover		.50
Block of 4	37.50	3.00
P# strip of 3, Impt., T V	37.50	
Never hinged	85.00	
P# block of 6, Impt., T V	200.00	
Never hinged	360.00	
P# strip of 4, Impt., T V		
(plate 802, UR position)	*250.00*	
P# block of 8, Impt., T V		
(plate 802, UR position)	*750.00*	
Double transfer	18.00	.75
Triple transfer		.75
Triangle at upper right		
without shading	22.50	6.00

c. 2c **rose carmine,** type IV, *Mar. 1899* 300.00 200.00
   bright carmine rose, *Mar. 1899* 300.00 200.00
   Never hinged 850.00
   Block of 4 1,250.
   P# strip of 3, Impt., T V 1,200.
   Never hinged 2,500.
   P# block of 6, Impt., T V 3,250.

d. 2c **orange red,** type IV, horizontal watermark, *June 1900* 11.50 .55
   pale orange red 11.50 .55
   dark orange red, *Sept. 1902* 11.50 .55
   deep orange red, *Jan. 1903* 11.50 .55
   Never hinged 32.50
   On cover .70
   Block of 4 50.00 4.00
   P# strip of 3, Impt., T V 42.50
   Never hinged 115.00
   P# block of 6, Impt., T V 220.00
   Never hinged 400.00

e. 2c **orange red,** type IV, vertical watermark (error), *May 1902* 35.00 5.00
   Never hinged *110.00*
   On cover 17.50
   Block of 4 *175.00*
   P# strip of 3, Impt., T V *300.00*
   Never hinged *750.00*
   P# block of 6, Impt., T V, never hinged *2,750.*

f. 2c **carmine,** type IV, *Nov. 1897* 10.00 .50
   reddish carmine, *Dec. 1898* 10.00 .50
   Never hinged 27.50
   On cover .65
   Block of 4 42.50 3.00
   P# strip of 3, Impt., T V 40.00
   Never hinged 95.00
   P# block of 6, Impt., T V 220.00
   Never hinged 385.00

g. 2c **pink,** type IV, *Nov. 1897* 50.00 1.75
   Never hinged 150.00
   bright pink 60.00 2.00
   Never hinged 180.00
   On cover 2.00
   Block of 4 225.00 12.50
   P# strip of 3, Impt., T V 175.00
   Never hinged 525.00
   P# block of 6, Impt., T V 600.00
   Never hinged 1,200.

h. 2c **vermilion,** type IV, *Jan. 1899* 11.00 .55
   pale vermilion 11.00 .55
   Never hinged 30.00
   On cover .75
   Block of 4 47.50 4.00
   P# strip of 3, Impt., T V 45.00
   Never hinged 120.00
   P# block of 6, Impt., T V 235.00
   Never hinged 425.00

i. 2c **brown orange,** type IV, *Jan. 1899* *150.00* *15.00*
   Never hinged *425.00*
   P# strip of 3, Impt., T V *650.00*

j. Booklet pane of 6, **red,** type IV, horizontal watermark, *Apr. 18, 1900* *500.00* *1,250.*
   light red *500.00* *1,250.*
   orange red, *1901* *500.00* *1,250.*
   Never hinged *1,000.*

k. Booklet pane of 6, **red,** type IV, vertical watermark ('02) *500.00* *1,250.*
   Never hinged *1,000.*

Earliest documented uses:
No. 279B, July 6, 1899;
No. 279Bc, Mar 30, 1899;
No. 279Bc in bright rose carmine, July 16, 1899;
No. 279Bd, June 8, 1900;
No. 279Bf, Nov. 18, 1897;
No. 279Bg, Dec. 1, 1897;
No. 279Bh, Feb. 27, 1899.
No. 279Bj booklet single (red), May 4, 1900;
No. 279Bj booklet single (orange red), May 7, 1902;

Cancellations

Puerto Rico, 1898	—
Philippines, 1898	—
Guam, 1899 or 1900	—
Supplementary Mail Type G	+4.00
Cuba, 1898	—
China	—
Samoa	—

280 A90 4c **rose brown,** *Oct. 1898* 27.50 3.50
   Never hinged 82.50
a. 4c **lilac brown** 27.50 3.50
   brownish claret 27.50 3.50
   Never hinged 82.50
b. 4c **orange brown** 27.50 3.50
   Never hinged 82.50
   On cover 11.00
   Block of 4 120.00 27.50

Margin block of 4, arrow, R or L	130.00	
P# strip of 3, Impt., T V	115.00	
Never hinged	290.00	
P# block of 6, Impt., T V	700.00	
Never hinged	1,250.	
Double transfer	32.50	5.00
Extra frame line at top (Plate 793 R 62)	50.00	9.50

Earliest documented use: Nov. 13, 1898.

Cancellations

Supplementary Mail Type G	+3.00
China	—
Philippines	—

281 A91 5c **dark blue,** *Mar. 1898* 32.50 2.25
   blue 32.50 2.25
   bright blue 32.50 2.25
   Never hinged 100.00
   On cover 10.00
   Block of 4 140.00 14.00
   Margin block of 4, arrow, R or L 150.00
   P# strip of 3, Impt., T V 135.00
   Never hinged 340.00
   P# block of 6, Impt., T V 650.00
   Never hinged 1,250.
   Double transfer 42.50 4.50
   Worn plate (diagonal lines missing in oval background) 37.50 2.75

Earliest documented use: Mar. 19, 1898.

Cancellations

Puerto Rico, 1898	—
Supplementary Mail Type G	+4.00
China	—
Cuba	—
Guam	—
Philippines	—

282 A92 6c **lake,** *Dec. 1898* 45.00 6.50
   claret 45.00 6.50
   Never hinged 140.00
   On cover 17.50
   Block of 4 190.00 50.00
   Margin block of 4, arrow, R or L 200.00
   P# strip of 3, Impt., T V 190.00
   Never hinged 475.00
   P# block of 6, Impt., T V 900.00
   Never hinged 1,650.
   Double transfer 55.00 9.00
a. 6c **purple lake** 70.00 15.00
   Never hinged 210.00
   Block of 4 300.00 90.00
   Margin block of 4, arrow 325.00
   P# strip of 3, Impt., T V 290.00
   Never hinged 725.00
   P# block of 6, Impt., T V 1,250.
   Never hinged 2,200.

Earliest documented use: Mar. 13, 1899.

Cancellations

Supplementary Mail Type G	+4.00
China	—
Philippines	—

Type I. The tips of the foliate ornaments do not impinge on the white curved line below "ten cents."

282C A94 10c **brown,** type I, *Nov. 1898* 190.00 6.50
   dark brown 190.00 6.50
   Never hinged 575.00
   On cover 18.00
   Block of 4 800.00 57.50
   P# strip of 3, Impt., T IV or V 775.00
   Never hinged 1,900.
   P# block of 6, Impt., T IV or V 2,600.
   Never hinged 4,500.
   Double transfer 230.00 11.00

Earliest documented use: Dec. 10, 1898.

Cancellation

Supplementary Mail Type G	+2.50

Type II. The tips of the ornaments break the curved line below the "e" of "ten" and the "t" of "cents."

283 A94 10c **orange brown,** type II, horizontal watermark 150.00 5.50
   brown 150.00 5.50
   yellow brown 150.00 5.50
   Never hinged 450.00

On cover		17.50
Block of 4	650.00	50.00
P# strip of 3, Impt., T V	550.00	
Never hinged	1,500.	
P# block of 6, Impt., T V	1,900.	
Never hinged	3,750.	
Pair, type I and type II	15,000.	—

a. 10c **orange brown,** type II, vertical watermark, *early 1900* 225.00 11.00
   Never hinged 700.00
   On cover 35.00
   Block of 4 950.00
   Margin block of 4, arrow, R or L 1,000.
   P# strip of 3, Impt., T V 1,000.
   Never hinged 2,500.
   P# block of 6, Impt., T V 2,850.
   Never hinged 5,250.

Earliest documented use: Mar. 13, 1899.

Cancellations

Supplementary Mail Type G	+2.50
China	—
Puerto Rico	—

On the 400 subject plate 932, all are Type I except the following: UL 20; UR 11, 12, 13; LL 61, 71, 86, these 7 being Type II.

284 A95 15c **olive green,** *Nov. 1898* 160.00 13.00
   dark olive green 160.00 13.00
   Never hinged 500.00
   On cover 32.50
   Block of 4 700.00 90.00
   Margin block of 4, arrow, R or L 750.00
   P# strip of 3, Impt., T IV 650.00
   Never hinged 1,700.
   P# block of 6, Impt., T IV 2,250.
   Never hinged 4,250.

Earliest documented use: Mar. 3, 1899.

Cancellations

Supp. Mail Type F or G	+2.50
China	—
Samoa	—

Nos. 279-284 (8) 623.00 38.15

VALUES FOR VERY FINE STAMPS
Please note: Stamps are valued in the grade of Very Fine unless otherwise indicated.

TRANS-MISSISSIPPI EXPOSITION ISSUE
Omaha, Nebr., June 1 - Nov. 1, 1898.

Jacques Marquette on the Mississippi A100

Farming in the West — A101

Indian Hunting Buffalo — A102

John Charles Frémont on the Rocky Mountains A103

Troops Guarding Wagon Train — A104

Hardships of Emigration A105

Western Mining Prospector A106

Western Cattle in Storm — A107

Mississippi River Bridge, St. Louis — A108

Exposition Station Handstamp Postmark

Designed by Raymond Ostrander Smith.

Plates of 100 (10x10) subjects, divided vertically into 2 panes of 50.

See Nos. 3209-3210 for bi-colored reproductions of Nos. 285-293.

1898, June 17   Wmk. 191   Perf. 12

285	A100	1c **dark yellow green**	25.00	7.00
		yellow green	25.00	7.00
		green	25.00	7.00
		Never hinged	75.00	
		On cover		10.00
		On card, Expo. station canc.		200.00
		Pair, on cover, Expo. station canc.		300.00
		Block of 4	110.00	47.50
		Margin block of 4, arrow, R or L	120.00	—
		P# pair, Impt., T VIII	60.00	
		Never hinged	165.00	
		P# strip of 3, Impt., T VIII	105.00	
		Never hinged	270.00	
		P# block of 4, Impt., T VIII	240.00	
		Never hinged	410.00	
		P# block of 6, Impt., T VIII	450.00	
		Never hinged	750.00	
		Double transfer	35.00	8.00

Earliest documented use: June 17, 1898 (FDC).

Cancellations

		Supp. Mail Type F or G		+1.50
		China		—
		Philippines		—
		Puerto Rico, 1898		—
286	A101	2c **copper red**	25.00	2.75
		brown red	25.00	2.75
		light brown red	25.00	2.75
		Never hinged	75.00	
		On cover		3.75
		On cover, Expo. station canc.		175.00
		Block of 4	110.00	16.00
		Margin block of 4, arrow, R or L	120.00	—
		P# pair, Impt., T VIII	60.00	
		Never hinged	165.00	
		P# strip of 3, Impt., T VIII	105.00	
		Never hinged	270.00	
		P# block of 4, Impt., T VIII	240.00	
		Never hinged	410.00	
		P# block of 6, Impt., T VIII	450.00	
		Never hinged	750.00	
		Double transfer	40.00	4.00
		Worn plate	27.50	3.25

Earliest documented use: June 17, 1898 (FDC).

Cancellations

		China		—
		Hawaii		—
		Puerto Rico, 1898		—
		Philippines		—
287	A102	4c **orange**	120.00	27.50
		deep orange	120.00	27.50
		Never hinged	360.00	
		On cover		60.00
		On cover, Expo. station canc.		750.00
		Block of 4	500.00	200.00
		Margin block of 4, arrow, R or L	525.00	
		P# pair, Impt., T VIII	300.00	
		Never hinged	800.00	
		P# strip of 3, Impt., T VIII	525.00	
		Never hinged	1,300.	
		P# block of 4, Impt., T VIII	950.00	
		Never hinged	1,700.	
		P# block of 6, Impt., T VIII	1,750.	
		Never hinged	3,250.	

Earliest documented use: June 17, 1898 (FDC).

Cancellations

Supp. Mail Type F or G		+5.00
China		—
Philippines		—
288 A103 5c **dull blue**	120.00	25.00
bright blue	120.00	25.00
Never hinged	360.00	
On cover		50.00
On cover, Expo. station canc.		500.00
Block of 4	500.00	160.00
Margin block of 4, arrow, R or L	525.00	—
P# pair, Impt., T VIII	300.00	
Never hinged	800.00	
P# strip of 3, Impt., T VIII	550.00	
Never hinged	1,300.	
P# block of 4, Impt., T VIII	850.00	
Never hinged	1,700.	
P# block of 6, Impt., T VIII	1,600.	
Never hinged	3,250.	

Earliest documented use: June 17, 1898 (FDC).

Cancellations

Supp. Mail Type F or G		+5.00
China		—
Philippines		—
Puerto Rico, 1898		—
289 A104 8c **violet brown**	175.00	50.00
dark violet brown	175.00	50.00
Never hinged	525.00	
On cover		120.00
On cover, Expo. station canc.		1,000.
Block of 4	750.00	300.00
Margin block of 4, arrow, R or L	775.00	
P# pair, Impt., T VIII	425.00	
P# strip of 3, Impt., T VIII	750.00	
P# block of 4, Impt., T VIII	1,950.	
Never hinged	3,400.	
P# block of 6, Impt., T VIII	3,250.	
Never hinged	5,500.	
a. Vert. pair, imperf. horiz.	27,500.	
P# block of 4, Impt., T VIII	125,000.	

Earliest documented use: June 17, 1898 (FDC).

Cancellations

Philippines		—
Samoa		—
290 A105 10c **gray violet**	160.00	35.00
blackish violet	160.00	35.00
Never hinged	475.00	
On cover		90.00
On cover, Expo. station canc.		750.00
Block of 4	700.00	210.00
Margin block of 4, arrow, R or L	725.00	—
P# pair, Impt., T VIII	425.00	
Never hinged	1,200.	
P# strip of 3, Impt., T VIII	600.00	
Never hinged	1,650.	
P# block of 4, Impt., T VIII	2,100.	
Never hinged	3,600.	
P# block of 6, Impt., T VIII	3,500.	
Never hinged	6,000.	

Earliest documented use: June 17, 1898 (FDC).

Cancellations

Supplementary Mail Type G		+5.00
China		—
Philippines		—
291 A106 50c **sage green**	650.00	210.00
dark sage green	650.00	210.00
Never hinged	2,000.	
On cover		1,750.
Block of 4	3,000.	1,325.
Margin block of 4, arrow, R or L	3,200.	
P# pair, Impt., T VIII	1,850.	
Never hinged	4,500.	
P# strip of 3, Impt., T VIII	2,750.	
Never hinged	6,600.	
P# block of 4, Impt., T VIII	15,000.	
Never hinged	25,000.	
P# block of 6, Impt., T VIII	27,500.	

Earliest documented use: June 17, 1898 (FDC).

Cancellations

Supp. Mail Type F or G		+25.00
Cuba		—
Philippines		—
292 A107 $1 **black**	1,100.	650.
Never hinged	3,400.	
No gum	500.00	
On cover		4,000.
Block of 4	5,500.	4,000.
Margin block of 4, arrow, R or L	5,750.	
P# pair, Impt., T VIII	3,000.	
Never hinged	7,750.	

P# strip of 3, Impt., T VIII	5,250.	
Never hinged	12,000.	
P# block of 4, Impt., T VIII	35,000.	
Never hinged	50,000.	
P# block of 6, Impt., T VIII	50,000.	
Never hinged	70,000.	

Earliest documented use: June 17, 1898 (FDC).

Cancellation

Philippines		—
293 A108 $2 **orange brown**	1,900.	1,050.
dark orange brown	1,900.	1,050.
Never hinged	6,000.	
No gum	900.	
On cover		12,500.
Block of 4	8,250.	6,250.
Margin block of 4, arrow, R or L	8,750.	
P# pair, Impt., T VIII	4,750.	
P# strip of 3, Impt., T VIII	8,500.	
P# block of 4, Impt., T VIII	85,000.	
Never hinged	—	
P# block of 6, Impt., T VIII	150,000.	

Earliest documented use: June 24, 1898.

Nos. 285-293 (9)   4,275.   2,057.

Never-Hinged Stamps

See note before No. 182 regarding premiums for never-hinged stamps.

PAN-AMERICAN EXPOSITION ISSUE
Buffalo, N.Y., May 1 - Nov. 1, 1901.
On sale May 1-Oct. 31, 1901.

Fast Lake Navigation (Steamship "City of Alpena") — A109

Empire State Express — A110

Electric Automobile in Washington — A111

Bridge at Niagara Falls — A112

Canal Locks at Sault Ste. Marie — A113

Fast Ocean Navigation (Steamship "St. Paul") — A114

Exposition Station Machine Cancellation

Designed by Raymond Ostrander Smith.

Plates of 200 subjects in two panes of 100 each.

1901, May 1	Wmk. 191	Perf. 12	
294 A109 1c **green & black**		17.50	3.00
dark blue green & black		17.50	3.00
Never hinged		45.00	
On cover			4.50
On Expo. cover or card, Expo. station machine canc.			50.00
On Expo. cover or card, Expo. station duplex handstamp canc.			150.00
Block of 4		75.00	25.00
Margin block of 4, top arrow & markers		77.50	
Margin block of 4, bottom arrow & markers & black P#		80.00	
P# strip of 3, Impt., T V		80.00	
Never hinged		160.00	
P# block of 6, Impt., T V		300.00	
Never hinged		475.00	
Margin strip of 5, bottom Impt. T V, two P#, arrow & markers		115.00	
Never hinged		260.00	
Margin block of 10, bottom Impt., T V, two P#, arrow & markers		700.00	
Never hinged		1,100.	
Double transfer		25.00	5.25
a. Center inverted		12,500.	16,500.
Never hinged		22,500.	
On cover		—	
Block of 4		75,000.	
P# strip of 4, Impt.		150,000.	

Earliest documented uses: May 1, 1901 (No. 294 FDC); Aug. 2, 1901 (No. 294a). The No. 294a cover sold at auction in 1999 for $121,000. Two other uses on cover are recorded.

295 A110 2c **carmine & black**		16.50	1.00
carmine & gray black		16.50	1.00
dark carmine & black		16.50	1.00
rose carmine & black		16.50	1.00
scarlet & black		16.50	1.00
Never hinged		42.50	
On cover			1.50
On Expo. cover or card, Expo. sta. machine cancel			60.00
On Expo. cover or card, Expo. sta. duplex handstamp canc.			200.00
Block of 4		70.00	8.00
Margin block of 4, top arrow & markers		72.50	
P# block of 4, bottom arrow & markers and black P#		75.00	
P# strip of 3, Impt., T V		70.00	
Never hinged		150.00	
P# block of 6, Impt., T V		300.00	
Never hinged		475.00	
P# strip of 5, bottom Impt., T V, two P#, arrow & markers		130.00	
Never hinged		250.00	
P# block of 10, bottom Impt., T V, two P#, arrow & markers		700.00	
Never hinged		1,100.	
Double transfer		24.00	2.25
a. Center inverted		55,000.	60,000.
Block of 4		920,000.	

Almost all unused examples of No. 295a have partial or disturbed gum. Values are for examples with full original gum that is slightly disturbed. Value for No. 295a is for a well-centered example with faults, as there are no known fault-free examples.

Earliest documented uses: May 1, 1901 (No. 295 FDC); Feb. 26, (1902?) (No. 295a, dated cancel on off-cover stamp). The dated No. 295a stamp is the only used example showing a date of any kind. Sold at auction in 2001 for $66,000.

The block of 4 of No. 295a is unique. Value reflects sale price at 2009 auction.

296 A111 4c **deep red brown & black**		75.00	19.00
chocolate & black		75.00	19.00
Never hinged		190.00	
On cover			42.50
On cover, Expo. station machine cancel			350.00
On cover, Expo. station duplex handstamp canc.			750.00
Block of 4		320.00	140.00
Margin block of 4, top arrow & markers		340.00	
P# block of 4, bottom arrow & markers & black P#		360.00	
P# strip of 3, Impt., T V		310.00	
Never hinged		675.00	
P# block of 6, Impt., T V		2,100.	
Never hinged		3,500.	

	P# strip of 5, bottom Impt., T V, two P#, arrow & markers	575.00	
	Never hinged	1,150.	
	P# block of 10, bottom Impt., T V, two P#, arrow & markers	4,250.	
	Never hinged	6,000.	
a.	Center inverted	70,000.	—
	Block of 4	400,000.	
	P# strip of 4, Impt.	450,000.	

No. 296a was a Special Printing and not regularly issued. Almost all unused examples of No. 296a have partial or disturbed gum. Values are for examples with full orginal gum that is slightly disturbed.
See No. 296a-S, "Specimen" Stamps.
Earliest documented use: May 1, 1901 (FDC).

297	A112	5c ultramarine & black	800.00	18.00
		dark ultramarine & black	800.00	18.00
		Never hinged	200.00	
		On cover		45.00
		On cover, Expo. station machine cancel		350.00
		On cover, Expo. station duplex handstamp canc.		750.00
		Block of 4	350.00	130.00
		Margin block of 4, top arrow & markers	375.00	
		P# block of 4, bottom arrow & markers & black P#	400.00	
		P# strip of 3, Impt., T V	325.00	
		Never hinged	650.00	
		P# block of 6, Impt., T V	2,250.	
		Never hinged	3,750.	
		P# strip of 5, bottom Impt., T V, two P#, arrow & markers	650.00	
		Never hinged	1,300.	
		P# block of 10, bottom Impt., T V, two P#, arrow & markers	4,250.	
		Never hinged	6,000.	

Earliest documented use: May 1, 1901 (FDC).

298	A113	8c brown violet & black	100.00	55.00
		purplish brown & black	100.00	55.00
		Never hinged	250.00	
		On cover		110.00
		On cover, Expo. station machine cancel		750.00
		On cover, Expo. station duplex handstamp canc.		1,250.
		Block of 4	450.00	425.00
		Margin block of 4, top arrow & markers	475.00	
		P# block of 4, bottom arrow & markers & black P#	500.00	
		P# strip of 3, Impt., T V	425.00	
		Never hinged	900.00	
		P# block of 6, Impt., T V	4,000.	
		Never hinged	6,250.	
		P# strip of 5, bottom Impt., T V, two P#, arrow & markers	825.00	
		Never hinged	1,650.	
		P# block of 10, bottom Impt., T V, two P#, arrow & markers	7,000.	
		Never hinged	9,500.	

Earliest documented use: May 1, 1901 (FDC).

299	A114	10c yellow brown & black	130.00	32.50
		dark yellow brown & black	130.00	35.00
		Never hinged	325.00	
		On cover		125.00
		On cover, Expo. station machine cancel		1,000.
		On cover, Expo. station duplex handstamp canc.		1,500.
		Block of 4	575.00	260.00
		Margin block of 4, top arrow & markers	600.00	
		P# block of 4, bottom arrow & markers & black P#	650.00	
		P# strip of 3, Impt., T V	550.00	
		Never hinged	1,250.	
		P# block of 6, Impt., T V	6,750.	
		Never hinged	9,000.	
		P# strip of 5, bottom Impt., T V, two P#, arrow & markers	1,125.	
		Never hinged	2,250.	
		P# block of 10, bottom Impt., T V, two P#, arrow & markers	10,000.	
		Never hinged	14,000.	
		Nos. 294-299 (6)	1,139.	128.50
		Nos. 294-299, never hinged	1,052.	

Earliest documented use: May 1, 1901 (FDC).

VALUES FOR VERY FINE STAMPS
Please note: Stamps are valued in the grade of Very Fine unless otherwise indicated.

Franklin — A115

Jackson — A117

Lincoln — A119

Martha Washington — A121

Benjamin Harrison — A123

Jefferson — A125

Madison — A127

Washington — A116

Grant — A118

Garfield — A120

Daniel Webster — A122

Henry Clay — A124

David G. Farragut — A126

Marshall — A128

REGULAR ISSUE
Designed by Raymond Ostrander Smith and/or Clair Aubrey Huston.

Plates of 400 subjects in four panes of 100 each for all values from 1c to 15c inclusive. Certain plates of 1c, 2c type A129, 3c and 5c show a round marker in margin opposite the horizontal guide line at right or left.

Plates of 200 subjects in two panes of 100 each for 15c, 50c, $1, $2 and $5.

1902-03		Wmk. 191		Perf. 12

Many stamps of this issue are known with blurred printing due to having been printed on dry paper.

300	A115	1c blue green, Feb. 1903	12.00	.25
		green	12.00	.25
		deep green	12.00	.25
		gray green	12.00	.25
		yellow green	12.00	.25
		Never hinged	30.00	
		On cover		.30
		Block of 4	50.00	3.50
		P# strip of 3, Impt., T V	47.50	
		Never hinged	95.00	
		P# block of 6, Impt., T V	225.00	
		Never hinged	350.00	
		Double transfer	17.50	1.00
		Worn plate	13.00	.35
		Cracked plate	14.00	.30
b.		Booklet pane of 6, Mar. 6, 1907	600.00	12,500.
		Never hinged	1,150.	

Earliest documented uses: Feb. 3, 1903 (No. 300); Mar. 22, 1907 (No. 300b single).

301	A116	2c carmine, Jan. 22, 1903	16.00	.50
		bright carmine	16.00	.50
		deep carmine	16.00	.50
		carmine rose	16.00	.50
		Never hinged	40.00	
		On cover		.55
		Block of 4	67.50	5.50
		P# strip of 3, Impt., T V	65.00	
		Never hinged	130.00	
		P# block of 6, Impt., T V	275.00	
		Never hinged	425.00	
		Double transfer	27.50	1.40
		Cracked plate	—	1.40
c.		Booklet pane of 6, Jan. 24, 1903	500.00	4,500.
		Never hinged	950.00	

Earliest documented use: Jan. 28, 1903 (No. 301); Mar. 28, 1903 (No. 301c single); Apr. 4, 1903 (No. 301c pane).
Four unused single imperforate sheet margin examples of No. 301 are recorded. These are considered printer's waste.

302	A117	3c bright violet, Feb. 1903	55.00	4.00
		violet	55.00	4.00
		deep violet	55.00	4.00
		Never hinged	140.00	
		On cover		11.00
		Block of 4	230.00	32.50
		P# strip of 3, Impt., T V	220.00	
		Never hinged	450.00	
		P# block of 6, Impt., T V	800.00	
		Never hinged	1,350.	
		Double transfer	77.50	4.75
		Cracked plate	—	

Earliest documented use: Mar. 19, 1903.

303	A118	4c brown, Feb. 1903	60.00	2.50

dark brown	60.00	2.50	
yellow brown	60.00	2.50	
orange brown	60.00	2.50	
red brown	60.00	2.50	
Never hinged	150.00		
On cover		12.50	
Block of 4	250.00	25.00	
P# strip of 3, Impt., T V	240.00		
Never hinged	500.00		
P# block of 6, Impt., T V	825.00		
Never hinged	1,425.		
Double transfer	77.50	2.75	

Earliest documented use: Mar. 10, 1903 (on cover front).

304 A119 5c **blue,** *Jan. 1903* | 60.00 | 2.25
pale blue	60.00	2.25
bright blue	60.00	2.25
dark blue	60.00	2.25
Never hinged	150.00	
On cover		7.50
Block of 4	250.00	16.00
P# strip of 3, Impt., T V	240.00	
Never hinged	500.00	
P# block of 6, Impt., T V	825.00	—
Never hinged	1,375.	
Double transfer	82.50	3.75
Cracked plate	70.00	4.75

Earliest documented use: Feb. 9, 1903.

305 A120 6c **claret,** *Feb. 1903* | 60.00 | 5.75
deep claret	60.00	5.75
brownish lake	60.00	5.75
dull brownish lake	60.00	5.75
Never hinged	150.00	
On cover		16.00
Block of 4	260.00	50.00
P# strip of 3, Impt., T V	260.00	
Never hinged	575.00	
P# block of 6, Impt., T V	900.00	
Never hinged	1,600.	
Double transfer	65.00	4.50

Earliest documented use: May 8, 1903.

306 A121 8c **violet black,** *Dec. 1902* | 40.00 | 3.50
black	40.00	3.50
slate black	40.00	3.50
gray lilac	40.00	3.50
Never hinged	100.00	
lavender	50.00	4.25
Never hinged	125.00	
On cover		8.00
Block of 4	175.00	30.00
P# strip of 3, Impt., T V	160.00	
Never hinged	330.00	
P# block of 6, Impt., T V	750.00	
Never hinged	1,250.	
Double transfer	45.00	4.50

Earliest documented use: Dec. 27, 1902.

307 A122 10c **pale red brown,** *Feb. 1903* | 60.00 | 3.25
red brown	60.00	3.25
dark red brown	60.00	3.25
Never hinged	150.00	
On cover		9.50
Block of 4	260.00	19.00
P# strip of 3, Impt., T V	250.00	
Never hinged	525.00	
P# block of 6, Impt., T V	1,050.00	
Never hinged	1,850.	
Double transfer	70.00	11.00

Earliest documented use: Mar. 12, 1903.

308 A123 13c **purple black,** *Nov. 1902* | 40.00 | 11.00
brown violet	40.00	11.00
Never hinged	100.00	
On cover		37.50
Block of 4	175.00	100.00
P# strip of 3, Impt., T V	165.00	
Never hinged	350.00	
P# block of 6, Impt., T V	675.00	
Never hinged	1,150.	

Earliest documented use: Nov. 18, 1902.

309 A124 15c **olive green,** *May 27, 1903* | 200.00 | 14.00
dark olive green	200.00	14.00
Never hinged	500.00	
On cover		80.00
Block of 4	800.00	105.00
Margin block of 4, arrow	825.00	
P# strip of 3, Impt., T V	750.00	
Never hinged	1,650.	
P# block of 6, Impt., T V	3,400.	
Never hinged	5,750.	
Double transfer	230.00	14.00

Earliest documented use: July 1903 (on registry tag); Sept. 11, 1903 (on cover).

310 A125 50c **orange,** *Mar. 23, 1903* | 425. | 35.00
deep orange	425.	35.00
Never hinged	1,250.	
On cover		700.00
Block of 4	1,800.	250.00
Margin block of 4, arrow	1,900.	
P# strip of 3, Impt., T V	1,650.	
Never hinged	4,250.	
P# block of 6, Impt., T V	7,500.	

Earliest documented use: Oct. 6, 1903 (on cover front).

311 A126 $1 **black,** *June 5, 1903* | 700.00 | 90.00
grayish black	700.00	90.00
Never hinged	2,100.	
No gum	150.00	
On cover		1,500.
Block of 4	3,000.	575.00

Margin block of 4, arrow	3,250.		
P# strip of 3, Impt., T V	3,000.		
P# block of 6, Impt., T V	25,000.		

Earliest documented use: Sept. 30, 1903.

312 A127 $2 **dark blue,** *June 5, 1903* | 1,000. | 250.00
blue	1,000.	250.00
Never hinged	3,000.	
No gum	225.00	
On cover		2,500.
Block of 4	4,250.	2,000.
Margin block of 4, arrow	4,750.	
P# strip of 3, Impt., T V	4,500.	
P# block of 6, Impt., T V	37,500.	

Earliest documented use: Feb. 17, 1904.

313 A128 $5 **dark green,** *June 5, 1903* | 2,500. | 800.00
Never hinged	6,500.	
No gum	550.00	
On cover		5,000.
Block of 4	12,000.	6,250.
Margin block of 4, arrow	12,500.	
P# strip of 3, Impt., T V	10,500.	
P# block of 6, Impt., T V	180,000.	

Earliest documented use: Feb. 17, 1904.

Nos. 300-313 (14) | 5,228. | 1,222.

For listings of designs A127 and A128 with Perf. 10 see Nos. 479 and 480.

Earliest documented use dates for imperforates are for the imperforate sheet stamps, not for imperforate stamps with vending and affixing machine perforations or for flat plate imperforate coil stamps. EDU dates for VAMP and flat plate imperf coil stamps are shown in their respective sections later in the catalogue.

1906-08   **Imperf.**

314 A115 1c **blue green,** *Oct. 2, 1906* | 16.00 | 18.00
green	16.00	18.00
deep green	16.00	18.00
Never hinged	35.00	
On cover		32.50
Pair	35.00	40.00
Never hinged	70.00	
Block of 4	70.00	90.00
Never hinged	140.00	
Corner margin block of 4	77.50	95.00
Margin block of 4, arrow	80.00	97.50
Margin block of 4, arrow & round marker	175.00	145.00
Center line block	135.00	125.00
Never hinged	260.00	
P# block of 6, Impt.	200.00	—
Never hinged	325.00	
Double transfer	30.00	21.00

Earliest documented use: Dec. 20, 1906.

314A A118 4c **brown,** *Apr. 1908* | 90,000. | 50,000.
Never hinged	140,000.	
On cover		140,000.
Pair	225,000.	
Guide line pair	375,000.	

This stamp was issued imperforate but all examples were privately perforated with large oblong perforations at the sides (Schermack type III).
Beware of examples of No. 303 with trimmed perforations and fake private perfs. added.
Used and on-cover values are for contemporaneous usage.

Earliest documented use: May 27, 1908.

315 A119 5c **blue,** *May 12, 1908* | 200. | 1,250.
Never hinged	350.	
On cover, pair		70,000.
Pair	425.	12,500.
Never hinged	750.	
Block of 4	900.	27,500.
Never hinged	1,600.	
Corner margin block of 4	1,000.	
Margin block of 4, arrow	1,500.	
Margin block of 4, arrow & round marker	2,400.	
Center line block	10,000.	
P# block of 6, Impt.	2,750.	—
Never hinged	4,000.	

Earliest documented use: Sept. 15, 1908 (pair on piece).

Beware of examples of No. 304 with perforations removed. Used examples of No. 315 must have contemporaneous cancels. Single examples of No. 315 on cover are not known to exist.

COIL STAMPS

Warning! Imperforate stamps are known fraudulently perforated to resemble coil stamps and part-perforate varieties. Fully perforated stamps and booklet stamps also are known with perforations fraudulently trimmed off to resemble coil stamps.

1908   **Perf. 12 Horizontally**

316 A115 1c **blue green,** *Feb. 18* | 70,000.
| Pair | 200,000. |
| Guide line pair | 325,000. |
317 A119 5c **blue,** *Feb. 24* | 6,000. | —
| Never hinged | 17,500. | |
| Pair | 17,500. | |

Never hinged	50,000.	
Guide line pair	70,000.	
Never hinged	160,000.	

Earliest documented use: Sept. 18, 1908.

Perf. 12 Vertically

318 A115 1c **blue green,** *July 31* | 6,000. |
Never hinged	11,500.	
Pair	16,500.	
Guide line pair	35,000.	
Double transfer		

The No. 318 mint never hinged single is valued in the grade of fine.

Coil stamps for use in vending and affixing machines are perforated on two sides only, either horizontally or vertically. They were first issued in 1908, using perf. 12. This was changed to 8½ in 1910, and to 10 in 1914.

Imperforate sheets of certain denominations were sold to the vending machine companies which applied a variety of private perforations and separations (see Vending and Affixing Machine Perforations section of this catalogue).

Several values of the 1902 and later issues are found on an apparently coarse-ribbed paper. This is caused by worn blankets on the printing presses and is not a true paper variety.

All examples of Nos. 316-318 must be accompanied by certificates of authenticity issued by recognized expertizing committees.

Washington — A129

Plate of 400 subjects in four panes of 100 each.

Type I

Type II

Designed by Clair Aubrey Huston.

1903   **Wmk. 191**   **Perf. 12**

319 A129 2c **carmine,** type I, *Nov. 12, 1903* | 6.00 | .25
bright carmine	6.00	.25
red	6.00	.25
Never hinged	15.00	
On cover		.30
Block of 4	25.00	2.50
P# strip of 3, Impt., T V	24.00	
Never hinged	45.00	
P# block of 6, Impt., T V	180.00	
Never hinged	310.00	
Double transfer	12.50	2.00
a. 2c **lake,** type I	—	
carmine lake		
b. 2c **carmine rose,** type I	10.00	.40
Never hinged	25.00	
On cover		.60
Block of 4	42.50	9.00
P# strip of 3, Impt., T V	40.00	
Never hinged	75.00	
P# block of 6, Impt., T V	250.00	
Never hinged	375.00	
c. 2c **scarlet,** type I	10.00	.30
Never hinged	25.00	
On cover		.40
Block of 4	42.50	6.00
P# strip of 3, Impt., T V	40.00	
Never hinged	75.00	
P# block of 6, Impt., T V	250.00	
Never hinged	375.00	
d. Vert. pair, imperf. horiz., No. 319	7,500.	
Never hinged	15,000.	
e. Vertical pair, imperf. between, No. 319	2,500.	
As "e," rouletted between	3,250.	

No. 319e comes from a single pane of stamps on which a line of horizontal perfs were omitted between rows 9 and 10. Additionally, during the use of this stamp, the Postmaster at San Francisco discovered in his stock sheets of No. 319, each of which had the horizontal perforations missing between the two top rows of stamps. To facilitate their separation, the imperf. rows were rouletted, and the stamps sold over the counter. So vertical pairs are found from this source with regular perforations all around and rouletted between.

"Gash on Face"
Variety

The gash may appear as double lines due to different plate wiping techniques.

f.	2c **lake**, type II	10.00	.30
	carmine lake	10.00	.30
	Never hinged	25.00	
	On cover		.35
	Block of 4	42.50	5.50
	P# strip of 3, Impt., T V	45.00	
	Never hinged	95.00	
	P# block of 6, Impt., T V	325.00	
	Never hinged	475.00	
	"Gash on face" plate flaw (carmine lake, 4671 LL 16)	—	
g.	Booklet pane of 6, **car.**, type I	125.00	550.00
	Never hinged	240.00	
	Wmk. horizontal	4,000.	
	Never hinged	6,500.	
h.	Booklet pane of 6, **car.**, type II	900.00	
	Never hinged	1,500.	
i.	2c **carmine**, type II	75.00	50.00
	red	75.00	50.00
	Never hinged	175.00	
	On cover		150.00
j.	2c **carmine rose**, type II	70.00	1.75
	Never hinged	160.00	
	Block of 4	300.00	20.00
	P# block of 6, Impt., T V	1,100.	
k.	2c **scarlet**, type II	70.00	.65
	Never hinged	160.00	
	Block of 4	300.00	5.00
	P# block of 6, Impt., T V	1,100.	
n.	Booklet pane of 6, **car. rose** (I)	250.00	650.00
	Never hinged	450.00	
p.	Booklet pane of 6, **scarlet** (I)	185.00	575.00
	Never hinged	350.00	
q.	Booklet pane of 6, **lake** (II)	300.00	750.00
	Never hinged	575.00	

Earliest documented uses:
No. 319, Nov. 19, 1903;
No. 319a, Sept. 23, 1904;
No. 319b, Nov. 3, 1903;
No. 319c, Dec. 16, 1903;
No. 319f, Sept. 25, 1908;
No. 319g single, Dec. 7, 1903;
No. 319h single, June 8, 1908;
No. 319i, June 5, 1908;
No. 319j, June 30, 1908;
No. 319k, June 11, 1908;
No. 319p single, Apr. 12, 1904.

1906 — **Imperf.**

320	A129 2c **carmine**, type I *Oct. 2*	16.00	19.00
	Never hinged	35.00	
	On cover		25.00
	Pair	35.00	42.50
	Never hinged	72.50	
	Block of 4	70.00	87.50
	Corner margin block of 4	72.50	110.00
	Margin block of 4, arrow	75.00	120.00
	Margin block of 4, arrow & round marker	—	
	Center line block	150.00	225.00
	Never hinged	250.00	
	P# block of 6, Impt., T V, carmine	200.00	—
	Never hinged	325.00	
	Double transfer	24.00	21.50

Earliest documented use: Oct. 16, 1906.

a.	2c **lake**, type II	45.00	50.00
	carmine lake	45.00	50.00
	Never hinged	100.00	
	On cover		100.00
	Pair	100.00	120.00
	Never hinged	225.00	
	Block of 4	200.00	275.00
	Corner margin block of 4	205.00	
	Margin block of 4, arrow	210.00	
	Center line block	425.00	—
	Never hinged	700.00	
	P# block of 6, Impt., T V	725.00	—
	Never hinged	1,150.	
	"Gash on face" plate flaw (see No. 319f)		
b.	2c **scarlet**, type I	18.50	15.00
	Never hinged	40.00	
	On cover		22.50
	Pair	39.00	
	Never hinged	85.00	
	Block of 4	77.50	
	Corner margin block of 4	80.00	—
	Margin block of 4, arrow	82.50	—
	Center line block	205.00	—
	Never hinged	325.00	
	P# block of 6, Impt., T V	225.00	
	Never hinged	350.00	
c.	2c **carmine rose**, type I	60.00	42.50
	Never hinged	130.00	
d.	2c **carmine**, type II	120.00	250.00
	Never hinged	175.00	
	On cover		600.00

	Pair	225.00	
	Never hinged	425.00	
	Guide line pair	450.00	

No. 320d was issued imperforate, but all examples were privately perforated with large oblong perforations at the sides (Schermack type III).

COIL STAMPS

1908 — **Perf. 12 Horizontally**

321	A129 2c **carmine**, type I, pair, *Feb. 18*	—	450,000.
	On cover, single	—	250,000.
	Guide line pair	—	

Four authenticated unused pairs of No. 321 are known and available to collectors. A fifth, unauthenticated pair is in the New York Public Library Miller collection. The value for an unused pair is for a fine-very fine example. Two fine pairs are recorded and one very fine pair. There are no authenticated unused single stamps recorded. There are 2 authenticated examples of the single used on cover, both used from Indianapolis in 1908. Numerous counterfeits exist.

Earliest documented use: Oct. 2, 1908.

Perf. 12 Vertically

322	A129 2c **carmine**, type II, *July 31*	7,000.	
	Never hinged	13,500.	
	Pair	18,000.	
	Guide line pair	35,000.	
	Double transfer		

This Government Coil Stamp should not be confused with those of the International Vending Machine Co., which are perforated 12½.

All examples of Nos. 321-322 must be accompanied by certificates of authenticity issued by recognized expertizing committees.

VALUES FOR VERY FINE STAMPS
Please note: Stamps are valued in the grade of Very Fine unless otherwise indicated.

LOUISIANA PURCHASE EXPOSITION ISSUE
St. Louis, Mo., Apr. 30 - Dec. 1, 1904

Robert R. Livingston — A130

Thomas Jefferson — A131

James Monroe — A132

William McKinley — A133

Map of Louisiana Purchase — A134

Designed by Clair Aubrey Huston.

Plates of 100 (10x10) subjects, divided vertically into 2 panes of 50.

EXPOSITION STA.

Exposition Station Machine Cancellation

		Wmk. 191		Perf. 12
1904, Apr. 30				
323	A130 1c **green**		25.00	5.00
	dark green		25.00	5.00
	Never hinged		70.00	
	On cover			7.00
	On Expo. card, Expo. station machine canc.			40.00

On Expo. card, Expo. station duplex handstamp canc.	100.00	
Block of 4	110.00	35.00
Margin block of 4, arrow, R or L	120.00	—
P# pair, Impt., T V	75.00	
Never hinged	180.00	
P# strip of 3, Impt., T V	105.00	
Never hinged	240.00	
P# block of 4, Impt., T V	190.00	
Never hinged	350.00	
P# block of 6, Impt., T V	350.00	
Never hinged	550.00	
Diagonal line through left "1" (2138 L 2)	47.50	12.50
Double transfer		

Earliest documented use: Apr. 30, 1904 (FDC).

324	A131	2c	**carmine**	25.00	2.00
			bright carmine	25.00	2.00
			Never hinged	70.00	
			On cover		3.00
			On Expo. cover, Expo. station machine canc.		60.00
			On Expo. cover, Expo. station duplex handstamp canc.		150.00
			Block of 4	110.00	17.50
			Margin block of 4, arrow, R or L	120.00	—
			P# pair, Impt., T V	75.00	
			Never hinged	180.00	
			P# strip of 3, Impt., T V	100.00	
			Never hinged	230.00	
			P# block of 4, Impt., T V	190.00	
			Never hinged	350.00	
			P# block of 6, Impt., T V	350.00	
			Never hinged	550.00	
a.			Vertical pair, imperf. horiz.	17,500.	
			Block of 4	40,000.	
			P# block of 4	55,000.	

Earliest documented use: Apr. 30, 1904 (FDC).

325	A132	3c	**violet**	75.00	30.00
			Never hinged	200.00	
			On cover		65.00
			On cover, Expo. station machine canc.		200.00
			On cover, Expo. station duplex handstamp canc.		400.00
			Block of 4	325.00	225.00
			Margin block of 4, arrow, R or L	350.00	—
			P# pair, Impt., T V	200.00	
			Never hinged	460.00	
			P# strip of 3, Impt., T V	325.00	
			Never hinged	750.00	
			P# block of 4, Impt., T V	600.00	
			Never hinged	1,100.	
			P# block of 6, Impt., T V	950.00	
			Never hinged	1,750.	
			Double transfer		

Earliest documented use: Apr. 30, 1904 (FDC).

326	A133	5c	**dark blue**	80.00	25.00
			Never hinged	210.00	
			On cover		50.00
			On cover, Expo. station machine canc.		400.00
			On cover, Expo. station duplex handstamp canc.		500.00
			Block of 4	350.00	200.00
			Margin block of 4, arrow, R or L	375.00	—
			P# pair, Impt., T V	200.00	
			Never hinged	460.00	
			P# strip of 3, Impt., T V	350.00	
			Never hinged	800.00	
			P# block of 4, Impt., T V	650.00	
			Never hinged	1,200.	
			P# block of 6, Impt., T V	1,000.	
			Never hinged	1,850.	

Earliest documented use: Apr. 30, 1904 (FDC).

327	A134	10c	**red brown**	145.00	30.00
			dark red brown	145.00	30.00
			Never hinged	375.00	
			On cover		125.00
			On cover, Expo. station machine canc.		450.00
			On cover, Expo. station duplex handstamp canc.		750.00
			Block of 4	625.00	225.00
			Margin block of 4, arrow, R or L	675.00	—
			P# pair, Impt., T V	375.00	
			Never hinged	900.00	
			P# strip of 3, Impt., T V	650.00	
			Never hinged	1,500.	
			P# block of 4, Impt., T V	1,300.	
			Never hinged	2,250.	
			P# block of 6, Impt., T V	2,250.	
			Never hinged	4,000.	

Earliest documented use: Apr. 30, 1904 (FDC).

Nos. 323-327 (5)	350.00	92.00
Nos. 323-327, never hinged	925.00	

JAMESTOWN EXPOSITION ISSUE
Hampton Roads, Va., Apr. 26 - Dec. 1, 1907

Captain John Smith — A135

Founding of Jamestown — A136

Pocahontas — A137

Plates of 200 subjects in two panes of 100 each.

Exposition Station Machine Cancellation

Designed by Clair Aubrey Huston.

1907		**Wmk. 191**		**Perf. 12**
328	A135	1c **green**, *Apr. 26*	25.00	5.00
		dark green	25.00	5.00
		Never hinged	70.00	
		On cover		8.00
		On Expo. card, Expo. station machine canc.		25.00
		On Expo. card, Expo. station duplex handstamp canc.		125.00
		Block of 4	105.00	50.00
		Margin block of 4, arrow	110.00	—
		P# strip of 3, Impt., T V	100.00	
		Never hinged	230.00	
		P# block of 6, Impt., T V	475.00	
		Never hinged	725.00	
		Double transfer	32.50	6.00

Earliest documented use: Apr. 26, 1907 (FDC).

329	A136	2c **carmine**, *Apr. 26*	30.00	4.50
		bright carmine	30.00	4.50
		Never hinged	80.00	
		On cover		6.00
		On Expo. cover, Expo. station machine canc.		100.00
		On Expo. cover, Expo. station duplex handstamp canc.		150.00
		Block of 4	130.00	35.00
		Margin block of 4, arrow	140.00	—
		P# strip of 3, Impt., T V	115.00	
		Never hinged	280.00	
		P# block of 6, Impt., T V	525.00	
		Never hinged	800.00	
		Double transfer	37.50	6.00
a.		2c carmine lake		

Earliest documented use: Apr. 26, 1907 (FDC).

330	A137	5c **blue**	130.00	32.50
		deep blue	130.00	32.50
		Never hinged	325.00	
		On cover		85.00
		On cover, Expo. station machine canc.		350.00
		On cover, Expo. station duplex handstamp canc.		500.00
		Block of 4	550.00	225.00
		Margin block of 4, arrow	575.00	—
		P# strip of 3, Impt., T V	475.00	
		Never hinged	1,200.	
		P# block of 6, Impt., T V	2,750.	
		Never hinged	5,250.	
		Double transfer	140.00	37.50

Earliest documented use: May 8, 1907.

Nos. 328-330 (3)	185.00	42.00
Nos. 328-330, never hinged	475.00	

REGULAR ISSUE

Plates of 400 subjects in four panes of 100 each for all values 1c to 15c inclusive.

Plates of 200 subjects in two panes of 100 each for 50c and $1 denominations.

In 1909 the Bureau prepared certain plates with horizontal spacings of 3mm between the outer seven vertical stamp rows and 2mm between the others. This was done to try to counteract the effect of unequal shrinkage of the paper. *However, some unequal shrinkage still did occur and intermediate spacings are frequently found.* The listings of 2mm and 3mm spacings are for exact measurements. Intermediate spacings sell for approximately the same as the cheaper of the two listed spacings.

All such plates were marked with an open star added to the imprint and exist on the 1c, 2c, 3c, 4c, and 5c denominations only. A small solid star was added to the imprint and plate number for 1c plate No. 4980, 2c plate No. 4988 and for the 2c Lincoln. All other plates for this issue are spaced 2mm throughout.

There are several types of some of the 2c and 3c stamps of this and succeeding issues. These types are described under the dates at which they first appeared. Illustrations of Types I-VII of the 2c (A140) and Types I-IV of the 3c (A140) are reproduced by permission of H. L. Lindquist.

Imprint, plate number and open star

Imprint, plate number and small solid star

Imprint, plate number and "A"

(Illustrations reduced in size)

"A" and number only

Number only

The above illustrations are several of the styles used on plates of issues from 1908 to date.

The previously listed "China Clay Paper" stamps, formerly Scott 331b-332b and 333a-340a, have been removed from the catalogue. Research has shown that the "experimental paper" explanation for the existence of these stamps was incorrect. The only paper experiment during this time period was the 35 percent rag stock paper (Blue Paper, Scott 357-366, 369) of 1909. The stamps previously known as "China Clay Paper" stamps were, in fact, normal stamps printed on paper that was defective to varying degrees. These interesting varieties, which have nothing to do with China clay, can appear to be thin, thick, translucent, opaque, somewhat dark or very dark, but they are not the kind of items that the Scott catalogue or other catalogues normally list. This is not to say that these various paper varieties are of no value or are not of great interest to specialists of the stamps from this period. It is only to say that these various types and degrees of paper varieties are subjects which are beyond the scope of stamp catalogues. Specialist collectors will no doubt continue to study and treasure these varieties.

Franklin — A138   Washington — A139

1908-09		**Wmk. 191**		**Perf. 12**
331	A138	1c **green**, *Dec. 1908*	6.75	.40
		bright green	6.75	.40
		dark green	6.75	.40
		yellow green	6.75	.40
		Never hinged	17.00	
		On cover		.55
		Block of 4 (2mm spacing)	30.00	2.50
		Block of 4 (3mm spacing)	32.50	3.00
		P# block of 6, Impt., T V	100.00	
		Never hinged	175.00	
		P# block of 6, Impt. & star	95.00	
		Never hinged	160.00	
		P# block of 6, Impt. & small solid star (plate 4980)	1,500.	
		Never hinged	2,250.	
		Double transfer	9.00	.75
		Cracked plate		
a.		Booklet pane of 6, *Dec. 1908*	160.00	450.00
		Never hinged	285.00	

No. 331 exists in horizontal pair, imperforate between, a variety resulting from booklet experiments. Not regularly issued. Value, $2,500.

No. 331a used is valued with a contemporary cancel. A certificate of authenticity is advised.

Earliest documented uses: Dec. 1, 1908 (No. 331); Dec. 2, 1908 (No. 331a single) (FDC).

332	A139	2c **carmine**, *Nov. 1908*	6.25	.35
		light carmine	6.25	.35
		dark carmine	6.25	.35
		Never hinged	15.00	
		On cover		.40
		Block of 4 (2mm spacing)	27.50	2.00
		Block of 4 (3mm spacing)	30.00	2.50
		P# block of 6, Impt., T V	90.00	
		Never hinged	150.00	
		P# block of 6, Impt. & star	85.00	
		Never hinged	140.00	
		P# block of 6, Impt. & small		
		solid star (plate 4988)	*1,750.*	
		Never hinged	*2,750.*	
		Double transfer	12.50	—
		Foreign entry, design of 1c		
		(plate 5299)	*2,250.*	*2,750.*
		On cover		*5,000.*
		Rosette crack	—	
		Cracked plate	—	
a.		Booklet pane of 6	135.00	400.00
		Never hinged	230.00	
b.		2c **lake**		

No. 332a used is valued with a contemporary cancel. A certificate of authenticity is advised.

No. 332 with foreign entry, used, is valued in the grade of fine.

Earliest documented uses: Dec. 3, 1908 (No. 332), Nov. 16, 1908 (No. 332a single).

Washington — A140

TYPE I

THREE CENTS.
Type I. The top line of the toga rope is weak and the rope shading lines are thin. The 5th line from the left is missing. The line between the lips is thin. (For descriptions of 3c types II, III and IV, see notes and illustrations preceding Nos. 484, 529-530.)
Used on both flat plate and rotary press printings.

333	A140	3c **deep violet**, type I, *Dec.*		
		1908	30.00	3.00
		violet	30.00	3.00
		light violet	30.00	3.00
		Never hinged	75.00	
		On cover		8.50
		Block of 4 (2mm spacing)	125.00	26.50
		Block of 4 (3mm spacing)	130.00	29.00
		P# block of 6, Impt., T V	375.00	
		Never hinged	600.00	
		P# block of 6, Impt. & star	400.00	
		Never hinged	650.00	
		Double transfer	37.50	5.75

Earliest documented use: Jan. 12, 1909.

334	A140	4c **orange brown**, *Dec. 1908*	37.50	1.50
		brown	37.50	1.50
		light brown	37.50	1.50
		dark brown	37.50	1.50
		Never hinged	92.50	
		On cover		7.00
		Block of 4 (2mm spacing)	160.00	12.50
		Block of 4 (3mm spacing)	170.00	14.00
		P# block of 6, Impt., T V	450.00	
		Never hinged	725.00	
		P# block of 6, Impt. & star	450.00	
		Never hinged	725.00	
		Double transfer	55.00	—

Earliest documented use: Jan. 12, 1909.

335	A140	5c **blue**, *Dec. 1908*	50.00	2.50
		bright blue	50.00	2.50
		dark blue	50.00	2.50
		Never hinged	120.00	
		On cover		8.50
		Block of 4 (2mm spacing)	210.00	20.00
		Block of 4 (3mm spacing)	220.00	17.50
		P# block of 6, Impt., T V	525.00	

Never hinged	1,000.		
P# block of 6, Impt. & star	550.00		
Never hinged	1,050.		
Double transfer	60.00	—	

Earliest documented use: Jan. 12, 1909.

336	A140	6c **red orange**, *Jan. 1909*	65.00	6.50
		pale red orange	65.00	6.50
		orange	65.00	6.50
		Never hinged	150.00	
		On cover		22.50
		Block of 4	275.00	50.00
		P# block of 6, Impt., T V	750.00	
		Never hinged	1,400.	
		Never hinged		

Earliest documented use: Jan. 6, 1909.

337	A140	8c **olive green**, *Dec. 1908*	45.00	3.00
		deep olive green	45.00	3.00
		Never hinged	105.00	
		On cover		18.00
		Block of 4	190.00	25.00
		P# block of 6, Impt., T V	525.00	
		Never hinged	875.00	
		Double transfer	57.50	—

Earliest documented use: Jan. 8, 1909.

338	A140	10c **yellow**, *Jan. 1909*	67.50	2.00
		Never hinged	160.00	
		On cover		10.00
		Block of 4	280.00	15.00
		P# block of 6, Impt., T V	800.00	
		Never hinged	1,500.	
		Double transfer	—	
		Very thin paper	—	

Earliest documented use: Jan. 18, 1909.

339	A140	13c **blue green**, *Jan. 1909*	37.50	19.00
		deep blue green	37.50	19.00
		Never hinged	90.00	
		On cover		110.00
		Block of 4	160.00	175.00
		P# block of 6, Impt., T V	500.00	
		Never hinged	875.00	
		Line through "TAG" of		
		"POSTAGE" (4948 LR 96)	70.00	—

Earliest documented use: Mar. 5, 1909.

340	A140	15c **pale ultramarine**, *Jan. 1909*	65.00	6.50
		ultramarine	65.00	6.50
		Never hinged	150.00	
		On cover		125.00
		Block of 4	270.00	65.00
		P# block of 6, Impt., T V	650.00	
		Never hinged	1,175.	

Earliest documented use: Mar. 12, 1909.

341	A140	50c **violet**, *Jan. 1909*	300.00	20.00
		dull violet	300.00	20.00

Never hinged	690.00		
On cover		5,000.	
Block of 4	1,300.	150.00	
Margin block of 4, arrow,			
right or left	1,350.		
P# block of 6, Impt., T V	*7,000.*	—	
Never hinged	15,000.		

Earliest documented use: Oct. 23, 1909 (on registry tag); June 2, 1916 (on cover).

342	A140	$1 **violet brown**, *Jan. 29, 1909*	500.00	100.00
		light violet brown	500.00	100.00
		Never hinged	1,150.	
		On cover		*6,000.*
		Block of 4	2,200.	700.00
		Margin block of 4, arrow,		
		right or left	2,300.	725.00
		P# block of 6, Impt., T V	20,000.	
		Never hinged	35,000.	
		Double transfer	—	—

Earliest documented use: July 26, 1909.

Nos. 331-342 (12)	1,210.	164.75	

For listings of other perforated sheet stamps of A138, A139 and A140 see:
Nos. 357-366 Bluish paper
Nos. 374-382, 405-407 Single line wmk. Perf. 12
Nos. 423A-423C Single line wmk. Perf 12x10
Nos. 423D-423E Single line wmk. Perf 10x12
Nos. 424-430 Single line wmk. Perf. 10
Nos. 461 Single line wmk. Perf. 11
Nos. 462-469 unwmk. Perf. 10
Nos. 498-507 unwmk. Perf. 11
Nos. 519 Double line wmk. Perf. 11
Nos. 525-530 and 536 Offset printing
Nos. 538-546 Rotary press printing

Plate Blocks
Scott values for plate blocks printed from flat plates are for very fine side and bottom positions. Top position plate blocks with full wide selvage sell for more.

Earliest documented use dates for imperforates are for the imperforate sheet stamps, not for imperforate stamps with vending and affixing machine perforations or for flat plate imperforate coil stamps. EDU dates for VAMP and flat plate imperf coil stamps are shown in their respective sections later in the catalogue.

		Imperf		
343	A138	1c **green**, *Dec. 1908*	4.00	5.50
		dark green	4.00	5.50
		yellowish green	4.00	5.50
		Never hinged	8.50	

		Unused	Used
On cover			12.00
Pair		8.50	12.00
Never hinged		18.00	
Block of 4 (2mm or 3mm spacing)		18.00	25.00
Corner margin block of 4, 2mm or 3mm		19.00	27.50
Margin block of 4, arrow, 2mm or 3mm		21.50	27.50
Center line block		30.00	40.00
Never hinged		55.00	
P# block of 6, Impt., T V		47.50	—
Never hinged		75.00	
P# block of 6, Impt. & star		57.50	—
Never hinged		90.00	
P# block of 6, Impt. & small solid star (plate 4980)		675.00	
Never hinged		1,050.	
Double transfer		11.00	8.50

Earliest documented use: Jan. 4, 1909.

344	A139	2c	**carmine**, Dec. 1908	4.75	3.25
			light carmine	4.75	3.25
			dark carmine	4.75	3.25
			Never hinged	10.00	
			On cover		8.25
			Pair	10.00	8.00
			Never hinged	22.00	
			Block of 4 (2mm or 3mm spacing)	21.00	16.00
			Corner margin block of 4, 2mm or 3mm	23.00	22.50
			Margin block of 4, arrow, 2mm or 3mm	25.00	22.50
			Center line block	37.50	40.00
			Never hinged	67.50	
			P# block of 6, Impt., T V	77.50	—
			Never hinged	120.00	
			P# block of 6, Impt. & star	70.00	—
			Never hinged	110.00	
			Double transfer	12.50	4.00
			Foreign entry, design of 1c (plate 5299)	1,250.	—

Earliest documented use: Dec. 7, 1908.

The existence of the foreign entry on the imperforate sheet stamp No. 344 has been questioned by specialists. The editors would like to see evidence of the existence of the item, either unused or used.

345	A140	3c	**deep violet**, type I, 1909	9.00	22.50
			violet	9.00	22.50
			Never hinged	19.00	
			On cover		65.00
			Pair	19.00	55.00
			Never hinged	40.00	
			Block of 4	39.00	110.00
			Corner margin block of 4	40.00	115.00
			Margin block of 4, arrow	45.00	115.00
			Center line block	75.00	140.00
			Never hinged	135.00	
			P# block of 6, Impt., T V	155.00	—
			Never hinged	240.00	
			Double transfer	22.50	—

Earliest documented use: Feb. 13, 1909.

346	A140	4c	**orange brown**, Feb. 25, 1909	13.50	25.00
			brown	13.50	25.00
			Never hinged	29.00	
			On cover		100.00
			Pair	29.00	62.50
			Never hinged	62.50	
			Block of 4 (2 or 3mm spacing)	60.00	125.00
			Corner margin block of 4 (2 or 3mm spacing)	65.00	130.00
			Margin block of 4, arrow, (2 or 3mm spacing)	70.00	130.00
			Center line block	120.00	220.00
			Never hinged	220.00	
			P# block of 6, Impt., T V	175.00	—
			Never hinged	275.00	
			P# block of 6, Impt. & star	210.00	—
			Never hinged	325.00	
			Double transfer	35.00	—

Earliest documented use: Mar. 13, 1909.

347	A140	5c	**blue**, Feb. 25, 1909	27.50	37.50
			dark blue	27.50	37.50
			Never hinged	60.00	
			On cover		140.00
			Pair	60.00	110.00
			Never hinged	130.00	
			Block of 4	125.00	220.00
			Corner margin block of 4	135.00	235.00
			Margin block of 4, arrow	145.00	245.00
			Center line block	220.00	325.00
			Never hinged	400.00	
			P# block of 6, Impt., T V	275.00	—
			Never hinged	500.00	
			Cracked plate		—

Earliest documented use: Mar. 4, 1909.

Nos. 343-347 (5)	58.75	93.75
Nos. 343-347, never hinged	126.50	

For listings of other imperforate stamps of designs A138, A139 and A140 see Nos. 383, 384, 408, 409 and 459 Single line wmk.
Nos. 481-485 unwmk.
Nos. 531-535 Offset printing

Used values for coil singles, pairs and line pairs reflect examples with contemporaneous cancels.

COIL STAMPS

1908-10   *Perf. 12 Horizontally*

348	A138	1c	**green**, Dec. 29, 1908	37.50	50.00
			dark green	37.50	50.00
			Never hinged	80.00	
			On cover		70.00
			Pair	95.00	140.00
			Never hinged	210.00	
			Guide line pair	275.00	625.00
			Never hinged	600.00	

Earliest documented use: Jan. 25, 1909.

349	A139	2c	**carmine**, Jan. 1909	80.00	100.00
			dark carmine	80.00	100.00
			Never hinged	180.00	
			On cover		125.00
			Pair	210.00	300.00
			Never hinged	500.00	
			Guide line pair	550.00	1,100.
			Never hinged	1,300.	
			Foreign entry, design of 1c (plate 5299)	—	3,000.

Earliest documented use: May 14, 1909.

350	A140	4c	**orange brown**, Aug. 15, 1910	150.00	210.00
			Never hinged	350.00	
			On cover		275.00
			Pair	370.00	625.00
			Never hinged	825.00	
			Guide line pair	1,250.	2,750.
			Never hinged	2,750.	

Earliest documented use: Mar. 22, 1912.

351	A140	5c	**blue**, Jan. 1909	160.00	275.00
			dark blue	160.00	275.00
			Never hinged	375.00	
			On cover		625.00
			Pair	425.00	825.00
			Never hinged	950.	
			Guide line pair	1,150.	3,000.
			Never hinged	2,500.	

Earliest documented use: Sept. 21, 1909.

1909   *Perf. 12 Vertically*

352	A138	1c	**green**, Jan. 1909	95.00	190.00
			dark green	95.00	190.00
			Never hinged	210.00	
			On cover		225.00
			Pair (2mm spacing)	250.00	600.00
			Never hinged	550.00	
			Pair (3mm spacing)	235.00	575.00
			Never hinged	525.00	
			Guide line pair	825.00	1,650.
			Never hinged	1,800.	
			Double transfer	—	

353	A139	2c	**carmine**, Jan. 12, 1909	95.00	220.00
			dark carmine	95.00	220.00
			Never hinged	215.00	
			On cover		275.00
			Pair (2mm spacing)	250.00	575.00
			Never hinged	550.00	
			Pair (3mm spacing)	235.00	550.00
			Never hinged	525.00	
			Guide line pair	750.00	1,300.
			Never hinged	1,750.	

Earliest documented use: June 14, 1909.

354	A140	4c	**orange brown**, Feb. 23, 1909	220.00	275.00
			Never hinged	475.00	
			On cover		325.00
			Pair (2mm spacing)	550.00	825.00
			Never hinged	1,200.	
			Pair (3mm spacing)	525.00	825.00
			Never hinged	1,150.	
			Guide line pair	1,500.	1,550.
			Never hinged	3,250.	

Earliest documented use: June 9, 1909.

355	A140	5c	**blue**, Feb. 23, 1909	225.00	300.00
			Never hinged	500.00	
			On cover		375.00
			Pair	575.00	875.00
			Never hinged	1,250.	
			Guide line pair	1,500.	2,050.
			Never hinged	3,250.	

Earliest documented use: Oct. 25, 1909.

These Government Coil Stamps, Nos. 352-355, should not be confused with those of the International Vending Machine Co., which are perf. 12½-13.

356	A140	10c	**yellow**, Jan. 7, 1909	3,250.	4,500.
			Never hinged	7,000.	
			On cover		10,000.
			Pair	7,000.	10,500.
			Never hinged	15,000.	
			Guide line pair	17,500.	29,000.
			Never hinged	55,000.	

Earliest documented use: Mar. 9, 1909 (dated cancel on off-cover stamp).

The used guide line pair of No. 356 is unique. Value reflects price realized at auction in 2002.
For listings of other coil stamps of designs A138 A139 and A140 see:
Nos. 385-396, 410-413, 441-459, single line watermark.
Nos. 486-496, unwatermarked.

Beware of stamps offered as No. 356 which may be examples of No. 338 with perfs. trimmed at top and/or bottom. Beware also of plentiful fakes in the marketplace of Nos. 348-355, made by fraudulently perforating imperforate stamps or by fraudulently trimming perforations off fully perforated stamps. Authentication of all these coils is advised.

BLUISH PAPER

This was made with 35 percent rag stock instead of all wood pulp. The "bluish" color (actually grayish blue) goes through the paper showing clearly on the back as well as on the face.

1909   *Perf. 12*

357	A138	1c	**green**, Feb. 16, 1909	85.00	100.00
			Never hinged	180.00	
			On postcard		120.00
			On cover		220.00
			Block of 4 (2mm spacing)	360.00	600.00
			Block of 4 (3mm spacing)	750.00	
			P# block of 6, Impt., T V	1,100.	
			Never hinged	1,850.	
			P# block of 6, Impt. & star	3,100.	
			Never hinged	5,200.	

Earliest documented use: Feb. 21, 1909.

358	A139	2c	**carmine**, Feb. 16, 1909	80.00	100.00
			Never hinged	170.00	
			On cover		190.00
			Block of 4 (2mm spacing)	350.00	650.00
			Block of 4 (3mm spacing)	450.00	
			P# block of 6, Impt., T V	1,000.	
			Never hinged	1,800.	
			P# block of 6, Impt. & star	1,650.	
			Never hinged	2,750.	
			Double transfer	—	

Earliest documented use: Feb. 23, 1909.

359	A140	3c	**deep violet**, type I	1,800.	5,000.
			Never hinged	4,000.	
			On cover		—
			Block of 4	7,750.	
			P# block of 6, Impt., T V	25,000.	
			Never hinged	35,000.	

Earliest documented use: Dec. 27, 1910.

360	A140	4c	**orange brown**	27,500.	
			Never hinged	80,000.	
			Block of 4	140,000.	
			P# strip of 3, Impt., T V	140,000.	

The No. 360 plate number strip of three is unique.

361	A140	5c	**blue**	5,750.	15,000.
			Never hinged	14,500.	
			On cover		27,500.
			Block of 4	25,000.	
			P# block of 6, Impt., T V	90,000.	

The No. 361 plate block is unique.

Earliest documented use: May 18, 1910.

362	A140	6c	**red orange**	1,350.	15,000.
			Never hinged	3,250.	
			On cover		22,500.
			Block of 4	5,750.	
			P# block of 6, Impt., T V	17,500.	
			Never hinged	30,000.	

Earliest documented use: Sept. 14, 1911.

363	A140	8c	**olive green**	30,000.	
			Never hinged	85,000.	
			Block of 4	135,000.	
			P# strip of 3, Impt., T V	150,000.	

The No. 363 plate number strip of three is unique.

364	A140	10c	**yellow**	1,750.	7,000.
			Never hinged	4,500.	
			On cover		—
			Block of 4	7,500.	
			P# block of 6, Impt., T V	40,000.	

Earliest documented use: Feb. 3, 1910.

365	A140	13c	**blue green**	2,750.	2,250.
			Never hinged	6,500.	
			On cover		—
			Block of 4	12,000.	10,000.
			P# block of 6, Impt., T V	32,500.	

366	A140	15c	**pale ultramarine**	1,350.	11,000.
			Never hinged	3,250.	
			On cover		—
			Block of 4	6,500.	
			P# block of 6, Impt., T V	17,500.	
			Never hinged	30,000.	

Earliest documented use: Jan. 15, 1911.

Nos. 360 and 363 were not regularly issued.
Used examples of Nos. 357-366 must bear contemporaneous cancels, and Nos. 359-366 used must be accompanied by certificates of authenticity issued by recognized expertizing committees.

IMPORTANT INFORMATION REGARDING VALUES FOR NEVER-HINGED STAMPS

Collectors should be aware that the values given for never-hinged stamps from No. 182 on are for stamps in the grade of very fine, just as the values for all stamps in the catalogue are for very fine stamps unless indicated otherwise. The never-hinged premium as a percentage of value will be larger for stamps in extremely fine or superb grades, and the premium will be smaller for fine-very fine, fine or poor examples. This is particularly true of the issues of the late-19th and early-20th centuries. For example, in the grade of very fine, an unused stamp from this time period may be valued at $100 hinged and $200 never hinged. The never-hinged premium is thus 100%. But in a grade of extremely fine, this same stamp will not only sell for more hinged, but the never-hinged premium will increase, perhaps to 200%-400% or more over the higher extremely fine value. In a grade of superb, a hinged stamp will sell for much more than a very fine stamp, and additionally the never-hinged premium will be much larger, perhaps as large as 500%-1,000%. On the other hand, the same stamp in a grade of fine or fine-very fine not only will sell for less than a very fine stamp in hinged condition, but additionally the never-hinged premium will be smaller than the never-hinged premium on a very fine stamp, perhaps as small as 40%-60%.

Please note that the above statements and percentages are NOT a formula for arriving at the values of stamps in hinged or never-hinged condition in the grades of very good, fine, fine to very fine, very fine, very fine to extremely fine, extremely fine or superb. The percentages given apply only to the size of the premium for never-hinged condition that might be added to the stamp value for hinged condition. Further, the percentages given are only generalized estimates. Some stamps or grades may have percentages for never-hinged condition that are higher or lower than the ranges given. For values of the most popular U.S. stamps in the grades of very good, fine, fine to very fine, very fine, very fine to extremely fine, extremely fine and superb, see the *Scott United States Specialized Valuing Supplement*, updated and issued twice each year in April and October.

VALUES FOR NEVER-HINGED STAMPS PRIOR TO SCOTT 182

This catalogue does not value pre-1879 stamps in never-hinged condition. Premiums for never-hinged condition in the classic era invariably are even larger than those premiums listed for the 1879 and later issues. Generally speaking, the earlier the stamp is listed in the catalogue, the larger will be the never-hinged premium. On some early classics, the premium will be several multiples of the unused, hinged values given in the catalogue.

NEVER-HINGED PLATE BLOCKS

Values given for never-hinged plate blocks are for blocks in which all stamps have original gum that has never been hinged and has no disturbances, and all selvage, whether gummed or ungummed, has never been hinged.

Lincoln — A141   William H. Seward — A142

LINCOLN CENTENARY OF BIRTH ISSUE
Designed by Clair Aubrey Huston.

Plates of 400 subjects in four panes of 100 each

1909	Wmk. 191		Perf. 12
367	A141 2c **carmine**, *Feb. 12*	5.00	2.00
	bright carmine	5.00	2.00
	Never hinged	10.50	
	On cover		4.00
	Block of 4 (2mm spacing)	21.00	16.00
	Block of 4 (3mm spacing)	21.00	15.00
	P# block of 6, Impt. & small sol-		
	id star	200.00	
	Never hinged	275.00	
	Double transfer	7.25	2.75

Earliest documented use: Feb. 12, 1909 (FDC).

Imperf

368	A141 2c **carmine**, *Feb. 12*	15.00	22.50
	Never hinged	30.00	
	On cover		35.00
	Pair	32.50	50.00
	Never hinged	70.00	
	Block of 4 (2mm or 3mm spac-		
	ing)	67.50	95.00

	Corner margin block of 4	72.50	95.00
	Margin block of 4, arrow	75.00	100.00
	Center line block	145.00	125.00
	Never hinged	260.00	
	P# block of 6, Impt. & small sol-		
	id star	200.00	—
	Never hinged	390.00	
	Double transfer	40.00	30.00

Earliest documented use: Feb. 12, 1909 (FDC).

BLUISH PAPER
Perf. 12

369	A141 2c **carmine**, *Feb.*	180.00	*275.00*
	Never hinged	380.00	
	On cover		425.00
	Block of 4 (2mm or 3mm spac-		
	ing)	800.	*1,250.*
	P# block of 6, Impt. & small sol-		
	id star	*2,750.*	
	Never hinged	*4,250.*	

Earliest documented use: Feb. 27, 1909 (dated cancel on off-cover stamp); Mar. 27, 1909 (on cover).

ALASKA-YUKON-PACIFIC EXPOSITION ISSUE
Seattle, Wash., June 1 - Oct. 16, 1909

Designed by Clair Aubrey Huston.

Plates of 280 subjects in four panes of 70 each

1909	Wmk. 191		Perf. 12
370	A142 2c **carmine**, *June 1*	7.50	2.25
	bright carmine	7.50	2.25
	Never hinged	16.00	
	On cover		5.00
	On Expo. card or cover, Expo. station machine canc.		65.00
	On Expo. card or cover, Expo. station duplex handstamp canc.		250.00
	Block of 4	32.50	19.00
	P# block of 6, Impt., T V	200.00	
	Never hinged	320.00	
	Double transfer (5249 UL 8)	10.50	5.00

Earliest documented use: June 1, 1909 (FDC).

Imperf

371	A142 2c **carmine**, *June*	17.50	24.00
	Never hinged	37.50	
	On cover		42.50
	On cover, Expo. station machine canc.		*450.00*
	Pair	37.50	52.50
	Never hinged	77.50	
	Block of 4	85.00	130.00
	Corner margin block of 4	90.00	
	Margin block of 4, arrow	92.50	140.00
	Center line block	175.00	175.00
	Never hinged	300.00	
	P# block of 6, Impt., T V	225.00	—
	Never hinged	350.00	
	Double transfer	32.50	30.00

Earliest documented use: June 7, 1909.

HUDSON-FULTON CELEBRATION ISSUE
Tercentenary of the discovery of the Hudson River and the centenary of Robert Fulton's steamship, the "Clermont."

Henry Hudson's "Half Moon" and Fulton's Steamship "Clermont" A143

Designed by Clair Aubrey Huston.

Plates of 240 subjects in four panes of 60 each

1909, Sept. 25	Wmk. 191		Perf. 12
372	A143 2c **carmine**	10.00	4.75
	Never hinged	21.00	
	On cover		8.50
	Block of 4	42.50	30.00
	P# block of 6, Impt., T V	280.00	
	Never hinged	425.00	
	Double transfer (5393 and 5394)	15.00	5.00

Earliest documented use: Sept. 25, 1909 (FDC).

Imperf

373	A143 2c **carmine**	20.00	27.50
	Never hinged	42.50	
	On cover		40.00
	Pair	42.50	60.00
	Never hinged	90.00	
	Block of 4	90.00	130.00
	Corner margin block of 4	95.00	
	Margin block of 4, arrow	100.00	135.00
	Center line block	210.00	160.00
	Never hinged	360.00	
	P# block of 6, Impt., T V	240.00	
	Never hinged	375.00	
	Double transfer (5393 and 5394)	45.00	32.50

Earliest documented use: Sept. 25, 1909 (FDC).

Earliest documented use dates for imperforates are for the imperforate sheet stamps, not for imperforate stamps with vending and affixing machine perforations or for flat plate imperforate coil stamps. EDU dates for VAMP and flat plate imperf coil stamps are shown in their respective sections later in the catalogue.

REGULAR ISSUE
DESIGNS OF 1908-09 ISSUES

In this issue the Bureau used three groups of plates:

(1) The old standard plates with uniform 2mm spacing throughout (6c, 8c, 10c and 15c values);

(2) Those having an open star in the margin and showing spacings of 2mm and 3mm between stamps (for all values 1c to 10c); and

(3) A third set of plates with uniform spacing of approximately 2¾mm between all stamps. These plates have imprints showing
a. "Bureau of Engraving & Printing," "A" and number.
b. "A" and number only.
c. Number only.
(See above No. 331)

These were used for the 1c, 2c, 3c, 4c and 5c values.

On or about Oct. 1, 1910 the Bureau began using paper watermarked with single-lined letters:

(Actual size of letter)

repeated in rows, this way:

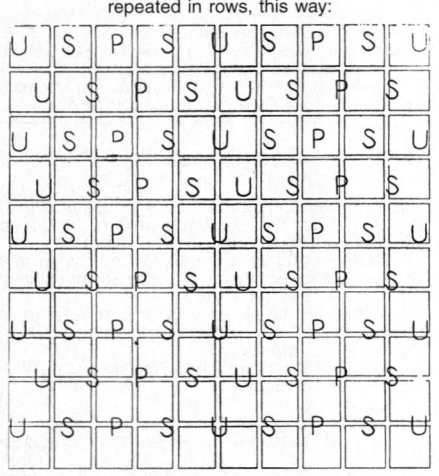

Watermark 190

Plates of 400 subjects in four panes of 100 each

1910-11	Wmk. 190		Perf. 12	
374 A138	1c **green**, *Nov. 23, 1910*		6.50	.25
	light green		6.50	.25
	dark green		6.50	.25
	Never hinged		15.00	
	On cover			.30
	Block of 4 (2mm spacing)		28.00	3.25
	Block of 4 (3mm spacing)		30.00	3.00
	P# block of 6, Impt., & star		100.00	
	Never hinged		160.00	
	P# block of 6, Impt. & "A"		125.00	—
	Never hinged		175.00	
	Double transfer		14.00	—
	Cracked plate		—	—
	Pane of 60		1,750.	—
a.	Booklet pane of 6, *Oct. 7, 1910*		225.00	300.00
	Never hinged		375.00	

Earliest documented uses: Feb. 7, 1911 (No. 374); Feb. 28, 1911 (No. 374a single).

Panes of 60 of No. 374 were regularly issued in Washington, D.C. during Sept. and Oct., 1912. They were made from the six outer vertical rows of imperforate "Star Plate" sheets that had been rejected for use in vending machines on account of the 3mm spacing.

These panes have sheet margins on two adjoining sides and are imperforate along the other two sides. Upper and lower right panes show plate number, star and imprint on both margins; upper and lower left panes show plate number, star and imprint on side margins, but only the imprint on top or bottom margins.

375 A139	2c **carmine**, *Nov. 23, 1910*		6.50	.25
	bright carmine		6.50	.25
	dark carmine		6.50	.25
	Never hinged		15.00	
	On cover			.30
	Block of 4 (2mm spacing)		28.00	2.00
	Block of 4 (3mm spacing)		27.00	1.75
	P# block of 6, Impt. & star		125.00	
	Never hinged		185.00	
	P# block of 6, Impt. & "A"		135.00	
	Never hinged		200.00	
	Cracked plate		—	—
	Double transfer		12.00	—
	Foreign entry, design of 1c (plate 5299)		—	1,450.
a.	Booklet pane of 6, *Nov. 30, 1910*		125.00	200.00
	Never hinged		200.00	
b.	2c **lake**		900.00	
	Never hinged		1,900.	
c.	Double impression		600.00	
	Never hinged		1,200.	

Earliest documented use: Dec. 29, 1910 (No. 375); May 10, 1911 (No. 375a single).

376 A140	3c **deep violet**, type I, *Jan. 16, 1911*		20.00	2.00
	violet		20.00	2.00
	Never hinged		45.00	
	lilac		25.00	2.25
	Never hinged		55.00	
	On cover			8.00
	Block of 4 (2mm spacing)		85.00	15.00
	Block of 4 (3mm spacing)		87.50	14.00
	P# block of 6, Impt. & star		300.00	
	Never hinged		450.00	
	P# block of 6		325.00	
	Never hinged		475.00	

Earliest documented use: June 9, 1911.

377 A140	4c **brown**, *Jan. 20, 1911*		30.00	1.00
	dark brown		30.00	1.00
	orange brown		30.00	1.00
	Never hinged		70.00	
	On cover			7.50
	Block of 4 (2mm spacing)		135.00	6.50
	Block of 4 (3mm spacing)		130.00	6.00
	P# block of 6, Impt. & star		325.00	
	Never hinged		475.00	

	P# block of 6	350.00	
	Never hinged	550.00	—
	Double transfer		

Earliest documented use: Mar. 7, 1911.

378 A140	5c **blue**, *Jan. 25, 1911*	30.00	.75
	light blue	30.00	.75
	dark blue	30.00	.75
	bright blue	30.00	.75
	Never hinged	70.00	
	On cover		5.25
	Block of 4 (2mm spacing)	135.00	6.00
	Block of 4 (3mm spacing)	130.00	5.00
	P# block of 6, Impt., T V	350.00	
	Never hinged	550.00	
	P# block of 6, Impt. & star	350.00	
	Never hinged	550.00	
	P# block of 6, "A"	400.00	
	Never hinged	625.00	
	P# block of 6	400.00	
	Never hinged	625.00	
	Double transfer		

Earliest documented use: Feb. 14, 1911.

379 A140	6c **red orange**, *Jan. 1911*	35.00	1.00
	light red orange	35.00	1.00
	Never hinged	80.00	
	On cover		13.00
	Block of 4 (2mm spacing)	150.00	12.50
	Block of 4 (3mm spacing)	145.00	11.00
	P# block of 6, Impt., T V	500.00	
	Never hinged	800.00	
	P# block of 6, Impt. & star	440.00	
	Never hinged	700.00	

Earliest documented use: Jan. 12, 1911.

380 A140	8c **olive green**, *Feb. 8, 1911*	100.00	15.00
	dark olive green	100.00	15.00
	Never hinged	225.00	
	On cover		45.00
	Block of 4 (2mm spacing)	425.00	100.00
	Block of 4 (3mm spacing)	425.00	95.00
	P# block of 6, Impt., T V	1,100.	
	Never hinged	1,900.	
	P# block of 6, Impt. & star	1,300.	
	Never hinged	2,200.	

Earliest documented use: May 27, 1911.

381 A140	10c **yellow**, *Jan. 24, 1911*	95.00	6.00
	Never hinged	220.00	
	On cover		22.50
	Block of 4 (2mm spacing)	400.00	50.00
	Block of 4 (3mm spacing)	400.00	47.50
	P# block of 6, Impt., T V	1,150.	
	Never hinged	2,000.	
	P# block of 6, Impt. & star	1,250.	
	Never hinged	2,250.	

Earliest documented use: Feb. 17, 1911.

382 A140	15c **pale ultramarine**, *Mar. 1, 1911*	250.00	19.00
	Never hinged	575.00	
	On cover		100.00
	Block of 4	1,050.	130.00
	P# block of 6, Impt., T V	2,500.	
	Never hinged	4,500.	

Earliest documented use: April 25, 1911.

Nos. 374-382 (9)	573.00	45.25

Earliest documented use dates for imperforates are for the imperforate sheet stamps, not for imperforate stamps with vending and affixing machine perforations or for flat plate imperforate coil stamps. EDU dates for VAMP and flat plate imperf coil stamps are shown in their respective sections later in the catalogue.

1910, Dec.			*Imperf.*
383 A138	1c **green**	2.00	*2.25*
	dark green	2.00	*2.25*
	yellowish green	2.00	*2.25*
	bright green	2.00	*2.25*
	Never hinged	4.25	
	On cover		5.50
	Pair	4.25	*5.00*
	Never hinged	9.50	
	Block of 4 (2mm or 3mm spacing)	9.00	*17.50*
	Corner margin block of 4	10.00	
	Margin block of 4, arrow	10.50	*16.00*
	Center line block	24.00	18.00
	Never hinged	40.00	
	P# block of 6, Impt. & star	45.00	—
	Never hinged	72.50	—
	P# block of 6, Impt. & "A"	82.50	—
	Never hinged	125.00	
	Double transfer	6.50	—

Earliest documented use: Jan. 28, 1911.

Rosette plate crack on head

384 A139	2c **carmine**	3.25	2.75
	light carmine	3.25	2.75
	Never hinged	7.00	
	dark carmine	55.00	14.00
	On cover		4.00
	Horizontal pair	10.00	8.25
	Never hinged	22.00	
	Vertical pair	7.50	6.75
	Never hinged	17.00	
	Block of 4 (2mm or 3mm spacing)	22.50	17.50
	Corner margin block of 4	25.00	21.50
	Margin block of 4, arrow	26.00	22.50
	Center line block	50.00	*55.00*
	Never hinged	85.00	
	P# block of 6, Impt. & star	130.00	—
	Never hinged	200.00	
	P# block of 6, Impt. & "A"	170.00	—
	Never hinged	260.00	
	Double transfer	7.50	—
	Rosette plate crack on head	*150.00*	—

Earliest documented use: Dec. 8, 1910.

COIL STAMPS

1910, Nov. 1			*Perf. 12 Horizontally*
385 A138	1c **green**	45.00	45.00
	dark green	45.00	45.00
	Never hinged	100.00	
	On cover		70.00
	Pair	110.00	*135.00*
	Never hinged	240.00	
	Guide line pair	450.00	*675.00*
	Never hinged	1,000.	
386 A139	2c **carmine**	110.00	100.00
	light carmine	110.00	100.00
	Never hinged	250.00	
	On cover		125.00
	Pair	300.00	280.00
	Never hinged	650.00	
	Guide line pair	1,400.	*1,150.*
	Never hinged	3,250.	

Earliest documented use: Dec. 9, 1910.

1910-11			*Perf. 12 Vertically*
387 A138	1c **green**, *Nov. 1, 1910*	200.00	140.00
	Never hinged	425.00	
	On cover		175.00
	Pair (2mm spacing)	475.00	425.00
	Never hinged	1,050.	
	Pair (3mm spacing)	500.00	410.00
	Never hinged	1,100.	
	Guide line pair	1,200.	*1,150.*
	Never hinged	2,600.	

Earliest documented use: Nov. 5, 1910.

388 A139	2c **carmine**, *Nov. 1, 1910*	1,400.	*2,250.*
	Never hinged	3,300.	
	On cover		*2,500.*
	Pair (2mm spacing)	3,250.	*7,500.*
	Never hinged	7,500.	
	Pair (3mm spacing)	3,500.	*8,000.*
	Never hinged	7,750.	
	Guide line pair	*8,250.*	*23,000.*
	Never hinged	*24,000.*	

The used guide line pair of No. 388 is unique. It is the center pair in a strip of four, is fine-very fine and is valued thus.

Stamps offered as No. 388 frequently are privately perforated examples of No. 384, or copies of No. 375 with top and/or bottom perfs trimmed.

Earliest documented use: Jan. 4, 1911.

389 A140	3c **deep vio.**, type I, *Jan. 24, 1911*	110,000.	11,000.
	Never hinged	225,000.	
	On cover		27,500.
	Pair	250,000.	37,500.

No. 389 is valued in the grade of fine.

Only a small supply of this coil was used at Orangeburg, N.Y. The used pair listed is part of a strip of 3 (three such strips exist). Each strip is in average grade or condition, and the pairs are valued thus. No other used multiples are recorded. There is only one mint, never-hinged example recorded.

Stamps offered as No. 389 sometimes are examples of No. 376 with top and/or bottom perfs trimmed. Expertization by competent authorities is recommended.

Earliest documented use: Mar. 8, 1911.

Beware of plentiful fakes in the marketplace of Nos. 385-389, made by fraudulently perforating the 1c and 2c imperforate stamps or by fraudulently trimming perforations off fully perforated stamps.

1910 — Perf. 8½ Horizontally

390	A138	1c **green,** *Dec. 12, 1910*	5.00	14.00
		dark green	5.00	14.00
		Never hinged	11.00	
		On cover		17.50
		Pair	11.50	45.00
		Never hinged	24.00	
		Guide line pair	37.50	125.00
		Never hinged	80.00	
		Double transfer	—	—

Earliest documented use: Oct. 5, 1911.

391	A139	2c **carmine,** *Dec. 23, 1910*	42.50	50.00
		light carmine	42.50	50.00
		Never hinged	90.00	
		On cover		70.00
		Pair	110.00	170.00
		Never hinged	240.00	
		Guide line pair	260.00	*1,350.*
		Never hinged	575.00	

Earliest documented use: May 3, 1911.

1910-13 — Perf. 8½ Vertically

392	A138	1c **green,** *Dec. 12, 1910*	30.00	55.00
		dark green	30.00	55.00
		Never hinged	65.00	
		On cover		75.00
		Pair	75.00	155.00
		Never hinged	160.00	
		Guide line pair	200.00	500.00
		Never hinged	425.00	
		Double transfer	—	—

Earliest documented use: Dec. 16, 1910.

393	A139	2c **carmine,** *Dec. 16, 1910*	47.50	45.00
		dark carmine	47.50	45.00
		Never hinged	110.00	
		On cover		65.00
		Pair	125.00	130.00
		Never hinged	275.00	
		Guide line pair	300.00	275.00
		Never hinged	650.00	

Earliest documented use: Dec. 27, 1910.

394	A140	3c **deep violet,** type I, *Sept. 1911*	60.00	67.50
		violet	60.00	67.50
		red violet	60.00	67.50
		Never hinged	135.00	
		On cover		115.00
		Pair (2mm spacing)	150.00	220.00
		Never hinged	350.00	
		Pair (3mm spacing)	145.00	210.00
		Never hinged	325.00	
		Guide line pair	425.00	650.00
		Never hinged	925.00	

Earliest documented use: Sept. 18, 1911.

395	A140	4c **brown,** *Apr. 15, 1912*	62.50	*70.00*
		dark brown	62.50	*70.00*
		Never hinged	140.00	
		On cover		115.00
		Pair (2mm spacing)	160.00	200.00
		Never hinged	375.00	
		Pair (3mm spacing)	150.00	200.00
		Never hinged	350.00	
		Guide line pair	475.00	650.00
		Never hinged	1,100.	

Earliest documented use: June 21, 1912.

396	A140	5c **blue,** *Mar. 1913*	60.00	67.50
		dark blue	60.00	67.50
		Never hinged	135.00	
		On cover		115.00
		Pair	160.00	190.00
		Never hinged	375.00	
		Guide line pair	425.00	*825.00*
		Never hinged	975.00	

Earliest documented use: April 5, 1913.

Beware of plentiful fakes in the marketplace of Nos. 390-393, made by fraudulently perforating imperforate stamps.

PANAMA-PACIFIC EXPOSITION ISSUE
San Francisco, Cal., Feb. 20 - Dec. 4, 1915

Vasco Nunez de Balboa — A144

Pedro Miguel Locks, Panama Canal — A145

Golden Gate — A146

Discovery of San Francisco Bay — A147

Exposition Station Cancellation.

Designed by Clair Aubrey Huston.

Plates of 280 subjects in four panes of 70 each.

1913 — Wmk. 190 — Perf. 12

397	A144	1c **green,** *Jan. 1, 1913*	16.50	2.00
		deep green	16.50	2.00
		yellowish green	16.50	2.00
		Never hinged	40.00	
		On cover		3.50
		On Expo. card, Expo. station 1915 machine cancel		30.00
		Pair on cover, Expo. station 1915 duplex handstamp cancel		150.00
		Block of 4	70.00	14.00
		P# block of 6	300.00	
		Never hinged	450.00	
		Double transfer	22.50	3.25

Earliest documented use: Jan. 1, 1913 (FDC).

398	A145	2c **carmine,** *Jan. 1913*	18.00	1.00
		deep carmine	18.00	1.00
		Never hinged	40.00	
		On cover		1.75
		On cover, Expo. station 1915 machine cancel		75.00
		On cover, Expo. station 1915 duplex handstamp cancel		*250.00*
		Block of 4	75.00	10.00
		P# block of 6	400.00	
		Never hinged	625.00	
		Double transfer	37.50	3.50
a.		2c **carmine lake**	*1,500.*	
		Never hinged	*2,500.*	
b.		2c **lake**	*5,000.*	
		Never hinged	*8,500.*	

Earliest documented use: Jan. 17, 1913.

399	A146	5c **blue,** *Jan. 1, 1913*	70.00	10.00
		dark blue	70.00	10.00
		Never hinged	160.00	
		On cover		27.50
		On cover, Expo. station 1915 machine cancel		300.00
		Block of 4	300.00	70.00
		P# block of 6	1,900.	
		Never hinged	3,200.	

Earliest documented use: Jan. 1, 1913 (FDC).

400	A147	10c **orange yellow,** *Jan. 1, 1913*	120.00	22.50
		Never hinged	270.00	
		On cover		57.50
		On cover, Expo. station 1915 machine cancel		500.00
		Block of 4	525.00	150.00
		P# block of 6	2,350.	
		Never hinged	3,850.	

Earliest documented use: Jan. 1, 1913 (FDC).

400A	A147	10c **orange,** *Aug. 1913*	200.00	20.00
		Never hinged	450.00	
		On cover		75.00
		On cover, Expo. station 1915 machine cancel		550.00
		Block of 4	850.00	110.00
		P# block of 6	*12,000.*	
		Never hinged	*22,500.*	

Earliest documented use: Nov. 12, 1913.

Nos. 397-400A (5)		424.50	55.50
Nos. 397-400A, never hinged		960.00	

1914-15 — Perf. 10

401	A144	1c **green,** *Dec. 1914*	25.00	7.00
		dark green	25.00	7.00
		Never hinged	60.00	
		On cover		16.00
		On Expo. card, Expo. station 1915 machine cancel		75.00

	Block of 4	110.00	47.50
	P# block of 6	400.00	
	Never hinged	650.00	

Earliest documented use: Dec. 21, 1914.

402	A145	2c **carmine**, *Jan. 1915*	70.00	2.75
		deep carmine	70.00	2.75
		red	70.00	2.75
		Never hinged	170.00	
		On cover		6.50
		On cover, Expo. station 1915		
		machine cancel		150.00
		On cover, Expo. station 1915		
		duplex handstamp cancel		450.00
		Block of 4	300.00	19.00
		P# block of 6	1,950.	
		Never hinged	3,250.	

Earliest documented use: Jan. 13, 1915.

403	A146	5c **blue**, *Feb. 1915*	160.00	20.00
		dark blue	160.00	20.00
		Never hinged	390.00	
		On cover		55.00
		On cover, Expo. station 1915		
		machine cancel		450.00
		Block of 4	700.00	130.00
		P# block of 6	4,000.	
		Never hinged	6,750.	

Earliest documented use: Feb. 6, 1915.

404	A147	10c **orange**, *July 1915*	750.00	70.00
		Never hinged	1,750.	
		On cover		175.00
		On cover, Expo. station 1915		
		machine cancel		600.00
		Block of 4	3,500.	500.00
		P# block of 6	12,000.	
		Never hinged	22,000.	

Earliest documented use: Aug. 27, 1915.

Nos. 401-404 (4)	1,005.	99.75
Nos. 401-404, never hinged	2,370.	

VALUES FOR VERY FINE STAMPS
Please note: Stamps are valued in the grade of Very Fine unless otherwise indicated.

REGULAR ISSUE

Washington — A140

The plates for this and later issues were the so-called "A" plates with uniform spacing of 2¾mm between stamps.

Plates of 400 subjects in four panes of 100 each for all values 1c to 50c inclusive.

Plates of 200 subjects in two panes of 100 each for $1 and some of the 50c (No. 422) denomination.

1912-14		**Wmk. 190**		***Perf. 12***
405	A140	1c **green**, *Feb. 1912*	6.50	.25
		light green	6.50	.25
		dark green	6.50	.25
		yellowish green	6.50	.25
		Never hinged	15.00	
		On cover		.30
		Block of 4	28.00	2.50
		P# block of 6, Impt. & "A"	125.00	
		Never hinged	200.00	
		P# block of 6, "A"	115.00	
		Never hinged	185.00	
		P# block of 6	110.00	
		Never hinged	170.00	
		Cracked plate	14.50	—
		Double transfer	8.50	—
a.		Vert. pair, imperf. horiz.	2,000.	—
b.		Booklet pane of 6, *1912*	65.00	75.00
		Never hinged	110.00	
c.		Double impression		1,250.

Earliest documented uses: Feb. 2, 1912 (No. 405); Jan. 16, 1912 (No. 405b single).

TYPE I

TYPE I

TWO CENTS
Type I. There is one shading line in the first curve of the ribbon above the left "2" and one in the second curve of the ribbon above the right "2."

The button of the toga has only a faint outline.

The top line of the toga rope, from the button to the front of the throat, is also very faint.

The shading lines of the face terminate in front of the ear with little or no joining, to form a lock of hair.

Used on both flat plate and rotary press printings.

406	A140	2c **carmine**, type I, *Feb. 1912*	6.50	.25
		bright carmine	6.50	.25
		Never hinged	15.00	
		dark carmine	7.00	.25
		Never hinged	16.00	
		On cover		.30
		Block of 4	28.00	2.50
		P# block of 6, Impt. & "A"	150.00	
		Never hinged	240.00	
		P# block of 6, "A"	140.00	
		Never hinged	230.00	
		P# block of 6	125.00	
		Never hinged	200.00	
		P# single, Electrolytic, (Pl. 6023)	650.00	
		Never hinged	1,100.	
		Double transfer	9.00	—
a.		Booklet pane of 6, *Feb. 8, 1912*	65.00	90.00
		Never hinged	110.00	
b.		Double impression		
c.		2c **lake**, type I	2,000.	2,750.
		Never hinged	4,500.	

Earliest documented uses: Feb. 15, 1912 (No. 406); May 2, 1912 (No. 406a single).

407	A140	7c **black**, *Apr. 1914*	70.00	14.00
		grayish black	70.00	14.00
		intense black	70.00	14.00
		Never hinged	160.00	
		On cover		75.00
		Block of 4	310.00	100.00
		P# block of 6	1,200.	
		Never hinged	2,000.	

Earliest documented use: May 1, 1914.

Earliest documented use dates for imperforates are for the imperforate sheet stamps, not for imperforate stamps with vending and affixing machine perforations or for flat plate imperforate coil stamps. EDU dates for VAMP and flat plate imperf coil stamps are shown in their respective sections later in the catalogue.

Plate Blocks
Scott values for plate blocks printed from flat plates are for very fine side and bottom positions. Top position plate blocks with full wide selvage sell for more.

1912				***Imperf.***
408	A140	1c **green**, *Mar. 1912*	1.00	1.00
		yellowish green	1.00	1.00
		dark green	1.00	1.00
		Never hinged	2.00	
		On cover		1.75
		Pair	2.10	2.10
		Never hinged	4.20	
		Block of 4	4.20	4.20
		Corner margin block of 4	4.30	4.30
		Margin block of 4, arrow	4.40	4.40
		Center line block	10.00	10.00
		Never hinged	17.50	
		P# block of 6, Impt. & "A," T, B or L	45.00	—
		Never hinged	75.00	
		P# block of 6, Impt. & "A," at right	550.00	—
		Never hinged	850.00	
		P# block of 6, "A"	26.00	—
		Never hinged	45.00	
		P# block of 6	18.00	—
		Never hinged	29.00	
		Double transfer	2.40	2.40
		Cracked plate		—

Earliest documented use: April 26, 1912.

409	A140	2c **carmine**, type I, *Feb. 1912*	1.20	1.20
		deep carmine	1.20	1.20
		scarlet	1.20	1.20
		Never hinged	2.40	
		On cover		2.00
		Pair	2.50	2.50
		Never hinged	5.00	
		Block of 4	5.00	5.00
		Corner margin block of 4	5.25	
		Margin block of 4, arrow	5.50	5.50
		Center line block	11.00	11.00
		Never hinged	19.00	
		P# block of 6, Impt. & "A"	47.50	—
		Never hinged	80.00	
		P# block of 6, "A"	45.00	—
		Never hinged	75.00	
		P# block of 6	35.00	—
		Never hinged	57.50	
		Cracked plate (Plates 7580, 7582)	14.00	—

Earliest documented use: Apr. 15, 1912.

In late 1914, the Post Office at Kansas City, Missouri, had on hand a stock of imperforate sheets of 400 of stamps Nos. 408 and 409, formerly sold for use in vending machines, but not then in demand. In order to make them salable, they were rouletted with ordinary tracing wheels and were sold over the counter with official approval of the Post Office Department given January 5, 1915.

These stamps were sold until the supply was exhausted. Except for one full sheet of 400 of each value, all were cut into panes of 100 before being rouletted and sold. They are known as "Kansas City Roulettes". Value, authenticated blocks of 4, 1c *$100*, 2c *$200*.

Earliest documented uses of "Kansas City Roulettes": Oct. 22, 1914 (No. 408); Nov. 25, 1914 (No. 409).

COIL STAMPS

1912			***Perf. 8½ Horizontally***	
410	A140	1c **green**, *Mar. 1912*	6.00	12.50
		dark green	6.00	12.50
		Never hinged	13.00	
		On cover		17.50
		Pair	15.00	42.50
		Never hinged	32.50	
		Guide line pair	30.00	90.00
		Never hinged	65.00	
		Double transfer	—	—

Earliest documented use: Apr. 17, 1912.

411	A140	2c **carmine**, type I, *Mar. 1912*	10.00	15.00
		deep carmine	10.00	15.00
		Never hinged	22.50	
		On cover		20.00
		Pair	25.00	45.00
		Never hinged	55.00	
		Guide line pair	55.00	90.00
		Never hinged	125.00	
		Double transfer	12.50	

Earliest documented use: June 12, 1912.

			Perf. 8½ Vertically	
412	A140	1c **green**, *Mar. 18, 1912*	25.00	25.00
		deep green	25.00	25.00
		Never hinged	55.00	
		On cover		35.00
		Pair	60.00	75.00
		Never hinged	130.00	
		Guide line pair	120.00	175.00
		Never hinged	260.00	

Earliest documented use: May 21, 1912.

413	A140	2c **carmine**, type I, *Mar. 1912*	55.00	25.00
		dark carmine	55.00	25.00
		Never hinged	120.00	
		On cover		32.50
		Pair	115.00	75.00
		Never hinged	250.00	
		Guide line pair	300.00	175.00
		Never hinged	625.00	
		Double transfer	52.50	—

Earliest documented use: April 16, 1912.

Beware of plentiful fakes in the marketplace of Nos. 410-413, made by fraudulently perforating imperforate stamps.

Franklin — A148

1912-14		**Wmk. 190**		***Perf. 12***
414	A148	8c **pale olive green**, *Feb. 1912*	40.00	2.00
		olive green	40.00	2.00
		Never hinged	100.00	
		On cover		15.00
		Block of 4	180.00	15.00
		P# block of 6, Impt. & "A"	475.00	
		Never hinged	800.00	
415	A148	9c **salmon red**, *Apr. 1914*	50.00	14.00
		rose red	50.00	14.00
		Never hinged	120.00	
		On cover		50.00
		Block of 4	220.00	125.00
		P# block of 6	650.00	
		Never hinged	1,100.	

Earliest documented use: May 1, 1914.

416	A148	10c **orange yellow**, *Jan. 1912*	40.00	.80
		yellow	40.00	.80
		Never hinged	100.00	
		On cover		2.75
		Block of 4	180.00	5.25
		P# block of 6, Impt. & "A"	500.00	
		Never hinged	825.00	
		P# block of 6, "A"	550.00	
		Never hinged	900.00	
		Double transfer		—
a.		10c **brown yellow**	1,250.	
		Never hinged	2,750.	

Earliest documented use: Feb. 12, 1912.

417	A148	12c **claret brown**, *Apr. 1914*	45.00	5.00
		deep claret brown	45.00	5.00
		Never hinged	110.00	
		On cover		25.00
		Block of 4	200.00	37.50
		P# block of 6	625.00	

Never hinged	1,050.	
Double transfer	55.00	—
Triple transfer	72.50	—

Earliest documented use: May 5, 1914.

418 A148 15c **gray**, *Feb. 1912*	80.00	4.50
dark gray	80.00	4.50
Never hinged	190.00	
On cover		17.50
Block of 4	340.00	35.00
P# block of 6, Impt. & "A"	675.00	
Never hinged	1,400.	
P# block of 6, "A"	850.00	
Never hinged	1,550.	
P# block of 6	1,000.	
Never hinged	1,700.	
Double transfer		—

Earliest documented use: Apr. 26, 1912.

419 A148 20c **ultramarine**, *Apr. 1914*	180.00	19.00
dark ultramarine	180.00	19.00
Never hinged	400.00	
On cover		150.00
Block of 4	750.00	135.00
P# block of 6	2,000.	
Never hinged	3,500.	

Earliest documented use: May 1, 1914.

420 A148 30c **orange red**, *Apr. 1914*	110.00	19.00
dark orange red	110.00	19.00
Never hinged	250.00	
On cover		250.00
Block of 4	475.00	140.00
P# block of 6	1,450.	
Never hinged	2,400.	

Earliest documented use: May 1, 1914.

421 A148 50c **violet**, *1914*	400.00	30.00
bright violet	400.00	30.00
Never hinged	900.00	
On cover		2,000.
Block of 4	1,700.	200.00
P# block of 6	10,000.	
Never hinged	16,000.	

Earliest documented use: May 1, 1914.

No. 421 almost always has an offset of the frame lines on the back under the gum. No. 422 does not have this offset.

1912, Feb. 12   **Wmk. 191**

422 A148 50c **violet**	240.00	22.50
Never hinged	550.00	
On cover		2,000.
Block of 4	1,000.	150.00
Margin block of 4, arrow, R or L	1,050.	
P# block of 6, Impt. & "A"	4,750.	
Never hinged	7,500.	

Earliest documented use: Oct. 31, 1914.

423 A148 $1 **violet brown**	500.00	75.00
Never hinged	1,100.	
On cover		7,000.
Block of 4	2,100.	1,000.
Margin block of 4, arrow, R or L	2,150.	
P# block of 6, Impt. & "A"	15,000.	
Never hinged	22,500.	
Double transfer (5782 L 66)	625.00	—

Earliest documented use: July 15, 1915.

During the United States occupation of Vera Cruz, Mexico, from April to November, 1914, letters sent from there show Provisional Postmarks.

For other listings of perforated sheet stamps of design A148, see:

Nos. 431-440 — Single line wmk. Perf. 10
Nos. 460 — Double line wmk. Perf. 10
Nos. 470-478 — Unwmkd. Perf. 10
Nos. 508-518 — Unwmkd. Perf. 11

1914 Compound Perforations

As the Bureau of Engraving and Printing made the changeover to perf 10 from perf 12, in the normal course of their stamp production they perforated limited quantities of 1c, 2c and 5c stamps with the old 12-gauge perforations in one direction and the new 10-gauge perforations in the other direction. These were not production errors. These compound-perforation stamps previously were listed as Nos. 424a, 424b, 425c, 425d and 428a.

All examples of Nos. 423A-423E must be accompanied by certificates of authenticity issued by a recognized expertizing committee. Fakes made from perf 12, perf 10 and imperfs exist.

1914   **Wmk. 190**   *Perf. 12x10*

423A A140 1c **green**	20,000.	10,000.
Never hinged	—	
Pair	—	22,500.
Block of 4	—	45,000.
On postcard		15,000.
On cover, pair		20,000.

Formerly No. 424a. Seventeen unused and 59 used examples are recorded. Value for unused is for a sound stamp with perfs touching or just cutting the design. Value for used is for a sound stamp in the grade of fine-very fine. Of the used examples, 23 are precanceled Quincy IL (very scarce) or Chicago (usually inverted). The unused block of four, used block of four and pair on cover are each unique (top stamp of pair on cover

---

with small piece missing and valued thus). The block of 4 has perfs slightly cutting at top and is valued thus.

423B A140 2c **rose red**, type I	175,000.	32,500.

Formerly No. 425c. One unused (a plate #7082 single) and 30 used examples are recorded. Value for used is for a sound stamp in the grade of fine-very fine. There are no precancels known on this issue.

423C A140 5c **blue**		37,500.
Pair		

Formerly No. 428a. 24 used examples are recorded. No unused examples are recorded. Three examples are precanceled: Tampa FL (2) and Rahway NJ (1). Value is for a sound stamp in the grade of fine-very fine. The pair is unique (one stamp creased, the other with a small tear).

Earliest documented use: April 14, 1915 (dated cancel on off-cover stamp).

1914   **Wmk. 190**   *Perf. 10x12*

423D A140 1c **green**		20,000.

Formerly No. 424b. 41 used examples are recorded. No unused examples are recorded. 36 examples are precanceled: Dayton OH (33), Buffalo NY (2) and Elkhart IN (1). Value is for a sound stamp in the grade of fine-very fine.

423E A140 2c **rose red**, type I		—

Formerly No. 425c. Only one used example has been certified (by the Philatelic Foundation). It is well centered, has a machine cancel, and has small thinning and a crease.

Plates of 400 subjects in four panes of 100 each.

Type of plate number and imprint used for the 12 special 1c and 2c plates designed for the production of coil stamps.

1913-15   **Wmk. 190**   *Perf. 10*

424 A140 1c **green**, *Sept. 5, 1914*		2.50	.20
	bright green	2.50	.20
	deep green	2.50	.20
	yellowish green	2.50	.20
	Never hinged	5.25	
	On cover		.25
	Block of 4	10.50	1.50
	P# block of 6	60.00	
	Never hinged	90.00	
	Block of ten with imprint "COIL STAMPS" and number (6581-82, 85, 89)	150.00	
	Never hinged	250.00	
	Cracked plate		—
	Double transfer	4.75	
c.	Vert. pair, imperf. horiz.	2,800.	2,500.
	Never hinged	4,250.	
d.	Booklet pane of 6	5.25	7.50
	Never hinged	8.75	
e.	As "d," imperf.	2,000.	
f.	Vert. pair, imperf. between and with straight edge at top	9,000.	

For former Nos. 424a and 424b, see Nos. 423A and 423D.
All known examples of No. 424e are without gum.
The unique example of No. 424f is never hinged, and it is valued thus.

Earliest documented uses: Oct. 21, 1914 (No. 424); Dec. 18, 1913 (No. 424d single); Sept. 24, 1915 (block with "COIL STAMPS" and plate # in selvage).

425 A140 2c **rose red**, type I, *Sept. 5, 1914*		2.30	.20
	dark rose red	2.30	.20
	carmine rose	2.30	.20
	carmine	2.30	.20
	dark carmine	2.30	.20
	scarlet	2.30	.20
	red	2.30	.20
	Never hinged	4.75	
	On cover		.25
	Block of 4	9.50	1.50
	P# block of 6	40.00	
	Never hinged	75.00	
	Block of 10 with imprint "COIL STAMPS" and number (6568, 70-72)	160.00	
	Never hinged	250.00	
	Cracked plate	9.50	—
	Double transfer		—
e.	Booklet pane of 6, *1913*	17.50	25.00
	Never hinged	30.00	

For former Nos. 425c and 425d, see Nos. 423E and 423B.
The aniline inks used on some printings of Nos. 425, 426 and 435a caused a pink tinge to permeate the paper and appear on the back. These are called "pink backs."

Earliest documented uses: Oct. 27, 1914 (No. 425); Dec. 23, 1913 (No. 425e pair).

426 A140 3c **deep violet**, type I, *Sept. 18, 1914*		14.00	1.50
	violet	15.00	1.50
	bright violet	15.00	1.50
	reddish violet	15.00	1.50
	Never hinged	32.50	
	On cover		3.50

	Block of 4	57.50	12.50
	P# block of 6	250.00	
	Never hinged	400.00	

See "pink backs" note after No. 425.

Earliest documented use: Oct. 11, 1914.

427 A140 4c **brown**, *Sept. 7, 1914*		32.50	1.00
	dark brown	32.50	1.00
	orange brown	32.50	1.00
	yellowish brown	32.50	1.00
	Never hinged	75.00	
	On cover		5.25
	Block of 4	135.00	9.00
	P# block of 6	475.00	
	Never hinged	775.00	
	Double transfer	42.50	—

Earliest documented use: Jan. 2, 1915.

428 A140 5c **blue**, *Sept. 14, 1914*		32.50	1.00
	bright blue	32.50	1.00
	dark blue	32.50	1.00
	indigo blue	32.50	1.00
	Never hinged	75.00	
	On cover		3.00
	Block of 4	135.00	8.00
	P# block of 6	425.00	
	Never hinged	650.00	

For former No. 428a, see No. 423C.

Earliest documented use: Dec. 2, 1914.

429 A140 6c **red orange**, *Sept. 28, 1914*		45.00	2.00
	deep red orange	45.00	2.00
	pale red orange	45.00	2.00
	Never hinged	105.00	
	On cover		9.00
	Block of 4 (2mm spacing)	200.00	16.00
	Block of 4 (3mm spacing)	190.00	15.00
	P# block of 6, Impt. & star	425.00	
	Never hinged	725.00	
	P# block of 6	525.00	
	Never hinged	875.00	

430 A140 7c **black**, *Sept. 10, 1914*		90.00	5.00
	gray black	90.00	5.00
	intense black	90.00	5.00
	Never hinged	200.00	
	On cover		37.50
	Block of 4	400.00	40.00
	P# block of 6	1,000.	
	Never hinged	1,650.	

Earliest documented use: April 14, 1915.

431 A148 8c **pale olive green**, *Sept. 26, 1914*		35.00	3.00
	olive green	35.00	3.00
	Never hinged	82.50	
	On cover		8.00
	Block of 4	150.00	25.00

P# block of 6, Impt. & "A"		450.00	
Never hinged		725.00	
P# block of 6, "A"		550.00	
Never hinged		900.00	
Double transfer		—	—
a. Double impression		—	

Earliest documented use: Jan. 20, 1915.

432	A148	9c **salmon red,** *Oct. 6, 1914*	45.00	9.00
		dark salmon red	45.00	9.00
		Never hinged	105.00	
		On cover		27.50
		Block of 4	190.00	70.00
		P# block of 6	725.00	
		Never hinged	1,150.	

Earliest documented use: Oct. 7, 1915 (dated cancel on off-cover block of 4); Feb. 25, 1916 (on cover).

433	A148	10c **orange yellow,** *Sept. 9, 1914*	45.00	1.00
		golden yellow	45.00	1.00
		Never hinged	105.00	
		On cover		7.75
		Block of 4	190.00	6.50
		P# block of 6, Impt. & "A"	650.00	
		Never hinged	1,100.	
		P# block of 6, "A"	950.00	
		Never hinged	1,600.	
		P# block of 6	825.00	
		Never hinged	1,400.	

Earliest documented use: Nov. 13, 1914.

434	A148	11c **dark green,** *Aug. 11, 1915*	22.50	8.50
		bluish green	22.50	8.50
		Never hinged	55.00	
		On cover		25.00
		Block of 4	95.00	65.00
		P# block of 6	300.00	
		Never hinged	475.00	

435	A148	12c **claret brown,** *Sept. 10, 1914*	25.00	6.00
		deep claret brown	25.00	6.00
		Never hinged	60.00	
		On cover		17.50
		Block of 4	110.00	45.00
		P# block of 6	350.00	
		Never hinged	525.00	
		Double transfer	35.00	—
		Triple transfer	40.00	—
a.		12c **copper red**	30.00	7.00
		Never hinged	72.50	
		On cover		20.00
		Block of 4	130.00	50.00
		P# block of 6	350.00	
		Never hinged	550.00	

All so-called vertical pairs, imperf. between, have at least one perf. hole or "blind perfs" between the stamps.
See "pink backs" note after No. 425.

Earliest documented use: Feb. 22, 1915.

437	A148	15c **gray,** *Sept. 16, 1914*	125.00	7.25
		dark gray	125.00	7.25
		Never hinged	280.00	
		On cover		52.50
		Block of 4	550.00	70.00
		P# block of 6, Impt. & "A"	1,050.	
		Never hinged	2,100.	
		P# block of 6, "A"	1,225.	
		Never hinged	2,250.	
		P# block of 6	1,125.	
		Never hinged	2,150.	

Earliest documented use: Sept. 21, 1915.

438	A148	20c **ultramarine,** *Sept. 19, 1914*	200.00	6.00
		dark ultramarine	200.00	6.00
		Never hinged	460.00	
		On cover		*150.00*
		Block of 4	850.00	45.00
		P# block of 6	3,250.	
		Never hinged	*5,500.*	

Earliest documented use: Nov. 28, 1914.

439	A148	30c **orange red,** *Sept. 19, 1914*	240.00	17.50
		dark orange red	240.00	17.50
		Never hinged	550.00	
		On cover		*250.00*
		Block of 4	1,000.	135.00
		P# block of 6	*4,100.*	
		Never hinged	*6,750.*	

Earliest documented use: Feb. 13, 1914.

440	A148	50c **violet,** *Dec. 10, 1915*	525.00	17.50
		Never hinged	1,175.	
		On cover		*1,750.*
		Block of 4	2,200.	135.00
		P# block of 6	*15,000.*	
		Never hinged	—	
		Nos. 424-440 (16)	*1,481.*	*86.65*

COIL STAMPS

1914   ***Perf. 10 Horizontally***

441	A140	1c **green,** *Nov. 14, 1914*	1.00	*1.50*
		deep green	1.00	*1.50*
		Never hinged	2.00	
		On cover		2.75
		Pair	2.75	*7.00*
		Never hinged	5.75	
		Guide line pair	8.00	*27.50*
		Never hinged	17.50	
442	A140	2c carmine, type I, *July 22, 1914*	10.00	*45.00*
		deep carmine	10.00	*45.00*
		Never hinged	22.50	
		On cover		60.00
		Pair	25.00	*130.00*

		Never hinged	55.00	
		Guide line pair	60.00	*180.00*
		Never hinged	130.00	

1914   ***Perf. 10 Vertically***

443	A140	1c **green,** *May 29, 1914*	30.00	*45.00*
		deep green	30.00	*45.00*
		Never hinged	65.00	
		On cover		60.00
		Pair	75.00	*135.00*
		Never hinged	160.00	
		Guide line pair	155.00	*225.00*
		Never hinged	325.00	

Earliest documented use: June. 19, 1914.

444	A140	2c **carmine,** type I, *Apr. 25, 1914*	50.00	35.00
		deep carmine	50.00	35.00
		red	50.00	35.00
		Never hinged	125.00	
		On cover		52.50
		Pair	130.00	125.00
		Never hinged	275.00	
		Guide line pair	325.00	190.00
		Never hinged	700.00	
a.		2c **lake**		*1,250.*

Earliest documented use: May 19, 1914.

445	A140	3c **violet,** type I, *Dec. 18, 1914*	250.00	250.00
		deep violet	250.00	250.00
		Never hinged	575.00	
		On cover		*325.00*
		Pair	575.00	*750.00*
		Never hinged	1,250.	
		Guide line pair	1,300.	*3,000.*
		Never hinged	2,800.	

Earliest documented use: August 13, 1915.

446	A140	4c **brown,** *Oct. 2, 1914*	140.00	*150.00*
		Never hinged	325.00	
		On cover		*200.00*
		Pair	325.00	*425.00*
		Never hinged	700.00	
		Guide line pair	750.00	*1,150.*
		Never hinged	1,650.	

Earliest documented use: Aug. 4, 1915.

447	A140	5c **blue,** *July 30, 1914*	50.00	*115.00*
		Never hinged	110.00	
		On cover		*125.00*
		Pair	115.00	*375.00*
		Never hinged	240.00	
		Guide line pair	260.00	*950.00*
		Never hinged	550.00	

Earliest documented use: May 9, 1916.

Beware of plentiful fakes in the marketplace of Nos. 441-447, made by fraudulently perforating imperforate stamps or by fraudulently trimming perforations off fully perforated stamps.

ROTARY PRESS STAMPS

The Rotary Press Stamps are printed from plates that are curved to fit around a cylinder. This curvature produces stamps that are slightly larger, either horizontally or vertically, than those printed from flat plates. Designs of stamps from flat plates measure about 18½-19mm wide by 22mm high.

When the impressions are placed sidewise on the curved plates the designs are 19½-20mm wide; when they are placed vertically the designs are 22½ to 23mm high. A line of color (not a guide line) shows where the curved plates meet or join on the press. Rotary Press Coil Stamps were printed from plates of 170 subjects for stamps coiled sidewise, and from plates of 150 subjects for stamps coiled endwise.

Double paper varieties of Rotary Press stamps are not listed in this catalogue. Collectors are referred to the note on "Rotary Press Double Paper" in the "Information for Collectors" in the front of the catalogue.

ROTARY PRESS COIL STAMPS
Stamp designs: 18½-19x22½mm

1915   ***Perf. 10 Horizontally***

448	A140	1c **green,** *Dec., 1915*	7.50	*17.50*
		light green	7.50	*17.50*
		Never hinged	16.00	
		On cover		22.50
		Pair	17.50	*50.00*
		Never hinged	40.00	
		Joint line pair	60.00	*115.00*
		Never hinged	125.00	

Earliest documented use: Dec. 11, 1915.

TYPE II

TWO CENTS.
Type II. Shading lines in ribbons as on type I.
The toga button, rope and rope shading lines are heavy.
The shading lines of the face at the lock of hair end in a strong vertical curved line.
Used on rotary press printings only.

TYPE III

Type III. Two lines of shading in the curves of the ribbons.
Other characteristics similar to type II.
Used on rotary press printings only.

449	A140	2c **red,** type I, *1915*	2,750.	650.00
		Never hinged	6,000.	
		carmine rose, type I	3,000.	
		On cover, type I		*1,350.*
		Pair, type I	6,500.	*5,250.*
		Never hinged	*13,500.*	
		Joint line pair, type I	*14,500.*	*25,000.*
		Never hinged	*30,000.*	

Earliest documented uses: Oct. 29, 1915 (on cover front or dated cancel on off-cover stamp); Nov. 4, 1915 (on cover).

450	A140	2c **carmine,** type III, *1915*	12.50	*22.50*
		carmine rose, type III	12.50	*22.50*
		red, type III	12.50	*22.50*
		Never hinged	27.50	
		On cover, type III		32.50
		Pair, type III	30.00	*67.50*
		Never hinged	65.00	
		Joint line pair, type III	230.00	*190.00*
		Never hinged	550.00	

Earliest documented use: Dec. 21, 1915.

1914-16   ***Perf. 10 Vertically***
Stamp designs: 19½-20x22mm

452	A140	1c **green,** *Nov. 11, 1914*	10.00	*17.50*
		Never hinged	21.00	
		On cover		22.50
		Pair	25.00	*55.00*
		Never hinged	55.00	
		Joint line pair	75.00	*100.00*
		Never hinged	160.00	

Earliest documented use: Nov. 25, 1914.

453	A140	2c **carmine rose,** type I, *July 3, 1914*	150.00	17.50
		Never hinged	325.00	
		On cover, type I		22.50
		Pair, type I	325.00	55.00
		Never hinged	675.00	
		Joint line pair, type I	725.00	500.00
		Never hinged	1,550.	
		Cracked plate, type I	—	—

Earliest documented use: Sept. 26, 1914.

454	A140	2c **red,** type II, *June, 1915*	75.00	22.50
		carmine, type II	75.00	22.50
		Never hinged	170.00	
		On cover, type II		40.00
		Pair, type II	175.00	70.00
		Never hinged	375.00	
		Joint line pair, type II	425.00	400.00
		Never hinged	900.00	

Earliest documented use: July 7, 1915.

455	A140	2c **carmine,** type III, *Dec. 1915*	8.50	3.50
		carmine rose, type III	8.50	3.50
		Never hinged	19.00	
		On cover, type III		5.00
		Pair, type III	21.00	27.50

Never hinged	45.00	
Joint line pair, type III	50.00	100.00
Never hinged	110.00	

Earliest documented use: Dec. 15, 1915.

Fraudulently altered examples of Type III (Nos. 455, 488, 492 and 540) have had one line of shading scraped off to make them resemble Type II (Nos. 454, 487, 491 and 539).

456 A140 3c **violet**, type I, *Feb. 2, 1916*	250.00	170.00
deep violet	250.00	170.00
red violet	250.00	170.00
Never hinged	525.00	
On cover		250.00
Pair	600.00	650.00
Never hinged	1,250.	
Joint line pair	1,250.	1,800.
Never hinged	2,600.	

Earliest documented use: Apr. 13, 1916.

457 A140 4c **brown**, *1915*	25.00	30.00
light brown	25.00	30.00
Never hinged	55.00	
On cover		50.00
Pair	60.00	95.00
Never hinged	130.00	
Joint line pair	150.00	230.00
Never hinged	325.00	
Cracked plate	35.00	—

Earliest documented use: Nov. 5, 1915.

458 A140 5c **blue**, *Mar. 9, 1916*	30.00	30.00
Never hinged	65.00	
On cover		50.00
Pair	72.50	95.00
Never hinged	160.00	
Joint line pair	175.00	230.00
Never hinged	375.00	
Double transfer	—	—

Earliest documented use: Apr. 6, 1916.

Horizontal Coil

1914, June 30 — *Imperf.*

459 A140 2c **carmine**, type I	175.	1,300.
Never hinged	275.	
Pair	360.	3,500.
Never hinged	575.	
Joint line pair, with crease	550.	
Never hinged	950.	
Joint line pair, without crease	850.	21,000.
Never hinged	1,500.	

Most line pairs of No. 459 are creased. The value for joint line pair with crease is for a pair creased vertically between the stamps, but not touching the design.

When the value for a used stamp is higher than the unused value, the stamp must have a contemporaneous cancel. Valuable stamps of this type should be accompanied by certificates of authenticity issued by recognized expertizing committees. The used value for No. 459 is for an example with such a certificate.

Beware of examples of No. 453 with perforations fraudulently trimmed to resemble single examples of No. 459.

Earliest documented use: Dec. 1914 (dated cancel on a used joint line pair, off cover).

FLAT PLATE PRINTINGS

1915 **Wmk. 191** *Perf. 10*

460 A148 $1 **violet black**, *Feb. 8*	775.	150.
Never hinged	1,750.	
On cover		12,000.
Block of 4	3,500.	750.
Margin block of 4, arrow, R or L	3,600.	
P# block of 6, Impt. & "A"	13,500.	
Never hinged	20,000.	
Double transfer (5782 L. 66)	850.	175.

Earliest documented uses: May 25, 1916 (dated cancel on stamp on mailing tag); June 2, 1916 (unique usage on cover is from Shanghai, China).

Wmk. 190 *Perf. 11*

461 A140 2c **pale car. red**, type I, *June 17*	140.	360.
Never hinged	325.	
On cover		1,200.
Block of 4	600.	3,000.
P# block of 6	1,500.	
Never hinged	2,600.	

Beware of fraudulently perforated examples of No. 409 being offered as No. 461.

See note on used stamps following No. 459.

Earliest documented use: June 24, 1915.

VALUES FOR VERY FINE STAMPS
Please note: Stamps are valued in the grade of Very Fine unless otherwise indicated.

FLAT PLATE PRINTINGS

Plates of 400 subjects in four panes of 100 each for all values 1c to 50c inclusive.

Plates of 200 subjects in two panes of 100 each for $1, $2 and $5 denominations.

The Act of Oct. 3, 1917, effective Nov. 2, 1917, created a 3 cent rate. Local rate, 2 cents.

1916-17 **Unwmk.** *Perf. 10*

462 A140 1c **green**, *Sept. 27, 1916*	7.00	.35
light green	7.00	.35
dark green	7.00	.35
bluish green	7.00	.35
Never hinged	16.00	
On cover		.50
Block of 4	30.00	3.25
P# block of 6	160.00	
Never hinged	275.00	
Experimental bureau precancel, New Orleans		10.00
Experimental bureau precancel, Springfield, Mass.		10.00
Experimental bureau precancel, Augusta, Me.		25.00
a. Booklet pane of 6, *Oct. 15, 1916*	9.50	12.50
Never hinged	16.00	

Earliest documented use: Apr. 5, 1917 (No. 462a single).

463 A140 2c **carmine**, type I, *Sept. 1916*	4.50	.40
dark carmine	4.50	.40
rose red	4.50	.40
Never hinged	10.00	
On cover		.45
Block of 4	20.00	3.50
P# block of 6	150.00	
Never hinged	250.00	
Double transfer	6.50	—
Experimental bureau precancel, New Orleans		500.00
Experimental bureau precancel, Springfield, Mass.		22.50
a. Booklet pane of 6, *Oct. 8, 1916*	110.00	110.00
Never hinged	180.00	

See No. 467 for P# block of 6 from plate 7942.

Earliest documented uses: Sept. 12, 1916 (No. 463).

464 A140 3c **violet**, type I, *Nov. 11, 1916*	70.00	19.00
deep violet	70.00	19.00
Never hinged	160.00	
On cover		42.50
Block of 4	300.00	150.00
P# block of 6	1,350.	
Never hinged	2,250.	
Double transfer in "CENTS"	90.00	—
Experimental bureau precancel, New Orleans		1,000.
Experimental bureau precancel, Springfield, Mass.		200.00

Beware of fraudulently perforated examples of No. 483 being offered as No. 464.

Earliest documented use: Mar. 9, 1917.

465 A140 4c **orange brown**, *Oct. 7, 1916*	40.00	2.50
deep brown	40.00	2.50
brown	40.00	2.50
Never hinged	90.00	
On cover		11.00
Block of 4	170.00	25.00
P# block of 6	650.00	
Never hinged	1,100.	
Double transfer	—	—
Experimental bureau precancel, Springfield, Mass.		175.00

466 A140 5c **blue**, *Oct. 17, 1916*	70.00	2.50
dark blue	70.00	2.50
Never hinged	160.00	
On cover		13.00
Block of 4	290.00	22.50
P# block of 6	950.00	
Never hinged	1,600.	
Experimental bureau precancel, Springfield, Mass.		175.00

Earliest documented use: Dec. 7, 1916.

467 A140 5c **carmine** (error in plate of 2c)	475.00	850.00
Never hinged	950.00	
On cover		5,000.
Block of 9, #467 in middle	1,050.	1,600.
Never hinged	1,700.	
Block of 12, two middle stamps #467	1,950.	3,000.
Never hinged	3,100.	
P# block of 6 2c stamps (#463), P#7942	140.00	
Never hinged	250.00	

No. 467 is an error caused by using a 5c transfer roll in re-entering three subjects: 7942 UL 74, 7942 UL 84, 7942 LR 18; the balance of the subjects on the plate being normal 2c entries. No. 467 imperf. is listed as No. 485. The error perf 11 on unwatermarked paper is No. 505.

The first value given for the error in blocks of 9 and 12 is for blocks with the error stamp(s) never hinged. The second value given is for blocks in which all stamps are never hinged. See note on used stamps following No. 459.

Earliest documented use: May 22, 1917.

468 A140 6c **red orange**, *Oct. 10, 1916*	85.00	9.00
Never hinged	190.00	
On cover		37.50
Block of 4	360.00	70.00
P# block of 6	1,350.	
Never hinged	2,500.	
Double transfer	—	—
Experimental bureau precancel, New Orleans		2,500.
Experimental bureau precancel, Springfield, Mass.		175.00

Earliest documented use: April 19, 1917.

469 A140 7c **black**, *Oct. 10, 1916*	120.00	15.00
gray black	120.00	15.00
Never hinged	270.00	

On cover		45.00
Block of 4	500.00	125.00
P# block of 6	1,350.	
Never hinged	2,500.	
Experimental bureau precancel, Springfield, Mass.		175.00

Earliest documented use: Feb. 19, 1917.

470 A148 8c **olive green**, *Nov. 13, 1916*	55.00	8.00
dark olive green	55.00	8.00
Never hinged	125.00	
On cover		27.50
Block of 4	230.00	65.00
P# block of 6, Impt. & "A"	550.00	
Never hinged	900.00	
P# block of 6, "A"	600.00	
Never hinged	1,050.	
Experimental bureau precancel, Springfield, Mass.		165.00

Earliest documented use: Jan. 26, 1917 (dated cancel on off-cover stamp); Feb. 13, 1917 (on cover).

471 A148 9c **salmon red**, *Nov. 16, 1916*	55.00	18.50
Never hinged	125.00	
On cover		42.50
Block of 4	230.00	135.00
P# block of 6	750.00	
Never hinged	1,250.	
Experimental bureau precancel, Springfield, Mass.		150.00

Earliest documented use: Dec. 27, 1917.

472 A148 10c **orange yellow**, *Oct. 17, 1916*	100.00	2.50
Never hinged	230.00	
On cover		8.50
Block of 4	425.00	16.50
P# block of 6	1,350.	
Never hinged	2,250.	
Experimental bureau precancel, Springfield, Mass.		160.00

Earliest documented use: Oct. 24, 1916.

473 A148 11c **dark green**, *Nov. 16, 1916*	40.00	18.50
Never hinged	90.00	
On cover		47.50
Block of 4	170.00	140.00
P# block of 6	360.00	
Never hinged	625.00	
Experimental bureau precancel, Springfield, Mass.		575.00

Earliest documented use: Apr. 13, 1917.

474 A148 12c **claret brown**, *Oct. 1916*	50.00	7.50
Never hinged	115.00	
On cover		22.50
Block of 4	220.00	55.00
P# block of 6	625.00	
Never hinged	1,050.	
Double transfer	65.00	8.50
Triple transfer	77.50	11.00
Experimental bureau precancel, Springfield, Mass.		200.00

Earliest documented uses: Oct. 6, 1916 (dated cancel on off-cover pair); Oct. 13, 1916 (on cover).

475 A148 15c **gray**, *Nov. 16, 1916*	180.00	16.00
dark gray	180.00	16.00
Never hinged	400.00	
On cover		87.50
Block of 4	775.00	125.00
P# block of 6	3,000.	
Never hinged	5,250.	
P# block of 6, Impt. & "A"		
Experimental bureau precancel, Springfield, Mass.		150.00

Earliest documented use: Mar. 2, 1917.

476 A148 20c **light ultramarine**, *Dec. 5, 1916*	225.00	17.50
ultramarine	225.00	17.50
Never hinged	525.00	
On cover		725.00
Block of 4	950.00	135.00
P# block of 6	3,600.	
Never hinged	6,000.	
Experimental bureau precancel, Springfield, Mass.		125.00

476A A148 30c **orange red**	3,250.	
Never hinged	6,500.	
Block of 4	14,500.	
Never hinged	32,000.	
P# block of 6, never hinged	60,000.	

No. 476A is valued in the grade of fine.

477 A148 50c **light violet**, *Mar. 2, 1917*	1,000.	80.00
Never hinged	2,200.	
On cover		2,250.
Block of 4	4,400.	575.00
P# block of 6	57,500.	
Never hinged		

Earliest documented use: Aug. 31, 1917.

478 A148 $1 **violet black**, *Dec. 22, 1916*	700.00	25.00
Never hinged	1,550.	
On cover		3,000.
Block of 4	3,100.	175.00
Margin block of 4, arrow, R or L	3,250.	
P# block of 6, Impt. & "A"	13,500.	
Never hinged	21,000.	
Double transfer (5782 L 66)	750.00	32.50

Earliest documented use: May 24, 1917 (on large part of parcel label).

TYPES OF 1902-03 ISSUE

1917, Mar. 22	**Unwmk.**	**Perf. 10**
479 A127 $2 **dark blue**	225.00	42.50
Never hinged	500.00	
On cover (other than first flight or Zeppelin)		1,250.
On first flight cover		350.00
On Zeppelin flight cover		750.00
Block of 4	1,000.	325.00
Margin block of 4, arrow, R or L	1,150.	
P# block of 6	4,250.	
Never hinged	6,750.	
Double transfer		

Earliest documented use (on large piece of reg'd parcel wrapper): Apr. 6, 1917.

480 A128 $5 **light green**	180.00	40.00
Never hinged	390.00	
On cover		1,250.
Block of 4	800.00	300.00
Margin block of 4, arrow, R or L	900.00	
P# block of 6	3,300.	
Never hinged	5,500.	

Earliest documented use: Apr. 6, 1917 (on large piece of reg'd parcel wrapper).

Earliest documented use dates for imperforates are for the imperforate sheet stamps, not for imperforate stamps with vending and affixing machine perforations or for flat plate imperforate coil stamps. EDU dates for VAMP and flat plate imperf coil stamps are shown in their respective sections later in the catalogue.

1916-17		**Imperf.**
481 A140 1c **green,** *Nov. 1916*	.95	.95
bluish green	.95	.95
deep green	.95	.95
Never hinged	1.90	
On cover		1.50
Pair	2.00	2.00
Never hinged	4.00	
Block of 4	4.00	4.00
Corner margin block of 4	4.25	4.25
Margin block of 4, arrow	4.40	4.40
Center line block	8.50	8.50
Never hinged	14.00	
P# block of 6	30.00	—
Never hinged	45.00	
Margin block of 6, Electrolytic (Pl. 13376)	450.00	
Never hinged	800.00	
Margin block of 6, Electrolytic (Pl. 13377)	750.00	
Never hinged	1,250.	
Double transfer	2.50	2.50

Earliest documented use: Nov. 17, 1916.

During September, 1921, the Bureau of Engraving and Printing issued a 1c stamp printed from experimental electrolytic plates made in accordance with patent granted to George U. Rose. Tests at that time did not prove satisfactory and the method was discontinued. Four plates were made, viz., 13376, 13377, 13389 and 13390 from which stamps were issued. They are difficult to distinguish from the normal varieties. (See No. 498).

TYPE Ia

TWO CENTS

Type Ia. The design characteristics are similar to type I except that all of the lines of the design are stronger.

The toga button, toga rope and rope and rope shading lines are heavy.

The latter characteristics are those of type II, which, however, occur only on impressions from rotary plates.

Used only on flat plates 10208 and 10209.

482 A140 2c **carmine,** type I, *Dec. 8, 1916*	1.30	1.30
deep carmine	1.30	1.30
carmine rose	1.30	1.30
deep rose	1.30	1.30
Never hinged	2.60	
On cover		2.50
Pair	2.75	2.75
Never hinged	5.50	
Block of 4	5.50	6.50
Corner margin block of 4	5.75	6.75
Margin block of 4, arrow	6.00	7.00
Center line block	8.50	10.00
Never hinged	14.00	

P# block of 6	30.00	—
Never hinged	45.00	
Cracked plate		—

Earliest documented use: Dec. 16, 1916.

See No. 485 for P# block of 6 from plate 7942.

482A A140 2c **deep rose,** type Ia	—	65,000.
On cover		70,000.
Pair		140,000.

Earliest documented use: Feb. 17, 1920.

The imperforate, type Ia, was issued but all known examples were privately perforated with large oblong perforations at the sides (Schermack type III).
The No. 482A pair is unique.

TYPE II

THREE CENTS

Type II. The top line of the toga rope is strong and the rope shading lines are heavy and complete.
The line between the lips is heavy.
Used on both flat plate and rotary press printings.

483 A140 3c **violet,** type I, *Oct. 13, 1917*	10.00	10.00
light violet	10.00	10.00
Never hinged	22.00	
On cover		25.00
Pair	22.00	22.50
Never hinged	47.50	
Block of 4	45.00	45.00
Corner margin block of 4	47.50	47.50
Margin block of 4, arrow	50.00	50.00
Center line block	75.00	75.00
Never hinged	135.00	
P# block of 6	115.00	—
Never hinged	190.00	
Double transfer	17.50	—
Triple transfer		—

Earliest documented use: Nov. 8, 1917.

484 A140 3c **violet,** type II	8.00	8.00
deep violet	8.00	8.00
Never hinged	18.00	
On cover		14.00
Pair	17.00	17.00
Never hinged	36.00	
Block of 4	35.00	35.00
Corner margin block of 4	37.50	37.50
Margin block of 4, arrow	40.00	40.00
Center line block	67.50	67.50
Never hinged	120.00	
P# block of 6	87.50	—
Never hinged	150.00	
Double transfer	12.50	

Earliest documented use: Apr. 30, 1918.

485 A140 5c **carmine** (error), *Mar. 1917*	12,000.	
Never hinged	20,000.	
Block of 9, #485 in middle	22,500.	
Never hinged	32,500.	
Block of 12, two middle stamps #485	42,500.	
Never hinged	52,500.	
P# block of six 2c stamps (#482), P#7942	130.00	
Never hinged	220.00	

No. 485 is usually seen either as the center stamp in a block of 9 with 8 No. 482 (the first value given being with No. 485 never hinged) or as two center stamps in a block of 12 (the first value given being with both examples of No. 485 never hinged). A second value is given for each block with all stamps in the block never hinged.
See note under No. 467.

ROTARY PRESS COIL STAMPS
(See note over No. 448)

1916-18		**Perf. 10 Horizontally**
Stamp designs: 18½-19x22½mm		
486 A140 1c **green,** *Jan. 1918*	.85	.85
yellowish green	.85	.85
Never hinged	1.75	
On cover		1.15
Pair	2.00	2.50
Never hinged	4.25	
Joint line pair	4.50	12.50
Never hinged	9.50	
Cracked plate		—
Double transfer	2.25	—

Earliest documented use: June 30, 1918.

487 A140 2c **carmine,** type II, *Nov. 15, 1916*	12.50	14.00
Never hinged	26.00	
On cover		19.00
Pair	30.00	37.50

Never hinged	65.00	
Joint line pair	110.00	125.00
Never hinged	250.00	
Cracked plate		—

Earliest documented use: Sept. 21, 1917.

(See note after No. 455)

488 A140 2c **carmine,** type III, *1916*	3.00	5.00
carmine rose	3.00	5.00
Never hinged	6.50	
On cover		7.00
Pair	8.00	17.50
Never hinged	17.50	
Joint line pair	40.00	95.00
Never hinged	90.00	
Cracked plate	12.50	10.00

Earliest documented use: Apr. 25, 1917.

489 A140 3c **violet,** type I, *Oct. 10, 1917*	4.50	2.25
dull violet	4.50	2.25
bluish violet	4.50	2.25
Never hinged	10.00	
On cover		3.50
Pair	10.50	9.00
Never hinged	22.50	
Joint line pair	32.50	27.50
Never hinged	70.00	

Earliest documented use: Dec. 29, 1917.

Rosette plate crack on head

1916-22		**Perf. 10 Vertically**
Stamp designs: 19½-20x22mm		
490 A140 1c **green,** *Nov. 17, 1916*	.50	.60
yellowish green	.50	.60
Never hinged	1.05	
On cover		.80
Pair	1.25	2.25
Never hinged	2.60	
Joint line pair	3.25	9.00
Never hinged	7.00	
Double transfer	—	—
Cracked plate (horizontal)	7.50	—
Cracked plate (vertical) retouched	9.00	—
Rosette plate crack on head	60.00	—

Earliest documented use: Jan. 3, 1917 (dated cancel on off-cover pair); March 6, 1917 (on cover).

491 A140 2c **carmine,** type II, *Nov. 17, 1916*	2,500.	750.00
Never hinged	5,250.	
On cover, type II		1,100.
Pair, type II	5,750.	3,750.
Never hinged	12,500.	
Joint line pair, type II	13,000.	15,000.
Never hinged	26,000.	

Earliest documented use: Jan. 2, 1917.
See note after No. 455.

492 A140 2c **carmine,** type III	9.00	1.00
carmine rose, type III	9.00	1.00
Never hinged	19.00	
On cover, type III		1.40
Pair, type III	21.50	5.00
Never hinged	45.00	
Joint line pair, type III	55.00	25.00
Never hinged	115.00	
Double transfer, type III	—	—
Cracked plate	—	—

Earliest documented use: April 1, 1917.

493 A140 3c **violet,** type I, *July 23, 1917*	14.00	4.50
reddish violet, type I	14.00	4.50
Never hinged	30.00	
On cover, type I		8.00
Pair, type I	35.00	12.50
Never hinged	75.00	
Joint line pair, type I	110.00	75.00
Never hinged	230.00	

Earliest documented use: Nov. 2, 1917.

494 A140 3c **violet,** type II, *Feb. 4, 1918*	10.00	2.50
dull violet, type II	10.00	2.50
gray violet, type II	10.00	2.50
Never hinged	21.50	
On cover, type II		2.40
Pair, type II	24.00	9.00
Never hinged	50.00	
Joint line pair, type II	75.00	17.50
Never hinged	160.00	

Earliest documented use: Apr. 16, 1918.

495 A140 4c **orange brown,** *Apr. 15, 1917*	10.00	7.00
Never hinged	21.50	
On cover		10.00
Pair	24.00	20.00
Never hinged	50.00	

Joint line pair		75.00	35.00
Never hinged		160.00	
Cracked plate		25.00	—
Earliest documented use: June 20, 1917.			
496 A140 5c **blue,** Jan. 15, 1919		3.25	2.50
Never hinged		7.00	
On cover			3.00
Pair		8.00	10.00
Never hinged		17.50	
Joint line pair		30.00	17.50
Never hinged		65.00	
Earliest documented use: April 15, 1919.			
497 A148 10c **orange yellow,** Jan. 31, 1922		19.00	17.50
Never hinged		40.00	
On cover			22.50
Pair		45.00	57.50
Never hinged		95.00	
Joint line pair		130.00	180.00
Never hinged		280.00	
Earliest documented use: Jan. 31, 1922 (FDC).			

Blind Perfs

Listings of imperforate-between varieties are for examples which show no trace of "blind perfs," traces of impressions from the perforating pins which do not cut into the paper.

Some unused stamps have had the gum removed to eliminate the impressions from the perforating pins. These stamps do not qualify as the listed varieties.

FLAT PLATE PRINTINGS
Plates of 400 subjects in four panes of 100.
TYPES OF 1913-15 ISSUE

1917-19	**Unwmk.**	**Perf. 11**	
498 A140 1c **green,** Mar. 1917	.35	.25	
light green		.35	.25
dark green		.35	.25
yellowish green		.35	.25
Never hinged		.75	
On cover			.30
Block of 4		1.40	1.50
P# block of 6		22.50	
Never hinged		35.00	
Margin block of 6, Electrolytic (Pl, 13376-7, 13389-90)			
See note after No. 481		1,000.	
Never hinged		1,750.	
Cracked plate (10656 UL and 10645 LR)		7.50	—
Double transfer		5.50	2.00
a. Vertical pair, imperf. horiz.		900.00	
Never hinged		1,750.	
b. Horizontal pair, imperf. between		575.00	
Never hinged		1,250.	
c. Vertical pair, imperf. between		700.00	
d. Double impression		250.00	4,000.
e. Booklet pane of 6, March 1917		2.50	2.00
Never hinged		4.25	
f. Booklet pane of 30, Aug. 1917		1,150.	
Never hinged		1,800.	
g. Perf. 10 at top or bottom		15,000.	45,000.
Never hinged		22,500.	

Earliest documented use: March 30, 1917 (No. 498e booklet pair); Aug. 8, 1917 (No. 498f single).

No. 498g also known as a transitional stamp gauging 10 at left bottom and 11 at right bottom (bottom center stamp in a plate block of 6).

No. 499g, Stamp 15mm Wide

499 A140 2c **rose,** type I, Mar. 1917	.35	.25	
dark rose, type I		.35	.25
carmine rose, type I		.35	.25
deep rose, type I		.35	.25
Never hinged		.75	
On cover, type I			.30
Block of 4, type I		1.40	1.50
P# block of 6, type I		22.50	
Never hinged		35.00	
Cracked plate, type I			—
Recut in hair, type I		1,500.	2,300.
Never hinged		3,000.	
Double transfer, type I		6.00	—
a. Vertical pair, imperf. horiz., type I		600.00	
Never hinged		1,200.	
b. Horiz. pair, imperf. vert., type I		375.00	225.00

c. Vert. pair, imperf. btwn., type I		750.00	
Never hinged		1,000.	300.00
e. Booklet pane of 6, type I, Mar. 31, 1917		4.00	2.50
Never hinged		6.75	
f. Booklet pane of 30, type I, Aug. 1917	28,000.	—	
Never hinged		38,000.	
g. Double impression, type I		200.00	—
Never hinged		400.00	
On cover			750.00
As "g," stamp 15mm wide			
h. 2c **lake,** type I		500.00	350.00
Never hinged		1,000.	
On cover			—

No. 499b is valued in the grade of fine.
See No. 505 for P# block of 6 from plate 7942.
No. 499h occurs in two different lake shades. The true lake is similar to the lake on other lake shades noted elsewhere in this catalogue. A somewhat more common lake shade is known as "Boston lake," and it is a very distinctive and duller lake shade. Certificates of authenticity recommended for these and all listed lake shades.

Earliest documented uses: Mar. 27, 1917 (No. 499); July 19, 1917 (No. 499e single); Aug. 7, 1917 (No. 499f single).

500 A140 2c **deep rose,** type Ia	250.00	240.00	
Never hinged		550.00	
On cover, type Ia			650.00
Block of 4, type Ia		1,100.	1,500.
P# block of 6, type Ia		2,000.	
Never hinged		3,750.	—
P# block of 6, two stamps type I (P# 10208 LL)		15,000.	
Never hinged		22,500.	
Pair, types I and Ia (10208 LL 95 or 96)		1,250.	

Earliest documented use: Dec. 15, 1919.
No. 500 exists with imperforate top sheet margin. Examples have been altered by trimming perforations. Some also have faked Schermack perfs.

501 A140 3c **light violet,** type I, Mar. 1917	10.00	.40	
violet, type I		10.00	.40
dark violet, type I		10.00	.40
reddish violet, type I		10.00	.40
Never hinged		23.00	
On cover, type I			.50
Block of 4, type I		42.50	4.00
P# block of 6, type I		140.00	
Never hinged		240.00	
Double transfer, type I		12.00	
b. Bklt. pane of 6, type I, Oct. 17, 1917		75.00	60.00
Never hinged		125.00	
c. Vert. pair, imper. horiz., type I		2,500.	
Never hinged		3,500.	
d. Double impression		3,500.	3,500.
Never hinged		5,500.	

Earliest documented uses: June 5, 1917 (No. 501); Feb. 8, 1918 (No. 501b single).

No. 501d is valued in the grade of fine.

502 A140 3c **dark violet,** type II	13.00	.75	
violet, type II		13.00	.75
Never hinged		30.00	
On cover, type II			1.00
Block of 4, type II		55.00	5.50
P# block of 6, type II		160.00	
Never hinged		275.00	
b. Bklt. pane of 6, type II, Feb. 25, 1918		60.00	55.00
Never hinged		100.00	
c. Vert. pair, imperf. horiz., type II		1,400.	750.00
Never hinged		2,750.	
On cover			1,500.
d. Double impression		850.00	750.00
Never hinged		1,700.	
e. Perf. 10 at top or bottom		15,000.	12,500.
Never hinged		21,500.	

Earliest documented uses: Jan. 30, 1918 (No. 502); June 12, 1918 (No. 502b single).

503 A140 4c **brown,** Mar. 1917	9.00	.40	
dark brown		9.00	.40
orange brown		9.00	.40
yellow brown		9.00	.40
Never hinged		20.00	
On cover			2.10
Block of 4		37.50	3.50
P# block of 6		150.00	
Never hinged		250.00	
Double transfer		14.00	—
b. Double impression			
504 A140 5c **blue,** Mar. 1917	8.00	.35	
light blue		8.00	.35
dark blue		8.00	.35
Never hinged		18.00	
On cover			.45
Block of 4		35.00	3.00
P# block of 6		140.00	
Never hinged		225.00	
Double transfer		10.00	—
a. Horizontal pair, imperf. between		20,000.	
b. Double impression		2,000.	900.00

Earliest documented use: June 5, 1917.

505 A140 5c **rose** (error)	300.00	550.00	
Never hinged		625.00	
On cover			2,250.
Block of 9, middle stamp #505		650.00	1,100.
Never hinged		1,000.	
Block of 12, two middle stamps #505		1,300.	2,100.
Never hinged		2,000.	

Margin block of six 2c stamps
　(#499), P# 7942　　40.00
　　Never hinged　　　70.00
Earliest documented use: Mar. 27, 1917.

Value notes under No. 467 also apply to No. 505.

506 A140　6c **red orange,** *Mar. 1917*　12.00　.40
　　　orange　　　　　　　　12.00　.40
　　　Never hinged　　　　　27.50
　　　On cover　　　　　　　　　　2.50
　　　Block of 4　　　　　　　52.50　4.00
　　　P# block of 6　　　　　180.00
　　　　Never hinged　　　　300.00　—
　　a.　Perf. 10 at top or bottom　*5,000.　9,000.*

No. 506a also exists as a transitional stamp gauging partly perf 10 and partly perf 11 at top. Value thus the same as normal 506a.

507 A140　7c **black,** *Mar. 1917*　26.00　1.25
　　　gray black　　　　　　26.00　1.25
　　　intense black　　　　26.00　1.25
　　　Never hinged　　　　60.00
　　　On cover　　　　　　　　　　7.75
　　　Block of 4　　　　　110.00　12.50
　　　P# block of 6　　　　250.00
　　　　Never hinged　　　450.00　—
　　a.　Perf. 10 at top　*20,000.*　—

Only two unused and one used example of No. 507a are recorded. The two unused stamps are the top two stamps in a block of four with two normal No. 507.

508 A148　8c **olive bister,** *Mar. 1917*　12.00　.65
　　　dark olive green　　　12.00　.65
　　　olive green　　　　　12.00　.65
　　　Never hinged　　　　27.50
　　　On cover　　　　　　　　　　2.75
　　　Block of 4　　　　　50.00　6.50
　　　P# block of 6, Impt. & "A"　170.00
　　　　Never hinged　　　285.00
　　　P# block of 6, "A"　　220.00
　　　　Never hinged　　　370.00
　　　P# block of 6　　　　140.00
　　　　Never hinged　　　240.00
　　b.　Vertical pair, imperf. between　—　—
　　c.　Perf. 10 at top or bottom　*16,000.*

509 A148　9c **salmon red,** *Mar. 1917*　12.00　1.75
　　　salmon　　　　　　　12.00　1.75
　　　Never hinged　　　　27.50
　　　On cover　　　　　　　　　13.00
　　　Block of 4　　　　　52.50　19.00
　　　P# block of 6　　　　150.00
　　　　Never hinged　　　250.00
　　　Double transfer　　　19.00　4.50
　　a.　Perf. 10 at top or bottom　*4,250.　7,000.*
　　　　Never hinged　　　*6,750.*

No. 509a also exists as a transitional stamp gauging partly perf 10 and partly perf 11 at top or bottom. Value thus the same as normal 509a.

510 A148　10c **orange yellow,** *Mar. 1917*　16.00　.25
　　　golden yellow　　　　16.00　.25
　　　Never hinged　　　　36.00
　　　On cover　　　　　　　　　2.00
　　　Block of 4　　　　　67.50　2.00
　　　P# block of 6, "A"　　290.00
　　　　Never hinged　　　475.00
　　　P# block of 6　　　　200.00
　　　　Never hinged　　　325.00
　　a.　10c **brown yellow**　*1,500.*
　　　　Never hinged　　　*2,500.*
Earliest documented use: Mar. 27, 1917.

511 A148　11c **light green,** *May 1917*　8.00　2.50
　　　green　　　　　　　　8.00　2.50
　　　Never hinged　　　　18.00
　　　dark green　　　　　9.00　2.50
　　　Never hinged　　　　18.00
　　　On cover　　　　　　　　　8.50
　　　Block of 4　　　　　35.00　22.50
　　　P# block of 6　　　　150.00
　　　　Never hinged　　　260.00
　　　Double transfer　　　12.00　3.25
　　a.　Perf. 10 at top or bottom　*5,000.　4,500.*
　　　　Never hinged　　　*7,500.*
　　　Block of 4, two stamps No.
　　　　511a　　　　　　—　*10,000.*

No. 511a also exists as a transitional stamp gauging partly perf 10 and partly perf 11 at top or bottom. Value thus the same as normal 511a.

512 A148　12c **claret brown,** *May 1917*　8.00　.40
　　　Never hinged　　　　18.00
　　　On cover　　　　　　　　　4.00
　　　Block of 4　　　　　35.00　3.75
　　　P# block of 6　　　　150.00
　　　　Never hinged　　　260.00
　　　Double transfer　　　12.00　—
　　　Triple transfer　　　20.00　—
　　a.　12c **brown carmine**　9.00　.50
　　　　Never hinged　　　20.00
　　　On cover　　　　　　　　　4.50
　　　Block of 4　　　　　37.50　4.50
　　　P# block of 6　　　　150.00
　　　　Never hinged　　　260.00
　　b.　Perf. 10 at top or bottom　*17,500.　10,000.*
　　　On cover
Earliest documented use: Aug. 15, 1917 (No. 512a); Aug. 26, 1924 (No. 512b).

513 A148　13c **apple green,** *Jan. 10, 1919*　10.00　6.00
　　　pale apple green　　　10.00　6.00
　　　Never hinged　　　　22.00
　　　deep apple green　　　12.00　6.50
　　　　Never hinged　　　27.50
　　　On cover　　　　　　　　　19.00

　　　Block of 4　　　　　42.50　45.00
　　　P# block of 6　　　　140.00
　　　　Never hinged　　　240.00
Earliest documented use: Jan. 25, 1919.

514 A148　15c **gray,** *May 1917*　35.00　1.50
　　　dark gray　　　　　　35.00　1.50
　　　Never hinged　　　　80.00
　　　On cover　　　　　　　　　25.00
　　　Block of 4　　　　　150.00　12.50
　　　P# block of 6　　　　550.00　—
　　　　Never hinged　　　900.00
　　　Double transfer　　　—　—
　　a.　Perf. 10 at bottom　*10,000.*
Earliest documented use: Nov. 15, 1917.

515 A148　20c **light ultramarine,** *May 1917*　42.50　.45
　　　gray blue　　　　　　42.50　.45
　　　Never hinged　　　　90.00
　　　deep ultramarine　　47.50　.55
　　　　Never hinged　　　100.00
　　　On cover　　　　　　　　　75.00
　　　Block of 4　　　　　190.00　3.50
　　　P# block of 6　　　　600.00
　　　　Never hinged　　1,000.00　—
　　b.　Vertical pair, imperf. between　*2,000.　1,750.*
　　c.　Double impression　*1,250.*
　　d.　Perf. 10 at top or bottom　—　*15,000.*

No. 515b is valued in the grade of fine.
Beware of pairs with blind perforations inside the design of the top stamp that are offered as No. 515b.

Earliest documented use: May 4, 1918.

516 A148　30c **orange red,** *May 1917*　35.00　1.50
　　　dark orange red　　　35.00　1.50
　　　Never hinged　　　　80.00
　　　On cover　　　　　　　　　150.00
　　　Block of 4　　　　　150.00　12.50
　　　P# block of 6　　　　600.00
　　　　Never hinged　　　925.00　—
　　a.　Perf. 10 at top or bottom　*20,000.　7,500.*
　　　　Never hinged　　　*40,000.*
　　b.　Double impression　—
Earliest documented use: Jan. 12, 1918.

517 A148　50c **red violet,** *May 1917*　55.00　.75
　　　Never hinged　　　　130.00
　　　violet　　　　　　　65.00　.75
　　　　Never hinged　　　130.00
　　　light violet　　　70.00　.75
　　　　Never hinged　　　170.00
　　　On cover　　　　　　　　　400.00
　　　Block of 4　　　　　250.00　5.00
　　　P# block of 6　　　　1,600.
　　　　Never hinged　　　2,550.
　　　Double transfer　　　90.00　1.75
　　b.　Vertical pair, imperf. between & at
　　　　bottom　　　　　　*6,000.*
　　c.　Perf. 10 at top or bottom　*10,000.*

No. 517b is valued in average condition and may be a unique used pair (precanceled). The editors would like to see authenticated evidence of an unused pair.

Earliest documented use: Dec. 28, 1917 (on registry tag).

518 A148　$1 **violet brown,** *May 1917*　40.00　1.50
　　　violet black　　　　40.00　1.50
　　　Never hinged　　　　100.00
　　　On cover　　　　　　　　　550.00
　　　Block of 4　　　　　175.00　12.50
　　　Margin block of 4, arrow
　　　　right or left　　　230.00
　　　P# block of 6, Impt. & "A"　1,300.　—
　　　　Never hinged　　　2,100.
　　　Double transfer (5782 L. 66)　60.00　2.00
　　b.　$1 **deep brown**　*1,900.　1,250.*
　　　　Never hinged　　　*4,000.*
　　　Block of 4　　　　　*5,500.*
　　　P# block of 6, Impt. & "A,"
　　　　never hinged　　　*32,500.*
Earliest documented use: May 19, 1917.

No. 518b is valued in the grade of fine to very fine.
　　Nos. 498-504, 506-518 (20)　602.20　261.30

TYPE OF 1908-09 ISSUE

1917, Oct. 10　　Wmk. 191　　Perf. 11

This is the result of an old stock of No. 344 which was returned to the Bureau in 1917 and perforated with the then current gauge 11. Only lower left panes of No. 344 were perforated 11, and therefore only left and bottom plate blocks exist.

519 A139　2c **carmine**　400.00　*1,750.*
　　　Never hinged　　　　850.00
　　　On cover　　　　　　　　　*3,500.*
　　　Block of 4　　　　　1,800.　—
　　　P# block of 6, T V, Impt.　3,500.　—
　　　　Never hinged　　　6,500.

Beware of examples of No. 344 fraudulently perforated and offered as No. 519. Obtaining a certificate from a recognized expertizing committee is strongly recommended.
Warning: See note following No. 459 regarding used stamps.

Earliest documented use: Oct. 10, 1917.

Franklin — A149

Plates of 100 subjects.

1918, Aug.　　Unwmk.　　Perf. 11

523 A149　$2 **orange red & black**　550.　250.
　　　red orange & black　　550.　250.
　　　Never hinged　　　　1,200.
　　　On cover　　　　　　　　　*2,000.*
　　　Block of 4　　　　　2,300.　1,300.
　　　Margin block of 4, arrow　2,400.
　　　Center line block　　　2,600.　1,400.
　　　P# block of 8, 2# & arrow　12,000.
　　　　Never hinged　　　18,000.

Earliest documented use: Dec. 17, 1918.

524 A149　$5 **deep green & black**　175.　35.
　　　Never hinged　　　　375.
　　　On cover　　　　　　　　　*2,500.*
　　　Block of 4　　　　　750.　200.
　　　Margin block of 4, arrow　800.　210.
　　　Center line block　　　1,000.　225.
　　　P# block of 8, 2# & arrow　4,000.
　　　　Never hinged　　　*6,500.*

Earliest documented use: Mar. 20, 1920.

For other listing of design A149 see No. 547.

OFFSET PRINTING

Plates of 400, 800 or 1600 subjects in panes of 100 each, as follows:
No. 525 — 400 and 1600 subjects
No. 526 — 400, 800 and 1600 subjects
No. 529 — 400 subjects
No. 531 — 400 subjects
No. 532 — 400, 800 and 1600 subjects
No. 535 — 400 subjects
No. 536 — 400 and 1600 subjects

TYPES OF 1917-19 ISSUE

1918-20　　　Unwmk.　　Perf. 11

525 A140　1c **gray green,** *Dec. 1918*　2.50　.90
　　　Never hinged　　　　6.00
　　　emerald　　　　　　　3.50　1.25
　　　　Never hinged　　　8.25
　　　On cover　　　　　　　　　1.75
　　　Block of 4　　　　　10.50　6.00
　　　P# block of 6　　　　30.00
　　　　Never hinged　　　50.00
　　　"Flat nose"
　　a.　1c **dark green**　7.00　1.75
　　　　Never hinged　　　17.50
　　c.　Horizontal pair, imperf. between　100.00　*700.00*
　　d.　Double impression　40.00
　　　　Never hinged　　　90.00

Earliest documented use: Dec. 24, 1918.

TYPE IV

TWO CENTS
Type IV — Top line of the toga rope is broken.
The shading lines in the toga button are so arranged that the curving of the first and last form "D (reversed) ID."
The line of color in the left "2" is very thin and usually broken.
Used on offset printings only.

TYPE V

Type V — Top line of the toga is complete.
There are five vertical shading lines in the toga button.
The line of color in the left "2" is very thin and usually broken.
The shading dots on the nose are as shown on the diagram.
Used on offset printings only.

TYPE Va

Type Va — Characteristics are the same as type V except in the shading dots of the nose. The third row of dots from the bottom has four dots instead of six. The overall height is ⅓mm shorter than type V.
Used on offset printings only.

TYPE VI

Type VI — General characteristics the same as type V except that the line of color in the left "2" is very heavy.
Used on offset printings only.

TYPE VII

Type VII — The line of color in the left "2" is invariably continuous, clearly defined and heavier than in type V or Va but not as heavy as type VI.
An additional vertical row of dots has been added to the upper lip.
Numerous additional dots have been added to the hair on top of the head.
Used on offset printings only.
Dates of issue of types after type IV are not known but official records show the first plate of each type to have been certified as follows:
Type IV, Mar. 6, 1920
Type V, Mar. 20, 1920

Type Va, May 4, 1920
Type VI, June 24, 1920
Type VII, Nov. 3, 1920

526	A140 2c **carmine**, type IV, *1920*	25.00	4.00
	rose carmine, type IV	25.00	4.00
	Never hinged	57.50	
	On cover, type IV		11.00
	Block of 4, type IV	110.00	30.00
	P# block of 6, type IV	240.00	
	Never hinged	450.00	
	Gash on forehead, type IV	60.00	—
	Never hinged	125.00	
	Malformed "2" at left, type IV (10823 LR 93)	40.00	6.00

Earliest documented use: Mar. 15, 1920 (FDC).

527	A140 2c **carmine**, type V, *1920*	18.00	1.25
	bright carmine, type V	18.00	1.25
	rose carmine, type V	18.00	1.25
	Never hinged	40.00	
	On cover		2.75
	Block of 4, type V	77.50	10.00
	Block of 6, P# only, type V	185.00	
	Never hinged	350.00	
	Line through "2" & "EN," type V	35.00	—
	Never hinged	75.00	
a.	Double impression, type V	75.00	—
	Never hinged	160.00	
b.	Vert. pair, imperf. horiz., type V	850.00	—
c.	Horiz. pair, imperf. vert., type V	1,000.	—

Earliest documented use: Apr. 16, 1920.

528	A140 2c **carmine**, type Va, *1920*	9.00	.40
	Never hinged	21.50	
	On cover, type Va		.75
	Block of 4, type Va	37.50	3.50
	Block of 6, P# only, type Va	100.00	
	Never hinged	175.00	
	Block of 6, monogram over P#	200.00	
	Never hinged	300.00	
	Retouches in "P" of Postage type Va	*52.50*	—
	Retouched on toga, type Va		
	Variety C"R"NTS, type Va	*37.50*	—
	Never hinged	85.00	
	Top margin P# block of 6 containing the C"R"NTS variety, type Va	*450.00*	
c.	Double impression, type Va	55.00	—
	Never hinged	125.00	
g.	Vert. pair, imperf. between	*3,500.*	

Earliest documented use: June 18, 1920.

528A	A140 2c **carmine**, type VI, *1920*	47.50	2.00
	bright carmine, type VI	47.50	2.00
	Never hinged	115.00	
	On cover, type VI		3.75
	Block of 4, type VI	200.00	15.00
	P# block of 6, type VI	425.00	
	Never hinged	800.00	
	Block of 6, monogram over P#	525.00	
	Never hinged	900.00	
d.	Double impression, type VI	180.00	—
	Never hinged	400.00	
f.	Vert. pair, imperf. horiz., type VI	—	
h.	Vert. pair, imperf. between	1,000.	

Earliest documented use: July 30, 1920.

528B	A140 2c **carmine**, type VII, *1920*	20.00	.75
	Never hinged	50.00	
	On cover, type VII		1.00
	Block of 4, type VII	85.00	6.00
	P# block of 6, type VII	200.00	
	Never hinged	375.00	
	Gash on cheek, type VII	*300.00*	—
	Retouched on cheek, type VII	*750.00*	—
	Vertical plate scratch through face, type VII	*200.00*	—
e.	Double impression, type VII	77.50	*400.00*

Earliest documented use: Nov. 10, 1920.

TYPE III

THREE CENTS
Type III — The top line of the toga rope is strong but the 5th shading line is missing as in type I.
Center shading line of the toga button consists of two dashes with a central dot.
The "P" and "O" of POSTAGE are separated by a line of color.
The frame line at the bottom of the vignette is complete.

Used on offset printings only.

TYPE IV

Type IV — The shading lines of the toga rope are complete.
The second and fourth shading lines in the toga button are broken in the middle and the third line is continuous with a dot in the center.
The "P" and "O" of "POSTAGE" are joined.
The frame line at the bottom of the vignette is broken.
Used on offset printings only.

529	A140 3c **violet**, type III, *Mar. 1918*	3.50	.50
	light violet, type III	3.50	.50
	dark violet, type III	3.50	.50
	Never hinged	7.75	
	On cover, type III		.60
	Block of 4, type III	14.50	4.00
	P# block of 6, type III	75.00	
	Never hinged	125.00	
a.	Double impression, type III	45.00	—
	Never hinged	100.00	
b.	Printed on both sides, type III	*2,500.*	

Earliest documented use: Apr. 8, 1918 (No. 529); June 24, 1918 (No. 529a).

530	A140 3c **purple**, *June 1918* type IV	2.00	.30
	light purple, type IV	2.00	.30
	deep purple, type IV	2.00	.30
	violet, type IV	2.00	.30
	Never hinged	4.50	
	On cover, type IV		.35
	Block of 4, type IV	8.50	2.00
	P# block of 6, type IV	32.50	
	Never hinged	55.00	
	"Blister" under "U.S.," type IV	5.00	—
	Recut under "U.S.," type IV	5.00	—
a.	Double impression, type IV	35.00	—

b.	On cover	*2,250.*	
	Printed on both sides, type IV	*350.00*	
	Never hinged	*650.00*	
c.	Triple impression, type IV	*1,750.*	—
	Nos. 525-530 (8)	127.50	10.10

Earliest documented use: June 30, 1918.

Earliest documented perforated use dates for imperforates are for the imperforate sheet stamps, not for imperforate stamps with vending and affixing machine perforations or for flat plate imperforate coil stamps. EDU dates for VAMP and flat plate imperf coil stamps are shown in their respective sections later in the catalogue.

1918-20   *Imperf.*

Dates of issue of 2c types are not known, but official records show that the first plate of each type known to have been issued imperforate was certified as follows:
Type IV, Mar. 1920
Type V,   May 4, 1920
Type Va, May 25, 1920
Type VI, July 26, 1920
Type VII, Dec. 2, 1920

531	A140	1c **green**, *Jan. 1919*	10.00	12.00
		gray green	10.00	12.00
		Never hinged	21.00	
		On cover		17.50
		Pair	21.00	52.50
		Never hinged	50.00	
		Block of 4	45.00	75.00
		Corner margin block of 4	47.50	—
		Margin block of 4, arrow	50.00	80.00
		Center line block	75.00	90.00
		Never hinged	135.00	
		P# block of 6	110.00	—
		Never hinged	190.00	

Earliest documented use: Mar. 17, 1919 (dated cancel on off-cover plate block); April 7, 1919 (cover).

532	A140	2c **carmine rose**, type IV, *1920*	32.50	35.00
		Never hinged	70.00	
		On cover		70.00
		Pair	70.00	110.00
		Never hinged	160.00	
		Block of 4	145.00	225.00
		Corner margin block of 4	155.00	
		Margin block of 4, arrow	160.00	
		Center line block	230.00	
		Never hinged	400.00	
		P# block of 6	370.00	—
		Never hinged	625.00	

Earliest documented use: Feb. 26, 1923 (dated cancel on used block of 4); April 12, 1923 (on cover).

533	A140	2c **carmine**, type V, *1920*	90.00	95.00
		Never hinged	190.00	
		On cover		210.00
		Pair	200.00	250.00
		Never hinged	420.00	
		Block of 4	425.00	550.00
		Corner margin block of 4	450.00	675.00
		Margin block of 4, arrow	475.00	675.00
		Center line block	750.00	700.00
		Never hinged	1,300.	
		P# block of 6	1,100.	—
		Never hinged	1,800.	
		Line through "2" and "EN," type V	225.00	
		Never hinged	450.00	

Earliest documented use: Sept. 29, 1920 (dated cancel on off-cover center line block of 4).

534	A140	2c **carmine**, type Va, *1920*	12.00	9.00
		carmine rose	12.00	9.00
		Never hinged	26.00	
		On cover		16.00
		Pair	26.00	22.50
		Never hinged	55.00	
		Block of 4	55.00	57.50
		Corner margin block of 4	57.50	
		Margin block of 4, arrow	60.00	60.00
		Center line block	70.00	90.00
		Never hinged	130.00	
		P# block of 6	130.00	—
		Never hinged	200.00	
		Block of 6, monogram over P#	225.00	
		Never hinged	360.00	

Earliest documented use: June 24, 1920.

534A	A140	2c **carmine**, type VI, *1920*	37.50	32.50
		Never hinged	80.00	
		On cover		45.00
		Pair	80.00	85.00
		Never hinged	170.00	
		Block of 4	160.00	230.00
		Corner block of 4	170.00	250.00
		Block of 4, arrow	180.00	—
		Center line block	260.00	300.00
		Never hinged	475.00	
		P# block of 6	400.00	—
		Never hinged	650.00	

Earliest documented use: Aug. 31, 1920.

534B	A140	2c **carmine**, type VII, *1920*	1,750.	1,250.
		Never hinged	3,250.	
		On cover		*5,000.*
		Pair	3,750.	*4,500.*
		Never hinged	6,400.	
		Block of 4	7,750.	*7,000.*
		Corner margin block of 4	8,000.	
		Margin block of 4, arrow	8,250.	
		Center line block	10,500.	

Never hinged	16,000.	
P# block of 6	17,000.	
Never hinged	25,000.	

Earliest documented use: Oct. 1, 1921 (dated cancel on on-piece pair); Mar. 22, 1923 (on cover). A cover purported to be an Oct. 20, 1920, usage is believed to exist. The editors would like to see authenticated evidence of its genuineness.

Beware of perforated 2c offset stamps that may have been fraudulently trimmed to resemble Nos. 532-534B.

Examples of the 2c type VII with Schermack type III vending machine perforations have been cut down at sides to simulate the rarer No. 534B imperforate. The No. 534B with Schermack type III perforations is much less expensive than the fully imperforate No. 534B listed here.

535	A140	3c **violet**, type IV, *1918*	8.00	5.00
		Never hinged	18.00	
		On cover		11.00
		Pair	18.00	15.00
		Never hinged	37.50	
		Block of 4	35.00	32.50
		Corner margin block of 4	37.50	35.00
		Margin block of 4, arrow	40.00	35.00
		Center line block	60.00	50.00
		Never hinged	105.00	
		P# block of 6	80.00	—
		Never hinged	125.00	
a.		Double impression	95.00	
		Never hinged	200.00	
		Nos. 531-534A,535 (6)	190.00	188.50

Earliest documented use: Sept. 30, 1918.

Cancellation
Haiti   —

1919, Aug. 15   *Perf. 12½*

536	A140	1c **gray green**	20.00	27.50
		Never hinged	45.00	
		On cover		200.00
		Block of 4	85.00	150.00
		P# block of 6	250.00	
		Never hinged	400.00	
a.		Horiz. pair, imperf. vert.	*1,250.*	

Earliest documented use: Aug. 18, 1919.

VICTORY ISSUE
Victory of the Allies in World War I

"Victory" and Flags of Allies — A150

Designed by Clair Aubrey Huston

FLAT PLATE PRINTING
Plates of 400 subjects in four panes of 100 each

1919, Mar. 3   Unwmk.   *Perf. 11*

537	A150	3c **violet**	10.00	3.25
		Never hinged	20.00	
		On cover		10.00
		Block of 4	42.50	17.50
		P# block of 6	275.00	
		Never hinged	400.00	
		Double transfer	—	—
a.		3c **deep red violet**	*1,250.*	*2,250.*
		Never hinged	*2,300.*	
		On cover		—
		Block of 4	*5,250.*	*11,000.*
		P# block of 6	10,000.	
		Never hinged	16,000.	
b.		3c **light reddish violet**	125.00	45.00
		Never hinged	250.00	
		On cover		225.00
		Block of 4	550.00	225.00
		P# block of 6	1,150.	
		Never hinged	1,750.	
c.		3c **red violet**	150.00	55.00
		Never hinged	300.00	
		On cover		250.00
		Block of 4	650.00	
		P# block of 6	1,250.	
		Never hinged	1,900.	

No. 537a is valued in the grade of fine.
Earliest documented date: Mar. 3, 1919 (FDC).

REGULAR ISSUE
ROTARY PRESS PRINTINGS
(See note over No. 448)

1919   Unwmk.   *Perf. 11x10*
Issued in panes of 170 stamps (coil waste), later in
panes of 70 and 100 (#538, 540)
Stamp designs: 19½-20x22-22¼mm

538	A140	1c **green**, *June*	10.00	9.00
		yellowish green	10.00	9.00
		bluish green	10.00	9.00
		Never hinged	23.00	
		On cover		22.50
		Block of 4	42.50	55.00
		P# block of 4 & "S 30"	95.00	
		Never hinged	160.00	
		P# block of 4	110.00	

Never hinged	180.00	
P# block of 4, star	140.00	
Never hinged	225.00	
Double transfer	16.00	—
a. Vert. pair, imperf. horiz.	50.00	*100.00*
Never hinged	90.00	
Block of 4	110.00	*250.00*
Never hinged	200.00	
P# block of 4	900.00	
Never hinged	1,375.	

No. 538a used is valued with a contemporary cancel. A certificate of authenticity is advised.
Earliest documented use: June 28, 1919 (No. 538); Sept. 5, 1927 (No. 538a).

539	A140	2c **carmine rose**, type II	2,750.	*5,500.*
		Never hinged	4,000.	
		On cover, type II		*60,000.*
		Block of 4, type II	12,000.	*35,000.*
		P# block of 4, type II, & "S 20"	*17,500.*	
		Never hinged	25,000.	

No. 539 is valued in the grade of fine.
(See note after No. 455.)
Earliest documented use: June 30, 1919. This is the unique usage on cover. The used block of four also is unique.

540	A140	2c **carmine rose**, type III, *June 14*	12.00	9.50
		carmine	12.00	9.50
		Never hinged	27.50	
		On cover, type III		25.00
		Block of 4, type III	50.00	60.00
		Never hinged	115.00	
		P# block of 4, type III, & "S 30"	105.00	
		Never hinged	175.00	
		P# block of 4, type III, & "S 30" inverted	450.00	
		Never hinged	725.00	
		P# block of 4, type III	105.00	
		Never hinged	175.00	
		P# block of 4, type III, star	160.00	
		Never hinged	275.00	
		Double transfer, type III	21.00	—

Earliest documented use: June 17, 1919.

a.		Vert. pair, imperf. horiz., type III	50.00	*100.00*
		Never hinged	100.00	
		Block of 4	110.00	*250.00*
		Never hinged	220.00	
		P# block of 4, type III	1,000.	
		Never hinged	1,500.	
		P# block of 4, type III, Star	1,050.	
		Never hinged	1,600.	
b.		Horiz. pair, imperf. vert., type III	*1,750.*	

No. 540a used is valued with a contemporary cancel. A certificate of authenticity is advised.
Earliest documented use: June 17, 1919 (No. 540); Nov. 4, 1922 (No. 540a).

541	A140	3c **violet**, type II, *June 14, 1919*	40.00	32.50
		gray violet, type II	40.00	32.50
		Never hinged	100.00	
		On cover		100.00
		Block of 4	170.00	260.00
		P# block of 4	360.00	
		Never hinged	625.00	

Earliest documented use: June 14, 1919 (FDC).

1920, May 26   *Perf. 10x11*
Plates of 400 subjects in four panes of 100.
Stamp design: 19x22½-22¾mm

542	A140	1c **green**	12.50	1.50
		bluish green	12.50	1.50
		Never hinged	31.00	
		On cover		5.50
		Block of 4	55.00	12.50
		Vertical margin block of 6, P# opposite center horizontal row	165.00	
		Never hinged	300.00	

Earliest documented use: May 26, 1920 (FDC).

1921, May   *Perf. 10*
Plates of 400 subjects in four panes of 100 each
Stamp design: 19x22½mm

543	A140	1c **green**	.70	.40
		deep green	.70	.40
		Never hinged	1.75	
		On cover		.45
		Block of 4	2.80	2.00
		Vertical margin block of 6, P# opposite center horizontal row	32.50	
		Never hinged	57.50	
		Corner margin block of 4, P# only	17.50	
		Never hinged	30.00	
		Double transfer	—	
		Triple transfer	—	
a.		Horizontal pair, imperf. between	*2,750.*	

Earliest documented use: May 21, 1921.

1922   *Perf. 11*
Rotary press sheet waste
Stamp design: 19x22½mm

544	A140	1c **green**	*22,500.*	*3,750.*
		Never hinged	*40,000.*	
		On cover		*7,500.*

No. 544 is valued in the grade of fine.

Earliest documented use: Dec. 21, 1922.

1921, May
Issued in panes of 170 stamps (coil waste), later in panes of 70 and 100
Stamp designs: 19½-20x22mm

545	A140	1c	**green**	180.00	210.00
			yellowish green	180.00	210.00
			Never hinged	425.00	
			On cover		*1,800.*
			Block of 4	750.00	*1,050.*
			P# block of 4, "S 30"	1,100.	
			Never hinged	2,150.	
			P# block of 4	1,150.	
			Never hinged	2,200.	
			P# block of 4, star	1,200.	
			Never hinged	2,300.	

Earliest documented use: June 25, 1921.

546	A140	2c	**carmine rose,** type III	110.00	*190.00*
			deep carmine rose	110.00	*190.00*
			Never hinged	240.00	
			On cover		*800.00*
			Block of 4	475.00	*1,000.*
			P# block of 4, "S 30"	750.00	
			Never hinged	1,400.	
			P# block of 4	775.00	
			Never hinged	1,450.	
			P# block of 4, star	800.00	
			Never hinged	1,500.	
			Recut in hair	140.00	210.00
a.			Perf. 10 on left side	7,500.	10,000.

Earliest documented use: May 5, 1921.

FLAT PLATE PRINTING
Plates of 100 subjects

1920, Nov. 1   ***Perf. 11***

547	A149	$2	**carmine & black**	130.	40.
			Never hinged	290.	
			On cover (commercial)		1,000.
			On flown cover (philatelic)		250.
			Block of 4	550.00	200.
			Margin block of 4, arrow	575.	
			Center line block	800.	—
			Margin block of 8, two P#, & arrow	4,500.	
			Never hinged	7,000.	
a.			$2 **lake & black**	190.	40.
			Never hinged	410.	

Earliest documented use: Dec. 6, 1920 (on piece).

From No. 548 forward, almost all U.S. stamps have had officially designated first days of sale and use. Therefore, from this point, earliest documented uses are given only for those stamps for which there were not designated first days of sale. For first day covers, see the First Day Cover section later in the catalogue.

PILGRIM TERCENTENARY ISSUE
Landing of the Pilgrims at Plymouth, Mass.

The "Mayflower" — A151

Landing of the Pilgrims — A152

Signing of the Compact — A153

Designed by Clair Aubrey Huston

Plates of 280 subjects in four panes of 70 each

1920, Dec. 21   Unwmk.   ***Perf. 11***

548	A151	1c	**green**	4.50	2.25
			dark green	4.50	2.25
			Never hinged	11.00	
			On cover		3.50
			Block of 4	19.00	14.00
			P# block of 6	70.00	
			Never hinged	100.00	
			Double transfer		
549	A152	2c	**carmine rose**	5.75	1.60
			carmine	5.75	1.60

		rose	5.75	1.60
		Never hinged	14.00	
		On cover		2.50
		Block of 4	25.00	9.00
		P# block of 6	85.00	
		Never hinged	125.00	

Cancellation

		China	—	
550	A153	5c	**deep blue**	40.00	14.00
		dark blue	40.00	14.00
		Never hinged	95.00	
		On cover		22.50
		Block of 4	190.00	75.00
		P# block of 6	475.00	
		Never hinged	750.00	
		Nos. 548-550 (3)	50.25	17.85
		Nos. 548-550, never hinged	120.00	

IMPORTANT INFORMATION REGARDING VALUES FOR NEVER-HINGED STAMPS

Collectors should be aware that the values given for never-hinged stamps from No. 182 on are for stamps in the grade of very fine, just as the values for all stamps in the catalogue are for very fine stamps unless indicated otherwise. The never-hinged premium as a percentage of value will be larger for stamps in extremely fine or superb grades, and the premium will be smaller for fine-very fine, fine or poor examples. This is particularly true of the issues of the late-19th and early-20th centuries. For example, in the grade of very fine, an unused stamp from this time period may be valued at $100 hinged and $200 never hinged. The never-hinged premium is thus 100%. But in a grade of extremely fine, this same stamp will not only sell for more hinged, but the never-hinged premium will increase, perhaps to 200%-400% or more over the higher extremely fine value. In a grade of superb, a hinged stamp will sell for much more than a very fine stamp, and additionally the never-hinged premium will be much larger, perhaps as large as 500%-1,000%. On the other hand, the same stamp in a grade of fine or fine-very fine not only will sell for less than a very fine stamp in hinged condition, but additionally the never-hinged premium will be smaller than the never-hinged premium on a very fine stamp, perhaps as small as 40%-60%.

Please note that the above statements and percentages are NOT a formula for arriving at values of stamps in hinged or never-hinged condition in the grades of very good, fine, fine to very fine, very fine, very fine to extremely fine, extremely fine or superb. The percentages given apply only to the size of the premium for never-hinged condition that might be added to the stamp value for hinged condition. Further, the percentages given are only generalized estimates. Some stamps or grades may have percentages for never-hinged condition that are higher or lower than the ranges given. For values of the most popular U.S. stamps in the grades of very good, fine, fine to very fine, very fine, very fine to extremely fine, extremely fine and superb, see the *Scott United States Specialized Valuing Supplement*, updated and issued twice each year in April and October.

VALUES FOR NEVER-HINGED STAMPS PRIOR TO SCOTT 182
This catalogue does not value pre-1879 stamps in never-hinged condition. Premiums for never-hinged condition in the classic era invariably are even larger than those premiums listed for the 1879 and later issues. Generally speaking, the earlier the stamp is listed in the catalogue, the larger will be the never-hinged premium. On some early classics, the premium will be several multiples of the unused, hinged values given in the catalogue.

NEVER-HINGED PLATE BLOCKS
Values given for never-hinged plate blocks are for blocks in which all stamps have original gum that has never been hinged and has no disturbances, and all selvage, whether gummed or ungummed, has never been hinged.

REGULAR ISSUE

Nathan Hale — A154

Franklin — A155

Warren G. Harding — A156

Washington — A157

Lincoln — A158

Martha Washington — A159

Theodore Roosevelt — A160

Garfield — A161

McKinley — A162

Grant — A163

Jefferson — A164

Monroe — A165

Rutherford B.
Hayes — A166

Grover
Cleveland — A167

American
Indian — A168

Statue of
Liberty — A169

Golden Gate — A170

Niagara Falls — A171

American
Buffalo — A172

Arlington
Amphitheater — A173

Lincoln
Memorial — A174

United States
Capitol — A175

Head of Freedom Statue,
Capitol Dome — A176

Plates of 400 subjects in four panes of 100 each for all values ½c to 50c inclusive.

Plates of 200 subjects for $1 and $2. The sheets were cut along the horizontal guide line into two panes, upper and lower, of 100 subjects each.

Plates of 100 subjects for the $5 denomination, and sheets of 100 subjects were issued intact.

The Bureau of Engraving and Printing in 1925 in experimenting to overcome the loss due to uneven perforations, produced what is known as the "Star Plate." The vertical rows of designs on these plates are spaced 3mm apart in place of 2¾mm as on the regular plates. Most of these plates were identified with a star added to the plate number.

Designed by Clair Aubrey Huston.

FLAT PLATE PRINTINGS

1922-25			Unwmk.		Perf. 11
551	A154	½c	**olive brown,** *Apr. 4, 1925*	.25	.20
			pale olive brown	.25	.20
			deep olive brown	.25	.20
			Never hinged	.50	
			On 1c stamped envelope (3rd class)		2.50
			Block of 4	1.00	.50
			P# block of 6	15.00	
			Never hinged	25.00	
			"Cap" on fraction bar (Pl. 17041)	.75	.20
552	A155	1c	**deep green,** *Jan. 17, 1923*	1.50	.20
			green	1.50	.20

			pale green	1.50	.20
			Never hinged	3.25	
			On postcard		.25
			Block of 4	6.25	.40
			P# block of 6	37.50	
			Never hinged	55.00	
			Double transfer	3.50	—
a.			Booklet pane of 6, *Aug. 11, 1923*	7.50	4.00
			Never hinged	12.50	

Earliest documented use: Dec. 21, 1923 (No. 552a pair).

553	A156	1½c	**yellow brown,** *Mar. 19, 1925*	2.30	.20
			pale yellow brown	2.30	.20
			brown	2.30	.20
			Never hinged	4.75	
			On 3rd class cover		2.25
			Block of 4	9.50	1.10
			P# block of 6	67.50	
			Never hinged	95.00	
			Double transfer	—	—
554	A157	2c	**carmine,** *Jan. 15, 1923*	1.40	.20
			light carmine	1.40	.20
			deep claret		
			Never hinged	3.25	
			On cover		.25
			Block of 4	5.75	.30
			P# block of 6	42.50	
			Never hinged	60.00	
			P# block of 6 & small 5 point star, top only	550.00	
			Never hinged	775.00	
			P# block of 6 & large 5 point star, side only	65.00	
			Never hinged	97.50	
			Same, large 5-pt. star, top	600.00	
			Never hinged	1,000.	
			Same, large 6-pt. star, top	750.00	
			Never hinged	1,200.	
			Same, large 6-pt. star, side only (Pl. 17196)	1,000.	
			Never hinged	1,500.	
			Double transfer	2.50	.80
a.			Horiz. pair, imperf. vert.	275.00	
b.			Vert. pair, imperf. horiz.	4,000.	
			Never hinged	—	
c.			Booklet pane of 6, *Feb. 10, 1923*	7.00	3.00
			Never hinged	12.00	
d.			Perf. 10 at top or bottom	7,000.	5,500.
			On cover		9,000.

No. 554d unused is unique. It is never hinged and has a natural straight edge at left. Value represents the sale price at 2001 auction.

Earliest documented use: Feb. 10, 1923 (No. 554c single); Nov. 23, 1923 (No. 554d).

555	A158	3c	**violet,** *Feb. 12, 1923*	16.00	1.25
			deep violet	16.00	1.25
			dark violet	16.00	1.25
			red violet	16.00	1.25
			bright violet	16.00	1.25
			Never hinged	34.00	
			On 2c stamped envelope (single UPU rate)		8.00
			Block of 4	67.50	9.00
			P# block of 6	225.00	
			Never hinged	375.00	
556	A159	4c	**yellow brown,** *Jan. 15, 1923*	18.00	.50
			brown	18.00	.50
			Never hinged	40.00	
			On cover		9.00
			Block of 4	77.50	3.00
			P# block of 6	250.00	
			Never hinged	400.00	
			Double transfer	—	—
a.			Vert. pair, imperf. horiz.	10,500.	
b.			Perf. 10 at top or bottom	3,500.	25,000.

No. 556a is unique. It resulted from a sheet that was damaged and patched during production.

No. 556b used also exists as a transitional stamp gauging 10 at left top and 11 at right top. Value the same.

557	A160	5c	**dark blue,** *Oct. 27, 1922*	18.00	.30
			deep blue	18.00	.30
			Never hinged	40.00	
			On UPU-rate cover		6.00
			Block of 4	77.50	2.00
			P# block of 6	250.00	
			Never hinged	400.00	
			Double transfer (15571 UL 86)	—	350.00
a.			Imperf., pair	2,000.	
			Never hinged	3,500.	
			P# block of 6	27,500.	
b.			Horiz. pair, imperf. vert.		
c.			Perf. 10 at top or bottom	—	11,000.
			On cover		17,500.

Earliest documented use: Nov. 12, 1923 (No. 557c).

558	A161	6c	**red orange,** *Nov. 20, 1922*	35.00	1.00
			pale red orange	35.00	1.00
			Never hinged	75.00	
			Pair on special delivery cover		17.50
			Block of 4	145.00	7.50
			P# block of 6	400.00	
			Never hinged	650.00	
			Double transfer (Plate 14169 LR 60 and 70)	55.00	2.00
			Same, recut	55.00	2.00
559	A162	7c	**black,** *May 1, 1923*	8.00	.75
			gray black	8.00	.75
			Never hinged	17.00	
			On registered cover with other values		27.50
			Block of 4	35.00	6.00
			P# block of 6	125.00	
			Never hinged	200.00	

			Double transfer	—	—
560	A163	8c	**olive green,** *May 1, 1923*	45.00	1.00
			pale olive green	45.00	1.00
			Never hinged	100.00	
			Pair on airmail cover		12.50
			Block of 4	190.00	7.50
			P# block of 6	575.00	
			Never hinged	900.00	
			Double transfer	—	—
561	A164	9c	**rose,** *Jan. 15, 1923*	13.00	1.25
			pale rose	13.00	1.25
			Never hinged	28.00	
			On registered cover with other values		22.50
			Block of 4	55.00	9.00
			P# block of 6	250.00	
			Never hinged	400.00	
562	A165	10c	**orange,** *Jan. 15, 1923*	16.00	.35
			pale orange	16.00	.35
			Never hinged	34.00	
			On special delivery cover with 2c		6.00
			Block of 4	67.50	2.00
			P# block of 6	275.00	
			Never hinged	425.00	
a.			Vert. pair, imperf. horiz.	2,250.	
			Never hinged	3,500.	
b.			Imperf., pair	2,500.	
			P# block of 6	25,000.	
c.			Perf. 10 at top or bottom	—	20,000.
			Pair		42,500.

No. 562b is valued without gum and without blue pencil defacing lines. No. 562c is valued in the grade of fine.

563	A166	11c	**greenish blue,** *Oct. 4, 1922*	1.50	.60
			Never hinged	3.25	
			light blue	1.85	.60
			Never hinged	3.75	
			On registered cover with other values		12.50
			Block of 4	6.25	3.50
			P# block of 6	55.00	
			Never hinged	80.00	
a.			11c **light bluish green**	1.50	.60
			light yellow green	1.50	.60
			Never hinged	3.25	
			On registered cover with other values		14.00
			Block of 4	6.25	4.00
			P# block of 6	40.00	
			Never hinged	60.00	
d.			Imperf., pair		20,000.

Many other intermediate shades exist for Nos. 563 and 563a, all falling within the blue or green color families.

564	A167	12c	**brown violet,** *Mar. 20, 1923*	5.50	.35
			deep brown violet	5.50	.35
			Never hinged	12.00	
			On special delivery cover		12.50
			Block of 4	23.00	3.00
			P# block of 6	115.00	
			Never hinged	175.00	
			P# block of 6 & large 5 point star, side only	150.00	
			Never hinged	230.00	
			P# block of 6 & large 6 point star, side only	250.00	
			Never hinged	400.00	
			Double transfer, (14404 UL 73 & 74)	12.00	1.10
a.			Horiz. pair, imperf. vert.	1,750.	
565	A168	14c	**blue,** *May 1, 1923*	4.75	.90
			deep blue	4.75	.90
			Never hinged	10.50	
			On registered cover with other values		15.00
			Block of 4	20.00	7.50
			P# block of 6	80.00	
			Never hinged	130.00	
			Double transfer	—	—

Horizontal pairs of No. 565 are known with spacings up to 3mm instead of 2mm between. These are from the 5th and 6th vertical rows of the right panes of Plate 14515 and also between stamps Nos. 3 and 4 of the same pane. A plate block of Pl. 14512 is known with 3mm spacing.

566	A169	15c	**gray,** *Nov. 11, 1922*	18.00	.30
			light gray	18.00	.30
			Never hinged	40.00	
			On registered cover with 2c		3.50
			Block of 4	75.00	2.00
			P# block of 6	275.00	
			Never hinged	425.00	
			P# block of 6 & large 5 point star, side only	550.00	
			Never hinged	825.00	
567	A170	20c	**carmine rose,** *May 1, 1923*	18.00	.30
			deep carmine rose	18.00	.30
			Never hinged	40.00	
			On registered UPU-rate cover		12.50
			Block of 4	75.00	2.00
			P# block of 6	300.00	
			Never hinged	450.00	
			P# block of 6 & large 5 point star, side only	575.00	
			Never hinged	850.00	
a.			Horiz. pair, imperf. vert.	2,000.	
			Never hinged	3,500.	

"Bridge over Falls" plate scratches

568	A171	25c yellow green, *Nov. 11, 1922*	17.50	.75
		green	17.50	.75
		deep green	17.50	.75
		Never hinged	37.50	
		On contract airmail cover		27.50
		Block of 4	72.50	6.00
		P# block of 6	300.00	
		Never hinged	425.00	
		Double transfer	—	
		Plate scratches ("Bridge over Falls") (17445 LL 26)	500.00	—
b.		Vert. pair, imperf. horiz.	2,500.	
c.		Perf. 10 at one side	5,000.	11,000.
		Never hinged	7,500.	

No. 568b is valued in the grade of fine.

Double Transfer

569	A172	30c olive brown, *Mar. 20, 1923*	27.50	.60
		Never hinged	60.00	
		On registered cover with other values		20.00
		Block of 4	130.00	5.00
		P# block of 6	325.00	
		Never hinged	475.00	
		Double transfer (16065 UR 52)	200.00	—
570	A173	50c lilac, *Nov. 11, 1922*	35.00	.40
		dull lilac	35.00	.40
		Never hinged	80.00	
		On Federal airmail cover		27.50
		Block of 4	150.00	2.00
		P# block of 6	575.00	
		Never hinged	900.00	
571	A174	$1 violet brown, *Feb. 12, 1923*	37.50	.65
		violet black	37.50	.65
		Never hinged	85.00	
		On post-1932 registered cover with other values		22.50
		Block of 4	160.00	4.50
		Margin block of 4, arrow, top or bottom	170.00	
		P# block of 6	350.00	
		Never hinged	650.00	
		Double transfers, Pl. 18642 L 30 and Pl. 18682	95.00	1.60
572	A175	$2 deep blue, *Mar. 20, 1923*	65.00	9.00
		Never hinged	140.00	
		On post-1932 registered cover with other values		55.00
		Block of 4	275.00	65.00
		Margin block of 4, arrow, top or bottom	290.00	
		P# block of 6	750.00	
		Never hinged	1,200.	
573	A176	$5 carmine & blue, *Mar. 20, 1923*	85.00	15.00
		Never hinged	190.00	
		On post-1932 registered cover with other values		175.00
		Block of 4	375.00	95.00
		Margin block of 4, arrow	400.00	
		Center line block	450.00	105.00
		Never hinged	800.00	
		P# block of 8, two P# & arrow	2,250.	—
		Never hinged	3,500.	
a.		$5 carmine lake & dark blue	175.00	20.00
		Never hinged	325.00	
		On post-1932 registered cover with other values		190.00
		Block of 4	775.00	140.00
		Margin block of 4, arrow	800.00	
		Center line block	875.00	175.00
		Never hinged	1,600.	
		P# block of 8, two P# & arrow	3,000.	
		Never hinged	4,500.	
		Nos. 551-573 (23)	489.70	36.05
		Nos. 551-573, never hinged	1,078.	

For other listings of perforated stamps of designs A154 to A176 see:
Nos. 578 & 579, Perf. 11x10
Nos. 581-591, Perf. 10
Nos. 594-596, Perf. 11
Nos. 632-642, 653, 692-696, Perf. 11x10½
Nos. 697-701, Perf. 10½x11

This series also includes #622-623 (perf. 11), 684-687 & 720-723.

Plate Blocks
Scott values for plate blocks printed from flat plates are for very fine side and bottom positions. Top position plate blocks with full wide selvage sell for more.

Earliest documented use dates for imperforates are for the imperforate sheet stamps, not for imperforate stamps with vending and affixing machine perforations or for flat plate imperforate coil stamps. EDU dates for VAMP and flat plate imperf coil stamps are shown in their respective sections later in the catalogue.

1923-25   Stamp design 19¼x22¼mm   *Imperf.*

575	A155	1c green, *Mar. 1923*	5.00	5.00
		deep green	5.00	5.00
		Never hinged	11.00	
		On commercial cover		100.00
		On philatelic cover		8.50
		Pair	11.00	12.50
		Never hinged	24.00	
		Block of 4	22.00	27.50
		Corner margin block of 4	25.00	27.50
		Corner margin block of 4 (UR), "O" in selvage		
		Margin block of 4, arrow	27.00	30.00
		Center line block	40.00	40.00
		Never hinged	70.00	
		P# block of 6	80.00	—
		Never hinged	115.00	

Earliest documented use: Mar. 16, 1923.

576	A156	1½c yellow brown, *Apr. 4, 1925*	1.25	1.50
		pale yellow brown	1.25	1.50
		brown	1.25	1.50
		Never hinged	2.70	
		On commercial cover		25.00
		On philatelic cover		6.00
		Pair	2.75	3.75
		Never hinged	6.00	
		Block of 4	5.75	8.50
		Corner margin block of 4	6.00	9.00
		Margin block of 4, arrow	6.25	10.00
		Center line block	11.00	20.00
		Never hinged	20.00	
		P# block of 6	30.00	—
		Never hinged	45.00	
		Double transfer	—	—

The 1½c A156 Rotary press imperforate is listed as No. 631.

577	A157	2c carmine	1.30	1.25
		light carmine	1.30	1.25
		Never hinged	2.90	
		On commercial cover		20.00
		On philatelic cover		6.00
		Pair	2.80	3.00
		Never hinged	6.00	
		Block of 4	5.75	7.00
		Corner margin block of 4	6.00	8.00
		Margin block of 4, arrow	6.25	10.00
		Center line block	13.00	15.00
		Never hinged	22.50	
		P# block of 6	30.00	—
		Never hinged	45.00	
		P# block of 6, large 5 point star	75.00	—
		Never hinged	110.00	
a.		2c carmine lake	—	—
		Nos. 575-577 (3)	7.55	7.75
		Nos. 575-577, never hinged	16.60	

ROTARY PRESS PRINTINGS
(See note over No. 448)
Issued in sheets of 70, 100 or 170 stamps, coil waste of Nos. 597, 599
Stamp designs: 19¾x22¼mm

1923   *Perf. 11x10*

578	A155	1c green	75.00	160.00
		Never hinged	170.00	
		On cover		700.00
		Block of 4	325.00	1,000.
		P# block of 4, star	925.00	
		Never hinged	1,450.	

Earliest documented use: Nov. 7, 1923.

579	A157	2c carmine	70.00	140.00
		deep carmine	70.00	140.00
		Never hinged	155.00	
		Block of 4	300.00	1,750.
		On cover		400.00
		P# block of 4, star	600.00	
		Never hinged	1,000.	
		Recut in eye, plate 14731	110.00	150.00

Earliest documented use: Feb. 20, 1923.

Warning: See note following No. 459 regarding used stamps.

Plates of 400 subjects in four panes of 100 each
Stamp designs: 19¼x22½mm

1923-26   *Perf. 10*

581	A155	1c green, *Apr. 21, 1923*	10.00	.75
		yellow green	10.00	.75
		pale green	10.00	.75
		Never hinged	22.50	
		On postcard		.85

		On 3rd class cover		1.35
		Block of 4	42.50	4.50
		P# block of 4	175.00	
		Never hinged	250.00	

Earliest documented use: May 18, 1923.

582	A156	1½c brown, *Mar. 19, 1925*	6.00	.65
		dark brown	6.00	.65
		Never hinged	13.50	
		On 3rd class cover		6.00
		Block of 4	26.00	4.00
		P# block of 4	85.00	
		Never hinged	125.00	
		Pair with full horiz. gutter btwn.	160.00	
		Pair with full vert. gutter btwn.	210.00	

No. 582 was available in full sheets of 400 subjects but was not regularly issued in that form.

583	A157	2c carmine, *Apr. 14, 1924*	3.00	.30
		deep carmine	3.00	.30
		Never hinged	6.50	
		On cover		2.50
		Block of 4	14.00	2.00
		P# block of 4	70.00	
		Never hinged	110.00	
a.		Booklet pane of 6, *Aug. 27, 1926*	95.00	150.00
		Never hinged	175.00	

Earliest documented use (unprecanceled): May 15, 1924.

584	A158	3c violet, *Aug. 1, 1925*	27.50	3.00
		Never hinged	62.50	
		On postcard (UPU rate)		12.50
		Block of 4	130.00	17.50
		P# block of 4	275.00	
		Never hinged	425.00	
585	A159	4c yellow brown, *Mar. 1925*	18.00	.65
		deep yellow brown	18.00	.65
		Never hinged	40.00	
		On cover		15.00
		Block of 4	80.00	4.00
		P# block of 4	275.00	
		Never hinged	425.00	
586	A160	5c blue, *Dec. 1924*	18.00	.40
		deep blue	18.00	.40
		Never hinged	40.00	
		On UPU-rate cover		6.00
		Block of 4	80.00	3.00
		P# block of 4	275.00	
		Never hinged	425.00	
		Double transfer	—	—
a.		Horizontal pair, imperf. vertically		8,000.

No. 586a is unique, precanceled, with average centering and small faults, and it is valued as such.

587	A161	6c red orange, *Mar. 1925*	9.25	.60
		pale red orange	9.25	.60
		Never hinged	21.00	

	On registered cover with other values		15.00	
	Block of 4	40.00	4.00	
	P# block of 4	225.00		
	Never hinged	325.00		
588 A162	7c **black,** *May 29, 1926*	12.50	6.25	
	Never hinged	27.50		
	On registered cover with other values		30.00	
	Block of 4	57.50	45.00	
	P# block of 4	200.00		
	Never hinged	300.00		
589 A163	8c **olive green,** *May 29, 1926*	27.50	4.50	
	pale olive green	27.50	4.50	
	Never hinged	60.00		
	On airmail cover		22.50	
	Block of 4	125.00	25.00	
	P# block of 4	300.00		
	Never hinged	450.00		
590 A164	9c **rose,** *May 29, 1926*	6.00	2.50	
	Never hinged	13.50		
	On registered cover with other values		22.50	
	Block of 4	26.00	17.50	
	P# block of 4	150.00		
	Never hinged	225.00		
591 A165	10c **orange,** *June 8, 1925*	50.00	.50	
	Never hinged	115.00		
	On airmail cover		17.50	
	Block of 4	250.00	3.00	
	P# block of 4	475.00		
	Never hinged	750.00		
	Nos. 581-591 (11)	187.75	20.10	
	Nos. 581-591, never hinged	422.00		

Bureau Precancels: 1c, 64 diff., 1½c, 76 diff., 2c, 58 diff., 3c, 41 diff., 4c, 36 diff., 5c, 38 diff., 6c, 36 diff., 7c, 18 diff., 8c, 18 diff., 9c, 13 diff., 10c, 39 diff.

Issued in sheets of 70 or 100 stamps, coil waste of
Nos. 597, 599
Stamp designs approximately 19¾x22¼mm

1923			**Perf. 11**
594 A155	1c **green**	27,500.	11,000.
	On cover		20,000.
	Pair		25,000.

No. 594 unused is valued without gum; both unused and used are valued with perforations just touching frameline on one side.

Earliest documented use: Mar. 25, 1924.

595 A157	2c **carmine**	275.00	375.00
	deep carmine	275.00	375.00
	Never hinged	550.00	
	On cover		550.00
	Block of 4	1,200.	1,750.
	P# block of 4, star	2,150.	—
	Never hinged	3,100.	—
	Recut in eye, plate 14731	—	

Earliest documented uses: Mar. 31, 1923 (dated cancel on off-cover pair of stamps); June 29, 1923 (on cover).

Rotary press sheet waste
Stamp design approximately 19¼x22½mm

596 A155	1c **green,** machine cancel	130,000.
	With Bureau precancel	110,000.

A majority of examples of No. 596 carry the Bureau precancel "Kansas City, Mo."
No. 596 is valued in the grade of fine.

COIL STAMPS
ROTARY PRESS

1923-29			**Perf. 10 Vertically**
	Stamp designs aproximately 19¾x22¼mm		
597 A155	1c **green,** *July 18, 1923*	.30	.20
	yellow green	.30	.20
	grayish green	—	
	Never hinged	.60	
	Three on cover		2.25
	Pair	.65	.25
	Never hinged	1.40	
	Joint line pair	2.00	.75
	Never hinged	4.00	
	Gripper cracks	2.60	1.00
	Double transfer	2.60	1.00
598 A156	1½c **brown,** *Mar. 19, 1925*	.90	.20
	deep brown	.90	.20
	Never hinged	1.80	
	On 3rd class cover		6.00
	Pair	1.90	.25
	Never hinged	3.80	
	Joint line pair	4.50	.75
	Never hinged	9.00	

TYPE I

TYPE II

TYPE I　　　　　　　　TYPE II

TYPE I. No heavy hair lines at top center of head. Outline of left acanthus scroll generally faint at top and toward base at left side.
TYPE II. Three heavy hair lines at top center of head; two being outstanding in the white area. Outline of left acanthus scroll very strong and clearly defined at top (under left edge of lettered panel) and at lower curve (above and to left of numeral oval). This type appears only on Nos. 599A and 634A.

599 A157	2c **carmine,** type I, *Jan. 1923*	.35	.20
	deep carmine, type I	.35	.20
	Never hinged	.70	
	On cover		1.10
	Pair, type I	.75	.20
	Never hinged	1.50	
	Joint line pair, type I	2.25	.50
	Never hinged	4.50	
	Double transfer, type I	1.90	1.00
	Gripper cracks, type I	2.30	2.00
b.	2c carmine lake, type I, never hinged	175.00	
	Pair, never hinged	375.00	
	Joint line pair		7,000.
	Never hinged	675.	

Earliest documented use: Jan. 10, 1923 (precanceled version)

599A A157	2c **carmine,** type II, *Mar. 1929*	105.00	17.50
	Never hinged	200.00	
	On cover		32.50
	Pair, type II	215.00	60.00
	Never hinged	425.00	
	Joint line pair, type II	575.00	350.00
	Never hinged	1,150.	
	Joint line pair, types I & II	650.00	1,000.
	Never hinged	1,250.	

Earliest documented use: Mar. 29, 1929.

600 A158	3c **violet,** *May 10, 1924*	6.25	.20
	deep violet	6.25	.20
	Never hinged	12.50	
	On cover		6.00
	Pair	13.00	.35
	Never hinged	25.00	
	Joint line pair	22.50	2.50
	Never hinged	45.00	
	Cracked plate	—	
601 A159	4c **yellow brown,** *Aug. 5, 1923*	3.75	.35
	brown	3.75	.35
	Never hinged	7.50	
	On cover		14.00
	Pair	8.25	.95
	Never hinged	16.50	
	Joint line pair	27.50	6.00
	Never hinged	55.00	

Earliest documented use: Sept. 14, 1923.

602 A160	5c **dark blue,** *Mar. 5, 1924*	1.75	.20
	Never hinged	3.50	
	On UPU-rate cover		6.00
	Pair	3.75	.35
	Never hinged	7.50	
	Joint line pair	11.00	1.50
	Never hinged	22.50	
603 A165	10c **orange,** *Dec. 1, 1924*	3.50	.20
	Never hinged	7.00	
	On special delivery cover with 2c		22.50
	Pair	8.00	.25
	Never hinged	16.00	
	Joint line pair	25.00	2.00
	Never hinged	50.00	

The 6c design A161 coil stamp is listed as No. 723.
Bureau Precancels: 1c, 296 diff., 1½c, 188 diff., 2c, type I, 113 diff., 2c, type II, Boston, Detroit, 3c, 62 diff., 4c, 34 diff., 5c, 36 diff., 10c, 32 diff.

1923-25			**Perf. 10 Horizontally**
	Stamp designs: 19¼x22½mm		
604 A155	1c **green,** *July 19, 1924*	.40	.20
	yellow green	.40	.20
	Never hinged	.80	
	Three on cover		6.00
	Pair	.85	.20
	Never hinged	1.70	
	Joint line pair	3.50	.55
	Never hinged	7.00	
605 A156	1½c **yellow brown,** *May 9, 1925*	.40	.20
	brown	.40	.20

	Never hinged	.80	
	On 3rd class cover		17.50
	Pair	.85	.35
	Never hinged	1.70	
	Joint line pair	3.50	.75
	Never hinged	7.00	
606 A157	2c **carmine,** *Dec. 31, 1923*	.40	.20
	Never hinged	.80	
	On cover		3.50
	Pair	.85	.45
	Never hinged	1.70	
	Joint line pair	2.50	1.00
	Never hinged	5.00	
	Cracked plate	5.25	2.00
a.	2c carmine lake	75.00	
	Never hinged	150.00	
	Pair, never hinged	325.00	
	Joint line pair, never hinged	1,000.	
	Nos. 597-599,600-606 (10)	18.00	2.15
	Nos. 597-599, 600-606, never hinged	36.00	

HARDING MEMORIAL ISSUE
Tribute to the memory of President Warren G. Harding, who died in San Francisco, Aug. 2, 1923.

Warren Gamaliel
Harding — A177

Plates of 400 subjects in four panes of 100 each
FLAT PLATE PRINTINGS
Stamp designs: 19¼x22¼mm

1923			**Perf. 11**
610 A177	2c **black,** *Sept. 1, 1923*	.55	.25
	intense black	.55	.25
	grayish black	.55	.25
	Never hinged	1.10	
	On cover		.30
	P# block of 6	25.00	
	Never hinged	35.00	
	Double transfer	1.75	.50
a.	Horiz. pair, imperf. vert.	1,750.	
b.	Imperf, P#14870 block of 6	25,000.	

No. 610b comes from a single upper left error pane found in a normal pad of No. 610 stamps before No. 611 was issued. Plate #14870 was not used to print No. 611. Loose stamps separated from the top and left plate blocks are indistinguishable from No. 611.

		Imperf	
611 A177	2c **black,** *Nov. 15, 1923*	4.75	4.00
	Never hinged	10.00	
	On philatelic cover		8.00
	On commercial cover		15.00
	Pair	10.50	10.00
	Never hinged	22.00	
	Corner margin block of 4	22.50	22.50
	Margin block of 4, arrow	23.50	22.50
	Center line block	60.00	40.00
	Never hinged	90.00	
	P# block of 6	75.00	—
	Never hinged	100.00	

ROTARY PRESS PRINTINGS
Stamp designs: 19¼x22½mm

		Perf. 10	
612 A177	2c **black,** *Sept. 12, 1923*	15.00	1.75
	gray black	15.00	1.75
	Never hinged	32.50	
	On cover		3.25
	P# block of 4	300.00	
	Never hinged	500.00	
	Pair with full vertical gutter between	350.00	

		Perf. 11	
613 A177	2c **black**		45,000.
	Pair		95,000.
	Horiz. strip of 3		175,000.

No. 613 was produced from rotary press sheet waste. It is valued in the grade of fine. The strip of three is the largest recorded multiple.

HUGUENOT-WALLOON TERCENTENARY ISSUE
300th anniversary of the settling of the Walloons, and in honor of the Huguenots.

Ship "Nieu
Nederland"
A178

Walloons Landing at Fort Orange (Albany) — A179

Jan Ribault Monument at Duval County, Fla. — A180

"Broken Circle" flaw

Designed by Clair Aubrey Huston
FLAT PLATE PRINTINGS
Plates of 200 subjects in four panes of 50 each

1924, May 1 — *Perf. 11*

614	A178	1c	**dark green**	2.25	*3.25*
			green	2.25	*3.25*
			Never hinged	4.50	
			On cover		4.50
			P# block of 6	40.00	
			Never hinged	70.00	—
			Double transfer	6.50	6.50
615	A179	2c	**carmine rose**	4.50	2.25
			dark carmine rose	4.50	2.25
			Never hinged	9.25	
			On cover		3.50
			P# block of 6	60.00	
			Never hinged	90.00	
			Double transfer	12.00	3.50
616	A180	5c	**dark blue**	18.00	13.00
			deep blue	18.00	13.00
			Never hinged	37.50	
			On UPU-rate cover		20.00
			P# block of 6	250.00	
			Never hinged	375.00	

Added line at bottom of white circle around right numeral, "broken circle" plate flaw (15754 UR 2, 3, 4, 5)   50.00   15.00
Nos. 614-616 (3)   24.75   18.50
Nos. 614-616, never hinged   51.25

LEXINGTON-CONCORD ISSUE
150th anniv. of the Battle of Lexington-Concord.

Washington at Cambridge
A181

"Birth of Liberty," by Henry Sandham
A182

The Minute Man, by Daniel Chester French — A183

Plates of 200 subjects in four panes of 50 each

1925, Apr. 4 — *Perf. 11*

617	A181	1c	**deep green**	2.10	2.50
			green	2.10	2.50
			Never hinged	4.25	
			On cover		3.75
			P# block of 6	40.00	
			Never hinged	65.00	
618	A182	2c	**carmine rose**	3.90	4.00
			pale carmine rose	3.90	4.00
			Never hinged	8.00	
			On cover		5.50
			P# block of 6	60.00	
			Never hinged	90.00	
619	A183	5c	**dark blue**	17.00	13.00
			blue	17.00	13.00
			Never hinged	35.00	
			On UPU-rate cover		20.00
			P# block of 6	200.00	
			Never hinged	310.00	

Line over head (16807 LL 48)   42.50   19.00
Nos. 617-619 (3)   23.00   19.50
Nos. 617-619, never hinged   47.25

NORSE-AMERICAN ISSUE
Arrival in New York, on Oct. 9, 1825, of the sloop "Restaurationen" with the first group of immigrants from Norway.

Sloop "Restaurationen"
A184

Viking Ship
A185

Designed by Clair Aubrey Huston.

Plates of 100 subjects.

1925, May 18 — *Perf. 11*

620	A184	2c	**carmine & black**	3.50	3.00
			deep carmine & black	3.50	3.00
			Never hinged	7.00	
			On cover		4.50
			Margin block of 4, arrow	17.50	
			Center line block	24.00	
			Never hinged	40.00	
			P# block of 8, two P# & arrow	200.00	—
			Never hinged	300.00	

P# block of 8, carmine & arrow; black P# omitted   3,250.

621	A185	5c	**dark blue & black**	11.00	11.00
			Never hinged	24.00	
			On UPU-rate cover		17.50
			Margin block of 4, arrow	62.50	
			Center line block	75.00	
			Never hinged	135.00	
			P# block of 8, two P# & arrow	500.00	—
			Never hinged	750.00	

REGULAR ISSUE

Benjamin Harrison — A186

Woodrow Wilson — A187

Plates of 400 subjects in four panes of 100.

1925-26 — *Perf. 11*

622	A186	13c	**green,** *Jan. 11, 1926*	11.00	.75
			light green	11.00	.75
			Never hinged	22.50	
			On registered cover with other values		17.50
			P# block of 6	215.00	
			Never hinged	325.00	

P# block of 6, large 5 point star, right side only   2,100.
Never hinged   3,000.

623	A187	17c	**black,** *Dec. 28, 1925*	12.00	.30
			gray black	12.00	.30
			Never hinged	25.00	

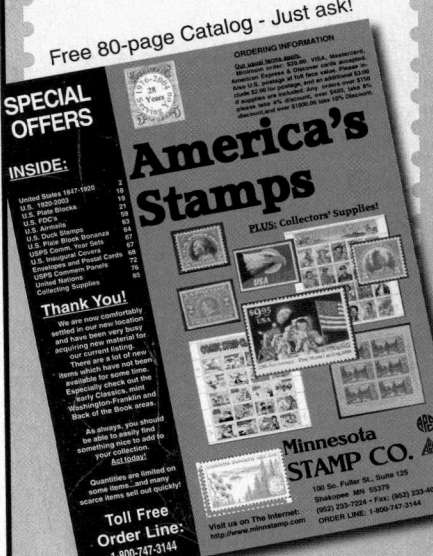

On registered cover		6.00
P# block of 6	250.00	—
Never hinged	350.00	

Plate Blocks

Scott values for plate blocks printed from flat plates are for very fine side and bottom positions. Top position plate blocks with full wide selvage sell for more.

SESQUICENTENNIAL EXPOSITION ISSUE

Sesquicentennial Exposition, Philadelphia, Pa., June 1 - Dec. 1, 1926, and 150th anniv. of the Declaration of Independence.

Liberty Bell — A188

Designed by Clair Aubrey Huston.

Plates of 200 subjects in four panes of 50.

1926, May 10   *Perf. 11*

627 A188 2c **carmine rose**		
	2.50	.50
Never hinged	4.50	
On cover		1.00
On cover, Expo. station machine canc.		7.50
On cover, Expo. station duplex handstamp canc.		35.00
P# block of 6	37.50	—
Never hinged	50.00	
Double transfer	—	—

ERICSSON MEMORIAL ISSUE

Unveiling of the statue of John Ericsson, builder of the "Monitor," by the Crown Prince of Sweden, Washington, D.C., May 29, 1926.

Statue of John Ericsson — A189

Designed by Clair Aubrey Huston.

Plates of 200 subjects in four panes of 50.

1926, May 29   *Perf. 11*

628 A189 5c **gray lilac**		
	5.50	3.25
Never hinged	9.50	
On UPU-rate cover		8.00
P# block of 6	60.00	—
Never hinged	95.00	

BATTLE OF WHITE PLAINS ISSUE

150th anniv. of the Battle of White Plains, N. Y.

Alexander Hamilton's Battery — A190

Designed by Clair Aubrey Huston.

Plates of 400 subjects in four panes of 100.

1926, Oct. 18   *Perf. 11*

629 A190 2c **carmine rose**		
	1.90	1.70
Never hinged	3.25	
On cover		2.25
P# block of 6	37.50	—
Never hinged	60.00	

INTERNATIONAL PHILATELIC EXHIBITION ISSUE
Souvenir Sheet

A190a

Illustration reduced.

Plates of 100 subjects in four panes of 25 each, separated by one inch wide gutters with central guide lines.

Condition valued:

Centering: Overall centering will average very fine, but individual stamps may be better or worse.

Perforations: No folds along rows of perforations.

Gum: There may be some light gum bends but no gum creases.

Hinging: There may be hinge marks in the selvage and on up to two or three stamps, but no heavy hinging or hinge remnants (except in the ungummed portion of the wide selvage).

Margins: Top panes should have about ½ inch bottom margin and 1 inch top margin.

Bottom panes should have about ½ inch top margin and just under ¾ inch bottom margin. Both will have one wide side (usually 1 inch plus) and one narrow (½ inch) side margin. The wide margin corner will have a small diagonal notch on top panes.

1926, Oct. 18   *Perf. 11*

630 A190a 2c **carmine rose**, sheet of 25	375.00	450.00
Never hinged	600.00	
On cover		—
Dot over first "S" of "States" 18774 LL 9 or 18773 LL 11, sheet	400.00	475.00

Issued in sheets measuring 158-160¼x136-146½mm containing 25 stamps with inscription "International Philatelic Exhibition, Oct. 16th to 23rd, 1926" in top margin.

VALUES FOR VERY FINE STAMPS
Please note: Stamps are valued in the grade of Very Fine unless otherwise indicated.

REGULAR ISSUE
ROTARY PRESS PRINTINGS
(See note over No. 448.)
Plates of 400 subjects in four panes of 100 each
Stamp designs 19¼x22½mm

1926, Aug. 27   *Imperf.*

631 A156 1½c **yellow brown**		
	2.00	1.70
light brown	2.00	1.70
Never hinged	3.00	
On philatelic cover		12.50
Pair	4.25	4.00
Never hinged	6.25	
Pair, vert. gutter between	4.75	5.00
Pair, horiz. gutter between	4.75	5.00
Margin block with dash (left, right, top or bottom)	11.00	14.00
Center block with crossed gutters and dashes	27.50	30.00
Never hinged	42.50	
P# block of 4	57.50	—
Never hinged	85.00	
Without gum breaker ridges	50.00	
Pair, vert. gutter between	*125.00*	
Pair, horiz. gutter btwn.	*125.00*	
Margin block with dash (left, right, top or bottom)	*350.00*	
Center block with crossed gutters and dashes	*700.00*	
Never hinged	*1,050.00*	
P# block of 4	450.00	
Never hinged	700.00	

1926-34   *Perf. 11x10½*

632 A155 1c **green**, *June 10, 1927*		
	.25	.20
yellow green	.25	.20
Never hinged	.35	
Three on cover		1.25
P# block of 4	2.00	
Never hinged	3.25	
Pair with full vertical gutter btwn.	150.00	—
Cracked plate	—	—
a. Booklet pane of 6, *Nov. 2, 1927*	5.00	4.00

Never hinged	8.00	
b. Vertical pair, imperf. between	*3,250.*	—
Never hinged	*5,000.*	
c. Horiz. pair, imperf. between	*5,000.*	

No. 632c is valued in the grade of fine and never hinged. It is possibly unique.

633 A156 1½c **yellow brown**, *May 17, 1927*		
	1.70	.20
deep brown	1.70	.20
Never hinged	2.60	
On 3rd class cover		2.50
P# block of 4	70.00	
Never hinged	120.00	

Normal   Recut ("long ear")

634 A157 2c **carmine**, type I, *Dec. 10, 1926*		
	.20	.20
Never hinged	.20	
On cover		.20
P# block of 4, type I, # opposite corner stamp	3.75	—
Never hinged	6.50	
Vertical P# block of 10, # opposite 3rd horizontal row from top or bottom (Experimental Electric Eye plates)	5.00	—
Never hinged	8.50	
Margin block of 4, Electric Eye marking	.45	.25
Pair with full vertical gutter between	200.00	
Recut ("long ear"), type I, 20342 UR 34	*400.00*	
Recut face, type I, 20234 LL 58		
b. 2c **carmine lake**, type I	*225.00*	—
Never hinged	*425.00*	
P# block of 4	*1,500.*	
Never hinged	*2,750.*	
c. Horizontal pair, type I, imperf. between	*7,000.*	
d. Booklet pane of 6, type I, *Feb. 25, 1927*	1.50	1.50
Never hinged	2.50	
e. As "d," carmine lake	*625.00*	
Never hinged	*1,250.*	
f. 2c **lake**, type I, on cover		—

Shades of the carmine exist.

No. 634, Type I, exists on a thin, tough experimental paper. No. 634c is valued in the grade of fine.

Earliest documented use: FDC (No. 634); Dec. 20, 1929 (No. 634b).

634A A157 2c **carmine**, type II, *Dec. 1928*		
	325.00	13.50
Never hinged	650.00	
On cover		21.00
P# block of 4, type II	2,200.	—
Never hinged	3,000.	
Pair with full horiz. gutter btwn.	850.00	—
Never hinged	*1,400.*	
Pair with full vert. gutter btwn.	850.00	—
Never hinged	*1,400.*	
Center block with crossed gutters	2,750.	
Never hinged	*4,250.*	

Earliest documented use: Dec. 15, 1928.

No. 634A, Type II, was available in full sheet of 400 subjects but was not regularly issued in that form.

635 A158 3c **violet**, *Feb. 3, 1927*		
	.50	.20
Never hinged	.75	
On cover		2.00
P# block of 4	17.50	
Never hinged	35.00	
a. 3c **bright violet**, *Feb. 7, 1934* re-issue, Plates 21185 & 21186	.20	.20
Never hinged	.30	
On cover		.25
P# block of 4	11.00	—
Never hinged	20.00	
Gripper cracks	3.25	2.00

636 A159 4c **yellow brown**, *May 17, 1927*		
	1.90	.20
Never hinged	3.00	
On cover		8.00
P# block of 4	75.00	—
Never hinged	120.00	
Pair with full vert. gutter btwn.	200.00	

637 A160 5c **dark blue**, *Mar. 24, 1927*		
	1.90	.20
Never hinged	3.00	
On UPU-rate cover		4.50
P# block of 4	15.00	—
Never hinged	22.50	
Pair with full vert. gutter btwn.	275.00	
Double transfer	—	

| 638 A161 6c **red orange**, *July 27, 1927* | 2.00 | .20 |

		Never hinged		3.20	
		On airmail cover			6.00
		P# block of 4		15.00	
		Never hinged		22.50	
		Pair with full horiz. gutter btwn.		—	
		Pair with full vert. gutter btwn.		200.00	
639	A162	7c **black,** *Mar. 24, 1927*		2.00	.20
		Never hinged		3.20	
		On registered cover with other values			15.00
		P# block of 4		15.00	
		Never hinged		22.50	
a.		Vertical pair, imperf. between		325.00	250.00
		Never hinged		500.00	
640	A163	8c **olive green,** *June 10, 1927*		2.00	.20
		olive bister		2.00	.20
		Never hinged		3.20	
		On airmail cover			8.00
		P# block of 4		15.00	
		Never hinged		22.50	
641	A164	9c **rose,** *May 17, 1927*		1.90	.20
		salmon rose		1.90	.20
		orange red, *1931*		1.90	.20
		Never hinged		3.00	
		On registered cover with other values			8.00
		P# block of 4		15.00	
		Never hinged		22.50	
		Pair with full vert. gutter btwn.		—	
642	A165	10c **orange,** *Feb. 3, 1927*		3.25	.20
		Never hinged		5.50	
		On special delivery cover with 2c			6.00
		P# block of 4		20.00	
		Never hinged		30.00	
		Double transfer		—	
		Nos. 632-634,635-642 (11)		17.60	2.20
		Nos. 632-634, 635-642 never hinged		27.85	

The 1½c, 2c, 4c, 5c, 6c, 8c imperf. (dry print) are printer's waste.
See No. 653.
Bureau Precancels: 1c, 292 diff., 1½c, 147 diff., 2c, type I, 99 diff., 2c, type II, 4 diff., 3c, 101 diff., 4c, 60 diff., 5c, 91 diff., 6c, 78 diff., 7c, 66 diff., 8c, 78 diff., 9c, 60 diff., 10c, 97 diff.

VERMONT SESQUICENTENNIAL ISSUE

Battle of Bennington, 150th anniv. and State independence.

Green Mountain Boy — A191

FLAT PLATE PRINTING
Plates of 400 subjects in four panes of 100.

1927, Aug. 3					*Perf. 11*
643	A191	2c **carmine rose**		1.20	.80
		Never hinged		2.00	
		On cover			1.50
		P# block of 6		35.00	
		Never hinged		55.00	

BURGOYNE CAMPAIGN ISSUE

Battles of Bennington, Oriskany, Fort Stanwix and Saratoga.

"The Surrender of General Burgoyne at Saratoga," by John Trumbull A192

Plates of 200 subjects in four panes of 50.

1927, Aug. 3					*Perf. 11*
644	A192	2c **carmine rose**		3.10	2.10
		Never hinged		5.50	
		On cover			3.00
		P# block of 6		32.50	
		Never hinged		45.00	

VALLEY FORGE ISSUE

150th anniversary of Washington's encampment at Valley Forge, Pa.

Washington at Prayer — A193

Plates of 400 subjects in four panes of 100.

1928, May 26					*Perf. 11*
645	A193	2c **carmine rose**		.95	.50
		Never hinged		1.50	
		On cover			.75
		P# block of 6		25.00	
		Never hinged		40.00	
a.		2c **lake**		—	
		Never hinged		—	

BATTLE OF MONMOUTH ISSUE

150th anniv. of the Battle of Monmouth, N.J., and "Molly Pitcher" (Mary Ludwig Hayes), the heroine of the battle.

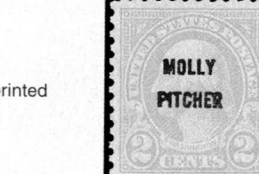

No. 634 Overprinted

ROTARY PRESS PRINTING

1928, Oct. 20					*Perf. 11x10½*
646	A157	2c **carmine**		1.00	1.00
		Never hinged		1.60	
		On cover			1.60
		P# block of 4		37.50	
		Never hinged		55.00	
		Wide spacing, vert. pair		50.00	—
a.		"Pitcher" only		*500.00*	

No. 646a is valued in the grade of fine.
Normally the overprints were placed 18mm apart vertically, but pairs exist with a space of 28mm between the overprints.

HAWAII SESQUICENTENNIAL ISSUE

Sesquicentennial Celebration of the discovery of the Hawaiian Islands.

Nos. 634 and 637 Overprinted

ROTARY PRESS PRINTING

1928, Aug. 13					*Perf. 11x10½*
647	A157	2c **carmine**		4.00	4.00
		Never hinged		7.25	
		On cover			5.75
		P# block of 4		125.00	—
		Never hinged		225.00	
		Wide spacing, vert. pair		125.00	
648	A160	5c **dark blue**		11.00	12.50
		Never hinged		21.50	
		On cover			20.00
		P# block of 4		275.00	—
		Never hinged		425.00	

Nos. 647-648 were sold at post offices in Hawaii and at the Postal Agency in Washington, D.C. They were valid throughout the nation.
Normally the overprints were placed 18mm apart vertically, but pairs exist with a space of 28mm between the overprints.

AERONAUTICS CONFERENCE ISSUE

Intl. Civil Aeronautics Conf., Washington, D.C., Dec. 12 - 14, 1928, and 25th anniv. of the 1st airplane flight by the Wright Brothers, Dec. 17, 1903.

Wright Airplane A194

Globe and Airplane A195

"Prairie Dog" plate flaw

FLAT PLATE PRINTING
Plates of 200 subjects in four panes of 50.

1928, Dec. 12					*Perf. 11*
649	A194	2c **carmine rose**		1.10	.80
		Never hinged		1.75	
		On cover			1.50
		P# block of 6		12.00	
		Never hinged		20.00	
650	A195	5c **blue**		4.50	3.25
		Never hinged		7.25	
		On UPU-rate cover			5.00
		P# block of 6		45.00	
		Never hinged		70.00	
		Plate flaw "prairie dog" (19658 LL 50)		27.50	12.50

GEORGE ROGERS CLARK ISSUE

150th anniv. of the surrender of Fort Sackville, the present site of Vincennes, Ind., to Clark.

Surrender of Fort Sackville A196

Plates of 100 subjects in two panes of 50.

1929, Feb. 25					*Perf. 11*
651	A196	2c **carmine & black**		.70	.50
		deep carmine & black		.70	.50
		Never hinged		1.10	
		On cover			1.00
		Margin block of 4, arrow (line only) right or left		3.25	
		P# block of 6, two P# & "Top"		12.00	—
		Never hinged		20.00	
		P# block of 10, red P# only		—	—
		Double transfer (19721 R 14, 29 & 44)		4.25	2.25

REGULAR ISSUE
Type of 1922-26 Issue
ROTARY PRESS PRINTING
Plates of 400 subjects in four panes of 100.

1929, May 25					*Perf. 11x10½*
653	A154	½c **olive brown**		.25	.20
		Never hinged		.35	
		On 1c stamped envelope (3rd class)			1.00
		P# block of 4		2.00	—
		Never hinged		3.00	
		Damaged plate, (19652 LL 72)		1.50	.75
		Retouched plate, (19652 LL 72)		1.50	.75
		Pair with full horiz. gutter btwn.		*150.00*	

Bureau Precancels: 99 diff.

Edison's First
Lamp — A197

Major General John
Sullivan — A198

ELECTRIC LIGHT'S GOLDEN JUBILEE ISSUE

Invention of the 1st incandescent electric lamp by
Thomas Alva Edison, Oct. 21, 1879, 50th anniv.

Designed by Alvin R. Meissner.

FLAT PLATE PRINTING
Plates of 400 subjects in four panes of 100.

1929					Perf. 11
654	A197	2c	carmine rose, *June 5*	.60	.65
		Never hinged		1.00	
		On cover			1.10
		P# block of 6		25.00	—
		Never hinged		45.00	
a.		2c lake		—	

ROTARY PRESS PRINTING
Perf. 11x10½

655	A197	2c	carmine rose, *June 11*	.55	.20
		Never hinged		.90	
		On cover			.25
		P# block of 4		35.00	—
		Never hinged		55.00	

ROTARY PRESS COIL STAMP
Perf. 10 Vertically

656	A197	2c	carmine rose, *June 11*	11.00	1.75
		Never hinged		21.00	
		On cover			2.75
		Pair		25.00	4.00
		Never hinged		45.00	
		Joint line pair		60.00	27.50
		Never hinged		110.00	

SULLIVAN EXPEDITION ISSUE

150th anniversary of the Sullivan Expedition in New
York State during the Revolutionary War.

FLAT PLATE PRINTING
Plates of 400 subjects in four panes of 100.

1929, June 17					Perf. 11
657	A198	2c	carmine rose	.60	.60
		Never hinged		1.00	
		On cover			1.00
		P# block of 6		22.50	
		Never hinged		37.50	
a.		2c lake		325.00	300.00
		Never hinged		575.00	
		P# block of 6		2,750.	
		Never hinged		3,750.	

REGULAR ISSUE

Nos. 632 to 642 Overprinted

Kans.

Officially issued May 1, 1929.
Some values known canceled as early as Apr. 15.

This special issue was authorized as a measure of preventing
losses from post office burglaries. Approximately a year's supply was printed and issued to postmasters. The P.O. Dept.
found it desirable to discontinue the State overprinted stamps
after the initial supply was used.

ROTARY PRESS PRINTING

1929, May 1					Perf. 11x10½
658	A155	1c	green	2.50	2.00
		Never hinged		5.00	
		P# block of 4		60.00	—
		Never hinged		90.00	
		Wide spacing, pair		32.50	
a.		Vertical pair, one without ovpt.		*300.00*	
		Never hinged		*500.00*	
659	A156	1½c	brown	3.10	2.90
		Never hinged		6.25	
		P# block of 4		60.00	—
		Never hinged		85.00	
		Wide spacing, pair		70.00	
a.		Vertical pair, one without ovpt.		*475.00*	
660	A157	2c	carmine	4.00	1.00
		Never hinged		7.50	
		P# block of 4		60.00	—
		Never hinged		85.00	
		Wide spacing, pair		55.00	
661	A158	3c	violet	18.50	15.00
		Never hinged		37.50	
		P# block of 4		225.00	

		Never hinged	325.00	
a.		Vertical pair, one without ovpt.	*525.00*	
		Never hinged	675.00	
662	A159	4c yellow brown	18.50	9.00
		Never hinged	37.50	
		P# block of 4	225.00	—
		Never hinged	325.00	
a.		Vertical pair, one without ovpt.	*500.00*	
663	A160	5c deep blue	12.00	9.75
		Never hinged	24.00	
		P# block of 4	200.00	—
		Never hinged	300.00	
664	A161	6c red orange	27.50	18.00
		Never hinged	55.00	
		P# block of 4	450.00	—
		Never hinged	650.00	
665	A162	7c black	27.50	27.50
		Never hinged	55.00	
		P# block of 4	500.00	—
		Never hinged	725.00	
666	A163	8c olive green	90.00	70.00
		Never hinged	180.00	
		P# block of 4	700.00	—
		Never hinged	1,000.	
667	A164	9c light rose	13.00	11.50
		Never hinged	26.00	
		P# block of 4	275.00	—
		Never hinged	400.00	
668	A165	10c orange yellow	22.50	12.50
		Never hinged	45.00	
		P# block of 4	375.00	—
		Never hinged	575.00	
		Pair with full horizontal gutter		
		between	4,750.	
		Nos. 658-668 (11)	239.10	179.15
		Nos. 658-668, never hinged	478.75	

See notes following No. 679.

Overprinted

Nebr.

1929, May 1					
669	A155	1c	green	3.25	2.25
		Never hinged		6.50	
		P# block of 4		60.00	—
		Never hinged		90.00	
		Wide spacing, pair		40.00	
b.		No period after "Nebr." (19338, 19339 UR 26, 36)		50.00	
670	A156	1½c	brown	3.00	2.50
		Never hinged		6.00	
		P# block of 4		65.00	—
		Never hinged		95.00	
		Wide spacing, pair		37.50	
671	A157	2c	carmine	3.00	1.30
		Never hinged		6.00	
		P# block of 4		60.00	—
		Never hinged		90.00	
		Wide spacing, pair		57.50	
672	A158	3c	violet	12.00	12.00
		Never hinged		24.00	
		P# block of 4		250.00	—
		Never hinged		375.00	
		Wide spacing, pair		80.00	
a.		Vertical pair, one without ovpt.		*500.00*	
673	A159	4c	yellow brown	17.50	15.00
		Never hinged		35.00	
		P# block of 4		275.00	—
		Never hinged		400.00	
		Wide spacing, pair		120.00	
674	A160	5c	deep blue	16.00	15.00
		Never hinged		32.50	
		P# block of 4		300.00	—
		Never hinged		425.00	
675	A161	6c	red orange	37.50	24.00
		Never hinged		75.00	
		P# block of 4		525.00	—
		Never hinged		750.00	
676	A162	7c	black	21.00	18.00
		Never hinged		42.50	
		P# block of 4		325.00	—
		Never hinged		525.00	
677	A163	8c	olive green	32.50	25.00
		Never hinged		65.00	
		P# block of 4		400.00	—
		Never hinged		600.00	
		Wide spacing, pair		175.00	
678	A164	9c	light rose	35.00	27.50
		Never hinged		70.00	
		P# block of 4		525.00	—
		Never hinged		750.00	
		Wide spacing, pair		160.00	
a.		Vertical pair, one without ovpt.		*750.00*	
679	A165	10c	orange yellow	115.00	22.50
		Never hinged		230.00	
		P# block of 4		925.	—
		Never hinged		1,300.	
		Nos. 669-679 (11)		295.75	165.05
		Nos. 669-679, never hinged		592.75	

Nos. 658-661, 669-673, 677-678 are known with the overprints on vertical pairs spaced 32mm apart instead of the normal 22mm.

Important: Nos. 658-679 with original gum have either one
horizontal gum breaker ridge per stamp or portions of two at the
extreme top and bottom of the stamps, 21mm apart. Multiple

complete gum breaker ridges indicate a fake overprint. Absence
of the gum breaker ridge indicates either regumming or regumming and a fake overprint.

General Wayne
Memorial — A199

Lock No. 5,
Monongahela
River — A200

BATTLE OF FALLEN TIMBERS ISSUE

Memorial to Gen. Anthony Wayne and for 135th
anniv. of the Battle of Fallen Timbers, Ohio.

FLAT PLATE PRINTING
Plates of 400 subjects in four panes of 100.

1929, Sept. 14					Perf. 11
680	A199	2c	carmine rose	.70	.70
		deep carmine rose		.70	.70
		Never hinged		1.10	
		On cover			1.10
		P# block of 6		20.00	—
		Never hinged		32.50	

OHIO RIVER CANALIZATION ISSUE

Completion of the Ohio River Canalization Project,
between Cairo, Ill. and Pittsburgh, Pa.

Plates of 400 subjects in four panes of 100.

1929, Oct. 19					Perf. 11
681	A200	2c	carmine rose	.60	.60
		Never hinged		.95	
		On cover			1.10
		P# block of 6		14.00	—
		Never hinged		25.00	
a.		2c lake		—	

Massachusetts Bay
Colony Seal — A201

Gov. Joseph West
and Chief Shadoo, a
Kiowa — A202

MASSACHUSETTS BAY COLONY ISSUE

300th anniversary of the founding of the Massachusetts Bay Colony.

Plates of 400 subjects in four panes of 100.

1930, Apr. 8					Perf. 11
682	A201	2c	carmine rose	.50	.50
		Never hinged		.85	
		On cover			1.00
		P# block of 6		22.50	—
		Never hinged		35.00	

CAROLINA-CHARLESTON ISSUE

260th anniv. of the founding of the Province of Carolina and the 250th anniv. of the city of Charleston, S.C.

Plates of 400 subjects in four panes of 100.

1930, Apr. 10					Perf. 11
683	A202	2c	carmine rose	1.05	1.05
		Never hinged		1.65	
		On cover			1.40
		P# block of 6		40.00	—
		Never hinged		57.50	

REGULAR ISSUE

Harding — A203

Taft — A204

Type of 1922-26 Issue
ROTARY PRESS PRINTING

1930   *Perf. 11x10½*

684	A203	1½c **brown**, *Dec. 1*	.40	.20
		yellow brown	.40	.20
		Never hinged	.55	
		On 3rd class cover		2.00
		P# block of 4	2.00	
		Never hinged	3.00	
		Pair with full horiz. gutter btwn.	175.00	
		Pair with full vert. gutter btwn.		
685	A204	4c **brown**, *June 4*	.80	.25
		deep brown	.80	.25
		Never hinged	1.25	
		On cover		5.00
		P# block of 4	15.00	
		Never hinged	25.00	
		Gouge on right "4" (20141 UL 24)	2.10	.60
		Recut right "4" (20141 UL 24)	2.10	.65
		Pair with full horiz. gutter btwn.		

Bureau Precancels: 1½c, 96 diff., 4c, 46 diff.

ROTARY PRESS COIL STAMPS
Perf. 10 Vertically

686	A203	1½c **brown**, *Dec. 1*	1.75	.20
		Never hinged	2.60	
		On 3rd class cover		5.00
		Pair	3.75	.20
		Never hinged	5.75	
		Joint line pair	7.50	.75
		Never hinged	11.50	
687	A204	4c **brown**, *Sept. 18*	3.00	.45
		Never hinged	4.50	
		On cover		10.00
		Pair	6.25	1.00
		Never hinged	9.50	
		Joint line pair	11.00	2.50
		Never hinged	22.00	

Bureau Precancels: 1½c, 107 diff., 4c, 23 diff.

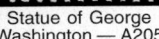
Statue of George Washington — A205

General von Steuben — A206

BRADDOCK'S FIELD ISSUE

175th anniversary of the Battle of Braddock's Field, otherwise the Battle of Monongahela.

Designed by Alvin R. Meissner.

FLAT PLATE PRINTING
Plates of 400 subjects in four panes of 100.

1930, July 9   *Perf. 11*

688	A205	2c **carmine rose**	.90	.85
		Never hinged	1.40	
		On cover		1.00
		P# block of 6	32.50	
		Never hinged	45.00	

VON STEUBEN ISSUE

Baron Friedrich Wilhelm von Steuben (1730-1794), participant in the American Revolution.

FLAT PLATE PRINTING
Plates of 400 subjects in four panes of 100.

1930, Sept. 17   *Perf. 11*

689	A206	2c **carmine rose**	.50	.50
		Never hinged	.75	
		On cover		1.05
		P# block of 6	17.50	
		Never hinged	30.00	
a.		Imperf., pair	2,750.	
		Never hinged	3,500.	
		P# block of 6	12,500.	

The No. 689a plate block is unique but damaged. The value is for the item in its damaged condition.

General Casimir Pulaski — A207

"The Greatest Mother" — A208

PULASKI ISSUE

150th anniversary (in 1929) of the death of Gen. Casimir Pulaski, Polish patriot and hero of the American Revolutionary War.

Plates of 400 subjects in four panes of 100.

1931, Jan. 16   *Perf. 11*

690	A207	2c **carmine rose**	.30	.25
		deep carmine rose	.30	.25
		Never hinged	.40	
		On cover		.50
		P# block of 6	10.00	
		Never hinged	17.50	

REGULAR ISSUE
TYPE OF 1922-26 ISSUES
ROTARY PRESS PRINTING

1931   *Perf. 11x10½*

692	A166	11c **light blue**, *Sept. 4*	2.50	.25
		Never hinged	3.75	
		On registered cover with other values		10.00
		P# block of 4	15.00	
		Never hinged	27.50	
		Retouched forehead (20617 LL 2, 3)	20.00	1.00
693	A167	12c **brown violet**, *Aug. 25*	5.00	.20
		violet brown	5.00	.20
		Never hinged	8.00	
		Pair on registered cover		8.00
		P# block of 4	22.50	
		Never hinged	40.00	
694	A186	13c **yellow green**, *Sept. 4*	2.25	.25
		light yellow green	2.25	.25
		blue green	2.25	.25
		Never hinged	3.50	
		On special delivery cover		27.50
		P# block of 4	15.00	
		Never hinged	27.50	
		Pair with full vert. gutter btwn.	150.00	
695	A168	14c **dark blue**, *Sept. 8*	4.00	.60
		Never hinged	6.25	
		On registered cover with other values		20.00
		P# block of 4	26.00	
		Never hinged	40.00	
696	A169	15c **gray**, *Aug. 27*	7.75	.25
		dark gray	8.00	.25
		Never hinged	12.00	
		On registered cover with 3c		5.00
		P# block of 4	37.50	
		Never hinged	52.50	

Perf. 10½x11

697	A187	17c **black**, *July 25*	4.75	.25
		Never hinged	7.25	
		On registered cover		5.00
		P# block of 4	37.50	
		Never hinged	52.50	
698	A170	20c **carmine rose**, *Sept. 8*	7.75	.25
		Never hinged	12.50	
		On registered UPU-rate cover		12.50
		P# block of 4	37.50	
		Never hinged	60.00	
		Double transfer (20538 LR 26)	20.00	
699	A171	25c **blue green**, *July 25*	8.00	.25
		Never hinged	13.00	
		On Federal airmail cover		20.00
		P# block of 4	42.50	
		Never hinged	75.00	
700	A172	30c **brown**, *Sept. 8*	13.00	.25
		Never hinged	22.50	
		On Federal airmail cover		17.50
		P# block of 4	72.50	
		Never hinged	110.00	
		Retouched in head (20552 UL 83)	27.50	.85
		Cracked plate (20552 UR 30)	26.00	.85
701	A173	50c **lilac**, *Sept. 4*	30.00	.25
		red lilac	30.00	.25
		Never hinged	52.50	
		On Federal airmail cover		25.00
		P# block of 4	175.00	
		Never hinged	250.00	
		Nos. 692-701 (10)	85.00	2.80
		Nos. 692-701, never hinged	141.10	

Bureau Precancels: 11c, 33 diff., 12c, 33 diff., 13c, 28 diff., 14c, 27 diff., 15c, 33 diff., 17c, 29 diff., 20c, 37 diff., 25c, 29 diff., 30c, 31 diff., 50c, 28 diff.

RED CROSS ISSUE

50th anniversary of the founding of the American Red Cross Society.

FLAT PLATE PRINTING
Plates of 200 subjects in two panes of 100.

1931, May 21   *Perf. 11*

702	A208	2c **black & red**	.20	.20
		Never hinged	.30	
		Margin block of 4, arrow right or left	1.05	
		P# block of 4, two P#	2.25	
		Never hinged	3.00	
		Double transfer	1.50	.50
a.		Red cross missing (FO)	40,000.	

The cross tends to shift, appearing in many slightly varied positions.

One example of No. 702a is documented; believed to be unique. Value reflects most recent sale price at auction in 1994.

YORKTOWN ISSUE

Surrender of Cornwallis at Yorktown, 1781.

Rochambeau, Washington, de Grasse
A209

First Plate Layout — Border and vignette plates of 100 subjects in two panes of 50 subjects each. Plate numbers between 20461 and 20602.

Second Plate Layout — Border plates of 100 subjects in two panes of 50 each, separated by a 1 inch wide vertical gutter with central guide line and vignette plates of 50 subjects. Plate numbers between 20646 and 20671.

Issued in panes of 50 subjects.

1931, Oct. 19   *Perf. 11*

703	A209	2c **carmine rose & black**	.35	.25
		Never hinged	.50	
		Margin block of 4, arrow marker, right or left	1.70	
		Center line block	1.80	
		P# block of 4, 2#	3.00	—
		Never hinged	4.00	
		P# block of 4, 2# & arrow & marker block	3.00	—
		Never hinged	4.00	
		P# block of 6, 2# & "TOP," arrow & marker	3.50	—
		Never hinged	4.50	
		P# block of 8, 2# & "TOP"	3.75	—
		Never hinged	5.00	
		Double transfer	1.75	.75
a.		2c **lake & black**	4.50	.75
		Never hinged	6.25	
b.		2c **dark lake & black**	400.00	
		Never hinged	750.00	
		P# block of 4, 2#	2,250.	
		Never hinged	3,000.	
c.		Horiz. pair, imperf. vertically	5,000.	
		Never hinged	6,250.	
		Center line block of 10	17,000.	
		P# block of 10, top, 2#, arrow, marker and "TOP," block	35,000.	
		P# block of 10, bottom, 2#, arrow and marker	25,000.	

No. 703c is valued in the grade of fine.

WASHINGTON BICENTENNIAL ISSUE

200th anniversary of the birth of George Washington. Various Portraits of George Washington.

By Charles Willson Peale, 1777 — A210

From Houdon Bust, 1785 — A211

By Charles Willson Peale, 1772 — A212

By Gilbert Stuart, 1796 — A213

By Charles Willson Peale, 1777 — A214

By Charles Peale Polk — A215

By Charles Willson
Peale, 1795 — A216

By John Trumbull,
1792 — A217

By John Trumbull,
1780 — A218

By Charles B. J. F.
Saint Memin,
1798 — A219

By W. Williams,
1794 — A220

By Gilbert Stuart,
1795 — A221

Broken Circle

ROTARY PRESS PRINTINGS
Plates of 400 subjects in four panes of 100 each

1932, Jan. 1   *Perf. 11x10½*

704	A210	½c	**olive brown**	.25 .20
			Never hinged	.35
			P# block of 4	6.50 —
			Never hinged	10.00
			Broken circle (20560 UR 8)	.75 .20
705	A211	1c	**green**	.25 .20
			Never hinged	.35
			P# block of 4	4.00 —
			Never hinged	6.00
			Gripper cracks (20742 UL and UR)	2.75 1.75
706	A212	1½c	**brown**	.45 .20
			Never hinged	.60
			P# block of 4	15.00 —
			Never hinged	30.00

Cracked Plate   Broken "E" Plate

707	A213	2c	**carmine rose**	.30 .20
			Never hinged	.45
			P# block of 4	1.40 —
			Never hinged	2.50
			Pair with full vert. gutter between	
			Cracked plate (20768 UL 1)	—
			Broken "E" plate flaw (20772 UR 8)	—
			Gripper cracks (20752 LR, 20755 LL & LR, 20756 LL, 20774 LR, 20792 LL & LR, 20796 LL & LR)	1.75 .65

No. 708
3 Cent Bicentennial
BROKEN TOP FRAME
L.L.20847 - Stamp Nº 8
King

Double Transfer

708	A214	3c	**deep violet**	.55 .20
			Never hinged	.80
			P# block of 4	17.50 —

Retouch in
Eyes — 4c

Cracked Plate
— 5c

			Never hinged	25.00
			Double transfer	1.75 .65
			Broken top frame line (20847 LL 8)	4.00 .90

709	A215	4c	**light brown**	.40 .20
			Never hinged	.60
			P# block of 4	5.00 —
			Never hinged	8.00
			Double transfer (20568 LR 60)	2.00 .25
			Retouch in eyes (20568 LR 89)	2.50 .35
			P# block of 4 with variety	
			Broken bottom frame line (20568 LR 100)	2.00 .50
			P# block of 4 with variety	
710	A216	5c	**blue**	1.50 .20
			Never hinged	2.25
			P# block of 4	15.00 —
			Never hinged	25.00
			Cracked plate (20637 UR 80)	5.25 1.10
711	A217	6c	**red orange**	3.00 .20
			Never hinged	4.50
			P# block of 4	52.50 —
			Never hinged	72.50

Double Transfer

712	A218	7c	**black**	.50 .20
			Never hinged	.75
			P# block of 4	9.00 —
			Never hinged	14.00
			Double transfer (20563 UL 1 or 20564 LL 91)	1.50 .25
			P# block of 4 with variety	
713	A219	8c	**olive bister**	2.75 .50
			Never hinged	4.00
			P# block of 4	50.00 —
			Never hinged	70.00
			Pair with full vert. gutter between	
714	A220	9c	**pale red**	2.25 .20
			orange red	2.25 .20
			Never hinged	3.25
			P# block of 4	35.00 —
			Never hinged	50.00
715	A221	10c	**orange yellow**	10.00 .20
			Never hinged	15.00
			P# block of 4	90.00 —
			Never hinged	130.00
			Nos. 704-715 (12)	22.20 2.70
			Nos. 704-715, never hinged	31.90

Skier — A222

Boy and Girl
Planting
Tree — A223

OLYMPIC WINTER GAMES ISSUE

3rd Olympic Winter Games, held at Lake Placid, N.Y., Feb. 4-13, 1932.

FLAT PLATE PRINTING
Plates of 400 subjects in four panes of 100.

1932, Jan. 25   *Perf. 11*

716	A222	2c	**carmine rose**	.40 .20
			carmine	.40 .20
			Never hinged	.55
			P# block of 6	10.00 —
			Never hinged	14.00
			Cracked plate (20823 UR 41, 42; UL 48, 49, 50)	5.00 1.65
			Recut (20823 UR 61)	3.50 1.50
			Colored "snowball" (20815 UR 64)	25.00 5.00
a.			2c lake	—
			Never hinged	—
			carmine lake	—
			Never hinged	—

ARBOR DAY ISSUE

1st observance of Arbor Day in the state of Nebraska, Apr. 1872, 60th anniv., and cent. of the birth of Julius Sterling Morton, who conceived the plan

and the name "Arbor Day," while he was a member of the Nebraska State Board of Agriculture.

ROTARY PRESS PRINTING
Plates of 400 subjects in four panes of 100.

1932, Apr. 22   *Perf. 11x10½*

717	A223	2c	**carmine rose**	.25 .20
			Never hinged	.35
			P# block of 4	5.50 —
			Never hinged	7.50

OLYMPIC GAMES ISSUE

Issued in honor of the 10th Olympic Games, held at Los Angeles, Calif., July 30 to Aug. 14, 1932.

Runner at Starting
Mark — A224

Myron's
Discobolus — A225

Designed by Victor S. McCloskey, Jr.

ROTARY PRESS PRINTING
Plates of 400 subjects in four panes of 100.

1932, June 15   *Perf. 11x10½*

718	A224	3c	**violet**	1.50 .20
			deep violet	1.50 .20
			Never hinged	2.00
			P# block of 4	12.00 —
			Never hinged	18.50
			Gripper cracks (20906 UL 1)	4.25 .75
			P# block of 4 with variety	
719	A225	5c	**blue**	2.25 .20
			deep blue	2.25 .20
			Never hinged	2.90
			P# block of 4	20.00 —
			Never hinged	27.50
			Gripper cracks (20868 UL & UR)	4.25 1.00

Washington, by Gilbert
Stuart — A226

REGULAR ISSUE
ROTARY PRESS PRINTING
Plates of 400 subjects in four panes of 100.

1932   *Perf. 11x10½*

720	A226	3c	**deep violet,** *June 16*	.20 .20
			light violet	.20 .20
			Never hinged	.25
			P# block of 4	1.60 —
			Never hinged	2.00
			Double transfer	1.00 .30
			Recut face (20986 UR 15)	2.00 .75
			Gripper cracks	1.25 .30
			Pair with full vert. gutter btwn.	200.00
			Pair with full horiz. gutter btwn.	200.00
b.			Booklet pane of 6, *July 25*	35.00 12.50
			Never hinged	60.00
c.			Vertical pair, imperf. between	700.00 1,350.
			Never hinged	1,400.

Bureau Precancels: 64 diff.

ROTARY PRESS COIL STAMPS

1932   *Perf. 10 Vertically*

721	A226	3c	**deep violet,** *June 24*	2.75 .20
			light violet	2.75 .20
			Never hinged	3.50
			Pair	5.75 .25
			Never hinged	7.00
			Joint line pair	10.00 1.50
			Never hinged	12.50
			Gripper cracks	—
			Recut face (20995, pos. 29)	— —
			Recut lines around eyes	— —

Perf. 10 Horizontally

722	A226	3c	**deep violet,** *Oct. 12*	1.50 .35
			light violet	1.50 .35
			Never hinged	2.00
			Pair	3.25 .80
			Never hinged	4.25
			Joint line pair	6.25 2.75
			Never hinged	8.00

Bureau Precancels: No. 721, 46 diff.

TYPE OF 1922-26 ISSUES

1932, Aug. 18			Perf. 10 Vertically	
723	A161 6c	**deep orange**	11.00	.30
		Never hinged	15.00	
		Pair	24.00	.70
		Never hinged	32.50	
		Joint line pair	60.00	5.00
		Never hinged	82.50	

Bureau Precancels: 5 diff.

William
Penn — A227

Daniel Webster
(1782-1852),
Statesman — A228

WILLIAM PENN ISSUE

250th anniv. of the arrival in America of Penn (1644-1718), English Quaker and founder of Pennsylvania.

FLAT PLATE PRINTING
Plates of 400 subjects in four panes of 100 each

1932, Oct. 24			Perf. 11	
724	A227 3c	**violet**	.45	.20
		Never hinged	.60	
		P# block of 6	8.50	—
		Never hinged	12.50	
a.		Vert. pair, imperf. horiz.		

DANIEL WEBSTER ISSUE
FLAT PLATE PRINTING
Plates of 400 subjects in four panes of 100.

1932, Oct. 24			Perf. 11	
725	A228 3c	**violet**	.45	.25
		light violet	.45	.25
		Never hinged	.60	
		P# block of 6	16.00	—
		Never hinged	22.50	

Gen. James
Edward
Oglethorpe — A229

Washington's
Headquarters at
Newburgh,
N.Y. — A230

GEORGIA BICENTENNIAL ISSUE

200th anniv. of the founding of the Colony of Georgia, and honoring Oglethorpe, who landed from England, Feb. 12, 1733, and personally supervised the establishing of the colony.

FLAT PLATE PRINTING
Plates of 400 subjects in four panes of 100.

1933, Feb. 12			Perf. 11	
726	A229 3c	**violet**	.45	.20
		Never hinged	.60	
		P# block of 6	10.00	—
		Never hinged	15.00	
		P# block of 10, "CS" in selvage	11.00	
		Never hinged	16.00	
		Bottom margin block of 20, no P#		

PEACE OF 1783 ISSUE

150th anniv. of the issuance by George Washington of the official order containing the Proclamation of Peace marking officially the ending of hostilities in the War for Independence.

ROTARY PRESS PRINTING
Plates of 400 subjects in four panes of 100 each

1933, Apr. 19			Perf. 10½x11	
727	A230 3c	**violet**	.20	.20
		Never hinged	.20	
		P# block of 4	3.00	—
		Never hinged	5.50	
		Pair with horiz. gutter between	100.00	—
		Pair with vert. gutter between	100.00	—
		Center block with crossed gutters and dashes		

No. 727 was available in full sheets of 400 subjects with gum, but was not regularly issued in that form. All examples of No. 727 must have original gum, including the gutter pairs and blocks, which are from the full sheets of 400. These should not be confused with similar blocks without gum, which are from the No. 752 Special Printing.

See No. 752 in the Special Printings following No. 751.

CENTURY OF PROGRESS ISSUES

"Century of Progress" Intl. Exhibition, Chicago, which opened June 1, 1933, and centenary of the incorporation of Chicago as a city.

Restoration of Fort
Dearborn — A231

Federal
Building — A232

ROTARY PRESS PRINTING
Plates of 400 subjects in four panes of 100.

1933, May 25			Perf. 10½x11	
728	A231 1c	**yellow green**	.20	.20
		Never hinged	.25	
		On card, Expo. station machine canc.		1.00
		On card, Expo. station duplex handstamp canc.		3.00
		P# block of 4	1.75	—
		Never hinged	3.00	
		Pair with horizontal gutter between	200.00	
		Pair with vertical gutter between	200.00	
		Center block with crossed gutters and dashes	5,000.	
		Gripper cracks (21133 UR & LR)	2.00	
729	A232 3c	**violet**	.25	.20
		Never hinged	.35	
		On cover, Expo. station machine canc.		2.00
		On cover, Expo. station duplex handstamp canc.		6.00
		P# block of 4	2.40	—
		Never hinged	4.00	
		Pair with horiz. gutter between	200.00	
		Pair with vert. gutter between	200.00	
		Center block with crossed gutters and dashes	5,000.	

Nos. 728 and 729 were not regularly issued in full sheets of 400 with gum. The gutter pairs and blocks come from a very few non-issued sheets that were retained by Postmaster James A. Farley.

AMERICAN PHILATELIC SOCIETY ISSUE
SOUVENIR SHEETS

A231a

A232a

Illustrations reduced.

FLAT PLATE PRINTING
Plates of 225 subjects in nine panes of 25 each.

1933, Aug. 25   *Imperf.*
Without Gum

730	A231a 1c **deep yellow green,** sheet of 25	27.50	27.50
a.	Single stamp	.75	.50
	Single on card, Expo. station machine canc.	1.50	
	Single on card, Expo. station duplex handstamp canc.	5.00	
731	A232a 3c **deep violet,** sheet of 25	25.00	25.00
a.	Single stamp	.65	.50
	Single on cover, Expo. station machine canc.	3.00	
	Single on cover, Expo. station duplex handstamp canc.	7.50	

Issued in sheets measuring 134x120mm containing twenty-five stamps, inscribed in the margins: PRINTED BY THE TREASURY DEPARTMENT, BUREAU OF ENGRAVING AND PRINTING, — UNDER AUTHORITY OF JAMES A. FARLEY, POSTMASTER-GENERAL, AT CENTURY OF PROGRESS, — IN COMPLIMENT TO THE AMERICAN PHILATELIC SOCIETY FOR ITS CONVENTION AND EXHIBITION — CHICAGO, ILLINOIS, AUGUST, 1933. PLATE NO. 21145.
Also used were plates 21159 (1c), 21146 and 21160 (3c).

See Nos. 766-767 in the Special Printings following No. 751.

NATIONAL RECOVERY ACT ISSUE

Issued to direct attention to and arouse the support of the nation for the National Recovery Act.

Group of Workers — A233

ROTARY PRESS PRINTING
Plates of 400 subjects in four panes of 100.

1933, Aug. 15   *Perf. 10½x11*

732	A233 3c **violet**	.20	.20
	Never hinged	.20	
	P# block of 4	1.50	—
	Never hinged	2.00	
	Gripper cracks (21151 UL & UR, 21153 UR & LR)	1.50	—
	Recut at right (21151 UR 47)	4.00	

BYRD ANTARCTIC ISSUE

Issued in connection with the Byrd Antarctic Expedition of 1933 and for use on letters mailed through the Little America Post Office established at the Base Camp of the Expedition in the territory of the South Pole.

A Map of the World (on van der Grinten's Projection) — A234

Designed by Victor S. McCloskey, Jr.

FLAT PLATE PRINTING
Plates of 200 subjects in four panes of 50 each.

1933, Oct. 9   *Perf. 11*

733	A234 3c **dark blue**	.50	.50
	Never hinged	.60	
	P# block of 6	12.00	—
	Never hinged	15.00	
	Double transfer (21167 LR 2)	2.75	1.00

In addition to the postage charge of 3 cents, letters sent by the ships of the expedition to be canceled in Little America were subject to a service charge of 50 cents each.

See No. 753 in the Special Printings following No. 751.

KOSCIUSZKO ISSUE

Kosciuszko (1746-1807), Polish soldier and statesman served in the American Revolution, on the 150th anniv. of the granting to him of American citizenship.

Statue of General Tadeusz Kosciuszko — A235

Designed by Victor S. McCloskey, Jr.

FLAT PLATE PRINTING
Plates of 400 subjects in four panes of 100 each.

1933, Oct. 13   *Perf. 11*

734	A235 5c **blue**	.55	.25
	Never hinged	.65	
	P# block of 6	24.00	—
	Never hinged	30.00	
	Cracked plate	—	
a.	Horizontal pair, imperf. vertically	2,250.	
	Never hinged	2,800.	
	P# block of 8	35,000.	

The No. 734a plate block is unique but damaged.

NATIONAL STAMP EXHIBITION ISSUE
SOUVENIR SHEET

A235a

Illustration reduced.

TYPE OF BYRD ISSUE
Plates of 150 subjects in 25 panes of six each.

1934, Feb. 10   *Imperf.*
Without Gum

735	A235a 3c **dark blue,** sheet of 6	12.00	10.00
a.	Single stamp	1.90	1.65

Issued in sheets measuring 87x93mm containing six stamps, inscribed in the margins: "Printed by the Treasury Department, Bureau of Engraving and Printing, under authority of James A. Farley, Postmaster General, in the National Stamp Exhibition of

1934. New York, N. Y., February 10-18, 1934. Plate No. 21184." Plate No. 21187 was used for sheets printed at the Exhibition, but all these were destroyed.

See No. 768 in the Special Printings following No. 751.

MARYLAND TERCENTENARY ISSUE
300th anniversary of the founding of Maryland.

"The Ark" and "The Dove" — A236

Designed by Alvin R. Meissner.

FLAT PLATE PRINTING
Plates of 400 subjects in four panes of 100.

1934, Mar. 23   *Perf. 11*

736	A236 3c **carmine rose**	.25	.20
	Never hinged	.35	
	P# block of 6	6.25	—
	Never hinged	9.50	
	Double transfer (21190 UL 1)	—	—
a.	Horizontal pair, imperf between	7,000.	

MOTHERS OF AMERICA ISSUE
Issued to commemorate Mother's Day.

Adaptation of Whistler's Portrait of his Mother — A237

Designed by Victor S. McCloskey, Jr.

Plates of 200 subjects in four panes of 50.
ROTARY PRESS PRINTING

1934, May 2   *Perf. 11x10½*

737	A237 3c **deep violet**	.20	.20
	Never hinged	.25	
	P# block of 4	1.00	—
	Never hinged	1.50	

FLAT PLATE PRINTING
Perf. 11

738	A237 3c **deep violet**	.20	.20
	Never hinged	.20	
	P# block of 6	4.25	—
	Never hinged	6.00	

See No. 754 in the Special Printings following No. 751.

WISCONSIN TERCENTENARY ISSUE

Arrival of Jean Nicolet, French explorer, on the shores of Green Bay, 300th anniv. According to historical records, Nicolet was the 1st white man to reach the territory now comprising the State of Wisconsin.

Nicolet's Landing A238

Designed by Victor S. McCloskey, Jr.

FLAT PLATE PRINTING
Plates of 200 subjects in four panes of 50.

1934. July 7   *Perf. 11*

739	A238 3c **deep violet**	.25	.20
	violet	.25	.20
	Never hinged	.40	
	P# block of 6	3.25	—
	Never hinged	4.75	
a.	Vert. pair, imperf. horiz.	350.00	
	Never hinged	600.00	
b.	Horiz. pair, imperf. vert.	500.00	
	Never hinged	850.00	
	P# block of 6	2,250.	

See No. 755 in the Special Printings following No. 751.

NATIONAL PARKS YEAR ISSUE

El Capitan, Yosemite
(California) — A239

Old Faithful,
Yellowstone
(Wyoming) — A243

View of Grand
Canyon
(Arizona)
A240

Mt. Rainier
and Mirror
Lake
(Washington)
A241

Cliff Palace,
Mesa Verde
Park (Colorado)
A242

Crater Lake
(Oregon)
A244

Great Head,
Acadia Park
(Maine)
A245

Great White Throne,
Zion Park
(Utah) — A246

Great Smoky
Mountains (North
Carolina) — A248

Mt. Rockwell
(Mt. Sinopah)
and Two
Medicine Lake,
Glacier
National Park
(Montana)
A247

FLAT PLATE PRINTING
Plates of 200 subjects in four panes of 50.

		1934 Unwmk.		Perf. 11	
740	A239	1c **green,** *July 16*		.25	.20
		light green		.25	.20
		Never hinged		.35	
		P# block of 6		1.00	—
		Never hinged		1.75	
		Recut		1.50	.50
a.		Vert. pair, imperf. horiz., with gum		1,500.	
		Never hinged		2,200.	
741	A240	2c **red,** *July 24*		.25	.20
		orange red		.25	.20
		Never hinged		.35	
		P# block of 6		1.50	—
		Never hinged		2.00	
		Double transfer		1.25	
a.		Vert. pair, imperf. horiz., with gum		575.00	
		Never hinged		1,000.	
		P# block of 6		—	
b.		Horiz. pair, imperf. vert., with gum		500.00	
		Never hinged		825.00	
		P# block of 6		2,000.	
		Never hinged		3,250.	
742	A241	3c **deep violet,** *Aug. 3*		.35	.20
		Never hinged		.45	
		P# block of 6		2.00	—
		Never hinged		2.50	
		Recut		1.50	
a.		Vert. pair, imperf. horiz., with gum		700.00	
		Never hinged		1,200.	
743	A242	4c **brown,** *Sept. 25*		.45	.40
		light brown		.45	.40
		Never hinged		.65	
		P# block of 6		7.00	—
		Never hinged		9.00	
a.		Vert. pair, imperf. horiz., with gum		1,000.	
		Never hinged		1,700.	
744	A243	5c **blue,** *July 30*		.75	.65
		light blue		.75	.65
		Never hinged		1.05	
		P# block of 6		9.00	—
		Never hinged		12.00	
a.		Horiz. pair, imperf. vert., with gum		600.00	
		Never hinged		1,050.	
745	A244	6c **dark blue,** *Sept. 5*		1.10	.85
		Never hinged		1.60	
		P# block of 6		16.00	—
		Never hinged		22.50	
746	A245	7c **black,** *Oct. 2*		.75	.75
		Never hinged		1.05	
		P# block of 6		9.00	—
		Never hinged		12.00	
		Double transfer		3.00	1.25
a.		Horiz. pair, imperf. vert., with gum		600.00	
		Never hinged		1,050.	
		P# block of 6, never hinged		6,000.	
747	A246	8c **sage green,** *Sept. 18*		1.60	1.50
		Never hinged		2.40	
		P# block of 6		17.50	—
		Never hinged		25.00	
748	A247	9c **red orange,** *Aug. 27*		1.50	.65
		orange		1.50	.65
		Never hinged		2.25	
		P# block of 6		15.00	—
		Never hinged		22.50	
749	A248	10c **gray black,** *Oct. 8*		3.00	1.25
		gray		3.00	1.25
		Never hinged		4.50	
		P# block of 6		22.50	—
		Never hinged		32.50	
		Nos. 740-749 (10)		10.00	6.65
		Nos. 740-749, never hinged		14.65	

Imperforate varieties of the 2c and 5c exist as errors of the perforated Parks set, but are virtually impossible to distinguish from gummed examples from the imperforate sheets of 200.

Also, beware of fakes of the part-perforate errors of Nos. 740-749, including those with gum (see "without gum" note before No. 752).

AMERICAN PHILATELIC SOCIETY ISSUE
SOUVENIR SHEET

A248a

Illustration reduced.

Plates of 120 subjects in 20 panes of 6 stamps each.

		1934, Aug. 28		*Imperf.*	
750	A248a	3c **deep violet,** sheet of 6		30.00	27.50
		Never hinged		37.50	
a.		Single stamp		3.75	3.25
		Never hinged		4.75	

Issued in sheets measuring approximately 98x93mm containing six stamps, inscribed in the margins: PRINTED BY THE TREASURY DEPARTMENT, BUREAU OF ENGRAVING AND PRINTING, — UNDER AUTHORITY OF JAMES A. FARLEY, POSTMASTER GENERAL, — IN COMPLIMENT TO THE AMERICAN PHILATELIC SOCIETY FOR ITS CONVENTION AND EXHIBITION, — ATLANTIC CITY, NEW JERSEY, AUGUST, 1934. PLATE NO. 21303.

See No. 770 in the Special Printings following No. 751.

TRANS-MISSISSIPPI PHILATELIC EXPOSITION ISSUE
SOUVENIR SHEET

A248b

Illustration reduced.

Plates of 120 subjects in 20 panes of 6 stamps
each.

1934, Oct. 10   *Imperf.*
751 A248b 1c **green**, sheet of 6   12.50   12.50
　　　　Never hinged   16.00
a.　Single stamp   2.00   1.60
　　　　Never hinged   2.60

Issued in sheets measuring approximately 92x99mm contain-
ing six stamps, inscribed in the margins: PRINTED BY THE
TREASURY DEPARTMENT, BUREAU OF ENGRAVING AND
PRINTING, — UNDER AUTHORITY OF JAMES A. FARLEY,
POSTMASTER GENERAL, — IN COMPLIMENT TO THE
TRANS-MISSISSIPPI PHILATELIC EXPOSITION AND CON-
VENTION, OMAHA, NEBRASKA, — OCTOBER, 1934. PLATE
NO. 21341.

See No. 769 in the Special Printings that follow.

SPECIAL PRINTING
(Nos. 752-771 inclusive)

"Issued for a limited time in full sheets as printed,
and in blocks thereof, to meet the requirements of
collectors and others who may be interested." — From
Postal Bulletin No. 16614.

Issuance of the following 20 stamps in complete
sheets resulted from the protest of collectors and
others at the practice of presenting, to certain government officials, complete sheets of unsevered panes,
imperforate (except Nos. 752 and 753) and generally
ungummed.

Designs of Commemorative Issues
Without Gum

NOTE: In 1940 the P.O. Department offered to and
did gum full sheets of Nos. 756-765 and 769-770 sent
in by owners. No other Special Printings were
accepted for gumming.

TYPE OF PEACE ISSUE

Issued in sheets of 400, consisting of four panes of
100 each, with vertical and horizontal gutters between
and plate numbers at outside corners at sides.

ROTARY PRESS PRINTING

1935, Mar. 15   **Unwmk.**   *Perf. 10½x11*
752 A230 3c **violet**   .25   .20
　　　　Pair with horiz. gutter between   5.75
　　　　Pair with vert. gutter between   9.50
　　　　Gutter block of 4 with dash (left or
　　　　　right)   17.50
　　　　Gutter block of 4 with dash (top or
　　　　　bottom)   22.50
　　　　Center block with crossed gutters
　　　　　and dashes   60.00
　　　　P# block of 4   30.00

TYPE OF BYRD ISSUE

Issued in sheets of 200, consisting of four panes of
50 each, with vertical and horizontal guide lines in
gutters between panes, and plate numbers centered at
top and bottom of each pane. This applies to Nos.
753-765 and 771.

FLAT PLATE PRINTING
Perf. 11
753 A234 3c **dark blue**   .50   .45
　　　　Pair with horiz. line between   2.25
　　　　Pair with vert. line between   32.50
　　　　Margin block of 4, arrow & guide
　　　　　line (left or right)   4.75
　　　　Margin block of 4, arrow & guide-
　　　　　line (top or bottom)   67.50
　　　　Center line block   80.00   15.00
　　　　P# block of 6, number at top or
　　　　　bottom   20.00

No. 753 is similar to No. 733. Positive identification is by
blocks or pairs showing guide line between stamps. These lines
between stamps are found only on No. 753.

TYPE OF MOTHERS OF AMERICA ISSUE
Issued in sheets of 200
FLAT PLATE PRINTING
Imperf
754 A237 3c **deep violet**   .60   .60
　　　　Pair with horiz. line between   1.75
　　　　Pair with vert. line between   1.50
　　　　Margin block of 4, arrow & guide-
　　　　　line (left or right)   3.75
　　　　Margin block of 4, arrow & guide-
　　　　　line (top or bottom)   3.25
　　　　Center line block   7.25
　　　　P# block of 6, number at top or bot-
　　　　　tom   12.00

TYPE OF WISCONSIN ISSUE
Issued in sheets of 200
FLAT PLATE PRINTING
Imperf
755 A238 3c **deep violet**   .60   .60
　　　　Pair with horiz. line between   1.75
　　　　Pair with vert. line between   1.50
　　　　Margin block of 4, arrow & guide-
　　　　　line (left or right)   3.75

　　　　Margin block of 4, arrow & guide-
　　　　　line (top or bottom)   3.25
　　　　Center line block   7.25
　　　　P# block of 6, number at top or bot-
　　　　　tom   11.00

TYPES OF NATIONAL PARKS ISSUE
Issued in sheets of 200
FLAT PLATE PRINTING
Imperf
756 A239 1c **green**   .20   .20
　　　　Pair with horiz. line between   .45
　　　　Pair with vert. line between   .55
　　　　Margin block of 4, arrow & guide-
　　　　　line (left or right)   1.00
　　　　Margin block of 4, arrow & guide-
　　　　　line (top or bottom)   1.25
　　　　Center line block   3.00
　　　　P# block of 6, number at top or
　　　　　bottom   4.50
　　　　　　See note above No. 766.

757 A240 2c **red**   .25   .25
　　　　Pair with horiz. line between   .70
　　　　Pair with vert. line between   .55
　　　　Margin block of 4, arrow & guide-
　　　　　line (left or right)   1.60
　　　　Margin block of 4, arrow & guide-
　　　　　line (top or bottom)   1.25
　　　　Center line block   4.00
　　　　P# block of 6, number at top or
　　　　　bottom   5.75
　　　　Double transfer   —

758 A241 3c **deep violet**   .50   .45
　　　　Pair with horiz. line between   1.40
　　　　Pair with vert. line between   1.25
　　　　Margin block of 4, arrow & guide-
　　　　　line (left or right)   3.10
　　　　Margin block of 4, arrow & guide-
　　　　　line (top or bottom)   2.75
　　　　Center line block   5.25
　　　　P# block of 6, number at top or
　　　　　bottom   14.00

759 A242 4c **brown**   .95   .95
　　　　Pair with horiz. line between   2.75
　　　　Pair with vert. line between   2.25
　　　　Margin block of 4, arrow & guide-
　　　　　line (left or right)   5.75
　　　　Margin block of 4, arrow & guide-
　　　　　line (top or bottom)   4.75
　　　　Center line block   8.50
　　　　P# block of 6, number at top or
　　　　　bottom   22.50

760 A243 5c **blue**   1.50   1.40
　　　　Pair with horiz. line between   3.50
　　　　Pair with vert. line between   4.25
　　　　Margin block of 4, arrow & guide-
　　　　　line (left or right)   7.50
　　　　Margin block of 4, arrow & guide-
　　　　　line (top or bottom)   9.00
　　　　Center line block   15.00
　　　　P# block of 6, number at top or
　　　　　bottom   30.00
　　　　Double transfer   —

761 A244 6c **dark blue**   2.25   2.25
　　　　Pair with horiz. line between   6.00
　　　　Pair with vert. line between   5.00
　　　　Margin block of 4, arrow & guide-
　　　　　line (left or right)   12.00
　　　　Margin block of 4, arrow & guide-
　　　　　line (top or bottom)   11.00
　　　　Center line block   17.50
　　　　P# block of 6, number at top or
　　　　　bottom)   37.50

762 A245 7c **black**   1.50   1.40
　　　　Pair with horiz. line between   4.25
　　　　Pair with vert. line between   3.75
　　　　Margin block of 4, arrow & guide-
　　　　　line (left or right)   9.25
　　　　Margin block of 4, arrow & guide-
　　　　　line (top or bottom)   8.25
　　　　Center line block   14.00
　　　　P# block of 6, number at top or
　　　　　bottom   30.00
　　　　Double transfer   —

763 A246 8c **sage green**   1.80   1.50
　　　　Pair with horiz. line between   4.25
　　　　Pair with vert. line between   5.25
　　　　Margin block of 4, arrow & guide-
　　　　　line (left or right)   12.50
　　　　Margin block of 4, arrow & guide-
　　　　　line (top or bottom)   15.00
　　　　Center line block   20.00
　　　　P# block of 6, number at top or
　　　　　bottom   37.50

764 A247 9c **red orange**   1.90   1.75
　　　　Pair with horiz. line between   5.00
　　　　Pair with vert. line between   4.50
　　　　Margin block of 4, arrow & guide-
　　　　　line (left or right)   11.50
　　　　Margin block of 4, arrow & guide-
　　　　　line (top or bottom)   10.50
　　　　Center line block   22.50
　　　　P# block of 6, number at top or
　　　　　bottom   42.50

765 A248 10c **gray black**   3.75   3.50
　　　　Pair with horiz. line between   9.00
　　　　Pair with vert. line between   10.50
　　　　Margin block of 4, arrow & guide-
　　　　　line (left or right)   20.00
　　　　Margin block of 4, arrow & guide-
　　　　　line (top or bottom)   24.00
　　　　Center line block   30.00
　　　　P# block of 6, number at top or
　　　　　bottom   50.00
　　　　Nos. 756-765 (10)   14.60   13.65

SOUVENIR SHEETS

Note: Single items from these sheets are identical
with other varieties, 766 and 730, 766a and 730a, 767
and 731, 767a and 731a, 768 and 735, 768a and
735a, 769a and 756, 770a and 758.

Positive identification is by blocks or pairs showing
wide gutters between stamps. These wide gutters
occur only on Nos. 766-770 and measure, horizontally,
13mm on Nos. 766-767; 16mm on No. 768, and 23mm
on Nos. 769-770.

TYPE OF CENTURY OF PROGRESS ISSUE

Issued in sheets of 9 panes of 25 stamps each, with
vertical and horizontal gutters between panes.

FLAT PLATE PRINTING
Imperf
766 A231a 1c **yellow green**, pane of 25   25.00   25.00
a.　Single stamp   .70   .50
　　　　Block of 4   2.80   1.70
　　　　Pair with horiz. gutter between   5.00   —
　　　　Pair with vert. gutter between   7.00   —
　　　　Block with crossed gutters   16.00
　　　　Block of 50 stamps (two panes)   70.00
767 A232a 3c **violet**, pane of 25   23.50   23.50
a.　Single stamp   .60   .50
　　　　Pair with horiz. gutter between   5.00
　　　　Pair with vert. gutter between   6.50
　　　　Block with crossed gutters   17.50
　　　　Block of 50 stamps (two panes)   65.00

NATIONAL EXHIBITION ISSUE
TYPE OF BYRD ISSUE

Issued in sheets of 25 panes of 6 stamps each, with
vertical and horizontal gutters between panes.

FLAT PLATE PRINTING
Imperf
768 A235a 3c **dark blue**, pane of six   20.00   15.00
a.　Single stamp   2.80   2.40
　　　　Pair with horiz. gutter between   7.00
　　　　Pair with vert. gutter between   8.00   —
　　　　Block of 4 with crossed gutters   20.00
　　　　Block of 12 stamps (two panes)   47.50

TYPES OF NATIONAL PARKS ISSUE

Issued in sheets of 20 panes of 6 stamps each, with
vertical and horizontal gutters between panes.

FLAT PLATE PRINTING
Imperf
769 A248b 1c **green**, pane of six   12.50   11.00
a.　Single stamp   1.85   1.80
　　　　Pair with horiz. gutter between   5.50
　　　　Pair with vert. gutter between   7.50   —
　　　　Block of 4 with crossed gutters   15.00   —
　　　　Block of 12 stamps (two panes)   30.00
770 A248a 3c **deep violet**, pane of six   30.00   24.00
a.　Single stamp   3.25   3.10
　　　　Pair with horiz. gutter between   12.00
　　　　Pair with vert. gutter between   10.50
　　　　Block of 4 with crossed gutters   27.50   —
　　　　Block of 12 stamps (two panes)   70.00

TYPE OF AIR POST SPECIAL DELIVERY
Issued in sheets of 200, with vertical and horizontal
guide lines between panes.
FLAT PLATE PRINTING
Imperf
771 APSD1 16c **dark blue**   2.60   2.60
　　　　Pair with horiz. line between   7.75   —
　　　　Pair with vert. line between   6.50   —
　　　　Margin block of 4, arrow &
　　　　　guideline (left or right)   17.50   —
　　　　Margin block of 4, arrow &
　　　　　guideline (top or bottom)   15.00   —
　　　　Center line block   65.00   —
　　　　P# block of 6, number at top or
　　　　　bottom   55.00   —

**Catalogue values for unused stamps in this
section, from this point to the end, are for Never
Hinged items.**

VALUES FOR HINGED STAMPS AFTER NO. 771
This catalogue does not value unused stamps
after No. 771 in hinged condition. Hinged unused
stamps from No. 772 to the present are worth considerably less than the values given for unused
stamps, which are for never-hinged examples.

CONNECTICUT TERCENTENARY ISSUE

300th anniv. of the settlement of Connecticut.

The Charter
Oak — A249

ROTARY PRESS PRINTING
Plates of 200 subjects in four panes of 50.

1935, Apr. 26	Unwmk.	Perf. 11x10½	
772 A249 3c **violet**		.30	.20
rose violet		.30	.20
P# block of 4		2.25	—
Defect in cent sign (21395 UR 4)		5.00	4.00

CALIFORNIA PACIFIC EXPOSITION ISSUE
California Pacific Exposition at San Diego.

View of San Diego Exposition A250

ROTARY PRESS PRINTING
Plates of 200 subjects in four panes of 50.

1935, May 29	Unwmk.	Perf. 11x10½	
773 A250 3c **purple**		.30	.20
On cover, Expo. station machine canc. (non-first day)			2.50
On cover, Expo. station duplex handstamp canc. (non-first day)			20.00
P# block of 4		1.30	—
Pair with full vertical gutter between			—

BOULDER DAM ISSUE
Dedication of Boulder Dam.

Boulder Dam (Hoover Dam) — A251

FLAT PLATE PRINTING
Plates of 200 subjects in four panes of 50.

1935, Sept. 30	Unwmk.	Perf. 11	
774 A251 3c **purple**		.30	.20
deep purple		.30	.20
P# block of 6		2.00	—

MICHIGAN CENTENARY ISSUE
Advance celebration of Michigan Statehood centenary.

Michigan State Seal — A252

Designed by Alvin R. Meissner.

ROTARY PRESS PRINTING
Plates of 200 subjects in 4 panes of 50.

1935, Nov. 1	Unwmk.	Perf. 11x10½	
775 A252 3c **purple**		.30	.20
P# block of 4		2.00	—

TEXAS CENTENNIAL ISSUE
Centennial of Texas independence.

Sam Houston, Stephen F. Austin and the Alamo — A253

Designed by Alvin R. Meissner.

ROTARY PRESS PRINTING
Plates of 200 subjects in four panes of 50.

1936, Mar. 2	Unwmk.	Perf. 11x10½	
776 A253 3c **purple**		.30	.20
On cover, Expo. station machine canc.			2.00
On cover, Expo. station duplex handstamp canc.			40.00
P# block of 4		1.75	—

RHODE ISLAND TERCENTENARY ISSUE
300th anniv. of the settlement of Rhode Island.

Statue of Roger Williams — A254

ROTARY PRESS PRINTING
Plates of 200 subjects in four panes of 50.

1936, May 4	Unwmk.	Perf. 10½x11	
777 A254 3c **purple**		.35	.20
rose violet		.35	.20
P# block of 4		1.50	—
Pair with full gutter between			200.00

THIRD INTERNATIONAL PHILATELIC EXHIBITION ISSUE
SOUVENIR SHEET

A254a

Illustration reduced.

Plates of 120 subjects in thirty panes of 4 each.
FLAT PLATE PRINTING

1936, May 9	Unwmk.	Imperf.	
778 A254a **violet**, sheet of 4		1.75	1.25
a. 3c Type A249		.40	.30
b. 3c Type A250		.40	.30
c. 3c Type A252		.40	.30
d. 3c Type A253		.40	.30

Issued in sheets measuring 98x66mm containing four stamps, inscribed in the margins: "Printed by the Treasury Department, Bureau of Engraving and Printing, under authority of James A. Farley, Postmaster General, in compliment to the third International Philatelic Exhibition of 1936. New York, N. Y., May 9-17, 1936. Plate No. 21557 (or 21558)."

ARKANSAS CENTENNIAL ISSUE
100th anniv. of the State of Arkansas.

Arkansas Post, Old and New State Houses A255

ROTARY PRESS PRINTING
Plates of 200 subjects in four panes of 50.

1936, June 15	Unwmk.	Perf. 11x10½	
782 A255 3c **purple**		.30	.20
P# block of 4		1.75	—

OREGON TERRITORY ISSUE
Opening of the Oregon Territory, 1836, 100th anniv.

Map of Oregon Territory A256

ROTARY PRESS PRINTING
Plates of 200 subjects in four panes of 50.

1936, July 14	Unwmk.	Perf. 11x10½	
783 A256 3c **purple**		.25	.20
P# block of 4		1.25	—
Double transfer (21579 UL 3)		4.00	2.50

SUSAN B. ANTHONY ISSUE
Susan Brownell Anthony (1820-1906), woman-suffrage advocate, and 16th anniv. of the ratification of the 19th Amendment which grants American women the right to vote.

Susan B. Anthony — A257

ROTARY PRESS PRINTING
Plates of 400 subjects in four panes of 100.

1936, Aug. 26	Unwmk.	Perf. 11x10½	
784 A257 3c **violet**		.25	.20
rose violet		.25	.20
P# block of 4		1.10	—
Period missing after "B" (21590 LR 100)		4.00	2.00

ARMY ISSUE
Issued in honor of the United States Army.

Generals George Washington, Nathanael Greene and Mt. Vernon A258

Maj. Gen. Andrew Jackson, Gen. Winfield Scott and the Hermitage A259

Generals William T. Sherman, Ulysses S. Grant and Philip H. Sheridan A260

Generals Robert E. Lee, "Stonewall" Jackson and Stratford Hall — A261

U. S. Military Academy, West Point — A262

ROTARY PRESS PRINTING
Plates of 200 subjects in four panes of 50.

1936-37		Unwmk.	Perf. 11x10½	
785	A258	1c green, *Dec. 15, 1936*	.25	.20
		yellow green	.25	.20
		P# block of 4	1.10	—
		Pair with full vertical gutter between		
786	A259	2c carmine, *Jan. 15, 1937*	.25	.20
		P# block of 4	1.10	—
787	A260	3c purple, *Feb. 18, 1937*	.35	.20
		P# block of 4	2.00	—
788	A261	4c gray, *Mar. 23, 1937*	.55	.20
		P# block of 4	8.50	—
789	A262	5c ultramarine, *May 26, 1937*	.65	.25
		P# block of 4	8.00	—
		Nos. 785-789 (5)	2.05	1.05

NAVY ISSUE
Issued in honor of the United States Navy.

John Paul Jones and John Barry — A263

Stephen Decatur and Thomas MacDonough A264

Admirals David G. Farragut and David D. Porter — A265

Admirals William T. Sampson, George Dewey and Winfield S. Schley A266

Seal of US Naval Academy and Naval Midshipmen A267

ROTARY PRESS PRINTING
Plates of 200 subjects in four panes of 50.

1936-37		Unwmk.	Perf. 11x10½	
790	A263	1c green, *Dec. 15, 1936*	.25	.20
		yellow green	.25	.20
		P# block of 4	1.10	—
791	A264	2c carmine, *Jan. 15, 1937*	.25	.20
		P# block of 4	1.10	—
792	A265	3c purple, *Feb. 18, 1937*	.35	.20
		P# block of 4	1.10	—
793	A266	4c gray, *Mar. 23, 1937*	.55	.20
		P# block of 4	9.50	—
794	A267	5c ultramarine, *May 26, 1937*	.65	.25

	P# block of 4	8.75	—
	Pair with full vert. gutter btwn.		
	Nos. 790-794 (5)	2.05	1.05

ORDINANCE OF 1787 SESQUICENTENNIAL ISSUE
150th anniv. of the adoption of the Ordinance of 1787 and the creation of the Northwest Territory.

Manasseh Cutler, Rufus Putnam and Map of Northwest Territory A268

ROTARY PRESS PRINTING
Plates of 200 subjects in four panes of 50.

1937, July 13		Unwmk.	Perf. 11x10½	
795	A268	3c red violet	.30	.20
		P# block of 4	1.50	—

VIRGINIA DARE ISSUE
350th anniv. of the birth of Virginia Dare, 1st child born in America of English parents (Aug. 18, 1587), and the settlement at Roanoke Island.

Virginia Dare and Parents — A269

FLAT PLATE PRINTING
Plates of 192 subjects in four panes of 48 each, separated by 1¼ inch wide gutters with central guide lines.

1937, Aug. 18		Unwmk.	Perf. 11	
796	A269	5c gray blue	.35	.20
		P# block of 6	6.50	—

SOCIETY OF PHILATELIC AMERICANS ISSUE
SOUVENIR SHEET

A269a

Illustration reduced.

TYPE OF NATIONAL PARKS ISSUE
Plates of 36 subjects
FLAT PLATE PRINTING

1937, Aug. 26		Unwmk.	Imperf.	
797	A269a	10c blue green	.60	.40

Issued in sheets measuring 67x78mm, inscribed in margins: "Printed by the Treasury Department, Bureau of Engraving and Printing — Under the Authority of James A. Farley, Postmaster General — In Compliment to the 43rd Annual Convention of the Society of Philatelic Americans - Asheville, N.C., August 26-28, 1937. Plate Number 21695 (6)."

CONSTITUTION SESQUICENTENNIAL ISSUE
150th anniversary of the signing of the Constitution on September 17, 1787.

"Adoption of the Constitution" A270

ROTARY PRESS PRINTING
Plates of 200 subjects in four panes of 50.

1937, Sept. 17		Unwmk.	Perf. 11x10½	
798	A270	3c bright red violet	.40	.20
		P# block of 4	1.90	—

TERRITORIAL ISSUES
Hawaii

Statue of Kamehameha I, Honolulu — A271

Alaska

Mt. McKinley A272

Puerto Rico

La Fortaleza, San Juan — A273

Virgin Islands

Charlotte Amalie Harbor, St. Thomas A274

ROTARY PRESS PRINTING
Plates of 200 subjects in panes of 50.

1937		Unwmk.	Perf. 10½x11	
799	A271	3c violet, *Oct. 18*	.35	.20
		P# block of 4	1.60	—
			Perf. 11x10½	
800	A272	3c violet, *Nov. 12*	.35	.20
		P# block of 4	1.60	—
		Pair with full gutter between	—	
801	A273	3c bright violet, *Nov. 25*	.35	.20
		P# block of 4	1.90	—
802	A274	3c light violet, *Dec. 15*	.35	.20
		P# block of 4	1.90	—
		Pair with full vertical gutter between	275.00	
		Nos. 799-802 (4)	1.40	.80

PRESIDENTIAL ISSUE

Benjamin
Franklin — A275

George
Washington — A276

Martha
Washington — A277

John
Adams — A278

Thomas
Jefferson — A279

James
Madison — A280

The White
House — A281

James
Monroe — A282

John Quincy
Adams — A283

Andrew
Jackson — A284

Martin Van
Buren — A285

William H.
Harrison — A286

John Tyler — A287

James K.
Polk — A288

Zachary
Taylor — A289

Millard
Fillmore — A290

Franklin
Pierce — A291

James
Buchanan — A292

Abraham
Lincoln — A293

Andrew
Johnson — A294

Ulysses S.
Grant — A295

Rutherford B.
Hayes — A296

James A.
Garfield — A297

Chester A.
Arthur — A298

Grover
Cleveland — A299

Benjamin
Harrison — A300

William
McKinley — A301

Theodore
Roosevelt — A302

William Howard
Taft — A303

Woodrow
Wilson — A304

Warren G.
Harding — A305

Calvin
Coolidge — A306

ROTARY PRESS PRINTING

Ordinary and Electric Eye (EE) Plates of 400 subjects in four panes of 100. (For details of EE Markings, see Information for Collectors in first part of this Catalogue.)

1938   Unwmk.   Perf. 11x10½

803	A275	½c **deep orange,** *May 19*	.20	.20
		P# block of 4	.50	—
804	A276	1c **green,** *Apr. 25*	.25	.20
		light green	.25	.20
		P# block of 4	1.10	—
		Pair with full vert. gutter btwn.	160.00	—
b.		Booklet pane of 6	2.00	.50
c.		Horiz. pair, imperf between (from booklet pane)		
805	A277	1½c **bister brown,** *May 5*	.20	.20
		buff ('43)	.20	.20
		P# block of 4	.40	—
		Pair with full horiz. gutter btwn.	175.00	
		Pair with full vert. gutter btwn.	—	
b.		Horiz. pair, imperf. between	125.00	20.00

No. 805b used is always Bureau precanceled St. Louis, Mo., and is generally with gum. Value is for gummed pair.

806	A278	2c **rose carmine,** *June 3*	.25	.20
		rose pink ('43)	.25	.20
		P# block of 4, # opposite corner stamp	1.10	—
		Vertical margin block of 10, P# opposite 3rd horizontal row (Experimental EE plates)	7.00	
		Recut at top of head, Pl. 22156 U.L. 3	3.00	1.50
		Pair with full horiz. gutter btwn.	125.00	
b.		Booklet pane of 6	5.50	1.00
807	A279	3c **deep violet,** *June 16*	.25	.20
		P# block of 4, # opposite corner stamp	1.10	.25
		Vertical margin block of 10, P# opposite 3rd horizontal row (Experimental EE plates)	95.00	
		Pair with full vert. gutter btwn.	150.00	
		Pair with full horiz. gutter btwn.	200.00	
a.		Booklet pane of 6	8.50	2.00
		Horiz. booklet pair with full vert. gutter between	—	
b.		Horiz. pair, imperf. between	1,750.	
c.		Imperf., pair	2,750.	
d.		As "a," imperf between vert.		
808	A280	4c **red violet,** *July 1*	.75	.20
		rose violet ('43)	.75	.20
		P# block of 4	3.50	—
809	A281	4½c **dark gray,** *July 11*	.30	.20
		gray ('43)	.30	.20
		P# block of 4	1.75	
810	A282	5c **bright blue,** *July 21*	.35	.20
		light blue	.35	.20
		P# block of 4	1.50	—
		Pair with full vert. gutter btwn.	—	
811	A283	6c **red orange,** *July 28*	.40	.20
		P# block of 4	2.00	—
812	A284	7c **sepia,** *Aug. 4*	.40	.20
		violet brown	.40	—
		P# block of 4	2.00	—
813	A285	8c **olive green,** *Aug. 11*	.40	.20
		light olive green ('43)	.40	.20
		olive ('42)	.40	.20
		P# block of 4	2.00	—
814	A286	9c **rose pink,** *Aug. 18*	.40	.20
		pink ('43)	.40	.20
		P# block of 4	1.75	
		Pair with full vert. gutter btwn.	—	
815	A287	10c **brown red,** *Sept. 2*	.40	.20
		pale brown red ('43)	.40	.20
		P# block of 4	2.00	—
816	A288	11c **ultramarine,** *Sept. 8*	.75	.20
		bright ultramarine	.75	.20
		P# block of 4	3.50	—
817	A289	12c **bright violet,** *Sept. 14*	1.00	.20
		P# block of 4	5.25	—
818	A290	13c **blue green,** *Sept. 22*	1.30	.20
		deep blue green	1.30	.20
		P# block of 4	7.00	—

819	A291	14c **blue,** *Oct. 6*	1.00	.20
		P# block of 4	5.00	—
820	A292	15c **blue gray,** *Oct. 13*	.70	.20
		P# block of 4	3.00	—
821	A293	16c **black,** *Oct. 20*	1.50	.25
		P# block of 4	7.50	—
822	A294	17c **rose red,** *Oct. 27*	1.00	.20
		deep rose red	1.10	.20
		P# block of 4	5.00	—
823	A295	18c **brown carmine,** *Nov. 3*	2.25	.20
		rose brown ('43)	2.25	.20
		P# block of 4	12.50	—
824	A296	19c **bright violet,** *Nov. 10*	1.30	.35
		P# block of 4	7.00	—
825	A297	20c **bright blue green,** *Nov. 10*	1.00	.20
		deep blue green ('43)	1.00	.20
		P# block of 4	4.75	—
826	A298	21c **dull blue,** *Nov. 22*	1.30	.20
		P# block of 4	7.50	—
827	A299	22c **vermilion,** *Nov. 22*	1.20	.40
		P# block of 4	9.00	—
828	A300	24c **gray black,** *Dec. 2*	3.50	.20
		P# block of 4	17.00	—
829	A301	25c **deep red lilac,** *Dec. 2*	1.00	.20
		rose lilac ('43)	1.00	.20
		P# block of 4	5.00	—
		Pair with full vert. gutter btwn.	900.00	—
830	A302	30c **deep ultramarine,** *Dec. 8*	4.00	.20
		P# block of 4	15.00	—
a.		30c **blue**	15.00	—
b.		30c **deep blue**	240.00	—
831	A303	50c **light red violet,** *Dec. 8*	5.00	.20
		P# block of 4	25.00	—

Bureau Precancels: ½c, 199 diff., 1c, 701 diff., 1½c, 404 diff., 2c, 161 diff., 3c, 87 diff., 4c, 30 diff., 4½c, 27 diff., 5c, 44 diff., 6c, 45 diff., 7c, 44 diff., 8c, 44 diff., 9c, 38 diff., 10c, 43 diff. Also, 11c, 41 diff., 12c, 33 diff., 13c, 28 diff., 14c, 23 diff., 15c, 38 diff., 16c, 6 diff., 17c, 27 diff., 18c, 5 diff., 19c, 4 diff., 20c, 39 diff., 21c, 5 diff., 22c, 4 diff., 24c, 8 diff., 25c, 23 diff., 30c, 27 diff., 50c, 24 diff.

FLAT PLATE PRINTING
Plates of 100 subjects

1938			**Perf. 11**
832 A304	$1 **purple & black,** *Aug. 29*	7.00	.20
	Margin block of 4, bottom or side arrow	30.00	—
	Center line block	32.50	4.00
	Top P# block of 4, 2#	35.00	—
	Top P# block of 20, 2#, arrow, 2 TOP, 2 registration markers and denomination	145.00	—
a.	Vert. pair, imperf. horiz.	1,500.	
	Top P# blk of 8, imperf horiz.	8,500.	
b.	Watermarked USIR ('51)	150.00	65.00
	Hinged	90.00	
	Center line block	1,500.	
	P# block of 4, 2#	1,800.	
	Top P# block of 20, 2#, arrow, 2 TOP, 2 registration markers and denomination	3,250.	
c.	$1 **red violet & black,** *Aug. 31, 1954*	6.00	.20
	Top or bottom P# block of 4, 2#	30.00	—
d.	As "c," vert. pair, imperf. horiz.	1,250.	
e.	Vertical pair, imperf. between	2,750.	
f.	As "c," vert. pair, imperf. btwn.	8,500.	

No. 832c is dry printed from 400-subject flat plates on thick white paper with smooth, colorless gum.

833 A305	$2 **yellow green & black,** *Sept. 29*	17.50	3.75
	green & black ('43)	17.50	3.75
	Margin block of 4, bottom or side arrow	75.00	—
	Center line block	82.50	35.00
	Top P# block of 4, 2#	95.00	—
	Top P# block of 20, 2#, arrow, 2 TOP, 2 registration markers and denominations	450.00	—
	Top P# block of 20, 2#, black # and marginal markings only (yellow green # and markings omitted)	3,000.	
834 A306	$5 **carmine & black,** *Nov. 17*	85.00	3.00
	Hinged	50.00	
	Margin block of 4, bottom or side arrow	350.00	—
	Center line block	375.00	25.00
	Top P# block of 4, 2#	375.00	—
	Top P# block of 20, 2#, arrow, 2 TOP, 2 registration markers and denominations	2,200.	
a.	$5 **red brown & black**	3,000.	7,000.
	Hinged	2,000.	
	Top P# block of 4, 2#	15,000.	
	Hinged	9,500.	
	Nos. 803-834 (32)	141.85	13.15
	Nos. 803-834, P# blocks of 4	674.95	

Top plate number blocks of Nos. 832, 833 and 834 are found both with and without top arrow or registration markers.
No. 834 can be chemically altered to resemble Scott 834a. No. 834a should be purchased only with competent expert certification.

Watermarks
All stamps from No. 835 on are unwatermarked.

CONSTITUTION RATIFICATION ISSUE
150th anniversary of the ratification of the United States Constitution.

Old Courthouse, Williamsburg, Va. — A307

ROTARY PRESS PRINTING
Plates of 200 subjects in four panes of 50.

1938, June 21		**Perf. 11x10½**	
835 A307	3c **deep violet**	.45	.20
	P# block of 4	3.50	—

SWEDISH-FINNISH TERCENTENARY ISSUE
Tercentenary of the founding of the Swedish and Finnish Settlement at Wilmington, Delaware.

"Landing of the First Swedish and Finnish Settlers in America," by Stanley M. Arthurs — A308

FLAT PLATE PRINTING
Plates of 192 subjects in four panes of 48 each, separated by 1¼ inch wide gutters with central guide lines.

1938, June 27		**Perf. 11**	
836 A308	3c **red violet**	.35	.20
	P# block of 6	2.25	—

NORTHWEST TERRITORY SESQUICENTENNIAL

"Colonization of the West," by Gutzon Borglum — A309

ROTARY PRESS PRINTING
Plates of 400 subjects in four panes of 100.

1938, July 15		**Perf. 11x10½**	
837 A309	3c **bright violet**	.30	.20
	rose violet	.30	.20
	P# block of 4	6.00	—

IOWA TERRITORY CENTENNIAL ISSUE

Old Capitol, Iowa City — A310

ROTARY PRESS PRINTING
Plates of 200 subjects in four panes of 50.

1938, Aug. 24		**Perf. 11x10½**	
838 A310	3c **violet**	.35	.20
	P# block of 4	6.00	—
	Pair with full vertical gutter between	—	

REGULAR ISSUE
ROTARY PRESS COIL STAMPS
Types of 1938

1939, Jan. 20			**Perf. 10 Vertically**	
839	A276	1c **green**	.30	.20
		light green	.30	.20
		Pair	.60	.20
		Joint line pair	1.40	.35
840	A277	1½c **bister brown**	.30	.20
		buff	.30	.20
		Pair	.60	.20
		Joint line pair	1.50	.75
841	A278	2c **rose carmine**	.40	.20
		Pair	.80	.20
		Joint line pair	1.75	.35
842	A279	3c **deep violet**	.50	.20
		violet	.50	.20
		Pair	1.00	.20
		Joint line pair	2.00	.35

		Gripper cracks	—	
		Thin translucent paper	2.50	
843	A280	4c **red violet**	7.50	.40
		Pair	16.50	.90
		Joint line pair	27.50	5.00
844	A281	4½c **dark gray**	.70	.40
		Pair	1.50	.90
		Joint line pair	5.00	2.25
845	A282	5c **bright blue**	5.00	.35
		Pair	10.50	.75
		Joint line pair	27.50	5.00
846	A283	6c **red orange**	1.10	.20
		Pair	2.25	.40
		Joint line pair	7.50	1.50
847	A287	10c **brown red**	11.00	1.00
		Pair	24.00	2.50
		Joint line pair	42.50	4.50

Bureau Precancels: 1c, 269 diff., 1½c, 179 diff., 2c, 101 diff., 3c, 46 diff., 4c, 13 diff., 4½c, 3 diff., 5c, 6 diff., 6c, 8 diff., 10c, 4 diff.

1939, Jan. 27			**Perf. 10 Horizontally**	
848	A276	1c **green**	.85	.20
		Pair	1.75	.30
		Joint line pair	2.75	.75
849	A277	1½c **bister brown**	1.25	.30
		Pair	2.50	.65
		Joint line pair	4.50	2.00
850	A278	2c **rose carmine**	2.50	.40
		Pair	5.00	.90
		Joint line pair	7.50	3.50
851	A279	3c **deep violet**	2.50	.40
		Pair	5.00	.90
		Joint line pair	8.50	3.75
		Thin translucent paper		
		Nos. 839-851 (13)	33.90	4.45
		Nos. 839-851, joint line pairs (13)	139.90	29.65

"Tower of the Sun" — A311

Trylon and Perisphere — A312

GOLDEN GATE INTL. EXPOSITION, SAN FRANCISCO
ROTARY PRESS PRINTING
Plates of 200 subjects in four panes of 50.

1939, Feb. 18		**Perf. 10½x11**	
852 A311	3c **bright purple**	.30	.20
	On cover, Expo. station machine canc. (non-first day)		3.00
	On cover, Expo. station duplex handstamp canc. (non-first day)		15.00
	P# block of 4	1.40	

NEW YORK WORLD'S FAIR ISSUE
ROTARY PRESS PRINTING
Plates of 200 subjects in four panes of 50.

1939, Apr. 1		**Perf. 10½x11**	
853 A312	3c **deep purple**	.30	.20
	On cover, Expo. station machine canc. (non-first day)		3.00
	On cover, Expo. station duplex handstamp canc.		10.00
	P# block of 4	1.75	

WASHINGTON INAUGURATION ISSUE
Sesquicentennial of the inauguration of George Washington as First President.

Washington Taking Oath of Office, Federal Building, New York City — A313

FLAT PLATE PRINTING
Plates of 200 subjects in four panes of 50.

1939, Apr. 30			**Perf. 11**	
854 A313 3c **bright red violet**			.55	.20
P# block of 6			3.50	—

BASEBALL CENTENNIAL ISSUE

Sandlot Baseball Game — A314

Designed by William A. Roach.

ROTARY PRESS PRINTING
Plates of 200 subjects in four panes of 50.

1939, June 12			**Perf. 11x10½**	
855 A314 3c **violet**			1.75	.20
P# block of 4			7.50	—

PANAMA CANAL ISSUE
25th anniv. of the opening of the Panama Canal.

Theodore Roosevelt, Gen. George W. Goethals and Ship in Gaillard Cut — A315

Designed by William A. Roach.

FLAT PLATE PRINTING
Plates of 200 subjects in four panes of 50.

1939, Aug. 15			**Perf. 11**	
856 A315 3c **deep red violet**			.35	.20
P# block of 6			3.50	—

PRINTING TERCENTENARY ISSUE
Issued in commemoration of the 300th anniversary of printing in Colonial America. The Stephen Daye press is in the Harvard University Museum.

Stephen Daye Press — A316

Designed by William K. Schrage.

ROTARY PRESS PRINTING
E.E. Plates of 200 subjects in four panes of 50.

1939, Sept. 25			**Perf. 10½x11**	
857 A316 3c **violet**			.25	.20
P# block of 4			1.10	—

50th ANNIVERSARY OF STATEHOOD ISSUE

Map of North and South Dakota, Montana and Washington A317

ROTARY PRESS PRINTING
E.E. Plates of 200 subjects in four panes of 50.

1939, Nov. 2			**Perf. 11x10½**	
858 A317 3c **rose violet**			.35	.20
P# block of 4			2.00	—

FAMOUS AMERICANS ISSUES
ROTARY PRESS PRINTING
E.E. Plates of 280 subjects in four panes of 70.
AMERICAN AUTHORS

Washington Irving — A318   James Fenimore Cooper — A319

Ralph Waldo Emerson — A320   Louisa May Alcott — A321

Samuel L. Clemens (Mark Twain) — A322

1940			**Perf. 10½x11**	
859 A318 1c **bright blue green**, *Jan. 29*			.20	.20
P# block of 4			.95	—
860 A319 2c **rose carmine**, *Jan. 29*			.20	.20
P# block of 4			.95	—
861 A320 3c **bright red violet**, *Feb. 5*			.25	.20
P# block of 4			1.25	—
862 A321 5c **ultramarine**, *Feb. 5*			.35	.20
P# block of 4			8.25	—
863 A322 10c **dark brown**, *Feb. 13*			1.75	1.20
P# block of 4			32.50	—
Nos. 859-863 (5)			2.75	2.00

AMERICAN POETS

Henry Wadsworth Longfellow — A323   John Greenleaf Whittier — A324

James Russell Lowell — A325   Walt Whitman — A326

James Whitcomb Riley — A327

864 A323 1c **bright blue green**, *Feb. 16*			.20	.20
P# block of 4			2.00	—
865 A324 2c **rose carmine**, *Feb. 16*			.20	.20
P# block of 4			1.75	—
866 A325 3c **bright red violet**, *Feb. 20*			.25	.20
P# block of 4			2.25	—
867 A326 5c **ultramarine**, *Feb. 20*			.50	.20
P# block of 4			9.50	—
868 A327 10c **dark brown**, *Feb. 24*			1.75	1.25
P# block of 4			32.50	—
Nos. 864-868 (5)			2.90	2.05

AMERICAN EDUCATORS

Horace Mann — A328   Mark Hopkins — A329

Charles W. Eliot — A330   Frances E. Willard — A331

Booker T. Washington — A332

869 A328 1c **bright blue green**, *Mar. 14*			.20	.20
P# block of 4			2.25	—
870 A329 2c **rose carmine**, *Mar. 14*			.20	.20
P# block of 4			1.50	—
871 A330 3c **bright red violet**, *Mar. 28*			.25	.20
P# block of 4			2.00	—
872 A331 5c **ultramarine**, *Mar. 28*			.50	.20
P# block of 4			9.00	—
873 A332 10c **dark brown**, *Apr. 7*			2.25	1.10
P# block of 4			27.50	—
Nos. 869-873 (5)			3.40	1.90

AMERICAN SCIENTISTS

John James Audubon — A333   Dr. Crawford W. Long — A334

94   POSTAGE

Luther Burbank — A335

Dr. Walter
Reed — A336

Jane Addams — A337

874	A333	1c	**bright blue green,** *Apr. 8*	.20	.20
			P# block of 4	.90	—
875	A334	2c	**rose carmine,** *Apr. 8*	.20	.20
			P# block of 4	.95	—
876	A335	3c	**bright red violet,** *Apr. 17*	.25	.20
			P# block of 4	1.10	—
877	A336	5c	**ultramarine,** *Apr. 17*	.50	.20
			P# block of 4	5.50	—
878	A337	10c	**dark brown,** *Apr. 26*	1.50	.85
			P# block of 4	16.00	—
			Nos. 874-878 (5)	2.65	1.65

AMERICAN COMPOSERS

Stephen Collins
Foster — A338

John Philip
Sousa — A339

Victor Herbert — A340

Edward A.
MacDowell — A341

Ethelbert Nevin — A342

879	A338	1c	**bright blue green,** *May 3*	.20	.20
			P# block of 4	.95	—
880	A339	2c	**rose carmine,** *May 3*	.20	.20
			P# block of 4	1.00	—
881	A340	3c	**bright red violet,** *May 13*	.25	.20
			P# block of 4	1.10	—
882	A341	5c	**ultramarine,** *May 13*	.50	.20
			P# block of 4	9.25	—
883	A342	10c	**dark brown,** *June 10*	3.75	1.35
			P# block of 4	32.50	—
			Nos. 879-883 (5)	4.90	2.15

AMERICAN ARTISTS

Gilbert Charles
Stuart — A343

James A. McNeill
Whistler — A344

Augustus Saint-
Gaudens — A345

Daniel Chester
French — A346

Frederic Remington — A347

884	A343	1c	**bright blue green,** *Sept. 5*	.20	.20
			P# block of 4	1.00	—
885	A344	2c	**rose carmine,** *Sept. 5*	.20	.20
			P# block of 4	.95	—
886	A345	3c	**bright red violet,** *Sept. 16*	.30	.20
			P# block of 4	1.50	—
887	A346	5c	**ultramarine,** *Sept. 16*	.50	.20
			P# block of 4	8.00	—
888	A347	10c	**dark brown,** *Sept. 30*	1.75	1.25
			P# block of 4	17.50	—
			Nos. 884-888 (5)	2.95	2.05

AMERICAN INVENTORS

Eli Whitney — A348

Samuel F. B.
Morse — A349

Cyrus Hall
McCormick — A350

Elias Howe — A351

Alexander Graham
Bell — A352

889	A348	1c	**bright blue green,** *Oct. 7*	.25	.20
			P# block of 4	2.25	—
890	A349	2c	**rose carmine,** *Oct. 7*	.30	.20
			P# block of 4	2.00	—

891	A350	3c	**bright red violet,** *Oct. 14*	.30	.20
			P# block of 4	1.50	—
892	A351	5c	**ultramarine,** *Oct. 14*	1.10	.30
			P# block of 4	12.50	—
893	A352	10c	**dark brown,** *Oct. 28*	11.00	2.00
			P# block of 4	50.00	—
			Nos. 889-893 (5)	12.95	2.90
			Nos. 859-893 (35)	32.50	14.70
			Nos. 859-893, P# blocks of 4	303.10	

PONY EXPRESS, 80th ANNIV. ISSUE

Pony Express
Rider — A353

ROTARY PRESS PRINTING
E.E. Plates of 200 subjects in four panes of 50.

1940, Apr. 3   *Perf. 11x10½*

| 894 | A353 | 3c | **henna brown** | .50 | .20 |
| | | | P# block of 4 | 3.50 | — |

PAN AMERICAN UNION ISSUE
Founding of the Pan American Union, 50th anniv.

The Three Graces
(Botticelli) — A354

ROTARY PRESS PRINTING
E.E. Plates of 200 subjects in four panes of 50.

1940, Apr. 14   *Perf. 10½x11*

| 895 | A354 | 3c | **light violet** | .30 | .20 |
| | | | P# block of 4 | 2.75 | — |

IDAHO STATEHOOD, 50th ANNIV.

Idaho State
Capitol
A355

ROTARY PRESS PRINTING
E.E. Plates of 200 subjects in four panes of 50.

1940, July 3   *Perf. 11x10½*

| 896 | A355 | 3c | **bright violet** | .35 | .20 |
| | | | P# block of 4 | 2.25 | — |

WYOMING STATEHOOD, 50th ANNIV.

Wyoming State
Seal — A356

ROTARY PRESS PRINTING
E.E. Plates of 200 subjects in four panes of 50.

1940, July 10   *Perf. 10½x11*

| 897 | A356 | 3c | **brown violet** | .30 | .20 |
| | | | P# block of 4 | 2.25 | — |

CORONADO EXPEDITION, 400th ANNIV.

"Coronado and His Captains" Painted by Gerald Cassidy A357

ROTARY PRESS PRINTING
E.E. Plates of 200 subjects in four panes of 50.

1940, Sept. 7			**Perf. 11x10½**
898	A357	3c **violet**	.25 .20
		P# block of 4	2.00 —

NATIONAL DEFENSE ISSUE

Statue of Liberty — A358

90-millimeter Anti-aircraft Gun — A359

Torch of Enlightenment — A360

ROTARY PRESS PRINTING
E.E. Plates of 400 subjects in four panes of 100

1940, Oct. 16			**Perf. 11x10½**
899	A358	1c **bright blue green**	.20 .20
		P# block of 4	.45 —
		Cracked plate (22684 UR 10)	3.00
		Gripper cracks	3.00
		Pair with full vert. gutter between	200.00
a.		Vertical pair, imperf. between	600.00 —
b.		Horizontal pair, imperf. between	32.50 —
900	A359	2c **rose carmine**	.20 .20
		P# block of 4	.45 —
		Pair with full vert. gutter between	275.00
a.		Horizontal pair, imperf. between	37.50 —
901	A360	3c **bright violet**	.20 .20
		P# block of 4	.60 —
		Pair with full vert. gutter between	
a.		Horizontal pair, imperf. between	22.50 —
		Nos. 899-901 (3)	.60 .60

Bureau Precancels: 1c, 316 diff., 2c, 25 diff., 3c, 22 diff.

THIRTEENTH AMENDMENT ISSUE

75th anniv. of the 13th Amendment to the Constitution abolishing slavery.

Emancipation Monument; Lincoln and Kneeling Slave, by Thomas Ball — A361

Designed by William A. Roach.

ROTARY PRESS PRINTING
E.E. Plates of 200 subjects in four panes of 50.

1940, Oct. 20			**Perf. 10½x11**
902	A361	3c **deep violet**	.30 .20
		dark violet	.30 .20
		P# block of 4	3.00 —

VERMONT STATEHOOD, 150th ANNIV.

State Capitol, Montpelier A362

Designed by Alvin R. Meissner.

ROTARY PRESS PRINTING
E.E. Plates of 200 subjects in four panes of 50.

1941, Mar. 4			**Perf. 11x10½**
903	A362	3c **light violet**	.45 .20
		P# block of 4	3.00 —

KENTUCKY STATEHOOD, 150th ANNIV.

Daniel Boone and Three Frontiersmen, from Mural by Gilbert White — A363

Designed by William A. Roach.

ROTARY PRESS PRINTING
E.E. Plates of 200 subjects in four panes of 50.

1942, June 1			**Perf. 11x10½**
904	A363	3c **violet**	.30 .20
		P# block of 4	1.75 —

WIN THE WAR ISSUE

American Eagle — A364

ROTARY PRESS PRINTING
E.E. Plates of 400 subjects in four panes of 100.

1942, July 4			**Perf. 11x10½**
905	A364	3c **violet**	.20 .20
		light violet	.20 .20
		P# block of 4	.65 —
		Pair with full vert. or horiz. gutter between	175.00
b.		3c **reddish violet**	750.00 500.00

Bureau Precancels: 26 diff.

All examples of No. 905b are precanceled either Los Angeles, Calif., or Fremont, Ohio. Value is for Los Angeles, which is the more common.

CHINESE RESISTANCE ISSUE

Issued to commemorate the Chinese people's five years of resistance to Japanese aggression.

Map of China, Abraham Lincoln and Sun Yat-sen, Founder of the Chinese Republic A365

ROTARY PRESS PRINTING
E.E. Plates of 200 subjects in four panes of 50.

1942, July 7			**Perf. 11x10½**
906	A365	5c **bright blue**	1.40 .20
		P# block of 4	8.25 —

ALLIED NATIONS ISSUE

Allegory of Victory — A366

Designed by Leon Helguera.

ROTARY PRESS PRINTING
E.E. Plates of 400 subjects in four panes of 100.

1943, Jan. 14			**Perf. 11x10½**
907	A366	2c **rose carmine**	.20 .20
		P# block of 4	.30 —
		Pair with full vert. or horiz. gutter between	225.00

Bureau Precancels: Denver, Baltimore.

FOUR FREEDOMS ISSUE

Liberty Holding the Torch of Freedom and Enlightenment — A367

Designed by Paul Manship.

ROTARY PRESS PRINTING
E.E. Plates of 400 subjects in four panes of 100.

1943, Feb. 12			**Perf. 11x10½**
908	A367	1c **bright blue green**	.20 .20
		P# block of 4	.70 —

Bureau Precancels: 20 diff.

OVERRUN COUNTRIES ISSUE
Printed by the American Bank Note Co.
FRAMES ENGRAVED, CENTERS OFFSET LETTERPRESS
ROTARY PRESS PRINTING
Plates of 200 subjects in four panes of 50.

Due to the failure of the printers to divulge detailed information as to printing processes used, the editors omit listings of irregularities, flaws and blemishes which are numerous in this issue. Exceptions are made for certified double impressions, the widely recognized "KORPA" variety, and "reverse" vs. "normal" printings of the flag colors.

Flag of Poland A368

1943-44			**Perf. 12**
909	A368	5c **blue violet, bright red & black,** *June 22, 1943*	.25 .20
		Margin block of 4, Inscribed "Poland"	3.50
		Top margin block of 6, with red & blue violet guide markings and "Poland"	4.75
		Bottom margin block of 6, with red & black guide markings	1.65
a.		Double impression of "Poland"	—
b.		Double impression of black flag color and red "Poland"	—
c.		Reverse printing of flag colors (bright red over black)	— —

Flag of Czechoslovakia — A368a

910 A368a 5c **blue violet, blue, bright red & black,** *July 12, 1943* .25 .20
 Margin block of 4, inscribed "Czechoslovakia" 2.75 —
 Top margin block of 6, with red & blue violet guide markings and "Czechoslovakia" 3.25 —
 a. Double impression of "Czechoslovakia" —
 b. Reverse printing of flag colors (blue and bright red over black) —
 c. Partial reverse printing of flag colors (bright red over black and black over blue) —

Flag of Norway — A368b

911 A368b 5c **blue violet, dark rose, deep blue & black,** *July 27, 1943* .25 .20
 Margin block of 4, inscribed "Norway" 1.30 —
 Bottom margin block of 6 with dark rose & blue violet guide markings 1.65 —
 a. Double impression of "Norway" —
 b. Reverse printing of flag colors (dark rose and deep blue over black) —

Flag of Luxembourg — A368c

912 A368c 5c **blue violet, dark rose, light blue & black,** *Aug. 10, 1943* .25 .20
 Margin block of 4, inscribed "Luxembourg" 1.30 —
 Top margin block of 6 with light blue & blue violet guide markings & "Luxembourg" 1.65 —
 a. Double impression of "Luxembourg" —
 b. Reverse printing of flag colors (dark rose and light blue over black) —
 c. Partial reverse printing of flag colors (dark rose over black and black over light blue) —

Flag of Netherlands — A368d

913 A368d 5c **blue violet, dark rose, blue & black,** *Aug. 24, 1943* .25 .20
 Margin block of 4, inscribed "Netherlands" 1.25 —
 Bottom margin block of 6 with blue & blue violet guide markings 1.65 —
 a. Reverse printing of flag colors (dark rose and blue over black) —
 b. Partial reverse printing of flag colors (blue over black and black over dark rose) .25 .20
 c. Double impression of black —

Flag of Belgium — A368e

914 A368e 5c **blue violet, dark rose, yellow & black,** *Sept. 14, 1943* .20 .20
 Margin block of 4, inscribed "Belgium" 1.10 —
 Top margin block of 6, with yellow & blue violet guide markings and "Belgium" 1.50 —
 a. Double impression of "Belgium" —
 b. Reverse printing of flag colors (red and yellow over black) —
 c. Partial reverse printing of flag colors (yellow over black and black over red) —

Flag of France — A368f

915 A368f 5c **blue violet, deep blue, dark rose & black,** *Sept. 28, 1943* .25 .20
 Margin block of 4, inscribed "France" 1.25 —
 Bottom margin block of 6 with dark rose & blue violet guide markings 1.65 —
 a. Reverse printing of flag colors (deep blue and dark rose over black) —
 b. Partial reverse printing of flag colors (dark rose over black and black over deep blue) —

Flag of Greece — A368g

916 A368g 5c **blue violet, pale blue, greenish blue & black,** reverse printing of flag colors (pale blue flag stripes over pale blue shading), *1943* .50 .25
 Margin block of 4, inscribed "Greece" 11.00 —
 Top margin block of 6 with pale blue & blue violet guide markings & "Greece" 11.50 —
 a. "Normal" printing of flag colors (dark blue shading over pale blue flag stripes) — —

Flag of Yugoslavia — A368h

Normal

Reverse Printing of Flag Colors

917 A368h 5c **blue violet, blue, dark rose & black,** *Oct. 26, 1943* .40 .20
 Margin block of 4, inscribed "Yugoslavia" 4.25 —
 Bottom margin block of 6 with dark rose & blue violet guide markings 2.60 —
 a. Reverse printing of flag colors (blue and dark rose over black) —
 b. Double impression of black —
 c. Partial reverse printing of flag colors (dark rose over black and black over blue) —

Flag of Albania — A368i

918 A368i 5c **blue violet, dark red & black,** *Nov. 9, 1943* .25 .20
 Margin block of 4, inscribed "Albania" 4.25 —
 Top margin block of 6, with dark red & blue violet guide markings & "Albania" 6.50 —
 a. Double impression of "Albania" —

Flag of Austria — A368j

919 A368j 5c **blue violet, red & black,** *Nov. 23, 1943* .30 .20
 Margin block of 4, inscribed "Austria" 3.50 —
 Bottom margin block of 6, with red & blue violet guide markings 2.00 —
 a. Double impression of "Austria" —
 b. Reverse printing of flag colors (red over black) —
 c. Double impression of black —

Flag of Denmark — A368k

920 A368k 5c **blue violet, red & black,** *Dec. 7, 1943* .30 .20
 Margin block of 4, inscribed "Denmark" 5.25 —
 Top margin block of 6, with red & blue violet guide markings & "Denmark" 6.00 —
 a. Reverse printing of flag colors (red over black) —
 b. 5c **blue violet, red & gray** .30 .20
 c. As "b," reverse printing of flag colors (red over gray) —

Flag of Korea — A368m

"KORPA" plate flaw

921 A368m 5c **blue violet, red, light blue & gray,** reverse printing of flag colors (light blue over gray), *Nov. 2, 1944* .25 .20
    Margin block of 4, inscribed "Korea" 4.50 —
    Top margin block of 6 with blue & black guide markings and "Korea" 5.25 —
    "KORPA" plate flaw 19.00 12.50
  a. Double impression of "Korea" —
  b. "Normal" printing of flag colors (gray over light blue) .25 .20

The "P" of "KORPA" is actually a mangled "E." Occurs only on some panes, position 26.

    Nos. 909-921 (13) 3.70 2.65
    Nos. 909-921, Name blocks of 4 47.10

TRANSCONTINENTAL RAILROAD ISSUE

Completion of the 1st transcontinental railroad, 75th anniv.

"Golden Spike Ceremony" Painted by John McQuarrie A369

ENGRAVED
ROTARY PRESS PRINTING
E.E. Plates of 200 subjects in four panes of 50.

1944, May 10 *Perf. 11x10½*
922 A369 3c **violet** .25 .20
    P# block of 4 2.00 —

STEAMSHIP ISSUE

1st steamship to cross the Atlantic, 125th anniv.

"Savannah" A370

ROTARY PRESS PRINTING
E.E. Plates of 200 subjects in four panes of 50.

1944, May 22 *Perf. 11x10½*
923 A370 3c **violet** .20 .20
    P# block of 4 1.25 —

TELEGRAPH ISSUE

1st message transmitted by telegraph, cent.

Telegraph Wires and Morse's First Transmitted Words "What Hath God Wrought" A371

ROTARY PRESS PRINTING
E.E. Plates of 200 subjects in four panes of 50.

1944, May 24 *Perf. 11x10½*
924 A371 3c **bright red violet** .20 .20
    P# block of 4 1.00 —

PHILIPPINE ISSUE

Final resistance of the US and Philippine defenders on Corregidor to the Japanese invaders in 1942.

Aerial View of Corregidor, Manila Bay — A372

ROTARY PRESS PRINTING
E.E. Plates of 200 subjects in four panes of 50.

1944, Sept. 27 *Perf. 11x10½*
925 A372 3c **deep violet** .20 .20
    P# block of 4 1.25 —

MOTION PICTURE, 50th ANNIV.

Motion Picture Showing for Armed Forces in South Pacific — A373

ROTARY PRESS PRINTING
E.E. Plates of 200 subjects in four panes of 50.

1944, Oct. 31 *Perf. 11x10½*
926 A373 3c **deep violet** .20 .20
    P# block of 4 1.10 —

FLORIDA STATEHOOD, CENTENARY

State Seal, Gates of St. Augustine and Capitol at Tallahassee A374

ROTARY PRESS PRINTING
E.E. Plates of 200 subjects in four panes of 50.

1945, Mar. 3 *Perf. 11x10½*
927 A374 3c **bright red violet** .20 .20
    P# block of 4 1.10 —

UNITED NATIONS CONFERENCE ISSUE

United Nations Conference, San Francisco, Calif.

"Toward United Nations, April 25, 1945" — A375

ROTARY PRESS PRINTING
E.E. Plates of 200 subjects in four panes of 50.

1945, Apr. 25 *Perf. 11x10½*
928 A375 5c **ultramarine** .20 .20
    P# block of 4 .60 —

IWO JIMA (MARINES) ISSUE

Battle of Iwo Jima and honoring the achievements of the US Marines.

Marines Raising American Flag on Mount Suribachi, Iwo Jima, from a photograph by Joe Rosenthal — A376

ROTARY PRESS PRINTING
E.E. Plates of 200 subjects in four panes of 50.

1945, July 11 *Perf. 10½x11*
929 A376 3c **yellow green** .30 .20
    P# block of 4 2.00 —

FRANKLIN D. ROOSEVELT ISSUE

Franklin Delano Roosevelt (1882-1945).

Roosevelt and Hyde Park Residence A377

Roosevelt and the "Little White House" at Warm Springs, Ga. — A378

Roosevelt and White House — A379

Roosevelt, Map of Western Hemisphere and Four Freedoms A380

ROTARY PRESS PRINTING
E.E. Plates of 200 subjects in four panes of 50.

1945-46 *Perf. 11x10½*
930 A377 1c **blue green,** *July 26, 1945* .20 .20
    P# block of 4 .35 —
931 A378 2c **carmine rose,** *Aug. 24, 1945* .20 .20
    P# block of 4 .60 —
932 A379 3c **purple,** *June 27, 1945* .20 .20
    P# block of 4 .60 —
933 A380 5c **bright blue,** *Jan. 30, 1946* .20 .20
    P# block of 4 .45 —
    Nos. 930-933 (4) .80 .80

ARMY ISSUE

Achievements of the US Army in World War II.

United States Troops Passing Arch of Triumph, Paris — A381

ROTARY PRESS PRINTING
E.E. Plates of 200 subjects in four panes of 50.
1945, Sept. 28   *Perf. 11x10½*
934 A381 3c olive   .20 .20
    P# block of 4   .60 —

NAVY ISSUE
Achievements of the U.S. Navy in World War II.

United States
Sailors — A382

ROTARY PRESS PRINTING
E.E. Plates of 200 subjects in four panes of 50.
1945, Oct. 27   *Perf. 11x10½*
935 A382 3c blue   .20 .20
    P# block of 4   .60 —

COAST GUARD ISSUE
Achievements of the US Coast Guard in World War II.

Coast Guard
Landing Craft
and Supply
Ship — A383

ROTARY PRESS PRINTING
E.E. Plates of 200 subjects in four panes of 50.
1945, Nov. 10   *Perf. 11x10½*
936 A383 3c bright blue green   .20 .20
    P# block of 4   .70 —

ALFRED E. SMITH ISSUE

Alfred E. Smith, Governor of
New York — A384

ROTARY PRESS PRINTING
E.E. Plates of 400 subjects in four panes of 100.
1945, Nov. 26   *Perf. 11x10½*
937 A384 3c purple   .20 .20
    P# block of 4   .50
    Pair with full vert. gutter btwn.
    Pair with full horiz. gutter btwn.   300.00

TEXAS STATEHOOD, 100th ANNIV.

Flags of the
United States
and the State
of
Texas — A385

ROTARY PRESS PRINTING
E.E. Plates of 200 subjects in four panes of 50.
1945, Dec. 29   *Perf. 11x10½*
938 A385 3c dark blue   .20 .20
    P# block of 4   .60 —

MERCHANT MARINE ISSUE
Achievements of the US Merchant Marine in World War II.

Liberty Ship
Unloading
Cargo — A386

ROTARY PRESS PRINTING
E.E. Plates of 200 subjects in four panes of 50.
1946, Feb. 26   *Perf. 11x10½*
939 A386 3c blue green   .20 .20
    P# block of 4   .60 —

VETERANS OF WORLD WAR II ISSUE
Issued to honor all veterans of World War II.

Honorable Discharge
Emblem — A387

ROTARY PRESS PRINTING
E.E. Plates of 400 subjects in four panes of 100.
1946, May 9   *Perf. 11x10½*
940 A387 3c dark violet   .20 .20
    P# block of 4   .50
    Pair with full vert. gutter btwn.   225.00

TENNESSEE STATEHOOD, 150th ANNIV.

Andrew
Jackson, John
Sevier and
State Capitol,
Nashville
A388

ROTARY PRESS PRINTING
E.E. Plates of 200 subjects in four panes of 50.
1946, June 1   *Perf. 11x10½*
941 A388 3c dark violet   .20 .20
    P# block of 4   .50

IOWA STATEHOOD, 100th ANNIV.

Iowa State
Flag and
Map — A389

ROTARY PRESS PRINTING
E.E. Plates of 200 subjects in four panes of 50.
1946, Aug. 3   *Perf. 11x10½*
942 A389 3c deep blue   .20 .20
    P# block of 4   .45 —

SMITHSONIAN INSTITUTION ISSUE
100th anniversary of the establishment of the Smithsonian Institution, Washington, D.C.

Smithsonian
Institution
A390

ROTARY PRESS PRINTING
E.E. Plates of 200 subjects in four panes of 50.
1946, Aug. 10   *Perf. 11x10½*
943 A390 3c violet brown   .20 .20
    P# block of 4   .45 —

KEARNY EXPEDITION ISSUE
100th anniversary of the entry of General Stephen Watts Kearny into Santa Fe.

"Capture of
Santa Fe" by
Kenneth M.
Chapman
A391

ROTARY PRESS PRINTING
E.E. Plates of 200 subjects in four panes of 50.
1946, Oct. 16   *Perf. 11x10½*
944 A391 3c brown violet   .20 .20
    P# block of 4   .45 —

THOMAS A. EDISON ISSUE

Thomas A. Edison (1847-
1931), Inventor — A392

ROTARY PRESS PRINTING
E.E. Plates of 280 subjects in four panes of 70.
1947, Feb. 11   *Perf. 10½x11*
945 A392 3c bright red violet   .20 .20
    P# block of 4   .40 —

JOSEPH PULITZER ISSUE

Joseph
Pulitzer (1847-
1911),
Journalist, and
Statue of
Liberty
A393

Designed by Victor S. McCloskey, Jr.

ROTARY PRESS PRINTING
E.E. Plates of 200 subjects in four panes of 50.
1947, Apr. 10   *Perf. 11x10½*
946 A393 3c purple   .20 .20
    P# block of 4   .40 —

POSTAGE STAMP CENTENARY ISSUE
Centenary of the first postage stamps issued by the United States Government

Washington
and Franklin,
Early and
Modern Mail-
carrying
Vehicles
A394

Designed by Leon Helguera.

ROTARY PRESS PRINTING
E.E. Plates of 200 subjects in four panes of 50.
1947, May 17   *Perf. 11x10½*
947 A394 3c deep blue   .20 .20
    P# block of 4   .40 —

CENTENARY INTERNATIONAL PHILATELIC EXHIBITION ISSUE
SOUVENIR SHEET

A395

Illustration reduced.

FLAT PLATE PRINTING
Plates of 30 subjects

1947, May 19   *Imperf.*
948 A395   Sheet of 2   .55   .45
a.   5c **blue**, type A1   .20   .20
b.   10c **brown orange**, type A2   .25   .25

Sheet inscribed below stamps: "100th Anniversary United States Postage Stamps" and in the margins: "PRINTED BY THE TREASURY DEPARTMENT, BUREAU OF ENGRAVING AND PRINTING. — UNDER AUTHORITY OF ROBERT E. HANNEGAN, POSTMASTER GENERAL. — IN COMPLIMENT TO THE CENTENARY INTERNATIONAL PHILATELIC EXHIBITION. — NEW YORK, N.Y., MAY 17-25, 1947." Sheet size varies: 96-98x66-68mm.

DOCTORS ISSUE

Issued to honor the physicians of America.

"The Doctor" by Sir Luke Fildes — A396

Designed by Charles R. Chickering.
ROTARY PRESS PRINTING
E.E. Plates of 200 subjects in four panes of 50.

1947, June 9   *Perf. 11x10½*
949 A396 3c **brown violet**   .20   .20
     P# block of 4   .40

UTAH ISSUE

Centenary of the settlement of Utah.

Pioneers Entering the Valley of Great Salt Lake — A397

Designed by Charles R. Chickering.
ROTARY PRESS PRINTING
E.E. Plates of 200 subjects in four panes of 50.

1947, July 24   *Perf. 11x10½*
950 A397 3c **dark violet**   .20   .20
     P# block of 4   .60

U.S. FRIGATE CONSTITUTION ISSUE

150th anniversary of the launching of the U.S. frigate Constitution ("Old Ironsides").

Naval Architect's Drawing of Frigate Constitution A398

Designed by Andrew H. Hepburn.

ROTARY PRESS PRINTING
E.E. Plates of 200 subjects in four panes of 50.

1947, Oct. 21   *Perf. 11x10½*
951 A398 3c **blue green**   .20   .20
     P# block of 4   .40

Great White Heron and Map of Florida — A399   Dr. George Washington Carver — A400

EVERGLADES NATIONAL PARK ISSUE

Dedication of the Everglades National Park, Florida, Dec. 6, 1947.

Designed by Robert I. Miller, Jr.
ROTARY PRESS PRINTING
E.E. Plates of 200 subjects in four panes of 50.

1947, Dec. 5   *Perf. 10½x11*
952 A399 3c **bright green**   .20   .20
     P# block of 4   .40

GEORGE WASHINGTON CARVER ISSUE

5th anniversary of the death of Dr. George Washington Carver, (1864-1943), botanist.

ROTARY PRESS PRINTING
E.E. Plates of 280 subjects in four panes of 70.

1948, Jan. 5   *Perf. 10½x11*
953 A400 3c **bright red violet**   .20   .20
     P# block of 4   .45

CALIFORNIA GOLD CENTENNIAL ISSUE

Sutter's Mill, Coloma, California A401

Designed by Charles R. Chickering.
ROTARY PRESS PRINTING
E.E. Plates of 200 subjects in four panes of 50.

1948, Jan. 24   *Perf. 11x10½*
954 A401 3c **dark violet**   .20   .20
     P# block of 4   .40

MISSISSIPPI TERRITORY ISSUE

Mississippi Territory establishment, 150th anniv.

Map, Seal of Mississippi Territory and Gov. Winthrop Sargent A402

Designed by William K. Schrage.
ROTARY PRESS PRINTING
E.E. Plates of 200 subjects in four panes of 50.

1948, Apr. 7   *Perf. 11x10½*
955 A402 3c **brown violet**   .20   .20
     P# block of 4   .50

FOUR CHAPLAINS ISSUE

George L. Fox, Clark V. Poling, John P. Washington and Alexander D. Goode, the 4 chaplains who sacrificed their lives in the sinking of the S.S. Dorchester, Feb. 3, 1943.

Four Chaplains and Sinking S.S. Dorchester A403

Designed by Charles R. Chickering.
ROTARY PRESS PRINTING
E.E. Plates of 200 subjects in four panes of 50.

1948, May 28   *Perf. 11x10½*
956 A403 3c **gray black**   .20   .20
     P# block of 4   .50

WISCONSIN STATEHOOD, 100th ANNIV.

Map on Scroll and State Capitol — A404

Designed by Victor S. McCloskey, Jr.
ROTARY PRESS PRINTING
E.E. Plates of 200 subjects in four panes of 50.

1948, May 29   *Perf. 11x10½*
957 A404 3c **dark violet**   .20   .20
     P# block of 4   .50

SWEDISH PIONEER ISSUE

Centenary of the coming of the Swedish pioneers to the Middle West.

Swedish Pioneer with Covered Wagon Moving Westward A405

Designed by Charles R. Chickering.
ROTARY PRESS PRINTING
E.E. Plates of 200 subjects in four panes of 50.

1948, June 4   *Perf. 11x10½*
958 A405 5c **deep blue**   .20   .20
     P# block of 4   .45

PROGRESS OF WOMEN ISSUE

Century of progress of American Women.

Elizabeth Stanton, Carrie Chapman and Lucretia Mott — A406

Designed by Victor S. McCloskey, Jr.
ROTARY PRESS PRINTING
E.E. Plates of 200 subjects in four panes of 50.

1948, July 19
959 A406 3c **dark violet**
     P# block of 4

WILLIAM ALLEN WHITE ISSUE

William Allen White (1868-1944), Writer and Journalist — A407

ROTARY PRESS PRINTING
E.E. Plates of 280 subjects in four panes of 70.

1948, July 31		Perf. 10½x11	
960 A407 3c **bright red violet**		.20	.20
P# block of 4		.40	—

UNITED STATES-CANADA FRIENDSHIP ISSUE
Century of friendship between the US and Canada.

Niagara Railway Suspension Bridge — A408

Designed by Leon Helguera, modeled by V. S. McCloskey, Jr.

ROTARY PRESS PRINTING
E.E. Plates of 200 subjects in four panes of 50.

1948, Aug. 2		Perf. 11x10½	
961 A408 3c **blue**		.20	.20
P# block of 4		.40	—

FRANCIS SCOTT KEY ISSUE
Francis Scott Key (1779-1843), Maryland lawyer and author of "The Star-Spangled Banner" (1813).

Francis Scott Key and American Flags of 1814 and 1948 — A409

Designed by Victor S. McCloskey, Jr.

ROTARY PRESS PRINTING
E.E. Plates of 200 subjects in four panes of 50.

1948, Aug. 9		Perf. 11x10½	
962 A409 3c **rose pink**		.20	.20
P# block of 4		.40	—

SALUTE TO YOUTH ISSUE
...ed to honor the Youth of America and to publi-
...uth Month," September, 1948.

Girl and Boy Carrying Books — A410

..., Carrie
..., an Catt
...cretia
... A406

...ESS PRINTING
...ects in four panes of 50.

		Perf. 11x10½	
		.20	.20
		.40	—

...RY ISSUE
... of Oregon Territory.

...es of 50.
...rf. 11x10½
.20   .20
.55

...SUE

...10½
.20   .20
.65

HARLAN F. STONE ISSUE

Harlan Fiske Stone (1872-1946) of New York, Associate Justice of the Supreme Court, 1925-1941, and Chief Justice, 1941-1946 — A412

ROTARY PRESS PRINTING
E.E. Plates of 280 subjects in four panes of 70.

1948, Aug. 25		Perf. 10½x11	
965 A412 3c **bright violet**		.20	.20
P# block of 4		.60	—

PALOMAR MOUNTAIN OBSERVATORY ISSUE
Dedication, August 30, 1948.

Observatory, Palomar Mountain, California — A413

Designed by Victor S. McCloskey, Jr.

ROTARY PRESS PRINTING
E.E. Plates of 280 subjects in four panes of 70.

1948, Aug. 30		Perf. 10½x11	
966 A413 3c **blue**		.20	.20
P# block of 4		.95	—
a. Vert. pair, imperf. between		350.00	

CLARA BARTON ISSUE

Clara Barton (1821-1912), Founder of the American Red Cross in 1882 — A414

Designed by Charles R. Chickering.

ROTARY PRESS PRINTING
E.E. Plates of 200 subjects in four panes of 50.

1948, Sept. 7		Perf. 11x10½	
967 A414 3c **rose pink**		.20	.20
P# block of 4		.60	—

POULTRY INDUSTRY CENTENNIAL ISSUE

Light Brahma Rooster A415

Designed by Charles R. Chickering.

ROTARY PRESS PRINTING
E.E. Plates of 200 subjects in four panes of 50.

1948, Sept. 9		Perf. 11x10½	
968 A415 3c **sepia**		.20	.20
P# block of 4		.60	—

GOLD STAR MOTHERS ISSUE
Issued to honor the mothers of deceased members of the United States armed forces.

Star and Palm Frond — A416

Designed by Charles R. Chickering.

ROTARY PRESS PRINTING
E.E. Plates of 200 subjects in four panes of 50.

1948, Sept. 21		Perf. 10½x11	
969 A416 3c **orange yellow**		.20	.20
P# block of 4		.45	—

FORT KEARNY ISSUE
Establishment of Fort Kearny, Neb., centenary.

Fort Kearny and Pioneer Group — A417

ROTARY PRESS PRINTING
E.E. Plates of 200 subjects in four panes of 50.

1948, Sept. 22		Perf. 11x10½	
970 A417 3c **violet**		.20	.20
P# block of 4		.60	—

VOLUNTEER FIREMEN ISSUE
300th anniv. of the organization of the 1st volunteer firemen in America by Peter Stuyvesant.

Peter Stuyvesant, Early and Modern Fire Engines A418

ROTARY PRESS PRINTING
E.E. Plates of 200 subjects in four panes of 50.

1948, Oct. 4		Perf. 11x10½	
971 A418 3c **bright rose carmine**		.20	.20
P# block of 4		.70	—

INDIAN CENTENNIAL ISSUE
Centenary of the arrival in Indian Territory, later Oklahoma, of the Five Civilized Indian Tribes: Cherokee, Chickasaw, Choctaw, Muscogee and Seminole.

Map of Indian Territory and Seals of Five Tribes — A419

ROTARY PRESS PRINTING
E.E. Plates of 200 subjects in four panes of 50.

1948, Oct. 15		Perf. 11x10½	
972 A419 3c **dark brown**		.20	.20
P# block of 4		.60	—

ROUGH RIDERS ISSUE
50th anniversary of the organization of the Rough Riders of the Spanish-American War.

ROTARY PRESS PRINTING
E.E. Plates of 280 subjects in four panes of 70.

1948, July 31		**Perf. 10½x11**
960 A407 3c **bright red violet**	.20	.20
P# block of 4	.40	—

UNITED STATES-CANADA FRIENDSHIP ISSUE

Century of friendship between the US and Canada.

Niagara Railway Suspension Bridge — A408

Designed by Leon Helguera, modeled by V. S. McCloskey, Jr.

ROTARY PRESS PRINTING
E.E. Plates of 200 subjects in four panes of 50.

1948, Aug. 2		**Perf. 11x10½**
961 A408 3c **blue**	.20	.20
P# block of 4	.40	—

FRANCIS SCOTT KEY ISSUE

Francis Scott Key (1779-1843), Maryland lawyer and author of "The Star-Spangled Banner" (1813).

Francis Scott Key and American Flags of 1814 and 1948 — A409

Designed by Victor S. McCloskey, Jr.

ROTARY PRESS PRINTING
E.E. Plates of 200 subjects in four panes of 50.

1948, Aug. 9		**Perf. 11x10½**
962 A409 3c **rose pink**	.20	.20
P# block of 4	.40	—

SALUTE TO YOUTH ISSUE

Issued to honor the Youth of America and to publicize "Youth Month," September, 1948.

Girl and Boy Carrying Books — A410

ROTARY PRESS PRINTING
E.E. Plates of 200 subjects in four panes of 50.

1948, Aug. 11		**Perf. 11x10½**
963 A410 3c **deep blue**	.20	.20
P# block of 4	.40	—

OREGON TERRITORY ISSUE

Centenary of the establishment of Oregon Territory.

John McLoughlin, Jason Lee and Wagon on Oregon Trail — A411

ROTARY PRESS PRINTING
E.E. Plates of 200 subjects in four panes of 50.

1948, Aug. 14		**Perf. 11x10½**
964 A411 3c **brown red**	.20	.20
P# block of 4	.65	—

HARLAN F. STONE ISSUE

Harlan Fiske Stone (1872-1946) of New York, Associate Justice of the Supreme Court, 1925-1941, and Chief Justice, 1941-1946 — A412

ROTARY PRESS PRINTING
E.E. Plates of 280 subjects in four panes of 70.

1948, Aug. 25		**Perf. 10½x11**
965 A412 3c **bright violet**	.20	.20
P# block of 4	.60	—

PALOMAR MOUNTAIN OBSERVATORY ISSUE

Dedication, August 30, 1948.

Observatory, Palomar Mountain, California — A413

Designed by Victor S. McCloskey, Jr.

ROTARY PRESS PRINTING
E.E. Plates of 280 subjects in four panes of 70.

1948, Aug. 30		**Perf. 10½x11**
966 A413 3c **blue**	.20	.20
P# block of 4	.95	—
a. Vert. pair, imperf. between	350.00	

CLARA BARTON ISSUE

Clara Barton (1821-1912), Founder of the American Red Cross in 1882 — A414

Designed by Charles R. Chickering.

ROTARY PRESS PRINTING
E.E. Plates of 200 subjects in four panes of 50.

1948, Sept. 7		**Perf. 11x10½**
967 A414 3c **rose pink**	.20	.20
P# block of 4	.60	—

POULTRY INDUSTRY CENTENNIAL ISSUE

Light Brahma Rooster — A415

Designed by Charles R. Chickering.

ROTARY PRESS PRINTING
E.E. Plates of 200 subjects in four panes of 50.

1948, Sept. 9		**Perf. 11x10½**
968 A415 3c **sepia**	.20	.20
P# block of 4	.60	—

GOLD STAR MOTHERS ISSUE

Issued to honor the mothers of deceased members of the United States armed forces.

Star and Palm Frond — A416

Designed by Charles R. Chickering.

ROTARY PRESS PRINTING
E.E. Plates of 200 subjects in four panes of 50.

1948, Sept. 21		**Perf. 10½x11**
969 A416 3c **orange yellow**	.20	.20
P# block of 4	.45	—

FORT KEARNY ISSUE

Establishment of Fort Kearny, Neb., centenary.

Fort Kearny and Pioneer Group — A417

ROTARY PRESS PRINTING
E.E. Plates of 200 subjects in four panes of 50.

1948, Sept. 22		**Perf. 11x10½**
970 A417 3c **violet**	.20	.20
P# block of 4	.60	—

VOLUNTEER FIREMEN ISSUE

300th anniv. of the organization of the 1st volunteer firemen in America by Peter Stuyvesant.

Peter Stuyvesant, Early and Modern Fire Engines A418

ROTARY PRESS PRINTING
E.E. Plates of 200 subjects in four panes of 50.

1948, Oct. 4		**Perf. 11x10½**
971 A418 3c **bright rose carmine**	.20	.20
P# block of 4	.70	—

INDIAN CENTENNIAL ISSUE

Centenary of the arrival in Indian Territory, later Oklahoma, of the Five Civilized Indian Tribes: Cherokee, Chickasaw, Choctaw, Muscogee and Seminole.

Map of Indian Territory and Seals of Five Tribes — A419

ROTARY PRESS PRINTING
E.E. Plates of 200 subjects in four panes of 50.

1948, Oct. 15		**Perf. 11x10½**
972 A419 3c **dark brown**	.20	.20
P# block of 4	.60	—

ROUGH RIDERS ISSUE

50th anniversary of the organization of the Rough Riders of the Spanish-American War.

CENTENARY INTERNATIONAL PHILATELIC EXHIBITION ISSUE
SOUVENIR SHEET

A395

Illustration reduced.

FLAT PLATE PRINTING
Plates of 30 subjects

1947, May 19 *Imperf.*
948 A395 Sheet of 2 .55 .45
  a. 5c **blue**, type A1 .20 .20
  b. 10c **brown orange**, type A2 .25 .25
Sheet inscribed below stamps: "100th Anniversary United States Postage Stamps" and in the margins:
"PRINTED BY THE TREASURY DEPARTMENT, BUREAU OF ENGRAVING AND PRINTING. — UNDER AUTHORITY OF ROBERT E. HANNEGAN, POSTMASTER GENERAL. — IN COMPLIMENT TO THE CENTENARY INTERNATIONAL PHILATELIC EXHIBITION. — NEW YORK, N.Y., MAY 17-25, 1947."
Sheet size varies: 96-98x66-68mm.

DOCTORS ISSUE
Issued to honor the physicians of America.

"The Doctor" by Sir Luke Fildes — A396

Designed by Charles R. Chickering.

ROTARY PRESS PRINTING
E.E. Plates of 200 subjects in four panes of 50.

1947, June 9 *Perf. 11x10½*
949 A396 3c **brown violet** .20 .20
  P# block of 4 .40 —

UTAH ISSUE
Centenary of the settlement of Utah.

Pioneers Entering the Valley of Great Salt Lake — A397

Designed by Charles R. Chickering.

ROTARY PRESS PRINTING
E.E. Plates of 200 subjects in four panes of 50.

1947, July 24 *Perf. 11x10½*
950 A397 3c **dark violet** .20 .20
  P# block of 4 .60 —

U.S. FRIGATE CONSTITUTION ISSUE
150th anniversary of the launching of the U.S. frigate Constitution ("Old Ironsides").

Naval Architect's Drawing of Frigate Constitution A398

Designed by Andrew H. Hepburn.

ROTARY PRESS PRINTING
E.E. Plates of 200 subjects in four panes of 50.

1947, Oct. 21 *Perf. 11x10½*
951 A398 3c **blue green** .20 .20
  P# block of 4 .40

Great White Heron and Map of Florida — A399

Dr. George Washington Carver — A400

EVERGLADES NATIONAL PARK ISSUE
Dedication of the Everglades National Park, Florida, Dec. 6, 1947.

Designed by Robert I. Miller, Jr.

ROTARY PRESS PRINTING
E.E. Plates of 200 subjects in four panes of 50.

1947, Dec. 5 *Perf. 10½x11*
952 A399 3c **bright green** .20 .20
  P# block of 4 .40 —

GEORGE WASHINGTON CARVER ISSUE
5th anniversary of the death of Dr. George Washington Carver, (1864-1943), botanist.

ROTARY PRESS PRINTING
E.E. Plates of 280 subjects in four panes of 70.

1948, Jan. 5 *Perf. 10½x11*
953 A400 3c **bright red violet** .20 .20
  P# block of 4 .45 —

CALIFORNIA GOLD CENTENNIAL ISSUE

Sutter's Mill, Coloma, California A401

Designed by Charles R. Chickering.

ROTARY PRESS PRINTING
E.E. Plates of 200 subjects in four panes of 50.

1948, Jan. 24 *Perf. 11x10½*
954 A401 3c **dark violet** .20 .20
  P# block of 4 .40 —

MISSISSIPPI TERRITORY ISSUE
Mississippi Territory establishment, 150th anniv.

Map, Seal of Mississippi Territory and Gov. Winthrop Sargent A402

Designed by William K. Schrage.

ROTARY PRESS PRINTING
E.E. Plates of 200 subjects in four panes of 50.

1948, Apr. 7 *Perf. 11x10½*
955 A402 3c **brown violet** .20 .20
  P# block of 4 .50 —

FOUR CHAPLAINS ISSUE
George L. Fox, Clark V. Poling, John P. Washington and Alexander D. Goode, the 4 chaplains who sacrificed their lives in the sinking of the S.S. Dorchester, Feb. 3, 1943.

Four Chaplains and Sinking S.S. Dorchester A403

Designed by Charles R. Chickering.

ROTARY PRESS PRINTING
E.E. Plates of 200 subjects in four panes of 50.

1948, May 28 *Perf. 11x10½*
956 A403 3c **gray black** .20 .20
  P# block of 4 .50 —

WISCONSIN STATEHOOD, 100th ANNIV.

Map on Scroll and State Capitol — A404

Designed by Victor S. McCloskey, Jr.

ROTARY PRESS PRINTING
E.E. Plates of 200 subjects in four panes of 50.

1948, May 29 *Perf. 11x10½*
957 A404 3c **dark violet** .20 .20
  P# block of 4 .50 —

SWEDISH PIONEER ISSUE
Centenary of the coming of the Swedish pioneers to the Middle West.

Swedish Pioneer with Covered Wagon Moving Westward A405

Designed by Charles R. Chickering.

ROTARY PRESS PRINTING
E.E. Plates of 200 subjects in four panes of 50.

1948, June 4 *Perf. 11x10½*
958 A405 5c **deep blue** .20 .20
  P# block of 4 .45 —

PROGRESS OF WOMEN ISSUE
Century of progress of American Women.

Elizabeth Stanton, Carrie Chapman Catt and Lucretia Mott — A406

Designed by Victor S. McCloskey, Jr.

ROTARY PRESS PRINTING
E.E. Plates of 200 subjects in four panes of 50.

1948, July 19 *Perf. 11x10½*
959 A406 3c **dark violet** .20 .20
  P# block of 4 .55 —

WILLIAM ALLEN WHITE ISSUE

William Allen White (1868-1944), Writer and Journalist — A407

Statue of Capt. William O. (Bucky) O'Neill by Solon H. Borglum A420

Designed by Victor S. McCloskey, Jr.

ROTARY PRESS PRINTING
E.E. Plates of 200 subjects in four panes of 50.

1948, Oct. 27			Perf. 11x10½	
973 A420 3c violet brown			.20	.20
P# block of 4			.60	—

JULIETTE LOW ISSUE
Low (1860-1927), founder of the Girl Scouts of America. Mrs. Low organized the 1st Girl Guides troop in 1912 at Savannah. The name was changed to Girl Scouts in 1913 and headquarters moved to New York.

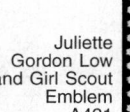

Juliette Gordon Low and Girl Scout Emblem A421

Designed by William K. Schrage.

ROTARY PRESS PRINTING
E.E. Plates of 200 subjects in four panes of 50.

1948, Oct. 29			Perf. 11x10½	
974 A421 3c blue green			.20	.20
P# block of 4			.50	—

Will Rogers, (1879-1935), Humorist and Political Commentator. — A422

Fort Bliss, El Paso, Texas, and Rocket Firing — A423

WILL ROGERS ISSUE
ROTARY PRESS PRINTING
E.E. Plates of 280 subjects in four panes of 70.

1948, Nov. 4			Perf. 10½x11	
975 A422 3c bright red violet			.20	.20
P# block of 4			.45	—

FORT BLISS CENTENNIAL ISSUE
Designed by Charles R. Chickering.

ROTARY PRESS PRINTING
E.E. Plates of 280 subjects in four panes of 70.

1948, Nov. 5			Perf. 10½x11	
976 A423 3c henna brown			.20	.20
P# block of 4			1.00	—

MOINA MICHAEL ISSUE
Moina Michael (1870-1944), educator who originated (1918) the Flanders Field Poppy Day idea as a memorial to the war dead.

Moina Michael and Poppy Plant — A424

ROTARY PRESS PRINTING
E.E. Plates of 200 subjects in four panes of 50.

1948, Nov. 9			Perf. 11x10½	
977 A424 3c rose pink			.20	.20
			.50	—

GETTYSBURG ADDRESS ISSUE
85th anniversary of Abraham Lincoln's address at Gettysburg, Pennsylvania.

Abraham Lincoln and Quotation from Gettysburg Address A425

Designed by Charles R. Chickering.

ROTARY PRESS PRINTING
E.E. Plates of 200 subjects in four panes of 50.

1948, Nov. 19			Perf. 11x10½	
978 A425 3c bright blue			.20	.20
P# block of 4			.60	—

Torch and Emblem of American Turners A426

Joel Chandler Harris (1848-1908), Georgia Writer, Creator of "Uncle Remus" and newspaperman. A427

AMERICAN TURNERS ISSUE
Formation of the American Turners Soc., cent.

Designed by Alvin R. Meissner.

ROTARY PRESS PRINTING
E.E. Plates of 200 subjects in four panes of 50.

1948, Nov. 20			Perf. 10½x11	
979 A426 3c carmine			.20	.20
P# block of 4			.40	—

JOEL CHANDLER HARRIS ISSUE
ROTARY PRESS PRINTING
E.E. Plates of 280 subjects in four panes of 70.

1948, Dec. 9			Perf. 10½x11	
980 A427 3c bright red violet			.20	.20
P# block of 4			.55	—

MINNESOTA TERRITORY ISSUE
Establishment of Minnesota Territory, cent.

Pioneer and Red River Oxcart — A428

ROTARY PRESS PRINTING
E.E. Plates of 200 subjects in four panes of 50.

1949, Mar. 3			Perf. 11x10½	
981 A428 3c blue green			.20	.20
P# block of 4			.45	—

WASHINGTON AND LEE UNIVERSITY ISSUE
Bicentenary of Washington and Lee University.

George Washington, Robert E. Lee and University Building, Lexington, Va. — A429

ROTARY PRESS PRINTING
E.E. Plates of 200 subjects in four panes of 50.

1949, Apr. 12			Perf. 11x10½	
982 A429 3c ultramarine			.20	.20
P# block of 4			.40	—

PUERTO RICO ELECTION ISSUE
First gubernatorial election in the Territory of Puerto Rico, Nov. 2, 1948.

Puerto Rican Farmer Holding Cogwheel and Ballot Box — A430

ROTARY PRESS PRINTING
E.E. Plates of 200 subjects in four panes of 50.

1949, Apr. 27			Perf. 11x10½	
983 A430 3c green			.20	.20
P# block of 4			.70	—

ANNAPOLIS TERCENTENARY ISSUE
Founding of Annapolis, Maryland, 300th anniv.

James Stoddert's 1718 Map of Regions about Annapolis, Redrawn A431

ROTARY PRESS PRINTING
E.E. Plates of 200 subjects in four panes of 50.

1949, May 23			Perf. 11x10½	
984 A431 3c aquamarine			.20	.20
P# block of 4			.40	—

G.A.R. ISSUE
Final encampment of the Grand Army of the Republic, Indianapolis, Aug. 28 - Sept. 1, 1949.

Union Soldier and G.A.R. Veteran of 1949 — A432

Designed by Charles R. Chickering.

ROTARY PRESS PRINTING
E.E. Plates of 200 subjects in four panes of 50.

1949, Aug. 29			Perf. 11x10½	
985 A432 3c bright rose carmine			.20	.20
P# block of 4			.40	—

EDGAR ALLAN POE ISSUE

Edgar Allan Poe (1809-1849), Boston-born Poet, Story Writer and Editor — A433

ROTARY PRESS PRINTING
E.E. Plates of 280 subjects in four panes of 70.

1949, Oct. 7		Perf. 10½x11	
986 A433 3c bright red violet		.20	.20
P# block of 4		.45	—
Thin outer frame line at top, inner			
line missing (24143 LL 42)		6.00	

AMERICAN BANKERS ASSOCIATION ISSUE

75th anniv. of the formation of the Association.

Coin, Symbolizing Fields of Banking Service A434

Designed by Charles R. Chickering.

ROTARY PRESS PRINTING
E.E. Plates of 200 subjects in four panes of 50.

1950, Jan. 3		Perf. 11x10½	
987 A434 3c yellow green		.20	.20
P# block of 4		.45	—

SAMUEL GOMPERS ISSUE

Samuel Gompers (1850-1924), British-born American Labor Leader — A435

ROTARY PRESS PRINTING
E.E. Plates of 280 subjects in four panes of 70.

1950, Jan. 27		Perf. 10½x11	
988 A435 3c bright red violet		.20	.20
P# block of 4		.40	—

NATIONAL CAPITAL SESQUICENTENNIAL ISSUE

150th anniversary of the establishment of the National Capital, Washington, D.C.

Statue of Freedom on Capitol Dome — A436

Executive Mansion A437

Supreme Court Building A438

United States Capitol — A439

ROTARY PRESS PRINTING
E.E. Plates of 200 subjects in four panes of 50.

1950		Perf. 10½x11, 11x10½	
989 A436 3c bright blue, Apr. 20		.20	.20
P# block of 4		.45	—
990 A437 3c deep green, June 12		.20	.20
P# block of 4		.50	—
991 A438 3c light violet, Aug. 2		.20	.20
P# block of 4		.35	—
992 A439 3c bright red violet, Nov. 22		.20	.20
P# block of 4		.55	—
Gripper cracks (24285 UL 11)		4.50	3.00
Nos. 989-992 (4)		.80	.80

RAILROAD ENGINEERS ISSUE

Issued to honor the Railroad Engineers of America. Stamp portrays John Luther (Casey) Jones (1864-1900), locomotive engineer killed in train wreck near Vaughn, Miss.

"Casey" Jones and Locomotives of 1900 and 1950 — A440

ROTARY PRESS PRINTING
E.E. Plates of 200 subjects in four panes of 50.

1950, Apr. 29		Perf. 11x10½	
993 A440 3c violet brown		.20	.20
P# block of 4		.50	—

KANSAS CITY, MISSOURI, CENTENARY ISSUE

Kansas City, Missouri, incorporation.

Kansas City Skyline, 1950 and Westport Landing, 1850 — A441

ROTARY PRESS PRINTING
E.E. Plates of 200 subjects in four panes of 50.

1950, June 3		Perf. 11x10½	
994 A441 3c violet		.20	.20
P# block of 4		.40	—

BOY SCOUTS ISSUE

Honoring the Boy Scouts of America on the occasion of the 2nd National Jamboree, Valley Forge, Pa.

Three Boys, Statue of Liberty and Scout Badge A442

ROTARY PRESS PRINTING
E.E. Plates of 200 subjects in four panes of 50.

1950, June 30		Perf. 11x10½	
995 A442 3c sepia		.20	.20
P# block of 4		.60	—

INDIANA TERRITORY ISSUE

Establishment of Indiana Territory, 150th anniv.

Gov. William Henry Harrison and First Indiana Capitol, Vincennes A443

ROTARY PRESS PRINTING
E.E. Plates of 200 subjects in four panes of 50.

1950, July 4		Perf. 11x10½	
996 A443 3c bright blue		.20	.20
P# block of 4		.50	—

CALIFORNIA STATEHOOD ISSUE

Gold Miner, Pioneers and S.S. Oregon A444

ROTARY PRESS PRINTING
E.E. Plates of 200 subjects in four panes of 50.

1950, Sept. 9		Perf. 11x10½	
997 A444 3c yellow orange		.20	.20
P# block of 4		.50	—

UNITED CONFEDERATE VETERANS FINAL REUNION ISSUE

Final reunion of the United Confederate Veterans, Norfolk, Virginia, May 30, 1951.

Confederate Soldier and United Confederate Veteran A445

ROTARY PRESS PRINTING
E.E. Plates of 200 subjects in four panes of 50.

1951, May 30		Perf. 11x10½	
998 A445 3c gray		.20	.20
P# block of 4		.45	—

NEVADA CENTENNIAL ISSUE

Centenary of the settlement of Nevada.

Carson Valley, c. 1851 — A446

Designed by Charles R. Chickering.

ROTARY PRESS PRINTING
E.E. Plates of 200 subjects in four panes of 50.

1951, July 14		Perf. 11x10½	
999 A446 3c light olive green		.20	.20
P# block of 4		.50	—

LANDING OF CADILLAC ISSUE

250th anniversary of the landing of Antoine de la Mothe Cadillac at Detroit.

Detroit Skyline and Cadillac Landing A447

ROTARY PRESS PRINTING
E.E. Plates of 200 subjects in four panes of 50.

1951, July 24 — Perf. 11x10½
1000 A447 3c blue .20 .20
P# block of 4 .30

COLORADO STATEHOOD, 75th ANNIV.

Colorado Capitol, Mount of the Holy Cross, Columbine and Bronco Buster by Proctor A448

ROTARY PRESS PRINTING
E.E. Plates of 200 subjects in four panes of 50.

1951, Aug. 1 — Perf. 11x10½
1001 A448 3c blue violet .20 .20
P# block of 4 .45

AMERICAN CHEMICAL SOCIETY ISSUE
75th anniv. of the formation of the Society.

A.C.S. Emblem and Symbols of Chemistry A449

ROTARY PRESS PRINTING
E.E. Plates of 200 subjects in four panes of 50.

1951, Sept. 4 — Perf. 11x10½
1002 A449 3c violet brown .20 .20
P# block of 4 .50

BATTLE OF BROOKLYN, 175th ANNIV.

Gen. George Washington Evacuating Army; Fulton Ferry House at Right — A450

ROTARY PRESS PRINTING
E.E. Plates of 200 subjects in four panes of 50.

1951, Dec. 10 — Perf. 11x10½
1003 A450 3c violet .20 .20
P# block of 4 .40

BETSY ROSS ISSUE
200th anniv. of the birth of Betsy Ross, maker of the first American flag.

"Birth of Our Nation's Flag," by Charles H. Weisgerber — Betsy Ross Showing Flag to Gen. George Washington, Robert Morris and George Ross — A451

ROTARY PRESS PRINTING
E.E. Plates of 200 subjects in four panes of 50.

1952, Jan. 2 — Perf. 11x10½
1004 A451 3c carmine rose .20 .20
P# block of 4 .40

4-H CLUB ISSUE

Farm, Club Emblem, Boy and Girl — A452

ROTARY PRESS PRINTING
E.E. Plates of 200 subjects in four panes of 50.

1952, Jan. 15 — Perf. 11x10½
1005 A452 3c blue green .20 .20
P# block of 4 .55

B. & O. RAILROAD ISSUE
125th anniv. of the granting of a charter to the Baltimore and Ohio Railroad Company by the Maryland Legislature.

Charter and Three Stages of Rail Transportation A453

ROTARY PRESS PRINTING
E.E. Plates of 200 subjects in four panes of 50.

1952, Feb. 28 — Perf. 11x10½
1006 A453 3c bright blue .20 .20
P# block of 4 .60

A. A. A. ISSUE
50th anniversary of the formation of the American Automobile Association.

School Girls and Safety Patrolman Automobiles of 1902 and 1952 — A454

ROTARY PRESS PRINTING
E.E. Plates of 200 subjects in four panes of 50.

1952, Mar. 4 — Perf. 11x10½
1007 A454 3c deep blue .20 .20
P# block of 4 .40

NATO ISSUE
Signing of the North Atlantic Treaty, 3rd anniv.

Torch of Liberty and Globe — A455

ROTARY PRESS PRINTING
E.E. Plates of 400 subjects in four panes of 100.

1952, Apr. 4 — Perf. 11x10½
1008 A455 3c deep violet .20 .20
P# block of 4 .40

GRAND COULEE DAM ISSUE
50 years of Federal cooperation in developing the resources of rivers and streams in the West.

Spillway, Grand Coulee Dam — A456

ROTARY PRESS PRINTING
E.E. Plates of 200 subjects in four panes of 50.

1952, May 15 — Perf. 11x10½
1009 A456 3c blue green .20 .20
P# block of 4 .40

LAFAYETTE ISSUE
175th anniversary of the arrival of Marquis de Lafayette in America.

Marquis de Lafayette, Flags, Cannon and Landing Party — A457

Designed by Victor S. McCloskey, Jr.

ROTARY PRESS PRINTING
E.E. Plates of 200 subjects in four panes of 50.

1952, June 13 — Perf. 11x10½
1010 A457 3c bright blue .20 .20
P# block of 4 .45

MT. RUSHMORE MEMORIAL ISSUE
Dedication of the Mt. Rushmore National Memorial in the Black Hills of South Dakota, 25th anniv.

Sculptured Heads on Mt. Rushmore — A458

Designed by William K. Schrage.

ROTARY PRESS PRINTING
E.E. Plates of 200 subjects in four panes of 50.

1952, Aug. 11 — Perf. 10½x11
1011 A458 3c blue green .20 .20
P# block of 4 .75

ENGINEERING CENTENNIAL ISSUE
American Society of Civil Engineers founding.

George Washington Bridge and Covered Bridge of 1850's — A459

ROTARY PRESS PRINTING
E.E. Plates of 200 subjects in four panes of 50.

1952, Sept. 6 — Perf. 11x10½
1012 A459 3c violet blue .20 .20
P# block of 4 .45

SERVICE WOMEN ISSUE
Women in the United States Armed Services.

Women of the Marine Corps, Army, Navy and Air Force — A460

ROTARY PRESS PRINTING
E.E. Plates of 200 subjects in four panes of 50.

1952, Sept. 11			*Perf. 11x10½*
1013 A460 3c **deep blue**		.20	.20
P# block of 4		.40	—

GUTENBERG BIBLE ISSUE

Printing of the 1st book, the Holy Bible, from movable type, by Johann Gutenberg, 500th anniv.

Gutenberg Showing Proof to the Elector of Mainz — A461

ROTARY PRESS PRINTING
E.E. Plates of 200 subjects in four panes of 50.

1952, Sept. 30			*Perf. 11x10½*
1014 A461 3c **violet**		.20	.20
P# block of 4		.40	—

NEWSPAPER BOYS ISSUE

Newspaper Boy, Torch and Group of Homes A462

ROTARY PRESS PRINTING
E.E. Plates of 200 subjects in four panes of 50.

1952, Oct. 4			*Perf. 11x10½*
1015 A462 3c **violet**		.20	.20
P# block of 4		.40	—

RED CROSS ISSUE

Globe, Sun and Cross — A463

ROTARY PRESS PRINTING
Cross Typographed
E.E. Plates of 200 subjects in four panes of 50.

1952, Nov. 21			*Perf. 11x10½*
1016 A463 3c **deep blue & carmine**		.20	.20
P# block of 4		.40	—

NATIONAL GUARD ISSUE

National Guardsman, Amphibious Landing and Disaster Service A464

ROTARY PRESS PRINTING
E.E. Plates of 200 subjects in four panes of 50.

1953, Feb. 23			*Perf. 11x10½*
1017 A464 3c **bright blue**		.20	.20
P# block of 4		.40	—

OHIO STATEHOOD, 150th ANNIV.

Ohio Map, State Seal, Buckeye Leaf — A465

ROTARY PRESS PRINTING
E.E. Plates of 280 subjects in four panes of 70.

1953, Mar. 2			*Perf. 11x10½*
1018 A465 3c **chocolate**		.20	.20
P# block of 4		.45	—

WASHINGTON TERRITORY ISSUE

Organization of Washington Territory, cent.

Medallion, Pioneers and Washington Scene — A466

ROTARY PRESS PRINTING
E.E. Plates of 200 subjects in four panes of 50.

1953, Mar. 2			*Perf. 11x10½*
1019 A466 3c **green**		.20	.20
P# block of 4		.45	—

LOUISIANA PURCHASE, 150th ANNIV.

James Monroe, Robert R. Livingston and Marquis Francois de Barbé-Marbois A467

ROTARY PRESS PRINTING
E.E. Plates of 200 subjects in four panes of 50.

1953, Apr. 30			*Perf. 11x10½*
1020 A467 3c **violet brown**		.20	.20
P# block of 4		.90	—

OPENING OF JAPAN CENTENNIAL ISSUE

Centenary of Commodore Matthew Calbraith Perry's negotiations with Japan, which opened her doors to foreign trade.

Commodore Matthew C. Perry and First Anchorage off Tokyo Bay — A468

ROTARY PRESS PRINTING
E.E. Plates of 200 subjects in four panes of 50.

1953, July 14			*Perf. 11x10½*
1021 A468 5c **green**		.20	.20
P# block of 4		.65	—

AMERICAN BAR ASSOCIATION, 75th ANNIV.

Section of Frieze, Supreme Court Room — A469

ROTARY PRESS PRINTING
E.E. Plates of 200 subjects in four panes of 50.

1953, Aug. 24			*Perf. 11x10½*
1022 A469 3c **rose violet**		.20	.20
P# block of 4		.45	—

SAGAMORE HILL ISSUE

Opening of Sagamore Hill, Theodore Roosevelt's home, as a national shrine.

Home of Theodore Roosevelt A470

ROTARY PRESS PRINTING
E.E. Plates of 200 subjects in four panes of 50.

1953, Sept. 14			*Perf. 11x10½*
1023 A470 3c **yellow green**		.20	.20
P# block of 4		.40	—

FUTURE FARMERS ISSUE

25th anniversary of the organization of Future Farmers of America.

Agricultural Scene and Future Farmer A471

ROTARY PRESS PRINTING
E.E. Plates of 200 subjects in four panes of 50.

1953, Oct. 13			*Perf. 11x10½*
1024 A471 3c **deep blue**		.20	.20
P# block of 4		.40	—

TRUCKING INDUSTRY ISSUE

50th anniv. of the Trucking Industry in the US.

Truck, Farm and Distant City — A472

ROTARY PRESS PRINTING
E.E. Plates of 200 subjects in four panes of 50.

1953, Oct. 27			*Perf. 11x10½*
1025 A472 3c **violet**		.20	.20
P# block of 4		.40	—

GENERAL PATTON ISSUE

Honoring Gen. George S. Patton, Jr. (1885-1945), and the armored forces of the US Army.

Gen. George S. Patton, Jr., and Tanks in Action — A473

ROTARY PRESS PRINTING
E.E. Plates of 200 subjects in four panes of 50.

1953, Nov. 11			*Perf. 11x10½*
1026 A473 3c **blue violet**		.20	.20
P# block of 4		.45	—

NEW YORK CITY, 300th ANNIV.

Dutch Ship in New Amsterdam Harbor A474

ROTARY PRESS PRINTING
E.E. Plates of 200 subjects in four panes of 50.

1953, Nov. 20   *Perf. 11x10½*
1027 A474 3c **bright red violet**   .20   .20
    P# block of 4   .40   —

GADSDEN PURCHASE ISSUE
Centenary of James Gadsden's purchase of territory from Mexico to adjust the US-Mexico boundary.

Map and Pioneer Group — A475

ROTARY PRESS PRINTING
E.E. Plates of 200 subjects in four panes of 50.

1953, Dec. 30   *Perf. 11x10½*
1028 A475 3c **copper brown**   .20   .20
    P# block of 4   .40   —

COLUMBIA UNIVERSITY, 200th ANNIV.

Low Memorial Library A476

ROTARY PRESS PRINTING
E.E. Plates of 200 subjects in four panes of 50.

1954, Jan. 4   *Perf. 11x10½*
1029 A476 3c **blue**   .20   .20
    P# block of 4   .40   —

Wet and Dry Printings
In 1953 the Bureau of Engraving and Printing began experiments in printing on "dry" paper (moisture content 5-10 per cent). In previous "wet" printings the paper had a moisture content of 15-35 per cent.

The new process required a thicker, stiffer paper, special types of inks and greater pressure to force the paper into the recessed plates. The "dry" printings show whiter paper, a higher sheen on the surface, feel thicker and stiffer, and the designs stand out more clearly than on the "wet" printings.

Nos. 832c and 1041 (flat plate) were the first "dry" printings to be issued of flat-plate, regular-issue stamps. No. 1063 was the first rotary press stamp to be produced entirely by "dry" printing.

Stamps printed by both the "wet" and "dry" process are Nos. 1030, 1031, 1035, 1035a, 1036, 1039, 1049, 1050-1052, 1054, 1055, 1057, 1058, C34-C36, C39, C39a, J78, J80-J84, QE1-QE3, RF26-RF28, S1, S1a, S2, S2a, S3. The "wet" printed 4c coil, No. 1058, exists only Bureau precanceled.

In the Liberty Issue listings that follow, wet printings are listed first, followed by dry printings. Where only one type of printing of a stamp is indicated, it is "dry."

All postage stamps have been printed by the "dry" process since the late 1950s.

LIBERTY ISSUE

Benjamin Franklin — A477

George Washington — A478

Palace of the Governors, Santa Fe — A478a

Thomas Jefferson — A480

Statue of Liberty — A482

The Hermitage, Home of Andrew Jackson, near Nashville — A484

Theodore Roosevelt — A486

Statue of Liberty — A488

John J. Pershing — A489a

Mount Vernon — A479

Bunker Hill Monument and Massachusetts Flag, 1776 — A481

Abraham Lincoln — A483

James Monroe — A485

Woodrow Wilson — A487

Statue of Liberty — A489

The Alamo, San Antonio — A490

Independence Hall — A491

Benjamin Harrison — A492

Monticello, Home of Thomas Jefferson, near Charlottesville, Va. — A494

Robert E. Lee — A496

Susan B. Anthony — A498

Statue of Liberty — A491a

John Jay — A493

Paul Revere — A495

John Marshall — A497

Patrick Henry — A499

Alexander Hamilton — A500

ROTARY PRESS PRINTING
E.E. Plates of 400 subjects in four panes of 100

1954-68   *Perf. 11x10½*
1030a A477 ½c **red orange,** wet printing, *Oct. 20, 1955*   .20   .20
    P# block of 4   .35   —
1030 A477 ½c **red orange,** dry printing, *May 1958*   .20   .20
    P# block of 4 (#25980 and up)   .30   —
1031b A478 1c **dark green,** wet printing, *Aug. 26, 1954*   .20   .20
    P# block of 4   .25   —
1031 A478 1c **dark green,** dry printing, *Mar. 1956*   .20   .20
    P# block of 4 (#25326 and up)   .25   —
    Pair with full vert. gutter between   150.00
    Pair with full horiz. gutter between   150.00

Perf. 10½x11

1031A	A478a	1¼c **turquoise**, June 17, 1960		.20	.20
		P# block of 4		.45	
1032	A479	1½c **brown carmine**, Feb. 22, 1956		.20	.20
		P# block of 4		1.00	

Perf. 11x10½

1033	A480	2c **carmine rose**, Sept. 15, 1954		.20	.20
		P# block of 4		.30	
		Pair with full vert. gutter between		—	
		Pair with full horiz. gutter between		—	
a.		Silkote paper		350.	
		P# block of 4		2,250.	
		On cover		—	

Silkote paper was used in 1954 for an experimental printing of 50,000 stamps. The stamps were put on sale at the Westbrook, Maine post office in Dec. 1954. Only plates 25061 and 25062 were used to print No. 1033a (these plates also used to print No. 1033 on normal paper). Competent expertization is required for No. 1033a.

1034	A481	2½c **gray blue**, June 17, 1959		.20	.20
		P# block of 4		.50	
1035e	A482	3c **deep violet**, wet printing, June 24, 1954		.20	.20
		P# block of 4		.40	
a.		Booklet pane of 6, June 30, 1954		4.00	1.25
g.		As "a," vert. imperf. between		—	
1035	A482	3c **deep violet**, dry printing		.20	.20
		P# block of 4 (#25235 and up)		.30	—
		Pair with full vert. gutter between		150.00	
		Pair with full horiz. gutter between		150.00	
b.		Tagged, July 6, 1966		.35	.25
		P# block of 4		5.75	
c.		Imperf., pair		1,750.	
d.		Horiz. pair, imperf. between		—	
f.		Booklet pane of 6, dry printing		5.00	1.50

No. 1057a measures about 19½x22mm; No. 1035c, about 18¾x22½mm.

1036c	A483	4c **red violet**, wet printing, Nov. 19, 1954		.20	.20
		P# block of 4		.50	
1036	A483	4c **red violet**, dry printing		.20	.20
		P# block of 4 (#25445 and up)		.35	—
		Pair with full vert. gutter between		675.00	
		Pair with full horiz. gutter between		900.00	
a.		Booklet pane of 6, July 31, 1958		2.75	1.25
b.		Tagged, Nov. 2, 1963		.65	.40
		P# block of 4		9.00	
d.		As "a," imperf. horiz.		—	
e.		Horiz. pair, imperf between		3,500.	

No. 1036e resulted from a booklet pane foldover after perforating and before cutting into panes.

Perf. 10½x11

1037	A484	4½c **blue green**, Mar. 16, 1959		.20	.20
		P# block of 4		.65	

Perf. 11x10½

1038	A485	5c **deep blue**, Dec. 2, 1954		.20	.20
		P# block of 4		.60	
		Pair with full vert. gutter btwn.		200.00	
1039a	A486	6c **carmine**, wet printing, Nov. 18, 1955		.40	.20
		P# block of 4		2.00	
1039	A486	6c **carmine**, dry printing		.25	.20
		P# block of 4 (#25427 and up)		1.25	
b.		Imperf, block of 4 (unique)		23,000.	
1040	A487	7c **rose carmine**, Jan. 10, 1956		.20	.20
		P# block of 4		1.00	
a.		7c **dark rose carmine**		.20	.20
		P# block of 4		1.00	

FLAT PLATE PRINTING
Plates of 400 subjects in four panes of 100 each
Size: 22.7mm high
Perf. 11

1041	A488	8c **dark violet blue & carmine**, Apr. 9, 1954		.25	.20
		P# block of 4, 2#		2.00	—
		Corner P# block of 4, blue # only		—	
		Corner P# block of 4, red # only		—	
a.		Double impression of carmine		575.00	

FLAT PRINTING PLATES
Frame: 24912-13-14-15, 24926, 24929-30, 24932-33.
Vignette: 24916-17-18-19-20, 24935-36-37, 24939.
See note following No. 1041B.

ROTARY PRESS PRINTING
Plates of 400 subjects in four panes of 100 each
Size: 22.9mm high
Perf. 11

1041B	A488	8c **dark violet blue & carmine**, Apr. 9, 1954		.40	.20
		P# block of 4, 2#		3.50	—

ROTARY PRINTING PLATES
Frame: 24923-24, 24928, 24940, 24942.
Vignette: 24927, 24938.
No. 1041B is slightly taller than No. 1041, about the thickness of one line of engraving.

GIORI PRESS PRINTING
Plates of 400 subjects in four panes of 100 each
Redrawn design
Perf. 11

1042	A489	8c **dark violet blue & carmine rose**, Mar. 22, 1958		.20	.20
		P# block of 4		.90	—

ROTARY PRESS PRINTING
E.E. Plates of 400 subjects in four panes of 100 each
Perf. 11x10½

1042A	A489a	8c **brown**, Nov. 17, 1961		.20	.20
		P# block of 4		1.00	

Many collectors do not consider No. 1042A to be part of the Liberty issue. Instead, they prefer to group it with Nos. 1209 and 1213.

Perf. 10½x11

1043	A490	9c **rose lilac**, June 14, 1956		.30	.20
		P# block of 4		1.50	—
a.		9c **dark rose lilac**		.30	.20
		P# block of 4		1.50	
1044	A491	10c **rose lake**, July 4, 1956		.30	.20
		P# block of 4		1.40	
b.		10c **dark rose lake**		.25	.20
		P# block of 4		1.10	
d.		Tagged, July 6, 1966		2.00	1.00
		P# block of 4		35.00	

No. 1044b is from later printings and is on a harder, whiter paper than No. 1044.

GIORI PRESS PRINTING
Plates of 400 subjects in four panes of 100.
Perf. 11

1044A	A491a	11c **carmine & dark violet blue**, June 15, 1961		.30	.20
		P# block of 4		1.50	—
c.		Tagged, Jan. 11, 1967		2.50	1.60
		P# block of 4		45.00	—

ROTARY PRESS PRINTING
E.E. Plates of 400 subjects in four panes of 100 each
Perf. 11x10½

1045	A492	12c **red**, June 6, 1959		.35	.20
		P# block of 4		1.60	—
a.		Tagged, 1968		.35	.20
		P# block of 4		4.00	
1046	A493	15c **rose lake**, Dec. 12, 1958		.60	.20
		P# block of 4		3.00	—
a.		Tagged, July 6, 1966		1.10	.80
		P# block of 4		13.00	

Perf. 10½x11

1047	A494	20c **ultramarine**, Apr. 13, 1956		.50	.20
		P# block of 4		2.25	—
a.		20c **deep bright ultramarine**		.50	.20
		P# block of 4		2.25	

No. 1047a is from later printings and is on a harder, whiter paper than No. 1047.

Perf. 11x10½

1048	A495	25c **green**, Apr. 18, 1958		1.10	.75
		P# block of 4		4.75	
1049a	A496	30c **black**, wet printing, Sept. 21, 1955		1.20	.75
		P# block of 4		5.25	
1049	A496	30c **black**, dry printing, June 1957		1.00	.20
		P# block of 4 (#25487 and up)		4.50	—
b.		30c **intense black**		.80	.20
		P# block of 4		3.75	

No. 1049b is from later printings and is on a harder, whiter paper than No. 1049.

1050a	A497	40c **brown red**, wet printing, Sept. 24, 1955		1.75	.25
		P# block of 4		9.00	
1050	A497	40c **brown red**, dry printing, Apr. 1958		1.50	.20
		P# block of 4 (#25571 and up)		7.50	—
1051a	A498	50c **bright purple**, wet printing, Aug. 25, 1955		1.75	.20
		P# block of 4		11.00	
		Cracked plate (25231 UL 1)		—	—

1051	A498	50c **bright purple**, dry printing, Apr. 1958		1.50	.20
		P# block of 4 (#25897 and up)		7.50	
1052a	A499	$1 **purple**, wet printing, Oct. 7, 1955		5.25	1.00
		P# block of 4		22.50	
1052	A499	$1 **purple**, dry printing, Oct. 1958		4.50	.20
		P# block of 4 (#25541 and up)		19.00	—

FLAT PLATE PRINTING
Plates of 400 subjects in four panes of 100.
Perf. 11

1053	A500	$5 **black**, Mar. 19, 1956		57.50	6.75
		P# block of 4		260.00	

Bureau Precancels: ½c, 37 diff., 1c, 113 diff., 1¼c, 142 diff., 1½c, 45 diff.

2c, 86 diff., 2½c, 123 diff., 3c, 106 diff., 4c, 95 diff., 4½c, 23 diff., 5c, 20 diff., 6c, 23 diff., 7c, 16 diff.

Also, No. 1041, 12 diff., No. 1042, 12 diff., No. 1042A, 16 diff., 9c, 15 diff., 10c, 16 diff., 11c, New York, 12c, 6 diff.

15c, 12 diff., 20c, 20 diff., 25c, 11 diff., 30c, 17 diff., 40c, 10 diff., 50c, 19 diff., $1, 5 diff.

Large Holes

Small Holes

With the change from 384-subject plates to 432-subject plates the size of the perforation holes was reduced. While both are perf. 10 the later holes are smaller than the paper between them. The difference is most noticible on pairs.

ROTARY PRESS COIL STAMPS

1954-80   **Perf. 10 Vertically**

1054c	A478	1c **dark green**, large holes, wet printing, Oct. 8, 1954		.35	.20
		Pair		.70	.40
		Joint line pair		1.75	.90
1054	A478	1c **dark green**, small holes, Feb. 1960		.20	.20
		Pair		.40	.25
		Joint line pair		1.00	.65
		Large holes, dry printing, Aug. 1957		1.00	.20
		Pair		2.00	.25
		Joint line pair		4.00	.65
b.		Imperf., pair		2,500.	

Perf. 10 Horizontally

1054A	A478a	1¼c **turquoise**, June 17, 1960, small holes		.20	.20
		Pair		.25	.25
		Joint line pair		2.25	1.00
		Large holes		6.00	.20
		Pair		15.00	.20
		Joint line pair		150.00	1.25
c.		Imperf., pair		—	
		Joint line pair		—	

Perf. 10 Vertically

1055d	A480	2c **carmine rose**, large holes, wet printing, Oct. 22, 1954		.40	.20
		Pair		.80	.20
		Joint line pair		3.50	.40
		Small holes		—	
		Pair		—	
1055	A480	2c **carmine rose**, large holes, dry printing, May 1957		.35	.20
		Pair		.80	.20
		Joint line pair		1.50	.20
		Small holes, Aug. 1961		7.00	.20
		Pair		17.50	.20
		Joint line pair		50.00	.40
a.		Tagged, small holes, shiny gum, May 6, 1968		.20	.20
		Pair		.20	.20
		Joint line pair		.75	.20
		Dull gum, tagged, small holes		.75	

	Pair	1.50		
	Joint line pair	6.00		
b.	Imperf., pair, untagged, shiny gum (Bureau precanceled, Riverdale, MD)		425.00	
	Joint line pair		1,200.	
c.	Imperf. pair, tagged, shiny gum	550.00		
	Joint line pair	1,200.		
1056	A481 2½c **gray blue,** large holes *Sept. 9, 1959*		.30	.25
	Pair		.60	.50
	Joint line pair		3.50	1.75
	Small holes, *Jan. 1961*		400.00	100.00
	Pair		850.00	200.00
	Joint line pair		3,000.	400.00

No. 1056 with small holes only known with Bureau precancels. It was against postal regulations to make mint precanceled stamps available other than to permit holders for their use. Resale was prohibited. Since some mint examples do exist in the marketplace, values are furnished here.

1057c	A482 3c **deep violet,** large holes, wet printing, *July 20, 1954*	.35	.20
	Pair	.80	.25
	Joint line pair	2.75	.60
	Small holes, *Jan. 1961*		
	Pair	—	
	Joint line pair	—	
1057	A482 3c **deep violet,** large holes, dry printing, *Oct. 1956*	.35	.20
	Pair	.80	.20
	Joint line pair	2.75	.25
	Gripper cracks	—	
	Small holes, *Mar. 1958*	.20	.20
	Pair	.20	.20
	Joint line pair	.55	.20
a.	Imperf., pair	1,750.	800.00
	Joint line pair	2,750.	
b.	Tagged, small holes, philatelic printing, *June 26, 1967*	1.00	.50
	Pair	3.00	1.00
	Joint line pair	25.00	
d.	Tagged, small holes, Look magazine printing, *Oct. 1966*	5.00	4.00
	On "Look" cover	1.00	
	Pair	11.00	8.00
	Joint line pair	300.00	

Earliest known use No. 1057d: Dec. 29, 1966.

No. 1057a measures about 19½x22mm; No. 1035c, about 18¾x22½mm.
The second tagged printing (No. 1057b) was a "philatelic reprint" made when the original stock of tagged stamps was exhausted. The original tagged printing (No. 1057d, specially printed for "Look" magazine) has a less intense color, the impression is less sharp and the tagging is brighter.
The reprint was printed on a slightly fluorescent paper, while the original paper is dead under longwave UV light.

1058b	A483 4c **red violet,** large holes, wet printing (Bureau precanceled)	22.50	.50
	Pair	47.50	
	Joint line pair	325.00	

It was against postal regulations to make mint precanceled examples of No. 1058b available other than to permit holders for their use. Resale was prohibited. Since some mint examples do exist in the marketplace, values are furnished here.

1058	A483 4c **red violet,** large holes, dry printing, *July 31, 1958*	.50	.20
	Pair	1.50	.30
	Joint line pair	2.50	.40
	Small holes	.20	.20
	Pair	.55	.20
	Joint line pair	.70	.25
a.	Imperf., pair	75.00	70.00
	Joint line pair	200.00	

Perf. 10 Horizontally

1059	A484 4½c **blue green,** large holes, *May 1, 1959*	1.50	1.00
	Pair	3.00	2.25
	Joint line pair	14.00	3.00
	Small holes	12.00	—
	Pair	35.00	—
	Joint line pair	450.00	—

Perf. 10 Vertically

1059A	A495 25c **green,** *Feb. 25, 1965*	.50	.30
	Pair	1.00	.60
	Joint line pair	2.00	1.20
b.	Tagged, shiny gum, *Apr. 3, 1973*	.80	.20
	Pair	1.60	.40
	Joint line pair	3.25	1.25
	Tagged, dull gum, *1980*	4.00	
	Pair	8.00	
	Joint line pair	12.00	
c.	Imperf., pair, untagged	—	
	Joint line pair	—	
d.	Imperf., pair, tagged	30.00	
	Joint line pair	60.00	

Value for No. 1059Ac is for fine centering.
Bureau Precancels: 1c, 118 diff., 1¼c, 105 diff., 2c, 191 diff., 2½c, 94 diff., 3c, 142 diff., 4c, 83 diff., 4½c, 23 diff.

NEBRASKA TERRITORY ISSUE
Establishment of the Nebraska Territory, centenary.

"The Sower," Mitchell Pass and Scotts Bluff — A507

ROTARY PRESS PRINTING
E.E. Plates of 200 subjects in four panes of 50.

1954, May 7		Perf. 11x10½
1060 A507 3c **violet**	.20	.20
P# block of 4	.45	—

KANSAS TERRITORY ISSUE
Establishment of the Kansas Territory, centenary

Wheat Field and Pioneer Wagon Train — A508

ROTARY PRESS PRINTING
E.E. Plates of 200 subjects in four panes of 50.

1954, May 31		Perf. 11x10½
1061 A508 3c **brown orange**	.20	.20
P# block of 4	.55	—

GEORGE EASTMAN ISSUE

Eastman (1854-1932), inventor of photographic dry plates, flexible film and the Kodak camera; Rochester, N.Y., industrialist. — A509

ROTARY PRESS PRINTING
E.E. Plates of 280 subjects in four panes of 70.

1954, July 12		Perf. 10½x11
1062 A509 3c **violet brown**	.20	.20
P# block of 4	.40	—

LEWIS AND CLARK EXPEDITION
150th anniv. of the Lewis and Clark expedition.

Meriwether Lewis, William Clark and Sacagawea Landing on Missouri Riverbank A510

ROTARY PRESS PRINTING
E.E. Plates of 200 subjects in four panes of 50.

1954, July 28		Perf. 11x10½
1063 A510 3c **violet brown**	.20	.20
P# block of 4	.75	—

PENNSYLVANIA ACADEMY OF THE FINE ARTS ISSUE
150th anniversary of the founding of the Pennsylvania Academy of the Fine Arts, Philadelphia.

Charles Willson Peale in his Museum, Self-portrait — A511

ROTARY PRESS PRINTING
E.E. Plates of 200 subjects in four panes of 50.

1955, Jan. 15		Perf. 10½x11
1064 A511 3c **rose brown**	.20	.20
P# block of 4	.45	—

LAND GRANT COLLEGES ISSUE
Centenary of the founding of Michigan State College and Pennsylvania State University, first of the land grant institutions.

Open Book and Symbols of Subjects Taught — A512

ROTARY PRESS PRINTING
E.E. Plates of 200 subjects in four panes of 50.

1955, Feb. 12		Perf. 11x10½
1065 A512 3c **green**	.20	.20
P# block of 4	.45	—

ROTARY INTERNATIONAL, 50th ANNIV.

Torch, Globe and Rotary Emblem A513

ROTARY PRESS PRINTING
E.E. Plates of 200 subjects in four panes of 50.

1955, Feb. 23		Perf. 11x10½
1066 A513 8c **deep blue**	.25	.20
P# block of 4	1.25	—

ARMED FORCES RESERVE ISSUE

Marine, Coast
Guard, Army,
Navy and Air
Force
Personnel
A514

ROTARY PRESS PRINTING
E.E. Plates of 200 subjects in four panes of 50.

1955, May 21   *Perf. 11x10½*
1067 A514 3c **purple**   .20 .20
      P# block of 4   .40 —

NEW HAMPSHIRE ISSUE

Sesquicentennial of the discovery of the "Old Man of the Mountains."

Great Stone Face — A515

ROTARY PRESS PRINTING
E.E. Plates of 200 subjects in four panes of 50.

1955, June 21   *Perf. 10½x11*
1068 A515 3c **green**   .20 .20
      P# block of 4   .70 —

SOO LOCKS ISSUE
Centenary of the opening of the Soo Locks.

Map of Great
Lakes and Two
Steamers
A516

ROTARY PRESS PRINTING
E.E. Plates of 200 subjects in four panes of 50.

1955, June 28   *Perf. 11x10½*
1069 A516 3c **blue**   .20 .20
      P# block of 4   .45 —

ATOMS FOR PEACE ISSUE
Issued to promote an Atoms for Peace policy.

Atomic Energy
Encircling the
Hemispheres
A517

Designed by George R. Cox.

ROTARY PRESS PRINTING
E.E. Plates of 200 subjects in four panes of 50.

1955, July 28   *Perf. 11x10½*
1070 A517 3c **deep blue**   .20 .20
      P# block of 4   .45 —

FORT TICONDEROGA ISSUE
Bicentenary of Fort Ticonderoga, New York.

Map of the
Fort, Ethan
Allen and
Artillery
A518

Designed by Enrico Arno.

ROTARY PRESS PRINTING
E.E. Plates of 200 subjects in four panes of 50.

1955, Sept. 18   *Perf. 11x10½*
1071 A518 3c **light brown**   .20 .20
      P# block of 4   .40 —

Andrew W. Mellon
(1855-1937), US
Secretary of the
Treasury (1921-32),
Financier and Art
Collector — A519

"Franklin Taking
Electricity from the
Sky," by Benjamin
West — A520

ANDREW W. MELLON ISSUE
Designed by Victor S. McCloskey, Jr.

ROTARY PRESS PRINTING
E.E. Plates of 280 subjects in four panes of 70.

1955, Dec. 20   *Perf. 10½x11*
1072 A519 3c **rose carmine**   .20 .20
      P# block of 4   .40 —

BENJAMIN FRANKLIN ISSUE
250th anniv. of the birth of Benjamin Franklin.

Designed by Charles R. Chickering.

ROTARY PRESS PRINTING
E.E. Plates of 200 subjects in four panes of 50.

1956, Jan. 17   *Perf. 10½x11*
1073 A520 3c **bright carmine**   .20 .20
      P# block of 4   .40 —

BOOKER T. WASHINGTON ISSUE
Washington (1856-1915), black educator, founder and head of Tuskegee Institute in Alabama.

Log
Cabin — A521

Designed by Charles R. Chickering.

ROTARY PRESS PRINTING
E.E. Plates of 200 subjects in four panes of 50.

1956, Apr. 5   *Perf. 11x10½*
1074 A521 3c **deep blue**   .20 .20
      P# block of 4   .40 —

FIFTH INTERNATIONAL PHILATELIC EXHIBITION ISSUES
FIPEX, New York City, Apr. 28 - May 6, 1956.

SOUVENIR SHEET

A522

Illustration reduced.

FLAT PLATE PRINTING
Plates of 24 subjects

1956, Apr. 28   *Imperf.*
1075 A522   Sheet of 2   1.80 1.50
   a.   A482 3c deep violet   .80 .60
   b.   A488 8c dark violet blue & carmine   .90 .75

No. 1075 measures 108x73mm. Nos. 1075a and 1075b measure 24x28mm.
Inscriptions printed in dark violet blue; scrolls and stars in carmine.

New York
Coliseum and
Columbus
Monument
A523

Designed by William K. Schrage.

ROTARY PRESS PRINTING
E.E. Plates of 200 subjects in four panes of 50.

1956, Apr. 30   *Perf. 11x10½*
1076 A523 3c **deep violet**   .20 .20
      P# block of 4   .35 —

WILDLIFE CONSERVATION ISSUE
Issued to emphasize the importance of Wildlife Conservation in America.

Wild Turkey
A524

Pronghorn
Antelope
A525

King
Salmon — A526

Designed by Robert W. (Bob) Hines.

ROTARY PRESS PRINTING
E.E. Plates of 200 subjects in four panes of 50.

1956   *Perf. 11x10½*
1077 A524 3c **rose lake,** *May 5*   .20 .20
      P# block of 4   .40 —
1078 A525 3c **brown,** *June 22*   .20 .20
      P# block of 4   .35 —

1079 A526 3c **blue green,** *Nov. 9*   .20 .20
    P# block of 4   .35 —
    Nos. 1077-1079 (3)   .60 .60

PURE FOOD AND DRUG LAWS, 50th ANNIV.

Harvey Washington
Wiley — A527

Designed by Robert L. Miller

ROTARY PRESS PRINTING
E.E. Plates of 200 subjects in four panes of 50.

1956, June 27   ***Perf. 10½x11***
1080 A527 3c **dark blue green**   .20 .20
    P# block of 4   .50 —

WHEATLAND ISSUE

Pres.
Buchanan's
Home,
Lancaster,
Pa. — A528

ROTARY PRESS PRINTING
E.E. Plates of 200 subjects in four panes of 50.

1956, Aug. 5   ***Perf. 11x10½***
1081 A528 3c **black brown**   .20 .20
    P# block of 4   .40 —

LABOR DAY ISSUE

Mosaic, AFL-CIO
Headquarters — A529

Designed by Victor S. McCloskey, Jr.

ROTARY PRESS PRINTING
E.E. Plates of 200 subjects in four panes of 50.

1956, Sept. 3   ***Perf. 10½x11***
1082 A529 3c **deep blue**   .20 .20
    P# block of 4   .45 —

NASSAU HALL ISSUE

200th anniv. of Nassau Hall, Princeton University.

Nassau Hall,
Princeton,
N.J. — A530

ROTARY PRESS PRINTING
E.E. Plates of 200 subjects in four panes of 50.

1956, Sept. 22   ***Perf. 11x10½***
1083 A530 3c **black,** *orange*   .20 .20
    P# block of 4   .50 —

DEVILS TOWER ISSUE

Issued to commemorate the 50th anniversary of the Federal law providing for protection of American natural antiquities. Devils Tower National Monument, Wyoming, is an outstanding example.

Devils Tower — A531

Designed by Charles R. Chickering.

ROTARY PRESS PRINTING
E.E. Plates of 200 subjects in four panes of 50.

1956, Sept. 24   ***Perf. 10½x11***
1084 A531 3c **violet**   .20 .20
    P# block of 4   .50 —
    Pair with full horiz. gutter btwn.   —

CHILDREN'S ISSUE

Issued to promote friendship among the children of the world.

Children of the
World — A532

Designed by Ronald Dias.

ROTARY PRESS PRINTING
E.E. Plates of 200 subjects in four panes of 50.

1956, Dec. 15   ***Perf. 11x10½***
1085 A532 3c **dark blue**   .20 .20
    P# block of 4   .40 —

ALEXANDER HAMILTON (1755-1804)

Alexander
Hamilton and
Federal
Hall — A533

Designed by William K. Schrage.

ROTARY PRESS PRINTING
E.E. Plates of 200 subjects in four panes of 50.

1957, Jan. 11   ***Perf. 11x10½***
1086 A533 3c **rose red**   .20 .20
    P# block of 4   .40 —

POLIO ISSUE

Honoring "those who helped fight polio," and on for 20th anniv. of the Natl. Foundation for Infantile Paralysis and the March of Dimes.

25605

Allegory — A534   Major Plate Crack

Designed by Charles R. Chickering.

ROTARY PRESS PRINTING
E.E. Plates of 200 subjects in four panes of 50.

1957, Jan. 15   ***Perf. 10½x11***
1087 A534 3c **red lilac**   .20 .20
    P# block of 4   .40 —
    Major plate crack (25605 UL 1)   —

COAST AND GEODETIC SURVEY ISSUE

150th anniversary of the establishment of the Coast and Geodetic Survey.

Flag of Coast
and Geodetic
Survey and
Ships at
Sea — A535

Designed by Harold E. MacEwen.

ROTARY PRESS PRINTING
E.E. Plates of 200 subjects in four panes of 50.

1957, Feb. 11   ***Perf. 11x10½***
1088 A535 3c **dark blue**   .20 .20
    P# block of 4   .40 —

ARCHITECTS ISSUE

American Institute of Architects, centenary.

Corinthian
Capital and
Mushroom
Type Head and
Shaft — A536

Designed by Robert J. Schultz.

ROTARY PRESS PRINTING
E.E. Plates of 200 subjects in four panes of 50.

1957, Feb. 23   ***Perf. 11x10½***
1089 A536 3c **red lilac**   .20 .20
    P# block of 4   .40 —

STEEL INDUSTRY ISSUE

Centenary of the steel industry in America.

American Eagle and
Pouring Ladle — A537

Designed by Anthonio Petruccelli.

ROTARY PRESS PRINTING
E.E. Plates of 200 subjects in four panes of 50.

1957, May 22   ***Perf. 10½x11***
1090 A537 3c **bright ultramarine**   .20 .20
    P# block of 4   .40 —

INTERNATIONAL NAVAL REVIEW ISSUE

Issued to commemorate the International Naval Review and the Jamestown Festival.

Aircraft Carrier
and
Jamestown
Festival
Emblem
A538

Designed by Richard A. Genders.

ROTARY PRESS PRINTING
E.E. Plates of 200 subjects in four panes of 50.

1957, June 10			Perf. 11x10½
1091 A538 3c blue green		.20	.20
P# block of 4		.40	—

OKLAHOMA STATEHOOD, 50th ANNIV.

Map of Oklahoma, Arrow and Atom Diagram A539

Designed by William K. Schrage.

ROTARY PRESS PRINTING
E.E. Plates of 200 subjects in four panes of 50.

1957, June 14			Perf. 11x10½
1092 A539 3c dark blue		.20	.20
P# block of 4		.50	—

SCHOOL TEACHERS ISSUE

Teacher and Pupils — A540

ROTARY PRESS PRINTING
E.E. Plates of 200 subjects in four panes of 50.

1957, July 1			Perf. 11x10½
1093 A540 3c rose lake		.20	.20
P# block of 4		.40	—

FLAG ISSUE

"Old Glory" (48 Stars) — A541

Designed by Victor S. McCloskey, Jr.

GIORI PRESS PRINTING
Plates of 200 subjects in four panes of 50.

1957, July 4			Perf. 11
1094 A541 4c dark blue & deep carmine		.20	.20
P# block of 4		.45	—

"Virginia of Sagadahock" and Seal of Maine — A542

Ramon Magsaysay — A543

SHIPBUILDING ISSUE

350th anniversary of shipbuilding in America.

Designed by Ervine Metzel, Mrs. William Zorach, A. M. Main, Jr., and George F. Cary II.

ROTARY PRESS PRINTING
E.E. Plates of 280 subjects in four panes of 70.

1957, Aug. 15			Perf. 10½x11
1095 A542 3c deep violet		.20	.20
P# block of 4		.45	—

CHAMPION OF LIBERTY ISSUE

Magsaysay (1907-57), Pres. of the Philippines.

Designed by Arnold Copeland, Ervine Metzl and William H. Buckley.

GIORI PRESS PRINTING
Plates of 192 subjects in four panes of 48 each.

1957, Aug. 31			Perf. 11
1096 A543 8c carmine, ultramarine & ocher		.20	.20
P# block of 4, 2#		.85	—
P# block of 4, ultra. # omitted		—	

Marquis de Lafayette (1757-1834) — A544

Whooping Cranes — A545

LAFAYETTE BICENTENARY ISSUE

Designed by Ervine Metzl.

ROTARY PRESS PRINTING
E.E. Plates of 200 subjects in four panes of 50.

1957, Sept. 6			Perf. 10½x11
1097 A544 3c rose lake		.20	.20
P# block of 4		.40	—

WILDLIFE CONSERVATION ISSUE

Issued to emphasize the importance of Wildlife Conservation in America.

Designed by Bob Hines and C.R. Chickering.

GIORI PRESS PRINTING
Plates of 200 subjects in four panes of 50.

1957, Nov. 22			Perf. 11
1098 A545 3c blue, ocher & green		.20	.20
P# block of 4		.40	—

Bible, Hat and Quill Pen — A546

"Bountiful Earth" — A547

RELIGIOUS FREEDOM ISSUE

300th anniv. of the Flushing Remonstrance.

Designed by Robert Geissmann.

ROTARY PRESS PRINTING
E.E. Plates of 200 subjects in four panes of 50.

1957, Dec. 27			Perf. 10½x11
1099 A546 3c black		.20	.20
P# block of 4		.40	—

GARDENING HORTICULTURE ISSUE

Issued to honor the garden clubs of America and in connection with the centenary of the birth of Liberty Hyde Bailey, horticulturist.

Designed by Denver Gillen.

ROTARY PRESS PRINTING
E.E. Plates of 200 subjects in four panes of 50.

1958, Mar. 15			Perf. 10½x11
1100 A547 3c green		.20	.20
P# block of 4		.40	—

BRUSSELS EXHIBITION ISSUE

Issued in honor of the opening of the Universal and International Exhibition at Brussels, April 17.

US Pavilion at Brussels A551

Designed by Bradbury Thompson.

ROTARY PRESS PRINTING
E.E. Plates of 200 subjects in four panes of 50.

1958, Apr. 17			Perf. 11x10½
1104 A551 3c deep claret		.20	.20
On cover, Expo. station ("U.S. Pavilion") canc.		3.00	
P# block of 4		.40	—

JAMES MONROE ISSUE

James Monroe (1758-1831), 5th President of the US — A552

Designed by Frank P. Conley.

ROTARY PRESS PRINTING
E.E. Plates of 280 subjects in four panes of 70.

1958, Apr. 28			Perf. 11x10½
1105 A552 3c purple		.20	.20
P# block of 4		.60	—

MINNESOTA STATEHOOD, 100th ANNIV.

Minnesota Lakes and Pines — A553

Designed by Homer Hill.

ROTARY PRESS PRINTING
E.E. Plates of 200 subjects in four panes of 50.

1958, May 11			Perf. 11x10½
1106 A553 3c green		.20	.20
P# block of 4		.45	—

GEOPHYSICAL YEAR ISSUE

International Geophysical Year, 1957-58.

Solar Disc and Hands from Michelangelo's "Creation of Adam" — A554

Designed by Ervine Metzl.

GIORI PRESS PRINTING
Plates of 200 subjects in four panes of 50.

1958, May 31			Perf. 11
1107 A554 3c black & red orange		.20	.20
P# block of 4		.40	—

GUNSTON HALL ISSUE

Issued for the bicentenary of Gunston Hall and to honor George Mason, author of the Constitution of Virginia and the Virginia Bill of Rights.

Gunston Hall, Virginia — A555

Designed by Rene Clarke.

ROTARY PRESS PRINTING
E.E. Plates of 200 subjects in four panes of 50.

1958, June 12		Perf. 11x10½	
1108 A555 3c light green		.20	.20
P# block of 4		.40	—

Mackinac Bridge — A556

Simon Bolívar — A557

MACKINAC BRIDGE ISSUE

Dedication of Mackinac Bridge, Michigan.

Designed by Arnold J. Copeland.

ROTARY PRESS PRINTING
E.E. Plates of 200 subjects in four panes of 50.

1958, June 25		Perf. 10½x11	
1109 A556 3c bright greenish blue		.20	.20
P# block of 4		.50	—

CHAMPION OF LIBERTY ISSUE

Simon Bolívar, South American freedom fighter.

ROTARY PRESS PRINTING
E.E. Plates of 280 subjects in four panes of 70.

1958, July 24		Perf. 10½x11	
1110 A557 4c olive bister		.20	.20
P# block of 4		.40	—

GIORI PRESS PRINTING
Plates of 288 subjects in four panes of 72 each.

	Perf. 11		
1111 A557 8c carmine, ultramarine & ocher		.20	.20
P# block of 4, 2#		1.25	—
P# block of 4, ocher # only			

ATLANTIC CABLE CENTENNIAL ISSUE

Centenary of the Atlantic Cable, linking the Eastern and Western hemispheres.

Neptune, Globe and Mermaid A558

Designed by George Giusti.

ROTARY PRESS PRINTING
E.E. Plates of 200 subjects in four panes of 50.

1958, Aug. 15		Perf. 11x10½	
1112 A558 4c reddish purple		.20	.20
P# block of 4		.40	—

LINCOLN SESQUICENTENNIAL ISSUE

Sesquicentennial of the birth of Abraham Lincoln. No. 1114 also for the centenary of the founding of Cooper Union, New York City. No. 1115 marks the centenary of the Lincoln-Douglas Debates.

Lincoln by George Healy — A559

Lincoln by Gutzon Borglum — A560

Lincoln and Stephen A. Douglas Debating, from Painting by Joseph Boggs Beale — A561

Daniel Chester French Statue of Lincoln as Drawn by Fritz Busse — A562

Designed by Ervine Metzl.

ROTARY PRESS PRINTING
E.E. Plates of 200 subjects in four panes of 50.

1958-59		Perf. 10½x11	
1113 A559 1c green, Feb. 12, 1959		.20	.20
P# block of 4		.25	
1114 A560 3c purple, Feb. 27, 1959		.20	.20
P# block of 4		.45	
	Perf. 11x10½		
1115 A561 4c sepia, Aug. 27, 1958		.20	.20
P# block of 4		.60	
1116 A562 4c dark blue, May 30, 1959		.20	.20
P# block of 4		.40	
Nos. 1113-1116 (4)		.80	.80

Lajos Kossuth — A563

Early Press and Hand Holding Quill — A564

CHAMPION OF LIBERTY ISSUE

Lajos Kossuth, Hungarian freedom fighter.

ROTARY PRESS PRINTING
E.E. Plates of 280 subjects in four panes of 70.

1958, Sept. 19		Perf. 10½x11	
1117 A563 4c green		.20	.20
P# block of 4		.40	—

GIORI PRESS PRINTING
Plates of 288 subjects in four panes of 72 each.

	Perf. 11		
1118 A563 8c carmine, ultramarine & ocher		.20	.20
P# block of 4, 2#		1.10	—

FREEDOM OF PRESS ISSUE

Honoring Journalism and freedom of the press in connection with the 50th anniv. of the 1st School of Journalism at the University of Missouri.

Designed by Lester Beall and Charles Goslin.

ROTARY PRESS PRINTING
E.E. Plates of 200 subjects in four panes of 50.

1958, Sept. 22		Perf. 10½x11	
1119 A564 4c black		.20	.20
P# block of 4		.40	—

OVERLAND MAIL ISSUE

Centenary of Overland Mail Service.

Mail Coach and Map of Southwest US — A565

Designed by William H. Buckley.

ROTARY PRESS PRINTING
E.E. Plates of 200 subjects in four panes of 50.

1958, Oct. 10		Perf. 11x10½	
1120 A565 4c crimson rose		.20	.20
P# block of 4		.40	—

Noah Webster — A566

Forest Scene — A567

NOAH WEBSTER ISSUE

Webster (1758-1843), lexicographer and author.

Designed by Charles R. Chickering.

ROTARY PRESS PRINTING
E.E. Plates of 280 subjects in four panes of 70.

1958, Oct. 16		Perf. 10½x11	
1121 A566 4c dark carmine rose		.20	.20
P# block of 4		.40	—

FOREST CONSERVATION ISSUE

Issued to publicize forest conservation and the protection of natural resources and to honor Theodore Roosevelt, a leading forest conservationist, on the centenary of his birth.

Designed by Rudolph Wendelin.

GIORI PRESS PRINTING
Plates of 200 subjects in four panes of 50.

1958, Oct. 27		Perf. 11	
1122 A567 4c green, yellow & brown		.20	.20
P# block of 4		.45	—

FORT DUQUESNE ISSUE

Bicentennial of Fort Duquesne (Fort Pitt) at future site of Pittsburgh.

British Capture of Fort Duquesne, 1758; Brig. Gen. John Forbes on Litter, Colonel Washington Mounted A568

Designed by William H. Buckley and Douglas Gorsline.

ROTARY PRESS PRINTING
E.E. Plates of 200 subjects in four panes of 50.

1958, Nov. 25		Perf. 11x10½	
1123 A568 4c blue		.20	.20
P# block of 4		.40	—

OREGON STATEHOOD, 100th ANNIV.

Covered
Wagon and Mt.
Hood — A569

Designed by Robert Hallock.

ROTARY PRESS PRINTING
E.E. Plates of 200 subjects in four panes of 50.

1959, Feb. 14		Perf. 11x10½
1124 A569 4c **blue green**	.25	.20
P# block of 4	1.10	—

José de San
Martin — A570

NATO Emblem — A571

CHAMPION OF LIBERTY ISSUE
San Martin, So. American soldier and statesman.

ROTARY PRESS PRINTING
E.E. Plates of 280 subjects in four panes of 70.

1959, Feb. 25		Perf. 10½x11
1125 A570 4c **blue**	.20	.20
P# block of 4	.40	—
a. Horiz. pair, imperf. between	1,000.	

GIORI PRESS PRINTING
Plates of 288 subjects in four panes of 72 each.
Perf. 11

1126 A570 8c **carmine, ultramarine & ocher**	.20	.20
P# block of 4	.90	—

NATO ISSUE
North Atlantic Treaty Organization, 10th anniv.

Designed by Stevan Dohanos.

ROTARY PRESS PRINTING
E.E. Plates of 280 subjects in four panes of 70.

1959, Apr. 1		Perf. 10½x11
1127 A571 4c **blue**	.20	.20
P# block of 4	.40	—

ARCTIC EXPLORATIONS ISSUE
Conquest of the Arctic by land by Rear Admiral Robert Edwin Peary in 1909 and by sea by the submarine "Nautilus" in 1958.

North Pole,
Dog Sled and
"Nautilus"
A572

Designed by George Samerjan.

ROTARY PRESS PRINTING
E.E. Plates of 200 subjects in four panes of 50.

1959, Apr. 6		Perf. 11x10½
1128 A572 4c **bright greenish blue**	.20	.20
P# block of 4	.40	—

WORLD PEACE THROUGH WORLD TRADE ISSUE
Issued in conjunction with the 17th Congress of the International Chamber of Commerce, Washington, D.C., April 19-25.

Globe and
Laurel — A573

Designed by Robert Baker.

ROTARY PRESS PRINTING
E.E. Plates of 200 subjects in four panes of 50.

1959, Apr. 20		Perf. 11x10½
1129 A573 8c **rose lake**	.20	.20
P# block of 4	.85	—

SILVER CENTENNIAL ISSUE
Discovery of silver at the Comstock Lode, Nevada.

Henry
Comstock at
Mount
Davidson
Site — A574

Designed by Robert L. Miller and W.K. Schrage.

ROTARY PRESS PRINTING
E.E. Plates of 200 subjects in four panes of 50.

1959, June 8		Perf. 11x10½
1130 A574 4c **black**	.20	.20
P# block of 4	.40	—

ST. LAWRENCE SEAWAY ISSUE
Opening of the St. Lawrence Seaway.

Great Lakes,
Maple Leaf
and Eagle
Emblems
A575

Designed by Arnold Copeland, Ervine Metzl, William H. Buckley and Gerald Trottier.

GIORI PRESS PRINTING
Plates of 200 subjects in four panes of 50.

1959, June 26		Perf. 11
1131 A575 4c **red & dark blue**	.20	.20
P# block of 4	.40	—
Pair with full horiz. gutter btwn.	—	

See Canada No. 387.

49-STAR FLAG ISSUE

U.S. Flag,
1959 — A576

Designed by Stevan Dohanos.

GIORI PRESS PRINTING
Plates of 200 subjects in four panes of 50.

1959, July 4		Perf. 11
1132 A576 4c **ocher, dark blue & deep carmine**	.20	.20
P# block of 4	.40	—

SOIL CONSERVATION ISSUE
Issued as a tribute to farmers and ranchers who use soil and water conservation measures.

Modern
Farm — A577

Designed by Walter Hortens.

GIORI PRESS PRINTING
Plates of 200 subjects in four panes of 50.

1959, Aug. 26		Perf. 11
1133 A577 4c **blue, green & ocher**	.20	.20
P# block of 4	.40	—

PETROLEUM INDUSTRY ISSUE
Centenary of the completion of the nation's first oil well at Titusville, Pa.

Oil Derrick — A578

Designed by Robert Foster.

ROTARY PRESS PRINTING
E.E. Plates of 200 subjects in four panes of 50.

1959, Aug. 27		Perf. 10½x11
1134 A578 4c **brown**	.20	.20
P# block of 4	.40	—

DENTAL HEALTH ISSUE
Issued to publicize Dental Health and for the centenary of the American Dental Association.

Children
A579

Designed by Charles Henry Carter.

ROTARY PRESS PRINTING
E.E. Plates of 200 subjects in four panes of 50.

1959, Sept. 14		Perf. 11x10½
1135 A579 4c **green**	.20	.20
P# block of 4	.40	—

Ernst Reuter — A580

Dr. Ephraim
McDowell — A581

CHAMPION OF LIBERTY ISSUE
Ernst Reuter, Mayor of Berlin, 1948-53.

ROTARY PRESS PRINTING
E.E. Plates of 280 subjects in four panes of 70.

1959, Sept. 29		Perf. 10½x11
1136 A580 4c **gray**	.20	.20
P# block of 4	.40	—

GIORI PRESS PRINTING
Plates of 288 subjects in four panes of 72 each.
Perf. 11

1137	A580	8c **carmine, ultramarine & ocher**	.20	.20
		P# block of 4	.90	
a.		Ocher missing (EP)	3,500.	
b.		Ultramarine missing (EP)	4,250.	
c.		Ocher & ultramarine missing (EP)	4,500.	
d.		All colors missing (EP)	2,500.	

DR. EPHRAIM McDOWELL ISSUE
Honoring McDowell (1771-1830) on the 150th anniv. of the 1st successful ovarian operation in the US, performed at Danville, Ky., 1809.

Designed by Charles R. Chickering.

ROTARY PRESS PRINTING
E.E. Plates of 280 subjects in four panes of 70.

1959, Dec. 3			**Perf. 10½x11**	
1138	A581	4c **rose lake**	.20	.20
		P# block of 4	.40	
a.		Vert. pair, imperf. btwn.	400.00	
b.		Vert. pair, imperf. horiz.	275.00	

VALUES FOR HINGED STAMPS AFTER NO. 771
This catalogue does not value unused stamps after No. 771 in hinged condition. Hinged unused stamps from No. 772 to the present are worth considerably less than the values given for unused stamps, which are for never-hinged examples.

AMERICAN CREDO ISSUE
Issued to re-emphasize the ideals upon which America was founded and to honor those great Americans who wrote or uttered the credos.

Quotation from Washington's Farewell Address, 1796 — A582

Benjamin Franklin Quotation A583

Thomas Jefferson Quotation A584

Francis Scott Key Quotation A585

Abraham Lincoln Quotation A586

Patrick Henry Quotation A587

Designed by Frank Conley.

GIORI PRESS PRINTING
Plates of 200 subjects in four panes of 50.

1960-61			**Perf. 11**	
1139	A582	4c **dark violet blue, & carmine,** Jan. 20, 1960	.20	.20
		P# block of 4	.40	—
1140	A583	4c **olive bister & green,** Mar. 31, 1960	.20	.20
		P# block of 4	.40	—
1141	A584	4c **gray & vermilion,** May 18, 1960	.20	.20
		P# block of 4	.60	—
1142	A585	4c **carmine & dark blue,** Sept. 14, 1960	.20	.20
		P# block of 4	.50	—
1143	A586	4c **magenta & green,** Nov. 19, 1960	.20	.20
		P# block of 4	.50	—
		Pair with full horiz. gutter between	525.	
1144	A587	4c **green & brown,** Jan. 11, 1961	.20	.20
		P# block of 4	.65	—
		Nos. 1139-1144 (6)	1.20	1.20

BOY SCOUT JUBILEE ISSUE
50th anniv. of the Boy Scouts of America.

Boy Scout Giving Scout Sign — A588

Designed by Norman Rockwell.

GIORI PRESS PRINTING
Plates of 200 subjects in four panes of 50.

1960, Feb. 8			**Perf. 11**	
1145	A588	4c **red, dark blue & dark bister**	.20	.20
		P# block of 4	.55	—

Olympic Rings and Snowflake — A589

Thomas G. Masaryk — A590

OLYMPIC WINTER GAMES ISSUE
Opening of the 8th Olympic Winter Games, Squaw Valley, Feb. 18-29, 1960.

Designed by Ervine Metzl.

ROTARY PRESS PRINTING
E.E. Plates of 200 subjects in four panes of 50.

1960, Feb. 18			**Perf. 10½x11**	
1146	A589	4c **dull blue**	.20	.20
		P# block of 4	.40	—

CHAMPION OF LIBERTY ISSUE
Issued to honor Thomas G. Masaryk, founder and president of Czechoslovakia (1918-35), on the 110th anniversary of his birth.

ROTARY PRESS PRINTING
E.E. Plates of 280 subjects in four panes of 70.

1960, Mar. 7			**Perf. 10½x11**	
1147	A590	4c **blue**	.20	.20
		P# block of 4	.40	—
a.		Vert. pair, imperf. between	2,750.	

GIORI PRESS PRINTING
Plates of 288 subjects in four panes of 72 each.
Perf. 11

1148	A590	8c **carmine, ultramarine & ocher**	.20	.20
		P# block of 4	.95	—
a.		Horiz. pair, imperf. between	—	

WORLD REFUGEE YEAR ISSUE
World Refugee Year, July 1, 1959-June 30, 1960.

Family Walking Toward New Life — A591

Designed by Ervine Metzl.

ROTARY PRESS PRINTING
E.E. Plates of 200 subjects in four panes of 50.

1960, Apr. 7			**Perf. 11x10½**	
1149	A591	4c **gray black**	.20	.20
		P# block of 4	.40	—

WATER CONSERVATION ISSUE
Issued to stress the importance of water conservation and to commemorate the 7th Watershed Congress, Washington, D.C.

Water: From Watershed to Consumer A592

Designed by Elmo White.

GIORI PRESS PRINTING
Plates of 200 subjects in four panes of 50.

1960, Apr. 18			**Perf. 11**	
1150	A592	4c **dark blue, brown orange & green**	.20	.20
		P# block of 4	.40	—
a.		Brown orange missing (EP)	2,250.	

SEATO ISSUE
South-East Asia Treaty Organization and for the SEATO Conf., Washington, D.C., May 31-June 3.

SEATO Emblem — A593

Designed by John Maass.

ROTARY PRESS PRINTING
E.E. plates of 280 subjects in four panes of 70.

1960, May 31			**Perf. 10½x11**	
1151	A593	4c **blue**	.20	.20
		P# block of 4	.40	—
a.		Vertical pair, imperf. between	140.00	

AMERICAN WOMAN ISSUE
Issued to pay tribute to American women and their accomplishments in civic affairs, education, arts and industry.

Mother and Daughter A594

Designed by Robert Sivard.

ROTARY PRESS PRINTING
E.E. Plates of 200 subjects in four panes of 50.

1960, June 2		**Perf. 11x10½**	
1152 A594 4c **deep violet**		.20	.20
P# block of 4		.40	—

50-STAR FLAG ISSUE

US Flag, 1960 — A595

Designed by Stevan Dohanos.

GIORI PRESS PRINTING
Plates of 200 subjects in four panes of 50.

1960, July 4		**Perf. 11**	
1153 A595 4c **dark blue & red**		.20	.20
P# block of 4		.40	—

PONY EXPRESS CENTENNIAL ISSUE

Pony Express Rider — A596

Designed by Harold von Schmidt.

ROTARY PRESS PRINTING
E.E. Plates of 200 subjects in four panes of 50.

1960, July 19		**Perf. 11x10½**	
1154 A596 4c **sepia**		.20	.20
P# block of 4		.65	—

Man in Wheelchair Operating Drill Press — A597

World Forestry Congress Seal — A598

EMPLOY THE HANDICAPPED ISSUE

Promoting the employment of the physically handicapped and publicizing the 8th World Congress of the Intl. Soc. for the Welfare of Cripples, New York City.

Designed by Carl Bobertz.

ROTARY PRESS PRINTING
E.E. Plates of 200 subjects in four panes of 50.

1960, Aug. 28		**Perf. 10½x11**	
1155 A597 4c **dark blue**		.20	.20
P# block of 4		.40	—

WORLD FORESTRY CONGRESS ISSUE

5th World Forestry Cong., Seattle, Wash., Aug. 29-Sept. 10.

ROTARY PRESS PRINTING
E.E. Plates of 200 subjects in four panes of 50.

1960, Aug. 29		**Perf. 10½x11**	
1156 A598 4c **green**		.20	.20
P# block of 4		.40	—

Independence Bell — A599

Washington Monument and Cherry Blossoms — A600

MEXICAN INDEPENDENCE, 150th ANNIV.

Designed by Leon Helguera and Charles R. Chickering.

GIORI PRESS PRINTING
Plates of 200 subjects in four panes of 50.

1960, Sept. 16		**Perf. 11**	
1157 A599 4c **green & rose red**		.20	.20
P# block of 4		.40	—

See Mexico No. 910.

US-JAPAN TREATY ISSUE

Centenary of the United States-Japan Treaty of Amity and Commerce.

Designed by Gyo Fujikawa.

GIORI PRESS PRINTING
Plates of 200 subjects in four panes of 50.

1960, Sept. 28		**Perf. 11**	
1158 A600 4c **blue & pink**		.20	.20
P# block of 4		.65	—

Ignacy Jan Paderewski — A601

Robert A. Taft — A602

CHAMPION OF LIBERTY ISSUE

Jan Paderewski, Polish statesman and musician.

ROTARY PRESS PRINTING
E.E. Plates of 280 subjects in four panes of 70.

1960, Oct. 8		**Perf. 10½x11**	
1159 A601 4c **blue**		.20	.20
P# block of 4		.40	—

GIORI PRESS PRINTING
Plates of 288 subjects in four panes of 72 each.
Perf. 11

1160 A601 8c **carmine, ultramarine & ocher**		.20	.20
P# block of 4		.90	—

SENATOR TAFT MEMORIAL ISSUE

Senator Robert A. Taft (1889-1953) of Ohio.

Designed by William K. Schrage.

ROTARY PRESS PRINTING
E.E. Plates of 280 subjects in four panes of 70.

1960, Oct. 10		**Perf. 10½x11**	
1161 A602 4c **dull violet**		.20	.20
P# block of 4		.45	—

WHEELS OF FREEDOM ISSUE

Issued to honor the automotive industry and in connection with the National Automobile Show, Detroit, Oct. 15-23.

Globe and Steering Wheel with Tractor, Car and Truck — A603

Designed by Arnold J. Copeland.

ROTARY PRESS PRINTING
E.E. Plates of 200 subjects in four panes of 50.

1960, Oct. 15		**Perf. 11x10½**	
1162 A603 4c **dark blue**		.20	.20
P# block of 4		.40	—

BOYS' CLUBS OF AMERICA ISSUE

Boys' Clubs of America movement, centenary.

Profile of Boy — A604

Designed by Charles T. Coiner.

GIORI PRESS PRINTING
Plates of 200 subjects in four panes of 50.

1960, Oct. 18		**Perf. 11**	
1163 A604 4c **indigo, slate & rose red**		.20	.20
P# block of 4		.40	—

FIRST AUTOMATED POST OFFICE IN THE US ISSUE

Publicizing the opening of the 1st automated post office in the US at Providence, R.I.

Architect's Sketch of New Post Office, Providence, R.I. — A605

Designed by Arnold J. Copeland and Victor S. McCloskey, Jr.

GIORI PRESS PRINTING
Plates of 200 subjects in four panes of 50.

1960, Oct. 20		**Perf. 11**	
1164 A605 4c **dark blue & carmine**		.20	.20
P# block of 4		.40	—

Baron Gustaf Mannerheim — A606

Camp Fire Girls Emblem — A607

CHAMPION OF LIBERTY ISSUE

Baron Karl Gustaf Emil Mannerheim (1867-1951), Marshal and President of Finland.

ROTARY PRESS PRINTING
E.E. Plates of 280 subjects in four panes of 70.

1960, Oct. 26		**Perf. 10½x11**	
1165 A606 4c **blue**		.20	.20
P# block of 4		.40	—

GIORI PRESS PRINTING
Plates of 288 subjects in four panes of 72 each.
Perf. 11

1166 A606 8c **carmine, ultramarine & ocher**		.20	.20
P# block of 4		.80	—

CAMP FIRE GIRLS ISSUE

50th anniv. of the Camp Fire Girls' movement and in connection with the Golden Jubilee Convention celebration of the Camp Fire Girls.

Designed by H. Edward Oliver.

GIORI PRESS PRINTING

Plates of 200 subjects in four panes of 50.

1960, Nov. 1   *Perf. 11*
1167 A607 4c **dark blue & bright red**   .20 .20
              P# block of 4   .65 —

Giuseppe Garibaldi — A608

Walter F. George — A609

CHAMPION OF LIBERTY ISSUE

Giuseppe Garibaldi (1807-1882), Italian patriot and freedom fighter.

ROTARY PRESS PRINTING

E.E. Plates of 280 subjects in four panes of 70.

1960, Nov. 2   *Perf. 10½x11*
1168 A608 4c **green**   .20 .20
              P# block of 4   .40 —

GIORI PRESS PRINTING

Plates of 288 subjects in four panes of 72 each.
Perf. 11
1169 A608 8c **carmine, ultramarine & ocher** .20 .20
              P# block of 4   .85 —

SENATOR GEORGE MEMORIAL ISSUE

Walter F. George (1878-1957) of Georgia.

Designed by William K. Schrage.

ROTARY PRESS PRINTING

E.E. Plates of 280 subjects in four panes of 70.

1960, Nov. 5   *Perf. 10½x11*
1170 A609 4c **dull violet**   .20 .20
              P# block of 4   .45 —

Andrew Carnegie — A610

John Foster Dulles — A611

ANDREW CARNEGIE ISSUE

Carnegie (1835-1919), industrialist & philanthropist.

Designed by Charles R. Chickering.

ROTARY PRESS PRINTING

E.E. Plates of 280 subjects in four panes of 70.

1960, Nov. 25   *Perf. 10½x11*
1171 A610 4c **deep claret**   .20 .20
              P# block of 4   .40 —

JOHN FOSTER DULLES MEMORIAL ISSUE

Dulles (1888-1959), Secretary of State (1953-59).

Designed by William K. Schrage.

ROTARY PRESS PRINTING

E.E. Plates of 280 subjects in four panes of 70.

1960, Dec. 6   *Perf. 10½x11*
1172 A611 4c **dull violet**   .20 .20
              P# block of 4   .40 —

ECHO I — COMMUNICATIONS FOR PEACE ISSUE

World's 1st communications satellite, Echo I, placed in orbit by the Natl. Aeronautics and Space Admin., Aug. 12, 1960.

Radio Waves Connecting Echo I and Earth — A612

Designed by Ervine Metzl.

ROTARY PRESS PRINTING

E.E. Plates of 200 subjects in four panes of 50.

1960, Dec. 15   *Perf. 11x10½*
1173 A612 4c **deep violet**   .20 .20
              P# block of 4   .65 —

CHAMPION OF LIBERTY ISSUE

Mohandas K. Gandhi, leader in India's struggle for independence.

Mahatma Gandhi — A613

ROTARY PRESS PRINTING

E.E. Plates of 280 subjects in four panes of 70.

1961, Jan. 26   *Perf. 10½x11*
1174 A613 4c **red orange**   .20 .20
              P# block of 4   .40 —

GIORI PRESS PRINTING

Plates of 288 subjects in four panes of 72 each.
Perf. 11
1175 A613 8c **carmine, ultramarine & ocher** .20 .20
              P# block of 4   1.00 —

RANGE CONSERVATION ISSUE

Issued to stress the importance of range conservation and to commemorate the meeting of the American Society of Range Management. "The Trail Boss" from a drawing by Charles M. Russell is the Society's emblem.

The Trail Boss and Modern Range — A614

Designed by Rudolph Wendelin.

GIORI PRESS PRINTING

Plates of 200 subjects in four panes of 50.

1961, Feb. 2   *Perf. 11*
1176 A614 4c **blue, slate & brown orange**   .20 .20
              P# block of 4   .60 —

HORACE GREELEY ISSUE

Horace Greeley (1811-1872), Publisher and Editor — A615

Designed by Charles R. Chickering.

ROTARY PRESS PRINTING

E.E. Plates of 280 subjects in four panes of 70.

1961, Feb. 3   *Perf. 10½x11*
1177 A615 4c **dull violet**   .20 .20
              P# block of 4   .45 —

CIVIL WAR CENTENNIAL ISSUE

Centenaries of the firing on Fort Sumter (No. 1178), the Battle of Shiloh (No. 1179), the Battle of Gettysburg (No. 1180), the Battle of the Wilderness (No. 1181) and the surrender at Appomattox (No. 1182).

Sea Coast Gun of 1861 — A616

Rifleman at Battle of Shiloh, 1862 — A617

Blue and Gray at Gettysburg, 1863 — A618

Battle of the Wilderness, 1864 — A619

Appomattox, 1865 — A620

Designed by Charles R. Chickering (Sumter), Noel Sickles (Shiloh), Roy Gjertson (Gettysburg), B. Harold Christenson (Wilderness), Leonard Fellman (Appomattox).

ROTARY PRESS PRINTING

E.E. Plates of 200 subjects in four panes of 50.

1961-65   *Perf. 11x10½*
1178 A616 4c **light green,** *Apr. 12, 1961*   .25 .20
              P# block of 4   1.10 —
1179 A617 4c **black,** *peach blossom, Apr. 7, 1962* .20 .20
              P# block of 4   .75 —

GIORI PRESS PRINTING

Plates of 200 subjects in four panes of 50.
Perf. 11
1180 A618 5c **gray & blue,** *July 1, 1963*   .20 .20
              P# block of 4   .65 —
1181 A619 5c **dark red & black,** *May 5, 1964* .20 .20
              P# block of 4   .60 —
              Margin block of 4, Mr. Zip and
              "Use Zip Code"   .55 —
1182 A620 5c **Prus. blue & black,** *Apr. 9, 1965* .30 .20
              P# block of 4   1.40 —
              Margin block of 4, Mr. Zip and
              "Use Zip Code"   1.30 —
    a.   Horiz. pair, imperf. vert.   4,500.
              Nos. 1178-1182 (5)   1.15 1.00

KANSAS STATEHOOD, 100th ANNIV.

Sunflower, Pioneer Couple and Stockade A621

GIORI PRESS PRINTING
Plates of 200 subjects in four panes of 50.

1961, May 10			Perf. 11
1183 A621 4c **brown, dark red & green**, *yellow*	.20	.20
P# block of 4		.55	—

SENATOR NORRIS ISSUE

Senator George W. Norris of Nebraska, and Norris Dam — A622

Designed by Charles R. Chickering.

ROTARY PRESS PRINTING
E.E. Plates of 200 subjects in four panes of 50.

1961, July 11			Perf. 11x10½
1184 A622 4c **blue green**	.20	.20
P# block of 4		.40	—

NAVAL AVIATION, 50th ANNIV.

Navy's First Plane (Curtiss A-1 of 1911) and Naval Air Wings — A623

Designed by John Maass.

ROTARY PRESS PRINTING
E.E. Plates of 200 subjects in four panes of 50.

1961, Aug. 20			Perf. 11x10½
1185 A623 4c **blue**	.20	.20
P# block of 4		.40	—
Pair with full vert. gutter btwn.		150.00	

WORKMEN'S COMPENSATION ISSUE

50th anniv. of the 1st successful Workmen's Compensation Law, enacted by the Wisconsin legislature.

Scales of Justice, Factory, Worker and Family — A624

Designed by Norman Todhunter.

ROTARY PRESS PRINTING
E.E. Plates of 200 subjects in four panes of 50.

1961, Sept. 4			Perf. 10½x11
1186 A624 4c **ultramarine**, *grayish*	.20	.20
P# block of 4		.40	—
P# block of 4 inverted		.60	—

"The Smoke Signal" — A625   Sun Yat-sen — A626

FREDERIC REMINGTON ISSUE

Remington (1861-1909), artist of the West. The design is from an oil painting, Amon Carter Museum of Western Art, Fort Worth, Texas.

Designed by Charles R. Chickering.

GIORI PRESS PRINTING
Panes of 200 subjects in four panes of 50.

1961, Oct. 4			Perf. 11
1187 A625 4c **multicolored**	.20	.20
P# block of 4		.40	—

REPUBLIC OF CHINA ISSUE

50th anniversary of the Republic of China.

ROTARY PRESS PRINTING
E.E. Plates of 200 subjects in four panes of 50.

1961, Oct. 10			Perf. 10½x11
1188 A626 4c **blue**	.20	.20
P# block of 4		.60	—

Basketball — A627   Student Nurse Lighting Candle — A628

NAISMITH — BASKETBALL ISSUE

Honoring basketball and James Naismith (1861-1939), Canada-born director of physical education, who invented the game in 1891 at Y.M.C.A. College, Springfield, Mass.

Designed by Charles R. Chickering.

ROTARY PRESS PRINTING
E.E. Plates of 200 subjects in four panes of 50.

1961, Nov. 6			Perf. 10½x11
1189 A627 4c **brown**	.20	.20
P# block of 4		.50	—

NURSING ISSUE

Issued to honor the nursing profession.

Designed by Alfred Charles Parker.

GIORI PRESS PRINTING
Plates of 200 subjects in four panes of 50.

1961, Dec. 28			Perf. 11
1190 A628 4c **blue, green, orange & black**	.20	.20
P# block of 4, 2#		.50	—

NEW MEXICO STATEHOOD, 50th ANNIV.

Shiprock A629

Designed by Robert J. Jones.

GIORI PRESS PRINTING
Plates of 200 subjects in four panes of 50.

1962, Jan. 6			Perf. 11
1191 A629 4c **lt. blue, maroon & bister**	.20	.20
P# block of 4		.50	—

ARIZONA STATEHOOD, 50th ANNIV.

Giant Saguaro Cactus — A630

Designed by Jimmie E. Ihms and James M. Chemi.

GIORI PRESS PRINTING
Plates of 200 subjects in four panes of 50.

1962, Feb. 14			Perf. 11
1192 A630 4c **carmine, violet blue & green**	.20	.20
P# block of 4		.50	—

PROJECT MERCURY ISSUE

1st orbital flight of a US astronaut, Lt. Col. John H. Glenn, Jr., Feb. 20, 1962.

"Friendship 7" Capsule and Globe — A631

GIORI PRESS PRINTING
Plates of 200 subjects in four panes of 50.

1962, Feb. 20			Perf. 11
1193 A631 4c **dark blue & yellow**	.20	.20
P# block of 4		.40	—

Imperfs. are printers waste.

MALARIA ERADICATION ISSUE

World Health Organization's drive to eradicate malaria.

Great Seal of US and WHO Symbol A632

Designed by Charles R. Chickering.

GIORI PRESS PRINTING
Plates of 200 subjects in four panes of 50.

1962, Mar. 30			Perf. 11
1194 A632 4c **blue & bister**	.20	.20
P# block of 4		.40	—

Charles Evans Hughes — A633   "Space Needle" and Monorail — A634

CHARLES EVANS HUGHES ISSUE

Hughes (1862-1948), Governor of New York, Chief Justice of the US.

Designed by Charles R. Chickering.

ROTARY PRESS PRINTING
E.E. Plates of 200 subjects in four panes of 50.

1962, Apr. 11   *Perf. 10½x11*
1195 A633 4c black, *buff*   .20   .20
      P# block of 4   .40 —

SEATTLE WORLD'S FAIR ISSUE

"Century 21" International Exposition, Seattle, Wash., Apr. 21-Oct. 21.

Designed by John Maass.

GIORI PRESS PRINTING
Plates of 200 subjects in four panes of 50.

1962, Apr. 25   *Perf. 11*
1196 A634 4c red & dark blue   .20   .20
      On cover, "Century 21" Expo. cancel   5.00
      On cover, "Space Needle" Expo. cancel   2.00
      P# block of 4   .40 —

LOUISIANA STATEHOOD, 150th ANNIV.

Riverboat on the Mississippi
A635

Designed by Norman Todhunter.

GIORI PRESS PRINTING
Plates of 200 subjects in four panes of 50.

1962, Apr. 30   *Perf. 11*
1197 A635 4c blue, dark slate green & red   .20   .20
      P# block of 4   .50 —

HOMESTEAD ACT, CENTENARY

Sod Hut and Settlers
A636

Designed by Charles R. Chickering.

ROTARY PRESS PRINTING
E.E. Plates of 200 subjects in four panes of 50.

1962, May 20   *Perf. 11x10½*
1198 A636 4c slate   .20   .20
      P# block of 4   .40 —

GIRL SCOUTS ISSUE

50th anniversary of the Girl Scouts of America.

Senior Girl Scout and Flag — A637

Designed by Ward Brackett.

ROTARY PRESS PRINTING
E.E. Plates of 200 subjects in four panes of 50.

1962, July 24   *Perf. 11x10½*
1199 A637 4c rose red   .20   .20
      P# block of 4   .40 —
      Pair with full vertical gutter between   250.00

SENATOR BRIEN McMAHON ISSUE

McMahon (1903-52) of Connecticut had a role in opening the way to peaceful uses of atomic energy through the Atomic Energy Act establishing the Atomic Energy Commission.

Brien McMahon and Atomic Symbol
A638

Designed by V. S. McCloskey, Jr.

ROTARY PRESS PRINTING
E.E. Plates of 200 subjects in four panes of 50.

1962, July 28   *Perf. 11x10½*
1200 A638 4c purple   .20   .20
      P# block of 4   .40 —

APPRENTICESHIP ISSUE

National Apprenticeship Program and 25th anniv. of the National Apprenticeship Act.

Machinist Handing Micrometer to Apprentice
A639

Designed by Robert Geissmann.

ROTARY PRESS PRINTING
E.E. Plates of 200 subjects in four panes of 50.

1962, Aug. 31   *Perf. 11x10½*
1201 A639 4c black, *yellow bister*   .20   .20
      P# block of 4   .40 —

SAM RAYBURN ISSUE

Sam Rayburn (1882-1961), Speaker of the House of Representatives — A640

Designed by Robert L. Miller.

GIORI PRESS PRINTING
Plates of 200 subjects in four panes of 50.

1962, Sept. 16   *Perf. 11*
1202 A640 4c dark blue & red brown   .20   .20
      P# block of 4   .45 —

DAG HAMMARSKJOLD ISSUE

UN Headquarters and Dag Hammarskjold, UN Sec. Gen., 1953-61
A641

Designed by Herbert M. Sanborn.

GIORI PRESS PRINTING
Plates of 200 subjects in four panes of 50.

1962, Oct. 23   *Perf. 11*
1203 A641 4c black, brown & yellow   .20   .20
      P# block of 4, 2#   .40 —
   a.   Yellow inverted, on cover, see note

No. 1203a can only be collected on a cover postmarked before Nov. 16, 1962 (the date the Hammarskjold Special Printing, No. 1204, was issued). Covers are known machine postmarked Cuyahoga Falls, Ohio, Nov. 14, 1962, and notarized in the lower left corner by George W. Schwartz, Notary Public. Other covers are reported postmarked Oct. 26, 1962, Brooklyn, NY, Vanderveer Station. Unaddressed, uncacheted first day covers also exist. Other covers may exist. All covers must be accompanied by certificates from recognized expertizing committees. Value of first-day cover, $3,000.

An unused pane of 50 was signed in the selvage by ten well-known philatelists attesting to its genuineness. This pane was donated to the American Philatelic Society in 1987.

An unknown number of "first day covers" exist bearing Artmaster cachets. These were contrived using examples of No. 1204.

Hammarskjold Special Printing

No. 1204 was issued following discovery of No. 1203 with yellow background inverted.

GIORI PRESS PRINTING
Plates of 200 subjects in four panes of 50.

1962, Nov. 16   *Perf. 11*
1204 A641 4c black, brown & yel (yellow inverted)   .20   .20
      P# block of 4, 2#, yellow # inverted   1.10 —

The inverted yellow impression is shifted to the right in relation to the black and brown impression. Stamps of first vertical row of UL and LL panes show no yellow at left side for a space of 11-11½mm in from the perforations.

Stamps of first vertical row of UR and LR panes show vertical no-yellow strip 9¾mm wide, covering UN Building. On all others, the vertical no-yellow strip is 3½mm wide, and touches UN Building.

CHRISTMAS ISSUE

Wreath and Candles — A642

Designed by Jim Crawford.

GIORI PRESS PRINTING
Plates of 400 subjects in four panes of 100.
Panes of 90 and 100 exist
without plate numbers due to provisional use of smaller paper.
Value per pane thus $50.

1962, Nov. 1   *Perf. 11*
1205 A642 4c green & red   .20   .20
      P# block of 4   .40 —

HIGHER EDUCATION ISSUE

Higher education's role in American cultural and industrial development and the centenary celebrations of the signing of the law creating land-grant colleges and universities.

Map of U.S. and Lamp — A643

Designed by Henry K. Bencsath.

GIORI PRESS PRINTING
Plates of 200 subjects in panes of 50.

1962, Nov. 14   *Perf. 11*
1206 A643 4c blue green & black   .20   .20
      P# block of 4, 2#   .40 —

WINSLOW HOMER ISSUE

Homer (1836-1910), painter, showing his oil, "Breezing Up," which hangs in the National Gallery, Washington, D.C.

"Breezing Up" — A644

Designed by Victor S. McCloskey, Jr.

GIORI PRESS PRINTING
Plates of 200 subjects in four panes of 50.

1962, Dec. 15			**Perf. 11**
1207 A644 4c **multicolored**		.20	.20
	P# block of 4	.45	
a.	Horiz. pair, imperf. btwn. and at right	6,750.	

FLAG ISSUE

Flag over White House — A645

Designed by Robert J. Jones.

GIORI PRESS PRINTING
Plates of 400 subjects in four panes of 100.

1963-66			**Perf. 11**
1208 A645 5c **blue & red**, *Jan. 9, 1963*		.20	.20
	P# block of 4	.40	—
	Pair with full horiz. gutter between		—
a.	Tagged, *Aug. 25, 1966*	.20	.20
	P# block of 4	2.00	—
b.	Horiz. pair, imperf. between, tagged	1,500.	

Beware of pairs with faint blind perfs between offered as No. 1208b.

REGULAR ISSUE

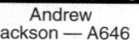

Andrew Jackson — A646

George Washington — A650

Designed by William K. Schrage.

ROTARY PRESS PRINTING
E.E. Plates of 400 subjects in four panes of 100.

1962-66			**Perf. 11x10½**
1209 A646 1c **green**, *Mar. 22, 1963*		.20	.20
	P# block of 4	.20	
	Pair with full vert. gutter btwn.		—
a.	Tagged, *July 6, 1966*	.20	.20
	P# block of 4	.40	
1213 A650 5c **dark blue gray**, *Nov. 23, 1962*		.20	.20
	P# block of 4	.40	
	Pair with full vert. gutter btwn.		—
	Pair with full horiz. gutter btwn.	425.00	
a.	Booklet pane of 5 + label	3.00	2.00
b.	Tagged, *Oct. 28, 1963*	.50	.20
	P# block of 4	4.50	
c.	As "a," tagged, *Oct. 28, 1963*	2.25	1.50
d.	Horiz. pair, imperf between	1,500.	

Bureau Precancels: 1c, 10 diff., 5c, 18 diff.

No. 1213d resulted from a paper foldover after perforating and before cutting into panes. At least six individually unique panes exist, including at least one that contains two error pairs. Recent auction prices for panes have ranged between $1,400 and $4,000.

COIL STAMPS
(Rotary Press)

1962-66			**Perf. 10 Vertically**
1225 A646 1c **green**, *May 31, 1963*		.20	.20
	Pair	.30	.20
	Joint line pair	2.25	.20
a.	Tagged, *July 6, 1966*	.20	.20
	Joint line pair	.75	.20
1229 A650 5c **dark blue gray**, *Nov. 23, 1962*		1.50	.20
	Pair	3.00	.20
	Joint line pair	4.00	.35
a.	Tagged, *Oct. 28, 1963*	1.80	.20
	Joint line pair	12.00	.20
b.	Imperf., pair	325.00	
	Joint line pair	900.00	

Bureau Precancels: 1c, 5 diff., 5c, 14 diff.

See Luminescence note in "Basic Stamp Information" in the introduction.

CAROLINA CHARTER ISSUE

Tercentenary of the Carolina Charter granting to 8 Englishmen lands extending coast-to-coast roughly along the present border of Virginia to the north and Florida to the south. Original charter on display at Raleigh.

First Page of Carolina Charter A662

Designed by Robert L. Miller.

GIORI PRESS PRINTING
Plates of 200 subjects in four panes of 50.

1963, Apr. 6			**Perf. 11**
1230 A662 5c **dark carmine & brown**		.20	.20
	P# block of 4	.45	—

FOOD FOR PEACE-FREEDOM FROM HUNGER ISSUE

American "Food for Peace" program and the "Freedom from Hunger" campaign of the FAO.

Wheat — A663

Designed by Stevan Dohanos.

GIORI PRESS PRINTING
Plates of 200 subjects in four panes of 50.

1963, June 4			**Perf. 11**
1231 A663 5c **green, buff & red**		.20	.20
	P# block of 4	.40	—

WEST VIRGINIA STATEHOOD, 100th ANNIV.

Map of West Virginia and State Capitol A664

Designed by Dr. Dwight Mutchler.

GIORI PRESS PRINTING
Plates of 200 subjects in four panes of 50.

1963, June 20			**Perf. 11**
1232 A664 5c **green, red & black**		.20	.20
	P# block of 4	.50	—

EMANCIPATION PROCLAMATION ISSUE

Centenary of Lincoln's Emancipation Proclamation freeing about 3,000,000 slaves in 10 southern states.

Severed Chain — A665

Designed by Georg Olden.

GIORI PRESS PRINTING
Plates of 200 subjects in four panes of 50.

1963, Aug. 16			**Perf. 11**
1233 A665 5c **dark blue, black & red**		.20	.20
	P# block of 4	.50	—

ALLIANCE FOR PROGRESS ISSUE

2nd anniv. of the Alliance for Progress, which aims to stimulate economic growth and raise living standards in Latin America.

Alliance Emblem A666

Designed by William K. Schrage.

GIORI PRESS PRINTING
Plates of 200 subjects in four panes of 50.

1963, Aug. 17			**Perf. 11**
1234 A666 5c **ultramarine & green**		.20	.20
	P# block of 4	.40	—

CORDELL HULL ISSUE

Hull (1871-1955), Secretary of State (1933-44).

Cordell Hull — A667

Designed by Robert J. Jones.

ROTARY PRESS PRINTING
E.E. Plates of 200 subjects in four panes of 50.

1963, Oct. 5			**Perf. 10½x11**
1235 A667 5c **blue green**		.20	.20
	P# block of 4	.50	—

ELEANOR ROOSEVELT ISSUE

Mrs. Franklin D. Roosevelt (1884-1962).

Eleanor Roosevelt A668

Designed by Robert L. Miller.

ROTARY PRESS PRINTING
E.E. Plates of 200 subjects in four panes of 50.

1963, Oct. 11			**Perf. 11x10½**
1236 A668 5c **bright purple**		.20	.20
	P# block of 4	.45	—

SCIENCE ISSUE

Honoring the sciences and in connection with the centenary of the Natl. Academy of Science.

"The Universe" A669

Designed by Antonio Frasconi.

GIORI PRESS PRINTING
Plates of 200 subjects in four panes of 50.

1963, Oct. 14			**Perf. 11**
1237 A669 5c **Prussian blue & black**		.20	.20
	P# block of 4	.40	—

CITY MAIL DELIVERY ISSUE

Centenary of free city mail delivery.

Letter Carrier, 1863 — A670

Designed by Norman Rockwell.

GIORI PRESS PRINTING
Plates of 200 subjects in four panes of 50.

1963, Oct. 26	**Tagged**	**Perf. 11**	
1238 A670 5c **gray, dark blue & red**		.20	.20
	P# block of 4	.50	—
a.	Tagging omitted	9.50	

RED CROSS CENTENARY ISSUE

Cuban Refugees on S.S. Morning Light and Red Cross Flag — A671

Designed by Victor S. McCloskey, Jr.

GIORI PRESS PRINTING
Plates of 200 subjects in four panes of 50.

1963, Oct. 29		**Perf. 11**	
1239 A671 5c **bluish black & red**		.20	.20
	P# block of 4	.50	

CHRISTMAS ISSUE

National Christmas Tree and White House — A672

Designed by Lily Spandorf; modified by Norman Todhunter.

GIORI PRESS PRINTING
Plates of 400 subjects in four panes of 100.

1963, Nov. 1		**Perf. 11**	
1240 A672 5c **dark blue, bluish black & red**		.20	.20
	P# block of 4	.50	
a.	Tagged, *Nov. 2, 1963*	.65	.50
	P# block of 4	5.00	—
	Pair with full horiz. gutter between	—	
b.	Horiz. pair, imperf between	7,750.	
c.	Red missing (PS)		

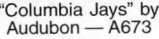

"Columbia Jays" by Audubon — A673

Sam Houston — A674

JOHN JAMES AUDUBON ISSUE

Audubon (1785-1851), ornithologist and artist. The birds pictured are actually Collie's magpie jays. See No. C71.

Designed by Robert L. Miller.

GIORI PRESS PRINTING
Plates of 200 subjects in four panes of 50.

1963, Dec. 7		**Perf. 11**	
1241 A673 5c **dark blue & multicolored**		.20	.20
	P# block of 4	.45	—

SAM HOUSTON ISSUE

Houston (1793-1863), soldier, president of Texas, US senator.

Designed by Tom Lea.

ROTARY PRESS PRINTING
E.E. Plates of 200 subjects in four panes of 50.

1964, Jan. 10		**Perf. 10½x11**	
1242 A674 5c **black**		.25	.20
	P# block of 4	1.05	
	Margin block of 4, Mr. Zip and "Use Zip Code"	1.00	—

CHARLES M. RUSSELL ISSUE

Russell (1864-1926), painter. The design is from a painting, Thomas Gilcrease Institute of American History and Art, Tulsa, Okla.

"Jerked Down" — A675

Designed by William K. Schrage.

GIORI PRESS PRINTING
Plates of 200 subjects in four panes of 50.

1964, Mar. 19		**Perf. 11**	
1243 A675 5c **multicolored**		.20	.20
	P# block of 4	.40	
	Margin block of 4, Mr. Zip and "Use Zip Code"	.35	—

NEW YORK WORLD'S FAIR ISSUE

New York World's Fair, 1964-65.

Mall with Unisphere and "Rocket Thrower" by Donald De Lue — A676

Designed by Robert J. Jones.

ROTARY PRESS PRINTING
E.E. Plates of 200 subjects in four panes of 50.

1964, Apr. 22		**Perf. 11x10½**	
1244 A676 5c **blue green**		.20	.20
	On cover, Expo. station machine cancel (non-first day)	2.00	
	On cover, Expo. station hand-stamp cancel (non-first day)	10.00	
	P# block of 4	.45	
	Margin block of 4, Mr. Zip and "Use Zip Code"	.40	—

JOHN MUIR ISSUE

Muir (1838-1914), naturalist and conservationist.

John Muir and Redwood Forest — A677

Designed by Rudolph Wendelin.

GIORI PRESS PRINTING
Plates of 200 subjects in four panes of 50.

1964, Apr. 29		**Perf. 11**	
1245 A677 5c **brown, green, yellow green & olive**		.20	.20
	P# block of 4	.45	—

KENNEDY MEMORIAL ISSUE

President John Fitzgerald Kennedy, (1917-1963).

John F. Kennedy and Eternal Flame — A678

Designed by Raymond Loewy/William Snaith, Inc.

Photograph by William S. Murphy.

ROTARY PRESS PRINTING
E.E. Plates of 200 subjects in four panes of 50.

1964, May 29		**Perf. 11x10½**	
1246 A678 5c **blue gray**		.20	.20
	P# block of 4	.50	—

NEW JERSEY TERCENTENARY ISSUE

300th anniv. of English colonization of New Jersey. The design is from a mural by Howard Pyle in the Essex County Courthouse, Newark, N.J.

Philip Carteret Landing at Elizabethtown, and Map of New Jersey — A679

Designed by Douglas Allen.

ROTARY PRESS PRINTING
E.E. Plates of 200 subjects in four panes of 50.

1964, June 15		**Perf. 10½x11**	
1247 A679 5c **brt. ultramarine**		.20	.20
	P# block of 4	.50	—
	Margin block of 4, Mr. Zip and "Use Zip Code"	.40	

NEVADA STATEHOOD, 100th ANNIV.

Virginia City and Map of Nevada A680

Designed by William K. Schrage.

GIORI PRESS PRINTING
Plates of 200 subjects in four panes of 50.

1964, July 22		**Perf. 11**	
1248 A680 5c **red, yellow & blue**		.25	.20
	P# block of 4	1.05	
	Margin block of 4, Mr. Zip and "Use Zip Code"	1.00	—

Flag — A681

William
Shakespeare — A682

REGISTER AND VOTE ISSUE

Campaign to draw more voters to the polls.

Designed by Victor S. McCloskey, Jr.

GIORI PRESS PRINTING
Plates of 200 subjects in four panes of 50.

1964, Aug. 1				Perf. 11	
1249	A681	5c	dark blue & red	.20	.20
			P# block of 4	.45	—
			Margin block of 4, Mr. Zip and "Use Zip Code"	.40	—

SHAKESPEARE ISSUE

William Shakespeare (1564-1616).

Designed by Douglas Gorsline.

ROTARY PRESS PRINTING
E.E. Plates of 200 subjects in four panes of 50.

1964, Aug. 14				Perf. 10½x11	
1250	A682	5c	black brown, tan	.20	.20
			P# block of 4	.40	—
			Margin block of 4, Mr. Zip and "Use Zip Code"	.35	—

DOCTORS MAYO ISSUE

Dr. William James Mayo (1861-1939) and his brother, Dr. Charles Horace Mayo (1865-1939), surgeons who founded the Mayo Foundation for Medical Education and Research in affiliation with the Univ. of Minnesota at Rochester. Heads on stamp are from a sculpture by James Earle Fraser.

Drs. William and Charles
Mayo — A683

ROTARY PRESS PRINTING
E.E. Plates of 200 subjects in four panes of 50.

1964, Sept. 11				Perf. 10½x11	
1251	A683	5c	green	.20	.20
			P# block of 4	.70	—
			Margin block of 4, Mr. Zip and "Use Zip Code"	.40	—

AMERICAN MUSIC ISSUE

50th anniv. of the founding of the American Society of Composers, Authors and Publishers (ASCAP).

Lute, Horn,
Laurel, Oak
and Music
Score — A684

Designed by Bradbury Thompson.

GIORI PRESS PRINTING
Plates of 200 subjects in four panes of 50.

1964, Oct. 15				Perf. 11	
		Gray Paper with Blue Threads			
1252	A684	5c	red, black & blue	.20	.20
			P# block of 4	.40	—
			Margin block of 4, Mr. Zip and "Use Zip Code"	.35	—
a.			Blue omitted	800.00	
b.			Blue missing (PS)	—	

Beware of copies offered as No. 1252a which have traces of blue.

HOMEMAKERS ISSUE

Honoring American women as homemakers and for the 50th anniv. of the passage of the Smith-Lever Act. By providing economic experts under an extension service of the U.S. Dept. of Agriculture, this legislation helped to improve homelife.

Farm Scene
Sampler
A685

Designed by Norman Todhunter.

Plates of 200 subjects in four panes of 50.

Engraved (Giori Press); Background Lithographed

1964, Oct. 26				Perf. 11	
1253	A685	5c	multicolored	.20	.20
			P# block of 4	.50	—
			Margin block of 4, Mr. Zip and "Use Zip Code"	.40	—

CHRISTMAS ISSUE

Holly — A686

Mistletoe — A687

Poinsettia — A688

Sprig of
Conifer — A689

Designed by Thomas F. Naegele.

GIORI PRESS PRINTING
Plates of 400 subjects in four panes of 100.
Panes contain 25 subjects each of Nos. 1254-1257

1964, Nov. 9				Perf. 11	
1254	A686	5c	green, carmine & black	.25	.20
a.			Tagged, Nov. 10	.75	.50
b.			Printed on gummed side	—	
1255	A687	5c	carmine, green & black	.25	.20
a.			Tagged, Nov. 10	.75	.50
1256	A688	5c	carmine, green & black	.25	.20
a.			Tagged, Nov. 10	.75	.50
1257	A689	5c	black, green & carmine	.25	.20
a.			Tagged, Nov. 10	.75	.50
b.			Block of 4, #1254-1257	1.00	1.00
			P# block of 4	1.10	—
			Margin block of 4, Zip and "Use Zip Code"	1.00	—
c.			Block of 4, tagged	3.00	2.25
			P# block of 4	6.00	—
			Zip block of 4	3.25	—

No. 1254b resulted from a paper foldover before printing and perforating.

VERRAZANO-NARROWS BRIDGE ISSUE

Opening of the Verrazano-Narrows Bridge connecting Staten Island and Brooklyn.

Verrazano-Narrows Bridge
and Map of New York
Bay — A690

ROTARY PRESS PRINTING
E.E. Plates of 200 subjects in four panes of 50.

1964, Nov. 21				Perf. 10½x11	
1258	A690	5c	blue green	.20	.20
			P# block of 4	.45	—
			Margin block of 4, Mr. Zip and "Use Zip Code"	.40	—

FINE ARTS ISSUE

Abstract
Design by
Stuart
Davis — A691

GIORI PRESS PRINTING
Plates of 200 subjects in four panes of 50.

1964, Dec. 2				Perf. 11	
1259	A691	5c	ultra., black & dull red	.20	.20
			P# block of 4, 2#	.45	—
			Margin block of 4, Mr. Zip and "Use Zip Code"	.40	—

AMATEUR RADIO ISSUE

Issued to honor the radio amateurs on the 50th anniversary of the American Radio Relay League.

Radio Waves and
Dial — A692

Designed by Emil J. Willett.

ROTARY PRESS PRINTING
E.E. Plates of 200 subjects in four panes of 50.

1964, Dec. 15				Perf. 10½x11	
1260	A692	5c	red lilac	.20	.20
			P# block of 4	.85	—
			Margin block of 4, Mr. Zip and "Use Zip Code"	.40	—

BATTLE OF NEW ORLEANS ISSUE

Battle of New Orleans, Chalmette Plantation, Jan. 8-18, 1815, established 150 years of peace and friendship between the US and Great Britain.

General Andrew Jackson and Sesquicentennial
Medal — A693

Designed by Robert J. Jones.

GIORI PRESS PRINTING
Plates of 200 subjects in four panes of 50.

1965, Jan. 8			Perf. 11	
1261	A693	5c deep carmine, violet blue & gray	.20	.20
		P# block of 4	.60	—
		Margin block of 4, Mr. Zip and "Use Zip Code"	.50	

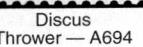

Discus Thrower — A694

Microscope and Stethoscope — A695

PHYSICAL FITNESS-SOKOL ISSUE

Publicizing the importance of physical fitness and for the centenary of the founding of the Sokol (athletic) organization in America.

Designed by Norman Todhunter.

GIORI PRESS PRINTING
Plates of 200 subjects in four panes of 50.

1965, Feb. 15			Perf. 11	
1262	A694	5c maroon & black	.20	.20
		P# block of 4	.50	—
		Margin block of 4, Mr. Zip and "Use Zip Code"	.40	

CRUSADE AGAINST CANCER ISSUE

Issued to publicize the "Crusade Against Cancer" and to stress the importance of early diagnosis.

Designed by Stevan Dohanos.

GIORI PRESS PRINTING
Plates of 200 subjects in four panes of 50.

1965, Apr. 1			Perf. 11	
1263	A695	5c black, purple & red orange	.20	.20
		P# block of 4, 2#	.40	—
		Margin block of 4, Mr. Zip and "Use Zip Code"	.35	

CHURCHILL MEMORIAL ISSUE

Sir Winston Spencer Churchill (1874-1965), British statesman and World War II leader.

Winston Churchill — A696

Designed by Richard Hurd.

ROTARY PRESS PRINTING
E.E. Plates of 200 subjects in four panes of 50.

1965, May 13			Perf. 10½x11	
1264	A696	5c black	.20	.20
		P# block of 4	.40	—
		Margin block of 4, Mr. Zip and "Use Zip Code"	.35	

MAGNA CARTA ISSUE

750th anniversary of the Magna Carta, the basis of English and American common law.

Procession of Barons and King John's Crown — A697

Designed by Brook Temple.

GIORI PRESS PRINTING
Plates of 200 subjects in four panes of 50.

1965, June 15			Perf. 11	
1265	A697	5c black, yellow ocher & red lilac	.20	.20
		P# block of 4, 2#	.40	—
		Margin block of 4, Mr. Zip and "Use Zip Code"	.35	—
		Corner block of 4, black # omitted		—

INTERNATIONAL COOPERATION YEAR

ICY, 1965, and 20th anniv. of the UN.

International Cooperation Year Emblem A698

Designed by Herbert M. Sanborn and Olav S. Mathiesen.

GIORI PRESS PRINTING
Plates of 200 subjects in four panes of 50.

1965, June 26			Perf. 11	
1266	A698	5c dull blue & black	.20	.20
		P# block of 4	.40	—
		Margin block of 4, Mr. Zip and "Use Zip Code"	.35	—

SALVATION ARMY ISSUE

Centenary of the founding of the Salvation Army by William Booth in London.

A699

Designed by Sam Marsh.

GIORI PRESS PRINTING
Plates of 200 subjects in four panes of 50.

1965, July 2			Perf. 11	
1267	A699	5c red, black & dark blue	.20	.20
		P# block of 4	.40	—
		Margin block of 4, Mr. Zip and "Use Zip Code"	.35	—

Dante after a 16th Century Painting — A700

Herbert Hoover — A701

DANTE ISSUE

Dante Alighieri (1265-1321), Italian poet.

Designed by Douglas Gorsline.

ROTARY PRESS PRINTING
E.E. Plates of 200 subjects in four panes of 50.

1965, July 17			Perf. 10½x11	
1268	A700	5c maroon, tan	.20	.20
		P# block of 4	.40	—
		Margin block of 4, Mr. Zip and "Use Zip Code"	.35	—

HERBERT HOOVER ISSUE

President Herbert Clark Hoover, (1874-1964).

Designed by Norman Todhunter; photograph by Fabian Bachrach, Sr.

ROTARY PRESS PRINTING
E.E. Plates of 200 subjects in four panes of 50.

1965, Aug. 10			Perf. 10½x11	
1269	A701	5c rose red	.20	.20
		P# block of 4	.55	—
		Margin block of 4, Mr. Zip and "Use Zip Code"	.40	—

ROBERT FULTON ISSUE

Fulton (1765-1815), inventor of the 1st commercial steamship.

Robert Fulton and the Clermont A702

Designed by John Maass; bust by Jean Antoine Houdon.

GIORI PRESS PRINTING
Plates of 200 subjects in four panes of 50.

1965, Aug. 19			Perf. 11	
1270	A702	5c black & blue	.20	.20
		P# block of 4	.40	—
		Margin block of 4, Mr. Zip and "Use Zip Code"	.35	—

FLORIDA SETTLEMENT ISSUE

400th anniv. of the settlement of Florida, and the 1st permanent European settlement in the continental US, St. Augustine, Fla.

Spanish Explorer, Royal Flag of Spain and Ships — A703

Designed by Brook Temple.

GIORI PRESS PRINTING
Plates of 200 subjects with four panes of 50.

1965, Aug. 28			Perf. 11	
1271	A703	5c red, yellow & black	.20	.20
		P# block of 4, 3#	.50	—
		Margin block of 4, Mr. Zip and "Use Zip Code"	.40	—
a.		Yellow omitted	250.00	

See Spain No. 1312.

TRAFFIC SAFETY ISSUE

Issued to publicize traffic safety and the prevention of traffic accidents.

Traffic Signal — A704

Designed by Richard F. Hurd.

GIORI PRESS PRINTING
Plates of 200 subjects in four panes of 50.

1965, Sept. 3   *Perf. 11*
1272 A704 5c emerald, black & red   .20   .20
              P# block of 4, 2#   .45   —
              Margin block of 4, Mr. Zip and "Use
                Zip Code"   .40   —

JOHN SINGLETON COPLEY ISSUE
Copley (1738-1815), painter. The portrait of the artist's daughter is from the oil painting "The Copley Family," which hangs in the National Gallery of Art, Washington, D.C.

Elizabeth Clarke
Copley — A705

Designed by John Carter Brown.

GIORI PRESS PRINTING
Plates of 200 subjects in four panes of 50.

1965, Sept. 17   *Perf. 11*
1273 A705 5c black, brown & olive   .20   .20
              P# block of 4   .50   —
              Margin block of 4, Mr. Zip and "Use
                Zip Code"   .40   —

INTERNATIONAL TELECOMMUNICATION UNION, 100th ANNIV.

Galt Projection
World Map
and Radio
Sine
Wave — A706

Designed by Thomas F. Naegele.

GIORI PRESS PRINTING
Plates of 200 subjects with four panes of 50.

1965, Oct. 6   *Perf. 11*
1274 A706 11c black, carmine & bister   .35   .20
              P# block of 4, 2#   1.75   —
              Margin block of 4, Mr. Zip and
                "Use Zip Code"   1.50   —

ADLAI STEVENSON ISSUE
Adlai Ewing Stevenson (1900-65), governor of Illinois, US ambassador to the UN.

Adlai E. Stevenson — A707

Designed by George Samerjan; photograph by Philippe Halsman.

LITHOGRAPHED, ENGRAVED (Giori)
Plates of 200 subjects in four panes of 50.

1965, Oct. 23   *Perf. 11*
1275 A707 5c pale blue, black, carmine & violet
                blue   .20   .20
              P# block of 4   .40   —

CHRISTMAS ISSUE

Angel with Trumpet, 1840
Weather Vane — A708

Designed by Robert Jones.

After a watercolor by Lucille Gloria Chabot of the 1840 weather vane from the People's Methodist Church, Newburyport, Mass.

GIORI PRESS PRINTING
Plates of 400 subjects in four panes of 100.

1965, Nov. 2   *Perf. 11*
1276 A708 5c carmine, dark olive green & bister
                                               .20   .20
              P# block of 4   .45   —
              Margin block of 4, Mr. Zip and "Use
                Zip Code"   .35   —
              Pair with full vert. gutter btwn. —   —
  a.   Tagged, *Nov. 15*   .75   .25
              P# block of 4   5.50   —
              Zip block of 4   3.50   —

PROMINENT AMERICANS ISSUE

Thomas   Albert
Jefferson — A710   Gallatin — A711

Frank Lloyd Wright   Francis
and Guggenheim   Parkman — A713
Museum, New
York — A712

Abraham   George
Lincoln — A714   Washington — A715

George Washington   Franklin D.
(redrawn) — A715a   Roosevelt — A716

Albert   Andrew
Einstein — A717   Jackson — A718

Henry Ford and 1909   John F.
Model T — A718a   Kennedy — A719

Oliver Wendell   George Catlett
Holmes — A720   Marshall — A721

Frederick   John Dewey — A723
Douglass — A722

Thomas   Lucy Stone — A725
Paine — A724

Eugene   John Bassett
O'Neill — A726   Moore — A727

Designers: 1c, Robert Geissmann, after portrait by Rembrandt Peale. 1¼c, Robert Gallatin. 2c, Patricia Amarantides; photograph by Blackstone-Shelburne. 3c, Bill Hyde. 4c, Bill Hyde; photograph by Mathew Brady. 5c, Bill Hyde, after portrait by Rembrandt Peale. 5c, No. 1283B, Redrawn by Stevan Dohanos. 6c, 30c, Richard L. Clark. 8c, Frank Sebastiano; photograph by Philippe Halsman. 10c, Lester Beall. 12c, Norman Todhunter. 13c, Stevan Dohanos; photograph by Jacques Lowe. 15c, Richard F. Hurd. 20c, Robert Geissmann. 25c, Walter DuBois Richards. 40c, Robert Geissmann, after portrait by John Wesley Jarvis. 50c, Mark English. $1, Norman Todhunter. $5, Tom Laufer.

ROTARY PRESS PRINTING
E.E. Plates of 400 subjects in four panes of 100

1965-78   *Perf. 11x10½, 10½x11*

Types of 15c:
I. Necktie barely touches coat at bottom; crosshatching of tie strong and complete. Flag of "5" is true horizontal. Crosshatching of "15" is colorless when visible.

II. Necktie does not touch coat at bottom; LL to UR crosshatching lines strong, UL to LR lines very faint. Flag of "5" slants down slightly at right. Crosshatching of "15" is colored and visible when magnified.

A third type, used only for No. 1288B, is smaller in overall size and "15c" is ¾-inch closer to head.

1278 A710 1c green, tagged, shiny
                gum, *Jan. 12, 1968*   .20   .20
              P# block of 4   .20   —
              Margin block of 4, "Use
                Zip Codes"   .20   —
              Dull gum (from bklt. pane)   .20
  a.   Booklet pane of 8, shiny gum, *Jan.
        12, 1968*   1.00   .75

	Dull gum	2.00		
b.	Bklt. pane of 4+2 labels, *May 10, 1971*	.80	.60	
c.	Untagged (Bureau precanceled)	6.25	1.25	
	P# block of 4	175.00		
	Margin block of 4, "Use Zip Codes"	30.00		
d.	Tagging omitted (not Bureau precanceled)	3.50	—	
e.	As "a," dull gum, tagging omitted	75.00		
1279 A711	1¼c **light green**, *Jan. 30, 1967*	.20	.20	
	P# block of 4	4.00		
1280 A712	2c **dark blue gray**, tagged, shiny gum, *June 8, 1966*	.20	.20	
	P# block of 4	.25	—	
	Margin block of 4, "Use Zip Codes"	.20	—	
	Pair with full vert. gutter between	—		
	Dull gum (from bklt. pane)	.20		
a.	Bklt. pane of 5 + label, *Jan. 8, 1968*	1.25	.80	
b.	Untagged (Bureau precanceled)	1.35	.40	
	P# block of 4	27.50		
	Margin block of 4, "Use Zip Codes"	7.50		
c.	Bklt. pane of 6, shiny gum, *May 7, 1971*	1.00	.75	
	Dull gum	1.10		
d.	Tagging omitted (not Bureau precanceled)	4.00	—	
1281 A713	3c **violet**, tagged, *Sept. 16, 1967*	.20	.20	
	P# block of 4	.25	—	
	Margin block of 4, "Use Zip Codes"	.20	—	
	Pair with full horiz. gutter between	—		
a.	Untagged (Bureau precanceled)	3.00	.75	
	P# block of 4	—		
	Margin block of 4, "Use Zip Codes"	30.00		
b.	Tagging omitted (not Bureau precanceled)	5.00	—	
1282 A714	4c **black**, *Nov. 19, 1965*	.20	.20	
	P# block of 4	.40	—	
a.	Tagged, *Dec. 1, 1965*	.20	.20	
	P# block of 4	.55	—	
	Pair with full horiz. gutter between	700.00		
1283 A715	5c **blue**, *Feb. 22, 1966*	.20	.20	
	P# block of 4	.50	—	
a.	Tagged, *Feb. 23, 1966*	.20	.20	
	P# block of 4	.60	—	
	Pair with full vert. gutter between	—		
1283B A715a	5c **blue**, tagged, shiny gum, *Nov. 17, 1967*	.20	.20	
	P# block of 4	.50	—	
	Pair with full horiz. gutter between	175.00		
	Dull gum	.20		
	P# block of 4	1.40		
d.	Untagged (Bureau precanceled)	12.50	1.00	
	P# block of 4	—		
e.	Tagging omitted (not Bureau precanceled), shiny gum	4.00		
	Dull gum	5.50		

No. 1283B is redrawn; highlights, shadows softened.

1284 A716	6c **gray brown**, *Jan. 29, 1966*	.20	.20	
	P# block of 4	.60	—	
	Margin block of 4, "Use Zip Codes" (Bureau precanceled)	3.00		
	Pair with full horiz. gutter between	150.00		
	Pair with full vert. gutter between	150.00		
a.	Tagged, *Dec. 29, 1966*	.20	.20	
	P# block of 4	.80	—	
	Margin block of 4, "Use Zip Codes"	.65	—	
b.	Booklet pane of 8, *Dec. 28, 1967*	1.50	1.00	
c.	Bklt. pane of 5+ label, *Jan. 9, 1968*	1.50	1.00	
d.	Horiz. pair, imperf. between	2,400.		
e.	As "b," tagging omitted	50.00		

For untagged sheet stamps, "Use Zip Codes" and "Mail Early in the Day" marginal markings are found only on panes with Bureau precancels.

1285 A717	8c **violet**, *Mar. 14, 1966*	.20	.20	
	P# block of 4	.85	—	
a.	Tagged, *July 6, 1966*	.20	.20	
	P# block of 4	.95	—	
	Margin block of 4, "Use Zip Codes"	.85	—	
1286 A718	10c **lilac**, tagged, *Mar. 15, 1967*	.20	.20	
	P# block of 4	1.25	—	
	Margin block of 4, "Use Zip Codes"	.85	—	
b.	Untagged (Bureau precanceled)	57.50	1.75	
	Margin block of 4, "Use Zip Codes"	275.00		
e.	Tagging omitted (not Bureau precanceled)	10.00		
1286A 718a	12c **black**, tagged, *July 30, 1968*	.25	.20	
	P# block of 4	1.30		
	Margin block of 4, "Use Zip Codes"	1.00	—	
c.	Untagged (Bureau precanceled)	4.75	1.00	

	P# block of 4	145.00		
	Margin block of 4, "Use Zip Codes"	27.50		
d.	Tagging omitted (not Bureau precanceled)	35.00		
1287 A719	13c **brown**, tagged, *May 29, 1967*	.30	.20	
	P# block of 4	1.50	—	
	Pair with full horiz. gutter between	—		
a.	Untagged (Bureau precanceled)	6.00	1.00	
	P# block of 4	100.00		
b.	Tagging omitted (not Bureau precanceled)	15.00		
1288 A720	15c **magenta**, type I, tagged, *Mar. 8, 1968*	.30	.20	
	P# block of 4	1.25	—	
	Margin block of 4, "Use Zip Codes"	1.25	—	
	Pair with full horiz. gutter between	200.00		
	Pair with full vert. gutter between	325.00		
a.	Untagged (Bureau precanceled)	.75	.75	
	P# block of 4	29.50		
	Margin block of 4, "Use Zip Codes"	7.50	—	
d.	Type II	.55	.20	
	P# block of 4	8.00	—	
	Zip block of 4	3.50	—	
	Pair with full vert. gutter between	—		
f.	As "d," tagging omitted (not Bureau precanceled)	7.50	—	
h.	As No. 1288, tagging omitted (not Bureau precanceled)	20.00		
	Imperforates exist from printer's waste.			

Values for No. 1288a are for the bars-only precancel. Also exists with city precancels, and worth more thus.

The existence of the No. 1288d pair with vert. gutter between has been questioned by specialists. The editors would like to see evidence of its existence.

1288B A720	15c **magenta**, tagged, perf. 10 (from blkt. pane)	.35	.20	
c.	Booklet pane of 8, *June 14, 1978*	2.80	1.75	
e.	As "c," vert. imperf. between	1,750.		
g.	Tagging omitted	10.00	—	
i.	As "c," tagging omitted	85.00	50.00	

No. 1288B issued in booklets only. All stamps have one or two straight edges. Plates made from redrawn die.

1289 A721	20c **deep olive**, shiny gum, *Oct. 24, 1967*	.40	.20	
	P# block of 4	1.75	—	
	Margin block of 4, "Use Zip Codes"	1.65	—	
	Dull gum	.45		
	P# block of 4	2.10		
	Zip block of 4	1.90		
a.	Tagged, shiny gum, *Apr. 3, 1973*	.40	.20	
	P# block of 4	1.75	—	
	Zip block of 4	1.65	—	
b.	20c **black olive**, tagged, shiny gum	.50	.20	
	P# block of 4	3.50	—	
	Zip block of 4	2.25	—	
	Dull gum	.50		
	P# block of 4	3.50		
	Zip block of 4	2.25		
1290 A722	25c **rose lake**, *Feb. 14, 1967*	.55	.20	
	P# block of 4	2.25	—	
	Margin block of 4, "Use Zip Codes"	2.20	—	
a.	Tagged, shiny gum, *Apr. 3, 1973*	.45	.20	
	P# block of 4	2.00	—	
	Zip block of 4	1.90	—	
	Dull gum	.45		
	P# block of 4	2.00		
	Zip block of 4	1.90		
b.	25c **magenta**	25.00	—	
	On cover	—		
	P# block of 4	150.00		
1291 A723	30c **red lilac**, *Oct. 21, 1968*	.65	.20	
	P# block of 4	2.90	—	
	Margin block of 4, "Use Zip Codes"	2.70	—	
a.	Tagged, *Apr. 3, 1973*	.50	.20	
	P# block of 4	2.25	—	
	Zip block of 4	2.10	—	
1292 A724	40c **blue black**, *Jan. 29, 1968*	.80	.20	
	P# block of 4	3.25	—	
	Margin block of 4, "Use Zip Codes"	3.25	—	
a.	Tagged, shiny gum, *Apr. 3, 1973*	.65	.20	
	P# block of 4	2.75	—	
	Zip block of 4	2.65	—	
	Dull gum	.70		
	P# block of 4	3.00		
	Zip block of 4	2.90		
1293 A725	50c **rose magenta**, *Aug. 13, 1968*	1.00	.20	
	P# block of 4	4.25	—	
	Margin block of 4, "Use Zip Codes"	4.00	—	
	Pair with full vert. gutter btwn.	—		
a.	Tagged, *Apr. 3, 1973*	.80	.20	
	P# block of 4	3.50	—	
	Zip block of 4	3.25	—	
1294 A726	$1 **dull purple**, *Oct. 16, 1967*	2.25	.20	
	P# block of 4	10.00	—	
	Margin block of 4, "Use Zip Codes"	9.25	—	
a.	Tagged, *Apr. 3, 1973*	1.65	.20	

	P# block of 4	6.75	—	
	Zip block of 4	6.65	—	
1295 A727	$5 **gray black**, *Dec. 3, 1966*	10.00	2.25	
	P# block of 4	42.50		
a.	Tagged, *Apr. 3, 1973*	8.50	2.00	
	P# block of 4	35.00	—	
	Nos. 1278-1295 (21)	18.85	6.25	
	Nos. 1278-1288, 1289-1295, P# blocks of 4 (20)	78.65		

Bureau Precancels: 1c, 19 diff., 1 ¼c, 14 diff., 2c, 41 diff., 3c, 11 diff., 4c, 49 diff. No. 1283, 7 diff., No. 1283B, 29 diff., 6c, 35 diff., 8c, 18 diff., 10c, 12 diff., 12c, 3 diff., 13c, 3 diff., No. 1288a, 9 diff., 20c, 14 diff., 25c, 9 diff., 30c, 14 diff., 40c, 7 diff., 50c, 14 diff., $1, 8 diff.

See Luminescence note in "Information for Collectors" at front of book.

COIL STAMPS

1967-75		**Tagged**	*Perf. 10 Horizontally*	
1297 A713	3c **violet**, shiny gum, *Nov. 4, 1975*	.20	.20	
	Pair	.20	.20	
	Joint line pair	.45	.20	
	Dull gum	.75		
	Joint line pair	3.00		
a.	Imperf., pair, shiny gum	22.50		
	Imperf., joint line pair	45.00		
	Imperf, pair, dull gum	22.50		
	Imperf, joint line pair	45.00		
b.	Untagged (Bureau precanceled), shiny gum	.40	.25	
	Pair	.80	.50	
	Joint line pair	62.50	3.75	
	Dull gum	.25		
	Pair	.50		
	Joint line pair	3.75		
c.	As "b," imperf. pair	6.00	—	
	Joint line pair	22.50		

No. 1297c is precanceled "Nonprofit Org. / CAR RT SORT."

1298 A716	6c **gray brown**, *Dec. 28, 1967*	.20	.20	
	Pair	.30	.20	
	Joint line pair	1.10	.25	
a.	Imperf., pair	1,750.		
	Imperf., joint line pair	4,500.		
b.	Tagging omitted	3.50		

Bureau Precancels: 3c, 9 diff.

Franklin D. Roosevelt — A727a

Revised design by Robert J. Jones and Howard C. Mildner.

COIL STAMPS

1966-81		**Tagged**	*Perf. 10 Vertically*	
1299 A710	1c **green**, *Jan. 12, 1968*	.20	.20	
	Pair	.20	.20	
	Joint line pair	.25	.20	
a.	Untagged (Bureau precanceled)	8.00	1.75	
	Pair	17.50	4.00	
	Joint line pair	295.00		
b.	Imperf., pair	22.50	—	
	Imperf., joint line pair	50.00		
1303 A714	4c **black**, *May 28, 1966*	.20	.20	
	Pair	.30	.20	
	Joint line pair	.75	.20	
a.	Untagged (Bureau precanceled)	8.75	.75	
	Pair	19.00	1.75	
	Joint line pair	250.00		
b.	Imperf., pair	700.00		
	Imperf., joint line pair	1,650.		
c.	Tagging omitted (not Bureau precanceled)	15.00		
1304 A715	5c **blue**, shiny gum, *Sept. 8, 1966*	.20	.20	
	Pair	.25	.20	
	Joint line pair	.40	.20	
	Dull gum	.75		
	Joint line pair	5.00		
a.	Untagged (Bureau precanceled)	6.50	.65	
	Pair	14.00	1.40	
	Joint line pair	175.00		
b.	Imperf., pair	125.00		
	Joint line pair	250.00		
e.	As "a," imperf., pair	275.00		
	Joint line pair	800.00		
f.	Tagging omitted (not Bureau precanceled)	—		

No. 1304b is valued in the grade of fine.

No. 1304e is precanceled Mount Pleasant, Iowa. Also exists from Chicago, Illinois; value $1,500 for pair.

1304C A715a	5c **blue**, *Jan., 1981*	.20	.20	
	Pair	.30	.20	
	Joint line pair	1.25		
f.	Imperf., pair	475.00		
	Joint line pair	850.00		
1305 A727a	6c **gray brown**, *Feb. 28, 1968*	.20	.20	
	Pair	.30	.20	
	Joint line pair	.55	.20	
a.	Imperf., pair	60.00		

	Joint line pair	115.00	
b.	Untagged (Bureau precanceled)	20.00	1.00
	Pair	42.50	2.25
	Joint line pair	675.00	
k.	Tagging omitted (not Bureau pre-canceled)	3.50	—
1305E A720	15c **magenta,** type I, shiny gum, *June 14, 1978*	.25	.20
	Pair	.50	.20
	Joint line pair	1.10	.30
	Dull gum	.75	
	Joint line pair	4.25	
f.	Untagged (Bureau precanceled, Chicago, IL)	32.50	—
	Pair	75.00	—
	Joint line pair	1,250.	—
g.	Imperf., pair, shiny gum	20.00	
	Joint line pair	50.00	
	Imperf., pair, dull gum	25.00	
	Joint line pair	60.00	
h.	Pair, imperf. between	150.00	
	Joint line pair	450.00	
i	Type II, dull gum	1.50	.20
	Joint line pair	5.00	
j.	Type II, dull gum, Imperf., pair	65.00	
	Joint line pair	125.00	
l	Tagging omitted		—
1305C A726	$1 **dull purple,** shiny gum, *Jan. 12, 1973*	2.75	.40
	Pair	5.50	.80
	Joint line pair	9.00	1.50
	Dull gum	4.00	
	Joint line pair	14.00	
d.	Imperf., pair	1,750.	
	Joint line pair	3,000.	
	Nos. 1297-1305C (9)	4.40	2.00

Bureau Precancels: 1c, 5 diff., 4c, 35 diff., No. 1304a, 45 diff., 6c, 30 diff.

MIGRATORY BIRD TREATY ISSUE

Migratory Birds over Canada-US Border A728

Designed by Burt E. Pringle.

GIORI PRESS PRINTING
Plates of 200 subjects in four panes of 50.

1966, Mar. 16			*Perf. 11*	
1306 A728	5c	**black, crimson & dark blue**	.20	.20
		P# block of 4, 2#	.40	—
		Margin block of 4, Mr. Zip and "Use Zip Code"	.35	—

HUMANE TREATMENT OF ANIMALS ISSUE
Issued to promote humane treatment of all animals and for the centenary of the American Society for the Prevention of Cruelty to Animals.

Mongrel A729

Designed by Norman Todhunter.

LITHOGRAPHED, ENGRAVED (Giori)
Plates of 200 subjects in four panes of 50.

1966, Apr. 9			*Perf. 11*	
1307 A729	5c	**orange brown & black**	.20	.20
		P# block of 4	.50	—
		Margin block of 4, Mr. Zip and "Use Zip Code"	.35	—

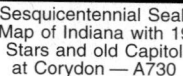

Sesquicentennial Seal; Map of Indiana with 19 Stars and old Capitol at Corydon — A730

Clown — A731

INDIANA STATEHOOD, 150th ANNIV.
Designed by Paul A. Wehr.

GIORI PRESS PRINTING
Plates of 200 subjects in four panes of 50.

1966, Apr. 16			*Perf. 11*	
1308 A730	5c	**ocher, brown & violet blue**	.20	.20
		P# block of 4, 2#	.50	—
		Margin block of 4, Mr. Zip and "Use Zip Code"	.40	—

AMERICAN CIRCUS ISSUE
Issued to honor the American Circus on the centenary of the birth of John Ringling.

Designed by Edward Klauck.

GIORI PRESS PRINTING
Plates of 200 subjects in four panes of 50.

1966, May 2			*Perf. 11*	
1309 A731	5c	**multicolored**	.20	.20
		P# block of 4, 2#	.50	—
		Margin block of 4, Mr. Zip and "Use Zip Code"	.40	—

SIXTH INTERNATIONAL PHILATELIC EXHIBITION ISSUES
Sixth International Philatelic Exhibition (SIPEX), Washington, D.C., May 21-30.

Stamped Cover — A732

Designed by Thomas F. Naegele.

LITHOGRAPHED, ENGRAVED (Giori)
Plates of 200 subjects in four panes of 50.

1966			*Perf. 11*	
1310 A732	5c	**multicolored,** *May 21*	.20	.20
		P# block of 4	.40	—
		Margin block of 4, Mr. Zip and "Use Zip Code"	.35	—

A733

Illustration reduced.

Designed by Brook Temple.

SOUVENIR SHEET
Plates of 24 subjects
Imperf

1311 A733	5c	**multicolored,** *May 23*	.20	.20

No. 1311 measures 108x74mm. Below the stamp appears a line drawing of the Capitol and Washington Monument. Marginal inscriptions and drawing are green.

"Freedom" Checking "Tyranny" — A734

Polish Eagle and Cross — A735

BILL OF RIGHTS, 175th ANNIV.
Designed by Herbert L. Block (Herblock).

GIORI PRESS PRINTING
Plates of 200 subjects in four panes of 50.

1966, July 1			*Perf. 11*	
1312 A734	5c	**carmine, dark & light blue**	.20	.20
		P# block of 4, 2#	.65	—
		Margin block of 4, Mr. Zip and "Use Zip Code"	.40	—

POLISH MILLENNIUM ISSUE
Adoption of Christianity in Poland, 1000th anniv.

Designed by Edmund D. Lewandowski.

ROTARY PRESS PRINTING
E.E. Plates of 200 subjects in four panes of 50.

1966, July 30			*Perf. 10½x11*	
1313 A735	5c	**red**	.20	.20
		P# block of 4	.45	—
		Margin block of 4, Mr. Zip and "Use Zip Code"	.40	—

NATIONAL PARK SERVICE ISSUE
50th anniv. of the Natl. Park Service of the Interior Dept. The design "Parkscape U.S.A." identifies Natl. Park Service facilities.

National Park Service Emblem A736

Designed by Thomas H. Geismar.

LITHOGRAPHED, ENGRAVED (Giori)
Plates of 200 subjects in four panes of 50.

1966, Aug. 25			*Perf. 11*	
1314 A736	5c	**yellow, black & green**	.20	.20
		P# block of 4	.60	—
		Margin block of 4, Mr. Zip and "Use Zip Code"	.40	—
a.		Tagged, *Aug. 26*	.35	.35
		P# block of 4	2.25	—
		Zip block of 4	1.50	—

MARINE CORPS RESERVE ISSUE
US Marine Corps Reserve founding, 50th anniv.

Combat Marine, 1966; Frogman; World War II Flier; World War I "Devil Dog" and Marine, 1775 — A737

Designed by Stella Grafakos.

LITHOGRAPHED, ENGRAVED (Giori)
Plates of 200 subjects in four panes of 50.

1966, Aug. 29			***Perf. 11***	
1315	A737 5c	**black, bister, red & ultra.**	.20	.20
		P# block of 4	.50	
		Margin block of 4, Mr. Zip and		
		"Use Zip Code"	.40	—
a.		Tagged	.40	.20
		P# block of 4	2.25	—
		Zip block of 4	1.70	—
b.		Black & bister (engraved) missing (EP)	16,000.	

GENERAL FEDERATION OF WOMEN'S CLUBS ISSUE

75 years of service by the General Federation of Women's Clubs.

Women of 1890 and 1966 — A738

Designed by Charles Henry Carter.

GIORI PRESS PRINTING
Plates of 200 subjects in four panes of 50.

1966, Sept. 12			***Perf. 11***	
1316	A738 5c	**black, pink & blue**	.20	.20
		P# block of 4, 2#	.45	
		Margin block of 4, Mr. Zip and "Use		
		Zip Code"	.40	—
a.		Tagged, *Sept. 13*	.40	.20
		P# block of 4, 2#	2.25	—
		Zip block of 4	1.70	—

AMERICAN FOLKLORE ISSUE
Johnny Appleseed

Issued to honor Johnny Appleseed (John Chapman 1774-1845), who wandered over 100,000 square miles planting apple trees, and who gave away and sold seedlings to Midwest pioneers.

Johnny Appleseed — A739

Designed by Robert Bode.

GIORI PRESS PRINTING
Plates of 200 subjects in four panes of 50.

1966, Sept. 24			***Perf. 11***	
1317	A739 5c	**green, red & black**	.20	.20
		P# block of 4, 2#	.45	—
		Margin block of 4, Mr. Zip and "Use		
		Zip Code"	.40	—
a.		Tagged, *Sept. 26*	.40	.20
		P# block of 4, 2#	2.25	—
		Zip block of 4	1.70	—

BEAUTIFICATION OF AMERICA ISSUE

Issued to publicize President Johnson's "Plant for a more beautiful America" campaign.

Jefferson Memorial, Tidal Basin and Cherry Blossoms A740

Designed by Miss Gyo Fujikawa.

GIORI PRESS PRINTING
Plates of 200 subjects in four panes of 50.

1966, Oct. 5			***Perf. 11***	
1318	A740 5c	**emerald, pink & black**	.20	.20
		P# block of 4, 2#	.50	
		Margin block of 4, Mr. Zip and "Use		
		Zip Code"	.40	—
a.		Tagged	.40	.20
		P# block of 4, 2#	2.25	—
		Zip block of 4	1.70	—

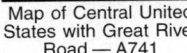

Map of Central United States with Great River Road — A741

Statue of Liberty and "Old Glory" — A742

GREAT RIVER ROAD ISSUE

Issued to publicize the 5,600-mile Great River Road connecting New Orleans with Kenora, Ontario, and following the Mississippi most of the way.

Designed by Herbert Bayer.

LITHOGRAPHED, ENGRAVED (Giori)
Plates of 200 subjects in four panes of 50.

1966, Oct. 21			***Perf. 11***	
1319	A741 5c	**vermilion, yellow, blue & green**	.20	.20
		P# block of 4	.60	—
		Margin block of 4, Mr. Zip and "Use		
		Zip Code"	.40	—
a.		Tagged, *Oct. 22*	.40	.20
		P# block of 4	2.50	—
		Zip block of 4	1.70	—

SAVINGS BOND-SERVICEMEN ISSUE

25th anniv. of US Savings Bonds, and honoring American servicemen.

Designed by Stevan Dohanos, photo by Bob Noble.

LITHOGRAPHED, ENGRAVED (Giori)
Plates of 200 subjects in four panes of 50.

1966, Oct. 26			***Perf. 11***	
1320	A742 5c	**red, dark blue, light blue & black**	.20	.20
		P# block of 4	.45	
		Margin block of 4, Mr. Zip and "Use Zip Code"	.40	—
a.		Tagged, *Oct. 27*	.40	.20
		P# block of 4	2.00	—
		Zip block of 4	1.70	—
b.		Red, dark blue & black missing (EP)	4,500.	
c.		Dark blue (engr.) missing (EP)	5,500.	

CHRISTMAS ISSUE

Madonna and Child, by Hans Memling — A743

Designed by Howard C. Mildner.

Modeled after "Madonna and Child with Angels," by the Flemish artist Hans Memling (c.1430-1494), Mellon Collection, National Gallery of Art, Washington, D.C.

LITHOGRAPHED, ENGRAVED (Giori)
Plates of 400 subjects in four panes of 100.

1966, Nov. 1			***Perf. 11***	
1321	A743 5c	**multicolored**	.20	.20
		P# block of 4	.40	—
		Margin block of 4, Mr. Zip and "Use		
		Zip Code"	.35	—
a.		Tagged, *Nov. 2*	.40	.20
		P# block of 4	2.00	—
		Zip block of 4	1.70	—

MARY CASSATT ISSUE

Cassatt (1844-1926), painter. The painting "The Boating Party" is in the Natl. Gallery of Art, Washington, D.C.

"The Boating Party" — A744

Designed by Robert J. Jones.

GIORI PRESS PRINTING
Plates of 200 subjects in four panes of 50.

1966, Nov. 17			***Perf. 11***	
1322	A744 5c	**multicolored**	.20	.20
		P# block of 4, 2#	.60	—
		Margin block of 4, Mr. Zip and "Use		
		Zip Code"	.50	—
a.		Tagged	.40	.25
		P# block of 4, 2#	2.00	—
		Zip block of 4	1.70	—

NATIONAL GRANGE ISSUE

Centenary of the founding of the National Grange, American farmers' organization.

Grange Poster, 1870 — A745

Designed by Lee Pavao.

GIORI PRESS PRINTING
Plates of 200 subjects in four panes of 50.

1967, Apr. 17		**Tagged**		***Perf. 11***	
1323	A745 5c	**orange, yellow, brown, green & black**		.20	.20
		P# block of 4, 2#		.40	
		Margin block of 4, Mr. Zip and "Use			
		Zip Code"		.35	—
a.		Tagging omitted		6.00	

CANADA CENTENARY ISSUE

Centenary of Canada's emergence as a nation.

Canadian Landscape A746

Designed by Ivan Chermayeff.

GIORI PRESS PRINTING
Plates of 200 subjects in four panes of 50.

1967, May 25		**Tagged**		***Perf. 11***	
1324	A746 5c	**lt. blue, dp. green, ultra., olive & black**		.20	.20
		On cover, Expo. station ("U.S. Pavilion") machine canc.		1.00	
		On cover, Expo. station handstamp canc.		2.50	
		P# block of 4, 2#		.40	
		Margin block of 4, Mr. Zip and "Use			
		Zip Code"		.35	—
a.		Tagging omitted		7.50	—

ERIE CANAL ISSUE

150th anniversary of the Erie Canal ground-breaking ceremony at Rome, N.Y. The canal links Lake Erie and New York City.

Stern of Early Canal Boat — A747

Designed by George Samerjan.

LITHOGRAPHED, ENGRAVED (Giori)
Plates of 200 subjects in four panes of 50.

1967, July 4	Tagged	Perf. 11	
1325 A747 5c ultra., greenish blue, black & crimson		.20	.20
P# block of 4		.40	
Margin block of 4, Mr. Zip and "Use Zip Code"		.35	—
a. Tagging omitted		22.50	—

"SEARCH FOR PEACE" — LIONS ISSUE

Issued to publicize the search for peace. "Search for Peace" was the theme of an essay contest for young men and women sponsored by Lions International on its 50th anniversary.

Peace Dove — A748

Designed by Bradbury Thompson.

GIORI PRESS PRINTING
Plates of 200 subjects in four panes of 50.

1967, July 5	Tagged	Perf. 11	
	Gray Paper with Blue Threads		
1326 A748 5c blue, red & black		.20	.20
P# block of 4		.40	
Margin block of 4, Mr. Zip and "Use Zip Code"		.35	—
a. Tagging omitted		7.50	—

HENRY DAVID THOREAU ISSUE

Henry David Thoreau (1817-62), Writer — A749

Designed by Leonard Baskin.

GIORI PRESS PRINTING
Plates of 200 subjects in four panes of 50.

1967, July 12	Tagged	Perf. 11	
1327 A749 5c carmine, black & blue green		.20	.20
P# block of 4		.50	—
Margin block of 4, Mr. Zip and "Use Zip Code"		.40	—
a. Tagging omitted		200.00	—

NEBRASKA STATEHOOD, 100th ANNIV.

Hereford Steer and Ear of Corn — A750

Designed by Julian K. Billings.

LITHOGRAPHED, ENGRAVED (Giori)
Plates of 200 subjects in four panes of 50.

1967, July 29	Tagged	Perf. 11	
1328 A750 5c dark red brown, lemon & yellow		.20	.20
P# block of 4		.70	
Margin block of 4, Mr. Zip and "Use Zip Code"		.40	—
a. Tagging omitted		7.50	—

VOICE OF AMERICA ISSUE

25th anniv. of the radio branch of the United States Information Agency (USIA).

Radio Transmission Tower and Waves — A751

Designed by Georg Olden.

LITHOGRAPHED, ENGRAVED (Giori)
Plates of 200 subjects in four panes of 50.

1967, Aug. 1	Tagged	Perf. 11	
1329 A751 5c red, blue, black & carmine		.20	.20
P# block of 4		.40	
Margin block of 4, Mr. Zip and "Use Zip Code"		.35	—
a. Tagging omitted		20.00	—

AMERICAN FOLKLORE ISSUE

Davy Crockett (1786-1836), frontiersman, hunter, and congressman from Tennessee who died at the Alamo.

Davy Crockett and Scrub Pine — A752

Designed by Robert Bode.

LITHOGRAPHED, ENGRAVED (Giori)
Plates of 200 subjects in four panes of 50.

1967, Aug. 17	Tagged	Perf. 11	
1330 A752 5c green, black, & yellow		.20	.20
P# block of 4		.60	
Margin block of 4, Mr. Zip and "Use Zip Code"		.40	—
a. Vertical pair, imperf. between		7,000.	
b. Green (engr.) missing (FO)		—	
c. Black & green (engr.) missing (FO)		—	
e. Tagging omitted		9.00	—

A foldover on a pane of No. 1330 resulted in one example each of Nos. 1330b-1330c. Part of the colors appear on the back of the selvage and one freak stamp. An engraved black-and-green-only impression appears on the gummed side of one almost-complete "stamp."

ACCOMPLISHMENTS IN SPACE ISSUE

US accomplishments in space. Printed with continuous design in horizontal rows of 5. In the left panes the astronaut stamp is 1st, 3rd and 5th, the spaceship 2nd and 4th. This arrangement is reversed in the right panes.

Space-Walking Astronaut A753

Gemini 4 Capsule A754

Designed by Paul Calle.

LITHOGRAPHED, ENGRAVED (Giori)
Plates of 200 subjects in four panes of 50.

1967, Sept. 29	Tagged	Perf. 11	
1331 A753 5c multicolored		.50	.20
a. Tagging omitted		25.00	
1332 A754 5c multicolored		.50	.20
P# block of 4		2.25	
Margin block of 4, Mr. Zip and "Use Zip Code"		2.10	
Plate flaw (red stripes of flag on capsule omitted; 29322, 29325 UL 19)		210.00	
a. Tagging omitted		25.00	
b. Pair, #1331-1332		1.10	1.25
c. As "b," tagging omitted		60.00	—

View of Model City — A755

Finnish Coat of Arms — A756

URBAN PLANNING ISSUE

Publicizing the importance of Urban Planning in connection with the Intl. Conf. of the American Institute of Planners, Washington, D.C., Oct. 1-6.

Designed by Francis Ferguson.

LITHOGRAPHED, ENGRAVED (Giori)
Plates of 200 subjects in four panes of 50.

1967, Oct. 2	Tagged	Perf. 11	
1333 A755 5c dark blue, light blue & black		.20	.20
P# block of 4		.50	
Margin block of 4, Mr. Zip and "Use Zip Code"		.40	—
a. Tagging omitted		50.00	

FINNISH INDEPENDENCE, 50th ANNIV.

Designed by Bradbury Thompson.

ENGRAVED (Giori)
Plates of 200 subjects in four panes of 50.

1967, Oct. 6	Tagged	Perf. 11	
1334 A756 5c blue		.20	.20
P# block of 4		.50	
Margin block of 4, Mr. Zip and "Use Zip Code"		.40	—
a. Tagging omitted		100.00	

THOMAS EAKINS ISSUE

Eakins (1844-1916), painter and sculptor. The painting is in the Natl. Gallery of Art, Washington, D.C.

"The Biglin Brothers Racing" (Sculling on Schuylkill River, Philadelphia) A757

Printed by Photogravure & Color Co., Moonachie, N.J.

PHOTOGRAVURE
Plates of 200 subjects in four panes of 50.

1967, Nov. 2	Tagged	Perf. 12	
1335 A757 5c gold & multicolored		.20	.20
P# block of 4, 6#		.50	
a. Tagging omitted		40.00	—

Plate number blocks from upper left or lower left panes show clipped corner of margin.

CHRISTMAS ISSUE

Madonna and Child, by
Hans Memling — A758

LITHOGRAPHED, ENGRAVED (Giori)
Plates of 200 subjects in four panes of 50.

1967, Nov. 6		Tagged	Perf. 11	
1336	A758	5c **multicolored**	.20	.20
		P# block of 4	.40	—
		Margin block of 4, Mr. Zip and "Use Zip Code"	.35	—
a.		Tagging omitted	5.50	—

See note on painting above No. 1321.

MISSISSIPPI STATEHOOD, 150th ANNIV.

Magnolia
A759

Designed by Andrew Bucci.

GIORI PRESS PRINTING
Plates of 200 subjects in four panes of 50.

1967, Dec. 11		Tagged	Perf. 11	
1337	A759	5c **brt. greenish blue, green & red brown**	.20	.20
		P# block of 4, 2#	.75	—
		Margin block of 4, Mr. Zip and "Use Zip Code"	.40	—
a.		Tagging omitted	10.00	—

FLAG ISSUE

Flag and White House — A760

Designed by Stevan Dohanos.

GIORI PRESS PRINTING
Plates of 400 subjects in four panes of 100.

1968, Jan. 24		Tagged	Perf. 11	
		Size: 19x22mm		
1338	A760	6c **dark blue, red & green**	.20	.20
		P# block of 4	.45	—
		Margin block of 4, "Use Zip Code"	.40	—
		Pair with full vert. gutter btwn.	—	—
k.		Vert. pair, imperf. btwn.	325.00	175.00
m.		Tagging omitted	4.50	—
s.		Red missing (FO)	—	—
u.		Vert. pair, imperf horiz.	475.00	—

Beware of regumming on No. 1338u. Most examples have had the gum washed off to make it difficult or impossible to detect blind perfs. Check carefully for blind perfs. Value is for pair with original gum.
No. 1338s is unique.

COIL STAMP
MULTICOLOR HUCK PRESS

1969, May 30		Tagged	Perf. 10 Vertically	
		Size: 18¼x21mm		
1338A	A760	6c **dark blue, red & green**	.20	.20
		Pair	.30	.20
b.		Imperf., pair	400.00	—
q.		Tagging omitted	10.00	—

MULTICOLOR HUCK PRESS
Panes of 100 (10x10) each

1970-71		Tagged	Perf. 11x10½	
		Size: 18¼x21mm		
1338D	A760	6c **dark blue, red & green,** Aug. 7, 1970	.20	.20
		Margin block of 20+	2.60	—
e.		Horiz. pair, imperf. between	125.00	—
n.		Tagging omitted	4.00	—
1338F	A760	8c **dark blue, red & slate green,** May 10, 1971	.20	.20
		Margin block of 20+	3.00	—
i.		Imperf., vert. pair	35.00	—
j.		Horiz. pair, imperf. between	45.00	—
o.		Tagging omitted	4.00	—
p.		Slate green omitted	325.00	—
t.		Horiz. pair, imperf. vertically	—	—

+ Margin blocks of 20 come in four versions: (1) 2 P#, 3 ME, 3 zip; (2) 3 P#, 2 ME, 2 zip; (3) 2 P#, 3 ME, 2 zip; (4) 3 P#, 2 ME, 3 zip.

COIL STAMP
MULTICOLOR HUCK PRESS

1971, May 10		Tagged	Perf. 10 Vertically	
		Size: 18¼x21mm		
1338G	A760	8c **dk blue, red & slate green**	.30	.20
		Pair	.60	.20
h.		Imperf., pair	45.00	—
r.		Tagging omitted	5.00	—

Farm Buildings and
Fields of Ripening
Grain — A761

Map of North and
South America and
Lines Converging on
San Antonio — A762

ILLINOIS STATEHOOD, 150th ANNIV.

Designed by George Barford.

LITHOGRAPHED, ENGRAVED (Giori)
Plates of 200 subjects in four panes of 50.

1968, Feb. 12		Tagged	Perf. 11	
1339	A761	6c **dk blue, blue, red & ocher**	.20	.20
		P# block of 4	.60	—
		Margin block of 4, Mr. Zip and "Use Zip Code"	.45	—
a.		Tagging omitted	—	—

HEMISFAIR '68 ISSUE

HemisFair '68 exhibition, San Antonio, Texas, Apr. 6-Oct. 6, for the 250th anniv. of San Antonio.

Designed by Louis Macouillard.

LITHOGRAPHED, ENGRAVED (Giori)
Plates of 200 subjects in four panes of 50.

1968, Mar. 30		Tagged	Perf. 11	
1340	A762	6c **blue, rose red & white**	.20	.20
		On cover, Expo. station machine canc.	10.00	
		On cover, Expo. roller canc.	25.00	
		P# block of 4	.50	—
		Margin block of 4, Mr. Zip and "Use Zip Code"	.45	—
a.		White omitted	925.00	—

AIRLIFT ISSUE

Issued to pay for airlift of parcels from and to US ports to servicemen overseas and in Alaska, Hawaii and Puerto Rico. Valid for all regular postage. On Apr. 26, 1969, the Post Office Department ruled that henceforth No. 1341 "may be used toward paying the postage or fees for special services on *airmail* articles."

Eagle Holding
Pennant
A763

Designed by Stevan Dohanos.

After a late 19th century wood carving, part of the Index of American Design, National Gallery of Art.

LITHOGRAPHED, ENGRAVED (Giori)
Plates of 200 subjects in four panes of 50.

1968, Apr. 4		Untagged	Perf. 11	
1341	A763	$1 **sepia, dk. blue, ocher & brown red**	2.00	1.25
		P# block of 4	8.50	—
		Margin block of 4, Mr. Zip and "Use Zip Code"	8.25	—
		Pair with full horiz. gutter btwn.	—	—

"SUPPORT OUR YOUTH" — ELKS ISSUE

Support Our Youth program, and honoring the Benevolent and Protective Order of Elks, which extended its youth service program in observance of its centennial year.

Girls and
Boys — A764

Designed by Edward Vebell.

LITHOGRAPHED, ENGRAVED (Giori)
Plates of 200 subjects in four panes of 50.

1968, May 1		Tagged	Perf. 11	
1342	A764	6c **ultramarine & orange red**	.20	.20
		P# block of 4	.55	—
		Margin block of 4, Mr. Zip and "Use Zip Code"	.45	—
a.		Tagging omitted	9.50	—

Policeman and
Boy — A765

Eagle Weather
Vane — A766

LAW AND ORDER ISSUE

Publicizing the policeman as protector and friend and to encourage respect for law and order.

Designed by Ward Brackett.

GIORI PRESS PRINTING
Plates of 200 subjects in four panes of 50 each

1968, May 17		Tagged	Perf. 11	
1343	A765	6c **chalky blue, black & red**	.20	.20
		P# block of 4	.55	—
		Margin block of 4, Mr. Zip and "Use Zip Code"	.45	—
a.		Tagging omitted	175.00	90.00

REGISTER AND VOTE ISSUE

Campaign to draw more voters to the polls. The weather vane is from an old house in the Russian Hill section of San Francisco, Cal.

Designed by Norman Todhunter and Bill Hyde; photograph by M. Halberstadt.

LITHOGRAPHED, ENGRAVED (Giori)
Plates of 200 subjects in four panes of 50.

1968, June 27		Tagged	Perf. 11	
1344	A766	6c **black, yellow & orange**	.20	.20
		P# block of 4	.50	—
		Margin block of 4, Mr. Zip and "Use Zip Code"	.45	—
a.		Tagging omitted	—	—

HISTORIC FLAG SERIES

Flags carried by American colonists and by citizens of the new United States. Printed se-tenant in vertical columns of 10. The flag sequence on the 2 upper panes is as listed. On the 2 lower panes the sequence is reversed with the Navy Jack in the 1st row and the Fort Moultrie flag in the 10th.

Ft. Moultrie,
1776 — A767

Ft. McHenry,
1795-1818
A768

Washington's
Cruisers,
1775 — A769

Bennington,
1777 — A770

Rhode Island,
1775 — A771

First Stars and
Stripes,
1777 — A772

Bunker Hill,
1775 — A773

Grand Union,
1776 — A774

Philadelphia
Light Horse,
1775 — A775

First Navy
Jack,
1775 — A776

ENGR. (Giori) (#1345-1348, 1350);
ENGR. & LITHO. (#1349, 1351-1354)
Plates of 200 subjects in four panes of 50.

				1968, July 4	**Tagged**		**Perf. 11**
1345	A767	6c	dark blue		.40		.25
1346	A768	6c	dark blue & red		.40		.25
1347	A769	6c	dark blue & olive green		.30		.25
1348	A770	6c	dark blue & red		.30		.25
1349	A771	6c	dark blue, yellow & red		.30		.25
1350	A772	6c	dark blue & red		.30		.25
1351	A773	6c	dark blue, olive green & red		.30		.25
1352	A774	6c	dark blue, yellow & red		.30		.25
1353	A775	6c	dark blue, yellow & red		.30		.25
1354	A776	6c	dark blue, red & yellow		.30		.25
a.			Strip of ten, #1345-1354		3.25		*3.25*
			P# block of 20, inscriptions, #1345-1354		6.75		—
b.			#1345b-1354b, any single, tagging omitted		—		
c.			As "a," imperf		*4,500.*		

WALT DISNEY ISSUE

Walt Disney (1901-1966), cartoonist, film producer
and creator of Mickey Mouse.

Walt Disney and Children of
the World — A777

Designed by C. Robert Moore.

Designed after portrait by Paul E. Wenzel.
Printed by Achrovure Division of Union-Camp Corp., Englewood, N.J.

PHOTOGRAVURE
Plates of 400 subjects in eight panes of 50.

			1968, Sept. 11	**Tagged**		**Perf. 12**
1355	A777	6c	multicolored		.40	.20
			P# block of 4, 5#		1.75	—
			P# block of 4, 5#, 5 dashes		1.75	—
			Margin block of 4, Mr. Zip and "Use Zip Code"		1.60	—
a.			Ocher omitted ("Walt Disney," "6c," etc.)		400.00	—
b.			Vert. pair, imperf. horiz.		575.00	—
c.			Imperf., pair		425.00	—
d.			Black omitted		1,850.	—
e.			Horiz. pair, imperf. between		3,500.	—
f.			Blue omitted		1,850.	—
g.			Tagging omitted		18.00	—

FATHER MARQUETTE ISSUE

Father Jacques Marquette (1637-1675), French Jesuit missionary, who together with Louis Jolliet explored
the Mississippi River and its tributaries.

Father
Marquette and
Louis Jolliet
Exploring the
Mississippi
A778

Designed by Stanley W. Galli.

GIORI PRESS PRINTING
Plates of 200 subjects in four panes of 50.

			1968, Sept. 20	**Tagged**		**Perf. 11**
1356	A778	6c	black, apple green & orange brown		.20	.20
			P# block of 4		.60	—
			Margin block of 4, Mr. Zip and "Use Zip Code"		.65	—
a.			Tagging omitted		6.00	—

AMERICAN FOLKLORE ISSUE

Daniel Boone (1734-1820), frontiersman and trapper.

Pennsylvania
Rifle, Powder
Horn,
Tomahawk
Pipe and
Knife — A779

Designed by Louis Macouillard.

LITHOGRAPHED, ENGRAVED (Giori)
Plates of 200 subjects in four panes of 50.

			1968, Sept. 26	**Tagged**		**Perf. 11**
1357	A779	6c	yellow, deep yellow, maroon & black		.20	.20
			P# block of 4		.50	—
			Margin block of 4, Mr. Zip and "Use Zip Code"		.45	—
a.			Tagging omitted		—	

ARKANSAS RIVER NAVIGATION ISSUE

Opening of the Arkansas River to commercial
navigation.

Ship's Wheel,
Power
Transmission
Tower and
Barge — A780

Designed by Dean Ellis.

LITHOGRAPHED, ENGRAVED (Giori)
Plates of 200 subjects in four panes of 50.

			1968, Oct. 1	**Tagged**		**Perf. 11**
1358	A780	6c	bright blue, dark blue & black		.20	.20
			P# block of 4		.50	—
			Margin block of 4, Mr. Zip and "Use Zip Code"		.45	—
a.			Tagging omitted		—	

LEIF ERIKSON ISSUE

Leif Erikson, 11th century Norse explorer, called the
1st European to set foot on the American continent, at
a place he called Vinland. The statue by the American
sculptor A. Stirling Calder is in Reykjavik, Iceland.

Leif Erikson by A. Stirling
Calder — A781

Designed by Kurt Weiner.

LITHOGRAPHED & ENGRAVED
Plates of 200 subjects in four panes of 50.

			1968, Oct. 9	**Tagged**		**Perf. 11**
1359	A781	6c	light gray brown & black brown		.20	.20
			P# block of 4		.50	—
			Margin block of 4, Mr. Zip and "Use Zip Code"		.45	—

The luminescent element is in the light gray brown ink of the
background. The engraved parts were printed on a rotary currency press.

CHEROKEE STRIP ISSUE

75th anniversary of the opening of the Cherokee Strip to settlers, Sept. 16, 1893.

Racing for Homesteads in Cherokee Strip, 1893 — A782

Designed by Norman Todhunter.

ROTARY PRESS PRINTING
E.E. Plates of 200 subjects in four panes of 50.

1968, Oct. 15	Tagged	Perf. 11x10½	
1360 A782 6c **brown**		.20	.20
P# block of 4		1.00	—
Margin block of 4, Mr. Zip and "Use Zip Code"		.50	—
a. Tagging omitted		7.50	—

JOHN TRUMBULL ISSUE

Trumbull (1756-1843), painter. The stamp shows Lt. Thomas Grosvenor and his attendant Peter Salem. The painting hangs at Yale University.

Detail from "The Battle of Bunker's Hill" — A783

Modeled by Robert J. Jones.

LITHOGRAPHED, ENGRAVED (Giori)
Plates of 200 subjects in four panes of 50.

1968, Oct. 18	Tagged	Perf. 11	
1361 A783 6c **multicolored**		.20	.20
P# block of 4		.70	
Margin block of 4, Mr. Zip and "Use Zip Code"		.50	—
a. Tagging omitted		125.00	—
b. Black (engr.) missing (FO)		11,000.	—

WATERFOWL CONSERVATION ISSUE

Wood Ducks — A784

Designed by Stanley W. Galli.

LITHOGRAPHED, ENGRAVED (Giori)
Plates of 200 subjects in four panes of 50.

1968, Oct. 24	Tagged	Perf. 11	
1362 A784 6c **black & multicolored**		.20	.20
P# block of 4		.75	
Margin block of 4, Mr. Zip and "Use Zip Code"		.60	—
a. Vertical pair, imperf. between		275.00	—
b. Red & dark blue omitted		475.00	—
c. Red omitted		1,750.	

Dangerous fakes exist of Nos. 1362b and 1362c. Authentication by experts is required.

Angel Gabriel, from "The Annunciation" by Jan van Eyck — A785

Chief Joseph, by Cyrenius Hall — A786

CHRISTMAS ISSUE

"The Annunciation" by the 15th century Flemish painter Jan van Eyck is in the National Gallery of Art, Washington, D.C.

Designed by Robert J. Jones.

ENGRAVED (Multicolor Huck press)
Panes of 50 (10x5)

1968, Nov. 1	Tagged	Perf. 11	
1363 A785 6c **multicolored**		.20	.20
P# block of 10 +		2.00	
a. Untagged, Nov. 2		.20	.20
P# block of 10 +		2.00	
b. Imperf., pair, tagged		175.00	—
c. Light yellow omitted		50.00	—
d. Imperf., pair, untagged		250.00	—

+ P# blocks come in two versions: (1) 7 P#, 3 ME; (2) 8 P#, 2 ME.

AMERICAN INDIAN ISSUE

Honoring the American Indian and to celebrate the opening of the Natl. Portrait Gallery, Washington, D.C. Chief Joseph (Indian name, Thunder Traveling over the Mountains), a leader of the Nez Percé, was born in eastern Oregon about 1840 and died at the Colesville Reservation in Washington State in 1904.

Designed by Robert J. Jones; lettering by Crimilda Pontes.

LITHOGRAPHED, ENGRAVED (Giori)
Plates of 200 subjects in four panes of 50.

1968, Nov. 4	Tagged	Perf. 11	
1364 A786 6c **black & multicolored**		.20	.20
P# block of 4		.75	
Margin block of 4, Mr. Zip and "Use Zip Code"		.60	—
a. Tagging omitted		—	—

BEAUTIFICATION OF AMERICA ISSUE

Publicizing the Natural Beauty Campaign for more beautiful cities, parks, highways and streets. In the left panes Nos. 1365 and 1367 appear in 1st, 3rd and 5th place, Nos. 1366 and 1368 in 2nd and 4th place. This arrangement is reversed in the right panes.

Capitol, Azaleas and Tulips — A787

Washington Monument, Potomac River and Daffodils A788

Poppies and Lupines along Highway A789

Blooming Crabapples Lining Avenue A790

Designed by Walter DuBois Richards.

LITHOGRAPHED, ENGRAVED (Giori)
Plates of 200 subjects in four panes of 50.

1969, Jan. 16	Tagged	Perf. 11	
1365 A787 6c **multicolored**		.25	.20
1366 A788 6c **multicolored**		.25	.20
1367 A789 6c **multicolored**		.25	.20
1368 A790 6c **multicolored**		.25	.20
a. Block of 4, #1365-1368		1.00	1.25
P# block of 4		1.25	
Margin block of 4, Mr. Zip and "Use Zip Code"		1.10	
b. #1365b-1368b, tagging omitted, any single		—	

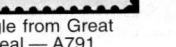

Eagle from Great Seal — A791

July Fourth, by Grandma Moses — A792

AMERICAN LEGION, 50th ANNIV.

Designed by Robert Hallock.

LITHOGRAPHED, ENGRAVED (Giori)
Plates of 200 subjects in four panes of 50.

1969, Mar. 15	Tagged	Perf. 11	
1369 A791 6c **red, blue & black**		.20	.20
P# block of 4		.45	
Margin block of 4, Mr. Zip and "Use Zip Code"		.40	—
a. Tagging omitted		—	

AMERICAN FOLKLORE ISSUE

Grandma Moses (Anna Mary Robertson Moses, 1860-1961), primitive painter of American life.

Designed by Robert J. Jones.

LITHOGRAPHED, ENGRAVED (Giori)
Plates of 200 subjects in four panes of 50.

1969, May 1	Tagged	Perf. 11	
1370 A792 6c **multicolored**		.20	.20
P# block of 4		.50	—
Margin block of 4, Mr. Zip and "Use Zip Code"		.45	—
a. Horizontal pair, imperf. between		165.00	—
b. Engraved black ("6c U.S. Postage") & Prus. blue ("Grandma Moses") omitted		575.00	—
c. Tagging omitted		7.50	—

Beware of pairs with blind perfs. being offered as No. 1370a. No. 1370b often comes with mottled or disturbed gum. Such stamps sell for about two-thirds as much as copies with perfect gum.

APOLLO 8 ISSUE

Apollo 8 mission, which 1st put men into orbit around the moon, Dec. 21-27, 1968. The astronauts were: Col. Frank Borman, Capt. James Lovell and Maj. William Anders.

Moon Surface and
Earth — A793

Designed by Leonard E. Buckley after a photograph by the Apollo 8 astronauts.

GIORI PRESS PRINTING
Plates of 200 subjects in four panes of 50.

1969, May 5		Tagged	Perf. 11	
1371	A793 6c	black, blue & ocher	.20	.20
		P# block of 4	1.00	—
		Margin block of 4, Mr. Zip and "Use Zip Code"	.60	—

Imperfs. exist from printer's waste.

W.C. HANDY ISSUE

Handy (1873-1958), jazz musician and composer.

William
Christopher
Handy — A794

Designed by Bernice Kochan.

LITHOGRAPHED, ENGRAVED (Giori)
Plates of 200 subjects in four panes of 50.

1969, May 17		Tagged	Perf. 11	
1372	A794 6c	violet, deep lilac & blue	.20	.20
		P# block of 4	.65	—
		Margin block of 4, Mr. Zip and "Use Zip Code"	.45	—
a.		Tagging omitted	9.00	—

CALIFORNIA SETTLEMENT, 200th ANNIV.

Carmel Mission
Belfry — A795

Designed by Leonard Buckley and Howard C. Mildner.

LITHOGRAPHED, ENGRAVED (Giori)
Plates of 200 subjects in four panes of 50.

1969, July 16		Tagged	Perf. 11	
1373	A795 6c	orange, red, black & light blue	.20	.20
		P# block of 4	.60	—
		Margin block of 4, Mr. Zip and "Use Zip Code"	.45	—
a.		Tagging omitted	10.00	—
b.		Red (engr.) missing (CM)	—	

JOHN WESLEY POWELL ISSUE

Powell (1834-1902), geologist who explored the Green and Colorado Rivers 1869-75, and ethnologist.

Major Powell
Exploring
Colorado River,
1869 — A796

Designed by Rudolph Wendelin.

LITHOGRAPHED, ENGRAVED (Giori)
Plates of 200 subjects in four panes of 50.

1969, Aug. 1		Tagged	Perf. 11	
1374	A796 6c	black, ocher & light blue	.20	.20
		P# block of 4	.60	—
		Margin block of 4, Mr. Zip and "Use Zip Code"	.45	—
a.		Tagging omitted	10.00	—

ALABAMA STATEHOOD, 150th ANNIV.

Camellia and
Yellow-shafted
Flicker — A797

Designed by Bernice Kochan

LITHOGRAPHED, ENGRAVED (Giori)
Plates of 200 subjects in four panes of 50.

1969, Aug. 2		Tagged	Perf. 11	
1375	A797 6c	magenta, rose red, yellow, dark green & brown	.20	.20
		P# block of 4	.75	—
		Margin block of 4, Mr. Zip and "Use Zip Code"	.45	—
a.		Tagging omitted	140.00	—

BOTANICAL CONGRESS ISSUE

11th Intl. Botanical Cong., Seattle, Wash., Aug. 24-Sept. 2. In left panes Nos. 1376 and 1378 appear in 1st, 3rd and 5th place; Nos. 1377 and 1379 in 2nd and 4th place. This arrangement is reversed in right panes.

Douglas Fir
(Northwest)
A798

Lady's-slipper
(Northeast)
A799

Ocotillo
(Southwest)
A800

Franklinia
(Southeast)
A801

Designed by Stanley Galli.

LITHOGRAPHED, ENGRAVED (Giori)
Plates of 200 subjects in four panes of 50.

1969, Aug. 23		Tagged	Perf. 11	
1376	A798 6c	multicolored	.35	.20
1377	A799 6c	multicolored	.35	.20
1378	A800 6c	multicolored	.35	.20
1379	A801 6c	multicolored	.35	.20
a.		Block of 4, #1376-1379	1.50	1.75
		P# block of 4	1.75	—
		Margin block of 4, Mr. Zip and "Use Zip Code"	1.60	—

DARTMOUTH COLLEGE CASE ISSUE

150th anniv. of the Dartmouth College Case, which Daniel Webster argued before the Supreme Court, reasserting the sanctity of contracts.

Daniel Webster and
Dartmouth Hall — A802

Designed by John R. Scotford, Jr.

ROTARY PRESS PRINTING
E.E. Plates of 200 subjects in four panes of 50.

1969, Sept. 22		Tagged	Perf. 10½x11	
1380	A802 6c	green	.20	.20
		P# block of 4	.60	—
		Margin block of 4, Mr. Zip and "Use Zip Code"	.45	—

PROFESSIONAL BASEBALL, 100th ANNIV.

Batter — A803

Designed by Alex Ross.

LITHOGRAPHED, ENGRAVED (Giori)
Plates of 200 subjects in four panes of 50.

1969, Sept. 24		Tagged	Perf. 11	
1381	A803 6c	yellow, red, black & green	.55	.20
		P# block of 4	2.50	—
		Margin block of 4, Mr. Zip and "Use Zip Code"	2.25	—
a.		Black omitted ("1869-1969, United States, 6c, Professional Baseball")	800.00	
b.		Tagging omitted	—	

INTERCOLLEGIATE FOOTBALL, 100th ANNIV.

Football Player
and
Coach — A804

Designed by Robert Peak.

LITHOGRAPHED, ENGRAVED (Giori)
Plates of 200 subjects in four panes of 50.

1969, Sept. 26		Tagged	Perf. 11	
1382	A804 6c	red & green	.20	.20
		P# block of 4	1.00	—
		Margin block of 4, Mr. Zip and "Use Zip Code"	.60	—
a.		Tagging omitted	—	
b.		Vert. pair, imperf between	—	

The engraved parts were printed on a rotary currency press.

DWIGHT D. EISENHOWER ISSUE

Dwight D. Eisenhower, 34th President (1890-1969) — A805

Designed by Robert J. Jones; photograph by Bernie Noble.

GIORI PRESS PRINTING
Plates of 128 subjects in 4 panes of 32 each.

1969, Oct. 14	Tagged	Perf. 11	
1383 A805 6c blue, black & red		.20	.20
P# block of 4		.55	—
Margin block of 4, Mr. Zip and "Use Zip Code"		.45	—
a. Tagging omitted			
b. Blue ("U.S. 6c Postage") missing (PS)			

CHRISTMAS ISSUE

The painting, painted about 1870 by an unknown primitive artist, is the property of the N.Y. State Historical Association, Cooperstown, N.Y.

Winter Sunday in Norway, Maine A806

Designed by Stevan Dohanos.

ENGRAVED (Multicolor Huck)
Panes of 50 (5x10)

1969, Nov. 3	Tagged	Perf. 11x10½	
1384 A806 6c dark green & multicolored		.20	.20
P# block of 10, 5#, 2-3 zip, 2-3 Mail Early		1.40	—
Precancel		.50	.20
b. Imperf., pair		800.00	
c. Light green omitted		25.00	
d. Light green, red & yellow omitted		700.00	
e. Yellow omitted		2,000.	
f. Tagging omitted		5.00	
g. Red & yellow omitted		2,750.	
h. Light green and yellow omitted		—	
i. Light green and red omitted		—	
j. Vert. pair, top stamp Baltimore precancel, bottom stamp precancel missing (FO)		—	
k. Baltimore precancel printed on gum side		—	

The precancel value applies to the least expensive of experimental precancels printed locally in four cities, on tagged stamps, with the names between lines 4½mm apart: in black or green, "ATLANTA, GA" and in green only "BALTIMORE, MD," "MEMPHIS, TN" and "NEW HAVEN, CT." They were sold freely to the public and could be used on any class of mail at all post offices during the experimental program and thereafter. The Baltimore precancel is known with tagging omitted; value, unused $50.

Most examples of No. 1384c show orange where the offset green was. Value is for this variety. Examples without orange sell for more.

On No. 1384i, almost all of the yellow is also omitted. Do not confuse with No. 1384d.

Cured Child — A807

HOPE FOR CRIPPLED ISSUE

Issued to encourage the rehabilitation of crippled children and adults and to honor the National Society for Crippled Children and Adults (Easter Seal Society) on its 50th anniversary.

Designed by Mark English.

LITHOGRAPHED, ENGRAVED (Giori)
Plates of 200 subjects in four panes of 50.

1969, Nov. 20	Tagged	Perf. 11	
1385 A807 6c multicolored		.20	.20
P# block of 4		.55	—
Margin block of 4, Mr. Zip and "Use Zip Code"		.45	—
a. Tagging omitted			

WILLIAM M. HARNETT ISSUE

"Old Models" — A808

Harnett (1848-1892), painter. The painting hangs in the Museum of Fine Arts, Boston.

Designed by Robert J. Jones.

LITHOGRAPHED, ENGRAVED (Giori)
Plates of 128 subjects in 4 panes of 32 each.

1969, Dec. 3	Tagged	Perf. 11	
1386 A808 6c multicolored		.20	.20
P# block of 4		.55	—
Margin block of 4, Mr. Zip and "Use Zip Code"		.45	—

NATURAL HISTORY ISSUE

Centenary of the American Museum of Natural History, New York City. Nos. 1387-1388 alternate in 1st row, Nos. 1389-1390 in 2nd row. This arrangement is repeated throughout the pane.

American Bald Eagle — A809

African Elephant Herd — A810

Tlingit Chief in Haida Ceremonial Canoe — A811

Brontosaurus, Stegosaurus and Allosaurus from Jurassic Period — A812

Designers: No. 1387, Walter Richards; No. 1388, Dean Ellis; No. 1389, Paul Rabut; No. 1390, detail from mural by Rudolph Zallinger in Yal Peabody Museum, adapted by Robert J. Jones.

LITHOGRAPHED, ENGRAVED (Giori)
Plates of 128 subjects in 4 panes of 32 each (4x8).

1970, May 6	Tagged	Perf. 11	
1387 A809 6c multicolored		.20	.20
1388 A810 6c multicolored		.20	.20
1389 A811 6c multicolored		.20	.20
1390 A812 6c multicolored		.20	.20
a. Block of 4, #1387-1390		.55	.60
P# block of 4		.70	—
Margin block of 4, Mr. Zip and "Use Zip Code"		.60	—
b. As "a," tagging omitted			

MAINE STATEHOOD, 150th ANNIV.

The painting hangs in the Metropolitan Museum of Art, New York City.

The Lighthouse at Two Lights, Maine, by Edward Hopper A813

Designed by Stevan Dohanos.

LITHOGRAPHED, ENGRAVED (Giori)
Plates of 200 subjects in four panes of 50.

1970, July 9	Tagged	Perf. 11	
1391 A813 6c black & multicolored		.20	.20
P# block of 4		.60	—
Margin block of 4, Mr. Zip and "Use Zip Code"		.45	—
a. Tagging omitted			

WILDLIFE CONSERVATION ISSUE

American Buffalo — A814

Designed by Robert Lougheed.

ROTARY PRESS PRINTING
E.E. Plates of 200 subjects in four panes of 50.

1970, July 20	Tagged	Perf. 11x10½	
1392 A814 6c black, light brown		.20	.20
P# block of 4		.75	—
Margin block of 4, Mr. Zip and "Use Zip Code"		.45	—

REGULAR ISSUE
Dwight David Eisenhower

Dot between "R" and "U" — A815

No Dot between "R" and "U" — A815a

Benjamin Franklin — A816

U.S. Postal Service Emblem — A817

Fiorello H. LaGuardia   A817a

Ernest Taylor Pyle — A818

Dr. Elizabeth Blackwell — A818a

Amadeo P. Giannini A818b

Designers: Nos. 1393-1395, 1401-1402, Robert Geissman; photograph by George Tames. 7c, Bill Hyde. No. 1396, Raymond Loewy/William Smith, Inc. 14c, Robert Geissman; photograph by George Fayer. 16c, Robert Geissman; photograph by Alfred Eisenstadt. 18c, Robert Geissman; painting by Joseph Kozlowski. 21c, Robert Geissman.

ROTARY PRESS PRINTING
E.E. Plates of 400 subjects in four panes of 100.

1970-74   **Tagged**   **Perf. 11x10½**

1393	A815 6c **dark blue gray,** shiny gum, *Aug. 6, 1970*	.20	.20
	P# block of 4	.50	—
	Margin block of 4, "Use Zip Codes"	.45	—
	Dull gum	.20	
	P# block of 4	1.00	
	Zip block of 4	.55	
a.	Booklet pane of 8, shiny gum	1.50	.75
	Dull gum	1.90	
b.	Booklet pane of 5 + label	1.50	.75
c.	Untagged (Bureau precanceled)	12.75	3.00
	P# block of 4	175.00	
	Margin block of 4, "Use Zip Codes"	75.00	
g.	Tagging omitted (not Bureau precanceled)	150.00	—
h.	As "a," tagging omitted, shiny gum	250.00	—
	Dull gum	—	

Perf. 10½x11

1393D	A816 7c **bright blue,** shiny gum, *Oct. 20, 1972*	.20	.20
	P# block of 4	.60	—
	Margin block of 4, "Use Zip Codes"	.55	—
	Dull gum	.20	
	P# block of 4	1.25	
	Zip block of 4	.90	
e.	Untagged (Bureau precanceled)	4.25	1.00
	P# block of 4	52.50	
	Margin block of 4, "Use Zip Codes"	22.50	
f.	Tagging omitted (not Bureau-canceled)	4.00	—

GIORI PRESS PRINTING
Plates of 400 subjects in four panes of 100.
Perf. 11

1394	A815a 8c **black, red & blue gray,** *May 10, 1971*	.20	.20
	P# block of 4	.60	—
	Margin block of 4, "Use Zip Codes"	.55	
	Pair with full vert. gutter btwn.		
a.	Tagging omitted	4.50	—
b.	Red missing (PS)	175.00	—
c.	Red and blue missing (PS)		

ROTARY PRESS PRINTING
Perf. 11x10½ on 2 or 3 sides

1395	A815 8c **deep claret,** shiny gum (from blkt. pane)	.20	.20
	Dull gum	.20	
a.	Booklet pane of 8, shiny gum, *May 10, 1971*	1.80	1.25
b.	Booklet pane of 6, shiny gum, *May 10, 1971*	1.25	1.10
c.	Booklet pane of 4 + 2 labels, dull gum, *Jan. 28, 1972*	1.65	1.00
d.	Booklet pane of 7 + label, dull gum, *Jan. 28, 1972*	1.90	1.10
e.	Vert. pair, imperf between	800.00	—
f.	As "a," tagging omitted	—	—
g.	As "b," tagging omitted	40.00	—
h.	As "c," tagging omitted	40.00	—
i.	As "d," tagging omitted	—	—

No. 1395 was issued only in booklets.
1395e resulted from a paper foldover after perforating and before cutting into panes. At least 4 pairs are recorded from 3 panes (one No. 1395a and two 1395d) with different foldover patterns. A pane of No. 1395d also is known with a foldover resulting in a vertical pair of stamp and label, imperf between.

PHOTOGRAVURE (Andreotti)
Plates of 400 subjects in four panes of 100.
Perf. 11x10½

1396	A817 8c **multicolored,** *July 1, 1971*	.20	.20
	P# block of 12, 6#	2.00	
	P# block of 20, 6#, "Mail Early in the Day," "Use Zip Codes" and rectangular color contents (UL pane)	3.25	
	Margin block of 4, "Use Zip Codes"	.65	—

ROTARY PRESS PRINTING
E.E. Plates of 400 subjects in four panes of 100.

1397	A817a 14c **gray brown,** *Apr. 24, 1972*	.25	.20
	P# block of 4	1.15	—
	Margin block of 4, "Use Zip Codes"		
a.	Untagged (Bureau precanceled)	140.00	17.50
	P# block of 4	—	
	Margin block of 4, "Use Zip Codes"		
1398	A818 16c **brown,** *May 7, 1971*	.35	.20
	P# block of 4	2.50	
	Margin block of 4, "Use Zip Codes"	1.50	—
a.	Untagged (Bureau precanceled)	22.50	5.00
	P# block of 4	—	
	Margin block of 4, "Use Zip Codes"	175.00	
b.	Tagging omitted (not Bureau precanceled)	—	—
1399	A818a 18c **violet,** *Jan. 23, 1974*	.35	.20
	P# block of 4	1.50	
	Margin block of 4, "Use Zip Codes"	1.40	—
1400	A818b 21c **green,** *June 27, 1973*	.40	.20
	P# block of 4	1.65	
	Margin block of 4, "Use Zip Codes"	1.60	—
	Nos. 1393-1400 (9)	2.35	1.80

Bureau Precancels: 6c, 6 diff., 7c, 13 diff., No. 1394, 24 diff., 14c, 3 diff., 16c, NYC, 3 diff. Greensboro, NC.

COIL STAMPS
ROTARY PRESS PRINTING

1970-71   **Tagged**   **Perf. 10 Vert.**

1401	A815 6c **dark blue gray,** shiny gum, *Aug. 6, 1970*	.20	.20
	Pair	.30	.20
	Joint line pair	.50	.20
	Dull gum	.85	
	Joint line pair	7.00	
a.	Untagged (Bureau precanceled)	19.50	3.00
	Pair	42.50	6.50
	Joint line pair	525.00	
b.	Imperf., pair	1,750.	
	Joint line pair		
1402	A815 8c **deep claret,** *May 10, 1971*	.20	.20
	Pair	.30	.20
	Joint line pair	.60	.20
a.	Imperf., pair	37.50	
	Joint line pair	65.00	
b.	Untagged (Bureau precanceled)	6.75	.75
	Pair	15.00	1.60
	Joint line pair	185.00	
c.	Pair, imperf. between	6,250.	

Bureau Precancels: 6c, 4 diff., 8c, 34 diff.

EDGAR LEE MASTERS ISSUE

Edgar Lee Masters (1869-1950), Poet — A819

Designed by Fred Otnes.

LITHOGRAPHED, ENGRAVED (Giori)
E.E. Plates of 200 subjects in four panes of 50.

1970, Aug. 22   **Tagged**   **Perf. 11**

1405	A819 6c **black & olive bister**	.20	.20
	P# block of 4	.50	—
	Margin block of 4, Mr. Zip and "Use Zip Code"	.45	
a.	Tagging omitted	125.00	—

WOMAN SUFFRAGE ISSUE

50th anniversary of the 19th Amendment, which gave the vote to women.

Suffragettes, 1920, and Woman Voter, 1970 — A820

Designed by Ward Brackett.

GIORI PRESS PRINTING
Plates of 200 subjects in four panes of 50.

1970, Aug. 26   **Tagged**   **Perf. 11**

1406	A820 6c **blue**	.20	.20
	P# block of 4	.50	—
	Margin block of 4, Mr. Zip and "Use Zip Code"	.45	—

SOUTH CAROLINA ISSUE

300th anniv. of the founding of Charles Town (Charleston), the 1st permanent settlement of South Carolina. Against a background of pine wood the line drawings of the design represent the economic and historic development of South Carolina: the spire of St. Phillip's Church, Capitol, state flag, a ship, 17th century man and woman, a Fort Sumter cannon, barrels, cotton, tobacco and yellow jasmine.

Symbols of South Carolina A821

Designed by George Samerjan.

LITHOGRAPHED, ENGRAVED (Giori)
Plates of 200 subjects in four panes of 50.

1970, Sept. 12   **Tagged**   **Perf. 11**

1407	A821 6c **bister, black & red**	.20	.20
	P# block of 4	.55	—
	Margin block of 4, Mr. Zip and "Use Zip Code"	.45	—

STONE MOUNTAIN MEMORIAL ISSUE

Dedication of the Stone Mountain Confederate Memorial, Georgia, May 9, 1970.

Robert E. Lee, Jefferson Davis and "Stonewall" Jackson
A822

Designed by Robert Hallock.

GIORI PRESS PRINTING
Plates of 200 subjects in four panes of 50.

1970, Sept. 19	Tagged	Perf. 11	
1408 A822 6c gray		.20	.20
P# block of 4		.50	—
Margin block of 4, Mr. Zip and "Use Zip Code"		.45	—

FORT SNELLING ISSUE
150th anniv. of Fort Snelling, Minnesota, an important outpost for the opening of the Northwest.

Fort Snelling, Keelboat and Tepees
A823

Designed by David K. Stone.

LITHOGRAPHED, ENGRAVED (Giori)
Plates of 200 in four panes of 50.

1970, Oct. 17	Tagged	Perf. 11	
1409 A823 6c yellow & multicolored		.20	.20
P# block of 4		.55	—
Margin block of 4, Mr. Zip and "Use Zip Code"		.45	—
a. Tagging omitted		—	

ANTI-POLLUTION ISSUE
Issued to focus attention on the problems of pollution.
In left panes Nos. 1410 and 1412 appear in 1st, 3rd and 5th place; Nos. 1411 and 1413 in 2nd and 4th place. This arrangement is reversed in right panes.

Globe and Wheat — A824

Globe and City — A825

Globe and Bluegill
A826

Globe and Seagull
A827

Designed by Arnold Copeland and Walter DuBois Richards. Printed by Bureau of Engraving and Printing at Guilford Gravure, Inc., Guilford, Conn.

PHOTOGRAVURE
Plates of 200 subjects in four panes of 50.

1970, Oct. 28	Tagged	Perf. 11x10½	
1410 A824 6c multicolored		.25	.20
1411 A825 6c multicolored		.25	.20
1412 A826 6c multicolored		.25	.20
1413 A827 6c multicolored		.25	.20
a. Block of 4, #1410-1413		1.10	1.25
P# block of 10, 5#		2.25	—
Margin block of 4, Mr. Zip and "Use Zip Code"		1.25	—

CHRISTMAS ISSUE
In left panes Nos. 1415 and 1417 appear in 1st, 3rd and 5th place; Nos. 1416 and 1418 in 2nd and 4th place. This arrangement is reversed in right panes.

Nativity, by Lorenzo Lotto — A828

Tin and Cast-iron Locomotive
A829

Toy Horse on Wheels
A830

Mechanical Tricycle
A831

Doll Carriage
A832

Designers: No. 1414, Howard C. Mildner, from a painting by Lorenzo Lotto (1480-1556) in the National Gallery of Art, Washington, D.C. Nos. 1415-1418, Stevan Dohanos, from a drawing (locomotive) by Charles Hemming and from "Golden Age of Toys" by Fondin and Remise.
Printed by Guilford Gravure, Inc., Guilford, Conn.

PHOTOGRAVURE
Plates of 200 subjects in four panes of 50.

1970, Nov. 5	Tagged	Perf. 10½x11	
1414 A828 6c multicolored		.20	.20
P# block of 8, 4#		1.10	—
Margin block of 4, Mr. Zip and "Use Zip Code"		.50	—
a. Precanceled		.20	.20

Margin block of 4, Mr. Zip and "Use Zip Code"		.70	—
b. Black omitted		450.00	
c. As "a," blue omitted		1,450.	
d. Type II		.20	.20
P# block of 8, 4#		2.75	—
Zip block of 4		.85	—
e. Type II, precanceled		.25	.20
P# block of 8, 4#		4.00	—
Zip block of 4		1.25	—

No. 1414 has pregummed paper, a slightly blurry impression, snowflaking in the sky and no gum breaker ridges. No. 1414d has shiny surfaced paper, sharper impression, no snowflaking and vertical and horizontal gum breaker ridges.
No. 1414a has a slightly blurry impression, snowflaking in the sky, no gum breaker ridges and the precancel is grayish black. No. 1414e has sharper impression, no snowflaking, gum breaker ridges and the precancel is intense black.

	Perf. 11x10½		
1415 A829 6c multicolored		.30	.20
a. Precanceled		.75	.20
b. Black omitted		2,500.	
c. Tagging omitted		—	
1416 A830 6c multicolored		.30	.20
a. Precanceled		.75	.20
b. Black omitted		2,500.	
c. Imperf., pair (#1416, 1418)			2,500.
1417 A831 6c multicolored		.30	.20
a. Precanceled		.75	.20
b. Black omitted		2,500.	
c. Tagging omitted		—	
1418 A832 6c multicolored		.30	.20
a. Precanceled		.75	.20
b. Block of 4, #1415-1418		1.25	1.40
P# block of 8, 4#		3.00	—
Margin block of 4, Mr. Zip and "Use Zip Code"		1.25	—
c. As "b," precanceled		3.25	3.50
P# block of 8, 4P#		6.25	—
Margin block of 4, Mr. Zip and "Use Zip Code"		3.50	—
d. Black omitted		2,500.	
e. As "b," black omitted		10,000.	
f. As "b," black omitted on #1417 & 1418		5,000.	
g. P# block of 8, black omitted on #1415 & 1416		5,000.	

Nos. 1415-1418 and 1415a-1418a are known both without gum breaker ridges (common) and with gum breaker ridges (scarce).
The precanceled stamps, Nos. 1414a-1418a, were furnished to 68 cities. The plates include two straight (No. 1414a) or two wavy (Nos. 1415a-1418a) black lines that make up the precancellation. Unused values are for stamps with gum and used values are for stamps with an additional cancellation or without gum.

UNITED NATIONS, 25th ANNIV.

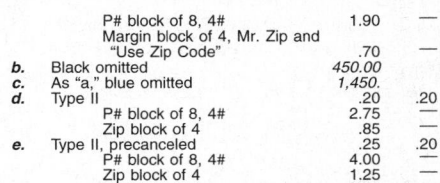

"UN" and UN Emblem
A833

Designed by Arnold Copeland.

LITHOGRAPHED, ENGRAVED (Giori)
Plates of 200 subjects in four panes of 50.

1970, Nov. 20	Tagged	Perf. 11	
1419 A833 6c black, verm. & ultra.		.20	.20
P# block of 4		.65	—
Margin block of 4, Mr. Zip and "Use Zip Code"		.45	—
Pair with full horiz. gutter btwn.			—
a. Tagging omitted		85.00	—

LANDING OF THE PILGRIMS ISSUE
350th anniv. of the landing of the Mayflower.

Mayflower and Pilgrims — A834

Designed by Mark English.

LITHOGRAPHED, ENGRAVED (Giori)
Plates of 200 subjects in four panes of 50.

1970, Nov. 21	Tagged	Perf. 11
1420 A834 6c blk., org., yel., magenta, bl. & brn.	.20	.20
P# block of 4	.50	
Margin block of 4, Mr. Zip and "Use Zip Code"	.45	—
a. Orange & yellow omitted	625.00	
b. Tagging omitted	—	

DISABLED AMERICAN VETERANS AND SERVICEMEN ISSUE

No. 1421 for the 50th anniv. of the Disabled Veterans of America Organization; No. 1422 honors the contribution of servicemen, particularly those who were prisoners of war, missing or killed in action. Nos. 1421-1422 are printed se-tenant in horizontal rows of 10.

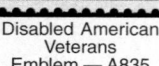

Disabled American Veterans Emblem — A835

A836

Designed by Stevan Dohanos.

LITHOGRAPHED, ENGRAVED (Giori)
Plates of 200 subjects in four panes of 50.

1970, Nov. 24	Tagged	Perf. 11
1421 A835 6c dark blue, red & multicolored	.20	.20

ENGRAVED

1422 A836 6c dark blue, black & red	.20	.20
a. Pair, #1421-1422	.30	.30
P# block of 4	1.00	—
Margin block of 4, Mr. Zip and "Use Zip Code"	.65	—
b. As "a," tagging omitted	75.00	—

Ewe and Lamb — A837

Gen. Douglas MacArthur — A838

AMERICAN WOOL INDUSTRY ISSUE

450th anniv. of the introduction of sheep to the North American continent and the beginning of the American wool industry.

Designed by Dean Ellis.

LITHOGRAPHED, ENGRAVED (Giori)
Plates of 200 subjects in four panes of 50.

1971, Jan. 19	Tagged	Perf. 11
1423 A837 6c multicolored	.20	.20
P# block of 4	.55	
Margin block of 4, Mr. Zip and "Use Zip Code"	.45	—
a. Tagging omitted	11.00	—
b. Teal blue ("United States") missing (CM)	350.00	

GEN. DOUGLAS MacARTHUR ISSUE

MacArthur (1880-1964), Chief of Staff, Supreme Commander for the Allied Powers in the Pacific Area during World War II and Supreme Commander in Japan after the war.

Designed by Paul Calle; Wide World photograph.

GIORI PRESS PRINTING
Plates of 200 subjects in four panes of 50.

1971, Jan. 26	Tagged	Perf. 11
1424 A838 6c black, red & dark blue	.20	.20
P# block of 4	.60	
Margin block of 4, Mr. Zip and "Use Zip Code"	.45	—
a. Red missing (PS)	—	
b. Tagging omitted	125.00	
c. Blue missing (PS)	—	

BLOOD DONOR ISSUE

Salute to blood donors and spur to increased participation in the blood donor program.

"Giving Blood Saves Lives" — A839

Designed by Howard Munce.

LITHOGRAPHED, ENGRAVED (Giori)
Plates of 200 subjects in four panes of 50.

1971, Mar. 12	Tagged	Perf. 11
1425 A839 6c blue, scarlet & indigo	.20	.20
P# block of 4	.50	—
Margin block of 4, Mr. Zip and "Use Zip Code"	.45	—
a. Tagging omitted	10.00	—

MISSOURI STATEHOOD, 150th ANNIV.

The stamp design shows a Pawnee facing a hunter-trapper and a group of settlers. It is from a mural by Thomas Hart Benton in the Harry S Truman Library, Independence, Mo.

"Independence and the Opening of the West," Detail, by Thomas Hart Benton — A840

Designed by Bradbury Thompson.

PHOTOGRAVURE (Andreotti)
Plates of 200 subjects in four panes of 50.

1971, May 8	Tagged	Perf. 11x10½
1426 A840 8c multicolored	.20	.20
P# block of 12, 6#	3.00	
Margin block of 4, Mr. Zip and "Use Zip Code"	.65	—
a. Tagging omitted	—	

See note on Andreotti printings and their color control markings in Information for Collectors under Printing, Photogravure.

WILDLIFE CONSERVATION ISSUE

Nos. 1427-1428 alternate in first row, Nos. 1429-1430 in second row. This arrangement repeated throughout pane.

Trout A841

Alligator — A842

Polar Bear and Cubs A843

California Condor — A844

Designed by Stanley W. Galli.

LITHOGRAPHED, ENGRAVED (Giori)
Plates of 128 subjects in 4 panes of 32 each (4x8).

1971, June 12	Tagged	Perf. 11
1427 A841 8c multicolored	.20	.20
a. Red omitted	1,250.	
b. Green (engr.) omitted		
1428 A842 8c multicolored	.20	.20
1429 A843 8c multicolored	.20	.20
1430 A844 8c multicolored	.20	.20
a. Block of 4, #1427-1430	.80	.90
P# block of 4	1.00	—
Margin block of 4, Mr. Zip and "Use Zip Code"	.85	
b. As "a," light green & dark green omitted from #1427-1428	4,500.	
c. As "a," red omitted from #1427, 1429-1430	3,500.	
d. As "a," tagging omitted	—	

ANTARCTIC TREATY ISSUE

Map of Antarctica A845

Designed by Howard Koslow.

Adapted from emblem on official documents of Consultative Meetings.

GIORI PRESS PRINTING
Plates of 200 subjects in four panes of 50.

1971, June 23	Tagged	Perf. 11
1431 A845 8c red & dark blue	.20	.20
P# block of 4	.65	—
Margin block of 4, Mr. Zip and "Use Zip Code"	.60	—
a. Tagging omitted	10.00	
b. Both colors missing (EP)	500.00	

No. 1431b should be collected se-tenant with a normal stamp and/or a partially printed stamp.

AMERICAN REVOLUTION BICENTENNIAL

Bicentennial Commission Emblem — A846

Designed by Chermayeff & Geismar.

LITHOGRAPHED, ENGRAVED (Giori)
Plates of 200 subjects in four panes of 50.

1971, July 4	Tagged	Perf. 11	
1432 A846 8c **gray, red, blue & black**		.20	.20
P# block of 4		.85	—
Margin block of 4, Mr. Zip and "Use Zip Code"		.80	—
a. Gray & black missing (EP)		500.00	
b. Gray ("U.S. Postage 8c") missing (EP)		750.00	
c. Tagging omitted		125.00	

JOHN SLOAN ISSUE

John Sloan (1871-1951), painter. The painting hangs in the Phillips Gallery, Washington, D.C.

The Wake of the Ferry — A847

Designed by Bradbury Thompson.

LITHOGRAPHED, ENGRAVED (Giori)
Plates of 200 subjects in four panes of 50.

1971, Aug. 2	Tagged	Perf. 11	
1433 A847 8c **multicolored**		.20	.20
P# block of 4		.70	—
Margin block of 4, Mr. Zip and "Use Zip Code"		.65	—
a. Tagging omitted		—	
b. Red engr. ("John Sloan" and "8") missing (CM)		950.00	

SPACE ACHIEVEMENT DECADE ISSUE

Decade of space achievements and the Apollo 15 moon exploration mission, July 26-Aug. 7. In the left panes the earth and sun stamp is 1st, 3rd and 5th, the rover 2nd and 4th. This arrangement is reversed in the right panes.

Earth, Sun and Landing Craft on Moon — A848

Lunar Rover and Astronauts A849

Designed by Robert McCall.

LITHOGRAPHED, ENGRAVED (Giori)
Plates of 200 subjects in four panes of 50.

1971, Aug. 2	Tagged	Perf. 11	
1434 A848 8c **black, blue, gray, yellow & red**		.20	.20
a. Tagging omitted		45.00	
1435 A849 8c **black, blue, gray, yellow & red**		.20	.20
a. Tagging omitted		45.00	
b. Pair, #1434-1435		.40	.45

	P# block of 4	.65	
	Margin block of 4, Mr. Zip and "Use Zip Code"	.60	—
c.	As "b," tagging omitted	125.00	
d.	As "b," blue & red (litho.) omitted	1,200.	

Emily Elizabeth Dickinson (1830-1886), Poet — A850

Sentry Box, Morro Castle, San Juan — A851

EMILY DICKINSON ISSUE

Designed by Bernard Fuchs after a photograph.

LITHOGRAPHED, ENGRAVED (Giori)
Plates of 200 subjects in four panes of 50.

1971, Aug. 28	Tagged	Perf. 11	
1436 A850 8c **multicolored,** *greenish*		.20	.20
P# block of 4		.65	—
Margin block of 4, Mr. Zip and "Use Zip Code"		.60	—
a. Black & olive (engr.) omitted		525.00	
b. Pale rose missing (EP)		6,000.	
c. Red omitted			
d. Tagging omitted		150.00	

SAN JUAN ISSUE

450th anniversary of San Juan, Puerto Rico.

Designed as a woodcut by Walter Brooks.

LITHOGRAPHED, ENGRAVED (Giori)
Plates of 200 subjects in four panes of 50.

1971, Sept. 12	Tagged	Perf. 11	
1437 A851 8c **pale brown, black, yellow & dark brown**		.20	.20
P# block of 4		1.00	—
Margin block of 4, Mr. Zip and "Use Zip Code"		.60	—
a. Tagging omitted		9.00	

VALUES FOR HINGED STAMPS AFTER NO. 771
This catalogue does not value unused stamps after No. 771 in hinged condition. Hinged unused stamps from No. 772 to the present are worth considerably less than the values given for unused stamps, which are for never-hinged examples.

Young Woman Drug Addict — A852

Hands Reaching for CARE — A853

PREVENT DRUG ABUSE ISSUE

Drug Abuse Prevention Week, Oct. 3-9.

Designed by Miggs Burroughs.

PHOTOGRAVURE (Andreotti)
Plates of 200 subjects in four panes of 50.

1971, Oct. 4	Tagged	Perf. 10½x11	
1438 A852 8c **blue, deep blue & black**		.20	.20
P# block of 6, 3#		1.00	—
Margin block of 4, "Use Zip Code"		.65	—

CARE ISSUE

25th anniversary of CARE, a US-Canadian Cooperative for American Relief Everywhere.

Designed by Soren Noring

PHOTOGRAVURE (Andreotti)
Plates of 200 subjects in four panes of 50.

1971, Oct. 27	Tagged	Perf. 10½x11	
1439 A853 8c **blue, blk., vio. & red lilac**		.20	.20
P# block of 8, 4#		1.25	—
Margin block of 4, Mr. Zip and "Use Zip Code"		.65	—
a. Black omitted		1,750.	
b. Tagging omitted		5.00	

HISTORIC PRESERVATION ISSUE

Nos. 1440-1441 alternate in 1st row, Nos. 1442-1443 in 2nd row. This arrangement is repeated throughout the pane.

Decatur House, Washington, D.C. — A854

Whaling Ship Charles W. Morgan, Mystic, Conn. — A855

Cable Car, San Francisco — A856

San Xavier del Bac Mission, Tucson, Ariz. — A857

Designed by Melbourne Brindle.

LITHOGRAPHED, ENGRAVED (Giori)

1971, Oct. 29	Tagged	Perf. 11	
1440 A854 8c **black brown & ocher,** *buff*		.20	.20
1441 A855 8c **black brown & ocher,** *buff*		.20	.20
1442 A856 8c **black brown & ocher,** *buff*		.20	.20
1443 A857 8c **black brown & ocher,** *buff*		.20	.20
a. Block of 4, #1440-1443		.75	.85
P# block of 4		.90	—
Margin block of 4, Mr. Zip and "Use Zip Code"		.80	—
b. As "a," black brown omitted		1,250.	
c. As "a," ocher omitted		3,000.	
d. As "a," tagging omitted		75.00	

CHRISTMAS ISSUE

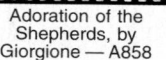

Adoration of the
Shepherds, by
Giorgione — A858

"Partridge in a Pear
Tree" — A859

Designers: No. 1444, Bradbury Thompson, using a painting by Giorgione in the National Gallery of Art, Washington, D.C. No. 1445, Jamie Wyeth.

PHOTOGRAVURE (Andreotti)
Plates of 200 subjects in four panes of 50.

1971, Nov. 10	Tagged	Perf. 10½x11	
1444 A858 8c **gold & multicolored**		.20	.20
P# block of 12, 6#		1.80	—
Margin block of 4, Mr. Zip and "Use Zip Code"		.60	
a. Gold omitted		400.00	
b. Tagging omitted		—	
1445 A859 8c **dark green, red & multicolored**		.20	.20
P# block of 12, 6#		1.80	—
Margin block of 4, Mr. Zip and "Use Zip Code"		.60	

Sidney Lanier — A860

Peace Corps Poster, by
David Battle — A861

SIDNEY LANIER ISSUE

Lanier (1842-81), poet, musician, lawyer, educator.

Designed by William A. Smith.

GIORI PRESS PRINTING
Plates of 200 subjects in four panes of 50.

1972, Feb. 3	Tagged	Perf. 11	
1446 A860 8c **black, brown & light blue**		.20	.20
P# block of 4		.65	—
Margin block of 4, Mr. Zip and "Use Zip Code"		.60	—
a. Tagging omitted		55.00	

PEACE CORPS ISSUE

Designed by Bradbury Thompson.

PHOTOGRAVURE (Andreotti)
Plates of 200 subjects in four panes of 50.

1972, Feb. 11	Tagged	Perf. 10½x11	
1447 A861 8c **dark blue, light blue & red**		.20	.20
P# block of 6, 3#		1.00	—
Margin block of 4, Mr. Zip and "Use Zip Code"		.65	—
a. Tagging omitted		5.00	

NATIONAL PARKS CENTENNIAL ISSUE

Centenary of Yellowstone National Park, the 1st National Park, and of the entire National Park System. See No. C84.

A862   A863
A864   A865
Cape Hatteras National Seashore

Wolf Trap
Farm,
Va. — A866

Old Faithful,
Yellowstone — A867

Mt. McKinley,
Alaska — A868

Designers: 2c, Walter D. Richards; 6c, Howard Koslow; 8c, Robert Handville; 15c, James Barkley.

LITHOGRAPHED, ENGRAVED (Giori)

1972	Tagged	Perf. 11	
Plates of 400 subjects in 4 panes of 100 each			
1448 A862 2c **black & multi.,** *Apr. 5*		.20	.20
1449 A863 2c **black & multi.,** *Apr. 5*		.20	.20
1450 A864 2c **black & multi.,** *Apr. 5*		.20	.20
1451 A865 2c **black & multi.,** *Apr. 5*		.20	.20
a. Block of 4, #1448-1451		.25	*.30*
P# block of 4		.50	
Margin block of 4, "Use Zip Codes"		.30	
b. As "a," black (litho.) omitted		1,400.	
c. As "a," tagging omitted		150.00	
Plates of 200 subjects in four panes of 50 each			
1452 A866 6c **black & multicolored,** *June 26*		.20	.20
P# block of 4		.55	—
Margin block of 4, Mr. Zip and "Use Zip Code"		.50	—
a. Tagging omitted		10.00	
Plates of 128 subjects in four panes of 32 (8x4)			
1453 A867 8c **blk., blue, brn. & multi.,** *Mar. 1*		.20	.20
P# block of 4		.80	—
Margin block of 4, Mr. Zip and "Use Zip Code"		.65	—
a. Tagging omitted		140.00	
Plates of 200 subjects in four panes of 50 each			
1454 A868 15c **black & multi.,** *July 28*		.30	.20
P# block of 4		1.30	—
Margin block of 4, Mr. Zip		1.25	—
a. Tagging omitted		125.00	
b. Yellow omitted		*3,500.*	

FAMILY PLANNING ISSUE

Family — A869

LITHOGRAPHED, ENGRAVED (Giori)
Plates of 200 subjects in four panes of 50.

1972, Mar. 18	Tagged	Perf. 11	
1455 A869 8c **black & multicolored**		.20	.20
P# block of 4		.65	—
Margin block of 4, Mr. Zip and "Use Zip Code"		.60	—
a. Yellow omitted		400.00	
c. Dark brown missing (FO)		9,000.	
d. Tagging omitted		—	

AMERICAN BICENTENNIAL ISSUE
Colonial American Craftsmen

In left panes Nos. 1456 and 1458 appear in 1st, 3rd and 5th place; Nos. 1457 and 1459 in 2nd and 4th place. This arrangement is reversed in right panes.

Glass Blower
A870

Silversmith
A871

Wigmaker
A872

Hatter — A873

Designed by Leonard Everett Fisher.

ENGRAVED
E.E. Plates of 200 subjects in four panes of 50.

1972, July 4	Tagged	Perf. 11x10½	
1456 A870 8c **deep brown,** *dull yellow*		.20	.20
1457 A871 8c **deep brown,** *dull yellow*		.20	.20
1458 A872 8c **deep brown,** *dull yellow*		.20	.20
1459 A873 8c **deep brown,** *dull yellow*		.20	.20
a. Block of 4, #1456-1459		.65	*.75*
P# block of 4		.80	—
Margin block of 4, Mr. Zip and "Use Zip Code"		.70	—
b. As "a," tagging omitted		150.00	

Margin includes Bicentennial Commission emblem and inscription: USA BICENTENNIAL / HONORS COLONIAL / AMERICAN CRAFTSMEN.

OLYMPIC GAMES ISSUE

11th Winter Olympic Games, Sapporo, Japan, Feb. 3-13 and 20th Summer Olympic Games, Munich, Germany, Aug. 26-Sept. 11. See No. C85.

Bicycling and Olympic Rings — A874

Bobsledding and Olympic Rings — A875

Running and Olympic Rings — A876

"Broken red ring" Cylinder Flaw

Designed by Lance Wyman.

PHOTOGRAVURE (Andreotti)
Plates of 200 subjects in four panes of 50.

1972, Aug. 17	Tagged	Perf. 11x10½
1460 A874 6c black, blue, red, emerald & yellow	.20	.20
P# block of 10, 5#	1.25	
Margin block of 4, Mr. Zip and "Use Zip Code"	.50	
Cylinder flaw (broken red ring) (33313 UL 43)	10.00	
1461 A875 8c black, blue, red, emerald & yellow	.20	.20
P# block of 10, 5#	1.60	
Margin block of 4, Mr. Zip and "Use Zip Code"	.65	
a. Tagging omitted	7.50	
1462 A876 15c black, blue, red, emerald & yel	.30	.20
P# block of 10, 5#	3.00	
Margin block of 4, Mr. Zip and "Use Zip Code"	1.15	
Nos. 1460-1462 (3)	.70	.60

PARENT TEACHER ASSN., 75th ANNIV.

Blackboard A877

Designed by Arthur S. Congdon III.

PHOTOGRAVURE (Andreotti)
Plates of 200 subjects in four panes of 50.

1972, Sept. 15	Tagged	Perf. 11x10½
1463 A877 8c yellow & black	.20	.20
P# block of 4, 2#	.65	
P# block of 4, yellow # reversed	.75	
Margin block of 4, Mr. Zip and "Use Zip Code"	.60	
a. Tagging omitted		

WILDLIFE CONSERVATION ISSUE

Nos. 1464-1465 alternate in 1st row, Nos. 1468-1469 in 2nd row. This arrangement repeated throughout pane.

Fur Seals A878

Cardinal — A879

Brown Pelican — A880

Bighorn Sheep — A881

Designed by Stanley W. Galli.

LITHOGRAPHED, ENGRAVED (Giori)
Plates of 128 subjects in 4 panes of 32 (4x8).

1972, Sept. 20	Tagged	Perf. 11
1464 A878 8c multicolored	.25	.20
1465 A879 8c multicolored	.25	.20
1466 A880 8c multicolored	.25	.20
1467 A881 8c multicolored	.25	.20
a. Block of 4, #1464-1467	1.00	.75
P# block of 4	1.10	
Margin block of 4, Mr. Zip and "Use Zip Code"	1.00	
b. As "a," brown omitted	3,750.	
c. As "a," green & blue omitted	3,750.	
d. As "a," red & brown omitted	4,000.	
e. As "a," tagging omitted	—	

MAIL ORDER BUSINESS ISSUE

Centenary of mail order business, originated by Aaron Montgomery Ward, Chicago. Design based on Headsville, W.Va., post office in Smithsonian Institution, Washington, D.C.

Rural Post Office Store — A882

Designed by Robert Lambdin.

PHOTOGRAVURE (Andreotti)
Plates of 200 subjects in four panes of 50.

1972, Sept. 27	Tagged	Perf. 11x10½
1468 A882 8c multicolored	.20	.20
P# block of 12, 6#	1.75	
Margin block of 4, Mr. Zip and "Use Zip Code"	.60	

The tagging on No. 1468 consists of a vertical bar of phosphor 10mm wide.

Man's Quest for Health — A883

Tom Sawyer, by Norman Rockwell — A884

OSTEOPATHIC MEDICINE ISSUE

75th anniv. of the American Osteopathic Assoc., founded by Dr. Andrew T. Still (1828-1917), who developed the principles of osteopathy in 1874.

Designed by V. Jack Ruther.

PHOTOGRAVURE (Andreotti)
Plates of 200 subjects in four panes of 50.

1972, Oct. 9	Tagged	Perf. 10½x11
1469 A883 8c multicolored	.20	.20
P# block of 6, 3#	1.10	
Margin block of 4, Mr. Zip and "Use Zip Code"	.65	

AMERICAN FOLKLORE ISSUE
Tom Sawyer

Designed by Bradbury Thompson.

LITHOGRAPHED, ENGRAVED (Giori)
Plates of 200 subjects in four panes of 50.

1972, Oct. 13	Tagged	Perf. 11
1470 A884 8c black, red, yellow, tan, blue & rose red	.20	.20
P# block of 4	.65	
Margin block of 4, Mr. Zip and "Use Zip Code"	.60	
a. Horiz. pair, imperf. between	7,500.	
b. Red & black (engr.) omitted	1,250.	
c. Yellow & tan (litho.) omitted	1,750.	
d. Tagging omitted	125.	

CHRISTMAS ISSUE

Angels from "Mary, Queen of Heaven" — A885

Santa Claus — A886

Designers: No. 1471, Bradbury Thompson, using detail from a painting by the Master of the St. Lucy legend, in the National Gallery of Art, Washington, D.C. No. 1472, Stevan Dohanos.

PHOTOGRAVURE (Andreotti)
Plates of 200 subjects in four panes of 50.

1972, Nov. 9	Tagged	Perf. 10½x11
1471 A885 8c multicolored	.20	.20
P# block of 12, 6#	1.75	
Margin block of 4, Mr. Zip and "Use Zip Code"	.60	
a. Pink omitted	120.00	
b. Black omitted	3,250.	
1472 A886 8c multicolored	.20	.20
P# block of 12, 6#	1.75	
Margin block of 4, Mr. Zip and "Use Zip Code"	.60	

PHARMACY ISSUE

Honoring American druggists in connection with the 120th anniversary of the American Pharmaceutical Association.

Mortar and Pestle, Bowl of Hygeia, 19th Century Medicine Bottles — A887

Designed by Ken Davies.

LITHOGRAPHED, ENGRAVED (Giori)
Plates of 200 subjects in four panes of 50.

1972, Nov. 10	Tagged	Perf. 11	
1473 A887 8c **black & multicolored**		.20	.20
P# block of 4		.65	—
Margin block of 4, Mr. Zip and "Use Zip Code"		.60	—
a. Blue & orange omitted		675.00	
b. Blue omitted		1,750.	
c. Orange omitted		1,750.	
d. Tagging omitted		120.00	—
e. Vertical pair, imperf horiz.		2,100.	

STAMP COLLECTING ISSUE

Issued to publicize stamp collecting.

U.S. No. 1 under Magnifying Glass — A888

Designed by Frank E. Livia.

LITHOGRAPHED, ENGRAVED (Giori)
Plates of 160 subjects in four panes of 40.

1972, Nov. 17	Tagged	Perf. 11	
1474 A888 8c **multicolored**		.20	.20
P# block of 4		.65	—
Margin block of 4, Mr. Zip and "Use Zip Code"		.60	—
a. Black (litho.) omitted		475.00	
b. Tagging omitted		4.50	

LOVE ISSUE

"Love," by Robert Indiana A889

Designed by Robert Indiana.

PHOTOGRAVURE (Andreotti)
Plates of 200 subjects in four panes of 50.

1973, Jan. 26	Tagged	Perf. 11x10½	
1475 A889 8c **red, emerald & violet blue**		.20	.20
P# block of 6, 3#		1.00	—
Margin block of 4, Mr. Zip and "Use Zip Code"		.65	—

AMERICAN BICENTENNIAL ISSUE
Communications in Colonial Times

Posting a Broadside A891

Postrider A892

Drummer A893

Designed by William A. Smith.

GIORI PRESS PRINTING
Plates of 200 subjects in four panes of 50.

1973	Tagged	Perf. 11	
1476 A890 8c **ultra., greenish blk. & red,** *Feb. 16*		.20	.20
P# block of 4		.65	—
Margin block of 4, Mr. Zip and "Use Zip Code"		.60	—
a. Tagging omitted		50.00	
1477 A891 8c **black, vermilion & ultra.,** *Apr. 13*		.20	.20
P# block of 4		.65	—
Margin block of 4, Mr. Zip and "Use Zip Code"		.60	—
Pair with full horiz. gutter btwn,			—
a. Tagging omitted			—

LITHOGRAPHED, ENGRAVED (Giori)

1478 A892 8c **blue, black, red & green,** *June 22*		.20	.20
P# block of 4		.65	—
Margin block of 4, Mr. Zip and "Use Zip Code"		.60	—
a. Red missing (CM)			—
1479 A893 8c **blue, black, yellow & red,** *Sept. 28*		.20	.20
P# block of 4		.65	—
Margin block of 4, Mr. Zip and "Use Zip Code"		.60	—
Nos. 1476-1479 (4)		.80	.80

Margin of Nos. 1477-1479 includes Bicentennial Commission emblem and inscription.

AMERICAN BICENTENNIAL ISSUE
Boston Tea Party

In left panes Nos. 1480 and 1482 appear in 1st, 3rd and 5th place, Nos. 1481 and 1483 appear in 2nd and 4th place. This arrangement is reversed in right panes.

British Merchantman A894

British Three-master A895

Boats and Ship's Hull — A896

Boat and Dock — A897

Designed by William A. Smith.

LITHOGRAPHED, ENGRAVED (Giori)
Plates of 200 subjects in four panes of 50.

1973, July 4	Tagged	Perf. 11	
1480 A894 8c **black & multicolored**		.20	.20
1481 A895 8c **black & multicolored**		.20	.20
1482 A896 8c **black & multicolored**		.20	.20
1483 A897 8c **black & multicolored**		.20	.20
a. Block of 4, #1480-1483		.65	.75
P# block of 4		.75	—
Margin block of 4, Mr. Zip and "Use Zip Code"		.70	—
b. As "a," black (engraved) omitted		1,100.	
c. As "a," black (litho.) omitted		1,000.	
d. As "a," tagging omitted			—

Margin includes Bicentennial Commission emblem and inscription.

AMERICAN ARTS ISSUE

George Gershwin (1898-1937), composer (No. 1484); Robinson Jeffers (1887-1962), poet (No. 1485); Henry Ossawa Tanner (1859-1937), black painter (No. 1486); Willa Cather (1873-1947), novelist (No. 1487).

Gershwin, Sportin' Life, Porgy and Bess — A898

Robinson Jeffers, Man and Children of Carmel with Burro — A899

Henry Ossawa Tanner, Palette and Rainbow A900

Willa Cather, Pioneer Family and Covered Wagon A901

Designed by Mark English.

PHOTOGRAVURE (Andreotti)
Plates of 160 subjects in four panes of 40.

1973		Tagged	Perf. 11	
1484	A898	8c **dp. green & multi.**, Feb. 28	.20	.20
		P# block of 12, 6#	1.75	
		Margin block of 4, Mr. Zip, "Use Zip Code" and "Mail Early in the Day"	.60	—
		P# block of 16, 6#, Mr. Zip and slogans	2.50	
a.		Vertical pair, imperf. horiz.	175.00	
1485	A899	8c **Prussian blue & multi.**, Aug. 13	.20	.20
		P# block of 12, 6#	1.75	
		Margin block of 4, Mr. Zip, "Use Zip Code" "Mail Early in the Day"	.60	—
		P# block of 16, 6#, Mr. Zip and slogans	2.50	
a.		Vertical pair, imperf. horiz.	200.00	
1486	A900	8c **yellow brown & multi.**, Sept. 10	.20	.20
		P# block of 12, 6#	1.75	
		Margin block of 4, Mr. Zip, "Use Zip Code" "Mail Early in the Day"	.60	—
		P# block of 16, 6#, Mr. Zip and slogans	2.50	
1487	A901	8c **deep brown & multi.**, Sept. 20	.20	.20
		P# block of 12, 6#	2.50	—
		Margin block of 4, Mr. Zip, "Use Zip Code" "Mail Early in the Day"	.60	
		P# block of 16, 6#, Mr. Zip and slogans	2.50	
a.		Vertical pair, imperf. horiz.	225.00	
		Nos. 1484-1487 (4)	.80	.80

COPERNICUS ISSUE

Nicolaus Copernicus (1473-1543), Polish Astronomer — A902

Designed by Alvin Eisenman after 18th century engraving.

LITHOGRAPHED, ENGRAVED (Giori)
Plates of 200 subjects in four panes of 50.

1973, Apr. 23		Tagged	Perf. 11	
1488	A902	8c **black & orange**	.20	.20
		P# block of 4	.65	
		Margin block of 4, Mr. Zip and "Use Zip Code"	.60	—
a.		Orange omitted	775.00	
b.		Black (engraved) omitted	875.00	
c.		Tagging omitted	125.00	

The orange can be chemically removed. Expertization of No. 1488a is required.

POSTAL SERVICE EMPLOYEES ISSUE

A tribute to US Postal Service employees. Nos. 1489-1498 are printed se-tenant in horizontal rows of 10. Emerald inscription on back, printed beneath gum in water-soluble ink, includes Postal Service emblem, "People Serving You" and a statement, differing for each of the 10 stamps, about some aspect of postal service.

Each stamp in top or bottom row has a tab with blue inscription enumerating various jobs in postal service.

Stamp Counter — A903

Mail Collection — A904

Letter Facing on Conveyor Belt — A905

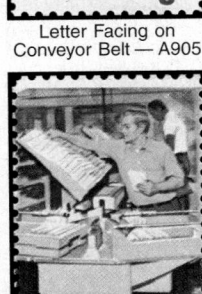

Parcel Post Sorting — A906

Mail Canceling — A907

Manual Letter Routing — A908

Electronic Letter Routing — A909

Loading Mail on Truck — A910

Mailman — A911

Rural Mail Delivery — A912

Designed by Edward Vebell.

PHOTOGRAVURE (Andreotti)
Plates of 200 subjects in four panes of 50.

1973, Apr. 30		Tagged	Perf. 10½x11	
1489	A903	8c multicolored	.20	.20
1490	A904	8c multicolored	.20	.20
1491	A905	8c multicolored	.20	.20
1492	A906	8c multicolored	.20	.20
1493	A907	8c multicolored	.20	.20
1494	A908	8c multicolored	.20	.20
1495	A909	8c multicolored	.20	.20
1496	A910	8c multicolored	.20	.20
1497	A911	8c multicolored	.20	.20
1498	A912	8c multicolored	.20	.20
a.		Strip of 10, #1489-1498	1.75	1.90
		P# block of 20, 5# and 10 tabs	3.75	—
b.		As "a," tagging omitted	300.00	—

The tagging on Nos. 1489-1498 consists of a ½-inch horizontal band of phosphor.

HARRY S. TRUMAN ISSUE

Harry S Truman, 33rd President, (1884-1972) — A913

Designed by Bradbury Thompson; photograph by Leo Stern.

GIORI PRESS PRINTING
Plates of 128 subjects in four panes of 32 each.

1973, May 8		Tagged	Perf. 11	
1499	A913	8c **carmine rose, black & blue**	.20	.20
		P# block of 4	.75	—
a.		Tagging omitted	7.50	

ELECTRONICS PROGRESS ISSUE
See No. C86.

Marconi's Spark Coil and Spark Gap — A914

Transistors and Printed Circuit Board — A915

Microphone, Speaker, Vacuum Tube and TV Camera Tube — A916

Designed by Walter and Naiad Einsel.

LITHOGRAPHED, ENGRAVED (Giori)
Plates of 200 subjects in four panes of 50.

1973, July 10		Tagged	Perf. 11	
1500	A914	6c **lilac & multicolored**	.20	.20
		P# block of 4	.55	
		Margin block of 4, Mr. Zip and "Use Zip Code"	.50	—
a.		Tagging omitted	100.00	
1501	A915	8c **tan & multicolored**	.20	.20
		P# block of 4	.70	
		Margin block of 4, Mr. Zip and "Use Zip Code"	.65	—
a.		Black (inscriptions & "U.S. 8c") omitted	350.00	
b.		Tan (background) & lilac omitted	850.00	
c.		Tagging omitted	—	

Many examples of No. 1501b are hinged. Value about one-half never hinged value.

1502	A916	15c **gray green & multicolored**	.30	.20
		P# block of 4	1.30	
		Margin block of 4, Mr. Zip and "Use Zip Code"	1.20	—
a.		Black (inscriptions & "U.S. 15c") omitted	1,250.	
		Nos. 1500-1502 (3)	.70	.60

LYNDON B. JOHNSON ISSUE

Lyndon B. Johnson, 36th President (1908-1973) — A917

Designed by Bradbury Thompson, portrait by Elizabeth Shoumatoff.

PHOTOGRAVURE (Andreotti)
Plates of 128 subjects in four panes of 32 each.

1973, Aug. 27	**Tagged**		**Perf. 11**
1503 A917 8c **black & multicolored**, *Aug. 27*		.20	.20
P# block of 12, 6#		2.20	—
a. Horiz. pair, imperf. vert.		250.00	

RURAL AMERICA ISSUE

Centenary of the introduction of Aberdeen Angus cattle into the US (#1504); of the Chautauqua Institution (#1505); and of the introduction of hard winter wheat into Kansas by Mennonite immigrants (#1506).

Angus and Longhorn Cattle — A918

Chautauqua Tent and Buggies A919

Wheat Fields and Train — A920

No. 1504 modeled by Frank Waslick after painting by F. C. "Frank" Murphy. Nos. 1505-1506 designed by John Falter.

LITHOGRAPHED, ENGRAVED (Giori)
Plates of 200 subjects in four panes of 50.

1973-74	**Tagged**		**Perf. 11**
1504 A918 8c **multicolored**, *Oct. 5, 1973*		.20	.20
P# block of 4		.65	—
Margin block of 4, Mr. Zip and "Use Zip Code"		.60	—
a. Green & red brown omitted		750.00	
b. Vert. pair, imperf. between			5,000.
c. Tagging omitted		80.00	
1505 A919 10c **multicolored**, *Aug. 6, 1974*		.20	.20
P# block of 4		.85	—
Margin block of 4, Mr. Zip and "Use Zip Code"		.80	—
a. Black (litho.) omitted		1,750.	
b. Tagging omitted			
1506 A920 10c **multicolored**, *Aug. 16, 1974*		.20	.20
P# block of 4		.85	—
Margin block of 4, Mr. Zip and "Use Zip Code"		.80	—
a. Black and blue (engr.) omitted		650.00	
b. Tagging omitted		100.00	
Nos. 1504-1506 (3)		.60	.60

CHRISTMAS ISSUE

Small Cowper Madonna, by Raphael — A921

Christmas Tree in Needlepoint — A922

Designers: No. 1507, Bradbury Thompson, using a painting in the National Gallery of Art, Washington, D.C. No. 1508, Dolli Tingle.

PHOTOGRAVURE (Andreotti)
Plates of 200 subjects in four panes of 50.

1973, Nov. 7	**Tagged**		**Perf. 10½x11**
1507 A921 8c **multicolored**		.20	.20
P# block of 12, 6#		1.75	—
Margin block of 4, Mr. Zip and "Use Zip Code"		.60	—
Pair with full vert. gutter btwn.			
1508 A922 8c **multicolored**		.20	.20
P# block of 12, 6#		1.75	—
Margin block of 4, Mr. Zip and "Use Zip Code"		.60	—
Pair with full horiz. gutter btwn.			
a. Vertical pair, imperf. between		225.00	

The tagging on Nos. 1507-1508 consists of a 20x12mm horizontal bar of phosphor.

50-Star and 13-Star Flags — A923

Jefferson Memorial and Signature — A924

Mail Transport — A925

Liberty Bell — A926

Designers: No. 1509, Ren Wicks. No. 1510, Dean Ellis. No. 1511, Randall McDougall. 6.3c, Frank Lionetti.

MULTICOLOR HUCK PRESS
Panes of 100 (10x10)

1973-74	**Tagged**		**Perf. 11x10½**
1509 A923 10c **red & blue**, *Dec. 8, 1973*		.20	.20
P# block of 20, 4-6#, 2-3 "Mail Early" and 2-3 "Use Zip Code"		4.25	—
a. Horizontal pair, imperf. between		40.00	—
b. Blue omitted		160.00	—
c. Imperf., vert. pair		750.00	—
d. Horiz. pair, imperf. vert.		900.00	—
e. Tagging omitted		9.00	—
f. Vert. pair, imperf between		—	

No. 1509 exists imperf and with red omitted from printer's waste.

ROTARY PRESS PRINTING
E.E. Plates of 400 subjects in four panes of 100.

1510 A924 10c **blue**, *Dec. 14, 1973*		.20	.20
P# block of 4		.85	—
Margin block of 4, "Use Zip Codes"		.80	—
a. Untagged (Bureau precanceled)		4.00	1.00
P# block of 4		50.00	
Margin block of 4, "Use Zip Codes"		25.00	
b. Booklet pane of 5 + label		1.65	.90
c. Booklet pane of 8		1.65	1.00
Pair with full vert.. gutter btwn.		225.00	
d. Booklet pane of 6, *Aug. 5, 1974*		5.25	1.75
e. Vert. pair, imperf. horiz.		375.00	
f. Vert. pair, imperf. between		475.00	

g. As No. 1510, tagging omitted (not Bureau precanceled)		5.00	
h. As "c," tagging omitted			
Bureau Precancels: 10 different.			

No. 1510f resulted from a paper foldover after perforating and before cutting into booklet panes.

PHOTOGRAVURE (Andreotti)
Plates of 400 subjects in four panes of 100.

1511 A925 10c **multicolored**, *Jan. 4, 1974*		.20	.20
P# block of 8, 4#		1.75	
Margin block of 4, "Use Zip Codes"		.80	
a. Yellow omitted		45.00	

Beware of stamps with yellow chemically removed offered as No. 1511a.

COIL STAMPS
ROTARY PRESS PRINTING

1973-74	**Tagged**		**Perf. 10 Vert.**
1518 A926 6.3c **brick red**, *Oct. 1, 1974*		.20	.20
Pair		.25	.20
Joint line pair		.80	—
a. Untagged (Bureau precanceled)		.35	.20
Pair		.70	.30
Joint line pair		1.65	1.65
b. Imperf., pair		150.00	
Joint line pair		400.00	
c. As "a," imperf., pair		80.00	
Joint line pair		175.00	

A total of 129 different Bureau precancels were used by 117 cities.

No. 1518c is precanceled Washington, DC. Columbus, Ohio and Garden City, N.Y. Values for Columbus pair $425, for Garden City pair $850.

MULTICOLOR HUCK PRESS

1519 A923 10c **red & blue**, *Dec. 8, 1973*		.20	.20
Pair		.40	.20
a. Imperf., pair		35.00	
b. Tagging omitted		9.00	

ROTARY PRESS PRINTING

1520 A924 10c **blue**, *Dec. 14, 1973*		.25	.20
Pair		.50	.20
Joint line pair		.75	—
a. Untagged (Bureau precanceled)		5.50	1.25
Pair		12.00	2.75
Joint line pair		185.00	—
b. Imperf., pair		30.00	
Joint line pair		50.00	

Bureau Precancels: No. 1520a, 14 diff.

VETERANS OF FOREIGN WARS ISSUE

75th anniversary of Veterans of Spanish-American and Other Foreign Wars.

Emblem and Initials of Veterans of Foreign Wars — A928

Designed by Robert Hallock.

GIORI PRESS PRINTING
Plates of 200 subjects in 4 plates of 50.

1974, Mar. 11	**Tagged**		**Perf. 11**
1525 A928 10c **red & dark blue**		.20	.20
P# block of 4		.85	—
Margin block of 4, Mr. Zip and "Use Zip Code"		.80	—
a. Tagging omitted		90.00	
b. Blue missing (PS)			

ROBERT FROST ISSUE

Robert Frost (1873-1963), Poet — A929

Designed by Paul Calle; photograph by David Rhinelander.

ROTARY PRESS PRINTING
E.E. Plates of 200 subjects in four panes of 50.

1974, Mar. 26	Tagged	Perf. 10½x11
1526 A929 10c **black**	.20	.20
P# block of 4	.85	—
Margin block of 4, Mr. Zip and "Use Zip Code"	.80	—

EXPO '74 WORLD'S FAIR ISSUE
EXPO '74 World's Fair "Preserve the Environment," Spokane, Wash., May 4-Nov. 4.

"Cosmic Jumper" and "Smiling Sage" — A930

Designed by Peter Max.

PHOTOGRAVURE (Andreotti)
Plates of 160 subjects in four panes of 40.

1974, Apr. 18	Tagged	Perf. 11
1527 A930 10c **multicolored**	.20	.20
On cover, Expo. station hand-stamp canc.		12.50
P# block of 12, 6#	2.50	
Margin block of 4, Mr. Zip, "Use Zip Code" and "Mail Early in the Day"	.80	—
P# block of 16, 6#, Mr. Zip and slogans	3.40	—

HORSE RACING ISSUE
Kentucky Derby, Churchill Downs, centenary.

Horses Rounding Turn — A931

Designed by Henry Koehler.

PHOTOGRAVURE (Andreotti)
Plates of 200 subjects in four panes of 50.

1974, May 4	Tagged	Perf. 11x10½
1528 A931 10c **yellow & multicolored**	.25	.20
P# block of 12, 6#	3.50	
Margin block of 4, Mr. Zip and "Use Zip Code"	1.10	—
a. Blue ("Horse Racing") omitted	800.00	
b. Red ("U.S. postage 10 cents") omitted	2,250.	
c. Tagging omitted	150.00	

Beware of stamps offered as No. 1528b that have traces of red.

SKYLAB ISSUE
First anniversary of the launching of Skylab I, honoring all who participated in the Skylab project.

Skylab — A932

Designed by Robert T. McCall.

LITHOGRAPHED, ENGRAVED (Giori)
Plates of 200 subjects in four panes of 50.

1974, May 14	Tagged	Perf. 11
1529 A932 10c **multicolored**	.20	.20
P# block of 4	.85	
Margin block of 4, Mr. Zip and "Use Zip Code"	.80	—
a. Vert. pair, imperf. between		
b. Tagging omitted		
c. Vert. pair, imperf. horiz.	10.00	

UNIVERSAL POSTAL UNION ISSUE
UPU cent. In the 1st row Nos. 1530-1537 are in sequence as listed. In the 2nd row Nos. 1534-1537 are followed by Nos. 1530-1533. Every row of 8 and every horizontal block of 8 contains all 8 designs. The letter writing designs are from famous works of art; some are details. The quotation on every second stamp, "Letters mingle souls," is from a letter by poet John Donne.

Michelangelo, from "School of Athens," by Raphael, 1509 — A933

"Five Feminine Virtues," by Hokusai, c. 1811 — A934

"Old Scraps," by John Fredrick Peto, 1894 — A935

"The Lovely Reader," by Jean Etienne Liotard, 1746 — A936

"Lady Writing Letter," by Gerard Terborch, 1654 — A937

Inkwell and Quill, from "Boy with a Top," by Jean-Baptiste Simeon Chardin, 1738 — A938

Mrs. John Douglas, by Thomas Gainsborough, 1784 — A939

Don Antonio Noriega, by Francisco de Goya, 1801 — A940

Designed by Bradbury Thompson.

PHOTOGRAVURE (Andreotti)
Plates of 128 subjects in four panes of 32 each.

1974, June 6	Tagged	Perf. 11
1530 A933 10c **multicolored**	.20	.20
1531 A934 10c **multicolored**	.20	.20
1532 A935 10c **multicolored**	.20	.20
1533 A936 10c **multicolored**	.20	.20
1534 A937 10c **multicolored**	.20	.20
1535 A938 10c **multicolored**	.20	.20
1536 A939 10c **multicolored**	.20	.20
1537 A940 10c **multicolored**	.20	.20
a. Block or strip of 8 (#1530-1537)	1.75	1.75

P# block of 16, 5#, "Mail Early
in the Day," Mr. Zip and "Use
Zip Code"   3.50   —
       P# block of 10, 5#; no slogans   2.25   —
b.   As "a," (block), imperf. vert.   *3,500.*

MINERAL HERITAGE ISSUE

The sequence of stamps in 1st horizontal row is
Nos. 1538-1541, 1538-1539. In 2nd row Nos. 1540-
1541 are followed by Nos. 1538-1541.

Petrified
Wood
A941

Tourmaline — A942

Amethyst
A943

Rhodochrosite — A944

Designed by Leonard F. Buckley.

LITHOGRAPHED, ENGRAVED (Giori)
Plates of 192 subjects in four panes of 48 (6x8).

1974, June 13	Tagged	Perf. 11	
1538 A941 10c **blue & multicolored**		.20	.20
a. Light blue & yellow (litho.) omitted		—	
1539 A942 10c **blue & multicolored**		.20	.20
a. Light blue (litho.) omitted		—	
b. Black & purple (engr.) omitted		—	

1540 A943 10c **blue & multicolored**		.20	.20
a. Light blue & yellow (litho.) omitted		—	
1541 A944 10c **blue & multicolored**		.20	.20
a. Block or strip of 4, #1538-1541		.80	.90
P# block of 4		.90	
Margin block of 4, Mr. Zip and			
"Use Zip Code"		.85	
b. As "a," light blue & yellow (litho.) omitted		*1,500.*	
c. Light blue (litho.) omitted		—	
d. Black & red (engr.) omitted		—	
e. Block of 4, two right stamps being Nos. 1539b and 1541d		*7,000.*	
f. As "a," tagging omitted		*225.00*	

No. 1541e is usually collected as a transition block of six or
larger.

KENTUCKY SETTLEMENT, 150th ANNIV.
Fort Harrod, first settlement in Kentucky.

Covered Wagons at Fort
Harrod — A945

Designed by David K. Stone.

LITHOGRAPHED, ENGRAVED (Giori)
Plates of 200 subjects in four panes of 50.

1974, June 15	Tagged	Perf. 11	
1542 A945 10c **green & multicolored**		.20	.20
P# block of 4		.85	
Margin block of 4, Mr. Zip and "Use Zip Code"		.80	
a. Dull black (litho.) omitted		*575.00*	
b. Green (engr. & litho.), black (engr. & litho.) & blue missing (EP)		*3,000.*	
c. Green (engr.) missing (EP)		*3,750.*	
d. Green (engr.) & black (litho.) missing (EP)		—	
e. Tagging omitted		*150.00*	
f. Blue (litho.) omitted		—	

No. 1542f was caused by an occurrence that seems to be
unique for U.S. total color omitted/missing errors. According to
the BEP, oil on the printing blanket made a small area unrecep-
tive to the blue ink. No blue at all was printed on one unique
error stamp.

AMERICAN REVOLUTION BICENTENNIAL ISSUE
First Continental Congress

Nos. 1543-1544 alternate in 1st row, Nos. 1545-
1546 in 2nd row. This arrangement is repeated
throughout the pane.

Carpenters'
Hall,
Philadelphia
A946

"We ask but
for peace . . ."
A947

"Deriving their
just
powers . . ."
A948

Independence
Hall — A949

Designed by Frank P. Conley

GIORI PRESS PRINTING
Plates of 200 subjects in four panes of 50.

1974, July 4	Tagged	Perf. 11	
1543 A946 10c **dark blue & red**		.20	.20
1544 A947 10c **gray, dark blue & red**		.20	.20
1545 A948 10c **gray, dark blue & red**		.20	.20
1546 A949 10c **red & dark blue**		.20	.20
a. Block of 4, #1543-1546		.80	.90
P# block of 4		.90	
Margin block of 4, Mr. Zip and "Use Zip Code"		.85	
b. As "a," tagging omitted		*65.00*	

Margin includes Bicentennial Commission emblem and
inscription.

ENERGY CONSERVATION ISSUE
Publicizing the importance of conserving all forms of
energy.

Molecules and Drops of
Gasoline and Oil — A950

Designed by Robert W. Bode.

LITHOGRAPHED, ENGRAVED (Giori)
Plates of 200 subjects in four panes of 50.

1974, Sept. 23	Tagged	Perf. 11	
1547 A950 10c **multicolored**		.20	.20
P# block of 4		.85	
Margin block of 4, Mr. Zip and "Use Zip Code"		.80	
a. Blue & orange omitted		*750.00*	
b. Orange & green omitted		*500.00*	
c. Green omitted		*700.00*	
d. Tagging omitted		*7.00*	

AMERICAN FOLKLORE ISSUE
Legend of Sleepy Hollow

The Headless Horseman in pursuit of Ichabod
Crane from "Legend of Sleepy Hollow," by Washington
Irving.

Headless
Horseman and
Ichabod
A951

Designed by Leonard Everett Fisher.

LITHOGRAPHED, ENGRAVED (Giori)
Plates of 200 subjects in four panes of 50.

1974, Oct. 12	Tagged	Perf. 11	
1548 A951 10c **dk. bl., blk., org. & yel.**		.20	.20
P# block of 4		.85	
Margin block of 4, Mr. Zip and "Use Zip Code"		.80	
a. Tagging omitted		*200.00*	

RETARDED CHILDREN ISSUE

Retarded Children Can Be Helped, theme of annual
convention of the National Association of Retarded
Citizens.

Retarded Child — A952

Designed by Paul Calle.

GIORI PRESS PRINTING
Plates of 200 subjects in four panes of 50.

1974, Oct. 12	Tagged	Perf. 11	
1549 A952 10c **brown red & dark brown**		.20	.20
P# block of 4		.85	—
Margin block of 4, Mr. Zip and "Use Zip Code"		.80	—
a. Tagging omitted		9.00	

CHRISTMAS ISSUE

Angel — A953

"The Road-Winter," by Currier and Ives — A954

Dove Weather Vane atop Mount Vernon — A955

Designers: No. 1550, Bradbury Thompson, using detail from the Pérussis altarpiece painted by anonymous French artist, 1480, in Metropolitan Museum of Art, New York City. No. 1551, Stevan Dohanos, using Currier and Ives print from drawing by Otto Knirsch. No. 1552, Don Hedin and Robert Geissman.

PHOTOGRAVURE (Andreotti)
Plates of 200 subjects in four panes of 50.

1974, Oct. 23	Tagged	Perf. 10½x11	
1550 A953 10c **multicolored**		.20	.20
P# block of 10, 5#		2.10	—
Margin block of 4, Mr. Zip and "Use Zip Code"		.80	—

	Perf. 11x10½		
1551 A954 10c **multicolored**		.20	.20
P# block of 12, 6#		2.50	—
Margin block of 4, Mr. Zip and "Use Zip Code"		.80	—
a. Buff omitted		12.50	
b. Tagging omitted			

No. 1551a is difficult to identify. Competent expertization is necessary.

Die Cut, Paper Backing Rouletted
Self-adhesive; Inscribed "Precanceled"

1974, Nov. 15		Untagged	
1552 A955 10c **multicolored**		.20	.20
P# block of 20, 6#, 5 slogans		4.25	
P# block of 12, 6#, 5 different slogans		2.60	
Nos. 1550-1552 (3)		.60	.60

Unused value of No. 1552 is for stamp on rouletted paper backing as issued. Used value is for stamp on piece, with or without postmark. **Most examples are becoming discolored from the adhesive. The Catalogue value is for discolored examples.**

Die cutting includes crossed slashes through dove, applied to prevent removal and re-use of the stamp. The stamp will separate into layers if soaked.

Two different machines were used to roulette the sheet.

AMERICAN ARTS ISSUE
Benjamin West (1738-1820), painter (No. 1553); Paul Laurence Dunbar (1872-1906), poet (No. 1554); David (Lewelyn) Wark Griffith (1875-1948), motion picture producer (No. 1555).

Self-portrait — A956

A957

A958

Designers: No. 1553, Bradbury Thompson; No. 1554, Walter D. Richards; No. 1555, Fred Otnes.

PHOTOGRAVURE (Andreotti)
Plates of 200 subjects in four panes of 50.

1975	Tagged	Perf. 10½x11	
1553 A956 10c **multicolored**, *Feb. 10*		.20	.20
P# block of 10, 5#		2.10	—
Margin block of 4, Mr. Zip and "Use Zip Code"		.80	—

	Perf. 11		
1554 A957 10c **multicolored**, *May 1*		.20	.20
P# block of 10, 5#		2.10	—
Margin block of 4, Mr. Zip and "Use Zip Code"		.80	—
a. Imperf., pair		1,100.	

LITHOGRAPHED, ENGRAVED (Giori)
Perf. 11

1555 A958 10c **brown & multicolored**, *May 27*		.20	.20
P# block of 4		.85	—
Margin block of 4, Mr. Zip and "Use Zip Code"		.80	—
a. Brown (engr.) omitted		575.00	
b. Tagging omitted		160.00	
Nos. 1553-1555 (3)		.60	.60

SPACE ISSUES
US space accomplishments with unmanned craft. Pioneer 10 passed within 81,000 miles of Jupiter, Dec. 10, 1973. Mariner 10 explored Venus and Mercury in 1974 and Mercury again in 1975.

Pioneer 10 Passing Jupiter A959

Mariner 10, Venus and Mercury A960

Designed by Robert McCall (No. 1556); Roy Gjertson (No. 1557).

LITHOGRAPHED, ENGRAVED (Giori)
Plates of 200 subjects in four panes of 50.

1975	Tagged	Perf. 11	
1556 A959 10c **light yellow, dark yellow, red, blue & 2 dark blues**			
Feb. 28		.20	.20
P# block of 4, Mr. Zip and "Use Zip Code"		.85	
		.80	—
a. Red & dark yellow omitted		1,000.	
b. Dark blues (engr.) omitted		675.00	
c. Tagging omitted		11.00	—
d. Dark yellow omitted		—	
	Imperfs. exist from printer's waste.		
1557 A960 10c **black, red, ultra. & bister**,			
Apr. 14		.20	.20
P# block of 4, Mr. Zip and "Use Zip Code"		.85	
		.80	—
a. Red omitted		375.00	
b. Ultramarine & bister omitted		1,575.	
c. Tagging omitted		11.00	
d. Red missing (PS)		575.00	

COLLECTIVE BARGAINING ISSUE
Collective Bargaining law, enacted 1935, in Wagner Act.

"Labor and Management" A961

Designed by Robert Hallock.

PHOTOGRAVURE (Andreotti)
Plates of 200 subjects in four panes of 50.

1975, Mar. 13	Tagged	Perf. 11	
1558 A961 10c **multicolored**		.20	.20
P# block of 8, 4#		1.75	—
Margin block of 4, Mr. Zip and "Use Zip Code"		.80	—

Imperforates exist from printer's waste.

AMERICAN BICENTENNIAL ISSUE
Contributors to the Cause
Sybil Ludington, age 16, rallied militia, Apr. 26, 1777; Salem Poor, black freeman, fought in Battle of Bunker Hill; Haym Salomon, Jewish immigrant, raised money to finance Revolutionary War; Peter Francisco, Portuguese-French immigrant, joined Continental Army at 15. Emerald inscription on back, printed beneath gum in water-soluble ink, gives thumbnail sketch of portrayed contributor.

Sybil Ludington A962

Salem Poor — A963

Haym Salomon A964

Peter Francisco
A965

Designed by Neil Boyle.

PHOTOGRAVURE (Andreotti)
Plates of 200 subjects in four panes of 50.

1975, Mar. 25	Tagged	Perf. 11x10½	
1559 A962 8c **multicolored**		.20	.20
P# block of 10, 5#		1.50	—
Margin block of 4, Mr. Zip and "Use Zip Code"		.65	—
a. Back inscriptions omitted		175.00	
1560 A963 10c **multicolored**		.20	.20
P# block of 10, 5#		2.10	—
Margin block of 4, Mr. Zip and "Use Zip Code"		.80	—
a. Back inscription omitted		175.00	
1561 A964 10c **multicolored**		.20	.20
P# block of 10, 5#		2.10	—
Margin block of 4, Mr. Zip and "Use Zip Code"		.80	—
a. Back inscription omitted		175.00	
b. Red omitted		225.00	
1562 A965 18c **multicolored**		.35	.20
P# block of 10, 5#		3.60	—
Margin block of 4, Mr. Zip and "Use Zip Code"		1.45	—
Nos. 1559-1562 (4)		.95	.80

Lexington-Concord Battle, 200th Anniv.

"Birth of Liberty," by Henry Sandham A966

Designed by Bradbury Thompson.

PHOTOGRAVURE (Andreotti)
Plates of 160 subjects in four panes of 40.

1975, Apr. 19	Tagged	Perf. 11	
1563 A966 10c **multicolored**		.20	.20
P# block of 12, 6#		2.50	—
Margin block of 4, Mr. Zip, "Use Zip Code" and "Mail Early in the Day"		.80	—
P# block of 16, 6 P#, Mr. Zip and slogans		3.40	—
a. Vert. pair, imperf. horiz.		400.00	

Bunker Hill Battle, 200th Anniv.

Battle of Bunker Hill, by John Trumbull — A967

Designed by Bradbury Thompson.

PHOTOGRAVURE (Andreotti)
Plates of 160 subjects in four panes of 40.

1975, June 17	Tagged	Perf. 11	
1564 A967 10c **multicolored**		.20	.20
P# block of 12, 6#		2.50	—
Margin block of 4, Mr. Zip, "Use Zip Code" and "Mail Early in the Day"		.80	—
P# block of 16, 6#, Mr. Zip and slogans		3.40	—

Military Uniforms

Bicentenary of US Military Services. Nos. 1565-1566 alternate in one row, Nos. 1567-1568 in next row.

Soldier with Flintlock Musket, Uniform Button — A968

Sailor with Grappling Hook, First Navy Jack, 1775 — A969

Marine with Musket, Fullrigged Ship — A970

Militiaman with Musket and Powder Horn — A971

Designed by Edward Vebell.

PHOTOGRAVURE (Andreotti)
Plates of 200 subjects in four panes of 50.

1975, July 4	Tagged	Perf. 11	
1565 A968 10c **multicolored**		.20	.20
a. Tagging omitted		—	
1566 A969 10c **multicolored**		.20	.20
1567 A970 10c **multicolored**		.20	.20
1568 A971 10c **multicolored**		.20	.20
a. Block of 4, #1565-1568		.85	.90
P# block of 12, 6#		2.50	—
P# block of 20, 6#, Mr. Zip and slogans		4.50	—
Margin block of 4, Mr. Zip and "Use Zip Code"		1.00	—

APOLLO SOYUZ SPACE ISSUE

Apollo Soyuz space test project, Russo-American cooperation, launched July 15; link-up, July 17. Nos. in the 1st row, No. 1569 is in 1st and 3rd space, No. 1570 is in 2nd space; in the 2nd row No. 1570 is in 1st and 3rd space, No. 1569 in 2nd space, etc.

Participating US and USSR crews: Thomas P. Stafford, Donald K. Slayton, Vance D. Brand, Aleksei A. Leonov, Valery N. Kubasov.

Apollo and Soyuz after Link-up, and Earth — A972

Spacecraft before Link-up, Earth and Project Emblem — A973

Illustrations reduced.

Designed by Robert McCall (No. 1569) and Anatoly M. Aksamit of USSR (No. 1570).

PHOTOGRAVURE (Andreotti)
Plates of 96 subjects in four panes of 24 each.

1975, July 15	Tagged	Perf. 11	
1569 A972 10c **multicolored**		.20	.20
Pair with full horiz. gutter btwn.		—	
1570 A973 10c **multicolored**		.20	.20
a. Pair, #1569-1570		.45	.40
P# block of 12, 6#		2.50	—
Margin block of 4, Mr. Zip, "Use Zip Code"		.85	
P# block of 16, 6#, Mr. Zip, "Use Zip Code"		3.40	—
Pair with full horiz. gutter btwn.			
b. As "a," tagging omitted		30.00	
c. As "a," vert. pair imperf. horiz.		2,100.	
d. As "a," yellow omitted		1,000.	

Nos. 1569-1570 totally imperforate are printer's waste. See Russia Nos. 4339-4340.

INTERNATIONAL WOMEN'S YEAR ISSUE
International Women's Year 1975.

Worldwide Equality for Women A974

Designed by Miriam Schottland.

PHOTOGRAVURE (Andreotti)
Plates of 200 subjects in four panes of 50.

1975, Aug. 26	Tagged	Perf. 11x10½	
1571 A974 10c **blue, orange & dark blue**		.20	.20
P# block of 6, 3#		1.30	—
Margin block of 4, Mr. Zip and "Use Zip Code"		.80	—
a. Tagging omitted		10.00	

US POSTAL SERVICE BICENTENNIAL ISSUE

Nos. 1572-1573 alternate in 1st row, Nos. 1574-1575 in 2nd row. This arrangement is repeated throughout the pane.

Stagecoach and Trailer Truck — A975

Old and New Locomotives A976

Early Mail Plane and Jet — A977

Satellite for Transmission of Mailgrams A978

Designed by James L. Womer.

PHOTOGRAVURE (Andreotti)
Plates of 200 subjects in four panes of 50.

1975, Sept. 3		Tagged	Perf. 11x10½	
1572	A975 10c	multicolored	.20	.20
1573	A976 10c	multicolored	.20	.20
1574	A977 10c	multicolored	.20	.20
1575	A978 10c	multicolored	.20	.20
a.		Block of 4, #1572-1575	.85	.90
		P# block of 12, 6#	2.50	—
		P# block of 20, 6#, Mr. Zip and slogans	4.50	—
		Margin block of 4, Mr. Zip and "Use Zip Code"	1.00	—
b.		As "a," red "10c" omitted		

WORLD PEACE THROUGH LAW ISSUE
A prelude to 7th World Law Conference of the World Peace Through Law Center at Washington, D.C., Oct. 12-17.

Law Book, Gavel, Olive Branch and Globe — A979

Designed by Melbourne Brindle.

GIORI PRESS PRINTING
Plates of 200 subjects in four panes of 50.

1975, Sept. 29		Tagged	Perf. 11	
1576	A979 10c	green, Prussian blue & rose brown	.20	.20
		P# block of 4	.85	
		Margin block of 4, Mr. Zip and "Use Zip Code"	.80	—
a.		Tagging omitted	7.50	
b.		Horiz. pair, imperf vert.	7,500.	

BANKING AND COMMERCE ISSUE
Banking and commerce in the U.S., and for the Centennial Convention of the American Bankers Association.

Designed by V. Jack Ruther.

Engine Turning, Indian Head Penny, Morgan-type Silver Dollar — A980

Seated Liberty Quarter, $20 Gold Double Eagle and Engine Turning — A981

LITHOGRAPHED, ENGRAVED (Giori)
Plates of 160 subjects in four panes of 40.

1975, Oct. 6		Tagged	Perf. 11	
1577	A980 10c	multicolored	.25	.20
1578	A981 10c	multicolored	.25	.20
a.		Pair, #1577-1578	.50	.40
		P# block of 4	1.10	
		Margin block of 4, Mr. Zip and "Use Zip Code"	1.00	—
b.		As "a," brown & blue (litho) omitted	2,000.	
c.		As "a," brown, blue & yellow (litho) omitted	2,500.	
d.		As No. 1578, tagging omitted		—

CHRISTMAS ISSUE

Madonna and Child, by Domenico Ghirlandaio — A982

Christmas Card, by Louis Prang, 1878 — A983

Designed by Stevan Dohanos.

PHOTOGRAVURE (Andreotti)
Plates of 200 subjects in four panes of 50.

1975, Oct. 14		Tagged	Perf. 11	
1579	A982 (10c)	multicolored	.20	.20
		P# block of 12, 6#	2.50	—
		Margin block of 4, Mr. Zip and "Use Zip Code"	.80	—
		Plate flaw ("d" damaged) (36741-36746 LL 47)	5.00	—
a.		Imperf., pair	90.00	
		Perf. 11.2		
1580	A983 (10c)	multicolored	.20	.20
		P# block of 12, 6#	2.50	—
		Margin block of 4, Mr. Zip and "Use Zip Code"	.80	—
a.		Imperf., pair	90.00	
c.		Perf. 10.9	.25	.20
		P# block of 12, 6#	3.50	—
		Margin block of 4, Mr. Zip and "Use Zip Code"	1.00	—
		Perf. 10.5x11.3		
1580B	A983 (10c)	multicolored,	.65	.20
		P# block of 12, 6#	15.00	—
		Margin block of 4, Mr. Zip and "Use Zip Code"	2.75	—

AMERICANA ISSUE

Inkwell and Quill — A984

Speaker's Stand — A985

Early Ballot Box — A987

Books, Bookmark, Eyeglasses — A988

Dome of Capitol — A994

Contemplation of Justice, by J. E. Fraser — A995

Early American Printing Press — A996

Torch, Statue of Liberty — A997

Liberty Bell — A998

Eagle and Shield — A999

Fort McHenry Flag (15 Stars) — A1001

Head, Statue of Liberty — A1002

Old North Church, Boston — A1003

Fort Nisqually, Wash. — A1004

Sandy Hook Lighthouse, NJ — A1005

Morris Township School No. 2, Devils Lake, ND — A1006

Iron "Betty" Lamp, Plymouth Colony, 17th-18th Centuries — A1007

Rush Lamp and Candle Holder — A1008

Kerosene Table Lamp — A1009

Railroad Conductor's Lantern, c. 1850 — A1010

Designed by: 2c, 4c, 15c, V. Jack Ruther Robert Hallock. 3c, Clarence Holbert. 9c, 10c, 11c, Walter Brooks. 12c, George Mercer. No. 1595, Bernard Glassman. No. 1596, James L. Womer.

ROTARY PRESS PRINTING
E.E. Plates of 400 subjects in four panes of 100.

1975-81   **Tagged**   *Perf. 11x10½*
Size: 18½x22½mm

1581 A984	1c **dark blue**, *greenish*, shiny gum, *Dec. 8, 1977*		.20	.20
	P# block of 4		.25	—
	Margin block of 4, "Use Zip Codes"		.20	—
	Dull gum		.20	
	P# block of 4		.50	
	Zip block of 4		.20	
	Pair with full vert. gutter btwn.		—	
a.	Untagged (Bureau precanceled)		4.50	1.50
	P# block of 4		22.50	
	Margin block of 4, "Use Zip Codes"		18.50	
c.	White paper, dull gum		—	
d.	Tagging omitted (not Bureau precanceled), shiny gum		4.50	
	Dull gum		4.00	
1582 A985	2c **red brown**, *greenish*, shiny gum, *Dec. 8, 1977*		.20	.20
	P# block of 4		.25	—
	Margin block of 4, "Use Zip Codes"		.20	—
	Dull gum		.20	
	P# block of 4		2.50	
	Zip block of 4		.50	
a.	Untagged (Bureau precanceled)		4.50	1.50
	P# block of 4		22.50	
			18.50	
b.	Cream paper, dull gum, *1981*		.20	.20
	P# block of 4		.25	
	Zip block of 4		.20	
c.	Tagging omitted (not Bureau precanceled)		4.50	
1584 A987	3c **olive**, *greenish*, shiny gum, *Dec. 8, 1977*		.20	.20
	P# block of 4		.35	—
	Margin block of 4, "Use Zip Codes"		.25	—
	Dull gum		.20	
	P# block of 4		.50	
	Zip block of 4		.30	
	Pair with full horiz. gutter btwn.		—	
a.	Untagged (Bureau precanceled)		.75	.50
	P# block of 4		9.50	
	Zip block of 4		5.00	
b.	Tagging omitted (not Bureau precanceled)		7.50	

Values for No. 1584a are for the lines-only precancel. Also known with city precancels, and valued at $100 thus.

1585 A988	4c **rose magenta**, *cream*, shiny gum, *Dec. 8, 1977*		.20	.20
	P# block of 4		.50	—
	Margin block of 4, "Use Zip Code"		.35	—
	Dull gum		.20	
	P# block of 4		1.10	
	Zip block of 4		.65	
a.	Untagged (Bureau precanceled)		1.00	.75
	P# block of 4		13.50	
	Zip block of 4		6.00	
b.	Tagging omitted (not Bureau precanceled), dull gum		65.00	
	Shiny gum		35.00	

Values for No. 1585a are for the lines-only precancel. Also known with city precancels, and worth more thus.

Size: 17½x20½mm

1590 A994	9c **slate green** (from bklt. pane #1623a), *Mar. 11, 1977*		.45	.20
	Pair with full horiz. gutter between		—	

Perf. 10x9¾

1590A A994	9c **slate green** (from bklt. pane #1623Bc), *Mar. 11, 1977*		17.50	15.00

Size: 18½x22½mm

Perf. 11x10½

1591 A994	9c **slate green**, *gray*, shiny gum, *Nov. 24, 1975*		.20	.20
	P# block of 4		.85	—
	Margin block of 4, "Use Zip Code"		.80	—
	Dull gum		1.00	
	P# block of 4		5.00	
	Zip block of 4		4.25	
a.	Untagged (Bureau precanceled)		1.75	1.00
	P# block of 4		50.00	
	Zip block of 4		11.50	
b.	Tagging omitted (not Bureau precanceled)		5.00	

Values for No. 1591a are for the lines-only precancel. Also known with city precancels, and valued at $32.50 thus.

1592 A995	10c **violet**, *gray*, shiny gum, *Nov. 17, 1977*		.20	.20
	P# block of 4		.90	—
	Margin block of 4, "Use Zip Code"		.80	—
	Dull gum		.20	
	P# block of 4		.90	
	Zip block of 4		.80	
a.	Untagged (Bureau precanceled, Chicago)		9.50	5.00

	P# block of 4		95.00	
	Zip block of 4		42.50	
b.	Tagging omitted (not Bureau precanceled)		7.50	
1593 A996	11c **orange**, *gray*, *Nov. 13, 1975*		.20	.20
	P# block of 4		.90	
	Margin block of 4, "Use Zip Code"		.85	
	Pair with full horiz. gutter between		—	
a.	Tagging omitted		4.00	
1594 A997	12c **red brown**, *beige*, *Apr. 8, 1981*		.25	.20
	P# block of 4		1.60	
	Zip block of 4		1.10	
a.	Tagging omitted		5.00	
1595 A998	13c **brown** (from bklt. pane), *Oct. 31, 1975*		.30	.20
a.	Booklet pane of 6		2.25	1.00
b.	Booklet pane of 7 + label		2.25	1.00
c.	Booklet pane of 8		2.25	1.00
d.	Booklet pane of 5 + label, *Apr. 2, 1976*		1.75	1.00
e.	Vert. pair, imperf. btwn.		1,250.	
f.	Booklet pane of 6		—	
g.	Horiz. pair, imperf. btwn.		—	
h.	As "a," miscut and inserted upside down into booklet cover, imperf below bottom stamps and with "tab" at bottom		—	

Nos. 1595e and 1595g resulted from paper foldovers after perforating and before cutting into panes. Beware of printer's waste consisting of complete panes with perfs around all outside edges.

PHOTOGRAVURE (Andreotti)
Plates of 400 subjects in four panes of 100.
Perf. 11.2

1596 A999	13c **multicolored**, *Dec. 1, 1975*		.25	.20
	P# block of 12, 6#		3.25	
	P# block of 20, 6# and slogans		5.50	
	Margin block of 4, "Use Zip Code"		1.00	
	Pair with full horiz. gutter btwn.		150.00	
a.	Imperf., pair		40.00	
b.	Yellow omitted		115.00	
d.	Line perforated		27.50	
	P# block of 12, 6#		375.00	

On No. 1596 the entire sheet is perforated at one time so the perforations meet perfectly at the corners of the stamp. On No. 1596d the perforations do not line up perfectly and are perf. 11.

ENGRAVED (Combination Press)
Plates of 460 subjects (20x23) in panes of 100 (10x10)

1597 A1001	15c **gray, dark blue & red**, large block tagging, *June 30, 1978*		.30	.20
	P# block of 6		1.90	
	P# block of 20, 1-2#		6.50	
a.	Small block tagging		.30	.20
	P# block of 6		1.90	
	P# block of 20, 1-2#		6.50	
b.	Gray omitted		350.00	
c.	Vert. strip of 3, imperf. btwn. and at top or bottom		375.00	
d.	Tagging omitted		3.00	
e.	Imperf., vert. pair		15.00	

Plate number appears 3 times on each plate of 23 rows. With no separating gutters, each pane has only left or right sheet margin. Plate numbers appear on both margins; there are no slogans.

ENGRAVED
Perf. 11x10½

1598 A1001	15c **gray, dark blue & red** (from bklt. pane), *June 30, 1978*		.40	.20
a.	Booklet pane of 8		4.25	.80
1599 A1002	16c **blue**, *Mar. 31, 1978*		.35	.20
	P# block of 4		1.90	
	Margin block of 4, "Use Correct Zip Code"		1.40	
1603 A1003	24c **red**, *blue*, *Nov. 14, 1975*		.50	.20
	P# block of 4		2.25	
	Margin block of 4, "Use Zip Code"		2.00	
a.	Tagging omitted		7.50	
1604 A1004	28c **brown**, *blue*, shiny gum, *Aug. 11, 1978*		.55	.20
	P# block of 4		2.75	
	Margin block of 4, "Use Correct Zip Code"		2.25	
	Dull gum		1.10	
	P# block of 4		10.00	
	Zip block of 4		5.00	
1605 A1005	29c **blue**, *light blue*, shiny gum, *Apr. 14, 1978*		.60	.20
	P# block of 4		3.00	
	Margin block of 4, "Use Correct Zip Code"		2.40	
	Dull gum		2.00	
	P# block of 4		15.00	
	Zip block of 4		9.00	
1606 A1006	30c **green**, *blue*, *Aug. 27, 1979*		.55	.20
	P# block of 4		2.40	
	Margin block of 4, "Use Correct Zip Code"		2.25	
a.	Tagging omitted		65.00	

LITHOGRAPHED AND ENGRAVED
Perf. 11

1608 A1007	50c **tan, black & orange**, *Sept. 11, 1979*		.85	.20
	P# block of 4		3.75	
	Margin block of 4, "Use Correct Zip Code"		3.50	
a.	Black omitted		250.00	
b.	Vert. pair, imperf. horiz.		1,500.	
c.	Tagging omitted		16.00	

Beware of examples offered as No. 1608b that have blind perfs.

1610 A1008	$1 **tan, brown, orange & yellow**, *July 2, 1979*		2.00	.20
	P# block of 4		8.50	
	Margin block of 4, "Use Correct Zip Code"		8.00	
	Pair with full vert. gutter btwn.		—	
a.	Brown (engraved) omitted		225.00	
b.	Tan, orange & yellow omitted		250.00	
c.	Brown inverted		21,000.	
d.	Tagging (engraved) omitted		12.50	
1611 A1009	$2 **tan, dark green, orange & yellow**, *Nov. 16, 1978*		3.75	.75
	P# block of 4		16.00	
	Margin block of 4, "Use Correct Zip Code"		15.00	
a.	Tagging omitted		—	
1612 A1010	$5 **tan, red brown, yellow & orange**, *Aug. 23, 1979*		8.50	1.75
	P# block of 4		36.00	
	Margin block of 4, "Use Correct Zip Code"		34.00	
	Nos. 1581-1612 (23)		38.50	21.50

Nos. 1590, 1590A, 1595, 1598, 1623 and 1623b were issued only in booklets. All stamps have one or two straight edges.

Bureau Precancels: 1c, 3 diff., 2c, Chicago, Greensboro, NC, 3c, 6 diff., 4c, Chicago, lines only, No. 1591a, 4 diff., No. 1596, 5 diff., 30c, lines only, 50c, 2 spacings, lines only, $1, 2 spacings, lines only. The 30c, 50c, $1 and No. 1596 are precanceled on tagged stamps.

Six-string Guitar — A1011

Saxhorns — A1012

Drum — A1013

Steinway Grand Piano, 1857 — A1014

Designers: 3.1c, George Mercer. 7.7c, Susan Robb. 7.9c, Bernard Glassman. 10c, Walter Brooks. 15c, V. Jack Ruther.

COIL STAMPS
ENGRAVED

1975-79   *Perf. 10 Vertically*

1613 A1011	3.1c **brown**, *yellow*, *Oct. 25, 1979*		.20	.20
	Pair		.25	.20
	Joint line pair		1.25	—
a.	Untagged (Bureau precanceled, lines only)		.35	.35
	Pair		.70	.70
	Joint line pair		7.00	
b.	Imperf., pair		1,200.	
	Joint line pair		—	
1614 A1012	7.7c **brown**, *bright yellow*, *Nov. 20, 1976*		.20	.20
	Pair		.40	.20
	Joint line pair		.90	
a.	Untagged (Bureau precanceled)		.40	.30
	Pair		.80	.60
	Joint line pair		3.25	
b.	As "a," imperf., pair		1,400.	
	Joint line pair		3,250.	

A total of 160 different Bureau precancels were used by 153 cities.

No. 1614b is precanceled Washington, DC. Also exists with Marion, OH precancel; value $1,950 for pair.

1615 A1013	7.9c **carmine**, *yellow*, shiny gum, *Apr. 23, 1976*		.20	.20
	Pair		.40	.20
	Joint line pair		.75	
	Dull gum		1.00	
	Pair		2.00	
	Joint line pair		6.00	
a.	Untagged (Bureau precanceled), shiny gum		.40	.40

		Pair	.80	.80
		Joint line pair	2.75	
	Dull gum		.45	
		Pair	.90	
		Joint line pair	4.50	
b.	Imperf., pair		525.00	

A total of 109 different Bureau precancels were used by 107 cities plus two types of CAR. RT./SORT.

1615C A1014	8.4c **dark blue,** *yellow,* shiny gum, *July 13, 1978*	.20	.20
	Pair	.40	.20
	Joint line pair	3.25	.30
d.	Untagged (Bureau precanceled), shiny gum	.50	.40
	Pair	1.00	.80
	Joint line pair	4.25	
	Dull gum	.40	
	Pair	.80	
	Joint line pair	3.25	
e.	As "d," pair, imperf. between	45.00	
	Joint line pair	110.00	
f.	As "d," imperf., pair	15.00	
	Joint line pair	25.00	

A total of 145 different Bureau precancels were used by 144 cities.

No. 1615Ce is precanceled with lines only. No. 1615Cf is precanceled (value shown) and also exists in pairs precanceled Newark, N.J. ($25.), Brownstown, Ind. ($900), Oklahoma City, Okla. ($1,500.) and Washington, DC ($1,250.).

1616 A994	9c **slate green,** *gray,* Mar. 5, 1976	.20	.20
	Pair	.40	.20
	Joint line pair	.90	
a.	Imperf., pair	135.00	
	Joint line pair	275.00	
b.	Untagged (Bureau precanceled), shiny gum	1.15	.75
	Pair	2.30	1.50
	Joint line pair	42.50	
	Dull gum	.75	
	Pair	1.50	
	Joint line pair	19.50	
c.	As "b," imperf., pair	650.00	
	Joint line pair		

Values for No. 1616b with shiny gum are for the lines-only precancel. Also known with city precancels, and worth more thus.

No. 1616c is precanceled Pleasantville, NY.

1617 A995	10c **violet,** *gray,* shiny gum, Nov. 4, 1977	.20	.20
	Pair	.40	.20
	Joint line pair	1.00	
	Dull gum	.30	
	Pair	.60	
	Joint line pair	2.50	
a.	Untagged (Bureau precanceled, shiny gum)	42.50	1.35
	Pair	90.00	2.75
	Joint line pair	1,150.	
	Dull gum	1.35	
	Pair	2.75	
	Joint line pair	47.50	
b.	Imperf., pair, shiny gum	55.00	
	Joint line pair, shiny gum	115.00	
	Imperf., pair, dull gum	50.00	
	Joint line pair, dull gum	100.00	
c.	As "a," imperf pair, dull gum	3,500.	
	Joint line pair, dull gum	4,500.	
1618 A998	13c **brown,** shiny gum, Nov. 25, 1975	.25	.20
	Pair	.50	.20
	Joint line pair	.75	
	Dull gum	1.50	
	Pair	3.00	
	Joint line pair	9.00	
a.	Untagged (Bureau precanceled), shiny gum	5.75	.75
	Pair	12.00	1.50
	Joint line pair	90.00	
	Dull gum	.75	
	Pair	1.50	
	Joint line pair	35.00	
b.	Imperf., pair	22.50	
	Joint line pair	45.00	
g.	Vertical pair, imperf. between		
h.	As "a," imperf., pair		
j.	As No. 1618, shiny gum, tagging omitted		

Values for No. 1618a with shiny gum are for the lines-only precancel. Also known with city precancels, and worth more thus.

1618C A1001	15c **gray, dark blue & red,** June 30, 1978	.75	.20
	Pair	1.50	.20
d.	Imperf., pair	20.00	
e.	Pair, imperf. between	125.00	
f.	Gray omitted	30.00	
i.	Tagging omitted	50.00	
1619 A1002	16c **ultramarine,** overall tagging, Mar. 31, 1978	.35	.20
	Pair	.70	.20
	Joint line pair	1.50	
a.	Block tagging	.50	.20
	Pair	1.00	.20
	Nos. 1613-1619 (9)	2.55	1.80

No. 1619a (the Huck press printing) has a white background without bluish tinge, is a fraction of a millimeter smaller than No. 1619 (the Cottrell press printing) and has no joint lines.
Bureau Precancels: 9c, 7 diff., 10c, 3 diff., 13c, 12 diff.
See Nos. 1811, 1813, 1816.

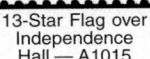

13-Star Flag over Independence Hall — A1015

Flag over Capitol — A1016

Designers: No. 1622, Melbourne Brindle. No. 1623, Esther Porter.

Panes of 100 (10x10) each.

1975-81			**Perf. 11x10¾**
1622 A1015 13c **dk blue, red & brown red,** Nov. 15, 1975	.25	.20
	P# block of 20, 2-3#, 2-3 Zip, 2-3 Mail Early	5.75	
a.	Horiz. pair, imperf. between	40.00	
b.	Vertical pair, imperf.	375.00	
e.	Horiz. pair, imperf. vert.		
f.	Tagging omitted	4.00	

No. 1622 was printed on the Multicolored Huck Press. Plate markings are at top or bottom of pane. It has large block tagging and nearly vertical multiple gum ridges.
See note after No. 1338F for marginal markings.

		Perf. 11¼	
1622C A1015 13c **dk blue, red & brown red,** 1981	1.00	.25
	P# block of 20, 1-2#, 1-2 Zip	32.50	
	P# block of 6	20.00	
d.	Vertical pair, imperf	120.00	

No. 1622C was printed on the Combination Press. Plate markings are at sides of pane. It has small block tagging and shiny flat gum.
See note after No. 1703.

BOOKLET STAMPS

1977, Mar. 11	**Engr.**	**Perf. 11x10½**	
1623 A1016 13c **blue & red**	.25	.20
a.	Booklet pane, 1 #1590 + 7 #1623	2.25	1.25
d.	Pair, #1590 & #1623	.70	1.00
f.	Tagging omitted		
g.	As "a," tagging omitted		

		Perf. 10x9¾	
1623B A1016 13c **blue & red**	.80	.80
c.	Booklet pane, 1 #1590A + 7 #1623B	22.50	
e.	Pair, #1590A & #1623B	18.50	18.50

COIL STAMP

1975, Nov. 15		**Perf. 10 Vertically**	
1625 A1015 13c **dk blue, red & brown red**	.35	.20
	Pair	.70	.20
a.	Imperf., pair	20.00	
b.	Tagging omitted		

No. 1625 was printed on both the Huck and "B" presses. Huck press printings have pebbled gum (gummed on press), while "B" press printings have smooth gum (pregummed paper). Huck press printings often show portions of a joint line, but this feature is not consistent. Values for coils and imperf coils are the same for both varieties.

AMERICAN BICENTENNIAL ISSUE
The Spirit of '76

Designed after painting by Archibald M. Willard in Abbot Hall, Marblehead, Massachusetts. Nos. 1629-1631 printed in continuous design.

Left panes contain 3 No. 1631a and one No. 1629; right panes contain one No. 1631 and 3 No. 1631a.

Drummer Boy — A1019

Old Drummer — A1020

Fifer — A1021

Designed by Vincent E. Hoffman.

PHOTOGRAVURE (Andreotti)
Plates of 200 subjects in four panes of 50.

1976, Jan. 1	**Tagged**	**Perf. 11**	
1629 A1019 13c **blue violet & multi**	.25	.20
a.	Imperf., vert. pair		
1630 A1020 13c **blue violet & multi**	.25	.20
1631 A1021 13c **blue violet & multi**	.25	.20
a.	Strip of 3, #1629-1631	.75	.75
	P# block of 12, 5#	3.50	
	P# block of 20, 5#, slogans	5.75	
b.	As "a," imperf.	800.00	
c.	Imperf., vert. pair, #1631	700.00	

INTERPHIL ISSUE

Interphil 76 International Philatelic Exhibition, Philadelphia, Pa., May 29-June 6.

"Interphil 76" A1022

Designed by Terrence W. McCaffrey.

LITHOGRAPHED, ENGRAVED (Giori)
Plates of 200 subjects of four panes of 50.

1976, Jan. 17	**Tagged**	**Perf. 11**	
1632 A1022 13c **dark blue & red (engr.), ultra. & red (litho.)**	.20	.20
	P# block of 4	1.00	
	Margin block of 4, Mr. Zip and "Use Zip Code"	1.00	
a.	Dark blue & red (engr.) missing (CM)		
b.	Tagging omitted	85.00	
c.	Red (engr,) missing (CM)		

AMERICAN BICENTENNIAL ISSUE

Illustration reduced.

Designed by Walt Reed.

PHOTOGRAVURE (Andreotti)
Plates of 200 subjects in four panes of 50.

1976, Feb. 23	**Tagged**	**Perf. 11**	
1633 A1023 13c Delaware	.30	.25
1634 A1024 13c Pennsylvania	.30	.25
1635 A1025 13c New Jersey	.30	.25
1636 A1026 13c Georgia	.30	.25
1637 A1027 13c Connecticut	.30	.25
1638 A1028 13c Massachusetts	.30	.25
1639 A1029 13c Maryland	.30	.25
1640 A1030 13c South Carolina	.30	.25
1641 A1031 13c New Hampshire	.30	.25
1642 A1032 13c Virginia	.30	.25
1643 A1033 13c New York	.30	.25
1644 A1034 13c North Carolina	.30	.25
1645 A1035 13c Rhode Island	.30	.25
1646 A1036 13c Vermont	.30	.25
1647 A1037 13c Kentucky	.30	.25
1648 A1038 13c Tennessee	.30	.25
1649 A1039 13c Ohio	.30	.25
1650 A1040 13c Louisiana	.30	.25
1651 A1041 13c Indiana	.30	.25
1652 A1042 13c Mississippi	.30	.25
1653 A1043 13c Illinois	.30	.25
1654 A1044 13c Alabama	.30	.25
1655 A1045 13c Maine	.30	.25
1656 A1046 13c Missouri	.30	.25
1657 A1047 13c Arkansas	.30	.25
1658 A1048 13c Michigan	.30	.25
1659 A1049 13c Florida	.30	.25
1660 A1050 13c Texas	.30	.25
1661 A1051 13c Iowa	.30	.25
1662 A1052 13c Wisconsin	.30	.25
1663 A1053 13c California	.30	.25
1664 A1054 13c Minnesota	.30	.25
1665 A1055 13c Oregon	.30	.25
1666 A1056 13c Kansas	.30	.25
1667 A1057 13c West Virginia	.30	.25
a.	Tagging omitted		
1668 A1058 13c Nevada	.30	.25
1669 A1059 13c Nebraska	.30	.25

1670	A1060	13c	Colorado	.30	.25
1671	A1061	13c	North Dakota	.30	.25
1672	A1062	13c	South Dakota	.30	.25
1673	A1063	13c	Montana	.30	.25
1674	A1064	13c	Washington	.30	.25
1675	A1065	13c	Idaho	.30	.25
1676	A1066	13c	Wyoming	.30	.25
1677	A1067	13c	Utah	.30	.25
1678	A1068	13c	Oklahoma	.30	.25
1679	A1069	13c	New Mexico	.30	.25
1680	A1070	13c	Arizona	.30	.25
1681	A1071	13c	Alaska	.30	.25
1682	A1072	13c	Hawaii	.30	.25
a.			Pane of 50	17.50	15.00

TELEPHONE CENTENNIAL ISSUE

Centenary of first telephone call by Alexander Graham Bell, March 10, 1876.

Bell's Telephone Patent Application, 1876 — A1073

Designed by George Tscherny.

ENGRAVED (Giori)
Plates of 200 subjects in four panes of 50.

				Perf. 11	
1976, Mar. 10			**Tagged**		
1683	A1073	13c	**black, purple & red,** *tan*	.25	.20
			P# block of 4	1.10	—
			Margin block of 4, Mr. Zip and		
			"Use Zip Code"	1.00	—
a.			Black & purple missing (EP)	450.00	
b.			Red missing (EP)	—	
c.			All colors missing (EP)	—	

On No. 1683a, the errors have only tiny traces of red present, so are best collected as a horiz. strip of 5 with 2 or 3 error stamps. No. 1683c also must be collected as a transitional strip.

State Flags A1023-A1072

COMMERCIAL AVIATION ISSUE

50th anniversary of first contract airmail flights: Dearborn, Mich. to Cleveland, Ohio, Feb. 15, 1926; and Pasco, Wash. to Elko, Nev., Apr. 6, 1926.

Ford-Pullman Monoplane and Laird Swallow Biplane
A1074

Designed by Robert E. Cunningham.

PHOTOGRAVURE (Andreotti)
Plates of 200 subjects in four panes of 50 each

1976, Mar. 19		Tagged	Perf. 11	
1684 A1074	13c	blue & multicolored	.25	.20
		P# block of 10, 5#	2.75	—
		Margin block of 4, Mr. Zip and "Use Zip Code"	1.00	—
a.		Tagging omitted	—	

CHEMISTRY ISSUE

Honoring American chemists, in conjunction with the centenary of the American Chemical Society.

Various Flasks, Separatory Funnel, Computer Tape — A1075

Designed by Ken Davies.

PHOTOGRAVURE (Andreotti)
Plates of 200 subjects in four panes of 50.

1976, Apr. 6		Tagged	Perf. 11	
1685 A1075	13c	multicolored	.25	.20
		P# block of 12, 6#	3.25	—
		Margin block of 4, Mr. Zip and "Use Zip Code"	1.00	—
		Pair with full vert. gutter btwn.	—	

AMERICAN BICENTENNIAL ISSUES
SOUVENIR SHEETS

Designs, from Left to Right, No. 1686: a, Two British officers. b, Gen. Benjamin Lincoln. c, George Washington. d, John Trumbull, Col. Cobb, von Steuben, Lafayette, Thomas Nelson. e, Alexander Hamilton, John Laurens, Walter Stewart (all vert.).

No. 1687: a, John Adams, Roger Sherman, Robert R. Livingston. b, Jefferson, Franklin. c, Thomas Nelson, Jr., Francis Lewis, John Witherspoon, Samuel Huntington. d, John Hancock, Charles Thomson. e, George Read, John Dickinson, Edward Rutledge (a, d, vert., b, c, e, horiz.).

No. 1688: a, Boatsman. b, Washington. c, Flag bearer. d, Men in boat. e, Men on shore (a, d, horiz., b, c, e, vert.).

No. 1689: a, Two officers. b, Washington. c, Officer, black horse. d, Officer, white horse. e, Three soldiers (a, c, e, horiz., b, d, vert.).

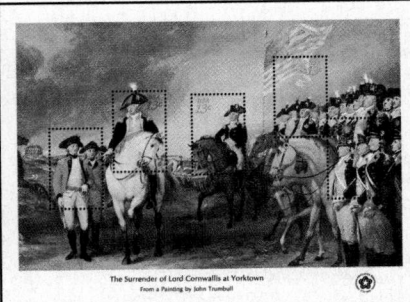

Surrender of Cornwallis at Yorktown, by John Trumbull — A1076

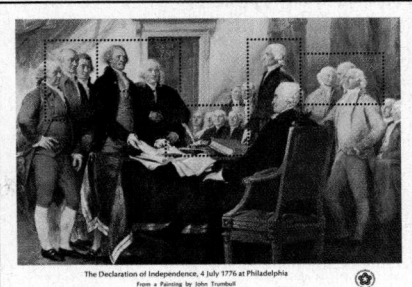

Declaration of Independence, by John Trumbull — A1077

Washington Crossing the Delaware, by Emmanuel Leutze / Eastman Johnson — A1078

Washington Reviewing Army at Valley Forge, by William T. Trego — A1079

Illustrations reduced.

Designed by Vincent E. Hoffman.

LITHOGRAPHED
Plates of 30 subjects in six panes of 5 each.

1976, May 29		Tagged	Perf. 11	
1686 A1076	Sheet of 5		3.25	2.25
a.-e.	13c multicolored		.45	.40
f.	"USA/13c" omitted on "b," "c" & "d," imperf, tagging omitted	—	1,750.
g.	"USA/13c" omitted on "a" & "e"	450.00	—
h.	Imperf., tagging omitted	—	2,250.
i.	"USA/13c" omitted on "b," "c" & "d"	450.00	
j.	"USA/13c" double on "b"	—	
k.	"USA/13c" omitted on "c" & "d"	750.00	
l.	"USA/13c" omitted on "e"	550.00	
m.	"USA/13c" omitted, imperf., tagging omitted	—	
n.	As "g," imperf., tagging omitted	—	
o.	"USA/13c" missing on "a" (PS)	—	
p.	As No. 1686, tagging omitted	—	
q.	"USA/13c" omitted on "a"	—	
r.	Imperf., tagged	—	
1687 A1077	Sheet of 5		4.25	3.25
a.-e.	18c multicolored		.55	.55
f.	Design & marginal inscriptions omitted	3,000.	
g.	"USA/18c" omitted on "a" & "c"	600.00	—
h.	"USA/18c" omitted on "b," "d" & "e"	400.00	
i.	"USA/18c" omitted on "d"	425.00	475.00
j.	Black omitted in design	2,000.	
k.	"USA/18c" omitted, imperf., tagging omitted	2,000.	
m.	"USA/18c" omitted on "b" & "e"	500.00	
n.	"USA/18c" omitted on "b" & "d"	1,000.	
p.	Imperf. (tagged)	1,000.	
q.	"USA/18c" omitted on "c"	—	
r.	Yellow omitted	—	
s.	"USA/18c" missing on "a," "c" and "d" (PS)	—	

t.	"USA/18c" missing on "a" and "d" (PS)	—	
1688 A1078	Sheet of 5		5.25	4.25
a.-e.	24c multicolored		.70	.70
f.	"USA/24c" omitted, imperf., tagging omitted	950.00	
g.	"USA/24c" omitted on "d" & "e"	450.00	450.00
h.	Design & marginal inscriptions omitted	2,750.	
i.	"USA/24c" omitted on "a," "b" & "c"	450.00	400.00
j.	Imperf., tagging omitted	1,500.	
k.	"USA/24c" on "d" & "e" inverted	40,000.	
l.	As "i," imperf, tagging omitted	3,250.	—
m.	Tagging omitted on "e" and "f"	—	
n.	As No. 1688, perfs inverted and reversed	450.00	
o.	As No. 1688, tagging omitted	—	
1689 A1079	Sheet of 5		6.25	5.25
a.-e.	31c multicolored		.85	.85
f.	"USA/31c" omitted, imperf.	1,500.	
g.	"USA/31c" omitted on "a" & "c"	375.00	
h.	"USA/31c" omitted on "b," "d" & "e"	500.00	
i.	"USA/31c" omitted on "e"	375.00	
j.	Black omitted in design	1,500.	
k.	Imperf., tagging omitted	—	1,250.
l.	"USA/31c" omitted on "b" & "d"	375.00	
m.	"USA/31c" omitted on "a," "c" & "e"	—	
n.	As "m," imperf., tagging omitted	—	
p.	As "h," imperf., tagging omitted	—	1,250.
q.	As "g," imperf., tagging omitted	2,750.	
r.	"USA/31c" omitted on "d" & "e"	500.00	
s.	As "f," tagging omitted	2,250.	
t.	"USA/31c" omitted on "d"	500.00	
u.	As No. 1689, tagging omitted	—	
v.	As No. 1689, perfs and tagging inverted	10,000.	
w.	"USA/31c" missing on "a," "b," "c" and "d" (PS)	—	
	Nos. 1686-1689 (4)	19.00	

Issued in connection with Interphil 76 International Philatelic Exhibition, Philadelphia, Pa., May 29-June 6. Size of sheets: 153x204mm; size of stamps: 25x39½mm, 39½x25mm.

Benjamin Franklin

American Bicentennial: Benjamin Franklin (1706-1790), deputy postmaster general for the colonies (1753-1774) and statesman. Design based on marble bust by anonymous Italian sculptor after terra cotta bust by Jean Jacques Caffieri, 1777. Map published by R. Sayer and J. Bennett in London.

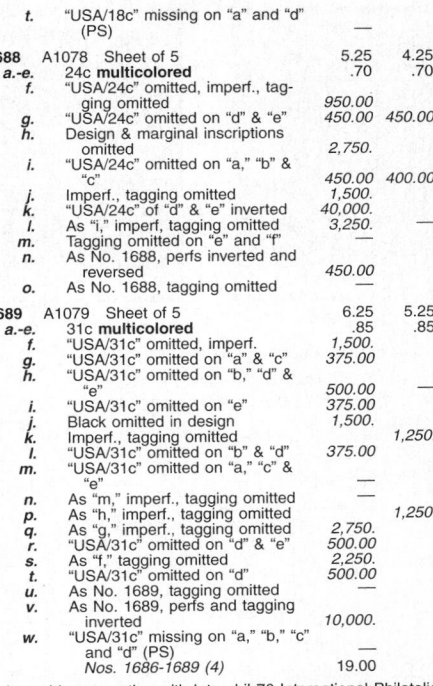

Franklin and Map of North America, 1776 — A1080

Designed by Bernard Reilander (Canada).

LITHOGRAPHED, ENGRAVED (Giori)
Plates of 200 subjects in four panes of 50.

1976, June 1		Tagged	Perf. 11	
1690 A1080	13c	ultramarine & multicolored	.25	.20
		P# block of 4	1.10	—
		Margin block of 4, Mr. Zip and "Use Zip Code"	1.00	—
a.		Light blue omitted	200.00	
b.		Tagging omitted	7.50	

See Canada No. 691.

Declaration of Independence

Designed after painting of Declaration of Independence, by John Trumbull, in the Rotunda of the Capitol, Washington, D.C. Nos. 1691-1694 printed in continuous design. Left panes contain 10 No. 1694a and 5 each of Nos. 1691-1692; right panes contain 5 each of Nos. 1693-1694 and 10 No. 1694a.

A1081   A1082

A1083 A1084

Designed by Vincent E. Hoffman.

PHOTOGRAVURE (Andreotti)
Plates of 200 subjects in four panes of 50.

1976, July 4		Tagged		Perf. 11	
1691	A1081	13c **blue & multicolored**		.30	.20
1692	A1082	13c **blue & multicolored**		.30	.20
1693	A1083	13c **blue & multicolored**		.30	.20
1694	A1084	13c **blue & multicolored**		.30	.20
a.		Strip of 4, #1691-1694		1.20	1.10
		P# block of 20, 5#, "Mail Early in the Day," Mr. Zip and "Use Zip Code"		7.25	—
		P# block of 16, 5#, "Mail Early in the Day"		6.00	—
		Margin block of 4, Mr. Zip and "Use Zip Code"		1.25	—

OLYMPIC GAMES ISSUE

12th Winter Olympic Games, Innsbruck, Austria, Feb. 4-15, and 21st Summer Olympic Games, Montreal, Canada, July 17-Aug. 1. Nos. 1695-1696 alternate in one row, Nos. 1697-1698 in other row.

Diving — A1085 Skiing — A1086

Running — A1087 Skating — A1088

Designed by Donald Moss.

PHOTOGRAVURE (Andreotti)
Plates of 200 subjects in four panes of 50.

1976, July 16		Tagged		Perf. 11	
1695	A1085	13c **multicolored**		.30	.20
1696	A1086	13c **multicolored**		.30	.20
1697	A1087	13c **multicolored**		.30	.20
1698	A1088	13c **multicolored**		.30	.20
a.		Block of 4, #1695-1698		1.20	1.20
		P# block of 12, 6#		4.00	—
		P# block of 20, 6#, Mr. Zip and slogans		8.75	—
		Margin block of 4, Mr. Zip and "Use Zip Code"		1.40	—
b.		As "a," imperf.		550.00	

CLARA MAASS ISSUE

Clara Louise Maass (1876-1901), volunteer in fight against yellow fever, birth centenary.

Clara Maass and Newark German Hospital Pin — A1089

Designed by Paul Calle.

PHOTOGRAVURE (Andreotti)
Plates of 160 subjects in four panes of 40.

1976, Aug. 18		Tagged		Perf. 11	
1699	A1089	13c **multicolored**		.25	.20
		P# block of 12, 6#		4.00	
		Margin block of 4, Mr. Zip, "Use Zip Code" and "Mail Early in the Day"		1.00	
a.		Horiz. pair, imperf. vert.		400.00	

ADOLPH S. OCHS ISSUE

Adolph S. Ochs (1858-1935), publisher of the New York Times, 1896-1935.

Adolph S. Ochs — A1090

Designed by Bradbury Thompson; photograph by S. J. Woolf.

GIORI PRESS PRINTING
Plates of 128 subjects in four panes of 32 (8x4).

1976, Sept. 18		Tagged		Perf. 11	
1700	A1090	13c **black & gray**		.25	.20
		P# block of 4		1.10	—
		Margin block of 4, Mr. Zip and "Use Zip Code"		.90	—
a.		Tagging omitted		50.00	—

CHRISTMAS ISSUE

Nativity, by John Singleton Copley A1091

"Winter Pastime," by Nathaniel Currier A1092

Designers: No. 1701, Bradbury Thompson after 1776 painting in Museum of Fine Arts, Boston. No. 1702, Stevan Dohanos after 1855 lithograph in Museum of the City of New York.

PHOTOGRAVURE (Andreotti)
Plates of 200 subjects in four panes of 50.

1976, Oct. 27		Tagged		Perf. 11	
1701	A1091	13c **multicolored**		.25	.20
		P# block of 12, 6#		3.25	—
		Margin block of 4, Mr. Zip and "Use Zip Code"		1.00	—
a.		Imperf., pair		85.00	

1702	A1092	13c **multi,** overall tagging		.25	.20
		P# block of 10, 5#		2.75	
		Margin block of 4, Mr. Zip and "Use Zip Code"		1.00	
a.		Imperf., pair		90.00	

Plates of 230 (10x23) subjects in panes of 50 (5x10)
Tagged, Block

1703	A1092	13c **multicolored**		.25	.20
		P# block of 20, 5-8#		6.00	—
a.		Imperf., pair		85.00	
b.		Vert. pair, imperf. between		325.00	
c.		Tagging omitted		12.50	
d.		Red omitted		650.00	
e.		Yellow omitted			

No. 1702 has overall tagging. Lettering at base is black and usually ½mm below design. As a rule, no "snowflaking" in sky or pond. Pane of 50 has margins on 4 sides with slogans. Plate Nos. 37465-37478.
No. 1703 has block tagging the size of printed area. Lettering at base is gray black and usually ¾mm below design. "Snowflaking" generally in sky and pond. Plate Nos. 37617-37621 or 37634-37638.
Examples of No. 1703 are known with various amounts of red or yellow missing. Nos. 1703d-1703e are stamps with the colors totally omitted. Expertization is recommended.

COMBINATION PRESS

Cylindrical plates consist of 23 rows of subjects, 10 across for commemoratives (230 subjects), 20 across for definitives (460 subjects), with selvage on the two outer edges only. Guillotining through the perforations creates individual panes of 50 or 100 with selvage on one side only.
Failure of the guillotine to separate through the perforations resulted in straight edges on some stamps. Perforating teeth along the center column and the tenth rows were removed for issues released on or after May 31, 1984 (the 10c Richard Russell, for definitives; the 20c Horace Moses, for commemoratives), creating panes with straight edged stamps on three sides.
Three sets of plate numbers, copyright notices (starting with No. 1787), and zip insignia (starting with No. 1927) are arranged identically on the left and right sides of the plate so that each pane has at least one of each marking. The markings adjacent to any particular row are repeated either seven or eight rows away on the cylinder.
Fifteen combinations of the three marginal markings and blank rows are possible on panes.

AMERICAN BICENTENNIAL ISSUE
Washington at Princeton

Washington's Victory over Lord Cornwallis at Princeton, N.J., bicentenary.

Washington, Nassau Hall, Hessian Prisoners and 13-star Flag, by Charles Willson Peale — A1093

Designed by Bradbury Thompson.

PHOTOGRAVURE (Andreotti)
Plates of 160 subjects in four panes of 40.

1977, Jan. 3		Tagged		Perf. 11	
1704	A1093	13c **multicolored**		.25	.20
		P# block of 10, 5#		2.75	—
		Margin block of 4, Mr. Zip and "Use Zip Code", "Mail Early in the Day"		1.00	—
a.		Horiz. pair, imperf. vert.		500.00	—
b.		Black (inscriptions) missing (PS)			

SOUND RECORDING ISSUE

Centenary of the invention of the phonograph by Thomas Alva Edison and development of sophisticated recording industry.

Tin Foil
Phonograph
A1094

Designed by Walter and Naiad Einsel.

LITHOGRAPHED, ENGRAVED (Giori)
Plates of 200 subjects in four panes of 50.

1977, Mar. 23	Tagged	Perf. 11	
1705 A1094 13c black & multicolored		.25	.20
P# block of 4		1.10	—
Margin block of 4, Mr. Zip and "Use Zip Code"		1.00	—

AMERICAN FOLK ART SERIES
Pueblo Pottery

Pueblo art, 1880-1920, from Museums in New Mexico, Arizona and Colorado.

Nos. 1706-1709 are printed in blocks and strips of 4 in panes of 40. In the 1st row Nos. 1706-1709 are in sequence as listed. In the 2nd row Nos. 1708-1709 are followed by Nos. 1706-1709, 1708-1709.

Zia Pot — A1095

San Ildefonso
Pot — A1096

Hopi Pot — A1097

Acoma Pot — A1098

Designed by Ford Ruthling.

PHOTOGRAVURE (Andreotti)
Plates of 160 subjects in four panes of 40.

1977, Apr. 13	Tagged	Perf. 11	
1706 A1095 13c multicolored		.25	.20
1707 A1096 13c multicolored		.25	.20
1708 A1097 13c multicolored		.25	.20
1709 A1098 13c multicolored		.25	.20
a.	Block or strip of 4, #1706-1709	1.00	1.00
	P# block of 10, 5#	2.75	—
	P# block of 16, 5#; Mr. Zip and slogans	4.25	—
	Margin block of 6, Mr. Zip and "Use Zip Code" "Mail Early in the Day"	1.50	—
b.	As "a," imperf. vert.	2,000.	

LINDBERGH FLIGHT ISSUE

Charles A. Lindbergh's solo transatlantic flight from New York to Paris, 50th anniversary.

Spirit of St.
Louis — A1099

Designed by Robert E. Cunningham.

PHOTOGRAVURE (Andreotti)
Plates of 200 subjects in four panes of 50.

1977, May 20	Tagged	Perf. 11	
1710 A1099 13c multicolored		.25	.20
	P# block of 12, 6#	3.25	—
	Margin block of 4, Mr. Zip and "Use Zip Code"	1.00	—
a.	Imperf., pair	825.00	

Beware of private overprints on No. 1710.

COLORADO STATEHOOD ISSUE

Issued to honor Colorado as the "Centennial State." It achieved statehood in 1876.

Columbine and Rocky
Mountains — A1100

Designed by V. Jack Ruther.

PHOTOGRAVURE (Andreotti)
Plates of 200 subjects in four panes of 50.

1977, May 21	Tagged	Perf. 11	
1711 A1100 13c multicolored		.25	.20
	P# block of 12, 6#	3.25	—
	Margin block of 4, Mr. Zip and "Use Zip Code"	1.00	—
a.	Horiz. pair, imperf. between and with natural straight edge at right	—	
b.	Horiz. pair, imperf. vertically	750.00	
c.	Perf. 11.2	.35	.25
	P# block of 12, 6#	20.00	

Perforations do not run through the sheet margin on about 10 percent of the sheets of No. 1711.

BUTTERFLY ISSUE

Nos. 1712-1713 alternate in 1st row, Nos. 1714-1715 in 2nd row. This arrangement is repeated throughout the pane. Butterflies represent different geographic US areas.

Swallowtail
A1101

Checkerspot
A1102

Dogface
A1103

Orange-Tip
A1104

Designed by Stanley Galli.

PHOTOGRAVURE (Andreotti)
Plates of 200 subjects in four panes of 50.

1977, June 6	Tagged	Perf. 11	
1712 A1101 13c tan & multicolored		.25	.20
1713 A1102 13c tan & multicolored		.25	.20
1714 A1103 13c tan & multicolored		.25	.20
1715 A1104 13c tan & multicolored		.25	.20
a.	Block of 4, #1712-1715	1.00	1.00
	P# block of 12, 6#	3.25	—
	P# block of 20, 6#, Mr. Zip and slogans	5.50	—
	Margin block of 4, Mr. Zip and "Use Zip Code"	1.05	—
b.	As "a," imperf. horiz.	15,000.	

AMERICAN BICENTENNIAL ISSUES
Marquis de Lafayette

200th anniversary of Lafayette's Landing on the coast of South Carolina, north of Charleston.

Marquis de
Lafayette — A1105

Designed by Bradbury Thompson.

GIORI PRESS PRINTING
Plates of 160 subjects in four panes of 40.

1977, June 13	Tagged	Perf. 11	
1716 A1105 13c blue, black & red		.25	.20
	P# block of 4	1.10	—
	Margin block of 4, Mr. Zip and "Use Zip Code"	1.00	—
a.	Red missing (PS)	200.00	

Skilled Hands for Independence

Nos. 1717-1718 alternate in 1st row, Nos. 1719-1720 in 2nd row. This arrangement is repeated throughout the pane.

Seamstress
A1106

Blacksmith
A1107

Wheelwright
A1108

Leatherworker
A1109

Designed by Leonard Everett Fisher.

PHOTOGRAVURE (Andreotti)
Plates of 200 subjects in four panes of 50.

1977, July 4	Tagged	Perf. 11	
1717 A1106 13c multicolored		.25	.20
1718 A1107 13c multicolored		.25	.20
1719 A1108 13c multicolored		.25	.20
1720 A1109 13c multicolored		.25	.20
a. Block of 4, #1717-1720		1.00	1.00
P# block of 12, 6#		3.25	
P# block of 20, 6#, Mr. Zip and slogans		5.50	—
Margin block of 4, Mr. Zip and "Use Zip Code"		1.05	—

PEACE BRIDGE ISSUE

50th anniversary of the Peace Bridge, connecting Buffalo (Fort Porter), N.Y. and Fort Erie, Ontario.

Peace Bridge and Dove — A1110

Designed by Bernard Brussel-Smith (wood-cut).

ENGRAVED
Plates of 200 subjects in four panes of 50.

1977, Aug. 4	Tagged	Perf. 11x10½	
1721 A1110 13c blue		.25	.20
P# block of 4		1.10	
Margin block of 4, Mr. Zip and "Use Zip Code"		1.00	—

AMERICAN BICENTENNIAL ISSUE
Battle of Oriskany

200th anniv. of the Battle of Oriskany, American Militia led by Brig. Gen. Nicholas Herkimer (1728-77).

Herkimer at Oriskany, by Frederick Yohn — A1111

Designed by Bradbury Thompson after painting in Utica, N.Y. Public Library.

PHOTOGRAVURE (Andreotti)
Plates of 160 subjects in four panes of 40.

1977, Aug. 6	Tagged	Perf. 11	
1722 A1111 13c multicolored		.25	.20
P# block of 10, 5#		2.75	—
Margin block of 6, Mr. Zip and "Use Zip Code" and "Mail Early in the Day"		1.50	—

ENERGY ISSUE

Conservation and development of nation}s energy resources. Nos. 1723-1724 se-tenant vertically.

"Conservation"
A1112

"Development"
A1113

Designed by Terrance W. McCaffrey.

PHOTOGRAVURE (Andreotti)
Plates of 160 subjects in four panes of 40.

1977, Oct. 20	Tagged	Perf. 11	
1723 A1112 13c multicolored		.25	.20
1724 A1113 13c multicolored		.25	.20
a. Pair, #1723-1724		.50	.50
P# block of 12, 6#		3.25	
Margin block of 4, Mr. Zip, "Use Zip Code" and "Mail Early in the Day"		1.00	—

ALTA CALIFORNIA ISSUE

Founding of El Pueblo de San José de Guadalupe, first civil settlement in Alta California, 200th anniversary.

Farm Houses
A1114

Designed by Earl Thollander.

LITHOGRAPHED, ENGRAVED (Giori)
Plates of 200 subjects in four panes of 50.

1977, Sept. 9	Tagged	Perf. 11	
1725 A1114 13c black & multicolored		.25	.20
P# block of 4		1.10	
Margin block of 4, Mr. Zip and "Use Zip Code"		1.00	—
a. Tagging omitted			

AMERICAN BICENTENNIAL ISSUE
Articles of Confederation

200th anniversary of drafting the Articles of Confederation, York Town, Pa.

Members of Continental Congress in Conference
A1115

Designed by David Blossom.

ENGRAVED (Giori)
Plates of 200 subjects in four panes of 50.

1977, Sept. 30	Tagged	Perf. 11	
1726 A1115 13c red & brown, cream		.25	.20
P# block of 4		1.10	—
Margin block of 4, Mr. Zip and "Use Zip Code"		1.00	—
a. Tagging omitted		125.00	
b. Red omitted		600.00	
c. Red & brown omitted		400.00	

No. 1726b also has most of the brown omitted. No. 1726c must be collected as a transition multiple, certainly with No. 1726b and preferably also with No. 1726.

TALKING PICTURES, 50th ANNIV.

Movie Projector and Phonograph
A1116

Designed by Walter Einsel.

LITHOGRAPHED, ENGRAVED (Giori)
Plates of 200 subjects in four panes of 50.

1977, Oct. 6	Tagged	Perf. 11	
1727 A1116 13c multicolored		.25	.20
P# block of 4, Mr. Zip and "Use Zip Code"		1.10	
		1.00	—

AMERICAN BICENTENNIAL ISSUE
Surrender at Saratoga

200th anniversary of Gen. John Burgoyne's surrender at Saratoga.

Surrender of Burgoyne, by John Trumbull
A1117

Designed by Bradbury Thompson.

PHOTOGRAVURE (Andreotti)
Plates of 160 subjects in four panes of 40.

1977, Oct. 7	Tagged	Perf. 11	
1728 A1117 13c multicolored		.25	.20
P# block of 10, 5#		2.75	—
Margin block of 6, Mr. Zip, "Use Zip Code" and "Mail Early in the Day"		1.50	—

CHRISTMAS ISSUE

Washington at Valley Forge — A1118

Rural Mailbox — A1119

Designers: No. 1729, Stevan Dohanos, after painting by J. C. Leyendecker. No. 1730, Dolli Tingle.

PHOTOGRAVURE (Combination Press)
Plates of 460 subjects (20x23) in panes of 100 (10x10)

1977, Oct. 21	Tagged	Perf. 11	
1729 A1118 13c multicolored		.25	.20
P# block of 20, 5-8#		5.75	—
a. Imperf., pair		65.00	

See Combination Press note after No. 1703.

PHOTOGRAVURE (Andreotti)
Plates of 400 subjects in 4 panes of 100.

1730	A1119	13c **multicolored**	.25	.20
		P# block of 10, 5#	2.75	—
		Margin block of 4, Mr. Zip and "Use Zip Code"	1.00	—
		Pair with full vert. gutter btwn.		—
a.		Imperf., pair	*200.00*	

CARL SANDBURG ISSUE
Carl Sandburg (1878-1967), poet, biographer and collector of American folk songs, birth centenary.

Carl Sandburg, by William A. Smith, 1952 — A1120

Designed by William A. Smith.

GIORI PRESS PRINTING
Plates of 200 subjects in four panes of 50.

1978, Jan. 6		Tagged	Perf. 11	
1731	A1120	13c **black & brown**	.25	.20
		P# block of 4	1.25	—
		Margin block of 4, Mr. Zip	1.05	—
a.		Brown omitted	*2,250.*	
b.		Tagging omitted		

CAPTAIN COOK ISSUE
Capt. James Cook, 200th anniversary of his arrival in Hawaii, at Waimea, Kauai, Jan. 20, 1778, and of his anchorage in Cook Inlet, near Anchorage, Alaska, June 1, 1778. Nos. 1732-1733 printed in panes of 50, containing 25 each of Nos. 1732-1733 including 5 No. 1733b.

Capt. Cook, by Nathaniel Dance — A1121

"Resolution" and "Discovery," by John Webber A1122

Designed by Robert F. Szabo (No. 1732; Jak Katalan (No. 1733.

GIORI PRESS PRINTING
Plates of 200 subjects in four panes of 50.

1978, Jan. 20		Tagged	Perf. 11	
1732	A1121	13c **dark blue**	.25	.20
1733	A1122	13c **green**	.25	.20
a.		Vert. pair, imperf. horiz.		
b.		Pair, #1732-1733	.50	.50
		P# block of 4, #1732 or 1733	1.10	—
		Margin block of 4, Mr. Zip, #1732 or 1733	1.05	—
		P# block of 20, 10 each #1732-1733, P# and slogans	5.25	—
c.		As "b," imperf. between	*4,250.*	
d.		As "b," tagging omitted	*25.00*	

Indian Head Penny, 1877 — A1123

Red Masterpiece and Medallion Roses — A1126

ENGRAVED (Giori)
Plates of 600 subjects in four panes of 150.

1978		Tagged	Perf. 11	
1734	A1123	13c **brown & blue green,** *bister, Jan. 11, 1978*	.25	.20
		P# block of 4	1.25	—
		Margin block of 4, "Use Correct Zip Code"	1.00	—
		Vert. pair with full horiz. gutter between		
a.		Horiz. pair, imperf. vert.	*225.00*	
b.		Tagging omitted		—

PHOTOGRAVURE (Andreotti)
Plates of 400 subjects in four panes of 100.

1735	A1124	(15c) **orange,** *May 22, 1978*	.30	.20
		P# block of 4	1.40	—
		Margin block of 4, "Use Zip Code"	1.25	—
		Vert. pair with full horiz. gutter between		—
a.		Imperf., pair	*80.00*	
b.		Vert. pair, imperf. horiz.	*600.00*	
c.		Perf. 11.2	.35	.20
		P# block of 4	1.80	—
		Zip block of 4	1.50	—

BOOKLET STAMPS
ENGRAVED
Perf. 11x10½ on 2 or 3 sides

1736	A1124	(15c) **orange**	.30	.20
a.		Booklet pane of 8, *May 22, 1978*	2.50	1.50
b.		As "a," tagging omitted		
c.		Vert. pair, imperf between	*750.00*	

Perf. 10

1737	A1126	15c **multicolored**	.30	.20
a.		Booklet pane of 8, *July 11, 1978*	2.50	1.50
b.		Imperf, pair	*450.00*	
c.		As "a," imperf	*2,200.*	
d.		As "a," tagging omitted	*50.00*	

A1127   A1128   A1129

A1130   A1131

Designed by Ronald Sharpe.

BOOKLET STAMPS
ENGRAVED

1980, Feb. 7		Tagged	Perf. 11 on 2 or 3 sides	
1738	A1127	15c **sepia,** *yellow*	.30	.20
1739	A1128	15c **sepia,** *yellow*	.30	.20
1740	A1129	15c **sepia,** *yellow*	.30	.20
1741	A1130	15c **sepia,** *yellow*	.30	.20
1742	A1131	15c **sepia,** *yellow*	.30	.20
a.		Booklet pane of 10, 2 each #1738-1742	3.50	3.00
b.		Strip of 5, #1738-1742	1.50	1.40

Eagle — A1124

COIL STAMP

1978, May 22			Perf. 10 Vert.	
1743	A1124	(15c) **orange**	.30	.20
		Pair	.60	.20
		Joint line pair	.75	
a.		Imperf., pair	*75.00*	
		Joint line pair	*150.00*	

No. 1743a is valued in the grade of fine.

BLACK HERITAGE SERIES
Harriet Tubman (1820-1913), born a slave, helped more than 300 slaves escape to freedom.

Harriet Tubman and Cart Carrying Slaves — A1133

Designed by Jerry Pinkney after photograph.

PHOTOGRAVURE (Andreotti)
Plates of 200 subjects in four panes of 50.

1978, Feb. 1		Tagged	Perf. 10½x11	
1744	A1133	13c **multicolored**	.25	.20
		P# block of 12, 6#	3.25	—
		Margin block of 4, Mr. Zip	1.00	—

AMERICAN FOLK ART SERIES
Quilts
Nos. 1745-1746 alternate in 1st row, Nos. 1747-1748 in 2nd.

Basket Design

A1134

A1135

A1136

A1137

Designed by Christopher Pullman after 1875 quilt made in New York City. Illustration reduced.

PHOTOGRAVURE (Andreotti)
Plates of 192 subjects in four panes of 48 (6x8).

1978, Mar. 8				Perf. 11	
1745	A1134	13c	multicolored	.25	.20
1746	A1135	13c	multicolored	.25	.20
1747	A1136	13c	multicolored	.25	.20
1748	A1137	13c	multicolored	.25	.20
a.		Block of 4, #1745-1748		1.00	1.00
		P# block of 12, 6#		3.25	—
		P# block of 16, 6#, Mr. Zip and copyright		4.50	—
		Margin block of 4, Mr. Zip, copyright		1.05	—

AMERICAN DANCE ISSUE
Nos. 1749-1750 alternate in 1st row, Nos. 1751-1752 in 2nd.

Ballet
A1138

Theater
A1139

Folk Dance
A1140

Modern Dance
A1141

Designed by John Hill.

PHOTOGRAVURE (Andreotti)
Plates of 192 subjects in four panes of 48 (6x8).

1978, Apr. 26				Tagged	Perf. 11	
1749	A1138	13c	multicolored		.25	.20
1750	A1139	13c	multicolored		.25	.20
1751	A1140	13c	multicolored		.25	.20
1752	A1141	13c	multicolored		.25	.20
a.		Block of 4, #1749-1752			1.00	1.00
		P# block of 12, 6#			3.25	—
		P# block of 16, 6#, Mr. Zip and copyright			4.50	—
		Margin block of 4, Mr. Zip, copyright			1.05	—

AMERICAN BICENTENNIAL ISSUE
French Alliance, signed in Paris, Feb. 6, 1778 and ratified by Continental Congress, May 4, 1778.

King Louis XVI and Benjamin Franklin, by Charles Gabriel Sauvage — A1142

Designed by Bradbury Thompson after 1785 porcelain sculpture in Du Pont Winterthur Museum, Delaware.

GIORI PRESS PRINTING
Plates of 160 subjects in four panes of 40.

1978, May 4				Tagged	Perf. 11	
1753	A1142	13c	blue, black & red		.25	.20
		P# block of 4			1.10	—
		Margin block of 4, Mr. Zip			1.00	—
a.		Red missing (PS)				

EARLY CANCER DETECTION ISSUE
George Papanicolaou, M.D. (1883-1962), cytologist and developer of Pap Test, early cancer detection in women.

Dr. Papanicolaou and Microscope — A1143

Designed by Paul Calle.

ENGRAVED
Plates of 200 subjects in four panes of 50.

1978, May 18				Tagged	Perf. 10½x11	
1754	A1143	13c	brown		.25	.20
		P# block of 4			1.10	—
		Margin block of 4, Mr. Zip			1.00	—

PERFORMING ARTS SERIES
Jimmie Rodgers (1897-1933), the "Singing Brakeman, Father of Country Music" (No. 1755); George M. Cohan (1878-1942), actor and playwright (No. 1756).

Jimmie Rodgers with Guitar and Brakeman's Cap, Locomotive — A1144

George M. Cohan, "Yankee Doodle Dandy" and Stars — A1145

Designed by Jim Sharpe.

PHOTOGRAVURE (Andreotti)
Plates of 200 subjects in four panes of 50.

1978				Tagged	Perf. 11	
1755	A1144	13c	multicolored,	May 24	.25	.20
		P# block of 12, 6#			4.00	—
		Margin block of 4, Mr. Zip			1.25	—
1756	A1145	15c	multicolored,	July 3	.30	.20
		P# block of 12, 6#			4.00	—
		Margin block of 4, Mr. Zip			1.25	—

CAPEX ISSUE
CAPEX '78, Canadian International Philatelic Exhibition, Toronto, Ont., June 9-18.

Wildlife from Canadian-United States Border — A1146

Illustration reduced.

Designed by Stanley Galli.

LITHOGRAPHED, ENGRAVED (Giori)
Plates of 24 subjects in four panes of 6 each.

1978, June 10				Tagged	Perf. 11	
1757	A1146		Block of 8, multicolored		2.00	1.75
a.		13c	Cardinal		.25	.20
b.		13c	Mallard		.25	.20
c.		13c	Canada goose		.25	.20
d.		13c	Blue jay		.25	.20
e.		13c	Moose		.25	.20
f.		13c	Chipmunk		.25	.20
g.		13c	Red fox		.25	.20
h.		13c	Raccoon		.25	.20
		P# block of 8, Mr. Zip and copyright			2.25	—
		Margin block of 8, Mr. Zip and copyright			2.10	—
		Pane of 6 No. 1757, P#, Mr. Zip and copyright			13.00	—
i.		As No. 1757, yellow, green, red, brown, blue, black (litho) omitted			7,000.	
j.		Strip of 4 (a-d), imperf. vert.			5,000.	
k.		Strip of 4 (e-h), imperf. vert.			3,000.	
l.		As No. 1757, "d" and "h" with black (engr.) omitted			—	
m.		As No. 1757, "b" with blue missing (PS)			—	

No. 1757k is worth more when contained in the sheet of 8. Value is for strip only.

PHOTOGRAPHY ISSUE
Photography's contribution to communications and understanding.

Camera, Lens, Color
Filters, Adapter Ring,
Studio Light Bulb and
Album — A1147

Designed by Ben Somoroff.

PHOTOGRAVURE (Andreotti)
Plates of 160 subjects in four panes of 40.

1978, June 26	Tagged	Perf. 11	
1758 A1147 15c **multicolored**		.30	.20
P# block of 12, 6#		4.00	—
Margin block of 4, Mr. Zip and copyright		1.25	—
P# block of 16, 6#, Mr. Zip and copyright		5.00	—

VIKING MISSIONS TO MARS ISSUE
Second anniv. of landing of Viking 1 on Mars.

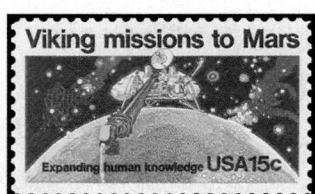

Viking 1
Lander
Scooping up
Soil on
Mars — A1148

Designed by Robert McCall.

LITHOGRAPHED, ENGRAVED (Giori)
Plates of 200 subjects in four panes of 50.

1978, July 20	Tagged	Perf. 11	
1759 A1148 15c **multicolored**		.30	.20
P# block of 4		1.35	—
Margin block of 4, Mr. Zip		1.25	—
a.	Tagging omitted	60.00	

WILDLIFE CONSERVATION
Nos. 1760-1761 alternate in one horizontal row.
Nos. 1762-1763 in the next.

Great Gray
Owl — A1149

Saw-whet
Owl — A1150

Barred Owl — A1151

Great Horned
Owl — A1152

Designed by Frank J. Waslick.

LITHOGRAPHED, ENGRAVED (Giori)
Plates of 200 subjects in four panes of 50.

1978, Aug. 26	Tagged	Perf. 11	
1760 A1149 15c **multicolored**		.30	.20
1761 A1150 15c **multicolored**		.30	.20
1762 A1151 15c **multicolored**		.30	.20
1763 A1152 15c **multicolored**		.30	.20
a.	Block of 4, #1760-1763	1.25	1.25
	P# block of 4	1.40	—
	Margin block of 4, Mr. Zip	1.25	—
b.	As "a," tagging omitted	—	

AMERICAN TREES ISSUE
Nos. 1764-1765 alternate in 1st row, Nos. 1766-
1767 in 2nd.

Giant Sequoia
A1153

White
Pine — A1154

White
Oak — A1155

Gray
Birch — A1156

Designed by Walter D. Richards.

PHOTOGRAVURE (Andreotti)
Plates of 160 subjects in four panes of 40.

1978, Oct. 9	Tagged	Perf. 11	
1764 A1153 15c **multicolored**		.30	.20
1765 A1154 15c **multicolored**		.30	.20
1766 A1155 15c **multicolored**		.30	.20
1767 A1156 15c **multicolored**		.30	.20
a.	Block of 4, #1764-1767	1.25	1.25
	P# block of 12, 6#	4.00	—
	P# block of 16, 6#, Mr. Zip and copyright	5.25	—
	Margin block of 4, Mr. Zip, copyright	1.30	—
b.	As "a," imperf. horiz.	17,500.	

No. 1767b is unique.

CHRISTMAS ISSUE

Madonna and Child
with Cherubim, by
Andrea della
Robbia — A1157

Child on Hobby
Horse and
Christmas
Trees — A1158

Designed by Bradbury Thompson (No. 1768) after terra cotta
sculpture in National Gallery, Washington, D.C. by Dolli Tingle
(No. 1769).

PHOTOGRAVURE (Andreotti)
Plates of 400 subjects in four panes of 100.

1978, Oct. 18		Perf. 11	
1768 A1157 15c **blue & multicolored**		.30	.20
P# block of 12, 6#		4.00	—
Margin block of 4, "Use Correct Zip Code"		1.25	—
a.	Imperf., pair	80.00	

Value for No. 1768a is for an uncreased pair.

1769 A1158 15c **red & multicolored**		.30	.20
P# block of 12, 6#		4.00	—
Margin block of 4, "Use Correct Zip Code"		1.25	—
Pair with full horiz. gutter btwn.		—	
a.	Imperf., pair	85.00	
b.	Vert. pair, imperf. horiz.	1,250.	

Robert F.
Kennedy — A1159

Martin Luther King, Jr. and
Civil Rights
Marchers — A1160

ROBERT F. KENNEDY ISSUE
Designed by Bradbury Thompson after photograph by Stanley Tretick.

ENGRAVED
Plates of 192 subjects in four panes of 48 (8x6).

1979, Jan. 12	Tagged	Perf. 11	
1770 A1159 15c **blue**		.35	.20
P# block of 4		1.75	—
Margin block of 4, Mr. Zip		1.50	—
a.	Tagging omitted	60.00	

BLACK HERITAGE SERIES
Dr. Martin Luther King, Jr. (1929-1968), Civil Rights
leader.

Designed by Jerry Pinkney.

PHOTOGRAVURE (Andreotti)
Plates of 200 subjects in four panes of 50.

1979, Jan. 13	Tagged	Perf. 11	
1771 A1160 15c **multicolored**		.40	.20
P# block of 12, 6#		5.75	—
Margin block of 4, Mr. Zip		1.75	—
a.	Imperf., pair	1,400.	

INTERNATIONAL YEAR OF THE CHILD ISSUE

Children of Different Races A1161

Designed by Paul Calle.

ENGRAVED

Plates of 200 subjects in four panes of 50.

1979, Feb. 15	Tagged	Perf. 11	
1772 A1161 15c **orange red**		.30	.20
P# block of 4		1.40	—
Margin block of 4, Mr. Zip		1.25	—

John Steinbeck (1902-1968), Novelist — A1162

Albert Einstein (1879-1955), Theoretical Physicist — A1163

LITERARY ARTS SERIES

Designed by Bradbury Thompson after photograph by Philippe Halsman.

ENGRAVED

Plates of 200 subjects in four panes of 50.

1979, Feb. 27	Tagged	Perf. 10½x11	
1773 A1162 15c **dark blue**		.30	.20
P# block of 4		1.40	—
Margin block of 4, Mr. Zip		1.25	—

ALBERT EINSTEIN ISSUE

Designed by Bradbury Thompson after photograph by Hermann Landshoff.

ENGRAVED

Plates of 200 subjects in four panes of 50.

1979, Mar. 4	Tagged	Perf. 10½x11	
1774 A1163 15c **chocolate**		.35	.20
P# block of 4		1.75	—
Margin block of 4, Mr. Zip		1.50	—
Pair, horiz. gutter btwn.		—	

AMERICAN FOLK ART SERIES
Pennsylvania Toleware, c. 1800

Coffeepot — A1164

Tea Caddy — A1165

Sugar Bowl — A1166

Coffeepot — A1167

Designed by Bradbury Thompson.

PHOTOGRAVURE (Andreotti)
Plates of 160 subjects in four panes of 40.

1979, Apr. 19	Tagged	Perf. 11	
1775 A1164 15c **multicolored**		.30	.20
1776 A1165 15c **multicolored**		.30	.20
1777 A1166 15c **multicolored**		.30	.20
1778 A1167 15c **multicolored**		.30	.20
a. Block of 4, #1775-1778		1.25	1.25
P# block of 10, 5#		3.25	—
P# block of 16, 5#; Mr. Zip and copyright		5.25	—
Margin block of 6, Mr. Zip and copyright		2.00	—
b. As "a," imperf. horiz.		3,000.	

AMERICAN ARCHITECTURE SERIES

Nos. 1779-1780 alternate in 1st row, Nos. 1781-1782 in 2nd.

Virginia Rotunda, by Thomas Jefferson — A1168

Baltimore Cathedral, by Benjamin Latrobe — A1169

Boston State House, by Charles Bulfinch — A1170

Philadelphia Exchange, by William Strickland — A1171

Designed by Walter D. Richards.

ENGRAVED (Giori)
Plates of 192 subjects in four panes of 48 (6x8).

1979, June 4	Tagged	Perf. 11	
1779 A1168 15c **black & brick red**		.30	.20
1780 A1169 15c **black & brick red**		.30	.20
1781 A1170 15c **black & brick red**		.30	.20
1782 A1171 15c **black & brick red**		.30	.20
a. Block of 4, #1779-1782		1.25	1.25
P# block of 4		1.45	—
Margin block of 4, Mr. Zip		1.30	—
b. As "a," tagging omitted		—	

ENDANGERED FLORA ISSUE

Nos. 1783-1784 alternate in one horizontal row. Nos. 1785-1786 in the next.

Persistent Trillium — A1172

Hawaiian Wild Broadbean — A1173

Contra Costa Wallflower — A1174

Antioch Dunes Evening Primrose — A1175

Designed by Frank J. Waslick.

PHOTOGRAVURE (Andreotti)
Plates of 200 subjects in four panes of 50.

1979, June 7	Tagged	Perf. 11	
1783 A1172 15c **multicolored**		.30	.20
1784 A1173 15c **multicolored**		.30	.20
1785 A1174 15c **multicolored**		.30	.20
1786 A1175 15c **multicolored**		.30	.20
a. Block of 4, #1783-1786		1.25	1.25
P# block of 12, 6#		4.00	—
P# block of 20, 6#; Mr. Zip and copyright		6.50	—
Margin block of 4, Mr. Zip		1.30	—
As "a," full vert. gutter btwn.		—	
b. As "a," imperf.		275.00	

SEEING EYE DOGS ISSUE
1st guide dog program in the US, 50th anniv.

German Shepherd Leading
Man — A1176

Designed by Joseph Csatari.

PHOTOGRAVURE (Combination Press)
Plates of 230 (10x23) subjects in panes of 50 (10x5).

1979, June 15	Tagged	Perf. 11	
1787 A1176 15c multicolored		.30	.20
	P# block of 20, 5-8#, 1-2 copyright	6.50	—
a.	Imperf., pair	375.00	
b.	Tagging omitted	12.00	

See Combination Press note after No. 1703.

Child Holding Winner's
Medal — A1177

John Paul Jones, by
Charles Willson
Peale — A1178

SPECIAL OLYMPICS ISSUE
Special Olympics for special children, Brockport, N.Y., Aug. 8-13.

Designed by Jeff Cornell.

PHOTOGRAVURE (Andreotti)
Plates of 200 subjects in four panes of 50.

1979, Aug. 9	Tagged	Perf. 11	
1788 A1177 15c multicolored		.30	.20
	P# block of 10, 5#	3.25	—
	Zip block of 4	1.25	—

JOHN PAUL JONES ISSUE
John Paul Jones (1747-1792), Naval Commander, American Revolution.

Designed after painting in Independence National Historical Park, Philadelphia.
Printed by American Bank Note Co. and J. W. Fergusson and Sons.

Designed by Bradbury Thompson.

PHOTOGRAVURE (Champlain)
Plates of 200 subjects in four panes of 50.

1979, Sept. 23	Tagged	Perf. 11x12	
1789 A1178 15c multicolored		.30	.20
	P# block of 10, 5#+A	3.25	—
	Zip block of 4	1.25	—
c.	Vert. pair, imperf. horiz.	150.00	

Imperforates on gummed stamp paper, including gutter pairs and blocks, are proofs from the ABNCo. archives. See No. 1789P in Proofs section.

		Perf. 11	
1789A A1178 15c multicolored		.55	.20
	P# block of 10, 5#+A	4.00	—
	Zip block of 4	3.25	—
d.	Vertical pair, imperf. horiz.	125.00	

		Perf. 12	
1789B A1178 15c multicolored		3,500.	3,500.
	P# block of 10, 5#+A	40,000.	—
	Zip block of 4	15,000.	—

OLYMPIC GAMES ISSUE
22nd Summer Olympic Games, Moscow, July 19-Aug. 3, 1980. Nos. 1791-1792 alternate in one horizontal row, Nos. 1793-1794 in next.

Javelin — A1179

Running
A1180

Swimming
A1181

Rowing
A1182

Equestrian
A1183

Designed by Robert M. Cunningham.

PHOTOGRAVURE
Plates of 200 subjects in four panes of 50.

1979, Sept. 5	Tagged	Perf. 11	
1790 A1179 10c multicolored		.20	.20
	P# block of 12, 6#	3.00	—
	Zip block of 4	.85	—

1979, Sept. 28			
1791 A1180 15c multicolored		.30	.20
1792 A1181 15c multicolored		.30	.20
1793 A1182 15c multicolored		.30	.20
1794 A1183 15c multicolored		.30	.20
a.	Block of 4, #1791-1794	1.25	1.25
	P# block of 12, 6#	4.00	—
	Zip block of 4	1.30	—
	P# block of 20, 6#, zip, copyright	6.50	—
b.	As "a," imperf.	1,400.	

OLYMPIC GAMES ISSUE
13th Winter Olympic Games, Lake Placid, N.Y., Feb. 12-24. Nos. 1795-1796 alternate in one horizontal row, Nos. 1797-1798 in next.

Speed Skating
A1184

Downhill Skiing
A1185

Ski Jump
A1186

Ice Hockey
A1187

Designed by Robert M. Cunningham

PHOTOGRAVURE
Plates of 200 subject in four panes of 50.

1980, Feb. 1	Tagged	Perf. 11¼x10½	
1795 A1184 15c multicolored		.35	.20
1796 A1185 15c multicolored		.35	.20
1797 A1186 15c multicolored		.35	.20
1798 A1187 15c multicolored		.35	.20
b.	Block of 4, #1795-1798	1.50	1.40
	P# block of 12, 6#	4.50	—
	Zip block of 4	1.55	—
	P# block of 20, 6#, zip and copyright	7.50	—

		Perf. 11	
1795A A1184 15c multicolored		1.10	.60
1796A A1185 15c multicolored		1.10	.60
1797A A1186 15c multicolored		1.10	.60
1798A A1187 15c multicolored		1.10	.60
c.	Block of 4, #1795A-1798A	4.50	3.50
	P# block of 12, 6#	15.00	—
	Zip block of 4	4.75	—
	P# block of 20, 6#, zip and copyright	27.50	—

CHRISTMAS ISSUE

Virgin and Child by
Gerard
David — A1188

Santa Claus,
Christmas Tree
Ornament — A1189

Designed by Bradbury Thompson (No. 1799) and by Eskil Ohlsson (No. 1800).

No. 1799 is designed after a painting in National Gallery of Art, Washington, D.C.

PHOTOGRAVURE (Andreotti)
Plates of 400 subjects in four panes of 100.

1979, Oct. 18	Tagged	Perf. 11	
1799 A1188 15c multicolored		.30	.20
	P# block of 12, 6#	4.00	—
	Zip block of 4	1.25	—
	P# block of 20, 6#, zip, copyright	6.50	—
a.	Imperf., pair	80.00	
b.	Vert. pair, imperf. horiz.	575.00	
c.	Vert. pair, imperf. between	1,100.	
d.	Tagging omitted		
1800 A1189 15c multicolored		.30	.20
	P# block of 12, 6#	4.00	—
	Zip block of 4	1.25	—
	P# block of 20, 6#, zip, copyright	6.50	—
a.	Green & yellow omitted	500.00	
b.	Green, yellow & tan omitted	450.00	
c.	Vert. se-tenant pair, #1800a & 1800b	1,000.	

Nos. 1800a and 1800b always have the remaining colors misaligned.
Nos. 1800a, 1800b and 1800c are valued in the grade of fine.

PERFORMING ARTS SERIES

Will Rogers (1879-1935), actor and humorist.

Will Rogers — A1190

Designed by Jim Sharpe.

PHOTOGRAVURE (Andreotti)
Plates of 200 subjects in four panes of 50.

1979, Nov. 4		Tagged		Perf. 11
1801	A1190	15c **multicolored**	.30	.20
		P# block of 12, 6#	4.00	—
		Zip block of 4	1.25	—
		P# block of 20, 6#, zip, copy-right	6.50	—
a.		Imperf., pair	175.00	

VIETNAM VETERANS ISSUE

A tribute to veterans of the Vietnam War.

Ribbon for
Vietnam
Service Medal
A1191

Designed by Stevan Dohanos.

PHOTOGRAVURE (Andreotti)
Plates of 200 subjects in four panes of 50.

1979, Nov. 11		Tagged		Perf. 11
1802	A1191	15c **multicolored**	.30	.20
		P# block of 10, 5#	3.25	—
		Zip block of 4	1.25	—

W.C. Fields — A1192

Benjamin
Banneker — A1193

PERFORMING ARTS SERIES

W.C. Fields (1880-1946), actor and comedian.

Designed by Jim Sharpe.

PHOTOGRAVURE
Plates of 200 subjects in four panes of 50.

1980, Jan. 29		Tagged		Perf. 11
1803	A1192	15c **multicolored**	.30	.20
		P# block of 12, 6#	4.00	—
		Zip block of 4	1.25	—
		P# block of 20, 6#, zip, copyright	6.50	—
a.		Imperf., pair	—	

BLACK HERITAGE SERIES

Benjamin Banneker (1731-1806), astronomer and
mathematician.

Designed by Jerry Pinkney.

Printed by American Bank Note Co. and J. W. Fergusson and
Sons.

PHOTOGRAVURE
Plates of 200 subjects in four panes of 50.

1980, Feb. 15		Tagged		Perf. 11
1804	A1193	15c **multicolored**	.35	.20
		P# block of 12, 6#+A	4.50	—
		Zip block of 4	1.50	—
		Plate block of 20, 6#+A, zip, copyright	6.50	—
a.		Horiz. pair, imperf. vert.	400.00	

Imperfs, including gutter pairs and blocks, exist from printer's
waste. These have been fraudulently perforated to simulate No.
1804a. Genuine examples of No. 1804a do not have colors
misregistered.

NATIONAL LETTER WRITING WEEK ISSUE

National Letter Writing Week, Feb. 24-Mar. 1. Nos.
1805-1810 are printed vertically se-tenant.

Letters Preserve
Memories — A1194

P.S. Write
Soon — A1195

Letters Lift
Spirits — A1196

Letters Shape
Opinions — A1197

Designed by Randall McDougall.

Plates of 240 subjects in four panes of 60 (10x6)
each.
PHOTOGRAVURE

1980, Feb. 25		Tagged		Perf. 11
1805	A1194	15c **multicolored**	.30	.20
1806	A1195	15c **purple & multi**	.30	.20
1807	A1196	15c **multicolored**	.30	.20
1808	A1197	15c **green & multi**	.30	.20
1809	A1197	15c **multicolored**	.30	.20
1810	A1195	15c **red & multi**	.30	.20
a.		Vertical strip of 6, #1805-1810	1.85	*2.00*
		P# block of 36, 6#	13.00	
		Zip block of 12	3.75	
		Nos. 1805-1810 (6)	1.80	1.20

AMERICANA TYPE

Weaver Violins — A1199

Designer: 3.5c, George Mercer.

COIL STAMPS

1980-81		Engr.		Perf. 10 Vertically
1811	A984	1c **dark blue**, *greenish, shiny gum, Mar. 6, 1980*	.20	.20
		Pair	.20	.20
		Joint line pair	.40	
		Dull gum	.35	
		Joint line pair	1.75	
a.		Imperf., pair	125.00	

		Joint line pair	200.00	
b.		Tagging omitted		
1813	A1199	3.5c **purple**, *yellow, June 23, 1980*	.20	.20
		Pair	.20	.20
		Joint line pair	1.00	
a.		Untagged (Bureau precanceled, lines only)	.20	.20
		Pair	.35	.35
		Joint line pair	1.95	
b.		Imperf., pair	150.00	
		Joint line pair	425.00	
1816	A997	12c **red brown**, *beige, Apr. 8, 1981*	.25	.20
		Pair	.50	.20
		Joint line pair	2.00	—
a.		Untagged (Bureau precanceled), **red brown**, *beige*	1.15	1.15
		Pair	2.40	2.40
		Joint line pair	47.50	
b.		Imperf., pair	150.00	
		Joint line pair	300.00	
c.		As "a," **brownish red**, *reddish beige*	—	—
		Pair	—	—
		Joint line pair	—	—
		Nos. 1811-1816 (3)	.65	.60

Bureau Precancels: No. 1816a, lines only, (valued)
PRESORTED/FIRST CLASS (value unused $135); No. 1816c,
PRESORTED/FIRST CLASS.

Eagle — A1207

PHOTOGRAVURE
Plates of 400 subjects in four panes of 100.

1981, Mar. 15		Tagged		Perf. 11x10½
1818	A1207	(18c) **violet**	.35	.20
		P# block of 4	1.60	—
		Zip block of 4	1.50	—
		Pair with full vert. gutter between	—	

BOOKLET STAMP
ENGRAVED
Perf. 10

1819	A1207	(18c) **violet**	.40	.20
a.		Booklet pane of 8	3.75	2.25

COIL STAMP
Perf. 10 Vert.

1820	A1207	(18c) **violet**	.40	.20
		Pair	.80	.20
		Joint line pair	1.60	—
a.		Imperf., pair	80.00	
		Joint line pair	125.00	

Frances Perkins
A1208

Dolley Madison
A1209

FRANCES PERKINS ISSUE

Frances Perkins (1882-1965), Secretary of Labor,
1933-1945 (first woman cabinet member).

Designed by F.R. Petrie.

ENGRAVED
Plates of 200 subjects in four panes of 50.

1980, Apr. 10		Tagged		Perf. 10½x11
1821	A1208	15c **Prussian blue**	.30	.20
		P# block of 4	1.30	—
		Zip block of 4	1.25	—

DOLLEY MADISON ISSUE

Dolley Madison (1768-1849), First Lady, 1809-1817.

Designed by Esther Porter.

ENGRAVED
Plates of 600 subjects in four panes of 150.

1980, May 20	Tagged	Perf. 11	
1822 A1209 15c red brown & sepia		.30	.20
P# block of 4		1.40	—
Zip block of 4		1.25	—
a. Red brown missing (PS)			

Emily Bissell — A1210

Helen Keller and Anne Sullivan — A1211

EMILY BISSELL ISSUE
Emily Bissell (1861-1948), social worker; introduced Christmas seals in United States.

Designed by Stevan Dohanos.

ENGRAVED
Plates of 200 subjects in four panes of 50.

1980, May 31	Tagged	Perf. 11	
1823 A1210 15c black & red		.35	.20
P# block of 4		1.75	—
Zip block of 4		1.50	—
a. Vert. pair, imperf. horiz.		325.00	
b. All colors missing (EP)		—	
c. Red missing (FO)		—	

HELEN KELLER ISSUE
Helen Keller (1880-1968), blind and deaf writer and lecturer taught by Anne Sullivan (1867-1936).

Designed by Paul Calle.

LITHOGRAPHED AND ENGRAVED
Plates of 200 subjects in four panes of 50.

1980, June 27	Tagged	Perf. 11	
1824 A1211 15c multicolored		.30	.20
P# block of 4		1.30	—
Zip block of 4		1.25	—

Veterans Administration Emblem — A1212

Gen. Bernardo de Galvez — A1213

VETERANS ADMINISTRATION, 50th ANNIV.
Designed by Malcolm Grear.

Printed by American Bank Note Co. and J. W. Fergusson and Sons.

PHOTOGRAVURE
Plates of 200 subjects in four panes of 50.

1980, July 21	Tagged	Perf. 11	
1825 A1212 15c carmine & violet blue		.30	.20
P# block of 4, 2#+A		1.30	—
Zip block of 4		1.25	—
a. Horiz. pair, imperf. vert.		400.00	

BERNARDO DE GALVEZ ISSUE
Gen. Bernardo de Galvez (1746-1786), helped defeat British in Battle of Mobile, 1780.

Designed by Roy H. Andersen.

LITHOGRAPHED & ENGRAVED
Plates of 200 subjects in four panes of 50.

1980, July 23	Tagged	Perf. 11	
1826 A1213 15c multicolored		.30	.20
P# block of 4		1.30	—
Zip block of 4		1.25	—
a. Red, brown & blue (engr.) omitted		625.00	
b. Blue, brown, red (engr.) & yellow (litho.) omitted		1,150.	

CORAL REEFS ISSUE
Nos. 1827-1828 alternate in one horizontal row, Nos. 1829-1830 in the next.

Brain Coral, Beaugregory Fish — A1214

Elkhorn Coral, Porkfish — A1215

Chalice Coral, Moorish Idol — A1216

Finger Coral, Sabertooth Blenny — A1217

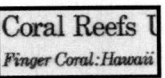

Normal — Cylinder Flaw

Designed by Chuck Ripper.

PHOTOGRAVURE
Plates of 200 subjects in four panes of 50.

1980, Aug. 26	Tagged	Perf. 11	
1827 A1214 15c multi		.30	.20
1828 A1215 15c multi		.30	.20
1829 A1216 15c multi		.30	.20
1830 A1217 15c multi		.30	.20
Cylinder flaw (period between "Finger coral" and "Hawaii" instead of colon) (39390 LR 48)			
a. Block of 4, #1827-1830		1.25	1.10
P# block of 12, 6#		4.00	—
Zip block of 4		1.30	—
b. As "a," imperf.		450.00	
c. As "a," vert. imperf. between		2,000.	
d. As "a," imperf. vert.		3,000.	

American Bald Eagle — A1218

Edith Wharton — A1219

ORGANIZED LABOR ISSUE
Designed by Peter Cocci.

PHOTOGRAVURE
Plates of 200 subjects in four panes of 50.

1980, Sept. 1	Tagged	Perf. 11	
1831 A1218 15c multi		.30	.20
P# block of 12, 6#		3.50	—
Zip block of 4		1.25	—
a. Imperf., pair		300.00	

LITERARY ARTS SERIES
Edith Wharton (1862-1937), novelist.

Designed by Bradbury Thompson after 1905 photograph.

ENGRAVED
Plates of 200 subjects in four panes of 50.

1980, Sept. 5	Tagged	Perf. 10½x11	
1832 A1219 15c purple		.30	.20
P# block of 4		1.30	—
Zip block of 4		1.25	—

EDUCATION ISSUE

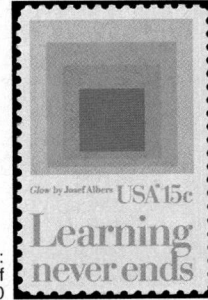

"Homage to the Square: Glow" by Josef Albers — A1220

Designed by Bradbury Thompson

Printed by American Bank Note Co. and J. W. Fergusson and Sons.

PHOTOGRAVURE
Plates of 200 subjects in four panes of 50.

1980, Sept. 12	Tagged	Perf. 11	
1833 A1220 15c multi		.30	.20
P# block of 6, 3#+A		1.90	—
Zip block of 4		1.25	—
a. Horiz. pair, imperf. vert.		175.00	

AMERICAN FOLK ART SERIES
Pacific Northwest Indian Masks

Heiltsuk, Bella Bella Tribe — A1221

Chilkat Tlingit Tribe — A1222

Tlingit
Indian Art USA 15c

Tlingit Tribe — A1223

Bella Coola
Indian Art USA 15c

Bella Coola
Tribe — A1224

Designed by Bradury Thompson after photographs.

PHOTOGRAVURE
Plates of 160 subjects in four panes of 40.

1980, Sept. 25		Tagged		*Perf. 11*	
1834	A1221	15c	**multi**	.35	.20
1835	A1222	15c	**multi**	.35	.20
1836	A1223	15c	**multi**	.35	.20
1837	A1224	15c	**multi**	.35	.20
a.		Block of 4, #1834-1837		1.50	1.25
		P# block of 10, 5#		5.00	—
		Zip, copyright block of 6		2.25	—

AMERICAN ARCHITECTURE SERIES

Renwick 1818-1895 Smithsonian Washington
Architecture USA 15c

Smithsonian
A1225

Richardson 1838-1886 Trinity Church Boston
Architecture USA 15c

Trinity Church
A1226

Furness 1839-1912 Penn Academy Philadelphia
Architecture USA 15c

Penn Academy
A1227

AJ Davis 1803-1892 Lyndhurst Tarrytown NY
Architecture USA 15c

Lyndhurst
A1228

Designed by Walter D. Richards.

ENGRAVED (Giori)
Plates of 160 subjects in four panes of 40.

1980, Oct. 9		Tagged		*Perf. 11*	
1838	A1225	15c	**black & red**	.30	.20
1839	A1226	15c	**black & red**	.30	.20
1840	A1227	15c	**black & red**	.30	.20
1841	A1228	15c	**black & red**	.30	.20
a.		Block of 4, #1838-1841		1.25	1.25
		P# block of 4		1.50	—
		Zip block of 4		1.30	—
b.		As "a," red missing on Nos. 1838, 1839 (PS)		400.00	
c.		As "a," tagging omitted		—	

CHRISTMAS ISSUE

Christmas USA 15c

Madonna and
Child — A1229

USA 15c
Season's Greetings

Wreath and
Toys — A1230

Designed by Esther Porter (No. 1842) after Epiphany Window, Washington Cathedral, and by Bob Timberlake (No. 1843).

PHOTOGRAVURE
Plate of 200 subjects in four panes of 50.

1980, Oct. 31		Tagged		*Perf. 11*	
1842	A1229	15c	**multi**	.30	.20
		P# block of 12, 6#		4.00	—
		Zip block of 4		1.25	—
		Pair with full vert. gutter btwn.		—	
a.		Imperf., pair		50.00	

PHOTOGRAVURE (Combination Press)
Plates of 230 subjects (10x23) in panes of 50 (10x5).

1843	A1230	15c	**multi**	.30	.20
		P# block of 20, 5-8 #, 1-2 copyright		6.50	—
a.		Imperf., pair		60.00	
b.		Buff omitted		22.50	
c.		Vert. pair, imperf. horiz.		—	
d.		Horiz. pair, imperf. between		3,750.	
e.		Tagging omitted		125.00	—

No. 1843b is difficult to identify and should have a competent certificate.
See Combination Press note after No. 1703.

GREAT AMERICANS ISSUE

Dorothea Dix
USA 1c

A1231

Igor Stravinsky
USA 2c

A1232

Henry Clay
USA 3c

A1233

Carl Schurz
4c USA

A1234

Pearl Buck
USA 5c

A1235

Walter Lippmann
6 USA

A1236

Abraham Baldwin
USA 7

A1237

Henry Knox
USA 8

A1238

Sylvanus Thayer
USA 9

A1239

Richard Russell
USA 10c

A1240

Alden Partridge
USA 11

A1241

USA 13c
Crazy Horse

A1242

Sinclair Lewis
USA 14

A1243

Rachel Carson
USA 17c

A1244

George Mason
USA 18c

A1245

USA 19c
Sequoyah

A1246

Ralph Bunche
USA 20c

A1247

Thomas H. Gallaudet
USA 20c

A1248

A1249

A1250

A1251

A1252

A1253

A1254

A1255

A1256

Designers: 1c, Bernie Fuchs. 2c, Burt Silverman, 3c, 17c, 40c, Ward Brackett. 4c, 7c, 10c, 18c, 30c, Richard Sparks. 5c, Paul Calle. 6c, No. 1861, Dennis Lyall. 8c, Arthur Lidov. 9c, 11c, Robert Alexander Anderson. 13c, Brad Holland. 14c, Bradbury Thompson. 19c, 39c, Roy H. Andersen. No. 1860, Jim Sharpe. No. 1862, 22c, 50c, 37c, Christopher Calle. 35c, Nathan Jones.

ENGRAVED

1980-85   Tagged   Perf. 11x10½
Perf. 11 (1c, 6c-11c, 14c, No. 1862, 22c, 30c, 39c, 40c, 50c)

1844	A1231	1c **black,** perf. 11.2, small block tagging, *Sept. 23, 1983*	.20	.20
		P# block of 6	.35	
		P# block of 20, 1-2 #, 1-2 copyright	2.00	—
a.		Imperf., pair	375.00	
b.		Vert. pair, imperf. btwn. and at bottom	1,900.	
c.		Perf. 10.9, small block tagging	.20	.20
		P# block of 6	.35	
		P# block of 20, 1-2 #, 1-2 copyright	2.00	—
d.		Perf. 10.9, large block tagging, *1985*	.20	.20
		P# block of 6	.35	
		P# block of 20, 1-2 #, 1-2 copyright	2.00	—
e.		Vert. pair, imperf. horiz.		
1845	A1232	2c **brn blk,** overall tagging, *Nov. 18, 1982*	.20	.20
		P# block of 4	.35	—
		Zip block of 4	.25	—
		Vert. pair, full gutter between		
a.		Tagging omitted	150.00	
1846	A1233	3c **olive green,** overall tagging, *July 13, 1983*	.20	.20
		P# block of 4	1.00	—
		Zip block of 4	.40	—
a.		Tagging omitted	7.50	
1847	A1234	4c **violet,** overall tagging, *June 3, 1983*	.20	.20
		P# block of 4	.65	—
		Zip block of 4	.35	—
a.		Tagging omitted	7.50	
1848	A1235	5c **henna brown,** overall tagging, *June 25, 1983*	.30	.20
		P# block of 4	1.50	—
		Zip block of 4	1.25	—
1849	A1236	6c **orange vermilion,** large block tagging, *Sept. 19, 1985*	.20	.20
		P# block of 6	.85	
		P# block of 20, 1-2 #, 1-2 zip, 1-2 copyright	5.00	—
a.		Vert. pair, imperf. between and with natural straight edge at bottom	1,750.	
1850	A1237	7c **bright carmine,** small block tagging, *Jan. 25, 1985*	.20	.20
		P# block of 6	.95	

		P# block of 20, 1-2 #, 1-2 zip, 1-2 copyright	4.00	—
1851	A1238	8c **olive black,** overall tagging, *July 25, 1985*	.20	.20
		P# block of 4	.85	—
		Zip block of 4	.60	—
a.		Tagging omitted		
1852	A1239	9c **dark green,** small block tagging, *June 7, 1985*	.20	.20
		P# block of 6	1.30	
		P# block of 20, 1-2 #. 1-2 zip, 1-2 copyright	5.00	
1853	A1240	10c **Prus. blue,** small block tagging, *May 31, 1984*	.25	.20
		P# block of 6	2.00	
		P# block of 20, 1-2 #, 1-2 copyright, 1-2 zip	9.00	—
a.		Large block tagging	.30	.20
		P# block of 6	2.25	
		P# block of 20, 1-2 #, 1-2 copyright, 1-2 zip	9.00	—
b.		Vert. pair, imperf. between	750.00	
c.		Horiz. pair, imperf. between	1,850.	
d.		Vert. pair, imperf horiz.		

Completely imperforate tagged or untagged stamps are from printer's waste.

1854	A1241	11c **dark blue,** overall tagging, *Feb. 12, 1985*	.40	.20
		P# block of 4	2.00	—
		Zip block of 4	1.60	—
a.		Tagging omitted	35.00	
1855	A1242	13c **light maroon,** overall tagging, *Jan. 15, 1982*	.40	.20
		P# block of 4	2.25	—
		Zip block of 4	1.60	—
a.		Tagging omitted	7.50	
1856	A1243	14c **slate green,** small block tagging, *Mar. 21, 1985*	.30	.20
		P# block of 6	2.25	
		P# block of 20, 1-2 #, 1-2 zip, 1-2 copyright	8.00	—
a.		Large block tagging	.30	.20
		P# block of 6	2.25	
		P# block of 20, 1-2 #, 1-2 zip, 1-2 copyright	9.00	—
b.		Vert. pair, imperf. horiz.	110.00	
c.		Horiz. pair, imperf. between	8.00	
d.		Vert. pair, imperf. between	1,650.	
e.		All color omitted		

No. 1856e comes from a partially printed pane and should be collected as a vertical strip of 10, one stamp normal, one stamp transitional and 8 stamps with color omitted.

1857	A1244	17c **green,** overall tagging, *May 28, 1981*	.35	.20
		P# block of 4	2.00	—
		Zip block of 4	1.40	—
a.		Tagging omitted	17.50	
1858	A1245	18c **dark blue,** overall tagging, *May 7, 1981*	.35	.20
		P# block of 4	3.00	—
		Zip block of 4	1.40	—
		Pair with full horiz. gutter between		
a.		Tagging omitted	7.50	
1859	A1246	19c **brown,** overall tagging, *Dec. 27, 1980*	.45	.20
		P# block of 4	2.75	—
		Zip block of 4	1.90	—
1860	A1247	20c **claret,** overall tagging, *Jan. 12, 1982*	.40	.20
		P# block of 4	3.25	—
		Zip block of 4	1.65	—
a.		Tagging omitted	7.50	
1861	A1248	20c **green,** overall tagging, *June 10, 1983*	.50	.20
		P# block of 4	4.00	—
		Zip block of 4	2.00	—
a.		Tagging omitted		
1862	A1249	20c **black,** perf 10.9, small block tagging, dull gum, *Jan. 26, 1984*	.40	.20
		P# block of 6	4.50	
		P# block of 20, 1-2 #, 1-2 copyright, 1-2 zip	12.00	—
a.		Perf. 11.2, large block tagging, dull gum	.40	.20
		Corner P# block of 4	3.00	—
		Zip block of 4	1.60	—
b.		Perf. 11.2, overall tagging, dull gum, *1990*	.40	
		Corner P# block of 4	3.75	—
		Zip block of 4	1.60	—
c.		Tagging omitted, perf. 11.2	11.50	
d.		Prephosphored uncoated paper with embedded tagging showing a mottled appearance, shiny gum, perf. 11.2, *1993*	.40	.20
		Corner P# block of 4	2.50	—
		Zip block of 4	1.60	—
1863	A1250	22c **dark chalky blue,** small block tagging, *Apr. 23, 1985*	.75	.20
		P# block of 6	9.00	
		P# block of 20, 1-2 #, 1-2 zip, 1-2 copyright	16.00	—
a.		Large block tagging	1.00	.20
		P# block of 6	12.50	
		P# block of 20, 1-2 #, 1-2 zip, 1-2 copyright	22.50	—
b.		Perf. 11.2, large block tagging, *1987*	.65	.20
		Corner P# block of 4	7.00	—
		Zip block of 4	2.75	—
c.		Tagging omitted	7.50	
d.		Vert. pair, imperf. horiz.	1,750.	
e.		Vert. pair, imperf. between		
f.		Horiz. pair, imperf. between	1,750.	
1864	A1251	30c **olive gray,** small block tagging, *Sept. 2, 1984*	.60	.20

		P# block of 6	3.50	—
		P# block of 20, 1-2 #, 1-2 copyright, 1-2 zip	17.50	—
a.		Perf. 11.2, large block tagging	.55	.20
		Corner P# block of 4	3.25	—
		Zip block of 4	2.50	—
b.		Perf. 11.2, overall tagging	2.50	.20
		Corner P# block of 4	27.50	—
		Zip block of 4	11.00	—
c.		Tagging omitted		
1865	A1252	35c **gray,** overall tagging, *June 3, 1981*	.75	.20
		P# block of 4	4.25	—
		Zip block of 4	3.25	—
a.		Tagging omitted	85.00	
1866	A1253	37c **blue,** overall tagging, *Jan. 26, 1982*	.80	.20
		P# block of 4	3.75	—
		Zip block of 4	3.25	—
a.		Tagging omitted	12.50	
1867	A1254	39c **rose lilac,** perf 10.9, small block tagging, *Mar. 20, 1985*	.90	.20
		P# block of 6	5.75	
		P# block of 20, 1-2 #, 1-2 zip, 1-2 copyright	22.50	—
a.		Vert. pair, imperf. horiz.	475.00	
b.		Vert. pair, imperf. between	1,650.	
c.		Large block tagging, perf 10.9	.90	.20
		P# block of 6	5.75	
		P# block of 20, 1-2 #, 1-2 zip, 1-2 copyright	20.00	—
d.		Perf. 11.2, large block tagging	.90	.20
		Corner P# block of 4	7.00	—
		Zip block of 4	3.75	—
1868	A1255	40c **dark green,** perf 10.9, small block tagging, *Feb. 24, 1984*	.90	.20
		P# block of 6	6.50	
		P# block of 20, 1-2 #, 1-2 copyright, 1-2 zip	20.00	—
a.		Perf. 11.2, large block tagging	.90	.20
		Corner P# block of 4	6.50	—
		Zip block of 4	3.75	—
1869	A1256	50c **brown,** perf 10.9, overall tagging, shiny gum, *Feb. 22, 1985*	.95	.20
		P# block of 4	7.50	—
		Zip block of 4	4.00	—
a.		Perf. 11.2, large block tagging, dull gum	.95	.20
		P# block of 4	6.25	—
		Zip block of 4	4.00	—
b.		Tagging omitted	11.00	
c.		Tagging omitted, perf. 11.2, dull gum	9.00	
d.		Perf. 11.2, overall tagging, dull gum	2.50	.20
		P# block of 4	35.00	—
		Zip block of 4	11.00	—
e.		Perf. 11.2, prephosphored uncoated paper with embedded tagging showing a mottled appearance, shiny gum, *1992*	.90	.20
		P# block of 4	5.00	—
		Zip block of 4	4.00	—
		Nos. 1844-1869 (26)	11.35	5.20

A1261

A1262

EVERETT DIRKSEN (1896-1969)
Senate minority leader, 1960-1969.

Designed by Ron Adair.

ENGRAVED
Plates of 200 subjects in four panes of 50.

1981, Jan. 4		**Tagged**	**Perf. 11**	
1874	A1261	15c **gray**	.30	.20
		P# block of 4	1.40	
		Zip block of 4	1.25	—
a.		All color omitted	500.00	

No. 1874a comes from a partially printed pane and may be collected as a vertical strip of 3 or 5 (1 or 3 stamps normal, one stamp transitional and one stamp with color omitted) or as a pair with one partially printed stamp.

BLACK HERITAGE SERIES
Whitney Moore Young, Jr. (1921-1971), civil rights leader.

Designed by Jerry Pinkney.

PHOTOGRAVURE
Plates of 200 subjects in four panes of 50.

1981, Jan. 30   **Tagged**   *Perf. 11*
1875 A1262 15c **multi**   .35   .20
          P# block of 4, 6#   1.75   —
          Zip block of 4   1.50   —

FLOWER ISSUE

A1263

A1264

A1265

A1266

Illustration reduced.

Designed by Lowell Nesbitt.

PHOTOGRAVURE
Plates of 192 subjects in four panes of 48 (8x6).

1981, Apr. 23   **Tagged**   *Perf. 11*
1876 A1263 18c **multicolored**   .35   .20
1877 A1264 18c **multicolored**   .35   .20
1878 A1265 18c **multicolored**   .35   .20
1879 A1266 18c **multicolored**   .35   .20
  a.   Block of 4, #1876-1879   1.40   1.25
          P# block of 4, 6#   1.75   —
          Zip block of 4   1.45   —

AMERICAN WILDLIFE

A1267

A1268

A1269

A1270

A1271

A1272

A1273

A1274

A1275

A1276

Designs from photographs by Jim Brandenburg.

ENGRAVED
1981, May 14   **Tagged**   *Perf. 11*
Dark brown
1880 A1267 18c Bighorn   .80   .20
  a.   Tagging omitted   —
1881 A1268 18c Puma   .80   .20
1882 A1269 18c Harbor seal   .80   .20
1883 A1270 18c American Buffalo   .80   .20
1884 A1271 18c Brown bear   .80   .20
1885 A1272 18c Polar bear   .80   .20
1886 A1273 18c Elk (wapiti)   .80   .20
  a.   Tagging omitted   —
1887 A1274 18c Moose   .80   .20
  a.   Tagging omitted   —
1888 A1275 18c White-tailed deer   .80   .20
1889 A1276 18c Pronghorn   .80   .20
  a.   Booklet pane of 10, #1880-1889 8.50   6.00
  b.   Tagging omitted   —

Nos. 1880-1889 issued in booklet only. All stamps have one or two straight edges.
Imperfs are from printer's waste.

FLAG AND ANTHEM ISSUE

A1277

A1278

A1279

A1280

Designed by Peter Cocci.

ENGRAVED
Plates of 460 subjects (20x23) in panes of 100 (10x10).

1981, Apr. 24   **Tagged**   *Perf. 11*
1890 A1277 18c **multicolored**   .35   .20
          P# block of 6   2.25   —
          P# block of 20, 1-2 #   10.00   —
  a.   Imperf., pair   80.00
  b.   Vert. pair, imperf. horiz.   *600.00*
  c.   Vert. pair, imperf. between *600.00*

See Combination Press note after No. 1703.

Coil Stamp
Perf. 10 Vert.
1891 A1278 18c **multicolored**   .35   .20
          Pair   .70   .20
          P# strip of 3, #1   45.00
          P# strip of 3, #2   8.00
          P# strip of 3, #3   45.00
          P# strip of 3, #4   2.25
          P# strip of 3, #5   2.25
          P# strip of 3, #6   *700.00*

          P# strip of 3, #7   6.00
          P# strip of 5, #1   175.00
          P# strip of 5, #2   30.00
          P# strip of 5, #3   525.00
          P# strip of 5, #4   3.50
          P# strip of 5, #5   3.50
          P# strip of 5, #6   *2,500.*
          P# strip of 5, #7   8.00
          P# single, #1   2.50
          P# single, #2   —   1.00
          P# single, #3   —   9.00
          P# single, #4   —   1.00
          P# single, #5   —   1.00
          P# single, #6   —   *675.00*
          P# single, #7   —   25.00
  a.   Imperf., pair   18.00
  b.   Pair, imperf. between   *1,850.*
  c.   Tagging omitted   —

Beware of pairs offered as No. 1891b that have faint blind perfs.
Vertical pairs and blocks exist from printer's waste.

Booklet Stamps
Perf. 11
1892 A1279 6c **dark blue & red**   .50   .20
1893 A1280 18c **multicolored**   .30   .20
  a.   Booklet pane of 8 (2 #1892, 6
          #1893)   3.00   2.50
  b.   As "a," vert. imperf. between 70.00
  c.   Se-tenant pair, #1892 & #1893 .90   1.00
  d.   As "a," tagging omitted   —

Bureau Precanceled Coils
Starting with No. 1895b, Bureau precanceled coil stamps are valued unused as well as used. The coils issued with dull gum may be difficult to distinguish.

When used normally these stamps do not receive any postal markings so that used stamps with an additional postal cancellation of any kind are worth considerably less than the values shown here.

FLAG OVER SUPREME COURT ISSUE

A1281

Designed by Dean Ellis.

ENGRAVED
Plates of 460 subjects (20x23) in panes of 100 (10x10)

1981, Dec. 17   **Tagged**   *Perf. 11*
1894 A1281 20c **black, dark blue & red**, dull
          gum   .40   .20
          P# block of 6   2.75   —
          P# block of 20, 1-2 #   9.00   —
  a.   Vert. pair, imperf.   30.00
  b.   Vert. pair, imperf. horiz. 400.00
  c.   Dark blue omitted   70.00
  d.   Black omitted   275.00
  e.   Perf. 11.2, shiny gum   .35   .20
          P# block of 6   2.50   —
          P# block of 20, 1-2 #   8.50   —
  f.   Tagging omitted   —

Coil Stamp
Perf. 10 Vert.
1895 A1281 20c **black, dark blue & red**, wide
          block tagging   .40   .20
          Pair   .80   .20
          P# strip of 3, #1   1.75
          P# strip of 3, #2   3.00
          P# strip of 3, #3   3.00
          P# strip of 3, #5   3.00
          P# strip of 3, #11   3.00
          P# strip of 3, #13, 14   2.75
          P# strip of 5, #1   30.00
          P# strip of 5, #2   4.00
          P# strip of 5, #3   4.00
          P# strip of 5, #5   4.00
          P# strip of 5, #11   4.00
          P# strip of 5, #13, 14   4.00
          P# single, #1   .75
          P# single, #2-3   —   .50
          P# single, #5   —   .50
          P# single, #11   —   3.00
          P# single, #13, 14   —   .50
  a.   Narrow block tagging   .40   .20
          Pair   .80   .20
          P# strip of 3, #4   5.00
          P# strip of 3, #6   7.50
          P# strip of 3, #8   3.00
          P# strip of 3, #9-10   2.75
          P# strip of 3, #12   3.00
          P# strip of 5, #4   *300.00*
          P# strip of 5, #6   125.00
          P# strip of 5, #8   11.00
          P# strip of 5, #9   3.75
          P# strip of 5, #10   4.00
          P# strip of 5, #12   4.00

P# single, #4	—	.80
P# single, #6	—	2.25
P# single, #8	—	.40
P# single, #9	—	.40
P# single, #10	—	.60
P# single, #12	—	.75
b. Untagged (Bureau precanceled, lines only)	.50	.50
P# strip of 3, #14	32.50	
P# strip of 5, #14	37.50	
P# single, #14		30.00
c. Tagging omitted (not Bureau precanceled)	15.00	
P# strip of 3, #4	—	
P# strip of 3, #3, 5, 8, 10, 11, 14	—	
P# strip of 5, #5, 10, 11, 14	—	
P# single, #5, 8-11, 14	—	
d. Imperf., pair	8.00	—
e. Pair, imperf. between	800.00	—
f. Black omitted	45.00	—
g. Dark blue omitted	1,350.	—
h. Black field of stars instead of blue	—	

The wide block tagging on No. 1895 and narrow block tagging on No. 1895a differentiate stamps printed on two different presses. The wide blocks are approximately 20-21mm high by 18mm wide with a 4mm untagged gutter between tagging blocks.

The narrow blocks are approximately 21-22mm high and approximately 16-16½mm wide with a 5½-6½ untagged gutter between tagging blocks.

BOOKLET STAMP
Perf. 11x10½

1896 A1281 20c **black, dark blue & red,** small block tagging	.40	.20
a. Booklet pane of 6	3.00	2.25
Scored perforations	3.00	2.25
b. Booklet pane of 10, *June 1, 1982*	5.25	3.25
c. Tagging omitted	100.00	—
d. Large block tagging ('83)	.40	.20
e. As "d," booklet pane of 10	5.25	3.25
Scored perforations	5.25	3.25
f. As "a," tagging omitted	—	

Booklets containing two panes of ten of No. 1896e were issued Nov. 17, 1983.

The small block tagging is 16x18mm (Nos. 1896-1896b). The large block tagging is 18x21mm (Nos. 1896d-1896e).

TRANSPORTATION ISSUE

A1283

A1284

Designer: 1c, 2c, David Stone.

COIL STAMPS
ENGRAVED

1981-84	**Tagged**	**Perf. 10 Vert.**	
1897 A1283 1c **violet,** *Aug. 19, 1983*	.20	.20	
Pair	.20	.20	
P# strip of 3, line, #1, 2	.30		
P# strip of 3, line, #3, 4	.30		
P# strip of 3, line, #5, 6	.30		
P# strip of 5, line, #1, 2	.40		
P# strip of 5, line, #3, 4	.40		
P# strip of 5, line, #5, 6	.40		
P# single, #1, 2	—	.25	
P# single, #3, 4	—	.65	
P# single, #5, 6	—	.30	
b. Imperf., pair	500.00		
Joint line pair	—		
e. Tagging omitted	—		
1897A A1284 2c **black,** *May 20, 1982*	.20	.20	
Pair	.20	.20	
P# strip of 3, line, #2-4, 6, 8, 10	.40		
P# strip of 5, line, #2-4, 6, 8, 10	.45		
P# single, #2-4, 6, 8, 10	—	.40	
c. Imperf., pair	45.00		
Joint line pair	—		
d. Tagging omitted	27.50		

A1284a

A1285

Designers: 3c, Walter Brooks. 4c, Jim Schleyer.

1898 A1284a 3c **dark green,** *Mar. 25, 1983*	.20	.20
Pair	.20	.20

P# strip of 3, line, #1-4	.45	
P# strip of 5, line, #1-4	.55	
P# single, #1-4		.55
1898A A1285 4c **reddish brown,** *Aug. 19, 1982*	.20	.20
Pair	.20	.20
P# strip of 3, line, #1-4	.50	
P# strip of 3, line, #5-6	1.25	
P# strip of 5, line, #1-4	.75	
P# strip of 5, line, #5-6	1.50	
P# single, #1-4	—	.75
P# single, #5-6	—	1.50
b. Untagged (Bureau precanceled, Nonprofit Org.)	.20	.20
P# strip of 3, line, #3-6	2.25	
P# strip of 3, line, #3-6	3.00	
P# single, #3, 4	—	3.00
P# single, #5, 6	—	3.25
c. As "b," imperf., pair	675.00	
d. As No. 1898A, imperf. pair	700.00	—
e. Tagging omitted (not Bureau precanceled)	35.00	15.00

See also No. 2228.

A1286

A1287

Designers: 5c, 5.2c, Walter Brooks.

1899 A1286 5c **gray green,** *Oct. 10, 1983*	.20	.20
Pair	.25	.20
P# strip of 3, line, #1-4	.45	
P# strip of 5, line, #1-4	.60	
P# single, #1-4	—	.45
a. Imperf., pair	2,500.	
b. Tagging omitted	22.50	—
1900 A1287 5.2c **carmine,** *Mar. 21, 1983*	.20	.20
Pair	.25	.20
P# strip of 3, line, #1-2	1.10	
P# strip of 3, line, #3	80.00	
P# strip of 3, line, #5	50.00	
P# strip of 5, line, #1-2	3.00	
P# strip of 5, line, #3	210.00	
P# strip of 5, line, #5	140.00	
P# single, #1-2	—	5.50
P# single, #3	—	170.00
P# single, #5	—	140.00
a. Untagged (Bureau precanceled, lines only)	.20	.20
P# strip of 3, line, #1-3	3.00	
P# strip of 3, line, #4	4.00	
P# strip of 3, line, #5	3.00	
P# strip of 3, line, #6	4.00	
P# strip of 5, line, #1-3	5.00	
P# strip of 5, line, #4, 6	7.00	
P# strip of 5, line, #5	5.00	
P# single, #1, 2	—	2.25
P# single, #3	—	1.50
P# single, #4	—	7.00
P# single, #5	—	1.75
P# single, #6	—	7.00
b. Tagging omitted	—	

A1288

A1289

Designers: 5.9c, David Stone. 7.4c, Jim Schleyer.

1901 A1288 5.9c **blue,** *Feb. 17, 1982*	.25	.20
Pair	.50	.20
P# strip of 3, line, #3-4	2.25	
P# strip of 5, line, #3-4	3.50	
P# single, #3-4	—	5.00
a. Untagged (Bureau precanceled, lines only)	.20	.20
P# strip of 3, line, #3-4	9.00	
P# strip of 3, line, #5-6	75.00	
P# strip of 5, line, #3-4	12.00	
P# strip of 5, line, #5-6	90.00	
P# single, #3-4	—	5.00
P# single, #5-6	—	60.00
b. As "a," imperf., pair	150.00	
1902 A1289 7.4c **brown,** *Apr. 7, 1984*	.20	.20
Pair	.40	.20
P# strip of 3, #2	3.50	
P# strip of 5, #2	4.00	
P# single, #2	—	5.75
a. Untagged (Bureau precanceled, Blk. Rt. CAR-RT SORT)	.20	.20
P# strip of 3, #2	3.50	
P# strip of 5, #2	4.00	
P# single, #2	—	3.75

A1290

A1291

Designers: 9.3c, Jim Schleyer. 10.9c, David Stone.

1903 A1290 9.3c **carmine rose,** *Dec. 15*	.30	.20
Pair	.60	.20
P# strip of 3, line, #1-2	2.00	
P# strip of 3, line, #3-4	4.00	
P# strip of 3, line, #5-6	75.00	
P# strip of 5, line, #1-2	4.50	
P# strip of 5, line, #3-4	10.00	
P# strip of 5, line, #5-6	325.00	
P# single, #1-2	—	7.00
P# single, #3-4	—	15.00
P# single, #5-6	—	175.00
a. Untagged (Bureau precanceled, lines only)	.25	.25
P# strip of 3, line, #1	3.25	
P# strip of 3, line, #2	3.25	
P# strip of 3, line, #3	6.00	
P# strip of 3, line, #4	3.25	
P# strip of 3, line, #5-6	1.25	
P# strip of 3, line, #8	150.00	
P# strip of 5, line, #1	4.75	
P# strip of 5, line, #2	4.75	
P# strip of 5, line, #3	10.00	
P# strip of 5, line, #4	4.75	
P# strip of 5, line, #5-6	1.75	
P# strip of 5, line, #8	225.00	
P# single, #1-2	—	4.00
P# single, #3	—	7.00
P# single, #4	—	4.00
P# single, #5-6	—	1.25
P# single, #8	—	180.00
b. As "a," imperf., pair	100.00	
1904 A1291 10.9c **purple,** *Mar. 26, 1982*	.30	.20
Pair	.60	.20
P# strip of 3, line, #1-2	4.00	
P# strip of 5, line, #1-2	10.00	
P# single, #1-2	—	12.00
a. Untagged (Bureau precanceled, lines only)	.30	.25
P# strip of 3, line, #1-2	10.00	
P# strip of 3, line, #3-4	75.00	
P# strip of 5, line, #1-2	15.00	
P# strip of 5, line, #3-4	200.00	
P# single, #1-2	—	7.50

	P# single, #3-4	—	65.00
b.	As "a," imperf., pair	140.00	
	Joint line pair		

A1292

A1293

Designers: 11c, Jim Schleyer. 17c Chuck Jaquays.

1905	A1292	**11c red,** *Feb. 3, 1984*	.30	.20
		Pair	.60	.20
		P# strip of 3, #1	1.60	
		P# strip of 5, #1	2.75	
		P# single, #1	—	2.50
a.		Untagged *Sept. 1991*	.25	.20
		Pair	.50	.20
		P# strip of 3, #1	1.60	
		P# strip of 3, #2	1.75	
		P# strip of 5, #1	2.50	
		P# strip of 5, #2	2.25	
		P# single, #1	—	2.25
		P# single, #2	—	2.00

Untagged stamps from plate 1 come only Bureau precanceled with lines. Untagged stamps from plate 2 come both without and with Bureau precancel lines; values are for non-precanceled examples.

1906	A1293	**17c ultramarine,** *June 25*	.35	.20
		Pair	.70	.20
		P# strip of 3, line, #1-5	1.25	
		P# strip of 3, line, #6	6.00	
		P# strip of 3, line, #7	2.25	
		P# strip of 5, line, #1-5	2.25	
		P# strip of 5, line, #6	8.00	
		P# strip of 5, line, #7	3.50	
		P# single, #1-5	—	1.50
		P# single, #6	—	8.00
		P# single, #7	—	3.25
a.		Untagged (Bureau precanceled, Presorted First Class)	.35	.35
		P# strip of 3, line, #1, 2	6.00	
		P# strip of 3, line, #3-5	2.50	
		P# strip of 3, line, #6, 7	7.00	
		P# strip of 5, line, #1, 2	8.75	
		P# strip of 5, line, #3-5	3.75	
		P# strip of 5, line, #6-7	10.50	
		P# single, #1, 2	—	7.25
		P# single, #3-5	—	8.00
		P# single, #6, 7	—	9.00

Three different precancel styles exist with differences in the font used: Type A has thin lines and the "T" in "PRESORTED" is tall with a short cross bar; Type B has thicker lines and the "T" is shorter with a longer cross bar; Type C has thicker lines still and the "T" has a shorter stem with a cross bar longer than on Types A or B. Lengths of the precancel increase with the types and the wider spacing of the letters, though the imprecise manufacture of the precancel mats led to significant variations in length. Combination pairs exist of Types A and B.

b.	Imperf., pair		140.00
c.	As "a," imperf., pair		*550.00*

A1294

A1295

Designers: 18c, David Stone. 20c, Jim Schleyer.

1907	A1294	**18c dark brown,** *May 18*	.35	.20
		Pair	.70	.20
		P# strip of 3, line, #1	16.00	
		P# strip of 3, line, #2	2.00	
		P# strip of 3, line, #3, 4	16.00	
		P# strip of 3, line, #5, 6	2.00	
		P# strip of 3, line, #7	5.00	
		P# strip of 3, line, #8	2.00	
		P# strip of 3, line, #9-12	5.00	
		P# strip of 3, line, #13, 14	2.00	
		P# strip of 3, line, #15, 16	5.00	
		P# strip of 3, line, #17, 18	2.00	
		P# strip of 5, line, #1	75.00	
		P# strip of 5, line, #2	2.75	
		P# strip of 5, line, #3-4	75.00	
		P# strip of 5, line, #5, 6	2.75	
		P# strip of 5, line, #7	8.00	
		P# strip of 5, line, #8	2.75	
		P# strip of 5, line, #9-12	8.00	
		P# strip of 5, line, #13, 14	2.75	
		P# strip of 5, line, #15, 16	8.00	
		P# strip of 5, line, #17, 18	2.75	

		P# single, #1	—	8.00
		P# single, #2	—	.75
		P# single, #3, 4	—	9.25
		P# single, #5, 6	—	.75
		P# single, #7	—	5.00
		P# single, #8	—	.75
		P# single, #9-14	—	3.50
		P# single, #15, 16	—	7.00
		P# single, #17, 18	—	3.25
a.		Imperf., pair	110.00	
b.		Tagging omitted		
1908	A1295	**20c vermilion,** *Dec. 10*	.35	.20
		Pair	.70	.20
		P# strip of 3, line, #1	15.00	
		P# strip of 3, line, #2	40.00	
		P# strip of 3, line, #3, 4	2.00	
		P# strip of 3, line, #5	2.00	
		P# strip of 3, line, #6	8.00	
		P# strip of 3, line, #7, 8	20.00	
		P# strip of 3, line, #9, 10	1.75	
		P# strip of 3, line, #11	7.50	
		P# strip of 3, line, #12	2.00	
		P# strip of 3, line, #13	2.25	
		P# strip of 3, line, #14	2.00	
		P# strip of 3, line, #15, 16	2.00	
		P# strip of 5, line, #1	125.00	
		P# strip of 5, line, #2	500.00	
		P# strip of 5, line, #3, 4	4.25	
		P# strip of 5, line, #5	2.75	
		P# strip of 5, line, #6	35.00	
		P# strip of 5, line, #7-8	200.00	
		P# strip of 5, line, #9-10	2.75	
		P# strip of 5, line, #11	85.00	
		P# strip of 5, line, #12	7.25	
		P# strip of 5, line, #13	4.25	
		P# strip of 5, line, #14	7.25	
		P# strip of 5, line, #15-16	4.25	
		P# single, #1	—	.75
		P# single, #2	—	7.50
		P# single, #3, 4	—	.65
		P# single, #5	—	.75
		P# single, #6	—	1.25
		P# single, #7, 8	—	1.00
		P# single, #9, 10	—	.75
		P# single, #11	—	.75
		P# single, #12	—	6.25
		P# single, #13	—	.65
		P# single, #14	—	6.25
		P# single, #15, 16	—	2.00
a.		Imperf., pair	90.00	
b.		Tagging omitted		—
		Nos. 1897-1908 (14)	3.60	2.80

See Nos. 2225-2228.

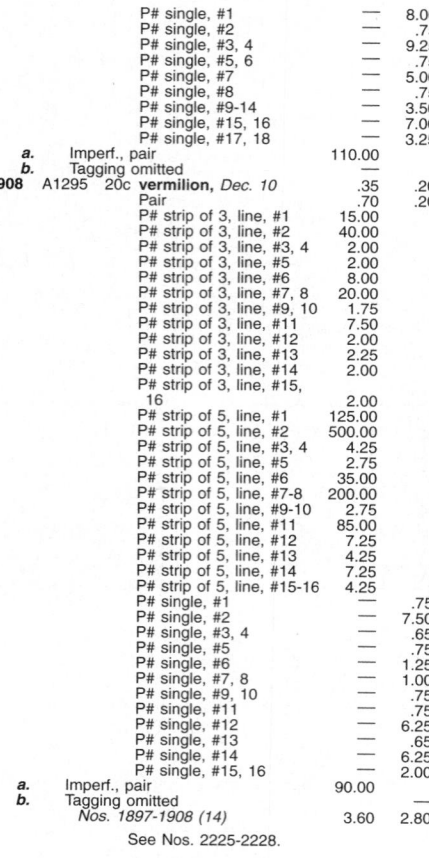

Eagle
and
Moon
A1296

Booklet Stamp
PHOTOGRAVURE

1983, Aug. 12		**Untagged**	*Perf. 10 Vert.*	
1909	A1296	**$9.35 multicolored**	20.00	15.00
a.		Booklet pane of 3	60.00	—

A1297

AMERICAN RED CROSS CENTENNIAL
Designed by Joseph Csatari.

PHOTOGRAVURE
Plates of 200 subjects in four panes of 50.

1981, May 1		**Tagged**	*Perf. 10½x11*	
1910	A1297	**18c multicolored**	.35	.20
		P# block of 4, 6#	1.75	
		Zip block of 4	1.40	—

SAVINGS & LOAN SESQUICENTENNIAL
Designed by Don Hedin.

PHOTOGRAVURE
Plates of 200 subjects in four panes of 50.

1981, May 8		**Tagged**	*Perf. 11*	
1911	A1298	**18c multicolored**	.35	.20
		P# block of 4, 6#	1.75	
		Zip block of 4	1.40	—

A1298

SPACE ACHIEVEMENT ISSUE

A1299

A1302

A1300

A1301

A1303

A1306

A1304

A1305

Designed by Robert McCall.

Designs: A1299, Moon walk. A1300-A1301, Columbia space shuttle. A1302, Skylab. A1303, Pioneer 11. A1306, Telescope. Se-tenant in blocks of 8.

PHOTOGRAVURE

Plates of 192 subjects in four panes of 48 each.

1981, May 21		Tagged	Perf. 11	
1912 A1299	18c multicolored		.40	.20
1913 A1300	18c multicolored		.40	.20
1914 A1301	18c multicolored		.40	.20
1915 A1302	18c multicolored		.40	.20
1916 A1303	18c multicolored		.40	.20
1917 A1304	18c multicolored		.40	.20
1918 A1305	18c multicolored		.40	.20
1919 A1306	18c multicolored		.40	.20
a.	Block of 8, #1912-1919		3.25	3.00
	P# block of 8, 6#		3.75	—
	Zip, copyright block of 8		3.25	—
b.	As "a," imperf.		6,750.	
c.	As "a," imperf. vert.		—	
d.	As "a," tagging omitted		—	

No. 1919c has blind horiz. perfs.

PROFESSIONAL MANAGEMENT EDUCATION CENTENARY

Joseph Wharton (Founder of Wharton School of Business) A1307

Designed by Rudolph de Harak.

PHOTOGRAVURE

Plates of 200 subject in four panes of 50.

1981, June 18		Tagged	Perf. 11	
1920 A1307	18c blue & black		.35	.20
	P# block of 4, 2#		1.50	—
	Zip block of 4		1.40	—

PRESERVATION OF WILDLIFE HABITATS

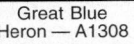

Great Blue Heron — A1308

Badger — A1309

Grizzly Bear — A1310

Ruffed Grouse — A1311

Designed by Chuck Ripper.

PHOTOGRAVURE

Plates of 200 subjects in four panes of 50.

1981, June 26		Tagged	Perf. 11	
1921 A1308	18c multicolored		.35	.20
1922 A1309	18c multicolored		.35	.20
1923 A1310	18c multicolored		.35	.20
1924 A1311	18c multicolored		.35	.20
a.	Block of 4, #1921-1924		1.50	1.25
	P# block of 4, 5#		2.00	—
	Zip block of 4		1.55	—

INTERNATIONAL YEAR OF THE DISABLED

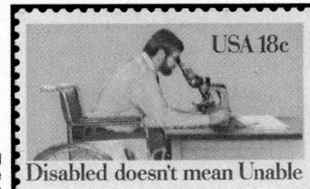

Man Using Microscope A1312

Designed by Martha Perske.

PHOTOGRAVURE

Plates of 200 subjects in four panes of 50.

1981, June 29		Tagged	Perf. 11	
1925 A1312	18c multicolored		.35	.20
	P# block of 4, 6#		1.50	—
	Zip block of 4		1.40	—
a.	Vert. pair, imperf. horiz.		2,500.	

EDNA ST. VINCENT MILLAY ISSUE

A1313

Designed by Glenora Case Richards.

LITHOGRAPHED AND ENGRAVED

Plates of 200 subjects in four panes of 50.

1981, July 10		Tagged	Perf. 11	
1926 A1313	18c multicolored		.35	.20
	P# block of 4, 7#		1.50	—
	Zip block of 4		1.40	—
a.	Black (engr., inscriptions) omitted		275.00	

ALCOHOLISM

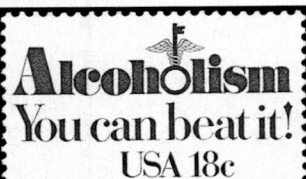

A1314

Designed by John Boyd.

ENGRAVED

Plates of 230 (10x23) subjects in panes of 50 (5x10)

1981, Aug. 19		Tagged	Perf. 11	
1927 A1314	18c blue & black		.45	.20
	P# block of 6		10.00	
	P# block of 20, 1-2 #, 1-2 copyright, 1-2 Zip		20.00	
a.	Imperf., pair		375.00	
b.	Vert. pair, imperf. horiz.		2,400.	

See Combination Press note after No. 1703.

AMERICAN ARCHITECTURE SERIES

New York University Library by Stanford White A1315

Biltmore House By Richard Morris Hunt — A1316

Palace of the Arts by Bernard Maybeck A1317

National Farmer's Bank by Louis Sullivan A1318

Designed by Walter D. Richards.

ENGRAVED

Plates of 160 subjects in four panes of 40.

1981, Aug. 28		Tagged	Perf. 11	
1928 A1315	18c black & red		.40	.20
a.	Tagging omitted		—	
1929 A1316	18c black & red		.40	.20
1930 A1317	18c black & red		.40	.20
a.	Tagging omitted		—	
1931 A1318	18c black & red		.40	.20
a.	Block of 4, #1928-1931		1.65	1.65
	P# block of 4		2.10	—
	Zip block of 4		1.80	—
b.	As "a," tagging omitted		—	

SPORTS PERSONALITIES

Mildred Didrikson Zaharias — A1319

Robert Tyre Jones — A1320

Designed by Richard Gangel.

ENGRAVED

Plates of 200 subjects in four panes of 50.

1981, Sept. 22		Tagged	Perf. 10½x11	
1932 A1319	18c purple		.40	.20
	P# block of 4		3.00	—
	Zip block of 4		1.75	—
1933 A1320	18c green		.60	.20
	P# block of 4		3.25	—
	Zip block of 4		2.50	—

FREDERIC REMINGTON

Coming Through the Rye — A1321

Designed by Paul Calle

LITHOGRAPHED AND ENGRAVED
Plates of 200 in four panes of 50.

1981, Oct. 9	Tagged	Perf. 11	
1934 A1321 18c **gray, olive green & brown**		.35	.20
	P# block of 4, 3#	1.60	—
	Zip block of 4	1.50	—
a.	Vert. pair, imperf. between	225.00	
b.	Brown omitted	325.00	

JAMES HOBAN

Irish-American
Architect of
the White
House
A1322

Designed by Ron Mercer and Walter D. Richards.

PHOTOGRAVURE
Plates of 200 in four panes of 50.

1981, Oct. 13	Tagged	Perf. 11	
1935 A1322 18c **multicolored**		.35	.20
	P# block of 4, 6#	1.60	—
	Zip block of 4	1.50	—
1936 A1322 20c **multicolored**		.35	.20
	P# block of 4, 6#	1.75	—
	Zip block of 4	1.50	—

See Ireland No. 504.

AMERICAN BICENTENNIAL

Battle of
Yorktown
A1323

Battle of the
Virginia Capes
A1324

Designed by Cal Sacks.

LITHOGRAPHED AND ENGRAVED
Plates of 200 in four panes of 50.

1981, Oct. 16	Tagged	Perf. 11	
1937 A1323 18c **multicolored**		.35	.20
1938 A1324 18c **multicolored**		.35	.20
a.	Pair, #1937-1938	.90	.75
	P# block of 4, 7#	2.00	—
	Zip block of 4	1.65	—
b.	As "a," black (engr., inscriptions) omitted	350.00	
c.	As "a," tagging omitted	100.00	

CHRISTMAS

Madonna and Child,
Botticelli — A1325

Felt Bear
on Sleigh
A1326

Designed by Bradbury Thompson (No. 1939) and by Naiad Einsel (No. 1940).

PHOTOGRAVURE
Plates of 400 in four panes of 100 (No. 1939)
Plates of 200 in four panes of 50 (No. 1940)

1981, Oct. 28	Tagged	Perf. 11	
1939 A1325 (20c) **multicolored**		.40	.20
	P# block of 4, 6#	1.75	—
	Zip block of 4	1.65	—
a.	Imperf., pair	100.00	
b.	Vert. pair, imperf. horiz.	1,000.	
c.	Tagging omitted	17.50	
1940 A1326 (20c) **multicolored**		.40	.20
	P# block of 4, 5#	1.75	—
	Zip block of 4	1.65	—
a.	Imperf., pair	200.00	
b.	Vert. pair, imperf. horiz.	2,750.	

JOHN HANSON

First President of the
Continental
Congress — A1327

Designed by Ron Adair.

PHOTOGRAVURE
Plates of 200 in panes of 50

1981, Nov. 5	Tagged	Perf. 11	
1941 A1327 20c **multicolored**		.40	.20
	P# block of 4, 5#	1.75	—
	Zip block of 4	1.65	—

DESERT PLANTS

Barrel Cactus — A1328

Agave — A1329

Beavertail Cactus — A1330

Saguaro — A1331

Designed by Frank J. Waslick.

LITHOGRAPHED AND ENGRAVED
Plates of 160 in four panes of 40

1981 Dec. 11	Tagged	Perf. 11	
1942 A1328 20c **multicolored**		.35	.20
1943 A1329 20c **multicolored**		.35	.20
1944 A1330 20c **multicolored**		.35	.20
1945 A1331 20c **multicolored**		.35	.20
a.	Block of 4, #1942-1945	1.50	1.25
	P# block of 4, 7#	1.90	
	Zip block of 4	1.55	—
b.	As "a," deep brown (litho.) omitted	4,250.	
c.	No. 1945 imperf., vert. pair	3,500.	
d.	As "a," dark green & dark blue (engr.) missing (EP)	—	
e.	As "a," dark green (engr.) missing on left stamp (EP)	—	
f.	As "a," tagging omitted	—	

A1332

A1333

Designed by Bradbury Thompson.

PHOTOGRAVURE
Plates of 400 in panes of 100.

1981, Oct. 11	Tagged	Perf. 11x10½	
1946 A1332 (20c) **brown**		.40	.20
	P# block of 4	2.00	—
	Zip block of 4	1.65	—
a.	Tagging omitted	7.00	
b.	All color omitted	—	

No. 1946b comes from a partially printed pane with most
stamps normal. It must be collected as a vertical pair or strip
with normal or partially printed stamps attached.

ENGRAVED
COIL STAMP
Perf. 10 Vert.

1947 A1332 (20c) **brown**		.60	.20
	Pair	1.20	.20
	Joint line pair	1.50	—
a.	Imperf. pair	950.00	
	Joint line pair	—	

BOOKLET STAMPS
Perf. 11

1948 A1333 (20c) **brown**		.40	.20
a.	Booklet pane of 10	4.50	3.25

Rocky Mountain
Bighorn — A1334

BOOKLET STAMP
ENGRAVED

1982, Jan. 8	Tagged	Perf. 11	
1949 A1334 20c **dark blue**		.55	.20
a.	Booklet pane of 10	5.50	2.50
b.	As "a," imperf. between	95.00	
c.	Type II	1.40	.20

d.	Type II, booklet pane of 10	14.00	—
e.	As #1949, tagging omitted	5.00	—
f.	As "e," booklet pane of 10	50.00	—

No. 1949 is 18¾mm wide and has overall tagging. No. 1949c is 18½mm wide and has block tagging.

FRANKLIN DELANO ROOSEVELT

A1335

Designed by Clarence Holbert.

ENGRAVED
Plates of 192 in four panes of 48.

1982, Jan. 30		**Tagged**		***Perf. 11***	
1950	A1335	20c blue		.40	.20
		P# block of 4		1.75	—
		Zip block of 4		1.65	—

LOVE ISSUE

A1336

Designed by Mary Faulconer.

PHOTOGRAVURE
Plates of 200 in four panes of 50.

1982, Feb. 1		**Tagged**		***Perf. 11¼***	
1951	A1336	20c multicolored		.40	.20
		P# block of 4, 5#		1.75	
		Zip block of 4		1.65	—
b.		Imperf., pair		225.00	
c.		Blue omitted		200.00	
d.		Yellow omitted		650.00	
e.		Purple omitted		—	
f.		Tagging omitted		100.00	—

No. 1951c is valued in the grade of fine.

Perf. 11¼x10½

1951A	A1336	20c multicolored		.75	.25
		P# block of 4, 5#		3.50	
		Zip block of 4		3.00	—

GEORGE WASHINGTON

A1337

Designed by Mark English.

PHOTOGRAVURE
Plates of 200 in four panes of 50.

1982, Feb. 22		**Tagged**		***Perf. 11***	
1952	A1337	20c multicolored		.40	.20
		P# block of 4, 6#		1.75	—
		Zip block of 4		1.65	—

State Birds and Flowers
A1338-A1387

STATE BIRDS AND FLOWERS ISSUE
Illustration reduced.

Designed by Arthur and Alan Singer.

PHOTOGRAVURE (Andreotti)
Plates of 200 subjects in four panes of 50.

1982, Apr. 14   **Tagged**   *Perf. 10½x11¼*

1953 A1338 20c Alabama	.55	.30
1954 A1339 20c Alaska	.55	.30
1955 A1340 20c Arizona	.55	.30
1956 A1341 20c Arkansas	.55	.30
1957 A1342 20c California	.55	.30
1958 A1343 20c Colorado	.55	.30
1959 A1344 20c Connecticut	.55	.30
1960 A1345 20c Delaware	.55	.30
1961 A1346 20c Florida	.55	.30
1962 A1347 20c Georgia	.55	.30
1963 A1348 20c Hawaii	.55	.30
1964 A1349 20c Idaho	.55	.30
1965 A1350 20c Illinois	.55	.30
1966 A1351 20c Indiana	.55	.30
1967 A1352 20c Iowa	.55	.30
1968 A1353 20c Kansas	.55	.30
1969 A1354 20c Kentucky	.55	.30
1970 A1355 20c Louisiana	.55	.30
1971 A1356 20c Maine	.55	.30
1972 A1357 20c Maryland	.55	.30
1973 A1358 20c Massachusetts	.55	.30
1974 A1359 20c Michigan	.55	.30
1975 A1360 20c Minnesota	.55	.30
1976 A1361 20c Mississippi	.55	.30
1977 A1362 20c Missouri	.55	.30
1978 A1363 20c Montana	.55	.30
1979 A1364 20c Nebraska	.55	.30
1980 A1365 20c Nevada	.55	.30
1981 A1366 20c New Hampshire	.55	.30
b. Black missing (EP)	5,000.	
1982 A1367 20c New Jersey	.55	.30
1983 A1368 20c New Mexico	.55	.30
1984 A1369 20c New York	.55	.30
1985 A1370 20c North Carolina	.55	.30
1986 A1371 20c North Dakota	.55	.30
1987 A1372 20c Ohio	.55	.30
1988 A1373 20c Oklahoma	.55	.30
1989 A1374 20c Oregon	.55	.30
1990 A1375 20c Pennsylvania	.55	.30
1991 A1376 20c Rhode Island	.55	.30
b. Black missing (EP)	5,000.	
1992 A1377 20c South Carolina	.55	.30
1993 A1378 20c South Dakota	.55	.30
1994 A1379 20c Tennessee	.55	.30
1995 A1380 20c Texas	.55	.30
1996 A1381 20c Utah	.55	.30
1997 A1382 20c Vermont	.55	.30
1998 A1383 20c Virginia	.55	.30
1999 A1384 20c Washington	.55	.30
2000 A1385 20c West Virginia	.55	.30
2001 A1386 20c Wisconsin	.55	.30
b. Black missing (EP)	5,000.	
2002 A1387 20c Wyoming	.55	.30
b. A1338-A1387 Pane of 50, Nos.		
1953-2002	27.50	20.00
d. Pane of 50, imperf.	27,500.	

Perf. 11¼x11

1953A A1338 20c Alabama	.65	.30
1954A A1339 20c Alaska	.65	.30
1955A A1340 20c Arizona	.65	.30
1956A A1341 20c Arkansas	.65	.30
1957A A1342 20c California	.65	.30
1958A A1343 20c Colorado	.65	.30
1959A A1344 20c Connecticut	.65	.30
1960A A1345 20c Delaware	.65	.30
1961A A1346 20c Florida	.65	.30
1962A A1347 20c Georgia	.65	.30
1963A A1348 20c Hawaii	.65	.30
1964A A1349 20c Idaho	.65	.30
1965A A1350 20c Illinois	.65	.30
1966A A1351 20c Indiana	.65	.30
1967A A1352 20c Iowa	.65	.30
1968A A1353 20c Kansas	.65	.30
1969A A1354 20c Kentucky	.65	.30
1970A A1355 20c Louisiana	.65	.30
1971A A1356 20c Maine	.65	.30
1972A A1357 20c Maryland	.65	.30
1973A A1358 20c Massachusetts	.65	.30
1974A A1359 20c Michigan	.65	.30
1975A A1360 20c Minnesota	.65	.30
1976A A1361 20c Mississippi	.65	.30
1977A A1362 20c Missouri	.65	.30
1978A A1363 20c Montana	.65	.30
1979A A1364 20c Nebraska	.65	.30
1980A A1365 20c Nevada	.65	.30
1981A A1366 20c New Hampshire	.65	.30
1982A A1367 20c New Jersey	.65	.30
1983A A1368 20c New Mexico	.65	.30
1984A A1369 20c New York	.65	.30
1985A A1370 20c North Carolina	.65	.30
1986A A1371 20c North Dakota	.65	.30
1987A A1372 20c Ohio	.65	.30
1988A A1373 20c Oklahoma	.65	.30
1989A A1374 20c Oregon	.65	.30
1990A A1375 20c Pennsylvania	.65	.30
1991A A1376 20c Rhode Island	.65	.30
1992A A1377 20c South Carolina	.65	.30
1993A A1378 20c South Dakota	.65	.30
1994A A1379 20c Tennessee	.65	.30
1995A A1380 20c Texas	.65	.30
1996A A1381 20c Utah	.65	.30
1997A A1382 20c Vermont	.65	.30
1998A A1383 20c Virginia	.65	.30
1999A A1384 20c Washington	.65	.30
2000A A1385 20c West Virginia	.65	.30
2001A A1386 20c Wisconsin	.65	.30

2002A A1387 20c Wyoming	.65	.30
c. A1338-A1387 Pane of 50, Nos.		
1953A-2002A	32.50	22.50

US-NETHERLANDS

200th Anniv. of Diplomatic Recognition by The Netherlands
A1388

Designed by Heleen Tigler Wybrandi-Raue.

PHOTOGRAVURE
Plates of 230 (10x23) subjects in panes of 50 (5x10).

1982, Apr. 20   **Tagged**   *Perf. 11*

2003 A1388 20c **verm., brt. blue & gray blk.**	.40	.20
P# block of 6	3.50	
P# block of 20, 1-2 #, 1-2 copyright, 1-2 zip	10.00	—
a. Imperf., pair	275.00	

See Combination Press note after No. 1703.
See Netherlands Nos. 640-641.

LIBRARY OF CONGRESS

A1389

Designed by Bradbury Thompson.

ENGRAVED
Plates of 200 subjects in four panes of 50.

1982, Apr. 21   **Tagged**   *Perf. 11*

2004 A1389 20c **red & black**	.40	.20
P# block of 4	1.75	
Zip block of 4	1.65	
a. All color missing		

No. 2004a must be collected as a right margin horiz. strip of 3, 4 or 5 with one No. 2004a, one transitional stamp and one or more normal stamps.

A1390

Designed by John Boyd.

ENGRAVED
Coil Stamp

1982, Apr. 27   **Tagged**   *Perf. 10 Vert.*

2005 A1390 20c **sky blue**	.55	.20
Pair	1.10	.20
P# strip of 3, line, #1-4	9.00	
P# strip of 5, line, #1-2	90.00	
P# strip of 5, line, #3-4	45.00	
P# single, #1-4		1.50
a. Imperf., pair	85.00	
b. Tagging omitted	7.50	

KNOXVILLE WORLD'S FAIR

Solar energy   Knoxville World's Fair   A1391

Synthetic fuels   Knoxville World's Fair
A1392

Breeder reactor   Knoxville World's Fair   A1393

Fossil fuels   Knoxville World's Fair
A1394

Illustration reduced.

Designed by Charles Harper.

PHOTOGRAVURE
Plates of 200 in four panes of 50.

1982, Apr. 29   **Tagged**   *Perf. 11*

2006 A1391 20c **multicolored**	.45	.20
2007 A1392 20c **multicolored**	.45	.20
2008 A1393 20c **multicolored**	.45	.20
2009 A1394 20c **multicolored**	.45	.20
Any single on cover, Expo. station handstamp cancel		10.00
a. Block of 4, #2006-2009	1.80	1.50
P# block of 4, 6#	2.40	—
Zip block of 4	1.90	—

HORATIO ALGER

A1395

Designed by Robert Hallock.

ENGRAVED
Plates of 200 in four panes of 50.

1982, Apr. 30   **Tagged**   *Perf. 11*

2010 A1395 20c **red & black,** *tan*	.40	.20
P# block of 4	1.75	
Zip block of 4	1.65	—
a. Red and black omitted		
b. Tagging omitted		

The Philatelic Foundation has issued a certificate for a pane of 50 with red and black colors omitted. Recognition of this error is by the paper and by a tiny residue of red ink from the tagging roller. The engraved plates did not strike the paper.

AGING TOGETHER

A1396

Designed by Paul Calle.

ENGRAVED
Plates of 200 in four panes of 50.

1982, May 21		Tagged		Perf. 11
2011 A1396 20c **brown**			.40	.20
	P# block of 4		1.75	—
	Zip block of 4		1.65	—

John, Ethel and Lionel
Barrymore — A1397   A1398

PERFORMING ARTS SERIES
Designed by Jim Sharpe.

PHOTOGRAVURE
Plates of 200 in four panes of 50.

1982, June 8		Tagged		Perf. 11
2012 A1397 20c **multicolored**			.40	.20
	P# block of 4, 6#		1.75	—
	Zip block of 4		1.65	—
a.	Black missing (EP)			—

DR. MARY WALKER
Designed by Glenora Richards.

PHOTOGRAVURE
Plate of 200 in four panes of 50.

1982, June 10		Tagged		Perf. 11
2013 A1398 20c **multicolored**			.40	.20
	P# block of 4, 6#		1.75	—
	Zip block of 4		1.65	—

INTERNATIONAL PEACE GARDEN

Dunseith, ND-
Boissevain,
Manitoba
A1399

Designed by Gyo Fujikawa.

LITHOGRAPHED AND ENGRAVED
Plate of 200 in four panes of 50.

1982, June 30		Tagged		Perf. 11
2014 A1399 20c **multicolored**			.50	.20
	P# block of 4, 5#		2.25	—
	Zip block of 4		2.00	—
a.	Black (engr.) omitted		225.00	

A1400   A1401

AMERICA'S LIBRARIES
Designed by Bradbury Thompson.

ENGRAVED
Plate of 200 subjects in four panes of 50.

1982, July 13		Tagged		Perf. 11
2015 A1400 20c **red & black**			.40	.20
	P# block of 4		1.75	—
	Zip block of 4		1.65	—
a.	Vert. pair, imperf. horiz.		250.00	
b.	Tagging omitted		9.00	
c.	All colors missing (EP)		175.00	

On No. 2015c, an albino impression of the design is present.

BLACK HERITAGE SERIES
Jackie Robinson (1919-72), baseball player.

Designed by Jerry Pinkney.

PHOTOGRAVURE
Plate of 200 subjects in four panes of 50.

1982, Aug. 2		Tagged		Perf. 10½x11
2016 A1401 20c **multicolored**			1.10	.20
	P# block of 4, 5#		6.00	—
	Zip block of 4		4.75	—

TOURO SYNAGOGUE

Oldest Existing
Synagogue
Building in the
U.S. — A1402

Designed by Donald Moss and Bradbury Thompson.

PHOTOGRAVURE AND ENGRAVED
Plates of 230 (10x23) subjects in panes of 50 (5x10).

1982, Aug. 22		Tagged		Perf. 11
2017 A1402 20c **multicolored**			.45	.20
	P# block of 20, 6-12 #, 1-2 copyright, 1-2 zip		12.50	—
a.	Imperf., pair		2,250.	

See Combination Press note after No. 1703.

WOLF TRAP FARM PARK

A1403

Designed by Richard Schlecht.

PHOTOGRAVURE
Plates of 200 in four panes of 50.

1982, Sept. 1		Tagged		Perf. 11
2018 A1403 20c **multicolored**			.40	.20
	P# block of 4, 5#		1.75	—
	Zip block of 4		1.65	—

AMERICAN ARCHITECTURE SERIES

A1404

A1405

A1406

A1407

Designed by Walter D. Richards.

ENGRAVED
Plates of 160 subjects in four panes of 40.

1982, Sept. 30		Tagged		Perf. 11
2019 A1404 20c **black & brown**			.45	.20
a.	Tagging omitted			—
b.	Red missing (PS)			—
2020 A1405 20c **black & brown**			.45	.20
a.	Red missing (PS)			—
2021 A1406 20c **black & brown**			.45	.20
2022 A1407 20c **black & brown**			.45	.20
a.	Block of 4, #2019-2022		2.00	1.75
	P# block of 4		2.50	
	Zip block of 4		2.10	

FRANCIS OF ASSISI

A1408

Designed by Ned Seidler.

Printed by American Bank Note Co. and J.W. Fergusson and Sons.

PHOTOGRAVURE
Plates of 200 subjects in four panes of 50.

1982, Oct. 7		Tagged		Perf. 11
2023 A1408 20c **multicolored**			.40	.20
	P# block of 4, 6#+A		1.75	—
	Zip block of 4		1.65	—

PONCE DE LEON

A1409

Designed by Richard Schlecht.

PHOTOGRAVURE (Combination press)
Plates of 230 subjects (10x23) in panes of 50 (5x10).

1982, Oct. 12		Tagged		Perf. 11
2024 A1409 20c **multicolored**			.50	.20
	P# block of 6, 5#		3.50	
	P# block of 20, 5 or 10 #, 1-2 zip, 1-2 copyright		12.00	—
a.	Imperf., pair		425.00	
b.	Vert. pair, imperf. between and at top			—

See Combination Press note after No. 1703.

CHRISTMAS ISSUES

A1410

A1411

A1412

A1413

A1414

A1415

PHOTOGRAVURE
Plates of 200 subjects in four panes of 50
Designed by Chuck Ripper.

1982, Nov. 3		Tagged	
2025	A1410 13c **multicolored**	.25	.20
	P# block of 4	1.40	—
	Zip block of 4	1.10	—
a.	Imperf., pair	350.00	

PHOTOGRAVURE (Combination Press)
Plates of 230 subjects (10x23) in panes of 50 (5x10).
Designed by Bradbury Thompson.

1982, Oct. 28		Tagged	
2026	A1411 20c **multicolored**	.40	.20
	P# block of 20, 5 or 10 #, 1-2		
	copyright, 1-2 zip	11.00	—
a.	Imperf. pair	125.00	—
b.	Horiz. pair, imperf. vert.		—
c.	Vert. pair, imperf. horiz.		—

See Combination Press note after No. 1703.

PHOTOGRAVURE
Plates of 200 in four panes of 50.

Designed by Dolli Tingle.

2027	A1412 20c **multicolored**	.60	.20
2028	A1413 20c **multicolored**	.60	.20
2029	A1414 20c **multicolored**	.60	.20
2030	A1415 20c **multicolored**	.60	.20
a.	Block of 4, #2027-2030	2.40	1.50
	P# block of 4, 4#	2.75	—
	Zip block of 4	2.50	—
b.	As "a," imperf.	1,750.	
c.	As "a," imperf. horiz.	800.00	

SCIENCE & INDUSTRY

A1416

Designed by Saul Bass.

LITHOGRAPHED AND ENGRAVED
Plates of 200 in four panes of 50.

1983, Jan. 19		Tagged	
2031	A1416 20c **multicolored**	.40	.20
	P# block of 4, 4#	1.75	—
	Zip block of 4	1.65	—
a.	Black (engr.) omitted	1,250.	
b.	Tagging omitted		

BALLOONS

Intrepid — A1417

Explorer II — A1420

A1418

A1419

Designed by Davis Meltzer.

PHOTOGRAVURE
Plates of 160 in four panes of 40.

1983, Mar. 31		Tagged	
2032	A1417 20c **multicolored**	.50	.20
2033	A1418 20c **multicolored**	.50	.20
2034	A1419 20c **multicolored**	.50	.20
2035	A1420 20c **multicolored**	.50	.20
a.	Block of 4, #2032-2035	2.00	1.50

	P# block of 4, 5#	2.25	—
	Zip block of 4	2.10	—
b.	As "a," imperf.	3,750.	
c.	As "a," right stamp perf., otherwise imperf.	3,750.	

US-SWEDEN

Benjamin
Franklin
A1421

Designed by Czeslaw Slania, court engraver of Sweden.

ENGRAVED
Plates of 200 in four panes of 50.

1983, Mar. 24		Tagged		Perf. 11
2036	A1421 20c **blue, blk & red brn**	.40	.20	
	P# block of 4	1.75	—	
	Zip block of 4	1.65	—	

See Sweden No. 1453.

CCC, 50th ANNIV.

A1422

Designed by David K. Stone.

PHOTOGRAVURE
Plates of 200 in four panes of 50.

1983, Apr. 5		Tagged		Perf. 11
2037	A1422 20c **multicolored**	.40	.20	
	P# block of 4, 6#	1.75	—	
	Zip block of 4	1.65	—	
a.	Imperf., pair	2,750.		
b.	Vert. pair, imperf. horiz.		—	

JOSEPH PRIESTLEY

Discoverer of
Oxygen — A1423

Designed by Dennis Lyall.

Printed by American Bank Note Company and J.W. Fergusson and Sons.

PHOTOGRAVURE
Plates of 200 in four panes of 50.

1983, Apr. 13		Tagged		Perf. 11
2038	A1423 20c **multicolored**	.40	.20	
	P# block of 4, 6#+A	1.75	—	
	Zip block of 4	1.65	—	

VOLUNTARISM

A1424

Designed by Paul Calle.

POSTAGE   171

ENGRAVED (Combination Press)
Plates of 230 subjects (10x23) in panes of 50 (5x10).

1983, Apr. 20	Tagged	Perf. 11	
2039 A1424 20c red & black		.40	.20
P# block of 6		3.00	
P# block of 20, 1-2 #, 1-2 copyright, 1-2 zip		10.00	
a. Imperf., pair		300.00	

See Combination Press note after No. 1703.

US-GERMANY

A1425

Designed by Richard Schlecht.

ENGRAVED
Plates of 200 in four panes of 50.

1983, Apr. 29	Tagged	Perf. 11	
2040 A1425 20c brown		.40	.20
P# block of 4		1.75	
Zip block of 4		1.65	
a. Tagging omitted			

See Germany No. 1397.

BROOKLYN BRIDGE

A1426

Normal

"Unfinished Bridge" Short Transfer

Designed by Howard Koslow.

ENGRAVED
Plates of 200 in four panes of 50.

1983, May 17	Tagged	Perf. 11	
2041 A1426 20c blue		.40	.20
P# block of 4		1.75	
Zip block of 4		1.65	
Short transfer (unfinished bridge) (UL 2)		9.00	.75
P# block of 4		15.00	
a. Tagging omitted		150.00	
b. All color missing (EP)		75.00	

On No. 2041b, an albino impression of the stamp is evident.

TVA

Norris Hydroelectric Dam — A1427

Designed by Howard Koslow.

PHOTOGRAVURE AND ENGRAVED (Combination Press)
Plates of 230 in panes of 50

1983, May 18	Tagged	Perf. 11	
2042 A1427 20c multicolored		.40	.20
P# block of 20, 5-10 #, 1-2 copyright, 1-2 zip		10.00	

Runners, Electrocardiograph Tracing — A1428

Designed by Donald Moss.

PHOTOGRAVURE (Combination Press)
Plates of 230 in panes of 50.

1983, May 14	Tagged	Perf. 11	
2043 A1428 20c multicolored		.40	.20
P# block of 6, 4#		3.00	
P# block of 20, 4-8 #, 1-2 copyright, 1-2 zip		10.00	

BLACK HERITAGE SERIES
Scott Joplin (1868-1917), Ragtime composer.

A1429

Designed by Jerry Pinkney.

PHOTOGRAVURE
Plates of 200 in four panes of 50.

1983, June 9	Tagged	Perf. 11	
2044 A1429 20c multicolored		.50	.20
P# block of 4, 6#		2.40	
Zip block of 4		2.10	
a. Imperf., pair		400.00	
b. Tagging omitted			

MEDAL OF HONOR

A1430

Designed by Dennis J. Hom.

LITHOGRAPHED AND ENGRAVED
Plates of 160 in four panes of 40.

1983, June 7	Tagged	Perf. 11	
2045 A1430 20c multicolored		.55	.20
P# block of 4, 5#		2.50	
Zip block of 4		2.25	
a. Red omitted		200.00	

A1431   A1432

GEORGE HERMAN RUTH (1895-1948)
Designed by Richard Gangel.

ENGRAVED
Plates of 200 in four panes of 50.

1983, July 6	Tagged	Perf. 10½x11	
2046 A1431 20c blue		1.40	.20
P# block of 4		6.25	
Zip block of 4		5.75	

LITERARY ARTS SERIES
Nathaniel Hawthorne (1804-1864), novelist.

Designed by Bradbury Thompson after 1851 painting by Cephus Giovanni Thompson.

PHOTOGRAVURE
Plates of 200 in four panes of 50.

1983, July 8	Tagged	Perf. 11	
2047 A1432 20c multicolored		.45	.20
P# block of 4, 4#		2.10	
Zip block of 4		1.90	

1984 SUMMER OLYMPICS
Los Angeles, July 28-August 12

Discus A1433

High Jump — A1434

Archery A1435

Boxing A1436

Designed by Bob Peak.

PHOTOGRAVURE
Plates of 200 in four panes of 50.

1983, July 28	Tagged	Perf. 11	
2048 A1433 13c multicolored		.35	.20
2049 A1434 13c multicolored		.35	.20
2050 A1435 13c multicolored		.35	.20
2051 A1436 13c multicolored		.35	.20
a. Block of 4, #2048-2051		1.50	1.25
P# block of 4, 4#		1.75	
Zip block of 4		1.65	

SIGNING OF TREATY OF PARIS

John Adams, B. Franklin, John Jay, David Hartley A1437

Designed by David Blossom after an unfinished painting by Benjamin West in Winterthur Museum.

PHOTOGRAVURE
Plates of 160 in four panes of 40.

1983, Sept. 2   **Tagged**   *Perf. 11*
2052 A1437 20c multicolored   .40   .20
   P# block of 4, 4#   1.75 —
   Zip block of 4   1.65 —
a.   Tagging omitted —

CIVIL SERVICE

A1438

Designed by MDB Communications, Inc.

PHOTOGRAVURE AND ENGRAVED
Plates of 230 in four panes of 50.

1983, Sept. 9   **Tagged**   *Perf. 11*
2053 A1438 20c buff, blue & red   .40   .20
   P# block of 6   3.00 —
   P# block of 20, 1-2P#, 1-2 Zip, 1-2 Copyright   10.00 —
a.   Tagging omitted —

METROPOLITAN OPERA

Original State Arch and Current 5-arch Entrance A1439

Designed by Ken Davies.

LITHOGRAPHED AND ENGRAVED
Plates of 200 in four panes of 50.

1983, Sept. 14   **Tagged**   *Perf. 11*
2054 A1439 20c yellow & maroon   .40   .20
   P# block of 4, 2#   1.75 —
   Zip block of 4   1.65 —
a.   Tagging omitted   8.50

AMERICAN INVENTORS

Charles Steinmetz and Curve on Graph A1440

Edwin Armstrong and Frequency Modulator A1441

Nikola Tesla and Induction Motor — A1442

Philo T. Farnsworth and First Television Camera A1443

Designed by Dennis Lyall.

LITHOGRAPHED AND ENGRAVED
Plates of 200 in four panes of 50.

1983, Sept. 21   **Tagged**   *Perf. 11*
2055 A1440 20c multicolored   .50   .20
2056 A1441 20c multicolored   .50   .20
2057 A1442 20c multicolored   .50   .20
2058 A1443 20c multicolored   .50   .20
a.   Block of 4, #2055-2058   2.00   1.50
   P# block of 4, 2#   2.75 —
   Zip block of 4   2.10 —
b.   As "a," black omitted   325.00

STREETCARS

First American streetcar, New York City, 1832 — A1444

Early electric streetcar, Montgomery, Ala., 1886 — A1445

"Bobtail" horsecar, Sulphur Rock, Ark., 1926 — A1446

St. Charles streetcar, New Orleans, La., 1923 — A1447

Designed by Richard Leech.

PHOTOGRAVURE AND ENGRAVED
Plates of 200 in four panes of 50.

1983, Oct. 8   **Tagged**   *Perf. 11*
2059 A1444 20c multicolored   .50   .20
2060 A1445 20c multicolored   .50   .20
a.   Horiz. pair, black (engr.) missing on Nos. 2059, 2060 (EP) —
2061 A1446 20c multicolored   .50   .20
a.   Vert. pair, black (engr.) missing on Nos. 2059, 2061 (EP) —
2062 A1447 20c multicolored   .50   .20
a.   Block of 4, #2059-2062   2.00   1.50
   P# block of 4, 5#   2.60 —
   Zip block of 4   2.10 —
b.   As "a," black (engr.) omitted   300.00
c.   As "a," black (engr.) omitted on #2059, 2061 —

CHRISTMAS

Niccolini-Cowper Madonna, by Raphael — A1448

Santa Claus — A1449

Designed by Bradbury Thompson (No. 2063), and John Berkey (No. 2064).

PHOTOGRAVURE
Plates of 200 in four panes of 50 (No. 2063), Plates of 230 in panes of 50 (Combination Press, No. 2064).

1983, Oct. 28   **Tagged**   *Perf. 11*
2063 A1448 20c multicolored   .40   .20
   P# block of 4, 5#   1.75 —
   Zip block of 4   1.65 —
2064 A1449 20c multicolored   .40   .20
   P# block of 6, 5#   3.00 —
   P# block of 20, 5-10 P#, 1-2 copyright, 1-2 zip   11.50 —
a.   Imperf., pair   125.00
b.   Tagging omitted —

See Combination Press note after No. 1703.

German Religious Leader, Founder of Lutheran Church (1483-1546) — A1450

Caribou and Alaska Pipeline — A1451

MARTIN LUTHER

Designed by Bradbury Thompson.

Printed by American Bank Note Company.

PHOTOGRAVURE
Plates of 200 in four panes of 50.

1983, Nov. 11   **Tagged**   *Perf. 11*
2065 A1450 20c multicolored   .40   .20
   P# block of 4, 5#+A   1.75 —
   Zip block of 4   1.65 —

ALASKA STATEHOOD, 25th ANNIV.

Designed by Bill Bond.

Printed by American Bank Note Company and J.W. Fergusson and Sons.

PHOTOGRAVURE
Plates of 200 in four panes of 50.

1984, Jan. 3	Tagged		Perf. 11	
2066 A1451 20c multicolored			.40	.20
P# block of 4, 5#+A			1.75	—
Zip block of 4			1.65	—

14th WINTER OLYMPIC GAMES,
Sarajevo, Yugoslavia, Feb. 8-19

Ice Dancing — A1452

Downhill Skiing — A1453

Cross-country Skiing — A1454

Hockey — A1455

Designed by Bob Peak.

PHOTOGRAVURE
Plates of 200 in four panes of 50.

1984, Jan. 6	Tagged		Perf. 10½x11	
2067 A1452 20c multicolored			.55	.20
2068 A1453 20c multicolored			.55	.20
2069 A1454 20c multicolored			.55	.20
2070 A1455 20c multicolored			.55	.20
a. Block of 4, #2067-2070			2.20	1.75
P# block of 4, 4#			3.00	—
Zip block of 4			2.25	—

Pillar, Dollar Sign — A1456

A1457

FEDERAL DEPOSIT INSURANCE CORPORATION, 50TH ANNIV.

Designed by Michael David Brown.

PHOTOGRAVURE
Plates of 200 in four panes of 50
(1 pane each #2071, 2074, 2075 and 2081)

1984, Jan. 12	Tagged		Perf. 11	
2071 A1456 20c multicolored			.40	.20
P# block of 4, 6#, UL only			2.00	—
Zip block of 4			1.65	—

LOVE

Designed by Bradbury Thompson.

PHOTOGRAVURE AND ENGRAVED (Combination Press)
Plates of 230 in four panes of 50.

1984, Jan. 31	Tagged		Perf. 11x10½	
2072 A1457 20c multicolored			.40	.20
P# block of 20, 6-12#, 1-2 copyright, 1-2 zip			10.00	
a. Horiz. pair, imperf. vert.			150.00	
b. Tagging omitted			5.00	

See Combination Press note after No. 1703.

A1458

A1459

BLACK HERITAGE SERIES

Carter G. Woodson (1875-1950), Black Historian.

Designed by Jerry Pinkney.

Printed by American Bank Note Company.

PHOTOGRAVURE
Plates of 200 in four panes of 50.

1984, Feb. 1	Tagged		Perf. 11	
2073 A1458 20c multicolored			.40	.20
P# block of 4, 6#+A			2.00	—
Zip block of 4			1.65	—
a. Horiz. pair, imperf. vert.			1,000.	

SOIL & WATER CONSERVATION

Designed by Michael David Brown.

See No. 2071 for printing information.

1984, Feb. 6	Tagged		Perf. 11	
2074 A1459 20c multicolored			.40	.20
P# block of 4, 6#, UR only			1.75	—
Zip block of 4			1.65	—

50TH ANNIV. OF CREDIT UNION ACT

Dollar Sign, Coin — A1460

Designed by Michael David Brown.

See No. 2071 for printing information.

1984, Feb. 10	Tagged		Perf. 11	
2075 A1460 20c multicolored			.40	.20
P# block of 4, 6#, LR only			1.75	—
Zip block of 4			1.65	—

ORCHIDS

Wild Pink — A1461

Yellow Lady's-slipper A1462

Spreading Pogonia — A1463

Pacific Calypso — A1464

Designed by Manabu Saito.

PHOTOGRAVURE
Plates of 192 in four panes of 48.

1984, Mar. 5	Tagged		Perf. 11	
2076 A1461 20c multicolored			.50	.20
2077 A1462 20c multicolored			.50	.20
2078 A1463 20c multicolored			.50	.20
2079 A1464 20c multicolored			.50	.20
a. Block of 4, #2076-2079			2.00	1.50
P# block of 4, 5#			2.50	—
Zip block of 4			2.10	—

HAWAII STATEHOOD, 25th ANNIV.

Eastern Polynesian Canoe, Golden Plover, Mauna Loa Volcano A1465

Designed by Herb Kane.

Printed by American Bank Note Company.

PHOTOGRAVURE
Plates of 200 in four panes of 50.

1984, Mar. 12	Tagged		Perf. 11	
2080 A1465 20c multicolored			.40	.20
P# block of 4, 5#+A			1.70	—
Zip block of 4			1.65	—

50TH ANNIV., NATIONAL ARCHIVES

Abraham Lincoln, George Washington — A1466

Designed by Michael David Brown.

See No. 2071 for printing information.

1984, Apr. 16	Tagged	Perf. 11	
2081 A1466 20c multicolored		.40	.20
P# block of 4, 6#, LL only		1.70	—
Zip block of 4		1.65	—

LOS ANGELES SUMMER OLYMPICS
July 28-August 12

Diving — A1467

Long Jump — A1468

Wrestling — A1469

Kayak — A1470

Designed by Bob Peak.

PHOTOGRAVURE
Plates of 200 in four panes of 50.

1984, May 4	Tagged	Perf. 11	
2082 A1467 20c multicolored		.55	.20
2083 A1468 20c multicolored		.55	.20
2084 A1469 20c multicolored		.55	.20
2085 A1470 20c multicolored		.55	.20
a. Block of 4, #2082-2085		2.40	1.90
P# block of 4, 4#		3.00	—
Zip block of 4		2.50	—
b. As "a," imperf between vertically		9,500.	

LOUISIANA WORLD EXPOSITION
New Orleans, May 12-Nov. 11

Bayou Wildlife
A1471

Designed by Chuck Ripper.

PHOTOGRAVURE
Plates of 160 in four panes of 40.

1984, May 11	Tagged	Perf. 11	
2086 A1471 20c multicolored		.50	.20
On cover, Expo. station pictorial handstamp cancel		2.50	
P# block of 4, 5#		2.60	—
Zip block of 4		2.10	—

HEALTH RESEARCH

Lab Equipment
A1472

Designed by Tyler Smith.

Printed by American Bank Note Company.

PHOTOGRAVURE
Plates of 200 in four panes of 50.

1984, May 17	Tagged	Perf. 11	
2087 A1472 20c multicolored		.40	.20
P# block of 4, 5#+A		1.75	—
Zip block of 4		1.65	—

Actor Douglas Fairbanks (1883-1939) — A1473

A1474

PERFORMING ARTS
Designed by Jim Sharpe.

PHOTOGRAVURE AND ENGRAVED (Combination Press)
Plates of 230 in panes of 50.

1984, May 23	Tagged	Perf. 11	
2088 A1473 20c multicolored		.50	.20
P# block of 20, 5-10#, 1-2 copyright, 1-2 zip		13.00	—
a. Tagging omitted		25.00	—
b. Horiz. pair, imperf between			

See Combination Press note after No. 1703.

JIM THORPE, 1888-1953
Designed by Richard Gangel.

ENGRAVED
Plates of 200 in four panes of 50.

1984, May 24	Tagged	Perf. 11	
2089 A1474 20c dark brown		.60	.20
P# block of 4		3.25	—
Zip block of 4		1.90	—

PERFORMING ARTS

John McCormack (1884-1945), Operatic Tenor — A1475

Designed by Jim Sharpe (US) and Ron Mercer (Ireland).

PHOTOGRAVURE
Plates of 200 in four panes of 50.

1984, June 6	Tagged	Perf. 11	
2090 A1475 20c multicolored		.40	.20
P# block of 4, 5#		1.80	—
Zip block of 4		1.65	—

See Ireland No. 594.

ST. LAWRENCE SEAWAY, 25th ANNIV.

Aerial View of Seaway, Freighters A1476

Designed by Ernst Barenscher (Canada).

Printed by American Bank Note Company.

PHOTOGRAVURE
Plates of 200 in four panes of 50.

1984, June 26	Tagged	Perf. 11	
2091 A1476 20c multicolored		.40	.20
P# block of 4, 4#+A		1.75	—
Zip block of 4		1.65	—

WATERFOWL PRESERVATION ACT, 50th ANNIV.

"Mallards Dropping In" by Jay N. Darling
A1477

Design adapted from Darling's work (No. RW1) by Donald M. McDowell.

ENGRAVED
Plates of 200 in four panes of 50.

1984, July 2	Tagged	Perf. 11	
2092 A1477 20c blue		.50	.20
P# block of 4		2.50	—
Zip block of 4		2.25	—
a. Horiz. pair, imperf. vert.		325.00	

The Elizabeth — A1478

A1479

ROANOKE VOYAGES
Designed by Charles Lundgren.

Printed by American Bank Note Company.

PHOTOGRAVURE
Plates of 200 in four panes of 50.

1984, July 13	Tagged	Perf. 11	
2093 A1478 20c multicolored		.40	.20
P# block of 4, 5#+A		1.75	—
Zip block of 4		1.65	—
Pair with full horiz. gutter btwn.			—

LITERARY ARTS SERIES
Herman Melville (1819-1891), Author

Designed by Bradbury Thompson.

ENGRAVED
Plates of 200 in four panes of 50.

1984, Aug. 1	Tagged	Perf. 11	
2094 A1479 20c sage green		.40	.20
P# block of 4		1.75	—
Zip block of 4		1.65	—
a. Tagging omitted		60.00	—

Founder of Junior Achievement — A1480

Smokey Bear — A1481

HORACE MOSES (1862-1947)
Designed by Dennis Lyall.

ENGRAVED (Combination Press)
Plates of 200 in panes of 50.

1984, Aug. 6	Tagged	*Perf. 11*	
2095 A1480 20c **orange & dark brown**		.45	.20
P# block of 6		3.50	—
P# block of 20, 1-2#, 1-2 copyright, 1-2 zip		12.50	—

See Combination Press note after No. 1703.

SMOKEY BEAR
Designed by Rudolph Wendelin.

LITHOGRAPHED AND ENGRAVED
Plates of 200 in panes of 50.

1984, Aug. 13	Tagged	*Perf. 11*	
2096 A1481 20c **multicolored**		.40	.20
P# block of 4, 5#		2.00	—
Zip block of 4		1.65	—
a. Horiz. pair, imperf. btwn.		250.00	
b. Vert. pair, imperf. btwn.		200.00	
c. Block of 4, imperf. btwn. vert. and horiz.		4,000.	
d. Horiz. pair, imperf. vert.		1,000.	
e. Tagging omitted			

ROBERTO CLEMENTE (1934-1972)

Clemente Wearing Pittsburgh Pirates Cap, Puerto Rican Flag — A1482

Designed by Juan Lopez-Bonilla.

PHOTOGRAVURE
Plates of 200 in panes of 50.

1984, Aug. 17	Tagged	*Perf. 11*	
2097 A1482 20c **multicolored**		1.40	.20
P# block of 4, 6#		6.00	—
Zip block of 4		5.75	—
a. Horiz. pair, imperf. vert.		1,800.	

DOGS

Beagle and Boston Terrier A1483

Chesapeake Bay Retriever and Cocker Spaniel A1484

Alaskan Malamute and Collie — A1485

Black and Tan Coonhound and American Foxhound A1486

Designed by Roy Andersen.

PHOTOGRAVURE
Plates of 160 in panes of 40.

1984, Sept. 7	Tagged	*Perf. 11*	
2098 A1483 20c **multicolored**		.50	.20
2099 A1484 20c **multicolored**		.50	.20
2100 A1485 20c **multicolored**		.50	.20
2101 A1486 20c **multicolored**		.50	.20
a. Block of 4, #2098-2101		2.00	1.90
P# block of 4, 4#		3.00	—
Zip block of 4		2.10	—
b. As "a," imperf horiz.		—	

CRIME PREVENTION

McGruff, the Crime Dog — A1487

Designed by Randall McDougall.

Printed by American Bank Note Company.

PHOTOGRAVURE
Plates of 200 in panes of 50.

1984, Sept. 26	Tagged	*Perf. 11*	
2102 A1487 20c **multicolored**		.40	.20
P# block of 4, 4#+A		1.90	—
Zip block of 4		1.65	—

HISPANIC AMERICANS

A1488

Designed by Robert McCall.

PHOTOGRAVURE
Plates of 160 in four panes of 40.

1984, Oct. 31	Tagged	*Perf. 11*	
2103 A1488 20c **multicolored**		.40	.20
P# block of 4, 6#		1.90	—
Zip block of 4		1.65	—
a. Vert. pair, imperf. horiz.		2,000.	

FAMILY UNITY

Stick Figures — A1489

Designed by Molly LaRue.

PHOTOGRAVURE AND ENGRAVED (Combination Press)
Plates of 230 in panes of 50.

1984, Oct. 1	Tagged	*Perf. 11*	
2104 A1489 20c **multicolored**		.40	.20
P# block of 20, 3-6#, 1-2 copyright, 1-2 zip		12.50	—
a. Horiz. pair, imperf. vert.		425.00	
b. Tagging omitted		7.50	
c. Vert. pair, imperf. btwn. and at bottom		—	
d. Horiz. pair, imperf. between		—	

See Combination Press note after No. 1703.
Used untagged imperfs exist from printer's waste.

A1490

Abraham Lincoln Reading to Son, Tad — A1491

ELEANOR ROOSEVELT (1884-1962)
Designed by Bradbury Thompson.

ENGRAVED
Plates of 192 in panes of 48.

1984, Oct. 11	Tagged	*Perf. 11*	
2105 A1490 20c **deep blue**		.40	.20
P# block of 4		2.00	—
Zip block of 4		1.65	—

NATION OF READERS
Design adapted from Anthony Berger daguerrotype by Bradbury Thompson.

ENGRAVED
Plates of 200 in panes of 50.

1984, Oct. 16	Tagged	*Perf. 11*	
2106 A1491 20c **brown & maroon**		.40	.20
P# block of 4		1.90	—
Zip block of 4		1.65	—

CHRISTMAS

Madonna and Child by Fra Filippo Lippi — A1492

Santa Claus — A1493

Designed by Bradbury Thompson (No. 2107) and Danny La Boccetta (No. 2108).

PHOTOGRAVURE
Plates of 200 in panes of 50.

1984, Oct. 30	Tagged	*Perf. 11*	
2107 A1492 20c **multicolored**		.40	.20
P# block of 4, 5#		1.90	—
Zip block of 4		1.65	—
2108 A1493 20c **multicolored**		.40	.20

	P# block of 4, 5#	1.90	—
	Zip block of 4	1.65	—
a.	Horiz. pair, imperf. vert.	*875.00*	

No. 2108a is valued in the grade of fine.

VIETNAM VETERANS MEMORIAL

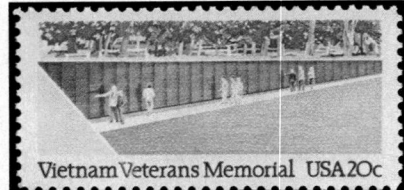

Memorial and Visitors — A1494

Designed by Paul Calle.

ENGRAVED
Plates of 160 in panes of 40.

1984, Nov. 10		**Tagged**		**Perf. 11**	
2109	A1494	20c **multicolored**		.50	.20
		P# block of 4		3.00	—
		Zip block of 4		2.10	—
a.		Tagging omitted		*75.00*	

PERFORMING ARTS

Jerome Kern (1885-1945),
Composer — A1495

Designed by Jim Sharpe.

Printed by the American Bank Note Company.

PHOTOGRAVURE
Plates of 200 in four panes of 50.

1985, Jan. 23		**Tagged**		**Perf. 11**	
2110	A1495	22c **multicolored**		.40	.20
		P# block of 4, 5#+A		1.90	—
		Zip block of 4		1.65	—
a.		Tagging omitted		*9.00*	

A1496   A1497

Designed by Bradbury Thompson.

PHOTOGRAVURE
Plates of 460 (20x23) in panes of 100.

1985, Feb. 1		**Tagged**		**Perf. 11**	
2111	A1496	(22c) **green**		.60	.20
		P# block of 6		4.50	—
		P# block of 20, 1-2 #, 1-2			
		Zip, 1-2 Copyright		17.50	—
a.		Vert. pair, imperf.		35.00	
b.		Vert. pair, imperf. horiz.		*1,000.*	
c.		Tagging omitted		—	

COIL STAMP
Perf. 10 Vert.

2112	A1496	(22c) **green**		.60	.20
		Pair		1.20	.20
		P# strip of 3, #1, 2		3.00	
		P# strip of 5, #1, 2		4.50	
		P# single, #1, 2		—	.50
a.		Imperf., pair		40.00	
b.		As "a," tagging omitted		*125.00*	
c.		As No. 2112, tagging omitted		—	

BOOKLET STAMP
ENGRAVED
Perf. 11

2113	A1497	(22c) **green**		.80	.20
a.		Booklet pane of 10		8.50	3.00
b.		As "a," imperf. btwn. horiz.		—	

A1498

Flag Over
Capitol
Dome
A1499

Designed by Frank Waslick.

ENGRAVED
Plates of 400 subjects in panes of 100.

1985, Mar. 29		**Tagged**		**Perf. 11**	
2114	A1498	22c **blue, red & black**		.40	.20
		P# block of 4		1.90	—
		Zip block of 4		1.65	—
		Pair with full horizontal gutter		—	
a.		All color missing (EP)		—	
b.		Tagging omitted		—	

No. 2114a should be collected se-tenant with a normal or a partially printed stamp.

COIL STAMP
Perf. 10 Vert.

2115	A1498	22c **blue, red & black,** wide block tagging, 19mmx21.5mm (B press)		.40	.20
		Pair		.80	.20
		P# strip of 3, #2, 4, 6, 10		2.00	
		P# strip of 3, #13		4.50	
		P# strip of 3, #14		12.00	
		P# strip of 3, #15, 16, 21		2.00	
		P# strip of 5, #2, 4, 6, 10		2.75	
		P# strip of 5, #13		6.00	
		P# strip of 5, #14		17.50	
		P# strip of 5, #15, 16, 21		2.75	
		P# single, #2		—	.50
		P# single, #4		—	.50
		P# single, #6		—	6.50
		P# single, #10		—	.65
		P# single, #13		—	9.00
		P# single, #14		—	22.00
		P# single, #15		—	1.50
		P# single, #16		—	2.25
		P# single, #21		—	2.25
a.		Narrow block tagging, 17.5mmx21.5mm (C press)		.40	.20
		P# strip of 3, #1		4.00	
		P# strip of 3, #3		7.50	
		P# strip of 3, #5		2.00	
		P# strip of 3, #7		4.00	
		P# strip of 3, #8, 11-12, 17-20, 22		2.00	
		P# strip of 5, #1		6.00	
		P# strip of 5, #3		27.50	
		P# strip of 5, #5		2.50	
		P# strip of 5, #7		6.00	
		P# strip of 5, #8, 11-12, 17-20, 22		2.50	
		P# single, #1, 3, 5		—	1.00
		P# single, #7-8		—	1.00
		P# single, #11		—	1.00
		P# single, #12		—	1.00
		P# single, #17-18		—	2.00
		P# single, #19		—	1.00
		P# single, #20		—	2.25
		P# single, #22		—	1.00
b.		Wide and tall block tagging, 19.5mmx23mm (D press)		.40	.20
		P# strip of 3, #2 (B press)		—	
		P# strip of 3, #8		—	
		P# strip of 3, #18		40.00	
		P# strip of 3, #20		40.00	
		P# strip of 3, #22		40.00	
		P# strip of 5, #2 (B press)		—	
		P# strip of 5, #8		200.00	
		P# strip of 5, #18		60.00	
		P# strip of 5, #20		60.00	
		P# strip of 5, #22		60.00	
		P# single, #2 (B press)		—	—
		P# single, #8		—	50.00
		P# single, #18		—	50.00
		P# single, #20		—	50.00
		P# single, #22		—	50.00
c.		Inscribed "T" at bottom, *May 23, 1987*		.50	.40
		P# strip of 3, #1		2.00	
		P# strip of 5, #1		3.00	
		P# single, #1		—	3.00
d.		Black field of stars		—	
e.		Tagging omitted		*12.50*	
f.		Imperf., pair		10.00	

No. 2115 is known with capitol in bluish black color, apparently from contaminated ink. Specialists often refer to this as "Erie blue."

No. 2115b from plate #2 is an anomaly because the plates used on the B press did not fit on the D press, from which the other wide and tall block tagged varieties come.

BOOKLET STAMP
Perf. 10 Horiz.

2116	A1499	22c **blue, red & black**		.50	.20
a.		Booklet pane of 5		2.50	1.25
		Scored perforations		2.50	—

BOOKLET STAMPS

Frilled Dogwinkle — A1500   Reticulated Helmet — A1501

New England Neptune — A1502   Calico Scallop — A1503

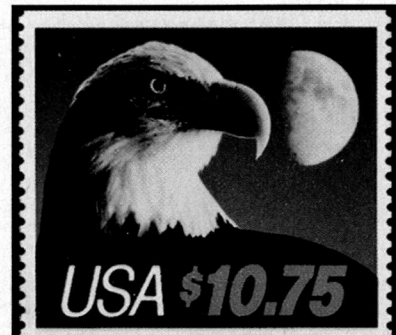

Lightning Whelk — A1504

Designed by Pete Cocci.

ENGRAVED

1985, Apr. 4		**Tagged**		**Perf. 10**	
2117	A1500	22c **black & brown**		.40	.20
a.		Tagging omitted			
2118	A1501	22c **black & multi**		.40	.20
2119	A1502	22c **black & brown**		.40	.20
a.		Tagging omitted			
2120	A1503	22c **black & violet**		.40	.20
2121	A1504	22c **black & multi**		.40	.20
a.		Booklet pane of 10, 2 ea #2117-2121		4.00	3.00
b.		As "a," violet omitted on both Nos. 2120		*475.00*	
c.		As "a," vert. imperf. between		*450.00*	
d.		As "a," imperf.		—	
e.		Strip of 5, Nos. 2117-2121		2.00	

Eagle and Half Moon — A1505

Designed by Young & Rubicam.

TYPE I: washed out, dull appearance most evident in the black of the body of the eagle, and the red in the background between the eagle's shoulder and the moon. "$10.75" appears splotchy or grainy (P# 11111).

TYPE II: brighter, more intense colors most evident in the black on the eagle's body, and red in the background. "$10.75" appears smoother, brighter, and less grainy (P# 22222).

PHOTOGRAVURE

1985, Apr. 29		**Untagged**		**Perf. 10 Vert.**	
2122	A1505	$10.75 **multicolored,** type I		19.00	7.50
a.		Booklet pane of 3		60.00	—
b.		Type II, *June 19, 1989*		21.00	10.00
c.		As "b," booklet pane of 3		65.00	—

Coil Plate No. Strips of 3
Beginning with No. 2123, coil plate No. strips of 3 usually sell at the level of strips of 5 minus the face value of two stamps.

TRANSPORTATION ISSUE

School Bus 1920s
3.4 USA

A1506

Buckboard 1880s
USA
4.9

A1507

Star Route Truck
5.5 USA 1910s

A1508

Tricycle 1880s
6 USA

A1509

Tractor 1920s
7.1 USA

A1510

Ambulance 1860s
8.3 USA

A1511

Tow Truck 1920s
8.5 USA

A1512

Oil Wagon 1890s
10.1 USA
OIL

A1513

Stutz Bearcat 1933
11 USA

A1514

Stanley Steamer 1909
USA
12

A1515

Pushcart 1880s
12.5
USA

A1516

Iceboat 1880s
USA
14

A1517

Dog Sled 1920s
17 USA

A1518

Bread Wagon 1880s
25 USA

A1519

Designers: 3.4c, 17c, Lou Nolan. 4.9c, 8.5c, 14c, 25c, William H. Bond. 5.5c, David K. Stone. 6c, 8.3c, 10.1c, 12.5c. James Schleyer. 7.1c, 11c, 12c, Ken Dallison.

COIL STAMPS
ENGRAVED

1985-89	Tagged		Perf. 10 Vert.	
2123 A1506	3.4c **dark bluish green,** *June 8*		.20	.20
	Pair		.20	.20
	P# strip of 5, line, #1-2		.80	
	P# single, #1-2		—	.75
a.	Untagged (Bureau precancel, Non-profit Org. CAR-RT SORT)		.20	.20
	P# strip of 5, line, #1-2		3.00	
	P# single, #1-2		—	3.00
2124 A1507	4.9c **brown black,** *June 21*		.20	.20
	Pair		.20	.20
	P# strip of 5, line, #3-4		.65	
	P# single, #3-4		—	.65
a.	Untagged (Bureau precancel, Non-profit Org.)		.20	.20
	P# strip of 5, line, #1-6		1.10	
	P# single, #1-6		—	1.00
b.	Tagging omitted		—	
2125 A1508	5.5c **deep magenta,** *Nov. 1, 1986*		.20	.20
	Pair		.20	.20
	P# strip of 5, #1		1.40	
	P# single, #1		—	1.25
a.	Untagged (Bureau precancel, Non-profit Org. CAR-RT SORT)		.20	.20
	P# strip of 5, #1		1.25	
	P# strip of 5, #2		1.50	
	P# single, #1		—	1.10
	P# single, #2		—	1.50

On No. 2125a, both vignette and the precancel inscription were printed from a single printing sleeve.

2126 A1509	6c **red brown,** *May 6*		.35	.20
	Pair		.70	.20
	P# strip of 5, #1		2.00	
	P# single, #1		—	1.00
a.	Untagged (Bureau precancel, Non-profit Org.)		.20	.20
	P# strip of 5, #1		1.50	
	P# strip of 5, #2		4.00	
	P# single, #1		—	1.00
	P# single, #2		—	2.75
b.	As "a," imperf., pair		200.00	
c.	Tagging omitted			
2127 A1510	7.1c **lake,** *Feb. 6, 1987*		.20	.20
	Pair		.30	.20
	P# strip of 5, #1		1.50	
	P# single, #1		—	1.00
a.	Untagged (Bureau precancel "Non-profit Org." in black), *Feb. 6, 1987*		.20	.20
	P# strip of 5, #1		2.00	
	P# single, #1		—	1.50
b.	Untagged (Bureau precancel "Non-profit 5-Digit Zip + 4" in black), *May 26, 1989*		.20	.20
	P# strip of 5, #1		1.25	
	P# single, #1		—	1.00
c.	As "a," black (precancel) omitted			

On Nos. 2127a and 2127b, both the vignette and the precancel inscription were printed from a single printing sleeve.
On No. 2127c, an albino impression of the precancel is present.

2128 A1511	8.3c **green,** *June 21*		.20	.20
	Pair		.40	.20
	P# strip of 5, line, #1-2		1.25	
	P# single, #1-2		—	1.00
a.	Untagged (Bureau precancel, Blk. Rt. CAR-RT SORT)		.20	.20
	P# strip of 5, line, #1-2		1.25	
	P# strip of 5, line, #3-4		3.50	
	P# single, #1-2		—	1.10
	P# single, #3-4		—	2.75

On No. 2231 "Ambulance 1860s" is 18mm long; on No. 2128, 18 ⅓mm long.

2129 A1512	8.5c **dark Prussian green,** *Jan. 24, 1987*		.20	.20
	Pair		.40	.20
	P# strip of 5, #1		2.25	
	P# single, #1		—	2.00
a.	Untagged (Bureau precancel, Non-profit Org.)		.20	.20
	P# strip of 5, #1		2.00	
	P# strip of 5, #2		7.00	
	P# single, #1		—	1.75
	P# single, #2		—	5.75
2130 A1513	10.1c **slate blue,** *Apr. 18*		.55	.20
	Pair		1.10	.20
	P# strip of 5, #1		3.50	
	P# single, #1		—	2.00
a.	Untagged (Bureau precancel "Bulk Rate Carrier Route Sort" in red)		.25	.25
	P# strip of 5, #2-3		2.00	
	P# single, #2-3		—	1.60
	Untagged (Bureau precancel "Bulk Rate" and lines in black)		.25	.25
	P# strip of 5, #1-2		2.00	
	P# single, #1-2		—	1.60
b.	As "a," red precancel, imperf, pair		15.00	
	As "a," black precancel, imperf, pair		80.00	
2131 A1514	11c **dark green,** *June 11*		.25	.20
	Pair		.50	.20
	P# strip of 5, line, #1-4		1.40	
	P# single, #1-4		—	1.00
a.	Tagging omitted		—	
2132 A1515	12c **dark blue,** type I, *Apr. 2*		.25	.20
	Pair		.50	.20
	P# strip of 5, line, #1-2		2.00	
	P# single, #1-2		—	1.25
a.	Untagged, type I (Bureau precancel, PRESORTED FIRST-CLASS), *Apr. 2*		.25	.25

	P# strip of 5, line, #1-2		2.00	
	P# single, #1-2		—	1.75
b.	Untagged, type II, (Bureau precancel, PRESORTED FIRST-CLASS) *1987*		.40	.30
	P# strip of 5, no line, #1		16.00	
	P# single, #1		—	15.00
c.	Tagging omitted, type I, (not Bureau precanceled), *1987*		15.00	

Type II has "Stanley Steamer 1909" ½mm shorter (17⅜mm) than No. 2132 (18mm).

2133 A1516	12.5c **olive green,** *Apr. 18*		.35	.20
	Pair		.70	.20
	P# strip of 5, #1		2.50	
	P# strip of 5, #2		3.50	
	P# single, #1		—	2.25
	P# single, #2		—	3.00
a.	Untagged (Bureau precancel, Bulk Rate)		.25	.25
	P# strip of 5, #1		2.00	
	P# strip of 5, #2		2.25	
	P# single, #1		—	1.25
	P# single, #2		—	2.25
b.	As "a," imperf., pair		40.00	

All No. 2133 from plate 1 and some No. 2133a from plate 1 were printed with luminescent ink that is orange under long wave UV light.

2134 A1517	14c **sky blue,** type I, *Mar. 23*		.30	.20
	Pair		.60	.20
	P# strip of 5, line, #1-4		2.00	
	P# single, #1-4		—	1.50
a.	Imperf., pair		90.00	
b.	Type II, *Sept. 30, 1986*		.30	.20
	P# strip of 5, no line, #2		2.50	
	P# single, #2		—	2.50
c.	Tagging omitted, type I		15.00	

Type II design is ¼mm narrower (17¼mm) than the original stamp (17½mm) and has block tagging. No. 2134 has overall tagging.

2135 A1518	17c **sky blue,** *Aug. 20, 1986*		.55	.20
	Pair		1.10	.20
	P# strip of 5, #2		4.00	
	P# single, #2		—	1.50
a.	Imperf., pair		375.00	
2136 A1519	25c **orange brown,** *Nov. 22, 1986*		.45	.20
	Pair		.90	.20
	P# strip of 5, #1-5		3.00	
	P# single, #1		—	1.00
	P# single, #2-4		—	.65
	P# single, #5		—	2.25
a.	Imperf., pair		10.00	
b.	Pair, imperf. between		600.00	
c.	Tagging omitted		27.50	
	Nos. 2123-2136 (14)		4.25	2.80

Precancellations on Nos. 2125a, 2127a do not have lines. Precancellation on No. 2129a is in red. See No. 2231.

BLACK HERITAGE SERIES

Mary McLeod Bethune
Black Heritage USA 22

Mary McLeod Bethune (1875-1955), Educator — A1520

Designed by Jerry Pinkney from a photograph.

Printed by American Bank Note Company.

PHOTOGRAVURE
Plates of 200 in four panes of 50.

1985, Mar. 5	Tagged		Perf. 11	
2137 A1520	22c **multicolored**		.60	.20
	P# block of 4, 6#+A		3.25	—
	Zip block of 4		2.50	—
a.	Tagging omitted		—	

AMERICAN FOLK ART SERIES
Duck Decoys

Broadbill Decoy
Folk Art USA 22

Broadbill
A1521

Mallard
A1522

Canvasback
A1523

Redhead
A1524

Designed by Stevan Dohanos.

Printed by American Bank Note Company.

PHOTOGRAVURE
Plates of 200 in four panes of 50.

1985, Mar. 22		Tagged	Perf. 11	
2138	A1521	22c multicolored	1.00	.20
2139	A1522	22c multicolored	1.00	.20
2140	A1523	22c multicolored	1.00	.20
2141	A1524	22c multicolored	1.00	.20
a.		Block of 4, #2138-2141	4.00	2.75
		P# block of 4, 5#+A	4.50	—
		Zip block of 4	4.25	—

WINTER SPECIAL OLYMPICS

Ice Skater,
Emblem,
Skier — A1525

Designed by Jeff Carnell.

PHOTOGRAVURE
Plates of 160 in four panes of 40.

1985, Mar. 25		Tagged	Perf. 11	
2142	A1525	22c multicolored	.50	.20
		P# block of 4, 6#	2.25	—
		Zip block of 4	2.10	—
a.		Vert. pair, imperf. horiz.	400.00	

LOVE

A1526

Designed by Corita Kent.

PHOTOGRAVURE
Plates of 200 in four panes of 50.

1985, Apr. 17		Tagged	Perf. 11	
2143	A1526	22c multicolored	.40	.20
		P# block of 4, 6#	1.70	
		Zip block of 4	1.65	
a.		Imperf., pair	1,250.	

RURAL ELECTRIFICATION ADMINISTRATION

REA Power
Lines,
Farmland
A1527

Designed by Howard Koslow.

PHOTOGRAVURE & ENGRAVED (Combination Press)
Plates of 230 in panes of 50.

1985, May 11		Tagged	Perf. 11	
2144	A1527	22c multicolored	.60	.20
		P# block of 20, 5-10 #, 1-2 Zip, 1-2 Copyright	20.00	—
a.		Vert. pair, imperf between	—	

See Combination Press note after No. 1703.

AMERIPEX '86

US No. 134 — A1528

Designed by Richard Sheaff.

LITHOGRAPHED & ENGRAVED
Plates of 192 in four panes of 48

1985, May 25		Tagged	Perf. 11	
2145	A1528	22c multicolored	.40	.20
		P# block of 4, 3#	1.75	—
		Zip block of 4	1.65	—
a.		Red, black & blue (engr.) omitted	175.00	
b.		Red & black omitted		
c.		Red omitted	2,350.	
d.		Black missing (PS)	—	

ABIGAIL ADAMS (1744-1818)

A1529

Designed by Bart Forbes.

PHOTOGRAVURE
Plates of 200 in four panes of 50.

1985, June 14		Tagged	Perf. 11	
2146	A1529	22c multicolored	.40	.20
		P# block of 4, 4#	2.00	—
		Zip block of 4	1.65	—
a.		Imperf., pair	225.00	

FREDERIC AUGUSTE BARTHOLDI (1834-1904)

Architect and
Sculptor,
Statue of
Liberty
A1530

Designed by Howard Paine from paintings by Jose Frappa and James Dean.

LITHOGRAPHED & ENGRAVED
Plates of 200 in four panes of 50.

1985, July 18		Tagged	Perf. 11	
2147	A1530	22c multicolored	.40	.20
		P# block of 4, 5#	2.00	—
		Zip block of 4	1.65	—

Examples of No. 2147 exist with most, but not all, of the engraved black omitted.

George Washington,
Washington
Monument — A1532

Sealed
Envelopes — A1533

Designed by Thomas Szumowski (#2149) based on a portrait by Gilbert Stuart, and Richard Sheaff (#2150).

COIL STAMPS
PHOTOGRAVURE

1985				Perf. 10 Vertically	
2149	A1532	18c multicolored, low gloss gum, Nov. 6		.40	.20
		Pair		.80	.20
		P# strip of 5, #1112		3.00	
		P# strip of 5, #3333		3.50	
		P# single, #1112		—	2.00
		P# single, #3333		—	3.00
a.		Untagged (Bureau precanceled), low gloss gum		.35	.35
		P# strip of 5, #11121		5.00	
		P# strip of 5, #33333		3.00	
		P# single, #11121		—	5.00
		P# single, #33333		—	2.00
		Dull gum		.35	
		P# strip of 5, #33333		4.00	
		P# strip of 5, #43444		6.50	
		P# single, #43444		—	5.50
b.		Imperf., pair		825.00	
c.		As "a," imperf., pair		625.00	
d.		Tagging omitted (not Bureau precanceled)		75.00	—
e.		As "a," tagged (error), dull gum		2.00	1.75
		Pair		4.00	3.75
		P# strip of 5, #33333		150.00	
		P# single, #33333		—	35.00
		Low gloss gum		2.00	
		P# strip of 5, #33333		150.00	
		P# single, #33333		—	35.00
2150	A1533	21.1c multicolored, Oct. 22		.40	.20
		Pair		.80	.20
		P# strip of 5, #111111		3.00	
		P# strip of 5, #111121		4.00	
		P# single, #111111		—	2.50
		P# single, #111121		—	3.50
a.		Untagged (Bureau Precancel)		.40	.40
		Pair		.80	.80
		P# strip of 5, #111111		3.50	
		P# strip of 5, #111121		4.75	
		P# single, #111111		—	2.50
		P# single, #111121		—	3.75
b.		As "a," tagged (error)		.50	.50
		Pair		1.00	1.00
		P# strip of 5, #111111		2.50	
		P# strip of 5, #111121		3.00	
		P# single, #111111		—	—
		P# single, #111121		—	3.00

Precancellations on Nos. 2149a ("PRESORTED FIRST-CLASS"), 2150a and 2150b ("ZIP+4") do not have lines.

KOREAN WAR VETERANS

American
Troops in
Korea
A1535

Designed by Richard Sheaff from a photograph by David D. Duncan.

ENGRAVED
Plates of 200 in four panes of 50.

1985, July 26	Tagged	Perf. 11	
2152 A1535 22c gray green & rose red		.40	.20
P# block of 4		2.50	—
Zip block of 4		1.75	—

SOCIAL SECURITY ACT, 50th ANNIV.

Men, Women, Children, Corinthian Columns A1536

Designed by Robert Brangwynne.

Printed by American Bank Note Company.

PHOTOGRAVURE
Plates of 200 in four panes of 50.

1985, Aug. 14	Tagged	Perf. 11	
2153 A1536 22c deep & light blue		.40	.20
P# block of 4, 2#+A		2.00	—
Zip block of 4		1.70	—

WORLD WAR I VETERANS

The Battle of Marne, France A1537

Designed by Richard Sheaff from Harvey Dunn's charcoal drawing.

ENGRAVED
Plates of 200 in four panes of 50.

1985, Aug. 26	Tagged	Perf. 11	
2154 A1537 22c gray green & rose red		.40	.20
P# block of 4		2.25	—
Zip block of 4		1.85	—
a. Red missing (PS)		400.00	
b. Tagging omitted			—

HORSES

Quarter Horse A1538

Morgan A1539

Saddlebred A1540

Appaloosa A1541

Designed by Roy Andersen.

PHOTOGRAVURE
Plates of 160 in four panes of 40.

1985, Sept. 25	Tagged	Perf. 11	
2155 A1538 22c multicolored		1.25	.20
2156 A1539 22c multicolored		1.25	.20
2157 A1540 22c multicolored		1.25	.20
2158 A1541 22c multicolored		1.25	.20
a. Block of 4, #2155-2158		5.00	4.00
P# block of 4, 5#		7.00	—
Zip block of 4		5.25	—

PUBLIC EDUCATION IN AMERICA

Quill Pen, Apple, Spectacles, Penmanship Quiz — A1542

Designed by Uldis Purins.

Printed by American Bank Note Company

PHOTOGRAVURE
Plates of 200 in four panes of 50.

1985, Oct. 1	Tagged	Perf. 11	
2159 A1542 22c multicolored		.45	.20
P# block of 4, 5#		2.75	—
Zip block of 4		1.85	—
a. Tagging omitted			—

INTERNATIONAL YOUTH YEAR

YMCA Youth Camping, Cent. — A1543

Boy Scouts, 75th Anniv. A1544

Big Brothers / Big Sisters Federation, 40th Anniv. A1545

Camp Fire Inc., 75th Anniv. A1546

Designed by Dennis Luzak.

Printed by American Bank Note Company.

PHOTOGRAVURE
Plates of 200 in four panes of 50.

1985, Oct. 7	Tagged	Perf. 11	
2160 A1543 22c multicolored		.70	.20
2161 A1544 22c multicolored		.70	.20
2162 A1545 22c multicolored		.70	.20
2163 A1546 22c multicolored		.70	.20
a. Block of 4, #2160-2163		3.00	2.25
P# block of 4, 5#+A		4.00	—
Zip block of 4		3.25	—

HELP END HUNGER

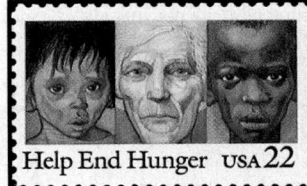

Youths and Elderly Suffering from Malnutrition A1547

Designed by Jerry Pinkney.

Printed by the American Bank Note Company.

PHOTOGRAVURE
Plates of 200 in four panes of 50.

1985, Oct. 15	Tagged	Perf. 11	
2164 A1547 22c multicolored		.45	.20
P# block of 4, 5#+A		2.25	—
Zip block of 4		1.90	—
a. Tagging omitted			—

CHRISTMAS

Genoa Madonna, Enameled Terra-Cotta by Luca Della Robbia (1400-1482) — A1548

Poinsettia Plants A1549

Designed by Bradbury Thompson (No. 2165) and James Dean (No. 2166).

PHOTOGRAVURE
Plates of 200 in panes of 50.

1985, Oct. 30	Tagged	Perf. 11	
2165 A1548 22c multicolored		.40	.20
P# block of 4, 4#		1.75	—
Zip block of 4		1.65	—
a. Imperf., pair		65.00	
b. Tagging omitted			—
2166 A1549 22c multicolored		.40	.20
P# block of 4, 5#		1.70	—
Zip block of 4		1.65	—
Vert. pair with full horiz. gutter between			—
a. Imperf., pair		100.00	

ARKANSAS STATEHOOD, 150th ANNIV.

Old State House, Little Rock — A1550

Designed by Roger Carlisle.

Printed by the American Bank Note Company

PHOTOGRAVURE
Plates of 200 in four panes of 50.

1986, Jan. 3   **Tagged**   ***Perf. 11***

2167	A1550	22c multicolored		.75	.20
		P# block of 4, 6#+A		3.75	—
		Zip block of 4		3.10	—
a.		Vert. pair, imperf. horiz.		—	—
b.		Tagging omitted		—	—

Marginal Inscriptions
Beginning with the Luis Munoz Marin issue a number of stamps include a descriptive inscription in the selvage.

GREAT AMERICANS ISSUE

A1551   A1552

Designed by Ron Adair.

Printed by the Bureau of Engraving & Printing.

ENGRAVED
Panes of 100 (#2168-2193, 2195), Panes of 20 (#2194, 2196)

Perf. 11, 11½x11 (#2185), 11.2x11.1 (20c)

1986-94   **Tagged**

2168	A1551	1c brownish vermilion, large block tagging, *June 30*		.20	.20
		P# block of 4		.30	—
		Zip block of 4		.20	—
a.		Tagging omitted		7.50	
2169	A1552	2c bright blue, large block tagging, *Feb. 28, 1987*		.20	.20
		P# block of 4		.30	—
		Zip block of 4		.20	—
a.		Untagged		.20	.20
		P# block of 4		.35	—
		Zip block of 4		.20	—
b.		Tagging omitted		—	—

The tagging omitted error No. 2169b appeared before No. 2169a was issued. Plate blocks from plate 1 are the error if untagged. No. 2169a is from plate 2. Other blocks and singles can be distinguished if se-tenant with tagged stamps. No. 2169a and 2169b also can be distinguished using a long wave ultraviolet light. The paper of No. 2169b will appear brownish, while the paper of No. 2169a appears almost white.

A1553   A1554

Designed by Christopher Calle.

Printed by the Bureau of Engraving & Printing.

2170	A1553	3c bright blue, large block tagging, dull gum, *Sept. 15*		.20	.20
		P# block of 4		.50	—
		Zip block of 4		.25	—
a.		Untagged, dull gum, *1994*		.20	.20
		P# block of 4		.50	—
		Zip block of 4		.25	—
		Shiny gum, *1994*		.20	

		P# block of 4		.50	—
		Zip block of 4		.25	—
b.		Tagging omitted		—	

The tagging omitted error No. 2170b appeared before No. 2170a was issued. Plate blocks from plates 2 and 3 are the error if untagged. No. 2170a is from plate 4. Other blocks and singles are indistiguishable, unless se-tenant with tagged stamps.

2171	A1554	4c blue violet, large block tagging, *July 14*		.20	.20
		P# block of 4		.60	—
		Zip block of 4		.40	—
a.		4c grayish violet, untagged		.20	.20
		P# block of 4		.40	—
		Zip block of 4		.35	—
b.		4c deep grayish blue, untagged, *1993*		.20	.20
		P# block of 4		.50	—
		Zip block of 4		.40	—
c.		As No. 2171, tagging omitted		—	

No. 2171c was found on a USPS souvenir page with first day cancel. No. 2171a and 2171b were not available on the first day of issue.

A1555   A1556

Designers: No. 2172, Christopher Calle. No. 2173, Juan Maldonado.

Printed by the Bureau of Engraving & Printing.

2172	A1555	5c dark olive green, large block tagging, *Feb. 27*		.20	.20
		P# block of 4		1.00	—
		Zip block of 4		.45	—
a.		Tagging omitted		150.00	—
2173	A1556	5c carmine, overall tagging, *Feb. 18, 1990*		.20	.20
		P# block of 4		1.00	—
		P# zip block of 4		.90	—
		Zip block of 4		.45	—
a.		Untagged, *1991*		.20	.20
		P# block of 4		.60	—
		P# zip block of 4		.75	—
		Zip block of 4		.45	—
b.		Tagging omitted		—	

The tagging omitted error No. 2173b appeared before No. 2173a was issued. Plate blocks from plate 1 are the error if untagged. No. 2173a is from plate 2. Other blocks and singles are indistinguishable, unless se-tenant with tagged stamps.

A1557   A1558

Designers: 10c, Robert Anderson. 14c, Ward Brackett.

Printed by the Bureau of Engraving & Printing.

2175	A1557	10c lake, large block tagging, dull gum, *Aug. 15, 1987*		.25	.20
		P# block of 4		1.10	—
		Zip block of 4		1.00	—
a.		Overall tagging, dull gum, *1990*		.60	.25
		P# block of 4		10.00	—
		Zip block of 4		2.00	—
b.		Tagging omitted		12.50	
c.		Prephosphored coated paper with surface tagging showing a solid appearance, dull gum, *1991*		.60	.20
		P# block of 4		3.00	—
		Zip block of 4		2.50	—
d.		Prephosphored uncoated paper with embedded tagging showing a mottled appearance, shiny gum, *1993*		.90	.20
		P# block of 4		4.00	—
		Zip block of 4		3.60	—
e.		10c carmine, prephosphored uncoated paper with embedded tagging showing a mottled appearance, shiny gum, *1994*		.40	.20
		P# block of 4		2.00	—
		Zip block of 4		1.75	—
f.		As "c," all color omitted		—	

No. 2157f must be collected se-tenant with a partially printed stamp or longer vertical strip.

2176	A1558	14c crimson, large block tagging, *Feb. 12, 1987*		.30	.20

		P# block of 4		1.50	—
		Zip block of 4		1.20	—
a.		Tagging omitted		—	

A1559   A1560

Designers: 15c, Jack Rosenthal. 17c, Christopher Calle.

Printed by the Bureau of Engraving & Printing.

2177	A1559	15c claret, large block tagging, *June 6, 1988*		.35	.20
		P# block of 4		10.00	—
		Zip block of 4		1.50	—
a.		Overall tagging, *1990*		.30	—
		P# block of 4		3.25	—
		Zip block of 4		1.20	—
b.		Prephosphored coated paper with surface tagging showing a solid appearance		.40	—
		P# block of 4		3.25	—
		Zip block of 4		1.60	—
c.		Tagging omitted		15.00	
d.		All color omitted		—	

No. 2177d resulted from partially printed panes. It must be collected se-tenant with a partially printed stamp or in a longer horizontal strip showing error stamps plus partially/completely printed stamps.

2178	A1560	17c dull blue green, large block tagging, *June 18*		.35	.20
		P# block of 4		2.00	—
		Zip block of 4		1.40	—
		Pair with full horizontal gutter between		—	
a.		Tagging omitted		10.00	

A1561   A1562

Designers: 20c, Robert Anderson. 21c, Susan Sanford.

Printed by: 20c, Banknote Corporation of America. 21c, Bureau of Engraving & Printing.

2179	A1561	20c red brown, prephosphored coated paper with surface tagging showing a grainy solid appearance, *Oct. 24, 1994*		.40	.20
		P# block of 4, 1#+B		2.00	
a.		20c orange brown, prephosphored coated paper with surface tagging showing a grainy solid appearance		.45	.20
		P# block of 4, 1#+B		2.25	
b.		20c bright red brown, prephosphored coated paper with surface tagging showing a grainy solid appearance		1.00	.25
		P# block of 4, 1#+B		6.00	
2180	A1562	21c blue violet, large block tagging, *Oct. 21, 1988*		.45	.20
		P# block of 4		2.50	—
		Zip block of 4		1.65	—
a.		Tagging omitted		—	

No. 2180 is known with worn tagging mats on which horizontal untagged areas have taggant giving the appearance of vertical band tagging.

A1563   A1564

A1565

A1570

A1573

A1574

Designers: 23c, Dennis Lyall. 25c, Richard Sparks. 28c, Robert Anderson.

Printed by the Bureau of Engraving & Printing.

2181	A1563	23c **purple,** large block tagging, dull gum, *Nov. 4, 1988*	.45	.20
		P# block of 4	2.50	—
		Zip block of 4	1.90	—
a.		Overall tagging, dull gum	.75	—
		P# block of 4	5.75	—
		Zip block of 4	3.25	—
b.		Prephosphored coated paper with surface tagging showing a solid appearance, dull gum	.65	—
		P# block of 4	4.50	—
		Zip block of 4	2.75	—
c.		Prephosphored uncoated paper with embedded tagging showing a mottled appearance, shiny gum	.75	.20
		P# block of 4	5.75	—
		Zip block of 4	3.25	—
d.		Tagging omitted	7.50	
2182	A1564	25c **blue,** large block tagging, *Jan. 11*	.50	.20
		P# block of 4	2.75	—
		Zip block of 4	2.00	—
a.		Booklet pane of 10, *May 3, 1988*	5.00	3.75
b.		As #2182, tagging omitted	—	
c.		As "a," tagging omitted	—	
d.		Horiz. pair, imperf between	850.00	
e.		As "a," all color omitted on right stamps	—	
f.		As No. 2182 (sheet stamp), vert. pair, bottom stamp all color omitted	—	

No. 2182f may be collected se-tenant with a partially printed stamp or longer vertical strip.
See Nos. 2197, 2197a.

2183	A1565	28c **myrtle green,** large block tagging, *Sept. 14, 1989*	.65	.35
		P# block of 4	3.75	—
		Zip block of 4	2.60	—

A1566

A1567

Designed by Christopher Calle.

Printed by: No. 2184, Canadian Bank Note Co. for Stamp Venturers. No. 2185, Stamp Venturers.

2184	A1566	29c **blue,** prephosphored uncoated paper with embedded tagging showing a mottled appearance, *Mar. 9, 1992*	.70	.20
		P# block of 4, #+S	4.00	—
		Zip block of 4	3.00	—
2185	A1567	29c **indigo,** prephosphored coated paper with surface tagging showing a solid appearance, *Apr. 13, 1993*	.65	.20
		P# block of 4, 1#+S	3.50	—
		Zip block of 4	2.60	—

A1568

A1569

Designers: 35c, 40c, Christopher Calle. 45c, Bradbury Thompson.

Printed by: 35c, Canadian Bank Note Co. for Stamp Venturers. 40c, 45c, Bureau of Engraving & Printing.

2186	A1568	35c **black,** prephosphored uncoated paper with embedded tagging showing a mottled appearance, *Apr. 3, 1991*	.75	.20
		P# block of 4, #+S	4.25	—
		Zip block of 4	3.00	—
2187	A1569	40c **dark blue,** overall tagging, dull gum, *Sept. 6, 1990*	.85	.20
		P# block of 4	5.00	—
		Zip block of 4	3.50	—
a.		Prephosphored coated paper with surface tagging, dull gum	1.00	.35
		P# block of 4	5.50	—
		Zip block of 4	4.25	—
		Low gloss gum, *1998*	.90	.35
		P# block of 4	5.50	—
		Zip block of 4	3.75	—
c.		Prephosphored uncoated paper with embedded tagging showing a mottled appearance, shiny gum, *1994*	1.00	.20
		P# block of 4	10.00	—
		Zip block of 4	4.25	—
d.		Tagging omitted		

No. 2187a exists on two types of surface-tagged paper that exhibit either a solid appearance (dull gum) or a grainy solid appearance (low gloss gum).

2188	A1570	45c **bright blue,** large block tagging, *June 17, 1988*	1.00	.20
		P# block of 4	5.00	—
		Zip block of 4	4.00	—
a.		45c **blue,** overall tagging, *1990*	2.50	.20
		P# block of 4	27.50	—
		Zip block of 4	12.00	—
b.		Tagging omitted	17.50	

The blue on No. 2188a is noticeably lighter than on No. 2188. Color variety specialists, as well as tagging specialists, will want to consider it as a second variety of this stamp.
Almost all examples of No. 2188a are in the grade of fine or fine-very fine. Values are for stamps in the grade of fine-very fine.

A1571

A1572

Designers: 52c, John Berkey. 56c, Robert Anderson.

Printed by the Bureau of Engraving & Printing.

2189	A1571	52c **purple,** prephosphored coated paper with surface tagging showing a solid appearance, dull gum, *June 3, 1991*	1.10	.20
		P# block of 4	7.50	—
		Zip block of 4	4.50	—
a.		Prephosphored uncoated paper with embedded tagging showing a mottled appearance, shiny gum, *1993*	1.25	—
		P# block of 4	10.00	—
		Zip block of 4	5.50	—

Selvage inscriptions from the original printing of No. 2189 from plate 1 show the incorrect dates for Humphrey's vice-presidential term ("1964 to 1968"). Corrected plate 1 and plate 2 printings (No. 2189a) show the dates correctly as 1965 to 1969. Values for the two varieties of inscription blocks of 6 are approximately the same: $8.50.

2190	A1572	56c **scarlet,** large block tagging, *Sept. 3*	1.20	.20
		P# block of 4	6.50	—
		Zip block of 4	4.80	—
a.		Tagging omitted		

No. 2190 known with a "tagging spill" making stamp appear overall tagged.

Designed by Christopher Calle.

Printed by the Bureau of Engraving & Printing.

2191	A1573	65c **dark blue,** large block tagging, *Nov. 5, 1988*	1.30	.20
		P# block of 4	6.50	—
		Zip block of 4	5.20	—
a.		Tagging omitted	22.50	
2192	A1574	75c **deep magenta,** prephosphored coated paper with surface tagging showing a solid appearance, dull gum, *Feb. 16, 1992*	1.60	.20
		P# block of 4	7.50	—
		Zip block of 4	6.40	—
a.		Prephosphored uncoated paper with embedded tagging showing a mottled appearance, shiny gum	1.75	—
		P# block of 4	9.00	—
		Zip block of 4	7.00	—

A1575

A1576

"Lipstick on Shirt Front" double gouge plate flaw

Designers: No. 2193, Tom Broad. No. 2194, Bradbury Thompson.

Printed by the Bureau of Engraving & Printing.

2193	A1575	$1 **dark Prussian green,** large block tagging, *Sept. 23*	3.00	.50
		P# block of 4	14.00	—
		Zip block of 4	12.00	—
a.		All color omitted	—	

No. 2193a must be collected se-tenant vertically with partially printed stamps.

2194	A1576	$1 **intense deep blue,** large block tagging, dull gum, *June 7, 1989*	2.25	.50
		P# block of 4	11.00	—
		Pane of 20	48.00	—
		Double gouge plate flaw ("Lipstick on Shirt Front"), (pos. 6 on one plate #1 pane)	—	
b.		$1 **deep blue,** overall tagging, dull gum, *1990*	2.50	.50
		P# block of 4	13.00	—
		Pane of 20	52.50	—
c.		Tagging omitted	10.00	
d.		$1 **dark blue,** prephosphored coated paper with surface tagging showing a solid appearance, dull gum, *1992*	2.50	.50
		P# block of 4	13.00	—
		Pane of 20	52.50	—
e.		$1 **blue,** prephosphored uncoated paper with embedded tagging showing a mottled appearance, shiny gum, *1993*	2.75	.60
		P# block of 4	14.00	—
		Pane of 20	58.00	—
f.		$1 **blue,** prephosphored coated paper with surface tagging showing a grainy solid appearance, low gloss gum, *1998*	2.75	.50
		P# block of 4	14.00	—
		Pane of 20	58.00	—

No. 2194 issued in pane of 20 (see No. 2196.)
The intense deep blue of No. 2194 is much deeper than the deep blue and dark blue of the other $1 varieties.
The "Lipstick on Shirt Front" flaw was discovered during production and the position was repaired. Very few have been found.

A1577

A1578

Designers: $2, Tom Broad. $5, Arthur Lidov.

Printed by the Bureau of Engraving & Printing.

2195	A1577	$2 bright violet, large block tagging, *Mar. 19*		4.50	.50
		P# block of 4		20.00	—
		Zip block of 4		17.00	—
a.		Tagging omitted		*250.00*	

No. 2195 is known with worn tagging mats on which horizontal untagged areas have taggant giving the appearance of vertical band tagging.

2196	A1578	$5 copper red, large block tagging, *Aug. 25, 1987*		9.00	1.00
		P# block of 4		42.50	—
		Pane of 20		185.00	—
a.		Tagging omitted		*225.00*	
b.		Prephosphored coated paper with surface tagging showing a solid appearance, *1992*		11.00	—
		P# block of 4		45.00	—
		Pane of 20		220.00	—
		Nos. 2168-2196 (28)		32.80	7.45

Booklet Stamp
Perf. 10 on 2 or 3 sides

2197	A1564	25c blue, large block tagging, *May 3, 1988*		.55	.20
a.		Booklet pane of 6		3.30	2.50
b.		Tagging omitted		8.00	
c.		As "b," booklet pane of 6		50.00	

UNITED STATES - SWEDEN
STAMP COLLECTING

Handstamped Cover, Philatelic Memorabilia A1581

Boy Examining Stamp Collection A1582

No. 836 Under Magnifying Glass, Sweden Nos. 268, 271 — A1583

1986 Presidents Miniature Sheet on First Day Cover — A1584

Designed by Richard Sheaff and Eva Jern (No. 2200).

BOOKLET STAMPS
LITHOGRAPHED & ENGRAVED
Perf. 10 Vert. on 1 or 2 Sides

1986, Jan. 23				Tagged	
2198	A1581	22c multicolored		.45	.20
2199	A1582	22c multicolored		.45	.20
2200	A1583	22c multicolored		.45	.20
2201	A1584	22c multicolored		.45	.20
a.		Bklt. pane of 4, #2198-2201		2.00	1.75
b.		As "a," black omitted on Nos. 2198, 2201		47.50	
c.		As "a," blue (litho.) omitted on Nos. 2198-2200		2,250.	
d.		As "a," buff (litho.) omitted			

See Sweden Nos. 1585-1588.

LOVE ISSUE

A1585

Designed by Saul Mandel.

Plates of 200 in four panes of 50.
PHOTOGRAVURE

1986, Jan. 30			Tagged		Perf. 11
2202	A1585	22c multicolored		.55	.20
		P# block of 4, 5#		2.75	—
		Zip block of 4		2.25	—
a.		Tagging omitted		—	

Sojourner Truth (c. 1797-1883), Human Rights Activist — A1586

Texas State Flag and Silver Spur — A1587

BLACK HERITAGE SERIES
Designed by Jerry Pinkney.

Printed by American Bank Note Co.

Plates of 200 in four panes of 50
PHOTOGRAVURE

1986, Feb. 4			Tagged		Perf. 11
2203	A1586	22c multicolored		.55	.20
		P# block of 4, 6#+A		2.75	
		Zip block of 4		2.25	

REPUBLIC OF TEXAS, 150th ANNIV.
Designed by Don Adair.

Printed by the American Bank Note Co.

Plates of 200 in four panes of 50.
PHOTOGRAVURE

1986, Mar. 2			Tagged		Perf. 11
2204	A1587	22c dark blue, dark red & grayish black		.55	.20
		P# block of 4, 3#+A		2.75	—
		Zip block of 4		2.25	—
a.		Horiz. pair, imperf. vert.		900.00	
b.		Dark red omitted		2,250.	
c.		Dark blue omitted		8,000.	

FISH

Muskellunge — A1588

Atlantic Cod A1589

Largemouth Bass — A1590

Bluefin Tuna A1591

Catfish A1592

Designed by Chuck Ripper.

BOOKLET STAMPS
PHOTOGRAVURE

1986, Mar. 21			Tagged	Perf. 10 Horiz.	
2205	A1588	22c multicolored		1.00	.20
2206	A1589	22c multicolored		1.00	.20
2207	A1590	22c multicolored		1.00	.20
2208	A1591	22c multicolored		1.00	.20
2209	A1592	22c multicolored		1.00	.20
a.		Bklt. pane of 5, #2205-2209		6.00	2.75

The magenta used to print this issue is extremely fugitive. Dangerous fakes purported to be magenta omitted exist. No genuine examples are known. Panes apparently lacking red must be certified, and examples presently with certificates should be recertified.

PUBLIC HOSPITALS

A1593

Designed by Uldis Purins.

Printed by the American Bank Note Co.

PHOTOGRAVURE
Plates of 200 in four panes of 50.

1986, Apr. 11	Tagged		Perf. 11	
2210 A1593 22c multicolored			.40	.20
	P# block of 4, 5#+A		1.75	—
	Zip block of 4		1.65	—
a.	Vert. pair, imperf. horiz.		275.00	
b.	Horiz. pair, imperf. vert.		1,150.	

PERFORMING ARTS

Edward Kennedy "Duke" Ellington (1899-1974), Jazz Composer — A1594

Designed by Jim Sharpe.
Printed by the American Bank Note Co.

PHOTOGRAVURE
Plates of 200 in four panes of 50.

1986, Apr. 29	Tagged		Perf. 11	
2211 A1594 22c multicolored			.40	.20
	P# block of 4, 6#+A		1.90	—
	Zip block of 4		1.75	—
a.	Vert. pair, imperf. horiz.		750.00	

AMERIPEX '86 ISSUE
Miniature Sheets

35 Presidents — A1599a

A1599b

A1599c

A1599d

Illustrations reduced.

Designs: No. 2216: a, George Washington. b, John Adams. c, Thomas Jefferson. d, James Madison. e, James Monroe. f, John Quincy Adams. g, Andrew Jackson. h, Martin Van Buren. i, William H. Harrison.

No. 2217: a, John Tyler. b, James Knox Polk. c, Zachary Taylor. d, Millard Fillmore. e, Franklin Pierce. f, James Buchanan. g, Abraham Lincoln. h, Andrew Johnson. i, Ulysses S. Grant.

No. 2218: a, Rutherford B. Hayes. b, James A. Garfield. c, Chester A. Arthur. d, Grover Cleveland. e, Benjamin Harrison. f, William McKinley. g, Theodore Roosevelt. h, William H. Taft. i, Woodrow Wilson.

No. 2219: a, Warren G. Harding. b, Calvin Coolidge. c, Herbert Hoover. d, Franklin Delano Roosevelt. e, White House. f, Harry S. Truman. g, Dwight D. Eisenhower. h, John F. Kennedy. i, Lyndon B. Johnson.

Designed by Jerry Dadds.

LITHOGRAPHED & ENGRAVED

1986, May 22	Tagged		Perf. 11	
2216 A1599a Sheet of 9			7.50	4.00
a.-i.	22c, any single		.75	.40
j.	Blue (engr.) omitted		2,500.	
k.	Black inscription omitted		2,000.	
l.	Imperf.		10,500.	
m.	As "k," double impression of red		—	
n.	Blue omitted on stamps 1-3, 5-6, 8, 9			
2217 A1599b Sheet of 9			7.50	4.00
a.-i.	22c, any single		.75	.40
j.	Black inscription omitted		2,500.	
k.	Tagging omitted		—	
2218 A1599c Sheet of 9			7.50	4.00
a.-i.	22c, any single		.75	.40
j.	Brown (engr.) omitted			
k.	Black inscription omitted		2,500.	
l.	Tagging omitted		—	
2219 A1599d Sheet of 9			7.50	4.00
a.-i.	22c, any single		.75	.40
j.	Blackish blue (engr.) inscription omitted on a-b, d-e, g-h		2,500.	
k.	Tagging omitted on c, f, i		4,000.	
l.	Blackish blue (engr.) omitted on all stamps			
Nos. 2216-2219 (4)			30.00	16.00

Issued in conjunction with AMERIPEX '86 Intl. Philatelic Exhibition, Chicago, IL May 22-June 1. Sheet size: 120x207mm (sheet size varied).

ARCTIC EXPLORERS

Elisha Kent Kane — A1600

Adolphus W. Greely
A1601

Vilhjalmur Stefansson
A1602

Robert E. Peary, Matthew Henson
A1603

Designed by Dennis Lyall.
Printed by the American Bank Note Company

PHOTOGRAVURE
Plates of 200 in four panes of 50.

1986, May 28		Tagged	Perf. 11	
2220	A1600	22c **multicolored**	.65	.20
2221	A1601	22c **multicolored**	.65	.20
2222	A1602	22c **multicolored**	.65	.20
2223	A1603	22c **multicolored**	.65	.20
a.		Block of 4, #2220-2223	2.75	2.25
		P# block of 4, 5#+A	4.50	
		Zip block of 4	3.00	—
b.		As "a," black omitted	6,000.	
c.		As "a," Nos. 2220, 2221 black omitted	—	
d.		As "a," Nos. 2222, 2223 black omitted	—	

STATUE OF LIBERTY, 100th ANNIV.

A1604

Designed by Howard Paine.

ENGRAVED
Plates of 200 in four panes of 50.

1986, July 4		Tagged	Perf. 11	
2224	A1604	22c **scarlet & dark blue**	.40	.20
		P# block of 4	2.25	—
		Zip block of 4	1.65	—
a.		Scarlet omitted		

On No. 2224a, virtually all of the dark blue also is omitted, so the error stamp should be collected as part of a transition strip. See France No. 2014.

> **Coil Plate No. Strips of 3**
> Beginning with No. 2123, coil plate no. strips of 3 usually sell at the level of strips of 5 minus the face value of two stamps.

TRANSPORTATION ISSUE

A1604a

A1604b

Designers: 1c, 2c, David Stone.

COIL STAMPS
ENGRAVED

1986-87		Tagged	Perf. 10 Vert.	
2225	A1604a	1c **violet,** large block tagging, dull gum, *Nov. 26*	.20	.20
		Pair	.20	.20
		P# strip of 5, #1, 2	.45	
		P# single, #1, 2		.40
a.		Prephosphored uncoated paper with embedded tagging showing a mottled appearance (error), shiny gum	.20	.20
		Pair	.20	.20
		P# strip of 5, #3	40.00	
		P# single, #3		25.00
b.		Untagged, dull gum	.20	.20
		Pair	.20	.20
		P# strip of 5, #2-3	.55	
		P# single, #2-3		.45
		Shiny gum	.20	
		P# strip of 5, #3	.60	
		Low gloss gum	.20	
		P# strip of 5, #3	2.75	
c.		Imperf., pair	2,000.	
2226	A1604b	2c **black,** dull gum, *Mar. 6, 1987*	.20	.20
		Pair	.20	.20
		P# strip of 5, #1	.40	
		P# single, #1		.35
a.		Untagged, dull gum	.20	.20
		Pair	.20	.20
		P# strip of 5, #2	2.00	
		P# single, #2		.50
		Shiny gum	.20	
		P# strip of 5, #2	2.00	

REDUCED SIZE

2228	A1285	4c **reddish brown,** large block tagging, *Aug.*	.20	.20
		Pair	.20	.20
		P# strip of 5, #1	1.50	
		P# single, #1		.95
a.		Overall tagging, *1990*	.70	.20
		Pair	1.40	.20
		P# strip of 5, #1	6.00	
		P# single, #1		5.00
b.		Imperf., pair	225.00	

Earliest known usage of No. 2228: Aug. 15, 1986.
On No. 2228 "Stagecoach 1890s" is 17¾mm long; on No. 1898A, 19½mm long.

UNTAGGED

2231	A1511	8.3c **green** (Bureau precancel, Blk.·Rt./CAR-RT/SORT), *Aug. 29*	.65	.20
		Pair	1.30	.40
		P# strip of 5, #1	4.50	
		P# strip of 5, #2	5.25	
		P# single, #1	—	3.00
		P# single, #2	—	5.00

On No. 2231 "Ambulance 1860s" is 18mm long; on No. 2128, 18⅛mm long.
Joint lines do not appear on Nos. 2225-2231.

AMERICAN FOLK ART SERIES
Navajo Art

A1605

A1606

A1607

A1608

Designed by Derry Noyes.

LITHOGRAPHED & ENGRAVED
Plates of 200 in four panes of 50.

1986, Sept. 4		Tagged	Perf. 11	
2235	A1605	22c **multicolored**	.80	.20
2236	A1606	22c **multicolored**	.80	.20
2237	A1607	22c **multicolored**	.80	.20
2238	A1608	22c **multicolored**	.80	.20
a.		Block of 4, #2235-2238	3.25	2.25
		P# block of 4, 5#	4.25	
		Zip block of 4	3.50	—
b.		As "a," black (engr.) omitted	325.00	

LITERARY ARTS SERIES

T.S. Eliot (1888-1965), Poet — A1609

Designed by Bradbury Thompson.

ENGRAVED
Plates of 200 in four panes of 50.

1986, Sept. 26		Tagged	Perf. 11	
2239	A1609	22c **copper red**	.55	.20
		P# block of 4	2.75	
		Zip block of 4	2.25	
a.		Tagging omitted		

AMERICAN FOLK ART SERIES
Woodcarved Figurines

A1610

A1611

A1612

A1613

Designed by Bradbury Thompson.
Printed by the American Bank Note Company

PHOTOGRAVURE
Plates of 200 in four panes of 50.

1986, Oct. 1		Tagged	Perf. 11	
2240	A1610	22c **multicolored**	.50	.20
2241	A1611	22c **multicolored**	.50	.20
2242	A1612	22c **multicolored**	.50	.20
2243	A1613	22c **multicolored**	.50	.20
a.		Block of 4, #2240-2243	2.00	1.50
		P# block of 4, 5#+A	3.75	
		Zip block of 4	2.25	—
b.		As "a," imperf. vert.	1,000.	

CHRISTMAS

Madonna, National
Gallery, by Perugino
(c. 1450-1513)
A1614

Village Scene
A1615

Designed by Bradbury Thompson (#2244) & Dolli Tingle
(#2245).

PHOTOGRAVURE
Plates of 200 in four panes of 50.

1986, Oct. 24	Tagged	Perf. 11	
2244 A1614 22c **multicolored**		.40	.20
P# block of 4, 5#		2.00	—
Zip block of 4		1.65	—
a. Imperf, pair		600.00	
2245 A1615 22c **multicolored**		.40	.20
P# block of 4, 6#		1.90	—
Zip block of 4		1.65	—

MICHIGAN STATEHOOD, 150th ANNIV.

White Pine — A1616

Designed by Robert Wilbert.

PHOTOGRAVURE
Plates of 200 in four panes of 50.

1987, Jan. 26	Tagged	Perf. 11	
2246 A1616 22c **multicolored**		.55	.20
P# block of 4, 5#		2.50	—
Zip block of 4		2.25	—
Pair with full vert. gutter between		—	

PAN AMERICAN GAMES
Indianapolis, Aug. 7-25

Runner in Full
Stride
A1617

Designed by Lon Busch.

PHOTOGRAVURE
Plates of 200 in four panes of 50.

1987, Jan. 29	Tagged	Perf. 11	
2247 A1617 22c **multicolored**		.40	.20
P# block of 4, 5#		1.90	—
Zip block of 4		1.65	—
a. Silver omitted		1,250.	

No. 2247a is valued in the grade of fine.

LOVE ISSUE

A1618

Designed by John Alcorn.

PHOTOGRAVURE
Panes of 100

1987, Jan. 30	Tagged	Perf. 11½x11	
2248 A1618 22c **multicolored**		.40	.20
P# block of 4, 5#		1.90	—
Zip block of 4		1.65	—
Pair with full horiz. gutter between		—	

BLACK HERITAGE SERIES

Jean Baptiste Pointe du
Sable (c. 1750-1818),
Pioneer Trader, Founder of
Chicago — A1619

Designed by Thomas Blackshear.

PHOTOGRAVURE
Plates of 200 in four panes of 50.

1987, Feb. 20	Tagged	Perf. 11	
2249 A1619 22c **multicolored**		.50	.20
P# block of 4, 5#		2.60	—
Zip block of 4		2.10	—
a. Tagging omitted		10.00	

Enrico Caruso (1873-
1921), Opera
Tenor — A1620

Fourteen Achievement
Badges — A1621

PERFORMING ARTS SERIES
Designed by Jim Sharpe.
Printed by American Bank Note Co.

PHOTOGRAVURE & ENGRAVED
Plates of 200 in four panes of 50.

1987, Feb. 27	Tagged	Perf. 11	
2250 A1620 22c **multicolored**		.40	.20
P# block of 4, 4#+A		1.90	—
Zip block of 4		1.65	—
a. Black (engr.) omitted		4,500.	

GIRL SCOUTS, 75TH ANNIVERSARY
Designed by Richard Sheaff.

LITHOGRAPHED & ENGRAVED
Plates of 200 in four panes of 50.

1987, Mar. 12	Tagged	Perf. 11	
2251 A1621 22c **multicolored**		.40	.20
P# block of 4, 6#		1.90	—
Zip block of 4		1.65	—
a. All litho. colors omitted		2,450.	
b. Red & black (engr.) omitted		1,950.	

All known examples of No. 2251a have been expertized and
certificate must accompany purchase. The unique pane of No.
2251b has been expertized and a certificate exists for the pane
of 50.

Coil Plate No. Strips of 3
Beginning with No. 2123, coil plate no. strips of 3
usually sell at the level of strips of 5 minus the face
value of two stamps.

TRANSPORTATION ISSUE

A1622

A1623

A1624

Milk Wagon 1900s
5 USA — A1623

Elevator 1900s
5.3 USA — A1624

Carreta 1770s
7.6 USA — A1625

A1626

Wheel Chair 1920s
8.4 USA — A1626

Canal Boat 1880s
10 USA — A1627

A1628

Patrol Wagon 1880s
13 USA — A1628

Coal Car 1870s
13.2 USA — A1629

A1630

Tugboat 1900s
15 USA — A1630

Popcorn Wagon
16.7 USA 1902 — A1631

A1632

Racing Car 1911
17.5 USA — A1632

Cable Car 1880s
USA 20 — A1633

A1633

A1634

Fire Engine 1900s
20.5 USA — A1634

Railroad Mail Car
1920s
21 USA — A1635

Conestoga Wagon
1800s
3 USA — A1622

Tandem Bicycle
1890s
24.1 USA — A1636

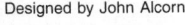
A1636

Designers: 3c, 7.6c, 13.2c, 15c, Richard Schlecht. 5c, 5.3c,
16.7c, Lou Nolan. 8.4c, 20.5c, 24.1c, Christopher Calle. 10c,

William H. Bond. 13c, Joe Brockert. 17.5c, Tom Broad. 20c, Dan Romano. 21c, David Stone.

COIL STAMPS
ENGRAVED

1987-95　　　　　　　　　　**Perf. 10 Vert.**
Tagged, Untagged (5.3c, 7.6c, 8.4c, 13c, 13.2c, 16.7c, 20.5c, 21c, 24.1c)

2252	A1622	3c **claret**, dull gum, *Feb. 29, 1988*	.20	.20
		Pair	.20	.20
		P# strip of 5, #1	.60	
		P# single, #1	—	.60
a.		Untagged, dull gum	.20	.20
		P# strip of 5, #2-3	1.25	
		P# single, #2	—	.95
		P# single, #3	—	.80
		Shiny gum, *1995*	.20	
		P# strip of 5, #3	1.25	
		P# strip of 5, #5	6.00	
		P# strip of 5, #6	1.25	
		P# single, #5	—	7.00
		P# single, #6	—	1.10
		Low gloss gum	.40	
		P# strip of 5, #5	8.00	
		P# single, #5	—	6.75
b.		As "a," imperf pair, shiny gum		

The plate #5 on No. 2252a with low gloss gum is smaller than the #5 on No. 2252a with shiny gum. The smaller plate #5 represents a different printing sleeve (plate).

2253	A1623	5c **black**, *Sept. 25*	.20	.20
		Pair	.20	.20
		P# strip of 5, #1	.80	
		P# single, #1	—	.75
2254	A1624	5.3c **black** (Bureau precancel "Nonprofit Carrier Route Sort" in red), *Sept. 16, 1988*	.20	.20
		Pair	.20	.20
		P# strip of 5, #1	1.40	
		P# single, #1	—	.70
2255	A1625	7.6c **brown** (Bureau precancel "Nonprofit" in red), *Aug. 30, 1988*	.20	.20
		Pair	.30	.30
		P# strip of 5, #1-2	1.75	
		P# strip of 5, #3	3.50	
		P# single, #1-2	—	1.50
		P# single, #3	—	4.00
2256	A1626	8.4c **deep claret** (Bureau precancel "Nonprofit" in red), *Aug. 12, 1988*	.20	.20
		Pair	.30	.30
		P# strip of 5, #1-2	1.90	
		P# strip of 5, #3	7.50	
		P# single, #1-2	—	1.00
		P# single, #3	—	5.50
a.		Imperf., pair	550.00	
2257	A1627	10c **blue**, large block tagging, dull gum, *Apr. 11*	.40	.20
		Pair	.80	.20
		P# strip of 5, #1	1.75	
		P# single, #1	—	1.00
a.		Overall tagging, dull gum, *1993*	1.50	.20
		Pair	3.00	.20
		P# strip of 5, #1	10.00	
		P# single, #1	—	4.75
		Shiny gum, *1994*	.20	.20
		Pair	.20	.20
		P# strip of 5, #4	3.25	
		P# single, #4	—	2.00
b.		Prephosphored uncoated paper with embedded tagging showing a mottled appearance, shiny gum	.20	.20
		Pair	.40	.20
		P# strip of 5, #1, 2	2.50	
		P# strip of 5, #3, 4	3.00	
		P# single, #1, 2	—	2.50
		P# single, #3, 4	—	2.75
c.		Prephosphored coated paper with surface tagging showing a solid appearance, low gloss gum	.25	.20
		Pair	.50	.20
		P# strip of 5, #5	4.25	
		P# single, #5	—	4.00
d.		Tagging omitted	30.00	
e.		Imperf, pair, large block tagging	1,750.	
2258	A1628	13c **black** (Bureau precancel "Presorted First-Class" in red), *Oct. 29, 1988*	.65	.25
		Pair	1.30	.50
		P# strip of 5, #1	5.00	
		P# single, #1	—	2.00
2259	A1629	13.2c **slate green** (Bureau precancel "Bulk Rate" in red), *July 19, 1988*	.25	.25
		Pair	.50	.50
		P# strip of 5, #1-2	2.75	
		P# single, #1-2	—	1.50
a.		Imperf., pair	80.00	
2260	A1630	15c **violet**, large block tagging, *July 12, 1988*	.25	.20
		Pair	.50	.20
		P# strip of 5, #1	1.75	
		P# strip of 5, #2	2.25	
		P# single, #1-2	—	1.50
a.		Overall tagging, *1990*	.25	.20
		Pair	.50	.20
		P# strip of 5, #2	3.00	
		P# single, #2	—	2.75
b.		Tagging omitted	3.75	
c.		Imperf., pair	625.00	
2261	A1631	16.7c **rose** (Bureau precancel "Bulk Rate " in black), *July 7, 1988*	.30	.30
		Pair	.60	.60

		P# strip of 5, #1	2.25	
		P# strip of 5, #2	2.50	
		P# single, #1	—	1.60
		P# single, #2	—	2.50
a.		Imperf., pair	150.00	

All known examples of No. 2261a are miscut top to bottom.

2262	A1632	17.5c **dark violet**, *Sept. 25*	.65	.20
		Pair	1.30	.20
		P# strip of 5, #1	4.00	
		P# single, #1	—	2.50
a.		Untagged (Bureau precancel "ZIP + 4 Presort" in red)	.65	.30
		P# strip of 5, #1	4.00	
		P# single, #1	—	2.50
b.		Imperf., pair	2,250.	
2263	A1633	20c **blue violet**, large block tagging, *Oct. 28, 1988*	.35	.20
		Pair	.70	.20
		P# strip of 5, #1-2	3.00	
		P# single, #1-2	—	1.75
a.		Imperf., pair	50.00	
b.		Overall tagging, *1990*	1.00	.20
		Pair	2.00	.20
		P# strip of 5, #2	8.00	
		P# single, #2	—	5.00
2264	A1634	20.5c **rose** (Bureau precancel "ZIP + 4 Presort" in black), *Sept. 28, 1988*	.75	.40
		Pair	1.50	.80
		P# strip of 5, #1	5.75	
		P# single, #1	—	3.00
2265	A1635	21c **olive green** (Bureau precancel "Presorted First-Class" in red), *Aug. 16, 1988*	.40	.40
		Pair	.80	.80
		P# strip of 5, #1-2	3.00	
		P# single, #1-2	—	2.50
a.		Imperf., pair	42.50	
2266	A1636	24.1c **deep ultra** (Bureau precancel ZIP + 4 in red), *Oct. 26, 1988*	.80	.45
		Pair	1.60	.90
		P# strip of 5, #1	3.75	
		P# single, #1	—	2.25
		Nos. 2252-2266 (15)	5.80	3.85

5.3c, 7.6c, 8.4c, 13.2c, 16.7c, 20.5c, 21c and 24.1c only available precanceled.

SPECIAL OCCASIONS

A1637

A1638

A1639

A1640

A1641

A1642

A1643

A1644

Designed by Oren Sherman.

BOOKLET STAMPS
PHOTOGRAVURE

1987, Apr. 20　Tagged　Perf. 10 on 1, 2 or 3 Sides

2267	A1637	22c **multicolored**	.65	.20
2268	A1638	22c **multicolored**	.80	.20
2269	A1639	22c **multicolored**	.80	.20
2270	A1640	22c **multicolored**	.80	.20
2271	A1641	22c **multicolored**	.80	.20
2272	A1642	22c **multicolored**	.65	.20
2273	A1643	22c **multicolored**	1.40	.20
2274	A1644	22c **multicolored**	.80	.20
a.		Bklt. pane of 10 (#2268-2271, 2273-2274, 2 each #2267, 2272)	10.00	5.00

UNITED WAY, 100th ANNIV.

Six Profiles
A1645

Designed by Jerry Pinkney.

LITHOGRAPHED & ENGRAVED
Plates of 200 in four panes of 50.

1987, Apr. 28　　　Tagged　　　Perf. 11

2275	A1645	22c **multicolored**	.40	.20
		P# block of 4, 6#	1.90	—
		Zip block of 4	1.65	—

A1646

A1647

A1648

A1649

Pheasant — A1649a

Grosbeak — A1649b

Owl — A1649c

Honeybee — A1649d

Designs: Nos. 2276, 2278, 2280, Peter Cocci. Nos. 2277, 2279, 2282, Robert McCall. Nos. 2281, 2283-2285, Chuck Ripper.

PHOTOGRAVURE (Nos. 2276-2279)
Panes of 100

1987-88		Tagged	Perf. 11	
2276	A1646	22c multicolored, May 9	.40	.20
		P# block of 4, 4#	1.90	—
		Zip block of 4	1.65	—
a.		Booklet pane of 20, Nov. 30	8.50	—
b.		As "a," vert. pair, imperf. btwn.	1,500.	
c.		As "a," miscut and inserted upside down into booklet cover, imperf between stamps and right selvage	—	
2277	A1647	(25c) multi, Mar. 22, 1988	.45	.20
		P# block of 4, 4#	2.00	—
		Zip block of 4	1.85	—
2278	A1648	25c multi, May 6, 1988	.45	.20
		P# block of 4, 4#	1.90	—
		Zip block of 4	1.85	—
		Pair with full vert. gutter between	125.00	

COIL STAMPS
Perf. 10 Vert.

2279	A1647	(25c) multi, Mar. 22, 1988	.45	.20
		Pair	.90	.20
		P# strip of 5, #1111	2.75	
		P# strip of 5, #1211	3.25	
		P# strip of 5, #1222	2.75	
		P# strip of 5, #2222	3.25	
		P# single, #1111	—	.50
		P# single, #1211	—	1.10
		P# single, #1222	—	.80
		P# single, #2222	—	3.25
a.		Imperf., pair	60.00	—

ENGRAVED

2280	A1649	25c multi, large block tagging, May 20, 1988	.45	.20
		Pair	.90	.20
		P# strip of 5, #1	3.50	
		P# strip of 5, #2-5	3.00	
		P# strip of 5, #7	3.50	
		P# strip of 5, #8	3.00	
		P# strip of 5, #9	3.50	
		P# single, #1	—	2.50
		P# single, #2-5	—	.75
		P# single, #7	—	2.00
		P# single, #8	—	.75
		P# single, #9	—	2.00
a.		Prephosphored uncoated paper with embedded tagging showing a mottled appearance Feb. 14, 1989	.45	.20
		P# strip of 5, #1	8.50	
		P# strip of 5, #2, 3	3.00	
		P# strip of 5, #5	3.50	
		P# strip of 5, #6	4.00	
		P# strip of 5, #7-11, 13-14	3.00	
		P# strip of 5, #15	3.50	
		P# single, #1	—	7.00
		P# single, #2	—	.60
		P# single, #3	—	.60
		P# single, #5	—	1.25
		P# single, #6	—	5.25

	P# single, #7-11, 13-14	—	.60
	P# single, #15	—	2.00
b.	Imperf., pair, large block tagging	25.00	—
c.	Imperf., pair, prephosphored uncoated paper with embedded tagging showing a mottled appearance	10.00	
d.	Tagging omitted	5.00	
e.	Black trees	100.00	—
	P# strip of 5, #4, 5, 9	700.00	
f.	Pair, imperf. between	450.00	—

LITHOGRAPHED AND ENGRAVED

2281	A1649d	25c multi, small block tagging Sept. 2, 1988	.45	.20
		Pair	.90	.20
		P# strip of 5, #1	3.50	
		P# single, #1	—	.50
a.		As No. 2281, imperf., pair P#1-2	45.00	
b.		Black (engr.) omitted	50.00	—
c.		Black (litho.) omitted	450.00	
d.		Pair, imperf. between	700.00	—
e.		Yellow (litho.) omitted	1,000.	
f.		Large block tagging	.45	.20
		Pair	.90	
		P# strip of 5, #2	3.50	
		P# single, #2	—	.50
g.		As "f," imperf, pair	45.00	
h.		As "f," tagging omitted	85.00	

NORTH AMERICAN WILDLIFE ISSUE — A1650-A1699

No. 2281h can be distinguished as having come from the large block tagging stamp by its deeper colors and jet black "25," which is a characteristic of the plate 2 large block tagged printing.

No. 2281 from plate #1 is known with two types of "1" on the plate-numbered stamps. The original tall "1" was later shortened manually by removing the top of the "1," including the serif, so it would not penetrate the design. Value of plate # strip of 5 with tall "1," $20.

Beware of stamps with traces of the litho. black that are offered as No. 2281c.

Vertical pairs or blocks of No. 2281 and imperfs. with the engr. black missing are from printer's waste.

BOOKLET STAMPS

Printed by American Bank Note Co. (#2283)

PHOTOGRAVURE
Perf. 10, 11 (#2283)

2282	A1647	(25c) multi, *Mar. 22, 1988*	.50	.20
a.		Booklet pane of 10	6.50	3.50
		Scored perforations	6.50	—
2283	A1649a	25c multi, *Apr. 29, 1988*	.50	.20
a.		Booklet pane of 10	6.00	3.50
b.		25c multicolored, red removed		
		from sky	6.50	.20
c.		As "b," bklt. pane of 10	65.00	—
d.		Vert. pair, imperf. btwn.		

Imperf. panes exist from printers waste, and a large number exist. No. 2283d resulted from a foldover. Non-foldover pairs and multiples are printer's waste.

2284	A1649b	25c multi, *May 28, 1988*	.50	.20
2285	A1649c	25c multi, *May 28, 1988*	.50	.20
b.		Bklt. pane of 10, 5 each #2284-		
		2285	5.00	3.50
d.		Pair, Nos. 2284-2285	1.10	.25
e.		As "d," tagging omitted	12.50	
2285A	A1648	25c multi, *July 5, 1988*	.50	.20
c.		Booklet pane of 6	3.00	2.00

NORTH AMERICAN WILDLIFE

Illustration reduced.

Designed by Chuck Ripper.

PHOTOGRAVURE
Plates of 200 in four panes of 50.

1987, June 13			**Tagged**	**Perf. 11**	
2286	A1650	22c	Barn swallow	1.00	.50
2287	A1651	22c	Monarch butterfly	1.00	.50
2288	A1652	22c	Bighorn sheep	1.00	.50
2289	A1653	22c	Broad-tailed hummingbird	1.00	.50
2290	A1654	22c	Cottontail	1.00	.50
2291	A1655	22c	Osprey	1.00	.50
2292	A1656	22c	Mountain lion	1.00	.50
2293	A1657	22c	Luna moth	1.00	.50
2294	A1658	22c	Mule deer	1.00	.50
2295	A1659	22c	Gray squirrel	1.00	.50
2296	A1660	22c	Armadillo	1.00	.50
2297	A1661	22c	Eastern chipmunk	1.00	.50
2298	A1662	22c	Moose	1.00	.50
2299	A1663	22c	Black bear	1.00	.50
2300	A1664	22c	Tiger swallowtail	1.00	.50
2301	A1665	22c	Bobwhite	1.00	.50
2302	A1666	22c	Ringtail	1.00	.50
2303	A1667	22c	Red-winged blackbird	1.00	.50
2304	A1668	22c	American lobster	1.00	.50
2305	A1669	22c	Black-tailed jack rabbit	1.00	.50
2306	A1670	22c	Scarlet tanager	1.00	.50
2307	A1671	22c	Woodchuck	1.00	.50
2308	A1672	22c	Roseate spoonbill	1.00	.50
2309	A1673	22c	Bald eagle	1.00	.50
2310	A1674	22c	Alaskan brown bear	1.00	.50
2311	A1675	22c	Iiwi	1.00	.50
2312	A1676	22c	Badger	1.00	.50
2313	A1677	22c	Pronghorn	1.00	.50
2314	A1678	22c	River otter	1.00	.50
2315	A1679	22c	Ladybug	1.00	.50
2316	A1680	22c	Beaver	1.00	.50
2317	A1681	22c	White-tailed deer	1.00	.50
2318	A1682	22c	Blue jay	1.00	.50
2319	A1683	22c	Pika	1.00	.50
2320	A1684	22c	American buffalo	1.00	.50
2321	A1685	22c	Snowy egret	1.00	.50
2322	A1686	22c	Gray wolf	1.00	.50
2323	A1687	22c	Mountain goat	1.00	.50
2324	A1688	22c	Deer mouse	1.00	.50
2325	A1689	22c	Black-tailed prairie dog	1.00	.50
2326	A1690	22c	Box turtle	1.00	.50
2327	A1691	22c	Wolverine	1.00	.50
2328	A1692	22c	American elk	1.00	.50
2329	A1693	22c	California sea lion	1.00	.50
2330	A1694	22c	Mockingbird	1.00	.50
2331	A1695	22c	Raccoon	1.00	.50
2332	A1696	22c	Bobcat	1.00	.50
2333	A1697	22c	Black-footed ferret	1.00	.50
2334	A1698	22c	Canada goose	1.00	.50
2335	A1699	22c	Red fox	1.00	.50
a.		A1650-A1699 Pane of 50, #2286-		
		2335	50.00	35.00
2286b-2335b		Any single, red omitted	2,500.	

RATIFICATION OF THE CONSTITUTION BICENTENNIAL

Dec 7, 1787　USA
Delaware 22

A1700

22 USA
Dec 12, 1787
Pennsylvania

A1701

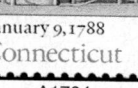
Dec 18, 1787　USA
New Jersey 22

A1702

22 USA
January 2, 1788
Georgia

A1703

22 USA
January 9, 1788
Connecticut

A1704

22 USA
Feb 6, 1788
Massachusetts

A1705

April 28, 1788　USA
Maryland 22

A1706

25 USA
May 23, 1788
South Carolina

A1707

25 USA
June 21, 1788
New Hampshire

A1708

June 25, 1788　USA
Virginia 25

A1709

July 26, 1788　USA
New York 25

A1710

25 USA
November 21, 1789
North Carolina

A1711

25 USA
May 29, 1790
Rhode Island

A1712

Designers: Nos. 2336-2337, 2341 Richard Sheaff. No. 2338, Jim Lamb. No. 2339, Greg Harlin. No. 2340, Christopher Calle. No. 2342, Stephen Hustvedt. Nos. 2343, 2347, Bob Timberlake. No. 2344, Thomas Szumowski. No. 2345, Pierre Mion. No. 2346, Bradbury Thompson. No. 2348, Robert Brangwynne.

Printed by the Bureau of Engraving & Printing, J.W. Fergusson and Sons (Nos. 2337, 2338), American Bank Note Co. (Nos. 2339, 2343-2344, 2347).

LITHOGRAPHED & ENGRAVED, PHOTOGRAVURE (#2337-2339, 2343-2344, 2347), ENGRAVED (#2341).

Plates of 200 in four panes of 50.

1987-90			**Tagged**		**Perf. 11**	
2336	A1700	22c	multi, *July 4*		.60	.20
			P# block of 4, 5#		2.75	—
			Zip block of 4		2.50	—
2337	A1701	22c	multi, *Aug. 26*		.60	.20
			P# block of 4, 5#+A		2.75	—
			Zip block of 4		2.50	—
2338	A1702	22c	multi, *Sept. 11*		.60	.20
			P# block of 4, 5#+A		2.75	—
			Zip block of 4		2.50	—
a.			Black (engr.) omitted		5,000.	
2339	A1703	22c	multi, *Jan. 6, 1988*		.60	.20
			P# block of 4, 5#+A		2.75	—
			Zip block of 4		2.50	—
2340	A1704	22c	multi, *Jan. 9, 1988*		.60	.20
			P# block of 4, 5#		2.75	—
			Zip block of 4		2.50	—
2341	A1705	22c	dark blue & dark red, *Feb.*			
			6, 1988		.60	.20
			P# block of 4, 1#		2.75	—
			Zip block of 4		2.50	—
2342	A1706	22c	multi, *Feb. 15, 1988*		.60	.20
			P# block of 4, 6#		2.75	—
			Zip block of 4		2.50	—
2343	A1707	25c	multi, *May 23, 1988*		.60	.20
			P# block of 4, 5#+A		2.75	—
			Zip block of 4		2.50	—
a.			Strip of 3, vert. imperf btwn.		12,500.	
b.			Red missing (PS)			
2344	A1708	25c	multi, *June 21, 1988*		.60	.20
			P# block of 4, 4#+A		2.75	—
			Zip block of 4		2.50	—
2345	A1709	25c	multi, *June 25, 1988*		.60	.20
			P# block of 4, 5#		2.75	—
			Zip block of 4		2.50	—
2346	A1710	25c	multi, *July 26, 1988*		.60	.20
			P# block of 4, 5#		2.75	—
			Zip block of 4		2.50	—
2347	A1711	25c	multi, *Aug. 22, 1989*		.60	.20
			P# block of 4, 5#+A		2.75	—
			Zip block of 4		2.50	—
2348	A1712	25c	multi, *May 29, 1990*		.60	.20
			P# block of 4, 7#		3.00	—
			Zip block of 4		2.50	—
			Nos. 2336-2348 (13)		7.80	2.60

No. 2343b resulted either from a shifting of all colors or from a shift of both the perforations and the cutting of the pane.

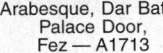

Arabesque, Dar Batha
Palace Door,
Fez — A1713

William Faulkner (1897-
1962),
Novelist — A1714

US-MOROCCO DIPLOMATIC RELATIONS, 200th ANNIV.

Designed by Howard Paine.

LITHOGRAPHED & ENGRAVED
Plates of 200 in four panes of 50.

1987, July 17	Tagged	Perf. 11	
2349 A1713 22c **scarlet & black**		.50	.20
	P# block of 4, 2#	2.10	—
	Zip block of 4	2.00	—
a.	Black (engr.) omitted	250.00	

See Morocco No. 642.

LITERARY ARTS SERIES

Designed by Bradbury Thompson.

ENGRAVED
Plates of 200 in four panes of 50

1987, Aug. 3	Tagged	Perf. 11	
2350 A1714 22c **bright green**		.55	.20
	P# block of 4	2.75	—
	Zip block of 4	2.25	—

Used untagged imperfs exist from printer's waste.

AMERICAN FOLK ART SERIES
Lacemaking

A1715

A1716

A1717

A1718

Designed by Libby Thiel.

LITHOGRAPHED & ENGRAVED
Plates of 160 in four panes of 40.

1987, Aug. 14	Tagged	Perf. 11	
2351 A1715 22c **ultra & white**		.45	.20
2352 A1716 22c **ultra & white**		.45	.20
2353 A1717 22c **ultra & white**		.45	.20
2354 A1718 22c **ultra & white**		.45	.20
a.	Block of 4, #2351-2354	1.90	1.90
	P# block of 4, 4#	3.25	—
	Zip block of 4	2.00	—
b.	As "a," white omitted	500.00	
c.	Single stamp, white omitted	—	

DRAFTING OF THE CONSTITUTION BICENTENNIAL
Excerpts from the Preamble

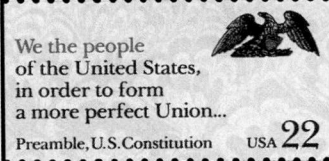
A1719

A1720

A1721

A1722

A1723

Designed by Bradbury Thompson.

BOOKLET STAMPS
PHOTOGRAVURE

1987, Aug. 28	Tagged	Perf. 10 Horiz.	
2355 A1719 22c **multicolored**		.90	.20
a.	Grayish green (background) omitted		
2356 A1720 22c **multicolored**		.90	.20
a.	Grayish green (background) omitted		
2357 A1721 22c **multicolored**		.90	.20
a.	Grayish green (background) omitted		
2358 A1722 22c **multicolored**		.90	.20
a.	Grayish green (background) omitted		
2359 A1723 22c **multicolored**		.90	.20
a.	Bklt. pane of 5, #2355-2359	4.50	2.25
b.	Grayish green (background) omitted		

A1724

A1725

SIGNING OF THE CONSTITUTION

Designed by Howard Koslow.

LITHOGRAPHED & ENGRAVED
Plates of 200 in four panes of 50.

1987, Sept. 17	Tagged	Perf. 11	
2360 A1724 22c **multicolored**		.55	.20
	P# block of 4, 6#	2.75	—
	Zip block of 4	2.25	—

CERTIFIED PUBLIC ACCOUNTING

Designed by Lou Nolan.

LITHOGRAPHED & ENGRAVED
Plates of 200 in four panes of 50.

1987, Sept. 21	Tagged	Perf. 11	
2361 A1725 22c **multicolored**		1.00	.20
	P# block of 4, 5#	5.50	—
	Zip block of 4	4.00	—
a.	Black (engr.) omitted	675.00	

LOCOMOTIVES

Stourbridge
Lion, 1829
A1726

Best Friend
of
Charleston,
183
A1727

John Bull,
1831
A1728

Brother
Jonathan,
1832
A1729

Gowan &
Marx, 1839
A1730

Designed by Richard Leech.

BOOKLET STAMPS
LITHOGRAPHED & ENGRAVED

1987, Oct. 1	Tagged	Perf. 10 Horiz.	
2362 A1726 22c **multicolored**		.55	.20
2363 A1727 22c **multicolored**		.55	.20
2364 A1728 22c **multicolored**		.55	.20

2365	A1729 22c **multicolored**	.55	.20
a.	Red omitted	1,100.	225.00
2366	A1730 22c **multicolored**	.55	.20
a.	Bklt. pane of 5, #2362-2366	2.75	2.50
b.	As No. 2366, black (engr.) omitted (single)	—	
c.	As No. 2366, blue omitted (single)	—	

CHRISTMAS

Moroni
Madonna — A1731

Christmas
Ornaments — A1732

Designed by Bradbury Thompson (No. 2367) and Jim Dean (No. 2368).

PHOTOGRAVURE
Plates of 800 in eight panes of 100.

1987, Oct. 23	**Tagged**	**Perf. 11**	
2367	A1731 22c **multicolored**	.45	.20
	P# block of 4, 6#	2.25	—
	Zip block of 4	1.90	—
2368	A1732 22c **multicolored**	.45	.20
	P# block of 4, 6#	2.10	—
	Zip block of 4	1.90	—
	Pair with full vert. gutter between	—	

1988 WINTER OLYMPICS, CALGARY

Skiing — A1733

Designed by Bart Forbes.

Printed by the American Bank Note Company

PHOTOGRAVURE
Plates of 200 in four panes of 50.

1988, Jan. 10	**Tagged**	**Perf. 11**	
2369	A1733 22c **multicolored**	.50	.20
	P# block of 4, 4#+A	3.00	—
	Zip block of 4	2.10	—

AUSTRALIA BICENTENNIAL

Caricature of an
Australian Koala and
an American Bald
Eagle — A1734

Designed by Roland Harvey.

PHOTOGRAVURE
Plates of 160 in four panes of 40.

1988, Jan. 26	**Tagged**	**Perf. 11**	
2370	A1734 22c **multicolored**	.45	.20
	P# block of 4, 5#	2.10	—
	Zip block of 4	1.90	—
	See Australia No. 1052.		

BLACK HERITAGE SERIES

James Weldon Johnson
(1871-1938), Author and
Lyricist — A1735

Designed by Thomas Blackshear.

Printed by the American Bank Note Co.

PHOTOGRAVURE
Plates of 200 in four panes of 50.

1988, Feb. 2		**Tagged**	
2371	A1735 22c **multicolored**	.50	.20
	P# block of 4, 5#+A	2.60	—
	Zip block of 4	2.10	—
a.	Tagging omitted	—	

CATS

Siamese and
Exotic
Shorthair
A1736

Abyssinian and
Himalayan
A1737

Maine Coon
and Burmese
A1738

American
Shorthair
and Persian
A1739

Designed by John Dawson.

Printed by the American Bank Note Co.

PHOTOGRAVURE
Plates of 160 in four panes of 40.

1988, Feb. 5		**Tagged**	
2372	A1736 22c **multicolored**	.70	.20
2373	A1737 22c **multicolored**	.70	.20
2374	A1738 22c **multicolored**	.70	.20
2375	A1739 22c **multicolored**	.70	.20
a.	Block of 4, #2372-2375	2.80	1.90
	P# block of 4, 5#+A	4.00	—
	Zip block of 4	3.00	—

AMERICAN SPORTS

Knute Rockne (1883-1931), Notre Dame football coach.

Francis Ouimet (1893-1967), 1st amateur golfer to win the US Open championship.

A1740   A1741

Designed by Peter Cocci and Thomas Hipschen.

LITHOGRAPHED & ENGRAVED
Plates of 200 in four panes of 50.

1988, Mar. 9		**Tagged**	
2376	A1740 22c **multicolored**	.50	.20
	P# block of 4, 7#	2.60	—
	Zip block of 4	2.10	—

Designed by M. Gregory Rudd.
Printed by the American Bank Note Co.

PHOTOGRAVURE
Plates of 200 in four panes of 50.

1988, June 13		**Tagged**	
2377	A1741 25c **multicolored**	.60	.20
	P# block of 4, 5#+A	3.00	—
	Zip block of 4	2.50	—

LOVE ISSUE
Roses

A1742

A1743

Designed by Richard Sheaff.

PHOTOGRAVURE
Plates of 400 in four panes of 100 (25c).
Plates of 200 in four panes of 50 (45c).

1988		**Tagged**	
2378	A1742 25c **multicolored**, *July 4*	.50	.20
	P# block of 4, 5#	2.25	—
	Zip block of 4	2.10	—
	Pair with full horiz. gutter between	—	
a.	Imperf., pair	2,000.	
2379	A1743 45c **multicolored**, *Aug. 8*	.85	.20
	P# block of 4, 4#	3.75	—
	Zip block of 4	3.50	—

1988 SUMMER OLYMPICS, SEOUL

Gymnastic
Rings — A1744

Designed by Bart Forbes.

PHOTOGRAVURE
Plates of 200 in four panes of 50

1988, Aug. 19		**Tagged**	
2380	A1744 25c **multicolored**	.50	.20
	P# block of 4, 5#	2.25	—
	Zip block of 4	2.10	—

CLASSIC AUTOMOBILES

1928
Locomobile
A1745

1929 Pierce-Arrow — A1746

1931 Cord
A1747

1932
Packard
A1748

1935 Duesenberg — A1749

Designed by Ken Dallison.

LITHOGRAPHED & ENGRAVED
BOOKLET STAMPS

1988, Aug. 25		Tagged	Perf. 10 Horiz.	
2381	A1745	25c **multicolored**	.80	.20
2382	A1746	25c **multicolored**	.80	.20
2383	A1747	25c **multicolored**	.80	.20
2384	A1748	25c **multicolored**	.80	.20
2385	A1749	25c **multicolored**	.80	.20
a.		Bklt. pane of 5, #2381-2385	6.00	3.50

ANTARCTIC EXPLORERS

Nathaniel
Palmer (1799-
1877)
A1750

Lt. Charles
Wilkes (1798-
1877)
A1751

Richard E.
Byrd (1888-
1957)
A1752

Lincoln
Ellsworth
(1880-1951)
A1753

Designed by Dennis Lyall.

Printed by the American Bank Note Co.

PHOTOGRAVURE
Plates of 160 in four panes of 40.

1988, Sept. 14		Tagged	Perf. 11	
2386	A1750	25c **multicolored**	.65	.20
2387	A1751	25c **multicolored**	.65	.20
2388	A1752	25c **multicolored**	.65	.20
2389	A1753	25c **multicolored**	.65	.20
a.		Block of 4, #2386-2389	2.75	2.00
		P# block of 4, 6#+A	4.50	
		Zip block of 4	3.00	
b.		As "a," black omitted	1,250.	
c.		As "a," imperf. horiz.	2,250.	

AMERICAN FOLK ART SERIES
Carousel Animals

Deer — A1754

Horse — A1755

Camel — A1756

Goat — A1757

Designed by Paul Calle.

LITHOGRAPHED & ENGRAVED
Plates of 200 in four panes of 50.

1988, Oct. 1		Tagged	Perf. 11	
2390	A1754	25c **multicolored**	.75	.20
2391	A1755	25c **multicolored**	.75	.20
2392	A1756	25c **multicolored**	.75	.20
2393	A1757	25c **multicolored**	.75	.20
a.		Block of 4, #2390-2393	3.00	2.00
		P# block of 4, 7#	4.00	
		Zip block of 4	3.25	
b.		As "a," red omitted	—	

EXPRESS MAIL RATE

Eagle and Moon — A1758

Designed by Ned Seidler.

LITHOGRAPHED & ENGRAVED
Panes of 20

1988, Oct. 4		Tagged	Perf. 11	
2394	A1758	$8.75 **multicolored**	13.50	8.00
		P# block of 4, 7#	60.00	—

SPECIAL OCCASIONS

Happy
Birthday
A1759

Best
Wishes
A1760

Thinking of
You
A1761

Love You
A1762

Designed by Harry Zelenko.

Printed by the American Bank Note Co.

BOOKLET STAMPS
PHOTOGRAVURE

1988, Oct. 22		Tagged	Perf. 11	
2395	A1759	25c **multicolored**	.50	.20
2396	A1760	25c **multicolored**	.50	.20
a.		Bklt. pane of 6, 3 #2395 + 3 #2396 with gutter between	3.50	3.25
2397	A1761	25c **multicolored**	.50	.20
2398	A1762	25c **multicolored**	.50	.20
a.		Bklt. pane of 6, 3 #2397 + 3 #2398 with gutter between	3.50	3.25
b.		As "a," imperf. horiz.	—	
c.		As "a," imperf.	—	

CHRISTMAS

Madonna and Child, by Botticelli — A1763

One-horse Open Sleigh and Village Scene — A1764

"Missing Curlicue on Sleigh Runner" Cylinder Flaw

Designed by Bradbury Thompson (No. 2399) and Joan Landis (No. 2400).

LITHOGRAPHED & ENGRAVED (No. 2399), PHOTOGRAVURE (No. 2400)
Plates of 300 in 6 Panes of 50

1988, Oct. 20		Tagged		Perf. 11½
2399 A1763 25c multicolored			.50	.20
	P# block of 4, 5+1#		2.25	—
	Zip, copyright block of 4		2.10	—
	Pair with full vert. gutter btwn.		—	
a.	Gold omitted		25.00	
2400 A1764 25c multicolored			.50	.20
	P# block of 4, 5#		2.25	—
	Zip, copyright block of 4		2.10	—
	Pair with full vert. gutter btwn.		—	
	Cylinder flaw (missing curlicue on sleigh runner, 11111 UR19)		9.00	

MONTANA STATEHOOD, 100th ANNIV.

C.M. Russell and Friends, by Charles M. Russell (1865-1926) A1765

Designed by Bradbury Thompson.

LITHOGRAPHED & ENGRAVED
Plates of 200 in four panes of 50.

1989, Jan. 15		Tagged		Perf. 11
2401 A1765 25c multicolored			.55	.20
	P# block of 4, 5#		2.75	—
	Zip block of 4		2.25	—

Imperfs without gum exist from printer's waste.

BLACK HERITAGE SERIES

Asa Philip Randolph (1889-1979), Labor and Civil Rights Leader — A1766

Designed by Thomas Blackshear.

PHOTOGRAVURE
Plates of 200 in four panes of 50.

1989, Feb. 3		Tagged		Perf. 11
2402 A1766 25c multicolored			.50	.20
	P# block of 4, 5#		2.50	—
	Zip block of 4		2.10	—

NORTH DAKOTA STATEHOOD, 100th ANNIV.

Grain Elevator on the Prairie A1767

Designed by Wendell Minor.

Printed by the American Bank Note Co.

PHOTOGRAVURE
Plates of 200 in four panes of 50.

1989, Feb. 21		Tagged		Perf. 11
2403 A1767 25c multicolored			.50	.20
	P# block of 4, 4#+A		3.00	—
	Zip block of 4		2.10	—

WASHINGTON STATEHOOD, 100th ANNIV.

Mt. Rainier — A1768

Designed by Howard Rogers.

Printed by the American Bank Note Co.

PHOTOGRAVURE
Plates of 200 in four panes of 50.

1989, Feb. 22		Tagged		Perf. 11
2404 A1768 25c multicolored			.50	.20
	P# block of 4, 4#+A		2.25	—
	Zip block of 4		2.10	—

STEAMBOATS

Experiment, 1788-90 — A1769

Phoenix, 1809 A1770

New Orleans, 1812 A1771

Washington, 1816 — A1772

Walk in the Water, 1818 A1773

Designed by Richard Schlecht.

LITHOGRAPHED & ENGRAVED
BOOKLET STAMPS
Perf. 10 Horiz. on 1 or 2 Sides

1989, Mar. 3			Tagged	
2405 A1769 25c multicolored			.50	.20
2406 A1770 25c multicolored			.50	.20
2407 A1771 25c multicolored			.50	.20
2408 A1772 25c multicolored			.50	.20
2409 A1773 25c multicolored			.50	.20
a.	Booklet pane of 5, #2405-2409		2.50	1.75
b.	As "a," tagging omitted			

No. 122 — A1774

Arturo Toscanini (1867-1957), Conductor — A1775

WORLD STAMP EXPO '89
Nov. 17-Dec. 3. Washington, D.C.

Designed by Richard Sheaff.

LITHOGRAPHED & ENGRAVED
Plates of 200 in four panes of 50.

1989, Mar. 16		Tagged		Perf. 11
2410 A1774 25c grayish brn, blk & car rose			.50	.20
	P# block of 4, 4#		2.25	—
	Zip block of 4		2.10	—

PERFORMING ARTS

Designed by Jim Sharpe

Printed by the American Bank Note Co.

PHOTOGRAVURE
Plates of 200 in four panes of 50.

1989, Mar. 25		Tagged		Perf. 11
2411 A1775 25c multicolored			.50	.20
	P# block of 4, 5#+A		2.25	—
	Zip block of 4		2.10	—

CONSTITUTION BICENTENNIAL SERIES

House of Representatives A1776

Senate A1777

Executive
Branch — A1778

Supreme
Court — A1779

Designed by Howard Koslow.

LITHOGRAPHED & ENGRAVED
Plates of 200 in four panes of 50.

1989-90		Tagged		Perf. 11	
2412	A1776 25c	**multi,** *Apr. 4, 1989*		.50	.20
		P# block of 4, 4#		2.25	
		Zip block of 4		2.10	—
2413	A1777 25c	**multi,** *Apr. 6, 1989*		.50	.20
		P# block of 4, 4#		2.75	
		Zip block of 4		2.10	—
2414	A1778 25c	**multi,** *Apr. 16, 1989*		.50	.20
		P# block of 4, 4#		2.25	
		Zip block of 4		2.10	—
2415	A1779 25c	**multi,** *Feb. 2, 1990*		.50	.20
		P# block of 4, 4#		2.25	
		Zip block of 4		2.10	—

SOUTH DAKOTA STATEHOOD, 100th ANNIV.

Pasque
Flowers,
Pioneer
Woman and
Sod House on
Grasslands
A1780

Designed by Marian Henjum.

Printed by the American Bank Note Co.

PHOTOGRAVURE
Plates of 200 in four panes of 50.

1989, May 3		Tagged		Perf. 11	
2416	A1780 25c	**multicolored**		.60	.20
		P# block of 4, 4#+A		3.00	
		Zip block of 4		2.50	—

AMERICAN SPORTS

Henry Louis "Lou" Gehrig
(1903-1941), New York
Yankee Baseball
Player — A1781

Designed by Bart Forbes.

Printed by the American Bank Note Co.

PHOTOGRAVURE
Plates of 200 in four panes of 50.

1989, June 10		Tagged		Perf. 11	
2417	A1781 25c	**multicolored**		.60	.20
		P# block of 4, 6#+A		3.00	—
		Zip block of 4		2.50	

LITERARY ARTS SERIES

Ernest Miller Hemingway
(1899-1961), Nobel Prize
winner for Literature in
1954 — A1782

Designed by M. Gregory Rudd.

Printed by the American Bank Note Co.

PHOTOGRAVURE
Plates of 200 in four panes of 50.

1989, July 17		Tagged		Perf. 11	
2418	A1782 25c	**multicolored**		.50	.20
		P# block of 4, 5#+A		2.25	
		Zip block of 4		2.10	—
a.		Vert. pair, imperf horiz.		1,500.	

Imperforates on gummed stamp paper, including gutter pairs and blocks, are proofs from the ABNCo. archives. See No. 2418P in Proofs section.

MOON LANDING, 20TH ANNIVERSARY

Raising of the
Flag on the Lunar
Surface, July 20,
1969 — A1783

Designed by Christopher Calle.

LITHOGRAPHED & ENGRAVED
Panes of 20

1989, July 20		Tagged		Perf. 11x11½	
2419	A1783 $2.40	**multicolored**		4.75	2.00
		P# block of 4, 6#		20.00	
		Pane of 20		100.00	
a.		Black (engr.) omitted		2,000.	
b.		Imperf., pair		650.00	
c.		Black (litho.) omitted		2,250.	

No. 2419 exists with a gray background instead of the normal dark blue. Some of these may have been caused by a chemical wiping of the blue plate. However, the same or extremely similar stamps can be produced by exposing normal stamps to sunlight or fluorescent light for varying time periods.

LETTER CARRIERS

A1784

Designed by Jack Davis.

Printed by the American Bank Note Co.

PHOTOGRAVURE
Plates of 160 in four panes of 40.

1989, Aug. 30		Tagged		Perf. 11	
2420	A1784 25c	**multicolored**		.50	.20
		P# block of 4, 5#+A		2.25	
		Zip block of 4		2.10	—

CONSTITUTION BICENTENNIAL

Bill of Rights — A1785

Designed by Lou Nolan.

LITHOGRAPHED & ENGRAVED
Plates of 200 in four panes of 50.

1989, Sept. 25		Tagged		Perf. 11	
2421	A1785 25c	**multicolored**		.50	.20
		P# block of 4		3.25	
		Zip block of 4		2.10	—
a.		Black (engr.) omitted		250.00	

PREHISTORIC ANIMALS

Tyrannosaurus
Rex — A1786

Pteranodon
A1787

Stegosaurus
A1788

Brontosaurus
A1789

Designed by John Gurche.

LITHOGRAPHED & ENGRAVED
Plates of 160 in four panes of 40.

1989, Oct. 1		Tagged		Perf. 11	
2422	A1786 25c	**multicolored**		.70	.20
a.		Black (engr.) omitted		80.00	
2423	A1787 25c	**multicolored**		.70	.20
a.		Black (engr.) omitted		80.00	
2424	A1788 25c	**multicolored**		.70	.20
a.		Black (engr.) omitted		80.00	
2425	A1789 25c	**multicolored**		.70	.20
a.		Black (engr.) omitted		80.00	
b.		Block of 4, #2422-2425		2.80	2.00

P# block of 4, 6#   3.50   —
Zip block of 4   3.00   —
c.   As "b," black (engr.) omitted   400.00

The correct scientific name for Brontosaurus is Apatosaurus. No. 2425b is valued in the grade of fine. Very fine blocks exist and sell for approximately $600.

PRE-COLUMBIAN AMERICA ISSUE

Southwest Carved Figure, A.D. 1150-1350 — A1790

Designed by Lon Busch.

Printed by the American Bank Note Company.

PHOTOGRAVURE
Plate of 200 in four panes of 50.

1989, Oct. 12	Tagged		Perf. 11	
2426 A1790 25c **multicolored**			.60	.20
	P# block of 4, 6#+A		3.00	—
	Zip block of 4		2.50	—
a.	Tagging omitted		—	

See No. C121.

CHRISTMAS

Madonna and Child, by Caracci — A1791   Sleigh Full of Presents — A1792

Designed by Bradbury Thompson (#2427 & 2429) and Steven Dohanos (#2428).

Printed by the Bureau of Engraving and Printing (#2427 & 2429) and American Bank Note Company (#2428).

LITHOGRAPHED & ENGRAVED, PHOTOGRAVURE (#2428-2429)
Sheets of 300 in six panes of 50.

1989, Oct. 19	Tagged		Perf. 11½	
2427 A1791 25c **multicolored**			.50	.20
	P# block of 4, 5#		2.25	—
	Zip, copyright block of 4		2.10	—
	Pair with full horiz. gutter between		—	
a.	Booklet pane of 10		5.00	3.50
b.	Red (litho.) omitted		650.00	
c.	As "a," imperf.		—	

	Perf. 11			
2428 A1792 25c **multicolored**			.50	.20
	P# block of 4, 5#+A		2.25	—
	Zip, copyright block of 4		2.10	—
a.	Vert. pair, imperf. horiz.		750.00	

BOOKLET STAMP
Perf. 11½ on 2 or 3 sides

2429 A1792 25c **multicolored**			.50	.20
a.	Booklet pane of 10		5.00	3.50
b.	Vert. pair, imperf between		—	
c.	As "a," imperf between		—	
d.	As "a," red omitted		3,500.	
e.	Imperf., pair		—	

Marked differences exist between Nos. 2428 and 2429: No. 2429 was printed in four colors, No. 2428 in five colors. The runners on the sleigh in No. 2429 are twice as thick as those on No. 2428. On No. 2429 the package at the upper left in the sleigh has a red bow, whereas the same package in No. 2428 has a red and black bow; and the ribbon on the upper right package in No. 2429 is green, whereas the same ribbon in No. 2428 is black.

Eagle and Shield — A1793

Designed by Jay Haiden.

Printed by the American Bank Note Company.

PHOTOGRAVURE
BOOKLET STAMP

1989, Nov. 10	Tagged	Self-Adhesive	*Die Cut*	
2431 A1793 25c **multicolored**			.50	.20
a.	Booklet pane of 18		11.00	
b.	Vert. pair, die cutting omitted between		350.00	
c.	Die cutting omitted, pair		225.00	

Panes sold for $5.
Also available in strips of 18 with stamps spaced for use in affixing machines to service first day covers. Sold for $5.
No. 2431c will include part of the margins around the stamps.
Sold only in 15 test cities (Atlanta, Chicago, Cleveland, Columbus, OH, Dallas, Denver, Houston, Indianapolis, Kansas City, MO, Los Angeles, Miami, Milwaukee, Minneapolis, Phoenix, St. Louis) and through the philatelic agency.

WORLD STAMP EXPO '89
Washington, DC, Nov. 17-Dec. 3

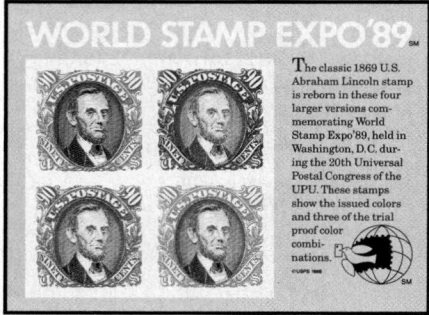

The classic 1869 U.S. Abraham Lincoln stamp is reborn in these four larger versions commemorating World Stamp Expo'89, held in Washington, D.C. during the 20th Universal Postal Congress of the UPU. These stamps show the issued colors and three of the trial proof color combinations.

A1794

Illustration reduced.

Designed by Richard Sheaff.

LITHOGRAPHED & ENGRAVED

1989, Nov. 17	Tagged		*Imperf.*	
2433 A1794	Sheet of 4		11.00	11.00
a.	90c like No. 122		2.75	2.75
b.	90c like No. 132TC (blue frame, brown center)		2.75	2.75
c.	90c like No. 132TC (green frame, blue center)		2.75	2.75
d.	90c like No. 132TC (scarlet frame, blue center)		2.75	2.75
e.	As No. 2433, tagging omitted		—	

20th UPU CONGRESS
Traditional Mail Delivery

Stagecoach, c. 1850 — A1795

Paddlewheel Steamer — A1796

Biplane — A1797

Depot-hack Type Automobile — A1798

Designed by Mark Hess.

LITHOGRAPHED & ENGRAVED
Plates of 160 in four panes of 40.

1989, Nov. 19	Tagged		Perf. 11	
2434 A1795 25c **multicolored**			.50	.20
2435 A1796 25c **multicolored**			.50	.20
2436 A1797 25c **multicolored**			.50	.20
2437 A1798 25c **multicolored**			.50	.20
a.	Block of 4, #2434-2437		2.00	1.75
	P# block of 4, 5#		3.75	—
	Zip block of 4		3.75	—
b.	As "a," dark blue (engr.) omitted		300.00	
c.	As No. 2437a, tagging omitted		—	

No. 2437b is valued in the grade of fine. Very fine blocks exist and sell for approximately $450.

Souvenir Sheet
LITHOGRAPHED & ENGRAVED

1989, Nov. 28	Tagged		*Imperf.*	
2438	Sheet of 4		4.50	3.75
a.	A1795 25c multicolored		1.10	.80
b.	A1796 25c multicolored		1.10	.80
c.	A1797 25c multicolored		1.10	.80
d.	A1798 25c multicolored		1.10	.80
e.	Dark blue & gray (engr.) omitted		5,000.	

20th Universal Postal Union Congress

VALUES FOR HINGED STAMPS AFTER NO. 771
This catalogue does not value unused stamps after No. 771 in hinged condition. Hinged unused stamps from No. 772 to the present are worth considerably less than the values given for unused stamps, which are for never-hinged examples.

IDAHO STATEHOOD, 100th ANNIV.

Mountain Bluebird, Sawtooth Mountains — A1799

Designed by John Dawson.

Printed by the American Bank Note Company.

PHOTOGRAVURE
Plates of 200 in four panes of 50.

1990, Jan. 6	Tagged		Perf. 11	
2439 A1799 25c **multicolored**			.55	.20
	P# block of 4, 5#+A		3.50	—
	Zip block of 4		2.25	—

LOVE

A1800

Designed by Jayne Hertko.

Printed by the U.S. Banknote Company (#2440) and the Bureau of Engraving and Printing (#2441).

PHOTOGRAVURE
Plates of 200 in four panes of 50.

1990, Jan. 18	Tagged	Perf. 12½x13		
2440	A1800	25c **black, bright blue, dark pink & emerald green**	.50	.20
		P# block of 4, 4#	2.25	—
		Zip, copyright block of 4	2.10	—
a.		Imperf., pair	675.00	

BOOKLET STAMP
Perf. 11½ on 2 or 3 sides

2441	A1800	25c **black, ultramarine, bright pink & dark green**	.50	.20
a.		Booklet pane of 10	5.00	3.50
b.		Bright pink omitted	125.00	
c.		As "a," bright pink omitted	1,500.	

No. 2441b may be obtained from booklet panes containing both normal and color-omitted stamps.

BLACK HERITAGE SERIES

Ida B. Wells (1862-1931), Journalist — A1801

Designed by Thomas Blackshear.

Printed by American Bank Note Company.

PHOTOGRAVURE
Plates of 200 in four panes of 50.

1990, Feb. 1	Tagged	Perf. 11		
2442	A1801	25c **multicolored**	.75	.20
		P# block of 4, 5#+A	3.75	—
		Zip block of 4	3.25	—

Beach Umbrella — A1802

Designed by Pierre Mion.

BOOKLET STAMP
PHOTOGRAVURE

1990, Feb. 3	Tagged	Perf. 11		
2443	A1802	15c **multicolored**	.30	.20
a.		Booklet pane of 10	3.00	2.00
b.		Blue omitted	125.00	
c.		As "a," blue omitted	1,250.	

WYOMING STATEHOOD, 100th ANNIV.

High Mountain Meadows, by Conrad Schwiering A1803

Designed by Jack Rosenthal.

LITHOGRAPHED & ENGRAVED
Plates of 200 in four panes of 50.

1990, Feb. 23	Tagged	Perf. 11		
2444	A1803	25c **multicolored**	.80	.20
		P# block of 4, 5#	4.00	—
		Zip block of 4	3.25	—
a.		Black (engr.) omitted	1,250.	

CLASSIC FILMS

Judy Garland and Toto (The Wizard of Oz) — A1804

Clark Gable & Vivien Leigh (Gone With the Wind) — A1805

Gary Cooper (Beau Geste) — A1806

John Wayne (Stagecoach) A1807

Designed by Thomas Blackshear.

Printed by the American Bank Note Company.

PHOTOGRAVURE
Plates of 160 in four panes of 40.

1990, Mar. 23		Tagged	Perf. 11		
2445	A1804	25c **multicolored**	1.50	.20	
2446	A1805	25c **multicolored**	1.50	.20	
2447	A1806	25c **multicolored**	1.50	.20	
2448	A1807	25c **multicolored**	1.50	.20	
a.		Block of 4, #2445-2448	6.00	3.50	
		P# block of 4, 5#+A	6.50	—	
		Zip block of 4	6.25	—	

LITERARY ARTS SERIES

Marianne Moore (1887-1972), Poet — A1808

Designed by M. Gregory Rudd.

Printed by the American Bank Note Company.

PHOTOGRAVURE
Plates of 200 in four panes of 50.

1990, Apr. 18	Tagged	Perf. 11		
2449	A1808	25c **multicolored**	.60	.20
		P# block of 4, 3#+A	2.75	—
		Zip block of 4	2.50	—
a.		All colors missing (EP)		

No. 2449a must be collected se-tenant with a partially printed stamp or in longer horizontal strips with a partially printed stamp and normal stamps.

> **Coil Plate No. Strips of 3**
> Beginning with No. 2123, coil plate no. strips of 3 usually sell at the level of strips of 5 minus the face value of two stamps.

TRANSPORTATION ISSUE

A1810

A1811

A1811a

A1816

A1812

A1822

A1823

A1825

A1827

Designers: 4c, 32c, Richard Schlecht. Nos. 2452, 2452B, 2452D, Susan Sanford. No. 2453, Paul Calle. 10c, David K. Stone. 20c, 23c, Robert Brangwynne. $1, Chuck Hodgson.

Printed by: Guilford Gravure for American Bank Note Co. (No. 2452B), J.W. Fergusson & Sons for Stamp Venturers (No. 2454), Stamp Venturers (No, 2452D), others by BEP.

COIL STAMPS
ENGRAVED, PHOTOGRAVURE (#2452B, 2452D, 2454, 2458)

Tagged, Untagged (Nos. 2452B, 2452D, 2453, 2454, 2457-2458)

1990-95				**Perf. 9.8 Vert.**	
2451	A1810	4c **claret**, Jan. 25, 1991		.20	.20
		Pair		.20	.20
		P# strip of 5, #1		.70	
		P# single, #1		—	.65
a.		Imperf., pair		525.00	
b.		Untagged		.20	.20
		Pair		.20	.20
		P# strip of 5, #1		.80	
		P# single, #1		—	.70
2452	A1811	5c **carmine**, dull gum, Aug. 31		.20	.20
		Pair		.20	.20
		P# strip of 5, #1		.85	
		P# single, #1		—	.85
a.		Untagged, dull gum		.20	.20
		Pair		.20	.20
		P# strip of 5, #1		3.00	
		P# single, #1		—	2.25
		Low gloss gum		.20	
		Pair		.20	
		P# strip of 5, #2		2.25	
		P# single, #2		—	1.60
c.		Imperf., pair		550.00	
2452B	A1811	5c **carmine**, Dec. 8, 1992		.20	.20
		Pair		.25	.20
		P# strip of 5, #A1-A2		1.25	
		P# single, #A1-A2		—	1.10
f.		Printed with luminescent ink		.20	.20
		Pair		.20	.20
		P# strip of 5, #A3		2.75	
		P# single, #A3		—	2.25
2452D	A1811a	5c **carmine**, low gloss gum, Mar. 20, 1995		.20	.20
		Pair		.20	.20
		P# strip of 5, #S1-S2		1.25	
		P# single, #S1-S2		—	1.25
e.		Imperf., pair		135.00	
g.		Printed with luminescent ink, shiny gum		.20	.20
		Pair		.20	.20
		P# strip of 5, #S2		2.25	
		P# single, #S2		—	1.75
		Low gloss gum		.20	
		P# strip of 5, #S3		2.25	
		P# single, #S3		—	2.50
h.		As "g," low gloss gum, imperf. pair		—	
2453	A1812	5c **brown** (Bureau precancel, Additional Nonprofit Postage Paid, in gray), May 25, 1991		.20	.20
		Pair		.50	.20
		P# strip of 5, #1-3		1.25	
		P# single, #1-3		—	.85
a.		Imperf., pair		225.00	
b.		Gray omitted		—	
2454	A1812	5c **red** (Bureau precancel, Additional Nonprofit Postage Paid, in gray), shiny gum, Oct. 22, 1991		.45	.20
		Pair		.90	.20
		P# strip of 5, #S11		1.25	
		P# single, #S11		—	1.00
		Low gloss gum		.65	
		Pair		1.30	
		P# strip of 5, #S11		5.00	
2457	A1816	10c **green** (Bureau precancel, Additional Presort Postage Paid, in gray), May 25, 1991		.35	.20
		Pair		.70	.40
		P# strip of 5, #1		2.00	
		P# single, #1		—	1.25
a.		Imperf., pair		125.00	
b.		All color omitted		—	

No. 2457b must be collected as part of a transitional strip with normal stamps having freak perfs.

2458	A1816	10c **green** (Bureau precancel, Additional Presort Postage Paid, in black), May 25, 1994		.45	.20
		Pair		.90	.40
		P# strip of 5, #11, 22		3.50	
		P# single, #11, 22		—	1.75
2463	A1822	20c **green**, June 9, 1995		.40	.20
		Pair		.80	.20
		P# strip of 5, #1-2		3.00	
		P# single, #1-2		—	2.00
a.		Imperf., pair		90.00	
2464	A1823	23c **dark blue**, prephosphored coated paper with surface tagging showing a solid appearance, dull gum, Apr. 12, 1991		.45	.20
		Pair		.90	.20
		P# strip of 5, #2-3		3.25	
		P# single, #2-3		—	2.00
a.		Prephosphored uncoated paper with embedded tagging showing a mottled appearance, dull gum, 1993		1.20	.20

		Pair		2.40	.20
		P# strip of 5, #3		9.00	
		Shiny gum, 1993		.45	
		Pair		.90	
		P# strip of 5, #3		3.75	
		P# strip of 5, #4		10.00	
		P# strip of 5, #5		4.50	
		P# single, #3-4		—	4.00
		P# single, #5		—	5.50
b.		Imperf., pair		110.00	
2466	A1825	32c **blue**, prephosphored uncoated paper with embedded tagging showing a mottled appearance, shiny gum, June 2, 1995		.80	.20
		Pair		1.60	.30
		P# strip of 5, #2		4.50	
		P# strip of 5, #4		4.75	
		P# strip of 5, #4		5.00	
		P# strip of 5, #5		9.00	
		P# single, #2, 3		—	2.25
		P# single, #4		—	2.75
		P# single, #5		—	3.50
		Low gloss gum		1.10	
		Pair		2.20	
		P# strip of 5, #3		10.00	
		P# strip of 5, #4		13.00	
		P# strip of 5, #5		10.00	
		P# single, #3		—	
		P# single, #4		—	
		P# single, #5		—	
a.		Imperf., pair, shiny gum		475.00	
		Low gloss gum		475.00	
b.		32c **bright blue**, prephosphored uncoated paper with embedded tagging showing a mottled appearance, low gloss gum		3.00	2.25
		Pair		6.00	5.50
		P# strip of 5, #5		95.00	
		P# single, #5		—	110.00

Some specialists refer to No. 2466b as "Bronx blue," and it is considered to be an error of color.

2468	A1827	$1 **blue & scarlet**, overall tagging, dull gum, Apr. 20		2.25	.50
		Pair		4.50	1.00
		P# strip of 5, #1		13.00	
		P# single, #1		—	5.00
a.		Imperf., pair		2,500.	1,350.
b.		Prephosphored uncoated paper with embedded tagging showing a mottled appearance, shiny gum, 1993		2.40	.50
		Pair		4.80	1.00
		P# strip of 5, #3		13.00	
		P# single, #3		—	5.00
c.		Prephosphored coated paper with surface tagging showing a grainy solid appearance, low gloss gum, 1998		3.50	.50
		Pair		7.00	1.00
		P# strip of 5, #3		18.00	
		P# single, #3		—	10.00
		Nos. 2451-2468 (12)		6.15	2.70

Some mint pairs of No. 2468 appear to be imperf. but have faint blind perforations on the gum. Beware of examples with the gum removed.

LIGHTHOUSES

Admiralty Head,
WA — A1829

Cape Hatteras,
NC — A1830

West Quoddy Head,
ME — A1831

American Shoals,
FL — A1832

Sandy Hook, NJ — A1833

Designed by Howard Koslow.

BOOKLET STAMPS
LITHOGRAPHED & ENGRAVED
Perf. 10 Vert. on 1 or 2 sides

				Tagged	
1990, Apr. 26					
2470	A1829	25c **multicolored**		1.90	.20
2471	A1830	25c **multicolored**		1.90	.20
2472	A1831	25c **multicolored**		1.90	.20
2473	A1832	25c **multicolored**		1.90	.20
2474	A1833	25c **multicolored**		1.90	.20
a.		Bklt. pane of 5, #2470-2474		9.50	2.00
b.		As "a," white ("USA 25") omitted		100.00	—

Perforations on Lighthouse booklet panes separate very easily. Careful handling is required.

FLAG

A1834

Designed by Harry Zelenko.

Printed by Avery International Corp.

PHOTOGRAVURE

1990, May 18		**Untagged Self-adhesive *Die Cut* Printed on Plastic**			
2475	A1834	25c **dark red & dark blue**		.55	.25
a.		Pane of 12		6.60	

Sold only in panes of 12; peelable plastic backing inscribed in light ultramarine. Available for a test period of six months at 22 First National Bank automatic teller machines in Seattle.

FLORA and FAUNA

American
Kestrel — A1840

A1841

Eastern
Bluebird — A1842

Fawn — A1843

Cardinal — A1844

Pumpkinseed
Sunfish — A1845

Bobcat
A1846

Blue Jay — A1847

African
Violets — A1849

Pear — A1851

Peach — A1850

Rose — A1853

Red
Squirrel — A1852

Wood Duck — A1848

Pine Cone — A1854

Designers: 1c, 3c, 45c, Michael Matherly. 19c, Peter Cocci. 30c, Robert Giusti. $2, Chuck Ripper.

Printed by: No. 2476 and No. 2478, American Bank Note Co. No. 2477, No. 2479, and No. 2482, Bureau of Engraving & Printing. No. 2480 and No. 2482, Stamp Venturers. No. 2481, Stamp Venturers (engraved) and The Press, Inc. (lithographed).

LITHOGRAPHED
Panes of 100

1990-95		**Untagged**	**Perf. 11, 11.2 (#2477)**	
2476	A1840	1c **multicolored,** *June 22, 1991*	.20	.20
		P# block of 4, 4#+A	.20	
		Zip block of 4	.20	—

Imperforates on gummed stamp paper, plus imperforate and perforated gutter pairs and blocks (including imperforate and perforated gutter pairs and blocks of No. 2476 se-tenant with No. 2478), are proofs from the ABNCo. archives. See Nos. 2476P and 2478P in Proofs section.

2477	A1841	1c **multicolored,** shiny gum, *May 10, 1995*	.20	.20
		P# block of 4, 4#	.20	
		Low gloss gum	.20	
		P# block of 4, 4#	.20	
a.		Tagged (error), shiny gum	.20	
2478	A1842	3c **multicolored,** *June 22, 1991*	.20	.20
		P# block of 4, 4#+A	.30	—
		Zip block of 4	.25	
a.		Vert. pair, imperf horiz.	—	
b.		Double impression of all colors except yellow	—	

Note for No. 2476 also applies to No. 2478.

See Nos. 3032/3053. Compare design A1842 with design A2336.

PHOTOGRAVURE
Plates of 400 in four panes of 100.

		Tagged	**Perf. 11**	
2479	A1843	19c **multicolored,** *Mar. 11, 1991*	.35	.20
		P# block of 4, 5#	1.75	
		Zip block of 4	1.50	—
a.		Tagging omitted	10.00	
b.		Red omitted	725.00	
c.		Imperf, pair	1,000.	

On No. 2479b other colors are shifted.

2480	A1844	30c **multicolored,** *June 22, 1991*	.60	.20
		P# block of 4, 4#+S	2.75	
		Zip block of 4	2.50	—

LITHOGRAPHED & ENGRAVED
Panes of 100
Perf. 11

2481	A1845	45c **multicolored,** *Dec. 2, 1992*	.90	.20
		P# block of 4, 5#+S	4.25	
		Zip block of 4	3.75	—
a.		Black (engr.) omitted	375.00	

Panes of 20

2482	A1846	$2 **multicolored,** *June 1, 1990*	3.50	1.25
		P# block of 4, 5#	14.00	
		Pane of 20	70.00	
a.		Black (engr.) omitted	225.00	
b.		Tagging omitted	12.50	

Designed by Robert Giusti (#2483-2485), Ned Seidler (#2486-2488, 2493-2495A), Michael R. Matherly (#2489), Gyo Fujikawa (#2490), Paul Breeden (#2491), Gyo Fujikawa (#2492).

Printed by Stamp Venturers (#2483, 2492), Bureau of Engraving and Printing (#2484, 2487-2488), J.W. Fergusson & Sons for KCS Industries, Inc. (#2485), KCS Industries (#2486), Dittler Brothers, Inc. (#2489), Stamp Venturers (#2490), Banknote Corporation of America (#2491), Avery-Dennison (#2493-2495, 2495A).

PHOTOGRAVURE
BOOKLET STAMPS

1991-95		**Tagged**	**Perf. 10.9x9.8**	
2483	A1847	20c **multicolored,** *June 15, 1995*	.50	.20
a.		Booklet pane of 10	5.25	2.25
b.		As "a," imperf	—	
		Perf. 10 on 2 or 3 sides		
2484	A1848	29c **black & multi,** overall tagging, *Apr. 12, 1991*	.60	.20
a.		Booklet pane of 10	6.00	3.75
b.		Vert. pair, imperf. horiz.	190.00	
c.		As "b," bklt. pane of 10	950.00	
d.		Prephosphored coated paper with surface tagging showing a solid appearance	.60	.20
e.		As "d," booklet pane of 10	6.00	3.75
f.		Vert. pair, imperf between and with natural straight edge at top or bottom	—	
g.		As "f," bklt. pane of 10	—	
		Perf. 11 on 2 or 3 Sides		
2485	A1848	29c **red & multi,** *Apr. 12, 1991*	.60	.20
a.		Booklet pane of 10	6.00	4.00
b.		Vert. pair, imperf. between	3,000.	
c.		Imperf, pair	2,000.	
		Perf. 10x11 on 2 or 3 Sides		
2486	A1849	29c **multicolored,** *Oct. 8, 1993*	.60	.20
a.		Booklet pane of 10	6.00	4.00
		Perf. 11x10 on 2 or 3 Sides		
2487	A1850	32c **multicolored,** *July 8, 1995*	.65	.20
2488	A1851	32c **multicolored,** *July 8, 1995*	.65	.20
a.		Booklet pane, 5 each #2487-2488	6.50	4.25
b.		Pair, #2487-2488	1.30	.30

1993-95		**Die Cut**	**Tagged**	
2489	A1852	29c **multicolored,** *June 25*	.65	.20
a.		Booklet pane of 18	12.00	
b.		As "a," die cutting omitted	—	

2490	A1853	29c **red, green & black,** *Aug. 19*	.65	.20
a.		Booklet pane of 18	12.00	

Nos. 2489-2490 also available in strips with stamps spaced for use in affixing machines to service first day covers. No plate numbers. Stamps removed from strips are indistinguishable from booklet stamps.

2491	A1854	29c **multicolored,** *Nov. 5*	.60	.20
a.		Booklet pane of 18	11.00	
b.		Horiz. pair, die cutting omitted between	200.00	150.00
c.		Coil with plate # B1	—	6.00
		P# strip of 5, #B1	8.50	

Stamps without plate # from coil strips are indistinguishable from booklet stamps once they are removed from the backing paper.

Serpentine Die Cut 11.3x11.7 on 2, 3 or 4 Sides

2492	A1853	32c **pink, green & black,** prephosphored coated paper *June 2, 1995*	.65	.20
a.		Booklet pane of 20+label	13.00	
b.		Booklet pane of 15+label	9.75	
c.		Horiz. pair, die cutting omitted between	—	
d.		As "a," 2 stamps and parts of 7 others printed on backing liner	—	
e.		Booklet pane of 14	21.00	
f.		Booklet pane of 16	21.00	
g.		Coil with plate # S111	—	5.50
		P# strip of 5, #S111	8.00	
h.		Vert. pair, die cutting omitted between (from No. 2492b)	—	

Nos. 2492, 2492a and 2492b exist on two types of surface-tagged paper that exhibit either a solid or a grainy solid appearance. Values are the same. Nos. 2492e, 2492f and 2492g have tagging with a solid appearance, while Nos. 2492c, 2492d and 2492h have tagging with a grainy solid appearance.

Stamps on plate # strips are separated on backing larger than the stamps. Stamps without plate # from coil strips are indistinguishable from interior position booklet stamps once they are removed from the backing paper.

For booklet panes containing No. 2492f with one stamp removed, see Nos. BK178B, BK178D-BK178E in Booklets section.

Serpentine Die Cut 8.8 on 2, 3 or 4 Sides

2493	A1850	32c **multicolored,** *July 8, 1995*	.65	.20
2494	A1851	32c **multicolored,** *July 8, 1995*	.65	.20
a.		Booklet pane, 10 each #2493-2494+label	13.00	
b.		Pair, #2493-2494	1.30	
c.		As "b," die cutting omitted	—	

COIL STAMPS
Serpentine Die Cut 8.8 Vert.

2495	A1850	32c **multicolored,** *July 8, 1995*	2.00	.20
2495A	A1851	32c **multicolored,** *July 8, 1995*	2.00	.20
b.		Pair, #2495-2495A	4.00	
		P# strip of 5, 3 #2495A, 2 #2495, #PV11111	13.00	
		P# single, #V11111	—	6.00

See Nos. 3048, 3053-3054.

Scott values for used self-adhesive stamps are for examples either on piece or off piece.

OLYMPIANS

Jesse Owens,
1936 — A1855

Ray Ewry,
1900-08
A1856

Hazel Wightman, 1924 — A1857

Eddie Eagan, 1920, 1932 — A1858

Helene Madison, 1932 — A1859

Designed by Bart Forbes.

Printed by the American Bank Note Company.

PHOTOGRAVURE
Panes of 35.

1990, July 6		Tagged	Perf. 11	
2496	A1855	25c multicolored	.60	.20
2497	A1856	25c multicolored	.60	.20
2498	A1857	25c multicolored	.60	.20
2499	A1858	25c multicolored	.60	.20
2500	A1859	25c multicolored	.60	.20
a.		Strip of 5, #2496-2500	3.25	2.50
		P# block of 10, 4#+A	8.00	—
		Zip, inscription block of 10	6.50	—
b.		As "a," blue omitted		

Imperforates on gummed stamp paper, including gutter pairs, strips and blocks, are proofs from the ABNCo. archives. See No. 2500aP in Proofs section.

INDIAN HEADDRESSES

Assiniboin A1860

Cheyenne A1861

Comanche A1862

Flathead A1863

Shoshone A1864

Designed by Lunda Hoyle Gill.

LITHOGRAPHED & ENGRAVED
BOOKLET STAMPS

1990, Aug. 17		Tagged	Perf. 11 on 2 or 3 Sides	
2501	A1860	25c multicolored	1.50	.20
2502	A1861	25c multicolored	1.50	.20
2503	A1862	25c multicolored	1.50	.20
2504	A1863	25c multicolored	1.50	.20
2505	A1864	25c multicolored	1.50	.20
a.		Bklt. pane of 10, 2 each #2501-2505	15.00	7.50
b.		As "a," black (engr.) omitted	3,500.	
c.		Strip of 5, #2501-2505	7.50	2.50
d.		As "a," horiz. imperf. between		

The one example of No. 2505d that has been reported is actually split at the booklet fold and is a block of 4 and a block of 6.

MICRONESIA & MARSHALL ISLANDS

Canoe and Flag of the Federated States of Micronesia A1865

Stick Chart, Canoe and Flag of the Republic of the Marshall Islands A1866

LITHOGRAPHED & ENGRAVED
Sheets of 200 in four panes of 50.

1990, Sept. 28		Tagged	Perf. 11	
2506	A1865	25c multicolored	.50	.20
2507	A1866	25c multicolored	.50	.20
a.		Pair, #2506-2507	1.00	.75
		P# block of 4, 6#	2.75	—
		Zip block of 4	2.10	—
b.		As "a," black (engr.) omitted	2,750.	

See Micronesia Nos. 124-126, Marshall Islands No. 381.

SEA CREATURES

Killer Whales A1867

Northern Sea Lions — A1868

Sea Otter — A1869

Common Dolphin A1870

Designed by Peter Cocci (Nos. 2508, 2511), Vladimir Beilin, USSR (Nos. 2509-2510).

LITHOGRAPHED & ENGRAVED
Sheets of 160 in four panes of 40.

1990, Oct. 3		Tagged	Perf. 11	
2508	A1867	25c multicolored	.55	.20
2509	A1868	25c multicolored	.55	.20
2510	A1869	25c multicolored	.55	.20
2511	A1870	25c multicolored	.55	.20
a.		Block of 4, #2508-2511	2.25	1.90
		P# block of 4, 5#	2.75	—
		Zip block of 4	2.30	—
b.		As "a," black (engr.) omitted	350.00	
c.		As "a," tagging omitted		

See Russia Nos. 5933-5936.

PRE-COLUMBIAN AMERICA ISSUE

Grand Canyon A1871

Designed by Mark Hess.

Printed by the American Bank Note Company.

PHOTOGRAVURE
Plates of 200 in four panes of 50.
(3 panes of #2512, 1 pane of #C127)

1990, Oct. 12		Tagged	Perf. 11	
2512	A1871	25c multicolored	.55	.20
		P# block of 4, 4#+A, UR, LL, LR	2.75	—
		Zip block of 4	2.25	

See No. C127.

DWIGHT D. EISENHOWER, BIRTH CENTENARY

A1872

Designed by Ken Hodges.

Printed by the American Bank Note Company.

PHOTOGRAVURE
Plates of 160 in four panes of 40.

1990, Oct. 13	Tagged	Perf. 11
2513 A1872 25c **multicolored**	.90	.20
P# block of 4, 5#+A	4.00	—
P# block of 8, 5#+A and inscriptions	8.00	—
Zip block of 4	3.75	—

Imperforates on gummed stamp paper are proofs from the ABNCo. archives. See No. 2513P in Proofs section.

CHRISTMAS

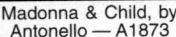

Madonna & Child, by Antonello — A1873

Christmas Tree — A1874

Designed by Bradbury Thompson (#2514) and Libby Thiel (#2515-2516).

Printed by the Bureau of Engraving and Printing or the American Bank Note Company (#2515).

LITHOGRAPHED & ENGRAVED
Sheets of 300 in six panes of 50 (#2414-2415).

1990, Oct. 18	Tagged	Perf. 11½
2514 A1873 25c **multicolored**, large block tagging	.50	.20
P# block of 4, 5#	2.25	—
Zip, copyright block of 4	2.10	—
a. Large block tagging over prephosphored coated paper with surface tagging showing a solid appearance	.50	.20
b. As "a," bklt. pane of 10	5.00	3.25

PHOTOGRAVURE
Perf. 11

2515 A1874 25c **multicolored**	.50	.20
P# block of 4, 4#+A	2.25	—
Zip block of 4	2.10	—
a. Vert. pair, imperf. horiz.	900.00	
b. All colors missing (EP)		

No. 2515b must be collected se-tenant with normal and/or partially printed stamp(s).

BOOKLET STAMP
Perf. 11½x11 on 2 or 3 sides

2516 A1874 25c **multicolored**	.50	.20
a. Booklet pane of 10	5.00	3.25

Marked differences exist between Nos. 2515 and 2516. The background red on No. 2515 is even while that on No. 2516 is splotchy. The bands across the tree and "Greetings" are blue green on No. 2515 and yellow green on No. 2516.

A1875

A1876

Designed by Wallace Marosek (Nos. 2517-2520), Richard Sheaff (No. 2521).

Printed by U.S. Bank Note Company (No. 2517), Bureau of Engraving and Printing (No. 2518-2519), KCS Industries (No. 2520), American Bank Note Company (No. 2521).

PHOTOGRAVURE
Sheets of 100

1991, Jan. 22	Tagged	Perf. 13
2517 A1875 (29c) **yel, blk, red & yel grn**	.60	.20
P# block of 4, 4#	2.75	—
Zip block of 4	2.50	—
b. Horiz. pair, imperf. vert.	1,150.	

Do not confuse imperforate proofs of No. 2517 with No. 2518a. See note after No. 2518.
Gutter pairs and blocks, and cross gutter blocks, all perforated, are proofs from the ABNCo. archives. See No. 2517P in Proofs section.

COIL STAMP
Perf. 10 Vert.

2518 A1875 (29c) **yel, blk, dull red & dk yel grn**	.60	.20
Pair	1.20	.20

P# strip of 5, #1111	3.00	
P# strip of 5, #1211	7.00	
P# strip of 5, #1222	3.50	
P# strip of 5, #2211	3.75	
P# strip of 5, #2222	3.50	
P# single, #1111	—	.60
P# single, #1211	—	8.50
P# single, #1222	—	.60
P# single, #2211	—	3.00
P# single, #2222	—	.60
a. Imperf., pair	27.50	

"For U.S. addresses only" is 17½mm long on No. 2517, 16½mm long on No. 2518. Design of No. 2517 measures 21½x17½mm, No. 2518, 21x18mm.

BOOKLET STAMPS
Perf. 11 on 2 or 3 Sides

2519 A1875 (29c) **yel, blk, dull red & dk grn**	.60	.20
a. Booklet pane of 10	6.50	4.50
2520 A1875 (29c) **pale yel, blk, red & brt**	1.75	.20
a. Booklet pane of 10	18.00	4.50
b. As "a," imperf. horiz.		
c. Horiz. pair, imperf btwn., in error booklet pane of 12 stamps	500.00	
d. Imperf. vert., pair		

No. 2519 has bullseye perforations that measure approximately 11.2. No. 2520 has less pronounced black lines in the leaf, which is a much brighter green than on No. 2519.
No. 2520c is from a paper foldover before perforating.

LITHOGRAPHED
Panes of 100

1991, Jan. 22	Untagged	Perf. 11
2521 A1876 (4c) **bister & carmine**	.20	.20
P# block of 4, 2#	.40	—
Zip block of 4	.30	—
a. Vert. pair, imperf. horiz.	95.00	
b. Imperf., pair	60.00	

FLAG

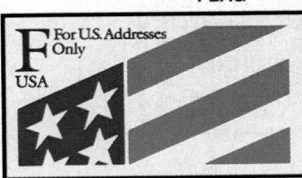

A1877

Designed by Harry Zelenko. Printed by Avery International Corp.

PHOTOGRAVURE
1991, Jan. 22 Untagged Self-Adhesive Die Cut
Printed on Plastic

2522 A1877 (29c) **blk, blue & dk red**	.60	.25
a. Pane of 12	7.25	

Sold only in panes of 12; peelable plastic backing inscribed in light ultramarine. Available during a test period at First National Bank automatic teller machines in Seattle.

Flag Over Mt. Rushmore — A1878

Designed by Clarence Holbert.

COIL STAMP
ENGRAVED

1991, Mar. 29	Tagged	Perf. 10 Vert.
2523 A1878 29c **blue, red & claret,** prephosphored uncoated paper with embedded tagging showing a mottled appearance	.65	.20
Pair	1.30	.20
P# strip of 5, #1-7	4.00	
P# strip of 5, #8	5.00	
P# strip of 5, #9	6.50	
P# single, #1	—	.40
P# single, #2-4	—	.50
P# single, #5	—	2.25
P# single, #6, 7	—	.50
P# single, #8	—	2.00
P# single, #9	—	2.00
b. Imperf., pair	20.00	
c. 29c **blue, red & brown,** prephosphored uncoated paper with embedded tagging showing a mottled appearance	3.00	—
Pair	6.00	
P# strip of 5, #1	4,000.	
P# strip of 5, #7	160.00	
P# single, #1	—	1,450.

P# single, 7	—	140.00
d. Prephosphored coated paper with surface tagging showing a solid appearance	5.00	
Pair	10.00	
P# strip of 5, #2	1,400.	
P# strip of 5, #6	260.00	
P# single, #2	—	250.00
P# single, #6	—	150.00

Specialists often call No. 2523c the "Toledo brown" variety, and No. 2523d "Lenz paper." It was from No. 2523d that it was discovered that "solid tagging" on prephosphored paper resulted from the application of taggant to coated paper.

COIL STAMP
PHOTOGRAVURE
Printed by American Bank Note Co.

1991, July 4		Perf. 10 Vert.
2523A A1878 29c **blue, red & brown**	.75	.20
Pair	1.50	.20
P# strip of 5, #A11111, A22211	4.00	—
P# single, #A11111, A22211	—	2.25

On No. 2523A, USA and 29 are not outlined in white and are farther from the bottom of the design.

A1879

Designed by Wallace Marosek.

Printed by U.S. Bank Note Co. (#2524), J.W. Fergusson & Sons for Stamp Venturers (#2525, 2526), J.W. Fergusson & Sons, Inc. for KCS Industries, Inc. (#2527).

PHOTOGRAVURE
Panes of 100

1991-92	Tagged	Perf. 11
2524 A1879 29c **dull yel, blk, red & yel grn,** *Apr. 5, 1991*	.60	.20
P# block of 4, 4#+U	2.75	—
Zip block of 4	2.50	—

See note after No. 2527.

	Perf. 13x12¾	
2524A A1879 29c **dull yel, blk, red & yel grn,** *Apr. 5, 1991*	1.00	.20
P# block of 4, 4#+U	45.00	—
Zip block of 4	7.50	—

COIL STAMPS
Rouletted 10 Vert.

2525 A1879 29c **pale yel, blk, red & yel grn,** *Aug. 16, 1991*	.60	.20
Pair	1.20	.30
P# strip of 5, #S1111, S2222	4.00	
P# single, #S1111, S2222	—	.75

No. 2525 was issued in attached coils so that "blocks" and "vertical pairs" exist.

	Perf. 10 Vert.	
2526 A1879 29c **pale yel, blk, red & yel grn,** *Mar. 3, 1992*	.80	.20
Pair	1.60	.30
P# strip of 5, #S2222	4.25	
P# single, #S2222	—	2.25

BOOKLET STAMP
Perf. 11 on 2 or 3 Sides

2527 A1879 29c **pale yel, blk, red & bright grn,** *Apr. 5*	.60	.20
a. Booklet pane of 10	6.00	3.50
b. Horiz. pair, imperf. between		
c. Horiz. pair, imperf. vert.	165.00	
d. As "a," imperf. horiz.	750.00	
d. As "a," imperf. vert.		

Flower on Nos. 2524-2524A has grainy appearance, inscriptions look rougher.
No. 2527b resulted from a foldover.

Flag, Olympic Rings — A1880

Designed by John Boyd.

Printed by KCS Industries, Inc.

BOOKLET STAMP
PHOTOGRAVURE

1991, Apr. 21   Tagged   Perf. 11 on 2 or 3 Sides

2528	A1880 29c multicolored	.60	.20
a.	Booklet pane of 10	6.00	3.50
c.	Vert. pair, imperf between, perfed at top and bottom	250.00	
d.	Vert. strip of 3, top or bottom pair imperf between	—	
e.	Vert. pair, imperf horiz.	700.00	

No. 2528c comes from misperfed booklet panes. No. 2528d resulted from paper foldovers after normal perforating and before cutting into panes. Two No. 2528d are known. No. 2528e is valued in the grade of fine.

Fishing
Boat — A1881

Balloon — A1882

Designed by Pierre Mion.

Printed by: Multi-Color Corp. for American Bank Note Co. (type I); Guilford Gravure (type II); J. W. Fergusson & Sons for Stamp Venturers (No. 2529C).

COIL STAMPS
PHOTOGRAVURE

1991, Aug. 8   Tagged   Perf. 9.8 Vert.

2529	A1881 19c multicolored	.40	.20
	Pair	.80	.30
	P# strip of 5, #A1111, A1212, A2424	3.00	
	P# strip of 5, #A1112	4.75	
	P# single, #A1111, A1212, A2424	—	2.25
	P# single, #A1112	—	4.50
a.	Type II, 1993	.40	.20
	Pair	.80	.30
	P# strip of 5, #A5555, A5556, A6667, A7667, A7679, A7766, A7779	3.50	
	P# single, same #	—	2.25
b.	As "a," untagged, 1993	1.00	.40
	Pair	2.00	.80
	P# strip of 5, #A5555	7.50	
	P# single, #A5555	—	5.50

Design on Type II stamps is created by a finer dot pattern. Vertical sides of "1" are smooth on Type II and jagged on Type I stamps.
Imperforates are from printer's waste. Also, No. 2529a, Plate #A7767 is known only from printer's waste.

1994, June 25   Tagged   Perf. 9.8 Vert.

2529C	A1881 19c multicolored	.50	.20
	Pair	1.00	.30
	P# strip of 5, #S111	4.00	
	P# single, #S111	—	2.75

No. 2529C has one loop of rope tying boat to piling.

BOOKLET STAMP

1991, May 17   Tagged   Perf. 10 on 2 or 3 Sides

2530	A1882 19c multicolored	.40	.20
a.	Booklet pane of 10	4.00	2.75

Flags on Parade — A1883

Designed by Frank J. Waslick and Peter Cocci.

PHOTOGRAVURE
Panes of 100

1991, May 30   Tagged   Perf. 11

2531	A1883 29c multicolored, overall tagging	.60	.20
	P# block of 4, 4#	2.75	
	Zip block of 4	2.50	—
b.	Prephosphored coated paper with surface tagging showing a solid appearance	.75	.25
	P# block of 4, 4#	6.50	
	Zip block of 4	3.25	—

Liberty Torch — A1884

Designed by Harry Zelenko.

Printed by Avery Dennison Co.

PHOTOGRAVURE

1991, June 25   Tagged   Die Cut
Self-Adhesive

2531A	A1884 29c black, gold & green, prephosphored coated paper with surface tagging showing a solid appearance	.60	.25
b.	Booklet pane of 18	11.00	
c.	Die cutting omitted, pair	1,750.	
d.	Overall tagging, 1992	.60	.25
e.	As "d," booklet pane of 18	11.00	

Sold only in panes of 18; peelable paper backing inscribed in light blue. Available for consumer testing at First National Bank automatic teller machines in Seattle, WA.

SWITZERLAND

Switzerland,
700th Anniv.
A1887

Designed by Hans Hartman, Switzerland.

Printed by the American Bank Note Company.

PHOTOGRAVURE
Plates of 160 in four panes of 40

1991, Feb. 22   Tagged   Perf. 11

2532	A1887 50c multicolored	1.00	.25
	P# block of 4, 5#+A	5.00	
	Zip block of 4	4.25	—
a.	Vert. pair, imperf. horiz.	2,250.	

See Switzerland No. 888.
Imperfs exist from printer's waste.

A1888

A1889

VERMONT STATEHOOD, 200th ANNIV.
Designed by Sabra Field.

Printed by the American Bank Note Company.

PHOTOGRAVURE
Plates of 200 in four panes of 50

1991, Mar. 1   Tagged   Perf. 11

2533	A1888 29c multicolored	.90	.20
	P# block of 4, 4#+A	4.50	
	Zip block of 4	3.75	—

SAVINGS BONDS, 50TH ANNIVERSARY
Designed by Primo Angeli.

1991, Apr. 30   Tagged   Perf. 11

2534	A1889 29c multicolored	.60	.20
	P# block of 4, 6#	2.75	
	Zip block of 4	2.50	—
a.	Tagging omitted		

LOVE

A1890

A1891

Designed by Harry Zelenko (#2535-2536) and Nancy L. Krause (#2537).

Printed by U.S. Banknote Co. (#2535), the Bureau of Engraving and Printing (#2536) and American Bank Note Co. (#2537).

PHOTOGRAVURE
Panes of 50

1991, May 9   Tagged   Perf. 12½x13

2535	A1890 29c multicolored	.60	.20
	P# block of 4, 5#+U	2.75	—
	Zip, copyright block of 4	2.50	—
b.	Imperf., pair	1,850.	

Perf. 11

2535A	A1890 29c multicolored	.85	.20
	P# block of 4, 5#+U	4.00	—
	Zip, copyright block of 4	3.50	—

BOOKLET STAMP
Perf. 11.1x11.3 on 2 or 3 Sides

2536	A1890 29c multicolored	.60	.20
a.	Booklet pane of 10	6.00	3.50

"29" is closer to edge of design on No. 2536 than on No. 2535.

Sheets of 200 in panes of 50
Perf. 11

2537	A1891 52c multicolored	.90	.20
	P# block of 4, 3#+A	4.50	—
	Zip block of 4	4.00	—

LITERARY ARTS SERIES

William
Saroyan
A1892

Designed by Ren Wicks.

Printed by J.W. Fergusson for American Bank Note Co.

PHOTOGRAVURE
Sheets of 200 in four panes of 50

1991, May 22   Tagged   Perf. 11

2538	A1892 29c multicolored	.60	.20
	P# block of 4, 5#+A	2.75	
	Zip block of 4	2.50	—
a.	All colors missing (EP)	—	
b.	All colors except black missing (EP)	—	

No. 2538a must be collected se-tenant with a partially printed stamp. On No. 2538b, only part of the black is present.
See Russia No. 6002.

Eagle, Olympic
Rings — A1893

A1894

A1895

A1896

Futuristic
Space Shuttle
A1897

Space Shuttle
Challenger
A1898

Space Shuttle
Endeavour —
A1898a

Designed by: Terrence McCaffrey (Nos. 2539-2541), Timothy Knapp (No. 2542), Ken Hodges (No. 2543), Phil Jordan (Nos. 2544-2544A).

Printed by: J.W. Fergusson & Sons for Stamp Venturers (No. 2539); American Bank Note Co (Nos. 2540-2541); Jeffries Banknote Co. for the American Bank Note Co (No. 2542).

Nos. 2540, 2543-2544 for priority mail rate. Nos. 2541, 2544A for domestic express mail rate. No. 2542 for international express mail rate.
Nos. 2544-2544A printed by Ashton-Potter (USA) Ltd.
Sheet of 180 in nine panes of 20 (No. 2539)
Sheet of 120 in six panes of 20 (Nos. 2540-2542, 2544-2544A)
Pane of 40 (No. 2543)

PHOTOGRAVURE
Copyright information appears in the center
of the top and bottom selvage.

1991, Sept. 29	Tagged	Perf. 11	
2539 A1893 $1 **gold & multi**		2.00	.50
P# block of 4, 6#+S		10.00	—
Pane of 20		40.00	
a. Black omitted		—	

LITHOGRAPHED & ENGRAVED

1991, July 7	Tagged	Perf. 11	
2540 A1894 $2.90 **multicolored**		6.00	1.50
P# block of 4, 5#+A		24.00	—
Pane of 20		120.00	
a. Vert. pair, imperf horiz.		*1,000.*	
b. Black (engr.) omitted		—	

Imperforates on gummed stamp paper, including gutter pairs and blocks, are proofs from the ABNCo. archives. From the same source also come imperforate progressive proofs. See No. 2540P in Proofs section.

1991, June 16	Untagged	Perf. 11	
2541 A1895 $9.95 **multicolored**		20.00	6.00
P# block of 4, 5#+A		80.00	
Pane of 20		400.00	
a. Imperf., pair		—	

No. 2541 exists imperf plus black (engr.) omitted from printer's waste.

1991, Aug. 31	Untagged	Perf. 11	
2542 A1896 $14 **multicolored**		25.00	15.00
P# block of 4, 5#+A		100.00	
Pane of 20		500.00	
a. Red (engr. inscriptions) omitted		—	

No. 2542 exists imperf plus red omitted from printer's waste.

1993, June 3	Tagged	Perf. 11x10½	
2543 A1897 $2.90 **multicolored**		6.00	1.75
P# block of 4, 6#		27.50	—
Zip block of 4		25.00	—
a. Tagging omitted		—	

1995, June 22	Tagged	Perf. 11.2	
2544 A1898 $3 **multicolored,** dated "1995"		5.75	1.75
b. Dated "1996"		5.75	1.75
P# block of 4, 5#+P		23.50	—
Pane of 20		120.00	
c. As "b," horiz. pair, imperf between		—	
d. As "b," imperf pair		*1,250.*	

1995, Aug. 4	Tagged	Perf. 11	
2544A A1898a $10.75 **multicolored**		20.00	9.00
P# block of 4, 5#+P		82.50	—
Pane of 20		425.00	

FISHING FLIES

Royal
Wulff — A1899

Jock
Scott — A1900

Apte Tarpon
Fly — A1901

Lefty's
Deceiver
A1902

Muddler
Minnow
A1903

Designed by Chuck Ripper.

Printed by American Bank Note Co.

PHOTOGRAVURE
BOOKLET STAMPS

1991, May 31	Tagged	Perf. 11 Horiz.	
2545 A1899 29c **multicolored**		2.50	.20
a. Black omitted		—	
b. Horiz. pair, imperf between		—	
2546 A1900 29c **multicolored**		2.50	.20
a. Black omitted		—	
2547 A1901 29c **multicolored**		2.50	.20
2548 A1902 29c **multicolored**		2.50	.20
2549 A1903 29c **multicolored**		2.50	.20
a. Bklt. pane of 5, #2545-2549		12.50	*3.50*

Horiz. pairs, imperf vert,. exist from printer's waste.
No. 2545b is unique and resulted from a foldover after perfing but before cutting. Both stamps are creased.

Cole Porter (1891-
1964),
Composer — A1904

S. W. Asia Service
Medal — A1905

PERFORMING ARTS

Designed by Jim Sharpe.

Printed by American Bank Note Co.

PHOTOGRAVURE
Panes of 50

1991, June 8	Tagged	Perf. 11	
2550 A1904 29c **multicolored**		.60	.20
P# block of 4, 5#+A		2.75	
Zip block of 4		2.50	
a. Vert. pair, imperf. horiz.		500.00	

OPERATIONS DESERT SHIELD & DESERT STORM

Designed by Jack Williams.

Printed by J.W. Fergusson Co. for Stamp Venturers (No. 2551), Multi-Color Corp. for the American Bank Note Co. (No. 2552).

PHOTOGRAVURE
Panes of 50

1991, July 2		Tagged	Perf. 11	
2551	A1905	29c multicolored	.60	.20
		P# block of 4, 7#+S	2.75	—
		Zip block of 4	2.50	—
a.		Vert. pair, imperf. horiz.	1,250.	

No. 2551 is 21mm wide.

BOOKLET STAMP
Perf. 11 Vert. on 1 or 2 Sides

2552	A1905	29c multicolored	.60	.20
a.		Booklet pane of 5	3.00	2.25

No. 2552 is 20½mm wide. Inscriptions are shorter than on No. 2551.

No. 2552 Vert. pairs, imperf. horiz., are from printer's waste.

1992 SUMMER OLYMPICS, BARCELONA

Pole Vault — A1907

Discus A1908

Women's Sprints A1909

Javelin A1910

Women's Hurdles A1911

Designed by Joni Carter.

Printed by the American Bank Note Co.

PHOTOGRAVURE
Panes of 40

1991, July 12		Tagged	Perf. 11	
2553	A1907	29c multicolored	.60	.20
2554	A1908	29c multicolored	.60	.20
2555	A1909	29c multicolored	.60	.20
2556	A1910	29c multicolored	.60	.20
2557	A1911	29c multicolored	.60	.20
a.		Strip of 5, #2553-2557	3.00	2.25
		P# block of 10, 5#+A	8.00	—
		Zip block of 10	6.00	—

NUMISMATICS

1858 Flying Eagle Cent, 1907 Standing Liberty Double Eagle, Series 1875 $1 Note, Series 1902 $10 National Currency Note — A1912

Designed by V. Jack Ruther.

LITHOGRAPHED & ENGRAVED
Sheets of 200 in four panes of 50

1991, Aug. 13		Tagged	Perf. 11	
2558	A1912	29c multicolored	.60	.20
		P# block of 4, 7#	2.75	—
		Zip block of 4	2.50	—

WORLD WAR II

A1913

Illustration reduced.

Designed by William H. Bond.

Designs and events of 1941: a, Military vehicles (Burma Road, 717-mile lifeline to China). b, Recruits (America's first peacetime draft). c, Shipments for allies (U.S. supports allies with Lend-Lease Act). d, Franklin D. Roosevelt, Winston Churchill (Atlantic Charter sets war aims of allies). e, Tank (America becomes the "arsenal of democracy.") f, Sinking of Destoyer Reuben James, Oct. 31. g, Gas mask, helmet (Civil defense mobilizes Americans at home). h, Liberty Ship, sea gull (First Liberty ship delivered December 30). i, Sinking ships (Japanese bomb Pearl Harbor, December 7). j, Congress in session (U.S. declares war on Japan, December 8.) Central label is the size of 15 stamps and shows world map, extent of axis control.

LITHOGRAPHED & ENGRAVED
Plates of eight subjects in four panes of 2 each

1991, Sept. 3		Tagged	Perf. 11	
2559	A1913	Block of 10	7.50	5.00
		Pane of 20	15.00	—
a.-j.		29c any single	.75	.45
k.		Black (engr.) omitted	12,500.	

No. 2559 has selvage at left and right and either top or bottom.

BASKETBALL, 100TH ANNIVERSARY

Basketball, Hoop, Players' Arms — A1914

Designed by Lon Busch.

PHOTOGRAVURE
Sheets of 200 in four panes of 50

1991, Aug. 28		Tagged	Perf. 11	
2560	A1914	29c multicolored	.60	.20
		P# block of 4, 4#	3.25	—
		Zip block of 4	2.50	—

DISTRICT OF COLUMBIA BICENTENNIAL

Capitol Building from Pennsylvania Avenue, Circa 1903 — A1915

Designed by Pierre Mion.

LITHOGRAPHED & ENGRAVED
Plates of 200 in four panes of 50

1991, Sept. 7		Tagged	Perf. 11	
2561	A1915	29c multicolored	.60	.20
		P# block of 4, 5#	2.75	—
		Zip block of 4	2.50	—
a.		Black (engr.) omitted	100.00	

COMEDIANS

Stan Laurel (1890-1965) and Oliver Hardy (1892-1957) A1916

Edgar Bergen (1903-1978) and Charlie McCarthy A1917

Jack Benny (1894-1974) A1918

Fanny Brice (1891-1951) A1919

Bud Abbott (1895-1974) and Lou Costello (1908-1959) A1920

Designed by Al Hirschfeld.

LITHOGRAPHED & ENGRAVED
BOOKLET STAMPS

1991, Aug. 29		Tagged	Perf. 11 on 2 or 3 Sides	
2562	A1916	29c multicolored	1.00	.20
2563	A1917	29c multicolored	1.00	.20
2564	A1918	29c multicolored	1.00	.20
2565	A1919	29c multicolored	1.00	.20
2566	A1920	29c multicolored	1.00	.20
a.		Bklt. pane of 10, 2 each #2562-2566	10.00	5.00
b.		As "a," scar & brt violet (engr.) omitted	550.00	
c.		Strip of 5, #2562-2566	5.00	2.50

BLACK HERITAGE SERIES

Jan E. Matzeliger (1852-1889), Inventor — A1921

Designed by Higgins Bond.
Printed by J.W. Fergusson & Sons for the American Bank Note Co.

PHOTOGRAVURE
Plates of 200 in four panes of 50

1991, Sept. 15	Tagged		Perf. 11
2567 A1921 29c multicolored		.60	.20
P# block of 4, 6#+A		2.75	—
Zip block of 4		2.40	—
a. Horiz. pair, imperf. vert.		1,150.	
b. Vert. pair, imperf. horiz.		1,150.	
c. Imperf., pair		400.00	

SPACE EXPLORATION

Mercury, Mariner 10 A1922

Venus, Mariner 2 A1923

Earth, Landsat A1924

Moon, Lunar Orbiter A1925

Mars, Viking Orbiter A1926

Jupiter, Pioneer 11 A1927

Saturn, Voyager 2 A1928

Uranus, Voyager 2 A1929

Neptune, Voyager 2 A1930

Pluto — A1931

Designed by Ron Miller.

PHOTOGRAVURE
BOOKLET STAMPS

1991, Oct. 1	Tagged	Perf. 11 on 2 or 3 Sides	
2568 A1922 29c multicolored		1.10	.20
2569 A1923 29c multicolored		1.10	.20
2570 A1924 29c multicolored		1.10	.20
2571 A1925 29c multicolored		1.10	.20
2572 A1926 29c multicolored		1.10	.20
2573 A1927 29c multicolored		1.10	.20
2574 A1928 29c multicolored		1.10	.20
2575 A1929 29c multicolored		1.10	.20
2576 A1930 29c multicolored		1.10	.20
2577 A1931 29c multicolored		1.10	.20
a. Bklt. pane of 10, #2568-2577		11.00	4.50

CHRISTMAS

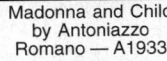
Madonna and Child by Antoniazzo Romano — A1933

Santa Claus in Chimney — A1934

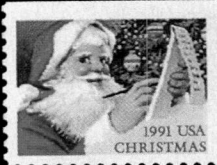
Santa Checking List — A1935

Santa with Present — A1936

Santa at Fireplace — A1937

Santa and Sleigh — A1938

Designed by Bradbury Thompson (#2578) and John Berkey (#2579-2585).
Printed by the Bureau of Engraving and Printing (#2578); J.W. Fergusson & Sons (#2579) and Multi-Color Corp. (#2580-2585) for the American Bank Note Co.

LITHOGRAPHED & ENGRAVED
Sheets of 300 in six panes of 50

1991, Oct. 17	Tagged		Perf. 11
2578 A1933 (29c) multicolored		.60	.20
P# block of 4, 5#		2.75	—
Zip, copyright block of 4		2.50	—
a. Booklet pane of 10		6.00	3.25
b. Red & black (engr.) omitted		3,250.	

PHOTOGRAVURE

2579 A1934 (29c) multicolored		.60	.20
P# block of 4, 3#+A		2.50	—
Zip block of 4		2.25	—
a. Horiz. pair, imperf. vert.		225.00	
b. Vert. pair, imperf. horiz.		375.00	

Booklet Stamps
Size: 25x18½mm
Perf. 11 on 2 or 3 Sides

2580 A1934 (29c) Type I	2.25	.20
2581 A1934 (29c) Type II	2.75	.50
a. Pair, #2580-2581	5.00	.50
b. Bklt. pane, 2 each, #2580, 2581	11.00	1.25
2582 A1935 (29c) multicolored	.60	.20
a. Bklt. pane of 4	2.40	1.25
2583 A1936 (29c) multicolored	.60	.20
a. Bklt. pane of 4	2.40	1.25
2584 A1937 (29c) multicolored	.60	.20
a. Bklt. pane of 4	2.40	1.25
2585 A1938 (29c) multicolored	.60	.20
a. Bklt. pane of 4	2.40	1.25
Nos. 2578-2585 (8)	8.60	1.60

The far left brick from the top row of the chimney is missing from Type II, No. 2581.
Imperfs of Nos. 2581, 2583-2585 are printer's waste.

James K. Polk (1795-1849) A1939

"The Surrender of General Burgoyne at Saratoga," by John Trumbull A1942

Washington and Jackson — A1944

Designed by John Thompson (No. 2587), based on painting by John Trumbull (No. 2590), Richard D. Sheaff (No. 2592). Printed by Banknote Corporation of America (No. 2587), Stamp Venturers (Nos. 2590, 2592).

ENGRAVED

Sheets of 400 in four panes of 100 (No. 2587)
Sheets of 120 in six panes of 20 (Nos. 2590, 2592)

1994-95		Tagged		Perf. 11.2
2587	A1939	32c **red brown,** Nov. 2, 1995	.65	.20
		P# block of 4, 1#+B	3.25	

		Perf. 11.5		
2590	A1942	$1 **blue,** May 5, 1994	1.90	.50
		P# block of 4, 1#+S	7.60	—
		Pane of 20	38.00	—
2592	A1944	$5 **slate green,** Aug. 19, 1994	8.00	2.50
		P# block of 4, 1#+S	40.00	—
		Pane of 20	160.00	—

Some plate blocks contain either inscription or plate position diagram.

USA29

I pledge allegiance...

A1946

Eagle and Shield — A1947

A1950

Statue of Liberty — A1951

Designed by Lou Nolan (#2593-2594), Jay Haiden (#2595-2597), Richard Sheaff (#2598), Tom Engeman (#2599). Printed by Bureau of Engraving & Printing (#2593), Stamp Venturers for KCS Industries (#2594), Banknote Corporation of America (#2595), Dittler Brothers, Inc. (#2596, 2599), Stamp Venturers (#2597), National Label Co. for 3M (#2598).

BOOKLET STAMPS
PHOTOGRAVURE

1992, Sept. 8		Tagged	*Perf. 9.8 on 2 or 3 sides*	
2593	A1946	29c **black & multi**	.60	.20
a.		Booklet pane of 10	6.00	4.25
d.		Imperf, pair		

		Perf. 11x10 on 2 or 3 sides		
2593B	A1946	29c **black & multi,** shiny gum	1.70	.50
		Low gloss gum	3.00	
c.		Bklt. pane of 10, shiny gum	17.00	7.50
		Low gloss gum	35.00	

1993, Apr. 8(?)			*Perf. 11x10 on 2 or 3 Sides*	
2594	A1946	29c **red & multi**	.65	.20
a.		Booklet pane of 10	6.50	4.25

Denomination is red on #2594 and black on #2593 and 2593B.

LITHOGRAPHED & ENGRAVED

1992, Sept. 25		Tagged		*Die Cut*
		Self-Adhesive		
2595	A1947	29c **brown & multicolored**	.60	.25
a.		Bklt. pane of 17 + label	13.00	
b.		Die cutting omitted, pair	135.00	
c.		Brown omitted	350.00	
d.		As "a," die cutting omitted	1,150.	

2596	A1947	29c **green & multicolored**	.60	.25
a.		Bklt. pane of 17 + label	12.00	

PHOTOGRAVURE

2597	A1947	29c **red & multicolored**	.60	.25
a.		Bklt. pane of 17 + label	10.50	

Plate No. and inscription reads down on No. 2595a and up on Nos. 2596a-2597a. Design is sharper and more finely detailed on Nos. 2595, 2597.
Nos. 2595a-2597a sold for $5 each.
Nos. 2595-2597 also available in strips with stamps spaced for use in affixing machines to service first day covers.

PHOTOGRAVURE

1994		Tagged		*Die Cut*
		Self-Adhesive, Feb. 4		
2598	A1950	29c **red, cream & blue,** Feb. 4	.60	.20
a.		Booklet pane of 18	11.00	
b.		Coil with P#111	—	5.00
		P# strip of 5, #111	8.00	
2599	A1951	29c **multicolored,** June 24	.60	.20
a.		Booklet pane of 18	11.00	
b.		Coil with P#D1111	—	5.00
		P# strip of 5, #D1111	8.00	

Except for Nos. 2598b and 2599b with plate numbers, coil stamps of these issues are indistinguishable from booklet stamps once they are removed from the backing paper.
See Nos. 3122-3122E.

> **Scott values for used self-adhesive stamps are for examples either on piece or off piece.**

Eagle and Shield — A1956

Eagle and Shield — A1957

Presorted First-Class USA23

A1959

USA Presorted First-Class 23

A1960

Flag Over White House — A1961

Designed by Chris Calle (#2602-2604), Terrence McCaffrey (#2605), Lon Busch (#2606-2608), V. Jack Ruther (29c). Printed by Guildford Gravure, Inc. for the American Bank Note Co. (#2602, 2606), Bureau of Engraving and Printing (#2603, 2607), Stamp Venturers (#2604, 2608), American Bank Note Co. (#2605).

PHOTOGRAVURE
COIL STAMPS

1991-93		Untagged		*Perf. 10 Vert.*
2602	A1956	**multi** (Bureau precancel, Bulk Rate, in blue), Dec. 13	.30	.20
		Pair	.60	.40
		P# strip of 5, #A11111, A11112, A21112, A21113, A22112, A22113, A33333, A43325, A43326, A43334, A43335, A53335, A54444, A54445, A77777, A88888	1.90	
		P# strip of 5, #A12213	4.00	
		P# strip of 5, #A34424, A34426, A43324, A88889	2.75	
		P# strip of 5, #A32333	725.00	
		P# strip of 5, #A33334	12.00	
		P# strip of 5, #A33335, A43426, A89999, A99998, A99999, A1010101010, A1011101011, A1011101012, A1110101010, A1110111010, A1111101010, A1111111010, A1411101010, A1411101011, A1412111110, A1412111111	2.50	
		P# strip of 5, #A1011101010	3.75	
		P# strip of 5, #A1211101010	4.00	
		P# strip of 5, #A1110101011	4.00	

	P# single, #A11111, A11112, A21112, A21113, A22112, A22113, A43324, A43325, A43326, A43334, A43335, A43426, A54444, A54445, A77777, A88888, A89999, A99998, A99999	—	1.75
	P# single, #A12213	—	5.00
	P# single, #A32333	—	225.00
	P# single, #A33333, A34424, A34426	—	2.50
	P# single, #A33334	—	75.00
	P# single, #A53335, A88889, A1010101010, A1011101011, A1011101012, A1110101010, A1110111010, A1111101010, A1111111010, A1411101010, A1411101011, A1412111110, A1412111111	—	2.50
	P# single, #A1011101010	—	3.00
	P# single, #A1211101010	—	4.00
	P# single, #A1110101011	—	4.00

a.		Imperf., pair		
2603	A1957	(10c) **org yel & multi,** shiny gum (Bureau precancel, Bulk Rate, in red), May 29, 1993	.30	.20
		Pair	.60	.40
		P# strip of 5, #11111, 22221, 22222	2.25	
		P# single, same	—	1.75
		Low gloss gum	.20	
		Pair	.40	
		P# strip of 5, #22222, 33333, 44444	3.00	
		P# strip of 5, #11111	15.00	
		P# single, #33333, 44444	—	2.00
a.		Imperf., pair	20.00	
b.		Tagged (error), shiny gum	2.00	1.50
		Pair	4.00	3.50
		P# strip of 5, #11111, 22221	10.00	
		P# strip of 5, #22222	425.00	
		P# single, #11111, 22221	—	10.00
		P# single, #22222	—	300.00

All examples of Nos. 2603, 2603a and 2603b were printed with luminescent ink.
See No. 2907.

2604	A1957	(10c) **gold & multi,** shiny gum (Bureau precancel, Bulk Rate, in red), May 29, 1993	.30	.20
		Pair	.60	.40
		P# strip of 5, #S22222	2.75	
		P# single, same	—	2.00
		Low gloss gum	.20	
		Pair	.40	
		P# strip of 5, #S11111	2.50	
		P# strip of 5, #S22222	2.25	
		P# single, #S11111	—	1.75
2605	A1959	23c **multi** (Bureau precancel in blue), Sept. 27	.45	.40
		Pair	.90	.80
		P# strip of 5, #A111, A212, A222	3.25	
		P# strip of 5, #A112, A122, A333	3.75	
		P# single, #A111, A112, A122, A212, A222, A333	—	2.25
a.		Imperf, pair		

Vertical pairs uncut between on gummed stamp paper are proofs from the ABNCo. archives. See No. 2605P in Proofs section.

2606	A1960	23c **multi** (Bureau precanceled), July 21, 1992	.45	.40
		Pair	.90	.80
		P# strip of 5, #A1111, A2222, A2232, A2233, A3333, A4364, A4443, A4444, A4453	3.75	
		P# single, same	—	2.50

"First-Class" is 9 ½mm long and "23" is 6mm long on No. 2606.

2607	A1960	23c **multi,** shiny gum (Bureau precanceled), Oct. 9, 1992	.45	.40
		Pair	.90	.80
		P# strip of 5, #1111	4.00	
		P# single, #1111	—	2.00
		Low gloss gum	.45	
		Pair	.90	
		P# strip of 5, #1111	4.00	
a.		Tagged (error), shiny gum	5.00	4.50
		Pair	10.00	9.00
		P# strip of 5, #1111	110.00	
		P# single, #1111	—	85.00
c.		Imperf., pair	70.00	

"First-Class" is 9mm long and "23" is 6 ½mm long on No. 2607.

2608	A1960	23c **vio bl, red & blk** (Bureau precanceled), May 14, 1993	.80	.40
		Pair	1.60	.80
		P# strip of 5, #S111	4.25	
		P# single, #S111	—	2.25

"First-Class" is 8 ½mm long and "23" is 6 ½mm long on No. 2608.

ENGRAVED
Tagged

2609	A1961	29c **blue & red,** *Apr. 23,*		
		1992	.60	.20
		Pair	1.20	.20
		P# strip of 5, #1-8	3.50	
		P# strip of 5, #9-16, 18	4.50	
		P# single, #1-4	—	.50
		P# single, #5	—	2.25
		P# single, #6-8	—	.50
		P# single, #9	—	2.50
		P# single, #10-16	—	.80
		P# single, #18	—	4.00
a.		Imperf., pair	15.00	
b.		Pair, imperf. between	85.00	

Beware of pairs with blind perfs sometimes offered as No. 2609b.

WINTER OLYMPICS

Hockey
A1963

Figure Skating
A1964

Speed Skating
A1965

Skiing
A1966

Bobsledding
A1967

Designed by Lon Busch. Printed by J.W. Fergusson & Sons for Stamp Venturers.

PHOTOGRAVURE
Panes of 35

			Perf. 11	
1992, Jan. 11		**Tagged**		
2611	A1963	29c **multicolored**	.60	.20
2612	A1964	29c **multicolored**	.60	.20
2613	A1965	29c **multicolored**	.60	.20
2614	A1966	29c **multicolored**	.60	.20

2615	A1967	29c **multicolored**	.60	.20
a.		Strip of 5, #2611-2615	3.00	2.50
		P# block of 10, 4#+S	7.00	—
		Zip, copyright block of 15	9.00	—

Inscriptions on six marginal tabs.

Features detail from No. 129 — A1968

W.E.B. Du Bois (1868-1963) — A1969

WORLD COLUMBIAN STAMP EXPO

Designed by Richard Sheaff.

LITHOGRAPHED & ENGRAVED
Plates of 200 in four panes of 50

			Perf. 11	
1992, Jan. 24		**Tagged**		
2616	A1968	29c **multicolored**	.60	.20
		P# block of 4, 4#	3.00	—
		Zip block of 4	2.50	—
a.		Tagging omitted	7.50	

BLACK HERITAGE SERIES
W.E.B. Du Bois (1868-1963), Writer and Civil Rights Leader

Designed by Higgins Bond.

LITHOGRAPHED & ENGRAVED
Plates of 200 in four panes of 50

			Perf. 11	
1992, Jan. 31		**Tagged**		
2617	A1969	29c **multicolored**	.60	.20
		P# block of 4, 7#	2.75	—
		Zip block of 4	2.50	—

A1970

A1971

LOVE
Designed by Uldis Purins. Printed by the U.S. Bank Note Co.

PHOTOGRAVURE
Panes of 50

			Perf. 11	
1992, Feb. 6		**Tagged**		
2618	A1970	29c **multicolored**	.60	.20
		P# block of 4, U+5#	2.75	—
		Zip, copyright block of 4	2.50	—
a.		Horiz. pair, imperf. vert.	625.00	
b.		As "a," green omitted on right stamp	2,500.	

OLYMPIC BASEBALL
Designed by Anthony DeLuz.

PHOTOGRAVURE
Plates of 200 in four panes of 50

			Perf. 11	
1992, Apr. 3		**Tagged**		
2619	A1971	29c **multicolored**	.60	.20
		P# block of 4, 5#	2.75	—
		Zip block of 4	2.50	—

VOYAGES OF COLUMBUS

Seeking Queen Isabella's Support
A1972

Crossing the Atlantic
A1973

Approaching Land
A1974

Coming Ashore
A1975

Designed by Richard Schlecht.

LITHOGRAPHED & ENGRAVED
Plates of 160 in four panes of 40

			Perf. 11	
1992, Apr. 24		**Tagged**		
2620	A1972	29c **multicolored**	.60	.20
2621	A1973	29c **multicolored**	.60	.20
2622	A1974	29c **multicolored**	.60	.20
2623	A1975	29c **multicolored**	.60	.20
a.		Block of 4, #2620-2623	2.40	2.00
		P# block of 4, 5#	2.75	—
		Zip block of 4	2.50	—

See Italy Nos. 1877-1880.

Souvenir Sheets

A1976

The Voyages of Columbus

Claiming a New World

A1977

The Voyages of Columbus

Seeking Royal Support

A1978

The Voyages of Columbus

Royal Favor Restored

A1979

The Voyages of Columbus

Reporting Discoveries

A1980

Christopher Columbus

The United States Postal Service celebrates the 500th anniversary of the voyages of Christopher Columbus. This set is based on the first U.S. stamps in commemorative format, engraved a century ago.

A1981

Illustrations reduced.

Designed by Richard Sheaff.

Printed by the American Bank Note Co. Margins on Nos. 2624-2628 are lithographed. Nos. 2624a-2628c, 2629 are similar in design to Nos. 230-245 but are dated 1492-1992.

LITHOGRAPHED & ENGRAVED

1992, May 22   **Perf. 10½**

Tagged (15c-$5), Untagged

2624	A1976	Sheet of 3	2.00	1.25
a.	A71	1c **deep blue**	.20	.20
b.	A74	4c **ultramarine**	.20	.20
c.	A82	$1 **salmon**	1.75	1.00
d.		As No. 2624, tagging omitted on "c"	—	
2625	A1977	Sheet of 3	7.25	5.00
a.	A72	2c **brown violet**	.20	.20
b.	A73	3c **green**	.20	.20
c.	A85	$4 **crimson lake**	7.00	4.00
2626	A1978	Sheet of 3	1.60	1.25
a.	A75	5c **chocolate**	.20	.20
b.	A80	30c **orange brown**	.60	.30
c.	A81	50c **slate blue**	.90	.50
d.		As No. 2626, tagging omitted on "c"	—	
2627	A1979	Sheet of 3	5.75	3.50
a.	A76	6c **purple**	.20	.20
b.	A77	8c **magenta**	.20	.20
c.	A84	$3 **yellow green**	5.50	3.00
2628	A1980	Sheet of 3	4.00	3.00
a.	A78	10c **black brown**	.20	.20
b.	A79	15c **dark green**	.30	.20
c.	A83	$2 **brown red**	3.50	2.00
d.		As No. 2628, tagging omitted on "b"	—	
2629	A1981	$5 Sheet of 1	8.75	6.00
a.	A86	$5 **black**, single stamp	8.50	5.00
		Nos. 2624-2629 (6)	29.35	20.00

See Italy Nos. 1883-1888, Portugal Nos. 1918-1923 and Spain Nos. 2677-2682.

Imperforate souvenir sheets on gummed stamp paper, singly or in pairs and blocks, are proofs from the ABNCo. archives. Additionally, one imperforate essay, with the background of No. 2622 combined with the stamps of No. 2620, is recorded. See Nos. 2624P-2629P in Proofs section.

NEW YORK STOCK EXCHANGE BICENTENNIAL

A1982

Designed by Richard Sheaff.

Printed by the Jeffries Bank Note Co. for the American Bank Note Co.

LITHOGRAPHED & ENGRAVED

1992, May 17   **Tagged**   **Perf. 11**

2630	A1982	29c **green, red & black**	.60	.20
		P# block of 4, 3#+A	2.75	
		Zip, Olympic block of 4	2.50	
a.		Black missing (EP)	—	
b.		Black missing (CM)	—	
c.		Center (black engr.) inverted	26,000.	

No. 2630a must be collected se-tenant with a normal stamp or with a stamp with half of black engraving missing, or se-tenant with a normal stamp and an additional 2630a.

No. 2630b may be collected alone or se-tenant with No. 2630c.

Two panes, each containing 28 No. 2630c and 12 No. 2630b, have been documented.

The unique pane containing 4 No. 2630a, one stamp with half of black center missing and 35 normal stamps sold at a 2002 auction for $18,400.

SPACE ACCOMPLISHMENTS

Cosmonaut, US Space Shuttle — A1983

Astronaut, Russian Space Station, Russian Space Shuttle — A1984

Sputnik, Vostok, Apollo Command & Lunar Modules — A1985

Soyuz, Mercury & Gemini Spacecraft — A1986

Designed by Vladimir Beilin (Russia) and Robert T. McCall.

PHOTOGRAVURE

Plates of 200 in four panes of 50

1992, May 29   **Tagged**   **Perf. 11**

2631	A1983	29c **multicolored**	.60	.20
2632	A1984	29c **multicolored**	.60	.20
2633	A1985	29c **multicolored**	.60	.20
2634	A1986	29c **multicolored**	.60	.20
a.		Block of 4, #2631-2634	2.40	1.90
		P# block of 4, 4#	3.25	—
		Zip block of 4	2.50	—
b.		As "a," yellow omitted		

See Russia Nos. 6080-6083.

ALASKA HIGHWAY, 50th ANNIVERSARY

A1987

Designed by Byron Birdsall.

LITHOGRAPHED & ENGRAVED

Plates of 200 in four panes of 50

1992, May 30   **Tagged**   **Perf. 11**

2635	A1987	29c **multicolored**	.60	.20
		P# block of 4, 6#	2.75	—
		Zip block of 4	2.50	—
a.		Black (engr.) omitted	700.00	

Almost half the recorded No. 2635a errors are poorly centered. These sell for approximately $400.

KENTUCKY STATEHOOD BICENTENNIAL

A1988

Designed by Joseph Petro.

Printed by J.W. Fergusson & Sons for Stamp Venturers.

PHOTOGRAVURE

Plates of 200 in four panes of 50

1992, June 1   **Tagged**   **Perf. 11**

2636	A1988	29c **multicolored**	.60	.20
		P# block of 4, 5#+S	2.75	
		Zip block of 4	2.50	
a.		Dark blue missing (EP)	—	
b.		Dark blue and red missing (EP)	—	
c.		All colors missing (EP)	—	

Nos. 2636a-2636c must be collected se-tenant with normal stamps.

SUMMER OLYMPICS

Soccer
A1989

Gymnastics
A1990

Volleyball
A1991

Boxing
A1992

Swimming
A1993

Designed by Richard Waldrep.

Printed by J.W. Fergusson & Sons for Stamp Venturers.

PHOTOGRAVURE

Panes of 35

1992, June 11			Tagged		Perf. 11	
2637	A1989	29c	**multicolored**		.60	.20
2638	A1990	29c	**multicolored**		.60	.20
2639	A1991	29c	**multicolored**		.60	.20
2640	A1992	29c	**multicolored**		.60	.20
2641	A1993	29c	**multicolored**		.60	.20
a.	Strip of 5, #2637-2641				3.00	2.50
	P# block of 10, 5#+S				6.50	—
	Zip, copyright block of 15				9.00	—

Inscriptions on six marginal tabs.

WILDFLOWERS
A1999-A2048

HUMMINGBIRDS

Ruby-throated
A1994

Broad-billed
A1995

Costa's — A1996

Rufous — A1997

Calliope — A1998

Designed by Chuck Ripper.

Printed by Multi-Color Corp. for the American Bank Note Co.

PHOTOGRAVURE
BOOKLET STAMPS
Perf. 11 Vert. on 1 or 2 sides

1992, June 15					Tagged	
2642	A1994	29c	multicolored		.60	.20
2643	A1995	29c	multicolored		.60	.20
2644	A1996	29c	multicolored		.60	.20
2645	A1997	29c	multicolored		.60	.20
2646	A1998	29c	multicolored		.60	.20
a.			Bklt. pane of 5, #2642-2646		3.00	2.50

Imperforate singles, booklet panes and pane multiples or varieties on gummed stamp paper are proofs from the ABNCo. archives. From the same source also come imperforate progressive proofs. See No. 2646aP in Proofs section.

WILDFLOWERS

Illustration reduced.

Designed by Karen Mallary.

Printed by Ashton-Potter America, Inc.

LITHOGRAPHED
Plates of 300 in six panes of 50 and
Plates of 200 in four panes of 50

1992, July 24				Tagged	Perf. 11
2647	A1999	29c	Indian paintbrush	.80	.60
2648	A2000	29c	Fragrant water lily	.80	.60
2649	A2001	29c	Meadow beauty	.80	.60
2650	A2002	29c	Jack-in-the-pulpit	.80	.60
2651	A2003	29c	California poppy	.80	.60
2652	A2004	29c	Large-flowered trillium	.80	.60
2653	A2005	29c	Tickseed	.80	.60
2654	A2006	29c	Shooting star	.80	.60
2655	A2007	29c	Stream violet	.80	.60
2656	A2008	29c	Bluets	.80	.60
2657	A2009	29c	Herb Robert	.80	.60
2658	A2010	29c	Marsh marigold	.80	.60
2659	A2011	29c	Sweet white violet	.80	.60
2660	A2012	29c	Claret cup cactus	.80	.60
2661	A2013	29c	White mountain avens	.80	.60
2662	A2014	29c	Sessile bellwort	.80	.60
2663	A2015	29c	Blue flag	.80	.60
2664	A2016	29c	Harlequin lupine	.80	.60

2665	A2017	29c	Twinflower	.80	.60
2666	A2018	29c	Common sunflower	.80	.60
2667	A2019	29c	Sego lily	.80	.60
2668	A2020	29c	Virginia bluebells	.80	.60
2669	A2021	29c	Ohi'a lehua	.80	.60
2670	A2022	29c	Rosebud orchid	.80	.60
2671	A2023	29c	Showy evening primrose	.80	.60
2672	A2024	29c	Fringed gentian	.80	.60
2673	A2025	29c	Yellow lady's slipper	.80	.60
2674	A2026	29c	Passionflower	.80	.60
2675	A2027	29c	Bunchberry	.80	.60
2676	A2028	29c	Pasqueflower	.80	.60
2677	A2029	29c	Round-lobed hepatica	.80	.60
2678	A2030	29c	Wild columbine	.80	.60
2679	A2031	29c	Fireweed	.80	.60
2680	A2032	29c	Indian pond lily	.80	.60
2681	A2033	29c	Turk's cap lily	.80	.60
2682	A2034	29c	Dutchman's breeches	.80	.60
2683	A2035	29c	Trumpet honeysuckle	.80	.60
2684	A2036	29c	Jacob's ladder	.80	.60
2685	A2037	29c	Plains prickly pear	.80	.60
2686	A2038	29c	Moss campion	.80	.60
2687	A2039	29c	Bearberry	.80	.60
2688	A2040	29c	Mexican hat	.80	.60
2689	A2041	29c	Harebell	.80	.60
2690	A2042	29c	Desert five spot	.80	.60
2691	A2043	29c	Smooth Solomon's seal	.80	.60
2692	A2044	29c	Red maids	.80	.60
2693	A2045	29c	Yellow skunk cabbage	.80	.60
2694	A2046	29c	Rue anemone	.80	.60
2695	A2047	29c	Standing cypress	.80	.60
2696	A2048	29c	Wild flax	.80	.60
a.		A1999-A2048	Pane of 50, #2647-2696	40.00	—

Sheet margin selvage contains a diagram of the plate layout with each pane's position shaded in gray.

WORLD WAR II

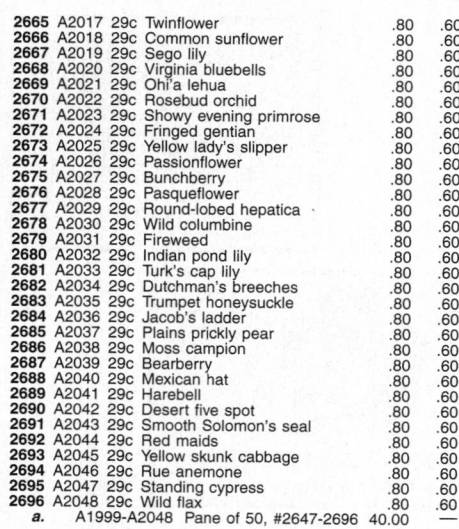

A2049

Illustration reduced.

Designed by William H. Bond.

Designs and events of 1942: a, B-25's take off to raid Tokyo, Apr. 18. b, Ration coupons (Food and other commodities rationed). c, Divebomber and deck crewman (US wins Battle of the Coral Sea, May). d, Prisoners of war (Corregidor falls to Japanese, May 6). e, Dutch Harbor buildings on fire (Japan invades Aleutian Islands, June). f, Headphones, coded message (Allies decipher secret enemy codes). g, Yorktown lost, U.S. wins at Midway. h, Woman with drill (Millions of women join war effort). i, Marines land on Guadalcanal, Aug. 7. j, Tank in desert (Allies land in North Africa, Nov.).
Central label is the size of 15 stamps and shows world map, extent of axis control.

LITHOGRAPHED & ENGRAVED
Plates of 80 in four panes of 20 each

1992, Aug. 17				Tagged	Perf. 11
2697	A2049		Block of 10	7.50	5.00
			Pane of 20	15.00	—
a.-j.			29c any single	.75	.30
k.			Red (litho.) omitted	5,000.	

No. 2697 has selvage at left and right and either top or bottom.

Dorothy
Parker — A2050

Von Karman (1881-1963), Rocket Scientist — A2051

LITERARY ARTS SERIES
Designed by Greg Rudd.

Printed by J.W. Fergusson & Sons for Stamp Venturers.

PHOTOGRAVURE
Plates of 200 in four panes of 50

1992, Aug. 22			Tagged	Perf. 11
2698	A2050	29c multicolored	.60	.20
		P# block of 4, 5# + S	2.75	—
		Zip block of 4	2.50	—

THEODORE VON KARMAN
Designed by Chris Calle.

Printed by J.W. Fergusson & Sons for Stamp Venturers.

PHOTOGRAVURE
Plates of 200 in four panes of 50

1992, Aug. 31			Tagged	Perf. 11
2699	A2051	29c multicolored	.60	.20
		P# block of 4, 4# + S	2.75	—
		Zip block of 4	2.50	—

MINERALS

Azurite — A2052

Copper — A2053

Variscite — A2054

Wulfenite — A2055

Designed by Len Buckley.

LITHOGRAPHED & ENGRAVED
Sheets of 160 in four panes of 40.

1992, Sept. 17			Tagged	Perf. 11
2700	A2052	29c multicolored	.60	.20
2701	A2053	29c multicolored	.60	.20
2702	A2054	29c multicolored	.60	.20
2703	A2055	29c multicolored	.60	.20
a.		Block or strip of 4, #2700-2703	2.40	2.00

	P# block of 4, 6#	3.50 —
	Zip block of 4	2.50 —
b.	As "a," silver (litho.) omitted	7,750.
c.	As "a," red (litho.) omitted	—
d.	As "a," silver omitted on two stamps	—

JUAN RODRIGUEZ CABRILLO

Cabrillo (d. 1543), Ship,
Map of San Diego Bay
Area — A2056

Designed by Ren Wicks.

Printed by The Press and J.W. Fergusson & Sons for Stamp Venturers.

LITHOGRAPHED & ENGRAVED
Plates of 200 in four panes of 50

1992, Sept. 28	Tagged	Perf. 11	
2704 A2056 29c **multicolored**		.60	.20
	P# block of 4, 7# + 2 "S"s	3.50	—
	Zip, Olympic block of 4	2.50	—
a.	Black (engr.) omitted	3,250.	

WILD ANIMALS

Giraffe
A2057

Giant Panda
A2058

Flamingo
A2059

King Penguins
A2060

White Bengal
Tiger — A2061

Designed by Robert Giusti.

Printed by J.W. Fergusson & Sons for Stamp Venturers.

PHOTOGRAVURE
BOOKLET STAMPS

1992, Oct. 1	Tagged	Perf. 11 Horiz.	
2705 A2057 29c **multicolored**		.65	.20
2706 A2058 29c **multicolored**		.65	.20
2707 A2059 29c **multicolored**		.65	.20
2708 A2060 29c **multicolored**		.65	.20
2709 A2061 29c **multicolored**		.65	.20
a.	Booklet pane of 5, #2705-2709	3.25	2.25
b.	As "a," imperf.	2,250.	

CHRISTMAS

Madonna and Child, by
Giovanni Bellini — A2062

A2063

A2064

A2065

A2066

Designed by Bradbury Thompson (#2710) and Lou Nolan (#2711-2719).

Printed by the Bureau of Engraving and Printing, Ashton-Potter America, Inc. (#2711-2714), the Multi-Color Corporation for American Bank Note Company (#2715-2718), and Avery Dennison (#2719).

LITHOGRAPHED & ENGRAVED
Sheets of 300 in six panes of 50 (#2710, 2714a)

1992	Tagged	Perf. 11½x11	
2710 A2062 29c **multicolored**, *Oct. 22*		.60	.20
	P# block of 4, 5#	2.75	—
	Zip, copyright block of 4	2.50	—
a.	Booklet pane of 10	6.00	3.50

LITHOGRAPHED

2711 A2063 29c **multicolored**, *Oct. 22*		.75	.20
2712 A2064 29c **multicolored**, *Oct. 22*		.75	.20
2713 A2065 29c **multicolored**, *Oct. 22*		.75	.20
2714 A2066 29c **multicolored**, *Oct. 22*		.75	.20
a.	Block of 4, #2711-2714	3.00	1.10
	P# block of 4, 5# + P	3.75	—
	Zip, copyright block of 6	4.50	—

Booklet Stamps
PHOTOGRAVURE
Perf. 11 on 2 or 3 Sides

2715 A2063 29c **multicolored**, *Oct. 22*		.85	.20
2716 A2064 29c **multicolored**, *Oct. 22*		.85	.20
2717 A2065 29c **multicolored**, *Oct. 22*		.85	.20
2718 A2066 29c **multicolored**, *Oct. 22*		.85	.20
a.	Booklet pane of 4, #2715-2718	3.50	1.25

Imperforates and part-perforates on gummed stamp paper are proofs from the ABNCo. archives. From the same source come imperforates with Toys only and imperforates without denominations. See No. 2718aP in Proofs section.

Self-Adhesive
Die Cut

2719 A2065 29c **multicolored**, *Oct. 28*		.60	.20
a.	Booklet pane of 18	11.00	

"Greetings" is 27mm long on Nos. 2711-2714, 25mm long on Nos. 2715-2718 and 21½mm long on No. 2719. Nos. 2715-2719 differ in color from Nos. 2711-2714.

CHINESE NEW YEAR

Year of the
Rooster
A2067

Designed by Clarence Lee.

Printed by the American Bank Note Co.

LITHOGRAPHED & ENGRAVED
Panes of 20

1992, Dec. 30	Tagged	Perf. 11	
2720 A2067 29c **multicolored**, prephosphored uncoated paper with embedded tagging showing a mottled appearance, plus block tagging under the engraved portion of the design		.60	.20
	P# block of 4, 5#+A	2.50	—
	Pane of 20	11.50	
a.	Prephosphored uncoated paper with embedded tagging showing a mottled appearance, plus block tagging on top of printed design		3.00	—
	P# block of 4, 5#+A		
b.	Prephosphored uncoated paper with embedded tagging showing a mottled appearance	125.00	—

See No. 3895i.

AMERICAN MUSIC SERIES

Elvis Presley
A2068

Oklahoma!
A2069

Hank Williams
A2070

Elvis Presley
A2071

Bill Haley
A2072

Clyde
McPhatter
A2073

Ritchie Valens
A2074

Otis Redding
A2075

Buddy
Holly — A2076

Dinah
Washington
A2077

Designed by Mark Stutzman (#2721, 2724-2725, 2727, 2729, 2731-2732, 2734, 2736), Wilson McLean (#2722), Richard Waldrep (#2723), John Berkey (#2726, 2728, 2730, 2733, 2735, 2737).

Printed by the Bureau of Engraving and Printing (#2721), Stamp Venturers (#2722-2730), Multi-color Corp. for American Bank Note Co. (#2731-2737).

PHOTOGRAVURE
Panes of 40, Panes of 35 (#2724-2730)

1993		Tagged	Perf. 11	
2721	A2068 29c	**multicolored**, Jan. 8	.60	.20
		P# block of 4, 5#	2.75	—
		Zip, copyright block of 4	2.50	—
a.		Imperf, pair		

		Perf. 10		
2722	A2069 29c	**multicolored**, Mar. 30	.60	.20
		P# block of 4, 4#+S	3.25	—
		Zip block of 4	2.50	—
2723	A2070 29c	**multicolored**, June 9	.75	.20
		P# block of 4, 6#+S	4.25	—
		Zip block of 4	3.25	—

		Perf. 11.2x11.5		
2723A	A2070 29c	**multicolored**, June 9	20.00	10.00
		P# block of 4, 6#+S	140.00	—
		Zip block of 4	90.00	—

1993, June 16			Perf. 10	
2724	A2071 29c	multicolored	.70	
2725	A2072 29c	multicolored	.70	
2726	A2073 29c	multicolored	.70	.20
2727	A2074 29c	multicolored	.70	.20
2728	A2075 29c	multicolored	.70	.20
2729	A2076 29c	multicolored	.70	.20
2730	A2077 29c	multicolored	.70	.20
a.		Vert. strip of 7, #2724-2730	5.50	
		Horiz. P# block of 10, 2 sets of 6P#+S, + top label	10.00	—
		Vert. P# block of 8, 6#+S	7.75	—
		Pane of 35	29.00	—

No. 2730a with Nos. 2724-2730 in numerical sequence cannot be obtained from the pane of 35.

Booklet Stamps
Perf. 11 Horiz.

2731	A2071 29c	multicolored	.60	.20
2732	A2072 29c	multicolored	.60	.20
2733	A2073 29c	multicolored	.60	.20
2734	A2074 29c	multicolored	.60	.20
2735	A2075 29c	multicolored	.60	.20
2736	A2076 29c	multicolored	.60	.20
2737	A2077 29c	multicolored	.60	.20
a.		Booklet pane, 2 #2731, 1 each #2732-2737	5.00	2.25
b.		Booklet pane, #2731, 2735-2737 + tab	2.40	1.50

Nos. 2731-2737 have smaller design sizes, brighter colors and shorter inscriptions than Nos. 2724-2730, as well as framelines around the designs and other subtle design differences.
No. 2737b without tab is indistinguishable from broken No. 2737a.
Imperforates of both No. 2737a and 2737b on gummed stamp paper are proofs from the ABNCo. archives. Perforated booklet pane multiples and varieties also exist from the same source. See Nos. 2737aP-2737bP in Proofs section.
See Nos. 2769, 2771, 2775 and designs A2112-A2117.

SPACE FANTASY

A2086

A2087

A2088

A2089

A2090

Designed by Stephen Hickman.

PHOTOGRAVURE
BOOKLET STAMPS

1993, Jan. 25		Tagged	Perf. 11 Vert.	
2741	A2086 29c	multicolored	.60	.20
2742	A2087 29c	multicolored	.60	.20
2743	A2088 29c	multicolored	.60	.20
2744	A2089 29c	multicolored	.60	.20
2745	A2090 29c	multicolored	.60	.20
a.		Booklet pane of 5, #2741-2745	3.00	2.25

BLACK HERITAGE SERIES

Percy Lavon Julian (1899-1975), Chemist — A2091

Designed by Higgins Bond.

LITHOGRAPHED & ENGRAVED
Panes of 50

1993, Jan. 29		Tagged	Perf. 11	
2746	A2091 29c	multicolored	.60	.20
		P# block of 4, 7#	2.75	—
		Zip block of 4	2.50	—

OREGON TRAIL

A2092

Designed by Jack Rosenthal.

LITHOGRAPHED & ENGRAVED
Panes of 50

1993, Feb. 12		Tagged	Perf. 11	
2747	A2092 29c	multicolored	.60	.20
		P# block of 4, 6#	2.75	—
		Zip block of 4	2.50	—
a.		Tagging omitted	22.50	
b.		Blue omitted		

WORLD UNIVERSITY GAMES

A2093

Designed by David Buck.

PHOTOGRAVURE
Panes of 50

1993, Feb. 25		Tagged	Perf. 11	
2748	A2093 29c multicolored		.60	.20
	P# block of 4, 5#		2.75	—
	Zip block of 4		2.50	—

GRACE KELLY (1929-1982)

Actress, Princess of Monaco — A2094

Designed by Czeslaw Slania.

Printed by Stamp Venturers.

ENGRAVED
Panes of 50

1993, Mar. 24		Tagged	Perf. 11	
2749	A2094 29c blue		.60	.20
	P# block of 4, 1# +S		2.75	—
	Zip block of 4		2.50	—

See Monaco No. 1851.

CIRCUS

Clown — A2095

Ringmaster — A2096

Trapeze Artist — A2097

Elephant — A2098

Designed by Steve McCracken.

Printed by Ashton Potter America.

LITHOGRAPHED
Panes of 40

1993, Apr. 6		Tagged	Perf. 11	
2750	A2095 29c multicolored		.60	.20
2751	A2096 29c multicolored		.60	.20
2752	A2097 29c multicolored		.60	.20
2753	A2098 29c multicolored		.60	.20
a.	Block of 4, #2750-2753		2.40	1.75
	P# block of 6, 5#+P		6.00	—
	Zip block of 6		3.75	—

Plate and zip blocks of 6 and copyright blocks of 9 contain one #2753a with continuous design (complete spotlight).

CHEROKEE STRIP LAND RUN, CENTENNIAL

A2099

Designed by Harold T. Holden.

Printed by American Bank Note. Co.

LITHOGRAPHED & ENGRAVED
Panes of 20

1993, Apr. 17		Tagged	Perf. 11	
2754	A2099 29c multicolored		.60	.20
	P# block of 4, 5#+A		2.50	—
	Pane of 20		12.50	—

Imperforates on gummed stamp paper, including gutter pairs and blocks, are proofs from the ABNCo. archives. From the same source also come perforated gutter pairs and blocks, plus imperforates missing the red text and black denomination and "USA." An approved die proof also is recorded. See No. 2754P in Proofs section.

DEAN ACHESON (1893-1971)

Secretary of State — A2100

Designed by Christopher Calle.

Printed by Stamp Venturers.

ENGRAVED
Sheets of 300 in six panes of 50

1993, Apr. 21		Tagged	Perf. 11	
2755	A2100 29c greenish gray		.60	.20
	P# block of 4, 1#+S		2.75	—
	Zip block of 4		2.50	—

SPORTING HORSES

Steeplechase A2101

Thoroughbred Racing A2102

Harness Racing A2103

Polo — A2104

Designed by Michael Dudash.

Printed by Stamp Venturers.

LITHOGRAPHED & ENGRAVED
Panes of 40

1993, May 1		Tagged	Perf. 11x11½	
2756	A2101 29c multicolored		.60	.20
2757	A2102 29c multicolored		.60	.20
2758	A2103 29c multicolored		.60	.20
2759	A2104 29c multicolored		.60	.20
a.	Block of 4, #2756-2759		2.40	2.00
	P# block of 4, 5#+S		2.75	—
	Zip block of 4		2.50	—
b.	As "a," black (engr.) omitted		700.00	

GARDEN FLOWERS

Hyacinth — A2105

Daffodil — A2106

Tulip — A2107

Iris — A2108

Lilac — A2109

Designed by Ned Seidler.

LITHOGRAPHED & ENGRAVED
BOOKLET STAMPS

1993, May 15		Tagged		Perf. 11 Vert.	
2760	A2105	29c	multicolored	.75	.20
2761	A2106	29c	multicolored	.75	.20
2762	A2107	29c	multicolored	.75	.20
2763	A2108	29c	multicolored	.75	.20
2764	A2109	29c	multicolored	.75	.20
a.		Booklet pane of 5, #2760-2764		3.75	2.25
b.		As "a," black (engr.) omitted		175.00	—
c.		As "a," imperf.		1,000.	

WORLD WAR II

A2110

Illustration reduced.

Designed by William H. Bond.

Designs and events of 1943: a, Destroyers (Allied forces battle German U-boats). b, Military medics treat the wounded. c, Amphibious landing craft on beach (Sicily attacked by Allied forces, July). d, B-24s hit Ploesti refineries, August. e, V-mail delivers letters from home. f, PT boat (Italy invaded by Allies, Sept.).
g, Nos. WS7, WS8, savings bonds, (Bonds and stamps help war effort). h, "Willie and Joe" keep spirits high. i, Banner in window (Gold Stars mark World War II losses). j, Marines assault Tarawa, Nov.
Central label is the size of 15 stamps and shows world map with extent of Axis control and Allied operations.

LITHOGRAPHED & ENGRAVED
Plates of 80 in four panes of 20 each

1993, May 31		Tagged		Perf. 11	
2765	A2110	Block of 10		7.50	5.00
		Pane of 20		15.00	—
a.-j.		29c any single		.75	.40
k.		As No. 2765, tagging omitted on a.-e.		—	
l.		As No. 2765, tagging omitted on f.-j.		—	

No. 2765 has selvage at left and right and either top or bottom.

JOE LOUIS (1914-1981)

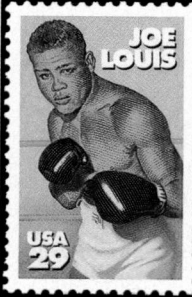

A2111

Designed by Thomas Blackshear.

LITHOGRAPHED & ENGRAVED
Plates of 200 in four panes of 50

1993, June 22		Tagged		Perf. 11	
2766	A2111	29c	multicolored	.60	.20
		P# block of 4, 5#		2.75	—
		Zip block of 4		2.50	—

AMERICAN MUSIC SERIES
Oklahoma! Type and

Show
Boat — A2112

Porgy &
Bess — A2113

My Fair
Lady — A2114

Designed by Wilson McLean.

Printed by Multi-Color Corp.

BOOKLET STAMPS
PHOTOGRAVURE
Perf. 11 Horiz. on 1 or 2 Sides

1993, July 14				Tagged	
2767	A2112	29c	multicolored	.60	.20
2768	A2113	29c	multicolored	.60	.20
2769	A2069	29c	multicolored	.60	.20
2770	A2114	29c	multicolored	.60	.20
a.		Booklet pane of 4, #2767-2770		2.75	2.25

No. 2769 has smaller design size, brighter colors and shorter inscription than No. 2722, as well as a frameline around the design and other subtle design differences.
Imperforate booklet panes, singly or in multiples, on gummed stamp paper are proofs from the ABNCo. archives. From the same source come imperforate progressive proofs, plus imperforate proofs/essays showing slightly altered designs. See No. 2770aP in Proofs section.

AMERICAN MUSIC SERIES
Hank Williams Type and

Patsy
Cline — A2115

The Carter
Family
A2116

Bob
Wills — A2117

Designed by Richard Waldrep.

Printed by Stamp Venturers (#2771-2774) and American Bank Note Co. (#2775-2778).

PHOTOGRAVURE
Panes of 20

1993, Sept. 25		Tagged		Perf. 10	
2771	A2070	29c	multicolored	.75	.20
2772	A2115	29c	multicolored	.75	.20
2773	A2116	29c	multicolored	.75	.20
2774	A2117	29c	multicolored	.75	.20
a.		Block or horiz. strip of 4, #2771-2774		3.00	1.75
		Horiz. P# block of 8, 2 sets of 6#+S + top label		6.50	—
		P# block of 4, 6#+S		3.25	—
		Pane of 20		16.00	—

Booklet Stamps
Perf. 11 Horiz. on one or two sides
With Black Frameline

2775	A2070	29c	multicolored	.60	.20
2776	A2116	29c	multicolored	.60	.20
2777	A2115	29c	multicolored	.60	.20
2778	A2117	29c	multicolored	.60	.20
a.		Booklet pane of 4, #2775-2778		2.50	2.00

Inscription at left measures 27½mm on No. 2723, 27mm on No. 2771 and 22mm on No. 2775. No. 2723 shows only two tuning keys on guitar, while No. 2771 shows those two and parts of two others.
Imperforate booklet panes on gummed stamp paper, singly or in multiples, are proofs from the ABNCo. archives. From the same source come panes perfed horiz. but uncut vertically, plus imperforate progressive proofs and other die proof varieties. See No. 2778aP in Proofs section.

NATIONAL POSTAL MUSEUM

Independence
Hall, Benjamin
Franklin,
Printing Press,
Colonial Post
Rider — A2118

Pony Express Rider, Civil War Soldier, Concord Stagecoach A2119

JN-4H Biplane, Charles Lindbergh, Railway Mail Car, 1931 Model A Ford Mail Truck — A2120

California Gold Rush Miner's Letter, Nos. 39, 295, C3a, C13, Barcode and Circular Date Stamp A2121

Designed by Richard Schlecht.

Printed by American Bank Note Co.

LITHOGRAPHED AND ENGRAVED

1993, July 30		Tagged		Perf. 11	
2779	A2118	29c multicolored		.60	.20
2780	A2119	29c multicolored		.60	.20
2781	A2120	29c multicolored		.60	.20
2782	A2121	29c multicolored		.60	.20
a.		Block or strip of 4, #2779-2782		2.40	2.00
		P# block of 4, 7#+A		2.50	—
		Pane of 20		12.50	—
b.		As "a," engr. maroon (USA/29) and black ("My dear...") omitted		—	
c.		As "a," imperf		3,250.	

AMERICAN SIGN LANGUAGE

A2122

A2123

Designed by Chris Calle.

Printed by Stamp Venturers.

PHOTOGRAVURE

1993, Sept. 20		Tagged		Perf. 11½	
2783	A2122	29c multicolored		.60	.20
2784	A2123	29c multicolored		.60	.20
a.		Pair, #2783-2784		1.20	.75
		P# block of 4, 4#+S		2.50	—
		Pane of 20		12.50	—

CLASSIC BOOKS

A2124

A2125

A2126

A2127

Designed by Jim Lamb.

Printed by American Bank Note Co.
Designs: No. 2785, Rebecca of Sunnybrook Farm, by Kate Douglas Wiggin. No. 2786, Little House on the Prairie, by Laura Ingalls Wilder. No. 2787, The Adventures of Huckleberry Finn, by Mark Twain. No. 2788, Little Women, by Louisa May Alcott.

LITHOGRAPHED & ENGRAVED
Panes of 40

1993, Oct. 23		Tagged		Perf. 11	
2785	A2124	29c multicolored		.60	.20
2786	A2125	29c multicolored		.60	.20
2787	A2126	29c multicolored		.60	.20
2788	A2127	29c multicolored		.60	.20
a.		Block or horiz. strip of 4, #2785-2788		2.40	2.00
		P# block of 4, 5#+A		5.00	—
		Zip block of 4		2.50	—

Imperforates on gummed stamp paper, including gutter pairs and blocks, are proofs from the ABNCo. archives. See No. 2788aP in Proofs section.

CHRISTMAS

Madonna and Child in a Landscape, by Giovanni Battista Cima — A2128

Jack-in-the-Box A2129

Red-Nosed Reindeer A2130

Snowman — A2131

Toy Soldier Blowing Horn — A2132

Designed by Bradbury Thompson (#2789-2790), Peter Good (#2791-2803).

Printed by Bureau of Engraving and Printing (#2789, 2791-2798), KCS Industries (#2790), Avery Dennison (#2799-2803).

LITHOGRAPHED & ENGRAVED
Panes of 50 (#2789, 2791-2794)

1993, Oct. 21		Tagged		Perf. 11	
2789	A2128	29c multicolored		.60	.20
		P# block of 4, 4#		2.75	—
		Zip, copyright block of 4		2.50	—

Booklet Stamp
Size: 18x25mm
Perf. 11½x11 on 2 or 3 Sides

2790	A2128	29c multicolored		.60	.20
a.		Booklet pane of 4		2.40	1.75
b.		Imperf., pair		—	
c.		As "a," imperf		—	

Nos. 2789-2790 have numerous design differences.

1993

PHOTOGRAVURE
Perf. 11½

2791	A2129	29c multicolored, Oct. 21		.60	.20
2792	A2130	29c multicolored, Oct. 21		.60	.20
2793	A2131	29c multicolored, Oct. 21		.60	.20
2794	A2132	29c multicolored, Oct. 21		.60	.20
a.		Block or strip of 4, #2791-2794		2.40	2.00
		P# block of 4, 6#		4.00	—
		Zip, copyright block of 4		2.50	—

Snowman on Nos. 2793, 2799 has three buttons and seven snowflakes beneath nose (placement differs on both stamps). No. 2796 has two buttons and five snowflakes beneath nose. No. 2803 has two orange buttons and four snowflakes beneath nose.

Booklet Stamps
Size: 18x21mm
Perf. 11x10 on 2 or 3 Sides

2795	A2132	29c multicolored, Oct. 21		.85	.20
2796	A2131	29c multicolored, Oct. 21		.85	.20
2797	A2130	29c multicolored, Oct. 21		.85	.20
2798	A2129	29c multicolored, Oct. 21		.85	.20
a.		Booklet pane, 3 each #2795-2796, 2 each #2797-2798		8.50	4.00
b.		Booklet pane, 3 each #2797-2798, 2 each #2795-2796		8.50	4.00
c.		Block of 4, #2795-2798		3.40	1.75

Self-Adhesive
Size: 19½x26½mm
Die Cut

2799	A2131	29c multicolored, Oct. 28		.65	.20
a.		Coil with plate # V1111111		—	6.00

P# strip of 5, 1 each #2799-
2801, 2 #2802, P#V1111111   8.00
P# strip of 8, 2 each #2799-
2802, P#V1111111   12.00
2800 A2132 29c **multicolored**, *Oct. 28*   .65   .20
2801 A2129 29c **multicolored**, *Oct. 28*   .65   .20
2802 A2130 29c **multicolored**, *Oct. 28*   .65   .20
a.   Booklet pane, 3 each #2799-2802   8.00
b.   Block of 4, #2799-2802   2.60

Except for No. 2799a with plate number, coil stamps are
indistinguishable from booklet stamps once they are removed
from the backing paper.

Size: 17x20mm

2803 A2131 29c **multicolored**, *Oct. 28*   .60   .20
a.   Booklet pane of 18   11.00

Snowman on Nos. 2793, 2799 has three buttons and seven
snowflakes beneath nose (placement differs on both stamps).
No. 2796 has two buttons and five snowflakes beneath nose.
No. 2803 has two orange buttons and four snowflakes beneath
nose.

MARIANA ISLANDS

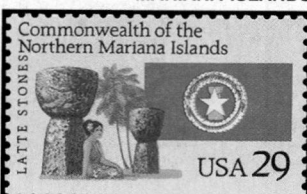

A2133

Designed by Herb Kane.

LITHOGRAPHED AND ENGRAVED
1993, Nov. 4   **Tagged**   *Perf. 11*
2804 A2133 29c **multicolored**   .60   .20
P# block of 4, 6#   2.50   —
Pane of 20   12.50 —

COLUMBUS' LANDING IN PUERTO RICO, 500th ANNIVERSARY

A2134

Designed by Richard Schlecht.

Printed by Stamp Venturers.

PHOTOGRAVURE
Panes of 50
1993, Nov. 19   **Tagged**   *Perf. 11.2*
2805 A2134 29c **multicolored**   .60   .20
P# block of 4, 5#+S   2.75   —
Zip block of 4   2.50   —

AIDS AWARENESS

A2135

Designed by Tom Mann.
Printed by Stamp Venturers.

PHOTOGRAVURE
Panes of 50
1993, Dec. 1   **Tagged**   *Perf. 11.2*
2806 A2135 29c **black & red**   .60   .20
P# block of 4, 3#+S   2.75   —
Zip, copyright block of 6   2.50   —
a.   Perf. 11 vert. on 1 or 2 sides, from bklt.
pane   .70   .20
b.   As "a," booklet pane of 5   3.50   2.00

WINTER OLYMPICS

Slalom — A2136   Luge — A2137

Ice Dancing — A2138   Cross-Country
Skiing — A2139

Ice Hockey — A2140

Designed by Lon Busch.
Printed by Ashton-Potter.

LITHOGRAPHED
Sheets of 120 in six panes of 20
1994, Jan. 6   **Tagged**   *Perf. 11.2*
2807 A2136 29c **multicolored**   .60   .20
2808 A2137 29c **multicolored**   .60   .20
2809 A2138 29c **multicolored**   .60   .20
2810 A2139 29c **multicolored**   .60   .20
2811 A2140 29c **multicolored**   .60   .20
a.   Strip of 5, #2807-2811   3.00   2.50
Horiz. P# block of 10, 2 sets of
4#+P and inscriptions   6.50   —
Horiz. P# block of 10, 2 sets of
4#+P   6.00   —
Pane of 20   12.50 —

EDWARD R. MURROW, JOURNALIST (1908-65)

A2141

Designed by Chris Calle.

ENGRAVED
Panes of 50
1994, Jan. 21   **Tagged**   *Perf. 11.2*
2812 A2141 29c **brown**   .60   .20
P# block of 4, 1#   3.25   —

LOVE

A2142   A2143

A2144

Designed by Peter Goode (#2813), Lon Busch (#2814-2815).

Printed by Banknote Corp. of America (#2813), American
Banknote Co. (#2814) and Bureau of Engraving and Printing
(#2814C, 2815).

Booklet Stamps
LITHOGRAPHED & ENGRAVED
1994   **Tagged**   *Die Cut*
Self-adhesive
2813 A2142 29c **multicolored**, *Jan. 27*   .60   .20
a.   Booklet pane of 18   11.00
b.   Coil with plate # B1   —   3.75
P# strip of 5, #B1   6.75

Except for No. 2813b with plate number, coil stamps are
indistinguishable from booklet stamps once they are removed
from the backing paper.

PHOTOGRAVURE
Perf. 10.9x11.1 on 2 or 3 sides
2814 A2143 29c **multicolored**, *Feb. 14*   .60   .20
a.   Booklet pane of 10   6.00   3.50
b.   Imperf, pair

Horiz. pairs, imperf between, are printer's waste.

LITHOGRAPHED & ENGRAVED
Sheets of 300 in six panes of 50
Tagged
Perf. 11.1
2814C A2143 29c **multicolored**, *June 11* .70   .20
P# block of 4, 5#   3.00   —

Size of No. 2814C is 20x28mm. No. 2814 is 18x24½mm.

PHOTOGRAVURE & ENGRAVED
Sheet of 300 in six panes of 50
Perf. 11.2
2815 A2144 52c **multicolored**, *Feb. 14*   1.00   .20
P# block of 4, 5#   5.00   —
P# block of 10, 2 sets of 5#,
plate diagram, copyright and
pane price inscriptions   11.00 —

BLACK HERITAGE SERIES

Dr. Allison Davis (1902-83),
Social Anthropologist,
Educator — A2145

Designed by Chris Calle.

Printed by Stamp Venturers.

ENGRAVED
1994, Feb. 1   **Tagged**   *Perf. 11.2*
2816 A2145 29c **red brown & brown**   .60   .20
P# block of 4, 1#+S   2.50   —
Pane of 20   12.50 —

CHINESE NEW YEAR

Year of the
Dog — A2146

Designed by Clarence Lee.

Printed by J.W. Fergusson & Sons for Stamp Venturers.

PHOTOGRAVURE
Sheets of 180 in nine panes of 20

1994, Feb. 5	Tagged		
2817 A2146 29c multicolored		.80	.20
P# block of 4, 4#+S		3.50	—
Pane of 20		17.50	—

See No. 3895j.

BUFFALO SOLDIERS

A2147

Designed by Mort Kuntsler.

Printed by Stamp Venturers.

LITHOGRAPHED & ENGRAVED
Plates of 180 in nine panes of 20

1994, Apr. 22	Tagged	Perf. 11.5x11.2	
2818 A2147 29c multicolored		.60	.20
P# block of 4, 5#+S		2.50	—
Pane of 20		12.50	—
a.	Double impression (second impression light) of red brown (engr. inscriptions)	—	

SILENT SCREEN STARS

Rudolph Valentino
(1895-1926) — A2148

Clara Bow (1905-
65) — A2149

Charlie Chaplin (1889-
1977) — A2150

Lon Chaney (1883-
1930) — A2151

John Gilbert (1895-
1936) — A2152

Zasu Pitts (1898-
1963) — A2153

Harold Lloyd (1894-
1971) — A2154

Keystone
Cops — A2155

Theda Bara (1885-
1955) — A2156

Buster Keaton (1895-
1966) — A2157

Designed by Al Hirschfeld.

LITHOGRAPHED & ENGRAVED
Plates of 160 in four panes of 40

1994, Apr. 27	Tagged	Perf. 11.2	
2819 A2148 29c red, black & bright violet		1.10	.30
2820 A2149 29c red, black & bright violet		1.10	.30
2821 A2150 29c red, black & bright violet		1.10	.30
2822 A2151 29c red, black & bright violet		1.10	.30
2823 A2152 29c red, black & bright violet		1.10	.30
2824 A2153 29c red, black & bright violet		1.10	.30
2825 A2154 29c red, black & bright violet		1.10	.30
2826 A2155 29c red, black & bright violet		1.10	.30
2827 A2156 29c red, black & bright violet		1.10	.30
2828 A2157 29c red, black & bright violet		1.10	.30
a.	Block of 10, #2819-2828	11.00	4.00
	P# block of 10, 4#, plate diagram and copyright inscription	12.00	—
	Half pane of 20	23.00	—
b.	As "a," black (litho.) omitted	—	
c.	As "a," blk, red & brt vio (litho.) omitted	—	

GARDEN FLOWERS

Lily — A2158

Zinnia — A2159

Gladiola — A2160

Marigold — A2161

Rose — A2162

Designed by Ned Seidler.

LITHOGRAPHED & ENGRAVED

1994, Apr. 28	Tagged	Perf. 10.9 Vert.	
Booklet Stamps			
2829 A2158 29c multicolored		.60	.20
2830 A2159 29c multicolored		.60	.20
2831 A2160 29c multicolored		.60	.20
2832 A2161 29c multicolored		.60	.20
2833 A2162 29c multicolored		.60	.20
a.	Booklet pane of 5, #2829-2833	3.00	2.25
b.	As "a," imperf	800.00	
c.	As "a," black (engr.) omitted	225.00	
d.	As "a," tagging omitted	—	

1994 WORLD CUP SOCCER CHAMPIONSHIPS

A2163

A2164

A2165

Illustration reduced.

Designed by Michael Dudash.

Printed by J.W. Fergusson & Sons for Stamp Venturers.
Design: 40c, Soccer player, diff.

PHOTOGRAVURE
Plates of 180 in nine panes of 20

1994, May 26		Tagged	*Perf. 11.1*	
2834	A2163	29c **multicolored**	.60	.20
		P# block of 4, 4#+S	2.50	—
		Pane of 20	12.50	—
2835	A2163	40c **multicolored**	.80	.20
		P# block of 4, 4#+S	3.20	—
		Pane of 20	16.00	—
2836	A2164	50c **multicolored**	1.00	.20
		P# block of 4, 4#+S	4.00	—
		Pane of 20	20.00	—

Souvenir Sheet

2837	A2165	Sheet of 3, #a.-c.	4.00	3.00

Nos. 2834-2836 are printed on phosphor-coated paper while Nos. 2837a (29c), 2837b (40c), 2837c (50c) are block tagged. No. 2837c has a portion of the yellow map in the LR corner.

WORLD WAR II

A2166

Illustration reduced.

Designed by William H. Bond.

Designs and events of 1944: a, Allied forces retake New Guinea. b, P-51s escort B-17s on bombing raids. c, Troops running from landing craft (Allies in Normandy, D-Day, June 6). d, Airborne units spearhead attacks. e, Officer at periscope (Submarines shorten war in Pacific). f, Parade (Allies free Rome, June 4; Paris, Aug. 25).

g, Soldier firing flamethrower (US troops clear Saipan bunkers). h, Red Ball Express speeds vital supplies. i, Battleship firing main battery (Battle for Leyte Gulf, Oct. 23-26). j, Soldiers in snow (Bastogne and Battle of the Bulge, Dec.).

Central label is size of 15 stamps and shows world map with extent of Axis control and Allied operations.

LITHOGRAPHED & ENGRAVED
Plates of eight subjects in four panes of 2 each

1994, June 6		Tagged	*Perf. 10.9*	
2838	A2166	Block of 10	18.00	10.00
		Pane of 20	36.00	—
a.-j.		29c any single	1.80	.50

No. 2838 has selvage at left and right and either top or bottom.

NORMAN ROCKWELL

A2167

A2168

Illustration reduced.

Designed by Richard Sheaff based on Rockwell's works.

LITHOGRAPHED & ENGRAVED
Sheets of 200 in four panes of 50

1994, July 1		Tagged	*Perf. 10.9x11.1*	
2839	A2167	29c **multicolored**	.60	.20
		P# block of 4, 5#	2.75	—

Souvenir Sheet
LITHOGRAPHED

2840	A2168	Sheet of 4	4.50	2.75
a.		50c Freedom From Want	1.10	.65
b.		50c Freedom From Fear	1.10	.65
c.		50c Freedom of Speech	1.10	.65
d.		50c Freedom of Worship	1.10	.65

Panes of No. 2839 contain two plate blocks, one containing a plate position diagram.

Moon Landing, 25th Anniv.

A2169

A2170

Designed by Paul and Chris Calle.

Printed by Stamp Venturers (#2841) and Banknote Corp. of America (#2842).

Miniature Sheet
LITHOGRAPHED

1994, July 20		Tagged	*Perf. 11.2x11.1*	
2841	A2169	29c Sheet of 12	11.00	—
a.		Single stamp	.90	.60

LITHOGRAPHED & ENGRAVED
Sheets of 120 in six panes of 20
Perf. 10.7x11.1

1994, July 20				
2842	A2170	$9.95 **multicolored**	20.00	16.00
		P# block of 4, 5#+B	82.50	—

LOCOMOTIVES

Hudson's
General
A2171

McQueen's
Jupiter
A2172

Eddy's No.
242 — A2173

Ely's No.
10 — A2174

Buchanan's
No.
999 — A2175

Designed by Richard Leech.

Printed by J.W. Ferguson & Sons for Stamp Venturers.

PHOTOGRAVURE

1994, July 28		Tagged	*Perf. 11 Horiz.*	
		Booklet Stamps		
2843	A2171	29c **multicolored**	.70	.20
2844	A2172	29c **multicolored**	.70	.20
2845	A2173	29c **multicolored**	.70	.20
2846	A2174	29c **multicolored**	.70	.20
2847	A2175	29c **multicolored**	.70	.20
a.		Booklet pane of 5, #2843-2847	3.50	2.00
b.		As "a," imperf.	*2,500.*	

GEORGE MEANY, LABOR LEADER (1894-1980)

A2176

Designed by Chris Calle.

ENGRAVED
Sheets of 200 in four panes of 50

1994, Aug. 16		Tagged	*Perf. 11.1x11*	
2848	A2176	29c **blue**	.60	.20
		P# block of 4, 1#	2.50	—

Panes of No. 2848 contain two plate blocks, one containing a plate position diagram.

AMERICAN MUSIC SERIES
Popular Singers

Al Jolson
(1886-1950)
A2177

Bing Crosby (1904-77) A2178

Ethel Waters (1896-1977) A2179

Nat "King" Cole (1919-65) A2180

Ethel Merman (1908-84) A2181

Jazz Singers

Bessie Smith (1894-1937) A2182

Muddy Waters (1915-83) A2183

Billie Holiday (1915-59) A2184

Robert Johnson (1911-38) A2185

Jimmy Rushing (1902-72) A2186

"Ma" Rainey (1886-1939) A2187

Mildred Bailey (1907-51) A2188

Howlin' Wolf (1910-76) A2189

Designed by Chris Payne (#2849-2853), Howard Koslow (#2854, 2856, 2858, 2860), Julian Allen (#2855, 2857, 2859, 2861).

Printed by J.W. Fergusson & Sons for Stamp Venturers (#2849-2853), Manhardt-Alexander for Ashton-Potter (USA) Ltd. (#2854-2861).

PHOTOGRAVURE
Plates of 180 in nine panes of 20, Plates of 210 in six panes of 35 (#2854-2861)

1994, Sept. 1		**Tagged**	*Perf. 10.1x10.2*	
2849	A2177	29c **multicolored**	.75	.20
2850	A2178	29c **multicolored**	.75	.20
2851	A2179	29c **multicolored**	.75	.20
2852	A2180	29c **multicolored**	.75	.20
2853	A2181	29c **multicolored**	.75	.20
a.		Vert. strip of 5, #2849-2853	3.75	2.00
		Vert. P# block of 6, 6#+S	8.00	—
		Horiz. P# block of 12, 2 sets of 6#+S, + top label	15.00	—
		Pane of 20	21.00	—
b.		Pane of 20, imperf	*4,600.*	

Some plate blocks of 6 will contain plate position diagram and copyright inscription, others will contain pane price inscription.

1994, Sept. 17			*Perf. 11x10.8*	
		LITHOGRAPHED		
2854	A2182	29c **multicolored**	1.60	.20
2855	A2183	29c **multicolored**	1.60	.20
2856	A2184	29c **multicolored**	1.60	.20
2857	A2185	29c **multicolored**	1.60	.20
2858	A2186	29c **multicolored**	1.60	.20
2859	A2187	29c **multicolored**	1.60	.20
2860	A2188	29c **multicolored**	1.60	.20
2861	A2189	29c **multicolored**	1.60	.20
a.		Block of 10, #2854-2861 +2 additional stamps	16.00	4.50
		Vert. P# block of 10, 5#+P	17.50	—
		P# block of 10, 2 sets of 5#+P, + top label	17.50	—
		Pane of 35	60.00	—

Vertical plate blocks contain either pane price inscription or copyright inscription.

LITERARY ARTS SERIES

James Thurber (1894-1961) — A2190

Designed by Richard Sheaff based on drawing by James Thurber.

LITHOGRAPHED & ENGRAVED
Plates of 200 in four panes of 50

1994, Sept. 10		**Tagged**	*Perf. 11*	
2862	A2190	29c **multicolored**	.60	.20
		P# block of 4, 2#	2.75	

Panes of No. 2862 contain two plate blocks, one containing a plate position diagram.

WONDERS OF THE SEA

Diver, Motorboat A2191

Diver, Ship — A2192

Diver, Ship's Wheel A2193

Diver, Coral — A2194

Designed by Charles Lynn Bragg.

Printed by Barton Press for Banknote Corporation of America.

LITHOGRAPHED
Plates of 216 in nine panes of 24

1994, Oct. 3		Tagged	Perf. 11x10.9	
2863	A2191 29c **multicolored**		.75	.20
2864	A2192 29c **multicolored**		.75	.20
2865	A2193 29c **multicolored**		.75	.20
2866	A2194 29c **multicolored**		.75	.20
a.	Block of 4, #2863-2866		3.00	1.50
	P# block of 4, 4#+B		3.25	—
	Pane of 24		19.00	—
b.	As "a," imperf		1,000.	

CRANES

Black-Necked
A2195

Whooping — A2196

Designed by Clarence Lee based on illustrations by Zhan Gengxi.

Printed by Barton Press for Banknote Corporation of America.

LITHOGRAPHED & ENGRAVED
Sheets of 120 in six panes of 20

1994, Oct. 9		Tagged	Perf. 10.8x11	
2867	A2195 29c **multicolored**		.70	.20
2868	A2196 29c **multicolored**		.70	.20
a.	Pair, #2867-2868		1.40	.75
	P# block of 4, 5#+B		3.00	—
	Pane of 20		14.50	
b.	As "a," black & magenta (engr.) omitted		1,650.	
c.	As "a," double impression of engr. black (Birds' names and "USA") & magenta ("29")		4,750.	
d.	As "a," double impression of engr. black ("USA") & magenta ("29")		—	

LEGENDS OF THE WEST

A2197

Illustration reduced.

g. Bill Pickett (1870-1932)
(Revised)

Vertical Pair with
Horizontal Gutter

Horizontal Pair with Vertical Gutter

Illustration reduced.

Designed by Mark Hess.

Printed by J.W. Fergusson & Sons for Stamp Venturers.

Designs: a, Home on the Range. b, Buffalo Bill Cody (1846-1917). c, Jim Bridger (1804-81). d, Annie Oakley (1860-1926). e, Native American Culture. f, Chief Joseph (c. 1840-1904). h, Bat Masterson (1853-1921). i, John C. Fremont (1813-90). j, Wyatt Earp (1848-1929). k, Nellie Cashman (c. 1849-1925). l, Charles Goodnight (1826-1929). m, Geronimo (1829-1909). n, Kit Carson (1809-68). o, Wild Bill Hickok (1837-76). p, Western Wildlife. q, Jim Beckwourth (c. 1798-1866). r, Bill Tilghman (1854-1924). s, Sacagawea (c. 1787-1812). t, Overland Mail.

PHOTOGRAVURE
Sheets of 120 in six panes of 20

1994, Oct. 18		Tagged	Perf. 10.1x10	
2869	A2197	Pane of 20	15.00	10.00
a.-t.	29c any single		.75	.50
		Sheet of 120 (6 panes)	90.00	—
		Cross gutter block of 20	25.00	—
		Vert. pairs with horiz. gutter (each)	2.50	—
		Horiz. pairs with vert. gutter (each)	2.50	—
u.	As No. 2869, a.-e. imperf. f.-j. part perf.			

Cross gutter block of 20 consists of six stamps from each of two panes and four stamps from each of two other panes with the cross gutter between.

LEGENDS OF THE WEST (Recalled)

g. Bill Pickett
(Recalled)

Nos. 2870b-2870d, 2870f-2870o, 2870q-2870s have a frameline around the vignette that is half the width of the frameline on similar stamps in No. 2869. Other design differences may exist.

PHOTOGRAVURE
Sheets of 120 in six panes of 20

1994		Tagged	Perf. 10.1x10	
2870	A2197 29c	Pane of 20	275.00	—

150,000 panes of No. 2870 were made available through a drawing. Panes were delivered in an envelope. Value is for pane without envelope.

CHRISTMAS

Madonna and Child,
by Elisabetta
Sirani — A2200

Stocking — A2201

Santa Claus — A2202

Greetings
Cardinal in
Snow — A2203

Designed by Bradbury Thompson (#2871), Lou Nolan (#2872), Harry Zelenko (#2873), Peter Good (#2874).

Printed by Bureau of Engraving and Printing (#2871), Ashton-Potter USA, Ltd. (#2872), Avery Dennison (#2873-2874).

LITHOGRAPHED & ENGRAVED
Sheets of 300 in six panes of 50

1994, Oct. 20		Tagged	Perf. 11¼	
2871	A2200 29c **multicolored,** shiny gum		.70	.20
	P# block of 4, 5#		2.75	
	Low gloss gum		.70	
	P# block of 4, 5#		2.75	

BOOKLET STAMP
Perf. 9¾x11

2871A	A2200 29c **multicolored**		.60	.20
b.	Booklet pane of 10		6.25	3.50
c.	Imperf, pair		475.00	

LITHOGRAPHED
Sheets of 400 in eight panes of 50
Perf. 11¼

2872	A2201 29c **multicolored**		.60	.20
	P# block of 4, 5#+P		2.50	
a.	Booklet pane of 20		12.50	4.00
b.	Imperf., pair		—	
c.	Vert. pair, imperf. horiz.		—	
d.	Quadruple impression of black, triple impression of blue, double impressions of red and yellow, green normal		—	
e.	Vert. pair, imperf between		—	

Panes of Nos. 2871-2872 contain four plate blocks, one containing pane position diagram.

PHOTOGRAVURE
BOOKLET STAMPS
Self-Adhesive
Die Cut

2873	A2202 29c **multicolored**		.70	.20
a.	Booklet pane of 12		8.50	
b.	Coil with plate # V1111		—	6.00
	P# strip of 5, P#V1111		8.00	

Except for No. 2873b with plate number, coil stamps are indistinguishable from booklet stamps once they are removed from the backing paper.

2874	A2203 29c **multicolored**		.60	.20
a.	Booklet pane of 18		11.00	

BUREAU OF ENGRAVING & PRINTING
Souvenir Sheet

A2204

Illustration reduced.

Major Double Transfer

Minor Double Transfer

Designed by Peter Cocci, using original die for Type A98.

LITHOGRAPHED & ENGRAVED
1994, Nov. 3	Tagged	Perf. 11	
2875	A2204 $2 Sheet of 4	16.00	13.50
a.	Single stamp	4.00	2.00
	Sheet of 4 with major double transfer on right stamp	80.00	—
	Major double transfer, single stamp		
	Sheet of 4 with minor double transfer on right stamp	32.50	—
	Minor double transfer, single stamp		

CHINESE NEW YEAR

Year of the Boar — A2205

Designed by Clarence Lee.

Printed by Stamp Venturers.

PHOTOGRAVURE
Panes of 20
1994, Dec. 30	Tagged	Perf. 11.2x11.1	
2876	A2205 29c multicolored	.70	.20
	P# block of 4, 5#+S	3.00	—
	Pane of 20	15.00	—

See No. 3895k.

The first class rate was increased to 32c on Jan. 1, 1995.

A2206

A2207

A2208

A2208a

A2208a

A2209

Designed by Richard D. Sheaff (#2877-2878), Lou Nolan (#2879-2892).

Printed by American Bank Note Co. (#2877, 2884, 2890), Bureau of Engraving and Printing (#2879, 2881, 2883, 2889), Stamp Venturers (#2878, 2880, 2882, 2888, 2891-2892), KCS Industries (#2885), Avery-Dennison (#2886-2887).

Coil Plate No. Strips of 3
Beginning with No. 2123, coil plate no. strips of 3 usually sell at the level of strips of 5 minus the face value of two stamps.

LITHOGRAPHED
Sheets of 100
1994, Dec. 13	Untagged	Perf. 11x10.8	
2877	A2206 (3c) tan, bright blue & red	.20	.20
	P# block of 4, 3#+A	.30	
	Zip block of 4	.25	—
a.	Imperf., pair	135.00	
b.	Double impression of red	190.00	

No. 2877 imperf and with blue omitted is known from printer's waste.

Perf. 10.8x10.9
2878	A2206 (3c) tan, dark blue & red	.20	.20
	P# block of 4, 3#+S	.40	
	Zip block of 4	.25	

Inscriptions on #2877 are in a thin typeface. Those on #2878 are in heavy, bold type.

PHOTOGRAVURE
Tagged
Perf. 11.2x11.1
2879	A2207 (20c) black "G," yellow & multi	.40	.20
	P# block of 4, 5#	8.50	
	Zip block of 4	1.75	
a.	Imperf., pair		

Perf. 11x10.9
2880	A2207 (20c) red "G," yellow & multi	.75	.20
	P# block of 4, 5#+S	17.50	
	Zip block of 4	3.25	

Perf. 11.2x11.1
2881	A2208 (32c) black "G" & multi	1.25	.20
	P# block of 4, 4#	70.00	
	Zip block of 4	5.50	
a.	Booklet pane of 10	12.50	5.00

Perf. 11x10.9
2882	A2208a (32c) red "G" & multi	.60	.20
	P# block of 4, 4#+S	4.00	
	Zip block of 4	2.75	

Distance on #2882 from bottom of red G to top of flag immediately above is 13¾mm. Illustration A2208a shows #2885 superimposed over #2882.

BOOKLET STAMPS
Perf. 10x9.9 on 2 or 3 Sides
2883	A2208 (32c) black "G" & multi	.65	.20
a.	Booklet pane of 10	6.50	3.75

Perf. 10.9 on 2 or 3 Sides
2884	A2208 (32c) blue "G" & multi	.65	.20
a.	Booklet pane of 10	6.50	3.75

b.	As "a," imperf	1,700.	

Perf. 11x10.9 on 2 or 3 Sides
2885	A2208a (32c) red "G" & multi	.90	.20
a.	Booklet pane of 10	9.00	4.50
b.	Horiz. pair, imperf vert.		
c.	Horiz. pair, imperf between		

Distance on #2885 from bottom of red G to top of flag immediately above is 13½mm. See note below #2882.
No. 2885c resulted from a paper foldover after perforating and before cutting into panes.

A2208b

A2208c

	Self-Adhesive	Die Cut	
2886	A2208b (32c) gray, blue, light blue, red & black	.75	.20
a.	Booklet pane of 18	14.00	
b.	Coil with plate # V11111		10.00
	P# strip of 5, same #	12.00	

No. 2886 is printed on surface-tagged paper which is opaque, thicker and brighter than that of No. 2887 and has only a small number of blue shading dots in the white stripes immediately below the flag's blue field.
Except for No. 2886b with plate number, coil stamps are indistinguishable from booklet stamps once they are removed from the backing paper.

2887	A2208c (32c) black, blue & red	.75	.20
a.	Booklet pane of 18	13.50	

No. 2887 has noticeable blue shading in the white stripes immediately below the blue field and has overall tagging. The paper is translucent, thinner and duller than No. 2886.

COIL STAMPS
Perf. 9.8 Vert.
2888	A2209 (25c) black "G," blue & multi	.90	.50
	Pair	1.80	1.00
	P# strip of 5, #S11111	4.00	
	P# single, #S11111		2.50
2889	A2208 (32c) black "G" & multi	1.50	.20
	Pair	3.00	.30
	P# strip of 5, #1111, 2222	8.00	
	P# single, #1111, 2222		4.50
a.	Imperf., pair	275.00	
2890	A2208 (32c) blue "G" & multi	.65	.20
	Pair	1.25	.30
	P# strip of 5, #A1111, A1112, A1113, A1211, A1212, A1311, A1313, A1324, A2211, A2212, A2213, A2214, A3314, A3314, A3323, A3324, A3433, A3435, A3436, A4427, A5327, A5417, A5427	3.50	
	P# strip of 5, #A1222, A1314, A4426, A5437	5.00	
	P# strip of 5, #A1417, A2223	7.50	
	P# strip of 5, #A1433	8.00	
	P# strip of 5, #A2313	7.75	
	P# strip of 5, #A3114, A3315, A3423	7.25	
	P# strip of 5, #A3426	5.50	
	P# strip of 5, #A4435	250.00	
	P# single, #A1111, A1313, A2214, A3113, A3314, A3324, A4427, A5427	—	1.00
	P# single, #A1212, A3323	—	3.00
	P# single, #A2212, A3435	—	3.50
	P# single, #A1112, A1311, A1324, A2213, A5327	—	2.50
	P# single, #A1113, A5437	—	3.75
	P# single, #A3315, A3423, A3426	—	4.75
	P# single, #A1222, A2211, A3114	—	4.25
	P# single, #A1211, A1314, A4426	—	4.00
	P# single, #A1417, A1433	—	6.75
	P# single, #A2223, A2313	—	6.00
	P# single, #A3433, A3436	—	2.00
	P# single, #A4435	—	250.00
	P# single, #A5417	—	3.00
2891	A2208 (32c) red "G" & multi	.85	.20
	Pair	1.70	.30
	P# strip of 5, #S1111	4.75	
	P# single, #S1111	—	1.00

Rouletted 9.8 Vert.
2892	A2208 (32c) red "G" & multi	.75	.20
	Pair	1.50	.30
	P# strip of 5, #S1111, S2222	4.75	
	P# single, #S1111, S2222	—	1.00

See note under No. 2525.

A2210

Flag Over
Porch — A2212

Designed by Lou Nolan (#2893), Dave LaFleur (#2897).

Printed by American Bank Note Co. (#2893), Stamp Venturers (#2897).

PHOTOGRAVURE
COIL STAMP

1995   Untagged   Perf. 9.8 Vert.

2893 A2210 (5c) green & multi	.50	.20
Pair	1.00	.20
P# strip of 5, #A11111, A21111	3.50	
P# single, #A11111, A21111	—	1.60

No. 2893 was only available through the Philatelic Fullfillment
Center (and, for a short time, at the L'Enfant Plaza Philatelic
Center in Washington, DC) after its announcement 1/12/95.
Covers submitted for first day cancels received a 12/13/94 can-
cel, even though the stamps were not available on that date.

Sheets of 400 in four panes of 100

1995, May 19   Tagged   Perf. 10.4

2897 A2212 32c multicolored,	.65	.20
P# block of 4, 5#+S	4.25	—
a. Imperf., vert. pair	60.00	

See Nos. 2913-2916, 2920-2921, 3133. For booklet see No.
BK243.

Butte — A2217

Mountain — A2218

Auto — A2220

Auto Tail
Fin — A2223

Juke Box — A2225

Flag Over
Field — A2230

Designed by Tom Engeman (#2902-2904B), Robert
Brangwynne (#2905-2906), Chris Calle (#2907), Bill Nelson
(#2908-2912B), Dave LaFleur (#2913-2916, 2921), Sabra Field
(#2919).

Printed by J.W. Fergusson & Sons for Stamp Venturers
(#2902, 2905, 2909, 2912, 2914), Bureau of Engraving and
Printing (#2903, 2904B, 2908, 2911, 2912B, 2913, 2915A,
2915C-2915D, 2916, 2921), Stamp Venturers (#2902B, 2904,

2906-2907, 2910, 2912A, 2915B), Avery Dennison (#2904A,
2915, 2919, 2920).

> **Coil Plate No. Strips of 3**
> Beginning with No. 2123, coil plate no. strips
> of 3 usually sell at the level of strips of 5 minus
> the face value of two stamps.

COIL STAMPS
PHOTOGRAVURE

1995-97   Untagged   Perf. 9.8 Vert.

**Self-Adhesive (#2902B, 2904A-2904B, 2906-2907,
2910, 2912A, 2912B, 2915-2915D, 2919-2921)**

2902 A2217 (5c) yellow, red & blue, Mar. 10	.20	.20
Pair	.20	.20
P# strip of 5, #S111, S222, S333	1.00	
P# single, #S111, S222, S333	—	.70
a. Imperf., pair	575.00	

Serpentine Die Cut 11.5 Vert.

2902B A2217 (5c) yellow, red & blue, June 15, 1996	.35	.20
Pair	.70	
P# strip of 5, #S111	2.25	
P# single, #S111	—	.80

Perf. 9.8 Vert.

2903 A2218 (5c) purple & multi, Mar. 16, 1996	.25	.20
Pair	.50	.20
P# strip of 5, #11111	1.25	
P# single, #11111	—	.90
a. Tagged (error)	4.00	3.50
P# strip of 5, #11111	60.00	
P# single, #11111	—	65.00

Letters of inscription "USA NONPROFIT ORG." outlined in
purple on #2903.

2904 A2218 (5c) blue & multi, Mar. 16, 1996	.20	.20
Pair	.40	.20
P# strip of 5, #S111	1.25	
P# single, #S111	—	.80
c. Imperf., pair	400.00	

Letters of inscription have no outline on #2904.

Serpentine Die Cut 11.2 Vert.

2904A A2218 (5c) purple & multi, June 15, 1996	.40	.20
Pair	.80	
P# strip of 5, #V222222, V333323, V333342	4.00	
P# strip of 5, #V333333	2.75	
P# strip of 5, #V333343	3.00	
P# single, #V222222, V333323, V333333, V333342	—	2.25
P# single, #V333343		3.75

Serpentine Die Cut 9.8 Vert.

2904B A2218 (5c) purple & multi, Jan. 24, 1997	.20	.20
pair	.40	
P# strip of 5, #1111	1.40	
P# single, #1111	—	1.00

Letters of inscription outlined in purple on No. 2904B, not outlined on No. 2904A.

Perf. 9.8 Vert.

2905 A2220 (10c) black, red brown & brown, small "1995" date, Mar. 10	.20	.20
Pair	.40	.40
P# strip of 5, #S111, S222	2.00	
P# single, #S111, S222	—	1.25
a. Large "1995" date, 1996	.20	.20
Pair	.40	.40
P# strip of 5, #S333	3.00	
P# single, #S333	—	1.50
b. As "a," brown omitted, P#S33 single		

Date on 2905 is approximately 1.9mm long, on No. 2905a
2.1mm long.

Serpentine Die Cut 11.5 Vert.

2906 A2220 (10c) black, brown & red brown, June 15, 1996	.50	.20
Pair	1.00	
P# strip of 5, #S111	2.50	
P# single, #S111	—	1.50
2907 A1957 (10c) gold & multi, May 21, 1996	.75	.20
Pair	1.50	
P# strip of 5, #S11111	4.00	
P# single, #S11111	—	2.25

Perf. 9.8 Vert.

2908 A2223 (15c) dark orange yellow & multi, Mar. 17	.30	.30
Pair	.60	.60
P# strip of 5, #11111	2.00	
P# single, #11111	—	1.75

No. 2908 has dark, bold colors, heavy shading lines and
heavily shaded chrome.

2909 A2223 (15c) buff & multi, Mar. 17	.30	.30

Pair	.60	.60
P# strip of 5, #S11111	2.00	
P# single, #S11111	—	1.50

No. 2909 has shinier chrome, more subdued colors and finer
details than No. 2908.

Serpentine Die Cut 11.5 Vert.

2910 A2223 (15c) buff & multi, June 15, 1996	.30	.30
Pair	.60	
P# strip of 5, #S11111	2.00	
P# single, #S11111	—	1.50

Perf. 9.8 Vert.

2911 A2225 (25c) dark red, dark yellow green & multi, Mar. 17	.50	.50
Pair	1.00	1.00
P# strip of 5, #111111, 212222, 222222, 332222	3.75	
P# single, #111111, 212222, 222222	—	2.25
P# single, #332222	—	2.75
a. Imperf, pair	425.00	

No. 2911 has dark, saturated colors and dark blue lines in the
music selection board.

2912 A2225 (25c) bright orange red, bright yellow green & multi, Mar. 17	.75	.50
Pair	1.50	1.00
P# strip of 5, #S11111, S22222	4.50	
P# single, same #	—	2.00

No. 2912 has bright colors, less shading and light blue lines
in the music selection board.

Serpentine Die Cut 11.5 Vert.

2912A A2225 (25c) bright orange red, bright yellow green & multi, June 15, 1996	.50	.50
Pair	1.00	
P# strip of 5, #S11111, S22222	3.75	
P# single, same #	—	1.60

Serpentine Die Cut 9.8 Vert.

2912B A2225 (25c) dark red, dark yellow green & multi, Jan. 24, 1997	.75	.50
pair	1.50	
P# strip of 5, #111111	4.00	
P# strip of 5, #222222	5.00	
P# single, #111111	—	1.50
P# single, #222222	—	3.50

See No. 3132.

Tagged
Perf. 9.8 Vert.

2913 A2212 32c blue, tan, brown, red & light blue, shiny gum, May 19	.65	.20
Pair	1.30	.30
P# strip of 5, #11111, 22221	5.00	
P# strip of 5, #22222	5.25	
P# single, #11111, 22222	—	2.75
P# single, #22221	—	3.50
Low gloss gum	.65	
Pair	1.30	
P# strip of 5, #11111, 22222, 33333, 34333, 44444, 45444, 66646, 77767, 78767, 91161, 99969	4.50	
P# strip of 5, #22322	8.00	
P# strip of 5, #66666	11.00	
P# single, #22322	—	5.75
P# single, #33333, 34333, 44444, 45444, 66646, 77767	—	1.50
P# single, #66666	—	8.00
P# single, #78767, 91161, 99969	—	2.25
a. Imperf., pair	30.00	

No. 2913 has pronounced light blue shading in the flag and
red "1995" at left bottom. See No. 3133.

2914 A2212 32c blue, yellow brown, red & gray, May 19	.80	.20
Pair	1.60	.30
P# strip of 5, #S11111	4.50	
P# single, #S11111	—	2.00

No. 2914 has pale gray shading in the flag and blue "1995" at
left bottom.

Serpentine Die Cut 8.7 Vert.

2915 A2212 32c multicolored, Apr. 18	1.25	.30
Pair	2.50	
P# strip of 5, #V11111	10.50	
P# single, #V11111	—	8.75

Serpentine Die Cut 9.8 Vert.

2915A	A2212	32c dk blue, tan, brown, red & light blue, *May 21, 1996*		.65	.20
		Pair		1.30	
		P# strip of 5, #11111, 22222, 23222, 33333, 44444, 45444, 55555, 66666, 78777, 88888, 99999, 11111A, 13231A, 13311A, 22222A, 33333A, 44444A, 55555A, 66666A, 77777A, 78777A, 88888A		4.25	
		P# strip of 5, #87888		20.00	
		P# strip of 5, #87898		11.00	
		P# strip of 5, #88898		75.00	
		P# strip of 5, #89878, 97898		9.00	
		P# strip of 5, #89888		14.00	
		P# strip of 5, #89898		8.00	
		P# strip of 5, #89899		*450.00*	
		P# strip of 5, #99899		13.00	
		P# strip of 5, #13211A		70.00	
		P# single, #11111, 22222, 23222, 33333, 44444, 45444, 55555, 66666, 78777, 88888, 99999, 11111A, 13231A,13311A, 22222A, 33333A, 44444A, 55555A, 66666A, 77777A, 78777A, 88888A	—	1.00	
		P# single, #87888	—	12.00	
		P# single, #87898, 89878, 97898	—	4.00	
		P# single, #88898	—	62.50	
		P# single, #89888	—	9.00	
		P# single, #89898	—	2.75	
		P# single, #89899	—	225.00	
		P# single, #99899	—	30.00	
		P# single, #13211A	—	65.00	
h.		Die cutting omitted, pair		32.50	—
i.		Tan omitted		—	
j.		Double die cutting		30.00	

No. 2915A has red "1996" at left bottom.

Die cutting on No. 2915A shows either 10 serpentine "peaks" on each side, 11 "peaks" on the left side and 10 "peaks" on the right side, or 10 "peaks" on the left side and 11 "peaks" on the right side. The last configuration is considered by specialists to be an error, and it is rare.

Sky on No. 3133 shows color gradation at LR not on No. 2915A.

On No. 2915Ai all other colors except brown are severely shifted.

On No. 2915Aj, the second die cutting is a different gauge than the normal 9.8.

Plate number 99999 strips of No. 2915A are known with the brown date number shifted one stamp to the right of the stamp with the other plate numbers. Such strips are scarce. Value of mint never hinged P# strip of 5 or 6, $1,500. Used examples are rare.

Serpentine Die Cut 11.5 Vert.

2915B	A2212	32c dk blue, tan, brown, red & light blue, *June 15, 1996*		1.00	.90
		Pair		2.00	
		P# strip of 5, #S11111		5.00	
		P# single, #S11111	—		2.75

Serpentine Die Cut 10.9 Vert.

2915C	A2212	32c dk blue, tan, brown, red & light blue, *May 21, 1996*		2.00	.40
		Pair		4.00	
		P# strip of 5, #55555, 66666		27.50	
		P# single, #55555, 66666	—		4.75
		P# single, #88888	—		*3,000.*

Plate number 55555 strips of No. 2915C are known with the tan plate number shifted one stamp to the left of the stamp with the other plate numbers. Extremely scarce. Last reported auction sale price (2006) was approximately $5,250.

Serpentine Die Cut 9.8 Vert.

2915D	A2212	32c dark blue, tan, brown, red & light blue, *Jan. 24, 1997*		2.00	.90
		pair		4.00	
		P# strip of 5, #11111		9.00	
		P# single, #11111	—		3.00

No. 2915D shows 9 "peaks" at left and 10 at right or 10 "peaks" at left and 10 at right.

Stamps on multiples of No. 2915A touch, and are on a peelable backing the same size as the stamps, while those of No. 2915D are separated on the peelable backing, which is larger than the stamps.

No. 2915D has red "1997" at left bottom; No. 2915A has red "1996" at left bottom.

Sky on No. 3133 shows color gradation at LR not on No. 2915D, and it has blue "1996" at left bottom.

BOOKLET STAMPS
Perf. 10.8x9.8 on 2 or 3 Adjacent Sides

2916	A2212	32c blue, tan, brown, red & light blue, *May 19*		.65	.20
a.		Booklet pane of 10		6.50	3.25
b.		As "a," imperf.		—	

Die Cut

2919	A2230	32c multicolored, *Mar. 17*		.65	.20
a.		Booklet pane of 18		12.00	
b.		Vert. pair, die cutting omitted btwn.		—	

Serpentine Die Cut 8.7 on 2, 3 or 4 Adjacent Sides

2920	A2212	32c multicolored, dated blue "1995," *Apr. 18*		.65	.20
a.		Booklet pane of 20+label		13.00	
b.		Small date		6.00	.35
c.		As "b," booklet pane of 20+label		120.00	
f.		As No. 2920, pane of 15+label		10.00	
g.		As "a," partial pane of 10, 3 stamps and parts of 7 stamps printed on backing liner		—	
h.		As No. 2920, booklet pane of 15		50.00	
i.		As No. 2920, die cutting omitted, pair		—	
j.		Dark blue omitted (from No. 2920a)		1,750.	
k.		Vert. pair, die cutting missing between (PS) (from No. 2920a)		—	

Date on No. 2920 is nearly twice as large as date on No. 2920b. No. 2920f comes in various configurations.

No. 2920h is a pane of 16 with one stamp removed. The missing stamp is the lower right stamp in the pane or (more rarely) the upper left stamp. No. 2920h cannot be made from No. 2920f, a pane of 15 + label. The label is located in the sixth or seventh row of the pane and is die cut. If the label is removed, an impression of the die cutting appears on the backing paper.

Serpentine Die Cut 11.3 on 3 sides

2920D	A2212	32c multicolored, dated blue "1996," *Jan. 20, 1996*		.80	.25
e.		Booklet pane of 10		8.00	

Serpentine Die Cut 9.8 on 2 or 3 Adjacent Sides

2921	A2212	32c dk bl, tan, brn, red & lt bl, dated red 1996, *May 21, 1996*		.90	.20
a.		Booklet pane of 10, dated red "1996"		9.00	
b.		As No. 2921, dated red "1997," *Jan. 24, 1997*		1.20	.20
c.		As "a," dated red "1997"		12.00	
d.		Booklet pane of 5 + label, dated red "1997," *Jan. 24, 1997*		7.00	
e.		As "a," die cutting omitted		200.00	

Scott values for used self-adhesive stamps are for examples either on piece or off piece.

GREAT AMERICANS ISSUE

A2248

A2249

A2250

A2251

A2253

A2255

A2256

A2257

A2258

Designed by Dennis Lyall (#2933-2934), Richard Sheaff (#2935), Howard Paine (#2936, 2941-2942), Roy Andersen (#2938), Chris Calle (#2940, 2943).

Printed by Banknote Corporation of America (#2933-2935, 2940-2943), Ashton-Potter (USA) Ltd. (#2936), Bureau of Engraving & Printing (#2938).

ENGRAVED
Sheets of 400 in four panes of 100
Sheets of 160 in eight panes of 20 (#2935)
Sheets of 120 in six panes of 20 (#2936, 2941-2942)

1995-99   **Tagged**

Self-Adhesive (#2941-2942)
Perf. 11.2, Serpentine Die Cut 11.7x11.5 (#2941-2942)

2933	A2248	32c brown, prephosphored coated paper with surface tagging showing a solid appearance, *Sept. 13, 1995*		.65	.20
		P# block of 4, 1#+B		3.00	
2934	A2249	32c green, prephosphored coated paper with surface tagging showing a solid appearance, *Apr. 26, 1996*		.65	.25
		P# block of 4, 1#+B		3.00	—

No. 2934 exists on two types of surface-tagged paper that exhibit either a solid or grainy solid appearance.

2935	A2250	32c lake, prephosphored coated paper with surface tagging showing a grainy solid appearance, *Apr. 3, 1998*		.65	.35
		P# block of 4, 1#+B		3.00	
		Pane of 20		14.75	
2936	A2251	32c blue, prephosphored coated paper with surface tagging showing a solid appearance, *July 16, 1998*		.65	.35
		P# block of 4, 1#+P		3.00	—
		Pane of 20		14.75	
a.		32c light blue		.65	.35
		P# block of 4, 1#+P		3.00	
		Pane of 20		14.75	
2938	A2253	46c carmine, prephosphored uncoated paper with embedded tagging showing a mottled appearance, *Oct. 20, 1995*		.90	.30
		P# block of 4, 1#		4.50	
2940	A2255	55c green, prephosphored coated paper with surface tagging showing a grainy solid appearance, *July 11, 1995*		1.10	.20
		P# block of 4, 1#+B		5.50	
a.		Imperf, pair			
2941	A2256	55c black, prephosphored coated paper with surface tagging showing a solid appearance, *July 17, 1999*		1.10	.20
		P# block of 4, 1#+B		4.40	
		Pane of 20		22.00	
2942	A2257	77c blue, prephosphored coated paper with surface tagging showing a solid appearance, *Nov. 9, 1998*		1.50	.40
		P# block of 4, 1#+B		6.00	
		Pane of 20		30.00	
2943	A2258	78c bright violet, prephosphored coated paper with surface tagging showing a solid appearance, *Aug. 18, 1995*		1.60	.20
		P# block of 4, 1#+B		7.50	
a.		78c dull violet, prephosphored coated paper with surface tagging showing a grainy solid appearance		1.60	.25
		P# block of 4, 1#+B		7.50	
b.		78c pale violet, prephosphored coated paper with surface tagging showing a grainy solid appearance		1.75	.30
		P# block of 4, 1#+B		12.00	—

The pale violet ink on No. 2943b luminesces bright pink under long-wave ultraviolet light.

LOVE

Cherub from Sistine Madonna, by Raphael
A2263   A2264

Designed by Terry McCaffrey.

Printed by the Bureau of Engraving and Printing (#2948) and Banknote Corp. of America (#2949).

LITHOGRAPHED & ENGRAVED
Sheets of 300 in six panes of 50

1995, Feb. 1	Tagged	Perf. 11.2	
2948 A2263 (32c) **multicolored**		.65	.20
P# block of 4, 5#		3.00	

Self-Adhesive
Die Cut

2949 A2264 (32c) **multicolored**		.65	.20
a. Booklet pane of 20 + label		13.00	
b. Red (engr.) omitted		275.00	
c. As "a," red (engr.) omitted		5,500.	
d. Red (engr.) missing (CM)			

No. 2949d must be collected se-tenant with a normal stamp. See Nos. 2957-2960, 3030.

Florida Statehood, 150th Anniv. A2265

Designed by Laura Smith.
Printed by Ashton-Potter (USA) Ltd.

LITHOGRAPHED
Sheets of 160 in eight panes of 20

1995, Mar. 3	Tagged	Perf. 11.1	
2950 A2265 32c **multicolored**		.65	.20
P# block of 4, 5#+P		3.00	
Pane of 20		15.00	

EARTH DAY

Earth Clean-Up A2266

Solar Energy A2267

Tree Planting A2268

Beach Clean-Up A2269

Designed by Christy Millard (#2951), Jennifer Michalove (#2952), Brian Hailes (#2953) and Melody Kiper (#2954).

Printed by Ashton-Potter (USA) Ltd.

LITHOGRAPHED
Sheets of 96 in six panes of 16

1995, Apr. 20	Tagged	Perf. 11.1x11	
2951 A2266 32c **multicolored**		.65	.20
2952 A2267 32c **multicolored**		.65	.20
2953 A2268 32c **multicolored**		.65	.20
2954 A2269 32c **multicolored**		.65	.20
a. Block of 4, #2951-2954		2.60	1.75
P# block of 4, 5#+P		2.60	
Horiz. P# block of 8, 2 sets of 5#+P, + top or bottom label		5.25	
Pane of 16		10.50	

A2270

A2271

RICHARD M. NIXON
37th President (1913-94)

Designed by Daniel Schwartz.
Printed by Barton Press and Bank Note Corp. of America.

LITHOGRAPHED & ENGRAVED
Sheets of 200 in four panes of 50

1995, Apr. 26	Tagged	Perf. 11.2	
2955 A2270 32c **multicolored**		.65	.20
P# block of 4, 5#+B		3.00	
a. Red (engr.) missing (CM)		950.	

No. 2955 is known with red (engr. "Richard Nixon") inverted, and with red engr. omitted but only half the Nixon portrait present, both from printer's waste. No. 2955a shows a complete Nixon portrait.

BLACK HERITAGE SERIES
Bessie Coleman (d. 1926), Aviator

Designed by Chris Calle.

ENGRAVED
Sheets of 200 in four panes of 50

1995, Apr. 27	Tagged	Perf. 11.2	
2956 A2271 32c **red & black**		.85	.20
P# block of 4, 1#		3.75	

LOVE

A2272

A2273

Cherubs from Sistine Madonna, by Raphael — A2274

Designed by Terry McCaffrey.
Printed by Bureau of Engraving and Printing (#2957-2959), Bank Note Corp. of America (#2960).

LITHOGRAPHED & ENGRAVED
Sheets of 300 in six panes of 50

1995, May 12	Tagged	Perf. 11.2	
2957 A2272 32c **multicolored**		.65	.20
P# block of 4, 5#		3.00	
Copyright block of 6		4.25	

Compare with No. 3030. For booklet see No. BK244.

2958 A2273 55c **multicolored**		1.10	.20
P# block of 4, 5#		5.50	

BOOKLET STAMPS
Perf. 9.8x10.8

2959 A2272 32c **multicolored**		.65	.20
a. Booklet pane of 10		6.50	3.25
b. Imperf, pair		100.00	

Self-Adhesive
Die Cut

2960 A2274 55c **multicolored**		1.10	.20
a. Booklet pane of 20 + label		22.50	

RECREATIONAL SPORTS

Volleyball A2275

Softball A2276

Bowling A2277

Tennis A2278

Golf — A2279

Designed by Don Weller.
Printed by Bank Note Corp. of America.

LITHOGRAPHED
Sheets of 120 in six panes of 20

1995, May 20	Tagged	Perf. 11.2	
2961 A2275 32c **multicolored**		.65	.20
2962 A2276 32c **multicolored**		.65	.20
2963 A2277 32c **multicolored**		.65	.20
2964 A2278 32c **multicolored**		.65	.20
2965 A2279 32c **multicolored**		.65	.20
a. Vert. strip of 5, #2961-2965		3.25	2.00
P# block of 10, 2 sets of 4#+B		6.50	
P# block of 8, 2 sets of 4#+B		5.50	
Pane of 20		13.00	
b. As "a," imperf		2,250.	
c. As "a," yellow omitted		2,000.	
d. As "a," yellow, blue & magenta omitted		2,000.	

PRISONERS OF WAR & MISSING IN ACTION

A2280

Designed by Carl Herrman.
Printed by Ashton-Potter (USA) Ltd.

LITHOGRAPHED
Sheets of 160 in eight panes of 20

1995, May 29	Tagged	Perf. 11.2
2966 A2280 32c multicolored		.65 .20
P# block of 4, 5#+P		2.50 —
Pane of 20		12.50 —

The five plate numbers do not include a sixth plate number for the plate that applied a transparent laquer "color."

LEGENDS OF HOLLYWOOD

Marilyn Monroe (1926-62) — A2281

Cross Gutter Block of 8

Illustration reduced.

Designed by Michael Deas.
Printed by Stamp Venturers.

PHOTOGRAVURE
Sheets of 120 in six panes of 20

1995, June 1	Tagged	Perf. 11.1
2967 A2281 32c multicolored		.85 .20
P# block of 4, 6#+S		5.50 —
Pane of 20		25.00
Sheet of 120 (six panes)		150.00
Cross gutter block of 8		55.00 —
Block of 8 with vertical gutter		45.00 —
Horiz. pair with vert. gutter		7.50 —
Vert. pair with horiz. gutter		4.00 —
a. Imperf., pair		400.00
Pane of 20, imperf.		5,000.

Perforations in corner of each stamp are star-shaped.

TEXAS STATEHOOD

A2282

Designed by Laura Smith.
Printed by Sterling Sommer for Ashton-Potter (USA) Ltd.

LITHOGRAPHED
Sheets of 120 in six panes of 20

1995, June 16	Tagged	Perf. 11.2
2968 A2282 32c multicolored		.75 .20
P# block of 4, 6#+P		3.00 —
Pane of 20		15.00 —

GREAT LAKES LIGHTHOUSES

Split Rock, Lake Superior — A2283   St. Joseph, Lake Michigan — A2284

Spectacle Reef, Lake Huron — A2285   Marblehead, Lake Erie — A2286

Thirty Mile Point, Lake Ontario — A2287

Designed by Howard Koslow.
Printed by Stamp Venturers.

PHOTOGRAVURE
BOOKLET STAMPS

1995, June 17	Tagged	Perf. 11.2 Vert.
2969 A2283 32c multicolored		1.25 .30
2970 A2284 32c multicolored		1.25 .30
2971 A2285 32c multicolored		1.25 .30
2972 A2286 32c multicolored		1.25 .30
2973 A2287 32c multicolored		1.25 .30
a. Booklet pane of 5, #2969-2973		6.25 3.00

U.N., 50th ANNIV.

A2288

Designed by Howard Paine.
Printed by Banknote Corp. of America.

ENGRAVED
Sheets of 180 in nine panes of 20

1995, June 26	Tagged	Perf. 11.2
2974 A2288 32c blue		.65 .20
P# block of 4, 1#+B		2.60 —
Pane of 20		13.00 —

CIVIL WAR

A2289

Illustration reduced.

Designed by Mark Hess.

Printed by Stamp Venturers.

Designs: a, Monitor and Virginia. b, Robert E. Lee. c, Clara Barton. d, Ulysses S. Grant. e, Battle of Shiloh. f, Jefferson Davis. g, David Farragut. h, Frederick Douglass. i, Raphael Semmes. j, Abraham Lincoln. k, Harriet Tubman. l, Stand Watie. m, Joseph E. Johnston. n, Winfield Hancock. o, Mary Chesnut. p, Battle of Chancellorsville. q, William T. Sherman. r, Phoebe Pember. s, "Stonewall" Jackson. t, Battle of Gettysburg.

PHOTOGRAVURE
Sheets of 120 in six panes of 20

1995, June 29	Tagged	Perf. 10.1
2975 A2289 Pane of 20		35.00 17.50
a.-t. 32c any single		1.50 .60
Sheet of 120 (6 panes)		200.00
Cross gutter block of 20		42.50 —
Vert. pairs with horiz. gutter (each)		5.00 —
Horiz. pairs with vert. gutter (each)		5.00 —
u. As No. 2975, a.-e. imperf, f.-j. part perf, others perf		—
v. As No. 2975, k.-t. imperf, f.-j. part perf, others perf		—
w. As No. 2975, imperf		1,500.
x. Block of 9 (f.-h., k.-m., p.-r.) k.-l. & p.-q. imperf. vert.		—
y. As No. 2975, a.-b. perf, c., f.-h. part perf, others imperf		—
z. As No. 2975, o. and t. imperf, j., n. & s. part perf, others perf		—

Cross gutter block of 20 consists of six stamps from each of two panes and four stamps from each of two other panes with the cross gutter between.

AMERICAN FOLK ART SERIES
Carousel Horses

A2290   A2291

A2292   A2293

Designed by Paul Calle.
Printed at Sterling Sommer for Ashton-Potter (USA) Ltd.

LITHOGRAPHED
Sheets of 160 in eight panes of 20

1995, July 21		Tagged	Perf. 11	
2976	A2290	32c **multicolored**	.65	.20
2977	A2291	32c **multicolored**	.65	.20
2978	A2292	32c **multicolored**	.65	.20
2979	A2293	32c **multicolored**	.65	.20
a.		Block of 4, #2976-2979	2.60	2.00
		P# block of 4, 5#+P	2.60	—
		Pane of 20	13.00	

WOMAN SUFFRAGE

A2294

Designed by April Greiman.
Printed by Ashton-Potter (USA) Ltd.

LITHOGRAPHED & ENGRAVED
Sheets of 160 in four panes of 40

1995, Aug. 26		Tagged	Perf. 11.1x11	
2980	A2294	32c **multicolored**	.65	.20
		P# block of 4, 5#+P	3.00	
a.		Black (engr.) omitted	375.00	
b.		Imperf., pair	1,250.	
c.		Vert. pair, imperf between and at bottom	750.00	

No. 2980a is valued in the grade of fine. Very fine examples exist and sell for much more.

WORLD WAR II

A2295

Illustration reduced.

Designed by Bill Bond.

Designs and events of 1945: a, Marines raise flag on Iwo Jima. b, Fierce fighting frees Manila by March 3, 1945. c, Soldiers advancing (Okinawa, the last big battle). d, Destroyed bridge (US and Soviets link up at Elbe River). e, Allies liberate Holocaust survivors. f, Germany surrenders at Reims. g, Refugees (By 1945, World War II has uprooted millions). h, Truman announces Japan's surrender. i, Sailor kissing nurse (News of victory hits home). j, Hometowns honor their returning veterans.
Central label is size of 15 stamps and shows world map with extent of Axis control and Allied operations.

LITHOGRAPHED & ENGRAVED
Plates of eight subjects in four panes of 2 each

1995, Sept. 2		Tagged	Perf. 11.1	
2981	A2295	Block of 10	15.00	7.50
		Pane of 20	30.00	—
a.-j.		32c any single	1.50	.50

No. 2981 has selvage at left and right and either top or bottom.

AMERICAN MUSIC SERIES

Louis Armstrong (1901-71) A2296

Coleman Hawkins (1904-69) A2297

James P. Johnson (1894-1955) A2298

Jelly Roll Morton (1890-1941) A2299

Charlie Parker (1920-55) A2300

Eubie Blake (1883-1983) A2301

Charles Mingus (1922-79) A2302

Thelonious Monk (1917-82) A2303

John Coltrane (1926-67) A2304

Erroll Garner (1921-77) A2305

Designed by Dean Mitchell (#2982-2984, 2987, 2989, 2991-2992) and Thomas Blackshear (others).

Printed by Ashton-Potter (USA) Ltd. (#2982), Sterling Sommer for Ashton-Potter (USA) Ltd. (#2983-2992).

LITHOGRAPHED
Plates of 120 in six panes of 20

1995		Tagged	Perf. 11.1x11	
2982	A2296	32c **white denomination,** Sept. 1	.90	.25
		P# block of 4, 4#+P	3.60	—
		Pane of 20	18.00	—
a.		Imperf, pair	—	
2983	A2297	32c **multicolored,** Sept. 16	2.25	.30
2984	A2296	32c **black denomination,** Sept. 16	2.25	.30
2985	A2298	32c **multicolored,** Sept. 16	2.25	.30
2986	A2299	32c **multicolored,** Sept. 16	2.25	.30
2987	A2300	32c **multicolored,** Sept. 16	2.25	.30
2988	A2301	32c **multicolored,** Sept. 16	2.25	.30
2989	A2302	32c **multicolored,** Sept. 16	2.25	.30
2990	A2303	32c **multicolored,** Sept. 16	2.25	.30
2991	A2304	32c **multicolored,** Sept. 16	2.25	.30
2992	A2305	32c **multicolored,** Sept. 16	2.25	.30
a.		Vert. block of 10, #2983-2992	23.00	7.50
		P# block of 10	23.00	
		Pane of 20	46.00	
b.		Pane of 20, dark blue (inscriptions) omitted	—	
c.		Imperf pair of Nos. 2991-2992	—	

GARDEN FLOWERS

Aster A2306

Chrysanthemum A2307

Dahlia — A2308

Hydrangea — A2309

Rudbeckia — A2310

Designed by Ned Seidler.

LITHOGRAPHED & ENGRAVED
BOOKLET STAMPS

1995, Sept. 19	Tagged	Perf. 10.9 Vert.	
2993	A2306 32c multicolored	.65	.20
2994	A2307 32c multicolored	.65	.20
2995	A2308 32c multicolored	.65	.20
2996	A2309 32c multicolored	.65	.20
2997	A2310 32c multicolored	.65	.20
a.	Booklet pane of 5, #2993-2997	3.25	2.25
b.	As "a," imperf	2,750.	

EDDIE RICKENBACKER (1890-1973), AVIATOR

A2311

Designed by Davis Meltzer.

PHOTOGRAVURE
Panes of 50

1995, Sept. 25	Tagged	Perf. 11¼	
2998	A2311 60c multicolored, small "1995" year date	1.40	.50
	P# block of 4, 5#	8.00	
a.	Large "1995" date, Oct., 1999	2.00	.50
	P# block of 4, 5#	12.00	

Date on No. 2998 is 1mm long, on No. 2998a 1½mm long.

REPUBLIC OF PALAU

A2312

Designed by Herb Kane.
Printed by Sterling Sommer for Ashton-Potter (USA) Ltd.

LITHOGRAPHED
Sheets of 200 in four panes of 50

1995, Sept. 29	Tagged	Perf. 11.1	
2999	A2312 32c multicolored	.65	.20
	P# block of 4, 5#+P	3.00	

See Palau Nos. 377-378.

COMIC STRIPS

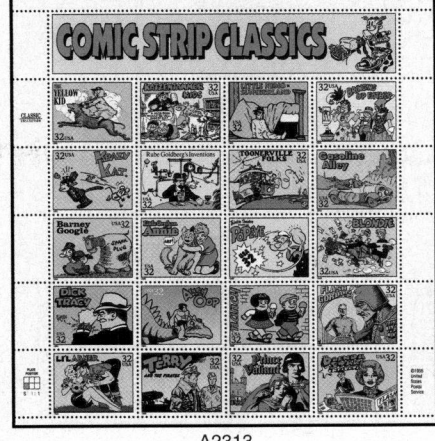

A2313

Illustration reduced.

Designed by Carl Herrman.

Printed by Stamp Venturers.

Designs: a, The Yellow Kid. b, Katzenjammer Kids. c, Little Nemo in Slumberland. d, Bringing Up Father. e, Krazy Kat. f, Rube Goldberg's Inventions. g, Toonerville Folks. h, Gasoline Alley. i, Barney Google. j, Little Orphan Annie. k, Popeye. l, Blondie. m, Dick Tracy. n, Alley Oop. o, Nancy. p, Flash Gordon. q, Li'l Abner. r, Terry and the Pirates. s, Prince Valiant. t, Brenda Starr, Reporter.

PHOTOGRAVURE
Sheets of 120 in six panes of 20

1995, Oct. 1	Tagged	Perf. 10.1	
3000	A2313 Pane of 20	13.00	10.00
a.-t.	32c any single	.65	.50
	Sheet of 120 (6 panes)	105.00	
	Cross gutter block of 20	35.00	—
	Vert. pairs with horiz. gutter (each)	3.75	—
	Horiz. pairs with vert. gutter (each)	3.75	—
u.	As No. 3000, a.-h. imperf., i.-l. part perf	—	
v.	As No. 3000, m.-t. imperf., i.-l. part perf	—	
w.	As No. 3000, a.-l. imperf.,m.-t. imperf vert.	—	
x.	As No. 3000, imperf	—	

Inscriptions on back of each stamp describe the comic strip.
Cross gutter block of 20 consists of six stamps from each of two panes and four stamps from each of two other panes with the cross gutter between.

U.S. NAVAL ACADEMY, 150th ANNIVERSARY

A2314

Designed by Dean Ellis. Printed by Sterling-Sommer for Aston-Potter (USA) Ltd.

LITHOGRAPHED
Sheets of 160 in eight panes of 20

1995, Oct. 10	Tagged	Perf. 10.9	
3001	A2314 32c multicolored	.65	.20
	P# block of 4, 5#+P	2.60	—
	Pane of 20	13.00	—

LITERARY ARTS SERIES

Tennessee Williams (1911-83)
A2315

Designed by Michael Deas. Printed by Sterling-Sommer for Ashton-Potter (USA) Ltd.

LITHOGRAPHED
Sheets of 160 in eight panes of 20

1995, Oct. 13	Tagged	Perf. 11.1	
3002	A2315 32c multicolored	.65	.20
	P# block of 4, 5#+P	2.80	
	Pane of 20	14.00	—

CHRISTMAS

Madonna and Child, by Giotto di Bondone — A2316

Santa Claus Entering Chimney — A2317

Child Holding Jumping Jack — A2318

Child Holding Tree — A2319

Santa Claus Working on Sled — A2320

Midnight Angel — A2321

Children Sledding — A2322

Designed by Richard Sheaff (#3003), John Grossman & Laura Alders (#3004-3018).

Printed by Bureau of Engraving and Printing (#3003), Sterling-Sommer for Ashton-Potter (USA) Ltd. (#3004-3007), Avery Dennison (#3008-3011, 3013-3017), Banknote Corporation of America (#3012, 3018).

LITHOGRAPHED & ENGRAVED
Sheets of 300 in six panes of 50

1995	Tagged	Perf. 11.2	
3003	A2316 32c multicolored, Oct. 19	.65	.20
	P# block of 4, 5#	3.00	
c.	Black (engr., denomination) omitted	200.00	

BOOKLET STAMP
Perf. 9.8x10.9

3003A	A2316 32c multicolored, Oct. 19	.65	.20
b.	Booklet pane of 10	6.50	4.00

LITHOGRAPHED
Sheets of 200 in four panes of 50
Perf. 11.25

3004	A2317 32c multicolored, Sept. 30	.70	.20
3005	A2318 32c multicolored, Sept. 30	.70	.20
3006	A2319 32c multicolored, Sept. 30	.70	.20
3007	A2320 32c multicolored, Sept. 30	.70	.20
a.	Block or strip of 4, #3004-3007	2.80	1.25
	P# block of 4, 4#+P	4.00	
b.	Booklet pane of 10, 3 each #3004-3005, 2 each #3006-3007	8.00	4.00
c.	Booklet pane of 10, 2 each #3004-3005, 3 each #3006-3007	8.00	4.00
d.	As "a," imperf	475.00	
e.	As "b," miscut and inserted upside down into booklet cover, with full bottom selvage	—	

PHOTOGRAVURE
Self-Adhesive Stamps
Serpentine Die Cut 11.25 on 2, 3 or 4 sides

3008	A2320	32c **multicolored**, *Sept. 30*		.95	.20
3009	A2318	32c **multicolored**, *Sept. 30*		.95	.20
3010	A2317	32c **multicolored**, *Sept. 30*		.95	.20
3011	A2319	32c **multicolored**, *Sept. 30*		.95	.20
a.		Booklet pane of 20, 5 each #3008-3011 + label		19.00	

LITHOGRAPHED
Serpentine Die Cut 11.3x11.6 on 2, 3 or 4 sides

3012	A2321	32c **multicolored**, *Oct. 19*		.65	.20
a.		Booklet pane of 20 + label		13.00	
b.		Vert. pair, die cutting omitted between		—	
c.		Booklet pane of 15 + label, *1996*		13.00	
d.		Booklet pane of 15		*30.00*	

No. 3012a comes either with no die cutting in the label (1995 printing) or with the die cutting (and deeper colors) from the 1996 printing.
No. 3012d is a pane of 16 with one stamp removed. The missing stamp can be from either row 1, 2, 3, 7 or 8 of the pane. No. 3012d cannot be made from No. 3012c, a pane of 15 + label. The label is die cut. If the label is removed, an impression of the die cutting appears on the backing paper.

PHOTOGRAVURE
Die Cut

3013	A2322	32c **multicolored**, *Oct. 19*		.65	.20
a.		Booklet pane of 18		12.00	
b.		As "a," tagging omitted		—	

Self-Adhesive Coil Stamps
Serpentine Die Cut 11.2 Vert.

3014	A2320	32c **multicolored**, *Sept. 30*		2.75	.30
3015	A2318	32c **multicolored**, *Sept. 30*		2.75	.30
3016	A2317	32c **multicolored**, *Sept. 30*		2.75	.30
3017	A2319	32c **multicolored**, *Sept. 30*		2.75	.30
a.		Strip of 4, #3014-3017		11.00	
		P# strip of 5, 1 each #3014-3017 + 1 stamp, P#V1111		17.50	
		P# strip of 8, 2 each #3014-3017, P#V1111		35.00	
		P# single (#3017), #V1111		—	10.00

LITHOGRAPHED
Serpentine Die Cut 11.6 Vert.

3018	A2321	32c **multicolored**, *Oct. 19*		1.10	.30
		Pair, #B1111		2.20	.60
		P# strip of 5, #B1111		9.00	
		P# single, #B1111		—	6.00

Nos. 3014-3018 were only available through the Philatelic Fulfillment Center in Kansas City.
Nos. 3005-3006 have "USA" printed in green. It is red on the self-adhesive stamps.

ANTIQUE AUTOMOBILES

1893 Duryea
A2323

1894 Haynes
A2324

1898 Columbia
A2325

1899 Winton
A2326

1901 White — A2327

Designed by Ken Dallison.
Printed by Stamp Venturers.

PHOTOGRAVURE
Sheets of 200 in eight panes of 25

1995, Nov. 3	Tagged		Perf. 10.1x11.1	
3019	A2323	32c **multicolored**	.90	.20
3020	A2324	32c **multicolored**	.90	.20
3021	A2325	32c **multicolored**	.90	.20
3022	A2326	32c **multicolored**	.90	.20
3023	A2327	32c **multicolored**	.90	.20
a.		Vert. or horiz. strip of 5, #3019-3023	4.50	2.00
		Vert. or Horiz. P# block of 10, 2 sets of 4#+S	10.00	—
		Pane of 25	24.00	—

Vert. and horiz. strips are all in different order.

UTAH STATEHOOD CENTENARY

Delicate Arch, Arches Natl. Park — A2328

Designed by McRay Magleby.
Printed by Sterling Sommer for Ashton-Potter (USA) Ltd.

LITHOGRAPHED
Sheets of 200 in four panes of 50

1996, Jan. 4	Tagged		Perf. 11.1	
3024	A2328	32c **multicolored**	.75	.20
		P# block of 4, 5#+P	4.00	—

For booklet see No. BK245.

GARDEN FLOWERS

Crocus — A2329

Winter Aconite — A2330

Pansy — A2331

Snowdrop — A2332

Anemone — A2333

Designed by Ned Seidler.

LITHOGRAPHED & ENGRAVED
BOOKLET STAMPS

1996, Jan. 19	Tagged		Perf. 10.9 Vert.	
3025	A2329	32c **multicolored**	.75	.20
3026	A2330	32c **multicolored**	.75	.20
3027	A2331	32c **multicolored**	.75	.20
3028	A2332	32c **multicolored**	.75	.20
3029	A2333	32c **multicolored**	.75	.20
a.		Booklet pane of 5, #3025-3029	3.75	2.50
b.		As "a," imperf.	—	

LOVE

Cherub from Sistine Madonna, by Raphael — A2334

Designed by Terry McCaffrey.
Printed by Banknote Corporation of America.

LITHOGRAPHED & ENGRAVED
BOOKLET STAMP
Serpentine Die Cut 11.3x11.7

1996, Jan. 20				Tagged
	Self-Adhesive			
3030	A2334	32c **multicolored**	.65	.20
a.	Booklet pane of 20 + label		13.00	
b.	Booklet pane of 15 + label		10.00	
c.	Red (engr. "Love") omitted		175.00	
d.	Red (engr. "Love") missing (CM)		—	
e.	Double impression of red (engr. "Love")		—	
f.	Die cutting omitted, pair		275.00	
g.	As "a," stamps 1-5 double impression of red (engr. "Love")		—	

No. 3030d must be collected se-tenant with a stamp bearing the red engraving.

FLORA AND FAUNA SERIES
Kestrel, Blue Jay and Rose Types of 1993-95 and

Red-headed Woodpecker
A2335

Eastern Bluebird
A2336

Red Fox — A2339

Ring-necked Pheasant — A2350

Coral Pink Rose — A2351

Designed by Michael Matherly (#3031-3033, 3044-3045); Terry McCaffrey (#3050-3051, 3055); Derry Noyes (#3036, 3052, 3052E).
Printed by Banknote Corporation of America (#3031A, 3036); Bureau of Engraving & Printing (#3031-3033, 3044-3045); Stamp Venturers (#3048-3049, 3053); Avery Dennison (#3050-3051A). American Packaging Corp. for Sennett Security Products (#3052); Sennett Security Products (#3052E).

LITHOGRAPHED
Sheets of 300 in six panes of 50 (#3031).
Sheets of 400 in eight panes of 50 (#3031A).
Sheets of 400 in four panes of 100 (#3032-3033).
Sheets of 120 in six panes of 20 (#3036).
Sheets of 200 in ten panes of 20 (#3036a).

1996-2002   Untagged   *Serpentine Die Cut 10½*
Self-Adhesive (#3031, 3031A)

| 3031 | A1841 1c multicolored, Nov. 19, 1999 | .20 | .20 |
| | P# block of 4, 4# or 4# + A | .25 | |

Serpentine Die Cut 11¼

3031A	A1841 1c multicolored, Oct. 2000	.20	.20
	P# block of 4, 6# + B	.20	
b.	Die cutting omitted, pair	.20	

No. 3031A has blue inscription and year.

Perf. 11

3032	A2335 2c multicolored, Feb. 2	.20	.20
	P# block of 4, 5#	.25	
3033	A2336 3c multicolored, Apr. 3	.20	.20
	P# block of 4, 5#	.25	

Some plate blocks contain plate position diagram.

Tagged
Serpentine Die Cut 11½x11¼
Self-Adhesive

3036	A2339 $1 multicolored, Aug. 14, 1998	2.00	.50
	P# block of 4, 4#+B	8.00	
	Pane of 20	40.00	
a.	Serpentine die cut 11¾x11, 2002	2.75	.50
	P# block of 4, 4#+B	11.00	
	Pane of 20	55.00	

The tagging of No. 3036 has a bright yellow-green appearance under shortwave ultraviolet light while that of No. 3036a appears light blue green. Nos. 3036 and 3036a are dated 1998 at left bottom.

COIL STAMPS
Untagged
Perf. 9¾ Vert.

3044	A1841 1c multicolored, small date, Jan. 20	.20	.20
	Pair	.20	.20
	P# strip of 5, #1111 in black, yellow, blue, magenta order	.50	
	P# single, same		.60
	P# strip of 5, #1111 in black, blue, yellow, magenta order	3.00	
	P# single, same	—	3.00
a.	Large date	.20	.20
	Pair	.20	.20
	P# strip of 5, #1111, 2222, 3333, 4444 in yellow, magenta, blue, black order	.70	
	P# single, same		.80

Date on No. 3044 is 1mm long, on No. 3044a 1.5mm long.

Untagged

3045	A2335 2c multicolored, June 22, 1999	.20	.20
	Pair	.20	.20
	P# strip of 5, #11111	.60	—
	P# strip of 5, #22222	1.10	
	P# single, #11111	—	.65
	P# single, #22222		1.50

BOOKLET STAMPS
PHOTOGRAVURE
Serpentine Die Cut 10.4x10.8 on 3 Sides
Tagged
Self-Adhesive

3048	A1847 20c multicolored, Aug. 2, 1996	.40	.20
a.	Booklet pane of 10	4.00	
b.	Booklet pane of 4	25.00	
c.	Booklet pane of 6	40.00	

Nos. 3048b-3048c are from the vending machine booklet No. BK237 that has a glue strip at the top edge of the top pane, the peelable strip removed and the rouletting line 2mm lower than on No. 3048a on some booklets, when the panes are compared with bottoms aligned. Vending booklets with plate #S2222 always have gauge 8½ rouletting on booklet covers. Convertible booklets (No. 3048a) with plate #S2222 always have gauge 12½ rouletting on booklet covers. Vending booklets with plate #S1111 can have either 8½ or 12½ gauge rouletting on booklet cover, and it may be impossible to tell a vending booklet with 12½ gauge rouletting and plate #S1111 from a convertible booklet with peelable strip removed.

Serpentine Die Cut 11.3x11.7 on 2, 3 or 4 Sides

3049	A1853 32c yellow, orange, green & black, Oct. 24, 1996	.65	.20
a.	Booklet pane of 20 + label	13.00	
b.	Booklet pane of 4, Dec. 1996	2.60	
c.	Booklet pane of 5 + label, Dec. 1996	3.50	
	P# single, #S1111	.85	1.00
d.	Booklet pane of 6, Dec. 1996	4.00	
	Booklet pane of 6 containing P# single	6.00	
	P# single, #S1111	2.50	1.00

The plate # single in No. 3049c is on the lower left stamp. In No. 3049d it is the lower right stamp on the bottom pane of the booklet.

Serpentine Die Cut 11.2 on 3 Sides

3050	A2350 20c multicolored, July 31, 1998	.60	.20
a.	Booklet pane of 10, all stamps upright	6.00	
b.	Serpentine die cut 11	1.75	.20
c.	As "b," booklet pane of 10, all stamps upright	20.00	

Serpentine Die Cut 10½x11 on 3 Sides

| 3051 | A2350 20c multicolored, July 1999 | .75 | .20 |

No. 3051 represents the eight upright stamps on the booklet panes Nos. 3051Ab and 3051Ac. The two stamps turned sideways on those panes are No. 3051A.
Specialists should note that 3051 can be either die cut 10.4 at top and 10.6 at bottom or 10.6 at top and 10.4 at bottom. These two varieties exist in equal numbers.

Serpentine Die Cut 10.6x10.4 on 3 Sides

3051A	A2350 20c multicolored,	6.00	.50
b.	Booklet pane of 5, 4 #3051, 1 #3051A turned sideways at top	9.00	
c.	Booklet pane of 5, 4 #3051, 1 #3051A turned sideways at bottom	9.00	

Serpentine Die Cut 11½x11¼ on 2, 3 or 4 Sides

3052	A2351 33c multicolored, Aug. 13, 1999	.90	.20
a.	Booklet pane of 4	3.60	
b.	Booklet pane of 5 + label	4.50	
c.	Booklet pane of 6	5.50	
d.	Booklet pane of 20 + label	17.50	
j.	Die cutting omitted, pair		

Serpentine Die Cut 10¾x10½ on 2 or 3 sides

3052E	A2351 33c multicolored, Apr. 7, 2000	.80	.20
f.	Booklet pane of 20	16.00	
g.	Black ("33 USA," etc.) omitted	375.00	
h.	As "f," all 12 stamps on one side with black omitted		
i.	Horiz. pair, die cutting omitted between		

No. 3052Ef is a double-sided booklet pane with 12 stamps on one side and 8 stamps plus label on the other side.

COIL STAMPS
Serpentine Die Cut 11½ Vert.

3053	A1847 20c multicolored, Aug. 2, 1996	.50	.20
	Pair	1.00	
	P# strip of 5, #S1111	4.75	
	P# single, #S1111		1.00

Yellow Rose, Ring-necked Pheasant Types of 1996-98

Printed by Bureau of Engraving and Printing (#3054-3055).

COIL STAMPS
LITHOGRAPHED
Serpentine Die Cut 9¾ Vert.
Tagged
Self-Adhesive

3054	A1853 32c yellow, magenta, black & green, Aug. 1, 1997	.65	.20
	Pair	1.30	
	P# strip of 5, #1111, 1112, 1122, 2222, 2223, 2333, 3344, 4455, 5455, 5555, 5556, 5566, 5666, 6666, 7777	4.50	
	P# strip of 5, #2233, 3444	6.00	
	P# strip of 5, #6677, 6777, 8888	7.50	
	P# single, #1111, 1112, 1122, 4455, 5555, 5556, 5566, 5666, 6666, 7777	—	1.75
	P# single, #2222, 2333	—	2.50
	P# single, #2223, 8888	—	2.75
	P# single, #2233, 3444	—	3.75
	P# single, #3344, 5455, 6677	—	3.50
	P# single, #6777	—	5.50
a.	Die cutting omitted, pair	85.00	
b.	Black, yellow & green omitted	—	
c.	Black, yellow & green omitted, die cutting omitted, pair	—	
d.	Black omitted	—	
e.	Black omitted, die cutting omitted, pair	—	
f.	All colors omitted, die cutting omitted	—	
g.	Pair, die cutting omitted, containing one stamp each of "c" and "e"	—	

Nos. 3054b and 3054d also are miscut and with shifted die cuttings.
No. 3054f must be collected se-tenant with a partially printed stamp(s).

3055	A2350 20c multicolored, July, 31, 1998	.40	.20
	Pair	.80	
	P# strip of 5, P#1111, 2222	3.00	
	P# single, same		1.50
a.	Die cutting omitted, pair	150.00	

No. 3055a exists miscut. It is more common in this form and is valued thus.

BLACK HERITAGE SERIES

Ernest E. Just (1883-1941), Marine Biologist — A2358

Designed by Richard Sheaff.
Printed by Banknote Corporation of America.

LITHOGRAPHED
Sheets of 160 in eight panes of 20

1996, Feb. 1	**Tagged**		***Perf. 11.1***
3058	A2358 32c gray & black	.65	.20
	P# block of 4, 4#+B	2.60	—
	Pane of 20	13.00	—

SMITHSONIAN INSTITUTION, 150TH ANNIVERSARY

A2359

Designed by Tom Engeman.
Printed by Ashton-Potter (USA) Ltd.

LITHOGRAPHED
Sheets of 160 in eight panes of 20

1996, Feb. 7	**Tagged**		***Perf. 11.1***
3059	A2359 32c multicolored	.65	.20
	P# block of 4, 4#+P	2.60	—
	Pane of 20	13.00	—

CHINESE NEW YEAR

Year of the Rat — A2360

Designed by Clarence Lee.
Printed by Stamp Venturers.

PHOTOGRAVURE
Sheets of 180 in nine panes of 20

1996, Feb. 8	**Tagged**		***Perf. 11.1***
3060	A2360 32c multicolored	.90	.20
	P# block of 4, 4#+S	4.25	—
	Pane of 20	19.00	—
a.	Imperf., pair	725.00	

See No. 3895a.

PIONEERS OF COMMUNICATION

Eadweard Muybridge (1830-1904), Photographer A2361

Ottmar
Mergenthaler
(1854-99),
Inventor of
Linotype
A2362

Frederic E.
Ives (1856-
1937),
Developer of
Halftone
Process
A2363

William
Dickson (1860-
1935), Co-
developer of
Kinetoscope
A2364

Designed by Fred Otnes.
Printed by Ashton-Potter USA.

LITHOGRAPHED
Sheets of 120 in six panes of 20

1996, Feb. 22	Tagged	Perf. 11.1x11
3061 A2361 32c multicolored	.65	.20
3062 A2362 32c multicolored	.65	.20
3063 A2363 32c multicolored	.65	.20
3064 A2364 32c multicolored	.65	.20
a. Block or strip of 4, #3061-3064	2.60	2.00
P# block of 4, 5#+P	2.60	
Pane of 20	13.00	—

FULBRIGHT SCHOLARSHIPS, 50th ANNIVERSARY

A2365

Designed by Richard D. Sheaff.

LITHOGRAPHED & ENGRAVED
Sheets of 200 in four panes of 50

1996, Feb. 28	Tagged	Perf. 11.1
3065 A2365 32c multicolored	.75	.20
P# block of 4, 5#	4.25	—

For booklet see No. BK246.

JACQUELINE COCHRAN (1910-80), PILOT

A2366

Designed by Davis Meltzer.

LITHOGRAPHED & ENGRAVED
Sheets of 300 in six panes of 50

1996, Mar. 9	Tagged	Perf. 11.1
3066 A2366 50c multicolored	1.00	.40
P# block of 4, 5#	5.00	
a. Black (engr.) omitted	55.00	

MARATHON

A2367

Designed by Michael Bartalos.

Printed by Banknote Corporation of America.

LITHOGRAPHED
Sheets of 160 in eight panes of 20

1996, Apr. 11	Tagged	Perf. 11.1
3067 A2367 32c multicolored	.65	.20
P# block of 4, 4#+B	2.60	—
Pane of 20	13.00	—

1996 SUMMER OLYMPIC GAMES

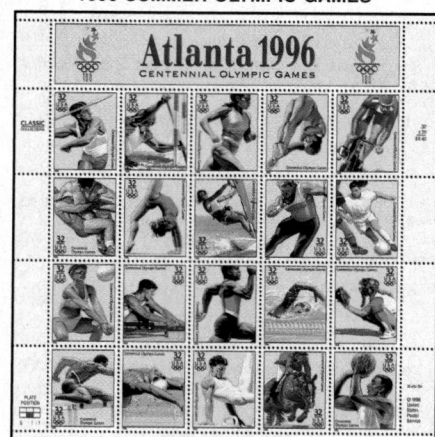

A2368

Illustration reduced.

Designed by Richard Waldrep. Printed by Stamp Venturers.

Designs: a, Decathlon (javelin). b, Men's canoeing. c, Women's running. d, Women's diving. e, Men's cycling. f, Freestyle wrestling. g, Women's gymnastics. h, Women's sailboarding. i, Men's shot put. j, Women's soccer. k, Beach volleyball. l, Men's rowing. m, Men's sprints. n, Women's swimming. o, Women's softball. p, Men's hurdles. q, Men's swimming. r, Men's gymnastics (pommel horse). s, Equestrian. t, Men's basketball.

PHOTOGRAVURE
Sheets of 120 in six panes of 20

1996, May 2	Tagged	Perf. 10.1
3068 A2368 Pane of 20	14.00	10.00
a.-t. 32c any single	.70	.50
Sheet of 120 (6 panes)	120.00	
Cross gutter block of 20	45.00	—
Vert. pairs with horiz. gutter (each)	4.00	—
Horiz. pairs with vert. gutter (each)	4.00	—
u. As No. 3068, imperf	1,000.	
v. As No. 3068, back inscriptions omitted on a., f., k. & p., incorrect back inscriptions on others	—	
w. As No. 3068, e. imperf, d., i.-j. part perf, all others perf	—	

Inscription on back of each stamp describes the sport shown.
Cross gutter block of 20 consists of six stamps from each of two panes and four stamps from each of two other panes with the cross gutter between.

GEORGIA O'KEEFFE (1887-1986)

A2369

Designed by Margaret Bauer. Printed by Stamp Venturers.

PHOTOGRAVURE
Sheets of 90 in six panes of 15

1996, May 23	Tagged	Perf. 11.6x11.4
3069 A2369 32c multicolored	.85	.20
P# block of 4, 5#+S	5.00	
Pane of 15	15.00	9.00
a. Imperf., pair	125.00	
Pane of 15, imperf.	900.00	—

For booklet see No. BK247.

TENNESSEE STATEHOOD BICENTENNIAL

A2370

Designed by Phil Jordan. Printed by Stamp Venturers.

PHOTOGRAVURE
Sheets of 200 in four panes of 50.

1996, May 31	Tagged	Perf. 11.1
3070 A2370 32c multicolored	.65	.20
P# block of 4, 5#+S	3.00	—

For booklet see No. BK248.

Booklet Stamp
Self-Adhesive
Serpentine Die Cut 9.9x10.8

3071 A2370 32c multicolored	.75	.30
a. Booklet pane of 20, #S11111	15.00	
b. Horiz. pair, die cutting omitted btwn.	—	
c. Die cutting omitted, pair	—	—
d. Horiz. pair, die cutting omitted vert.	—	—

AMERICAN INDIAN DANCES

Fancy — A2371   Butterfly — A2372

Traditional — A2373

Raven — A2374

Hoop — A2375

Designed by Keith Birdsong. Printed by Ashton-Potter (USA) Ltd.

LITHOGRAPHED
Sheets of 120 in six panes of 20.

1996, June 7		**Tagged**		**Perf. 11.1**	
3072	A2371	32c	multicolored	1.00	.20
3073	A2372	32c	multicolored	1.00	.20
3074	A2373	32c	multicolored	1.00	.20
3075	A2374	32c	multicolored	1.00	.20
3076	A2375	32c	multicolored	1.00	.20
a.		Strip of 5, #3072-3076		5.00	2.50
		P# block of 10, 4#+P		12.00	—
		Pane of 20		24.00	—

For booklet see No. BK249.

PREHISTORIC ANIMALS

Eohippus
A2376

Woolly
Mammoth
A2377

Mastodon
A2378

Saber-tooth
Cat — A2379

Designed by Davis Meltzer. Printed by Ashton-Potter (USA) Ltd.

LITHOGRAPHED
Sheets of 120 in six panes of 20

1996, June 8		**Tagged**		**Perf. 11.1x11**	
3077	A2376	32c	multicolored	.65	.20
3078	A2377	32c	multicolored	.65	.20
3079	A2378	32c	multicolored	.65	.20
3080	A2379	32c	multicolored	.65	.20
a.		Block or strip of 4, #3077-3080		2.60	2.00
		P# block of 4, 4#+P		2.60	—
		Pane of 20		13.00	—

A2380

A2381

BREAST CANCER AWARENESS
Designed by Tom Mann. Printed by Ashton-Potter (USA) Ltd.

LITHOGRAPHED
Sheets of 120 in six panes of 20

1996, June 15		**Tagged**		**Perf. 11.1**	
3081	A2380	32c	multicolored	.65	.20
		P# block of 4, 5#+P		2.60	—
		Pane of 20		13.00	—

LEGENDS OF HOLLYWOOD
James Dean (1931-55)

Designed by Michael Deas.

Printed by Stamp Venturers.

PHOTOGRAVURE
Sheets of 120 in six panes of 20.

1996, June 24		**Tagged**		**Perf. 11.1**	
3082	A2381	32c	multicolored	.65	.20
		P# block of 4, 7#+S		4.00	—
		Pane of 20		18.50	10.00
		Sheet of 120 (six panes)		110.00	—
		Cross gutter block of 8		30.00	—
		Block of 8 with vertical gutter		20.00	—
		Horiz. pair with vert. gutter		4.75	—
		Vert. pair with horiz. gutter		3.00	—
a.		Imperf., pair		150.00	—
		Pane of 20, imperf.		1,500.	
b.		As "a," red (USA 32c) missing (CM) and tan (JAMES DEAN) omitted		—	
c.		As "a," tan (JAMES DEAN) omitted		—	
d.		As "a," top stamp red missing (CM) and tan (JAMES DEAN) omitted, bottom stamp tan omitted		—	
e.		As No. 3082 pane of 20, right two columns perf, left three columns imperf		1,750.	

Perforations in corner of each stamp are star-shaped. No. 3082 was also available on the first day of issue in at least 127 Warner Bros. Studio stores.
Cross-gutter block consists of 3 stamps vertically from 2 upper panes and 1 stamp each from 2 lower panes.
For booklet see No. BK250.
Nos. 3082b-3082d come from the same error pane. The top row is No. 3082b; rows 2-4 are No. 3082c. No. 3082d is a vertical pair with one stamp from No. 3082b at top and one stamp from No. 3082c at bottom.

FOLK HEROES

A2382

A2383

A2384   A2385

Designed by David LaFleur.

Printed by Ashton-Potter (USA) Ltd.

LITHOGRAPHED
Sheets of 120 in six panes of 20

1996, July 11		**Tagged**		**Perf. 11.1x11**	
3083	A2382	32c	multicolored	.65	.20
3084	A2383	32c	multicolored	.65	.20
3085	A2384	32c	multicolored	.65	.20
3086	A2385	32c	multicolored	.65	.20
a.		Block or strip of 4, #3083-3086		2.60	2.00
		P# block of 4, 4#+P		2.60	—
		Pane of 20		13.00	—

For booklet see No. BK251.

Myron's
Discobolus — A2386

Young Corn, by Grant
Wood — A2387

CENTENNIAL OLYMPIC GAMES
Designed by Carl Herrman.

Printed by Ashton-Potter (USA) Ltd.

ENGRAVED
Sheets of 80 in four panes of 20

1996, July 19		**Tagged**		**Perf. 11.1**	
3087	A2386	32c	brown	.80	.20
		P# block of 4, 1#+P		4.50	—
		Pane of 20		21.50	10.00

Sheet margin of the pane of 20 is lithographed.
For booklet see No. BK252.

IOWA STATEHOOD, 150TH ANNIVERSARY
Designed by Carl Herrman.

Printed by Ashton-Potter (USA) Ltd. (#3088), Banknote Corporation of America (#3089)

LITHOGRAPHED
Sheets of 200 in four panes of 50

1996, Aug. 1		**Tagged**		**Perf. 11.1**	
3088	A2387	32c	multicolored	.80	.20
		P# block of 4, 4#+P		3.75	—

For booklet see No. BK253.

BOOKLET STAMP
Self-Adhesive
Serpentine Die Cut 11.6x11.4

3089	A2387 32c **multicolored**	.70	.30
a.	Booklet pane of 20	14.00	

RURAL FREE DELIVERY, CENT.

A2388

Designed by Richard Sheaff.

LITHOGRAPHED & ENGRAVED
Sheets of 120 in six panes of 20

1996, Aug. 7   Tagged   Perf. 11.2x11

3090	A2388 32c **multicolored**	.80	.20
	P# block of 4, 5#	3.25	—
	Pane of 20	16.50	—

For booklet see No. BK254.

RIVERBOATS

Robt. E.
Lee — A2389

Sylvan
Dell — A2390

Far
West — A2391

Rebecca
Everingham
A2392

Bailey Gatzert
A2393

Designed by Dean Ellis.

Printed by Avery Dennison.

PHOTOGRAVURE
Sheets of 200 in 10 panes of 20
Serpentine Die Cut 11x11.1

1996, Aug. 22   Tagged
Self-Adhesive

3091	A2389 32c **multicolored**	.65	.20
3092	A2390 32c **multicolored**	.65	.20
3093	A2391 32c **multicolored**	.65	.20

3094	A2392 32c **multicolored**	.65	.20
3095	A2393 32c **multicolored**	.65	.20
a.	Vert. strip of 5, #3091-3095	3.25	
	P# block of 10, 5#+V	6.50	
	Pane of 20	13.00	
b.	Strip of 5, #3091-3095, with special die cutting, die cut 11¼	75.00	50.00
	P# block of 10, 5#+V	150.00	
	Pane of 20	300.00	

The serpentine die cutting runs through the peelable backing to which Nos. 3091-3095 are affixed. No. 3095a exists with stamps in different sequences.

On the long side of each stamp in No. 3095b, the die cutting is missing 3 "perforations" between the stamps, one near each end and one in the middle. This allows a complete strip to be removed from the backing paper for use on a first day cover. No. 3095b was also used to make Souvenir Page No. 1215.

For booklet see No. BK255.

AMERICAN MUSIC SERIES
Big Band Leaders

Count
Basie — A2394

Tommy &
Jimmy Dorsey
A2395

Glenn
Miller — A2396

Benny
Goodman
A2397

Songwriters

Harold
Arlen — A2398

Johnny Mercer
A2399

Dorothy Fields
A2400

Hoagy
Carmichael
A2401

Designed by Bill Nelson (#3096-3099), Gregg Rudd (#3100-3103).

Printed by Ashton-Potter (USA) Ltd.

LITHOGRAPHED
Sheets of 120 in six panes of 20

1996, Sept. 11   Tagged   Perf. 11.1x11

3096	A2394 32c **multicolored**	.75	.20
3097	A2395 32c **multicolored**	.75	.20
3098	A2396 32c **multicolored**	.75	.20
3099	A2397 32c **multicolored**	.75	.20
a.	Block or strip of 4, #3096-3099	3.00	2.00
	P# block of 4, 6#+P	4.00	
	P# block of 8, 2 sets of P# + top label	6.75	—
	Pane of 20	19.00	—
3100	A2398 32c **multicolored**	.75	.20
3101	A2399 32c **multicolored**	.75	.20
3102	A2400 32c **multicolored**	.75	.20
3103	A2401 32c **multicolored**	.75	.20
a.	Block or strip of 4, #3100-3103	3.00	2.00
	P# block of 4, 6#+P	3.50	
	P# block of 8, 2 sets of P# + top label	5.75	—
	Pane of 20	16.00	—

LITERARY ARTS SERIES

F. Scott
Fitzgerald
(1896-1940)
A2402

Designed by Michael Deas.

PHOTOGRAVURE
Sheets of 200 in four panes of 50

1996, Sept. 27   Tagged   Perf. 11.1

3104	A2402 23c **multicolored**	.55	.20
	P# block of 4, 4#	4.00	—

ENDANGERED SPECIES

A2403

Illustration reduced.

Designed by James Balog. Printed by Ashton-Potter (USA) Ltd.

Designs: a, Black-footed ferret. b, Thick-billed parrot. c, Hawaiian monk seal. d, American crocodile. e, Ocelot. f, Schaus swallowtail butterfly. g, Wyoming toad. h, Brown pelican. i, California condor. j, Gila trout. k, San Francisco garter snake. l, Woodland caribou. m, Florida panther. n, Piping plover. o, Florida manatee.

LITHOGRAPHED
Sheets of 90 in six panes of 15

1996, Oct. 2	**Tagged**		*Perf. 11.1x11*
3105	A2403	Pane of 15	10.50 8.00
a.-o.		32c any single	.70 .50

See Mexico No. 1995. For booklet see No. BK256.

COMPUTER TECHNOLOGY

A2404

Designed by Nancy Skolos & Tom Wedell.

Printed by Ashton-Potter (USA) Ltd.

LITHOGRAPHED & ENGRAVED
Sheets of 160 in four panes of 40

1996, Oct. 8	**Tagged**		*Perf. 10.9x11.1*
3106	A2404	32c multicolored	.65 .20
		P# block of 4, 6#+P	3.00 —

CHRISTMAS

Madonna and Child from Adoration of the Shepherds, by Paolo de Matteis — A2405

Family at Fireplace — A2406

Decorating Tree — A2407

Dreaming of Santa Claus — A2408

Holiday Shopping — A2409

Skaters — A2410

Designed by Richard D. Sheaff (#3107, 3112), Julia Talcott (#3108-3111, 3113-3117).

Printed by Bureau of Engraving and Printing (#3107, 3112), Ashton-Potter (USA) Ltd. (#3108-3111), Banknote Corporation of America (#3113-3116), Avery-Dennison (#3117).

LITHOGRAPHED & ENGRAVED
Sheets of 300 in six panes of 50

1996	**Tagged**		*Perf. 11.1x11.2*
3107	A2405	32c multicolored, *Nov. 1*	.65 .20
		P# block of 4, 5#	3.00 —

For booklet see No. BK257.

LITHOGRAPHED
Perf. 11.3

3108	A2406	32c multicolored, *Oct. 8*	.65 .20
3109	A2407	32c multicolored, *Oct. 8*	.65 .20
3110	A2408	32c multicolored, *Oct. 8*	.65 .20
3111	A2409	32c multicolored, *Oct. 8*	.65 .20
a.		Block or strip of 4, #3108-3111	2.60 1.75
		P# block of 4, 4#+P	3.00 —
b.		Strip of 4, #3110-3111, 3108-3109, with #3109 imperf., #3108 imperf. at right	—
c.		Strip of 4, #3108-3111, with #3111 imperf, #3110 imperf at right	—

BOOKLET STAMPS
Self-Adhesive
LITHOGRAPHED & ENGRAVED
Serpentine Die Cut 10 on 2, 3 or 4 Sides

3112	A2405	32c multicolored, *Nov. 1*	.75 .20
a.		Booklet pane of 20 + label	15.00
b.		Die cutting omitted, pair	60.00
c.		As "a," die cutting omitted	—

LITHOGRAPHED
Serpentine Die Cut 11.8x11.5 on 2, 3 or 4 Sides

3113	A2406	32c multicolored, *Oct. 8*	.75 .20
3114	A2407	32c multicolored, *Oct. 8*	.75 .20
3115	A2408	32c multicolored, *Oct. 8*	.75 .20
3116	A2409	32c multicolored, *Oct. 8*	.75 .20
a.		Booklet pane of 20, 5 ea #3113-3116	15.00
b.		Strip of 4, #3113-3116, die cutting omitted	550.00
c.		Block of 6, die cutting omitted	775.00
d.		As "a," die cutting omitted	2,100.

PHOTOGRAVURE
Die Cut

3117	A2410	32c multicolored, *Oct. 8*	.65 .20
a.		Booklet pane of 18	12.00

HANUKKAH

A2411

Designed by Hannah Smotrich.

Printed by Avery Dennison.

PHOTOGRAVURE
Sheets of 200 in 10 panes of 20

1996, Oct. 22	**Tagged**		*Serpentine Die Cut 11.1*
		Self-Adhesive	
3118	A2411	32c multicolored	.65 .20
		P# block of 4, 5#+V	2.60
		Pane of 20	13.00

Backing on No. 3118 is die cut with a continuous horizontal wavy line. The 1997 reprint is die cut with two short horizontal lines on each side of a semi-circle on the backing of each stamp.

See Nos. 3352, 3547, 3672, Israel No. 1289. For booklet see No. BK258.

CYCLING
Souvenir Sheet

A2412

Illustration reduced.

Designed by McRay Magleby.

Printed by Stamp Venturers.

PHOTOGRAVURE

1996, Nov. 1	**Tagged**		*Perf. 11x11.1*
3119	A2412	Sheet of 2	2.50 2.00
a.		50c orange & multi	1.25 1.00
b.		50c blue green & multi	1.25 1.00

No. 3119 exists overprinted in gold for the Tour of China '96. This overprint is a private production.

CHINESE NEW YEAR

Year of the Ox — A2413

Designed by Clarence Lee.

Printed by Stamp Venturers.

PHOTOGRAVURE
Sheets of 180 in 9 panes of 20

1997, Jan. 5	**Tagged**		*Perf. 11.2*
3120	A2413	32c multicolored	.80 .20
		P# block of 4, 4#+S	3.20 —
		Pane of 20	16.00

See No. 3895b.

BLACK HERITAGE SERIES

Brig. Gen. Benjamin O. Davis, Sr. (1880-1970) — A2414

Designed by Richard Sheaff.

Printed by Banknote Corp. of America.

LITHOGRAPHED
Sheets of 120 in six panes of 20

1997, Jan. 28 **Tagged** *Serpentine Die Cut 11.4*
Self-Adhesive

3121	A2414	32c **multicolored**	.70	.20
		P# block of 4, 4#+B	2.75	
		Pane of 20	14.00	

Statue of Liberty Type of 1994
Printed by Avery-Dennison.

PHOTOGRAVURE
Serpentine Die Cut 11 on 2, 3 or 4 Sides
1997, Feb. 1 **Tagged**
Self-Adhesive

3122	A1951	32c **red, light blue, dark blue & yellow**	.70	.20
a.		Booklet pane of 20 + label	14.00	
b.		Booklet pane of 4	2.80	
c.		Booklet pane of 5 + label	3.75	
		P# single, #V1111	.95	1.00
d.		Booklet pane of 6	4.25	
		Booklet pane of 6 containing P# single	6.00	
		P# single, #V1111	2.50	1.00
h.		As "a," die cutting omitted	—	

The plate # single in No. 3122c is the lower left stamp and should be collected unused with the reorder label to its right to differentiate it from the plate # single in No. 3122d which is the lower left stamp in the bottom pane of the booklet and should be collected with a normal stamp adjoining it at right. In used condition, these plate # singles are indistinguishable.

Serpentine Die Cut 11.5x11.8 on 2, 3 or 4 Sides
1997 **Tagged**
Self-Adhesive

3122E	A1951	32c **red, light blue, dark blue & yellow**	1.50	.20
f.		Booklet pane of 20 + label	40.00	
g.		Booklet pane of 6	9.00	
		Booklet pane of 6 containing P# single	13.50	
		P# single, #V1111	5.50	2.00

The plate # single in No. 3122Eg is the lower left stamp in the bottom pane of the booklet.

LOVE

A2415   Swans   A2416

Designed by Marvin Mattelson.

Printed by Banknote Corp. of America.

LITHOGRAPHED
Serpentine Die Cut 11.8x11.6 on 2, 3 or 4 Sides
1997, Feb. 4 **Tagged**
Self-Adhesive

3123	A2415	32c **multicolored**	.65	.20
a.		Booklet pane of 20 + label	13.00	
b.		Die cutting omitted, pair	135.00	
c.		As "a," die cutting omitted	1,350.	
d.		As "a," black omitted	—	

Serpentine Die Cut 11.6x11.8 on 2, 3 or 4 Sides

3124	A2416	55c **multicolored**	1.10	.20
a.		Booklet pane of 20 + label	22.00	

HELPING CHILDREN LEARN

A2417

Designed by Chris Van Allsburg.

Printed by Avery-Dennison.

PHOTOGRAVURE
Sheets of 160 in eight panes of 20
Serpentine Die Cut 11.6x11.7
1997, Feb. 18 **Tagged**
Self-Adhesive

3125	A2417	32c **multicolored**	.65	.20
		P# block of 4, 4#+V	2.60	
		Pane of 20	13.00	

The die cut perforations of #3125 are fragile and separate easily.

MERIAN BOTANICAL PRINTS

Citron, Moth, Larvae, Pupa, Beetle
A2418

Flowering Pineapple, Cockroaches
A2419

No. 3128 (r), No. 3129 (l), No. 3128a below

Designed by Phil Jordan based on works by Maria Sibylla Merian (1647-1717).

Printed by Stamp Venturers.

PHOTOGRAVURE
Serpentine Die Cut 10.9x10.2 on 2, 3 or 4 Sides
1997, Mar. 3 **Tagged**
Self-Adhesive

3126	A2418	32c **multicolored**	.65	.20
3127	A2419	32c **multicolored**	.65	.20
a.		Booklet pane, 10 ea #3126-3127 + label	13.00	
b.		Pair, #3126-3127	1.30	
c.		Vert. pair, die cutting omitted between	475.00	

Size: 18.5x24mm
Serpentine Die Cut 11.2x10.8 on 2 or 3 Sides

3128	A2418	32c **multicolored**	1.00	.20
a.		See footnote	3.00	.25
b.		Booklet pane, 2 ea #3128-3129, 1 #3128a	7.00	

3129	A2419	32c **multicolored**	1.00	.20
a.		See footnote	4.50	.35
b.		Booklet pane, 2 ea #3128-3129, 1 #3129a	9.00	
c.		Pair, #3128-3129	2.00	

Nos. 3128a-3129a are placed sideways on the pane and are serpentine die cut 11.2 on top and bottom, 10.8 on left side. One of the two No. 3128a per pane has a straight edge at left. The right side is 11.2 broken by a sloping die cut where the stamp meets the vertical die cutting of the two stamps above it. See illustration above.

PACIFIC 97

Sailing Ship — A2420

Stagecoach — A2421

Designed by Richard Sheaff.

Printed by Banknote Corporation of America.

ENGRAVED
Sheets of 96 in six panes of 16

1997, Mar. 13		**Tagged**	***Perf. 11.2***	
3130	A2420	32c **blue**	.65	.30
3131	A2421	32c **red**	.65	.30
a.		Pair, #3130-3131	1.30	.75
		P# block of 4, 1#+B	2.60	—
		Pane of 16	10.50	7.50
		Sheet of 96 (6 panes)	80.00	
		Cross gutter block of 16 (8 #3131a)	30.00	—
		Vert. pairs with horiz. gutter (each)	10.00	—
		Horiz. pairs with vert. gutter (each)	5.00	—

Juke Box and Flag Over Porch Types of 1995
Designed by Bill Nelson (#3132), Dave LaFleur (#3133).

Printed by Stamp Venturers.

PHOTOGRAVURE
COIL STAMPS

1997, Mar. 14		**Untagged**	***Imperf.***	
Self-Adhesive				
3132	A2225	(25c) **bright orange red, bright yellow green & multi**	1.50	.50
		Pair	3.00	
		P# strip of 5, #M11111	8.00	
		P#, single, #M11111		6.50

Tagged
Serpentine Die Cut 9.9 Vert.

3133	A2212	32c **dark blue, tan, brown, red & light blue**	1.50	.20
		Pair	3.00	
		P# strip of 5, #M11111	7.25	
		P#, single, #M11111		4.00

Nos. 3132-3133 were issued without backing paper. No. 3132 has simulated perforations ending in black bars at the top and bottom edges of the stamp. Sky on No. 3133 shows color gradation at LR not on Nos. 2915A or 2915D, and it has blue "1996" at left bottom.

LITERARY ARTS SERIES

Thornton Wilder (1897-1975)
A2422

Designed by Phil Jordan.

Printed by Ashton-Potter (USA) Ltd.

LITHOGRAPHED
Sheets of 180 in nine panes of 20

1997, Apr. 17	Tagged	Perf. 11.1	
3134 A2422	32c multicolored	.65	.20
	P# block of 4, 4#+P	2.60	—
	Pane of 20	13.00	—

RAOUL WALLENBERG (1912-47)

Wallenberg and Jewish Refugees
A2423

Designed by Howard Paine.

Printed by Sterling Sommer for Ashton-Potter (USA) Ltd.

LITHOGRAPHED
Sheets of 180 in nine panes of 20

1997, Apr. 24	Tagged	Perf. 11.1	
3135 A2423	32c multicolored	.65	.20
	P# block of 4, 4#+P	2.60	—
	Pane of 20	13.00	—

DINOSAURS

A2424

Illustration reduced.

Designed by James Gurney.
Printed by Sterling Sommer for Ashton-Potter (USA) Ltd.

Designs: a, Ceratosaurus. b, Camptosaurus. c, Camarasaurus. d, Brachiosaurus. e, Goniopholis. f, Stegosaurus. g, Allosaurus. h, Opisthias. i, Edmontonia. j, Einiosaurus. k, Daspletosaurus. l, Palaeosaniwa. m, Corythosaurus. n, Ornithomimus. o, Parasaurolophus.

LITHOGRAPHED

1997, May 1	Tagged	Perf. 11x11.1	
3136 A2424	Sheet of 15	10.00	8.00
a.-o.	32c any single	.65	.50
p.	As No. 3136, bottom 7 stamps imperf.	3,750.	
q.	As No. 3136, top 8 stamps imperf.	3,750.	
r.	As No. 3136, all colors and tagging missing (EP)	—	

No. 3136r resulted from double sheeting in the sheet-fed press. It is properly gummed and perforated.

BUGS BUNNY

A2425

Cross Gutter Block of 12

Illustration reduced.

Designed by Warner Bros.

Printed by Avery Dennison.

PHOTOGRAVURE

1997, May 22	Tagged	Serpentine Die Cut 11	
		Self-Adhesive	
3137	Pane of 10	6.75	
a.	A2425 32c single	.65	.20
b.	Pane of 9 #3137a	6.00	
c.	Pane of 1 #3137a	.65	
	Sheet of 60 (six panes) top	250.00	
	Sheet of 60 (six panes) bottom, with plate #	450.00	
	Pane of 10 from uncut press sheet	70.00	
	Pane of 10 with plate #	350.00	
	Cross gutter block of 9 or 10	200.00	
	Cross gutter block of 12	250.00	
	Vert. pair with horiz. gutter	25.00	
	Horiz. pair with vert. gutter	50.00	

Die cutting on #3137 does not extend through the backing paper.
Pane of 10 with P# comes from bottom uncut sheet of 60.
Nos. 3137b-3137c and 3138b-3138c are separated by a vertical line of microperforations that are absent on the uncut sheet of 60.
The horiz. pair with vert. gutter consists of a stamp at the left, from No. 3137b, part of the illustration of Bugs Bunny, the small gutter between the panes, and a stamp at the right from the left row of 3137b. Some pairs may include the single stamp from No. 3137c in addition to the two stamps at the right and left.

3138	Pane of 10	150.00	
a.	A2425 32c single	3.50	
b.	Pane of 9 #3138a	32.50	
c.	Pane of 1, no die cutting	110.00	

Die cutting on #3138b extends through the backing paper.
An untagged promotional piece similar to No. 3137c exists on the same backing paper as the pane, with the same design image, but without Bugs' signature and the single stamp. Replacing the stamp is an enlarged "32 / USA" in the same style as used on the stamp. This promotional piece was not valid for postage.

PACIFIC 97

Franklin — A2426

Washington — A2427

Designed by Richard Sheaff. Selvage on Nos. 3139-3140 is lithographed.

LITHOGRAPHED & ENGRAVED

1997	Tagged	Perf. 10.5x10.4	
3139	Pane of 12, May 29	12.00	9.00
a.	A2426 50c single	1.00	.50
3140	Pane of 12, May 30	14.50	11.00
a.	A2427 60c single	1.20	.60

Nos. 3139-3140 were sold through June 8.

MARSHALL PLAN, 50TH ANNIV.

Gen. George C. Marshall, Map of Europe
A2428

Designed by Richard Sheaff.

Printed by Stevens Security Press for Ashton-Potter (USA) Ltd.

LITHOGRAPHED & ENGRAVED
Sheets of 120 in six panes of 20

1997, June 4	Tagged	Perf. 11.1	
3141 A2428	32c multicolored	.65	.20
	P# block of 4, 5#+P	2.60	—
	Pane of 20	13.00	—

CLASSIC AMERICAN AIRCRAFT

A2429

Illustration reduced.

Designed by Phil Jordan.

Printed by Stamp Venturers.

Designs: a, Mustang. b, Model B. c, Cub. d, Vega. e, Alpha. f, B-10. g, Corsair. h, Stratojet. i, GeeBee. j, Staggerwing. k, Flying Fortress. l, Stearman. m, Constellation. n, Lightning. o, Peashooter. p, Tri-Motor. q, DC-3. r, 314 Clipper. s, Jenny. t, Wildcat.

PHOTOGRAVURE
Sheets of 120 in six panes of 20

1997, July 19	Tagged	Perf. 10.1	
3142 A2429	Pane of 20	13.00	10.00
a.-t.	32c any single	.65	.50
	Sheet of 120 (6 panes)	85.00	
	Cross gutter block of 20	22.50	
	Vert. pairs with horiz. gutter (each)	2.40	—
	Horiz. pairs with vert. gutter (each)	2.40	—

Inscriptions on back of each stamp describe the airplane.
Cross gutter block of 20 consists of six stamps from each of two panes and four stamps from each of two other panes with the cross gutter between.

FOOTBALL COACHES

Bear Bryant
A2430

Pop Warner
A2431

Vince
Lombardi
A2432

George Halas
A2433

Designed by Carl Herrman.

Printed by Sterling Sommer for Ashton-Potter (USA) Ltd.

LITHOGRAPHED
Sheets of 120 in six panes of 20

1997	Tagged		Perf. 11.2	
3143	A2430	32c multicolored, July 25	.65	.25
3144	A2431	32c multicolored, July 25	.65	.25
3145	A2432	32c multicolored, July 25	.65	.25
3146	A2433	32c multicolored, July 25	.65	.25
a.		Block or strip of 4, #3143-3146	2.60	—
		P# block of 4, 5#+P	2.60	1.75
		P# block of 8, 2 sets of P# +		
		top label	5.25	—
		Pane of 20	13.00	

With Red Bar Above Coach's Name
Perf. 11

3147	A2432	32c multicolored, Aug. 5	.65	.45
		P# block of 4, 4#+P	3.00	—
		Pane of 20	14.50	—
3148	A2430	32c multicolored, Aug. 7	.65	.45
		P# block of 4, 4#+P	3.00	—
		Pane of 20	14.50	—
3149	A2431	32c multicolored, Aug. 8	.65	.45
		P# block of 4, 4#+P	3.00	—
		Pane of 20	14.50	—
3150	A2433	32c multicolored, Aug. 16	.65	.45
		P# block of 4, 4#+P	3.00	—
		Pane of 20	14.50	—

AMERICAN DOLLS

A2434

Illustration reduced.

Designed by Derry Noyes.

Printed by Sterling Sommer for Ashton-Potter (USA) Ltd.

Designs: a, "Alabama Baby," and doll by Martha Chase. b, "Columbian Doll." c, Johnny Gruelle's "Raggedy Ann." d, Doll by Martha Chase. e, "American Child." f, "Baby Coos." g, Plains Indian. h, Doll by Izannah Walker. i, "Babyland Rag." j, "Scootles." k, Doll by Ludwig Greiner. l, "Betsy McCall." m, Percy Crosby's "Skippy." n, "Maggie Mix-up." o, Dolls by Albert Schoenhut.

LITHOGRAPHED
Sheets of 90 in six panes of 15

1997, July 28		Tagged	Perf. 10.9x11.1	
3151	A2434	Pane of 15	13.50	—
a.-o.		32c any single	.90	.60

For booklet see No. BK266.

A2435

A2436

LEGENDS OF HOLLYWOOD
Humphrey Bogart (1899-1957).

Designed by Carl Herrman.

Printed by Stamp Venturers.

PHOTOGRAVURE
Sheets of 120 in six panes of 20

1997, July 31		Tagged	Perf. 11.1	
3152	A2435	32c multicolored	.85	.20
		P# block of 4, 5#+S	3.50	—
		Pane of 20	18.50	—
		Sheet of 120 (6 panes)	95.00	—
		Cross gutter block of 8	17.50	—
		Block of 8 with vertical gutter	13.50	—
		Horiz. pair with vert. gutter	3.50	—
		Vert. pair with horiz. gutter	2.50	—

Perforations in corner of each stamp are star-shaped. Cross-gutter block consists of 6 stamps from upper panes and 2 stamps from panes below.
For booklet see No. BK267.

"THE STARS AND STRIPES FOREVER!"
Designed by Richard Sheaff.

Sheets of 300 in six panes of 50
PHOTOGRAVURE

1997, Aug. 21		Tagged	Perf. 11.1	
3153	A2436	32c multicolored	.65	.20
		P# block of 4, 4#	3.00	—

For booklet see No. BK268.

AMERICAN MUSIC SERIES
Opera Singers

Lily
Pons — A2437

Richard Tucker
A2438

Lawrence
Tibbett
A2439

Rosa Ponselle
A2440

Classical Composers & Conductors

Leopold
Stokowski
A2441

Arthur Fiedler
A2442

George
Szell — A2443

Eugene
Ormandy
A2444

Samuel
Barber
A2445

Ferde Grofé
A2446

Charles
Ives — A2447

Louis Moreau
Gottschalk
A2448

Designed by Howard Paine.

Printed by Ashton-Potter (USA) Ltd.

LITHOGRAPHED
Sheets of 120 in six panes of 20

1997		Tagged	Perf. 11	
3154	A2437	32c multicolored, Sept. 10	.75	.20
3155	A2438	32c multicolored, Sept. 10	.75	.20
3156	A2439	32c multicolored, Sept. 10	.75	.20
3157	A2440	32c multicolored, Sept. 10	.75	.20
a.		Block or strip of 4, #3154-3157	3.00	2.00
		P# block of 4, 5#+P	3.00	—
		P# block of 8, 2 sets of P# +		
		top label	6.00	—
		Pane of 20	15.00	—
3158	A2441	32c multicolored, Sept. 12	1.10	.20
3159	A2442	32c multicolored, Sept. 12	1.10	.20
3160	A2443	32c multicolored, Sept. 12	1.10	.20
3161	A2444	32c multicolored, Sept. 12	1.10	.20
3162	A2445	32c multicolored, Sept. 12	1.10	.20
3163	A2446	32c multicolored, Sept. 12	1.10	.20
3164	A2447	32c multicolored, Sept. 12	1.10	.20
3165	A2448	32c multicolored, Sept. 12	1.10	.20
a.		Block of 8, #3158-3165	9.00	4.00
		P# block of 8, 2 sets of 5P#+P		
		+ top label	11.00	—
		Pane of 20	22.50	—

PADRE FÉLIX VARELA (1788-1853)

A2449

Designed by Carl Herrman.

Printed by Sterling Sommer for Ashton-Potter (USA) Ltd.

LITHOGRAPHED
Sheets of 120 in six panes of 20

1997, Sept. 15		Tagged	Perf. 11.2	
3166	A2449	32c purple	.65	.20
		P# block of 4, 1#+P	2.60	—
		Pane of 20	13.00	—

DEPARTMENT OF THE AIR FORCE, 50TH ANNIV.

Thunderbirds
Aerial
Demonstration
Squadron
A2450

Designed by Phil Jordan.

Printed by Sterling Sommer for Ashton-Potter (USA) Ltd.

LITHOGRAPHED
Sheets of 180 in nine panes of 20

1997, Sept. 18		Tagged	Perf. 11.2x11.1	
3167	A2450	32c multicolored	.65	.20
		P# block of 4, 4#+P	2.60	—
		Pane of 20	13.00	—

A hidden 3-D design can be seen on the stamp when it is viewed with a special viewer sold by the post office.

CLASSIC MOVIE MONSTERS

Lon Chaney as The
Phantom of the
Opera — A2451

Bela Lugosi as
Dracula — A2452

Boris Karloff as
Frankenstein's
Monster — A2453

Boris Karloff as The
Mummy — A2454

Lon Chaney, Jr. as
The Wolf
Man — A2455

Cross Gutter Block of 8

Illustration reduced.

Designed by Derry Noyes.

Printed by Stamp Venturers.

PHOTOGRAVURE
Sheets of 180 in nine panes of 20

1997, Sept. 30		Tagged	Perf. 10.2	
3168	A2451	32c multicolored	.75	.20
3169	A2452	32c multicolored	.75	.20
3170	A2453	32c multicolored	.75	.20
3171	A2454	32c multicolored	.75	.20
3172	A2455	32c multicolored	.75	.20
a.		Strip of 5, #3168-3172	3.75	2.25
		P# block of 10, 5#+S	7.50	—
		Pane of 20	15.00	—
		Sheet of 180 (9 panes)	130.00	
		Cross-gutter block of 8	17.50	
		Block of 10 with horiz. gutter	12.50	
		Vert. pairs with horiz. gutter (each)	2.50	—
		Horiz. pairs with vert. gutter (each)	2.50	—

Plate blocks may contain top label. See note after No. 3167.
For booklet see No. BK269.

FIRST SUPERSONIC FLIGHT, 50TH ANNIV.

A2456

Designed by Phil Jordan.

Printed by Banknote Corporation of America.

LITHOGRAPHED
Sheets of 180 in nine panes of 20

1997, Oct. 14		Tagged	Serpentine Die Cut 11.4	
			Self-Adhesive	
3173	A2456	32c multicolored	.65	.20
		P# block of 4, 4#+B	2.60	—
		Pane of 20	13.00	—

WOMEN IN MILITARY SERVICE

A2457

Designed by Derry Noyes.

Printed by Banknote Corporation of America.

LITHOGRAPHED
Sheets of 120 in six panes of 20

1997, Oct. 18	Tagged	Perf. 11.1
3174 A2457 32c **multicolored**	.65	.20
P# block of 4, 6#+B	2.60	—
Pane of 20	13.00	

KWANZAA

A2458

Designed by Synthia Saint James. Printed by Avery Dennison.

PHOTOGRAVURE
Sheets of 250 in five panes of 50

1997, Oct. 22	Tagged	Serpentine Die Cut 11
	Self-Adhesive	
3175 A2458 32c **multicolored**	.65	.20
P# block of 4, 4#+V	3.00	
Sheet of 250 (5 panes)	550.00	
P# block of 4, 4#+V and 4		
sets of #+VO	225.00	
Horiz. pair with vert. gutter	11.00	

See Nos. 3368, 3548, 3673.

CHRISTMAS

Madonna and Child,
by Sano di
Pietro — A2459

Holly — A2460

Designed by Richard D. Sheaff (#3176), Howard Paine (#3177).

Printed by Bureau of Engraving and Printing (#3176), Banknote Corporation of America (#3177).

LITHOGRAPHED
Serpentine Die Cut 9.9 on 2, 3 or 4 Sides
1997		Tagged
	Booklet Stamps	
	Self-Adhesive	
3176 A2459 32c **multicolored**, *Oct. 27*	.65	.20
a. Booklet pane of 20 + label	13.00	

Serpentine Die Cut 11.2x11.6 on 2, 3 or 4 Sides
3177 A2460 32c **multicolored**, *Oct. 30*	.65	.20
a. Booklet pane of 20 + label	13.00	
b. Booklet pane of 4	2.60	
c. Booklet pane of 5 + label	3.25	
d. Booklet pane of 6	3.90	

MARS PATHFINDER
Souvenir Sheet

Mars Rover Sojourner — A2461

Illustration reduced.

Designed by Terry McCaffrey. Printed by Stamp Venturers.

PHOTOGRAVURE

1997, Dec. 10	Tagged	Perf. 11x11.1
3178 A2461 $3 **multicolored**	6.00	4.00
a. $3, single stamp	5.50	3.00
b. Single souvenir sheet from sheet of 18	7.00	—
Sheet of 18	125.00	
Vert. pair with horiz. gutter	15.00	—

The perforations at the bottom of the stamp contain the letters "USA." Vertical rouletting extends from the vertical perforations of the stamp to the bottom of the souvenir sheet.

Sheet of 18 has vertical perforations separating the three columns of souvenir sheets. These were cut away when No. 3178 was produced. Thus, the souvenir sheet from the sheet of 18 is wider and has vertical perforations on one or two sides.

See note after No. 3167.

CHINESE NEW YEAR

Year of the
Tiger — A2462

Designed by Clarence Lee. Printed by Stamp Venturers.

PHOTOGRAVURE
Sheets of 180 in nine panes of 20

1998, Jan. 5	Tagged	Perf. 11.2
3179 A2462 32c **multicolored**	.80	.20
P# block of 4, 4#+S	3.75	—
Pane of 20	18.00	

See No. 3895c.

A2463

A2464

ALPINE SKIING
Designed by Michael Schwab.

Printed by Banknote Corporation of America.

LITHOGRAPHED
Sheets of 180 in nine panes of 20

1998, Jan. 22	Tagged	Perf. 11.2
3180 A2463 32c **multicolored**	.70	.20
P# block of 4, 6#+B	3.00	—
Pane of 20	15.00	

BLACK HERITAGE SERIES
Madam C.J. Walker (1867-1919), Entrepreneur

Designed by Richard Sheaff. Printed by Banknote Corp. of America.

LITHOGRAPHED
Sheets of 180 in nine panes of 20
Serpentine Die Cut 11.6x11.3

1998, Jan. 28		Tagged
	Self-Adhesive	
3181 A2464 32c **sepia & black**	.70	.20
P# block of 4, 3#+B	3.00	
Pane of 20	15.00	

CELEBRATE THE CENTURY

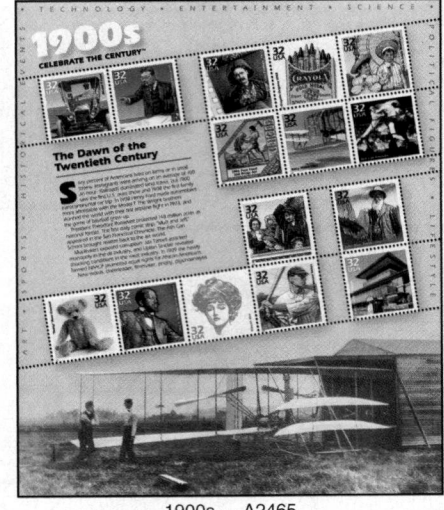

1900s — A2465

No. 3182: a, Model T Ford. b, Theodore Roosevelt. c, Motion picture "The Great Train Robbery," 1903. d, Crayola Crayons introduced, 1903. e, St. Louis World's Fair, 1904. f, Design used on Hunt's Remedy stamp (#RS56), Pure Food & Drug Act, 1906. g, Wright Brothers first flight, Kitty Hawk, 1903. h, Boxing match shown in painting "Stag at Sharkey's," by George Bellows of the Ash Can School. i, Immigrants arrive. j, John Muir, preservationist. k, "Teddy" Bear created. l, W.E.B. Du Bois, social activist. m, Gibson Girl. n, First baseball World Series, 1903. o, Robie House, Chicago, designed by Frank Lloyd Wright.

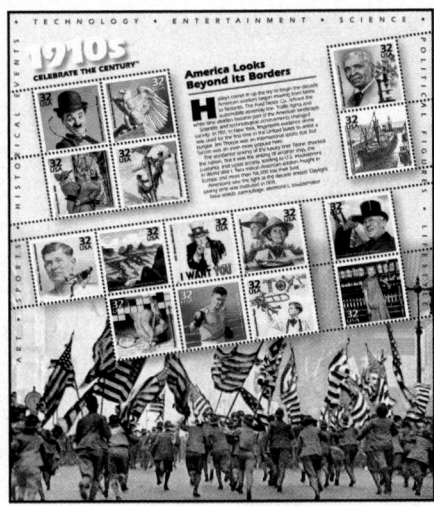

1910s — A2466

No. 3183: a, Charlie Chaplin as the Little Tramp. b, Federal Reserve System created, 1913. c, George Washington Carver. d, Avant-garde art introduced at Armory Show, 1913. e, First transcontinental telephone line, 1914. f, Panama Canal opens, 1914. g, Jim Thorpe wins decathlon at Stockholm Olympics, 1912. h, Grand Canyon National Park, 1919. i, U.S. enters World War I. j, Boy Scouts started in 1910, Girl Scouts formed in 1912. k, Woodrow Wilson. l, First crossword puzzle published, 1913. m, Jack Dempsey wins heavyweight title, 1919. n, Construction toys. o, Child labor reform.

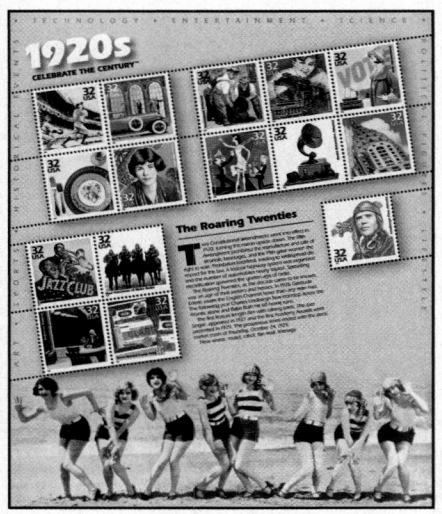

1920s — A2467

No. 3184: a, Babe Ruth. b, The Gatsby style. c, Prohibition enforced. d, Electric toy trains. e, 19th Amendment (woman voting). f, Emily Post's Etiquette. g, Margaret Mead, anthropologist. h, Flappers do the Charleston. i, Radio entertains America. j, Art Deco style (Chrysler Building). k, Jazz flourishes. l, Four Horsemen of Notre Dame. m, Lindbergh flies the Atlantic. n, American realism (Automat, by Edward Hopper). o, Stock Market crash, 1929.

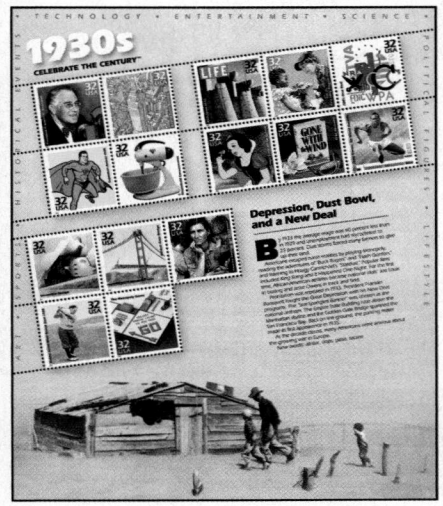

1930s — A2468

No. 3185: a, Franklin D. Roosevelt. b, The Empire State Building. c, 1st Issue of Life Magazine, 1936. d, Eleanor Roosevelt. e, FDR's New Deal. f, Superman arrives, 1938. g, Household conveniences. h, "Snow White and the Seven Dwarfs," 1937. i, "Gone with the Wind," 1936. j, Jesse Owens. k, Streamline design. l, Golden Gate Bridge. m, America survives the Depression. n, Bobby Jones wins golf Grand Slam, 1938. o, The Monopoly Game.

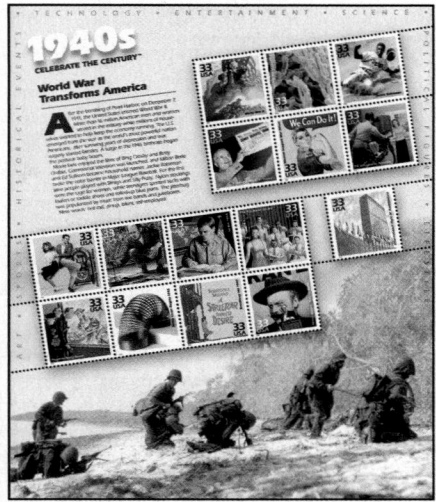

1940s — A2469

No. 3186: a, World War II. b, Antibiotics save lives. c, Jackie Robinson. d, Harry S Truman. e, Women support war effort. f, TV entertains America. g, Jitterbug sweeps nation. h, Jackson Pollock, Abstract Expressionism. i, GI Bill, 1944. j, Big Band Sound. k, Intl. style of architecture (UN Headquarters). l, Postwar baby boom. m, Slinky, 1945. n, "A Streecar Named Desire," 1947. o, Orson Welles' "Citizen Kane."

1950s — A2470

No. 3187: a, Polio vaccine developed. b, Teen fashions. c, The "Shot Heard 'Round the World." d, US launches satellites. e, Korean War. f, Desegregating public schools. g, Tail fins, chrome. h, Dr. Seuss' "The Cat in the Hat." i, Drive-in movies. j, World Series rivals. k, Rocky Marciano, undefeated boxer. l, "I Love Lucy." m, Rock 'n Roll. n, Stock car racing. o, Movies go 3-D.

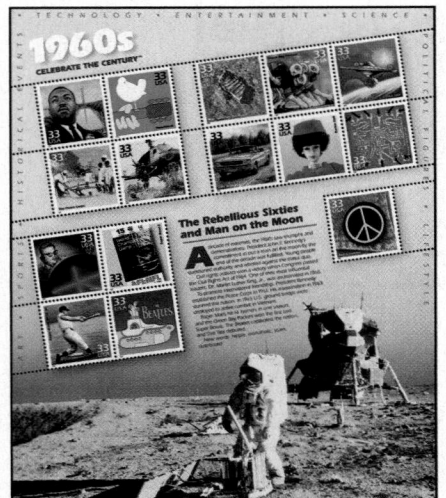

1960s — A2471

No. 3188: a, Martin Luther King, Jr., "I Have a Dream." b, Woodstock. c, Man walks on the moon. d, Green Bay Packers. e, Star Trek. f, The Peace Corps. g, Viet Nam War. h, Ford Mustang. i, Barbie Doll. j, Integrated circuit. k, Lasers. l, Super Bowl I. m, Peace symbol. n, Roger Maris, 61 in '61. o, The Beatles "Yellow Submarine."

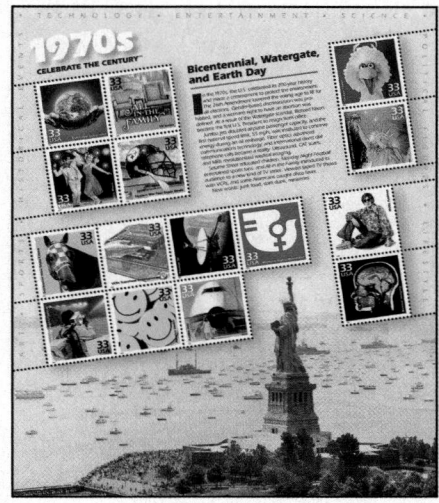

1970s — A2472

No. 3189: a, Earth Day celebrated. b, "All in the Family" television series. c, "Sesame Street" television series character, Big Bird. d, Disco music. e, Pittsburgh Steelers win four Super Bowls. f, US Celebrates 200th birthday. g, Secretariat wins Triple Crown. h, VCRs transform entertainment. i, Pioneer 10. j, Women's rights movement. k, 1970s fashions. l, "Monday Night Football." m, Smiley face buttons. n, Jumbo jets. o, Medical imaging.

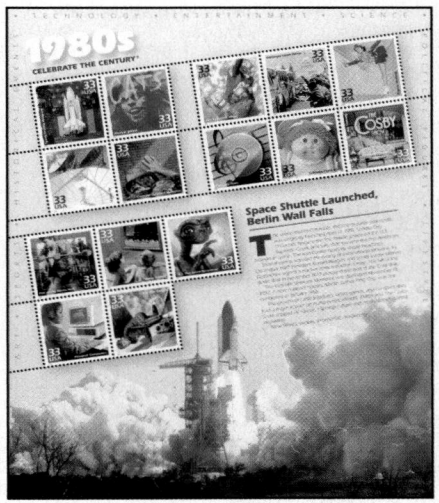

1980s — A2473

No. 3190: a, Space shuttle program. b, "Cats" Broadway show. c, San Francisco 49ers. d, Hostages in Iran come home. e, Figure skating. f, Cable TV. g, Vietnam Veterans Memorial. h, Compact discs. i, Cabbage Patch Kids. j, "The Cosby Show" television series. k, Fall of the Berlin Wall. l, Video games. m, "E. T. The Extra-Terrestrial" movie. n, Personal computers. o, Hip-hop culture.

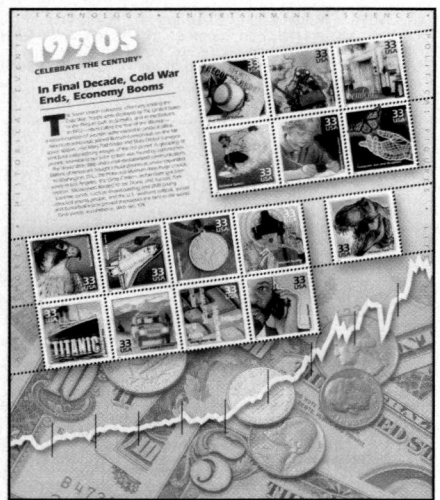

1990s — A2474

No. 3191: a, New baseball records. b, Gulf War. c, "Seinfeld" television series. d, Extreme sports. e, Improving education. f, Computer art and graphics. g, Recovering species. h, Return to space. i, Special Olympics. j, Virtual reality. k, Movie "Jurassic Park." l, Movie "Titanic." m, Sport utility vehicles. n, World Wide Web. o, Cellular phones.

Designed by Richard Waldrep (#3182), Dennis Lyall (#3183), Carl Herrman (#3184, 3188, 3190), Howard Paine (#3185-3187, 3189, 3191).

All illustrations reduced.

Printed by Ashton-Potter (USA) Ltd.

LITHOGRAPHED, ENGRAVED (#3182m, 3183f, 3184m, 3185b, 3186k, 3187a, 3188c, 3189h)

			1998-2000	**Tagged**	*Perf. 11½*	
3182	A2465	Pane of 15, *Feb. 3, 1998*			12.50	8.50
a.-o.		32c any single			.80	.65
		Sheet of 4 panes			50.00	
p.		Engr. red (No. 3182m, Gibson girl) omitted, in pane of 15			3,000.	
3183	A2466	Pane of 15, *Feb. 3, 1998*			12.50	8.50
a.-o.		32c any single			.80	.65
		Sheet of 4 panes			50.00	
p.		Nos. 3183g, 3183 l-3183o imperf, in pane of 15			7,000.	
3184	A2467	Pane of 15, *May 28, 1998*			12.50	8.50
a.-o.		32c any single			.80	.65
		Sheet of 4 panes			50.00	
3185	A2468	Pane of 15, *Sept. 10, 1998*			12.50	8.50
a.-o.		32c any single			.80	.65
		Sheet of 4 panes			50.00	
3186	A2469	Pane of 15, *Feb. 18, 1999*			13.00	8.50
a.-o.		33c any single			.85	.65
		Sheet of 4 panes			52.00	
p.		Tagging omitted on b-j and m-o			—	
3187	A2470	Pane of 15, *May 26, 1999*			13.00	8.50
a.-o.		33c any single			.85	.65
		Sheet of 4 panes			52.00	
p.		Tagging omitted			—	
3188	A2471	Pane of 15, *Sept. 17, 1999*			13.00	8.50
a.-o.		33c any single			.85	.65
		Sheet of 4 panes			52.00	
3189	A2472	Pane of 15, *Nov. 18, 1999*			13.00	8.50
a.-o.		33c any single			.85	.65
		Sheet of 4 panes			52.00	
3190	A2473	Pane of 15, *Jan. 12, 2000*			13.00	8.50
a.-o.		33c any single			.85	.65
		Sheet of 4 panes			52.00	
3191	A2474	Pane of 15, *May 2, 2000*			13.00	8.50
a.-o.		33c any single			.85	.65
		Sheet of 4 panes			52.00	
		Nos. 3182-3191 (10)			128.00	85.00

"REMEMBER THE MAINE"

A2475

Designed by Richard Sheaff.

LITHOGRAPHED & ENGRAVED
Sheets of 120 in six panes of 20

		1998, Feb. 15	**Tagged**	*Perf. 11.2x11*	
3192	A2475	32c **red & black**		.70	.20
		P# block of 4, 2#		2.75	—
		Pane of 20		14.00	

FLOWERING TREES

Southern Magnolia — A2476

Blue Paloverde — A2477

Yellow Poplar — A2478

Prairie Crab Apple — A2479

Pacific Dogwood — A2480

Designed by Howard Paine.

Printed by Banknote Corporation of America.

LITHOGRAPHED
Sheets of 120 in six panes of 20

		1998, Mar. 19	**Tagged**	*Die Cut Perf 11.3*	
		Self-Adhesive			
3193	A2476	32c **multicolored**		.65	.20
3194	A2477	32c **multicolored**		.65	.20
3195	A2478	32c **multicolored**		.65	.20
3196	A2479	32c **multicolored**		.65	.20

3197	A2480	32c **multicolored**		.65	.20
a.		Strip of 5, #3193-3197		3.25	
		P# block of 10, 2 sets of B+6#		6.50	
		Pane of 20		13.00	
b.		As "a," die cutting omitted		—	

ALEXANDER CALDER (1898-1976), SCULPTOR

Black Cascade, 13 Verticals, 1959 — A2481

Untitled, 1965 — A2482

Rearing Stallion, 1928 — A2483

Portrait of a Young Man, c. 1945 — A2484

Un Effet du Japonais, 1945 — A2485

Designed by Derry Noyes. Printed by Stamp Venturers.

PHOTOGRAVURE
Sheets of 120 in six panes of 20

		1998, Mar. 25	**Tagged**	*Perf. 10.2*	
3198	A2481	32c **multicolored**		.65	.20
3199	A2482	32c **multicolored**		.65	.20
3200	A2483	32c **multicolored**		.65	.20

3201	A2484	32c	multicolored	.65 .20
3202	A2485	32c	multicolored	.65 .20
a.			Strip of 5, #3198-3202	3.25 2.25
			P# block of 10, 2 sets of S+6#	7.00
			Pane of 20	13.50 —
			Sheet of 120 (6 panes)	110.00
			Cross gutter block of 20	37.50 —
			Block of 10 with horiz. gutter	22.50 —
			Vert. pairs with horiz. gutter (each)	4.00 —
			Horiz. pairs with vert. gutter (each)	5.50 —

Cross gutter block of 20 consists of six stamps from each of two panes and four stamps from each of two other panes with the cross gutter between. The sheet of 120 was quickly sold out.

A2486

CINCO DE MAYO

Designed by Carl Herrman.

Printed by Stamp Venturers.

PHOTOGRAVURE
Sheets of 180 in nine panes of 20
Serpentine Die Cut 11.7x10.9

1998, Apr. 16				Tagged

Self-Adhesive

3203	A2486	32c	multicolored	.65 .20
			P# block of 4, 5#+S	2.60
			Pane of 20	13.00
			Sheet of 180 (9 panes)	115.00
			Cross gutter block of 4	13.00
			Vert. pair with horiz. gutter	2.25
			Horiz. pair with vert. gutter	2.25

See Mexico #2066. For 33c version, see #3309.

A2487   A2488

SYLVESTER & TWEETY

Designed by Brenda Guttman.

Printed by Avery Dennison.

PHOTOGRAVURE

1998, Apr. 27	Tagged	*Serpentine Die Cut 11.1*

Self-Adhesive

3204			Pane of 10	6.75
a.	A2487		32c single	.65 .20
b.			Pane of 9 #3204a	6.00
c.			Pane of 1 #3204a	.65
			Sheet of 60 (six panes) top	70.00
			Sheet of 60 (six panes) bottom, with plate #	110.00
			Pane of 10 from sheet of 60	12.50
			Pane of 10 with plate #	50.00
			Cross gutter block of 9 or 10	45.00
			Cross gutter block of 12	50.00
			Vert. pair with horiz. gutter	7.00
			Horiz. pair with vert. gutter	14.00

Die cutting on #3204b does not extend through the backing paper. Pane with plate number comes from bottom uncut sheet of 60.

The horiz. pair with vert. gutter consists of a stamp at the left from either No. 3204b, part of the illustration of Sylvester & Tweety, the small gutter between the panes, and a stamp at the right from the left row of No. 3204b. Some pairs may include the single stamp from No. 3204c in addition to the two stamps at the right and left.

3205			Pane of 10	12.50
a.	A2487		32c single	1.00
b.			Pane of 9 #3205a	9.00
c.			Pane of 1, no die cutting	2.00

Die cutting on #3205a extends through the backing paper.

Nos. 3204b-3204c and 3205b-3205c are separated by a vertical line of microperforations, which is absent on the uncut sheets of 60.

WISCONSIN STATEHOOD

Designed by Phil Jordan.

Printed by Sennett Security Products.

PHOTOGRAVURE
Sheets of 120 in six panes of 20
Serpentine Die Cut 10.8x10.9

1998, May 29				Tagged

Self-Adhesive

3206	A2488	32c	multicolored	.65 .30
			P# block of 4, 4#+S	3.00
			Pane of 20	15.00

See note after No. 3167.

Wetlands — A2489   Diner — A2490

Designer by Phil Jordan (#3207-3207A), Carl Herrman (#3208, 308A).

Printed by Sennett Security Printers (#3207, 3208), Bureau of Engraving and Printing (#3207A, 3208A).

PHOTOGRAVURE
COIL STAMPS

1998			Untagged	*Perf. 10 Vert.*
3207	A2489	(5c)	multicolored, *June 5*	.20 .20
			Pair	.20 .20
			P# strip of 5, #S1111	1.40
			P#, single, #S1111	— .75

Serpentine Die Cut 9.8 Vert.

Self-adhesive

3207A	A2489	(5c)	multicolored, small date, *Dec.14*	.20 .20
			Pair	.20
			P# strip of 5, #1111, 2222, 3333	1.40
			P# single, same #	— .75
b.			Large date	.30 .20
			Pair	.60
			P# strip of 5, #4444, 5555, 6666	1.40
			P# single, same #	— .75

Date on No. 3207A is approximately 1.4mm long, on No. 3207Ab approx. 1.6mm long.

Perf. 10 Vert.

3208	A2490	(25c)	multicolored, *June 5*	.50 .50
			Pair	1.00 1.00
			P# strip of 5, #S11111	3.50
			P#, single, #S11111	— 2.00

Serpentine Die Cut 9.8 Vert.

Self-Adhesive

3208A	A2490	(25c)	multicolored, *Sept. 30*	.50 .50
			Pair	1.00
			P# strip of 5, #11111, 22211, 22222, 33333, 44444, 55555	3.50
			P# single, same #	— 1.75

1898 TRANS-MISSISSIPPI STAMPS, CENT.

A2491

Illustration reduced.

Designed by Raymond Ostrander Smith (1898), Richard Sheaff (1998).

Printed by Banknote Corporation of America.

LITHOGRAPHED & ENGRAVED
Sheets of 54 in six panes of 9

1998, June 18			Tagged	*Perf. 12x12.4*
3209	A2491		Pane of 9	9.00 7.00
a.	A100	1c	green & black	.20 .20
b.	A108	2c	red brown & black	.20 .20
c.	A102	4c	orange & black	.20 .20
d.	A103	5c	blue & black	.20 .20
e.	A104	8c	dark lilac & black	.20 .20
f.	A105	10c	purple & black	.20 .20
g.	A106	50c	green & black	1.25 .60
h.	A107	$1	red & black	2.25 1.25
i.	A101	$2	red brown & black	4.25 2.50
			Block of 9 with horiz. gutter	35.00
			Vert. pairs with horiz. gutter (each)	10.00

Vignettes on Nos. 3209b and 3209i are reversed in comparison to the original issue.

Vert. pairs consist of #3209g-3209a, 3209h-3209b, 3209i-3209c.

3210	A107	$1	Pane of 9 #3209h	18.00 —
			Sheet of 6 panes, 3 each #3209-3210	125.00
			Cross gutter block of 12	55.00
			Block of 18 (2 panes) with vert. gutter between and selvage on 4 sides	47.50 —
			Block of 12 with vert. gutter	32.50 —
			Vert. pair #3209h with horiz. gutter	10.00
			Horiz. pairs with vert. gutter (each)	10.00

Block of 12 contains #3209 and one column of 3 #3209h from #3210 separated by vert. gutter.

BERLIN AIRLIFT, 50th ANNIV.

A2492

Designed by Bill Bond.
Printed by Banknote Corporation of America.

PHOTOGRAVURE
Sheets of 120 in six panes of 20

1998, June 26			Tagged	*Perf. 11.2*
3211	A2492	32c	multicolored	.65 .20
			P# block of 4, 4#+B	2.60 —
			Pane of 20	13.00 —

AMERICAN MUSIC SERIES
Folk Singers

Huddie "Leadbelly" Ledbetter (1888-1949)
A2493

Woody Guthrie (1912-67)
A2494

Sonny Terry (1911-86)
A2495

Josh White
(1908-69)
A2496

Designed by Howard Paine.
Printed by American Packaging Corp. for Sennett Security Products.

PHOTOGRAVURE
Sheets of 180 in nine panes of 20

		1998, June 26	Tagged		Perf. 10.1x10.2	
3212	A2493	32c	multicolored		.75	.20
3213	A2494	32c	multicolored		.75	.20
3214	A2495	32c	multicolored		.75	.20
3215	A2496	32c	multicolored		.75	.20
a.	Block or strip of 4, #3212-3215				3.00	2.00
	P# block of 4, 5#+S				3.50	—
	P# block of 8, 2 sets of P# +					
	top label				7.50	—
	Pane of 20				17.50	—

AMERICAN MUSIC SERIES
Gospel Singers

Mahalia Jackson (1911-72)
A2497

Roberta Martin (1917-69)
A2498

Clara Ward (1924-73)
A2499

Sister Rosetta Tharpe (1921-73)
A2500

Designed by Howard Paine.
Printed by American Packaging Corp. for Sennett Security Products.

PHOTOGRAVURE
Sheets of 120 in six panes of 20

		1998, July 15	Tagged		Perf. 10.1x10.3	
3216	A2497	32c	multicolored		.75	.20
3217	A2498	32c	multicolored		.75	.20
3218	A2499	32c	multicolored		.75	.20
3219	A2500	32c	multicolored		.75	.20
a.	Block or strip of 4, #3216-3219				3.00	2.00

	P# block of 4, 6#+S	4.00	—
	P# block of 8, 2 sets of P# +		
	top label	8.00	—
	Pane of 20	19.00	—

SPANISH SETTLEMENT OF THE SOUTHWEST

La Mision de San Miguel de San Gabriel, Espanola, NM — A2501

Designed by Richard Sheaff.
Printed by Banknote Corporation of America.

LITHOGRAPHED
Sheets of 180 in nine panes of 20

		1998, July 11	Tagged		Perf. 11.2	
3220	A2501	32c	multicolored		.65	.20
	P# block of 4, 4#+B				2.60	—
	Pane of 20				13.00	—

LITERARY ARTS SERIES

Stephen Vincent Benét (1898-43)
A2502

Designed by Carl Herrman.
Printed by Ashton-Potter (USA) Ltd.

LITHOGRAPHED
Sheets of 180 in nine panes of 20

		1998, July 22	Tagged		Perf. 11.2	
3221	A2502	32c	multicolored		.65	.20
	P# block of 4, 4#+P				2.60	—
	Pane of 20				13.00	—

TROPICAL BIRDS

Antillean Euphonia
A2503

Green-throated Carib — A2504

Crested Honeycreeper
A2505

Cardinal Honeyeater
A2506

Designed by Phil Jordan.
Printed by Banknote Corporation of America.

LITHOGRAPHED
Sheets of 180 in nine panes of 20

		1998, July 29	Tagged		Perf. 11.2	
3222	A2503	32c	multicolored		.65	.20
3223	A2504	32c	multicolored		.65	.20
3224	A2505	32c	multicolored		.65	.20
3225	A2506	32c	multicolored		.65	.20
a.	Block or strip of 4, #3222-3225				2.60	2.00
	P# block of 4, 4#+B				2.60	—
	Pane of 20				13.00	—

For booklet see No. BK272.

LEGENDS OF HOLLYWOOD

Alfred Hitchcock (1899-1980) — A2507

Designed by Richard Sheaff.
Printed at American Packaging Corp. for Sennett Security Products.

PHOTOGRAVURE
Sheets of 120 in six panes of 20

		1998, Aug. 3	Tagged		Perf. 11.1	
3226	A2507	32c	multicolored		.75	.20
	P# block of 4, 4#+S				4.50	—
	Pane of 20				20.00	12.50
	Sheet of 120 (6 panes)				85.00	
	Cross gutter block of 8				19.00	—
	Block of 8 with vert. gutter				13.50	—
	Horiz. pair with vert. gutter				3.50	—
	Vert. pair with horiz. gutter				2.25	—

Perforations in corner of each stamp are star-shaped. Cross-gutter block consists of 6 stamps from upper panes and 2 stamps from panes below. Hitchcock's profile in the UL corner of each stamp is laser cut.

ORGAN & TISSUE DONATION

A2508

Designed by Richard Sheaff. Printed by Avery Dennison.

PHOTOGRAVURE
Sheets of 160 in eight panes of 20

		1998, Aug. 5	Tagged		Serpentine Die Cut 11.7	
			Self-Adhesive			
3227	A2508	32c	multicolored		.65	.20
	P# block of 4 5#+V				2.60	—
	Pane of 20				13.00	—

MODERN BICYCLE

A2509

Designed by Richard Sheaff. Printed by Bureau of Engraving and Printing (#3228), Sennett Security Printers (#3229).

POSTAGE

PHOTOGRAVURE
COIL STAMP
Serpentine Die Cut 9.8 Vert.

1998, Aug. 14			**Untagged**

Self-Adhesive (#3228)

3228	A2509	(10c) **multicolored,** small "1998"		
		year date	.20	.20
		Pair	.40	
		P# strip of 5, P#111, 221, 222,		
		333, 344, 444, 555	2.25	
		P# single, same #		1.75
a.		Large date	.25	.20
		Pair	.50	
		P# strip of 5, #666, 777, 888,		
		999	2.75	
		P# single, #666, 777, 888, 999	—	2.25

Date on No. 3228a is approximately 1½mm; on No. 3228 approximately 1mm.

Untagged
Perf. 9.9 Vert.

3229	A2509	(10c) **multicolored**	.20	.20
		Pair	.40	.25
		P# strip of 5, P#S111	2.50	
		P# single, same #	—	1.75

Date on No. 3229 is approximately 2mm wide.

BRIGHT EYES

Dog — A2510

Fish — A2511

Cat — A2512

Parakeet
A2513

Hamster
A2514

Designed by Carl Herrman. Printed at Guilford Gravure for Banknote Corp. of America.

PHOTOGRAVURE
Sheets of 180 in nine panes of 20

1998, Aug. 20	**Tagged**	*Serpentine Die Cut 9.9*

Self-Adhesive

3230	A2510	32c **multicolored**	.75	.20
3231	A2511	32c **multicolored**	.75	.20
3232	A2512	32c **multicolored**	.75	.20
3233	A2513	32c **multicolored**	.75	.20

3234	A2514	32c **multicolored**	.75	.20
a.		Strip of 5, #3230-3234	3.75	
		P# block of 8, 2 sets of 6#+B	7.50	
		Pane of 20	15.00	

Hidden 3-D designs can be seen on each stamp when viewed with a special viewer sold by the post office.
Plate blocks may contain top label.

KLONDIKE GOLD RUSH, CENTENNIAL

A2515

Designed by Howard Paine. Printed at Sterling Sommer for Ashton Potter (USA) Ltd.

LITHOGRAPHED
Sheets of 180 in nine panes of 20

1998, Aug. 21		**Tagged**	*Perf. 11.1*
3235	A2515	32c **multicolored**	.65	.20
		P# block of 4, 5#+P	2.60	—
		Pane of 20	13.00	—

AMERICAN ART

A2516

Illustration reduced.

Designed by Howard Paine. Printed by Sennett Security Products.

Paintings: a, "Portrait of Richard Mather," by John Foster. b, "Mrs. Elizabeth Freake and Baby Mary," by The Freake Limner. c, "Girl in Red Dress with Cat and Dog," by Ammi Phillips. d, "Rubens Peale with a Geranium," by Rembrandt Peale. e, "Long-billed Curlew, Numenius Longrostris," by John James Audubon. f, "Boatmen on the Missouri," by George Caleb Bingham. g, "Kindred Sprits," by Asher B. Durand. h, "The West-wood Children," by Joshua Johnson. i, "Music and Literature," by William Harnett. j, "The Fog Warning," by Winslow Homer. k, "The White Cloud, Head Chief of the Iowas," by George Catlin. l, "Cliffs of Green River," by Thomas Moran. m, "The Last of the Buffalo," by Alfred Bierstadt. n, "Niagara," by Frederic Edwin Church. o, "Breakfast in Bed," by Mary Cassatt. p, "Night-hawks," by Edward Hopper. q, "American Gothic," by Grant Wood. r, "Two Against the White," by Charles Sheeler. s, "Mahoning," by Franz Kline. t, "No. 12," by Mark Rothko.

PHOTOGRAVURE
Sheets of 120 stamps in six panes of 20

1998, Aug. 27		**Tagged**	*Perf. 10.2*
3236	A2516	Pane of 20	17.50	10.00
a.-t.		32c any single	.85	.60
		Sheet of 120 (six panes)	100.00	
		Cross gutter block of 20	30.00	—
		Vert. pairs with horiz. gutter (each)	3.25	—
		Horiz. pairs with vert. gutter (each)	3.25	—

Inscriptions on the back of each stamp describe the painting and the artist.
Cross gutter block of 20 consists of six stamps from each of two panes and four stamps from each of two other panes with the cross gutter between.

AMERICAN BALLET

A2517

Designed by Derry Noyes. Printed by Sterling Sommer for Ashton-Potter (USA) Ltd.

LITHOGRAPHED
Sheets of 120 in six panes of 20

1998, Sept. 16		**Tagged**	*Perf. 10.9x11.1*
3237	A2517	32c **multicolored**	.65	.20
		P# block of 4, 4#+P	3.00	—
		Pane of 20	14.50	—
		Sheet of 120 (six panes)	85.00	—
		Cross gutter block of 4	14.00	—
		Vert. pair with horiz. gutter	2.25	—
		Horiz. pair with vert. gutter	2.25	—

For booklet see No. BK273.

SPACE DISCOVERY

A2518

A2519

A2520

A2521

A2522

Designed by Phil Jordan. Printed at American Packaging Corp. for Sennett Security Products.

PHOTOGRAVURE
Sheets of 180 in nine panes of 20

1998, Oct. 1		**Tagged**	*Perf. 11.1*
3238	A2518	32c **multicolored**	.65	.20
3239	A2519	32c **multicolored**	.65	.20
3240	A2520	32c **multicolored**	.65	.20
3241	A2521	32c **multicolored**	.65	.20
3242	A2522	32c **multicolored**	.65	.20
a.		Strip of 5, #3238-3242	3.25	2.25

P# block of 10, 2 sets of 5#+S	6.50	—
Pane of 20	13.00	
Sheet of 180 (9 panes)	110.00	
Cross gutter block of 10	17.50	—
Vert. block of 10 with horiz. gutter	10.00	
Horiz. pair (#3238, 3242) with vert. gutter	2.00	—
Vert. pairs with horiz. gutter (each)	2.00	—
Pane of 20 from sheet of 180	12.00	—

Hidden 3-D designs can be seen on each stamp when viewed with a special viewer sold by the post office.
Plate blocks may contain top label.
Cross gutter block of 10 consists of two stamps from each of two panes and three stamps from each of two other panes with the cross gutter between. Pane of 20 from sheet of 180 has vertical perforations on one or both sides and is wider than pane sold in local post offices.
For booklet see No. BK274.

GIVING AND SHARING

A2523

Designed by Bob Dinetz.

Printed by Avery Dennison.

PHOTOGRAVURE
Sheets of 200 in ten panes of 20

1998, Oct. 7   Tagged   Serpentine Die Cut 11.1
Self-Adhesive

3243	A2523	32c multicolored	.65	.20
		P# block of 4, 4#+V	2.60	—
		Pane of 20	13.00	—

CHRISTMAS

Madonna and Child, Florence, 15th Cent. — A2524

Evergreen Wreath — A2525

Victorian Wreath — A2526

Chili Pepper Wreath — A2527

Tropical Wreath — A2528

Designed by Richard D. Sheaff (#3244), Lilian Dinihanian (A2525), George de Bruin (A2526), Chris Crinklaw (A2527), Micheale Thunin (A2528).

Printed by Bureau of Engraving and Printing (#3244), Banknote Corporation of America (#3245-3252).

LITHOGRAPHED
Sheets of 160 in 8 panes of 20 (#3249-3252)
Serpentine Die Cut 10.1x9.9 on 2, 3 or 4 Sides
1998, Oct. 15   Tagged
Self-Adhesive
Booklet Stamps

3244	A2524	32c multicolored	.65	.20
a.		Booklet pane of 20 + label	13.00	
b.		Die cutting omitted, pair		

Size: 22x25mm
Serpentine Die Cut 11.3x11.7 on 2 or 3 Sides

3245	A2525	32c multicolored	6.00	.20
3246	A2526	32c multicolored	6.00	.20
3247	A2527	32c multicolored	6.00	.20
3248	A2528	32c multicolored	6.00	.20
a.		Booklet pane of 4, #3245-3248	25.00	
b.		Booklet pane of 5, #3245-3246, 3248, 2 #3247 + label	32.50	
c.		Booklet pane of 6, #3247-3248, 2 each #3245-3246	40.00	
d.		As "a," die cutting omitted	—	
e.		As "b," die cutting omitted	—	
f.		As "c," die cutting omitted	—	

Size: 23x30mm
Serpentine Die Cut 11.4x11.5 on 2, 3, or 4 Sides

3249	A2525	32c multicolored	1.75	.20
a.		Serp. die cut 11.7x11.6 on 2, 3, or 4 sides	2.25	.20
3250	A2526	32c multicolored	1.75	.20
a.		Serp. die cut 11.7x11.6 on 3 or 4 sides	2.25	.20
3251	A2527	32c multicolored	1.75	.20
a.		Serp. die cut 11.7x11.6 on 3 or 4 sides	2.25	.20
3252	A2528	32c multicolored + label	1.75	.20
a.		Serp. die cut 11.7x11.6 on 2, 3, or 4 sides	2.25	.20
b.		Block or strip of 4, #3249-3252	7.00	
		P#block of 4, 6#+B	7.50	
		Pane of 20	37.50	
c.		Booklet pane of 20, 5 each #3249-3252 + label	35.00	
d.		Block or strip of 4, #3249a-3252a	9.00	
e.		Booklet pane of 20, 5 each #3249a-3252a + label	45.00	
f.		Block or strip of 4, #3249-3252, red ("Greetings 32 USA" and "1998") omitted on 3249, 3252	675.00	
g.		Block or strip of 4, #3249-3252, red ("Greetings 32 USA" and "1998") omitted on 3249, 3252; green (same) omitted on 3250, 3251	—	
h.		As "b," die cutting omitted	—	
i.		As "c," die cutting omitted	—	

Dedicated printing plates were used to print the red and green denominations, salutations and dates. Red and green appearing in the wreaths come from other plates and, therefore, are not part of the color omissions.
Specialists will want to note that the "1998" date on the flat pane of 20 is about .1mm wider than the date on the corresponding booklet pane (No. 3252c). The measurements are approximately 1.3mm versus 1.2mm, respectively. Therefore, unused and used singles can be distinguished.

Weather Vane — A2529

Uncle Sam — A2530

Uncle Sam's Hat — A2531

Space Shuttle Landing A2532

Piggyback Space Shuttle A2533

Designed by Terry McCaffrey (#3257-3258, 3260, 3264-3269), Richard Sheaff (#3259, 3263), Phil Jordan (#3261-3262).

Printed by Ashton Potter (USA) Ltd. (#3257), American Packaging Corp. for Sennett Security Products (#3259), Stamp Venturers (#3260), Banknote Corporation of America (#3258, 3261-3262), Bureau of Engraving and Printing (#3263-3267), Avery Dennison (#3268-3269).

LITHOGRAPHED
Sheets of 400 in eight panes of 50 (#3257, 3260), Sheets of 300 in six panes of 50 (#3258), Sheets of 160 in eight panes of 20 (#3259), Sheets of 120 in six panes of 20 (#3261-3262)

1998		Untagged		Perf. 11.2	
3257	A2529	(1c) multicolored Nov. 9		.20	.20
		P# block of 4, 5# + P		.25	
a.		Black omitted		135.00	
3258	A2529	(1c) multicolored, Nov. 9		.20	.20
		P# block of 4, 5# + B		.25	

No. 3257 is 18mm high, has thin letters, white USA, and black 1998. No. 3258 is 17mm high, has thick letters, pale blue USA and blue 1998.

PHOTOGRAVURE
Tagged
Serpentine Die Cut 10.8
Self-Adhesive (#3259, 3261-3263, 3265-3269)

3259	A2530	22c multicolored, Nov. 9	.45	.20
a.		Die cut 10.8x10.5	2.50	.25
b.		Vert. pair, No. 3259 + 3259a	3.50	
		P# block of 4, 4# + S, all No. 3259	2.50	
		P# block of 4, top stamps No. 3259, bottom stamps No. 3259a	—	
		P# block of 4, top stamps No. 3259a, bottom stamps No. 3259	7.50	
		Pane of 20, all No. 3259	9.00	
		Pane of 20, row 1 No. 3259a, rows 2-4 No. 3259	—	
		Pane of 20, row 2 No. 3259a, rows 1, 3-4 No. 3259	35.00	
		Pane of 20, row 3 No. 3259a, rows 1-2, 4 No. 3259	15.00	
		Pane of 20, row 4 No. 3259a, rows 1-3 No. 3259	30.00	

See No. 3353.

Perf. 11.2

3260	A2531	(33c) multicolored, shiny gum, Nov. 9	.65	.20
		P# block of 4 4#+S	2.75	
		Low-gloss gum	.65	.20
		P# block of 4 4#+S	2.75	—

LITHOGRAPHED
Serpentine Die Cut 11.5

3261	A2532	$3.20 multicolored, Nov. 9	6.00	1.50
		P# block of 4, 4#+B	24.00	
		Pane of 20	120.00	
3262	A2533	$11.75 multicolored, Nov. 19	22.50	10.00
		P# block of 4, 4#+B	90.00	
		Pane of 20	450.00	

COIL STAMPS

PHOTOGRAVURE
Serpentine Die Cut 9.9 Vert.

3263	A2530	22c multicolored, Nov. 9	.45	.20
		Pair	.90	
		P# strip of 5, #1111	4.25	
		P# single, same #		1.75
a.		Die cutting omitted, pair	—	

See No. 3353.

Perf. 9.8 Vert.

3264	A2531	(33c) multicolored, Nov. 9	.65	.20
		Pair	1.30	.30
		P# strip of 5, #1111, 3333, 3343, 3344, 3444	6.50	
		P# single, same #		3.75
a.		Imperf, pair	—	

On No. 3264, the black plate #1 of plate #1111 used in printing rolls of 100 places the plate digit "1" farther from the black printing in the vignette than does the black plate #1 of plate #1111 used in printing rolls of 3,000. These are referred to as "Low black 1" and "Hi black 1" and are used by plate number specialists to distinguish the different printings from plate #1111.

Serpentine Die Cut 9.9 Vert.

3265	A2531	(33c) **multicolored,** *Nov. 9*	.80	.20
		Pair	1.60	
		P# strip of 5, #1111,		
		1131, 2222, 3333	7.00	
		P# single, same #		4.50
a.		Die cutting omitted, pair	70.00	
b.		Red omitted	575.00	
c.		Black omitted	—	
d.		Black omitted, die cutting omitted, pair	*725.00*	
e.		Red omitted, die cutting omitted, pair	—	

Unused examples of No. 3265 are on backing paper the same size as the stamps. Corners of the stamp are 90 degree angles.

On No. 3265b, the blue and gray colors are shifted down and to the right.

Serpentine Die Cut 9.9 Vert.

3266	A2531	(33c) **multicolored,** *Nov. 9*	1.75	.20
		Pair	3.50	
		P# strip of 5, #1111	11.50	
		P# single, same #		3.50

Unused examples of No. 3266 are on backing paper larger than the stamps, and the stamps are spaced approximately 2mm. apart. Corners of stamps are rounded.

BOOKLET STAMPS

Serpentine Die Cut 9.9 on 2 or 3 Sides

3267	A2531	(33c) **multicolored,** *Nov. 9*	.75	.20
a.		Booklet pane of 10	7.50	

Serpentine Die Cut 11¼ on 3 Sides (#3268, 3268a)

or 11 on 2, 3 or 4 sides (#3268b, 3268c)

3268	A2531	(33c) **multicolored,** *Nov. 9*	.75	.20
a.		Booklet pane of 10	7.50	
b.		Serpentine die cut 11	.75	.20
c.		As "b," booklet pane of 20 + label	15.00	

Die Cut 8 on 2, 3 or 4 Sides

3269	A2531	(33c) **multicolored,** *Nov. 9*	.65	.20
a.		Booklet pane of 18	12.00	

Unused and used examples of an "H" nonde-nominated stamp inscribed "Postcard Rate" exist in the marketplace. There is no evidence that these stamps were ever officially issued. Values: unused $5,500; used $4,500.

A2534

Designed by Chris Calle.

PHOTOGRAVURE
COIL STAMPS

1998, Dec. 14		**Untagged**	**Perf. 9.8 Vert.**	
3270	A2534	(10c) **multicolored,** small date	.20	.20
		Pair	.40	.40
		P# strip of 5, #11111	2.25	
		P# single, #11111		2.00
a.		Large date	.45	.20
		Pair	.90	.40
		P# strip of 5, #22222	6.00	
		P# single, same #	—	5.00

Self-Adhesive
Serpentine Die Cut 9.9 Vert.

3271	A2534	(10c) **multicolored,** small date	.20	.20
		Pair	.40	
		P# strip of 5, #11111, 22222	2.25	
		P# single, #11111, 22222		1.75
a.		Large date	1.00	.20
		Pair	2.00	
		P# strip of 5, #33333	5.00	
		P# single, #33333	—	4.50
b.		Tagged (error)	1.25	.75
		Pair	2.50	
		P# strip of 5, #11111	9.00	
		P# single, #11111	—	8.50

No. 3271 is known with eagle in red brown rather than the normal golden brown, apparently from contaminated ink. Values slightly higher than normal No. 3271.

Dates on Nos. 3270a and 3271a are approximately 1¾mm; on Nos. 3270-3271 approximately 1¼mm.

Compare to Nos. 2602-2604, 2907.

Scott values for used self-adhesive stamps are for examples either on piece or off piece.

CHINESE NEW YEAR

Year of the Rabbit
A2535

Designed by Clarence Lee.

Printed at American Packaging Corp. for Sennett Security Printers.

PHOTOGRAVURE
Sheets of 180 in nine panes of 20

1999, Jan. 5		**Tagged**	**Perf. 11.2**	
3272	A2535	33c **multicolored**	.80	.20
		P# block of 4, 4#+S	3.25	—
		Pane of 20	17.00	—

See No. 3895d.

BLACK HERITAGE SERIES

Malcolm X (1925-65), Civil Rights Activist — A2536

Designed by Richard Sheaff. Printed by Banknote Corp. of America.

LITHOGRAPHED
Sheets of 180 in nine panes of 20

1999, Jan. 20	**Tagged**	**Serpentine Die Cut 11.4**		
		Self-Adhesive		
3273	A2536	33c **multicolored**	.85	.20
		P# block of 4, 3#+B	3.40	
		Pane of 20	17.00	

LOVE

A2537   A2538

Designed by John Grossman, Holly Sudduth.

Printed by Avery Dennison.

PHOTOGRAVURE

1999, Jan. 28		**Tagged**	**Die Cut**	
		Booklet Stamp		
		Self-Adhesive		
3274	A2537	33c **multicolored**	.65	.20
a.		Booklet pane of 20	13.00	
b.		Die cutting omitted, pair	*125.00*	
c.		As "a," die cutting omitted	*1,250.*	

Sheets of 160 in eight panes of 20

3275	A2538	55c **multicolored**	1.10	.20
		P# block of 4, 7#+B	4.40	
		Pane of 20	22.00	

HOSPICE CARE

A2539

Designed by Phil Jordan.

Printed by Banknote Corp. of America.

LITHOGRAPHED
Sheets of 120 in six panes of 20

1999, Feb. 9	A2539	33c **multicolored**	**Serpentine Die Cut 11.4**	
3276			.65	.20
		P# block of 4, 4#+B	2.80	
		Pane of 20	13.50	

Flag and City — A2540   Flag and Chalkboard — A2541

Designed by Richard Sheaff. Printed by Bureau of Engraving and Printing (#3277, 3279-3282), Avery Dennison (#3278, 3278F, 3283).

PHOTOGRAVURE
Sheets of 400 in four panes of 100 (#3277), Sheets of 200 in ten panes of 20 (#3278)

1999, Feb. 25		**Tagged**	**Perf. 11.2**	
Self-Adhesive (#3278, 3278F, 3279, 3281-3282)				
3277	A2540	33c **multicolored**	.70	.20
		P# block of 4, 4#	47.50	—

No. 3277 has red date.

Serpentine Die Cut 11 on 2, 3 or 4 Sides

3278	A2540	33c **multicolored**	.65	.20
		P# block of 4, 4#+V	4.25	
		Pane of 20	20.00	
a.		Booklet pane of 4	2.60	
b.		Booklet pane of 5 + label	3.25	
		P# single, #V1111, V1112,		
		V1121, V1122, V1212,		
		V2212	.80	1.00
c.		Booklet pane of 6	3.90	
d.		Booklet pane of 10	12.50	
e.		Booklet pane of 20 + label	17.00	
h.		As "e," die cutting omitted	—	
i.		Serpentine die cut 11¼	3.00	.20
j.		As "i," booklet pane of 10	30.00	

No. 3278 has black date.
The plate # single in No. 3278b is the lower left stamp.

BOOKLET STAMPS

Serpentine Die Cut 11½x11¾ on 2, 3 or 4 Sides

3278F	A2540	33c **multicolored**	1.25	.20
g.		Booklet pane of 20 + label	25.00	

No. 3278F has black date.

Serpentine Die Cut 9.8 on 2 or 3 Sides

3279	A2540	33c **multicolored**	.85	.20
a.		Booklet pane of 10	8.50	

No. 3279 has red date.

COIL STAMPS
Perf. 9.9 Vert.

3280	A2540	33c **multicolored,** small "1999"		
		year date	.65	.20
		Pair	1.30	.30
		P# strip of 5, #1111, 2222	4.00	
		P# single, same #		1.50
a.		Large date	1.25	.20
		Pair	2.50	.30
		P# strip of 5, #3333	9.00	
		P# single, same #	—	5.00
b.		As No. 3280, imperf pair	—	

Serpentine Die Cut 9.8 Vert.

Two types of No. 3281: Type I, Long vertical feature at left and right of tallest building consists of 3 separate lines; Type II, Same features consist of solid color.

3281	A2540	33c **multicolored,** type I,		
		large "1999" year date	.65	.20
		Pair	1.30	

P# strip of 5, #6666, 7777,
8888, 9999, 1111A,
2222A, 3333A, 4444A,
5555A, 6666A, 7777A,
8888A, 1111B, 2222B   4.75
P# single, same #   1.00
P# single, #7777A, 8888A,
1111B, 2222B   —   1.50

a.	Die cutting omitted, pair	30.00	
b.	Light blue and yellow omitted	*300.00*	
c.	Small date, type II	.65	.20
	Pair	1.30	
	P# strip of 5, #1111, 2222, 3333, 3433, 4443, 4444, 5555	5.50	
	P# single, same #	—	1.25
d.	Small date, type I	5.00	.30
	Pair	10.00	
	P# strip of 5, #9999A	30.00	
	P# single, same #	—	3.50
e.	As "c," die cutting omitted, pair	—	

Corners are square on #3281. Unused examples are on backing paper the same size as the stamps, and the stamps are adjoining.
Date on Nos. 3280a and 3281 is approximately 1¾mm; on Nos. 3280, 3281c and 3281d approximately 1¼mm.

3282	A2540 33c **multicolored**	.65	.20
	Pair	1.30	
	P# strip of 5, #1111, 2222	4.25	
	P# single, same #	3.25	

Corners are rounded on #3282. Unused examples are on backing paper larger than the stamps, and the stamps are spaced approximately 2mm. apart.

PHOTOGRAVURE
Serpentine Die Cut 7.9 on 2, 3 or 4 Sides

1999, Mar. 13			Tagged

Self-Adhesive
BOOKLET STAMP

3283	A2541 33c **multicolored**	.65	.20
a.	Booklet pane of 18	12.00	

IRISH IMMIGRATION

A2542

Designed by Howard Paine. Printed by Ashton-Potter (USA) Ltd.

LITHOGRAPHED
Sheets of 180 in nine panes of 20

1999, Feb. 26		Tagged		Perf. 11.2
3286	A2542 33c **multicolored**		.65	.20
	P# block of 4, 4#+P		2.60	—
	Pane of 20		13.00	—

See Ireland No. 1168.

PERFORMING ARTS SERIES
Alfred Lunt (1892-1977), Lynn Fontanne (1887-1983), Actors

A2543

Designed by Carl Herrman. Printed by Sterling Sommer for Ashton-Potter (USA) Ltd.

LITHOGRAPHED
Sheets of 180 in nine panes of 20

1999, Mar. 2		Tagged		Perf. 11.2
3287	A2543 33c **multicolored**		.65	.20
	P# block of 4, 4#+P		2.60	—
	Pane of 20		13.00	—

ARCTIC ANIMALS

Arctic Hare — A2544

Arctic Fox — A2545

Snowy Owl — A2546

Polar Bear — A2547

Gray Wolf — A2548

Designed by Derry Noyes. Printed by Banknote Corp. of America.

LITHOGRAPHED
Sheets of 90 in six panes of 15

1999, Mar. 12		Tagged		Perf. 11
3288	A2544 33c **multicolored**		.85	.20
3289	A2545 33c **multicolored**		.85	.20
3290	A2546 33c **multicolored**		.85	.20
3291	A2547 33c **multicolored**		.85	.20
3292	A2548 33c **multicolored**		.85	.20
a.	Strip of 5, #3288-3292		4.25	—
	Pane of 15, 6#+B		13.00	—

While the normal definition of a plate block dictates a block of 10, this would require collectors to discard the decorative label and top row of stamps from the pane of 15. To avoid destroying the more collectible entire, We list the entire pane as the plate block.

SONORAN DESERT

A2549

Illustration reduced.

Designed by Ethel Kessler. Printed by Banknote Corporation of America.

Designs: a, Cactus wren, brittlebush, teddy bear cholla. b, Desert tortoise. c, White-winged dove, prickly pear. d, Gambel quail. e, Saguaro cactus. f, Desert mule deer. g, Desert cottontail, hedgehog cactus. h, Gila monster. i, Western diamondback rattlesnake, cactus mouse. j, Gila woodpecker.

LITHOGRAPHED
Sheets of 60 in six panes of 10
Serpentine Die Cut Perf 11.2

1999, Apr. 6			Tagged

Self-Adhesive

3293	A2549 Pane of 10	6.50	
a.-j.	33c any single	.65	.50
	Sheet of 6 panes	40.00	

BERRIES

Blueberries
A2550

Raspberries
A2551

Strawberries
A2552

Blackberries
A2553

Designed by Howard Paine. Printed by Guilford Gravure for Banknote Corporation of America.

PHOTOGRAVURE
Serpentine Die Cut 11¼x11½ on 2, 3 or 4 Sides (Nos. 3294-3297), or 2 or 3 sides (Nos. 3294a-3297a)

1999, Apr. 10			Tagged

Self-Adhesive

3294	A2550 33c **multicolored**	.85	.20
a.	Dated "2000," *Mar. 15, 2000*	1.25	.20
3295	A2551 33c **multicolored**	.85	.20
a.	Dated "2000," *Mar. 15, 2000*	1.25	.20
3296	A2552 33c **multicolored**	.85	.20
a.	Dated "2000," *Mar. 15, 2000*	1.25	.20
3297	A2553 33c **multicolored**	.85	.20
a.	Dated "2000," *Mar. 15, 2000*	1.25	.20
b.	Booklet pane of 20, 5 each #3294-3297 + label	17.00	
c.	Block of 4, #3294-3297	3.40	
d.	Booklet pane of 20, 5 #3297e + label	25.00	
e.	Block of 4, #3294a-3297a	5.00	

No. 3297d is a double-sided booklet pane, with 12 stamps on one side and eight stamps plus label on the other side.

Serpentine Die Cut 9½x10 on 2 or 3 Sides

3298	A2550	33c multicolored	.90	.20
3299	A2552	33c multicolored	.90	.20
3300	A2551	33c multicolored	.90	.20
3301	A2553	33c multicolored	.90	.20
a.	Booklet pane of 4, #3298-3301		3.60	
b.	Booklet pane of 5, #3298, 3299, 3301, 2 #3300 + label		4.50	
c.	Booklet pane of 6, #3300, 3301, 2 #3298, 3299		5.50	
d.	Block of 4, #3298-3301		3.40	

COIL STAMPS
Serpentine Die Cut 8.5 Vert.

3302	A2550	33c multicolored	1.00	.20
3303	A2551	33c multicolored	1.00	.20
3304	A2553	33c multicolored	1.00	.20
3305	A2552	33c multicolored	1.00	.20
a.	Strip of 4, #3302-3305		4.00	
	P# strip of 5, 2 #3302, 1 ea #3303-3305, P#B1111, B1112, B2211, B2221, B2222		5.25	
	P# strip of 9, 2 ea #3302-3303, 3305, 3 #3304, same P#		9.00	
	P# single (#3304), same P#		—	1.25

A2554

A2555

DAFFY DUCK
Designed by Ed Wieczyk.
Printed by Avery Dennison.

PHOTOGRAVURE
1999, Apr. 16   Tagged   Serpentine Die Cut 11.1
Self-Adhesive

3306	Pane of 10	6.75	
a.	A2554 33c single	.65	.20
b.	Pane of 9 #3306a	6.00	
c.	Pane of 1 #3306a	.65	
	Sheet of 60 (six panes) top	40.00	
	Sheet of 60 (six panes) bottom, with plate # in selvage	47.50	
	Pane of 10 from sheet of 60	8.00	
	Pane of 10 with plate # in selvage	15.00	
	Cross gutter block of 9 or 10	15.00	
	Cross gutter block of 12	18.00	
	Vert. pair with horiz. gutter	2.00	
	Horiz. pair with vert. gutter	4.00	

Nos. 3306b-3306c and 3307b-3307c are separated by a vertical line of microperforations, which is absent on the uncut sheet of 60.
Die cutting on #3306b does not extend through the backing paper.

3307	Pane of 10	14.00	
a.	A2554 33c single	1.25	
b.	Pane of 9 #3307a	12.00	
c.	Pane of 1, no die cutting	1.75	
d.	As "a," vert. pair, die cutting omitted between	—	

Die cutting on #3307a extends through the backing paper.
Nos. 3306b-3306c and 3307b-3307c are separated by a vertical line of microperforations.

LITERARY ARTS SERIES
Ayn Rand (1905-82).

Designed by Phil Jordan.

Printed by Sterling Sommer for Ashton-Potter (USA) Ltd.

LITHOGRAPHED
Sheets of 180 in nine panes of 20

1999, Apr. 22	**Tagged**		**Perf. 11.2**
3308	A2555 33c multicolored	.65	.20
	P# block of 4, 4#+P	2.60	—
	Pane of 20	13.00	

Cinco De Mayo Type of 1998
Designed by Carl Herrman.

Printed by Banknote Corporation of America.

LITHOGRAPHED
Sheets of 160 in eight panes of 20
Serpentine Die Cut 11.6x11.3
1999, Apr. 27

Self-Adhesive   Tagged

3309	A2486 33c multicolored	.70	.20
	P# block of 4, 6#+B	3.00	
	Pane of 20	15.00	

TROPICAL FLOWERS

Bird of Paradise
A2556

Royal Poinciana
A2557

Gloriosa Lily — A2558

Chinese Hibiscus
A2559

Designed by Carl Herrman.

Printed by Sennett Security Products.

PHOTOGRAVURE
BOOKLET STAMPS
Serpentine Die Cut 10.9 on 2 or 1 Sides
1999, May 1   Tagged

Self-Adhesive

3310	A2556	33c multicolored	.65	.20
3311	A2557	33c multicolored	.65	.20
3312	A2558	33c multicolored	.65	.20
3313	A2559	33c multicolored	.65	.20
a.	Block of 4, #3310-3313		2.60	
b.	Booklet pane, 5 each #3313a		13.00	

No. 3313b is a double-sided booklet pane with 12 stamps on one side and 8 stamps plus label on the other side.

A2560

A2561

JOHN (1699-1777) & WILLIAM (1739-1823) BARTRAM, BOTANISTS
Designed by Phil Jordan. Printed by Banknote Corporation of America.

LITHOGRAPHED
Sheets of 180 in nine panes of 20
1999, May 18   Tagged   Serpentine Die Cut 11½
Self-Adhesive

3314	A2560 33c Franklinia alatamaha, by William Bartram	.65	.20
	P# block of 4, 4#+B	2.60	
	Pane of 20	13.00	

PROSTATE CANCER AWARENESS
Designed by Michael Cronan. Printed by Avery Dennison.

PHOTOGRAVURE
Sheets of 200 in ten panes of 20
1999, May 28   Tagged   Serpentine Die Cut 11
Self-Adhesive

3315	A2561 33c multicolored	.65	.20
	P# block of 4, 5#+V	2.60	
	Pane of 20	13.00	

CALIFORNIA GOLD RUSH, 150TH ANNIV.

A2562

Designed by Howard Paine. Printed by Ashton-Potter (USA) Ltd.

LITHOGRAPHED
Sheets of 180 in nine panes of 20

1999, June 18	**Tagged**		**Perf. 11¼**
3316	A2562 33c multicolored	.65	.20
	P# block of 4, 5#+P	2.60	—
	Pane of 20	13.00	—

AQUARIUM FISH
Reef Fish

A2563

A2564

A2565

A2566

Designed by Richard Sheaff. Printed by Banknote Corporation of America.

Designs: No. 3317, Yellow fish, red fish, cleaner shrimp. No. 3318, Fish, thermometer. No. 3319, Red fish, blue & yellow fish. No. 3320, Fish, heater/aerator.

LITHOGRAPHED
Sheets of 120 in six panes of 20

**1999, June 24   Tagged   *Serpentine Die Cut 11½*
Self-Adhesive**

3317	A2563 33c **multicolored,** block tagging		.65	.20
a.	Overall tagging		12.50	10.00
3318	A2564 33c **multicolored,** block tagging		.65	.20
a.	Overall tagging		12.50	10.00
3319	A2565 33c **multicolored,** block tagging		.65	.20
a.	Overall tagging		12.50	10.00
3320	A2566 33c **multicolored,** block tagging		.65	.20
a.	Overall tagging		12.50	10.00
b.	Strip of 4, #3317-3320		2.60	
	P# block of 8, 2 sets of 4#+B		5.20	
	Pane of 20		13.00	
	Sheet of 6 panes		80.00	
	Cross gutter block of 8		20.00	
	Block of 8 with horiz. gutter		9.00	
	Horiz. pair with vert. gutter		2.00	
	Vert. pairs with horiz. gutter (each)		2.25	
c.	Strip of 4, #3317a-3320a		55.00	
	P# block of 8, 2 sets of 4#+B		125.00	
	Pane of 20		300.00	

Plate blocks will have either top label or list of fish shown on bottom selvage. Cross gutter block of 8 consists of 4 horiz. pairs separated by vert. gutter with horiz. gutter between.
Press sheets were printed with large block tagging.

EXTREME SPORTS

Skateboarding — A2567

BMX Biking — A2568

Snowboarding — A2569

Inline Skating — A2570

Designed by Carl Herrman. Printed by Avery Dennison.

PHOTOGRAVURE
Sheets of 160 in eight panes of 20

**1999, June 25   Tagged   *Serpentine Die Cut 11*
Self-Adhesive**

3321	A2567 33c **multicolored**		.75	.20
3322	A2568 33c **multicolored**		.75	.20
3323	A2569 33c **multicolored**		.75	.20
3324	A2570 33c **multicolored**		.75	.20
a.	Block or strip of 4, #3321-3324		3.00	
	P# block of 4, 4#+V		3.00	
	Pane of 20		15.00	
	Sheet of 80 (four panes) top		62.50	
	Sheet of 80 (four panes) bottom, with plate # in sheet margin		67.50	
	Pane of 20 with extra selvage from sheet of 80		15.00	
	Pane of 20 with plate # in sheet margin		22.50	
	Cross gutter block of 8		7.50	
	Vert. pairs with horiz. gutter (each)		2.00	
	Horiz. pairs with vert. gutter (each)		2.00	
	Block of 4 with horiz. gutter		5.00	
	Block of 8 with vert. gutter		10.00	

Cross gutter block of 8 consists of 4 horiz. pairs separated by vert. gutter with horiz. gutter between

AMERICAN GLASS

Free-Blown Glass — A2571

Mold-Blown Glass — A2572

Pressed Glass — A2573

Art Glass — A2574

Designed by Richard Sheaff. Printed by Sterling Sommer for Ashton-Potter (USA) Ltd.

LITHOGRAPHED
Sheets of 90 in six panes of 15

1999, June 29		**Tagged**	**Perf. 11**	
3325	A2571 33c **multicolored**		1.50	.20
3326	A2572 33c **multicolored**		1.50	.20
3327	A2573 33c **multicolored**		1.50	.20
3328	A2574 33c **multicolored**		1.50	.20
a.	Strip or block of 4, #3325-3328		6.00	3.00
	Pane of 15, 4 each #3325, 3327-3328, 3 #3326		22.50	12.50

A2575

A2576

LEGENDS OF HOLLYWOOD
James Cagney (1899-1986)

Designed by Howard Paine.

Printed by Sennett Security Products.

PHOTOGRAVURE
Sheets of 120 in six panes of 20

1999, July 22		**Tagged**	**Perf. 11**	
3329	A2575 33c **multicolored**		.80	.20
	P# block of 4, 5#+S		4.25	—
	Pane of 20		20.00	—
	Sheet of 120 (6 panes)		85.00	—
	Cross gutter block of 8		17.50	—
	Block of 8 with vertical gutter		11.00	—
	Horiz. pair with vert. gutter		3.00	—
	Vert. pair with horiz. gutter		2.00	—

Perforations in corner of each stamp are star-shaped. Cross-gutter block consists of 2 stamps from upper panes and 6 stamps from panes below.

GEN. WILLIAM "BILLY" L. MITCHELL (1879-1936), AVIATION PIONEER

Designed by Phil Jordan.
Printed by Guilford Gravure for Banknote Corporation of America.

PHOTOGRAVURE
Sheets of 180 in nine panes of 20

**1999, July 30   Tagged   *Serpentine Die Cut 9¾x10*
Self-Adhesive**

3330	A2576 55c **multicolored**		1.10	.30
	P# block of 4, 5#+B		4.40	
	Pane of 20		22.00	

HONORING THOSE WHO SERVED

A2577

Designed by Richard Sheaff and Uldis Purins. Printed by Avery Dennison.

PHOTOGRAVURE
Sheets of 200 in 10 panes of 20

**1999, Aug. 16   Tagged   *Serpentine Die Cut 11*
Self-Adhesive**

3331	A2577 33c **black, blue & red**		.65	.20
	P# block of 4, 3#+V		2.60	
	Pane of 20		13.00	

UNIVERSAL POSTAL UNION

A2578

Designed by Gerald Gallo.
Printed by Sterling Sommer for Ashton-Potter (USA) Ltd.

LITHOGRAPHED
Sheets of 180 in nine panes of 20

1999, Aug. 25		**Tagged**	**Perf. 11**	
3332	A2578 45c **multicolored**		1.00	.45
	P# block of 4, 3#+P		4.00	—
	Pane of 20		20.00	—

FAMOUS TRAINS

Daylight A2579

Congressional A2580

20th Century Limited A2581

Hiawatha
A2582

Super Chief
A2583

Designed by Howard Paine.
Printed by Ashton-Potter (USA) Ltd.

LITHOGRAPHED
Sheets of 120 in six panes of 20

1999, Aug. 26	Tagged	Perf. 11	
3333 A2579 33c **multicolored**		.75	.20
3334 A2580 33c **multicolored**		.75	.20
3335 A2581 33c **multicolored**		.75	.20
3336 A2582 33c **multicolored**		.75	.20
3337 A2583 33c **multicolored**		.75	.20
a.	Strip of 5, #3333-3337	3.75	—
	Pane of 20, 4 #3337a	15.00	—
	P# block of 8, 2 sets of 4#+P	6.00	—
	Sheet of 120 (6 panes)	90.00	—
	Block of 10 with vert. gutter	15.00	—
	Cross gutter block of 8	17.50	—
	Horiz. pairs with vert. gutter		
	(each)	2.25	—
	Vert. pairs with horiz. gutter		
	(each)	2.25	—

Stamps in No. 3337a are arranged in four different orders.
Plate block may contain top label.

**FREDERICK LAW OLMSTED (1822-1903),
LANDSCAPE ARCHITECT**

A2584

Designed by Ethel Kessler.
Printed by Ashton-Potter (USA) Ltd.

LITHOGRAPHED
Sheets of 120 in six panes of 20

1999, Sept. 12	Tagged	Perf. 11	
3338 A2584 33c **multicolored**		.65	.20
	P# block of 4, 4#+P	2.60	—
	Pane of 20	13.00	—

**AMERICAN MUSIC SERIES
Hollywood Composers**

Max Steiner
(1888-1971)
A2585

Dimitri
Tiomkin
(1894-1975)
A2586

Bernard
Herrmann
(1911-75)
A2587

Franz Waxman
(1906-67)
A2588

Alfred
Newman
(1907-70)
A2589

Erich
Wolfgang
Korngold
(1897-1957)
A2590

Designed by Howard Paine.
Printed by Sterling Sommer for Ashton-Potter (USA) Ltd.

LITHOGRAPHED
Sheets of 120 in six panes of 20

1999, Sept. 16	Tagged	Perf. 11	
3339 A2585 33c **multicolored**		1.25	.20
3340 A2586 33c **multicolored**		1.25	.20
3341 A2587 33c **multicolored**		1.25	.20
3342 A2588 33c **multicolored**		1.25	.20
3343 A2589 33c **multicolored**		1.25	.20
3344 A2590 33c **multicolored**		1.25	.20
a.	Block of 6, #3339-3344	7.50	4.50
	P# block of 6, 5#+P	7.50	—
	P# block of 8, 2 sets of 5#+P +		
	top label	10.00	—
	Pane of 20	25.00	—

**AMERICAN MUSIC SERIES
Broadway Songwriters**

Ira (1896-
1983) &
George
(1898-1937)
Gershwin
A2591

Alan Jay
Lerner (1918-
86) &
Frederick
Loewe (1901-
88)
A2592

Lorenz Hart
(1895-1943)
A2593

Richard
Rodgers
(1902-79) &
Oscar
Hammerstein
II (1895-1960)
A2594

Meredith
Willson (1902-
84)
A2595

Frank Loesser
(1910-69)
A2596

Designed by Howard Paine.
Printed by Sterling Sommer for Ashton-Potter (USA) Ltd.

LITHOGRAPHED
Sheets of 120 in six panes of 20

1999, Sept. 21	Tagged	Perf. 11	
3345 A2591 33c **multicolored**		1.25	.20
3346 A2592 33c **multicolored**		1.25	.20
3347 A2593 33c **multicolored**		1.25	.20
3348 A2594 33c **multicolored**		1.25	.20
3349 A2595 33c **multicolored**		1.25	.20
3350 A2596 33c **multicolored**		1.25	.20
a.	Block of 6, #3345-3350	7.50	4.50

P# block of 6, 5#+P 7.50 —
P# block of 8, 2 sets of 5#+P +
top label 10.00 —
Pane of 20 25.00 —

INSECTS & SPIDERS

INSECTS & SPIDERS

A2597

Illustration reduced.

Designed by Carl Herrman.
Printed by Ashton-Potter (USA) Ltd.

Designs: a, Black widow. b, Elderberry longhorn. c, Lady beetle. d, Yellow garden spider. e, Dogbane beetle. f, Flower fly. g, Assassin bug. h, Ebony jewelwing. i, Velvet ant. j, Monarch caterpillar. k, Monarch butterfly. l, Eastern Hercules beetle. m, Bombardier beetle. n, Dung beetle. o, Spotted water beetle. p, True katydid. q, Spinybacked spider. r, Periodical cicada. s, Scorpionfly. t, Jumping spider.

LITHOGRAPHED
Sheets of 80 in four panes of 20

1999, Oct. 1	Tagged		Perf. 11
3351 A2597	Pane of 20	13.00	10.00
a.-t.	33c any single	.65	.50
	Sheet of 4 panes	52.50	
	Cross gutter block of 20	20.00	
	Vert. pair with horiz. gutter (each)	1.60	
	Horiz. pair with vert. gutter (each)	1.60	

Cross gutter block of 20 consists of six stamps from each of two panes and four stamps from each of the two other panes with the cross gutter between.

Hanukkah Type of 1996
Designed by Hannah Smotrich.
Printed by Avery Dennison.

PHOTOGRAVURE
Sheets of 200 in 10 panes of 20

1999, Oct. 8	Tagged	Serpentine Die Cut 11
	Self-Adhesive	
3352 A2411	33c multicolored	.65 .20
	P# block of 4, 5#+V	2.60
	Pane of 20	13.00

Uncle Sam Type of 1998
Designed by Richard Sheaff.
Printed by Bureau of Engraving and Printing.

COIL STAMP
PHOTOGRAVURE

1999, Oct. 8	Tagged	Perf. 9¾ Vert.
3353 A2530	22c multicolored	.45 .20
	Pair	.90 .30
	P# strip of 5, #1111	3.25 —
	P# single, same #	— 2.25

NATO, 50TH ANNIV.

A2598

Designed by Michael Cronan.
Printed by Ashton-Potter (USA) Ltd.

LITHOGRAPHED
Sheets of 180 in nine panes of 20

1999, Oct. 13	Tagged	Perf. 11¼
3354 A2598	33c multicolored	.65 .20
	P# block of 4, 4#+P	2.60 —
	Pane of 20	13.00 —

CHRISTMAS

Madonna and Child, by
Bartolomeo Vivarini — A2599

Deer — A2600

Designed by Richard Sheaff (#3355), Tom Nikosey (#3356-3367).
Printed by Banknote Corp. of America.

LITHOGRAPHED
Serpentine Die Cut 11¼ on 2 or 3 sides

1999, Oct. 20		Tagged
	Booklet Stamp	
	Self-Adhesive	
3355 A2599	33c multicolored	1.00 .20
a.	Booklet pane of 20	20.00

Sheets of 120 in six panes of 20
Serpentine Die Cut 11¼

3356 A2600	33c gold & red	1.75 .20
3357 A2600	33c gold & blue	1.75 .20
3358 A2600	33c gold & purple	1.75 .20
3359 A2600	33c gold & green	1.75 .20
a.	Block or strip of 4, #3356-3359	7.00
	P# block of 4, 6#+B	7.00
	Pane of 20	35.00

Booklet Stamps
Serpentine Die Cut 11¼ on 2, 3 or 4 sides

3360 A2600	33c gold & red	1.60 .20
3361 A2600	33c gold & blue	1.60 .20
3362 A2600	33c gold & purple	1.60 .20
3363 A2600	33c gold & green	1.60 .20
a.	Booklet pane of 20, 5 each #3360-3363	32.50
b.	Block of 4, #3360-3363	6.50
c.	As "b," die cutting omitted	—
d.	As "a," die cutting omitted	—

Size: 21x19mm
Serpentine Die Cut 11½x11¼ on 2 or 3 sides

3364 A2600	33c gold & red	2.25 .20
3365 A2600	33c gold & blue	2.25 .20
3366 A2600	33c gold & purple	2.25 .20
3367 A2600	33c gold & green	2.25 .20
a.	Booklet pane of 4, #3364-3367	9.00
b.	Booklet pane of 5, #3364, 3366, 3367, 2 #3365 + label	11.25
c.	Booklet pane of 6, #3365, 3367, 2 each #3364 & 3366	13.50
d.	Block of 4, #3364-3367	9.00

The frame on Nos. 3356-3359 is narrow and the space between it and the hoof is a hairline. The frame on Nos. 3360-3363 is much thicker, and the space between it and the hoof is wider.

Kwanzaa Type of 1997
Designed by Synthia Saint James
Printed by Avery Dennison.

PHOTOGRAVURE
Sheets of 240 in twelve pane of 20

1999, Oct. 29	Tagged	Serpentine Die Cut 11
	Self-Adhesive	
3368 A2458	33c multicolored	.65 .20
	P# block of 4, 4#+V	2.60
	Pane of 20	13.00

YEAR 2000

Baby New Year — A2601

Designed by Carl Herrman.
Printed by Banknote Corporation of America.

LITHOGRAPHED
Sheets of 120 in six panes of 20

1999, Dec. 27	Tagged	Serpentine Die Cut 11¼
	Self-Adhesive	
3369 A2601	33c multicolored	.65 .20
	P# block of 4, 5#+B	3.00
	Pane of 20	14.50

CHINESE NEW YEAR

Year of the
Dragon
A2602

Designed by Clarence Lee.
Printed by Sterling Sommer.

LITHOGRAPHED
Sheets of 180 in nine panes of 20

2000, Jan. 6	Tagged	Perf. 11¼
3370 A2602	33c multicolored	.80 .20
	P# block of 4, 4#+P	3.25 —
	Pane of 20	15.50 —

See No. 3895e.

BLACK HERITAGE SERIES

Patricia Roberts Harris
(1924-85), First Black
Woman Cabinet
Secretary — A2603

Designed by Richard Sheaff.
Printed by Ashton-Potter (USA) Ltd.

LITHOGRAPHED
Sheets of 180 in nine panes of 20
Serpentine Die Cut 11½x11¼

2000, Jan. 27		Tagged
	Self-Adhesive	
3371 A2603	33c indigo	.65 .20
	P# block of 4, 4#+P	2.75
	Pane of 20	13.50

SUBMARINES

S Class
A2604

Los Angeles Class A2605

Ohio Class A2606

USS Holland A2607

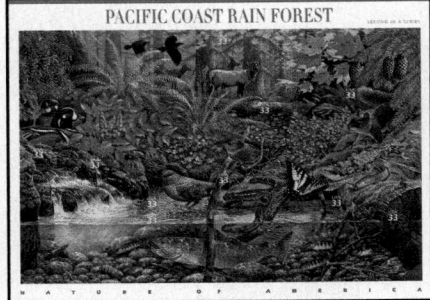

Gato Class — A2608

Illustration of No. 3377 reduced.

Designed by Carl Herrman.
Printed by Banknote Corporation of America.

LITHOGRAPHED
Sheets of 180 in nine panes of 20

2000, Mar. 27		Tagged	Perf. 11	
3372	A2605	33c multicolored, with microprinted "USPS" at base of sail	.75	.20
		P# block of 4, 4#+B	3.00	—
		Pane of 20	15.00	—

BOOKLET STAMPS

3373	A2604	22c multicolored	1.25	.75
3374	A2605	33c multicolored, no microprinting	1.75	1.00
3375	A2606	55c multicolored	2.75	1.25
3376	A2607	60c multicolored	3.00	1.50
3377	A2608	$3.20 multicolored	16.00	5.00
a.		Booklet pane of 5, #3373-3377	25.00	—

No. 3377a was issued with two types of text in the selvage.

PACIFIC COAST RAIN FOREST

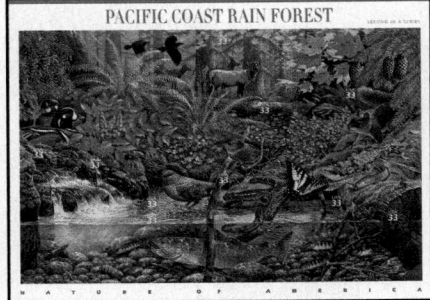

A2609

Illustration reduced.

Designed by Ethel Kessler.
Printed by Banknote Corporation of America.

Designs: a, Harlequin duck. b, Dwarf oregongrape, snail-eating ground beetle. c, American dipper, horiz. d, Cutthroat trout, horiz. e, Roosevelt elk. f, Winter wren. g, Pacific giant salamander, Rough-skinned newt. h, Western tiger swallowtail, horiz. i, Douglas squirrel, foliose lichen. j, Foliose lichen, banana slug.

LITHOGRAPHED
Sheets of 60 in six panes of 10
Serpentine Die Cut 11¼x11½, 11½ (horiz. stamps)

2000, Mar. 29			Tagged
Self-Adhesive			
3378	A2609	Pane of 10	8.00
a.-j.		33c any single	.80 .50
		Sheet of 6 panes	50.00

LOUISE NEVELSON (1899-1988), SCULPTOR

Silent Music I — A2610

Royal Tide I — A2611

Black Chord — A2612

Nightsphere-Light A2613

Dawn's Wedding Chapel I — A2614

Designed by Ethel Kessler.
Printed by Ashton-Potter (USA) Ltd.

LITHOGRAPHED
Sheets of 80 in four panes of 20.

2000, Apr. 6		Tagged	Perf. 11x11¼	
3379	A2610	33c multicolored	.65	.20
3380	A2611	33c multicolored	.65	.20
3381	A2612	33c multicolored	.65	.20
3382	A2613	33c multicolored	.65	.20
3383	A2614	33c multicolored	.65	.20
a.		Strip of 5, #3379-3383	3.25	—
		P# block of 10, 4#+P	6.50	—
		Pane of 20	13.00	—

HUBBLE SPACE TELESCOPE IMAGES

Eagle Nebula — A2615

Ring Nebula — A2616

Lagoon Nebula — A2617

Egg Nebula — A2618

Galaxy NGC 1316 — A2619

Designed by Phil Jordan. Printed at American Packaging Corp. for Sennett Security Products.

PHOTOGRAVURE
Sheets of 120 in six panes of 20.

2000, Apr. 10		Tagged	Perf. 11	
3384	A2615	33c multicolored	.65	.20
3385	A2616	33c multicolored	.65	.20
3386	A2617	33c multicolored	.65	.20
3387	A2618	33c multicolored	.65	.20
3388	A2619	33c multicolored	.65	.20
a.		Strip of 5, #3384-3388	3.25	—
		P# block of 10, 6#+S	6.50	—
		Pane of 20	13.00	—
b.		As "a," imperf	1,250.	
		As "b," pane of 20	5,000.	

AMERICAN SAMOA

Samoan Double Canoe A2620

Designed by Howard Paine.
Printed by Ashton-Potter (USA) Ltd.

LITHOGRAPHED
Sheets of 120 in six panes of 20

2000, Apr. 17		Tagged		Perf. 11
3389 A2620	33c multicolored		.85	.20
	P# block of 4, 4#+P		3.75	
	Pane of 20		18.50	—

LIBRARY OF CONGRESS

Interior Dome and Arched Windows in Main Reading Room, Thomas Jefferson Building — A2621

Designed by Ethel Kessler.
Printed by Ashton-Potter (USA) Ltd.

LITHOGRAPHED
Sheets of 120 in six panes of 20

2000, Apr. 24		Tagged		Perf. 11
3390 A2621	33c multicolored		.65	.20
	P# block of 4, 5#+P		2.60	
	Pane of 20		13.00	—

ROAD RUNNER & WILE E. COYOTE

A2622

Cross Gutter Block of 9

Illustration reduced.

Designed by Ed Wleczyk, Warner Bros.
Printed by Banknote Corp. of America, Inc.

LITHOGRAPHED

2000, Apr. 26	Tagged	Serpentine Die Cut 11
	Self-Adhesive	

3391	Pane of 10	10.00	
a.	A2622 33c single	.85	.20
b.	Pane of 9 #3391a	8.00	
c.	Pane of 1 #3391a	1.50	
	Sheet of 60 (six panes) top, with plate # in selvage on reverse	55.00	
	Sheet of 60 (six panes) bottom, with plate # in selvage	57.50	
	Pane of 10 from sheet of 60	9.50	
	Two panes of 10 with plate numbers on front	22.50	

	Cross gutter block of 9 or 10	16.00	
	Vert. pair with horiz. gutter	2.00	
	Horiz. pair with vert. gutter	4.00	
d.	All die cutting omitted, pane of 10	2,400.	

Die cutting on #3391b does not extend through the backing paper.

3392	Pane of 10	40.00	
a.	A2622 33c single	2.75	
b.	Pane of 9 #3392a	30.00	
c.	Pane of 1, imperf.	5.00	

Die cutting on #3392a extends through the backing paper. Used examples of No. 3392a are identical to those of No. 3391a.

Nos. 3391b-3391c and 3392b-3392c are separated by a vertical line of microperforations.

DISTINGUISHED SOLDIERS

Maj. Gen. John L. Hines (1868-1968) A2623

Gen. Omar N. Bradley (1893-1981) A2624

Sgt. Alvin C. York (1887-1964) A2625

Second Lt. Audie L. Murphy (1924-71) A2626

Designed by Phil Jordan.
Printed by Sterling Sommer for Ashton-Potter (USA) Ltd.

LITHOGRAPHED
Sheets of 120 in six panes of 20

2000, May 3		Tagged		Perf. 11
3393 A2623	33c multicolored		.65	.20
3394 A2624	33c multicolored		.65	.20
3395 A2625	33c multicolored		.65	.20
3396 A2626	33c multicolored		.65	.20
a.	Block or strip of 4, #3393-3396		2.60	—
	P# block of 4, 4#+P		2.60	—
	Pane of 20		13.00	—

SUMMER SPORTS

Runners A2627

Designed by Richard Sheaff.
Printed by Ashton-Potter (USA) Ltd.

LITHOGRAPHED
Sheets of 120 in six panes of 20

2000, May 5		Tagged		Perf. 11
3397 A2627	33c multicolored		.65	.20
	P# block of 4, 4#+P		2.60	
	Pane of 20		13.00	—

ADOPTION

Stick Figures — A2628

Designed by Greg Berger.
Printed by Banknote Corporation of America.

LITHOGRAPHED
Sheets of 120 in six panes of 20

2000, May 10	Tagged	Serpentine Die Cut 11½
		Self-Adhesive

3398 A2628	33c multicolored		.75	.20
	P# block of 4, 5#+B		3.00	
	Pane of 20		15.00	
a.	Die cutting omitted, pair		—	

YOUTH TEAM SPORTS

Basketball — A2629

Football — A2630

Soccer — A2631

Baseball — A2632

Designed by Derry Noyes.
Printed by Sterling Sommer for Ashton-Potter (USA) Ltd.

LITHOGRAPHED
Sheets of 120 in six panes of 20

2000, May 27			Tagged		Perf. 11
3399	A2629	33c	multicolored	.65	.20
3400	A2630	33c	multicolored	.65	.20
3401	A2631	33c	multicolored	.65	.20
3402	A2632	33c	multicolored	.65	.20
a.		Block or strip of 4, #3399-3402		2.60	—
		P# block of 4, 4#+P		2.60	—
		Pane of 20		13.00	—

THE STARS AND STRIPES

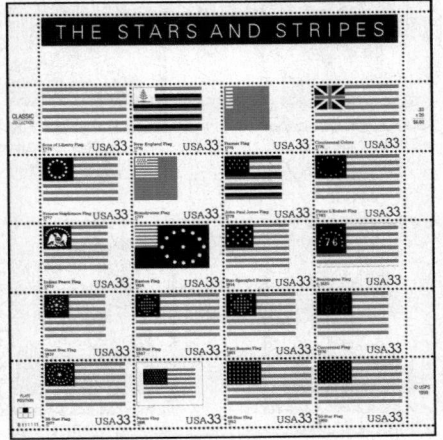

A2633

Illustration reduced.

Designed by Richard Sheaff.
Printed by Banknote Corp. of America.

Designs: a, Sons of Liberty Flag, 1775. b, New England Flag, 1775. c, Forster Flag, 1775. d, Continental Colors, 1776. e, Francis Hopkinson Flag, 1777. f, Brandywine Flag, 1777. g, John Paul Jones Flag, 1779. h, Pierre L'Enfant Flag, 1783. i, Indian Peace Flag, 1803. j, Easton Flag, 1814. k, Star-Spangled Banner, 1814. l, Bennington Flag, c. 1820. m, Great Star Flag, 1837. n, 29-Star Flag, 1847. o, Fort Sumter Flag, 1861. p, Centennial Flag, 1876. q, 38-Star Flag, 1877. r, Peace Flag, 1891. s, 48-Star Flag, 1912. t, 50-Star Flag, 1960.

LITHOGRAPHED

2000, June 14		Tagged		Perf. 10½x11
3403	A2633	Pane of 20	15.00	11.00
a.-t.		33c any single	.75	.50
		Sheet of 120 (6 panes)	85.00	—
		Cross gutter block of 20	25.00	—
		Vert. pairs with horiz. gutter (each)	2.50	—
		Horiz. pairs with vert. gutter (each)	2.50	—

Inscriptions on the back of each stamp describe the flag.
Cross gutter block of 20 consists of six stamps from each of two panes and four stamps from each of two other panes with the cross gutter between.

BERRIES

Blueberries — A2634

Strawberries — A2635

Blackberries — A2636

Raspberries — A2637

Designed by Howard Paine. Printed by Guilford Gravure.
See designs A2550-A2553.

PHOTOGRAVURE
COIL STAMPS
Serpentine Die Cut 8½ Horiz.

2000, June 16				Tagged

Self-Adhesive

3404	A2634	33c	multicolored	2.50	.20
3405	A2635	33c	multicolored	2.50	.20
3406	A2636	33c	multicolored	2.50	.20
3407	A2637	33c	multicolored	2.50	.20
a.		Strip of 4, #3404-3407		10.00	—
		P# strip of 5, 2 #3404, 1 each #3405-3407, #G1111		12.50	—
		P# strip of 9, 2 each #3404-3405, 3407, 3 #3406, #G1111		17.00	—
		P# single (#3406), #G1111			1.25

Nos. 3404-3407 are linerless coils issued without backing paper. The adhesive is strong and can remove the ink from stamps in the roll.

LEGENDS OF BASEBALL

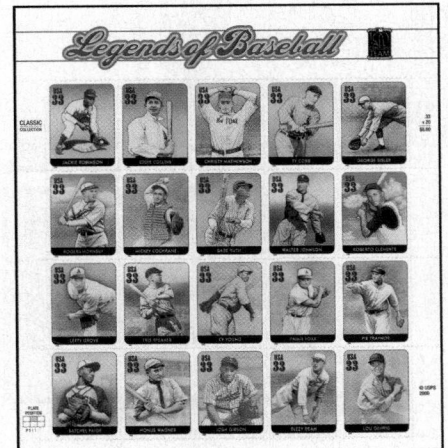

A2638

Illustration reduced.

Designed by Phil Jordan. Printed by Ashton-Potter (USA) Ltd.

Designs: a, Jackie Robinson. b, Eddie Collins. c, Christy Mathewson. d, Ty Cobb. e, George Sisler. f, Rogers Hornsby. g, Mickey Cochrane. h, Babe Ruth. i, Walter Johnson. j, Roberto Clemente. k, Lefty Grove. l, Tris Speaker. m, Cy Young. n, Jimmie Foxx. o, Pie Traynor. p, Satchel Paige. q, Honus Wagner. r, Josh Gibson. s, Dizzy Dean. t, Lou Gehrig.

LITHOGRAPHED
Sheets of 120 in six panes of 20

2000, July 6		Tagged	*Serpentine Die Cut 11¼*

Self-Adhesive

3408	A2638	Pane of 20	13.00	
a.-t.		33c any single	.65	.50
		Sheet of 120 (6 panes)	80.00	—
		Cross gutter block of 20	22.50	—
		Vert. pairs with horiz. gutter (each)	2.25	—
		Horiz. pairs with vert. gutter (each)	2.25	—

Cross gutter block of 20 consists of six stamps from each of two panes and four stamps from each of two other panes with the cross gutter between.

SPACE
Souvenir Sheets

Probing the Vastness of Space — A2639

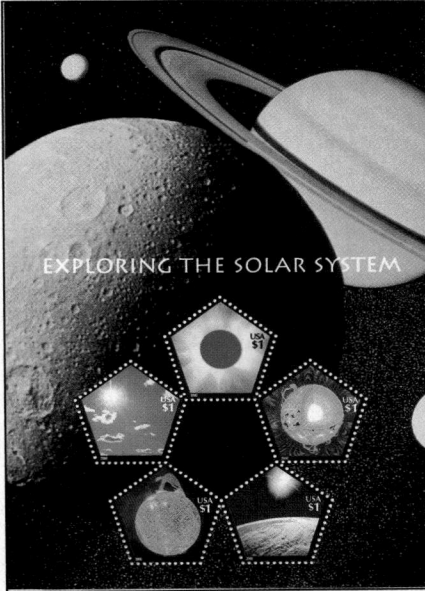

Exploring the Solar System — A2640

Escaping the Gravity of Earth — A2641

Space Achievement and Exploration — A2642

Landing on the Moon — A2643

Illustrations reduced.

Designed by Richard Sheaff. Printed by American Packaging Corporation for Sennett Security Products.

Designs: No. 3409: a, Hubble Space Telescope. b, Radio interferometer very large array, New Mexico. c, Optical and infrared telescopes, Keck Observatory, Hawaii. d, Optical telescopes, Cerro Tololo Observatory, Chile. e, Optical telescope, Mount Wilson Observatory, California. f, Radio telescope, Arecibo Observatory, Puerto Rico.

No. 3410: a, Sun and corona. b, Cross-section of sun. c, Sun and earth. d, Sun and solar flare. e, Sun and clouds.

No. 3411: a, Space Shuttle and Space Station. b, Astronauts working in space.

PHOTOGRAVURE

2000		Tagged		Perf. 10½x11	
3409	A2639	Sheet of 6, July 10		12.50	7.00
a.-f.		60c any single		2.00	1.00
		Perf. 10¾			
3410	A2640	Sheet of 5 + label, *July 11*		16.00	10.00
a.-e.		$1 any single		3.00	1.75
f.		As No. 3410, imperf		*3,250.*	
g		As No. 3410, with hologram from No. 3411b applied		—	

Untagged
Photogravure with Hologram Affixed
Perf. 10½, 10¾ (#3412)

3411	A2641	Sheet of 2, *July 9*	21.00	10.00
a.-b.		$3.20 any single	10.00	4.00
c.		Hologram omitted on right stamp	—	
3412	A2642	**multicolored**, *July 7*	37.50	17.50
a.		$11.75 single	35.00	15.00
b.		Hologram omitted	—	
c.		Hologram omitted on No. 3412 in uncut sheet of 5 panes	—	
3413	A2643	**multicolored**, *July 8*	37.50	17.50
		Uncut sheet of 5 panes, #3409-3413	115.00	
a.		$11.75 single	35.00	15.00
b.		Double hologram	—	
c.		Double hologram on No. 3413 in uncut sheet of 5 panes	—	
d.		Hologram omitted on No. 3413 in uncut sheet of 5 panes	—	
		Nos. 3409-3413 (5)	124.50	62.00

Warning: Soaking in water may affect holographic images.

STAMPIN' THE FUTURE CHILDREN'S STAMP DESIGN CONTEST WINNERS

By Zachary Canter A2644

By Sarah Lipsey A2645

By Morgan Hill — A2646

By Ashley Young A2647

Designed by Richard Sheaff. Printed by Ashton-Potter (USA) Ltd.

LITHOGRAPHED
Sheets of 120 in six panes of 20

2000, July 13		Tagged	*Serpentine Die Cut 11¼*		
			Self-Adhesive		
3414	A2644	33c multicolored		.65	.20
3415	A2645	33c multicolored		.65	.20
3416	A2646	33c multicolored		.65	.20
3417	A2647	33c multicolored		.65	.20
a.		Horiz. strip of 4, #3414-3417		2.60	
		P# block of 8, 2 sets of 5#+P		5.25	
		Pane of 20		13.00	

Plate block may contain top label.

DISTINGUISHED AMERICANS

Gen. Joseph W. Stilwell (1883-1946) A2650

Wilma Rudolph (1940-94), Athlete A2652

Sen. Claude Pepper (1900-89) A2656

Sen. Margaret Chase Smith (1897-1995) A2657

James A. Michener (1907-97), Author — A2657a

Dr. Jonas Salk (1914-95), Polio Vaccine Pioneer — A2658

Harriet Beecher Stowe (1811-96), Author A2660

Sen. Hattie Caraway (1878-1950) A2661

Edward Trudeau (1848-1915), Phthisiologist — A2661a

Mary Lasker (1900-94), Philanthropist — A2661b

Edna Ferber (1887-1968), Writer — A2662

Edna Ferber (With Curving Shoulder) — A2663

Dr. Albert Sabin (1906-93), Polio Vaccine Pioneer — A2664

Designed by: 10c, 23c, 33c, 58c, 59c, 63c, 75c, 76c, 83c, 87c Richard Sheaff; 76c, Howard E. Paine.
Printed by Banknote Corporation of America (#3420-3433). Ashton-Potter (USA) Ltd. (#3422, 3427, 3428, 3432A, 3234B 3434). Banknote Corporation of America for Sennett Security Products, (#3427A, 3430).

LITHOGRAPHED & ENGRAVED, LITHOGRAPHED
(#3436)
Sheets of 120 in six panes of 20
Sheets of 300 in fifteen panes of 20 (#3427A)
Perf. 11 (#3420, 3426), Serpentine Die Cut
11¼x10¾ (#3422, 3432B, 3430), 11¼x11 (#3427A,
3428, 3432A, 3435), 11 (#3427, 3431), 11½x11
(#3432), 11x11¾ (#3433), 11¼ (#3434),

2000-09					**Tagged**

Self-Adhesive (all except #3420, 3426)

3420	A2650	10c	red & black, *Aug. 24*	.20	.20
		P# block of 4, 3#+B		.80	
		Pane of 20		4.00	—
a.		Imperf, pair		350.00	
3422	A2652	23c	red & black, *July 14, 2004*	.45	.20
		P# block of 4, 2#+P		1.80	
		Pane of 20		9.00	
a.		Imperf, pair			
3426	A2656	33c	red & black, *Sept. 7*	.65	.20
		P# block of 4, 3#+B		2.60	—
		Pane of 20		13.00	—
3427	A2657	58c	red & black, *June 13, 2007*	1.25	.20
		P# block of 4, 3#+P		5.00	
		Pane of 20		25.00	
b.		Black (engr.) omitted			
3427A	A2657a	59c	multicolored, *May 12, 2008*	1.25	.20
		P# block of 4, 5#+S		5.00	
		Pane of 20		25.00	
3428	A2658	63c	red & black *Mar. 8, 2006*	1.25	.20
		P# block of 4, 3#+P		5.00	
		Pane of 20		25.00	
a.		Black (litho.) omitted			
3430	A2660	75c	red & black, *June 13, 2007*	1.50	.20
		P# block of 4, 3#+S		6.00	
		Pane of 20		30.00	
3431	A2661	76c	red & black, *Feb. 21, 2001*	1.50	.20
		P# block of 4, 3#+B		6.00	
		Pane of 20		30.00	
3432	A2661	76c	red & black,	3.50	2.00
		P# block of 4, 3#+B		14.00	
		Pane of 20		70.00	
3432A	A2661a	76c	multicolored, *May 12, 2008*	1.50	.20
		P# block of 4, 4#+P		6.00	
		Pane of 20		30.00	
3432B	A2661b	78c	multicolored, *May 15, 2009*	1.60	.20
		P# block of 4, 4#+P		6.50	
		Pane of 20		32.00	
3433	A2662	83c	red & black, *July 29, 2002*	1.60	.30
		P# block of 4, 3#+B1		6.50	
		Pane of 20		32.50	

The previously listed "Big Mouth" flaw on No. 3433 has been discovered to be not a constant plate flaw but rather the result of extraneous matter on the plate affecting a reported 15 panes before the matter fell off, or was removed from, the plate.

3434	A2663	83c	red & black, *Aug. 2003*	1.60	.30
		P# block of 4, 3#+P		6.50	
		Pane of 20		32.50	
3435	A2664	87c	red & black, *Mar. 8, 2006*	1.75	.30
		P# block of 4, 2#+S		7.00	
		Pane of 20		35.00	

BOOKLET STAMP
Serpentine Die Cut 11¼x10¾ on 3 Sides
Self-Adhesive

3436	A2652	23c	red & black, *July 14, 2004*	.45	.20
a.		Booklet pane of 4		1.80	
b.		Booklet pane of 6		2.70	
c.		Booklet pane of 10		4.50	
d.		As "c," die cutting omitted		—	

This is an ongoing set. Numbers may change.

CALIFORNIA STATEHOOD, 150TH ANNIV.

Big Sur and
Iceplant — A2668

Designed by Carl Herrman.
Printed by Avery Dennison.

PHOTOGRAVURE
Sheets of 200 in ten panes of 20

2000, Sept. 8			**Tagged**	*Serpentine Die Cut 11*

Self-Adhesive

3438	A2668	33c	multicolored	.75	.20
		P# block of 4, 5#+V		3.00	
		Pane of 20		15.00	

DEEP SEA CREATURES

Fanfin Anglerfish A2669

Sea Cucumber A2670

Fangtooth A2671

Amphipod A2672

Medusa A2673

Designed by Ethel Kessler.
Printed by American Packaging Corp. for Sennett Security Products.

PHOTOGRAVURE
Sheets of 135 in nine panes of 15

2000, Oct. 2			**Tagged**	*Perf. 10x10¼*

3439	A2669	33c	multicolored	.65	.20
3440	A2670	33c	multicolored	.65	.20
3441	A2671	33c	multicolored	.65	.20
3442	A2672	33c	multicolored	.65	.20
3443	A2673	33c	multicolored	.65	.20
a.		Vert. strip of 5, #3439-3443		3.25	2.00
		Pane of 15, 4#+S		9.75	
		Sheet of 135 (nine panes)		90.00	
		Cross gutter block of 10		15.00	
		Horiz. block of 10 with vert. gutter		10.00	
		Horiz. pairs with vert. gutter (each)		2.00	—
		Vert. pair with horiz. gutter		1.75	—

See note under No. 3292 regarding lack of plate block listing.
Cross gutter block of 10 consists of three stamps from each of two panes and two stamps from each of the other two panes with the cross gutter between.

LITERARY ARTS SERIES

Thomas Wolfe
(1900-38),
Novelist
A2674

Designed by Phil Jordan.
Printed by Ashton-Potter (USA) Ltd.

LITHOGRAPHED
Sheets of 120 in six panes of 20

2000, Oct. 3			**Tagged**	*Perf. 11*
3444	A2674	33c	multicolored	.65	.20
		P# block of 4, 5#+P		2.60	
		Pane of 20		13.00	—

WHITE HOUSE, 200TH ANNIV.

A2675

Designed by Derry Noyes.
Printed by Ashton-Potter (USA) Ltd.

LITHOGRAPHED
Sheets of 180 in nine panes of 20

2000, Oct. 18			**Tagged**	*Serpentine Die Cut 11¼*

Self-Adhesive

3445	A2675	33c	multicolored	1.00	.20
		P# block of 4, 4#+P		4.00	
		Pane of 20		20.00	

LEGENDS OF HOLLYWOOD

Edward G. Robinson (1893-
1973), Actor — A2676

Designed by Howard Paine.
Printed by American Packaging Corporation for Sennett Security Products.

PHOTOGRAVURE
Sheets of 120 in six panes of 20

2000, Oct. 24			**Tagged**	*Perf. 11*
3446	A2676	33c	multicolored	1.50	.20
		P# block of 4, 7#+S		7.00	
		Pane of 20		34.00	12.50
		Sheet of 120 (6 panes)		160.00	
		Cross gutter block of 8		25.00	
		Block of 8 with vertical gutter		15.00	
		Horiz. pair with vert. gutter		4.00	
		Vert. pair with horiz. gutter		3.00	

Perforations in corner of each stamp are star-shaped. Cross gutter block consists of 6 stamps from upper panes and 2 stamps from panes below.

New York Public Library
Lion — A2677

Designed by Carl Herrman.
Printed by American Packaging Corporation for Sennett Security Products.

PHOTOGRAVURE
COIL STAMP
Serpentine Die Cut 11½ Vert.

2000, Nov. 9   **Untagged**

Self-Adhesive

3447	A2677 (10c) **multicolored**, "2000" year date	.20	.20
	Pair	.40	
	P# strip of 5, #S11111, S22222, S33333, S44444, S66666	2.25	
	P# single, #S11111, S22222, S33333, S44444, S66666, S77777	—	1.75
a.	"2003" year date	.20	.20
	Pair	.40	
	P# strip of 5, #S55555	3.25	
	P# single, #S55555	—	2.00
b.	As "a.", prephosphored coated paper with surface tagging showing a solid appearance (error)	—	

No. 3447 also is known with extremely faint phosphor splotches. No. 3447b has full-strength tagging. Values with faint tagging: unused and used singles, $2; P# strip of 5, #S33333 and S44444 $8 each; #S77777 $25; P# single used, #S33333 and S44444 $6 each; #77777 $17.50.
   See No. 3769.

Flag Over Farm — A2678

Designed by Richard Sheaff.
Printed by Sterling Sommer for Ashton-Potter (USA) Ltd. (#3448), Ashton-Potter (USA) Ltd. (#3449), Avery Dennison (#3450).

LITHOGRAPHED (#3448-3449), PHOTOGRAVURE (#3450)
Sheets of 120 in six panes of 20

2000, Dec. 15   **Tagged**   *Perf. 11¼*

3448	A2678 (34c) **multicolored**	.75	.20
	P# block of 4, 4# + P	3.25	—
	Pane of 20	16.00	—

Self-Adhesive
Serpentine Die Cut 11¼

3449	A2678 (34c) **multicolored**	1.00	.20
	P# block of 4, 4# + P	5.00	
	Pane of 20	24.00	

Booklet Stamp
Self-Adhesive
Serpentine Die Cut 8 on 2, 3 or 4 sides

3450	A2678 (34c) **multicolored**	.85	.20
a.	Booklet pane of 18	16.00	
b.	Die cutting omitted, pair	—	

A2679   Statue of Liberty — A2680

Designed by Derry Noyes.
Printed by Avery Dennison (#3451), Bureau of Engraving and Printing (#3452-3453).

PHOTOGRAVURE
Serpentine Die Cut 11 on 2, 3 or 4 sides

2000, Dec. 15   **Tagged**

Self-Adhesive (#3451, 3453)
Booklet Stamp

3451	A2679 (34c) **multicolored**	.70	.20
a.	Booklet pane of 20	14.00	
b.	Booklet pane of 4	3.00	
	Booklet pane of 4 containing P# single	4.50	
	P# single, #V1111	1.50	.70
c.	Booklet pane of 6	5.75	
d.	As "a," die cutting omitted	—	

The plate # single in No. 3451b is the lower right stamp of the right pane of 4 of the booklet.

Coil Stamps
Perf. 9¾ Vert.

3452	A2680 (34c) **multicolored**	.70	.20
	Pair	1.40	.30
	P# strip of 5, #1111	5.00	
	P# single, same #	—	2.25

Serpentine Die Cut 10 Vert.

3453	A2680 (34c) **multicolored**, small date	.70	.20
	Pair	1.40	
	P# strip of 5, #1111	6.50	
	P# single, same #	—	1.50
a.	Die cutting omitted, pair	350.00	
b.	Large date	.75	.20
	Pair	1.50	
	P# strip of 5, #1111	7.50	
	P# single, same #	—	1.50

The date on No. 3453 is 1.4mm long, on No. 3453b 1.55mm long and darker in color.

A2681   A2682

A2683   Flowers — A2684

Designed by Derry Noyes.
Printed by American Packaging Corporation for Sennett Security Products (#3454-3461), Guilford Gravure for Banknote Corporation of America, Inc. (#3462-3465).

PHOTOGRAVURE
Serpentine Die Cut 10½x10¾ on 2 or 3 sides

2000, Dec. 15   **Tagged**

Booklet Stamps
Self-Adhesive

3454	A2681 (34c) **purple & multi**	1.00	.20
3455	A2682 (34c) **tan & multi**	1.00	.20
3456	A2683 (34c) **green & multi**	1.00	.20
3457	A2684 (34c) **red & multi**	1.00	.20
a.	Block of 4, #3454-3457	4.00	
b.	Booklet pane of 4, #3454-3457	4.00	
c.	Booklet pane of 6, #3456, 3457, 2 each #3454-3455	6.00	
d.	Booklet pane of 6, #3454, 3455, 2 each #3456-3457	6.00	
e.	Booklet pane of 20, 5 each #3454-3457 + label	20.00	

No. 3457e is a double-sided booklet pane, with 12 stamps on one side and eight stamps plus label on the other side.

Serpentine Die Cut 11½x11¾ on 2 or 3 sides

3458	A2681 (34c) **purple & multi**	3.00	.25
3459	A2682 (34c) **tan & multi**	3.00	.25
3460	A2683 (34c) **green & multi**	3.00	.25
3461	A2684 (34c) **red & multi**	3.00	.25
a.	Block of 4, #3458-3461	12.00	
b.	Booklet pane of 20, 2 each #3461a, 3 each #3457a	36.50	
c.	Booklet pane of 20, 2 each #3457a, 3 each #3461a	45.00	

Nos. 3461b and 3461c are double-sided booklet panes, with 12 stamps on one side and eight stamps plus label on the other side.

Coil Stamps
Serpentine Die Cut 8½ Vert.

3462	A2683 (34c) **green & multi**	3.50	.20
3463	A2684 (34c) **red & multi**	3.50	.20
3464	A2682 (34c) **tan & multi**	3.50	.20
3465	A2681 (34c) **purple & multi**	3.50	.20
a.	Strip of 4, #3462-3465	14.00	
	P# strip of 5, 2 #3462, 1 each #3463-3465, P#B1111	18.00	
	P# strip of 9, 2 each #3462-3463, 3465, 3 #3464, same P#	27.50	
	P# single (#3464)	—	1.25

Lettering on No. 3462 has black outline not found on No. 3456. Zeroes of "2000" are rounder on Nos. 3454-3457 than on Nos. 3462-3465.

Statue of Liberty A2685   George Washington A2686

American Buffalo — A2687   Flag Over Farm — A2688

Statue of Liberty — A2689   A2690

A2691   A2692

Flowers — A2693   Apple — A2694

Orange — A2695   Eagle — A2696

Capitol Dome — A2697

Washington
Monument — A2698

Designed by Sterling Sommer for Ashton-Potter (USA) Ltd.
(#3467), Carl Herrman (#3467, 3468, 3471, 3471A, 3475,
3484, 3484A), Richard Sheaff (#3468A, 3469, 3470, 3475A,
3482-3483, 3495), Derry Noyes (#3466, 3472-3473, 3476,
3477-3481, 3485, 3487-3490), Ned Seidler (#3491-3494).
Printed by Avery Dennison (#3468, 3475, 3485, 3495) Ashton-Potter (USA) Ltd. (#3469-3470, 3484-3484A), American
Packaging Corporation for Sennett Security Printers (#3471,
3471A, 3482-3483), Bureau of Engraving and Printing (#3466,
3476-3477), Guilford Gravure, Inc. for Banknote Corporation of
America (#3475A, 3487-3490), Banknote Corporation of
America (#3468A, 3472-3473, 3491-3494).

PHOTOGRAVURE
Serpentine Die Cut 9¾ Vert.

2001, Jan. 7   **Tagged**

Coil Stamp
Self-Adhesive

3466	A2685	34c multicolored	.70	.20
		Pair	1.40	
		P# strip of 5, #1111, 2222	5.00	
		P# single, same #	—	2.50

Sheets of 400 in four panes of 100 (#3467), Sheets
of 200 in ten panes of 20 (#3468), Sheets of 200 in
two panes of 100 (#3469), Sheets of 120 in six
panes of 20 (#3468A, 3470-3473), Sheets of 160 in
eight panes of 20 (#3471A).
Self-Adhesive (#3468-3468A, 3470-3473)

2001	**Photo.**	**Tagged**	**Perf. 11¼x11**	
3467	A2687	21c multicolored, *Sept. 20*	.50	.20
		P# block of 4, 6#+P	21.00	

Serpentine Die Cut 11

3468	A2687	21c multicolored, *Feb. 22*	.45	.20
		P# block of 4, 4#+V	3.50	
		Pane of 20	16.00	

Litho.
Serpentine Die Cut 11¼x11¾

3468A	A2686	23c green, *Sept. 20*	.50	.20
		P# block of 4, 3#+B	2.60	
		Pane of 20	12.50	

Photo.
Perf. 11¼

3469	A2688	34c multicolored, *Feb. 7*	.75	.20
		P# block of 4, 4#+P	25.00	

Serpentine Die Cut 11¼

3470	A2688	34c multicolored, *Mar. 6*	1.00	.20
		P# block of 4, 4#+P	6.00	
		Pane of 20	28.00	

Photo.
Serpentine Die Cut 10¾

3471	A2696	55c multicolored, *Feb. 22*	1.10	.20
		P# block of 4, 5#+S	4.40	
		Pane of 20	22.00	

Serpentine Die Cut 10¾

3471A	A2696	57c multicolored, *Sept. 20*	1.10	.20
		P# block of 4, 5#+S	4.40	
		Pane of 20	22.00	

LITHOGRAPHED
Serpentine Die Cut 11¼x11½

3472	A2697	$3.50 multicolored, *Jan. 29*	7.00	2.00
		P# block of 4, 4#+B	28.00	
		Pane of 20	140.00	
a.		Die cutting omitted, pair	—	
3473	A2698	$12.25 multicolored, *Jan. 29*	22.50	10.00
		P# block of 4, 4#+B	90.00	
		Pane of 20	450.00	

COIL STAMPS
Self-Adhesive (#3475-3475A, 3477-3481)
Photo.
Serpentine Die Cut 8½ Vert.

3475	A2687	21c multicolored, *Feb. 22*	.50	.20
		Pair	1.00	.30
		P# strip of 5, #V1111, V2222	3.50	
		P# single, same #	—	1.00
3475A	A2686	23c green, *Sept. 20*	.50	.20
		Pair	1.00	
		P# strip of 5, #B11	3.50	
		P# single, same #	—	1.00

Compare No. 3475A ("2001" date at lower left) with No. 3617
("2002" date at lower left).

Perf. 9¾ Vert.

3476	A2685	34c multicolored, prephosphored coated paper, *Feb. 7*	.70	.20
		Pair	1.40	.30
		P# strip of 5, #1111	5.00	
		P# single, same #	—	2.75

No. 3476 exists on two types of surface-tagged paper that
exhibit either a solid or a grainy solid appearance.

Serpentine Die Cut 9¾ Vert.

3477	A2685	34c multicolored, *Feb. 7*	.80	.20
		Pair	1.60	.30
		P# strip of 5, #1111, 2222, 3333, 4444, 5555, 6666	5.00	—
		P# single, same #	—	1.00
		P# strip of 5, #7777	11.00	
		P# single, #7777	—	8.50
a.		Die cutting omitted, pair	75.00	

No. 3477 has right angle corners and backing paper as high
as the stamp. No. 3466 has rounded corners and is on backing
paper larger than the stamp.

Serpentine Die Cut 8½ Vert.

3478	A2690	34c green & multi, *Feb. 7*	.70	.20
3479	A2691	34c red & multi, *Feb. 7*	.70	.20
3480	A2692	34c tan & multi, *Feb. 7*	.70	.20
3481	A2693	34c purple & multi, *Feb. 7*	.70	.20
a.		Strip of 4, #3478-3481	2.80	
		P# strip of 5, 2 #3478, 1 each #3479-3481, P#B1111, B2111, B2122, B2211, B2222	6.00	
		P# strip of 9, 3 #3480, 2 each #3478-3479, 3481, P# B1111, B2111, B2122, B2211, B2222	9.00	—
		P# single, (#3480), same #	—	2.00

BOOKLET STAMPS
Litho.
Self-Adhesive, Tagged
Serpentine Die Cut 11¼x11 on 3 Sides

3482	A2686	20c dark carmine, *Feb. 22*	.45	.20
a.		Booklet pane of 10	4.50	
b.		Booklet pane of 4	1.80	
c.		Booklet pane of 6	2.70	

Serpentine Die Cut 10½x11 on 3 Sides

3483	A2686	20c dark carmine, *Feb. 22*	5.00	1.25
a.		Booklet pane of 4, 2 #3482 at L, 2 #3483 at R	12.00	
b.		Booklet pane of 6, 3 #3482 at L, 3 #3483 at R	20.00	
c.		Booklet pane of 10, 5 #3482 at L, 5 #3483 at R	25.00	
d.		Booklet pane of 4, 2 #3483 at L, 2 #3482 at R	12.00	
e.		Booklet pane of 6, 3 #3483 at L, 3 #3482 at R	20.00	
f.		Booklet pane of 10, 5 #3483 at L, 5 #3482 at R	25.00	
g.		Pair, #3482 at L, #3483 at R	5.50	
h.		Pair, #3483 at L, #3482 at R	5.50	

Serpentine Die Cut 11¼ on 3 Sides

3484	A2687	21c multicolored, *Sept. 20*	.50	.20
b.		Booklet pane of 4	2.00	
c.		Booklet pane of 6	3.00	
d.		Booklet pane of 10	5.00	

Serpentine Die Cut 10½x11¼

3484A	A2687	21c multicolored, *Sept. 20*	5.50	1.50
e.		Booklet pane of 4, 2 #3484 at L, 2 #3484A at R	12.00	
f.		Booklet pane of 6, 3 #3484 at L, 3 #3484A at R	20.00	
g.		Booklet pane of 10, 5 #3484 at L, 5 #3484A at R	30.00	
h.		Booklet pane of 4, 2 #3484A at L, 2 #3484 at R	12.00	
i.		Booklet pane of 6, 3 #3484A at L, 3 #3484 at R	20.00	
j.		Booklet pane of 10, 5 #3484A at L, 5 #3484 at R	30.00	
k.		Pair, #3484 at L, #3484A at R	6.00	
l.		Pair, #3484A at L, #3484 at R	6.00	

Photo.
Serpentine Die Cut 11 on 2, 3 or 4 Sides

3485	A2689	34c multicolored, *Feb. 7*	.70	.20
a.		Booklet pane of 10	7.00	
b.		Booklet pane of 20	14.00	
c.		Booklet pane of 4	3.00	
		Booklet pane of 4 containing P# single	4.00	
		P# single, #V1111, V1122, V2212, V2222	1.50	1.50
		P# single, #V1112, V1121	—	
d.		Booklet pane of 6	4.50	
e.		Die cutting omitted, pair (from No. 3485b)	—	
f.		As "e," booklet pane of 20	—	

The plate # single in No. 3485c is the lower right stamp of the
right pane of 4 of the booklet.

Serpentine Die Cut 10½x10¾ on 2 or 3 Sides

3487	A2693	34c purple & multi, *Feb. 7*	.75	.20
3488	A2692	34c tan & multi, *Feb. 7*	.75	.20
3489	A2690	34c green & multi, *Feb. 7*	.75	.20

3490	A2691	34c red & multi, *Feb. 7*	.75	.20
a.		Block of 4, #3487-3490	3.00	
b.		Booklet pane of 4, #3487-3490	3.00	
c.		Booklet pane of 6, #3489-3490, 2 each #3487-3488	4.50	
d.		Booklet pane of 6, #3487-3488, 2 each #3489-3490	4.50	
e.		Booklet pane of 20, 5 each #3490a + label	15.00	

No. 3490e is a double-sided booklet pane, with 12 stamps on
one side and eight stamps plus label on the other side.

Litho.
Serpentine Die Cut 11¼ on 2, 3 or 4 Sides

3491	A2694	34c multicolored, *Mar. 6*	.70	.20
3492	A2695	34c multicolored, *Mar. 6*	.70	.20
a.		Pair, #3491-3492	1.40	
b.		Booklet pane, 10 each #3491-3492	14.00	
c.		As "a," black ("34 USA") omitted	—	
d.		As "a," die cutting omitted	—	
e.		As "b," die cutting omitted	—	
f.		As "b," right four stamps yellow omitted	—	

Serpentine Die Cut 11½x10¾ on 2 or 3 Sides

3493	A2694	34c multicolored, *May*	1.25	.20
3494	A2695	34c multicolored, *May*	1.25	.20
a.		Pair, #3493-3494	2.50	
b.		Booklet pane, 2 each #3493-3494	5.00	
		Booklet pane, 2 each #3493-3494, containing P# single	6.50	
		P# single, #B1111	2.50	2.00
c.		Booklet pane, 3 each #3493-3494, #3493 at UL	7.50	
d.		Booklet pane, 3 each #3493-3494, #3494 at UL	7.50	

Serpentine Die Cut 8 on 2, 3 or 4 sides

3495	A2688	34c multicolored, *Dec. 17*	1.00	.20
a.		Booklet pane of 18	18.00	

LOVE

Rose, Apr. 20, 1763
Love Letter by John
Adams — A2699

Rose, Apr. 20, 1763
Love Letter by John
Adams — A2700

Rose, Aug. 11, 1763
Love Letter by Abigail
Smith (Abigail Adams
in 1764) — A2701

Designed by Lisa Catalone. Printed by Banknote Corporation
of America, Inc.

LITHOGRAPHED
Sheets of 180 in nine panes of 20 (#3499)
Serpentine Die Cut 11¼ on 2, 3 or 4 Sides

2001			**Tagged**	

Self-Adhesive
Booklet Stamps (Nos. 3496-3498)

3496	A2699	(34c) multicolored, *Jan. 19*	.90	.20
a.		Booklet pane of 20	18.00	
b.		Vert. pair, die cutting omitted between	—	

Serpentine Die Cut 11¼ on 2, 3 or 4 Sides

3497	A2700	34c multicolored, *Feb. 14*	.90	.20
a.		Booklet pane of 20	18.00	
b.		Vertical pair, die cutting omitted between	—	

Size: 18x21mm
Serpentine Die Cut 11½x10¾ on 2 or 3 Sides

3498	A2700	34c multicolored, *Feb. 14*	1.00	.20
a.		Booklet pane of 4	4.00	
		Booklet pane of 4 containing P# single	6.00	
		P# single, #B1111	2.00	2.00
b.		Booklet pane of 6	6.00	

Plate number single on No. 3498 is on the lower left stamp of
the bottom pane of 4 of the booklet.

Serpentine Die Cut 11¼

3499	A2701	55c multicolored, *Feb. 14*	1.10	.20
		P# block of 4, 4#+B	4.50	
		Pane of 20	22.50	

See No. 3551.

CHINESE NEW YEAR

Year of the
Snake — A2702

Designed by Clarence Lee. Printed by Sterling Sommer for Ashton-Potter (USA) Ltd.

LITHOGRAPHED
Sheets of 180 in nine panes of 20

2001, Jan. 20	Tagged		Perf. 11¼	
3500 A2702	34c multicolored		.75	.20
	P# block of 4, 5#+P		3.00	—
	Pane of 20		15.00	—

See No. 3895f.

BLACK HERITAGE SERIES

Roy Wilkins (1901-81), Civil Rights Leader — A2703

Designed by Richard Sheaff. Printed by Ashton-Potter (USA) Ltd.

LITHOGRAPHED
Sheets of 180 in nine panes of 20
Serpentine Die Cut 11½x11¼

2001, Jan. 24		Tagged	
Self-Adhesive			
3501 A2703	34c blue	.70	.20
	P# block of 4, 2#+P	2.80	
	Pane of 20	14.00	

AMERICAN ILLUSTRATORS

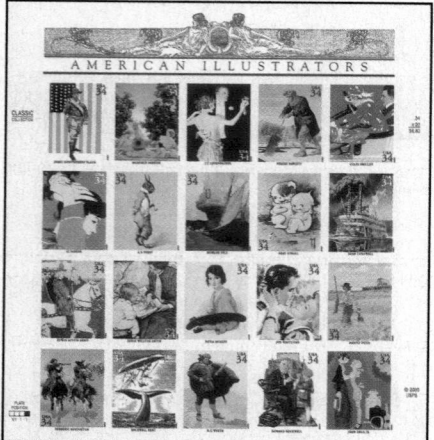

A2704

Illustration reduced.

Designed by Carl Herrman.
Printed by Avery Dennison.

Designs: a, Marine Corps poster "First in the Fight, Always Faithful," by James Montgomery Flagg. b, "Interlude (The Lute Players)," by Maxfield Parrish. c, Advertisement for Arrow Collars and Shirts, by J. C. Leyendecker. d, Advertisement for Carrier Corp. Refrigeration, by Robert Fawcett. e, Advertisement for Luxite Hosiery, by Coles Phillips. f, Illustration for correspondence school lesson, by Al Parker. g, "Br'er Rabbit," by A. B. Frost. h, "An Attack on a Galleon," by Howard Pyle. i, Kewpie and Kewpie Doodle Dog, by Rose O'Neill. j, Illustration for cover of True Magazine, by Dean Cornwell. k, "Galahad's Departure," by Edwin Austin Abbey. l, "The First Lesson," by Jessie Willcox Smith. m, Illustration for cover of McCall's Magazine, by Neysa McMein. n, "Back Home For Keeps," by Jon Whitcomb. o, "Something for Supper," by Harvey Dunn. p, "A Dash for the Timber," by Frederic Remington. q, Illustration for "Moby Dick," by Rockwell Kent. r, "Captain Bill Bones," by N. C.

Wyeth. s, Illustration for cover of The Saturday Evening Post, by Norman Rockwell. t, "The Girl He Left Behind," by John Held, Jr.

PHOTOGRAVURE
Sheets of 80 in four panes of 20

2001, Feb. 1	Tagged	*Serpentine Die Cut 11¼*		
	Self-Adhesive			
3502 A2704	Pane of 20		17.50	
a.-t.	34c any single		.85	.60
	Sheet of 80 (4 panes)		52.50	
	Block of 20 different stamps with vert. gutter between any 2 columns		27.50	
	Pairs with vert. gutter between (each)		2.00	

DIABETES AWARENESS

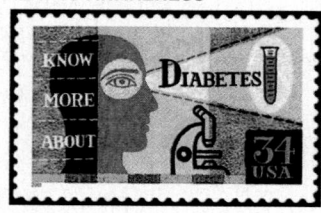

A2705

Designed by Richard Sheaff. Printed by Ashton-Potter (USA) Ltd.

LITHOGRAPHED
Sheets of 180 in nine panes of 20
Serpentine Die Cut 11¼x11½

2001, Mar. 16		Tagged	
	Self-Adhesive		
3503 A2705	34c multicolored	.65	.20
	P# block of 4, 4#+P	2.60	
	Pane of 20	13.00	

NOBEL PRIZE CENTENARY

Alfred Nobel and Obverse of Medals
A2706

Designed by Olof Baldursdottir of Sweden. Printed by De La Rue Security Printing.

LITHOGRAPHED & ENGRAVED
Sheets of 120 in six panes of 20

2001, Mar. 22	Tagged		Perf. 11	
3504 A2706	34c multicolored		.70	.20
	P# block of 4, 3#+S		2.80	—
	Pane of 20		14.00	—
a.	Imperf, pair			—

See Sweden No. 2415.

PAN-AMERICAN EXPOSITION INVERT STAMPS, CENT.

A2707

Illustration reduced.

Reproductions (dated 2001) of: a, #294a. b, #295a. c, #296a. d, Commemorative "cinderella" stamp depicting a buffalo.

Designed by Richard Sheaff. Printed by Banknote Corporation of America.

LITHOGRAPHED (#3505d), ENGRAVED (others)
Sheets of 28 in four panes of 7

2001, Mar. 29	*Perf. 12 (#3505d), 12½x12 (others)*			
	Tagged (#3505d), Untagged (others)			
3505 A2707	Pane of 7, #3505a-3505c, 4 #3505d		9.00	7.00
a.	A109 1c green & black		.60	.20
b.	A110 2c carmine & black		.60	.20
c.	A111 4c deep red brown & black		.60	.20
d.	80c red & blue		1.75	.35
	Sheet of 4 panes		45.00	
	Pane with vertical gutter, 80c stamps at left; "a," "b" & "c" at right (from sheet of 4 panes)		20.00	

GREAT PLAINS PRAIRIE

A2708

Illustration reduced.

Designed by Ethel Kessler. Printed by Ashton-Potter (USA) Ltd.

Wildlife and flowers: a, Pronghorns, Canada geese. b, Burrowing owls, American buffalos. c, American buffalo, Black-tailed prairie dogs, wild alfalfa, horiz. d, Black-tailed prairie dog, American buffalos,. e, Painted lady butterfly, American buffalo, prairie coneflowers, prairie wild roses, horiz. f, Western meadowlark, camel cricket, prairie coneflowers, prairie wild roses. g, Badger, harvester ants. h, Eastern short-horned lizard, plains pocket gopher. i, Plains spadefoot, dung beetle, prairie wild roses, horiz. j, Two-striped grasshopper, Ord's kangaroo rat.

LITHOGRAPHED
Sheets of 60 in six panes of 10

2001, Apr. 19	Tagged	*Serpentine Die Cut 10*		
	Self-Adhesive			
3506 A2708	Pane of 10		11.00	
a.-j.	34c Any single		1.00	.50
	Sheet of 6 panes		65.00	

PEANUTS COMIC STRIP

Snoopy
A2709

Designed by Paige Braddock. Printed by Ashton-Potter (USA) Ltd.

LITHOGRAPHED
Sheets of 180 in nine panes of 20
Serpentine Die Cut 11¼x11½

2001, May 17		Tagged	
Self-Adhesive			
3507	A2709 34c **multicolored**	.80	.20
	P# block of 4, 5#+P	3.50	
	Pane of 20	17.50	

HONORING VETERANS

A2710

Designed by Carl Herrman. Printed by Ashton-Potter (USA) Ltd.

LITHOGRAPHED
Sheets of 180 in nine panes of 20
Serpentine Die Cut 11¼x11½

2001, May 23		Tagged	
Self-Adhesive			
3508	A2710 34c **multicolored**	.75	.20
	P# block of 4, 4#+P	3.00	
	Pane of 20	15.00	11.00

FRIDA KAHLO (1907-54), PAINTER

Self-portrait — A2711

Designed by Richard Sheaff. Printed by Sterling Sommer for Ashton-Potter (USA) Ltd..

LITHOGRAPHED
Sheets of 80 in four panes of 20

2001, June 21	Tagged	Perf. 11¼
3509	A2711 34c **multicolored**	.75	.20
	P# block of 4, 4#+P	3.00	
	Pane of 20	15.00	—

LEGENDARY PLAYING FIELDS

Ebbets
Field — A2712

Tiger Stadium
A2713

Crosley
Field — A2714

Yankee
Stadium
A2715

Polo Grounds
A2716

Forbes
Field — A2717

Fenway
Park — A2718

Comiskey
Park — A2719

Shibe
Park — A2720

Wrigley
Field — A2721

Designed by Phil Jordan. Printed by Avery Dennison.

PHOTOGRAVURE
Sheets of 160 in eight panes of 20
Serpentine Die Cut 11¼x11½

2001, June 27	Tagged	Self-Adhesive	
3510	A2712 34c **multicolored**	.90	.60
3511	A2713 34c **multicolored**	.90	.60
3512	A2714 34c **multicolored**	.90	.60
3513	A2715 34c **multicolored**	.90	.60
3514	A2716 34c **multicolored**	.90	.60
3515	A2717 34c **multicolored**	.90	.60
3516	A2718 34c **multicolored**	.90	.60
3517	A2719 34c **multicolored**	.90	.60
3518	A2720 34c **multicolored**	.90	.60
3519	A2721 34c **multicolored**	.90	.60
a.	Block of 10, #3510-3519	9.00	
	P# block of 10, 4#+V	9.00	
	Pane of 20	18.00	
	Sheet of 160 (8 panes)	125.00	
	Cross-gutter block of 12	20.00	
	Horiz. block of 10 with vert. gutter	10.00	
	Block of 4 with horiz. gutter	4.50	
	Vert. pairs with horiz. gutter (each)	2.00	
	Horiz. pairs with vert. gutter (each)	2.00	

Cross gutter block contains one each Nos. 3510-3517, two each of Nos. 3518-3519, and vertical and horizontal gutters.

ATLAS STATUE, NEW YORK CITY

A2722

Designed by Kevin Newman. Printed by Banknote Corporation of America.

PHOTOGRAVURE
COIL STAMP
Serpentine Die Cut 8½ Vert.

2001, June 29		Untagged	
Self-Adhesive			
3520	A2722 (10c) **multicolored**	.20	.20
	Pair	.40	
	P# strip of 5, #B1111	2.00	
	P# single, same #	—	1.10

See No. 3770.

LEONARD BERNSTEIN (1918-90), CONDUCTOR

A2723

Designed by Howard Paine. Printed by Sterling Sommer for Ashton-Potter (USA) Ltd.

LITHOGRAPHED
Sheets of 180 in nine panes of 20

2001, July 10	Tagged	Perf. 11¼
3521	A2723 34c **multicolored**	.70	.20
	P# block of 4, 4#+P	2.80	
	Pane of 20	14.00	

WOODY WAGON

A2724

Designed by Kevin Newman. Printed by American Packaging Corporation for Sennett Security Products.

PHOTOGRAVURE
COIL STAMP
Serpentine Die Cut 11½ Vert.

2001, Aug. 3			**Untagged**	
		Self-Adhesive		
3522	A2724	(15c) **multicolored**	.30	.20
		Pair	.60	
		P# strip of 5, #S11111	3.75	
		P# single, same #	—	2.00

LEGENDS OF HOLLYWOOD

Lucille Ball (1911-89) — A2725

Designed by Derry Noyes. Printed by Banknote Corporation of America.

LITHOGRAPHED
Sheets of 180 in nine panes of 20

2001, Aug. 6	**Tagged**	***Serpentine Die Cut 11***		
		Self-Adhesive		
3523	A2725	34c **multicolored**	1.00	.20
		P# block of 4, 4#+B	4.50	
		Pane of 20	22.00	13.00
		Sheet of 180 (9 panes)	145.00	
		Cross-gutter block of 8	20.00	
		Block of 8 with vert. gutter	11.50	
		Horiz. pair with vert. gutter	3.25	
		Vert. pairs with horiz. gutter	2.25	
a.		Die cutting omitted, pair	*925.00*	
		As "a," pane of 20	—	

Cross gutter block consists of 6 stamps from upper panes and 2 stamps from lower panes.

AMERICAN TREASURES SERIES
Amish Quilts

Diamond in the Square, c. 1920 — A2726

Lone Star, c. 1920 — A2727

Sunshine and Shadow, c. 1910 — A2728

Double Ninepatch Variation — A2729

Designed by Derry Noyes. Printed by Ashton-Potter (USA) Ltd.

LITHOGRAPHED
Sheets of 120 in six panes of 20
Serpentine Die Cut 11¼x11½

2001, Aug. 9			**Tagged**	
		Self-Adhesive		
3524	A2726	34c **multicolored**	.70	.20
3525	A2727	34c **multicolored**	.70	.20
3526	A2728	34c **multicolored**	.70	.20
3527	A2729	34c **multicolored**	.70	.20
a.		Block or strip of 4, #3524-3527	2.80	
		P# block of 4, 5#+P	2.80	
		Pane of 20	14.00	

CARNIVOROUS PLANTS

Venus Flytrap — A2730

Yellow Trumpet — A2731

Cobra Lily — A2732

English Sundew — A2733

Designed by Steve Buchanan. Printed by Avery Dennison.

PHOTOGRAVURE
Sheets of 160 in eight panes of 20

2001, Aug. 23	**Tagged**	***Serpentine Die Cut 11½***		
		Self-Adhesive		
3528	A2730	34c **multicolored**	.70	.20
3529	A2731	34c **multicolored**	.70	.20
3530	A2732	34c **multicolored**	.70	.20

3531	A2733	34c **multicolored**	.70	.20
a.		Block or strip of 4, #3528-3531	2.80	
		P# block of 4, 4#+V	2.80	
		Pane of 20	14.00	

EID

"Eid Mubarak" — A2734

Designed by Mohamed Zakariya. Printed by Avery Dennison.

PHOTOGRAVURE
Sheets of 240 in twelve panes of 20

2001, Sept. 1	**Tagged**	***Serpentine Die Cut 11¼***		
		Self-Adhesive		
3532	A2734	34c **multicolored**	.70	.20
		P# block of 4, 3#+V	2.80	
		Pane of 20	14.00	

See No. 3674.

ENRICO FERMI (1901-54), PHYSICIST

A2735

Designed by Richard Sheaff. Printed by Sterling Sommer for Ashton-Potter (USA) Ltd.

LITHOGRAPHED
Sheets of 180 in nine panes of 20

2001, Sept. 29	**Tagged**		**Perf. 11**	
3533	A2735	34c **multicolored**	.70	.20
		P# block of 4, 4#+P	2.80	—
		Pane of 20	14.00	—

THAT'S ALL FOLKS!

Porky Pig at Mailbox — A2736

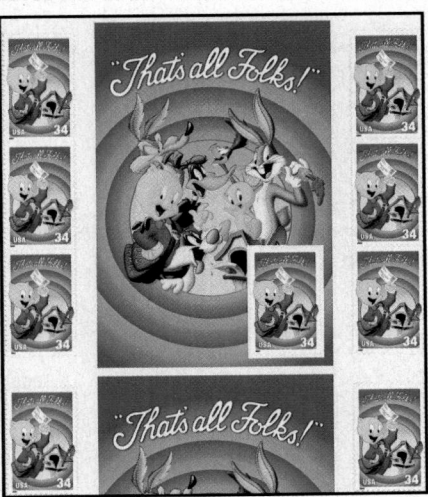

Cross Gutter Block of 9

Illustration reduced.

Designed by Ed Wleczyk, Warner Bros.
Printed by Avery Dennison.

PHOTOGRAVURE

**2001, Oct. 1   Tagged   *Serpentine Die Cut 11*
Self-Adhesive**

3534	Pane of 10	7.00	
a.	A2736 34c single	.70	.20
b.	Pane of 9 #3534a	6.25	
c.	Pane of 1 #3534a	.70	
	Sheet of 60 (six panes) no plate numbers	47.50	
	Sheet of 60 (six panes) with plate # in selvage on front and reverse	50.00	
	Pane of 10 from sheet of 60	8.00	
	Pane of 10 with plate numbers on front	12.50	
	Cross gutter block of 9 or 10	16.00	
	Cross gutter block of 12	18.00	
	Vert. pair with horiz. gutter	2.00	
	Horiz. pair with vert. gutter	4.00	

Die cutting on No. 3534b does not extend through the backing paper.

3535	Pane of 10	60.00	
a.	A2736 34c single	3.00	
b.	Pane of 9 #3535a	27.50	
c.	Pane of 1, no die cutting	30.00	

Die cutting on No. 3535a extends through backing paper.
Nos. 3534b-3534c and 3535b-3535c are separated by a vertical line of microperforations.

CHRISTMAS

Virgin and Child, by Lorenzo
Costa — A2737

A2738   A2739

A2740   A2741
**19th Century Chromolithographs of Santa
Claus**

Designed by Richard Sheaff.
Printed by Guilford Gravure, Inc., for Banknote Corporation of America (#3536), American Packaging Corporation for Sennett Security Products (#3537-3540), Avery Dennison (#3541-3544).

PHOTOGRAVURE
Sheets of 160 in eight panes of 20 (#3537-3540)
Serpentine Die Cut 11½ on 2, 3 or 4 Sides

2001, Oct. 10   Tagged

Self-Adhesive
Booklet Stamps (#3536, 3537a-3540a, 3537b, 3538b, 3539b, 3540e, 3541-3544)

3536	A2737 34c multicolored	.75	.20
a.	Booklet pane of 20	15.00	

Serpentine Die Cut 10¾x11
Black Inscriptions

3537	A2738 34c **multicolored**, large date	.70	.20
a.	Small date (from booklet pane)	.80	.20
b.	Large date (from booklet pane)	2.00	.20
3538	A2739 34c **multicolored**, large date	.70	.20
a.	Small date (from booklet pane)	.80	.20
b.	Large date (from booklet pane)	2.00	.20
3539	A2740 34c **multicolored**, large date	.70	.20
a.	Small date (from booklet pane)	.80	.20
b.	Large date (from booklet pane)	2.00	.20
3540	A2741 34c **multicolored**, large date	.70	.20
a.	Small date (from booklet pane)	.80	.20
b.	Block of 4, #3537-3540	2.80	
	P# block of 4, 4#+S	3.00	
	Pane of 20	15.00	
c.	Block of 4, small date, #3537a-3540a	3.25	
d.	Booklet pane of 20, 5 #3540c + label	16.50	
e.	Large date (from booklet pane)	2.00	.20
f.	Block of 4, large date, #3537b-3539b, 3540e	8.00	
g.	Booklet pane of 20, 5 #3540f + label	40.00	

Nos. 3540d and 3540g are double-sided booklet panes, with 12 stamps on one side and eight stamps plus label on the other side.

Numerals "3" and "4" are distinctly separate on Nos. 3537-3540, and touching or separated by a slight hairline on the booklet pane stamps.

Designs of Nos. 3537a-3540a are slightly taller than Nos. 3537-3540.

Serpentine Die Cut 11 on 2 or 3 Sides
Size: 21x18½mm
Green and Red Inscriptions

3541	A2738 34c **multicolored**	.70	.20
3542	A2739 34c **multicolored**	.70	.20
3543	A2740 34c **multicolored**	.70	.20
3544	A2741 34c **multicolored**	.70	.20
a.	Block of 4, #3541-3544	2.80	
b.	Booklet pane of 4, #3541-3544	2.80	
c.	Booklet pane of 6, #3543-3544, 2 #3541-3542	4.25	
d.	Booklet pane of 6, #3541-3542, 2 #3543-3544	4.25	
	Nos. 3536-3544 (9)	6.35	1.80

JAMES MADISON (1751-1836)

Madison and
His Home,
Montpelier
A2742

Designed by John Thompson.

Printed by Banknote Corporation of America.

LITHOGRAPHED & ENGRAVED
Sheets of 120 in six panes of 20

2001, Oct. 18   Tagged   *Perf. 11x11¼*

3545	A2742 34c **green & black**	.70	.20
	P# block of 4, 2#+B	2.80	—
	Pane of 20	14.00	—
	Sheet of 120 (6 panes)	80.00	—
	Cross gutter block of 4	8.25	—
	Horiz. pair with vert. gutter	3.00	—
	Vert. pair with horiz. gutter	2.00	—

THANKSGIVING

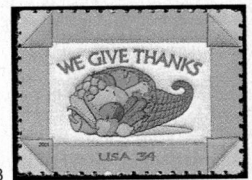

Cornucopia — A2743

Designed by Richard Sheaff.
Printed by Ashton-Potter (USA) Ltd.

LITHOGRAPHED
Sheets of 180 in nine panes of 20

**2001, Oct. 19   Tagged   *Serpentine Die Cut 11¼*
Self-Adhesive**

3546	A2743 34c **multicolored**	.70	.20
	P# block of 4, 4#+P	2.80	
	Pane of 20	14.00	

Hanukkah Type of 1996
Designed by Hannah Smotrich.
Printed by Avery Dennison.

PHOTOGRAVURE
Sheets of 200 in ten panes of 20

**2001, Oct. 21   Tagged   *Serpentine Die Cut 11*
Self-Adhesive**

3547	A2411 34c **multicolored**	.70	.20
	P# block of 4, 5#+V	2.80	
	Pane of 20	14.00	

Kwanzaa Type of 1997
Designed by Synthia Saint James.
Printed by Avery Dennison.

PHOTOGRAVURE
Sheets of 240 in twelve panes of 20

**2001, Oct. 21   Tagged   *Serpentine Die Cut 11*
Self-Adhesive**

3548	A2458 34c **multicolored**	.70	.20
	P# block of 4, 4#+V	2.80	
	Pane of 20	14.00	

UNITED WE STAND

A2744

Designed by Terry McCaffrey.
Printed by Banknote Corporation of America (#3549), Bureau of Engraving and Printing (#3550).

LITHOGRAPHED
BOOKLET STAMPS
Serpentine Die Cut 11¼ on 2, 3, or 4 Sides

2001, Oct. 24   Tagged

Self-Adhesive

3549	A2744 34c **multicolored**	.75	.20
a.	Booklet pane of 20	15.00	

PHOTOGRAVURE
Serpentine Die Cut 10½x10¾ on 2 or 3 Sides

2002, Jan.   Tagged

Self-Adhesive

3549B	A2744 34c **multicolored**, *Jan. 2002*	.90	.20
c.	Booklet pane of 4	3.60	
d.	Booklet pane of 6	5.40	
e.	Booklet pane of 20	18.00	

No. 3549Be is a double-sided booklet pane, with 12 stamps on one side and eight stamps plus label on the other side.
"First day covers" of No. 3549B are dated Oct. 24, 2001.

COIL STAMP

Serpentine Die Cut 9¾ Vert.
2001, Oct. 24   Tagged
Self-Adhesive

3550	A2744	34c	multicolored, perpendicular		
			corners	1.10	.20
			Pair	2.20	
			P# strip of 5, #1111, 2222	6.00	
			P# strip of 5, #3333	8.50	
			P# single, same #	—	1.00
			P# single, #3333	—	3.00
3550A	A2744	34c	multicolored	1.10	.20
			Pair	2.20	
			P# strip of 5, #1111	6.00	
			P# single, same #	—	3.00

No. 3550 has right angle corners and backing paper as high as the stamp. No. 3550A has rounded corners, the backing paper larger than the stamp, and the stamps are spaced approximately 2mm apart.

Love Letters Type of 2001
Designed by Lisa Catalone.
Printed by Banknote Corporation of America.
LITHOGRAPHED
Sheets of 160 in eight panes of 20
2001, Nov. 19 Tagged *Serpentine Die Cut 11¼*
Self-Adhesive

3551	A2701	57c	multicolored	1.10	.20
			P# block of 4, 4# + B	5.00	
			Pane of 20	24.00	

WINTER OLYMPICS

Ski Jumping
A2745

Snowboarding
A2746

Ice Hockey
A2747

Figure Skating
A2748

Designed by Jager Di Paola Kemp. Printed by American Packaging Corporation for Sennett Security Products.
PHOTOGRAVURE
Sheets of 180 in nine panes of 20
Serpentine Die Cut 11½x10¾
2002, Jan. 8   Tagged
Self-Adhesive

3552	A2745	34c	multicolored	.70	.20
3553	A2746	34c	multicolored	.70	.20
3554	A2747	34c	multicolored	.70	.20
3555	A2748	34c	multicolored	.70	.20
a.			Block or strip of 4, #3552-3555	2.80	
			P# block of 4, 6#+S (UL and		
			UR only)	4.00	
			Pane of 20	17.00	
			Sheet of 180 (9 panes)	125.00	
			Cross gutter block of 8	15.00	
			Block of 4 with vert. gutter	4.00	
			Block of 8 with horiz. gutter	8.00	
			Vert. pair with horiz. gutter,		
			each	1.75	

	Horiz. pair with vert. gutter,		
	each	1.75	
b.	Die cutting inverted, pane of 20	—	
c.	Die cutting omitted, block of 4	825.00	
	As "c," pane of 20	—	

Cross gutter blocks of 8 may be either 2x4 or 4x2 in configuration. The former will not show equal numbers of each stamp; the latter will.
Blocks of 4 with vertical gutter must show one of each of the stamps.

MENTORING A CHILD

Child and
Adult — A2749

Designed by Lance Hidy. Printed by American Packaging Corporation for Sennett Security Products.
PHOTOGRAVURE
Sheets of 120 in six panes of 20
Serpentine Die Cut 11x10¾
2002, Jan. 10   Tagged
Self-Adhesive

3556	A2749	34c	multicolored	.70	.20
			P# block of 4, 5#+S	2.80	
			Pane of 20	14.00	

BLACK HERITAGE SERIES

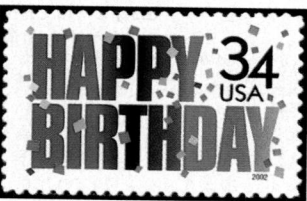

Langston Hughes (1902-67),
Writer — A2750

Designed by Richard Sheaff. Printed by Banknote Corporation of America.
LITHOGRAPHED
Sheets of 120 in six panes of 20
Serpentine Die Cut 10¼x10½
2002, Feb. 1   Tagged
Self-Adhesive

3557	A2750	34c	multicolored	.70	.20
			P# block of 4, 5#+B	3.00	
			Pane of 20	15.00	
a.		Die cutting omitted, pair	1,250.	
		As "a," pane of 20	—	

Beware of pairs/panes with extremely faint die cutting offered as imperf errors.

HAPPY BIRTHDAY

A2751

Designed by Harry Zelenko. Printed by Avery Dennison.
PHOTOGRAVURE
Sheets of 200 in ten panes of 20
2002, Feb. 8 Tagged *Serpentine Die Cut 11*
Self-Adhesive

3558	A2751	34c	multicolored	.70	.20
			P# block of 4, 4#+V	2.80	
			Pane of 20	14.00	

See Nos. 3695, 4079.

CHINESE NEW YEAR

Year of the
Horse
A2752

Designed by Clarence Lee. Printed by Banknote Corporation of America.
LITHOGRAPHED
Sheets of 120 in six panes of 20
Serpentine Die Cut 10½x10¼
2002, Feb. 11   Tagged
Self-Adhesive

3559	A2752	34c	multicolored	.75	.20
			P# block of 4, 5#+B	3.00	
			Pane of 20	15.00	

See No. 3895g.

U.S. MILITARY ACADEMY, BICENT.

Military Academy Coat
of Arms — A2753

Designed by Derry Noyes. Printed by American Packaging Corp. for Sennett Security Products.
PHOTOGRAVURE
Sheets of 180 in nine panes of 20
Serpentine Die Cut 10½x11
2002, Mar. 16   Tagged
Self-Adhesive

3560	A2753	34c	multicolored	.70	.20
			P# block of 4, 6#+S	2.80	
			Pane of 20	14.00	

GREETINGS FROM AMERICA

A2754-A2803

Illustration reduced.

Designed by Richard Sheaff. Printed by American Packaging Corp. for Sennett Security Products.
PHOTOGRAVURE
Sheets of 100 in two panes of 50
2002, Apr. 4 Tagged *Serpentine Die Cut 10¾*
Self-Adhesive

3561	A2754	34c	Alabama	.70	.45
3562	A2755	34c	Alaska	.70	.45
3563	A2756	34c	Arizona	.70	.45

3564	A2757	34c Arkansas	.70 .45
3565	A2758	34c California	.70 .45
3566	A2759	34c Colorado	.70 .45
3567	A2760	34c Connecticut	.70 .45
3568	A2761	34c Delaware	.70 .45
3569	A2762	34c Florida	.70 .45
3570	A2763	34c Georgia	.70 .45
3571	A2764	34c Hawaii	.70 .45
3572	A2765	34c Idaho	.70 .45
3573	A2766	34c Illinois	.70 .45
3574	A2767	34c Indiana	.70 .45
3575	A2768	34c Iowa	.70 .45
3576	A2769	34c Kansas	.70 .45
3577	A2770	34c Kentucky	.70 .45
3578	A2771	34c Louisiana	.70 .45
3579	A2772	34c Maine	.70 .45
3580	A2773	34c Maryland	.70 .45
3581	A2774	34c Massachusetts	.70 .45
3582	A2775	34c Michigan	.70 .45
3583	A2776	34c Minnesota	.70 .45
3584	A2777	34c Mississippi	.70 .45
3585	A2778	34c Missouri	.70 .45
3586	A2779	34c Montana	.70 .45
3587	A2780	34c Nebraska	.70 .45
3588	A2781	34c Nevada	.70 .45
3589	A2782	34c New Hampshire	.70 .45
3590	A2783	34c New Jersey	.70 .45
3591	A2784	34c New Mexico	.70 .45
3592	A2785	34c New York	.70 .45
3593	A2786	34c North Carolina	.70 .45
3594	A2787	34c North Dakota	.70 .45
3595	A2788	34c Ohio	.70 .45
3596	A2789	34c Oklahoma	.70 .45
3597	A2790	34c Oregon	.70 .45
3598	A2791	34c Pennsylvania	.70 .45
3599	A2792	34c Rhode Island	.70 .45
3600	A2793	34c South Carolina	.70 .45
3601	A2794	34c South Dakota	.70 .45
3602	A2795	34c Tennessee	.70 .45
3603	A2796	34c Texas	.70 .45
3604	A2797	34c Utah	.70 .45
3605	A2798	34c Vermont	.70 .45
3606	A2799	34c Virginia	.70 .45
3607	A2800	34c Washington	.70 .45
3608	A2801	34c West Virginia	.70 .45
3609	A2802	34c Wisconsin	.70 .45
3610	A2803	34c Wyoming	.70 .45
a.		Pane of 50, #3561-3610	35.00
		Sheet of 100 (two panes)	70.00
		Block of 50 different stamps with vert. gutter between any 2 columns	35.00
		Pair with vert. gutter between (each)	2.00

LONGLEAF PINE FOREST

A2804

Illustration reduced.

Designed by Ethel Kessler. Printed by American Packaging Corp. for Sennett Security Products.

Wildlife and flowers: a, Bachman's sparrow. b, Northern bobwhite, yellow pitcher plants. c, Fox squirrel, red-bellied woodpecker. d, Brown-headed nuthatch. e, Broadhead skink, yellow pitcher plants, pipeworts. f, Eastern towhee, yellow pitcher plants, Savannah meadow beauties, toothache grass. g, Gray fox, gopher tortoise, horiz. h, Blind click beetle, sweetbay, pine woods treefrog. i, Rosebud orchid, pipeworts, southern toad, yellow pitcher plants. j, Grass-pink orchid, yellow-sided skimmer, pipeworts, yellow pitcher plants, horiz.

PHOTOGRAVURE
Sheets of 90 in nine panes of 10
Serpentine Die Cut 10½x10¾, 10¾x10½

2002, Apr. 26			Tagged	
		Self-Adhesive		
3611	A2804	Pane of 10	16.00	
a.-j.		34c Any single	1.60	.50
		Sheet of 9 panes	145.00	
k.		As No. 3611, die cutting omitted	*2,500.*	

AMERICAN DESIGN SERIES

Toleware Coffeepot — A2805

Designed by Derry Noyes.
Printed by American Packaging Corp. for Sennett Security Products.

PHOTOGRAVURE
COIL STAMP

2002, May 31		Untagged	*Perf. 9¾ Vert.*	
3612	A2805	5c multicolored	.20	.20
		Pair	.20	.20
		P# strip of 5, #S1111111	1.00	
		P# single, #S1111111	—	.65
a.		Imperf, pair	—	

No. 3612a is valued with disturbed gum.

Star — A2806

Designed by Phil Jordan. Printed by Banknote Corporation of America.

LITHOGRAPHED, PHOTOGRAVURE (No. 3614, 3615)
Sheets of 400 in eight panes of 50

2002, June 7		Untagged	*Serpentine Die Cut 11*	
		Self-Adhesive (#3613-3614)		
		Year at Lower Left		
3613	A2806	3c red, blue & black	.20	.20
		P# block of 4, 3#+B	.25	
a.		Die cutting omitted, pair		

Serpentine Die Cut 10
Year at Lower Right

3614	A2806	3c red, blue & black	.20	.20
		P# block of 4, 3#+B	.25	

Coil Stamp
Perf. 10 Vert.
Year at Lower Left

3615	A2806	3c red, blue & black	.20	.20
		Pair	.20	.20
		P# strip of 5, #S111	.85	
		P# single, same #	—	.75
a.		Prephosphored paper with surface tagging showing a solid appearance (error)	.40	.20
		Pair	.80	.20
		P# strip of 5, #S111	6.00	
		P# single, same #	—	4.00

Washington Type of 2001

Designed by Richard Sheaff. Printed by Ashton-Potter (USA) Ltd. (#3616, 3618, 3619), Avery Dennison (#3617).

LITHOGRAPHED, PHOTOGRAVURE (#3617)
Sheets of 400 in four panes of 100 (#3616)

2002, June 7			Tagged	*Perf. 11¼*	
3616	A2686	23c green		.50	.20
		P# block of 4, 1#+P		20.00	

Self-Adhesive
Coil Stamp
Serpentine Die Cut 8½ Vert.

3617	A2686	23c gray green	.45	.20
		Pair	.90	
		P# strip of 5, #V11, V13, V21, V22, V24, V35, V36, V45, V46	3.50	
		P# single, same #	—	1.00
a.		Die cutting omitted, pair		

Compare No. 3617 ("2002" date at lower left) with No. 3475A ("2001" date at lower left).

Booklet Stamps
Serpentine Die Cut 11¼x11 on 3 Sides

3618	A2686	23c green	.50	.20
a.		Booklet pane of 4	2.00	
b.		Booklet pane of 6	3.00	
c.		Booklet pane of 10	5.00	

Serpentine Die Cut 10½x11 on 3 Sides

3619	A2686	23c green	4.00	1.75
a.		Booklet pane of 4, 2 #3619 at L, 2 #3618 at R	9.00	
b.		Booklet pane of 6, 3 #3619 at L, 3 #3618 at R	14.00	
c.		Booklet pane of 4, 2 #3618 at L, 2 #3619 at R	9.00	
d.		Booklet pane of 6, 3 #3618 at L, 3 #3619 at R	14.00	
e.		Booklet pane of 10, 5 #3619 at L, 5 #3618 at R	21.00	
f.		Booklet pane of 10, 5 #3618 at L, 5 #3619 at R	21.00	
g.		Pair, #3619 at L, #3618 at R	4.50	
h.		Pair, #3618 at L, #3619 at R	4.50	

Flag — A2807

Designed by Terrence W. McCaffrey. Printed by Sterling Sommer for Ashton-Potter (USA) Ltd. (#3620), Ashton-Potter (USA) Ltd. (#3621), Bureau of Engraving and Printing (#3622), Banknote Corporation of America (#3623), American Packaging Corporation for Sennett Security Products (#3624), Avery Dennison (#3625).

LITHOGRAPHED, PHOTOGRAVURE (#3622, 3624, 3625)
Sheets of 400 in four panes of 100 (#3620), Sheets of 120 in six panes of 20 (#3621)

2002, June 7			Tagged	*Perf. 11¼x11*	
3620	A2807	(37c) multicolored		.85	.20
		P# block of 4, 4#+P		25.00	—

Self-Adhesive
Serpentine Die Cut 11¼x11

3621	A2807	(37c) multicolored	1.00	.20
		P# block of 4, 4#+P	8.00	
		Pane of 20	36.00	

Coil Stamp
Serpentine Die Cut 10 Vert.

3622	A2807	(37c) multicolored	.75	.20
		Pair	1.50	
		P# strip of 5, #1111, 2222	7.00	
		P# single, same #	—	1.00
a.		Die cutting omitted, pair		

Booklet Stamps
Serpentine Die Cut 11¼ on 2, 3 or 4 Sides

3623	A2807	(37c) multicolored	.75	.20
a.		Booklet pane of 20	15.00	

Serpentine Die Cut 10½x10¾ on 2 or 3 Sides

3624	A2807	(37c) multicolored	.75	.20
a.		Booklet pane of 4	3.00	
b.		Booklet pane of 6	4.50	
c.		Booklet pane of 20	15.00	

Serpentine Die Cut 8 on 2, 3 or 4 sides

3625	A2807	(37c) multicolored	.75	.20
a.		Booklet pane of 18	13.50	

Toy Mail Wagon — A2808

Toy Locomotive — A2809

Toy Taxicab — A2810

Toy Fire Pumper — A2811

Designed by Derry Noyes. Printed by Avery Dennison

PHOTOGRAVURE
Serpentine Die Cut 11 on 2, 3 or 4 Sides

2002, June 7			Tagged	
		Booklet Stamps		
		Self-Adhesive		
3626	A2808	(37c) multicolored	.75	.20
3627	A2809	(37c) multicolored	.75	.20
3628	A2810	(37c) multicolored	.75	.20
3629	A2811	(37c) multicolored	.75	.20
a.		Block of 4, #3626-3629	3.00	
b.		Booklet pane of 4, #3626-3629	3.00	

c. Booklet pane of 6, #3627, 3629, 2 each
    #3626, 3628   4.50
d. Booklet pane of 6, #3626, 3628, 2 each
    #3627, 3629   4.50
e. Booklet pane of 20, 5 each #3626-3629   15.00

Flag — A2812

Designed by Terrence W. McCaffrey. Printed by Ashton-Potter (USA) Ltd. (#3629F, 3630, 3633B), American Packaging Corporation for Sennett Security Products (#3631, 3632A, 3632C, 3636), Bureau of Engraving and Printing (#3632), Banknote Corporation of America (#3633, 3635), Guilford Gravure for Banknote Corporation of America (#3633A), Avery Dennison (#3634, 3634b, 3636D, 3637).

LITHOGRAPHED, PHOTOGRAVURE (#3631-3633, 3634, 3636, 3636D)
Sheets of 400 in four panes of 100

2002-05		Tagged		Perf. 11¼
3629F	A2812 37c **multicolored**, *Nov. 24, 2003*		.90	.20
	P# block of 4, 4#+P	25.00	—	
g.	Imperf, pair	—		

No. 3629F has microprinted "USA" in top red stripe of flag.

Sheets of 120 in six panes of 20
Serpentine Die Cut 11¼x11
Self-Adhesive

3630	A2812 37c **multicolored** *June 7*		.90	.20
	P# block of 4, 4#+P	5.00		
	Pane of 20	23.50		

No. 3630 has microprinted "USA" in top red stripe of flag.

COIL STAMPS
Water-Activated Gum
Perf. 10 Vert.

3631	A2812 37c **multicolored** *June 7*		.75	.20
	Pair	1.50	—	
	P# strip of 5, #S1111	5.00	—	
	P# single, same #		—	2.00

No. 3631 is known printed with non-reactive red ink and also with luminescent yellow ink that glows orange under long wave ultraviolet light.

Self-Adhesive
Serpentine Die Cut 9¾ Vert.

3632	A2812 37c **multicolored** *June 7*		.75	.20
	Pair	1.50		
	P# strip of 5, #1111, 2222, 3333, 4444, 5555, 6666, 7777, 8888, 9999, 1111A, 2222A, 3333A, 4444A, 5555A, 6666A	4.75		
	P# single, same #		—	1.00
b.	Die cutting omitted, pair	55.00		

On plate #s 1111 through 9999 and 5555A-6666A, the color laydown order of plate numbers is yellow, magenta, cyan, black. Plate #s 1111A through 4444A have a laydown order of cyan, magenta, yellow, black.

Serpentine Die Cut 10¼ Vert.

3632A	A2812 37c **multicolored**, prephosphored coated paper, *Aug. 7, 2003*		.75	.20
	Pair	1.50		
	P# strip of 5, #S1111, S2222 S3333	5.25		
	P# strip of 5, #S4444	6.00		
	P# single, #S1111, S2222, S3333		—	1.25
	P# single, P#S4444		—	3.00
f.	Die cutting omitted, pair			

No. 3632A lacks points of stars at margin at left top, and was printed in "logs" of adjacent coil rolls that are connected at the top or bottom, wherein each roll could be separated from an adjacent roll as needed.
No. 3632 has "2002" date at left bottom. No. 3632A has "2003" date at left bottom.
No. 3632A exists on two types of surface-tagged paper that exhibit either a solid or an uneven appearance. Value of plate #S4444 strip of 5 with solid tagging, $150; used plate #S4444 single with solid tagging, $50.
On No. 3632A, P# S3333 was printed with yellow ink that glows orange under long wave ultraviolet light as well as with non-reactive red ink. P# S4444 was printed with and without luminescent red ink. Values the same.

Serpentine Die Cut 11¾ Vert.

3632C	A2812 37c **multicolored**, prephosphored coated paper, *2004*		.75	.20
	Pair	1.50		
	P# strip of 5, #S1111	5.50		
	P# single, same #		—	2.50

No. 3632C exists on two types of surface-tagged paper that exhibit either a solid or an uneven appearance. Values are the same.

Serpentine Die Cut 8½ Vert.

3633	A2812 37c **multicolored**, *June 7*		.75	.20
	Pair	1.50		
	P# strip of 5, #B1111	5.00		
	P# single, same #		—	1.50

Backing paper of No. 3633 is larger than the stamp.

3633A	A2812 37c **multicolored** *April, 2003*		2.00	.20
	Pair	4.00		
	P# strip of 5 B1111	12.00		
	P# single, same #		—	1.50

No. 3633A has right angle corners and backing paper as high as the stamp, and is dated "2003." No. 3633 is dated "2002," has rounded corners, the backing paper larger than the stamp, and the stamps are spaced approximately 2mm apart.

Serpentine Die Cut 9½ Vert.

3633B	A2812 37c **multicolored** *June 7, 2005*		3.50	.20
	Pair	7.00		
	P# strip of 5, #P1111	22.50		
	P# single, #P1111		—	3.00

No. 3633B has microprinted "USA" in top red stripe of flag, and has "2005" date at bottom left.

Booklet Stamps
Serpentine Die Cut 11.1 on 3 Sides (#3634) or 2 or 3 sides (#3634b-3634d)

3634	A2812 37c **multicolored**, large "2002" year date, *June 7*		.75	.20
a.	Booklet pane of 10	7.50		
b.	Small "2003," *Oct. 23, 2003*	.75		.20
c.	Booklet pane, 4 #3634b	3.00		
d.	Booklet pane, 6 #3634b	4.50		
e.	As #3634, die cut 11.3	.85		.25
f.	As "e," booklet pane of 10	8.50		

Serpentine Die Cut 11.3 on 2, 3 or 4 Sides

3635	A2812 37c **multicolored**, *June 7*		.75	.20
a.	Booklet pane of 20	15.00		
b.	Black omitted	—		

No. 3635 has "USPS" microprinted in the top red flag stripe and has a small "2002" year date.

Serpentine Die Cut 10½x10¾ on 2 or 3 Sides

3636	A2812 37c **multicolored**, *June 7*		.75	.20
a.	Booklet pane of 4	3.00		
b.	Booklet pane of 6	4.50		
c.	Booklet pane of 20	15.00		
f.	As "c," 11 stamps and part of 12th stamp on reverse printed on backing liner, the 8 stamps on front side imperf	—		

No. 3636c is a double-sided booklet pane, with 12 stamps on one side and eight stamps plus label on the other side.
Nos. 3636a and 3636b were issued on three types of prephosphored coated paper, with solid, grainy solid and uneven tagging characteristics. No. 3636c was issued on two types of prephosphored coated paper, with solid and uneven tagging.

Serpentine Die Cut 11¼x11 on 2 or 3 Sides

3636D	A2812 37c **multicolored**, *July, 2004*		1.10	.20
e.	Booklet pane of 20	22.50		

No. 3636D lacks points of stars at margin at UL. No. 3636De is a double-sided booklet pane with 12 stamps on one side and eight stamps plus label on the other side.

Serpentine Die Cut 8 on 2, 3 or 4 Sides
Tagged

3637	A2812 37c **multicolored**, *Feb. 4, 2003*		.75	.20
a.	Booklet pane of 18	13.50		

Toy Locomotive — A2813

Toy Mail Wagon — A2814

Toy Fire Pumper — A2815

Toy Taxicab — A2816

Designed by Derry Noyes. Printed by Banknote Corporation of America, Avery Dennison (#3642-3645).

PHOTOGRAVURE
Serpentine Die Cut 8½ Horiz.

2002, July 26				Tagged
	Self-Adhesive			
	Coil Stamps			
3638	A2813 37c **multicolored**		.85	.20
3639	A2814 37c **multicolored**		.85	.20
3640	A2815 37c **multicolored**		.85	.20

3641	A2816 37c **multicolored**		.85	.20
a.	Strip of 4, #3638-3641	3.40		
	P# strip of 5, 2 #3638, 1 each #3639-3641, #B11111, B12222	5.50		
	P# strip of 9, 2 each #3638-3639, 3641, 3 #3640, #B11111, B12222	8.50		
	P# single (#3640), #B11111, B12222		—	1.25

Serpentine Die Cut 11 on 2, 3 or 4 Sides
Booklet Stamps

3642	A2814 37c **multicolored**, "2002" year date		.75	.20
a.	Serpentine die cut 11x11¼ on 2 or 3 sides, dated "2003," *Sept. 3, 2003*	.75		.20
3643	A2813 37c **multicolored**, "2002" year date		.75	.20
a.	Serpentine die cut 11x11¼ on 2 or 3 sides, dated "2003," *Sept. 3, 2003*	.75		.20
3644	A2816 37c **multicolored**, "2002" year date		.75	.20
a.	Serpentine die cut 11x11¼ on 2 or 3 sides, dated "2003," *Sept. 3, 2003*	.75		.20
3645	A2815 37c **multicolored**, "2002" year date		.75	.20
a.	Block of 4, #3642-3645	3.00		
b.	Booklet pane of 4	3.00		
c.	Booklet pane of 6, #3643, 3645, 2 each #3642, 3644	4.50		
d.	Booklet pane of 6, #3642, 3644, 2 each #3643, 3645	4.50		
e.	Booklet pane of 20, 5 each #3642-3645	15.00		
f.	Serpentine die cut 11x11¼ on 2 or 3 sides, dated "2003," *Sept. 3, 2003*	.75		.20
g.	Block of 4, #3642a, 3643a, 3644a, 3645f	3.00		
h.	Booklet pane of 20, 5 #3645g	15.00		

No. 3645h is a double-sided booklet with 12 stamps on one side and 8 stamps plus label (booklet cover) on the other side. Nos. 3642a, 3643a, 3644a and 3645f have slightly narrower designs than Nos. 3642-3645.

Coverlet Eagle — A2817

Designed by Richard Sheaff. Printed by Ashton-Potter (USA) Ltd.

LITHOGRAPHED
Sheets of 120 in six panes of 20
Serpentine Die Cut 11x11¼

2002, July 12				Tagged
	Self-Adhesive			
3646	A2817 60c **multicolored**		1.25	.25
	P# block of 4, 4#+P	5.00		
	Pane of 20	25.00		

Jefferson Memorial A2818

Capitol Dome — A2819

Designed by Derry Noyes. Printed by Banknote Corporation of America (#3647-3648), American Packaging Corporation for Sennett Security Printers (#3647A).

LITHOGRAPHED
Sheets of 180 in nine panes of 20
Serpentine Die Cut 11¼ (#3647, 3648), 11x10¾ (#3647A)

2002-03				Tagged
	Self-Adhesive			
3647	A2818 $3.85 **multicolored**, *July 30*		7.50	2.00
	P# block of 4, 4#+B	30.00		
	Pane of 20	150.00		

3647A	A2818	$3.85 **multicolored,** *Nov. 2003*		8.50	2.00
		P# block of 4, 5#+S		35.00	
		Pane of 20		175.00	
3648	A2819	$13.65 **multicolored,** *July 30*		27.50	10.00
		P# block of 4, 4#+B		110.00	
		Pane of 20		550.00	

No. 3647A is dated 2003.

MASTERS OF AMERICAN PHOTOGRAPHY

A2820

Illustration reduced.

Designed by Derry Noyes. Printed by American Packaging Corporation for Sennett Security Products.

Designs: a, Portrait of Daniel Webster, by Albert Sands Southworth and Josiah Johnson Hawes. b, Gen. Ulysses S. Grant and Officers, by Timothy H. O'Sullivan. c, "Cape Horn, Columbia River," by Carleton E. Watkins. d, "Blessed Art Thou Among Women," by Gertrude Käsebier. e, "Looking for Lost Luggage, Ellis Island," by Lewis W. Hine. f, "The Octopus," by Alvin Langdon Coburn. g, "Lotus, Mount Kisco, New York," by Edward Steichen. h, "Hands and Thimble," by Alfred Stieglitz. i, "Rayograph," by Man Ray. j, "Two Shells," by Edward Weston. k, "My Corsage," by James VanDerZee. l, "Ditched, Stalled, and Stranded, San Joaquin Valley, California," by Dorothea Lange. m, "Washroom and Dining Area of Floyd Burroughs' Home, Hale County, Alabama," by Walker Evans. n, "Frontline Soldier with Canteen, Saipan," by W. Eugene Smith. o, "Steeple," by Paul Strand. p, "Sand Dunes, Sunrise," by Ansel Adams. q, "Age and Its Symbols," by Imogen Cunningham. r, New York cityscape, by André Kertész. s, Photograph of pedestrians, by Garry Winogrand. t, "Bristol, Vermont," by Minor White.

PHOTOGRAVURE
Sheets of 120 in six panes of 20
Serpentine Die Cut 10½x10¾

2002, June 13			**Tagged**
	Self-Adhesive		
3649	A2820	Pane of 20	15.00
a.-t.		37c Any single	.75 .50
		Sheet of 120 (6 panes)	90.00
		Cross-gutter block of 20	30.00
		Horiz. block of 8 with vert. gutter	11.00
		Vert. block of 10 with horiz. gutter	14.00
		Vert. pairs with horiz. gutter (each)	2.50
		Horiz. pairs with vert. gutter (each)	2.50
u.		As No. 3649, die cutting omitted	

Cross gutter block of 20 consists of six stamps from each of two panes and four stamps from each of two other panes with the cross gutter between.

AMERICAN TREASURES SERIES

Scarlet and Louisiana Tanagers, by John James Audubon — A2821

Designed by Derry Noyes. Printed by American Pacakaging Corporation for Sennett Security Products.

PHOTOGRAVURE
Sheets of 120 in six panes of 20

2002, June 27		**Tagged**	*Serpentine Die Cut 10¾*
	Self-Adhesive		
3650	A2821	37c **multicolored**	1.00 .20
		P# block of 4, 7#+S	6.00
		Pane of 20	27.50

HARRY HOUDINI (1874-1926), MAGICIAN

A2822

Designed by Richard Sheaff. Printed by Ashton-Potter (USA) Ltd.

LITHOGRAPHED
Sheets of 180 in nine panes of 20

2002, July 3		**Tagged**	*Serpentine Die Cut 11¼*
	Self-Adhesive		
3651	A2822	37c **multicolored**	.75 .20
		P# block of 4, 4#+P	3.00 —
		Pane of 20	15.00 —

ANDY WARHOL (1928-87), ARTIST

Self-Portrait — A2823

Designed by Richard Sheaff.
Printed by American Packaging Corporation for Sennett Security Products.

PHOTOGRAVURE
Sheets of 80 in four panes of 20
Serpentine Die Cut 10½x10¾

2002, Aug. 9			**Tagged**
	Self-Adhesive		
3652	A2823	37c **multicolored**	.75 .20
		P# block of 4, 6#+S	3.25
		Pane of 20	16.00

TEDDY BEARS, CENTENNIAL

Bruin Bear, c. 1907 — A2824

"Stick" Bear, 1920s — A2825

Gund Bear, c. 1948 — A2826

Ideal Bear, c. 1905 — A2827

Designed by Margaret Bauer.
Printed by American Packaging Corporation for Sennett Security Products.

PHOTOGRAVURE
Sheets of 120 in six panes of 20

2002, Aug. 15		**Tagged**	*Serpentine Die Cut 10½*
	Self-Adhesive		
3653	A2824	37c **multicolored**	1.00 .20
3654	A2825	37c **multicolored**	1.00 .20
3655	A2826	37c **multicolored**	1.00 .20
3656	A2827	37c **multicolored**	1.00 .20
a.		Block or vert. strip of 4, #3653-3656	4.00
		P# block of 4, 7#+S	5.00
		P# block of 10, 2 sets of P# + top label	15.00
		Pane of 20	27.50
		Sheet of 120 (six panes)	125.00
		Cross gutter block of 8	22.50
		Block of 8 with vert. gutter	11.00
		Block of 4 with horiz. gutter	6.00
		Vert. pair with horiz. gutter (each)	2.50
		Horiz. pair with vert. gutter (each)	2.50

Cross gutter block can be either a vertical or horizontal block showing all designs.

LOVE

A2828

A2829

Designed by Michael Osborne.
Printed by Banknote Corporation of America (#3657), Avery Dennison.

LITHOGRAPHED (#3657), PHOTOGRAVURE
Sheets of 200 in ten panes of 20 (#3658)
Serpentine Die Cut 11 on 2, 3 or 4 Sides

2002, Aug. 16			**Tagged**
	Booklet Stamp (#3657)		
	Self-Adhesive		
3657	A2828	37c **multicolored**	.75 .20
a.		Booklet pane of 20	15.00
b.		As "a," silver ("Love 37 USA") missing on top five stamps (CM)	750.00
	Serpentine Die Cut 11		
3658	A2829	60c **multicolored**	1.25 .25
		P# block of 4, 5#+V	5.00
		Pane of 20	25.00

LITERARY ARTS

Ogden Nash (1902-71), Poet — A2830

Designed by Carl T. Herrman.
Printed by Avery Dennison.

PHOTOGRAVURE
Sheets of 200 in ten panes of 20
2002, Aug. 19   Tagged   *Serpentine Die Cut 11*
Self-Adhesive

3659 A2830 37c **multicolored**		.75	.20
P# block of 4, 8#+V		3.00	
Pane of 20		15.00	

DUKE KAHANAMOKU (1890-1968), "FATHER OF SURFING" AND OLYMPIC SWIMMER

Kahanamoku and
Surfers at Waikiki
Beach — A2831

Designed by Carl T. Herrman.
Printed by Avery Dennison.

PHOTOGRAVURE
Sheets of 200 in ten panes of 20
Serpentine Die Cut 11½x11¾
2002, Aug. 24   Tagged
Self-Adhesive

3660 A2831 37c **multicolored**		.75	.20
P# block of 4, 4#+V		3.00	
Pane of 20		15.00	

AMERICAN BATS

Red
Bat — A2832

Leaf-nosed
Bat — A2833

Pallid
Bat — A2834

Spotted
Bat — A2835

Designed by Phil Jordan.
Printed by American Packaging Corporation for Sennett Security Products.

PHOTOGRAVURE
Sheets of 120 in six panes of 20
2002, Sept. 13   Tagged   *Serpentine Die Cut 10¾*
Self-Adhesive

3661 A2832 37c **multicolored**		.75	.20
3662 A2833 37c **multicolored**		.75	.20
3663 A2834 37c **multicolored**		.75	.20

3664	A2835 37c **multicolored**		.75	.20
a.	Block or horiz. strip of 4, #3661-3664		3.00	
	P# block of 4, 7#+S		3.25	
	P# block of 8, 2 sets of P# + top label		6.50	
	Pane of 20		16.00	

WOMEN IN JOURNALISM

Nellie Bly
(1864-1922)
A2836

Ida M. Tarbell
(1857-1944)
A2837

Ethel L. Payne
(1911-91)
A2838

Marguerite
Higgins (1920-
66)
A2839

Designed by Fred Otnes.
Printed by American Packaging Corporation for Sennett Security Products.

PHOTOGRAVURE
Sheets of 120 in six panes of 20
Serpentine Die Cut 11x10½
2002, Sept. 14   Tagged
Self-Adhesive

3665 A2836 37c **multicolored**		.75	.20
3666 A2837 37c **multicolored**		.75	.20
3667 A2838 37c **multicolored**		.75	.20
3668 A2839 37c **multicolored**		.75	.20
a.	Block or horiz. strip of 4, #3665-3668	3.00	
	P# block of 4, 5#+S	3.25	
	P# block of 8, 2 sets of P# + top label	6.50	
	Pane of 20	16.00	

IRVING BERLIN (1888-1989), COMPOSER

Berlin and Score of "God
Bless America" — A2840

Designed by Greg Berger.
Printed by Avery Dennison.

PHOTOGRAVURE
Sheets of 200 in ten panes of 20
2002, Sept. 15   Tagged   *Serpentine Die Cut 11*
Self-Adhesive

3669 A2840 37c **multicolored**		.75	.20
P# block of 4, 4#+V		3.00	
Pane of 20		15.00	

NEUTER AND SPAY

Kitten — A2841

Puppy
A2842

Designed by Derry Noyes. Printed by American Packaging Corporation for Sennett Security Products.

PHOTOGRAVURE
Sheets of 120 in six panes of 20
Serpentine Die Cut 10¾x10½
2002, Sept. 20   Tagged
Self-Adhesive

3670 A2841 37c **multicolored**		1.00	.20
3671 A2842 37c **multicolored**		1.00	.20
a.	Horiz. or vert. pair, #3670-3671	2.00	
	P# block of 4, 5#+S	4.00	
	P# block of 8, 2 sets of P# + top label	8.00	
	Pane of 20	20.00	

Hanukkah Type of 1996
Designed by Hannah Smotrich.
Printed by Avery Dennison.

PHOTOGRAVURE
Sheets of 200 in ten panes of 20
2002, Oct. 10   Tagged   *Serpentine Die Cut 11*
Self-Adhesive

3672 A2411 37c **multicolored**		.75	.20
P# block of 4, 5#+V		3.00	
Pane of 20		15.00	

Kwanzaa Type of 1997
Designed by Synthia Saint James.
Printed by Avery Dennison.

PHOTOGRAVURE
Sheets of 200 in ten panes of 20
2002, Oct. 10   Tagged   *Serpentine Die Cut 11*
Self-Adhesive

3673 A2458 37c **multicolored**		.75	.20
P# block of 4, 4#+V		3.00	
Pane of 20		15.00	

Eid Type of 2001
Designed by Mohamed Zakariya.
Printed by Avery Dennison.

PHOTOGRAVURE
Sheets of 240 in twelve panes of 20
2002, Oct. 10   Tagged   *Serpentine Die Cut 11*
Self-Adhesive

3674 A2734 37c **multicolored**		.75	.20
P# block of 4, 3#+V		3.00	
Pane of 20		15.00	

CHRISTMAS

Madonna and Child, by Jan
Gossaert — A2843

Designed by Richard Sheaff.
Printed by Banknote Corporation of America.

LITHOGRAPHED
Serpentine Die Cut 11x11¼ on 2, 3 or 4 Sides
2002, Oct. 10   **Tagged**
Self-Adhesive
Booklet Stamp
Design size: 19x27mm

3675 A2843 37c **multicolored**   .75 .20
  a. Booklet pane of 20   15.00
Compare to No. 3820, which measures 19½x28mm

CHRISTMAS

Snowman with Red
and Green Plaid
Scarf — A2844

Snowman with Blue
Plaid Scarf — A2845

Snowman with
Pipe — A2846

Snowman with Top
Hat — A2847

Snowman with Blue
Plaid Scarf — A2848

Snowman with
Pipe — A2849

Snowman with Top
Hat — A2850

Snowman with Red
and Green Plaid
Scarf — A2851

Designed by Derry Noyes.

Printed by Avery Dennison (#3676-3679, 3688-3691),
Guilford Gravure (#3680-3683), and American Packaging Corp.
for Sennett Security Products (#3684-3687).

PHOTOGRAVURE
Sheets of 200 in ten panes of 20
2002, Oct. 28   **Tagged**   *Serpentine Die Cut 11*
Self-Adhesive

3676 A2844 37c **multicolored**   .90   .20
3677 A2845 37c **multicolored**   .90   .20
3678 A2846 37c **multicolored**   .90   .20
3679 A2847 37c **multicolored**   .90   .20
 a. Block or vert. strip of 4, #3676-3679   3.75
   P# block of 4, 4#+V   3.75
   Pane of 20   19.00

COIL STAMPS
Serpentine Die Cut 8½ Vert.
3680 A2848 37c **multicolored**   2.00   .20
3681 A2849 37c **multicolored**   2.00   .20
3682 A2850 37c **multicolored**   2.00   .20
3683 A2851 37c **multicolored**   2.00   .20
 a. Strip of 4, #3680-3683   8.00
   P# strip of 5, 2 #3680, 1 each
   #3681-3683, #G1111, G1112   11.00
   P# strip of 9, 2 each #3680,
   3681, 3683, 3 #3682, same #   19.00
   P# single (#3682), same #   — 2.00

BOOKLET STAMPS
Serpentine Die Cut 10¾x11 on 2 or 3 Sides
3684 A2844 37c **multicolored**   1.25   .20
3685 A2845 37c **multicolored**   1.25   .20
3686 A2846 37c **multicolored**   1.25   .20
3687 A2847 37c **multicolored**   1.25   .20
 a. Block of 4, #3684-3687   5.00
 b. Booklet pane of 20, 5 #3687a + label 25.00
No. 3687b is a double-sided booklet pane with 12 stamps on
one side and eight stamps plus label on the other side.

Serpentine Die Cut 11 on 2 or 3 Sides
3688 A2851 37c **multicolored**   1.00   .20
3689 A2848 37c **multicolored**   1.00   .20
3690 A2849 37c **multicolored**   1.00   .20
3691 A2850 37c **multicolored**   1.00   .20
 a. Block of 4, #3688-3691   4.00
 b. Booklet pane of 4, #3688-3691 4.00
 c. Booklet pane of 6, #3690-3691, 2 each
   #3688-3689   6.00
 d. Booklet pane of 6, #3688-3689, 2 each
   #3690-3691   6.00
  Nos. 3676-3691 (16)   11.20 3.20
Colors of Nos. 3684-3687 are deeper and designs are slightly
smaller than those found on Nos. 3676-3679.

LEGENDS OF HOLLYWOOD

Cary Grant (1904-86),
Actor — A2852

Designed by Carl Herrman.

Printed by American Packaging Corporation for Sennett
Security Products.

PHOTOGRAVURE
Sheets of 120 in six panes of 20
2002, Oct. 15   **Tagged** *Serpentine Die Cut 10¾*
Self-Adhesive
3692 A2852 37c **multicolored**   1.00   .20
   P# block of 4, 6#+S   4.00
   Pane of 20   20.00
   Sheet of 120 (6 panes)   105.00
   Cross gutter block of 8   17.50
   Block of 8 with vertical gutter 12.50
   Horiz. pair with vert. gutter 3.00
   Vert. pair with horiz. gutter 2.00
Cross gutter block consists of 6 stamps from upper panes
and 2 stamps from panes below.

Sea Coast — A2853

Designed by Tom Engeman.

Printed by Banknote Corporation Of America.

PHOTOGRAVURE
COIL STAMP
Serpentine Die Cut 8½ Vert.
2002, Oct. 21   **Tagged**
Self-Adhesive
3693 A2853 (5c) **multicolored**   .20   .20
   Pair   .20
   P# strip of 5, #B111   1.25
   P# single, #B111   — 1.00
See Nos. 3775, 3785, 3864, 3874, 3875.

HAWAIIAN MISSIONARY STAMPS

A2854

Illustration reduced.

Designed by Richard Sheaff.

Printed by Banknote Corporation of America.

Designs: a, 2c stamp of 1851 (Hawaii Scott 1). b, 5c stamp of
1851 (Hawaii Scott 2) c, 13c stamp of 1851 (Hawaii Scott 3). d,
13c stamp of 1852 (Hawaii Scott 4).

LITHOGRAPHED
Sheets of 24 in six panes of 4
2002, Oct. 24   **Tagged**   *Perf. 11*
3694 A2854   Pane of 4   3.50 2.50
 a.-d. 37c Any single   .85   .50
   Sheet of 6 panes   25.00

Happy Birthday Type of 2002
Designed by Harry Zelenko.
Printed by Avery Dennison.

PHOTOGRAVURE
Sheets of 200 in ten panes of 20
2002, Oct. 25   **Tagged** *Serpentine Die Cut 11*
Self-Adhesive
3695 A2751 37c **multicolored**   .75   .20
   P# block of 4, 4#+V   3.00
   Pane of 20   15.00

Greetings From America Type of 2002
Designed by Richard Sheaff. Printed by American Packaging
Corp. for Sennett Security Products.

PHOTOGRAVURE
Sheets of 100 in two panes of 50
2002, Oct. 25   **Tagged** *Serpentine Die Cut 10¾*
Self-Adhesive
3696 A2754 37c Alabama   .75   .60
3697 A2755 37c Alaska   .75   .60
3698 A2756 37c Arizona   .75   .60
3699 A2757 37c Arkansas   .75   .60
3700 A2758 37c California   .75   .60
3701 A2759 37c Colorado   .75   .60
3702 A2760 37c Connecticut   .75   .60
3703 A2761 37c Delaware   .75   .60
3704 A2762 37c Florida   .75   .60
3705 A2763 37c Georgia   .75   .60
3706 A2764 37c Hawaii   .75   .60
3707 A2765 37c Idaho   .75   .60
3708 A2766 37c Illinois   .75   .60
3709 A2767 37c Indiana   .75   .60
3710 A2768 37c Iowa   .75   .60
3711 A2769 37c Kansas   .75   .60
3712 A2770 37c Kentucky   .75   .60
3713 A2771 37c Louisiana   .75   .60
3714 A2772 37c Maine   .75   .60
3715 A2773 37c Maryland   .75   .60
3716 A2774 37c Massachusetts   .75   .60
3717 A2775 37c Michigan   .75   .60
3718 A2776 37c Minnesota   .75   .60
3719 A2777 37c Mississippi   .75   .60
3720 A2778 37c Missouri   .75   .60
3721 A2779 37c Montana   .75   .60
3722 A2780 37c Nebraska   .75   .60
3723 A2781 37c Nevada   .75   .60
3724 A2782 37c New Hampshire   .75   .60

3725	A2783	37c	New Jersey	.75	.60
3726	A2784	37c	New Mexico	.75	.60
3727	A2785	37c	New York	.75	.60
3728	A2786	37c	North Carolina	.75	.60
3729	A2787	37c	North Dakota	.75	.60
3730	A2788	37c	Ohio	.75	.60
3731	A2789	37c	Oklahoma	.75	.60
3732	A2790	37c	Oregon	.75	.60
3733	A2791	37c	Pennsylvania	.75	.60
3734	A2792	37c	Rhode Island	.75	.60
3735	A2793	37c	South Carolina	.75	.60
3736	A2794	37c	South Dakota	.75	.60
3737	A2795	37c	Tennessee	.75	.60
3738	A2796	37c	Texas	.75	.60
3739	A2797	37c	Utah	.75	.60
3740	A2798	37c	Vermont	.75	.60
3741	A2799	37c	Virginia	.75	.60
3742	A2800	37c	Washington	.75	.60
3743	A2801	37c	West Virginia	.75	.60
3744	A2802	37c	Wisconsin	.75	.60
3745	A2803	37c	Wyoming	.75	.60
a.		Pane of 50, #3696-3745		37.50	

BLACK HERITAGE SERIES

Thurgood Marshall (1908-93), Supreme Court Justice — A2855

Designed by Richard Sheaff. Printed by Ashton-Potter (USA) Ltd.

LITHOGRAPHED
Sheets of 180 in nine panes of 20

2003, Jan. 7   Tagged   *Serpentine Die Cut 11½*
Self-Adhesive

3746	A2855	37c	black & gray	.75	.20
			P# block of 4, 3#+P	3.00	
			Pane of 20	15.00	

CHINESE NEW YEAR

Year of the Ram — A2856

Designed by Clarence Lee. Printed by Banknote Corporation of America.

LITHOGRAPHED
Sheets of 120 in six panes of 20

2003, Jan. 15   Tagged   *Serpentine Die Cut 11½*
Self-Adhesive

3747	A2856	37c	multicolored	.75	.20
			P# block of 4, 4#+B	3.00	
			Pane of 20	15.00	
a.		Tagging omitted		—	
		See No. 3895h.			

LITERARY ARTS

Zora Neale Hurston (1891-1960), Writer A2857

Designed by Howard E. Paine. Printed by American Packaging Corporation for Sennett Security Products.

PHOTOGRAVURE
Sheets of 120 in six panes of 20

2003, Jan. 24   Tagged   *Serpentine Die Cut 10¾*
Self-Adhesive

3748	A2857	37c	multicolored	.85	.20
			P# block of 4, 5#+S	3.50	
			Pane of 20	17.50	

AMERICAN DESIGN SERIES

Navajo Necklace — A2858

Chippendale Chair — A2859

American Clock — A2860

Tiffany Lamp — A2866

Silver Coffeepot — A2868

Designed by Derry Noyes. Printed by Ashton-Potter (USA) Ltd. (#3749, 3752, 3755, 3757), American Packaging Corp. for Sennett Security Products (#3751, 3756, 3759, 3761, 3762), Banknote Corporation of America for Sennett Security Products (#3749A, 3753, 3754, 3756A, 3758A, 3763), Avery Dennison (#3750).

LITHOGRAPHED, PHOTOGRAVURE (#3750, 3751, 3756, 3758, 3759, 3761, 3762)

Sheets of 300 in fifteen panes of 20 (#3749A), Sheets of 280 in fourteen panes of 20, Sheets of 240 in twelve panes of 20 (#3751, 3752, 3757), Sheets of 200 in ten panes of 20 (#3749, 3753, 3754, 3756A), Sheets of 120 in six panes of 20 (#3755), Sheets of 160 in eight panes of 20 (#3756).

Self-Adhesive

2003-08   Untagged

Serpentine Die Cut 11¼x11

3749	A2866	1c	multicolored, *Mar. 16, 2007*	.20	.20
			P# block of 4, 6#+P	.20	
			Pane of 20	.40	
3749A	A2866	1c	multicolored, *Mar. 7, 2008*	.20	.20
			P# block of 4, 5#+S	.20	
			Pane of 20	.40	

No. 3749A has "USPS" microprinted on a white field high on the lamp stand, just below the shade and is dated "2008." No. 3749 has "USPS" microprinted lower on the lamp stand and not on a white field and is dated "2007."

Serpentine Die Cut 11

3750	A2858	2c	multicolored, *Aug. 20, 2004*	.20	.20
			P# block of 4, 5#+V	.20	
			Pane of 20	.80	

A reprinting of No. 3750 shows the borders in a much brighter deep turquoise blue shade.

Serpentine Die Cut 11¼x11½

3751	A2858	2c	multicolored, *Dec. 8, 2005*	.20	.20
			P# block of 4, 6#+S	.20	
			Pane of 20	.80	

Serpentine Die Cut 11¼x11
With "USPS" Microprinting

3752	A2858	2c	multicolored, *Dec. 8, 2005*	.20	.20
			P# block of 4, 5#+P	.20	
			Pane of 20	.80	

Serpentine Die Cut 11¼x10¾

3753	A2858	2c	multicolored, *May 12, 2007*	.20	.20
			P# block of 4, 6#+S	.20	
			Pane of 20	.80	

Serpentine Die Cut 11¼x11

3754	A2868	3c	multicolored, *Mar. 16, 2007*	.20	.20
			P# block of 4, 4#+S	.25	
			Pane of 20	1.25	

Microprinted "USPS" on No. 3752 is found on top silver appendage next to and below the middle turquoise stone on the right side of the necklace. Microprinting on No. 3753 is found on the top silver appendage next to and below the turquoise stone on the left side of the necklace. Nos. 3751 and 3752 are dated "2006." No. 3753 is dated "2007."

Serpentine Die Cut 10¾x10¼

3755	A2859	4c	multicolored, *Mar. 5, 2004*	.20	.20
			P# block of 4, 4#+P	.35	
			Pane of 20	1.60	

Serpentine Die Cut 11¼x11¾

3756	A2805	5c	multicolored, *June 25, 2004*	.20	.20
			P# block of 4, 7#+S	.40	
			Pane of 20	2.00	

Serpentine Die Cut 11¼x10¾ on 2 or 3 Sides

3756A	A2805	5c	multicolored, *Aug. 2008*	.20	.20
			P# block of 4, 7#+S	.40	
			Pane of 20	2.00	

No. 3756A has microprinting on the lower part of the coffee-pot handle and is dated "2007." No. 3756 has no microprinting and is dated "2004." Existence of No. 3756A was reported in Aug. 2008.

Serpentine Die Cut 11¼x11
Tagged

3757	A2860	10c	multicolored, *Jan. 24*	.20	.20
			P# block of 4, 4#+P	.80	
			Pane of 20	4.00	
a.		Die cutting omitted, pair		—	

PHOTOGRAVURE
COIL STAMPS
Untagged
Perf. 9¾ Vert.

3758	A2866	1c	multicolored, *Mar. 1*	.20	.20
			Pair	.20	.20
			P# strip of 5, #S11111	.50	
			P# single, #S11111	—	.40
3758A	A2866	1c	multicolored, *June 7, 2008*	.20	.20
			Pair	.20	.20
			P# strip of 5, #S11111	.60	
			P# single, #S11111	—	.40

No. 3758A has microprinted "USPS" on lamp stand just below the lampshade and is dated "2008." No. 3758 lacks microprinting and is dated "2003."

3759	A2868	3c	multicolored, *Sept. 16, 2005*	.20	.20
			Pair	.20	.20
			P# strip of 5, #S1111	.65	
			P# single, #S1111	—	.55
3761	A2859	4c	multicolored, *July 19, 2007*	.20	.20
			Pair	.20	.20
			P# strip of 5, #S1111	1.25	
			P# single, #S1111	—	.75
3762	A2860	10c	multicolored, *Aug. 4, 2006*	.20	.20
			Pair	.40	.20
			P# strip of 5, #S1111	2.00	
			P# single, #S1111	—	1.50

Tagged

3763	A2860	10c	multicolored *July 15, 2008*	.20	.20
			Pair	.40	.20
			P# strip of 5, #S1111	2.50	
			P# single, #S1111	—	1.75

No. 3763 is dated "2008," has a microprinted "USPS" as the middle "I" in "VIII," and has network of beige dots on clock face. No. 3762 is dated "2006," lacks microprinting, and has network of gray dots on clock face.

This is an ongoing set. Numbers may change. See No. 3612.

AMERICAN CULTURE SERIES

Wisdom, Rockefeller Center, New York City — A2875

Designed by Carl Herrman. Printed by Ashton-Potter (USA) Ltd.

LITHOGRAPHED
Sheets of 120 in six panes of 20

Serpentine Die Cut 11¼x11

2003, Feb. 28   Tagged
Self-Adhesive

3766	A2875	$1	multicolored	2.00	.40
			P# block of 4, 5# + P	8.00	
			Pane of 20	40.00	
a.		Dated "2008"		2.00	.40

New York Public Library Lion Type of 2000
Designed by Carl Herrman. Printed by American Packaging Corporation for Sennett Security Products.

PHOTOGRAVURE
COIL STAMP

2003, Feb. 4   Untagged   *Perf. 10 Vert.*

3769	A2677	(10c)	multicolored	.20	.20
			Pair	.40	.20
			P# strip of 5, #S11111	2.50	
			P# single, #S11111	—	1.50

Atlas Statue Type of 2001
Designed by Kevin Newman. Printed by Avery Dennison.

PHOTOGRAVURE

2003, Oct. Untagged *Serpentine Die Cut 11 Vert.*
Coil Stamp
Self-Adhesive

3770	A2722 (10c) multicolored	.20	.20
	Pair	.40	
	P# strip of 5, #V11111,		
	V11222, V12222,		
	V21111, V21211,		
	V22111, V22112,		
	V22211, V23113,		
	V32332, V33333, V33332	2.25	
	P# strip of 5, #V12111	*275.00*	
	P# strip of 5, #V22222	10.00	
	P# single, #V11111,		
	V11222, V12222,		
	V21111, V21211,		
	V22111, V22112,		
	V22211, V23113,		
	V32332, V33333, V33332	—	1.50
	P# single, # V12111	*125.00*	
	P# single, # V13222	*150.00*	
	P# single, # V22222	3.00	
	P# single, # V21113	—	
a.	Tagged, error	—	
	P# single, # V21211	—	

No. 3770 is dated 2003.

SPECIAL OLYMPICS

Athlete with
Medal — A2879

Designed by Lance Hidy. Printed by Avery Dennison.

PHOTOGRAVURE
Sheets of 200 in ten panes of 20
2003, Feb. 13 Tagged *Serpentine Die Cut 11*
Self-Adhesive

3771	A2879 80c multicolored	1.60	.35
	P# block of 4, 6# + V	6.40	
	Pane of 20	32.00	

AMERICAN FILMMAKING: BEHIND THE SCENES

A2880

Block of 10 With Vertical Gutter Between

Illustrations reduced.

Designed by Imaginary Forces. Printed by American Packaging Corporation for Sennett Security Products.

Designs: a, Screenwriting (segment of script from
Gone With the Wind). b, Directing (John Cassavetes).
c, Costume design (Edith Head). d, Music (Max
Steiner working on score). e, Makeup (Jack Pierce
working on Boris Karloff's makeup for *Frankenstein*). f,
Art direction (Perry Ferguson working on sketch for
Citizen Kane). g, Cinematography (Paul Hill, assistant
cameraman for *Nagana*). h, Film editing (J. Watson
Webb editing *The Razor's Edge*). i, Special effects
(Mark Siegel working on model for *E.T. The Extra-
Terrestrial*). j, Sound (Gary Summers works on control
panel).

PHOTOGRAVURE
Sheets of 60 in six panes of 10
Serpentine Die Cut 11 Horiz.
2003, Feb. 25 **Tagged**
Self-Adhesive

3772	A2880 Pane of 10	10.00	
a.-j.	37c Any single	1.00	.50
	Sheet of 6 panes	60.00	
	Block of 10 with vertical gutter		
	between	12.50	

OHIO STATEHOOD BICENTENNIAL

Aerial View of Farm Near
Marietta — A2881

Designed by Phil Jordan. Printed by Banknote Corporation of
America.

LITHOGRAPHED
Sheets of 120 in six panes of 20
Serpentine Die Cut 11¾x11½
2003, Mar. 1 **Tagged**
Self-Adhesive

3773	A2881 37c multicolored	.75	.20
	P# block of 4, 4# + B	3.00	
	Pane of 20	15.00	

PELICAN ISLAND NATIONAL WILDLIFE REFUGE, CENT.

Brown Pelican — A2882

Designed by Carl T. Herrman. Printed by Banknote Corporation of America.

LITHOGRAPHED
Sheets of 120 in six panes of 20
Serpentine Die Cut 12x11½

2003, Mar. 14			Tagged
	Self-Adhesive		
3774	A2882 37c multicolored	.75	.20
	P# block of 4, 4#+B	3.00	
	Pane of 20	15.00	

Sea Coast Type of 2002

Designed by Tom Engeman. Printed by Banknote Corporation of America.

PHOTOGRAVURE
COIL STAMP

2003, Mar. 19	Untagged		*Perf. 9¾ Vert.*
3775	A2853 (5c) multicolored	.20	.20
	Pair	.20	
	P# strip of 5, #B111	1.25	
	P# single, #B111		1.00

See No. 3864. No. 3775 has "2003" year date in blue, dots
that run together in surf area, and a distinct small orange cloud.
No. 3864 has "2004" year date in black, rows of distinctly separated dots in surf area, and the small orange cloud is indistinct.

OLD GLORY

Uncle Sam on Bicycle
with Liberty Flag, 20th
Cent. — A2883

1888 Presidential
Campaign
Badge — A2884

1893 Silk
Bookmark — A2885

Modern Hand
Fan — A2886

Carving of Woman with Flag and Sword, 19th Cent. — A2887

Designed by Richard Sheaff. Printed by Ashton-Potter (USA) Ltd.

LITHOGRAPHED
BOOKLET STAMPS
2003, Apr. 3　Tagged　*Serpentine Die Cut 10x9¾*
Self-Adhesive

3776	A2883	37c	multicolored	.75	.50
3777	A2884	37c	multicolored	.75	.50
3778	A2885	37c	multicolored	.75	.50
3779	A2886	37c	multicolored	.75	.50
3780	A2887	37c	multicolored	.75	.50
a.		Horiz. strip of 5, #3776-3780		3.75
b.		Booklet pane, 2 #3780a		7.50

No. 3780b was issued with two types of backing.

CESAR E. CHAVEZ (1927-93), LABOR ORGANIZER

A2888

Designed by Carl Herrman. Printed by Banknote Corporation of America.

LITHOGRAPHED
Sheets of 120 in six panes of 20
Serpentine Die Cut 11¾x11½
2003, Apr. 23　　　　　　　　　**Tagged**
Self-Adhesive

3781	A2888	37c	multicolored	.75	.20
		P# block of 4, 4# + B		3.00	
		Pane of 20		15.00	

LOUISIANA PURCHASE, BICENT.

English Translation of Treaty, Map of U.S., Treaty Signers — A2889

Designed by Richard Sheaff. Printed by American Packaging Corporation for Sennett Security Products.

PHOTOGRAVURE
Sheets of 120 in six panes of 20
2003, Apr. 30　Tagged　*Serpentine Die Cut 10¾*
Self-Adhesive

3782	A2889	37c	multicolored	.95	.40
		P# block of 4, 6# + S		4.00	
		Pane of 20		20.00	

FIRST FLIGHT OF WRIGHT BROTHERS, CENT.

Orville Wright Piloting 1903 Wright Flyer — A2890

Designed by McRay Magleby. Printed by Avery Dennison.

PHOTOGRAVURE
2003, May 22　Tagged　*Serpentine Die Cut 11*
Self-Adhesive

3783		Pane of 10	7.50	
a.	A2890 37c single		.75	.40
b.	Pane of 9 #3783a		6.75	
c.	Pane of 1 #3783a		.75	

PURPLE HEART

A2891

Designed by Carl Herrman. Printed by Banknote Corporation of America (#3784), Ashton-Potter (USA) Ltd. (#3784A).

LITHOGRAPHED
Sheets of 200 in ten panes of 20 (#3784), Sheets of 120 in six panes of 20 (#3784A)
2003　Tagged　*Serpentine Die Cut 11¼x10¾*
Self-Adhesive

3784	A2891	37c	multicolored, *May 30*	.75	.20
		P# block of 4, 4#+B		3.00	
		Pane of 20		15.00	
b.		Printed on back of backing paper		—	
d.		Die cutting omitted, pair		—	

Serpentine Die Cut 10¾x10¼

3784A	A2891	37c	multicolored, *Aug. 1*	.75	.20
		P# block of 4, 4#+P		3.00	
		Pane of 20		15.00	
c.		Die cutting omitted, pane of 20		*1,600.*	

Sea Coast Type of 2002
Designed by Tom Engeman. Printed by J.W. Ferguson & Sons for Ashton-Potter (USA) Ltd.

PHOTOGRAVURE
COIL STAMP
2003, June　Untagged　*Serpentine Die Cut 9½x10*
Self-Adhesive

3785	A2853	(5c)	multicolored	.20	.20
		Pair		.20	
		P# strip of 5, #P1111		1.50	
		P# single, same #		—	1.00
a.		Serp. die cut 9¾x10		.20	.20
		Pair		.20	
		P# strip of 5, #P2222		1.50	
		P# single, same #		—	1.00
b.		As "a," tagged (error)		3.25	2.00
		P# strip of 5, #P2222		40.00	
		P# single, same #		—	7.00

One printing of No. 3785 has more of a scarlet shade in the sky than do other examples of Nos. 3785 and 3785a. Nos. 3785 and 3785a have black "2003" year date.

LEGENDS OF HOLLYWOOD

Audrey Hepburn (1929-93), Actress — A2892

Designed by Michael J. Deas. Printed by American Packaging Corporation for Sennett Security Products.

PHOTOGRAVURE
Sheets of 120 in six panes of 20
2003, June 11　Tagged　*Serpentine Die Cut 10¾*
Self-Adhesive

3786	A2892	37c	multicolored	1.00	1.00
		P# block of 4, 6#+S		4.50	
		Pane of 20		22.50	
		Sheet of 120 (6 panes)		85.00	
		Cross gutter block of 8		17.50	
		Block of 8 with vertical gutter		10.00	
		Horiz. pair with vert. gutter		3.00	
		Vert. pair with horiz. gutter		2.00	

Cross gutter block consists of 6 stamps from upper panes and 2 stamps from panes below.

SOUTHEASTERN LIGHTHOUSES

Old Cape Henry, Virginia — A2893

Cape Lookout, North Carolina — A2894

Morris Island, South Carolina — A2895

Tybee Island, Georgia — A2896

Hillsboro Inlet, Florida — A2897

Designed by Howard E. Paine. Printed by American Packaging Corporation for Sennett Security Products.

PHOTOGRAVURE
Sheets of 120 in six panes of 20
2003, June 13　Tagged　*Serpentine Die Cut 10¾*
Self-Adhesive

3787	A2893	37c	multicolored	1.10	.20
3788	A2894	37c	multicolored	1.10	.20
a.		Bottom of "USA" even with top of upper half-diamond of lighthouse (pos. 2)		4.00	2.50
3789	A2895	37c	multicolored	1.10	.20
3790	A2896	37c	multicolored	1.10	.20
3791	A2897	37c	multicolored	1.10	.20
a.		Strip of 5, #3587-3791		5.50	
b.		Strip of 5, #3787, 3788a, 3789-3791		9.50	
		P# block of 10, 2 sets of 6#+S		15.00	
		Pane of 20		30.00	

Eagle in Gold on
Colored Background
A2898

Colored Eagle on
Gold Background
A2899

Designed by Tom Engeman. Printed by American Packaging
Corporation for Sennett Security Products.

PHOTOGRAVURE
COIL STAMPS
Dated "2003"

Serpentine Die Cut 11¾ Vert.

2003, June 26			Untagged	
Self-Adhesive				
3792	A2898	(25c) gray & gold	.50	.20
3793	A2899	(25c) gold & red	.50	.20
3794	A2898	(25c) dull blue & gold	.50	.20
3795	A2898	(25c) gold & Prussian blue	.50	.20
3796	A2898	(25c) green & gold	.50	.20
3797	A2899	(25c) gold & gray	.50	.20
3798	A2898	(25c) Prussian blue & gold	.50	.20
3799	A2899	(25c) gold & dull blue	.50	.20
3800	A2898	(25c) red & gold	.50	.20
3801	A2899	(25c) gold & green	.50	.20
a.		Strip of 10, #3792-3801	5.00	
		P# strip of 11, 2 # 3801, 1 each #3792-3800, #S1111111, S2222222, S3333333	8.00	
		P# strip of 21, 3 # 3796, 2 each #3792-3795, 3797-3801, same #	16.00	
		P# single (#3796), same #	—	2.75

Dated "2005"

2005, Aug. 5		*Serpentine Die Cut 11½ Vert.*		
3792a	A2898	(25c) gray & gold	.50	.20
3793a	A2899	(25c) gold & red	.50	.20
3794a	A2898	(25c) dull blue & gold	.50	.20
3795a	A2898	(25c) gold & Prussian blue	.50	.20
3796a	A2898	(25c) green & gold	.50	.20
3797a	A2899	(25c) gold & gray	.50	.20
3798a	A2898	(25c) Prussian blue & gold	.50	.20
3799a	A2899	(25c) gold & dull blue	.50	.20
3800a	A2898	(25c) red & gold	.50	.20
3801b	A2899	(25c) gold & green	.50	.20
c.		Strip of 10, #3792a-3801b	5.00	
		P# strip of 11, 2 #3801b, 1 each #3792a-3800a, P#S1111111	8.00	
		P# strip of 21, 3 #3796a, 2 each #3792a-3795a, 3797a-3800a, 3801b, P#S1111111	16.00	
		P# single (#3796a), #S1111111		3.25

ARCTIC TUNDRA

A2900

Illustration reduced.

Designed by Ethel Kessler. Printed by Banknote Corporation
of America.

Wildlife and vegetation: a, Gyrfalcon. b, Gray wolf, vert. c,
Common raven, vert. d, Musk oxen and caribou, vert. e, Grizzly bears, caribou. f, Caribou, willow ptarmigans. g, Arctic
ground squirrel, vert. h, Willow ptarmigan, bearberry. i, Arctic
grayling. j, Singing vole, thin-legged wolf spider, lingonberry,
Labrador tea.

LITHOGRAPHED
Sheets of 80 in eight panes of 10
Serpentine Die Cut 10¾x10½, 10½x10¾

2003, July 2		Tagged	
Self-Adhesive			
3802	A2900	Pane of 10	7.50	
a.-j.		37c Any single	.75	.50
		Sheet of 8 panes	65.00	
		Pair of tete-beche panes	15.00	

KOREAN WAR VETERANS MEMORIAL

Memorial in
Snow — A2901

Designed by Richard Sheaff. Printed by Banknote Corporation of America.

LITHOGRAPHED
Sheets of 120 in six panes of 20
Serpentine Die Cut 11½x11¾

2003, July 27		Tagged	
Self-Adhesive			
3803	A2901	37c multicolored	.75	.20
		P# block of 4, 4#+B	3.00	
		Pane of 20	15.00	

MARY CASSATT PAINTINGS

Young Mother,
1888 — A2902

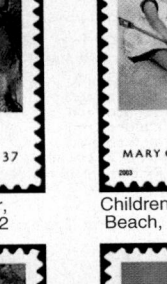

Children Playing on the
Beach, 1884 — A2903

On a Balcony, 1878-
79 — A2904

Child in a Straw Hat, c.
1886 — A2905

Designed by Derry Noyes. Printed by American Packaging
Corporation for Sennett Security Products.

PHOTOGRAVURE
Serpentine Die Cut 10¾ on 2 or 3 Sides

2003, Aug. 7		Tagged	
Self-Adhesive			
Booklet Stamps			
3804	A2902	37c multicolored	.75	.20
3805	A2903	37c multicolored	.75	.20
3806	A2904	37c multicolored	.75	.20
3807	A2905	37c multicolored	.75	.20
a.		Block of 4, #3804-3807	3.00	
b.		Booklet pane of 20, 5 #3807a	15.00	

No. 3807b is a double-sided booklet with 12 stamps on one
side and 8 stamps plus label (booklet cover) on the other side.

EARLY FOOTBALL HEROES

Bronko Nagurski
(1908-90) — A2906

Ernie Nevers (1903-
76) — A2907

Walter Camp (1859-
1925) — A2908

Red Grange (1903-
91) — A2909

Designed by Richard Sheaff. Printed by Avery Dennison.

PHOTOGRAVURE
Sheets of 200 in ten panes of 20
Serpentine Die Cut 11½x11¾

2003, Aug. 8		Tagged	
Self-Adhesive			
3808	A2906	37c multicolored	.75	.20
3809	A2907	37c multicolored	.75	.20
3810	A2908	37c multicolored	.75	.20
3811	A2909	37c multicolored	.75	.20
a.		Block of 4, #3808-3811	3.00	
		P# block of 4, 7#+V	3.00	
		Pane of 20	15.00	

ROY ACUFF

Acuff (1903-92), Country Music Artist, and Fiddle — A2910

Designed by Richard Sheaff.
Printed by Avery Dennison.

PHOTOGRAVURE
Sheets of 200 in ten panes of 20

2003, Sept. 13   Tagged   *Serpentine Die Cut 11*
Self-Adhesive

3812	A2910	37c	multicolored	.75	.20
		P# block of 4, 4#+V	3.00	
		Pane of 20	15.00	

DISTRICT OF COLUMBIA

Map, National Mall, Row Houses and Cherry Blossoms — A2911

Designed by Greg Berger.
Printed by American Packaging Corporation for Sennett Security Products.

PHOTOGRAVURE
Sheets of 128 in eight panes of 16

2003, Sept. 23   Tagged   *Serpentine Die Cut 11*
Self-Adhesive

3813	A2911	37c	multicolored	.85	.20
		P# block of 4, 8#+S	4.00	
		Pane of 16	20.00	

REPTILES AND AMPHIBIANS

Scarlet Kingsnake A2912

Blue-Spotted Salamander A2913

Reticulate Collared Lizard A2914

Ornate Chorus Frog — A2915

Ornate Box Turtle A2916

Designed by Steve Buchanan. Printed by Avery Dennison.

PHOTOGRAVURE
Sheets of 200 in ten panes of 20

2003, Oct. 7   Tagged   *Serpentine Die Cut 11*
Self-Adhesive

3814	A2912	37c	multicolored	.80	.20
3815	A2913	37c	multicolored	.80	.20
3816	A2914	37c	multicolored	.80	.20
3817	A2915	37c	multicolored	.80	.20
3818	A2916	37c	multicolored	.80	.20
a.		Vert. strip of 5, #3814-3818	4.00	
		P# block of 10, 4#+V	8.00	
		Pane of 20	16.00	

Washington Type of 2002
Designed by Richard Sheaff.

Printed by Avery Dennison.

PHOTOGRAVURE
Sheets of 200 in ten panes of 20

2003, Oct.   Tagged   *Serpentine Die Cut 11*
Self-Adhesive

3819	A2686	23c	gray green	1.00	.20
		P# block of 4, 2#+V	8.00	
		Pane of 20	36.00	

Christmas Type of 2002
Designed by Richard Sheaff.

Printed by Ashton-Potter (USA) Ltd.

LITHOGRAPHED
Serpentine Die Cut 11¼ on 2 or 3 Sides
2003, Oct. 23   Tagged

Self-Adhesive
Booklet Stamp
Size: 19½x28mm

3820	A2843	37c	multicolored	.75	.20
a.		Booklet pane of 20	15.00	
b.		Die cutting omitted, pair	—	

No. 3820a is a double-sided booklet with 12 stamps on one side and 8 stamps plus label (booklet cover) on the other side. Compare to No. 3675, which measures 19x27mm.

CHRISTMAS

Reindeer with Pan Pipes — A2917

Santa Claus with Drum — A2918

Santa Claus with Trumpet — A2919

Reindeer with Horn — A2920

Reindeer with Pan Pipes — A2921

Santa Claus with Drum — A2922

Santa Claus with Trumpet — A2923

Reindeer with Horn — A2924

Designed by Ethel Kessler.

Printed by American Packaging Corp. for Sennett Security Products.

PHOTOGRAVURE
Sheets of 160 in eight panes of 20
Serpentine Die Cut 11¾x11

2003, Oct. 23   Tagged
Self-Adhesive

3821	A2917	37c	multicolored	.80	.20
3822	A2918	37c	multicolored	.80	.20
3823	A2919	37c	multicolored	.80	.20
3824	A2920	37c	multicolored	.80	.20
a.		Block of 4, #3821-3824	3.20	
		P# block of 4, 4#+S	3.20	
		Pane of 20	16.00	
b.		Booklet pane of 20, 5 each #3821-3824	16.00	

BOOKLET STAMPS
Serpentine Die Cut 10½x10¾ on 2 or 3 Sides

3825	A2921	37c	multicolored	1.00	.20
3826	A2922	37c	multicolored	1.00	.20
3827	A2923	37c	multicolored	1.00	.20
3828	A2924	37c	multicolored	1.00	.20
a.		Block of 4, #3825-3828	4.00	
b.		Booklet pane of 4, #3825-3828	4.00	
c.		Booklet pane of 6, #3827-3828, 2 each #3825-3826	6.00	
d.		Booklet pane of 6, #3825-3826, 2 each #3827-3828	6.00	

No. 3824b is a double-sided booklet with 12 stamps on one side and 8 stamps plus label (booklet cover) on the other side.

Snowy Egret — A2925

Designed by Carl T. Herrman.

Printed by Avery Dennison (#3829), Ashton-Potter (USA) Ltd. (#3829A, 3830, 3830D).

COIL STAMPS

2003-05   Tagged   *Serpentine Die Cut 8½ Vert.* Self-Adhesive

PHOTOGRAVURE

3829	A2925 37c	multicolored, Oct. 24, 2003		.75	.20
		Pair		1.50	
		P# strip of 5, #V1111, V2111, V3212, V3222		4.50	
		P# strip of 5, #V3211		—	
		P# strip of 5, #V3221		300.00	
		P# single, #V1111, V2111, V3212, V3222		—	1.25
		P# single, #V2121		—	—
		P# single, #V3211		—	—
		P# single, #V3221		—	—
b.		Black omitted		—	—

LITHOGRAPHED
Serpentine Die Cut 9½ Vert.

3829A	A2925 37c	multicolored, Mar., 2004		.75	.20
		Pair		1.50	
		P# strip of 5, #P11111, P22222, P33333, P44444, P55555		6.00	
		P# single, same #		—	2.25

Serpentine Die Cut 11½x11 on 2, 3 or 4 Sides
Booklet Stamps

PHOTOGRAVURE

3830	A2925 37c	multicolored, Jan. 30, 2004		.75	.20
a.		Booklet pane of 20		15.00	

With "USPS" Microprinted on Bird's Breast

3830D	A2925 37c	multicolored, 2004		6.00	.25
e.		Booklet pane of 20		120.00	
f.		Die cutting omitted, pair		250.00	
g.		As "e," die cutting omitted		—	

PACIFIC CORAL REEF

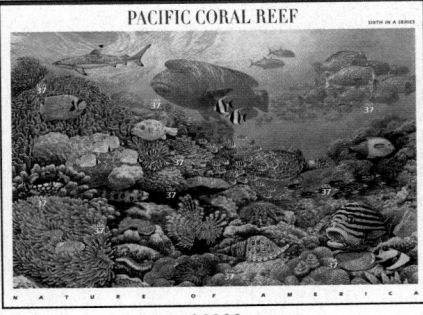

A2926

Illustration reduced.

Designed by Ethel Kessler. Printed by Avery Dennison.

Marine life: a, Emperor angelfish, blue coral, mound coral, vert. b, Humphead wrasse, Moorish idol. c, Bumphead parrotfish, vert. d, Black-spotted puffer, threadfin butterflyfish, staghorn coral. e, Hawksbill turtle, palette surgeonfish. f, Pink anemonefish, magnificent sea anemone, vert. g, Snowflake moray eel, Spanish dancer. h, Lionfish, vert. i, Triton's trumpet. j, Oriental sweetlips, bluestreak cleaner wrasse, mushroom coral, vert.

PHOTOGRAVURE
Sheets of 80 in eight panes of 10

2004, Jan. 2   Tagged   *Serpentine Die Cut 10¾* Self-Adhesive

3831	A2926	Pane of 10		7.50	
a.-j.		37c Any single		.75	.20
		Sheet of 8 panes		57.50	

CHINESE NEW YEAR

Year of the Monkey
A2927

Designed by Clarence Lee. Printed by American Packaging Corporation for Sennett Security Products.

PHOTOGRAVURE
Sheets of 120 in six panes of 20

2004, Jan. 13   Tagged   *Serpentine Die Cut 10¾* Self-Adhesive

3832	A2927 37c	multicolored		.75	.20
		P# block of 4, 4# + S		3.00	
		Pane of 20		15.00	

See No. 3895i.

LOVE

Candy Hearts — A2928

Designed by Michael Osborne. Printed by Avery Dennison.

PHOTOGRAVURE
BOOKLET STAMP
Serpentine Die Cut 10¾ on 2, 3 or 4 Sides

2004, Jan. 14   Tagged   Self-Adhesive

3833	A2928 37c	multicolored		.75	.20
a.		Booklet pane of 20		15.00	

BLACK HERITAGE SERIES

Paul Robeson (1898-1976), Actor, Singer, Athlete and Activist — A2929

Designed by Richard Sheaff. Printed by American Packaging Corporation for Sennett Security Products.

PHOTOGRAVURE
Sheets of 120 in six panes of 20

2004, Jan. 20   Tagged   *Serpentine Die Cut 10¾* Self-Adhesive

3834	A2929 37c	multicolored		.75	.20
		P# block of 4, 4# + S		3.00	
		Pane of 20		15.00	

THEODOR SEUSS GEISEL (DR. SEUSS)

Dr. Seuss (1904-91), Children's Book Writer, and Book Characters A2930

Designed by Carl T. Herrman. Printed by American Packaging Corporation for Sennett Security Products.

PHOTOGRAVURE
Sheets of 180 in nine panes of 20
Serpentine Die Cut 10¾x10½

2004, Mar. 2   Tagged   Self-Adhesive

3835	A2930 37c	multicolored		.85	.20
		P# block of 4, 6#+S		3.50	
		Pane of 20		17.50	
a.		Die cutting omitted, pair		2,750.	

FLOWERS

White Lilacs and Pink Roses — A2931

Five Varieties of Pink Roses — A2932

Designed by Richard Sheaff. Printed by Ashton-Potter (USA) Ltd. (#3836), American Packaging Corporation for Sennett Security Products.

LITHOGRAPHED (#3836), PHOTOGRAVURE
BOOKLET STAMP (#3836)
Sheets of 160 in eight panes of 20 (#3837)
Serpentine Die Cut 10¾ on 2, 3 or 4 Sides

2004, Mar. 4   **Tagged**   Self-Adhesive

3836	A2931 37c	multicolored		.75	.20
a.		Booklet pane of 20		15.00	

Serpentine Die Cut 11½x11

3837	A2932 60c	multicolored		1.25	.25
		P# block of 4, 5#+S		6.25	
		Pane of 20		25.00	

UNITED STATES AIR FORCE ACADEMY, 50TH ANNIV.

Cadet Chapel
A2933

Designed by Phil Jordan. Printed by American Packaging Corporation for Sennett Security Products.

PHOTOGRAVURE
Sheets of 120 in six panes of 20

2004, Apr. 1   Tagged   *Serpentine Die Cut 10¾* Self-Adhesive

3838	A2933 37c	multicolored		.75	.20
		P# block of 4, 6# + S		3.00	
		Pane of 20		15.00	

HENRY MANCINI

Henry Mancini (1924-94), Composer, and Pink Panther A2934

Designed by Carl Herrman. Printed by American Packaging Corporation for Sennett Security Products.

PHOTOGRAVURE
Sheets of 120 in six panes of 20

2004, Apr. 13   Tagged   *Serpentine Die Cut 10¾* Self-Adhesive

3839	A2934 37c	multicolored		.75	.20
		P# block of 4, 6#+S		3.00	
		Pane of 20		15.00	

LITHOGRAPHED
Sheets of 180 in nine panes of 20

**2004, May 29   Tagged   *Serpentine Die Cut 10¾*
Self-Adhesive**

3862	A2947	37c multicolored	.75	.20
		P# block of 4, 4#+P	3.00	
		Pane of 20	15.00	

> **Scott values for used self-adhesive stamps are for examples either on piece or off piece.**

SUMMER OLYMPIC GAMES, ATHENS, GREECE

Stylized
Runner
A2948

Designed by Richard Sheaff. Printed by Ashton-Potter (USA) Ltd.

LITHOGRAPHED
Sheets of 120 in six panes of 20

**2004, June 9   Tagged   *Serpentine Die Cut 10¾*
Self-Adhesive**

3863	A2948	37c multicolored	.75	.20
		P# block of 4, 4#+P	3.00	
		Pane of 20	15.00	

Sea Coast Type of 2002

Designed by Tom Engeman. Printed by American Packaging Corp. for Sennett Security Products.

PHOTOGRAVURE
COIL STAMP

2004, June 11   Untagged   Perf. 9¾ Vert.

3864	A2853	(5c) multicolored	.20	.20
		Pair	.20	—
		P# strip of 5, #S1111	1.50	—
		P# single, same #		— 1.00

No. 3864 has "2004" year date in black, rows of distinctly separated dots in surf area, and the small orange cloud is indistinct. No. 3775 has "2003" year date in blue, dots that run together in surf area, and a distinct small orange cloud.

No. 3864 known with red ink that glows orange under long wave ultraviolet light. Values the same.

THE ART OF DISNEY: FRIENDSHIP

Goofy, Mickey Mouse,
Donald Duck — A2949

Bambi,
Thumper — A2950

Mufasa,
Simba — A2951

Jiminy Cricket,
Pinocchio — A2952

Designed by David Pacheco. Printed by American Packaging Corporation for Bamknote Corporation of America/Sennett Security Products.

LITHOGRAPHED
Sheets of 180 in nine panes of 20
Serpentine Die Cut 10½x10¾

2004, June 23   Tagged

Self-Adhesive

3865	A2949	37c multicolored	1.00	.20
3866	A2950	37c multicolored	1.00	.20
3867	A2951	37c multicolored	1.00	.20
3868	A2952	37c multicolored	1.00	.20
a.		Block or vert. strip of 4, #3865-3868	4.00	
		P# block of 4, 4#+S	4.00	
		Pane of 20	20.00	

U.S.S. CONSTELLATION

A2953

Designed by Howard E. Paine. Printed by Ashton-Potter (USA) Ltd.

ENGRAVED
Sheets of 180 in nine panes of 20

**2004, June 30   Tagged   *Serpentine Die Cut 10½*
Self-Adhesive**

3869	A2953	37c brown	.75	.20
		P# block of 4, 1#+P	3.00	
		Pane of 20	15.00	

R. BUCKMINSTER FULLER (1895-1983),
ENGINEER

Time Magazine Cover
Depicting Fuller, by
Boris
Artzybasheff — A2954

Designed by Carl T. Herrman. Printed by Ashton-Potter (USA) Ltd.

LITHOGRAPHED
Sheets of 120 in six panes of 20
Serpentine Die Cut 10½x10¾

2004, July 12   Tagged

Self-Adhesive

3870	A2954	37c multicolored	.75	.20
		P# block of 4, 5#+P	3.00	
		Pane of 20	15.00	

LITERARY ARTS

James Baldwin
(1924-87),
Writer
A2955

Designed by Phil Jordan. Printed by Ashton-Potter (USA) Ltd.

LITHOGRAPHED
Sheets of 180 in nine panes of 20

**2004, July 23   Tagged   *Serpentine Die Cut 10¾*
Self-Adhesive**

3871	A2955	37c multicolored	.75	.20
		P# block of 4, 5#+P	3.00	
		Pane of 20	15.00	

AMERICAN TREASURES SERIES

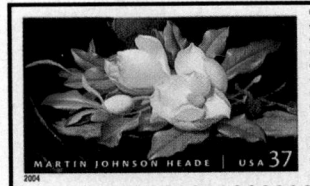

Giant
Magnolias on
a Blue Velvet
Cloth, by
Martin
Johnson
Heade
A2956

Designed by Derry Noyes. Printed by American Packaging Corporation for Sennett Security Products.

PHOTOGRAVURE
BOOKLET STAMP
Serpentine Die Cut 10¾ on 2 or 3 Sides

2004, Aug. 12   Tagged

Self-Adhesive

3872	A2956	37c multicolored	.70	.20
a.		Booklet pane of 20	15.00	
b.		Die cutting omitted, pair		—

No. 3872a is a double-sided booklet pane with 12 stamps on one side and eight stamps plus label on the other side.

ART OF THE AMERICAN INDIAN

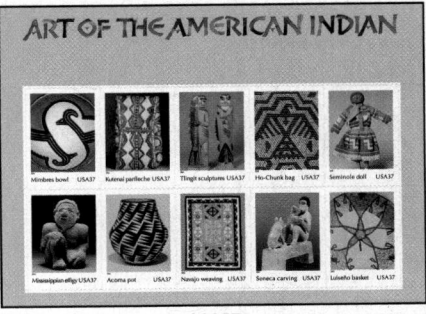

A2957

Illustration reduced.

Designed by Richard Sheaff. Printed by Avery Dennison.

Designs: a, Mimbres bowl. b, Kutenai parfleche. c, Tlingit sculptures. d, Ho-Chunk bag. e, Seminole doll. f, Mississippian effigy. g, Acoma pot. h, Navajo weaving. i, Seneca carving. j, Luiseño basket.

PHOTOGRAVURE
Serpentine Die Cut 10¾x11

2004, Aug. 21   Tagged

Self-Adhesive

3873	A2957	Pane of 10	19.00	
a.-j.		37c Any single	1.90	.20

Sea Coast Type of 2002

Designed by Tom Engeman.

Printed by Ashton-Potter (USA), Ltd. (#3874); American Packaging Corporation for Sennett Security Products (#3875).

PHOTOGRAVURE
COIL STAMPS

2004-05 Untagged *Serpentine Die Cut 10 Vert.*
Self-Adhesive

3874	A2853	(5c) **multicolored**, large "2003" year		
		date	.20	.20
		Pair	.20	
		P# strip of 5, #P2222	1.75	
		P# single, #P2222	—	1.00
a.		Small "2003" year date, *2005*	.20	.20
		Pair	.20	
		P# strip of 5, #P3333, P4444,		
		P5555, P6666, P7777, P8888,		
		P9999	1.75	
		P# single, same numbers	—	1.00

On Nos. 3874 and 3874a, the stamps are spaced on backing paper that is taller than the stamps.
On No. 3874 the color laydown order of plate numbers is cyan, magenta, yellow, black. On No. 3874a, the order is BCMY.

Serpentine Die Cut 11½ Vert.

3875	A2853	(5c) **multicolored**, "2004" year date	.20	.20
		Pair	.20	
		P# strip of 5, #S1111	1.75	
		P# single, #S1111	—	1.00

On No. 3875, the stamps are spaced on backing paper that is taller than the stamps.
No. 3875 exists with very faint traces of tagging.

LEGENDS OF HOLLYWOOD

John Wayne (1907-79),
Actor — A2958

Designed by Derry Noyes.

Printed by American Packaging Corporation for Sennett Security Products.

PHOTOGRAVURE
Sheets of 120 in six panes of 20

2004, Sept. 9 Tagged *Serpentine Die Cut 10¾*
Self-Adhesive

3876	A2958	37c **multicolored**	.75	.20
		P# block of 4, 6#+S	3.00	
		Pane of 20	15.00	
		Sheet of 120 (6 panes)	85.00	
		Cross gutter block of 8	17.50	
		Block of 8 with vertical gutter	10.00	
		Horiz. pair with vert. gutter	3.00	
		Vert. pair with horiz. gutter	2.00	

SICKLE CELL DISEASE AWARENESS

Mother and Child — A2959

Designed by Howard Paine.

Printed by Avery Dennison.

PHOTOGRAVURE
Sheets of 200 in ten panes of 20

2004, Sept. 29 Tagged *Serpentine Die Cut 11*
Self-Adhesive

3877	A2959	37c **multicolored**	.75	.20
		P# block of 4, 6#+V	3.00	
		Pane of 20	15.00	

CLOUDSCAPES

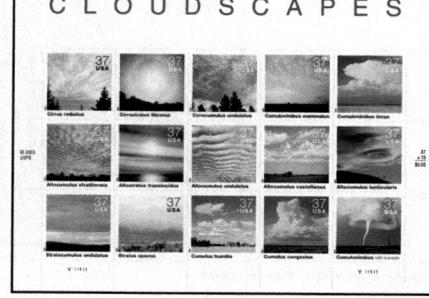

A2960

Illustration reduced.

Designed by Howard E. Paine.

Printed by Avery Dennison.

Clouds: a, Cirrus radiatus. b, Cirrostratus fibratus. c, Cirrocumulus undulatus. d, Cumulonimbus mammatus. e, Cumulonimbus incus. f, Altocumulus stratiformis. g, Altostratus translucidus. h, Altocumulus undulatus. i, Altocumulus castellanus. j, Altocumulus lenticularis. k, Stratocumulus undulatus. l, Stratus opacus. m, Cumulus humilis. n, Cumulus congestus. o, Cumulonimbus with tornado.

PHOTOGRAVURE

2004, Oct. 4 Tagged *Serpentine Die Cut 11*
Self-Adhesive

3878	A2960	Pane of 15	12.50	
a.-o.		37c Any single	.80	.20

CHRISTMAS

Madonna and Child, by
Lorenzo Monaco — A2961

Designed by Richard Sheaff.
Printed by Ashton-Potter (USA), Ltd.

LITHOGRAPHED
Serpentine Die Cut 10¾x11 on 2 or 3 Sides
BOOKLET STAMP

2004, Oct. 14   Tagged
Self-Adhesive

3879	A2961	37c **multicolored**	.75	.20
a.		Booklet pane of 20	15.00	
b.		As "a," die cutting omitted	—	

No. 3879a is a double-sided booklet pane with 12 stamps on one side and eight stamps plus label that serves as a booklet cover on the other side.

HANUKKAH

Dreidel — A2962

Designed by Ethel Kessler.
Printed by Banknote Corporation of America for Sennett Security Products.

LITHOGRAPHED
Sheets of 300 in fifteen panes of 20

2004, Oct. 15 Tagged *Serpentine Die Cut 10¾*
Self-Adhesive

3880	A2962	37c **multicolored**	.75	.20
		P# block of 4, 4#+S	3.00	
		Pane of 20	15.00	
a.		Die cuts applied to wrong sides of stamp		
		(hyphen-hole die cuts and wavy line		
		on face, die cut 10¾ on reverse)	—	—

KWANZAA

People in
Robes — A2963

Designed by Derry Noyes.
Printed by Ashton-Potter (USA), Ltd.

LITHOGRAPHED
Sheets of 160 in eight panes of 20

2004, Oct. 16 Tagged *Serpentine Die Cut 10¾*
Self-Adhesive

3881	A2963	37c **multicolored**	.75	.20
		P# block of 4, 6#+P	3.00	
		Pane of 20	15.00	

LITERARY ARTS

Moss Hart
(1904-61),
Playwright
A2964

Designed by Ethel Kessler.
Printed by Avery Dennison.

PHOTOGRAVURE
Sheets of 200 in ten panes of 20

2004, Oct. 25 Tagged *Serpentine Die Cut 11*
Self-Adhesive

3882	A2964	37c **multicolored**	.75	.20
		P# block of 4, 5#+V	3.00	
		Pane of 20	15.00	

CHRISTMAS

Purple Santa
Ornament — A2965

Green Santa
Ornament — A2966

Blue Santa
Ornament — A2967

Red Santa
Ornament — A2968

Purple Santa
Ornament — A2969

Green Santa
Ornament — A2970

Blue Santa
Ornament — A2971

Red Santa
Ornament — A2972

Designed by Derry Noyes. Printed by American Packaging Corporation for Sennett Security Printers. (#3883-3890), Avery Dennison (#3891-3894).

PHOTOGRAVURE
Sheets of 160 in eight panes of 20
Serpentine Die Cut 11½x11

2004, Nov. 16				Tagged

Self-Adhesive

3883	A2965	37c	purple & multicolored	.90	.20
3884	A2966	37c	green & multicolored	.90	.20
3885	A2967	37c	blue & multicolored	.90	.20
3886	A2968	37c	red & multicolored	.90	.20
a.			Block or strip of 4, #3883-3886	3.60	
			P# block of 4, 4#+S	3.60	
			Pane of 20	18.00	
b.			Booklet pane of 20, 5 #3886a blocks	18.00	

Booklet Stamps
Serpentine Die Cut 10¼x10¾ on 2 or 3 Sides

3887	A2969	37c	purple & multicolored	.90	.20
3888	A2970	37c	green & multicolored	.90	.20
3889	A2971	37c	blue & multicolored	.90	.20
3890	A2972	37c	red & multicolored	.90	.20
a.			Block of 4, #3887-3890	3.60	
b.			Booklet pane of 4, #3887-3890	3.60	
c.			Booklet pane of 6, #3889-3890, 2 each #3887-3888	5.50	
d.			Booklet pane of 6, #3887-3888, 2 each #3889-3890	5.50	

Serpentine Die Cut 8 on 2, 3 or 4 Sides

3891	A2970	37c	green & multicolored	1.10	.20
3892	A2969	37c	purple & multicolored	1.10	.20
3893	A2972	37c	red & multicolored	1.10	.20
3894	A2971	37c	blue & multicolored	1.10	.20
a.			Block of 4, #3891-3894	4.40	
b.			Booklet pane of 18, 6 each #3891, 3893, 3 each # 3892, 3894	20.00	
			Nos. 3883-3894 (12)	11.60	2.40

No. 3886b is a double-sided booklet with 12 stamps on one side and 8 stamps plus label that serves as a booklet cover on the other side.

The design of No. 3894b shows ornaments in a wooden box. The pattern of the wooden box dividers creates three types of each design. Rows 1 and 4 are Type 1, with a top horizontal strip of frame extending from edge to edge while the bottom strip of frame stops at the design's width. Rows 2 and 5 are Type 2, with both top and bottom strips of frame stopping at the design's width. Rows 3 and 6 are Type 3, with the top strip of frame stopping at design's width while the bottom strip of frame extends from edge to edge. Each variety is equally common.

Chinese New Year Types of 1992-2004

Designed by Clarence Lee. Printed by American Packaging Corporation for Sennett Security Products.

PHOTOGRAVURE

2005, Jan. 6			Tagged	*Serpentine Die Cut 10¾*

Self-Adhesive

3895			Double sided pane of 24, 2 each #a-l	18.00	
a.	A2360	37c	Rat	.75	.20
b.	A2413	37c	Ox	.75	.20
c.	A2462	37c	Tiger	.75	.20
d.	A2535	37c	Rabbit	.75	.20
e.	A2602	37c	Dragon	.75	.20
f.	A2702	37c	Snake	.75	.20
g.	A2752	37c	Horse	.75	.20
h.	A2856	37c	Ram	.75	.20
i.	A2927	37c	Monkey	.75	.20
j.	A2067	37c	Rooster	.75	.20
k.	A2146	37c	Dog	.75	.20
l.	A2205	37c	Boar	.75	.20
m.			As No. 3895, die cutting omitted on "a," "b," and "c" on reverse side	1,250.	

No. 3895h has "2005" year date and is photogravure while No. 3747 has "2003" year date and is lithographed.

Stamps are on the right side of the front and on the left side of the reverse.

BLACK HERITAGE SERIES

Marian Anderson (1897-1993), Singer — A2973

Designed by Richard Sheaff. Printed by American Packaging Corporation for Sennett Security Products.

PHOTOGRAVURE
Sheets of 120 in six panes of 20

2005, Jan. 27			Tagged	*Serpentine Die Cut 10¾*

Self-Adhesive

3896	A2973	37c	multicolored	.75	.20
			P# block of 4, 4# + S	3.00	
			Pane of 20	15.00	

RONALD REAGAN

Ronald Reagan (1911-2004), 40th President — A2974

Designed by Howard E. Paine. Printed by American Packaging Corporation for Sennett Security Products.

PHOTOGRAVURE
Sheets of 120 in six panes of 20

2005, Feb. 9			Tagged	*Serpentine Die Cut 10¾*

Self-Adhesive

3897	A2974	37c	multicolored	.75	.20
			P# block of 4, 4#+S	3.00	
			Pane of 20	15.00	
			Sheet of 120 (6 panes)	90.00	
			Cross gutter block of 4	8.25	
			Horiz. pair with vert. gutter	3.00	
			Vert. pair with horiz. gutter	2.00	

The bottom center stamp (pos. 18) shows a small portion of the pane position diagram in the bottom margin, due to the too-high placement of the diagram in the selvage. There are three varieties of the portion appearing on the stamp, depending on the pane position on the press sheet.

LOVE

Hand and Flower
Bouquet — A2975

Designed by Derry Noyes. Printed by Avery Dennison.

PHOTOGRAVURE
BOOKLET STAMP
Serpentine Die Cut 10¾x11 on 2, 3 or 4 Sides

2005, Feb. 18				Tagged

Self-Adhesive

3898	A2975	37c	multicolored	.75	.20
a.			Booklet pane of 20	15.00	

NORTHEAST DECIDUOUS FOREST

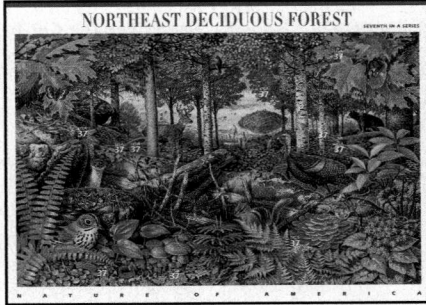

NORTHEAST DECIDUOUS FOREST

A2976

Illustration reduced.

Designed by Ethel Kessler. Printed by Avery Dennison.

Wildlife: a, Eastern buckmoth, vert. b, Red-shouldered hawk. c, Eastern red bat. d, White-tailed deer. e, Black bear. f, Long-tailed weasel, vert. g, Wild turkey, vert. h, Ovenbird, vert. i, Red eft. j, Eastern chipmunk.

PHOTOGRAVURE
Sheets of 80 in eight panes of 10

2005, Mar. 3			Tagged	*Serpentine Die Cut 10¾*

Self-Adhesive

3899	A2976		Pane of 10	7.50	
a.-j.		37c	Any single	.75	.20
			Sheet of 8 panes	60.00	

SPRING FLOWERS

Hyacinth — A2977

Daffodil — A2978

Tulip — A2979

Iris — A2980

Designed by Derry Noyes. Printed by Ashton-Potter (USA) Ltd.

LITHOGRAPHED
BOOKLET STAMPS
Serpentine Die Cut 10¾ on 2 or 3 Sides

2005, Mar. 15				Tagged

Self-Adhesive

3900	A2977	37c	multicolored	.85	.20
3901	A2978	37c	multicolored	.85	.20
3902	A2979	37c	multicolored	.85	.20
3903	A2980	37c	multicolored	.85	.20
a.			Block of 4, #3900-3903	3.40	
b.			Booklet pane of 20, 5 each #3900-3903	17.00	
c.			As "b," die cutting omitted on side with 8 stamps	—	

No. 3903b is a double-sided booklet with 12 stamps on one side and 8 stamps plus label (booklet cover) on the other side.

LITERARY ARTS

Robert Penn Warren (1905-89), Writer A2981

Designed by Carl Herrman. Printed by American Packaging Corporation for Sennett Security Products.

PHOTOGRAVURE
Sheets of 120 in six panes of 20

2005, Apr. 22 Tagged *Serpentine Die Cut 10¾*
Self-Adhesive

3904	A2981	37c multicolored	.75	.20
		P# block of 4, 5#+S	3.00	
		Pane of 20	15.00	

EDGAR Y. "YIP" HARBURG

Harburg (1896-1981), Lyricist
A2982

Designed by Ethel Kessler. Printed by Banknote Corporation of America for Sennett Security Products.

LITHOGRAPHED
Sheets of 120 in six panes of 20

2005, Apr. 28 Tagged *Serpentine Die Cut 10¾*
Self-Adhesive

3905	A2982	37c multicolored	.75	.20
		P# block of 4, 4#+S	3.00	
		Pane of 20	15.00	

AMERICAN SCIENTISTS

Barbara McClintock (1902-92), Geneticist
A2983

Josiah Willard Gibbs (1839-1903), Thermodynamicist — A2984

John von Neumann (1903-57), Mathematician
A2985

Richard Feynman (1918-88), Physicist
A2986

Designed by Carl Herrman. Printed by Banknote Corporation of America for Sennett Security Products.

LITHOGRAPHED
Sheets of 180 in nine panes of 20

2005, May 4 Tagged *Serpentine Die Cut 10¾*
Self-Adhesive

3906	A2983	37c multicolored	.75	.20
3907	A2984	37c multicolored	.75	.20
3908	A2985	37c multicolored	.75	.20
a.		Vert. pair, die cutting omitted, #3906 & 3908	—	
3909	A2986	37c multicolored	.75	.20
a.		Block or horiz. strip of 4, #3906-3909	3.00	
		P# block of 8, 2 sets of P# + top label, 5#+S	6.00	
		P# block of 4, 5#+S	3.00	
		Pane of 20	15.00	
b.		All colors omitted, tagging omitted, pane of 20	—	

c.		As "a," printing on back of stamps omitted	—	
d.		Vert. pair, die cutting omitted, #3907 & 3909	—	

On No. 3909b, the printing on the back of the pane and all die cutting is normal.

MODERN AMERICAN ARCHITECTURE

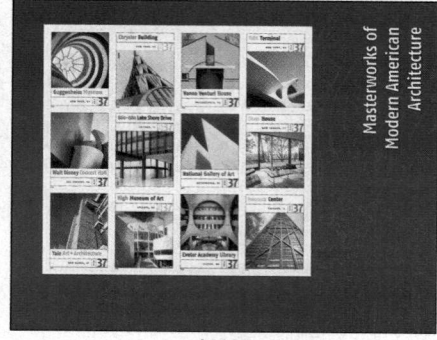

A2987

Illustration reduced.

Designed by Margaret Bauer. Printed by Ashton-Potter (USA) Ltd.

Buildings: a, Guggenheim Museum, New York. b, Chrysler Building, New York. c, Vanna Venturi House, Philadelphia. d, TWA Terminal, New York. e, Walt Disney Concert Hall, Los Angeles. f, 860-880 Lake Shore Drive, Chicago. g, National Gallery of Art, Washington, DC. h, Glass House, New Canaan, CT. i, Yale Art and Architecture Building, New Haven, CT. j, High Museum of Art, Atlanta. k, Exeter Academy Library, Exeter, NH. l, Hancock Center, Chicago.

LITHOGRAPHED
Serpentine Die Cut 10¾x11

2005, May 19 Tagged
Self-Adhesive

3910	A2987	Pane of 12	9.00	
a.-l.		37c Any single	.75	.20
m.		As No. 3910, orange yellow omitted	—	

No. 3910m exists on a first day cover.

LEGENDS OF HOLLYWOOD

Henry Fonda (1905-82), Actor — A2988

Designed by Derry Noyes. Printed by Ashton-Potter (USA) Ltd.

LITHOGRAPHED
Sheets of 180 in nine panes of 20
Serpentine Die Cut 11x10¾

2005, May 20 Tagged
Self-Adhesive

3911	A2988	37c multicolored	.90	.20
		P# block of 4, 5#+P	4.00	
		Pane of 20	20.00	
		Sheet of 180 (9 panes)	160.00	
		Cross gutter block of 8	17.50	
		Block of 8 with vert. gutter	10.00	
		Horiz. pair with vert. gutter	3.00	
		Vert. pair with horiz. gutter	2.00	

The cross gutter block consists of 4 stamps from the two upper panes and 4 stamps from the two lower panes.

THE ART OF DISNEY: CELEBRATION

Pluto, Mickey Mouse — A2989

Mad Hatter, Alice — A2990

Flounder, Ariel — A2991

Snow White, Dopey — A2992

Designed by David Pacheco. Printed by Banknote Corporation of America for Sennett Security Products.

LITHOGRAPHED
Sheets of 180 in nine panes of 20
Serpentine Die Cut 10½x10¾

2005, June 30 Tagged
Self-Adhesive

3912	A2989	37c multicolored	.75	.20
3913	A2990	37c multicolored	.75	.20
3914	A2991	37c multicolored	.75	.20
3915	A2992	37c multicolored	.75	.20
a.		Block or vert. strip of 4, #3912-3915	3.00	
		P# block of 4, 6#+S	3.00	
		P# block of 10, 2 sets of P# + top label	7.50	
		Pane of 20	15.00	
b.		Die cutting omitted, pane of 20	—	1,400.
c.		Printed on backing paper, pane of 20	—	

On the unique used pane of No. 3915b, the outer selvage was removed by cutting.

ADVANCES IN AVIATION

Boeing 247 — A2993

Consolidated PBY Catalina A2994

Grumman F6F Hellcat A2995

Republic P-47 Thunderbolt A2996

Engineering and Research Corporation Ercoupe 415 — A2997

Lockheed P-80 Shooting Star — A2998

Consolidated B-24 Liberator A2999

Boeing B-29 Superfortress A3000

Beechcraft 35 Bonanza A3001

Northrop YB-49 Flying Wing — A3002

Designed by Phil Jordan. Printed by Ashton-Potter (USA) Ltd.

LITHOGRAPHED
Sheets of 180 in nine panes of 20
Serpentine Die Cut 10¾x10½

2005, July 29			Tagged	
		Self-Adhesive		
3916	A2993	37c **multicolored**	.75	.20
3917	A2994	37c **multicolored**	.75	.20
3918	A2995	37c **multicolored**	.75	.20
3919	A2996	37c **multicolored**	.75	.20
3920	A2997	37c **multicolored**	.75	.20
3921	A2998	37c **multicolored**	.75	.20
3922	A2999	37c **multicolored**	.75	.20
3923	A3000	37c **multicolored**	.75	.20
3924	A3001	37c **multicolored**	.75	.20
3925	A3002	37c **multicolored**	.75	.20
a.		Block of 10, #3916-3925	7.50	
		P# block of 10, 7#+P	7.50	
		Pane of 20	15.00	

RIO GRANDE BLANKETS

A3003

A3005

A3004

A3006

Designed by Derry Noyes. Printed by Ashton-Potter (USA) Ltd.

LITHOGRAPHED
BOOKLET STAMPS
Serpentine Die Cut 10¾ on 2 or 3 Sides

2005, July 30			Tagged	
		Self-Adhesive		
3926	A3003	37c **multicolored**	.75	.20
3927	A3004	37c **multicolored**	.75	.20
3928	A3005	37c **multicolored**	.75	.20
3929	A3006	37c **multicolored**	.75	.20
a.		Block of 4, #3926-3929	3.00	
b.		Booklet pane, 5 each #3926-3929	15.00	

No. 3929b is a double-sided booklet with 12 stamps on one side and 8 stamps plus label (booklet cover) on the other side.

PRESIDENTIAL LIBRARIES ACT, 50th ANNIV.

Presidential Seal — A3007

Designed by Howard E. Paine. Printed by Banknote Corporation of America for Sennett Security Products.

LITHOGRAPHED
Sheets of 180 in nine panes of 20

2005, Aug. 4	Tagged	*Serpentine Die Cut 10¾*		
		Self-Adhesive		
3930	A3007	37c **multicolored**	.85	.20
		P# block of 4, 3#+S	3.50	
		Pane of 20	17.50	
		Sheet of 180 (9 panes)	155.00	
		Cross gutter block of 4	8.25	
		Horiz. pair with vert. gutter	3.00	
		Vert. pair with horiz. gutter	2.00	

SPORTY CARS OF THE 1950S

1953 Studebaker Starliner A3008

1954 Kaiser Darren A3009

1953 Chevrolet Corvette A3010

1952 Nash Healey A3011

1955 Ford
Thunderbird
A3012

Designed by Art M. Fitzpatrick. Printed by Ashton-Potter (USA) Ltd.

LITHOGRAPHED
BOOKLET STAMPS
Serpentine Die Cut 10¾ on 2 or 3 Sides

2005, Aug. 20			Tagged	
Self-Adhesive				
3931	A3008	37c multicolored	.90	.20
3932	A3009	37c multicolored	.90	.20
3933	A3010	37c multicolored	.90	.20
3934	A3011	37c multicolored	.90	.20
3935	A3012	37c multicolored	.90	.20
a.		Vert. strip of 5, #3931-3935	4.50	
b.		Booklet pane, 4 each #3931-3935	18.00	

Stamps in No. 3935a are not adjacent, as rows of selvage are between stamps one and two, and between stamps three and four.

No. 3935b is a double-sided booklet pane with 12 stamps on one side (2 each #3931, 3933, 3935, and 3 each #3932, 3934) and eight stamps (1 each #3932, 3934, and 2 each #3931, 3933, 3935) plus label on the other side.

ARTHUR ASHE

Arthur Ashe (1943-93),
Tennis Player — A3013

Designed by Carl T. Herrman. Printed by Ashton-Potter (USA) Ltd.

LITHOGRAPHED
Sheets of 240 in twelve panes of 20

2005, Aug. 27	Tagged	*Serpentine Die Cut 10¾*		
Self-Adhesive				
3936	A3013	37c multicolored	.75	.20
		P# block of 4, 5#+P	3.00	
		Pane of 20	15.00	

TO FORM A MORE PERFECT UNION

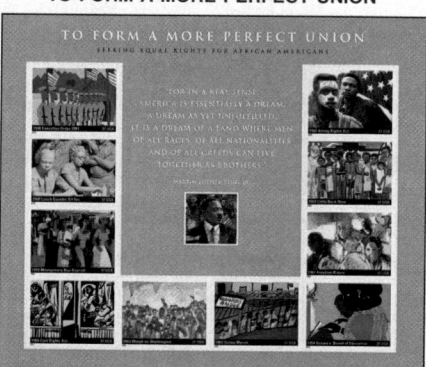

A3014

Illustration reduced.

Designed by Ethel Kessler. Printed by Ashton-Potter (USA) Ltd.

Inscriptions and artwork: a, 1948 Executive Order 9981 (Training for War, by William H. Johnson). b, 1965 Voting Rights Act (Youths on the Selma March, 1965, photograph by Bruce Davidson). c, 1960 Lunch Counter Sit-ins (National Civil Rights Museum exhibits, by StudioEIS). d, 1957 Little Rock Nine (America Cares, by George Hunt). e, 1955 Montgomery Bus Boycott (Walking, by Charles Alston). f, 1961 Freedom Riders (Freedom Riders, by May Stevens). g, 1964 Civil Rights Act (Dixie Café, by Jacob Lawrence). h,

1963 March on Washington (March on Washington, by Alma Thomas). i, 1965 Selma March (Selma March, by Bernice Sims). j, 1954 Brown v. Board of Education (The Lamp, by Romare Bearden).

LITHOGRAPHED
Serpentine Die Cut 10¾x10½

2005, Aug. 30			Tagged	
Self-Adhesive				
3937	A3014	Pane of 10	7.50	
a.-j.		37c Any single	.75	.20

CHILD HEALTH

Child and
Doctor — A3015

Designed by Craig Frazier.

Printed by Avery Dennison.

PHOTOGRAVURE
Sheets of 200 in ten panes of 20
Serpentine Die Cut 10½x11

2005, Sept. 7			Tagged	
Self-Adhesive				
3938	A3015	37c multicolored	.75	.20
		P# block of 4, 4#+V	3.00	
		Pane of 20	15.00	

LET'S DANCE

Merengue — A3016

Salsa — A3017

Cha Cha
Cha — A3018

Mambo — A3019

Designed by Ethel Kessler.

Printed by American Packaging Corporation for Sennett Security Products.

PHOTOGRAVURE
Sheets of 120 in six panes of 20

2005, Sept. 17	Tagged	*Serpentine Die Cut 10¾*		
Self-Adhesive				
3939	A3016	37c multicolored	.75	.20
3940	A3017	37c multicolored	.75	.20
3941	A3018	37c multicolored	.75	.20
3942	A3019	37c multicolored	.75	.20
a.		Vert. strip of 4, #3939-3942	3.00	
		P# block of 8, 8#+S	6.00	
		Pane of 20	15.00	

Stamps in the vertical strip are not adjacent as rows of selvage are between the stamps. The backing paper of stamps from the 2nd and 4th columns have Spanish inscriptions, while the other columns have English inscriptions.

GRETA GARBO

Garbo (1905-90),
Actress — A3020

Designed by Carl T. Herrman.

Printed by Banknote Corporation of America for Sennett Security Products.

ENGRAVED
Sheets of 120 in six panes of 20

2005, Sept. 23	Tagged	*Serpentine Die Cut 10¾*		
Self-Adhesive				
3943	A3020	37c black	.75	.20
		P# block of 4, 1#+S	3.00	
		Pane of 20	15.00	

See Sweden No. 2517.

JIM HENSON AND THE MUPPETS

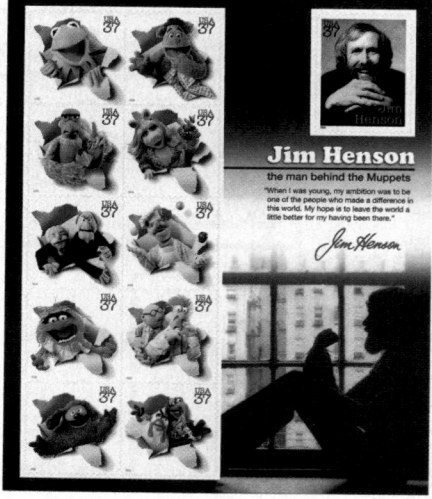

A3021

Illustration reduced.

Designed by Edward Eyth.

Printed by Avery Dennison.
No. 3944: a, Kermit the Frog. b, Fozzie Bear. c, Sam the
Eagle and flag. d, Miss Piggy. e, Statler and Waldorf. f, The
Swedish Chef and fruit. g, Animal. h, Dr. Bunsen Honeydew
and Beaker. i, Rowlf the Dog. j, The Great Gonzo and Camilla
the Chicken. k, Jim Henson.
Nos. 3944a-3944j are 30x30mm; No. 3944k, 28x37mm.

PHOTOGRAVURE
Serpentine Die Cut 10½, 10½x10¾ (#3944k)
2005, Sept. 28   **Tagged**

Self-Adhesive

3944	A3021	Pane of 11	8.25	
a.-k.		37c Any single	.75	.20

CONSTELLATIONS

Leo — A3022   Orion — A3023

Lyra — A3024   Pegasus — A3025

Designed by McRay Magleby.

Printed by Ashton-Potter (USA) Ltd.

LITHOGRAPHED
Sheets of 240 in twelve panes of 20
2005, Oct. 3   **Tagged**   *Serpentine Die Cut 10¾*
Self-Adhesive

3945	A3022	37c multicolored	.75	.20
3946	A3023	37c multicolored	.75	.20
3947	A3024	37c multicolored	.75	.20
3948	A3025	37c multicolored	.75	.20
a.		Block or vert. strip of 4, #3945-3948	3.00	
		P# block of 4, 6#+P	3.00	
		P# block of 10, 2 sets of P# + top label	7.50	
		Pane of 20	15.00	
b.		As "a," die cutting omitted	—	

CHRISTMAS COOKIES

Santa Claus — A3026   Snowmen — A3027

Angel — A3028   Elves — A3029

 Santa Claus — A3030   Snowmen — A3031

Angel — A3032   Elves — A3033

Designed by Derry Noyes.
Printed by Banknote Corporation of America for Sennett
Security Products (#3949-3952), American Packaging Corpora-
tion for Sennett Security Products (#3953-3960).

LITHOGRAPHED, PHOTOGRAVURE (#3953-3960)
Serpentine Die Cut 10¾x11
2005, Oct. 20   **Tagged**
Self-Adhesive
Design Size: 19x26mm

3949	A3026	37c multicolored	.85	.20
3950	A3027	37c multicolored	.85	.20
3951	A3028	37c multicolored	.85	.20
3952	A3029	37c multicolored	.85	.20
a.		Block or vert. strip of 4, #3949-3952	3.50	
		P# block of 4, 4#+S	3.50	
		Pane of 20	17.50	

Booklet Stamps
Serpentine Die Cut 10¾x11 on 2 or 3 Sides
Design Size: 19½x27mm

3953	A3026	37c multicolored	.75	.20
3954	A3027	37c multicolored	.75	.20
3955	A3028	37c multicolored	.75	.20
3956	A3029	37c multicolored	.75	.20
a.		Block of 4, #3953-3956	3.00	
b.		Booklet pane of 20, 5 #3956a	15.00	

Serpentine Die Cut 10½x10¾

3957	A3030	37c multicolored	1.50	.20
3958	A3031	37c multicolored	1.50	.20
3959	A3032	37c multicolored	1.50	.20
3960	A3033	37c multicolored	1.50	.20
a.		Block of 4, #3957-3960	6.00	
b.		Booklet pane of 4, #3957-3960	6.00	
c.		Booklet pane of 6, #3959-3960, 2 each #3957-3958	9.00	
d.		Booklet pane of 6, #3957-3958, 2 each #3959-3960	9.00	

No. 3956b is a double-sided booklet pane with 12 stamps on
one side and eight stamps plus label that serves as a booklet
cover on the other side. Nos. 3949-3952 have a small "2005"
year date, while Nos. 3953-3956 have a large year date. Other
design differences caused by different cropping of the images
can be found, with Nos. 3953-3956 showing slightly more
design features on one or more sides.

DISTINGUISHED MARINES

Lt. Gen. John A. Lejeune (1867-1942), 2nd Infantry Division Insignia A3034

Lt. Gen. Lewis B. Puller (1898-1971), 1st Marine Division Insignia A3035

Sgt. John Basilone (1916-45), 5th Marine Division Insignia A3036

Sgt. Major Daniel J. Daly (1873-1937), 73rd Machine Gun Company, 6th Marine Regiment Insignia A3037

Designed by Phil Jordan. Printed by Ashton-Potter (USA) Ltd.

LITHOGRAPHED
Sheets of 180 in nine panes of 20
Serpentine Die Cut 11x10½
2005, Nov. 10   **Tagged**
Self-Adhesive

3961	A3034	37c multicolored	1.00	.20
3962	A3035	37c multicolored	1.00	.20
3963	A3036	37c multicolored	1.00	.20
3964	A3037	37c multicolored	1.00	.20
a.		Block or horiz. strip of 4, #3961-3964	4.00	
		P# block of 4, 6#+P	4.00	
		P# block of 8, 2 sets of P# + top panel	8.00	
		Pane of 20	20.00	

Flag and Statue of Liberty — A3038

Designed by Carl and Ann Purcell. Printed by Sterling Sommer, Inc. for Ashton-Potter (USA) Ltd. (#3965), Ashton-Potter
(USA) Ltd. (#3966, 3970), American Packaging Corporation for
Sennett Security Printers (#3967, 3969, 3973), Avery Dennison
(#3968, 3972, 3975), Banknote Corporation of America for Sennett Security Products (#3974).

LITHOGRAPHED (#3965, 3966, 3970, 3974), PHOTOGRAVURE
Sheets of 400 in four panes of 100 (#3965), Sheets of 120 in six panes of 20 (#3966)
2005, Dec. 8   **Tagged**   **Perf. 11¼**

3965	A3038	(39c) multicolored	.80	.20
		P# block of 4, 4#+P	5.00	

Self-Adhesive (#3966, 3968-3975)
Serpentine Die Cut 11¼x10¾

3966	A3038	(39c) multicolored	.80	.20
		P# block of 4, 4#+P	3.20	
		Pane of 20	16.00	
a.		Booklet pane of 20	16.00	
b.		As "a," die cutting omitted	—	

COIL STAMPS
Perf. 9¾ Vert.

3967	A3038	(39c) multicolored	.80	.20
		Pair	1.60	—
		P# strip of 5, #S1111	5.25	—
		P# single, #S1111		2.00

Serpentine Die Cut 8½ Vert.

3968	A3038	(39c) multicolored	.80	.20
		Pair	1.60	
		P# strip of 5, #V1111	5.25	

	P# single, #V1111			1.50	

Serpentine Die Cut 10¼ Vert.

3969	A3038	(39c) multicolored		.80	.20
		Pair		1.60	
		P# strip of 5, #S1111		5.25	
		P# single, #S1111			1.50

Serpentine Die Cut 9½ Vert.

3970	A3038	(39c) multicolored		.80	.20
		Pair		1.60	
		P# strip of 5, #P1111, P2222		6.50	
		P# single, #P1111, P2222			2.00

BOOKLET STAMPS
Serpentine Die Cut 11¼x10¾ on 2 or 3 Sides

3972	A3038	(39c) multicolored		.80	.20
a.		Booklet pane of 20		16.00	

Serpentine Die Cut 10½x10¾ on 2 or 3 Sides

3973	A3038	(39c) multicolored		.80	.20
a.		Booklet pane of 20		16.00	

On both Nos. 3972 and 3973, the sky immediately above the date is bright blue and extends from the left side to beyond the "6" in the date, the left arm of the star at the upper left barely touches the frame line and is without the "USPS" microprinting. They are distinguishable by the die cutting. Nos. 3872a and 3973a are double-sided booklet panes with 12 stamps on one side and eight stamps plus label that serves as a booklet cover on the other side.

No. 3973 was not available until January 2006.

Serpentine Die Cut 11¼x10¾ on 2 or 3 Sides

3974	A3038	(39c) multicolored		.80	.20
a.		Booklet pane of 4		3.20	
b.		Booklet pane of 6		4.80	

Serpentine Die Cut 8 on 2, 3 or 4 Sides

3975	A3038	(39c) multicolored		.80	.20
a.		Booklet pane of 18		14.50	
		Nos. 3965-3975 (10)		8.00	2.00

Nos. 3965-3975 are dated "2006."

On No. 3966, the sky immediately above the date is bright blue and extends from the left side to beyond the "6" in the date, the left arm of the star at upper left is clear of the top frame, and "USPS" is microprinted on the top red flag stripe.

On No. 3974, the sky immediately above the date is dark blue and extends from the left side to the second "0" in the date, the left arm of the star at upper left touches the top frame, and lacks the microprinting found on No. 3966.

Nos. 3965 and 3970 also have "USPS" microprinted on the top red flag stripe.

Nos. 3966a and 3972a are double-sided booklet panes with 12 stamps on one side and eight stamps plus label that serves as a booklet cover on the other side. On No. 3966a, the stamps on one side are upside-down with relation to the stamps on the other side. On No. 3972a the stamps are all aligned the same on both sides.

LOVE

Birds — A3039

Designed by Craig Frazier. Printed by Avery Dennison.

PHOTOGRAVURE
Serpentine Die Cut 11 on 2, 3, or 4 Sides

2006, Jan. 3		**Tagged**

BOOKLET STAMP
Self-Adhesive

3976	A3039	(39c) multicolored		.90	.20
a.		Booklet pane of 20		18.00	

Flag and Statue of Liberty — A3040

Designed by Carl and Ann Purcell. Printed by American Packaging Corporation for Sennett Security Products (#3979, 3982), Ashton-Potter (USA) Ltd. (#3978, 3981). Avery Dennison (#3980).

LITHOGRAPHED (#3978, 3981), PHOTOGRAVURE (#3979-3980, 3983, 3985)
Sheets of 120 in six panes of 20

2006	**Tagged**	**Serpentine Die Cut 11¼x10¾**

Self-Adhesive

3978	A3040	39c multicolored, *Apr. 8*		.80	.20
		P# block of 4, 4#+P		3.20	
		Pane of 20		16.00	
a.		Booklet pane of 10		8.00	
b.		Booklet pane of 20		16.00	
c.		As "b," die cutting omitted on side with 8 stamps			

No. 3978 has "USPS" microprinted on top red flag stripe.
No. 3978b is a double-sided booklet with 12 stamps on one side and 8 stamps plus label (booklet cover) on the other side.

Perf. 10 Vert.
COIL STAMPS

3979	A3040	39c multicolored, *Mar. 8*		.80	.20
		Pair		1.60	
		P# strip of 5, #S1111		5.25	—
		P# single, #S1111		—	2.50

Serpentine Die Cut 11 Vert.

3980	A3040	39c multicolored, overall tagging, *Jan. 9*		.80	.20
		Pair		1.60	
		P# strip of 5, #V1111		5.25	
		P# single, #V1111		—	2.50
a.		Prephosphored coated paper with surface tagging showing a solid appearance			
		Pair		—	
		P# strip of 5, #V1111		—	

No. 3980 has rounded corners and lacks microprinting. Unused examples are on backing paper taller than the stamp, and the stamps are spaced approximately 3mm apart.

Serpentine Die Cut 9½ Vert.

3981	A3040	39c multicolored, *Apr. 8*		.80	.20
		Pair		1.60	
		P# strip of 5, #P1111		6.25	
		P# single, #P1111		—	2.00
a.		Die cutting omitted, pair		—	

No. 3981 has "USPS" microprinted on top red flag stripe.

Serpentine Die Cut 10¼ Vert.

3982	A3040	39c multicolored, *Apr. 8*		.80	.20
		Pair		1.60	
		P# strip of 5, #S1111		5.25	
		P# single, #S1111		—	2.00
a.		Vert. pair, unslit between		—	

No. 3982 was not made available until June, despite the official first day of issue.

Serpentine Die Cut 8½ Vert.

3983	A3040	39c multicolored, *Apr. 8*		.80	.20
		Pair		1.60	
		P# strip of 5, #V1111		5.25	
		P# single, #V1111		—	2.00

BOOKLET STAMP
Serpentine Die Cut 11¼x10¾ on 2 or 3 Sides

3985	A3040	39c multicolored, *Apr. 8*		.80	.20
a.		Booklet pane of 20		16.00	
b.		Serpentine die cut 11.1 on 2 or 3 sides		.80	.20
c.		Booklet pane of 4 #3985b		3.20	
d.		Booklet pane of 6 #3985b		4.80	

Nos. 3983 and 3985 lack the microprinting found on Nos. 3978 and 3981. No. 3983 was not made available until July and No. 3985 was not made available until August, despite the official first day of issue. No. 3985a is a double-sided booklet with 12 stamps on one side and 8 stamps plus label (booklet cover) on the other side.

CHILDREN'S BOOK ANIMALS

The Very Hungry Caterpillar, from *The Very Hungry Caterpillar*, by Eric Carle — A3041

Wilbur, from *Charlotte's Web*, by E. B. White — A3042

Fox in Socks, from *Fox in Socks*, by Dr. Seuss — A3043

Maisy, from *Maisy's ABC*, by Lucy Cousins — A3044

Wild Thing, from *Where the Wild Things Are*, by Maurice Sendak — A3045

Curious George, from *Curious George*, by Margaret and H. A. Rey — A3046

Olivia, from *Olivia*, by Ian Falconer — A3047

Frederick, from *Frederick*, by Leo Lionni — A3048

Designed by Derry Noyes. Printed by American Packaging Corporation for Sennett Security Products.

PHOTOGRAVURE
Sheets of 96 in six panes of 16

2006, Jan. 10 Tagged *Serpentine Die Cut 10¾*
Self-Adhesive

3987	A3041	39c multicolored	.80	.20
3988	A3042	39c multicolored	.80	.20
3989	A3043	39c multicolored	.80	.20
3990	A3044	39c multicolored	.80	.20
3991	A3045	39c multicolored	.80	.20
3992	A3046	39c multicolored	.80	.20
3993	A3047	39c multicolored	.80	.20
3994	A3048	39c multicolored	.80	.20
a.		Block of 8, #3987-3994	6.50	
		P# block of 8, 9# + S	6.50	
		Pane of 16	13.00	
		Sheet of 96 (6 panes)	80.00	
		Cross gutter block of 8	15.00	
		Block of 8 with horiz. gutter	9.00	
		Block of 8 different stamps with vert. gutter	8.00	
		Horiz. pair with vert. gutter	2.00	
		Vert. pair with horiz. gutter	2.00	

See Great Britain Nos. 2340-2341.

2006 WINTER OLYMPICS, TURIN, ITALY

Skier — A3049

Designed by Derry Noyes. Printed by Banknote Corporation of America for Sennett Security Products.

LITHOGRAPHED
Sheets of 240 in twelve panes of 20

2006, Jan. 11 Tagged *Serpentine Die Cut 10¾*
Self-Adhesive

3995	A3049	39c multicolored	.80	.20
		P# block of 4, 4# + S	3.20	
		Pane of 20	16.00	

BLACK HERITAGE SERIES

Hattie McDaniel (1895-1952), Actress — A3050

Designed by Ethel Kessler. Printed by Banknote Corporation of America for Sennett Security Products.

LITHOGRAPHED
Sheets of 240 in twelve panes of 20

2006, Jan. 25 Tagged *Serpentine Die Cut 10¾*
Self-Adhesive

3996	A3050	39c multicolored	.80	.20
		P# block of 4, 4# + S	3.20	
		Pane of 20	16.00	

Chinese New Year Types of 1992-2004
Designed by Clarence Lee. Printed by Banknote Corporation of America for Sennett Security Products.

LITHOGRAPHED

2006, Jan. 29 Tagged *Serpentine Die Cut 10¾*
Self-Adhesive

3997		Pane of 12	9.75	
a.	A2360	39c Rat	.80	.20
b.	A2413	39c Ox	.80	.20
c.	A2462	39c Tiger	.80	.20
d.	A2535	39c Rabbit	.80	.20
e.	A2602	39c Dragon	.80	.20
f.	A2702	39c Snake	.80	.20
g.	A2752	39c Horse	.80	.20
h.	A2856	39c Ram	.80	.20
i.	A2927	39c Monkey	.80	.20
j.	A2067	39c Rooster	.80	.20
k.	A2146	39c Dog	.80	.20
l.	A2205	39c Boar	.80	.20

WEDDING DOVES

Dove Facing Left — A3051

Dove Facing Right — A3052

Designed by Michael Osborne. Printed by Ashton-Potter (USA) Ltd.

LITHOGRAPHED
BOOKLET STAMPS
Serpentine Die Cut 10¾x11 on 2, 3 or 4 Sides
2006, Mar. 1   Tagged
Self-Adhesive

3998	A3051	39c pale lilac & bluish lilac	.80	.20
a.		Booklet pane of 20	16.00	

Serpentine Die Cut 10¾x11

3999	A3052	63c pale green & dull green	1.40	.50
a.		Booklet pane, 20 each #3998-3999	45.00	
b.		Horiz. pair, #3998-3999 with vertical gutter between	2.25	1.50

Common Buckeye Butterfly — A3053

Designed by Carl T. Herrman. Printed by Sterling Sommer, Inc. for Ashton-Potter (USA) Ltd. (#4000), Avery Dennison (#4001-4002).

LITHOGRAPHED (#4000), PHOTOGRAVURE (#4001-4002)
Sheets of 400 in four panes of 100 (#4000), Sheets of 280 in fourteen panes of 20 (#4001)

2006, Mar. 8   Tagged   Perf. 11¼

4000	A3053	24c multicolored	.50	.20
		P# block of 4, 4#+P	10.00	—

Self-Adhesive
Serpentine Die Cut 11

4001	A3053	24c multicolored	.55	.20
		P# block of 4, 4#+V	2.50	
		Pane of 20	12.00	
a.		Serpentine die cut 10¾x11¼ on 3 sides (from booklet panes)	.50	.20
b.		Booklet pane of 10 #4001a	5.00	
c.		Booklet pane of 4 #4001a	2.00	
d.		Booklet pane of 6 #4001a	3.00	

Some panes of No. 4001 contain bottom-row stamps that are 1mm taller than the other stamps on the pane. This most likely was caused by a shift of the die cutting blade cylinder on a low percentage of sheets in the press run.

No. 4001b is a convertible booklet that was sold flat. It has a self-adhesive panel that covers the rouletting on the inside of the booklet cover. Nos. 4001c and 4001d are component panes of a vending machine booklet, which was sold pre-folded and sealed, and which does not have the self-adhesive panel covering the rouletting on the inside of the booklet cover.

COIL STAMP
Serpentine Die Cut 8½ Horiz.

4002	A3053	24c multicolored	.50	.20
		Pair	1.00	
		P# strip of 5, #V1111	4.00	
		P# single, #V1111	—	2.00

CROPS OF THE AMERICAS

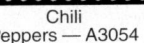

Chili Peppers — A3054

Beans — A3055

Sunflower and Seeds — A3056

Squashes — A3057

Corn — A3058

Designed by Phil Jordan. Printed by American Packaging Corporation for Sennett Security Products (#4003-4012), Banknote Corporation of America for Sennett Security Products (#4013-4017).

PHOTOGRAVURE (#4003-4012), LITHOGRAPHED (#4013-4017)
Serpentine Die Cut 10¼ Horiz.
2006, Mar. 16   Tagged
Self-Adhesive
Coil Stamps

4003	A3054	39c multicolored	.85	.20
4004	A3055	39c multicolored	.85	.20
4005	A3056	39c multicolored	.85	.20
4006	A3057	39c multicolored	.85	.20
4007	A3058	39c multicolored	.85	.20
a.		Strip of 5, #4003-4007	4.25	
		P# strip of 5, #4003-4007, #S1111	7.00	—
		P# strip of 11, 3 #4005, 2 each #4003-4004, 4006-4007	12.50	
		P# single (#4005), #S1111	—	2.00

Booklet Stamps
Serpentine Die Cut 10¾x10½ on 2 or 3 Sides

4008	A3058	39c multicolored	.80	.20
4009	A3057	39c multicolored	.80	.20
4010	A3056	39c multicolored	.80	.20
4011	A3055	39c multicolored	.80	.20
4012	A3054	39c multicolored	.80	.20
a.		Horiz. strip of 5, #4008-4012	4.00	
b.		Booklet pane, 4 each #4008-4012	16.00	

Stamps in Nos. 4012a and 4017a are not adjacent, as one or two rows of selvage is between stamps (or a blank space where selvage was removed by the manufacturer).

No. 4012b is a double-sided booklet with 12 stamps on one side and 8 stamps plus label (booklet cover) on the other side. "USA" is at right of "39" on No. 4004, at left of "39" on Nos. 4011, 4017. Top of "USA" is aligned with top of "39" on No. 4013, with bottom of "39" on Nos. 4003, 4012.

Serpentine Die Cut 10¾x11¼ on 2 or 3 Sides

4013	A3054	39c multicolored	.90	.20
4014	A3058	39c multicolored	.90	.20
4015	A3057	39c multicolored	.90	.20
4016	A3056	39c multicolored	.90	.20
a.		Booklet pane of 4, #4013-4016	3.60	
4017	A3055	39c multicolored	.90	.20
a.		Horiz. strip of 5, #4013-4017	4.50	
b.		Booklet pane of 4, #4013-4015, 4017	3.60	
c.		Booklet pane of 6, #4013-4016, 2 #4017	5.50	
d.		Booklet pane of 6, #4013-4015, 4017, 2 #4016	5.50	

The peelable selvage strips were removed by the manufacturer from 1 million of the 11 million vending booklets produced (containing Nos. 4017b, 4017c and 4017d).

X-PLANES

A3059

A3060

Designed by Phil Jordan. Printed by Banknote Corporation of America for Sennett Security Products.

LITHOGRAPHED WITH HOLOGRAM AFFIXED
Sheets of 120 in six panes of 20
Serpentine Die Cut 10¾x10½

2006, Mar. 17				Tagged	

Self-Adhesive

4018	A3059	$4.05	multicolored	8.00	5.00
			P# block of 4, 4#+S	40.00	
			Pane of 20	160.00	
a.			Silver foil ("X") omitted	—	
4019	A3060	$14.40	multicolored	27.50	15.00
			P# block of 4, 4#+S	110.00	
			Pane of 20	550.00	

SUGAR RAY ROBINSON (1921-89), BOXER

A3061

Designed by Carl T. Herrman. Printed by Avery Dennison.

PHOTOGRAVURE
Sheets of 200 in ten panes of 20

2006, Apr. 7	Tagged	*Serpentine Die Cut 11*

Self-Adhesive

4020	A3061	39c	red & blue	.80	.20
			P# block of 4, 2#+V	3.20	
			Pane of 20	16.00	

BENJAMIN FRANKLIN (1706-90)

Statesman A3062

Scientist A3063

Printer A3064

Postmaster A3065

Designed by Richard Sheaff. Printed by Avery Dennison.

PHOTOGRAVURE
Sheets of 200 in ten panes of 20

2006, Apr. 7	Tagged	*Serpentine Die Cut 11*

Self-Adhesive

4021	A3062	39c	multicolored	1.10	.20
4022	A3063	39c	multicolored	1.10	.20
4023	A3064	39c	multicolored	1.10	.20
4024	A3065	39c	multicolored	1.10	.20
a.			Block or horiz. strip of 4	4.40	
			P# block of 4, 4#+V	4.50	
			Pane of 20	22.50	

THE ART OF DISNEY: ROMANCE

Mickey and Minnie Mouse — A3066

Cinderella and Prince Charming — A3067

Beauty and the Beast — A3068

Lady and Tramp — A3069

Designed by David Pacheco. Printed by Ashton-Potter (USA) Ltd.

LITHOGRAPHED
Sheets of 180 in nine panes of 20
Serpentine Die Cut 10½x10¾

2006, Apr. 21				Tagged	

Self-Adhesive

4025	A3066	39c	multicolored	.80	.20
4026	A3067	39c	multicolored	.80	.20
4027	A3068	39c	multicolored	.80	.20
4028	A3069	39c	multicolored	.80	.20
a.			Block or vert. strip of 4, #4025-4028	3.20	
			P# block of 4, 6#+P	3.20	
			Pane of 20	16.00	

LOVE

Birds — A3070

Designed by Craig Frazier. Printed by Avery Dennison.

PHOTOGRAVURE
Serpentine Die Cut 11 on 2, 3 or 4 Sides

2006, May 1		Tagged	

Self-Adhesive
Booklet Stamp

4029	A3070	39c	multicolored	.80	.20
a.			Booklet pane of 20	16.00	

LITERARY ARTS

Katherine Anne Porter (1890-1980), Author A3071

Designed by Derry Noyes. Printed by Banknote Corporation of America for Sennett Security Products.

LITHOGRAPHED
Sheets of 240 in twelve panes of 20

2006, May 15	Tagged	*Serpentine Die Cut 10¾*

Self-Adhesive

4030	A3071	39c	multicolored	.80	.20
			P# block of 4, 4#+S	3.20	
			Pane of 20	16.00	

AMBER ALERT

Mother and Child — A3072

Designed by Derry Noyes. Printed by Avery Dennison.

PHOTOGRAVURE
Sheets of 160 in eight panes of 20

2006, May 25	Tagged	*Serpentine Die Cut 10¾*

Self-Adhesive

4031	A3072	39c	multicolored	.80	.20
			P# block of 4, 6#+V	3.20	
			Pane of 20	16.00	

Purple Heart Type of 2003

Designed by Carl T. Herrman. Printed by Ashton-Potter (USA) Ltd.

LITHOGRAPHED
Sheets of 120 in six panes of 20
Serpentine Die Cut 11¼x11

2006, May 26		Tagged	

Self-Adhesive

4032	A2891	39c	multicolored	.80	.20
			P# block of 4, 4#+P	3.20	
			Pane of 20	16.00	

WONDERS OF AMERICA

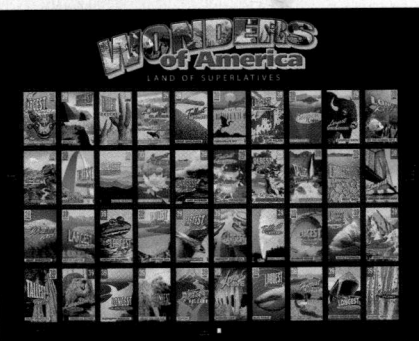

A3073-A3112

Illustration reduced.

Designed by Richard Sheaff. Printed by Avery Dennison.

Designs: No. 4033, American alligator, largest reptile. No. 4034, Moloka'i, highest sea cliffs. No. 4035, Saguaro, tallest cactus. No. 4036, Bering Glacier, largest glacier. No. 4037, Great Sand Dunes, tallest dune. No. 4038, Chesapeake Bay, largest estuary. No. 4039, Cliff Palace, largest cliff dwelling. No. 4040, Crater Lake, deepest lake. No. 4041, American bison, largest land mammal. No. 4042, Off the Florida Keys, longest reef. No. 4043, Pacific Crest Trail, longest hiking trail. No. 4044, Gateway Arch, tallest man-made monument. No. 4045, Appalachians, oldest mountains. No. 4046, American lotus, largest flower. No. 4047, Lake Superior, largest lake. No. 4048, Pronghorn, fastest land animal. No. 4049, Bristlecone pines, oldest trees. No. 4050, Yosemite Falls, tallest waterfall. No. 4051, Great Basin, largest desert. No. 4052, Verrazano-Narrows Bridge, longest span. No. 4053, Mount Washington, windiest place. No. 4054, Grand Canyon, largest canyon. No. 4055, American bullfrog, largest frog. No. 4056, Oroville Dam, tallest dam. No. 4057, Peregrine falcon, fastest bird. No. 4058, Mississippi River Delta, largest delta. No. 4059, Steamboat, tallest geyser. No. 4060, Rainbow Bridge, largest natural bridge. No. 4061, White sturgeon, largest freshwater fish. No. 4062, Rocky Mountains, longest mountain chain. No. 4063, Coast redwoods, tallest trees. No. 4064, American beaver, largest rodent. No. 4065, Mississippi-Missouri, longest river system. No. 4066, Mount Wai'ale'ale, rainiest spot. No. 4067, Kilauea, most active volcano. No. 4068, Mammoth Cave, longest cave. No. 4069, Blue whale, loudest animal. No. 4070, Death Valley, hottest spot. No. 4071, Cornish-Windsor Bridge, longest covered bridge. No. 4072, Quaking aspen, largest plant.

PHOTOGRAVURE
Sheets of 80 in two panes of 40

**2006, May 27   Tagged   *Serpentine Die Cut 10¾*
Self-Adhesive**

4033	A3073	39c	multicolored	.80	.45
4034	A3074	39c	multicolored	.80	.45
4035	A3075	39c	multicolored	.80	.45
4036	A3076	39c	multicolored	.80	.45
4037	A3077	39c	multicolored	.80	.45
4038	A3078	39c	multicolored	.80	.45
4039	A3079	39c	multicolored	.80	.45
4040	A3080	39c	multicolored	.80	.45
4041	A3081	39c	multicolored	.80	.45
4042	A3082	39c	multicolored	.80	.45
4043	A3083	39c	multicolored	.80	.45
4044	A3084	39c	multicolored	.80	.45
4045	A3085	39c	multicolored	.80	.45
4046	A3086	39c	multicolored	.80	.45
4047	A3087	39c	multicolored	.80	.45
4048	A3088	39c	multicolored	.80	.45
4049	A3089	39c	multicolored	.80	.45
4050	A3090	39c	multicolored	.80	.45
4051	A3091	39c	multicolored	.80	.45
4052	A3092	39c	multicolored	.80	.45
4053	A3093	39c	multicolored	.80	.45
4054	A3094	39c	multicolored	.80	.45
4055	A3095	39c	multicolored	.80	.45
4056	A3096	39c	multicolored	.80	.45
4057	A3097	39c	multicolored	.80	.45
4058	A3098	39c	multicolored	.80	.45
4059	A3099	39c	multicolored	.80	.45
4060	A3100	39c	multicolored	.80	.45
4061	A3101	39c	multicolored	.80	.45
4062	A3102	39c	multicolored	.80	.45
4063	A3103	39c	multicolored	.80	.45
4064	A3104	39c	multicolored	.80	.45
4065	A3105	39c	multicolored	.80	.45
4066	A3106	39c	multicolored	.80	.45
4067	A3107	39c	multicolored	.80	.45
4068	A3108	39c	multicolored	.80	.45
4069	A3109	39c	multicolored	.80	.45
4070	A3110	39c	multicolored	.80	.45
4071	A3111	39c	multicolored	.80	.45
4072	A3112	39c	multicolored	.80	.45
a.		Pane of 40, #4033-4072		32.00	
		Sheet of 80 (two panes)		65.00	
		Block of 40 different stamps with horiz. gutter between any two rows		32.00	
		Pair with horiz. gutter between (each)		2.00	

EXPLORATION OF EAST COAST BY SAMUEL DE CHAMPLAIN, 400TH ANNIV.

Ship and Map — A3113

A3114

Illustration reduced.

Designed by Rejean Myette and Francois Martin, Canada (#4073), Terrence W. McCaffrey and Francois Martin (#4074). Printed by Ashton-Potter (USA) Ltd. Illustration A3114 is reduced.

LITHOGRAPHED & ENGRAVED
Sheets of 120 in six panes of 20 (#4073), Sheets of 24 in six panes of 4 (#4074)

**2006, May 28   Tagged   *Serpentine Die Cut 10¾*
Self-Adhesive (#4073)**

4073	A3113	39c	multicolored	.85	.20
		P# block of 4, 6#+P		3.50	
		Pane of 20		17.50	

Souvenir Sheet
Perf. 11

4074	A3114		Sheet, 2 each #4074a, Canada #2156a	8.00	2.00
a.	A3113	39c	multicolored	1.75	.20
			Sheet of 24 (6 panes)	47.50	—
			Cross gutter block of 4 Canadian and 4 American stamps	14.00	—
			Block of 2 Canadian and 2 American stamps with horiz. gutter between	7.00	—
			Horiz. pair of Canadian and American stamps with vert. gutter between	3.50	—

Washington 2006 World Philatelic Exhibition (#4074). Canada No. 2156, which was sold only by Canada Post, has a bar code in the lower left margin of the sheet. No. 4074, which was sold only by the United States Postal Service for $1.75, lacks this bar code.

WASHINGTON 2006 WORLD PHILATELIC EXHIBITION
Souvenir Sheet

A3115

Illustration reduced.

Designed by Richard Sheaff. Printed by Banknote Corporation of America for Sennett Security Products.

LITHOGRAPHED (MARGIN) & ENGRAVED
Sheets of 18 in six panes of 3

2006, May 29   Tagged   *Perf. 10¾x10½*

4075	A3115		Pane of 3	16.00	6.00
a.	A174	$1	violet brown	2.00	.50
b.	A175	$2	deep blue	4.00	1.00
c.	A176	$5	carmine & blue	10.00	2.50
			Sheet of 6 panes	96.00	—
			Cross gutter block of 4 panes	64.00	—
			Vert. pair of panes with horiz. gutter between	32.00	—
			Horiz. pair of panes with vert. gutter between	32.00	—

DISTINGUISHED AMERICAN DIPLOMATS
Souvenir Sheet

A3116

Illustration reduced.

Designed by Howard E. Paine. Printed by Avery Dennison.

No. 4076: a, Robert D. Murphy (1894-1978). b, Frances E. Willis (1899-1983). c, Hiram Bingham IV (1903-88). d, Philip C. Habib (1920-92). e, Charles E. Bohlen (1904-74). f, Clifton R. Wharton, Sr. (1899-1990).

PHOTOGRAVURE
Sheets of 90 in fifteen panes of 6

**2006, May 29   Tagged   *Serpentine Die Cut 10¾*
Self-Adhesive**

4076	A3116		Pane of 6	4.80	
a.-f.		39c	any single	.80	.20
			Sheet of 15 panes	72.00	
			Cross gutter block of 6	7.00	
			Block of 6 with vert. gutter between	7.00	
			Block of 6 with horiz. gutter between	7.00	
			Horiz. pair with vert. gutter (each)	2.00	
			Vert. pair with horiz. gutter (each)	2.00	

The cross gutter block consists of 1 stamp from each of two panes and 2 stamps from each of two adjacent panes. Plate number, 1#+V, is on margin of backing paper.

LEGENDS OF HOLLYWOOD

Judy Garland (1922-69),
Actress — A3117

Designed by Ethel Kessler. Printed by Banknote Corporation
of America for Sennett Security Products.

LITHOGRAPHED
Sheets of 120 in six panes of 20
2006, June 10 **Tagged** *Serpentine Die Cut 10¾*
Self-Adhesive

4077	A3117	39c	**multicolored**	.85	.20
			P# block of 4, 4#+S	3.50	
			Pane of 20	17.50	
			Sheet of 120 (6 panes)	105.00	
			Cross gutter block of 8	17.50	
			Block of 8 with vertical gutter	10.00	
			Horiz. pair with vert. gutter	3.00	
			Vert. pair with horiz. gutter	2.00	
a.			Pair, die cutting omitted	—	

Cross gutter block consists of 6 stamps from upper panes
and 2 stamps from panes below.

Ronald Reagan Type of 2005
Designed by Howard E. Paine. Printed by American Packaging Corporation for Sennett Security Products.

PHOTOGRAVURE
Sheets of 120 in six panes of 20
2006, June 14 **Tagged** *Serpentine Die Cut 10¾*
Self-Adhesive

4078	A2974	39c	**multicolored**	.80	.20
			P# block of 4, 4#+S	3.20	
			Pane of 20	16.00	

Happy Birthday Type of 2002
Designed by Harry Zelenko. Printed by Avery Dennison.

PHOTOGRAVURE
Sheets of 200 in ten panes of 20
2006, June 23 **Tagged** *Serpentine Die Cut 11*
Self-Adhesive

4079	A2751	39c	**multicolored**	.80	.20
			P# block of 4, 4#+V	3.20	
			Pane of 20	16.00	

BASEBALL SLUGGERS

Roy Campanella
(1921-93) — A3118

Hank Greenberg
(1911-86) — A3119

Mel Ott (1909-
58) — A3120

Mickey Mantle (1931-
95) — A3121

Designed by Phil Jordan. Printed by Avery Dennison.

PHOTOGRAVURE
Sheets of 120 in six panes of 20
2006, July 15 **Tagged** *Serpentine Die Cut 10¾*
Self-Adhesive

4080	A3118	39c	**multicolored**	.80	.20
4081	A3119	39c	**multicolored**	.80	.20
4082	A3120	39c	**multicolored**	.80	.20
4083	A3121	39c	**multicolored**	.80	.20
a.			Block or vert. strip of 4, #4080-4083	3.20	
			P# block of 4, 6#+V	3.20	
			P# block of 10, 2 sets of P# + top label	8.00	
			Pane of 20	16.00	
			Sheet of 120 (6 panes)	97.50	
			Cross gutter block of 8	17.50	
			Block of 4 with horiz. gutter	6.00	
			Horiz. pair with vert. gutter	3.00	
			Vert. pair with horiz. gutter	3.00	

Cross gutter block of 8 consists of four stamps from top two
panes and four stamps from bottom two panes with the cross
gutter between.

DC COMICS SUPERHEROES

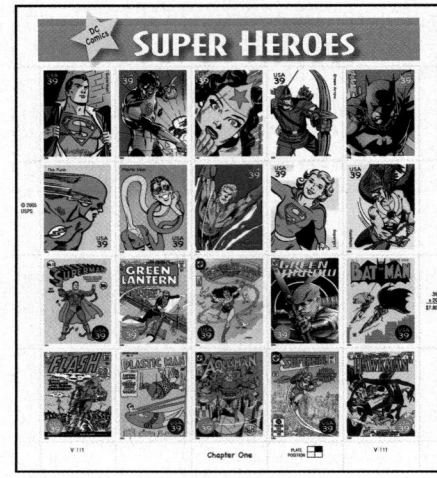

A3122

Illustration reduced.

Designed by Carl T. Herrman. Printed by Avery
Dennison.
No. 4084: a, Superman. b, Green Lantern. c, Wonder Woman. d, Green Arrow. e, Batman. f, The Flash.
g, Plastic Man. h, Aquaman. i, Supergirl. j, Hawkman.
k, Cover of *Superman #11*. l, Cover of *Green Lantern
#4*. m, Cover of *Wonder Woman #22 (Second Series)*.
n, Cover of *Green Arrow #15*. o, Cover of *Batman #1*.
p, Cover of *The Flash #111*. q, Cover of *Plastic Man
#4*. r, Cover of *Aquaman #5 (of 5)*. s, Cover of *The
Daring New Adventures of Supergirl #1*. t, Cover of
The Brave and the Bold Presents Hawkman #36.

PHOTOGRAVURE
Sheets of 80 in four panes of 20
Serpentine Die Cut 10½x10¾
2006, July 20 **Tagged**
Self-Adhesive

4084	A3122	Pane of 20	16.00	
a.-t.		39c Any single	.80	.20
		Sheet of 80 (4 panes)	65.00	
		Cross gutter block of 20	24.00	
		Horiz. pair with vert. gutter (each)	3.00	
		Vert. pair with horiz. gutter (each)	3.00	

Cross gutter block consists of 12 stamps from the panes on
one side of the sheet and 8 stamps from the panes on the other
side of the sheet.

MOTORCYCLES

1940 Indian
Four — A3123

1918 Cleveland
A3124

Generic
"Chopper," c.
1970 — A3125

1965 Harley-Davidson Electra-Glide — A3126

Designed by Richard Sheaff. Printed by Avery Dennison.

PHOTOGRAVURE
Sheets of 160 in eight panes of 20
Serpentine Die Cut 10¾x10½
2006, Aug. 7 **Tagged**
Self-Adhesive

4085	A3123	39c	**multicolored**	1.00	.20
4086	A3124	39c	**multicolored**	1.00	.20
4087	A3125	39c	**multicolored**	1.00	.20
4088	A3126	39c	**multicolored**	1.00	.20
a.			Block or horiz. strip of 4, #4085-4088	4.00	
			P# block of 4, 5#+V	4.00	
			P# block of 8, 2 sets of P# + top label	8.00	
			Pane of 20	20.00	

AMERICAN TREASURES SERIES
Quilts of Gee's Bend, Alabama

Housetop Variation, by
Mary Lee
Bendolph — A3127

Pig in a Pen Medallion,
by Minnie Sue
Coleman — A3128

Nine Patch, by Ruth P. Mosely — A3129

Housetop Four Block Half Log Cabin Variation, by Lottie Mooney — A3130

Roman Stripes Variation, by Loretta Pettway — A3131

Chinese Coins Variation, by Arlonzia Pettway — A3132

Blocks and Strips, by Annie Mae Young — A3133

Medallion, by Loretta Pettway — A3134

Bars and String-pieced Columns, by Jessie T. Pettway — A3135

Medallion With Checkerboard Center, by Patty Ann Williams — A3136

Designed by Derry Noyes. Printed by American Packaging Corporation for Sennett Security Products.

PHOTOGRAVURE
BOOKLET STAMPS
Serpentine Die Cut 10¾ on 2 or 3 Sides
2006, Aug. 24   **Tagged**
Self-Adhesive

4089	A3127	39c **multicolored**	1.00	.20
4090	A3128	39c **multicolored**	1.00	.20
4091	A3129	39c **multicolored**	1.00	.20
4092	A3130	39c **multicolored**	1.00	.20
4093	A3131	39c **multicolored**	1.00	.20
4094	A3132	39c **multicolored**	1.00	.20
4095	A3133	39c **multicolored**	1.00	.20
4096	A3134	39c **multicolored**	1.00	.20
4097	A3135	39c **multicolored**	1.00	.20

4098	A3136	39c **multicolored**	1.00	.20
a.		Block of 10, #4089-4098	10.00	
b.		Booklet pane of 20, 2 each #4089-4098	20.00	

No. 4098b is a double-sided booklet pane with 12 stamps on one side (1 each #4090-4093, 4095-4098, and 2 each #4089, 4094) and eight stamps (1 each #4090-4093, 4095-4098) plus label (booklet cover) on the other side.

SOUTHERN FLORIDA WETLAND

A3137

Illustration reduced.

Designed by Ethel Kessler.

Printed by Avery Dennison.

Wildlife: a, Snail kite. b, Wood storks. c, Florida panther. d, Bald eagle, horiz. e, American crocodile, horiz. f, Roseate spoonbills, horiz. g, Everglades mink, horiz. h, Cape Sable seaside sparrow, horiz. i, American alligator, horiz. j, White ibis.

PHOTOGRAVURE
Sheets of 80 in eight panes of 10
2006, Oct. 4   **Tagged**   *Serpentine Die Cut 10¾*
Self-Adhesive

4099	A3137	Pane of 10	8.00	
a.-j.		39c any single	.80	.20
		Sheet of 8 panes	65.00	

CHRISTMAS

Madonna and Child with Bird, by Ignacio Chacón — A3138

Snowflake — A3139

Snowflake — A3140

Snowflake — A3141

Snowflake — A3142

Designed by Michael Osborne (#4100), Richard Sheaff. Printed by Ashton-Potter (USA) Ltd. (#4100), Banknote Corporation of America for Sennett Security Products (#4101-4112), Avery Dennison (#4113-4116).

LITHOGRAPHED, PHOTOGRAVURE (#4113-4116)
Sheets of 240 in twelve panes of 20 (#4101-4104)
Serpentine Die Cut 10¾x11 on 2 or 3 Sides
2006   **Tagged**
Self-Adhesive
Booklet Stamps (#4100, 4105-4116)

4100	A3138	39c **multicolored**, *Oct. 17*	.80	.20
a.		Booklet pane of 20	16.00	

Base of Denomination Higher Than Year Date
Serpentine Die Cut 11¼x11

4101	A3139	39c **multicolored**, *Oct. 5*	.90	.20
4102	A3140	39c **multicolored**, *Oct. 5*	.90	.20
4103	A3141	39c **multicolored**, *Oct. 5*	.90	.20
4104	A3142	39c **multicolored**, *Oct. 5*	.90	.20
a.		Block or vert. strip of 4, #4101-4104	3.60	
		P# block of 4, 4#+S	3.60	
		Pane of 20	18.00	

Base of Denominations Even With Year Date
Serpentine Die Cut 11¼x11½ on 2 or 3 Sides

4105	A3139	39c **multicolored**, *Oct. 5*	.80	.20
a.		Red missing (PS)	—	
4106	A3140	39c **multicolored**, *Oct. 5*	.80	.20
a.		Red missing (PS)	—	
4107	A3141	39c **multicolored**, *Oct. 5*	.80	.20
4108	A3142	39c **multicolored**, *Oct. 5*	.80	.20
a.		Block of 4, #4105-4108	3.20	
b.		Booklet pane of 20, 5 #4108a	16.00	

Serpentine Die Cut 11¼x11 on 2 or 3 Sides

4109	A3139	39c **multicolored**, *Oct. 5*	.90	.20
4110	A3140	39c **multicolored**, *Oct. 5*	.90	.20
4111	A3141	39c **multicolored**, *Oct. 5*	.90	.20
4112	A3142	39c **multicolored**, *Oct. 5*	.90	.20
a.		Block of 4, #4109-4112	3.60	
b.		Booklet pane of 4, #4109-4112	3.60	
c.		Booklet pane of 6, #4111-4112, 2 each #4109-4110	5.50	
d.		Booklet pane of 6, #4109-4110, 2 each #4111-4112	5.50	

Serpentine Die Cut 8 on 2, 3 or 4 Sides

4113	A3139	39c **multicolored**, *Oct. 5*	1.00	.20
a.		Red and green missing (PS)	—	
4114	A3141	39c **multicolored**, *Oct. 5*	1.00	.20
4115	A3140	39c **multicolored**, *Oct. 5*	1.00	.20
4116	A3142	39c **multicolored**, *Oct. 5*	1.00	.20
a.		Block of 4, #4113-4116	4.00	
b.		Booklet pane of 18, 4 each #4114, 4116, 5 each #4113, 4115	20.00	
		Nos. 4100-4116 (17)	15.20	3.40

No. 4108b is a double-sided booklet pane with 12 stamps on one side and eight stamps plus label that serves as a booklet cover on the other side. Snowflakes on Nos. 4101-4104 are slightly smaller than those on Nos. 4105-4116.

Eid Type of 2001
Designed by Mohamed Zakariya. Printed by Avery Dennison.

PHOTOGRAVURE
Sheets of 240 in twelve panes of 20
2006, Oct. 6   **Tagged**   *Serpentine Die Cut 11*
Self-Adhesive

4117	A2734	39c **multicolored**	.80	.20
		P# block of 4, 3#+V	3.20	
		Pane of 20	16.00	

Hanukkah Type of 2004
Designed by Ethel Kessler. Printed by Banknote Corporation of America for Sennett Security Products.

LITHOGRAPHED
Sheets of 240 in twelve panes of 20
2006, Oct. 6   **Tagged**   *Serpentine Die Cut 10¾x11*
Self-Adhesive

4118	A2962	39c **multicolored**	.80	.20
		P# block of 4, 4#+S	3.20	
		Pane of 20	16.00	

Kwanzaa Type of 2004
Designed by Derry Noyes. Printed by Ashton-Potter (USA) Ltd.

LITHOGRAPHED
Sheets of 160 in eight panes of 20
2006, Oct. 6   **Tagged**   *Serpentine Die Cut 11x10¾*
Self-Adhesive

4119	A2963	39c **multicolored**	.80	.20
		P# block of 4, 6#+P	3.20	
		Pane of 20	16.00	

BLACK HERITAGE SERIES

Ella Fitzgerald (1917-96),
Singer — A3143

Designed by Ethel Kessler. Printed by Ashton-Potter (USA) Ltd.

LITHOGRAPHED
Sheets of 120 in six panes of 20

2007, Jan. 10   **Tagged**   *Serpentine Die Cut 11*
Self-Adhesive

4120 A3143 39c multicolored	.80	.20
P# block of 4, 6# + P	3.20	
Pane of 20	16.00	

OKLAHOMA STATEHOOD, 100TH ANNIV.

Cimarron
River — A3144

Designed by Phil Jordan. Printed by Ashton-Potter (USA) Ltd.

LITHOGRAPHED
Sheets of 120 in six panes of 20

2007, Jan. 11   **Tagged**   *Serpentine Die Cut 11*
Self-Adhesive

4121 A3144 39c multicolored	.80	.20
P# block of 4, 5# + P	3.20	
Pane of 20	16.00	

LOVE

Hershey's Kiss — A3145

Designed by Derry Noyes. Printed by Avery Dennison.

PHOTOGRAVURE
Serpentine Die Cut 10¾x11 on 2, 3 or 4 Sides
2007, Jan. 13   **Tagged**
BOOKLET STAMP
Self-Adhesive

4122 A3145 39c multicolored	.80	.20
a. Booklet pane of 20	16.00	

INTERNATIONAL POLAR YEAR
Souvenir Sheet

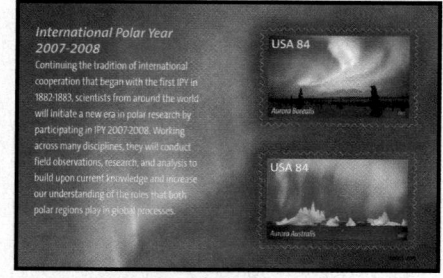

A3146

Illustration reduced.

Designed by Phil Jordan. Printed by Ashton-Potter (USA) Ltd.
No. 4123: a, Aurora borealis. b, Aurora australis.

LITHOGRAPHED
Sheets of 30 in fifteen panes of 2

2007, Feb. 21   **Tagged**   *Serpentine Die Cut 10¾*
Self-Adhesive

4123 A3146 Pane of 2	3.50	
a.-b. 84c Either single	1.75	.50
Sheet of 15 panes	52.50	
Cross gutter block of 4 stamps	9.00	
Vert. pair of panes with horiz. gutter between	7.00	
Horiz. pair of panes with vert. gutter between	7.00	
Vert. pair of stamps with horiz. gutter between	3.50	

LITERARY ARTS

Henry
Wadsworth
Longfellow
(1807-82),
Poet — A3147

Designed by Howard E. Paine. Printed by Ashton-Potter (USA) Ltd.

LITHOGRAPHED
Sheets of 120 in six panes of 20

2007, Mar. 15   **Tagged**   *Serpentine Die Cut 10¾*
Self-Adhesive

4124 A3147 39c multicolored	.80	.20
P# block of 4, 5#+P	3.20	
Pane of 20	16.00	

"FOREVER" STAMP

Liberty Bell — A3148

Large Microprinting
(#4125, 4128)

Small Microprinting
(#4126)

Medium Microprinting
(#4127)

Designed by Carl T. Herrman. Printed by Avery Dennison (#4125, 4128), Ashton-Potter (USA) Ltd. (#4126), Banknote Corporation of America for Sennett Security Products (#4127)

PHOTOGRAVURE, LITHOGRAPHED (#4126, 4127)
Serpentine Die Cut 11¼x10¾ on 2 or 3 Sides
2007, Apr. 12   **Tagged**
Booklet Stamps
Self-Adhesive
Large Microprinting, Bell 16mm Wide

4125 A3148 (41c) multicolored	.85	.20
a. Booklet pane of 20	17.00	
b. (42c) Dated "2008," Aug. 22, 2008	.85	.20
c. Booklet pane of 20 #4125b	17.00	
d. As "c," copper ("FOREVER") omitted	—	

e. As "c," copper ("FOREVER") omitted on side with 12 stamps, copper splatters on side with 8 stamps	—	

Small Microprinting, Bell 16mm Wide

4126 A3148 (41c) multicolored	.85	.20
a. Booklet pane of 20	17.00	
b. (42c) Dated "2008," Aug. 22, 2008	.85	.20
c. Booklet pane of 20 #4126b	17.00	

Medium Microprinting, Bell 15mm Wide

4127 A3148 (41c) multicolored, Dated "2007," prephosphored coated paper	.90	.20
a. Booklet pane of 20	18.00	
b. Booklet pane of 4	3.60	
c. Booklet pane of 6	5.50	
d. (42c) Dated "2008," 2008	.90	.20
e. As "d," booklet pane of 20	18.00	
f. (42c) Dated "2008," date in smaller type, 2008	.90	.20
g. As "f," booklet pane of 4	3.60	
h. As "f," booklet pane of 6	5.50	
i. (44c) Dated "2009" in copper, 2009	.90	.20
j. As "i," booklet pane of 20	18.00	

Large Microprinting, Bell 16mm Wide
Serpentine Die Cut 8 on 2, 3 or 4 Sides

4128 A3148 (41c) multicolored	.85	.20
a. Booklet pane of 18	15.50	
b. (42c) Dated "2009," 2009	.85	.20
c. As "b," booklet pane of 18	15.50	
Nos. 4125-4128 (4)	3.45	.80

Nos. 4125-4128 were sold for 41c on the day of issue and will be valid for the one ounce first class postage rate after any new rates go into effect. As of May 12, 2008, any "Forever" stamp (Nos. 4125-4128 and 4127d) in stock was sold for 42c. As of May 15, 2009, all "Forever" stamps in stock were sold for 44c.

Nos. 4125a, 4125c, 4126a, 4126c, 4127a, 4127e and 4127j are double-sided booklet panes, with 12 stamps on one side and eight stamps plus a label that serves as a booklet cover on the other side.

No. 4127 and its varieties exist on two types of surface-tagged paper that exhibit either an uneven or a solid appearance, as follows: tagging on Nos. 4127-4127d and 4127f-4127h appears uneven, tagging on Nos. 4127d-4127e and 4127i-4127j appears solid. Additionally, a version of No. 4127e exists that has tagging with a solid appearance on the front side with eight stamps and tagging with an uneven appearance on the side with 12 stamps. Values are the same.

Nos. 4127b and 4127c exist with rouletting on backing paper of either gauge 9½ or 13.

No. 4127d issued 5/12/08. No. 4127f issued 10/25/08. No. 4127i issued 5/15/09.

Flag — A3149

Designed by Richard Sheaff. Printed by Ashton-Potter (USA) Ltd. (#4129, 4130, 4132), Banknote Corporation of America for Sennett Security Products (#4131, 4133), Avery Dennison (#4134, 4135).

LITHOGRAPHED, PHOTOGRAVURE (#4134, 4135)
Sheets of 400 in four panes of 100 (#4129), Sheets of 120 in six panes of 20 (#4130)

2007, Apr. 12   **Tagged**   *Perf. 11¼*

4129 A3149 (41c) multicolored	.85	.40
P# block of 4, 4#+P	7.50	

Self-Adhesive (#4130, 4132-4135)
Serpentine Die Cut 11¼x10¾

4130 A3149 (41c) multicolored	.85	.20
P# block of 4, 4#+P	3.50	
Pane of 20	17.00	

COIL STAMPS
Perf. 9¾ Vert.

4131 A3149 (41c) multicolored	.85	.40
Pair	1.70	.80
P# strip of 5, #S1111	6.50	
P# single, #S1111	—	2.00

With Perpendicular Corners
Serpentine Die Cut 9½ Vert.

4132 A3149 (41c) multicolored	.85	.20
Pair	1.70	
P# strip of 5, #P1111	6.50	
P# single, #P1111	—	2.00

Serpentine Die Cut 11 Vert.

4133 A3149 (41c) multicolored	.85	.20
Pair	1.70	
P# strip of 5, #S1111	6.50	
P# single, #S1111	—	2.00
a. Die cutting omitted, pair	—	

Serpentine Die Cut 8½ Vert.

4134 A3149 (41c) multicolored	.85	.20
Pair	1.70	
P# strip of 5, #V1111	6.50	
P# single, #V1111	—	2.00

With Rounded Corners
Serpentine Die Cut 11 Vert.

4135	A3149 (41c)	**multicolored**	.85	.40
		Pair	1.70	
		P# strip of 5, #V1111	6.50	
		P# single, #V1111	—	2.00
		Nos. 4129-4135 (7)	5.95	2.00

Nos. 4132-4134 are on backing paper as high as the stamp. No. 4135 is on backing paper that is larger than the stamp.

SETTLEMENT OF JAMESTOWN, 400TH ANNIV.

Ships Susan Constant, Godspeed and Discovery — A3150

Illustration reduced.

Designed by Richard Sheaff. Printed by Banknote Corporation of America for Sennett Security Products.

LITHOGRAPHED
Double-sided panes of 20 (19 on one side, 1 on other side)
Serpentine Die Cut 10½x10½x10¾

2007, May 11		**Tagged**		
		Self-Adhesive		
4136	A3150 41c	**multicolored**	1.00	.20
		Pane of 20	20.00	

WILDLIFE

Bighorn Sheep — A3151

Florida Panther — A3152

Designed by Carl T. Herrman. Printed by Ashton-Potter (USA) Ltd. (#4137, 4139), Avery Dennison (#4138, 4142), Banknote Corporation of America for Sennett Security Products (#4140, 4141).

LITHOGRAPHED, PHOTOGRAVURE (#4138, 4142)
Sheets of 400 in four panes of 100 (#4137), Sheets of 280 in fourteen panes of 20 (#4138), Sheets of 120 in six panes of 20 (#4139)

2007		**Tagged**	**Perf. 11¼x11**	
4137	A3152 26c	**multicolored,** *May 12*	.55	.20
		P# block of 4, 4#+P	6.00	—
		Self-Adhesive		
		Serpentine Die Cut 11		
4138	A3151 17c	**multicolored,** *May 14*	.45	.20
		P# block of 4, 4#+V	1.75	
		Pane of 20	9.00	
		Serpentine Die Cut 11¼x11		
4139	A3152 26c	**multicolored,** *May 12*	.55	.20
		P# block of 4, 4#+P	2.25	
		Pane of 20	11.00	
		Coil Stamps		
		Serpentine Die Cut 11 Vert.		
4140	A3151 17c	**multicolored,** *May 21*	.35	.20
		Pair	.70	
		P# strip of 5, #S11111111	3.50	
		P# single, #S11111111	—	1.75
4141	A3152 26c	**multicolored,** prephosphored coated paper, *May 12*	.55	.20
		Pair	1.10	
		P# strip of 5, #S1111	4.25	
		P# single, #S1111	—	2.00
a.		Die cutting omitted, pair	—	

No. 4141 exists on two types of surface-tagged paper that exhibit either a solid or uneven appearance. Stamps with solid tagging are scarcer.

Booklet Stamp
Serpentine Die Cut 11¼x11 on 3 Sides

4142	A3152 26c	**multicolored,** *May 12*	.55	.20
a.		Booklet pane of 10	5.50	

Nos. 4137 and 4139 have microprinted "USPS" to the left and above the lower left whisker. No. 4140 has microprinted "USPS" on right horn. No. 4141 has microprinted "USPS" along the right edge of the stamp just above the panther. Nos. 4138 and 4142 lack microprinting.

PREMIERE OF MOVIE "STAR WARS," 30TH ANNI.

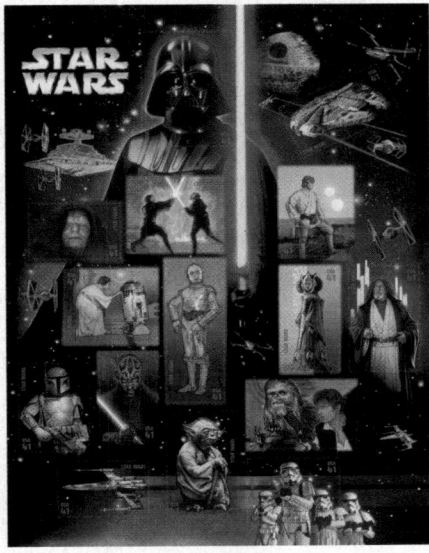

A3153

Illustration reduced.

Designed by Terrence McCaffrey and William J. Gicker, Jr.. Printed by Banknote Corporation of America for Sennett Security Products.

No. 4143: a, Darth Vader (40x53mm). b, Millennium Falcon (47x25mm). c, Emperor Palpatine (41x26mm). d, Anakin Skywalker and Obi-Wan Kenobi (41x33mm). e, Luke Skywalker (31x41mm). f, Princess Leia and R2-D2 (41x33mm). g, C-3PO (21x65mm). h, Queen Padmé Amidala (26x48mm). i, Obi-Wan Kenobi (31x48mm). j, Boba Fett (32x40mm). k, Darth Maul (26x41mm). l, Chewbacca and Han Solo (48x31mm). m, X-wing Starfighter (41x26mm). n, Yoda (31x48mm). o, Stormtroopers (41x31mm).

LITHOGRAPHED
Sheets of 45 in three panes of 15

2007, May 25		**Tagged**	**Serpentine Die Cut 11**	
		Self-Adhesive		
4143	A3153	Pane of 15	13.00	
a.-o.		41c Any single	.85	.20
		Sheet of 45 (3 panes)	40.00	
		Block of 15 with vertical gutter (6 stamps at left and 9 stamps at right)	16.50	

PRESIDENTIAL AIRCRAFT

Air Force One — A3154

Marine One — A3155

Designed by Phil Jordan. Printed by Ashton-Potter (USA) Ltd. (#4144), Banknote Corporation of America for Sennett Security Products (#4145).

LITHOGRAPHED & ENGRAVED (#4144),
LITHOGRAPHED (#4145)
Sheets of 120 in six panes of 20

2007, June 13		**Tagged**	**Serpentine Die Cut 10¾**	
		Self-Adhesive		
4144	A3154	$4.60 **multicolored**	9.25	5.00
		P# block of 4, 6#+P	37.50	
		Pane of 20	190.00	
a.		Black (engr.) omitted	—	

4145	A3155	$16.25 **multicolored**	27.50	16.00
		P# block of 4, 5#+S	110.00	
		Pane of 20	550.00	

PACIFIC LIGHTHOUSES

Diamond Head Lighthouse, Hawaii — A3156

Five Finger Lighthouse, Alaska — A3157

Grays Harbor Lighthouse, Washington — A3158

Umpqua River Lighthouse, Oregon — A3159

St. George Reef Lighthouse, California — A3160

Designed by Howard E. Paine. Printed by Avery Dennison.

PHOTOGRAVURE
Sheets of 160 in eight panes of 20

2007, June 21		**Tagged**	**Serpentine Die Cut 11**	
		Self-Adhesive		
4146	A3156 41c	**multicolored**	1.20	.20
4147	A3157 41c	**multicolored**	1.20	.20
4148	A3158 41c	**multicolored**	1.20	.20
4149	A3159 41c	**multicolored**	1.20	.20
4150	A3160 41c	**multicolored**	1.20	.20
a.		Horiz. strip of 5, #4146-4150	6.00	
		P# block of 10, 5#+V	12.00	
		Pane of 20	24.00	

WEDDING HEARTS

Heart With Lilac Background — A3161

Heart With Pink Background — A3162

Designed by Carl T. Herrman. Printed by Ashton-Potter (USA) Ltd. (#4151), Avery Dennison (#4152).

LITHOGRAPHED (#4151), PHOTOGRAVURE (#4152)
BOOKLET STAMP (#4151)
Sheets of 240 in twelve panes of 20 (#4152)
Serpentine Die Cut 10¾ on 2, 3 or 4 Sides
2007, June 27   **Tagged**

Self-Adhesive

4151	A3161	41c multicolored	.85	.20
a.		Booklet pane of 20	17.00	

Serpentine Die Cut 10¾x11

4152	A3162	58c multicolored	1.25	.25
		P# block of 4, 4#+V	5.00	
		Pane of 20	25.00	

POLLINATION

USA41

Purple
Nightshade,
Morrison's
Bumblebee
A3163

USA41

Hummingbird
Trumpet,
Calliope
Hummingbird
A3164

USA41

Saguaro,
Lesser Long-
nosed
Bat — A3165

USA41

Prairie
Ironweed,
Southern
Dogface
Butterfly
A3166

Designed by Steve Buchanan. Printed by Ashton-Potter (USA) Ltd.
No. 4153: Type I, Tip of bird wing is directly under center of "U" in "USA," straight edge at left. Type II, Tip of bird wing is directly under the right line of the "U" in "USA," straight edge at right.
No. 4154: Type I, Tip of bird wing is even with the top of denomination, straight edge at right. Type II, Tip of bird wing is well above denomination, straight edge at left.
No. 4155: Type I, Top of "USA" is even with the lower portion of the nearest unopened green saguaro flower bud, straight edge at left. Type II, Top of "USA" is even with the point where the flower and unopened green saguaro bud meet, straight edge at right.
No. 4156: Type I, Bottom of denomination is even with top point of the white triangle found between the bottom of the purple flower and the green leaf below it, straight edge at right. Type II, Bottom of denomination is even with the lower point of the white triangle found between the bottom of the purple flower and the green leaf below it, straight edge at left.

LITHOGRAPHED
Serpentine Die Cut 11 on 2, 3 or 4 Sides
2007, June 29   **Tagged**

Self-Adhesive
Booklet Stamps

4153	A3163	41c multicolored, Type I	.85	.20
a.		Type II	.85	.20
4154	A3164	41c multicolored, Type I	.85	.20
a.		Type II	.85	.20
4155	A3165	41c multicolored, Type I	.85	.20
a.		Type II	.85	.20
4156	A3166	41c multicolored, Type I	.85	.20
a.		Type II	.85	.20
b.		Block of 4, #4153-4156	3.40	
c.		Block of 4, #4153a-4156a	3.40	
d.		Booklet pane of 20, 3 each #4153-4156, 2 each #4153a-4156a	17.00	

No. 4156d is a double-sided booklet with 12 stamps (2 each #4153-4156, 1 each #4153a-4156a) on one side and 8 stamps plus label (booklet cover) on the other side.

USA
PRESORTED
STANDARD

Patriotic Banner — A3167

Designed by Michael Osborne. Printed by Avery-Dennison (#4157), Banknote Corporation of America for Sennett Security Products (#4158).

PHOTOGRAVURE (#4157), LITHOGRAPHED (#4158)
Serpentine Die Cut 11 Vert.
2007, July 4   **Untagged**

Coil Stamps
Self-Adhesive

4157	A3167	(10c) red, gold & blue	.20	.20
		Pair	.40	
		P# strip of 5, #V111, V222	2.50	
		P# single, #V111, V222	—	1.75

Serpentine Die Cut 11¾ Vert.

4158	A3167	(10c) red, gold & blue	.20	.20
		Pair	.40	
		P# strip of 5, #S111	2.50	
		P# single, #S111	—	1.75

A later printing of No. 4158 shows the red and blue in somewhat darker shades.

MARVEL COMICS SUPERHEROES

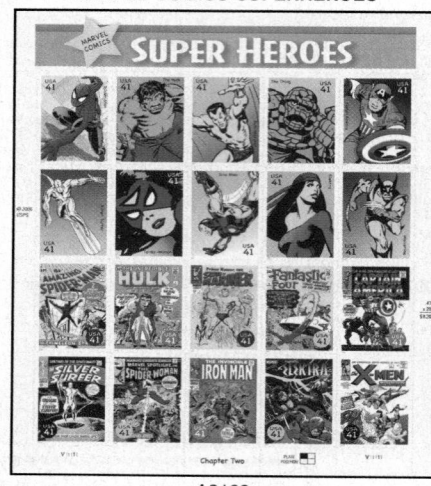

A3168

Illustration reduced.
Designed by Carl T. Herrman. Printed by Avery Dennison.
No. 4159: a, Spider-man. b, The Hulk. c, Sub-Mariner. d, The Thing. e, Captain America. f, Silver Surfer. g, Spider-Woman. h, Iron Man. i, Elektra. j, Wolverine. k, Cover of *The Amazing Spider-Man #1.* l, Cover of *The Incredible Hulk #1.* m, Cover of *Sub-Mariner #1.* n, Cover of *The Fantastic Four #3.* o, Cover of *Captain America #100.* p, Cover of *The Silver Surfer #1.* q, Cover of *Marvel Spotlight on The Spider-Woman #32.* r, Cover of *Iron Man #1.* s, Cover of *Daredevil #176 Featuring Elektra.* t, Cover of *The X-Men #1.*

PHOTOGRAVURE
Sheets of 80 in four panes of 20
Serpentine Die Cut 10½x10¾
2007, July 26   **Tagged**

Self-Adhesive

4159	A3168	Pane of 20	17.00	
a.-t.		41c Any single	.85	.20
		Sheet of 80 (4 panes)	68.00	
		Cross gutter block of 20	25.00	
		Horiz. pair with vert. gutter (each)	3.00	
		Vert. pair with horiz. gutter (each)	3.00	

Cross gutter block consists of 12 stamps from the panes on one side of the sheet and 8 stamps from the panes on the other side of the sheet.

VINTAGE MAHOGANY SPEEDBOATS

1915
Hutchinson — A3169

1954 Chris-
Craft — A3170

1939 Hacker-Craft
A3171

1931 Gar
Wood — A3172

Designed by Carl T. Herrman. Printed by Ashton-Potter (USA) Ltd.

LITHOGRAPHED
Sheets of 72 in six panes of 12
2007, Aug. 4   Tagged   *Serpentine Die Cut 10½*
Self-Adhesive

4160	A3169	41c multicolored	.85	.20
4161	A3170	41c multicolored	.85	.20
4162	A3171	41c multicolored	.85	.20
4163	A3172	41c multicolored	.85	.20
a.		Horiz. strip of 4, #4160-4163	3.40	
		P# block of 8, 4#+P	7.25	
		Pane of 12	10.50	

Purple Heart Type of 2003

Designed by Carl T. Herrman. Printed by Ashton-Potter (USA) Ltd.

LITHOGRAPHED
Sheets of 120 in six panes of 20
Serpentine Die Cut 11¼x10¾
2007, Aug. 7   **Tagged**

Self-Adhesive

4164	A2891	41c multicolored	.85	.20
		P# block of 4, 4#+P	3.40	
		Pane of 20	17.00	

AMERICAN TREASURES SERIES

Magnolia and Irises,
Stained Glass by Louis
Comfort Tiffany — A3173

Designed by Derry Noyes. Printed by Ashton-Potter (USA) Ltd.

LITHOGRAPHED
BOOKLET STAMP
Serpentine Die Cut 10¾ on 2 or 3 Sides
2007, Aug. 9 **Tagged**
Self-Adhesive

4165　A3173　41c **multicolored** .85 .20
　a.　Booklet pane of 20 17.00

No. 4165a is a double-sided booklet pane with 12 stamps on one side and eight stamps plus label (booklet cover) on the other side.

FLOWERS

Iris — A3174　　Dahlia — A3175

Magnolia — A3176　　Red Gerbera Daisy — A3177

Coneflower — A3178　　Tulip — A3179

Water Lily — A3180　　Poppy — A3181

Chrysanthemum
A3182　　Orange Gerbera Daisy A3183

Designed by Carl T. Herrman. Printed by Ashton-Potter (USA) Ltd. (#4166-4175), Avery Dennison (#4176-4185)

LITHOGRAPHED, PHOTOGRAVURE (#4176-4185)
Serpentine Die Cut 9½ Vert.
2007, Aug. 10 **Tagged**
COIL STAMPS
Self-Adhesive

4166　A3174　41c **multicolored** .85 .20
4167　A3175　41c **multicolored** .85 .20
4168　A3176　41c **multicolored** .85 .20
4169　A3177　41c **multicolored** .85 .20
4170　A3178　41c **multicolored** .85 .20
4171　A3179　41c **multicolored** .85 .20
4172　A3180　41c **multicolored** .85 .20
4173　A3181　41c **multicolored** .85 .20
4174　A3182　41c **multicolored** .85 .20
4175　A3183　41c **multicolored** .85 .20
　a.　Strip of 10, #4166-4175 8.50
　　　P# strip of 11, 2 # 4175, 1 each
　　　#4166-4174, #P1111, P2222 13.00 —
　　　P# single (#4170), same # — 2.00

BOOKLET STAMPS
Serpentine Die Cut 11¼x11½ on 2 or 3 Sides

4176　A3182　41c **multicolored** .85 .20
4177　A3183　41c **multicolored** .85 .20
4178　A3174　41c **multicolored** .85 .20
4179　A3175　41c **multicolored** .85 .20
4180　A3176　41c **multicolored** .85 .20
4181　A3177　41c **multicolored** .85 .20
4182　A3180　41c **multicolored** .85 .20
4183　A3181　41c **multicolored** .85 .20
4184　A3178　41c **multicolored** .85 .20
4185　A3179　41c **multicolored** .85 .20
　a.　Booklet pane of 20, 2 each #4176-4185 17.00
　b.　As "a," die cutting missing on Nos. 4178 & 4183 on side with 8 stamps (PS) —

No. 4185a is a double-sided booklet pane with 12 stamps on one side (2 each #4176-4177, 1 each #4178-4185) and eight stamps (#4178-4185) plus label (booklet cover) on the other side.

Flag — A3184

Designed by Richard Sheaff. Printed by Avery Dennison (#4188, 4189), Ashton-Potter (USA) Ltd. (#4186, 4190), Banknote Corporation of America for Sennett Security Products (#4187, 4191).

LITHOGRAPHED, PHOTOGRAVURE (#4188, 4189)
Serpentine Die Cut 9½ Vert.
2007, Aug. 15 **Tagged**
COIL STAMPS
Self-Adhesive
With "USPS" Microprinted on Right Side of Flagpole
With Perpendicular Corners

4186　A3184　41c **multicolored** .85 .20
　　　Pair 1.60
　　　P# strip of 5, #P11111 6.50
　　　P# single, #P11111 — 2.00

With "USPS" Microprinted on Left Side of Flagpole
Serpentine Die Cut 11 Vert.

4187　A3184　41c **multicolored,** prephosphored coated paper .85 .20
　　　Pair 1.60
　　　P# strip of 5, #S11111 6.50
　　　P# single, #S11111 — 2.00

No. 4187 exists on two types of surface-tagged paper that exhibit either a solid or an uneven appearance.

Without "USPS" Microprinting on Flagpole
Serpentine Die Cut 8½ Vert.

4188　A3184　41c **multicolored** .85 .20
　　　Pair 1.60
　　　P# strip of 5, #V11111, V22222 6.50
　　　P# single, same # — 2.00

Serpentine Die Cut 11 Vert.
With Rounded Corners

4189　A3184　41c **multicolored** .85 .20
　　　Pair 1.60
　　　P# strip of 5, #V11111 6.50
　　　P# single, #V11111 — 2.00

BOOKLET STAMPS
Serpentine Die Cut 11¼x10¾ on 3 Sides
With "USPS" Microprinted on Right Side of Flagpole

4190　A3184　41c **multicolored** .85 .20
　a.　Booklet pane of 10 8.50

With "USPS" Microprinted on Left Side of Flagpole
Serpentine Die Cut 11¼x10¾ on 2 or 3 Sides

4191　A3184　41c **multicolored** .85 .20
　a.　Booklet pane of 20 17.00

No. 4188 is on backing paper as high as the stamp. No. 4189 is on backing paper that is larger than the stamp. The microprinting on Nos. 4190 and 4191 is under the ball of the flagpole. The flagpole is light gray on No. 4190 and dark gray on No. 4191. No. 4191a is a double-sided booklet with 12 stamps on one side of the peelable backing and 8 stamps plus label (booklet cover) on the other side.

Nos. 4188-4189 lack "USPS" microprinting on the flagpole. No. 4186 was not sold to the public until October 2007 and No. 4187 was not sold to the public until November 2007.

THE ART OF DISNEY: MAGIC

Mickey
Mouse — A3185

Peter Pan and Tinker
Bell — A3186

Dumbo and Timothy
Mouse — A3187

Aladdin and
Genie — A3188

Designed by David Pacheco. Printed by Avery Dennison.

PHOTOGRAVURE
Sheets of 160 in eight panes of 20
Serpentine Die Cut 10½x10¾
2007, Aug. 16 **Tagged**
Self-Adhesive

4192　A3185　41c **multicolored** .85 .20
4193　A3186　41c **multicolored** .85 .20
4194　A3187　41c **multicolored** .85 .20
4195　A3188　41c **multicolored** .85 .20
　a.　Block of 4, #4192-4195 3.40

P# block of 4, 6#+V   3.40
P# block of 10, 2 sets of P# +
   top label   8.50
Pane of 20   17.00

CELEBRATE

A3189

Designed by Ethel Kessler. Printed by Banknote Corporation of America for Sennett Security Products.

LITHOGRAPHED
Sheets of 160 in eight panes of 20
2007, Aug. 17   Tagged   *Serpentine Die Cut 10¾*
Self-Adhesive

4196 A3189 41c **multicolored**   .85   .20
            P# block of 4, 4#+S   3.40
            Pane of 20   17.00

LEGENDS OF HOLLYWOOD

James Stewart (1908-97), Actor — A3190

Designed by Phil Jordan. Printed by Ashton-Potter (USA) Ltd.

LITHOGRAPHED
Sheets of 180 in nine panes of 20
2007, Aug. 17   Tagged   *Serpentine Die Cut 10¾*
Self-Adhesive

4197 A3190 41c **multicolored**   .85   .20
            P# block of 4, 4#+P   3.50
            Pane of 20   17.50
            Sheet of 180 (9 panes) 155.00
            Cross gutter block of 8 17.50
            Block of 8 with vert. gutter 10.00
            Horiz. pair with vert. gutter 3.00
            Vert. pair with horiz. gutter 2.00

The cross gutter block consists of 2 stamps from the two upper panes and 6 stamps from the two lower panes.

ALPINE TUNDRA

A3191

Illustration reduced.

Designed by Ethel Kessler. Printed by Banknote Corporation of America for Sennett Security Products.

Wildlife: a, Elk. b, Golden eagle, horiz. c, Yellow-bellied marmot. d, American pika. e, Bighorn sheep. f, Magdalena alpine butterfly. g, White-tailed ptarmigan. h, Rocky Mountain parnassian butterfly. i, Melissa arctic butterfly, horiz. j, Brown-capped rosy-finch, horiz.

PHOTOGRAVURE
Sheets of 80 in eight panes of 10
2007, Aug. 28   Tagged   *Serpentine Die Cut 10¾*
Self-Adhesive

4198 A3191   Pane of 10   8.50
a.-j.   41c any single   .85   .20
            Sheet of 8 panes   67.50

GERALD R. FORD

Gerald R. Ford (1913-2006), 38th President — A3192

Designed by Ethel Kessler. Printed by Ashton-Potter (USA) Ltd.

LITHOGRAPHED
Sheets of 120 in six panes of 20
2007, Aug. 31   Tagged   *Serpentine Die Cut 11*
Self-Adhesive

4199 A3192 41c **multicolored**   .85   .20
            P# block of 4, 5#+P   3.40
            Pane of 20   17.00
            Sheet of 120 (6 panes) 105.00
            Cross gutter block of 4   8.50
            Horiz. pair with vert. gutter 3.00
            Vert. pair with horiz. gutter 2.00

JURY DUTY

Twelve Jurors — A3193

Designed by Carl T. Herrman. Printed by Ashton-Potter (USA) Ltd.

LITHOGRAPHED
Sheets of 120 in six panes of 20
2007, Sept. 12   Tagged   *Serpentine Die Cut 10½*
Self-Adhesive

4200 A3193 41c **multicolored**   .85   .20
            P# block of 4, 5#+P   3.40
            Pane of 20   17.00

MENDEZ v. WESTMINSTER, 60th ANNIV.

A3194

Designed by Ethel Kessler. Printed by Ashton-Potter (USA) Ltd.

LITHOGRAPHED
Sheets of 120 in six panes of 20
2007, Sept. 14   Tagged   *Serpentine Die Cut 11*
Self-Adhesive

4201 A3194 41c **multicolored**   .85   .20
            P# block of 4, 4#+P   3.40
            Pane of 20   17.00

Eid Type of 2001
Designed by Mohamed Zakariya. Printed by Avery Dennison.

PHOTOGRAVURE
Sheets of 240 in twelve panes of 20
2007, Sept. 28   Tagged   *Serpentine Die Cut 11*
Self-Adhesive

4202 A2734 41c **multicolored**   .85   .20
            P# block of 4, 3#+V   3.40
            Pane of 20   17.00

AURORAS

Aurora Borealis A3195

Aurora Australis A3196

Designed by Phil Jordan. Printed by Ashton-Potter (USA) Ltd.

LITHOGRAPHED
Sheets of 120 in six panes of 20
2007, Oct. 1   Tagged   *Serpentine Die Cut 10¾*
Self-Adhesive

4203 A3195 41c **multicolored**   1.00   .20
4204 A3196 41c **multicolored**   1.00   .20
a.   Horiz. or vert. pair, #4203-4204   2.00
            P# block of 4, 5#+P   5.00
            Pane of 20   24.00

YODA

A3197

Designed by Greg Breeding. Printed by Banknote Corporation of America for Sennett Security Products.

LITHOGRAPHED
Sheets of 120 in six panes of 20
Serpentine Die Cut 10½x10¾
2007, Oct. 25   Tagged
Self-Adhesive

4205 A3197 41c **multicolored**   .85   .20
            P# block of 4, 5#+S   3.40
            Pane of 20   17.00
            Sheet of 60 (left or right) 51.00
            Vert. pair with horiz. gutter 2.00

CHRISTMAS

Madonna of the Carnation, by Bernardino Luini — A3198

Knit Reindeer — A3199

Knit Christmas
Tree — A3200

Knit
Snowman — A3201

Knit Bear — A3202

Knit
Reindeer — A3203

Knit Christmas
Tree — A3204

Knit
Snowman — A3205

Knit Bear — A3206

Designed by Richard Sheaff (#4206), Carl T. Herrman.
Printed by Ashton-Potter (USA) Ltd. (#4206), Banknote Corporation of America for Sennett Security Products (#4207-
4214), Avery Dennison (#4215-4218).

LITHOGRAPHED, PHOTOGRAVURE (#4215-4218)
Sheets of 160 in eight panes of 20 (#4207-4210)
Serpentine Die Cut 10¾x11 on 2 or 3 Sides
2007, Oct. 25   **Tagged**
Self-Adhesive
Booklet Stamps (#4206, 4211-4218)
4206 A3198 41c **multicolored**   .85   .20
  a. Booklet pane of 20   17.00
Serpentine Die Cut 10¾ on 2, 3 or 4 sides
4207 A3199 41c **multicolored**   .85   .20
4208 A3200 41c **multicolored**   .85   .20
4209 A3201 41c **multicolored**   .85   .20
4210 A3202 41c **multicolored**   .85   .20
  a. Block or vert. strip of 4, #4207-4210 3.40
      P# block of 4, 4#+S   3.40
      Pane of 20   17.00
  b. Booklet pane of 20   17.00

Nos. 4207-4210 in panes were printed on prephosphored
coated paper with surface tagging showing a solid appearance.
The booklet panes were printed on prephosphored coated
paper showing an uneven appearance.

Serpentine Die Cut 11¼x11 on 2 or 3 Sides
4211 A3203 41c **multicolored**   .85   .20
4212 A3204 41c **multicolored**   .85   .20
4213 A3205 41c **multicolored**   .85   .20
4214 A3206 41c **multicolored**   .85   .20
  a. Block of 4, #4211-4214   3.40
  b. Booklet pane of 4, #4211-4214   3.40
  c. Booklet pane of 6, #4213-4214, 2 each
      #4211-4212   5.10
  d. Booklet pane of 6, #4211-4212, 2 each
      #4213-4214   5.10
Serpentine Die Cut 8 on 2, 3 or 4 Sides
4215 A3203 41c **multicolored**   .85   .20
4216 A3204 41c **multicolored**   .85   .20
4217 A3205 41c **multicolored**   .85   .20

4218 A3206 41c **multicolored**   .85   .20
  a. Block of 4, #4215-4218   3.40
  b. Booklet pane of 18, 4 each #4215, 4218,
      5 each #4216, 4217   15.50
      Nos. 4206-4218 (13)   11.05 2.60

No. 4206a is a double-sided booklet pane with 12 stamps on
one side and eight stamps plus label that serves as a booklet
cover on the other side.
No. 4210b is a double-sided booklet pane with 12 stamps on
one side and eight stamps plus label that serves as a booklet
cover on the other side.

Hanukkah Type of 2004
Designed by Ethel Kessler. Printed by Banknote Corporation
of America for Sennett Security Products.

LITHOGRAPHED
Sheets of 160 in eight panes of 20
Serpentine Die Cut 10¾x11
2007, Oct. 26   **Tagged**
Self-Adhesive
4219 A2962 41c **multicolored**   .85   .20
      P# block of 4, 4#+S   3.40
      Pane of 20   17.00

Kwanzaa Type of 2004
Designed by Derry Noyes. Printed by Ashton-Potter (USA)
Ltd.

LITHOGRAPHED
Sheets of 160 in eight panes of 20
Serpentine Die Cut 11x10¾
2007, Oct. 26   **Tagged**
Self-Adhesive
4220 A2963 41c **multicolored**   .85   .20
      P# block of 4, 6#+P   3.40
      Pane of 20   17.00

CHINESE NEW YEAR

Year of the
Rat — A3207

Designed by Ethel Kessler. Printed by Avery Dennison

PHOTOGRAVURE
Sheets of 108 in nine panes of 12
2008, Jan. 9 **Tagged** *Serpentine Die Cut 10¾*
Self-Adhesive
4221 A3207 41c **multicolored**   .85   .20
      Pane of 12   10.50
      Sheet of 108 (9 panes)   95.00
      Cross gutter block of 4   8.00
      Horiz. pair with vert. gutter 2.00
      Vert. pair with horiz. gutter 2.00

BLACK HERITAGE SERIES

Charles W. Chesnutt (1858-
1932), Writer — A3208

Designed by Howard E. Paine. Printed by Avery Dennison.

PHOTOGRAVURE
Sheets of 200 in ten panes of 20
2008, Jan. 31 **Tagged** *Serpentine Die Cut 11*
Self-Adhesive
4222 A3208 41c **multicolored**   .85   .20
      P# block of 4, 4# + V   3.40
      Pane of 20   17.00

LITERARY ARTS SERIES

Marjorie
Kinnan
Rawlings
(1896-1953),
Writer
A3209

Designed by Carl T. Herrman. Printed by Avery Dennison.

PHOTOGRAVURE
Sheets of 200 in ten panes of 20
2008, Feb. 21 **Tagged** *Serpentine Die Cut 11*
Self-Adhesive
4223 A3209 41c **multicolored**   .85   .20
      P# block of 4, 4# + V   3.40
      Pane of 20   17.00

AMERICAN SCIENTISTS

Gerty Cori
(1896-1957),
Biochemist
A3210

Linus Pauling
(1901-94),
Structural
Chemist
A3211

Edwin Hubble
(1889-1953),
Astronomer
A3212

John Bardeen
(1908-91),
Theoretical
Physicist
A3213

Designed by Victor Stabin. Printed by Avery Dennison.

PHOTOGRAVURE
Sheets of 160 in eight panes of 20
2008, Mar. 6 **Tagged** *Serpentine Die Cut 11*
Self-Adhesive
4224 A3210 41c **multicolored**   .85   .20
4225 A3211 41c **multicolored**   .85   .20
4226 A3212 41c **multicolored**   .85   .20
4227 A3213 41c **multicolored**   .85   .20
  a. Horiz. strip of 4, #4224-4227   3.40
      P# block of 8, 2 sets of 4# + V 6.80
      Pane of 20   17.00

Plate block may contain top label.

Flag at
Dusk — A3214

Flag at
Night — A3215

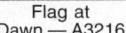

Flag at
Dawn — A3216

Flag at
Midday — A3217

Designed by Phil Jordan. Printed by American Packaging Corporation for Sennett Security Products (#4228-4231), Ashton-Potter (USA) Ltd. (#4232-4235), Banknote Corporation of America for Sennett Security Products (#4236-4239), Avery Dennison (#4240-4247).

PHOTOGRAVURE (#4228-4231, 4240-4247),
LITHOGRAPHED (#4232-4239)

2008, Apr. 18	Tagged		Perf. 10 Vert.	
COIL STAMPS				
4228	A3214	42c multicolored	.85	.40
4229	A3215	42c multicolored	.85	.40
4230	A3216	42c multicolored	.85	.40
4231	A3217	42c multicolored	.85	.40
a.	Horiz. strip of 4, #4228-4231		3.40	1.60
	P# strip of 5, 2 #4228, 1 each #4229-4231, #S1111111		6.00	—
	P# strip of 9, 3 #4230, 2 each #4228-4229, 4230, P#S1111111		10.00	—
	P# single, #S1111111 (#4230)		—	2.00

Self-Adhesive
With Perpendicular Corners
Serpentine Die Cut 9½ Vert.

4232	A3214	42c multicolored	.85	.20
4233	A3215	42c multicolored	.85	.20
4234	A3216	42c multicolored	.85	.20
4235	A3217	42c multicolored	.85	.20
a.	Horiz. strip of 4, #4232-4235		3.40	
	P# strip of 5, 2 #4232, 1 each #4233-4235, #P1111		6.00	
	P# strip of 9, 3 #4234, 2 each #4232-4233, 4235, P#P1111		10.00	
	P# single, #P1111 (#4234)		—	2.00

Serpentine Die Cut 11 Vert.

4236	A3214	42c multicolored	.85	.20
4237	A3215	42c multicolored	.85	.20
4238	A3216	42c multicolored	.85	.20
4239	A3217	42c multicolored	.85	.20
a.	Horiz. strip of 4, #4236-4239		3.40	
	P# strip of 5, 2 #4236, 1 each #4237-4239, #S1111		6.00	
	P# strip of 9, 3 #4238, 2 each #4236-4237, 4239, P#S1111		10.00	
	P# single, #S1111 (#4238)		—	2.00

Serpentine Die Cut 8½ Vert.

4240	A3214	42c multicolored	.85	.20
4241	A3215	42c multicolored	.85	.20
4242	A3216	42c multicolored	.85	.20
4243	A3217	42c multicolored	.85	.20
a.	Horiz. strip of 4, #4240-4243		3.40	
	P# strip of 5, 2 #4240, 1 each #4241-4243, #V1111, V2222		6.00	
	P# strip of 9, 3 #4242, 2 each #4240-4241, 4244, P#V1111, V2222		10.00	
	P# single, same # (#4242)		—	2.00

Serpentine Die Cut 11 Vert.
With Rounded Corners

4244	A3214	42c multicolored	.85	.30
4245	A3215	42c multicolored	.85	.30
4246	A3216	42c multicolored	.85	.30
4247	A3217	42c multicolored	.85	.30
a.	Horiz. strip of 4, #4244-4247		3.40	
	P# strip of 5, 2 #4244, 1 each #4245-4247, #V1111, V2222		6.00	
	P# strip of 9, 3 #4246, 2 each #4244-4245, 4247, P#V1111, V2222		10.00	
	P# single, same # (#4246)		—	2.00
	Nos. 4228-4247 (20)		17.00	5.20

Nos. 4232-4243 are on backing paper as high as the stamp. Nos. 4244-4247 are on backing paper that is larger than the stamp. Nos. 4232-4235 have "USPS" microprinted on the right side of a white flag stripe. On Nos. 4244-4247, the paper, vignette size and "2008" year date are slightly larger than those features on Nos. 4236-4239.

AMERICAN JOURNALISTS

Martha
Gellhorn
(1908-98)
A3218

John Hersey
(1914-93)
A3219

George Polk
(1913-48)
A3220

Ruben Salazar
(1928-70)
A3221

Eric Sevareid
(1912-92)
A3222

Designed by Howard E. Paine. Printed by Ashton-Potter (USA) Ltd.

LITHOGRAPHED
Serpentine Die Cut 10¾x10½

2008, Apr. 22			Tagged	
Self-Adhesive				
4248	A3218	42c multicolored	.85	.20
4249	A3219	42c multicolored	.85	.20
4250	A3220	42c multicolored	.85	.20
4251	A3221	42c multicolored	.85	.20
4252	A3222	42c multicolored	.85	.20
a.	Vert. strip of 5, #4248-4252		4.25	
	P# block of 10, 2 sets of 4# + P		10.00	
	P# block of 8, 2 sets of 4# +P		9.00	
	Pane of 20		20.00	

TROPICAL FRUIT

Pomegranate
A3223

Star Fruit
A3224

Kiwi — A3225

Papaya — A3226

Guava — A3227

Designed by Ethel Kessler. Printed by Ashton-Potter (USA) Ltd. (#4253-4257), Avery Dennison (#4258-4262)

LITHOGRAPHED (#4253-4257), PHOTOGRAVURE
(#4258-4262)
Serpentine Die Cut 11¼x10¾

2008, Apr. 25			Tagged	
Self-Adhesive				
4253	A3223	27c multicolored	.55	.20
4254	A3224	27c multicolored	.55	.20
4255	A3225	27c multicolored	.55	.20
4256	A3226	27c multicolored	.55	.20
4257	A3227	27c multicolored	.55	.20
a.	Horiz. strip of 5, #4253-4257		2.75	
	P# block of 10, 2 sets of 4# + P		5.50	
	Pane of 20		11.00	

COIL STAMPS
Serpentine Die Cut 8½ Vert.

4258	A3226	27c multicolored	.55	.20
4259	A3227	27c multicolored	.55	.20
4260	A3223	27c multicolored	.55	.20
4261	A3224	27c multicolored	.55	.20
4262	A3225	27c multicolored	.55	.20
a.	Horiz. strip of 5, #4258-4262		2.75	
	P# strip of 5, #V1111111		4.50	
	P# strip of 11, 3 #4260, 2 each #4258-4259, 4261, 4262, #V1111111		9.00	
	P# single, #V1111111 (#4260)		—	2.00
	Nos. 4253-4262 (10)		5.50	2.00

Purple Heart Type of 2003

Designed by Carl T. Herrman. Printed by Ashton-Potter (USA) Ltd.

LITHOGRAPHED
Sheets of 400 in four panes of 100 (#4263), Sheets of 120 in six panes of 20 (#4264)

2008, Apr. 30			Tagged	Perf. 11¼	
4263	A2891	42c multicolored		.85	.25
	P# block of 4, 4#+P			10.00	—

Self-Adhesive
Serpentine Die Cut 11¼x10¾

4264	A2891	42c multicolored	.85	.20
	P# block of 4, 4#+P		3.40	
	Pane of 20		17.00	

FRANK SINATRA

Frank Sinatra (1915-98),
Singer and Actor — A3228

Designed by Richard Sheaff. Printed by Ashton-Potter (USA) Ltd.

LITHOGRAPHED
Sheets of 120 in six panes of 20

2008, May 13	Tagged	*Serpentine Die Cut 10¾*		
Self-Adhesive				
4265	A3228	42c multicolored	.85	.20
	P# block of 4, 4#+P		3.40	
	Pane of 20		17.00	
	Sheet of 120 (6 panes)		105.00	
	Cross gutter block of 4		8.00	
	Horiz. pair with vert. gutter		2.00	
	Vert. pair with horiz. gutter		2.00	

MINNESOTA STATEHOOD, 150th ANNIV.

Bridge Over Mississippi River Near Winona — A3229

Designed by Ethel Kessler. Printed by Ashton-Potter (USA) Ltd.

LITHOGRAPHED
Sheets of 120 in six panes of 20

2008, May 17   Tagged   *Serpentine Die Cut 10¾*
Self-Adhesive

4266	A3229	42c **multicolored**	.85	.20
		P# block of 4, 4#+P	3.40	
		Pane of 20	17.00	

Dragonfly — A3230

Designed by Carl T. Herrman. Printed by Banknote Corporation of America for Sennett Security Products.

LITHOGRAPHED
Sheets of 400 in twenty panes of 20
Serpentine Die Cut 11¼x11

2008, May 19   Tagged
Self-Adhesive

4267	A3230	62c **multicolored**	1.25	.20
		P# block of 4, 4#+S	5.00	
		Pane of 20	25.00	

AMERICAN LANDMARKS

Mount Rushmore A3231

Hoover Dam — A3232

Designed by Carl T. Herrman. Printed by Ashton-Potter (USA) Ltd. (#4268), Banknote Corporation of America for Sennett Security Products (#4269).

LITHOGRAPHED
Sheets of 180 in nine panes of 20 (#4268), Sheets of 120 in six panes of 20 (#4269)

2008   Tagged   *Serpentine Die Cut 10¾x10½*
Self-Adhesive

4268	A3231	$4.80 **multicolored,** *June 6*	9.75	5.00
		P# block of 4, 4#+P	40.00	
		Pane of 20	200.00	
4269	A3232	$16.50 **multicolored,** *June 20*	30.00	17.00
		P# block of 4, 5#+S	120.00	
		Pane of 20	600.00	

LOVE

Man Carrying Heart — A3233

Designed by Ethel Kessler. Printed by Avery Dennison.

PHOTOGRAVURE
Serpentine Die Cut 10¾ on 2, 3, or 4 Sides
2008, June 10   Tagged
Booklet Stamp
Self-Adhesive

4270	A3233	42c **multicolored**	.85	.20
a.		Booklet pane of 20	17.00	

WEDDING HEARTS

Heart With Light Green Background — A3234   Heart With Buff Background — A3235

Designed by Carl T. Herrman. Printed by Ashton-Potter (USA) Ltd. (#4271), Avery Dennison (#4272).

LITHOGRAPHED (#4271), PHOTOGRAVURE (#4272)
BOOKLET STAMP (#4271)
Sheets of 240 in twelve panes of 20 (#4272)
Serpentine Die Cut 10¾ on 2, 3 or 4 Sides

2008, June 10   Tagged
Self-Adhesive

4271	A3234	42c **multicolored**	.85	.20
a.		Booklet pane of 20	17.00	

Serpentine Die Cut 10¾

4272	A3235	59c **multicolored**	1.25	.25
		P# block of 4, 3#+V	5.00	
		Pane of 20	25.00	

FLAGS OF OUR NATION

American Flag and Clouds A3236

Alabama Flag and Shrimp Boat A3237

Alaska Flag and Humpback Whale — A3238

American Samoa Flag and Island Peaks and Trees A3239

Arizona Flag and Saguaro Cacti A3240

Arkansas Flag and Wood Duck A3241

California Flag and Coast A3242

Colorado Flag and Mountain A3243

Connecticut Flag, Sailboats and Buoy — A3244

Delaware Flag and Beach A3245

Designed by Howard E. Paine. Printed by American Packaging Corp. for Sennett Security Products.

PHOTOGRAVURE
Serpentine Die Cut 11 Vert.
2008, June 14   Tagged
Self-Adhesive
Coil Stamps

4273	A3236	42c **multicolored**	.85	.25
4274	A3237	42c **multicolored**	.85	.25
4275	A3238	42c **multicolored**	.85	.25
4276	A3239	42c **multicolored**	.85	.25
4277	A3240	42c **multicolored**	.85	.25
a.		Strip of 5, #4273-4277	4.25	
4278	A3242	42c **multicolored**	.85	.25
4279	A3242	42c **multicolored**	.85	.25
4280	A3243	42c **multicolored**	.85	.25
4281	A3244	42c **multicolored**	.85	.25
4282	A3245	42c **multicolored**	.85	.25
a.		Strip of 5, #4278-4282	4.25	
b.		P # set of 10, #4277a + 4282a	8.50	

P# strip of 11, #4273-4277,
4279-4282, 2 #4278,
S#111111111   12.50

No. 4273 always has a plate number. No. 4282b may be collected as one continuous strip, but the item will not fit in any standard album.

District of Columbia Flag and Cherry Tree A3246

Florida Flag and Anhinga A3247

Georgia Flag, Fence and Lamppost A3248

Guam Flag, Fish and Tropicbird A3249

Hawaii Flag and Ohia Lehua Flowers A3250

Idaho Flag and Rainbow Trout A3251

Illinois Flag and Windmill A3252

Indiana Flag and Tractor A3253

Iowa Flag, Farm Field and Cornstalks — A3254

Kansas Flag and Farm Buildings A3255

Designed by Howard E. Paine. Printed by American Packaging Corp. for Sennett Security Products.

PHOTOGRAVURE
Serpentine Die Cut 11 Vert.

2008, Sept. 2   **Tagged**

Self-Adhesive
Coil Stamps

4283	A3246	42c	multicolored	.85 .25
4284	A3247	42c	multicolored	.85 .25
4285	A3248	42c	multicolored	.85 .25
4286	A3249	42c	multicolored	.85 .25
4287	A3250	42c	multicolored	.85 .25
a.		Strip of 5, #4283-4287		4.25
4288	A3251	42c	multicolored	.85 .25
4289	A3252	42c	multicolored	.85 .25
4290	A3253	42c	multicolored	.85 .25
4291	A3254	42c	multicolored	.85 .25
4292	A3255	42c	multicolored	.85 .25
a.		Strip of 5, #4288-4292		4.25
b.		P # set of 10, #4287a + 4192a		8.50
		P# strip of 11, #4283-4287, 4289-4292, 2 #4288, S#111111111		12.50

No. 4283 always has a plate number. No. 4292b may be collected as one continuous strip, but the item will not fit in any standard album.

CHARLES (1907-78) AND RAY (1912-88) EAMES, DESIGNERS

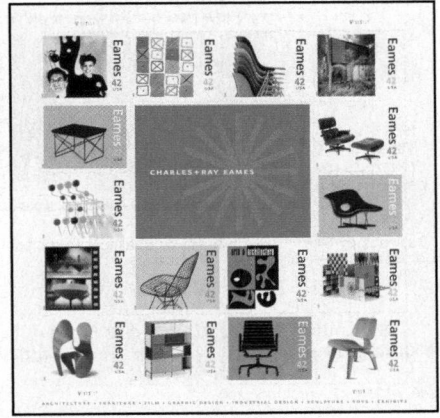

A3296

Illustration reduced.
Designed by Derry Noyes. Printed by Avery Dennison.
No. 4333: a, Christmas card depicting Charles and Ray Eames. b, "Crosspatch" fabric design. c, Stacking chairs. d, Case Study House #8, Pacific Palisades, CA. e, Wire-base table. f, Lounge chair and ottoman. g, Hang-it-all. h, La Chaise. i, Scene from film, "Tops." j, Wire mesh chair. k, Cover of May 1943 edition of *California Arts & Architecture* Magazine. l, House of Cards. m, Molded plywood sculpture. n, Eames Storage Unit. o, Aluminum group chair. p, Molded plywood chair.

PHOTOGRAVURE
Sheets of 160 in ten panes of 16
Serpentine Die Cut 10¾x10½

2008, June 17   **Tagged**

Self-Adhesive

4333	A3296	Pane of 16 + label		15.00
a.-p.		42c Any single		.85 .20

SUMMER OLYMPIC GAMES, BEIJING, CHINA

Gymnast A3297

Designed by Clarence Lee. Printed by Banknote Corporation of America for Sennett Security Products.

LITHOGRAPHED
Sheets of 180 in nine panes of 20

2008, June 19   **Tagged**   *Serpentine Die Cut 10¾*
Self-Adhesive

4334	A3297	42c	multicolored	.85 .20
		P# block of 4, 6#+S		3.40
		Pane of 20		17.00

Celebrate Type of 2007
Designed by Ethel Kessler. Printed by Banknote Corporation of America for Sennett Security Products.

LITHOGRAPHED
Sheets of 240 in twelve panes of 20

2008, July 10   **Tagged**   *Serpentine Die Cut 10¾*
Self-Adhesive

4335	A3189	42c	multicolored	.85 .20
		P# block of 4, 4# + S		3.40
		Pane of 20		17.00

VINTAGE BLACK CINEMA

Poster for "Black and Tan" — A3298

Poster for "The Sport of the Gods" — A3299

Poster for "Prinsesse Tam-Tam" — A3300

Poster for "Caldonia" — A3301

Poster for "Hallelujah" — A3302

Designed by Carl T. Herrman. Printed by Ashton-Potter (USA) Ltd.

LITHOGRAPHED
Sheets of 120 in six panes of 20
2008, July 16   Tagged   *Serpentine Die Cut 10¾*
Self-Adhesive

4336	A3298	42c	**multicolored**	.85	.20
4337	A3299	42c	**multicolored**	.85	.20
4338	A3300	42c	**multicolored**	.85	.20
4339	A3301	42c	**multicolored**	.85	.20
4340	A3302	42c	**multicolored**	.85	.20

a.	Horiz. strip of 5, #4336-4340	4.25
	P# block of 10, 2 sets of 4# + P	8.50
	Pane of 20	17.00
	Sheet of 120 (6 panes)	105.00
	Cross gutter block of 8	17.50
	Block of 10 with horiz. gutter	13.00
	Block of 8 with vert. gutter	11.00
	Vert. pair with horiz. gutter (each)	2.50
	Horiz. pair with vert. gutter (each)	2.50

Plate block may contain top label.

"TAKE ME OUT TO THE BALLGAME," CENT.

Baseball Players and First
Six Notes of Song — A3303

Designed by Richard Sheaff. Printed by Avery Dennison.

PHOTOGRAVURE
Sheets of 200 in ten panes of 20
2008, July 16   Tagged   *Serpentine Die Cut 11*
Self-Adhesive

4341	A3303	42c	**multicolored**	.85	.20
			P# block of 4, 4# + V	3.40	
			Pane of 20	17.00	

THE ART OF DISNEY: IMAGINATION

Pongo and
Pup — A3304

Steamboat
Willie — A3305

Princess Aurora,
Flora, Fauna and
Merryweather
A3306

Mowgli and
Baloo — A3307

Designed by David Pacheco. Printed by Avery Dennison.

PHOTOGRAVURE
Sheets of 160 in eight panes of 20
Serpentine Die Cut 10½x10¾
2008, Aug. 7   Tagged
Self-Adhesive

4342	A3304	42c	**multicolored**	.85	.20
4343	A3305	42c	**multicolored**	.85	.20
4344	A3306	42c	**multicolored**	.85	.20
4345	A3307	42c	**multicolored**	.85	.20

a.	Block of 4, #4342-4345	3.40
	P# block of 4, 6#+V	3.40
	P# block of 10, 2 sets of P# + top label	8.50
	Pane of 20	17.00

AMERICAN TREASURES SERIES

Valley of the
Yosemite, by
Albert Bierstadt
A3308

Designed by Derry Noyes. Printed by Banknote Corporation
of America for Sennett Security Products.

LITHOGRAPHED
BOOKLET STAMP
Serpentine Die Cut 11 on 2 or 3 Sides
2008, Aug. 14   Tagged
Self-Adhesive

4346	A3308	42c	**multicolored**	.85	.20
			a. Booklet pane of 20	17.00	

No. 4346a is a double-sided booklet pane with 12 stamps on
one side and eight stamps plus label (booklet cover) on the
other side.

Sunflower — A3309

Designed by Derry Noyes. Printed by Ashton-Potter (USA)
Ltd.

LITHOGRAPHED
BOOKLET STAMP
Serpentine Die Cut 11¼x10¾ on 2 or 3 Sides
2008, Aug. 15   Tagged
Self-Adhesive

4347	A3309	42c	**multicolored**	.85	.20
			a. Booklet pane of 20	17.00	

No. 4347a is a double-sided booklet pane with 12 stamps on
one side and eight stamps plus label (booklet cover) on the
other side.

Sea Coast Type of 2002
Designed by Tom Engeman. Printed by Banknote Corporation of America for Sennett Security Products.

LITHOGRAPHED
COIL STAMP
2008, Sept. 5   Untagged   *Perf. 9¾ Vert.*

4348	A2853	(5c)	**multicolored**	.20	.20
			Pair	.20	
			P# strip of 5, #S11111	1.25	
			P# single, #S11111		1.00

No. 4348 has "2008" year date in black, and microprinted
"USPS" at the end of the purple rock to the right of the crashing
wave.

LATIN JAZZ

Musicians
A3310

Designed by Richard Sheaff. Printed by Avery Dennison.

PHOTOGRAVURE
Sheets of 200 in ten panes of 20
Serpentine Die Cut 11x10¾
2008, Sept. 8   Tagged
Self-Adhesive

4349	A3310	42c	**multicolored**	.85	.20
			P# block of 4, 4#+V	3.40	
			Pane of 20	17.00	

LEGENDS OF HOLLYWOOD

Bette Davis (1908-89),
Actress — A3311

Designed by Richard Sheaff. Printed by Ashton-Potter (USA)
Ltd.

LITHOGRAPHED
Sheets of 180 in nine panes of 20
2008, Sept. 18   Tagged   *Serpentine Die Cut 10¾*
Self-Adhesive

4350	A3311	42c	**multicolored**	.85	.20
			P# block of 4, 4#+P	3.40	
			Pane of 20	17.00	
			Sheet of 180 (9 panes)	155.00	
			Cross gutter block of 8	17.50	
			Block of 8 with vert. gutter	10.00	
			Horiz. pair with vert. gutter	3.00	
			Vert. pair with horiz. gutter	2.00	

The cross gutter block consists of 4 stamps from the two
upper panes and 4 stamps from the two lower panes.

Eid Type of 2001
Designed by Mohamed Zakariya. Printed by Avery Dennison.

PHOTOGRAVURE
Sheets of 240 in twelve panes of 20
2008, Sept. 23   Tagged   *Serpentine Die Cut 11*
Self-Adhesive

4351	A2734	42c	**multicolored**	.85	.20
			P# block of 4, 3#+V	3.40	
			Pane of 20	17.00	

GREAT LAKES DUNES

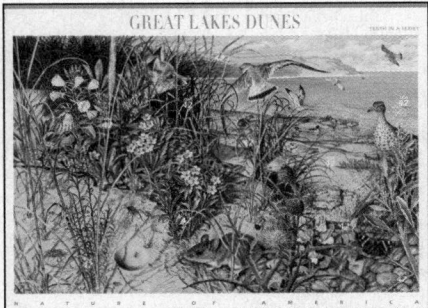

A3312

Illustration reduced.

Designed by Ethel Kessler. Printed by Avery Dennison.

Wildlife: a, Vesper sparrow. b, Red fox, vert. c, Piping plover. d, Eastern hognose snake. e, Common mergansers. f, Spotted sandpiper, vert. g, Tiger beetle, vert. h, White-footed mouse, vert. i, Piping plover nestlings. j, Red admiral butterfly, vert.

PHOTOGRAVURE
Sheets of 80 in eight panes of 10

2008, Oct. 2   Tagged   *Serpentine Die Cut 10¾*
Self-Adhesive

4352	A3312	Pane of 10	8.50	
a.-j.		42c Any single	.85	.20
		Sheet of 8 panes	67.50	

AUTOMOBILES OF THE 1950s

1959 Cadillac Eldorado
A3313

1957 Studebaker Golden Hawk
A3314

1957 Pontiac Safari
A3315

1957 Lincoln Premiere
A3316

1957 Chrysler 300C
A3317

Designed by Carl T. Herrman. Printed by Banknote Corporation of America for Sennett Security Products.

LITHOGRAPHED
Sheets of 180 in nine panes of 20

2008, Oct. 3   Tagged   *Serpentine Die Cut 10¾*
Self-Adhesive

4353	A3313	42c multicolored	.85	.20
4354	A3314	42c multicolored	.85	.20
4355	A3315	42c multicolored	.85	.20
4356	A3316	42c multicolored	.85	.20
4357	A3317	42c multicolored	.85	.20
a.		Vert. strip of 5, #4353-4357	4.25	
		Vert. P# block of 10, 2 sets of 4# + S	8.50	
		Horiz. P# block of 8, 2 sets of 4# + S	6.80	
		Pane of 20	17.00	

ALZHEIMER'S DISEASE AWARENESS

A3318

Designed by Ethel Kessler. Printed by Avery Dennison.

PHOTOGRAVURE
Sheets of 240 in twelve panes of 20

2008, Oct. 17   Tagged   *Serpentine Die Cut 10¾*
Self-Adhesive

4358	A3318	42c multicolored	.85	.20
		P# block of 4, 6#+V	3.40	
		Pane of 20	17.00	

CHRISTMAS

Virgin and Child with the Young John the Baptist, by Sandro Botticelli — A3319

Drummer Nutcracker — A3320

Santa Claus Nutcracker — A3321

King Nutcracker — A3322

Soldier Nutcracker — A3323

Drummer Nutcracker — A3324

Santa Claus Nutcracker — A3325

King Nutcracker — A3326

Soldier Nutcracker — A3327

Designed by Richard Sheaff (#4359), Derry Noyes. Printed by Ashton-Potter (USA) Ltd. (#4359), Banknote Corporation of America for Sennett Security Products (#4360-4367), Avery Dennison (#4368-4371).

LITHOGRAPHED, PHOTOGRAVURE (#4368-4371)
Serpentine Die Cut 10¾x11 on 2 or 3 Sides
2008, Oct. 23   Tagged
Self-Adhesive
Booklet Stamps

4359	A3319	42c multicolored	.85	.20
a.		Booklet pane of 20	17.00	
b.		Die cutting omitted, pair	—	
4360	A3320	42c multicolored	.85	.20
4361	A3321	42c multicolored	.85	.20
4362	A3322	42c multicolored	.85	.20
4363	A3323	42c multicolored	.85	.20
a.		Block of 4, #4360-4363	3.40	
b.		Booklet pane of 20, 5 each #4360-4363	17.00	

Serpentine Die Cut 11¼x11 on 2 or 3 Sides

4364	A3324	42c multicolored	.85	.20
4365	A3325	42c multicolored	.85	.20
4366	A3326	42c multicolored	.85	.20
4367	A3327	42c multicolored	.85	.20
a.		Block of 4, #4364-4367	3.40	
b.		Booklet pane of 4, #4364-4367	3.40	
c.		Booklet pane of 6, #4366-4367, 2 each #4364-4365	5.10	
d.		Booklet pane of 6, #4364-4365, 2 each #4366-4367	5.10	

Serpentine Die Cut 8 on 2, 3 or 4 Sides

4368	A3324	42c multicolored	.85	.20
4369	A3325	42c multicolored	.85	.20
4370	A3326	42c multicolored	.85	.20
4371	A3327	42c multicolored	.85	.20
a.		Block of 4, #4368-4371	3.40	
b.		Booklet pane of 18, 5 each #4368-4369, 4 each #4370-4371	15.50	
		Nos. 4359-4371 (13)	11.05	2.60

No. 4359a is a double-sided booklet pane with 12 stamps on one side and eight stamps plus label that serves as a booklet cover on the other side. No. 4363b is a double-sided booklet pane with 12 stamps on one side (3 each of Nos. 4360-4363) and eight stamps (2 each of Nos. 4360-4363) plus label that serves as a booklet cover on the other side.

Hanukkah Type of 2004

Designed by Ethel Kessler. Printed by Banknote Corporation of America for Sennett Security Products.

LITHOGRAPHED
Sheets of 240 in twelve panes of 20
Serpentine Die Cut 10¾x11

2008, Oct. 24　　　　　　　　**Tagged**
　　　　Self-Adhesive
4372　A2962　42c　multicolored　　　　.85　　.20
　　　　P# block of 4, 4#+S　　　　3.40
　　　　Pane of 20　　　　　　　17.00

Kwanzaa Type of 2004

Designed by Derry Noyes. Printed by Ashton-Potter (USA) Ltd.

LITHOGRAPHED
Sheets of 160 in eight panes of 20
Serpentine Die Cut 11x10¾

2008, Oct. 24　　　　　　　　**Tagged**
　　　　Self-Adhesive
4373　A2963　42c　multicolored　　　　.85　　.20
　　　　P# block of 4, 6#+P　　　　3.40
　　　　Pane of 20　　　　　　　17.00

ALASKA STATEHOOD, 50TH ANNIV.

Dogsledder Near Rainy Pass — A3328

Designed by Phil Jordan. Printed by Banknote Corporation of America for Sennett Security Products.

LITHOGRAPHED
Sheets of 180 in nine panes of 20

2009, Jan. 3　**Tagged**　*Serpentine Die Cut 10¾*
　　　　Self-Adhesive
4374　A3328　42c　multicolored　　　　.85　　.20
　　　　P# block of 4, 4#+S　　　　3.40
　　　　Pane of 20　　　　　　　17.00

CHINESE NEW YEAR

Year of the Ox — A3329

Designed by Ethel Kessler. Printed by Banknote Corporation of America for Sennett Security Products.

LITHOGRAPHED
Sheets of 108 in nine panes of 12

2009, Jan. 8　**Tagged**　*Serpentine Die Cut 10¾*
　　　　Self-Adhesive
4375　A3329　42c　multicolored　　　　.85　　.20
　　　　Pane of 12　　　　　　　10.50
　　　　Sheet of 108 (9 panes)　　95.00
　　　　Cross gutter block of 4　　8.00
　　　　Horiz. pair with vert. gutter　2.00
　　　　Vert. pair with horiz. gutter　2.00

OREGON STATEHOOD, 150TH ANNIV.

Pacific Coast of Oregon A3330

Designed by Derry Noyes. Printed by Banknote Corporation of America for Sennett Security Products.

LITHOGRAPHED
Sheets of 180 in nine panes of 20

2009, Jan. 14　**Tagged**　*Serpentine Die Cut 10¾*
　　　　Self-Adhesive
4376　A3330　42c　multicolored　　　　.85　　.20
　　　　P# block of 4, 5# + S　　　3.40
　　　　Pane of 20　　　　　　　17.00

EDGAR ALLAN POE

Edgar Allan Poe (1809-49), Writer — A3331

Designed by Carl T. Herrman. Printed by Avery Dennison.

PHOTOGRAVURE
Sheets of 160 in eight panes of 20

2009, Jan. 16　**Tagged**　*Serpentine Die Cut 10¾*
　　　　Self-Adhesive
4377　A3331　42c　multicolored　　　　.85　　.20
　　　　P# block of 4, 5# + V　　　3.40
　　　　Pane of 20　　　　　　　17.00

AMERICAN LANDMARKS

Redwood Forest A3332

Old Faithful A3333

Designed by Carl T. Herrman. Printed by Ashton-Potter (USA) Ltd.

LITHOGRAPHED
Sheets of 180 in nine panes of 20
Serpentine Die Cut 10¾x10½

2009, Jan. 16　　　　　　　　**Tagged**
　　　　Self-Adhesive
4378　A3332　$4.95　multicolored　　10.00　5.00
　　　　P# block of 4, 4# + P　　　40.00
　　　　Pane of 20　　　　　　　200.00
4379　A3333　$17.50　multicolored　32.50　18.00
　　　　P# block of 4, 4# + P　　　130.00
　　　　Pane of 20　　　　　　　650.00

ABRAHAM LINCOLN (1809-65), 16TH PRESIDENT

Lincoln as Railsplitter — A3334

Lincoln as Lawyer — A3335

Lincoln as Politician — A3336

Lincoln as President — A3337

Designed by Richard Sheaff. Printed by Ashton-Potter (USA) Ltd.

LITHOGRAPHED
Sheets of 120 in six panes of 20

2009, Feb. 9　**Tagged**　*Serpentine Die Cut 10¾*
　　　　Self-Adhesive
4380　A3334　42c　multicolored　　　　.85　　.20
4381　A3335　42c　multicolored　　　　.85　　.20
4382　A3336　42c　multicolored　　　　.85　　.20
4383　A3337　42c　multicolored　　　　.85　　.20
　a.　Horiz. strip of 4, #4380-4383　3.40
　　　　P# block of 8, 2 sets of 4# + P　6.80
　　　　Pane of 20　　　　　　　17.00
　　　　Sheet of 120 (6 panes)　　105.00
　　　　Cross gutter block of 8　　17.50
　　　　Block of 8 with horiz. gutter　10.00
　　　　Horiz. pair with vert. gutter　3.00
　　　　Vert. pair with horiz. gutter　2.00

The cross gutter block consists of 4 stamps from the two upper panes and 4 stamps from the two lower panes.

CIVIL RIGHTS PIONEERS

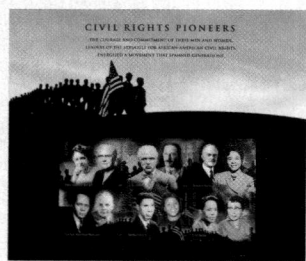

A3338

Illustration reduced.

Designed by Greg Berger. Printed by Avery Dennison.

Designs: a, Mary Church Terrell (1863-1954), writer, Mary White Ovington (1865-1951), journalist. b, J. R. Clifford (1848-1933), attorney, Joel Elias Spingarn (1875-1939), educator. c, Oswald Garrison Villard (1872-1949), co-founder of National Association for the Advancement of Colored People (NAACP), Daisy Gatson Bates (1914-99), mentor of black Little Rock Central High School students. d, Charles Hamilton Houston (1895-1950), lawyer, Walter White (1893-1955), chief secretary of NAACP. e, Medgar Evers (1925-63), assassinated Mississippi NAACP field secretary, Fannie Lou Hamer (1917-77), voting rights activist. f, Ella Baker (1903-86), activist, Ruby Hurley (1909-80), NAACP Southeast Regional Director.

PHOTOGRAVURE
Sheets of 48 in eight panes of 6

2009, Feb. 21　**Tagged**　*Serpentine Die Cut 10¾*
　　　　Self-Adhesive
4384　A3338　Pane of 6　　　　　5.10
a.-f.　42c Any single　　　　　.85　　.20

Patriotic Banner Type of 2007

Designed by Michael Osborne. Printed by Banknote Corporation of America for Sennett Security Products.

LITHOGRAPHED
COIL STAMP

2009, Feb. 24　**Untagged**　　**Perf. 9¾ Vert.**
4385　A3167　(10c)　multicolored　　.20　　.20
　　　　Pair　　　　　　　　　.40　　—
　　　　P# strip of 5, #S111　　2.50　　—
　　　　P# single, #S111　　　—　　1.75

LITERARY ARTS

Richard Wright (1908-60), Author A3339

Designed by Carl T. Herrman. Printed by Ashton-Potter (USA) Ltd.

LITHOGRAPHED
Sheets of 120 in six panes of 20

2009, Apr. 9	Tagged	*Serpentine Die Cut 10¾*		
Self-Adhesive				
4386	A3339	61c multicolored	1.25	.20
		P# block of 4, 6# + P	5.00	
		Pane of 20	25.00	

WILDLIFE

Polar Bear — A3340   Dolphin — A3341

Designed by Carl T. Herrman. Printed by Banknote Corporation of America for Sennett Security Products (#4387), Avery Dennison (#4388, 4389).

LITHOGRAPHED (#4387), PHOTOGRAVURE
Sheets of 300 in fifteen panes of 20 (#4387)
Sheets of 280 in fourteen panes of 20 (#4388)

2008-09	Tagged	*Serpentine Die Cut 11¼x11*		
Self-Adhesive				
4387	A3340	28c multicolored, *Apr. 16*	.60	.20
		P# block of 4, 4# + S	2.40	
		Pane of 20	12.00	
Serpentine Die Cut 11				
4388	A3341	64c multicolored, *June 12, 2009*	1.40	.25
		P# block of 4, 5#+V	5.60	
		Pane of 20	28.00	
COIL STAMP				
Serpentine Die Cut 8½ Vert.				
4389	A3340	28c multicolored, *Apr. 16*	.60	.20
		P# strip of 5, #V11111	4.25	
		P# single, #V11111	—	2.00

Purple Heart Type of 2003

Designed by Carl T. Herrman. Printed by Ashton-Potter (USA) Ltd.

LITHOGRAPHED
Sheets of 120 in six panes of 20
Serpentine Die Cut 11¼x10¾

2009, Apr. 28		Tagged		
Self-Adhesive				
4390	A2891	44c multicolored	.90	.20
		P# block of 4, 4#+P	3.60	
		Pane of 20	18.00	

Flag — A3342

Designed by Terrence W. McCaffrey. Printed by Banknote Corporation of America for Sennett Security Products (#4391, 4392), Ashton-Potter (USA) Ltd. (#4393), Avery Dennison (#4394, 4395, 4396).

LITHOGRAPHED, PHOTOGRAVURE (#4394, 4395, 4396)

2009	Tagged	*Perf. 9¾ Vert.*		
COIL STAMPS				
4391	A3342	44c multicolored, *May 1*	.90	.20
		Pair	1.80	
		P# strip of 5, #S111	6.25	
		P# single, #S111	—	2.00
Self-Adhesive				
Serpentine Die Cut 11 Vert.				
With Pointed Corners				
4392	A3342	44c multicolored, *May 8*	.90	.20
		Pair	1.80	
		P# strip of 5, #S111	6.25	
		P# single, #S111	—	2.00
Serpentine Die Cut 9½ Vert.				
4393	A3342	44c multicolored, *May 8*	.90	.20
		Pair	1.80	
		P# strip of 5, #P1111	6.25	
		P# single, #P1111	—	2.00
Serpentine Die Cut 8½ Vert.				
4394	A3342	44c multicolored, *May 8*	.90	.20
		Pair	1.80	
		P# strip of 5, #V1111	6.25	

		P# single, #V1111	—	2.00
Serpentine Die Cut 11 Vert.				
With Rounded Corners				
4395	A3342	44c multicolored, *May 1*	.90	.20
		Pair	1.80	
		P# strip of 5, #V1111	6.25	
		P# single, #V1111	—	2.00
BOOKLET STAMP				
Serpentine Die Cut 11¼x10¾ on 3 Sides				
4396	A3342	44c multicolored, *June 5*	.90	.20
a.		Booklet pane of 10	9.00	

Nos. 4392-4394 are on backing paper as high as the stamp. No. 4395 is on backing paper that is taller than the stamp. No. 4393 has microprinted "USPS" on white stripe below the blue field.

WEDDINGS

Wedding Rings — A3343   Wedding Cake — A3344

Designed by Ethel Kessler. Printed by Banknote Corporation of America for Sennett Security Products (#4397), Avery Dennison (#4398).

LITHOGRAPHED, PHOTOGRAVURE (#4398)
Sheets of 160 in eight panes of 20, Sheets of 240 in twelve panes of 20 (#4398)

2009, May 1	Tagged	*Serpentine Die Cut 10¾*		
Self-Adhesive				
4397	A3343	44c multicolored	.90	.20
		P# block of 4, 5#+S	3.60	
		Pane of 20	18.00	
4398	A3344	61c multicolored	1.25	.25
		P# block of 4, 6#+V	5.00	
		Pane of 20	25.00	

THE SIMPSONS TELEVISION SHOW, 20TH ANNIV.

Homer Simpson — A3345   Marge Simpson — A3346

Bart Simpson — A3347   Lisa Simpson — A3348

Maggie Simpson — A3349

Designed by Matt Groening. Printed by Banknote Corporation of America for Sennett Security Products.

LITHOGRAPHED
Serpentine Die Cut 10¾ on 2, 3 or 4 Sides

2009, May 7		Tagged		
BOOKLET STAMPS				
Self-Adhesive				
4399	A3345	44c multicolored	.90	.20
4400	A3346	44c multicolored	.90	.20
4401	A3347	44c multicolored	.90	.20
4402	A3348	44c multicolored	.90	.20
4403	A3349	44c multicolored	.90	.20
a.		Horiz. strip of 5, #4399-4403	4.50	
b.		Booklet pane of 20, 4 each #4399-4403	18.00	

LOVE

King of Hearts — A3350   Queen of Hearts — A3351

Designed by Jeanne Greco. Printed by Avery Dennison.

PHOTOGRAVURE
Serpentine Die Cut 10¾ on 2, 3 or 4 Sides

2009, May 8		Tagged		
BOOKLET STAMPS				
Self-Adhesive				
4404	A3350	44c multicolored	.90	.20
4405	A3351	44c multicolored	.90	.20
a.		Horiz. or vert. pair, #4404-4405	1.80	
b.		Booklet pane of 20, 10 each #4404-4405	18.00	

BOB HOPE

Bob Hope (1903-2003),
Actor, Comedian — A3352

Designed by Derry Noyes. Printed by Ashton-Potter (USA) Ltd.

LITHOGRAPHED
Sheets of 180 in nine panes of 20

| 2009, May 29 | Tagged | *Serpentine Die Cut 10¾* |
| | **Self-Adhesive** | |

4406	A3252 44c **multicolored**		.90	.20
	P# block of 4, 4#+P	3.60		
	Pane of 20	18.00		
	Sheet of 180 (9 panes)	165.00		
	Cross gutter block of 8	17.50		
	Block of 8 with vertical gutter	10.00		
	Horiz. pair with vert. gutter	2.00		
	Vert. pair with horiz. gutter	2.00		

The cross gutter block consists of 2 stamps from the two upper panes and 6 stamps from the two lower panes.

Celebrate Type of 2007

Designed by Ethel Kessler. Printed by Banknote Corporation of America for Sennett Security Products.

LITHOGRAPHED
Sheets of 240 in twelve panes of 20

| 2009, June 10 | Tagged | *Serpentine Die Cut 10¾* |
| | **Self-Adhesive** | |

4407	A3189 44c **multicolored**		.90	.20
	P# block of 4, 4#+S	3.60		
	Pane of 20	18.00		

BLACK HERITAGE

Anna Julia Cooper (c. 1858-1964), Educator — A3353

Designed by Ethel Kessler. Printed by Ashton-Potter (USA) Ltd.

LITHOGRAPHED
Sheets of 120 in six panes of 20

| 2009, June 11 | Tagged | *Serpentine Die Cut 10¾* |
| | **Self-Adhesive** | |

4408	A3353 44c **multicolored**		.90	.20
	P# block of 4, 5#+P	3.60		
	Pane of 20	18.00		

2009 END-OF-YEAR ISSUES

The USPS has announced that the following items will be released in late 2009. Dates, denominations and cities are tentative.

Gulf Coast Lighthouses 5 44c self-adhesive stamps depicting Matagorda Island Lighthouse, TX, Sabine Pass Lighthouse, LA, Biloxi Lighthouse, MS, Sand Island Lighthouse, AL, Fort Jefferson Lighthouse, FL, *July 23,* Biloxi, MS.

Gulf Coast Lighthouses 5 44c letter sheets depicting Matagorda Island Lighthouse, TX, Sabine Pass Lighthouse, LA, Biloxi Lighthouse, MS, Sand Island Lighthouse, AL, Fort Jefferson Lighthouse, FL, *July 23,* Biloxi, MS.

Gulf Coast Lighthouses 5 28c picture postal cards depicting Matagorda Island Lighthouse, TX, Sabine Pass Lighthouse, LA, Biloxi Lighthouse, MS, Sand Island Lighthouse, AL, Fort Jefferson Lighthouse, FL, in booklet of 20 containing five of each card *July 23,* Biloxi, MS.

Flags of Our Nation strip of 10 44c self-adhesive coil stamps depicting flags and scenery of United States, Kentucky, Louisiana, Maine, Maryland, Massachusetts, Michigan, Minnesota, Mississippi and Missouri *Aug. 6,* Pittsburgh, PA.

Early Television Memories pane of 20 44c self-adhesive stamps depicting Texaco Star Theater (Milton Berle), I Love Lucy (Lucy and Ethel), The Red Skelton Show (Red Skelton as Freddie the Freeloader), The Howdy Doody Show (Howdy Doody marionette), Dragnet (Jack Webb as Sergeant Joe Friday), Lassie (Lassie), Hopalong Cassidy (Hopalong, with his horse Topper), You Bet Your Life (Groucho Marx and the "secret word" duck), The Dinah Shore Show (Dinah Shore), The Ed Sullivan Show (Ed Sullivan), Kukla, Fran and Ollie (Fran Allison with puppets Kukla and Ollie), The Phil Silvers Show (Phil Silvers), The Lone Ranger (Lone Ranger with his horse Silver), Perry Mason (Hamilton Burger and Perry Mason), Alfred Hitchcock Presents (Alfred Hitchcock), George Burns and Gracie Allen Show (George Burns and Gracie Allen), The Adventures of Ozzie and Harriet (Ozzie and Harriet Nelson), The Tonight Show (Steve Allen), The Twilight Zone (Rod Serling) and The Honeymooners (Ralph Kramden and Ed Norton) *Aug. 11,* North Hollywood, CA.

Early Television Memories booklet of 20 28c picture postal cards depicting Texaco Star Theater (Milton Berle), I Love Lucy (Lucy and Ethel), The Red Skelton Show (Red Skelton as Freddie the Freeloader), The Howdy Doody Show (Howdy Doody marionette), Dragnet (Jack Webb as Sergeant Joe Friday), Lassie (Lassie), Hopalong Cassidy (Hopalong, with his horse Topper), You Bet Your Life (Groucho Marx and the "secret word" duck), The Dinah Shore Show (Dinah Shore), The Ed Sullivan Show (Ed Sullivan), Kukla, Fran and Ollie (Fran Allison with puppets Kukla and Ollie), The Phil Silvers Show (Phil Silvers), The Lone Ranger (Lone Ranger with his horse Silver), Perry Mason (Hamilton Burger and Perry Mason), Alfred Hitchcock Presents (Alfred Hitchcock), George Burns and Gracie Allen Show (George Burns and Gracie Allen), The Adventures of Ozzie and Harriet (Ozzie and Harriet Nelson), The Tonight Show (Steve Allen), The Twilight Zone (Rod Serling) and The Honeymooners (Ralph Kramden and Ed Norton) *Aug. 11,* North Hollywood, CA.

Hawaii Statehood, 44c self-adhesive stamp, *Aug. 21,* Honolulu, HI.

Eid, 44c self-adhesive stamp, *Sept. 3,* Washington, DC.

Thanksgiving Day Parade, horizontal strip of 4 44c self-adhesive stamps depicting boy pointing at bear balloon, drum major and trombone players, trumpeters, and turkey balloon and cowboy with lasso, *Sept. 9,* New York, NY. p>**Gary Cooper, Legends of Hollywood Series,** 44c self-adhesive stamp, *Sept. 10,* Los Angeles, CA.

Supreme Court Justices, 4 x 44c self-adhesive souvenir sheet depicting Louis D. Brandeis, William J. Brennan, Jr., Felix Frankfurter and Joseph Story, *Sept. 22,* Washington, DC.

Kelp Forest, Nature of America Series, pane of 10 x 44c self-adhesive stamps depicting: brown pelican; harbor seal; yellowtail rockfish and white-spotted anemone; Pacific rock crab and jeweled top snail; northern kelp crab, Monterey turban snail, brooding sea anemone and treefish; copper rockfish; lion's mane nudibranch; western gull, southern sea otter and red sea urchin; and vermilion rockfish , *Oct. 1,* Monterey, CA.

Kelp Forest, Nature of America Series, postal cards in a pack of 10 x 44c self-adhesive stamps depicting: brown pelican; harbor seal; yellowtail rockfish and white-spotted anemone; Pacific rock crab and jeweled top snail; northern kelp crab, Monterey turban snail, brooding sea anemone and treefish; copper rockfish; lion's mane nudibranch; western gull, southern sea otter and red sea urchin; and vermilion rockfish , *Oct. 1,* Monterey, CA.

Winter Holidays, 4 x 44c self-adhesive booklet stamps depicting reindeer, snowman, gingerbread man, nutcracker, in convertible booklet pane of 20, *Oct. 8,* New York, NY.

Winter Holidays, 4 x 44c self-adhesive ATM booklet stamps depicting reindeer, snowman, gingerbread man, nutcracker, in booklet pane of 18, *Oct. 8,* New York, NY.

Hanukkah, 44c self-adhesive stamp, *Oct. 9.*
Kwanzaa, 44c self-adhesive stamp, *Oct. 9.*
Christmas, Madonna and Child by Sassoferrato, 44c self-adhesive stamp in double-sided convertible booklet of 20, *Oct. 20,* San Simeon, CA.

Listings as of 9PM, Aug. 3, 2009.

National Album Series

The National series offers a panoramic view of our country's heritage through postage stamps. It is the most complete and comprehensive U.S. album series you can buy. There are spaces for every major U.S. stamp listed in the Scott Catalogue, including Special Printings, Newspaper stamps and much more.

- Pages printed on one side.

- All spaces identified by Scott numbers.

- All major variety of stamps are either illustrated or described.

- Chemically neutral paper protects stamps.

- Sold as page units only. Binders, slipcases and labels sold separately.

Item			Retail
100NTL1	1845-1934	108 pgs	$64.99
100NTL2	1935-1976	108 pgs	$64.99
100NTL3	1977-1993	114 pgs	$64.99
100NTL4	1994-1999	96 pgs	$64.99
100NTL5	2000-2005	126 pgs	$64.99

Supplemented in March.

U.S. National Kit

The most complete and comprehensive U.S. stamp album is now available in a money-saving complete kit package! This kit contains all five National album parts, 4 large National Series 3-ring binders, slipcases, protector sheets and National album labels, pre-cut value pack of black ScottMounts and the *U.S. Specialized Catalogue*.

Item	Retail
NATLKIT	$649.99

What ever your collecting specialty Scott Publishing has an album for you. For more information on the entire line of Scott albums and products visit your local stamp dealer or online at:
www.amosadvantage.com

SCOTT®

1-800-572-6885
P.O. BOX 828
Sidney OH 45365
www.amosadvantage.com

AMOS
PUBLISHING

SEMI-POSTAL STAMPS

The genesis of the U.S. semi-postal stamp program was a July 1997 bill passed by both houses of Congress that directed the USPS to issue a stamp to benefit breast-cancer research. On August 13, the President signed it into law. The surcharge was to be up to 25% of the current first-class rate.

BREAST CANCER RESEARCH

SP1

Designed by Ethel Kessler. Printed by Avery Dennison.

PHOTOGRAVURE
Sheets of 160 in eight panes of 20

1998, July 29   **Tagged**   *Serpentine Die Cut 11*
Self-Adhesive

B1	SP1	(32c+8c) **multicolored**	.80	.20
		P# block of 4, 6#+V	3.50	
		Pane of 20	16.00	

The 8c surtax was for cancer research. After the Jan. 10, 1999, first class postage rate changes, No. B1 became a 33c stamp with a 7c surtax; after Jan. 7, 2001, it became a 34c stamp with a 6c surtax. Effective Mar. 23, 2002, the stamp was sold for 45c, but the face value remained at 34c until June 30, 2002, at which time the face value rose to 37c. On Jan. 8, 2006, the face value rose to 39c, and on May 14, 2007, the face value rose to 41c and the stamp sold for 55c.

Sales of No. B1 were suspended Jan. 1, 2004, but resumed Feb. 2, 2004, after Congress extended the sales period through

Dec. 31, 2005. Subsequently, the sales period was again extended.

HEROES OF 2001

Firemen Atop World Trade Center Rubble — SP2

Designed by Derry Noyes. Printed by Ashton-Potter (USA) Ltd..

LITHOGRAPHED
Sheets of 120 in six panes of 20

2002, June 7   **Tagged**   *Serpentine Die Cut 11¼*
Self-Adhesive

B2	SP2	(34c+11c) **multicolored**	.80	.35
		P# block of 4, 4#+P	3.50	
		Pane of 20	16.00	

The 11c surtax was for assistance to families of emergency relief personnel killed or permanently disabled in the line of duty

in connection with the terrorist attacks of Sept. 11, 2001. No. B2 became a 37c stamp with an 8c surtax June 30, 2002.

STOP FAMILY VIOLENCE

SP3

Designed by Carl T. Herrman.

Printed by Avery Dennison.

PHOTOGRAVURE
Sheets of 200 in ten panes of 20

2003, Oct. 8   **Tagged**   *Serpentine Die Cut 11*
Self-Adhesive

B3	SP3	(37c+8c) **multicolored**	.85	.45
		P# block of 4, 4#+V	3.50	
		Pane of 20	17.50	

AIR POST STAMPS

Air mail in the U. S. postal system developed in three stages: pioneer period (with many unofficial or semi-official flights before 1918), government flights and contract air mail (C.A.M.). Contract air mail began on February 15, 1926.

All C.A.M. contracts were canceled on February 19, 1934, and air mail was carried by Army planes for six months. After that the contract plan was resumed. Separate domestic airmail service was abolished Oct. 11, 1975.

See Domestic Air Mail Rates chart in introduction.

Curtiss Jenny — AP1

No. C3 first used on airplane mail service between Washington, Philadelphia and New York, on May 15, 1918, but was valid for ordinary postage. The rate of postage was 24 cents per ounce, which included immediate individual delivery.

Rate of postage was reduced to 16 cents for the first ounce and 6 cents for each additional ounce, which included 10 cents for immediate individual delivery, on July 15, 1918, by Postmaster General's order of June 26, 1918. No. C2 was first used for air mail in the tri-city service on July 15.

Rate of postage was reduced on December 15, 1918, by Postmaster General's order of November 30, 1918, to 6 cents per ounce. No. C1 was first used for air mail (same three-way service) on Dec. 16.

FLAT PLATE PRINTINGS
Plates of 100 subjects.

1918		Unwmk. Engr.	Perf. 11	
C1	AP1	6c **orange**, *Dec. 10*	65.	30.
		pale orange	65.	30.
		Never hinged	135.	
		On cover		50.
		First flight cover, *Dec. 16*		2,000.
		Margin block of 4, arrow top or left	290.	140.
		Center line block	300.	150.
		P# block of 6, arrow	775.	—
		Never hinged	1,125.	
		Double transfer (#9155-14)	90.	45.
C2	AP1	16c **green**, *July 11*	70.	35.
		dark green	70.	35.
		Never hinged	150.	
		On cover		55.

		First flight cover, *July 15*		800.
		Margin block of 4, arrow top or left	310.	175.
		Center line block	340.	190.
		P# block of 6, arrow	1,000.	
		Never hinged	1,500.	
C3	AP1	24c **carmine rose & blue**, *May 13*	70.	35.
		dark carmine rose & blue	75.	35.
		Never hinged	150.	
		On cover		75.
		First flight cover, *May 15*		750.
		Margin block of 4, arrow top or left	310.	150.
		Margin block of 4, arrow bottom	360.	160.
		Margin block of 4, arrow right	400.	200.
		Center line block	350.	175.
		P# block of 4, red P# only	400.	—
		P# block of 12, two P#, arrow & two "TOP"	1,300.	—
		Never hinged	2,100.	
		P# block of 12, two P#, arrow & blue "TOP" only	12,500.	
a.		Center inverted	500,000.	
		Never hinged	1,100,000.	
		Block of 4	2,000,000.	
		Block of 4 with horiz. guide line	2,150,000.	
		Corner margin block of 4 with siderographer's initials	2,400,000.	
		Center line block	2,150,000.	
		P# block of 4, blue P#	3,500,000.	
		Nos. C1-C3 (3)	205.00	100.00
		Nos. C1-C3, never hinged	435.00	

Plate Blocks
Scott values for plate blocks printed from flat plates are for very fine side and bottom positions. Top position plate blocks with full wide selvage sell for more.

Airplane Radiator and
Wooden
Propeller — AP2

Air Service
Emblem — AP3

DeHavilland Biplane — AP4

Nos. C4-C6 were issued primarily for use in the new night-flying air mail service between New York and San Francisco, but valid for all purposes. Three zones were established; New York-Chicago, Chicago-Cheyenne, Cheyenne-San Francisco, and the rate of postage was 8 cents an ounce for each zone. Service was inaugurated on July 1, 1924.

These stamps were placed on sale at the Philatelic Agency at Washington on the dates indicated in the listings but were not issued to postmasters at that time.

Plates of 400 subjects in four panes of 100 each.

1923			Unwmk.		Perf. 11	
C4	AP2	8c	dark green, Aug. 15	21.00	14.00	
			deep green	21.00	14.00	
			Never hinged	42.50		
			On cover		22.50	
			P# block of 6	250.00		
			Never hinged	350.00		
			Double transfer	40.00	22.50	
C5	AP3	16c	dark blue, Aug. 17	70.00	30.00	
			Never hinged	150.00		
			On cover		47.50	
			P# block of 6	1,550.		
			Never hinged	2,350.		
			Double transfer	120.00	50.00	
C6	AP4	24c	carmine, Aug. 21	75.00	30.00	
			Never hinged	160.00		
			On cover		42.50	
			P# block of 6	2,050.		
			Never hinged	3,100.		
			Double transfer (Pl. 14841)	160.00	42.50	
			Nos. C4-C6 (3)	166.00	74.00	
			Nos. C4-C6, never hinged	352.50		

Map of United States and Two Mail Planes — AP5

Double Transfer

The Act of Congress of February 2, 1925, created a rate of 10 cents per ounce for distances to 1000 miles, 15 cents per ounce for 1500 miles and 20 cents for more than 1500 miles on contract air mail routes.

Plates of 200 subjects in four panes of 50 each.

1926-27			Unwmk.		Perf. 11	
C7	AP5	10c	dark blue, Feb. 13, 1926	2.50	.35	
			light blue	2.50	.35	
			Never hinged	4.50		
			P# block of 6	35.00		
			Never hinged	47.50		
			Double transfer (18246 UL 11)	5.75	1.10	
C8	AP5	15c	olive brown, Sept. 18, 1926	2.75	2.50	
			light brown	2.75	2.50	
			Never hinged	5.25		
			P# block of 6	35.00		
			Never hinged	50.00		
C9	AP5	20c	yellow green, Jan. 25, 1927	7.00	2.00	
			green	7.00	2.00	
			Never hinged	13.50		

	P# block of 6	75.00	—
	Never hinged	105.00	
	Nos. C7-C9 (3)	12.25	4.85
	Nos. C7-C9, never hinged	23.25	

Lindbergh's Plane "Spirit of St. Louis" and Flight
Route — AP6

A tribute to Col. Charles A. Lindbergh, who made the first non-stop (and solo) flight from New York to Paris, May 20-21, 1927.

Plates of 200 subjects in four panes of 50 each.

1927, June 18			Unwmk.		Perf. 11	
C10	AP6	10c	dark blue	7.00	2.50	
			Never hinged	13.00		
			P# block of 6	90.00	—	
			Never hinged	130.00		
			Double transfer	11.50	3.25	
a.			Booklet pane of 3, May 26, 1928	80.00	65.00	
			Never hinged	130.00		

Beacon on
Rocky
Mountains
AP7

Issued to meet the new rate, effective August 1, of 5 cents per ounce.

Plates of 100 subjects in two panes of 50

1928, July 25			Unwmk.		Perf. 11	
C11	AP7	5c	carmine and blue	5.00	.75	
			Never hinged	9.50		
			On cover, first day of 5c airmail rate, Aug. 1		3.00	
			Margin block of 4, arrow, (line) right or left	24.00	4.50	
			P# block of 6, two P# & red "TOP"	40.00	—	
			Never hinged	55.00		
			P# block of 6, two P# & blue "TOP"	40.00	—	
			Never hinged	55.00		
			P# block of 6, two P# & double "TOP"	110.00	—	
			Never hinged	160.00		
			P# block of 8, two P# only (no "TOP")	200.00	—	
			Never hinged	300.00		
			Recut frame line at left	7.50	1.50	
			Double transfer			
a.			Vert. pair, imperf. between	7,000.		

Winged Globe — AP8

Plates of 200 subjects in four panes of 50 each.

1930, Feb. 10			Unwmk.		Perf. 11	
			Stamp design: 46½x19mm			
C12	AP8	5c	violet	9.50	.50	
			Never hinged	18.00		
			P# block of 6	140.00	—	
			Never hinged	210.00		
			Double transfer (Pl. 20189)	19.00	1.25	
a.			Horiz. pair, imperf. between	4,500.		

See Nos. C16-C17, C19.

GRAF ZEPPELIN ISSUE

Zeppelin Over Atlantic Ocean — AP9

Zeppelin Between Continents — AP10

Zeppelin Passing Globe — AP11

Issued for use on mail carried on the first Europe-Pan-America round trip flight of the Graf Zeppelin in May, 1930. They were withdrawn from sale June 30, 1930.

Plates of 200 subjects in four panes of 50 each.

1930, Apr. 19		Unwmk.		Perf. 11	
C13	AP9	65c green		225.	150.
		Never hinged		400.	
		On cover or card			160.
		Block of 4		975.	700.
		P# block of 6		2,100.	—
		Never hinged		3,000.	
C14	AP10	$1.30 brown		475.	350.
		Never hinged		850.	
		On cover			375.
		Block of 4		2,100.	1,500.
		P# block of 6		5,400.	—
		Never hinged		7,600.	
C15	AP11	$2.60 blue		615.	550.
		Never hinged		1,200.	
		On cover			575.
		Block of 4		3,200.	2,500.
		P# block of 6		8,000.	—
		Never hinged		11,000.	
		Nos. C13-C15 (3)		1,315.	1,050.
		Nos. C13-C15, never hinged		2,450.	

ROTARY PRESS PRINTING
Plates of 200 subjects in four panes of 50 each.

1931-32		Unwmk.		Perf. 10½x11	
		Stamp design: 47½x19mm			
C16	AP8	5c violet, Aug. 19, 1931		5.00	.60
		Never hinged		8.75	
		Block of 4		22.00	2.00
		P# block of 4		75.00	—
		Never hinged		100.00	

Issued to conform with new air mail rate of 8 cents per ounce which became effective July 6, 1932.

C17	AP8	8c olive bister, Sept. 26, 1932		2.25	.40
		Never hinged		4.00	
		Block of 4		10.00	2.00
		P# block of 4		27.50	—
		Never hinged		37.50	

CENTURY OF PROGRESS ISSUE

"Graf Zeppelin," Federal Building at Chicago Exposition and Hangar at Friedrichshafen — AP12

Issued in connection with the flight of the airship "Graf Zeppelin" in October, 1933, to Miami, Akron and Chicago and from the last city to Europe.

FLAT PLATE PRINTING
Plates of 200 subjects in four panes of 50 each.

1933, Oct. 2		Unwmk.		Perf. 11	
C18	AP12	50c green		55.00	55.00
		Never hinged		100.00	
		On cover			80.00

	Block of 4	230.00	290.00
	P# block of 6	500.00	—
	Never hinged	750.00	

> **Catalogue values for unused stamps in this section, from this point to the end, are for Never Hinged items.**

Type of 1930 Issue
ROTARY PRESS PRINTING

Issued to conform with new air mail rate of 6 cents per ounce which became effective July 1, 1934.

Plates of 200 subjects in four panes of 50 each.

1934, June 30		Unwmk.	Perf. 10½x11	
C19	AP8	6c dull orange	3.50	.25
		On cover, first day of 6c airmail rate, July 1		10.00
		Block of 4	14.00	1.10
		P# block of 4	20.00	
		Horiz. pair with full vert. gutter btwn.	425.00	
		Vert. pair with full horiz. gutter btwn.	600.00	

TRANSPACIFIC ISSUES

"China Clipper" over Pacific — AP13

Issued to pay postage on mail transported by the Transpacific air mail service, inaugurated Nov. 22, 1935.

FLAT PLATE PRINTING
Plates of 200 subjects in four panes of 50 each.

1935, Nov. 22		Unwmk.	Perf. 11	
C20	AP13	25c blue	1.40	1.00
		P# block of 6	22.50	—

"China Clipper" over Pacific — AP14

Issued primarily for use on the Transpacific service to China, but valid for all air mail purposes.

FLAT PLATE PRINTING
Plates of 200 subjects in four panes of 50 each.

1937, Feb. 15		Unwmk.	Perf. 11	
C21	AP14	20c green	11.00	1.75
		dark green	11.00	1.75
		Block of 4	45.00	8.50
		P# block of 6	90.00	—
C22	AP14	50c carmine	11.00	5.00
		Block of 4	45.00	21.00
		P# block of 6	90.00	—

Wide full selvage top margin plate blocks of No. C22 are extremely scarce and sell for 10 or more times the value listed.

Eagle Holding Shield, Olive Branch and Arrows — AP15

FLAT PLATE PRINTING

Frame plates of 100 subjects in two panes of 50 each separated by a 1½-inch wide vertical gutter with central guide line, and vignette plates of 50 subjects. Some plates were made of iron, then chromed; several of these carry an additional imprint, "E.I." (Electrolytic Iron).

1938, May 14		Unwmk.	Perf. 11	
C23	AP15	6c dark blue & carmine	.50	.20
		Margin block of 4, bottom or side arrow	2.25	.55
		P# block of 4, 2 P#	8.00	—
		Center line block	2.75	.95

	Top P# block of 10, with two P#, arrow, two "TOP" and two registration markers	15.00	
a.	Vert. pair, imperf. horiz.	325.00	—
	On cover		1,750.
	Center line block	1,000.	
	P# block of 4, 2 P#	1,500.	
b.	Horiz. pair, imperf. vert.	12,500.	
	P# block of 4, 2 P#	37,500.	
c.	6c ultramarine & carmine	150.00	1,500.
	Center line block	1,200.	
	P# block of 4, 2 P#	1,500.	

Top plate number blocks of No. C23 are found both with and without top arrow.

The plate block of No. C23b is unique and never hinged; value is based on 1994 auction sale.

TRANSATLANTIC ISSUE

Winged Globe — AP16

Inauguration of Transatlantic air mail service.

FLAT PLATE PRINTING
Plates of 200 subjects in four panes of 50 each.

1939, May 16		Unwmk.	Perf. 11	
C24	AP16	30c dull blue	12.00	1.50
		P# block of 6	125.00	—

Twin-Motored Transport Plane — AP17

ROTARY PRESS PRINTING
E. E. Plates of 200 subjects in four panes of 50 each.

1941-44		Unwmk.	Perf. 11x10½	
C25	AP17	6c carmine, June 25, 1941	.20	.20
		P# block of 4	.60	—
		Pair with full vert. gutter btwn.	225.00	
		Pair with full horiz. gutter btwn.		
a.		Booklet pane of 3, Mar. 18, 1943	5.00	1.50
b.		Horiz. pair, imperf. between	2,250.	

Singles from No. C25a are imperf. at sides or at sides and bottom.

Value of No. C25b is for pair without blue crayon P. O. rejection mark on front. Very fine pairs with crayon mark sell for about $1,750.

C26	AP17	8c olive green, Mar. 21, 1944	.20	.20
		P# block of 4	1.10	—
		Pair with full horiz. gutter btwn.	325.00	
a.		All color omitted		

No. C26a has an albino impression and exists as a pair of stamps within a double-paper spliced strip of six stamps.

C27	AP17	10c violet, Aug. 15, 1941	1.25	.80
		P# block of 4	5.50	—
C28	AP17	15c brown carmine, Aug. 19, 1941	2.25	.35
		P# block of 4	9.50	—
C29	AP17	20c bright green, Aug. 27, 1941	2.25	.30
		P# block of 4	9.50	—
C30	AP17	30c blue, Sept. 25, 1941	2.25	.35
		P# block of 4	9.50	—
C31	AP17	50c orange, Oct. 29, 1941	11.00	3.25
		P# block of 4	50.00	—
		Nos. C25-C31 (7)	19.40	4.85

DC-4 Skymaster AP18

ROTARY PRESS PRINTING
E. E. Plates of 200 subjects in four panes of 50 each.

1946, Sept. 25		Unwmk.	Perf. 11x10½	
C32	AP18	5c carmine	.20	.20
		P# block of 4	.45	—

DC-4 Skymaster — AP19

ROTARY PRESS PRINTING
E. E. Plates of 400 subjects in four panes of 100
each.

1947, Mar. 26   Unwmk.   Perf. 10½x11
C33 AP19 5c **carmine**   .20 .20
P# block of 4   .60 —

Pan American
Union
Building,
Washington,
D.C., and
Martin 2-0-
2 — AP20

Statue of
Liberty, New
York Skyline
and Lockheed
Constellation
AP21

San Francisco-Oakland Bay Bridge and Boeing B377
Stratocruiser — AP22

Designed by Victor S. McCloskey, Jr., Leon Helguera and
William K. Schrage.

ROTARY PRESS PRINTING
E. E. Plates of 200 subjects in four panes of 50
each.

1947   Unwmk.   Perf. 11x10½
C34 AP20 10c **black,** *Aug. 30*   .25 .20
P# block of 4   1.10 —
a.   Dry printing   .40 .20
P# block of 4 (#25613, 25614)   1.75
C35 AP21 15c **bright blue green,** *Aug. 20*   .35 .20
blue green   .35 .20
P# block of 4   1.50 —
Pair with full horiz. gutter btwn.   650.00
a.   Horiz. pair, imperf. between   2,750.
b.   Dry printing   .55 .20
P# block of 4 (#25492 and up)   2.50 —
C36 AP22 25c **blue,** *July 30*   .90 .20
P# block of 4   4.00 —
a.   Dry printing   1.20 .20
P# block of 4 (#25615 and up)   5.25 —
Nos. C34-C36 (3)   1.50 .60

See note on wet and dry printings following No. 1029.
No. C35a is valued in the grade of fine.

ROTARY PRESS COIL STAMP
Type of 1947

1948, Jan. 15   Unwmk.   Perf. 10 Horizontally
C37 AP19 5c **carmine**   1.00 .80
Pair   2.10 1.75
Joint line pair   10.00 3.00

NEW YORK CITY ISSUE

Map of Five Boroughs,
Circular Band and
Planes — AP23

50th anniv. of the consolidation of the five boroughs of New
York City.

ROTARY PRESS PRINTING
E. E. Plates of 400 subjects in four panes of 100
each.

1948, July 31   Unwmk.   Perf. 11x10½
C38 AP23 5c **bright carmine**   .20 .20
P# block of 4   3.50

Type of 1947
ROTARY PRESS PRINTING
E. E. Plates of 400 subjects in four panes of 100
each.

1949   Unwmk.   Perf. 10½x11
C39 AP19 6c **carmine,** *Jan. 18*   .20 .20
P# block of 4   .50
Pair with full horiz. gutter btwn.   600.00
a.   Booklet pane of 6, *Nov. 18*   10.00 5.00
b.   Dry printing   .50 .20
P# block of 4 (#25340 and up)   2.25 —
c.   As "a," dry printing   25.00
See note on wet and dry printings following No. 1029.

ALEXANDRIA BICENTENNIAL ISSUE

Home of John
Carlyle,
Alexandria
Seal and
Gadsby's
Tavern
AP24

200th anniv. of the founding of Alexandria, Va.

ROTARY PRESS PRINTING
E. E. Plates of 200 subjects in four panes of 50
each.

1949, May 11   Unwmk.   Perf. 11x10½
C40 AP24 6c **carmine**   .20 .20
P# block of 4   .50

ROTARY PRESS COIL STAMP
Type of 1947

1949, Aug. 25   Unwmk.   Perf. 10 Horizontally
C41 AP19 6c **carmine**   3.00 .20
Pair   6.25 .20
Joint line pair   14.00 1.35

UNIVERSAL POSTAL UNION ISSUE

Post Office
Department
Building
AP25

Globe and
Doves Carrying
Messages
AP26

Boeing
Stratocruiser
and
Globe — AP27

Universal Postal Union, 75th Anniv.

ROTARY PRESS PRINTING
E. E. Plates of 200 subjects in four panes of 50
each.

1949   Unwmk.   Perf. 11x10½
C42 AP25 10c **violet,** *Nov. 18*   .20 .20
P# block of 4   1.40 —
C43 AP26 15c **ultramarine,** *Oct. 7*   .30 .25
P# block of 4   1.25 —
C44 AP27 25c **rose carmine,** *Nov. 30*   .60 .40
P# block of 4   4.00 —
Nos. C42-C44 (3)   1.10 .85

WRIGHT BROTHERS ISSUE

Wilbur and
Orville Wright
and their
Plane,
1903 — AP28

46th anniv. of the 1st successful flight in a motor-powered
airplane, Dec. 17, 1903, at Kill Devil Hill near Kitty Hawk, NC, by
Wilbur (1867-1912) and Orville Wright (1871-1948) of Dayton,
OH. The plane flew 852 feet in 59 seconds.

ROTARY PRESS PRINTING
E. E. Plates of 200 subjects in four panes of 50
each.

1949, Dec. 17   Unwmk.   Perf. 11x10½
C45 AP28 6c **magenta**   .20 .20
P# block of 4   .70 —

Diamond
Head,
Honolulu,
Hawaii
AP29

ROTARY PRESS PRINTING
E. E. Plates of 200 subjects in four panes of 50
each.

1952, Mar. 26   Unwmk.   Perf. 11x10½
C46 AP29 80c **bright red violet**   4.75 1.25
P# block of 4   21.00 —

POWERED FLIGHT, 50th ANNIV.

First Plane and
Modern
Plane — AP30

ROTARY PRESS PRINTING
E. E. Plates of 200 subjects in four panes of 50
each.

1953, May 29   Unwmk.   Perf. 11x10½
C47 AP30 6c **carmine**   .20 .20
P# block of 4   .55 —

Eagle in Flight — AP31

Issued primarily for use on domestic post cards.

ROTARY PRESS PRINTING
E. E. Plates of 400 subjects in four panes of 100
each.

1954, Sept. 3   Unwmk.   Perf. 11x10½
C48 AP31 4c **bright blue**   .20 .20
P# block of 4   1.10 —

AIR FORCE, 50th ANNIV.

B-52
Stratofortress
and F-104
Starfighter
AP32

Designed by Alexander Nagy, Jr.

ROTARY PRESS PRINTING
E. E. Plates of 200 subjects in four panes of 50 each.

1957, Aug. 1	Unwmk.	Perf. 11x10½	
C49 AP32 6c blue		.20	.20
P# block of 4		.70	—

Type of 1954
Issued primarily for use on domestic post cards.

1958, July 31	Unwmk.	Perf. 11x10½	
C50 AP31 5c red		.20	.20
P# block of 4		1.00	—

Silhouette of Jet Airliner — AP33

Designed by William H. Buckley and Sam Marsh.

ROTARY PRESS PRINTING
E. E. Plates of 400 subjects in four panes of 100 each.

1958, July 31	Unwmk.	Perf. 10½x11	
C51 AP33 7c blue		.20	.20
P# block of 4		.60	—
a. Booklet pane of 6		9.00	7.00
b. Vert. pair, imperf. between (from booklet pane)		—	

No. C51b resulted from a paper foldover after perforating and before cutting into panes. Two pairs are known.

ROTARY PRESS COIL STAMP
Perf. 10 Horizontally

C52 AP33 7c blue	2.00	.20
Pair	4.25	.40
Joint line pair	14.00	1.25
Small holes	7.50	—
Pair	15.00	—
Joint line pair	200.00	

ALASKA STATEHOOD ISSUE

Big Dipper, North Star and Map of Alaska — AP34

Designed by Richard C. Lockwood.

ROTARY PRESS PRINTING
E. E. Plates of 200 subjects in four panes of 50 each.

1959, Jan. 3	Unwmk.	Perf. 11x10½	
C53 AP34 7c dark blue		.20	.20
P# block of 4		.75	—

BALLOON JUPITER ISSUE

Balloon and Crowd — AP35

Designed by Austin Briggs.

Centenary of the carrying of mail by the balloon Jupiter from Lafayette to Crawfordsville, Ind.

GIORI PRESS PRINTING
Plates of 200 subjects in four panes of 50 each.

1959, Aug. 17	Unwmk.	Perf. 11	
C54 AP35 7c dark blue & red		.30	.20
P# block of 4		1.40	—

HAWAII STATEHOOD ISSUE

Alii Warrior, Map of Hawaii and Star of Statehood AP36

Designed by Joseph Feher.

ROTARY PRESS PRINTING
E. E. Plates of 200 subjects in four panes of 50 each.

1959, Aug. 21	Unwmk.	Perf. 11x10½	
C55 AP36 7c rose red		.20	.20
P# block of 4		.75	—

PAN AMERICAN GAMES ISSUE

Runner Holding Torch — AP37

Designed by Suren Ermoyan.

3rd Pan American Games, Chicago, Aug. 27-Sept. 7, 1959.

GIORI PRESS PRINTING
Plates of 200 subjects in four panes of 50 each.

1959, Aug. 27	Unwmk.	Perf. 11	
C56 AP37 10c red, white & blue		.25	.25
P# block of 4		1.25	—

Liberty Bell — AP38

Statue of Liberty AP39

Abraham Lincoln AP40

GIORI PRESS PRINTING
Plates of 200 subjects in four panes of 50 each.

1959-66	Unwmk.	Perf. 11	
C57 AP38 10c black & green, June 10, 1960		1.00	.70
P# block of 4		6.00	—
C58 AP39 15c black & orange, Nov. 20, 1959		.35	.20
P# block of 4		1.50	—
C59 AP40 25c black & maroon, Apr. 22, 1960		.50	.20
P# block of 4		2.00	—
a. Tagged, Dec. 29, 1966		.60	.30
P# block of 4		2.50	—
Nos. C57-C59 (3)		1.85	1.10

See Luminescence data in Information for Collectors section.

Type of 1958
ROTARY PRESS PRINTING
E. E. Plates of 400 subjects in four panes of 100 each.

1960, Aug. 12	Unwmk.	Perf. 10½x11	
C60 AP33 7c carmine		.20	.20
P# block of 4		.60	—
Pair with full horiz. gutter btwn.		125.00	—
a. Booklet pane of 6, Aug. 19		10.00	8.00
b. Vert. pair, imperf between (from booklet pane)		5,500.	

No. C60b resulted from a paper foldover after perforating and before cutting into panes. Two pairs are known.

Type of 1958
ROTARY PRESS COIL STAMP

1960, Oct. 22	Unwmk.	Perf. 10 Horizontally	
C61 AP33 7c carmine		4.00	.25
Pair		8.25	.55
Joint line pair		35.00	3.75

Type of 1959-60 and

Statue of Liberty AP41

GIORI PRESS PRINTING
Plates of 200 subjects in four panes of 50 each.

1961-67	Unwmk.	Perf. 11	
C62 AP38 13c black & red, June 28, 1961		.40	.20
P# block of 4		1.65	—
a. Tagged, Feb. 15, 1967		.75	.50
P# block of 4		7.50	—
C63 AP41 15c black & orange, Jan. 13, 1961		.30	.20
P# block of 4		1.25	—
a. Tagged, Jan. 11, 1967		.35	.20
P# block of 4		1.50	—
b. As "a," horiz. pair, imperf. vert.		15,000.	
c. As "a," horiz. pair, imperf between and at left		2,750.	
d. All color omitted		—	

On No. C63d, there is a clear albino plate impression.

Jet Airliner over Capitol — AP42

Designed by Henry K. Bencsath.

ROTARY PRESS PRINTING
E.E. Plates of 400 subjects in four panes of 100 each.

1962, Dec. 5	Unwmk.	Perf. 10½x11	
C64 AP42 8c carmine		.20	.20
P# block of 4		.65	—
a. Tagged, Aug. 1, 1963		.20	.20
P# block of 4		.65	—
As "a," pair with full horiz. gutter between		—	
b. Booklet pane of 5 + label		7.00	3.00
c. As "b," tagged, 1964		2.00	.75

Nos. C64a and C64c were made by overprinting Nos. C64 and C64b with phosphorescent ink. No. C64a was first issued at Dayton, O., for experiments in high speed mail sorting. The tagging is visible in ultraviolet light.

COIL STAMP; ROTARY PRESS
Perf. 10 Horizontally

C65 AP42 8c carmine		.40	.20
Pair		.80	.20
Joint line pair		3.75	.35
a. Tagged, Sept. 1964		.35	.20
Pair		.70	.20
Joint line pair		1.75	.30

Earliest documented use of C65a: Jan. 14, 1965.

MONTGOMERY BLAIR ISSUE

Montgomery
Blair — AP43

Designed by Robert J. Jones

Montgomery Blair (1813-83), Postmaster General (1861-64), who called the 1st Intl. Postal Conf., Paris, 1863, forerunner of the UPU.

GIORI PRESS PRINTING
Plates of 200 subjects in four panes of 50 each.

1963, May 3	Unwmk.	Perf. 11	
C66 AP43 15c dull red, dark brown & blue		.60	.55
P# block of 4		2.50	—

Bald Eagle — AP44

Designed by V. S. McCloskey, Jr.

Issued primarily for use on domestic post cards.

ROTARY PRESS PRINTING
E.E. Plates of 400 subjects in four panes of 100 each.

1963, July 12	Unwmk.	Perf. 11x10½	
C67 AP44 6c red		.20	.20
P# block of 4		1.40	—
a.	Tagged, Feb. 15, 1967	4.00	3.00
P# block of 4		65.00	—

AMELIA EARHART ISSUE

Amelia Earhart and
Lockheed Electra — AP45

Designed by Robert J. Jones.

Amelia Earhart (1898-1937), 1st woman to fly across the Atlantic.

GIORI PRESS PRINTING
Plates of 200 subjects in four panes of 50 each.

1963, July 24	Unwmk.	Perf. 11	
C68 AP45 8c carmine & maroon		.20	.20
P# block of 4		1.00	—

ROBERT H. GODDARD ISSUE

Robert H.
Goddard, Atlas
Rocket and
Launching
Tower, Cape
Kennedy
AP46

Designed by Robert J. Jones.

Dr. Robert H. Goddard (1882-1945), physicist and pioneer rocket researcher.

GIORI PRESS PRINTING
Plates of 200 subjects in four panes of 50 each.

1964, Oct. 5	Tagged	Perf. 11	
C69 AP46 8c blue, red & bister		.40	.20
P# block of 4		1.75	—
Margin block of 4, Mr. Zip and "Use Zip Code"		1.65	—
a.	Tagging omitted		

Luminescence
Air Post stamps issued after mid-1964 are tagged.

ALASKA PURCHASE ISSUE

Tlingit Totem, Southern
Alaska — AP47

Designed by Willard R. Cox

Centenary of the Alaska Purchase. The totem pole shown is in the Alaska State Museum, Juneau.

GIORI PRESS PRINTING
Plates of 200 subjects in four panes of 50 each.

1967, Mar. 30	Unwmk.	Perf. 11	
C70 AP47 8c brown		.25	.20
P# block of 4		1.10	—
Margin block of 4, Mr. Zip and "Use Zip Code"		1.05	—

"Columbia Jays" by
John James
Audubon — AP48

Fifty-Star
Runway — AP49

GIORI PRESS PRINTING
Designed by Robert J. Jones.

Plates of 200 subjects in four panes of 50 each.

1967, Apr. 26		Perf. 11	
C71 AP48 20c multicolored		.80	.20
P# block of 4		3.50	—
Margin block of 4, Mr. Zip and "Use Zip Code"		3.25	—
a.	Tagging omitted	10.00	

See note over No. 1241.

ROTARY PRESS PRINTING
Designed by Jaan Born.

E. E. Plates of 400 subjects in four panes of 100 each.

1968, Jan. 5	Unwmk.	Perf. 11x10½	
C72 AP49 10c carmine		.20	.20
P# block of 4		.90	—
Margin block of 4, "Use Zip Codes"		.85	—
Vert. pair with full horiz. gutter between		—	
b.	Booklet pane of 8	2.00	.75
c.	Booklet pane of 5 + label, Jan. 6	3.75	.75
d.	Vert. pair, imperf. between (from bklt. pane)	4,000.	
e.	Tagging omitted	12.00	—
f.	As "b," tagging omitted		

Red is the normal color of the tagging. Copies of No. C72b exist that have a mixture of the two tagging compounds.

No. C72d resulted from a paper foldover after perforating and before cutting into panes. Two pairs are recorded from different panes.

ROTARY PRESS COIL STAMP
Perf. 10 Vertically

C73 AP49 10c carmine		.30	.20
Pair		.65	.20
Joint line pair		1.75	.20
a.	Imperf., pair	550.00	
Joint line pair		900.00	

$1 Air Lift

This stamp, listed as No. 1341, was issued Apr. 4, 1968, to pay for airlift of parcels to and from U.S. ports to servicemen overseas and in Alaska, Hawaii and Puerto Rico.

It was "also valid for paying regular rates for other types of mail," the Post Office Department announced to the public in a philatelic release dated Mar. 10, 1968. The stamp is inscribed "U.S. Postage" and is untagged.

On Apr. 26, 1969, the P.O.D. stated in its Postal Manual (for postal employees) that this stamp "may be used toward paying the postage or fees for special services on airmail articles." On Jan. 1, 1970, the Department told postal employees through its Postal Bulletin that this $1 stamp "can only be used to pay the airlift fee or toward payment of postage or fees on airmail articles."

Some collectors prefer to consider No. 1341 an airmail stamp.

50th ANNIVERSARY OF AIR MAIL ISSUE

Curtiss
Jenny — AP50

Designed by Hordur Karlsson.

50th anniv. of regularly scheduled air mail service.

LITHOGRAPHED, ENGRAVED (GIORI)
Plates of 200 subjects in four panes of 50 each.

1968, May 15		Perf. 11	
C74 AP50 10c blue, black & red		.25	.20
P# block of 4		1.40	—
Margin block of 4, Mr. Zip and "Use Zip Code"		1.05	—
b.	Tagging omitted	8.00	

"USA" and
Jet — AP51

Designed by John Larrecq.

LITHOGRAPHED, ENGRAVED (GIORI)
Plates of 200 subjects in four panes of 50 each.

1968, Nov. 22		Perf. 11	
C75 AP51 20c red, blue & black		.35	.20
P# block of 4		1.75	—
Margin block of 4, Mr. Zip and "Use Zip Code"		1.50	—
a.	Tagging omitted	10.00	

MOON LANDING ISSUE

First
Man
on the
Moon
AP52

Designed by Paul Calle.

Man's first landing on the moon July 20, 1969, by U.S. astronauts Neil A. Armstrong and Col. Edwin E. Aldrin, Jr., with Lieut. Col. Michael Collins piloting Apollo 11.

LITHOGRAPHED, ENGRAVED (GIORI)
Plates of 128 subjects in four panes of 32 each.

1969, Sept. 9   *Perf. 11*
C76 AP52 10c **yellow, black, lt. blue, ultra.,
      rose red & carmine**   .25   .20
      P# block of 4   1.10   —
      Margin block of 4, Mr. Zip and
        "Use Zip Code"   1.05   —
  a.   Rose red (litho.) omitted   500.00   —
  b.   Tagging omitted   —   —

On No. C76a, the lithographed rose red is missing from the entire vignette-the dots on top of the yellow areas as well as the flag shoulder patch.

Silhouette of Delta
Wing Plane — AP53

Silhouette of Jet
Airliner — AP54

Winged Airmail
Envelope — AP55

Statue of
Liberty
AP56

Designed by George Vander Sluis (9c, 11c), Nelson Gruppo (13c) and Robert J. Jones (17c).

ROTARY PRESS PRINTING
E. E. Plates of 400 subjects in four panes of 100 each.

1971-73   *Perf. 10½x11*
C77 AP53 9c **red,** *May 15, 1971*   .20   .20
      P# block of 4   .90   —
      Margin block of 4, "Use Zip Codes"   .85   —

No. C77 issued primarily for use on domestic post cards.

Perf. 11x10½
C78 AP54 11c **carmine,** *May 7, 1971*   .20   .20
      P# block of 4   .90   —
      Margin block of 4, "Use Zip
        Codes"   .85   —
      Pair with full vert. gutter btwn.   —   —
  a.   Booklet pane of 4 + 2 labels   1.25   .75
  b.   Untagged (Bureau precanceled)   .85   .85
      P# block of 4   27.50   —
      Margin block of 4, "Use Zip
        Codes"   13.75   —
  c.   Tagging omitted (not Bureau precanceled) 7.50 —
C79 AP55 13c **carmine,** *Nov. 16, 1973*   .25   .20
      P# block of 4   1.10   —
      Margin block of 4, "Use Zip
        Codes"   1.05   —
  a.   Booklet pane of 5 + label, *Dec. 27, 1973* 1.50 .75
  b.   Untagged (Bureau precanceled)   .85   .85
      P# block of 4   20.00   —
      Margin block of 4, "Use Zip
        Codes"   9.50   —
  c.   Green instead of red tagging (single from
      booklet pane)   —   —
  d.   Tagging omitted (not precanceled) 7.50   —

No. C78b Bureau precanceled "WASHINGTON D.C." (or "DC" - more valuable thus), No. C79b "WASHINGTON DC" only; both for use of Congressmen, but available to any permit holder.
Red is the normal color of the tagging. Copies also exist that have a mixture of the two tagging compounds.

GIORI PRESS PRINTING
Panes of 200 subjects in four panes of 50 each.
Perf. 11
C80 AP56 17c **bluish black, red, & dark green,**
      July 13, 1971   .35   .20
      P# block of 4   1.60   —
      Margin block of 4, Mr. Zip and
        "Use Zip Code"   1.50   —
  a.   Tagging omitted   10.00   —

"USA" & Jet Type of 1968
LITHOGRAPHED, ENGRAVED (GIORI)
Plates of 200 subjects in four panes of 50 each.
Perf. 11

C81 AP51 21c **red, blue & black,** *May 21,*
      1971   .40   .20
      P# block of 4   2.00   —
      Margin block of 4, Mr. Zip and
        "Use Zip Code"   1.75   —
  a.   Tagging omitted   10.00   —
  b.   Black (engr.) missing (FO)   2,750.   —

The two recorded examples of No. C81b are in a single full pane. Catalogue value is for both errors.

COIL STAMPS
ROTARY PRESS PRINTING

1971-73   *Perf. 10 Vertically*
C82 AP54 11c **carmine,** *May 7, 1971*   .25   .20
      Pair   .50   .25
      Joint line pair   .85   .35
  a.   Imperf., pair   250.00   —
      Joint line pair   425.00   —
  b.   Tagging omitted   11.00   —
C83 AP55 13c **carmine,** *Dec. 27, 1973*   .30   .20
      Pair   .60   .25
      Joint line pair   1.10   —
  a.   Imperf., pair   65.00   —
      Joint line pair   150.00   —
  b.   Tagging omitted   —   —

NATIONAL PARKS CENTENNIAL ISSUE
City of Refuge, Hawaii

Kii Statue and
Temple — AP57

Designed by Paul Rabut.

Centenary of national parks. This 11c honors the City of Refuge National Historical Park, established in 1961 at Honaunau, island of Hawaii.

LITHOGRAPHED, ENGRAVED (GIORI)
Plates of 200 subjects in four panes of 50 each.

1972, May 3   *Perf. 11*
C84 AP57 11c **orange & multicolored**   .20   .20
      P# block of 4   .90   —
      Margin block of 4, Mr. Zip and
        "Use Zip Code"   .85   —
  a.   Blue & green (litho.) omitted   750.00   —
  b.   Tagging omitted   —   —

OLYMPIC GAMES ISSUE

Skiing and
Olympic
Rings — AP58

Designed by Lance Wyman.

11th Winter Olympic Games, Sapporo, Japan, Feb. 3-13, and 20th Summer Olympic Games, Munich, Germany, Aug. 26-Sept. 11.

PHOTOGRAVURE (Andreotti)
Plates of 200 subjects in four panes of 50 each.

1972, Aug. 17   *Perf. 11x10½*
C85 AP58 11c **black, blue, red, emerald & yel-
      low**   .20   .20
      P# block of 10, 5 P#   2.40   —
      Margin block of 4, "Use Zip Code"   .85   —

ELECTRONICS PROGRESS ISSUE

De Forest
Audions
AP59

Designed by Walter and Naiad Einsel.

LITHOGRAPHED, ENGRAVED (GIORI)
Plates of 200 subjects in four panes of 50 each.

1973, July 10   *Perf. 11*
C86 AP59 11c **vermilion, lilac, pale lilac, ol-
      ive, brown, deep carmine &
      black**   .30   .20
      P# block of 4   1.25   —
      Margin block of 4, Mr. Zip and
        "Use Zip Code"   1.20   —
  a.   Vermilion & olive (litho.) omitted 825.00 —
  b.   Tagging omitted   25.00   —
  c.   Olive omitted   1,150.   —

Statue of
Liberty
AP60

Mt. Rushmore
National
Memorial
AP61

Designed by Robert (Gene) Shehorn.

GIORI PRESS PRINTING
Panes of 200 subjects in four panes of 50 each.
1974   *Perf. 11*
C87 AP60 18c **carmine, black & ultramarine,**
      Jan. 11   .35   .30
      P# block of 4, 2#   1.50   —
      Margin block of 4, Mr. Zip and
        "Use Zip Code"   1.45   —
  a.   Tagging omitted   20.00   —
C88 AP61 26c **ultramarine, black & carmine,**
      Jan. 2   .60   .20
      P# block of 4   2.30   —
      Margin block of 4, Mr. Zip and
        "Use Zip Code"   2.20   —
      Pair with full vert. gutter btwn.   —   —
  a.   Tagging omitted   17.50   —
  b.   Yellow-green instead of orange-red tag-
      ging   —   —

Plane and
Globes
AP62

Plane, Globes
and
Flags — AP63

Designed by David G. Foote.

GIORI PRESS PRINTING

Panes of 200 subjects in four panes of 50 each.

1976, Jan. 2			***Perf. 11***
C89 AP62 25c	**red, blue & black**		.50 .20
	P# block of 4		2.25 —
	Margin block of 4, Mr. Zip and "Use Zip Code"		2.10 —
a.	Tagging omitted		45.00 —
C90 AP63 31c	**red, blue & black**		.60 .20
	P# block of 4		2.60 —
	Margin block of 4, Mr. Zip and "Use Zip Code"		2.50 —
a.	Tagging omitted		10.00 —

WRIGHT BROTHERS ISSUE

Orville and Wilbur Wright, and Flyer A — AP64

Wright Brothers, Flyer A and Shed — AP65

Designed by Ken Dallison.

75th anniv. of 1st powered flight, Kill Devil Hill, NC, Dec. 17, 1903.

LITHOGRAPHED, ENGRAVED (GIORI)

Plates of 400 subjects in four panes of 100 each.

1978, Sept. 23			***Perf. 11***
C91 AP64 31c	**ultramarine & multicolored**		.65 .30
C92 AP65 31c	**ultramarine & multicolored**		.65 .30
a.	Vert. pair, #C91-C92		1.30 1.20
	P# block of 4		3.00 —
	Margin block of 4, "Use Correct Zip Code"		2.75 —
b.	As "a," ultra. & black (engr.) omitted		600.00
c.	As "a," black (engr.) omitted		2,500.
d.	As "a," black, yellow, magenta, blue & brown (litho.) omitted		2,250.

OCTAVE CHANUTE ISSUE

Chanute and Biplane Hang-glider — AP66

Biplane Hang-glider and Chanute — AP67

Designed by Ken Dallison.

Octave Chanute (1832-1910), civil engineer and aviation pioneer.

LITHOGRAPHED, ENGRAVED (GIORI)

Plates of 400 subjects in four panes of 100 each.

1979, Mar. 29		**Tagged**	***Perf. 11***
C93 AP66 21c	**blue & multicolored**		.70 .35
C94 AP67 21c	**blue & multicolored**		.70 .35
a.	Vert. pair, #C93-C94		1.40 1.20
	P# block of 4		3.00 —
	Margin block of 4, Mr. Zip		2.85 —
b.	As "a," ultra & black (engr.) omitted		4,500.

WILEY POST ISSUE

Wiley Post and "Winnie Mae" — AP68

NR-105-W, Post in Pressurized Suit, Portrait — AP69

Designed by Ken Dallison.

Wiley Post (1899-1935), first man to fly around the world alone and high-altitude flying pioneer.

LITHOGRAPHED, ENGRAVED (GIORI)

Plates of 400 subjects in four panes of 100 each.

1979, Nov. 20		**Tagged**	***Perf. 11***
C95 AP68 25c	**blue & multicolored**		1.10 .45
C96 AP69 25c	**blue & multicolored**		1.10 .45
a.	Vert. pair, #C95-C96		2.25 1.50
	P# block of 4		4.75 —
	Margin block of 4, Mr. Zip		4.50 —

OLYMPIC GAMES ISSUE

High Jump — AP70

Designed by Robert M. Cunningham.

22nd Olympic Games, Moscow, July 19-Aug. 3, 1980.

PHOTOGRAVURE

Plates of 200 subjects in four panes of 50 each.

1979, Nov. 1		**Tagged**	***Perf. 11***
C97 AP70 31c	**multicolored**		.70 .30
	P# block of 12, 6#		9.50 —
	Zip block of 4		3.00 —

PHILIP MAZZEI (1730-1816)

Italian-born Political Writer — AP71

Designed by Sante Graziani.

PHOTOGRAVURE

Plates of 200 subjects in four panes of 50 each.

1980, Oct. 13		**Tagged**	***Perf. 11***
C98 AP71 40c	**multicolored**		.80 .20
	P# block of 12, 6#		10.00 —
	Zip block of 4		3.50 —
b.	Imperf., pair		3,500.
d.	Tagging omitted		11.00
1982		**Tagged**	***Perf. 10½x11¼***
C98A AP71 40c	**multicolored**		8.00 1.50
	P# block of 12, 6#		125.00 —
c.	Horiz. pair, imperf. vert.		4,250.

BLANCHE STUART SCOTT (1886-1970)

First Woman Pilot — AP72

Designed by Paul Calle.

PHOTOGRAVURE

Plates of 200 subjects in four panes of 50.

1980, Dec. 30		**Tagged**	***Perf. 11***
C99 AP72 28c	**multicolored**		.60 .20
	P# block of 12, 6#		8.50 —
	Zip block of 4		2.50 —
a.	Imperf., pair		2,350.

GLENN CURTISS (1878-1930)

Aviation Pioneer and Aircraft Designer AP73

Designed by Ken Dallison.

PHOTOGRAVURE

Plates of 200 subjects in four panes of 50.

1980, Dec. 30		**Tagged**	***Perf. 11***
C100 AP73 35c	**multicolored**		.65 .20
	P# block of 12, 6#		9.00 —
	Zip block of 4		2.75 —
a.	Light blue (background) omitted		2,000.

SUMMER OLYMPICS 1984

Women's Gymnastics — AP74

Hurdles — AP75

Women's Basketball — AP76

Soccer — AP77

Shot Put — AP78

Men's Gymnastics AP79

Women's Swimming AP80

Weight Lifting — AP81

Women's Fencing AP82

Cycling AP83

Women's Volleyball AP84

Pole Vaulting AP85

Designed by Robert Peak.

23rd Olympic Games, Los Angeles, July 28-Aug. 12, 1984.

PHOTOGRAVURE
Plates of 200 subjects in four panes of 50.

1983, June 17	Tagged	Perf. 11	
C101 AP74 28c multicolored		1.00	.30
C102 AP75 28c multicolored		1.00	.30
C103 AP76 28c multicolored		1.00	.30
C104 AP77 28c multicolored		1.00	.30
a. Block of 4, #C101-C104		4.25	2.50
P# block of 4, 4#		5.50	—
Zip block of 4		4.25	—
b. As "a," imperf. vert.		7,500.	

1983, Apr. 8	Tagged	Perf. 11.2 Bullseye	
C105 AP78 40c multicolored		.90	.40
a. Perf. 11 line		1.00	.45
C106 AP79 40c multicolored		.90	.40
a. Perf. 11 line		1.00	.45
C107 AP80 40c multicolored		.90	.40
a. Perf. 11 line		1.00	.45
C108 AP81 40c multicolored		.90	.40
a. Perf. 11 line		1.00	.45
b. Block of 4, #C105-C108		4.25	3.00
P# block of 4, 4#		5.00	—
Zip block of 4		4.50	—
c. Block of 4, #C105a-C108a		5.00	4.00
P# block of 4, 4#		7.50	—
d. Block of 4, imperf.		1,000.	

1983, Nov. 4	Tagged	Perf. 11	
C109 AP82 35c multicolored		.90	.55
C110 AP83 35c multicolored		.90	.55
C111 AP84 35c multicolored		.90	.55
C112 AP85 35c multicolored		.90	.55
a. Block of 4, #C109-C112		4.00	3.25
P# block of 4, 4#		6.50	—
Zip block of 4		4.25	—

AVIATION PIONEERS

Alfred V. Verville (1890-1970), Inventor, Verville-Sperry R-3 Army Racer — AP86

Lawrence Sperry (1892-1931), Aircraft Designer, and Father Elmer (1860-1930), Designer and Pilot, 1st Seaplane AP87

Designed by Ken Dallison (No. C113) and Howard Koslow (No. C114).

PHOTOGRAVURE
Plates of 200 in four panes of 50
(2 panes each, No. C113 and No. C114)
Plates of 200 in four panes of 50 (No. C114)

1985, Feb. 13	Tagged	Perf. 11	
C113 AP86 33c multicolored		.65	.20
P# block of 4, 5#, UL, LR		3.25	—
Zip block of 4		2.90	—
a. Imperf., pair		825.00	
C114 AP87 39c multicolored		.80	.25
P# block of 4, 5#, UR, LL		3.75	—
P# block of 4, 4#		3.75	—
Zip block of 4		3.50	—
a. Imperf., pair		1,750.	

Philatelic Foundation certificates issued prior to August 1994 for No. C114 with magenta missing have been rescinded. At this time no true magenta missing copies are known.

TRANSPACIFIC AIRMAIL
50th Anniversary

Martin M-130 China Clipper AP88

Designed by Chuck Hodgson.

PHOTOGRAVURE
Plates of 200 in four panes of 50

1985, Feb. 15	Tagged	Perf. 11	
C115 AP88 44c multicolored		.85	.25
P# block of 4, 4#		4.00	—
Zip block of 4		3.50	—
a. Imperf., pair		750.00	

FR. JUNIPERO SERRA (1713-1784)
California Missionary

Outline Map of Southern California, Portrait, San Gabriel Mission AP89

Designed by Richard Schlecht from a Spanish stamp.

PHOTOGRAVURE
Plates of 200 in four panes of 50

1985, Aug. 22	Tagged	Perf. 11	
C116 AP89 44c multicolored		1.00	.35
P# block of 4		7.50	—
Zip block of 4		4.25	—
a. Imperf., pair		1,300.	

SETTLING OF NEW SWEDEN, 350th ANNIV.

Settler, Two Indians, Map of New Sweden, Swedish Ships "Kalmar Nyckel" and "Fogel Grip" — AP90

Designed by Goran Osterland based on an 18th century illustration from a Swedish book about the Colonies.

LITHOGRAPHED AND ENGRAVED
Plates of 200 in four panes of 50

1988, Mar. 29	Tagged	Perf. 11	
C117 AP90 44c multicolored		1.00	.25
P# block of 4, 5#		6.50	—
Zip block of 4		5.00	—

See Sweden No. 1672 and Finland No. 768.

SAMUEL P. LANGLEY (1834-1906)

Langley and Unmanned Aerodrome No. 5 — AP91

Designed by Ken Dallison.

LITHOGRAPHED AND ENGRAVED
Plates of 200 in four panes of 50

1988, May 14	Tagged	Perf. 11	
C118 AP91 45c multicolored, large block tagging		.90	.20
P# block of 4, 7#		4.00	—
Zip block of 4		4.00	—
a. Overall tagging		3.00	.50
P# block of 4, 7#		50.00	—
Zip block of 4		15.00	—

IGOR SIKORSKY (1889-1972)

Sikorsky and 1939 VS300 Helicopter AP92

Designed by Ren Wicks.

PHOTOGRAVURE AND ENGRAVED
Plates of 200 in four panes of 50

1988, June 23	Tagged	Perf. 11	
C119 AP92 36c multicolored		.70	.25
P# block of 4, 6#		3.25	—
Zip block of 4		3.10	—
a. Red, dk blue & black (engraved) omitted		3,000.	

Beware of copies with traces of engraved red offered as "red omitted" varieties.

FRENCH REVOLUTION BICENTENNIAL

Liberty, Equality and Fraternity — AP93

Designed by Richard Sheaff.

LITHOGRAPHED AND ENGRAVED
Plates of 120 in four panes of 30.

1989, July 14	Tagged	Perf. 11½x11	
C120 AP93 45c multicolored		.95	.20
P# block of 4, 4#		4.75	—
Zip block of 4		4.00	—

See France Nos. 2143-2145a.

PRE-COLUMBIAN AMERICA ISSUE

Southeast Carved Figure,
700-1430 A.D. — AP94

Designed by Lon Busch.
Printed by American Bank Note Co.

PHOTOGRAVURE
Plates of 200 in four panes of 50

1989, Oct. 12		Perf. 11	
C121 AP94 45c multicolored		.90	.20
P# block of 4, 4#		5.25	—
Zip block of 4		3.75	—

20th UPU CONGRESS
Futuristic Mail Delivery

Spacecraft — AP95

Air-suspended Hover
Car — AP96

Moon Rover — AP97

Space Shuttle — AP98

Designed by Ken Hodges.

LITHOGRAPHED & ENGRAVED
Plates of 160 in four panes of 40.

1989, Nov. 27	Tagged	Perf. 11	
C122 AP95 45c multicolored		1.00	.50
C123 AP96 45c multicolored		1.00	.50
C124 AP97 45c multicolored		1.00	.50
C125 AP98 45c multicolored		1.00	.50
a.	Block of 4, #C122-C125	4.00	3.00
	P# block of 4, 5#	5.50	—
	Zip block of 4	4.50	—
b.	As "a," light blue (engr.) omitted	725.00	

Souvenir Sheet
LITHOGRAPHED & ENGRAVED

1989, Nov. 24	Tagged	Imperf.	
C126	Sheet of 4	5.00	4.00
a.	AP95 45c multicolored	1.25	.50
b.	AP96 45c multicolored	1.25	.50
c.	AP97 45c multicolored	1.25	.50
d.	AP98 45c multicolored	1.25	.50
e.	As No. C126, tagging omitted	—	

PRE-COLUMBIAN AMERICA ISSUE

Tropical
Coast — AP99

Designed by Mark Hess.
Printed by the American Bank Note Company.

PHOTOGRAVURE
Plates of 200 in four panes of 50
(3 panes of #2512, 1 pane of #C127)

1990, Oct. 12	Tagged	Perf. 11	
C127 AP99 45c multicolored		.90	.20
P# block of 4, 4#, UL only		7.00	—
Zip block of 4		3.75	—

HARRIET QUIMBY, 1ST AMERICAN WOMAN PILOT

Quimby (1884-
1912), Bleriot
Airplane
AP100

Designed by Howard Koslow. Printed by Stamp Venturers.

PHOTOGRAVURE
Panes of 200 in four panes of 50

1991, Apr. 27	Tagged	Perf. 11	
C128 AP100 50c multicolored, overall tagging		1.00	.25
P# block of 4, #S1111		5.25	—
Zip block of 4		4.25	—
a.	Vert. pair, imperf. horiz.	1,500.	
b.	Perf. 11.2, prephosphored uncoated paper (mottled tagging), 1993	1.10	.25
	P# block of 4, #S2222	5.75	—
	Zip block of 6	4.50	—

WILLIAM T. PIPER, AIRCRAFT MANUFACTURER

Piper and
Piper
Cub — AP101

Designed by Ren Wicks.
Printed by J. W. Fergusson and Sons for American Bank Note Co.

PHOTOGRAVURE
Panes of 200 in four panes of 50

1991, May 17	Tagged	Perf. 11	
C129 AP101 40c multicolored		.80	.20
P# block of 4, 4#+A		3.75	—
Zip block of 4		3.50	—

Blue sky is plainly visible all the way across stamp above Piper's head.
See No. C132.

ANTARCTIC TREATY, 30TH ANNIVERSARY

AP102

Designed by Howard Koslow. Printed by Stamp Venturers.

PHOTOGRAVURE
Panes of 50

1991, June 21	Tagged	Perf. 11	
C130 AP102 50c multicolored		1.00	.35
P# block of 4, 4#+S		5.00	—
Zip block of 4		4.25	—

PRE-COLUMBIAN AMERICA ISSUE

Bering Land
Bridge
AP103

Designed by Richard Schlect.

PHOTOGRAVURE
Plates of 200 in 4 panes of 50

1991, Oct. 12	Tagged	Perf. 11	
C131 AP103 50c multicolored		1.00	.35
P# block of 4, 6#		5.25	—
Zip block of 4		4.75	—

Piper Type of 1991
Printed by Stamp Venturers.

PHOTOGRAVURE
Panes of 200 in four panes of 50

1993	Tagged	Perf. 11.2	
C132 AP101 40c multicolored		2.75	.65
P# block of 4, 4#+S		52.50	—
Zip block of 4		12.00	—

Piper's hair touches top edge of design. No inscriptions.
Bullseye perf.

"All LC (Letters and Cards) mail receives First-Class Mail service in the United States, is dispatched by the fastest transportation available, and travels by airmail or priority service in the destination country. All LC mail should be marked 'AIRMAIL' or 'PAR AVION.'" (U.S. Postal Service, Pub. 51).

No. C133 listed below was issued to meet the LC rate to Canada and Mexico and is inscribed with the silhouette of a jet plane next to the denomination indicating the need for airmail service. This is unlike No. 2998, which met the LC rate to other countries, but contained no indication that it was intended for that use.

Future issues that meet a specific international airmail rate and contain the airplane silhouette will be treated by Scott as Air Post stamps. Stamps similar to No. 2998 will be listed in the Postage section.

SCENIC AMERICAN LANDSCAPES

Niagara
Falls — AP104

Designed by Ethel Kessler. Printed by Avery Dennison.

PHOTOGRAVURE
Sheets of 200 in ten panes of 20

1999, May 12	Tagged	Serpentine Die Cut 11	
		Self-Adhesive	
C133 AP104 48c multicolored		.95	.20
P# block of 4, 5#+V		4.00	
Pane of 20		20.00	

Rio Grande
AP105

Designed by Ethel Kessler. Printed by Avery Dennison.

PHOTOGRAVURE

Sheets of 200 in ten panes of 20

1999, July 30   Tagged   *Serpentine Die Cut 11*
Self-Adhesive

C134 AP105 40c **multicolored**   .80   .60
        P# block of 4, 5#+V   3.20
        Pane of 20   16.00

Grand Canyon
AP106

Designed by Ethel Kessler.
Printed by Banknote Corp. of America.

LITHOGRAPHED

Sheets of 180 in nine panes of 20

Serpentine Die Cut 11¼x11½

2000, Jan. 20   Tagged
        Self-Adhesive

C135 AP106 60c **multicolored**   1.25   .25
        P# block of 4, 4#+B   5.00
        Pane of 20   25.00
a.   Die cutting omitted, pair   2,250.
b.   Vert. pair, die cutting omitted horiz.   —
c.   Horiz. pair, die cutting omitted be-
        tween   —
d.   Horiz. pair, die cutting omitted vert.   —

Nine-Mile
Prairie,
Nebraska
AP107

Designed by Ethel Kessler. Printed by Ashton-Potter (USA)
Ltd.

LITHOGRAPHED

Sheets of 180 in nine panes of 20

Serpentine Die Cut 11¼x11½

2001, Mar. 6   Tagged
        Self-Adhesive

C136 AP107 70c **multicolored**   1.40   .30
        P# block of 4, 5#+P   5.60
        Pane of 20   28.00

Mt. McKinley
AP108

Designed by Ethel Kessler. Printed by Avery Dennison.

PHOTOGRAVURE

Sheets of 200 in ten panes of 20.

2001, Apr. 17   Tagged   *Serpentine Die Cut 11*
        Self-Adhesive

C137 AP108 80c **multicolored**   1.60   .35
        P# block of 4, 5 #+V   6.40
        Pane of 20   32.00

Acadia National
Park — AP109

Designed by Ethel Kessler. Printed by Banknote Corporation
of America.

LITHOGRAPHED

Sheets of 180 in nine panes of 20 (#C138), Sheets
of 120 in six panes of 20 (#C138a)

Serpentine Die Cut 11.25x11.5 (No. C138),
11.5x11.9 (No. C138a)

2001-05   Tagged
                Self-Adhesive

C138 AP109 60c **multicolored**,
        prephosphored coated pa-
        per (solid tagging), *May 30,
        2001*   1.25   .25
        P# block of 4, 4# + B   5.00
        Pane of 20   25.00
a.   Overall tagging, *March 2003*   1.25   .25
        P# block of 4, 4# + B   5.00
        Pane of 20   25.00
b.   As "a," with "2005" year date, *Jan.
        2005*   1.25   .25
        P# block of 4, 4#+S   5.00
        Pane of 20   25.00
c.   As "b," printed on back of backing
        paper   —

Bryce Canyon
National
Park — AP110

Great Smoky
Mountains
National
Park — AP111

Designed by Ethel Kessler. Printed by Banknote Corporation
of America for Sennett Security Products (#C139), Ashton-Potter (USA) Ltd. (#C140), Avery Dennison (#C141).

LITHOGRAPHED, PHOTOGRAVURE (#C141)

Sheets of 180 in nine panes of 20 and sheets of 160
in eight panes of 20 (#C139), Sheets of 120 in six
panes of 20 (#C140), Sheets of 200 in ten panes of
20 (#C141)

2006, Feb. 24   Tagged   *Serpentine Die Cut 10¾*
                Self-Adhesive

C139 AP110 63c **multicolored**   1.25   .25
        P# block of 4, 5#+S   5.00
        Pane of 20   25.00
a.   Die cutting omitted, pair   —
C140 AP111 75c **multicolored**   1.50   .35
        P# block of 4, 5#+P   6.00
        Pane of 20   30.00
a.   Die cutting omitted, pair   —

Two printings of No. C139 with different plate # order. Sheet
of 180 has gray plate # first (and has glossier finish). Sheet of
160 has gray plate # last.

Yosemite
National
Park — AP112

Serpentine Die Cut 11

C141 AP112 84c **multicolored**   1.75   .35
        P# block of 4, 5#+V   7.00
        Pane of 20   35.00
        Nos. C139-C141 (3)   4.50   .95

Okefenokee
Swamp,
Georgia and
Florida
AP113

Hagatña Bay,
Guam
AP114

Designed by Ethel Kessler. Printed by Ashton-Potter (USA)
Ltd. (#C142), Avery Dennison (#C143).

LITHOGRAPHED (#C142), PHOTOGRAVURE
(#C143)

Sheets of 120 in six panes of 20 (#C142), Sheets of
200 in ten panes of 20 (#C143)

2007, June 1   Tagged   *Serpentine Die Cut 10¾*
                Self-Adhesive

C142 AP113 69c **multicolored**   1.40   .30
        P# block of 4, 5#+P   5.60
        Pane of 20   28.00

Serpentine Die Cut 11

C143 AP114 90c **multicolored**   1.80   .40
        P# block of 4, 5#+V   7.20
        Pane of 20   36.00

13-Mile
Woods, New
Hampshire
AP115

Trunk Bay, St.
John, Virgin
Islands
AP116

Designed by Ethel Kessler. Printed by Banknote Corporation
of America for Sennett Security Products (#C144), Avery Dennison (#C145).

LITHOGRAPHED (#C144), PHOTOGRAVURE
(#C145)

Sheets of 180 in nine panes of 20 (#C144), Sheets
of 200 in ten panes of 20 (#C145)

2008, May 16   Tagged   *Serpentine Die Cut 10¾*
                Self-Adhesive

C144 AP115 72c **multicolored**   1.50   .30
        P# block of 4, 5#+S   6.00
        Pane of 20   30.00

Serpentine Die Cut 11

C145 AP116 94c **multicolored**   1.90   .45
        P# block of 4, 5#+V   7.60
        Pane of 20   38.00

Zion National
Park,
Utah — AP117

Grand Teton
National Park,
Wyoming
AP118

Designed by Ethel Kessler. Printed by Ashton-Potter (USA) Ltd. (#C146), Avery Dennison (#C147).

LITHOGRAPHED, PHOTOGRAVURE (#C147)
Sheets of 120 in six panes of 20 (#C146), Sheets of 200 in ten panes of 20 (#C147)

2009, June 28   Tagged   *Serpentine Die Cut 10¾*
Self-Adhesive

C146 AP117 79c **multicolored**   1.60   .35
P# block of 4, 5#+P   6.40

Pane of 20	32.00	
Serpentine Die Cut 11		
C147 AP118 98c **multicolored**	2.00	.45
P# block of 4, 5#+V	8.00	
Pane of 20	40.00	

AIR POST SPECIAL DELIVERY STAMPS

Great Seal of
United States
APSD1

No. CE1 was issued for the prepayment of the air postage and the special delivery fee in one stamp. First day sale was at the American Air Mail Society Convention.

FLAT PLATE PRINTING
Plates of 200 subjects in four panes of 50 each.

1934, Aug. 30   Unwmk.   *Perf. 11*
CE1 APSD1 16c **dark blue**   .60   .70
    blue   .60   .70
    Never hinged   .80
    P# block of 6   15.00   —

Never hinged	22.50	
First day cover, Chicago (40,171)	25.00	
First day cover, Washington, D.C., *Aug. 31*	15.00	

For imperforate variety see No. 771.

Type of 1934

Frame plates of 100 subjects in two panes of 50 each separated by a 1½ inch wide vertical gutter with central guide line, and vignette plates of 50 subjects.

The "seal" design for No. CE2 was from a new engraving, slightly smaller than that used for No. CE1.

Top plate number blocks of No. CE2 are found both with and without top arrow.

Issued in panes of 50 each.

1936, Feb. 10
CE2 APSD1 16c **red & blue**   .45   .25
    Never hinged   .60
    Margin block of 4, bottom or side arrow   2.00   1.50

Center line block	2.50	2.25
P# block of 4, 2#	8.50	
Never hinged	12.00	
P# block of 4, 2#, blue dotted registration marker	85.00	
Never hinged	110.00	
Same, arrow, thick red registration marker	80.00	
Never hinged	100.00	
P# block of 10, 2#, two "TOP" and two registration markers	20.00	6.00
Never hinged	25.00	
First day cover Washington, D.C. (72,981)		17.50
a. Horiz. pair, imperf. vert.	*3,750.*	
P# block of 6, 2#, two "TOP" and registration markers	*40,000.*	

The No. CE2a plate block is unique. Value represents sale in 1997.
Quantities issued: #CE1, 9,215,750; #CE2, 72,517,850.

AIR POST SEMI-OFFICIAL STAMPS

Buffalo Balloon

This stamp was privately issued by John F. B. Lillard, a Nashville reporter. It was used on covers carried on a balloon ascension of June 18, 1877, which began at Nashville and landed at Gallatin, Tenn., and possibly on other flights. The balloon was owned and piloted by Samuel Archer King. The stamp was reported to have been engraved by (Mrs.?) J. H. Snively and printed in tete beche pairs from a single die. Lillard wrote that 300 were printed and 23 used.

was sponsored by the Armour meat-packing company, makers of the soft drink, Vin Fiz.

The stamp probably was first available in Texas about October 19. Recorded dated examples exist from Oct. 19 to Nov. 8.

Each of the thirteen known examples is trimmed close to the design on one or more sides.

Buffalo Balloon —
APSO1

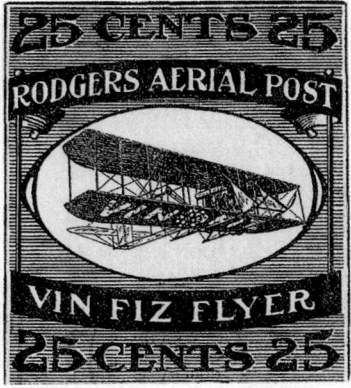

APSO2

1877, June 18   Typo.   *Imperf.*
CL1 APSO1 5c **deep blue**   *7,500.*
    Never hinged   *10,000.*
    On cover with 3c #158   *150,000.*
    On cover with 1c #156 & 2c #178   *130,000.*
a.   Tête bêche pair, vertical   *22,500.*
    Never hinged

A black proof exists of No. CL1, value *$7,500.*

Rodgers Aerial Post

This stamp was privately issued by Calbraith Perry Rodgers' wife who acted as unofficial postmaster during her husband's cross-country airplane flight in 1911. Rodgers was competing for the $50,000 prize offered by William Randolph Hearst to whomever completed the trip within a 30-day period. Rodgers' flight

1911, Oct.   *Imperf.*
CL2 APSO2 25c **black**   *55,000.*
    On postcard with 1c #374   *75,000.*
    Tied on cover with 1c #374   *115,000.*

No. CL2 is the first stamp in the world to picture an airplane.

Four examples are recorded off cover and without cancel (unused column). Only one of these has original gum. The unused value is for a stamp without gum. The example tied on cover is unique. Seven examples are recorded used on postcards.

R.F. OVERPRINTS

Authorized as a control mark by the United States Fleet Post Office during 1944-45 for the accommodation of and exclusive use by French naval personnel on airmail correspondence to the United States and Canada. All "R.F." (Republique Francaise) mail had to be posted on board French ships or at one of their western Mediterranean or northwest African naval bases and had to bear the return address, rank and/or serial number of a French officer or seaman. It also had to be reviewed by a censor.

All "R.F." overprints were handstamped by the French naval authorities after the stamps were affixed for mailing. The stamps had to be canceled by a special French naval cancellation. The status of unused stamps seems questionable; they are alleged to have been handstamped at a later date. Several types of "R.F." overprints other than those illustrated are known, but their validity is doubtful.

United States No. C25 Handstamped in Black

CM8	AP17 (h)	6c **carmine**, on cover			600.00
CM9	AP17 (i)	6c **carmine**, on cover			750.00
CM10	AP17 (j)	6c **carmine**, on cover			—
CM11	AP17 (k)	6c **carmine**, on cover			—
CM12	AP17 (l)	6c **carmine**, on cover			—

Counterfeits of several types exist.

No. 907 is known with type "c" overprint; Nos. 804 and 928 with type "f"; No. C19 with type "e"; No. C25a (single) with type "c," "d," "f," and "l"; No. C26 with type "a," "d" or "f."; and No. C28 with type "c." Type "i" exists in several very minor variations.

STAMPED ENVELOPES
Nos. UC3, UC4 or UC6 Handstamped in Black

1944-45

UCM1	UC2 (a)	6c **orange**, entire	300.00
UCM2	UC2 (b)	6c **orange**, entire	550.00
UCM3	UC2 (d)	6c **orange**, entire	450.00
UCM3A	UC2 (e)	6c **orange**, entire	1,000.
UCM4	UC2 (f)	6c **orange**, entire	550.00
UCM5	UC2 (h)	6c **orange**, entire	—
UCM6	UC2 (i)	6c **orange**, entire	—
UCM7	UC2 (j)	6c **orange**, entire	—
UCM8	UC2 (k)	6c **orange**, entire	—

Values for Nos. UCM1-UCM8 reflect the scarcity of the actual overprint types. Use of No. UC6 envelopes was by far the most common. Overprints on Nos. UC3 or UC4 merit a premium.

Specialist collectors question the existence of No. UCM6. The editors will be deleting this number if authenticated evidence of its existence is not provided.

1944-45   Unwmk.   Perf. 11x10½

CM1	AP17 (a)	6c **carmine**, on cover	300.00
CM2	AP17 (b)	6c **carmine**, on cover	475.00
CM3	AP17 (c)	6c **carmine**, on cover	300.00
CM4	AP17 (d)	6c **carmine**, on cover	350.00
CM5	AP17 (e)	6c **carmine**, on cover	425.00
CM6	AP17 (f)	6c **carmine**, on cover	350.00
CM7	AP17 (g)	6c **carmine**, on cover	600.00

SPECIAL DELIVERY STAMPS

Special Delivery service was instituted by the Act of Congress of March 3, 1885, and put into operation on October 1, 1885. The Act limited the service to free delivery offices and such others as served places with a population of 4,000 or more, and its privileges were thus operative in but 555 post offices. The Act of August 4, 1886, made the stamps and service available at all post offices and upon any article of mailable matter, beginning Oct. 1, 1886. To consume the supply of stamps of the first issue, Scott No. E2 was withheld until September 6, 1888.

A Special Delivery stamp, when affixed to any stamped letter or article of mailable matter, secured later delivery during daytime and evening at most post offices, so that the item did not have to wait until the next day for delivery.

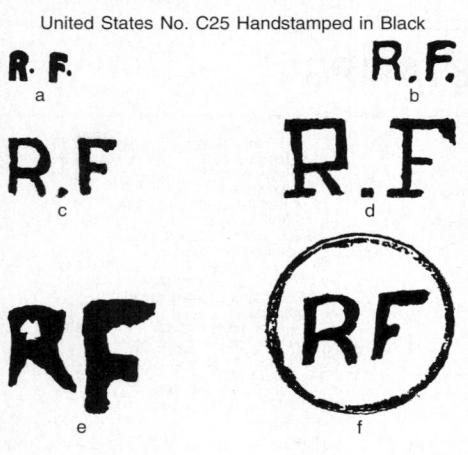

Messenger Running — SD1

ENGRAVED
Printed by the American Bank Note Co.
Plates of 100 subjects in two panes of 50 each

1885   Unwmk.   Perf. 12

E1	SD1 10c **blue**	550.00	75.00
	deep blue	550.00	75.00
	Never hinged	1,250.	
	On cover		150.00
	First day of service cover (Oct. 1)		22,500.
	Block of four	2,500.	
	P# block of 8, Impt. 495 or 496	19,000.	
	Margin strip of 4, same	5,500.	
	Double transfer at top	850.00	200.00

Earliest documented use: Sept. 29, 1885, on a cover delivered Oct. 1. There is also a Sept. 30 cover recorded, received for delivery at 7:00 a.m. Oct. 1.

Messenger Running SD2

1888, Sept. 6

E2	SD2 10c **blue**	500.00	40.00
	deep blue	500.00	40.00
	Never hinged	1,150.	
	On cover		95.00
	Block of four	2,250.	
	P# block of 8, Impt. 73 or 552	17,000.	
	Never hinged	24,000.	
	Margin strip of 4, same	4,750.	

Earliest documented use: Dec. 18, 1888.
See note above No. E3.

COLUMBIAN EXPOSITION ISSUE

Though not issued expressly for the Exposition, No. E3 is considered to be part of that issue. It was released in orange because No. E2 was easily confused with the 1c Columbian, No. 230.

From Jan. 24, 1893, until Jan. 5, 1894, the special delivery stamp was printed in orange; the issue in that color continued until May 19, 1894, when the stock on hand was exhausted. The stamp in blue was not issued from Jan. 24, 1893 to May 19, 1894. However, on Jan. 5, 1894, printing of the stamp in blue was resumed. Presumably it was reissued from May 19, 1894 until the appearance of No. E4 on Oct. 10, 1894. The emissions of the blue stamp of this design before Jan. 24, 1893 and after Jan. 5, 1894 are indistinguishable.

1893, Jan. 24

E3	SD2 10c **orange**	290.00	45.00
	deep orange	290.00	45.00
	Never hinged	675.00	
	On cover		150.00
	On cover, Columbian Expo. station machine canc.		1,100.
	On cover, Columbian Expo. station duplex handstamp cancel		1,350.
	Block of four	1,250.	

P# block of 8, Impt. 73 or 552	12,000.	
Never hinged	16,000.	
Margin strip of 4, same	3,900.	

Earliest documented use: Feb. 11, 1893.

Messenger Running SD3

| Type III | Type VI | Type VII |

Printed by the Bureau of Engraving and Printing.

1894, Oct. 10

Line under "TEN CENTS"

E4	SD3	10c **blue**	900.00	75.00
		dark blue	900.00	75.00
		bright blue	1,050.	100.00
		Never hinged	2,250.	
		On cover		225.00
		Block of four	3,900.	
		Margin block of 4, arrow	4,100.	
		P#77 block of 6, T III Impt.	*19,000.*	
		Never hinged	*27,500.*	
		Margin strip of 3, same	5,250.	
		Never hinged	7,750.	
		Double transfer	—	—

Earliest documented use: Oct. 25, 1894.

Imperfs of No. E4 on stamp paper, currently listed as No. E4aP, may not be proofs, but it is also unlikely that they were regularly issued. They most likely are from printer's waste.

1895, Aug. 16   **Wmk. 191**

E5	SD3	10c **blue**	210.00	10.00
		dark blue	210.00	10.00
		deep blue	210.00	10.00
		Never hinged	475.00	
		On cover		22.50
		Block of four	900.00	
		Margin block of 4, arrow	925.00	
		P# block of 6, T III, VI or VII Impt.	*4,750.*	
		Never hinged	*6,750.*	
		Margin strip of 3, same	900.00	
		Never hinged	1,600.	
		Double transfer		60.00
		Line of color through "POSTAL DELIVERY," from bottom row of Plates 1257-1260	300.00	40.00
		Never hinged	625.00	
a.		Dots in curved frame above messenger (Pl. 882)	300.00	20.00
		Never hinged	650.00	
b.		Printed on both sides		

Earliest documented use: Oct. 3, 1895.

The existence of No. E5b has been questioned by specialists. The editors would like to see authenticated evidence of its existence.

See Die and Plate Proofs for imperf. on stamp paper.

Messenger on Bicycle — SD4

1902, Dec. 9

E6	SD4	10c **ultramarine**	230.00	10.00
		pale ultramarine	230.00	10.00
		dark ultramarine	240.00	10.00
		Never hinged	525.00	

On cover		20.00
Block of four	1,000.	
Margin block of 4, arrow	1,050.	
P# block of 6, T VII Impt.	*3,250.*	
Never hinged	*4,750.*	
Margin strip of 3, same	825.00	
Never hinged	1,450.	
P# block of 6, "09"	*3,000.*	
Never hinged	*4,500.*	
Margin strip of 3, same	850.	
Never hinged	1,500.	
Double transfer	250.00	20.00
Damaged transfer under "N" of "CENTS"	250.00	15.00

a.	10c **blue**	250.00	10.00
	Never hinged	575.00	
	On cover		25.00
	Block of four	1,100.	
	Margin block of 4, arrow	1,150.	
	P# block of 6, T VII Impt.	*3,500.*	
	Never hinged	*5,000.*	
	Margin strip of 3, same	925.00	
	Never hinged	1,650.	
	Double transfer	—	—

Earliest documented use: Jan. 22, 1903.

No. E6 was re-issued in 1909 from new plates 5240, 5243-5245. After a few months use the Bureau added "09" to these plate numbers. The stamp can be identified only by plate number. The plate numbers without the "09" are scarcer and worth more.

Helmet of Mercury — SD5

Designed by Whitney Warren.

Plates of 280 subjects in four panes of 70 each

1908, Dec. 12

E7	SD5	10c **green**	70.00	45.00
		dark green	70.00	45.00
		yellowish green	70.00	45.00

Never hinged	150.00	
On cover		275.00
Block of four	300.00	
P# block of 6, T V Impt.	*1,000.*	—
Never hinged	*1,400.*	
Margin strip of 3, same	300.00	
Never hinged	500.00	
Double transfer	160.00	100.00

Earliest documented use: Dec. 14, 1908.

Plates of 200 subjects in four panes of 50 each

1911, Jan.   **Wmk. 190**   *Perf. 12*

E8	SD4	10c **ultramarine**	110.00	10.00
		pale ultramarine	110.00	10.00
		dark ultramarine	110.00	10.00
		Never hinged	240.00	
		On cover		25.00
		Block of four	460.00	
		P# block of 6, T VII Impt.	*1,850.*	
		Never hinged	*2,750.*	
		P# block of 6	*1,700.*	
		Never hinged	*2,500.*	
		Top frame line missing (Pl. 5514)	150.00	22.50
		Never hinged	325.00	
b.		10c **violet blue**	125.00	12.00
		Never hinged	275.00	
		On cover		25.00
		Block of four	550.00	
		P# block of 6, T VII Impt.	*1,950.*	
		Never hinged	*2,900.*	
		P# block of 6	*1,800.*	
		Never hinged	*2,650.*	

Earliest documented use: Jan. 14, 1911.

1914, Sept.   *Perf. 10*

E9	SD4 10c	**ultramarine**	190.00	12.00
		pale ultramarine	190.00	12.00
		Never hinged	425.00	
		On cover		45.00
		Block of four	800.00	
		P# block of 6, T VII Impt.	*4,000.*	—
		Never hinged	*6,000.*	
		P# block of 6	*3,000.*	—
		Never hinged	*4,500.*	
		Margin block of 8, T VII Impt. & P# (side)	—	
a.		**10c blue**	240.00	15.00
		Never hinged	525.00	
		On cover		45.00
		Block of four	1,050.	
		P# block of 6, T VII Impt.	*5,000.*	—
		Never hinged	*7,500.*	
		P# block of 6	*4,000.*	—
		Never hinged	*6,000.*	
		Margin block of 8, T VII Impt. & P# (side)	—	

Earliest documented use: Oct. 26, 1914.

1916, Oct. 19   Unwmk.   *Perf. 10*

E10	SD4 10c	**pale ultramarine**	320.00	45.00
		ultramarine	340.00	50.00
		Never hinged	700.00	
		On cover		140.00
		Block of four	1,400.	
		P# block of 6, T VII Impt.		
		5520	*5,500.*	—
		Never hinged	*7,750.*	
		P# block of 6	*5,000.*	—
		Never hinged	*7,250.*	
a.		**10c blue**	350.00	50.00
		Never hinged	750.00	
		On cover		110.00
		Block of four	1,550.	
		P# block of 6, T VII Impt.		
		5520	*5,750.*	—
		P# block of 6	*5,000.*	—

Earliest documented use: Nov. 4, 1916.

1917, May 2   Unwmk.   *Perf. 11*

E11	SD4 10c	**ultramarine**	20.00	.75
		pale ultramarine	20.00	.75
		dark ultramarine	25.00	2.00
		Never hinged	45.00	
		On cover		4.00
		Block of four	85.00	
		P# block of 6, T VII Impt.	725.00	—
		Never hinged	1,100.	
		P# block of 6	225.00	—
		Never hinged	340.00	
		Margin block of 8, T VII Impt. & P# (side)	—	
b.		**10c gray violet**	30.00	3.00
		Never hinged	65.00	
		On cover		4.00
		Block of four	130.00	
		P# block of 6, T VII Impt.	850.00	—
		Never hinged	1,300.	
		P# block of 6	300.00	—
		Never hinged	450.00	
		Margin block of 8, T VII Impt. & P# (side)	—	
c.		**10c blue**	65.00	4.00
		Never hinged	140.00	
		On cover		15.00
		Block of four	275.00	
		P# block of 6, T VII Impt.	2,000.	—
		P# block of 6	625.00	—
		Margin block of 8, T VII Impt. & P# (side)	—	
d.		Perf. 10 at left	—	

Earliest documented use: June 12, 1917.
The aniline ink used on some printings of No. E11 permeated the paper causing a pink tinge to appear on the back. Such stamps are called "pink backs." They are scarce and valued higher than the normal stamp.

Motorcycle Delivery SD6

Post Office Truck — SD7

1922, July 12   Unwmk.   *Perf. 11*

E12	SD6 10c	**gray violet**	50.00	1.75
		Never hinged	105.00	
		On cover		2.75

		First day cover		500.00
		P# block of 6	550.00	
		Never hinged	825.00	
		Double transfer	—	
a.		**10c deep ultramarine**	60.00	2.50
		Never hinged	140.00	
		On cover		4.00
		P# block of 6	625.00	
		Never hinged	950.00	
		Double transfer	—	

FLAT PLATE PRINTING

1925   Unwmk.   *Perf. 11*

Issued to facilitate special delivery service for parcel post.

E13	SD6 15c	**deep orange,** *Apr. 11, 1925*	30.00	2.00
		Never hinged	60.00	
		On cover		30.00
		First day cover		350.00
		P# block of 6	375.00	—
		Never hinged	550.00	
		Double transfer	37.50	3.00
E14	SD7 20c	**black,** *Apr. 25, 1925*	2.00	1.00
		Never hinged	4.25	
		On cover		10.00
		First day cover		125.00
		P# block of 6	45.00	—
		Never hinged	67.50	

Motorcycle Type of 1922
ROTARY PRESS PRINTING

1927-31   Unwmk.   *Perf. 11x10½*

E15	SD6 10c	**gray violet,** *Nov. 29, 1927*	.65	.25
		violet	.65	.25
		Never hinged	1.20	
a.		**10c red lilac**	.65	.25
		Never hinged	1.20	
b.		**10c gray lilac**	.65	.25
		Never hinged	1.20	
		On cover		.30
		First day cover		110.00
		First day cover, electric eye plate, *Sept. 8, 1941*		30.00
		P# block of 4	3.75	—
		Never hinged	6.25	
		Gashed plate 19280 LR 35	35.00	
c.		Horizontal pair, imperf. between	300.00	
		Never hinged	*525.00*	
E16	SD6 15c	**orange,** *Aug. 1931*	.70	.25
		Never hinged	1.05	
		On cover		1.50
		First day cover, Washington, D.C., *Aug. 13, 1931*		125.00
		P# block of 4	2.75	—
		Never hinged	4.50	

The Washington, D.C. Aug. 13, 1931 first day cover reflects the first day of sale at the philatelic agency. The actual earliest documented use of No. E16 is Aug. 6, 1931, at Easton, PA; value, $2,500.

> **Catalogue values for unused stamps in this section, from this point to the end, are for Never Hinged items.**

Motorcycle Type of 1922
ROTARY PRESS PRINTING
E. E. Plates of 200 subjects in four panes of 50 each.

1944-51   Unwmk.   *Perf. 11x10½*

E17	SD6 13c	**blue,** *Oct. 30, 1944*	.60	.20
		First day cover		15.00
		P# block of 4	2.75	—
E18	SD6 17c	**orange yellow,** *Oct. 30, 1944*	3.50	2.50
		First day cover		14.00
		First day cover, Nos. E17 & E18		35.00
		P# block of 4	24.00	—
E19	SD7 20c	**black,** *Nov. 30, 1951*	1.25	.20
		First day cover		5.00
		P# block of 4	5.50	—

Special Delivery Letter, Hand to Hand — SD8

ROTARY PRESS PRINTING
E.E. Plates of 200 subjects in four panes of 50 each

1954, Oct. 13   Unwmk.   *Perf. 11x10½*

E20	SD8 20c	**deep blue**	.40	.20
		light blue	—	
		First day cover, Boston *(194,043)*		3.00
		P# block of 4	2.00	—

1957, Sept. 3

E21	SD8 30c	**lake**	.50	.20
		First day cover, Indianapolis, Ind. *(111,451)*		2.25
		P# block of 4	2.25	—

Arrows SD9

Designed by Norman Ives.

GIORI PRESS PRINTING
Plates of 200 subjects in four panes of 50 each

1969, Nov. 21   Unwmk.   *Perf. 11*

E22	SD9 45c	**carmine & violet blue**	1.25	.25
		First day cover, New York, N.Y.		4.00
		P# block of 4	5.50	—
		Margin block of 4, Mr. Zip and "Use Zip Code"	5.10	—

1971, May 10   *Perf. 11*

E23	SD9 60c	**violet blue & carmine**	1.25	.20
		First day cover, Phoenix, Ariz. *(129,562)*		3.50
		P# block of 4	5.50	—
		Margin block of 4, Mr. Zip and "Use Zip Code"	5.25	—

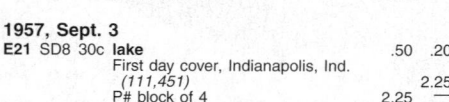

REGISTRATION STAMP

The Registry System for U.S. mail went into effect July 1, 1855, the fee being 5 cents. On June 30, 1863, the fee was increased to 20 cents. On January 1, 1869, the fee was reduced to 15 cents and on January 1, 1874, to 8 cents. On July 1, 1875, the fee was increased to 10 cents. On January 1, 1893 the fee was again reduced to 8 cents and again it was increased to 10 cents on November 1, 1909.

Early registered covers with various stamps, rates and postal markings are of particular interest to collectors.

Registry stamps (10c ultramarine) were issued on December 1, 1911, to prepay registry fees (not postage), but ordinary stamps were valid for registry fees then as now. These special stamps were abolished May 28, 1913, by order of the Postmaster General, who permitted their use until supplies on hand were exhausted.

Eagle — RS1

ENGRAVED					
1911, Dec. 1		**Wmk. 190**			*Perf. 12*
F1	RS1	10c	**ultramarine**	80.00	13.00
			pale ultramarine	80.00	13.00
			Never hinged	175.00	
			On cover		60.00

Block of 4	375.00	*100.00*
P# block of 6, Impt. & "A"	*1,800.*	—
Never hinged	*2,750.*	
First day cover		*19,000.*

CERTIFIED MAIL STAMP

Certified Mail service was started on June 6, 1955, for use on first class mail for which no indemnity value is claimed, but for which proof of mailing and proof of delivery are available at less cost than registered mail. The mailer receives one receipt and the addressee signs another when the postman delivers the letter. The second receipt is kept on file at the post office for six months. The Certified Mail charge, originally 15 cents, is in addition to regular postage, whether surface mail, air mail, or special delivery.

Catalogue value for the unused stamp in this section is for a Never Hinged item.

Letter Carrier — CM1

ROTARY PRESS PRINTING
E. E. Plates of 200 subjects in four panes of 50

1955, June 6		**Unwmk.**		*Perf. 10½x11*	
FA1	CM1	15c	**red**	.60	.40
			P# block of 4	5.50	—
			First day cover		8.00

POSTAGE DUE STAMPS

Postage due stamps were authorized by an act of Congress, approved March 3, 1879, and effective July 1, 1879. By law, postage due stamps were to be affixed by clerks to any piece of mailable matter to denote the amount collected from the addressee because of insufficient prepayment of postage.

Although the Post Office Department required postage to be prepaid beginning in 1855, there were many instances when full postage was not required, and postage due payment had to be collected in cash from the addressees. These instances included insufficiently prepaid letters, advertised letters, and unpaid ship letters and steamboat letters.

The reason for the appearance of postage due stamps may be summed up in one word: accountability. The 1880 *Report of the Postmaster General* noted that the former system of collecting postage due had one great weakness: "In securing the full returns of (the postage due collected in cash) the department was entirely dependent on the fidelity of the postmasters." Postage due stamps, affixed to underpaid mail as receipts for the underpayment collected, solved that problem by requiring postmasters to account for cash receipts that would balance any postage due stamps no longer in stock, in the same way that they had to account for regular postage stamp sales.

The last postage due stamps were printed in early November, 1985. With the advent of postage meters, the scrapping of the last Cottrell press in November 1985 (the last press capable of printing the current postage due stamps as designed), and finally new regulations requiring full prepayment of postage in all cases, postage due stamps became anachronistic, and their use ceased.

Printed by the American Bank Note Co.
Plates of 200 subjects in two panes of 100 each.

D1　　　　　　　D2

1879　　　Unwmk.　　　Engr.　　　Perf. 12

J1	D1	1c	**brown**	95.00	14.00
			pale brown	95.00	14.00
			deep brown	95.00	14.00
			Never hinged	275.00	
			Block of 4	425.00	75.00
			P# block of 10, Impt.	1,650.	

Earliest documented use: July 5, 1879.

J2	D1	2c	**brown**	425.00	18.00
			pale brown	425.00	18.00
			Never hinged	1,100.	
			Block of 4	1,800.	—

Earliest documented use: July 27, 1879.

J3	D1	3c	**brown**	105.00	6.00
			pale brown	105.00	6.00
			deep brown	105.00	6.00
			yellowish brown	115.00	7.00
			Never hinged	300.00	
			Block of 4	460.00	32.50
			P# block of 10, Impt.	1,800.	

Earliest documented use: June 18, 1879.

J4	D1	5c	**brown**	825.00	70.00
			Never hinged	2,100.	
			pale brown	825.00	70.00
			deep brown	825.00	70.00
			Block of 4	3,500.	—

Earliest documented use: July 7, 1879.

J5	D1	10c	**brown,** *Sept. 19*	1,000.	70.00
			pale brown	1,000.	70.00
			deep brown	1,000.	70.00
			Never hinged	2,750.	
			Block of 4	4,500.	—
a.			Imperf., pair	3,000.	

Earliest documented use: Oct. 7, 1879.

J6	D1	30c	**brown,** *Sept. 19*	400.00	65.00
			pale brown	400.00	65.00
			Never hinged	900.00	
			Block of 4	1,700.	—
			P# block of 10, Impt.	5,000.	

J7	D1	50c	**brown,** *Sept. 19*	650.00	90.00
			pale brown	650.00	90.00
			Never hinged	1,750.	
			Block of 4	2,900.	—
			P# block of 10, Impt.	12,500.	

SPECIAL PRINTING

1879　　　Unwmk.　　　Perf. 12

Soft porous paper

Printed by the American Bank Note Co.

J8	D1	1c	deep brown *(9,420)*	22,500.
J9	D1	2c	deep brown *(1,361)*	19,000.
J10	D1	3c	deep brown *(436)*	25,000.
J11	D1	5c	deep brown *(249)*	15,000.
J12	D1	10c	deep brown *(174)*	9,000.
J13	D1	30c	deep brown *(179)*	10,000.
J14	D1	50c	deep brown *(179)*	9,000.

Identifying characteristics for the final 8,920 examples of No. J8 delivered to the Post Office are unknown, and it is likely that these were regular issue stamps (No. J1) that were then sold as special printings.

1884　　　Unwmk.　　　Perf. 12

J15	D1	1c	**red brown**	75.00	7.00
			pale red brown	75.00	7.00
			deep red brown	75.00	7.00

			Never hinged	200.00	
			Block of 4	350.00	45.00
			P# block of 10, Impt.	1,450.	
J16	D1	2c	**red brown**	90.00	6.00
			pale red brown	90.00	6.00
			deep red brown	90.00	6.00
			Never hinged	250.00	
			Block of 4	400.00	37.50
			P# block of 10, Impt.	1,650.	
J17	D1	3c	**red brown**	1,150.	300.00
			deep red brown	1,150.	300.00
			Never hinged	2,750.	
			Block of 4	5,000.	—
J18	D1	5c	**red brown**	625.00	45.00
			pale red brown	625.00	45.00
			deep red brown	625.00	45.00
			Never hinged	1,500.	
			Block of 4	2,850.	—
J19	D1	10c	**red brown**	625.00	35.00
			deep red brown	625.00	35.00
			Never hinged	1,500.	
			Block of 4	2,850.	—
			P# block of 10, Impt.	14,000.	
J20	D1	30c	**red brown**	225.00	60.00
			deep red brown	225.00	60.00
			Never hinged	550.00	
			Block of 4	1,050.	350.00
			P# block of 10, Impt.	3,500.	
J21	D1	50c	**red brown**	1,900.	225.00
			Never hinged	4,250.	
			Block of 4	8,250.	—

1891　　　Unwmk.　　　Perf. 12

J22	D1	1c	**bright claret**	35.00	2.00
			light claret	35.00	2.00
			dark claret	35.00	2.00
			Never hinged	95.00	
			Block of 4	160.00	11.00
			P# block of 10, Impt.	625.00	
J23	D1	2c	**bright claret**	37.50	2.00
			light claret	37.50	2.00
			dark claret	37.50	2.00
			Never hinged	100.00	
			Block of 4	170.00	11.00
			P# block of 10, Impt.	700.00	
J24	D1	3c	**bright claret**	75.00	16.00
			dark claret	75.00	16.00
			Never hinged	200.00	
			Block of 4	350.00	80.00
			P# block of 10, Impt.	1,100.	
J25	D1	5c	**bright claret**	110.00	16.00
			light claret	110.00	16.00
			dark claret	110.00	16.00
			Never hinged	325.00	
			Block of 4	500.00	80.00
			P# block of 10, Impt.	1,500.	
J26	D1	10c	**bright claret**	180.00	30.00
			light claret	180.00	30.00
			Never hinged	550.00	
			Block of 4	800.00	190.00
			P# block of 10, Impt.	2,500.	
J27	D1	30c	**bright claret**	650.00	225.00
			Never hinged	1,900.	
			Block of 4	2,750.	—
			P# block of 10, Impt.	8,750.	
J28	D1	50c	**bright claret**	700.00	210.00
			dark claret	700.00	210.00
			Never hinged	2,000.	
			Block of 4	3,000.	—
			P# block of 10, Impt.	10,500.	
			Nos. J22-J28 (7)	1,787.	501.00

See Die and Plate Proofs for imperfs. on stamp paper.

Printed by the Bureau of Engraving and Printing.

1894　　　Unwmk.　　　Perf. 12

J29	D2	1c	**vermilion**	2,750.	725.
			pale vermilion	2,750.	725.
			Never hinged	6,750.	
			Block of 4	12,000.	3,250.
			P# block of 6, Impt.	—	
J30	D2	2c	**vermilion**	850.00	350.00
			deep vermilion	850.00	350.00
			Never hinged	2,100.	
			Block of 4	3,750.	—
			P# block of 6, Impt.	7,000.	

1894-95

J31	D2	1c	**deep claret,** *Aug. 14, 1894*	80.00	12.00
			claret	80.00	12.00
			lake	80.00	12.00
			Never hinged	300.00	
			Block of 4	360.00	65.00
			P# block of 6, Impt.	675.00	
			Never hinged	1,900.	
b.			Vertical pair, imperf. horiz.		

See Die and Plate Proofs for imperf. on stamp paper.

J32	D2	2c	**deep claret,** *July 20, 1894*	70.00	10.00
			claret	70.00	10.00
			lake	70.00	10.00
			Never hinged	275.00	
			Block of 4	300.00	65.00
			P# block of 6, Impt.	625.00	
			Never hinged	1,750.	
J33	D2	3c	**deep claret,** *Apr. 27, 1895*	220.00	50.00
			lake	220.00	50.00
			Never hinged	675.00	
			Block of 4	950.00	—
			P# block of 6, Impt.	2,750.	
			Never hinged	5,000.	
J34	D2	5c	**deep claret,** *Apr. 27, 1895*	350.00	55.00
			claret	350.00	55.00
			Never hinged	1,000.	
			Block of 4	1,500.	—
			P# block of 6, Impt.	3,000.	
			Never hinged	6,500.	
J35	D2	10c	**deep claret,** *Sept. 24, 1894*	400.00	40.00
			Never hinged	1,100.	
			Block of 4	1,750.	—
			P# block of 6, Impt.	3,250.	
J36	D2	30c	**deep claret,** *Apr. 27, 1895*	600.00	250.00
			claret	600.00	250.00
			Never hinged	1,400.	
			Block of 4	2,750.	—
			P# block of 6, Impt.	4,750.	
			Never hinged	9,000.	
a.		30c	carmine	750.00	275.00
			Never hinged	1,750.	
			Block of 4	3,500.	—
			P# block of 6, Impt.	5,750.	
			Never hinged	11,000.	
b.		30c	pale rose	500.00	200.00
			Never hinged	1,250.	
			Block of 4	2,250.	—
			P# block of 6, Impt.	4,250.	
			Never hinged	8,000.	
J37	D2	50c	**deep claret,** *Apr. 27, 1895*	2,000.	800.00
			Never hinged	4,750.	
			Block of 4	8,750.	—
			P# block of 6, Impt.	15,000.	
a.		50c	pale rose	1,800.	725.00
			Never hinged	4,250.	
			Block of 4	7,750.	—
			P# block of 6, Impt.	13,000.	

Shades are numerous in the 1894 and later issues.

Wmk. 191 Horizontally or Vertically

1895-97　　　　　　　　　Perf. 12

J38	D2	1c	**deep claret,** *Aug. 29, 1895*	15.00	1.00
			claret	15.00	1.00
			carmine	15.00	1.00
			lake	15.00	1.00
			Never hinged	45.00	
			Block of 4	65.00	8.50
			P# block of 6, Impt.	275.00	
			Never hinged	450.00	
J39	D2	2c	**deep claret,** *Sept. 14, 1895*	15.00	1.00
			claret	15.00	1.00
			carmine	15.00	1.00
			lake	15.00	1.00
			Never hinged	45.00	
			Block of 4	65.00	8.50
			P# block of 6, Impt.	275.00	
			Never hinged	450.00	
			Double transfer	—	—

In October, 1895, the Postmaster at Jefferson, Iowa, surcharged a few 2 cent stamps with the words "Due I cent" in black on each side, subsequently dividing the stamps vertically and using each half as a 1 cent stamp. Twenty of these were used.

J40	D2	3c	**deep claret,** *Oct. 30, 1895*	110.00	5.00
			claret	110.00	5.00
			rose red	110.00	5.00
			carmine	110.00	5.00

			Un	U
		Never hinged	275.00	
		Block of 4	475.00	27.50
		P# block of 6, Impt.	1,000.	
		Never hinged	1,800.	
J41	D2 5c	**deep claret**, *Oct. 15, 1895*	120.00	5.00
		claret	120.00	5.00
		carmine rose	120.00	5.00
		Never hinged	300.00	
		Block of 4	525.00	27.50
		P# block of 6, Impt.	1,050.	
		Never hinged	2,000.	
J42	D2 10c	**deep claret**, *Sept. 14, 1895*	120.00	7.50
		claret	120.00	7.50
		carmine	120.00	7.50
		lake	120.00	7.50
		Never hinged	300.00	
		Block of 4	525.00	47.50
		P# block of 6, Impt.	1,050.	
		Never hinged	2,000.	
J43	D2 30c	**deep claret**, *Aug. 21, 1897*	700.00	75.00
		claret	700.00	75.00
		Never hinged	1,800.	
		Block of 4	3,000.	450.00
		P# block of 6, Impt.	6,500.	
J44	D2 50c	**deep claret**, *Mar. 17, 1896*	450.00	60.00
		claret	450.00	60.00
		Never hinged	1,200.	
		Block of 4	2,000.	275.00
		P# block of 6, Impt.	4,750.	—
		Nos. J38-J44 (7)	1,530.	154.50

Plates of 400 subjects in four panes of 100.

1910-12   Wmk. 190   Perf. 12

			Un	U
J45	D2 1c	**deep claret**, *Dec., 1910*	45.00	5.00
		Never hinged	130.00	
a.		1c **rose carmine**	40.00	5.00
		Never hinged	120.00	
		Block of 4 (2 or 3mm spacing)	200.00	20.00
		P# block of 6, Impt. & star	525.00	
		Never hinged	875.00	
J46	D2 2c	**deep claret**, *Nov. 25, 1910*	45.00	2.00
		lake	45.00	2.00
		Never hinged	130.00	
a.		2c **rose carmine**	40.00	2.00
		Never hinged	120.00	
		Block of 4 (2 or 3mm spacing)	200.00	7.50
		P# block of 6, Impt. & star	500.00	
		Never hinged	850.00	
		P# block of 6	550.00	
		Never hinged	900.00	—
		Double transfer		
J47	D2 3c	**deep claret**, *Aug. 31, 1910*	675.00	60.00
		lake	675.00	60.00
		Never hinged	1,750.	
		Block of 4 (2 or 3mm spacing)	2,900.	325.00
		P# block of 6, Impt. & star	6,000.	
		Never hinged	11,500.	
J48	D2 5c	**deep claret**, *Aug. 31, 1910*	130.00	12.00
		Never hinged	300.00	
a.		5c **rose carmine**	130.00	12.00
		Never hinged	300.00	
		Block of 4 (2 or 3mm spacing)	550.00	60.00
		P# block of 6, Impt. & star	1,150.	
		Never hinged	2,000.	
J49	D2 10c	**deep claret**, *Aug. 31, 1910*	140.00	20.00
		Never hinged	360.00	
		Block of 4 (2 or 3mm spacing)	600.00	120.00
		P# block of 6, Impt. & star	1,500.	
a.		10c **rose carmine**	140.00	20.00
		Never hinged	360.00	
J50	D2 50c	**deep claret**, *Sept. 23, 1912*	1,150.	175.00
		Never hinged	3,000.	
		Block of 4 (2 or 3mm spacing)	5,000.	
		P# block of 6, Impt. & star	10,000.	
a.		50c **rose carmine**	1,200.	190.00
		Never hinged	3,250.	

1914   Perf. 10

			Un	U
J52	D2 1c	**carmine lake**	90.00	15.00
		deep carmine lake	90.00	15.00
		Never hinged	260.00	
		Block of 4 (2 or 3mm spacing)	400.00	80.00
		P# block of 6, Impt. & star	750.00	
		Never hinged	1,750.	
a.		1c **dull rose**	95.00	15.00
		Never hinged	270.00	
		Block of 4 (2 or 3mm spacing)	425.00	85.00
		P# block of 6, Impt. & star	775.00	
		Never hinged	1,800.	
J53	D2 2c	**carmine lake**	70.00	1.00
		Never hinged	200.00	
		Block of 4	300.00	8.00
		P# block of 6	650.00	—
		Never hinged	1,250.	
a.		2c **dull rose**	75.00	2.00
		Never hinged	210.00	
		Block of 4		15.00
b.		2c **vermilion**	75.00	2.00
		Never hinged	210.00	
		Block of 4	325.00	14.00
		P# block of 6	675.00	
		Never hinged	1,400.	
J54	D2 3c	**carmine lake**	1,150.	75.00
		Never hinged	3,300.	
		Block of 4 (2 or 3mm spacing)	5,250.	—
		P# block of 6, Impt. & star	9,500.	—
a.		3c **dull rose**	1,100.	75.00

			Un	U
		Never hinged	3,250.	
		Block of 4 (2 or 3mm spacing)	5,000.	—
		P# block of 6, Impt. & star	9,000.	—
J55	D2 5c	**carmine lake**	55.00	6.00
		Never hinged	160.00	
		Block of 4 (2 or 3mm spacing)	240.00	30.00
		P# block of 6, Impt. & star	475.00	—
		Never hinged	1,150.	
a.		5c **dull rose**	50.00	4.00
		carmine rose	50.00	4.00
		Never hinged	150.00	
		deep claret	—	
		Block of 4 (2 or 3mm spacing)	225.00	20.00
		P# block of 6, Impt. & star	450.00	—
		Never hinged	1,100.	
J56	D2 10c	**carmine lake**	85.00	4.00
		Never hinged	240.00	
		Block of 4 (2 or 3mm spacing)	375.00	22.50
		P# block of 6, Impt. & star	825.00	—
a.		10c **dull rose**	90.00	5.00
		carmine rose	90.00	5.00
		Never hinged	250.00	
		Block of 4 (2 or 3mm spacing)	400.00	25.00
		P# block of 6, Impt. & star	950.00	—
		Never hinged	1,700.	
J57	D2 30c	**carmine lake**	250.00	55.00
		Never hinged	600.00	
		Block of 4 (2 or 3mm spacing)	1,100.	325.00
		P# block of 6, Impt. & star	2,900.	—
J58	D2 50c	**carmine lake**	12,500.	1,500.
		Never hinged	22,500.	
		Precanceled		750.00
		Block of 4 (2 or 3mm spacing)	55,000.	6,500.
		P# block of 6, Impt. & star	100,000.	

No. J58 unused is valued in the grade of fine.
No. J58, precanceled, was used at Buffalo (normal, inverted) and Chicago (normal, inverted, double, double inverted).

1916   Unwmk.   Perf. 10

			Un	U
J59	D2 1c	**rose**	4,500.	725.00
		Never hinged	10,000.	
		Block of 4 (2 or 3mm spacing)	21,000.	3,500.
		P# block of 6, Impt. & star	31,500.	
		Experimental bureau precancel, New Orleans		400.00
J60	D2 2c	**rose**	300.00	75.00
		Never hinged	850.00	
		Block of 4	1,350.	350.00
		P# block of 6	2,500.	—
		Experimental bureau precancel, New Orleans		50.00

1917   Unwmk.   Perf. 11

			Un	U
J61	D2 1c	**carmine rose**	3.00	.25
		dull rose	3.00	.25
		Never hinged	10.00	
a.		1c **rose red**	3.00	.25
		Never hinged	10.00	
b.		1c **deep claret**	3.00	.25
		claret brown	3.00	.25
		Never hinged	10.00	
		Block of 4 (2 or 3mm spacing)	13.00	2.00
		P# block of 6, Impt. & star	150.00	—
		Never hinged	350.00	
		P# block of 6	45.00	—
		Never hinged	100.00	
J62	D2 2c	**carmine rose**	3.00	.25
		Never hinged	10.00	
a.		2c **rose red**	3.00	.25
		Never hinged	10.00	
b.		2c **deep claret**	3.00	.25
		claret brown	3.00	1.10
		Never hinged	10.00	
		Block of 4	13.00	2.00
		Never hinged	42.50	
		P# block of 6	55.00	—
		Never hinged	125.00	
		Double transfer	—	—
J63	D2 3c	**carmine rose**	15.00	.80
		Never hinged	40.00	
a.		3c **rose red**	15.00	.80
		Never hinged	40.00	
b.		3c **deep claret**	15.00	.80
		claret brown	15.00	.80
		Never hinged	40.00	
		Block of 4 (2 or 3mm spacing)	65.00	5.00
		P# block of 6, Impt. & star	150.00	—
		Never hinged	300.00	
		P# block of 6	125.00	—
		Never hinged	275.00	
J64	D2 5c	**carmine**	12.50	.80
		carmine rose	12.50	.80
		Never hinged	37.50	
a.		5c **rose red**	12.50	.80
		Never hinged	37.50	
b.		5c **deep claret**	12.50	.80
		claret brown	12.50	.80
		Never hinged	37.50	
		Block of 4 (2 or 3mm spacing)	52.50	6.00
		P# block of 6, Impt. & star	125.00	—
		Never hinged	275.00	
		P# block of 6	105.00	—
		Never hinged	250.00	
J65	D2 10c	**carmine rose**	25.00	1.00
		Never hinged	70.00	
a.		10c **rose red**	25.00	1.00
		Never hinged	70.00	
b.		10c **deep claret**	25.00	1.00

			Un	U
		claret brown	25.00	1.00
		Never hinged	70.00	
		Block of 4 (2 or 3mm spacing)	110.00	7.50
		P# block of 6, Impt. & star	220.00	—
		Never hinged	475.00	
		P# block of 6	240.00	—
		Never hinged	525.00	
		Double transfer		—
J66	D2 30c	**carmine rose**	90.00	2.00
		Never hinged	260.00	
a.		30c **deep claret**	90.00	2.00
		claret brown	90.00	2.00
		Never hinged	260.00	
		Block of 4 (2 or 3mm spacing)	390.00	14.00
		P# block of 6, Impt. & star	750.00	—
		P# block of 6	800.00	—
b.		As "a," perf 10 at top, precanceled		21,000.

No. J66b is valued with small faults and fine centering, as the two recorded examples are in this condition and grade. One is precanceled St. Louis, Mo., and the other is precanceled Minneapolis, Minn.

			Un	U
J67	D2 50c	**carmine rose**	150.00	1.00
		Never hinged	370.00	
a.		50c **rose red**	150.00	1.00
		Never hinged	370.00	
b.		50c **deep claret**	150.00	1.00
		claret brown	150.00	1.00
		Never hinged	370.00	
		Block of 4 (2 or 3mm spacing)	625.00	7.50
		P# block of 6, Impt. & star	1,150.	
		Never hinged	2,500.	
		P# block of 6	1,250.	

1925, Apr. 13

			Un	U
J68	D2 ½c	**dull red**	1.00	.25
		Never hinged	1.75	
		Block of 4	4.00	1.50
		P# block of 6	12.50	
		Never hinged	17.50	

D3

D4

1930   **Unwmk.**   *Perf. 11*
Design measures 19x22mm

J69	D3	½c **carmine**		4.50	1.90
		Never hinged		10.00	
		P# block of 6		50.00	—
		Never hinged		80.00	
J70	D3	1c **carmine**		3.00	.35
		Never hinged		7.00	
		P# block of 6		55.00	—
		Never hinged		100.00	
J71	D3	2c **carmine**		4.00	.35
		Never hinged		9.00	
		P# block of 6		50.00	—
		Never hinged		95.00	
J72	D3	3c **carmine**		21.00	2.75
		Never hinged		50.00	
		P# block of 6		300.00	—
		Never hinged		500.00	
J73	D3	5c **carmine**		19.00	5.00
		Never hinged		45.00	
		P# block of 6		300.00	—
		Never hinged		500.00	
J74	D3	10c **carmine**		45.00	2.00
		Never hinged		100.00	
		P# block of 6		475.00	—
		Never hinged		875.00	
J75	D3	30c **carmine**		150.00	4.00
		Never hinged		325.00	
		P# block of 6		1,150.	—
		Never hinged		*2,250.*	
J76	D3	50c **carmine**		200.00	2.00
		Never hinged		450.00	
		P# block of 6		1,750.	—
		Never hinged		*3,250.*	

Design measures 22x19mm

J77	D4	$1 **carmine**		35.00	.35
		Never hinged		70.00	
		P# block of 6		250.00	—
		Never hinged		475.00	
a.		$1 **scarlet**		30.00	.35
		Never hinged		60.00	
		P# block of 6		275.00	—
		Never hinged		500.00	
J78	D4	$5 **carmine**		40.00	.35
		Never hinged		90.00	
		P# block of 6		300.00	—
		Never hinged		600.00	
a.		$5 **scarlet**		35.00	.35
		Never hinged		75.00	
		P# block of 6		260.00	—
		Never hinged		525.00	
b.		As "a," wet printing		40.00	.35
		Never hinged		90.00	
		P# block of 6		300.00	—
		Never hinged		600.00	

See note on Wet and Dry Printings following No. 1029.

Type of 1930-31 Issue
Rotary Press Printing
Ordinary and Electric Eye Plates
Design measures 19x22½mm

1931   **Unwmk.**   *Perf. 11x10½*

J79	D3	½c **dull carmine**		.90	.20
		Never hinged		1.30	
a.		½c **scarlet**		.90	.20
		Never hinged		1.30	
		P# block of 4		20.00	—
		Never hinged		30.00	
J80	D3	1c **dull carmine**		.20	.20
		Never hinged		.30	
a.		1c **scarlet**		.20	.20
		Never hinged		.30	
		P# block of 4 (#25635, 25636)		1.50	—
		Never hinged		2.25	
b.		As "a," wet printing		.20	.20
		Never hinged		.20	
		P# block of 4		1.75	—
		Never hinged		2.60	
		Pair with full vertical gutter between			
J81	D3	2c **dull carmine**		.20	.20

		Never hinged		.30	
a.		2c **scarlet**		.20	.20
		Never hinged		.30	
		P# block of 4 (#25637, 25638)		1.50	—
		Never hinged		2.25	
b.		As "a," wet printing		.20	.20
		Never hinged		.30	
		P# block of 4		2.00	—
		Never hinged		3.00	
J82	D3	3c **dull carmine**		.25	.20
		Never hinged		.40	
a.		3c **scarlet**		.25	.20
		Never hinged		.40	
		P# block of 4 (#25641, 25642)		2.25	—
		Never hinged		3.40	
b.		As "a," wet printing		.30	.20
		Never hinged		.45	
		P# block of 4		2.50	—
		Never hinged		3.75	
J83	D3	5c **dull carmine**		.40	.20
		Never hinged		.60	
a.		5c **scarlet**		.40	.20
		Never hinged		.60	
		P# block of 4 (#25643, 25644)		3.00	—
		Never hinged		4.50	
b.		As "a," wet printing		.50	.20
		Never hinged		.75	
		P# block of 4		3.50	—
		Never hinged		5.25	
J84	D3	10c **dull carmine**		1.10	.20
		Never hinged		1.80	
a.		10c **scarlet**		1.10	.20
		Never hinged		1.80	
		P# block of 4 (#25645, 25646)		6.50	—
		Never hinged		9.75	
b.		As "a," wet printing		1.25	.20
		Never hinged		1.90	
		P# block of 4		7.00	—
		Never hinged		10.50	
J85	D3	30c **dull carmine**		7.50	.25
		Never hinged		11.50	
a.		30c **scarlet**		7.50	.25
		Never hinged		11.50	
		P# block of 4		35.00	—
		Never hinged		60.00	
J86	D3	50c **dull carmine**		9.00	.25
		Never hinged		15.00	
a.		50c **scarlet**		9.00	.25
		Never hinged		15.00	
		P# block of 4		52.50	—
		Never hinged		85.00	

Design measures 22½x19mm
1956   *Perf. 10½x11*

J87	D4	$1 **scarlet**		30.00	.25
		Never hinged		47.50	
		P# block of 4		190.00	—
		Never hinged		290.00	
		Nos. J79-J87 (9)		49.55	1.95

> **Catalogue values for unused stamps in this section, from this point to the end, are for Never Hinged items.**

D5

Rotary Press Printing
Denominations added in black by rubber plates in an operation similar to precanceling.

1959, June 19   **Unwmk.**   *Perf. 11x10½*
Denomination in Black

J88	D5	½c **carmine rose**		1.50	1.10
		P# block of 4		120.00	
J89	D5	1c **carmine rose**, shiny gum		.20	.20
		P# block of 4		.35	—
		Dull gum		.25	
		P# block of 4		4.50	
a.		Denomination omitted		225.00	
		P# block of 4		—	
b.		Pair, one without "1 CENT"		*400.00*	
J90	D5	2c **carmine rose**, shiny gum		.20	.20
		P# block of 4		.45	
		Wide spacing, pair		120.00	
		Dull gum		.40	
		P# block of 4		12.50	
J91	D5	3c **carmine rose**, shiny gum		.20	.20
		P# block of 4		.50	
		Dull gum		.50	
		P# block of 4		15.00	
a.		Pair, one without "3 CENTS"		*675.00*	
J92	D5	4c **carmine rose**		.20	.20
		P# block of 4		.60	
		Wide spacing, pair		190.00	
J93	D5	5c **carmine rose**, shiny gum		.20	.20
		P# block of 4		.65	
		Dull gum		.45	
		P# block of 4		8.00	
a.		Pair, one without "5 CENTS"		*1,500.*	
J94	D5	6c **carmine rose**, shiny gum		.20	.20
		P# block of 4		.70	
		Pair with full vertical gutter between			
		Dull gum		90.00	
		P# block of 4		*1,250.*	
a.		Pair, one without "6 CENTS"		*850.00*	
J95	D5	7c **carmine rose**, shiny gum		.20	.20
		P# block of 4		.80	
		Wide spacing, pair		120.00	
		Dull gum		700.00	
		P# block of 4		*7,500.*	
J96	D5	8c **carmine rose**		.20	.20
		P# block of 4		.90	
		Wide spacing, pair		120.00	
a.		Pair, one without "8 CENTS"		*850.00*	
J97	D5	10c **carmine rose**, shiny gum		.20	.20
		P# block of 4		1.00	
		Dull gum		.35	
		P# block of 4		5.00	
J98	D5	30c **carmine rose**, shiny gum		.75	.20
		P# block of 4		3.50	
		Dull gum		1.00	
		P# block of 4		16.00	
J99	D5	50c **carmine rose**, shiny gum		1.10	.20
		P# block of 4		5.00	
		Dull gum		1.75	
		P# block of 4		20.00	

Straight Numeral Outlined in Black

J100	D5	$1 **carmine rose**, shiny gum		2.00	.20
		P# block of 4		8.50	—
		Dull gum		2.50	
		P# block of 4		22.50	
J101	D5	$5 **carmine rose**, shiny gum		9.00	.20
		P# block of 4		40.00	—
		Dull gum		11.00	
		P# block of 4		65.00	—
		Nos. J88-J101 (14)		16.15	3.70

All single stamps with denomination omitted are catalogued as No. J89a.

Rotary Press Printing
1978-85   *Perf. 11x10½*
Denomination in Black

J102	D5	11c **carmine rose**, *Jan. 2, 1978*		.25	.20
		P# block of 4		2.00	—
J103	D5	13c **carmine rose**, *Jan. 2, 1978*		.25	.20
		P# block of 4		2.00	—
J104	D5	17c **carmine rose**, *June 10, 1985*		.40	.35
		P# block of 4		22.50	—

U.S. POSTAL AGENCY IN CHINA

Postage stamps of the 1917-19 U.S. series (then current) were issued to the U.S. Postal Agency, Shanghai, China, surcharged at double the original value of the stamps.

These stamps were intended for sale at Shanghai at their surcharged value in local currency, valid for prepayment on mail despatched from the U.S. Postal Agency at Shanghai to addresses in the U.S.

Stamps were first issued May 24, 1919, and were placed on sale at Shanghai on July 1, 1919. These stamps were not issued to postmasters in the U.S. The Shanghai post office, according to the U.S.P.O. Bulletin, was closed in December 1922. The stamps were on sale at the Philatelic Agency in Washington, D.C. for a short time after that.

Italicized numbers in parentheses indicate quantities shipped to the postal agency in Shanghai and to the Washington Philatelic Agency. In the case of Nos. K17-K18, the numbers are the quantity locally overprinted. All Nos. K16a, K17 and K18 are believed to have been sold. The final disposition of remainders of the others is not known. Neither the records of the Shanghai Postal Agency nor the records of the Washington Philatelic Agency have been located at this time. Authority for quantities shipped is the research of Joseph M. Napp, who in turn benefitted by the research of Meyer Tuchinsky.

The cancellations of the China office included "U.S. Postal Agency Shanghai China", "U.S. Pos. Service Shanghai China" duplexes, and the Shanghai parcel post roller cancel. Used stamps are valued bearing legible cancels showing Chinese origin.

United States Stamps #498-499, 502-504, 506-510, 512, 514-518 Surcharged in Black or Red (Nos. K7, K16)

1919   **Unwmk.**   **Perf. 11**

K1	A140	2c on 1c **green** (355,000)	25.00	60.00
		Never hinged	70.00	
		Block of 4	110.00	350.00
		P# block of 6	300.00	
		Never hinged	600.00	
		Double transfer	42.50	
		Never hinged	110.00	

Earliest documented use: July 2, 1919.

K2	A140	4c on 2c **rose**, type I (355,000)	25.00	60.00
		Never hinged	70.00	
		Block of 4	110.00	350.00
		P# block of 6	300.00	
		Never hinged	600.00	

Earliest documented use: July 2, 1919.

K3	A140	6c on 3c **violet**, type II, (113,000)	60.00	130.00
		Never hinged	150.00	
		Block of 4	260.00	650.00
		P# block of 6	675.00	
		Never hinged	1,150.	
K4	A140	8c on 4c **brown** (113,000)	60.00	130.00
		Never hinged	150.00	
		Block of 4	260.00	650.00
		P# block of 6	675.00	
		Never hinged	1,150.	
K5	A140	10c on 5c **blue** (113,000)	65.00	130.00
		Never hinged	170.00	
		Block of 4	280.00	650.00
		P# block of 6	600.00	
		Never hinged	1,100.	
K6	A140	12c on 6c **red orange** (113,000)	85.00	190.00
		Never hinged	220.00	
		Block of 4	375.00	1,000.
		P# block of 6	800.00	

K7	A140	14c on 7c **black** (113,000)	87.50	190.00
		Never hinged	225.00	
		Block of 4	400.00	1,050.
		P# block of 6	1,050.	
		Never hinged	1,650.	
K8	A148	16c on 8c **olive bister** (13,000)	70.00	145.00
		Never hinged	180.00	
		Block of 4	300.00	800.00
		P# block of 6	625.00	
		Never hinged	1,150.	
a.		16c on 8c **olive green** (100,000)	60.00	125.00
		Never hinged	160.00	
		Block of 4	260.00	725.00
		P# block of 6	575.00	
		Never hinged	1,000.	
K9	A148	18c on 9c **salmon red** (113,000)	65.00	160.00
		Never hinged	170.00	
		Block of 4	280.00	800.00
		P# block of 6	700.00	
		Never hinged	1,200.	
K10	A148	20c on 10c **orange yellow** (113,000)	60.00	130.00
		Never hinged	160.00	
		Block of 4	260.00	650.00
		P# block of 6	725.00	
		Never hinged	1,300.	
K11	A148	24c on 12c **brown carmine** (50,000)	80.00	150.00
		Never hinged	200.00	
		Block of 4	350.00	700.00
		P# block of 6	1,000.	
		Never hinged	1,750.	
a.		24c on 12c **claret brown** (8,000)	110.00	200.00
		Never hinged	275.00	
		Block of 4	475.00	975.00
		P# block of 6	1,200.	
		Never hinged	2,100.	
K12	A148	30c on 15c **gray** (58,000)	87.50	220.00
		Never hinged	210.00	
		Block of 4	375.00	—
		P# block of 6	1,150.	
		Never hinged	2,000.	
K13	A148	40c on 20c **deep ultramarine** (58,000)	130.00	310.00
		Never hinged	300.00	
		Block of 4	550.00	1,750.
		P# block of 6	1,300.	
		Never hinged	2,250.	
K14	A148	60c on 30c **orange red** (58,000)	120.00	260.00
		Never hinged	280.00	
		Block of 4	525.00	1,450.

		P# block of 6	1,050.	
		Never hinged	1,800.	
K15	A148	$1 on 50c **light violet** (14,000)	575.00	875.00
		Never hinged	1,300.	
		Block of 4	2,500.	5,250.
		P# block of 6	17,500.	
K16	A148	$2 on $1 **violet brown** (13,800)	450.00	725.00
		Never hinged	1,000.	
		Block of 4	2,000.	4,750.
		Margin block of 4, arrow, right or left	2,100.	
		P# block of 6	7,000.	
		Never hinged	11,000.	
a.		Double surcharge (200)	8,500.	8,000.
		Never hinged	14,000.	
		Block of 4		
		Nos. K1-K16 (16)	2,045.	3,865.

Fake surcharges exist, but most are rather crudely made.

United States Stamps Nos. 498 and 528B Locally Surcharged

1922, July 3

K17	A140	2c on 1c **green** (10,000)	110.00	200.00
		Never hinged	250.00	
		Block of 4	475.00	950.00
		P# block of 6	850.00	
		Never hinged	1,750.	
K18	A140	4c on 2c **carmine**, type VII (10,000)	100.00	175.00
		Never hinged	230.00	
		Block of 4	425.00	800.00
		P# block of 6	800.00	
		Never hinged	1,400.	
a.		"SHANGHAI" omitted	7,500.	
b.		"CHINA" only	15,000.	

OFFICIAL STAMPS

The original official stamps were authorized by Act of Congress, approved March 3, 1873, abolishing the franking privilege. Stamps for each executive government department were issued July 1, 1873.

Penalty franks were first authorized in 1877, and their expanded use after 1879 reduced the need for official stamps, the use of which was finally abolished on July 5, 1884.

DESIGNS. Stamps for departments other than the Post Office picture the same busts used in the regular postage issue: 1c Franklin, 2c Jackson, 3c Washington, 6c Lincoln, 7c Stanton, 10c Jefferson, 12c Clay, 15c Webster, 24c Scott, 30c Hamilton, and 90c Perry. William H. Seward appears on the $2, $5, $10 and $20.

Designs of the various denominations are not identical, but resemble those illustrated.

PLATES. Plates of 200 subjects in two panes of 100 were used for Post Office Department 1c, 3c, 6c; Treasury Department 1c, 2c, 3c, and War Department 2c, 3c. Plates of 10 subjects were used for State Department $2, $5, $10 and $20. Plates of 100 subjects were used for all other Official stamps up to No. O120.

CANCELLATIONS. Odd or Town cancellations on Departmental stamps are relatively much scarcer than those appearing on the general issues of the same period. Town cancellations, especially on the 1873 issue, are scarce. The "Kicking Mule" cancellation is found used on stamps of the War Department and has also been seen on some stamps of the other Departments. Black is usual.

As is done elsewhere in this catalogue, all Officials are valued in the grade of very fine. If unused, they will have original gum. Values for never-hinged stamps and unused stamps without gum are also given.

Printed by the Continental Bank Note Co.
Thin Hard Paper

O1   Franklin — O2

AGRICULTURE

1873   **Engr.**   **Unwmk.**   **Perf. 12**

O1	O1	1c **yellow**	280.00	180.00
		Never hinged	600.00	
		No gum	160.00	
		On wrapper		2,500.
		Block of 4	1,250.	
		Ribbed paper	340.00	200.00

Cancellations

Magenta		+7.50
Violet		+7.50
Blue		+5.00
Red		+50.00
Town		+7.50
Fort		+150.00

O2	O1	2c **yellow**	240.00	85.00
		Never hinged	500.00	
		No gum	100.00	
		On cover		4,000.
		Block of 4	1,050.	
		P# block of 12		—
		Ribbed paper	240.00	95.00

Cancellations

Blue		+3.00
Violet		+3.00
Red		+15.00
Magenta		+5.00
Town		+5.00

O3	O1	3c **yellow**	220.00	16.00
		Never hinged	460.00	
		No gum	80.00	
		On cover		900.00
		Block of 4	1,000.	
		P# block of 12, Impt., never hinged	3,900.	
		Ribbed paper	240.00	16.00
		Double transfer	—	
		Short transfer at upper left (pos. 10, 18, 28)	—	—

The never hinged, bottom left plate block of No. O3 is the only plate block of this number recorded.

Cancellations

Blue		+.50
Purple		+1.00
Magenta		+1.00
Violet		+1.00
Red		+17.50
Indigo		+10.00
Green		+200.00
Brown		+20.00
Town		+4.00
"Paid"		+27.50
Numeral		+35.00
Railroad		+75.00
Express Company		+900.00

O4	O1	6c **yellow**	260.00	60.00

		Never hinged	550.00		
		No gum	95.00		
		On cover		8,500.	
		Block of 4	1,250.		

Cancellations
Blue	+3.00
Magenta	+4.00
Violet	+5.00
Red	+50.00
Town	+7.00
"Paid"	+27.50
Numeral	+35.00
Express Company	—
Revenue	—

O5	O1	10c	**yellow**	525.00	200.00
			Never hinged	1,150.	
			No gum	220.00	
			On cover (parcel label)		6,000.
			Block of 4	2,500.	

Cancellations
Violet	+5.00
Blue	+5.00
Red	+50.00
Town	+25.00

O6	O1	12c	**yellow**	450.00	260.00
			Never hinged	950.00	
			No gum	250.00	
			On cover		12,000.
			Block of 4	1,950.	

Cancellations
Violet	+10.00
Blue	+10.00
Red	+50.00
Town	+30.00

O7	O1	15c	**yellow**	425.00	230.00
			Never hinged	950.00	
			No gum	225.00	
			Block of 4	1,850.	
			Recut top left frame line (pos. 100)	—	—

Cancellations
Purple	+10.00
Blue	+10.00

O8	O1	24c	**yellow**	425.00	220.00
			Never hinged	950.00	
			No gum	225.00	
			On parcel label		—
			Block of 4	1,850.	

Cancellation
Violet	+10.00

O9	O1	30c	**yellow**	550.00	270.00
			Never hinged	1,200.	
			No gum	275.00	
			Block of 4	2,500.	

Cancellations
Blue	+10.00
Red	+65.00

EXECUTIVE

1873

O10	O2	1c	**carmine**	850.00	475.00
			deep carmine	850.00	475.00
			Never hinged	2,250.	
			No gum	450.00	
			On cover with No. O11		3,250.
			On cover, single franking		3,000.
			Block of 6		4,250.

The only known block is with original gum and is off-center with perfs just cutting into design. It is valued thus.

Cancellations
Violet	+10.00
Blue favor	+10.00
Red	+50.00
Town	+30.00

O11	O2	2c	**carmine**	550.00	240.00

		deep carmine	550.00	240.00
		Never hinged	1,250.	
		No gum	240.00	
		On cover, single franking		3,750.
		Block of 4	3,250.	
		Foreign entry of 6c Agriculture (pos. 40)	2,500.	1,000.

Cancellations
Violet	+10.00
Blue favor	+10.00
Red	+50.00

O12	O2	3c	**carmine**	700.00	210.00
			Never hinged	1,600.	
			No gum	270.00	
			On cover		1,000.
			On cover from Long Branch, N.J.		4,500.
			Block of 4	3,250.	
a.		3c	**violet rose**	850.00	210.00
			Never hinged	1,950.	
			No gum	325.00	

Cancellations
Blue favor	+10.00
Violet	+10.00
Indigo	+20.00
Red	+50.00
Town	+35.00

O13	O2	6c	**carmine**	900.00	550.00
			pale carmine	900.00	550.00
			deep carmine	900.00	550.00
			Never hinged	325.00	
			No gum		
			On cover		5,000.
			Block of 4	4,000.	
			Double transfer (pos. 6)	2,600.	1,000.

Cancellations
Violet	+15.00
Blue favor	+15.00
Town	+50.00
New York Foreign Mail	

O14	O2	10c	**carmine**	1,200.	650.00
			pale carmine	1,200.	650.00
			deep carmine	1,200.	650.00
			Never hinged	600.00	
			No gum		
			On cover		—
			Block of 4	5,500.	

Cancellations
Violet	+15.00
Blue favor	+15.00

O3   O4

INTERIOR

1873

O15	O3	1c	**vermilion**	75.00	10.00
			dull vermilion	75.00	10.00
			bright vermilion	75.00	10.00
			Never hinged	170.00	
			No gum	30.00	
			On cover		160.00
			Block of 4	325.00	325.00
			P# block of 10, Impt.	1,000.	
			Never hinged	1,850.	
			Ribbed paper	85.00	20.00
			Short transfer at bottom right (pos. 91)	—	—

Cancellations
Violet	+1.00
Blue	+1.00
Red	+12.50
Ultramarine	+8.00
Town	+3.00

O16	O3	2c	**vermilion**	70.00	12.00
			dull vermilion	70.00	12.00
			bright vermilion	70.00	12.00
			Never hinged	160.00	
			No gum	30.00	
			On cover		65.00
			Block of 4	300.00	300.00
			P# block of 10, Impt.	950.00	
			P# block of 12, Impt.	1,050.	

Cancellations
Purple	+.75
Violet	+75
Blue	+.75
Red	+6.00
Town	+7.50
Numeral	+20.00
"Paid"	+20.00

O17	O3	3c	**vermilion**	80.00	6.00
			dull vermilion	80.00	6.00
			bright vermilion	80.00	6.00
			Never hinged	175.00	
			No gum	35.00	
			On cover		40.00
			First day cover, Nos. O17, O18, July 1, 1873		9,000.
			Block of 4	350.00	350.00
			P# block of 10, Impt.	975.00	
			Ribbed paper	100.00	10.00

Cancellations
Violet	+1.00
Blue	+1.00
Indigo	+3.00
Magenta	+5.00
Red	+15.00
Green	+65.00
Town	+7.50
Numeral	+20.00
Express Company	+75.00
"Paid"	+20.00
Fort	—

O18	O3	6c	**vermilion**	70.00	10.00
			dull vermilion	70.00	10.00
			bright vermilion	70.00	10.00
			scarlet vermilion	70.00	10.00
			Never hinged	160.00	
			No gum	27.50	
			On cover		95.00
			Block of 4	350.00	
			P# block of 10, Impt.	950.00	

Cancellations
Violet	+1.00
Blue	+1.00
Red	+15.00
Town	+7.50
Express Company	—
Railroad	—
Fort	—

See No. O17 for first day cover listing.

O19	O3	10c	**vermilion**	70.00	20.00
			dull vermilion	70.00	20.00
			bright vermilion	70.00	20.00
			Never hinged	160.00	
			No gum	27.50	
			On cover		600.00
			Block of 4	350.00	
			P# block of 12, Impt.	1,000.	

Cancellations
Violet	+1.00
Blue	+1.00
Indigo	+10.00
Red	+25.00
Town	+10.00
Fort	—
New York Foreign Mail	+300.00

O20	O3	12c	**vermilion**	90.00	12.00
			bright vermilion	90.00	12.00
			Never hinged	200.00	
			No gum	35.00	
			On cover		575.00
			Block of 4	400.00	500.00
			P# block of 10, Impt.	1,150.	
			Short transfer at right (pos. 6)		—

Cancellations
Violet	+1.00
Magenta	+1.00
Blue	+1.00
Red	+15.00
Brown	+20.00
Town	+7.50
Fort	—

O21	O3	15c	**vermilion**	200.00	25.00
			bright vermilion	200.00	25.00
			Never hinged	450.00	
			No gum	80.00	
			On cover		650.00
			Block of 4	900.00	
			P# block of 12, Impt.		
			Double transfer of left side	275.00	37.50

Cancellations
Blue	+1.50
Violet	+1.50
Town	+5.00

O22	O3	24c	**vermilion**	180.00	20.00
			dull vermilion	180.00	20.00
			bright vermilion	180.00	20.00
			Never hinged	400.00	
			No gum	60.00	
			On cover		2,500.
			Block of 4	775.00	2,000.
			P# block of 12, Impt.	2,500.	
a.			Double impression		—

Cancellations
Violet	+1.50
Blue	+1.50
Red	+15.00
Town	+5.00

O23	O3	30c	**vermilion**	290.00	20.00
			bright vermilion	290.00	20.00
			Never hinged	625.00	
			No gum	110.00	
			On parcel label		6,000.
			Block of 4	1,250.	
			P# block of 12, Impt.	4,250.	

Cancellations
Violet	+2.00
Blue	+2.00
Red	+50.00
Town	+7.50

O24	O3	90c	**vermilion**	325.00	50.00
			bright vermilion	325.00	50.00
			Never hinged	700.00	
			No gum	120.00	
			On cover		—
			Block of 4	1,650.	
			P# block of 12, Impt.	5,000.	
			Double transfer	390.00	
			Major double transfer (Pos. 17)		600.00	250.00
			Short transfer at right (Pos. 56)		—
			Silk paper		—

Cancellations
Violet	+4.00

Blue +4.00
Magenta +10.00
Red +50.00
Brown +60.00
Town +17.50

JUSTICE

1873

O25 O4 1c **purple** 250.00 100.00
dark purple 250.00 100.00
Never hinged 550.00
No gum 100.00
On cover 1,750.
On cover with No. O26 4,000.
Block of 4 1,100.
Double transfer — —

Cancellations
Violet +3.00
Blue +3.00
Indigo +5.00
Magenta +5.00
Red +20.00
Town +7.50

O26 O4 2c **purple** 310.00 110.00
light purple 310.00 110.00
Never hinged 700.00
No gum 120.00
On cover 1,500.
Block of 4 1,400.
Short transfer at right side (pos. 3) — —

Cancellations
Violet +4.00
Blue +4.00
Ultramarine +10.00
Indigo +5.00
Magenta +5.00
Red +20.00
Town +20.00

O27 O4 3c **purple** 320.00 35.00
dark purple 320.00 35.00
bluish purple 320.00 35.00
Never hinged 725.00
No gum 110.00
On cover 575.00
Block of 4 1,450.
Double transfer —

Cancellations
Violet +2.00
Magenta +2.00
Blue +2.00
Ultramarine +10.00
Indigo +5.00
Red +12.00
Green +100.00
Town +15.00

O28 O4 6c **purple** 310.00 45.00
light purple 310.00 45.00
bluish purple 310.00 45.00
Never hinged 700.00
No gum 110.00
On cover 1,200.
Block of 4 1,400.

Cancellations
Violet +2.00
Blue +2.00
Indigo +5.00
Magenta +5.00
Red +15.00
Town +17.50

O29 O4 10c **purple** 310.00 100.00
bluish purple 310.00 100.00
Never hinged 700.00
No gum 120.00
On cover 3,750.
Block of 4 1,400.
P# block of 10, Impt. 6,000.
Double transfer —

Cancellations
Violet +4.00
Blue +4.00
Magenta +5.00
Town +17.50

O30 O4 12c **purple** 260.00 75.00
dark purple 260.00 75.00
Never hinged 575.00
No gum 95.00
On cover 1,750.
Block of 4 1,200.

Cancellations
Purple +2.00
Violet +2.00
Blue +2.00
Magenta +5.00
Red +35.00
Town +17.50

O31 O4 15c **purple** 475.00 200.00
Never hinged 1,050.
No gum 210.00
On cover 1,250.
Block of 4 2,400.
Double transfer —

Cancellations
Violet +5.00
Blue +5.00
Indigo +5.00
Magenta +10.00
Red +35.00
Town +10.00

The block of 4 of No. O31 is unique. It is in the grade of fine and is valued thus.

O32 O4 24c **purple** 1,250. 425.00
Never hinged
No gum 550.00

On cover 8,000.
Short transfer (pos. 98) —

Cancellations
Violet +10.00
Blue +10.00
Magenta +10.00
Red +35.00
Town +40.00

O33 O4 30c **purple** 1,300. 350.00
Never hinged —
No gum 550.00
On cover with Nos. O27 & O28 17,500.
Block of 4 5,500.
Double transfer at top 1,400. 375.00

Cancellations
Purple +10.00
Violet +10.00
Blue +10.00
Magenta +10.00
Red +50.00
Town +40.00

The block of 4 of No. O33 is unique. It is in the grade of fine and is valued thus.

O34 O4 90c **purple** 1,900. 900.00
dark purple 1,900. 900.00
Never hinged —
No gum 800.00
On cover with No. O33 26,000.
Pair —
Double plate scratch —
Triple transfer at top —

Cancellations
Purple +25.00
Violet +25.00
Blue +25.00
Magenta +25.00

No. O34 on cover is unique. The cover bears three No. O34 and four No. O33.

O5

O6

NAVY

1873

O35 O5 1c **ultramarine** 160.00 50.00
dark ultramarine 160.00 50.00
Never hinged 350.00
No gum 65.00
On cover 750.00
On cover with No. O36 2,000.
Block of 4 750.00
P# block of 12, Impt. 2,250.
a. 1c **dull blue** 160.00 50.00
Never hinged 350.00
No gum 65.00

Cancellations
Violet +2.00
Blue +2.00
Indigo +5.00
Red +20.00
Town +7.50
Steamship +100.00
New York Foreign Mail

O36 O5 2c **ultramarine** 160.00 25.00
dark ultramarine 160.00 25.00
Never hinged 350.00
No gum 65.00
On cover 500.00
Block of 4 750.00
P# block of 12, Impt. 2,250.
Double transfer —
a. 2c **dull blue** 160.00 25.00
gray blue 160.00 25.00
Never hinged 350.00
No gum 65.00
Block of 4 750.00

The 2c deep green and the 2c black, both perforated and imperforate, are trial color proofs.

Cancellations
Violet +1.50
Blue +1.50
Indigo +5.00
Red +15.00
Green +75.00
Town +10.00
Steamship +100.00

O37 O5 3c **ultramarine** 170.00 15.00
pale ultramarine 170.00 15.00
dark ultramarine 170.00 15.00
Never hinged 375.00
No gum 60.00
On cover 250.00
Block of 4 775.00 1,000.
P# block of 12, Impt. 2,500.
Double transfer —
a. 3c **dull blue** 170.00 15.00
Never hinged 375.00
No gum 60.00

Cancellations
Violet +1.50
Blue +1.50
Indigo +5.00
Ultramarine +10.00
Magenta +5.00
Red +15.00
Town +5.00
Blue town +15.00
Steamship +75.00

O38 O5 6c **ultramarine** 150.00 25.00
bright ultramarine 150.00 25.00
Never hinged 325.00
No gum 55.00
On cover 750.00
Block of 4 700.00
P# block of 12, Impt. 2,400.
Vertical line through "N" of "Navy" 175.00 35.00
Double transfer —
a. 6c **dull blue** 150.00 25.00
Never hinged 325.00
No gum 55.00

Cancellations
Violet +1.50
Purple +1.50
Blue +1.50
Magenta +10.00
Red +17.50
Green +100.00
Town +5.00
Steamship +100.00
New York Foreign Mail

O39 O5 7c **ultramarine** 650.00 230.00
dark ultramarine 650.00 230.00
Never hinged —
No gum 250.00
On cover 3,000.
Block of 4 2,800.
Double transfer —
a. 7c **dull blue** 650.00 230.00
Never hinged —
No gum 250.00

Cancellations
Blue +10.00
Violet +10.00
Magenta +10.00
Red +45.00
Town +25.00

O40 O5 10c **ultramarine** 210.00 45.00
dark ultramarine 210.00 45.00
Never hinged 475.00
No gum 75.00
On cover —
Block of 4 1,150.
P# block of 12, Impt. 2,900.
Plate scratch (pos. 3) 325.00 —
Ribbed paper 225.00 60.00
a. 10c **dull blue** 210.00 45.00
Never hinged 475.00
No gum 75.00

Cancellations
Violet +2.00
Blue +2.00
Brown +20.00
Red +25.00
Town +10.00
Steamship +100.00
New York Foreign Mail

O41 O5 12c **ultramarine** 220.00 45.00
pale ultramarine 220.00 45.00
dark ultramarine 220.00 45.00
Never hinged 500.00
No gum 80.00
On cover —
Block of 4 1,100.
P# strip of 6, Impt. —
Short transfer at lower right (pos. 10) — —
Double transfer of left side (pos. 50) 400.00 250.00

Cancellations
Violet +2.50
Magenta +2.50
Blue +2.50
Red +25.00
Town +10.00
Supplementary Mail +80.00
Steamship +200.00
New York Foreign Mail +325.00

O42 O5 15c **ultramarine** 375.00 75.00
dark ultramarine 375.00 75.00
Never hinged —
No gum 135.00
On cover 21,000.
Block of 4 1,700.
P# strip of 6, Impt. —
Short transfer at upper left (pos. 26) —

Cancellations
Violet +2.50
Blue +2.50
Red +35.00
Yellow —
Town +20.00

O43 O5 24c **ultramarine** 400.00 85.00
dark ultramarine 400.00 85.00
Never hinged —
No gum 160.00
On cover 30,000.
Block of 4 2,000.
Recut at upper right (pos. 33, 92) — —
a. 24c **dull blue** 375.00 80.00
Never hinged —
No gum 150.00

Cancellations

Violet	+5.00
Magenta	+5.00
Red	+50.00
Blue	+5.00
Green	+150.00
Town	+40.00
Steamship	+125.00
New York Foreign Mail	—

O44	O5	30c **ultramarine**	325.00	50.00
		dark ultramarine	325.00	50.00
		Never hinged	—	
		No gum	125.00	
		On cover		42,500.
		Block of 4	1,600.	3,000.
		Double transfer	350.00	55.00

Cancellations

Blue	+4.00
Red	+30.00
Violet	+4.00
Town	+20.00
Supplementary Mail	+125.00
Steamship	+150.00
New York Foreign Mail	+400.00

O45	O5	90c **ultramarine**	1,050.	375.00
		Never hinged	—	
		No gum	450.00	
		Block of 4	6,250.	
		Short transfer at upper left (pos. 1, 5)	—	—
a.		Double impression		20,000.

Cancellations

Purple	+15.00
Violet	+15.00
Red	+75.00
Town	+40.00

POST OFFICE

Stamps of the Post Office Department are often on paper with a gray surface. This is due to insufficient wiping of the excess ink off plates during printing.

1873

O47	O6	1c **black**	25.00	12.00
		gray black	25.00	12.00
		Never hinged	60.00	
		No gum	12.00	
		On cover		60.00
		Block of 4	110.00	
		P# block of 12, Impt.	400.00	
		Never hinged	550.00	

Cancellations

Purple	+1.00
Violet	+1.00
Magenta	+1.00
Blue	+1.00
Red	+12.50
Town	+3.50

O48	O6	2c **black**	30.00	10.00
		gray black	30.00	10.00
		Never hinged	75.00	
		No gum	13.00	
		On cover		160.00
		Block of 4	140.00	
		P# block of 12, Impt.	475.00	
a.		Double impression	600.00	400.00

Cancellations

Purple	+1.00
Violet	+1.00
Blue	+1.00
Indigo	+5.00
Magenta	+1.00
Red	+12.50
Town	+3.50
Blue town	+7.50
New York Foreign Mail	—

O49	O6	3c **black**	10.00	2.00
		gray black	10.00	2.00
		Never hinged	25.00	
		No gum	3.00	
		On cover		20.00
		Block of 4	45.00	—
		P# block of 12, Impt.	200.00	
		Never hinged	350.00	
		Cracked plate	—	—
		Double transfer at bottom	—	—
		Double paper	—	—
		Vertical ribbed paper	—	—
a.		Printed on both sides		7,500.

Cancellations

Purple	+.75
Violet	+.75
Blue	+.75
Indigo	+5.00
Ultramarine	+1.50
Magenta	+.75
Red	+10.00
Brown	+20.00
Green	+60.00
Numeral	+20.00
Town	+1.50
Railroad	+25.00
"Paid"	+12.00

O50	O6	6c **black**	30.00	8.00
		gray black	30.00	8.00
		Never hinged	75.00	
		No gum	12.00	
		On cover		75.00
		Block of 4	150.00	
		P# block of 14, Impt.	550.00	
		Vertical ribbed paper	—	12.50

	Double transfer of top frame (pos. 96L, 99L)	—	—
a.	Diagonal half used as 3c on cover		4,750.
b.	Double impression		3,000.

Cancellations

Purple	+.75
Violet	+.75
Magenta	+.75
Blue	+.75
Indigo	+5.00
Red	+12.00
Brown	+20.00
Numeral	+20.00
Town	+2.50
"Paid"	+15.00

O51	O6	10c **black**	140.00	55.00
		gray black	140.00	55.00
		Never hinged	325.00	
		No gum	60.00	
		On cover		400.00
		Block of 4	700.00	
		P# block of 12, Impt.	1,950.	

Cancellations

Violet	+3.50
Red	+15.00
Magenta	+3.50
Blue	+3.50
Town	+10.00

O52	O6	12c **black**	120.00	12.00
		gray black	120.00	12.00
		Never hinged	275.00	
		No gum	40.00	
		On cover		1,000.
		Block of 4	575.00	1,250.
		P# block of 12, Impt.	1,850.	
		Plate scratch above small "12"	—	—

Cancellations

Purple	+1.00
Magenta	+1.00
Blue	+1.00
Indigo	+5.00
Red	+12.50
Town	+4.00

O53	O6	15c **black**	140.00	20.00
		gray black	140.00	20.00
		Never hinged	325.00	
		No gum	50.00	
		On cover		5,000.
		Block of 4	675.00	—
		P# block of 14, Impt.	2,250.	
		Double transfer	—	—

Cancellations

Violet	+1.50
Magenta	+1.50
Red	+20.00
Blue	+1.50
Town	+7.50
New York Foreign Mail	—

O54	O6	24c **black**	200.00	25.00
		gray black	200.00	25.00
		Never hinged	450.00	
		No gum	70.00	
		Block of 4	900.00	—
		P# block of 12, Impt.	—	
		Double paper	—	—

Cancellations

Violet	+1.50
Blue	+1.50
Red	+20.00
Town	+7.50
New York Foreign Mail	—

O55	O6	30c **black**	200.00	25.00
		gray black	200.00	25.00
		Never hinged	450.00	
		No gum	70.00	
		On cover		—
		Block of 4	900.00	750.00
		P# block of 12, Impt.	2,900.	

Cancellations

Purple	+1.50
Blue	+1.50
Red	+20.00
Magenta	+1.50
Town	+12.50

O56	O6	90c **black**	220.00	25.00
		gray black	220.00	25.00
		Never hinged	500.00	
		No gum	80.00	
		Block of 4	950.00	1,250.
		P# block of 12, Impt.	3,000.	
		Double transfer	—	—
		Double paper	—	—
		Silk paper	—	—

Cancellations

Purple	+1.50
Magenta	+1.50
Blue	+1.50
Town	+6.50

STATE

Franklin   William H. Seward — O8

1873

O57	O7	1c **dark green**	260.00	75.00
		dark yellow green	260.00	75.00
		light green	260.00	75.00
		Never hinged	575.00	
		No gum	110.00	
		On cover		—
		Block of 4	1,250.	
		Plate scratch at left (pos. 51)	—	—

Cancellations

Violet	+2.00
Blue favor	+2.00
Red	+17.50
Town	+7.50

O58	O7	2c **dark green**	310.00	100.00
		dark yellow green	310.00	100.00
		yellow green	—	
		Never hinged	700.00	
		No gum	120.00	
		On cover		1,000.
		Double transfer at bottom (pos. 98)	600.00	—

Cancellations

Violet	+5.00
Blue favor	+5.00
Indigo	+5.00
Red	+50.00
Town	+25.00

O59	O7	3c **bright green**	220.00	25.00
		yellow green	220.00	25.00
		dark green	220.00	25.00
		Never hinged	500.00	
		No gum	85.00	
		On cover		600.00
		First day cover, July 1, 1873	—	
		Block of 4	1,100.	
		Double paper	—	
		Short transfer at right (pos. 85)	—	—

Cancellations

Violet	+1.50
Blue favor	+1.50
Indigo	+1.50
Red	+10.00
Town	+6.50

O60	O7	6c **bright green**	220.00	30.00
		dark green	220.00	30.00
		yellow green	220.00	30.00
		Never hinged	500.00	
		No gum	85.00	
		On cover		800.00
		Block of 4	1,100.	
		P# block of 12, Impt.	—	
		Double transfer	—	—
		Foreign entry of 6c Executive (pos. 41, 91)	—	500.00
		Double transfer plus foreign entry of 6c Executive (pos. 61)	—	
		Plate scratch in margin (pos. 26, right; 27, left)	325.00	275.00

Cancellations

Violet	+2.00
Blue favor	+10.00
Indigo	+2.00
Red	+20.00
Town	+17.50

O61	O7	7c **dark green**	290.00	65.00
		dark yellow green	290.00	65.00
		Never hinged	650.00	
		No gum	95.00	
		On cover		1,000.
		Block of 4	1,500.	
		Ribbed paper	310.00	70.00

Cancellations

Violet	+2.00
Blue favor	+2.00
Indigo	+2.00
Red	+25.00
Town	+10.00

O62	O7	10c **dark green**	230.00	55.00
		bright green	230.00	55.00
		yellow green	230.00	—
		Never hinged	525.00	
		No gum	100.00	
		On cover		2,000.
		Block of 4	1,150.	
		P# block of 12, Impt.	—	
		Short transfer (pos. 34)	275.00	67.50

Cancellations

Violet	+2.50
Blue favor	+2.50

Indigo		+2.50
Red		+35.00
Town		+25.00
New York Foreign Mail		+325.00

O63 O7 12c dark green 310.00 125.00
dark yellow green
Never hinged 700.00
No gum 140.00
On cover *1,500.*
Block of 4 1,650.

Cancellations
Violet +5.00
Blue favor +5.00
Red +30.00
Town +15.00

O64 O7 15c dark green 320.00 90.00
dark yellow green 320.00 90.00
Never hinged 725.00
No gum 130.00
On cover *5,750.*
Block of 4 1,750.
Short transfer at upper right 450.00
Plate scratch at lower left (pos. 91) *450.00*
Plate scratch in margin (pos. 95, right; 96, left) —
Damaged plate at left (pos. 63) —

Cancellations
Violet +2.50
Blue favor +2.50
Red +30.00
Town +30.00

O65 O7 24c dark green 525.00 230.00
dark yellow green 525.00 230.00
Never hinged —
No gum 275.00
On cover *17,500.*
Block of 4 3,100.
Short transfer at bottom left (pos. 10) *600.00*
Plate gashes in forehead (pos. 76) *750.00* 725.00
Plate scratch (pos. 66) *800.00*

Cancellations
Violet +15.00
Blue favor +15.00
Indigo +15.00
Red +85.00
Town +55.00

O66 O7 30c dark green 500.00 180.00
dark yellow green 500.00 180.00
Never hinged —
No gum 240.00
On cover *12,500.*
Block of 4 *4,500.*

Cancellations
Violet +5.00
Blue favor +5.00
Indigo +5.00
Red +50.00
Town +50.00

O67 O7 90c dark green 1,050. 325.00
dark yellow green —
Never hinged —
No gum 525.00
On parcel wrapper front with Nos. O60 & O66 *62,500.*

Cancellations
Violet +15.00
Blue favor +15.00
Red +85.00
Red New York Foreign Mail +3,000.
Town +90.00

O68 O8 $2 green & black 1,500. 1,500.
yellow green & black 1,500. 1,500.
Never hinged 3,350.
No gum 750.00
On parcel label *175,000.*
Block of 4 *18,000.*
Ribbed paper —

Cancellations
Violet +25.00
Blue favor +25.00
Red +175.00
Town +125.00
Red New York Foreign Mail +3,000.
Pen *300.00*

O69 O8 $5 green & black 7,750. 12,000.
yellow green & black 7,750. 12,000.
Never hinged —
No gum 3,500.
Irregular block of 6 *60,000.*

Cancellations
Blue favor +250.00
Red favor +250.00
Pen *1,600.*

O70 O8 $10 green & black 5,000. 7,000.
yellow green & black 5,000. 7,000.
Never hinged 11,500.
No gum 2,750.
Block of 4 *26,500.*
P# sheet of 10, Impt. *62,500.*
Ribbed paper —

Cancellations
Blue favor +200.00
Pen *1,250.*

O71 O8 $20 green & black 5,250. 5,000.
yellow green & black 5,250. 5,000.
Never hinged 12,500.
No gum 2,500.
Block of 4 *27,500.*

Block of 4, presentation pen cancel *10,000.*
P# sheet of 10, Impt. *67,500.*
No. O71 used is valued with a blue or red handstamp favor cancel.

Cancellations
Blue favor 5,000.
Red favor 5,000.
Pen presentation 1,750.

The design of Nos. O68 to O71 measures 25½x39½mm.

TREASURY

O9

1873
O72 O9 1c brown 120.00 10.00
dark brown 120.00 10.00
yellow brown 120.00 10.00
Never hinged 250.00
No gum 45.00
On cover 100.00
Block of 4 525.00 *325.00*
P# block of 14, Impt. *2,100.*
  Never hinged *4,000.*
Double transfer 135.00 12.50

Cancellations
Purple +1.00
Violet +1.00
Magenta +1.00
Blue +1.00
Red +10.00
Brown +20.00
Green +200.00
Town +2.00
Blue town +4.00
New York Foreign Mail

O73 O9 2c brown 125.00 8.00
dark brown 125.00 8.00
yellow brown 125.00 8.00
Never hinged 275.00
No gum 45.00
On cover 75.00
Block of 4 550.00 *325.00*
P# block of 14, Impt. *2,000.*
Double transfer 12.50
Plate scratch (pos. 3R)

Cancellations
Purple +1.00
Violet +1.00
Magenta +1.00
Blue +1.00
Indigo +3.00
Red +10.00
Town +2.00
Blue town +4.00
New York Foreign Mail +275.00

O74 O9 3c brown 110.00 2.00
dark brown 110.00 2.00
yellow brown 110.00 2.00
Never hinged 230.00
No gum 40.00
On cover 100.00
First day cover, *July 1, 1873* *11,000.*
Block of 4 475.00 *250.00*
P# block of 14, Impt. *1,850.*
Double paper —
Shaded circle outside of right frame line — —
Short transfer at bottom (pos. 36 R 29) — —

a. Double impression *5,000.*

Cancellations
Purple +.50
Violet +.50
Blue +.50
Indigo +3.00
Ultramarine +2.00
Magenta +.50
Red +3.50
Brown +20.00
Green +200.00
Town +1.00
Railroad +20.00
"Paid" +10.00

O75 O9 6c brown 120.00 4.00
dark brown 120.00 4.00
yellow brown 120.00 4.00
Never hinged 250.00
No gum 45.00
On cover 75.00
On cover with 6c War #O86 *12,000.*
Block of 4 525.00 *500.00*
P# block of 12, Impt. *1,900.*
  Never hinged *3,500.*
Dirty plate 120.00 6.00
Double transfer — —

Cancellations
Purple +.50
Violet +.50

Magenta +.50
Blue +.50
Indigo +3.00
Ultramarine +1.50
Red +5.00
Green +200.00
"Paid" +20.00
Town +1.50
New York Foreign Mail

O76 O9 7c brown 250.00 35.00
dark brown 250.00 35.00
yellow brown 250.00 35.00
Never hinged 550.00
No gum 95.00
On cover 750.00
Block of 4 1,100. *1,000.*
P# block of 12, Impt. —

Cancellations
Purple +2.00
Violet +2.00
Blue +2.00
Indigo +3.00
Red +30.00
Green +200.00
Town +7.50
Blue town +12.50
New York Foreign Mail

O77 O9 10c brown 240.00 12.00
dark brown 240.00 12.00
yellow brown 240.00 12.00
Never hinged 525.00
No gum 90.00
On cover *450.00*
Block of 4 1,075. *325.00*
P# block of 12, Impt. —
Double paper — —
Double transfer — —

Cancellations
Purple +1.00
Violet +1.00
Blue +3.00
Indigo +3.00
Ultramarine +4.00
Magenta +1.00
Red +12.00
Brown +20.00
Green +200.00
Town +4.00
Blue town +8.50

O78 O9 12c brown 300.00 10.00
dark brown 300.00 10.00
yellow brown 300.00 10.00
Never hinged 650.00
No gum 100.00
On cover 600.00
Block of 4 1,400. *325.00*

Cancellations
Purple +.50
Blue +.50
Ultramarine +10.00
Red +10.00
Green +200.00
Town +2.50
Railroad +20.00

O79 O9 15c brown 300.00 12.00
yellow brown 300.00 12.00
Never hinged 650.00
No gum 100.00
On cover *850.00*
Block of 4 1,400. *325.00*
P# block of 12, Impt. *4,250.*
  Never hinged *6,000.*

Cancellations
Blue +1.00
Purple +1.00
Red +10.00
Green +200.00
Town +2.50
Blue town +7.50
Numeral +15.00
Steamship +100.00

O80 O9 24c brown 675.00 100.00
dark brown 675.00 100.00
yellow brown 675.00 100.00
Never hinged —
No gum 270.00
Block of 4 3,250.
Block of 14 —
Double transfer at top 725.00 —
Short transfer at top (pos. 61) —

Cancellations
Violet +10.00
Blue +5.00
Ultramarine +10.00
Magenta +5.00
Red +30.00
Brown +20.00
Town +15.00
Blue town +25.00
New York Foreign Mail

O81 O9 30c brown 400.00 12.00
dark brown 400.00 12.00
yellow brown 400.00 12.00
Never hinged —
No gum 140.00
On cover *5,000.*
Block of 4 1,750. *500.00*
Short transfer at left top (pos. 95) 450.00 25.00
Short transfer at right top (pos. 45) 450.00 25.00
  Block of 4, one pos. 45 —
Short transfer across entire top (pos. 41) 450.00 25.00

Cancellations
Purple +1.00
Blue +1.00

	Magenta		+1.00
	Red		+12.00
	Green		+200.00
	Town		+3.50
	Blue town		+7.50
O82 O9 90c	**brown**	400.00	15.00
	dark brown	400.00	15.00
	yellow brown	400.00	15.00
	Never hinged	—	
	No gum	140.00	
	Block of 4	1,750.	375.00
	Double paper	—	—

Cancellations

Purple		+1.00
Magenta		+1.00
Blue		+1.00
Red		+30.00
Brown		+7.50
Green		+200.00
Town		+3.50
Blue town		+7.50

WAR

O10

1873

O83 O10 1c	**rose**	240.00	15.00
	rose red	240.00	15.00
	Never hinged	525.00	
	No gum	90.00	
	On cover		140.00
	Block of 4	1,050.	
	Block of 10	—	
	P# block of 12, Impt.	3,250.	

Cancellations

Purple		+1.00
Blue		+1.00
Magenta		+5.00
Red		+15.00
Town		+3.50
Fort		+100.00
Numeral		+12.50
"Paid"		

O84 O10 2c	**rose**	240.00	15.00
	rose red	240.00	15.00
	Never hinged	525.00	
	No gum	90.00	
	On cover		70.00
	Block of 4	1,025.	—
	P# block of 14, Impt.	3,750.	
	Ribbed paper	250.00	17.50

Cancellations

Purple		+1.50
Magenta		+1.50
Blue		+1.50
Red		+15.00
Town		+4.00
Fort		+100.00

O85 O10 3c	**rose**	240.00	5.00
	rose red	240.00	5.00
	Never hinged	525.00	
	No gum	90.00	
	On cover		40.00
	Block of 4	1,025.	550.00
	P# block of 14, Impt.	3,750.	

Cancellations

Purple		+1.00
Blue		+1.00
Ultramarine		+10.00
Magenta		+1.00
Red		+20.00
Green		+35.00
Town		+1.50
Fort		+100.00
"Paid"		+12.00

O86 O10 6c	**rose**	625.00	10.00
	pale rose	625.00	10.00
	Never hinged	1,350.	
	No gum	250.00	
	On cover		60.00
	Block of 4	3,000.	—
	P# block of 12, Impt.	—	

Cancellations

Purple		+1.50
Blue		+1.50
Indigo		+3.00
Magenta		+3.00
Red		+15.00
Town		+3.50
Blue town		+6.50
Fort		+100.00

O87 O10 7c	**rose**	160.00	90.00
	pale rose	160.00	90.00
	rose red	160.00	90.00
	Never hinged	360.00	
	No gum	80.00	
	On cover		—
	Block of 4	675.00	
	P# block of 10, Impt.	2,250.	

Cancellations

Purple		+2.50
Blue		+3.50

	Magenta		+10.00
	Red		+25.00
	Town		+7.50
O88 O10 10c	**rose**	140.00	25.00
	rose red	140.00	25.00
	Never hinged	300.00	
	No gum	45.00	
	On cover		2,000.
	Block of 4	600.00	900.00
	P# block of 12, Impt.	2,000.	

All examples of No. O88 show a crack at lower left. It was on the original die.

Cancellations

Purple		+1.00
Blue		+1.00
Town		+3.50
Fort		+100.00

O89 O10 12c	**rose**	275.00	12.00
	Never hinged	600.00	
	No gum	110.00	
	On cover		450.00
	Block of 4	1,250.	550.00
	P# block of 12, Impt.	3,850.	
	Never hinged	7,750.	
	Ribbed paper	300.00	20.00

Cancellations

Purple		+1.00
Magenta		+1.00
Blue		+1.00
Indigo		+5.00
Red		+10.00
Town		+3.00
Fort		+100.00

O90 O10 15c	**rose**	85.00	15.00
	pale rose	85.00	15.00
	rose red	85.00	15.00
	Never hinged	190.00	
	No gum	30.00	
	On cover		3,250.
	Block of 4	375.00	—
	P# block of 10, Impt.	1,100.	
	Ribbed paper	92.50	20.00
	Short transfer at upper right (pos. 74)	—	

Cancellations

Purple		+1.00
Blue		+1.00
Ultramarine		+10.00
Magenta		+3.00
Red		+10.00
Town		+2.50
Fort		+200.00
Express Company		

O91 O10 24c	**rose**	85.00	12.00
	pale rose	85.00	12.00
	rose red	85.00	12.00
	Never hinged	190.00	
	No gum	30.00	
	On cover		—
	Block of 4	375.00	2,250.
	P# block of 10, Impt.	1,300.	

Cancellations

Purple		+1.00
Blue		+1.00
Magenta		+5.00
Town		+2.50
Fort		+100.00

O92 O10 30c	**rose**	130.00	12.00
	rose red	130.00	12.00
	Never hinged	275.00	
	No gum	45.00	
	On cover		—
	Block of 4	575.00	350.00
	P# block of 12, Impt.	1,850.	
	Ribbed paper	140.00	15.00

Cancellations

Purple		+1.00
Magenta		+1.00
Blue		+1.00
Red		+20.00
Town		+2.50
Fort		+100.00

O93 O10 90c	**rose**	225.00	50.00
	rose red	225.00	50.00
	Never hinged	500.00	
	No gum	80.00	
	On cover		—
	Block of 4	975.00	975.00
	P# block of 12, Impt.	3,750.	

Cancellations

Purple		+2.00
Magenta		+2.00
Blue		+2.00
Red		+20.00
Numeral		+40.00
Town		+7.50
Fort		+125.00

Printed by the American Bank Note Co.

The Continental Bank Note Co. was consolidated with the American Bank Note Co. on February 4, 1879. The American Bank Note Company used many plates of the Continental Bank Note Company to print the ordinary postage, Departmental and Newspaper stamps. Therefore, stamps bearing the Continental Company's imprint were not always its product.

1879   Soft Porous Paper

AGRICULTURE

O94 O1 1c	**yellow** (issued without gum)	6,000.	
	Block of 4	30,000.	
O95 O1 3c	**yellow**	550.00	110.00
	Never hinged	1,250.	
	No gum	240.00	
	Block of 4	2,750.	1,350.

	P# block of 12, Impt.	7,250.	

Cancellations

Purple		+5.00
Blue		+5.00
Town		+30.00

INTERIOR

O96 O3 1c	**vermilion**	300.00	275.00
	pale vermilion	300.00	275.00
	Never hinged	550.00	
	No gum	160.00	
	Block of 4	1,450.	—
	P# block of 12, Impt.	4,500.	
	Short transfer at lower right (pos. 91)	600.00	

Cancellations

Purple		+5.00
Blue		+5.00
Town		+15.00

O97 O3 2c	**vermilion**	10.00	3.00
	pale vermilion	10.00	3.00
	scarlet vermilion	10.00	3.00
	Never hinged	17.50	
	No gum	3.00	
	On cover		150.00
	Block of 4	47.50	250.00
	P# block of 12, Impt.	225.00	

Cancellations

Purple		+.50
Violet		+.50
Blue		+.50
Red		+5.00
Town		+1.50
Blue town		+3.00
Railroad		+40.00
Fort		+100.00

O98 O3 3c	**vermilion**	10.00	3.00
	pale vermilion	10.00	3.00
	Never hinged	22.50	
	No gum	3.00	
	On cover		30.00
	Block of 4	47.50	—
	P# block of 10, Impt.	225.00	

Cancellations

Purple		+.50
Violet		+.50
Blue		+.50
Red		+5.00
Town		+1.50
Blue town		+3.00
Railroad		+40.00
Numeral		+5.00

O99 O3 6c	**vermilion**	10.00	12.50
	pale vermilion	10.00	12.50
	scarlet vermilion	10.00	12.50
	Never hinged	17.50	
	No gum	3.00	
	On cover		200.00
	Block of 4	47.50	—
	P# block of 10, Impt.	225.00	

Cancellations

Purple		+.50
Blue		+.50
Red		+5.00
Town		+1.50
Fort		+100.00

O100 O3 10c	**vermilion**	110.00	75.00
	pale vermilion	110.00	75.00
	Never hinged	250.00	
	No gum	60.00	
	On cover		1,200.
	Block of 4	500.00	
	P# block of 12, Impt.	1,650.	

Cancellations

Purple		+5.00
Blue		+5.00
Town		+10.00

O101 O3 12c	**vermilion**	230.00	115.00
	pale vermilion	230.00	115.00
	Never hinged	525.00	
	No gum	130.00	
	On cover		—
	Block of 4	1,075.	575.00
	Block of 6		1,500.
	P# block of 12, Impt.	2,900.	
	Short transfer at lower right (pos. 6)	—	—

Cancellation

Violet		+5.00

O102 O3 15c	**vermilion**	400.00	260.00
	Never hinged	900.00	
	No gum	200.00	
	Block of 4	1,750.	
	P# block of 12, Impt.		
	On cover		6,500.
	Double transfer	450.00	—

Cancellations

Purple		+5.00
Blue		+5.00

O103 O3 24c	**vermilion**	4,500.	
	Never hinged	10,000.	
	No gum	2,100.	
	Block of 4	25,000.	
	P# strip of 6, Impt.	—	

Cancellation

Blue		—

JUSTICE

O106 O4 3c	**bluish purple**	175.00	100.00
	deep bluish purple	175.00	100.00
	Never hinged	400.00	
	No gum	80.00	
	On cover		1,250.
	Block of 4	750.00	

Cancellations

Violet		+5.00

	Blue			+5.00
	Indigo			+5.00
	Ultramarine			+10.00
O107	O4	6c **bluish purple**	475.00	275.00
	Never hinged		1,050.	
	No gum		210.00	
	On cover			1,000.
	Block of 4		2,250.	

Cancellations

Blue		+10.00
Indigo		+5.00
Town		+20.00

No. O107 on cover is unique, but the stamp is damaged. It is valued thus.

POST OFFICE

O108	O6	3c **black**	30.00	10.00
	gray black		30.00	10.00
	Never hinged		70.00	
	No gum		10.00	
	On cover			—
	Block of 4		130.00	
	P# block of 14, Impt.		475.00	

Cancellations

Purple	+1.00
Violet	+1.00
Blue	+1.00
Indigo	+10.00
Magenta	+1.00
Red	+20.00
Green	+40.00
Town	+2.00
"Paid"	+12.00

TREASURY

O109	O9	3c **brown**	80.00	10.00
	yellow brown		80.00	10.00
	Never hinged		175.00	
	No gum		35.00	
	On cover			110.00
	Block of 4		400.00	900.00
	P# block of 14, Impt.		1,450.	

Cancellations

Purple	+1.50
Blue	+1.50
Indigo	+3.00
Town	+2.00
Numeral	+7.50

O110	O9	6c **brown**	200.00	50.00
	yellow brown		200.00	50.00
	dark brown		200.00	50.00
	Never hinged		450.00	
	No gum		65.00	
	On cover			300.00
	Block of 4		950.00	—
	P# block of 12, Impt.		2,900.	

Cancellations

Purple	+6.00
Magenta	+6.00
Blue	+6.00

O111	O9	10c **brown**	260.00	80.00
	yellow brown		260.00	80.00
	dark brown		260.00	80.00
	Never hinged		575.00	
	No gum		90.00	
	On cover			750.00
	Block of 4		1,250.	—
	P# block of 12, Impt.		4,500.	

Cancellations

Purple	+2.50
Blue	+2.50
Magenta	+5.00
Town	+7.50

O112	O9	30c **brown**	2,400.	425.00
	Never hinged		—	
	No gum		875.00	
	Block of 4		12,000.	

Cancellations

Blue	+25.00
Indigo	+25.00
Town	+50.00

O113	O9	90c **brown**	5,500.	525.00
	dark brown		5,500.	525.00
	Never hinged		—	
	No gum		2,000.	
	Block of 4		25,000.	

Cancellations

Purple	+25.00
Blue	+25.00
Town	+75.00

WAR

O114	O10	1c **rose red**	6.00	4.00
	rose		6.00	4.00
	dull rose red		6.00	4.00
	brown rose		6.00	4.00
	Never hinged		11.00	
	No gum		2.50	
	On cover			55.00
	Block of 4		27.50	—
	P# block of 12, Impt.		150.00	
	Never hinged		220.00	

Cancellations

Purple	+.50
Blue	+.50
Town	+1.00
Fort	+100.00

O115	O10	2c **rose red**	12.00	4.00
	dark rose red		12.00	4.00
	dull vermilion		12.00	4.00
	Never hinged		22.50	
	No gum		4.00	
	On cover			40.00
	Block of 4		52.50	—
	P# block of 12, Impt.		200.00	

	Never hinged		325.00	

Cancellations

Purple	+.50
Blue	+.50
Magenta	+.50
Green	+35.00
Town	+2.00
Fort	+100.00

O116	O10	3c **rose red**	12.00	2.00
	dull rose red		12.00	2.00
	Never hinged		22.50	
	No gum		4.00	
	On cover			35.00
	Block of 4		52.50	—
	P# block of 12, Impt.		200.00	
	Never hinged		325.00	
	Double transfer		17.50	6.00
	Plate flaw at upper left (32 R 20)			—
a.	Imperf., pair		5,000.	
b.	Double impression		6,500.	

Cancellations

Purple	+.50
Violet	+.50
Blue	+.50
Ultramarine	+5.00
Magenta	+1.00
Red	+5.00
Town	+1.00
Fort	+100.00

O117	O10	6c **rose red**	11.00	3.00
	dull rose red		11.00	3.00
	dull vermilion			
	Never hinged		20.00	
	No gum		4.00	
	On cover			50.00
	Block of 4		47.50	—
	P# block of 12, Impt.		190.00	

Cancellations

Purple	+.50
Blue	+.50
Magenta	+1.00
Brown	+20.00
Town	+1.00
Fort	+100.00
Numeral	+7.50

O118	O10	10c **rose red**	65.00	50.00
	dull rose red		65.00	50.00
	Never hinged		120.00	
	No gum		26.00	
	On cover			1,800.
	Block of 4		300.00	—
	P# block of 10, Impt.		950.00	

Cancellations

Violet	+3.00
Town	+5.00
Fort	+100.00

O119	O10	12c **rose red**	60.00	14.00
	dull rose red		60.00	14.00
	brown rose		60.00	14.00
	Never hinged		110.00	
	No gum		20.00	
	On cover			—
	Block of 4		260.00	—
	P# block of 10, Impt.		775.00	

Cancellations

Purple	+1.00
Violet	+1.00
Red	+10.00
Town	+2.50
Fort	+150.00

O120	O10	30c **rose red**	225.00	100.00
	dull rose red		225.00	100.00
	Never hinged		450.00	
	No gum		90.00	
	Block of 4		975.00	—
	P# block of 10, Impt.		3,500.	

Cancellations

Violet	+5.00
Town	+10.00
Fort	+125.00

SPECIAL PRINTINGS

Special printings of Official stamps were made in 1875 at the time the other Reprints, Re-issues and Special Printings were printed. They are ungummed. Though overprinted "SPECIMEN," these stamps are Special Printings, and they are not considered to be in the same category as the stamps listed in the Specimen section of this catalogue.

Although perforated, these stamps were sometimes (but not always) cut apart with scissors. As a result the perforations may be mutilated and the design damaged.

Number sold indicated in parentheses.

All values exist imperforate.

Blocks of 4 are now listed. All are scarce, a few are rare. They will be valued when sufficient information has been received. Imprint and plate number strips or blocks are very scarce.

The "SEPCIMEN" error appears once on some panes of 100. The error was discovered and corrected part way through the printing. Blocks of 4 or larger with the "SEPCIMEN" error are rare and worth much more than the value of the individual stamps.

Printing flaws which resemble broken type (but are not) are commonly found on the SPECIMEN overprint on these and other overprinted stamps. The variety listed as a "small dotted i" is actually an "i"; it is not one of the printing flaws noted in the preceding sentence. All "small dotted 'i'" varieties are on ribbed paper from

the second special printings. They occur in positions 7 and 26.

Printed by the Continental Bank Note Co.

Overprinted in Block Letters

1875		**Thin, hard white paper**	**Perf. 12**
		Type D	

AGRICULTURE
Carmine Overprint

O1S	D	1c **yellow** (10,234)	30.00	
	Block of 4		350.00	
a.	"Sepcimen" error		2,500.	
b.	Horiz. ribbed paper (10,000)		37.50	
	Block of 4		425.00	
c.	As "b," small dotted "i" in "Sepcimen"		500.00	
O2S	D	2c **yellow** (4,192)	55.00	
	Block of 4		625.00	
a.	"Sepcimen" error		3,000.	
O3S	D	3c **yellow** (389)	300.00	
a.	"Sepcimen" error		11,000.	
O4S	D	6c **yellow** (373)	325.00	
a.	"Sepcimen" error		17,500.	
O5S	D	10c **yellow** (390)	325.00	
a.	"Sepcimen" error		17,500.	
O6S	D	12c **yellow** (379)	325.00	
a.	"Sepcimen" error		11,000.	
O7S	D	15c **yellow** (370)	325.00	
a.	"Sepcimen" error		11,000.	
O8S	D	24c **yellow** (352)	325.00	
a.	"Sepcimen" error		11,000.	
O9S	D	30c **yellow** (354)	325.00	
a.	"Sepcimen" error		13,500.	

EXECUTIVE
Blue Overprint

O10S	D	1c **carmine** (10,000)	30.00	
	Block of 4		350.00	
	P# block of 14, Impt.		18,000.	
a.	Horiz. ribbed paper (10,000)		35.00	
	Block of 4		375.00	
b.	As "a," small dotted "i" in "Specimen"		500.00	
O11S	D	2c **carmine** (7,430)	55.00	
	Block of 4		650.00	
	Foreign entry of 6c Agriculture (pos. 40)		2,250.	
O12S	D	3c **carmine** (3,735)	67.50	
	Block of 4		—	
O13S	D	6c **carmine** (3,485)	67.50	
	Block of 4		—	
O14S	D	10c **carmine** (3,461)	67.50	
	Block of 4		—	

INTERIOR
Blue Overprint

O15S	D	1c **vermilion** (7,194)	55.00	
	Block of 4		650.00	
	P# block of 12, impt.		5,750.	
O16S	D	2c **vermilion** (1,263)	120.00	
	Block of 4		1,500.	
	P# Block of 12, Impt.		10,000.	
a.	"Sepcimen" error		11,000.	
O17S	D	3c **vermilion** (88)	1,400.	
O18S	D	6c **vermilion** (83)	1,400.	
O19S	D	10c **vermilion** (82)	1,400.	
O20S	D	12c **vermilion** (75)	1,400.	
O21S	D	15c **vermilion** (78)	1,400.	
	Double transfer at left		2,250.	
O22S	D	24c **vermilion** (77)	1,400.	
O23S	D	30c **vermilion** (75)	1,400.	
O24S	D	90c **vermilion** (77)	1,400.	

JUSTICE
Blue Overprint

O25S	D	1c **purple** (10,000)	30.00	
	Block of 4		350.00	
	P# block of 12, Impt.		3,250.	
a.	"Sepcimen" error		1,900.	
b.	Horiz. ribbed paper (9,729)		35.00	
	Block of 4		550.00	
	P# block of 12, Impt.		4,000.	
c.	As "b," small dotted "i" in "Specimen"		500.00	
O26S	D	2c **purple** (3,395)	55.00	
	Block of 4		650.00	
	P# block of 12, Impt.		5,500.	
a.	"Sepcimen" error		2,500.	
O27S	D	3c **purple** (178)	900.00	
	Plate scratches			
a.	"Sepcimen" error		8,750.	
O28S	D	6c **purple** (163)	900.00	
O29S	D	10c **purple** (163)	900.00	
O30S	D	12c **purple** (154)	900.00	
a.	"Sepcimen" error		15,000.	
O31S	D	15c **purple** (157)	900.00	
a.	"Sepcimen" error		13,500.	
O32S	D	24c **purple** (150)	900.00	
a.	"Sepcimen" error		15,000.	

O33S D 30c **purple** (150) 900.00
a. "Sepcimen" error *13,500.*
O34S D 90c **purple** (152) 900.00

NAVY
Carmine Overprint
O35S D 1c **ultramarine** (10,000) 32.50
Block of 4 375.00
a. "Sepcimen" error 2,500.
b. Double "Specimen" overprint *1,900.*
O36S D 2c **ultramarine** (1,748) 60.00
Block of 4 750.00
a. "Sepcimen" error 3,250.
O37S D 3c **ultramarine** (126) 1,000.
O38S D 6c **ultramarine** (116) 1,100.
Vertical line through "N" of "Navy" *1,650.*
O39S D 7c **ultramarine** (501) 450.00
Block of 4 5,000.
a. "Sepcimen" error 8,250.
O40S D 10c **ultramarine** (112) 1,100.
a. "Sepcimen" error *17,500.*
O41S D 12c **ultramarine** (107) 1,000.
Double transfer at left side, pos. 50 —
a. "Sepcimen" error *17,500.*
O42S D 15c **ultramarine** (107) 1,000.
a. "Sepcimen" error *13,500.*
O43S D 24c **ultramarine** (106) 1,000.
a. "Sepcimen" error *13,500.*
O44S D 30c **ultramarine** (104) 1,000.
Double transfer —
a. "Sepcimen" error *17,500.*
O45S D 90c **ultramarine** (102) 1,000.

POST OFFICE
Carmine Overprint
O47S D 1c **black** (6,015) 42.50
Block of 4 475.00
a. "Sepcimen" error 1,900.
Block of 4, one stamp "SEPCIMEN" error *6,000.*
b. Inverted overprint 2,750.
O48S D 2c **black** (590) 250.00
Block of 4 *3,250.*
a. "Sepcimen" error 3,250.
O49S D 3c **black** (91) 1,200.
a. "Sepcimen" error —
O50S D 6c **black** (87) 1,100.
O51S D 10c **black** (177) 900.00
a. "Sepcimen" error *11,000.*
O52S D 12c **black** (93) 1,000.
O53S D 15c **black** (82) 1,100.
a. "Sepcimen" error *13,500.*
O54S D 24c **black** (84) 1,100.
a. "Sepcimen" error *11,000.*
O55S D 30c **black** (81) 1,200.
O56S D 90c **black** (82) 1,100.
a. "Sepcimen" error —

STATE
Carmine Overprint
O57S D 1c **bluish green** (10,000) 30.00
Block of 4 350.00
a. "Sepcimen" error 1,900.
b. Horiz. ribbed paper (10,000) 35.00
Block of 4 *425.00*
c. As "b," small dotted "i" in "Specimen" 550.00
d. Double "Specimen" overprint *3,850.*
Block of 4 —
O58S D 2c **bluish green** (5,145) 90.00
Block of 4 850.00
a. "Sepcimen" error *2,500.*
O59S D 3c **bluish green** (793) 120.00
Block of 4 —
a. "Sepcimen" error 6,000.
O60S D 6c **bluish green** (467) 275.00
Foreign entry of 6c Executive *600.00*
a. "Sepcimen" error 8,250.
O61S D 7c **bluish green** (791) 120.00
Block of 4 *1,500.*
a. "Sepcimen" error 8,250.
O62S D 10c **bluish green** (346) 500.00
Short transfer, pos. 34 *2,200.*
a. "Sepcimen" error *17,500.*
O63S D 12c **bluish green** (280) 550.00
a. "Sepcimen" error *11,000.*
O64S D 15c **bluish green** (257) 550.00
O65S D 24c **bluish green** (253) 550.00
a. "Sepcimen" error *11,000.*
O66S D 30c **bluish green** (249) 550.00
a. "Sepcimen" error *15,000.*
O67S D 90c **bluish green** (245) 550.00
a. "Sepcimen" error *11,000.*
O68S D $2 **green & black** (32) 20,000.
O69S D $5 **green & black** (12) 25,000.
O70S D $10 **green & black** (8) 50,000.
O71S D $20 **green & black** (7) 85,000.

TREASURY
Blue Overprint
O72S D 1c **dark brown** (2,185) 75.00
Block of 4 *975.00*
Double transfer —
O73S D 2c **dark brown** (309) 350.00
Block of 4 *4,250.*
O74S D 3c **dark brown** (84) 1,400.
O75S D 6c **dark brown** (85) 1,400.
O76S D 7c **dark brown** (198) 850.00
Block of 4 9,000.
P# block of 12, impt. 30,000.

The only recorded plate block of No. O76S is contained in a half sheet of 50 stamps.

O77S D 10c **dark brown** (82) 1,350.

O78S D 12c **dark brown** (75) 1,350.
O79S D 15c **dark brown** (75) 1,350.
O80S D 24c **dark brown** (99) 1,350.
O81S D 30c **dark brown** (74) 1,350.
Short transfer at left top (pos. 95) (1) —
Short transfer at right top (pos. 45) (1) —
O82S D 90c **dark brown** (72) 1,350.

WAR
Blue Overprint
O83S D 1c **deep rose** (9,610) 30.00
Block of 4 *375.00*
a. "Sepcimen" error 1,600.
O84S D 2c **deep rose** (1,618) 120.00
Block of 4 *1,400.*
P# block of 12 *9,000.*
a. "Sepcimen" error 2,000.
O85S D 3c **deep rose** (118) 1,000.
a. "Sepcimen" error *11,000.*
O86S D 6c **deep rose** (111) 1,000.
a. "Sepcimen" error *25,000.*
O87S D 7c **deep rose** (539) 325.00
Block of 4 *2,750.*
a. "Sepcimen" error 10,000.
O88S D 10c **deep rose** (119) 1,000.
a. "Sepcimen" error *13,500.*
O89S D 12c **deep rose** (105) 1,000.
a. "Sepcimen" error *13,500.*
O90S D 15c **deep rose** (105) 1,000.
a. "Sepcimen" error *13,500.*
O91S D 24c **deep rose** (106) 1,000.
a. "Sepcimen" error *13,500.*
O92S D 30c **deep rose** (104) 1,000.
a. "Sepcimen" error *13,500.*
O93S D 90c **deep rose** (106) 1,000.
a. "Sepcimen" error *13,500.*

Printed by the American Bank Note Co.
SOFT POROUS PAPER
EXECUTIVE
1881
Blue Overprint
O10xS D 1c **violet rose** (4,652) 95.00
Block of 4 *1,100.*
NAVY
Carmine Overprint
O35xS D 1c **gray blue** (4,182) 100.00
deep blue 100.00
Block of 4 *1,150.*
P# strip of 6, Impt. *4,000.*
a. Double overprint 1,200.
STATE
O57xS D 1c **yellow green** (1,672) 180.00
Block of 4 *2,500.*

POSTAL SAVINGS MAIL
The Act of Congress, approved June 25, 1910, establishing postal savings depositories, provided:
"Sec. 2. That the Postmaster General is hereby directed to prepare and issue special stamps of the necessary denominations for use, in lieu of penalty or franked envelopes, in the transmittal of free mail resulting from the administration of this act."
The use of postal savings official stamps was discontinued by the Act of Congress, approved September 23, 1914. Postmasters were notified of the discontinuance in mid-October 1914. The unused stamps in the hands of postmasters were returned and destroyed.

O11

Printed by the Bureau of Engraving & Printing
1910-11 Engr. Wmk. 191
O121 O11 2c **black**, *Dec. 22, 1910* 17.50 2.00
Never hinged 40.00
On cover 12.50
Block of 4 (2mm spacing) 80.00 11.00
Block of 4 (3mm spacing) 77.50 10.00
P# block of 6, Impt. & Star 350.00
Double transfer 22.50 4.00
O122 O11 50c **dark green**, *Feb. 1, 1911* 160.00 60.00
Never hinged 375.00
On cover 225.00
Block of 4 (2mm spacing) 675.00 300.00
Block of 4 (3mm spacing) 650.00 300.00
Margin block of 4, arrow 675.00
P# block of 6, Impt. & Star 2,400.
Never hinged *3,500.*
O123 O11 $1 **ultramarine**, *Feb. 1, 1911* 200.00 15.00
Never hinged 450.00
On cover 110.00
Block of 4 (2mm spacing) 850.00 75.00
Block of 4 (3mm spacing) 825.00 75.00
Margin block of 4, arrow 850.00

P# block of 6, Impt. & Star 2,400. —
Wmk. 190
O124 O11 1c **dark violet**, *Mar. 27, 1911* 10.00 2.00
Never hinged 22.50
On cover 15.00
Block of 4 (2mm spacing) 45.00 9.00
Block of 4 (3mm spacing) 42.50 8.50
P# block of 6, Impt. & Star 190.00
O125 O11 2c **black** 55.00 7.00
Never hinged 135.00
On cover 25.00
Block of 4 (2mm spacing) 240.00 32.50
Block of 4 (3mm spacing) 225.00 32.50
P# block of 6, Impt. & Star 700.00
Double transfer 60.00 8.00
O126 O11 10c **carmine**, *Feb. 1, 1911* 20.00 2.00
Never hinged 50.00
On cover 20.00
Block of 4 (2mm spacing) 87.50 30.00
Block of 4 (3mm spacing) 82.50 10.00
P# block of 6, Impt. & Star 370.00
Double transfer 25.00 3.50

> Catalogue values for unused stamps in this section, from this point to the end, are for Never Hinged items.

> Catalogue values for used stamps are for regularly used examples, not for examples removed from first day covers.

From No. O127 onward, all official stamps are tagged unless noted.

OFFICIAL MAIL

O12

Designed by Bradbury Thompson
Engraved
1983, Jan. 12-1985 Unwmk. Tagged Perf. 11
O127 O12 1c **red, blue & black** .20 .20
FDC, Washington, DC 1.00
P# block of 4, UL or UR .25
O128 O12 4c **red, blue & black** .20 .25
FDC, Washington, DC 1.00
P# block of 4, LR only .40
O129 O12 13c **red, blue & black** .50 *15.00*
FDC, Washington, DC 1.00
P# block of 4, UR only 2.25
O129A O12 14c **red, blue & black**, *May 15, 1985* .45 .50
FDC, Washington, DC 1.00
Zip-copyright block of 6 2.90
O130 O12 17c **red, blue & black** .60 .40
FDC, Washington, DC 1.00
P# block of 4, LL only 3.00
O132 O12 $1 **red, blue & black** 2.25 1.00
FDC, Washington, DC 2.25
P# block of 4, UL only 10.00
O133 O12 $5 **red, blue & black** 9.50 5.00
FDC, Washington, DC 12.50
P# block of 4, LL only 45.00
Nos. O127-O133 (7) 13.70 22.35

No. O129A does not have a "c" after the "14."

COIL STAMPS
Perf. 10 Vert.
O135 O12 20c **red, blue & black** 1.75 2.00
FDC, Washington, DC 1.00
Pair 3.50 4.00
P# strip of 3, P# 1 12.00
P# strip of 5, P# 1 55.00
P# single, #1 — 20.00
a. Imperf., pair *2,000.*
O136 O12 22c **red, blue & blk, low gloss gum**, *May 15, 1985* 1.00 *2.00*
FDC, Washington, DC 1.00
Pair 2.00 *4.00*
Dull finish gum *70.00*
a. Tagging omitted —

Inscribed: Postal Card Rate D
1985, Feb. 4 Perf. 11
O138 O12 (14c) **red, blue & black** 5.25 *10.00*
FDC, Washington, DC 1.00
P# block of 4, LR only 42.50

Frame line completely around
the design — O13

Inscribed: No. O139, Domestic Letter Rate D; No. O140,
Domestic Mail E.

COIL STAMPS

1985-88		**Litho., Engr. (#O139)**		*Perf. 10 Vert.*	
O138A	O13	15c **red, blue & blk,** *June 11, 1988*		.50	.50
		FDC, Corpus Christi, TX			1.25
		Pair		1.00	1.00
O138B	O13	20c **red, blue & blk,** *May 19, 1988*		.50	.30
		FDC, Washington			1.25
		Pair		1.00	.60
O139	O12	(22c) **red, blue & blk,** *Feb. 4*		5.25	10.00
		FDC, Washington, DC			1.00
		Pair		10.50	—
		P# strip of 3, P# 1		27.50	
		P# strip of 5, P# 1		55.00	
		P# single, #1		—	32.50
O140	O13	(25c) **red, blue & black,** *Mar. 22, 1988*		.75	2.00
		FDC, Washington			1.25
		Pair		1.50	
O141	O13	25c **red, blue & blk,** *June 11, 1988*		.65	.50
		FDC, Corpus Christi, TX			1.25
		Pair		1.30	1.00
a.		Imperf., pair		1,250.	—
		Nos. O138A-O141 (5)		7.65	13.30

First day cancellation was applied to 137,721 covers bearing
Nos. O138A and O141.

Plates of 400 in four panes of 100.

1989, July 5		**Litho.**		*Perf. 11*	
O143	O13	1c **red, blue & black**		.20	.20
		FDC, Washington, DC			1.25

On No. O143, the denomination is shown as "1". See No.
O154.

Type of 1985 and

O14

COIL STAMPS

1991		**Litho.**		*Perf. 10 Vert.*	
O144	O14	(29c) **red, blue & blk,** *Jan. 22*		.80	.50
		FDC, Washington, DC			1.25
		Pair		1.60	—
O145	O13	29c **red, blue & blk,** *May 24*		.70	.30
		FDC, Seattle, WA			1.25
		Pair		1.40	.60

Plates of 400 in four panes of 100.

1991-93		**Litho.**		*Perf. 11*	
O146	O13	4c **red, blue & blk,** *Apr. 6*		.20	.30
		FDC, Oklahoma City, OK			1.25
O146A	O13	10c **red, blue & black,** *Oct. 19, 1993*		.30	.30
		FDC, Washington, DC			1.25
O147	O13	19c **red, blue & blk,** *May 24*		.40	.50
		FDC, Seattle, WA			1.25
O148	O13	23c **red, blue & blk,** *May 24*		.50	.30
		FDC, Seattle, WA			1.25
		Horiz. pair with full vert. gutter between		—	
		Vert. pair with full horiz. gutter between		—	

See No. O156 for 23c with microscopic text below eagle.
Imperfs of No. O148 are printer's waste.

Perf. 11¼

O151	O13	$1 **red, blue & black,** *Sept. 1993*		5.00	.75
		Nos. O146-O151 (5)		6.40	2.15

COIL STAMPS

Inscribed: No. O152, For U.S. addresses only G.

Perf. 9.8 Vert.

O152	O14	(32c) **red, blue & black,** *Dec. 13, 1994*		.65	.50
		FDC, Washington, DC			1.25
		Pair		1.30	—
O153	O13	32c **red, blue & black,** *May 9, 1995*		1.50	.50
		FDC, Washington, DC			1.25
		Pair		3.00	—

Nos. O146A, O151, O153 have a line of microscopic text
below the eagle.

1995, May 9		**Litho.**		*Perf. 11.2*	
O154	O13	1c **red, blue & black,** untagged		.20	.50
		FDC, Washington, DC			1.25

Denomination on No. O154 has a cent sign. See No. O143.

O155	O13	20c **red, blue & black**		.55	.50
		FDC, Washington, DC			1.25
O156	O13	23c **red, blue & black**		.60	.50
		FDC, Washington, DC			1.25

COIL STAMP

1999, Oct. 8		**Litho.**		*Perf. 9¾ Vert.*	
O157	O13	33c **red, blue & black**		1.25	—
		FDC, Washington, DC			1.25
		Pair		2.50	—

Type of 1985
COIL STAMP

2001, Feb. 27		**Litho.** Tagged		*Perf. 9¾ Vert.*	
O158	O13	34c **red, blue & black**		1.25	.50
		FDC, Washington, DC			1.25
		Pair		2.50	—

Nos. O154-O158 have a line of microscopic text below the
eagle.

Type of 1985
COIL STAMP

2002, Aug. 2		**Photo.** Tagged		*Perf. 10 Vert.*	
O159	O13	37c **red, blue & black**		.70	.50
		First day cover, Washington, DC			1.25
		First day cover, any other city			1.25
		Pair		1.40	—
		P# strip of 5, P#S111		5.25	—
		P# single, same #		—	.70

Type of 1985
COIL STAMP

2006, Mar. 8		**Photo.** Tagged		*Perf. 10 Vert.*	
O160	O13	39c **red, blue & black**		.80	.50
		First day cover, Washington, DC			1.25
		First day cover, any other city			1.25
		Pair		1.60	—
		P# strip of 5, #S111		5.75	—
		P# single, #S111		—	2.25

Type of 1988

Designed by Bradbury Thompson.

Printed by Sterling Sommer for Ashton-Potter (USA) Ltd.

LITHOGRAPHED
Sheets of 240 in twelve panes of 20

2006, Sept. 29		**Tagged**		*Perf. 11¼*	
O161	O13	$1 **red, blue & black**		2.00	.90
		First day cover, Washington, DC			3.25
		First day cover, any other city			3.25
		Pane of 20		40.00	

No. O161 has a solid blue background. No. O151 has a
background of crosshatched lines.

Type of 1985
COIL STAMP

2007, June 25		**Litho.** Tagged		*Perf. 9¾*	
O162	O13	41c **red, blue & black**		1.00	.50
		First day cover, Kansas City, MO			2.10
		Pair		2.00	—
		P# strip of 5, #S111		8.00	—
		P# single, #S111		—	2.25

Nos. O159-O162 have solid blue backgrounds. Nos. O138A-
O158 have a background of crosshatched lines.

Type of 1985

Designed by Bradbury Thompson. Printed by Banknote Corporation of America for Sennett Security Products.

Serpentine Die Cut 11½x10¾

2009, Feb. 24					**Litho.**
Self-Adhesive					
O163	O13	1c **red, blue & black**		.20	.20
		First day cover, Washington, DC			2.10
		Pane of 20		.40	

NEWSPAPER AND PERIODICAL STAMPS

First issued in September 1865 for prepayment of postage on bulk shipments of newspapers and periodicals. From 1875 on, the stamps were affixed to pages of receipt books, sometimes canceled, and retained by the post office.

Virtually all used stamps of Nos. PR1-PR4 are canceled by blue brush strokes and have faults such as tears, stains, creases, etc. All are rare. Most used stamps of Nos. PR9-PR32, PR57-PR79 and PR81-PR89 are pen canceled (or uncanceled), with some of Nos. PR9-PR32 also known canceled by a thick blue brush stroke or a handstamp cancellation. Used values for Nos. PR90-PR125 are for stamps with handstamp cancellations.

Discontinued on July 1, 1898.

Washington — N1

Franklin — N2

Lincoln — N3

Values for Nos. PR1-PR8 are for examples with perforations on all four sides. Examples with natural straight edges sell for somewhat less. Some panes were fully perforated, while others have natural straight edges either at top or bottom affecting five stamps in the pane of ten.

Printed by the National Bank Note Co.
Plates of 20 subjects in two panes of 10 each.

Typographed and Embossed

1865			**Unwmk.**		*Perf. 12*

Thin hard paper, without gum
Size of design: 51x95mm

Colored Border

PR1	N1	5c	**dark blue**	750.00	*2,000.*
			blue	750.00	*2,000.*
			Block of 4	3,750.	—
a.			5c **light blue**	1,000.	—
PR2	N2	10c	**blue green**	300.00	*1,800.*
a.			10c **green**	300.00	*1,800.*
			Block of 4	1,400.	—
b.			Pelure paper	350.00	*1,800.*
PR3	N3	25c	**orange red**	375.00	*2,400.*
			Block of 4	1,600.	—
a.			25c **carmine red**	350.00	*2,400.*
			Block of 4	1,600.	—
b.			Pelure paper	375.00	—

Nos. PR1-PR3 used are valued with faults.

White Border
Yellowish paper

PR4	N1	5c	**light blue**	325.00	*2,400.*
			blue	350.00	—
			Block of 4	1,600.	—
a.			5c **dark blue**	325.00	—
b.			Pelure paper	375.00	—

REPRINTS of 1865 ISSUE

Printed by the Continental Bank Note Co. using the original National Bank Note Co. plates

1875				*Perf. 12*

Hard white paper, without gum
5c White Border, 10c and 25c Colored Border

PR5	N1	5c	**dull blue** *(10,000)*	225.00
			dark blue	225.00
			Block of 4	1,000.
a.			Printed on both sides	*5,750.*
PR6	N2	10c	**dark bluish green** *(7765)*	250.00
			deep green	250.00
			Block of 4	1,075.
a.			Printed on both sides	*4,250.*
PR7	N3	25c	**dark carmine** *(6684)*	250.00
			dark carmine red	250.00
			Block of 4	1,125.

750 examples of each value, which were remainders from the regular issue, were sold as reprints because of delays in obtaining Nos. PR5-PR7. These remainders cannot be distinguished from Nos. PR2-PR4, and are not included in the reprint quantities.

The Continental Bank Note Co. made another special printing from new plates, which did not have the colored border. These exist imperforate and perforated, but they were not regularly issued.

On No. PR5, there is no thin line of color in the second white area on each side of the stamp. On No. PR8, there is often a thin line of color in this area, but not all examples of No. PR8 show this line (see illustration below). Expertization is based on color and paper.

#PR5   #PR8

Printed by the American Bank Note Co.
Soft porous paper, without gum
White Border

1881				
PR8	N1	5c	**dark blue** *(5645)*	750.00
			Block of 4	3,750.

Statue of Freedom on Capitol
Dome, by Thomas
Crawford — N4

"Justice" — N5

Ceres — N6

"Victory" — N7

Clio — N8

Minerva — N9

Vesta — N10

"Peace" — N11

"Commerce" — N12

Hebe — N13

Indian Maiden — N14

Values for used examples of Nos. PR9-PR113 are for fine-very fine examples for denominations to $3, and fine for denominations of $3 or higher. Some used Scott numbers may not exist without faults.

Printed by the Continental Bank Note Co.
Plates of 100 subjects in two panes of 50 each
Size of design: 24x35mm

1875, Jan. 1   Engr.   Perf. 12
Thin hard paper

PR9	N4	2c	black	280.00	30.00
			gray black	280.00	30.00
			greenish black	280.00	30.00
			No gum	110.00	
			Handstamp or blue brush cancel		65.00
			Block of 4	1,250.	190.00
PR10	N4	3c	black	280.00	32.50
			gray black	280.00	32.50
			No gum	110.00	
			Handstamp or blue brush cancel		65.00
			Block of 4	1,250.	160.00
PR11	N4	4c	black	280.00	30.00
			gray black	280.00	30.00
			greenish black	280.00	30.00
			No gum	110.00	
			Handstamp or blue brush cancel		65.00
			Block of 4	1,250.	
PR12	N4	6c	black	280.00	32.50
			gray black	280.00	32.50
			greenish black	280.00	32.50
			No gum	110.00	
			Handstamp or blue brush cancel		65.00
			Block of 4	1,250.	
PR13	N4	8c	black	325.00	47.50
			gray black	325.00	47.50

			greenish black	325.00	47.50
			No gum	125.00	
			Handstamp or blue brush cancel		100.00
PR14	N4	9c	black	475.00	95.00
			gray black	475.00	95.00
			No gum	175.00	
			Handstamp or blue brush cancel		210.00
			Double transfer at top	525.00	110.00
PR15	N4	10c	black	350.00	37.50
			gray black	350.00	37.50
			greenish black	350.00	37.50
			No gum	125.00	
			Handstamp or blue brush cancel		75.00
			Block of 4	1,600.	
PR16	N5	12c	rose	800.00	100.00
			pale rose	800.00	100.00
			No gum	325.00	
			Handstamp or blue brush cancel		175.00
PR17	N5	24c	rose	875.00	125.00
			pale rose	875.00	125.00
			No gum	360.00	
			Handstamp or blue brush cancel		210.00
			Paper with silk fibers	2,000.	
PR18	N5	36c	rose	875.00	150.00
			pale rose	875.00	150.00
			No gum	360.00	
			Handstamp or blue brush cancel		275.00
PR19	N5	48c	rose	1,250.	200.00
			pale rose	1,250.	200.00
			No gum	450.00	
			Handstamp or blue brush cancel		375.00
PR20	N5	60c	rose	1,250.	115.00
			pale rose	1,250.	115.00
			No gum	450.00	
			Handstamp or blue brush cancel		225.00
PR21	N5	72c	rose	1,250.	250.00
			pale rose	1,250.	250.00
			No gum	450.00	
			Handstamp or blue brush cancel		475.00
PR22	N5	84c	rose	1,850.	375.00
			pale rose	1,850.	375.00
			No gum	650.00	
			Handstamp or blue brush cancel		625.00
PR23	N5	96c	rose	1,350.	250.00
			pale rose	1,350.	250.00
			No gum	525.00	
			Handstamp or blue brush cancel		575.00
PR24	N6	$1.92	dark brown	1,650.	250.00
			No gum	650.00	
			Handstamp or blue brush cancel		400.00
PR25	N7	$3	vermilion	1,800.	450.00
			No gum	700.00	
			Handstamp or blue brush cancel		700.00
PR26	N8	$6	ultramarine	3,600.	550.00
			dull ultramarine	3,600.	550.00
			No gum	1,400.	
			Handstamp or blue brush cancel		800.00
PR27	N9	$9	yellow orange	4,000.	600.00
			No gum	1,600.	
			Handstamp or blue brush cancel		1,000.
PR28	N10	$12	blue green	4,500.	750.00
			No gum	1,750.	
			Handstamp or blue brush cancel		1,250.
PR29	N11	$24	dark gray violet	4,750.	800.00
			No gum	1,850.	
			Handstamp or blue brush cancel		1,350.
PR30	N12	$36	brown rose	5,000.	950.00
			No gum	2,000.	
			Handstamp or blue brush cancel		1,600.
PR31	N13	$48	red brown	6,250.	1,150.
			No gum	2,300.	
			Handstamp or blue brush cancel		1,900.
PR32	N14	$60	violet	6,500.	1,250.
			No gum	2,400.	
			Handstamp or blue brush cancel		2,500.

SPECIAL PRINTING of 1875 ISSUE
Printed by the Continental Bank Note Co.
Hard white paper, without gum

1875   Perf. 12

PR33	N4	2c	gray black (5,000)	600.00
			Block of 4	3,000.
a.			Horizontally ribbed paper (10,000)	450.00
PR34	N4	3c	gray black (5,000)	600.00
			Block of 4	3,000.
a.			Horizontally ribbed paper (1,952)	450.00
PR35	N4	4c	gray black (4451)	650.00
			Block of 4	3,250.
a.			Horizontally ribbed paper	900.00
PR36	N4	6c	gray black (2348)	850.00
PR37	N4	8c	gray black (1930)	950.00
PR38	N4	9c	gray black (1795)	1,050.
PR39	N4	10c	gray black (1499)	1,300.
PR40	N5	12c	pale rose (1313)	1,500.
PR41	N5	24c	pale rose (411)	2,100.
PR42	N5	36c	pale rose (330)	2,800.
PR43	N5	48c	pale rose (268)	4,000.

PR44	N5	60c	pale rose (222)	4,000.
PR45	N5	72c	pale rose (174)	4,500.
PR46	N5	84c	pale rose (164)	5,000.
PR47	N5	96c	pale rose (141)	8,500.
PR48	N6	$1.92	dark brown (41)	22,500.
PR49	N7	$3	vermilion (20)	45,000.
PR50	N8	$6	ultramarine (14)	80,000.
PR51	N9	$9	yellow orange (4)	160,000.
PR52	N10	$12	blue green (5)	125,000.
PR53	N11	$24	dark gray violet (2)	—
PR54	N12	$36	brown rose (2)	250,000.
PR55	N13	$48	red brown (1)	—
PR56	N14	$60	violet (1)	—

Although four examples of No. PR51 were sold, only one is currently documented.

No. PR54 is valued in the grade of fine. Although two stamps were sold, only one is currently documented.

All values of this issue, Nos. PR33 to PR56, exist imperforate but were not regularly issued thus. Value, set $60,000.

Numbers in parentheses are quantities sold.

Printed by the American Bank Note Co.
Soft porous paper

1879   Unwmk.   Perf. 12

PR57	N4	2c	black	50.00	8.50
			gray black	50.00	8.50
			greenish black	50.00	8.50
			No gum	20.00	
			Handstamp cancel		25.00
			Block of 4	225.00	
			Double transfer at top	55.00	14.00
			Cracked plate	—	
PR58	N4	3c	black	60.00	10.50
			gray black	60.00	10.50
			intense black	60.00	10.50
			No gum	25.00	
			Handstamp cancel		35.00
			Block of 4	250.00	
			Double transfer at top	65.00	15.00
PR59	N4	4c	black	60.00	10.50
			gray black	60.00	10.50
			intense black	60.00	10.50
			greenish black	60.00	10.50
			No gum	25.00	
			Handstamp cancel		35.00
			Block of 4	250.00	
			Double transfer at top	65.00	15.00
PR60	N4	6c	black	105.00	21.00
			gray black	105.00	21.00
			intense black	105.00	21.00
			greenish black	105.00	21.00
			No gum	45.00	
			Handstamp cancel		75.00
			Block of 4	500.00	
			Double transfer at top	115.00	26.00
PR61	N4	8c	black	115.00	21.00
			gray black	115.00	21.00
			greenish black	115.00	21.00
			No gum	47.50	
			Handstamp cancel		75.00
			Block of 4	525.00	
			Double transfer at top	125.00	26.00
PR62	N4	10c	black	115.00	21.00
			gray black	115.00	21.00
			greenish black	115.00	21.00
			No gum	47.50	
			Handstamp cancel		75.00
			Block of 4	525.00	
			Double transfer at top	125.00	
PR63	N5	12c	red	475.00	85.00
			No gum	200.00	
			Handstamp cancel		225.00
			Block of 4	2,150.	
PR64	N5	24c	red	475.00	85.00
			No gum	200.00	
			Handstamp cancel		225.00
			Block of 4	2,150.	
PR65	N5	36c	red	1,000.	240.00
			No gum	475.00	
			Handstamp cancel		500.00
			Block of 4	4,500.	
PR66	N5	48c	red	1,000.	180.00
			No gum	450.00	
			Handstamp cancel		450.00
PR67	N5	60c	red	1,000.	160.00
			No gum	450.00	
			Handstamp cancel		400.00
			Block of 4	4,500.	
a.			Imperf., pair	4,000.	
PR68	N5	72c	red	1,250.	300.00
			No gum	575.00	
			Handstamp cancel		700.00
PR69	N5	84c	red	1,250.	225.00
			No gum	575.00	
			Handstamp cancel		575.00
			Block of 4	—	
PR70	N5	96c	red	1,200.	160.00
			No gum	525.00	
			Handstamp cancel		400.00
			Block of 4	5,500.	
PR71	N6	$1.92	pale brown	550.00	135.00
			brown	550.00	135.00
			No gum	225.00	
			Handstamp cancel		300.00
			Block of 4	2,500.	
			Cracked plate	600.00	
PR72	N7	$3	red vermilion	625.00	150.00
			No gum	250.00	
			Handstamp cancel		350.00
			Block of 4	2,850.	
PR73	N8	$6	blue	1,050.	230.00
			ultramarine	1,100.	230.00
			No gum	400.00	
			Handstamp cancel		500.00
PR74	N9	$9	orange	800.00	160.00
			No gum	325.00	

		Handstamp cancel		375.00
PR75	N10	$12 **yellow green**	850.00	210.00
		No gum	325.00	
		Handstamp cancel		500.00
PR76	N11	$24 **dark violet**	800.00	260.00
		No gum	300.00	
		Handstamp cancel		600.00
PR77	N12	$36 **Indian red**	850.00	280.00
		No gum	350.00	
		Handstamp cancel		650.00
PR78	N13	$48 **yellow brown**	900.00	390.00
		No gum	350.00	
		Handstamp cancel		775.00
PR79	N14	$60 **purple**	850.00	360.00
		bright purple	850.00	360.00
		No gum	350.00	
		Handstamp cancel		750.00

See Die and Plate Proofs for other imperfs. on stamp paper.

SPECIAL PRINTING of 1879 ISSUE
Printed by the American Bank Note Co.
Without gum

1883

PR80	N4	2c **intense black** (4,514)	1,350.	
		Block of 4	6,250.	

REGULAR ISSUE
Printed by the American Bank Note Co.
With gum

1885, July 1		**Unwmk.**		**Perf. 12**
PR81	N4	1c **black**	85.00	8.50
		gray black	85.00	8.50
		intense black	85.00	8.50
		No gum	35.00	
		Handstamp cancel		30.00
		Block of 4	375.00	
		Double transfer at top	90.00	11.00
PR82	N5	12c **carmine**	180.00	20.00
		deep carmine	180.00	20.00
		rose carmine	180.00	20.00
		No gum	75.00	
		Handstamp cancel		75.00
		Block of 4	875.00	
		Plate crack (pos. 41)	240.00	
PR83	N5	24c **carmine**	180.00	22.50
		deep carmine	180.00	22.50
		rose carmine	180.00	22.50
		No gum	75.00	
		Handstamp cancel		100.00
		Block of 4	875.00	
PR84	N5	36c **carmine**	280.00	37.50
		deep carmine	280.00	37.50
		rose carmine	280.00	37.50
		No gum	115.00	
		Handstamp cancel		125.00
		lilac rose		
		Block of 4	1,300.	
PR85	N5	48c **carmine**	400.00	55.00
		deep carmine	400.00	55.00
		No gum	175.00	
		Handstamp cancel		200.00
		Block of 4	1,750.	
PR86	N5	60c **carmine**	525.00	80.00
		deep carmine	525.00	80.00
		No gum	230.00	
		Handstamp cancel		280.00
		Block of 4	2,400.	
PR87	N5	72c **carmine**	525.00	85.00
		deep carmine	525.00	85.00
		rose carmine	525.00	85.00
		No gum	230.00	
		Handstamp cancel		310.00
		Block of 4	2,400.	
PR88	N5	84c **carmine**	800.00	200.00
		rose carmine	800.00	200.00
		No gum	300.00	
		Handstamp cancel		475.00
		Block of 4	3,650.	
PR89	N5	96c **carmine**	700.00	160.00
		rose carmine	700.00	160.00
		No gum	275.00	
		Handstamp cancel		425.00
		Block of 4	3,150.	

See Die and Plate Proofs for imperfs. on stamp paper.

Printed by the Bureau of Engraving and Printing

1894		**Unwmk.**		**Perf. 12**
		Soft wove paper, with pale, whitish gum		
PR90	N4	1c **intense black**	425.00	750.00
		Never hinged	1,000.	
		No gum	175.00	
		Block of 4	1,850.	
		Double transfer at top	450.00	
PR91	N4	2c **intense black**	475.00	
		Never hinged	1,100.	
		No gum	200.00	
		Block of 4	2,150.	
		Double transfer at top	500.00	
PR92	N4	4c **intense black**	500.00	—
		Never hinged	1,350.	
		No gum	225.00	
		Block of 4	2,400.	
PR93	N4	6c **intense black**	3,750.	
		No gum	1,750.	
		Block of 4	—	
PR94	N4	10c **intense black**	1,150.	
		No gum	500.00	
		Block of 4	5,000.	
PR95	N5	12c **pink**	2,600.	1,500.

		No gum	1,100.	
		Block of 4	12,000.	
PR96	N5	24c **pink**	3,750.	1,750.
		No gum	1,850.	
		Block of 4	17,500.	
PR97	N5	36c **pink**	50,000.	
		Block of 4		
PR98	N5	60c **pink**	55,000.	7,500.
		Block of 4		
PR99	N5	96c **pink**	52,500.	
PR100	N7	$3 **scarlet**	60,000.	
		Block of 4		
PR101	N8	$6 **pale blue**	60,000.	—
		No gum	30,000.	

Nos. PR90, PR95-PR98 used are valued with fine centering and small faults.

No. PR97 unused is valued in the grade of very good to fine. No. PR98 unused is valued in the grade of fine. Nos. PR99-PR100 unused are valued in the grade of fine-very fine.

Statue of Freedom — N15　　　　　N16

N17　　　　　N18

N19　　　　　N20

N21　　　　　N22

1895, Feb. 1		**Unwmk.**		**Perf. 12**
		Size of designs: 1c-50c, 21x34mm		
		$2-$100, 24x35mm		
PR102	N15	1c **black**	230.00	100.00
		Never hinged	500.00	
		No gum	90.00	
		Block of 4	1,050.	500.00
PR103	N15	2c **black**	230.00	100.00
		gray black	230.00	100.00
		Never hinged	500.00	
		No gum	90.00	
		Block of 4	1,050.	—
		Double transfer at top	250.00	
PR104	N15	5c **black**	300.00	150.00
		gray black	300.00	150.00
		Never hinged	650.00	
		No gum	125.00	
		Block of 4	1,350.	
PR105	N15	10c **black**	550.00	350.00
		Never hinged	1,150.	

		No gum	225.00	
		Block of 4	2,750.	
PR106	N16	25c **carmine**	750.00	500.00
		Never hinged	1,650.	
		No gum	300.00	
		Block of 4	3,500.	
PR107	N16	50c **carmine**	1,500.	800.00
		Never hinged	3,250.	
		No gum	575.00	
		Block of 4	7,000.	
PR108	N17	$2 **scarlet**	1,500.	600.00
		Never hinged	3,250.	
		No gum	575.00	
PR109	N18	$5 **ultramarine**	2,100.	1,100.
		Never hinged	4,500.	
		No gum	800.00	
PR110	N19	$10 **green**	2,500.	1,300.
		Never hinged	5,250.	
		No gum	900.00	
PR111	N20	$20 **slate**	3,250.	2,000.
		Never hinged	6,750.	
		No gum	1,200.	
PR112	N21	$50 **dull rose**	2,900.	750.00
		Never hinged	6,250.	
		No gum	1,100.	
PR113	N22	$100 **purple**	3,500.	2,500.
		Never hinged	7,250.	
		No gum	1,400.	

Nos. PR102-PR113 were printed from plates with arrows in the top, bottom and side margins, but no guidelines between the stamps.

1895-97		**Wmk. 191**		**Perf. 12**
PR114	N15	1c **black,** *Jan. 11, 1896*	8.00	25.00
		gray black	8.00	25.00
		Never hinged	20.00	
		No gum	2.75	
		Block of 4	35.00	
PR115	N15	2c **black,** *Nov. 21, 1895*	8.00	25.00
		gray black	15.00	25.00
		Never hinged	20.00	
		No gum	2.75	
		Block of 4	35.00	
PR116	N15	5c **black,** *Feb. 12, 1896*	13.00	40.00
		gray black	13.00	40.00
		Never hinged	27.50	
		No gum	4.25	
		Block of 4	57.50	
PR117	N15	10c **black,** *Sept. 13, 1895*	13.00	25.00
		gray black	13.00	25.00
		Never hinged	27.50	
		No gum	4.25	
		Block of 4	57.50	
PR118	N16	25c **carmine,** *Oct. 11, 1895*	20.00	65.00
		lilac rose	20.00	65.00
		Never hinged	45.00	
		No gum	7.00	
		Block of 4	87.50	
PR119	N16	50c **carmine,** *Sept. 19, 1895*	25.00	75.00
		rose carmine	25.00	75.00
		lilac rose	25.00	75.00
		Never hinged	55.00	
		No gum	8.50	
		Block of 4	110.00	—
PR120	N17	$2 **scarlet,** *Jan. 23, 1897*	30.00	110.00
		scarlet vermilion	30.00	110.00
		Never hinged	75.00	
		No gum	10.00	
		Block of 4	130.00	
PR121	N18	$5 **dark blue,** *Jan. 16, 1896*	40.00	160.00
		Never hinged	100.00	
		No gum	13.50	
		Block of 4	200.00	
a.		$5 light blue	200.00	500.00
		Never hinged	500.00	
		No gum	67.50	
		Block of 4	875.00	2,500.
PR122	N19	$10 **green,** *Mar. 5, 1896*	42.50	160.00
		Never hinged	105.00	
		No gum	14.00	
		Block of 4	200.00	—
PR123	N20	$20 **slate,** *Jan. 27, 1896*	45.00	180.00
		Never hinged	110.00	
		No gum	15.00	
		Block of 4	210.00	
PR124	N21	$50 **dull rose,** *July 31, 1897*	75.00	225.00
		Never hinged	170.00	
		No gum	27.50	
		Block of 4	350.00	
PR125	N22	$100 **purple,** *Jan. 23, 1896*	65.00	240.00
		Never hinged	150.00	
		No gum	22.50	
		Block of 4	300.00	
		Nos. PR114-PR125 (12)	384.50	1,330.
		Nos. PR114-PR125, never hinged	905.00	

Nos. PR114-PR125 were printed from the original plates with guide lines added in November 1895. Top and bottom plate strips and blocks of Nos. PR114-PR119 exist both with and without vertical guidelines.

In 1899 the Government sold 26,989 sets of these stamps, but, as the stock of high values was not sufficient to make up the required number, an additional printing was made of the $5, $10, $20, $50 and $100. These are virtually indistinguishable from earlier printings.

POSTAL NOTE STAMPS

Postal note stamps were issued to supplement the regular money order service. They were a means of sending amounts under $1. One or two Postal note stamps, totaling 1c to 99c, were affixed to United States Postal Notes and canceled by the clerk. The stamps were on the second of three parts, the one retained by the post office redeeming the Postal Note. They were discontinued March 31, 1951.

Catalogue Values for Unused Postal Note stamps are for Never Hinged items.

MO1

ROTARY PRESS PRINTING

1945, Feb. 1   Unwmk.   Perf. 11x10½

PN1	MO1	1c **black** (155950-155951)	.35	.30
PN2	MO1	2c **black** (156003-156004)	.35	.30
PN3	MO1	3c **black** (156062-156063)	.35	.30
PN4	MO1	4c **black** (156942-156943)	.35	.30
PN5	MO1	5c **black** (156261-156262)	.40	.30
PN6	MO1	6c **black** (156064-156065)	.45	.30
PN7	MO1	7c **black** (156075-156076)	.60	.30
PN8	MO1	8c **black** (156077-156078)	.85	.30
PN9	MO1	9c **black** (156251-156252)	1.00	.30
PN10	MO1	10c **black** (156274-156275)	1.20	.30
PN11	MO1	20c **black** (156276-156277)	1.80	.30
PN12	MO1	30c **black** (156303-156304)	2.50	.30

PN13	MO1	40c **black** (156283-156284)	3.50	.30
PN14	MO1	50c **black** (156322-156323)	3.75	.30
PN15	MO1	60c **black** (156324-156325)	4.50	.30
PN16	MO1	70c **black** (156344-156345)	7.00	.30
PN17	MO1	80c **black** (156326-156327)	8.25	.30
PN18	MO1	90c **black** (156352-156353)	10.00	.30
		Nos. PN1-PN18 (18)	47.20	5.40

Blocks of four and plate number blocks of four are valued at 4 and 15 times the unused single value.

Postal note stamps exist on postal note cards with first day cancellation.

Numbers in parentheses are plate Nos.

PARCEL POST STAMPS

The Act of Congress approved Aug. 24, 1912, created postage rates on 4th class mail weighing 4 ounces or less at 1 cent per ounce or fraction. On mail over 4 ounces, the rate was by the pound. These rates were to be prepaid by distinctive postage stamps. Under this provision, the Post Office Department prepared 12 parcel post and 5 parcel post postage due stamps, usable only on parcel post packages starting Jan. 1, 1913. Other stamps were not usable on parcel post starting on that date.

Beginning on Nov. 27, 1912, the stamps were shipped to post offices offering parcel post service. Approximate shipping dates were: 1c, 2c, 5c, 25c, 1c due, 5c due, Nov. 27; 10c, 2c due, Dec. 9; 4c, 10c due, Dec. 12; 15c, 20c, 25c due, Dec. 16; 75c, Dec. 18. There was no prohibition on sale of the stamps prior to Jan. 1, 1913. Undoubtedly many were used on 4th class mail in Dec. 1912. Fourth class mail was expanded by adding former 2nd and 3rd class categories and was renamed "parcel post" effective Jan. 1, 1913. Normally 4th class (parcel post) mail did not receive a dated cancel unless a special service was involved. Small pieces, such as samples, are known with 1st class cancels.

With the approval of the Interstate Commerce Commission, the Postmaster General directed, in Order No. 7241 dated June 26, 1913, and effective July 1, 1913, that regular postage stamps should be valid on parcels. Parcel post stamps then became usable as regular stamps.

Parcel post and parcel post postage due stamps remained on sale, but no further printings were made. Remainders, consisting of 3,510,345 of the 75c, were destroyed in Sept. 1921.

The 20c was the first government-issued postage stamp of any country to show an airplane.

Post Office Clerk — PP1

City Carrier — PP2

Railway Postal Clerk — PP3

Rural Carrier — PP4

Mail Train and Mail Bag on Rack — PP5

Steamship "Kronprinz Wilhelm" and Mail Tender, New York — PP6

Automobile Service — PP7

Airplane Carrying Mail — PP8

Manufacturing (Steel Plant, South Chicago) — PP9

Dairying — PP10

Harvesting PP11

Fruit Growing (Florida Orange Grove) — PP12

6161 TEN

Plate number and imprint consisting of value in words.

Marginal imprints, consisting of value in words, were added to the plates on January 27, 1913.

Designed by Clair Aubrey Huston.

Plates of 180 subjects in four panes of 45 each.

1913　　Wmk. 190　　Engr.　　Perf. 12

Q1	PP1	1c **carmine rose** (209,691,094)	5.25	1.75
		carmine	5.25	1.75
		Never hinged	13.00	
		First day cover, *July 1, 1913*		*1,500.*
		On cover, 1913-25		6.00
		Block of 4	22.50	9.00
		P# block of 4, Impt.	42.50	
		P# block of 6, Impt.	105.00	
		P# block of 6	110.00	
		Never hinged	180.00	
		Double transfer	9.50	4.00
Q2	PP2	2c **carmine rose** (206,417,253)	6.00	1.40
		carmine	6.00	1.40
		Never hinged	15.00	
		First day cover, *July 1, 1913*		*1,750.*
		On cover, 1913-25		5.75
		Block of 4	27.50	6.50
		P# block of 4, Impt.	45.00	
		P# block of 6, Impt.	125.00	
		P# block of 6	145.00	
		Never hinged	240.00	
		Double transfer	—	—
a.		2c **lake**	*1,750.*	
b.		2c **carmine lake**	*350.00*	

No. Q2a is valued in the grade of fine to very fine.

Q3	PP3	3c **carmine,** *Apr. 5, 1913* (29,027,433)	12.00	6.50
		deep carmine	12.00	6.50
		Never hinged	32.50	
		First day cover, *July 1, 1913*		*3,500.*
		On cover, 1913-25		19.00
		Block of 4	52.50	37.50
		P# block of 4, Impt.	95.00	
		P# block of 6, Impt.	260.00	
		P# block of 6	235.00	
		Never hinged	400.00	
		P# block of 8, Impt. (side)	310.00	

		Never hinged	550.00	
		Retouched at lower right corner (No. 6257 LL 7)	26.00	14.50
		Double transfer (No. 6257 LL 6)	26.00	14.50
Q4	PP4	4c **carmine rose** (76,743,813)	35.00	3.50
		carmine	35.00	3.50
		Never hinged	100.00	
		First day cover, *July 1, 1913*		*3,500.*
		On cover, 1913-25		65.00
		Block of 4	150.00	17.50
		P# block of 4, Impt.	350.00	
		P# block of 6, Impt.	1,050.00	
		Never hinged	1,750.	
		P# block of 6	1,000.00	
		Never hinged	1,700.	
		Double transfer	—	—
Q5	PP5	5c **carmine rose** (108,153,993)	30.00	2.50
		carmine	30.00	2.50
		Never hinged	85.00	
		First day cover, *July 1, 1913*		*3,500.*
		On cover, 1913-25		42.50
		Block of 4	125.00	15.00
		P# block of 4, Impt.	340.00	
		P# block of 6, Impt.	1,000.	
		P# block of 6	975.00	
		Never hinged	1,600.	
		Double transfer	45.00	6.25
Q6	PP6	10c **carmine rose** (56,896,653)	47.50	3.50
		carmine	47.50	3.50
		Never hinged	110.00	
		First day cover, *July 1, 1913*		*12,500.*
		On cover, 1913-25		55.00
		Block of 4	220.00	30.00
		P# block of 4, Impt.	425.00	
		P# block of 6, Impt.	1,150.	
		P# block of 6	1,000.	
		Never hinged	1,650.	
		Double transfer	—	—
Q7	PP7	15c **carmine rose** (21,147,033)	62.50	15.00
		carmine	62.50	15.00
		Never hinged	180.00	
		First day cover, *July 1, 1913*		—
		On cover, 1913-25		350.00
		Block of 4	290.00	100.00
		P# block of 4, Impt.	675.00	
		P# block of 6, Impt.	2,600.	
		P# block of 8, Impt.	3,100.	
		P# block of 6	2,300.	
		Never hinged	3,700.	
Q8	PP8	20c **carmine rose** (17,142,393)	135.00	30.00
		carmine	135.00	30.00
		Never hinged	350.00	

		On cover, 1913-25		750.00
		Block of 4	600.00	150.00
		P# block of 4, Impt.	1,450.	
		P# block of 6, Impt.	6,500.	
		P# block of 8, Impt. (side)	7,000.	
		P# block of 6	6,500.	
		Never hinged	10,000.	
Q9	PP9	25c **carmine rose** (21,940,653)	62.50	8.50
		carmine	62.50	8.50
		Never hinged	180.00	
		On cover, 1913-25		300.00
		Block of 4	290.00	60.00
		P# block of 6, Impt.	2,700.	
		P# block of 8, Impt. (side)	3,500.	
		P# block of 6	2,400.	
		Never hinged	3,850.	
Q10	PP10	50c **carmine rose,** *Mar. 15, 1913* (2,117,793)	275.00	50.00
		carmine	275.00	50.00
		Never hinged	700.00	
		On cover, 1913-25		—
		Block of 4	1,250.	325.00
		P# block of 4, Impt.	1,900.	
		Never hinged	3,000.	
		P# block of 6, Impt.	22,500.	
		Never hinged	30,000.	
Q11	PP11	75c **carmine rose** (2,772,615)	95.00	40.00
		carmine	95.00	40.00
		Never hinged	250.00	
		On cover, 1913-25		—
		Block of 4	450.00	225.00
		P# block of 6, Impt.	4,000.	
		P# block of 8, Impt. (side)	3,600.	
		P# block of 6	3,000.	
		Never hinged	4,500.	
Q12	PP12	$1 **carmine rose,** *Jan. 3, 1913* (1,053,273)	325.00	45.00
		carmine	325.00	45.00
		Never hinged	800.00	
		On cover, 1913-25		1,250.
		Block of 4	1,450.	225.00
		P# block of 6, Impt.	20,000.	
		Never hinged	29,000.	
		P# block of 8, Impt. (side)	21,000.	
		P# block of 6	18,000.	
		Never hinged	27,500.	
		Nos. Q1-Q12 (12)	1,090.	207.65
		Nos. Q1-Q12, never hinged	2,815.	

The 1c, 2c, 4c and 5c are known in parcel post usage postmarked Jan. 1, 1913.

PARCEL POST POSTAGE DUE STAMPS

See notes preceding Scott No. Q1. Parcel Post Postage Due stamps were allowed to be used as regular postage due stamps from July 1, 1913.

PPD1

Designed by Clair Aubrey Huston

Plates of 180 subjects in four panes of 45

1913　　Wmk. 190　　Engr.　　Perf. 12

JQ1	PPD1	1c **dark green** (7,322,400)	9.50	4.50
		yellowish green	9.50	4.50
		Never hinged	25.00	
		On cover, 1913-25		150.00
		Block of 4	42.50	35.00
		P# block of 6	475.00	
		Never hinged	800.00	

Earliest documented use: Feb. 26, 1913.

JQ2	PPD1	2c **dark green** (3,132,000)	75.00	20.00
		yellowish green	75.00	20.00
		Never hinged	190.00	
		On cover, 1913-25		200.00
		Block of 4	325.00	140.00
		P# block of 6	3,250.	
		Never hinged	5,250.	

Earliest documented use: July 7, 1913.

JQ3	PPD1	5c **dark green** (5,840,100)	12.50	5.50
		yellowish green	12.50	5.50
		Never hinged	32.50	
		On cover, 1913-25		185.00
		Block of 4	55.00	37.50
		P# block of 6	525.00	
		Never hinged	875.00	

Earliest documented use: Jan. 15, 1913 (dated cancel on off-cover stamp).

JQ4	PPD1	10c **dark green** (2,124,540)	150.00	47.50
		yellowish green	150.00	47.50
		Never hinged	375.00	
		On cover, 1913-25		650.00

		Block of 4	675.00	375.00
		P# block of 6	8,500.	
		Never hinged	12,000.	

Earliest documented use: July 19, 1913.

JQ5	PPD1	25c **dark green** (2,117,700)	85.00	5.00
		yellowish green	85.00	5.00
		Never hinged	225.00	
		On cover, 1913-25		—
		Block of 4	400.00	35.00
		P# block of 6	4,000.	
		Never hinged	7,000.	

Earliest documented use: Aug. 30, 1913.

Nos. JQ1-JQ5 (5)		332.00	82.50
Nos. JQ1-JQ5, never hinged		847.50	

SPECIAL HANDLING STAMPS

The Postal Service Act, approved February 28, 1925, provided for a special handling stamp of the 25-cent denomination for use on fourth-class mail matter, which would secure for such mail matter the expeditious handling accorded to mail matter of the first class.

PP13

FLAT PLATE PRINTING
Plates of 200 subjects in four panes of 50

1925-55	**Unwmk.**		**Perf. 11**
QE1 PP13 10c **yellow green**, wet printing,			
June 25, 1928		2.00	1.00
Never hinged		4.25	
Block of 4		10.00	—
P# block of 6		25.00	
Never hinged		40.00	
First day cover			45.00
a. Dry printing, *1955*		3.00	
Never hinged		6.50	
Block of 4		15.00	
P# block of 6		40.00	
Never hinged		65.00	
QE2 PP13 15c **yellow green**, wet printing,			
June 25, 1928		2.25	.90
Never hinged		4.75	
Block of 4		11.00	—
P# block of 6		30.00	
Never hinged		47.50	

First day cover	45.00	—
a. Dry printing, *1955*	4.00	
Never hinged	8.00	
Block of 4	19.00	
P# block of 6	50.00	
Never hinged	75.00	
QE3 PP13 20c **yellow green**, wet printing,		
June 25, 1928	3.75	1.50
Never hinged	7.75	
Block of 4	17.50	
P# block of 6	37.50	
Never hinged	60.00	
First day cover	45.00	
First day cover, Nos. QE1-QE3	350.00	—
a. Dry printing, *1955*	6.50	
Never hinged	12.50	
Block of 4	32.50	
P# block of 6	57.50	
Never hinged	85.00	

"AT" joined at top

"TA" joined at top

QE4 PP13 25c **deep green**, April 11, 1925	20.00	3.75
Never hinged	37.50	
Block of 4	115.00	24.00
P# block of 6	350.00	
Never hinged	525.00	
"A" and second "T" of "States" joined at top (Pl. 17103)	70.00	30.00
Never hinged	120.00	
"A" and second "T" of "States" and "T" and "A" of "Postage" joined at top (Pl. 17103)	110.00	100.00
Never hinged	190.00	
First day cover		225.00
a. 25c **yellow green**, *1928*	16.50	17.50
Never hinged	32.50	
Block of 4	90.00	85.00
P# block of 6	250.00	
Never hinged	360.00	
Nos. QE1-QE4 (4)	28.00	7.15
Nos. QE1-QE4, never hinged	62.00	

See note on Wet and Dry Printings following No. 1029.

POSTAL INSURANCE STAMPS

Postal insurance stamps were issued to pay insurance on parcels for loss or damage. The stamps come in a booklet of one which also carries instructions for use and a receipt form for use if there is a claim. The booklets were sold by vending machine. Values in unused column are for complete booklets. Values in used column are for used stamps. Booklet cover illustrations are reduced.

QI1 — PPI1

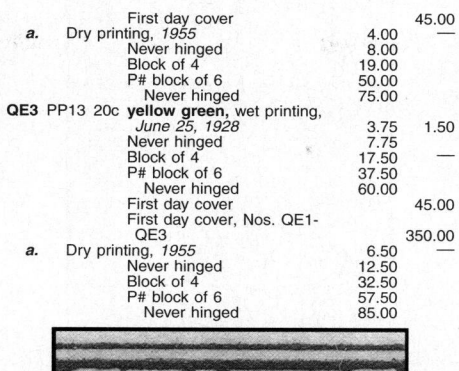
QI1 — PPIC1

1965, Aug.   Typo.   Rouletted 9 at Top
QI1 PPI1 (10c) **dark red**   150.00 —
No. QI1 paid insurance up to $10. It was sold at the Canoga Park, Calif., automatic post office, which opened Aug. 19, 1965. The "V" stands for "Vended."

QI2 — PPI2

QI2 — PPI2 Type I

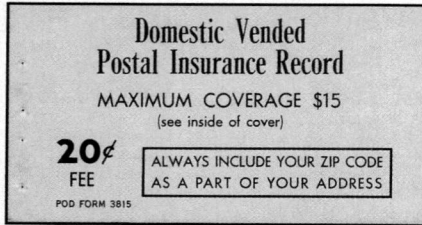

Domestic Vended
Postal Insurance Record
MAXIMUM COVERAGE $15
(see inside of cover)

20¢ FEE

ALWAYS INCLUDE YOUR ZIP CODE AS A PART OF YOUR ADDRESS

POD FORM 3815

QI2 — PPI2 Type II

1966, Mar. 26   Litho.   Perf. 11 at Top
QI2 PPI2 (20c) **red**   4.00 —

No. QI2 paid insurance up to $15. The rate increased from 20c to 25c on Apr. 18, 1976, and to 40c on July 18, 1976.

The QI2 booklet comes with two types of front covers, type I beginning "Vended..." and type II beginning "Domestic Vended...." There also are two types of back covers, the first with some white on black lettering, the second with all black on white lettering.

No 25c postal insurance stamps were printed. Existing examples of No. QI2 had 5c postage stamps added and the value on the cover was changed to 25c, usually by hand, but sometimes by handstamp or label. Twenty-cent stamps were added to make the 40c rate since new postal insurance stamps were not issued until 1977. Some 25c provisional booklets were further revalued to 40c by the addition of a 15c stamp. Each provisional booklet comes with both cover types.

DETACH THIS GUMMED LABEL AND AFFIX TO ADDRESS SIDE OF PARCEL

POSTMARK OF

MAILING OFFICE

INSURED U.S. MAIL

FEE PAID THROUGH VENDING MACHINE

QI3 — PPI3

THIS PACKAGE CONTAINS ONE:
DOMESTIC
PARCEL POST
INSURANCE STAMP
($15 MAXIMUM COVERAGE PER PARCEL)
DEPOSIT 40¢ FEE TO PURCHASE

QI3 — PPIC3

"FEE PAID THROUGH VENDING MACHINE"
Below "INSURED U.S. MAIL" Logo

1977-81   Litho.   Perf. 11 at Top
QI3 PPI3 (40c) **black**   10.00 —

Available for use by Nov. 28, 1977 or earlier.

QI3 is often found misperfed with horizontal perforations running between "Postmark of" and "Mailing Office." This variety is relatively common and does not merit a large premium.

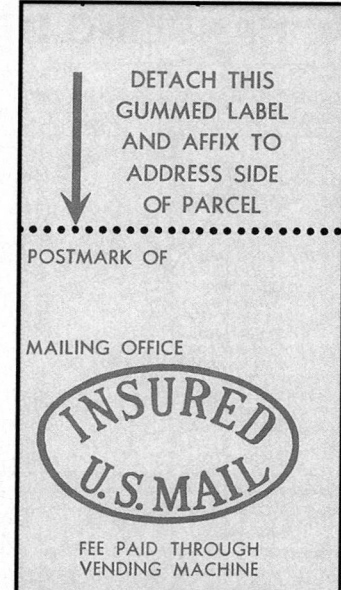

DETACH THIS GUMMED LABEL AND AFFIX TO ADDRESS SIDE OF PARCEL

POSTMARK OF

MAILING OFFICE

INSURED U.S. MAIL

FEE PAID THROUGH VENDING MACHINE

QI4 — PPI3

THIS PACKAGE CONTAINS ONE:
DOMESTIC
PARCEL POST
INSURANCE STAMP
($15 MAXIMUM COVERAGE PER PARCEL)
DEPOSIT 50¢ FEE TO PURCHASE

QI4 — PPIC4

QI4 PPI3 (50c) **green**   9.00 —

The rate increased to 50c on May 29, 1978. Examples of QI2 and QI3 exist revalued to 50c by the addition of stamps.

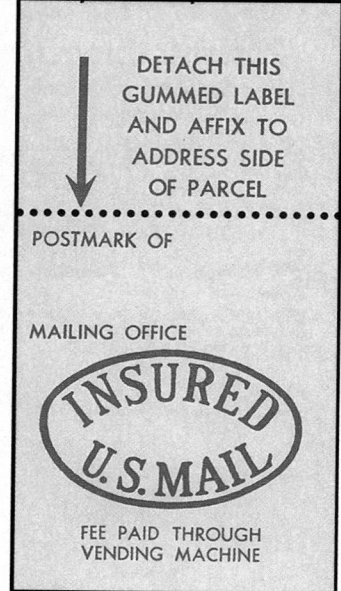

DETACH THIS GUMMED LABEL AND AFFIX TO ADDRESS SIDE OF PARCEL

POSTMARK OF

MAILING OFFICE

INSURED U.S. MAIL

FEE PAID THROUGH VENDING MACHINE

QI5 — PPI3

THIS PACKAGE CONTAINS ONE:
DOMESTIC
PARCEL POST
INSURANCE STAMP
($20 MAXIMUM COVERAGE PER PARCEL)
DEPOSIT 45¢ FEE TO PURCHASE

QI5 — PPIC5

QI5 PPI3 (45c) **red,** *1981*   10.00 —

No. QI3 booklets exist revalued to 45c by the addition of a 5c stamp, and the QI4 booklet is known revalued to 45c on its cover.

FIRST DAY COVERS

All envelopes or cards are postmarked Washington, D.C., unless otherwise stated. Minors and sublistings without dates have the same date and city (if none is otherwise mentioned) as the previous listing. Minors and sublistings with dates differing from the previous listing are postmarked in Washington, D.C. unless otherwise stated.

Values are for first day covers in very fine condition, without tears, stains or smeared postmarks, and with sound stamps that have fresh color and are not badly off center.

Printed cachets on covers before Scott Nos. 772 and C20 sell at a substantial premium. Values for covers of Nos. 772-986 and C20-C45 are for those with the most common cachets and addressed. Unaddressed covers sell at a substantial premium and covers without cachet sell at a substantial discount. Values for covers from Scott 987 and C46 onward are for those with the most common cachets and unaddressed.

Values for 1st class rate stamps are for covers bearing single stamps. Blocks of 4 on first day covers usually sell for about 1 ½ times as much as singles; Plate number blocks of 4 at about 3 times; Plate number blocks of 6 at about 4 times; coil line pairs at about 3 times. Stamps with denominations less than the first class rate will have the proper multiple to make the rate if practical or additional postage. (See Nos. 899, 907-908, 930-931, etc.)

Dates given are those on which the stamps were first *officially* placed on sale. Many instances are known of stamps being sold in advance, contrary to regulations.

Numbers in parentheses are quantities stated to have received the first day cancel.

Listings from Scott Nos. 551 and C4 are for covers canceled at cities officially designated by the Post Office Department or Postal Service. Some tagged varieties and cities of special interest are exceptions.

Air post first day covers are listed following the Postage first day covers. Envelope, postal card and other first day covers are with the regular listings.

Quantities given for se-tenant issues include the multiple and any single or combination of singles (see No. 2375a).

1851-57

5A	1c	**blue, type Ib,** *July 1, 1851,* Boston, Mass.	120,000.
7	1c	**blue, type II,** *July 1, 1851,* any city	25,000.
		Same on printed circular	4,000.
10	3c	**orange brown,** *July 1, 1851,* any city	12,500.

The No. 5A cover is unique. Value is based on 1996 auction sale. The No. 7 cover also is unique.

1861

64	3c	**pink,** *Aug. 17, 1861,* Baltimore, Md.	22,000.
64b	3c	**rose pink,** *Aug. 17, 1861,* Baltimore, Md.	23,000.

The Nos. 64 and 64b covers are each unique.

1883

210		2c **red brown,** *Oct. 1,* any city	2,000.
210, 211		2c, 4c **blue green,** *Oct. 1,* New York, N.Y.	50,000.

The Nos. 210, 211 cover is unique.

1890

219D		2c **lake,** *Feb. 22,* any city	35,000.

1893

COLUMBIAN EXPOSITION ISSUE

230	1c	**deep blue,** *Jan. 1,* any city	20,000.
		Jan. 2, any city	5,000.
231	2c	**brown violet,** *Jan. 1,* any city	20,000.
		Jan. 2, any city	5,000.
232	3c	**green,** *Jan. 1,* any city	20,000.
		Jan. 2, any city	7,000.
		230, 232 on one cover, *Jan. 2,* Boston, Mass.	8,250.
233	4c	**ultramarine,** *Jan. 1,* any city	20,000.
		Jan. 2, any city	14,000.
234	5c	**chocolate,** *Jan. 1,* any city	27,500.
		Jan. 2, any city	17,500.
235	6c	**purple,** *Jan. 2,* any city	22,500.
237	10c	**black brown,** *Jan. 1,* any city	32,500.
		Jan. 2, any city	27,500.
242	$2	**brown red,** *Jan. 2,* any city	65,000.

As Jan. 1, 1893, was a Sunday, specialists recognize both Jan. 1 and 2 as "first day."

1898

TRANS-MISSISSIPPI EXPOSITION ISSUE

285	1c	**green,** *June 17,* any city	12,000.
286	2c	**copper red,** *June 17,* any city	14,000.
		Pittsburgh, Pa,	13,000.
287	4c	**orange,** *June 17*	27,500.
288	5c	**dull blue,** *June 17,* any city	16,000.
		285, 287-288 on one cover	75,000.
		285-288 on one cover	75,000.
289	8c	**violet brown,** *June 17*	22,500.
290	10c	**gray violet,** *June 17*	27,500.
		285-290, all 6 on one cover, *June 17*	100,000.
291	50c	**sage green,** *June 17,* any city	50,000.
292	$1	**black,** *June 17,* any city	55,000.

1901

PAN AMERICAN EXPOSITION ISSUE

294	1c	**green & black,** *May 1,* any city	4,000.
295	2c	**carmine & black,** *May 1,* any city	2,500.
297	5c	**ultra. & blk.,** *May 1,* any city	35,000.
		294, 295, 297 on one cover, *May 1,* Boston, Mass.	17,500.
		294, 296, 297 on one cover, *May 1,* Boston, Mass.	16,000.
		295, 298 on one cover, *May 1,* Washington, D.C.	33,500.
		296, 298 on one cover, *May 1,* Boston, Mass.	27,500.
		297, 298 on one cover, *May 1,* Philadelphia, Pa.	27,500.
		294-299, complete set of 6 on one cover *May 1,* any city	30,000.

1904

LOUISIANA PURCHASE EXPOSITION ISSUE

323	1c	**green,** *Apr. 30,* any city	7,500.
324	2c	**carmine,** *Apr. 30,* any city	5,000.
325	3c	**violet,** *Apr. 30,* any city	20,000.
326	5c	**dark blue,** *Apr. 30,* any city	22,500.
327	10c	**red brown,** *Apr. 30,* any city	24,000.
		323-327, all 5 on one cover, *Apr. 30,* New York	65,000.

The Nos. 323-327 combination cover is unique.

1907

328	1c	**Jamestown,** *Apr. 26,* any city	10,000.
329	2c	**Jamestown,** *Apr. 26,* any city	15,000.

1908

331a		1c **green,** booklet single, *Dec. 2,* Washington, D.C.	17,500.

1909

367	2c	**Lincoln,** *Feb. 12,* any city	500.
		On pictorial postcard, *Feb. 12,* Boston	425.

Imperf

368	2c	**Lincoln,** *Feb. 12,* any city	13,000.

1909

ALASKA-YUKON ISSUE

370	2c	**carmine,** *June 1,* any city	3,000.
		On Expo-related picture postcard, *June 1*	5,000.

1909

HUDSON-FULTON ISSUE

372	2c	**carmine,** *Sept. 25,* any city	900.
		On Expo-related picture postcard, *Sept. 25*	1,400.

Imperf

373	2c	**carmine,** *Sept. 25,* any city	8,000.

1913

PANAMA-PACIFIC ISSUE

397	1c	**green,** *Jan. 1,* any city	5,000.
399	5c	**blue,** *Jan. 1*	31,000.
400	10c	**orange yellow,** *Jan. 1*	10,000.
		397, 399 & 400, all 3 on one cover, San Francisco, Cal.	—

The editors would like to see expertization of the above 3-stamp cover.

1916-22

COIL STAMP

497	10c	**orange yellow,** *Jan. 31, 1922,* any city	6,000.

1918-20

OFFSET PRINTING

526	2c	**carmine,** type IV, *Mar. 15, 1920*	850.

1919

537	3c	**Victory,** *Mar. 3,* any city	800.

1919 — **Perf. 11x10**

541	3c	**violet,** type II, *June 14, 1919,* any city	9,000.

1920 — **Perf. 10x11**

REGULAR ISSUE

542	1c	**green,** *May 26*	1,750.

1920

548	1c	**Pilgrim,** *Dec. 21,* any city, pair	1,000.
		Plymouth, Mass.	5,000.
549	2c	**Pilgrim,** *Dec. 21,* any city	700.
		Plymouth, Mass.	5,000.
550	5c	**Pilgrim,** *Dec. 21,* any city	2,500.
		548-550, complete set of 3 on one cover, *Dec. 21,* any city	1,750.
		Washington, D.C.	3,000.

1922-26 — **Perf. 11**

551	½c	**Hale,** *Apr. 4, 1925,* block of 4	19.00
		New Haven, Conn.	25.00
		551 & 576 on one cover, *Apr. 4, 1925,* New Haven, Conn.	165.00
552	1c	**Franklin,** *Jan. 17, 1923,* pair	27.50
		Philadelphia, Pa.	47.50
553	1½c	**Harding,** *Mar. 19, 1925,* pair	52.50
		553, 582, 598 on one cover, *Mar. 19, 1925*	190.00
554	2c	**Washington,** *Jan. 15, 1923*	42.50
555	3c	**Lincoln,** *Feb. 12, 1923*	40.00
		Hodgenville, Ky.	325.00
556	4c	**Martha Washington,** *Jan. 15, 1923*	65.00
557	5c	**Roosevelt,** *Oct. 27, 1922*	135.00
		New York, N.Y.	190.00
		Oyster Bay, N.Y.	1,750.
558	6c	**Garfield,** *Nov. 20, 1922*	235.00
559	7c	**McKinley,** *May 1, 1923*	185.00
		Niles, O.	275.00
560	8c	**Grant,** *May 1, 1923*	190.00
561	9c	**Jefferson,** *Jan. 15, 1923*	190.00
562	10c	**Monroe,** *Jan. 15, 1923*	190.00
		554, 556, 561 & 562, all 4 stamps issued Jan. 15 on one cover	3,500.
563	11c	**Hayes,** *Oct. 4, 1922*	650.00
		Fremont, O.	3,750.
564	12c	**Cleveland,** *Mar. 20, 1923*	185.00
		Boston, Mass. (Philatelic Exhibition)	185.00
		Caldwell, N.J.	210.00
565	14c	**American Indian,** *May 1, 1923*	400.00
		Muskogee, Okla.	1,250.
566	15c	**Statue of Liberty,** *Nov. 11, 1922*	575.00
567	20c	**Golden Gate,** *May 1, 1923*	600.00
		San Francisco, Cal.	2,000.
		559, 560, 565 & 567, all 4 stamps issued May 1 on one cover	10,000.
568	25c	**Niagara Falls,** *Nov. 11, 1922*	650.00
569	30c	**American Buffalo,** *Mar. 20, 1923*	800.00
570	50c	**Arlington,** *Nov. 11, 1922*	1,250.
571	$1	**Lincoln Memorial,** *Feb. 12, 1923*	7,000.
		Springfield, Ill.	6,500.
572	$2	**U.S. Capitol,** *Mar. 20, 1923*	20,000.
573	$5	**America,** *Mar. 20, 1923*	35,000.

Imperf

576	1½c	**Harding,** *Apr. 4, 1925*	42.50

Perf. 10

581	1c	**Franklin,** *Oct. 17, 1923,* not precanceled	6,000.
582	1½c	**Harding,** *Mar. 19, 1925*	40.00
583a	2c	**Washington booklet pane of 6,** *Aug. 27, 1926*	1,500.
584	3c	**Lincoln,** *Aug. 1, 1925*	55.00
585	4c	**Martha Washington,** *Apr. 4, 1925*	50.00
586	5c	**Roosevelt,** *Apr. 4, 1925*	60.00
587	6c	**Garfield,** *Apr. 4, 1925*	60.00
		585-587, all 3 stamps issued April 4 on one cover	1,000.
588	7c	**McKinley,** *May 29, 1926*	60.00
589	8c	**Grant,** *May 29, 1926*	70.00
590	9c	**Jefferson,** *May 29, 1926*	77.50
591	10c	**Monroe,** *June 8, 1925*	95.00

Perf. 10 Vertically

597	1c	**Franklin,** *July 18, 1923*	600.00
598	1½c	**Harding,** *Mar. 19, 1925*	65.00
599	2c	**Washington,** *Jan. 15, 1923*	1,750.

600	3c **Lincoln**, *May 10, 1924*		90.00
602	5c **Roosevelt**, *Mar. 5, 1924*		95.00
603	10c **Monroe**, *Dec. 1, 1924*		110.00

No. 599 is known used on Jan. 10, 11 and 13, 1923 (one each day). Jan. 15 was the first day of sale in Washington, D. C.

Perf. 10 Horizontally

604	1c **Franklin**, *July 19, 1924*		100.00
605	1½c **Harding**, *May 9, 1925*		80.00
606	2c **Washington**, *Dec. 31, 1923*		150.00

1923

610	2c **Harding**, perf. 11, *Sept. 1*		37.50
		Marion, O.	22.50
611	2c **Harding**, imperf., *Nov. 15*		90.00
612	2c **Harding**, perf. 10, *Sept. 12*		100.00

1924

614	1c **Huguenot-Walloon**, *May 1*, pair		30.00
		Albany, N.Y	30.00
		Allentown, Pa.	30.00
		Charleston, S.C.	30.00
		Jacksonville, Fla.	30.00
		Lancaster, Pa.	30.00
		Mayport, Fla.	30.00
		New Rochelle, N.Y.	30.00
		New York, N.Y.	30.00
		Philadelphia, Pa.	30.00
		Reading, Pa.	30.00
615	2c **Huguenot-Walloon**, *May 1*		45.00
		Albany, N.Y.	45.00
		Allentown, Pa.	45.00
		Charleston, S.C.	45.00
		Jacksonville, Fla.	45.00
		Lancaster, Pa.	45.00
		Mayport, Fla.	45.00
		New Rochelle, N.Y.	45.00
		New York, N.Y.	45.00
		Philadelphia, Pa.	45.00
		Reading, Pa.	45.00
616	5c **Huguenot-Walloon**, *May 1*		65.00
		Albany, N.Y.	65.00
		Allentown, Pa.	65.00
		Charleston, S.C.	65.00
		Jacksonville, Fla.	65.00
		Lancaster, Pa.	65.00
		Mayport, Fla.	65.00
		New Rochelle, N.Y.	65.00
		New York, N.Y.	65.00
		Philadelphia, Pa.	65.00
		Reading, Pa.	65.00
		614-616 on one cover, any city listed above	150.00
		614-616 on one cover, any other city	400.00

1925

617	1c **Lexington-Concord**, *Apr. 4*, pair		25.00
		Boston, Mass.	25.00
		Cambridge, Mass.	25.00
		Concord, Mass.	25.00
		Concord Junction, Mass.	25.00
		Lexington, Mass.	25.00
618	2c **Lexington-Concord**, *Apr. 4*		30.00
		Boston, Mass.	30.00
		Cambridge, Mass.	30.00
		Concord, Mass	30.00
		Concord Junction, Mass.	30.00
		Lexington, Mass.	42.50
619	5c **Lexington-Concord**, *Apr. 4*		75.00
		Boston, Mass.	75.00
		Cambridge, Mass.	75.00
		Concord, Mass.	75.00
		Concord Junction, Mass.	75.00
		Lexington, Mass.	75.00
		617-619 on one cover, Concord Junction or Lexington	175.00
		Set of 3 on one cover, any other city	150.00

1925

620	2c **Norse-American**, *May 18*		20.00
		Algona, Iowa	20.00
		Benson, Minn.	20.00
		Decorah, Iowa	20.00
		Minneapolis, Minn.	20.00
		Northfield, Minn.	20.00
		St. Paul, Minn.	20.00
621	5c **Norse-American**, *May 18*		25.00
		Algona, Iowa	25.00
		Benson, Minn.	25.00
		Decorah, Iowa	25.00
		Minneapolis, Minn.	25.00
		Northfield, Minn.	25.00
		St. Paul, Minn.	25.00
		620-621 on one cover, any city	50.00

1925-26

622	13c **Harrison**, *Jan. 11, 1926*		25.00
		Indianapolis, Ind.	40.00
		North Bend, Ohio *(500)*	200.00
623	17c **Wilson**, *Dec. 28, 1925*		15.00
		New York, N.Y.	15.00
		Princeton, N.J.	15.00
		Staunton, Va.	30.00

1926

627	2c **Sesquicentennial**, *May 10*		15.00
		Boston, Mass.	15.00
		Philadelphia, Pa.	15.00
628	5c **Ericsson**, *May 29*		40.00
		Chicago, Ill.	40.00
		Minneapolis, Minn.	40.00
		New York, N.Y.	40.00
629	2c **White Plains**, New York, N.Y., *Oct. 18*		6.25

	New York, N.Y., Inter-Philatelic Exhibition Agency cancellation		6.25
	White Plains, N.Y.		6.25
	Washington, D.C., *Oct. 28*		3.50
630	Sheet of 25, *Oct. 18*		1,800.
	Sheet of 25, *Oct. 28*		1,000.

1926-34   *Imperf.*

631	1½c **Harding**, *Aug. 27, 1926*, pair		35.00

Perf. 11x10½

632	1c **Franklin**, *June 10, 1927*, pair		45.00
632a	Booklet pane of 6, *Nov. 2, 1927*		4,000.
633	1½c **Harding**, *May 17, 1927*, pair		45.00
634	2c **Washington**, *Dec. 10, 1926*		50.00
635	3c **Lincoln**, *Feb. 3, 1927*		50.00
635a	3c bright violet, *Feb. 7, 1934*		25.00
636	4c **Martha Washington**, *May 17, 1927*		50.00
637	5c **Roosevelt**, *Mar. 24, 1927*		50.00
638	6c **Garfield**, *July 27, 1927*		60.00
639	7c **McKinley**, *Mar. 24, 1927*		60.00
		637, 639, both stamps issued *Mar. 24*	500.00
640	8c **Grant**, *June 10, 1927*		70.00
		632, 640, both stamps issued *June 10*	350.00
641	9c **Jefferson**, *May 17, 1927*		75.00
		633, 636, 641 all three stamps issued *May 17*	550.00
642	10c **Monroe**, *Feb. 3, 1927*		100.00

1927

643	2c **Vermont**, *Aug. 3*		6.00
		Bennington, Vt.	6.00
644	2c **Burgoyne**, *Aug. 3*		12.50
		Albany, N.Y.	12.50
		Rome, N.Y.	12.50
		Syracuse, N.Y.	12.50
		Utica, N.Y.	12.50

1928

645	2c **Valley Forge**, *May 26*		4.00
		Cleveland, O.	67.50
		Lancaster, Pa.	4.00
		Norristown, Pa.	4.00
		Philadelphia, Pa.	4.00
		Valley Forge, Pa.	4.00
		West Chester, Pa.	4.00
		Cleveland, Midwestern Philatelic Sta. cancellation	4.00
646	2c **Molly Pitcher**, *Oct. 20*		15.00
		Freehold, N.J.	15.00
		Red Bank, N.J.	15.00

1928

647	2c **Hawaii**, *Aug. 13*		15.00
		Honolulu, Hawaii	17.50
648	5c **Hawaii**, *Aug. 13*		22.50
		Honolulu, Hawaii	25.00
		647-648 on one cover	40.00
649	2c **Aero Conf.**, *Dec. 12*		7.00
650	5c **Aero Conf.**, *Dec. 12*		10.00
		649-650 on one cover	15.00

1929

651	2c **Clark**, Vincennes, Indiana, *Feb. 25*		6.00
		Washington, *Feb. 26*, first day of sale by Philatelic Agency	3.00

Perf. 11x10½

653	½c olive brown, *May 25*, block of four		27.50
654	2c **Electric Light**, perf. 11, Menlo Park, N.J., *June 5*		10.00
		Washington, D.C., *June 6*, first day of sale by Philatelic Agency	4.00
655	2c **Electric Light**, perf. 11x10½, *June 11*		80.00
656	2c **Electric Light**, perf. 10 vert., *June 11*		90.00
657	2c **Sullivan**, Auburn, N.Y., *June 17*		4.00
		Binghamton, N.Y.	4.00
		Canajoharie, N.Y.	4.00
		Canandaigua, N.Y.	4.00
		Elmira, N.Y.	4.00
		Geneseo, N.Y.	4.00
		Geneva, N.Y.	4.00
		Horseheads, N.Y.	4.00
		Owego, N.Y.	4.00
		Penn Yan, N.Y	4.00
		Perry, N.Y.	4.00
		Seneca Falls, N.Y.	4.00
		Waterloo, N.Y.	4.00
		Watkins Glen, N.Y.	4.00
		Waverly, N.Y.	4.00
		Washington, D.C., *June 18*	2.00

1929

658	1c **Kansas**, *May 1*, pair		50.00
		Newton, Kan., *Apr. 15*	325.00
659	1½c **Kansas**, *May 1*, pair		57.50
		Colby, Kan., *Apr. 16*	—
660	2c **Kansas**, *May 1*		57.50
		Colby, Kan., *Apr. 16*	—
661	3c **Kansas**, *May 1*		65.00
		Colby, Kan., *Apr. 16*	—
662	4c **Kansas**, *May 1*		100.00
		Colby, Kan., *Apr. 16*	—
663	5c **Kansas**, *May 1*		100.00
		Colby, Kan., *Apr. 16*	—
664	6c **Kansas**, *May 1*		125.00
		Newton, Kan., *Apr. 15*	900.00
665	7c **Kansas**, *May 1*		125.00
		Colby, Kan., *Apr. 16*	—
666	8c **Kansas**, *May 1*		125.00
		Newton, Kan., *Apr. 15*	900.00
667	9c **Kansas**, *May 1*		150.00
		Colby, Kan., *Apr. 16*	—

668	10c **Kansas**, *May 1*		200.00
		Colby, Kan., *Apr. 16*	—
		658-668 on 1 cover, Washington, D.C., *May 1*	1,500.
669	1c **Nebraska**, *May 1*, pair		50.00
		Beatrice, Neb., *Apr. 15*	250.00
670	1½c **Nebraska**, *May 1*, pair		52.50
		Hartington, Neb., *Apr. 15*	400.00
671	2c **Nebraska**, *May 1*		57.50
		Auburn, Neb., *Apr. 15*	1,200.
		Beatrice, Neb., *Apr. 15*	300.00
		Hartington, Neb., *Apr. 15*	400.00
672	3c **Nebraska**, *May 1*		70.00
		Beatrice, Neb., *Apr. 15*	400.00
		Hartington, Neb., *Apr. 15*	400.00
673	4c **Nebraska**, *May 1*		100.00
		Beatrice, Neb., *Apr. 15*	400.00
		Hartington, Neb., *Apr. 15*	400.00
674	5c **Nebraska**, *May 1*		100.00
		Beatrice, Neb., *Apr. 15*	275.00
		Hartington, Neb., *Apr. 15*	275.00
675	6c **Nebraska**, *May 1*		125.00
		Auburn, Neb., *Apr. 17*	400.00
		Ravenna, Neb., *Apr. 17*	—
		Wahoo, Neb., *Apr. 17*	—
676	7c **Nebraska**, *May 1*		150.00
		Auburn, Neb., *Apr. 17*	400.00
677	8c **Nebraska**, *May 1*		125.00
		Humbolt, Neb., *Apr. 17*	250.00
		Pawnee City, Neb., *Apr. 17*	400.00
678	9c **Nebraska**, *May 1*		150.00
		Cambridge, Neb., *Apr. 17*	400.00
679	10c **Nebraska**, *May 1*		200.00
		Tecumseh, Neb., *Apr. 18*	—
		669-679 on 1 cover, Washington, D.C., *May 1*	1,500.
		658-679 on 1 cover, Washington, D.C., *May 1*	5,000.
680	2c **Fallen Timbers**, Erie, Pa., *Sept. 14*		3.50
		Maumee, O.	3.50
		Perrysburg, O.	3.50
		Toledo, O.	3.50
		Waterville, O.	3.50
		Washington, D.C., *Sept. 16*	2.00
681	2c **Ohio River**, Cairo, Ill., *Oct. 19*		3.50
		Cincinnati, O.	3.50
		Evansville, Ind.	3.50
		Homestead, Pa.	3.50
		Louisville, Ky.	3.50
		Pittsburgh, Pa.	3.50
		Wheeling, W. Va.	3.50
		Washington, D.C., *Oct. 21*	2.00

1930

682	2c **Massachusetts Bay Colony**, Boston, Mass. *Apr. 8 (60,000)*		3.50
		Salem, Mass.	3.50
		Washington, D.C., *Apr. 11*	2.00
683	2c **Carolina-Charleston**, Charleston, S.C. *Apr. 10*		3.50
		Washington, D.C., *Apr. 11*	2.00

Perf. 11x10½

684	1½c **Harding**, Marion, O., *Dec. 1*, pair		4.50
		Washington, D.C., *Dec. 2*	2.50
685	4c **Taft**, Cincinnati, O., *June 4*		6.00
		Washington, D.C., *June 5*	3.00

Perf. 10 Vertically

686	1½c **Harding**, Marion, Ohio, *Dec. 1*		5.00
		Washington, D.C., *Dec. 2*	3.00
687	4c **Taft**, *Sept. 18*		20.00

Perf. 11

688	2c **Braddock**, Braddock, Pa., *July 9*		4.00
		Washington, D.C., *July 10*	2.00
689	2c **Von Steuben**, New York, N.Y., *Sept. 17*		4.00
		Washington, D.C., *Sept. 18*	2.00

1931

690	2c **Pulaski**, Brooklyn, N.Y., *Jan. 16*		4.00
		Buffalo, N.Y.	4.00
		Chicago, Ill.	4.00
		Cleveland, O.	4.00
		Detroit, Mich.	4.00
		Gary, Ind.	4.00
		Milwaukee, Wis.	4.00
		New York, N.Y.	4.00
		Pittsburgh, Pa.	4.00
		Savannah, Ga.	4.00
		South Bend, Ind.	4.00
		Toledo, O.	4.00
		Washington, D.C., *Jan. 17*	4.00

1931   Perf. 11x10½, 10½x11

692	11c **Hayes**, *Sept. 4*		100.
693	12c **Cleveland**, *Aug. 25*		100.
694	13c **Harrison**, *Sept. 4*		100.
695	14c **American Indian**, *Sept. 8*		100.
696	15c **Liberty**, *Aug. 27*		120.
697	17c **Wilson**, *July 25*, Brooklyn, N.Y.		2,750.
		Washington, D.C., *July 27*	400.
698	20c **Golden Gate**, *Sept. 8*		300.
699	25c **Niagara Falls**, *July 25*, Brooklyn, N.Y.		2,000.
		Washington, D.C., *July 27*	350.
		697, 699 on one cover, Brooklyn, *July 25*	5,750.
		697, 699 on one cover, Washington, *July 27*	2,500.
700	30c **American Buffalo**, *Sept. 8*		300.
701	50c **Arlington**, *Sept. 4*		400.
		Woolrich, Pa., *Sept. 4*	625.

1931

702	2c	**Red Cross**, *May 21*	3.50
		Dansville, N.Y.	3.50
703	2c	**Yorktown**, *Oct. 19*, Wethersfield, Conn.	3.50
		Yorktown, Va.	3.50
		Washington, D.C., *Oct. 20*	2.00

1932

WASHINGTON BICENTENNIAL ISSUE

704	½c	*Jan. 1*, block of 4	5.00
705	1c	*Jan. 1*, pair	5.00
706	1½c	*Jan. 1*, pair	5.00
707	2c	*Jan. 1*	5.00
708	3c	*Jan. 1*	5.00
709	4c	*Jan. 1*	5.00
710	5c	*Jan. 1*	5.00
711	6c	*Jan. 1*	5.00
712	7c	*Jan. 1*	5.00
713	8c	*Jan. 1*	5.50
714	9c	*Jan. 1*	5.50
715	10c	*Jan. 1*	5.50
		704-715, set of 12 on one cover, *Jan. 1*	70.00

1932

716	2c	**Olympic Winter Games**, *Jan. 25*, Lake Placid, N.Y.	6.00
		Washington, D.C., *Jan. 26*	1.50
717	2c	**Arbor Day**, *Apr. 22*, Nebraska City, Neb.	4.00
		Washington, D.C., *Apr. 23*	1.50
		Adams, N.Y., *Apr. 23*	6.50
718	3c	**Olympic Summer Games**, *June 15*, Los Angeles, Cal.	6.00
		Washington, D.C., *June 16*	2.75
719	5c	**Olympic Summer Games**, *June 15*, Los Angeles, Cal.	8.00
		Washington, D.C., *June 16*	2.75
		718, 719 on one cover, Los Angeles, Cal.	10.00
		718, 719 on one cover, Washington, D.C.	4.50
720	3c	**Washington**, *June 16*	7.50
720b		Booklet pane of 6, *July 25*	100.00
721	3c	**Washington Coil**, Sideways, *June 24*	15.00
722	3c	**Washington Coil**, Endways, *Oct. 12*	15.00
723	6c	**Garfield Coil**, Sideways, *Aug. 18*, Los Angeles, Cal.	15.00
		Washington, D.C., *Aug. 19*	4.00
724	3c	**William Penn**, *Oct. 24*, New Castle, Del.	3.25
		Chester, Pa.	3.25
		Philadelphia, Pa.	3.25
		Washington, D.C., *Oct. 25*	1.25
725	3c	**Daniel Webster**, *Oct. 24*, Franklin, N.H.	3.25
		Exeter, N.H.	3.25
		Hanover, N.H.	3.25
		Washington, D.C., *Oct. 25*	1.25

1933

726	3c	**Gen. Oglethorpe**, *Feb. 12*, Savannah, Ga., *(200,000)*	3.25
		Washington, D.C., *Feb. 13*	1.50
727	3c	**Peace Proclamation**, *Apr. 19*, Newburgh, N.Y. *(349,571)*	3.50
		Washington, D.C., *Apr. 20*	1.25
728	1c	**Century of Progress**, *May 25*, Chicago, Ill., strip of 3	3.00
		Washington, D.C., *May 26*	1.00
729	3c	**Century of Progress**, *May 25*, Chicago, Ill.	3.00
		Washington, D.C., *May 26*	1.00
		728, 729 on one cover	5.00

Covers mailed May 25, bearing Nos. 728 and 729 total 232,251.

730	1c	**American Philatelic Society**, sheet of 25, *Aug. 25*, Chicago, Ill.	100.00
730a	1c	**A.P.S.**, imperf., *Aug. 25*, Chicago, Ill., strip of 3	3.25
		Washington, D.C., *Aug. 28*	1.25
731	3c	**American Philatelic Society**, sheet of 25, *Aug. 25*, Chicago, Ill.	100.00
731a	3c	**A.P.S.**, single, imperf., *Aug. 25*, Chicago, Ill.	3.25
		Washington, D.C., *Aug. 28*	1.25
		730a, 731a on one cover	5.50

Covers mailed Aug. 25 bearing Nos. 730, 730a, 731, 731a total 65,218.

732	3c	**National Recovery Administration**, *Aug. 15*, *(65,000)*	3.25
		Nira, Iowa, *Aug. 17*	2.50
733	3c	**Byrd Antarctic**, *Oct. 9*	10.00
734	5c	**Kosciuszko**, *Oct. 13*, Boston, Mass. *(23,025)*	4.50
		Buffalo, N.Y. *(14,981)*	5.50
		Chicago, Ill. *(26,306)*	4.50
		Detroit, Mich. *(17,792)*	5.25
		Pittsburgh, Pa. *(6,282)*	15.00
		Kosciuszko, Miss. *(27,093)*	5.25
		St. Louis, Mo. *(17,872)*	5.25
		Washington, D.C., *Oct. 14*	1.60

1934

735	3c	**National Exhibition**, sheet of 6, Byrd imperf., *Feb. 10*, New York, N.Y.	40.00
		Washington, D.C., *Feb. 19*	27.50
735a	3c	**National Exhibition**, single, imperf., New York, N.Y., *Feb. 10 (450,715)*	5.00
		Washington, D.C., *Feb. 19*	2.75
736	3c	**Maryland Tercentenary**, *Mar. 23* St. Mary's City, Md. *(148,785)*	1.60
		Washington, D.C., *Mar. 24*	1.00

737	3c	**Mothers of America**, perf. 11x10½, *May 2*, any city	1.60
738	3c	**Mothers of America**, perf. 11, *May 2*, any city	1.60
		737, 738 on one cover	4.00

Covers mailed at Washington, May 2 bearing Nos. 737 and 738 total 183,359.

739	3c	**Wisconsin**, *July 7*, Green Bay, Wisc. *(130,000)*	1.10
		Washington, D.C., *July 9*	1.00
740	1c	**Parks, Yosemite**, *July 16*	2.25
		Yosemite, Cal., *(60,000)*, strip of 3	2.75
741	2c	**Parks, Grand Canyon**, *July 24*	2.25
		Grand Canyon, Ariz., *(75,000)*, pair	2.75
742	3c	**Parks, Mt. Rainier**, *Aug. 3*	2.50
		Longmire, Wash., *(64,500)*	3.00
743	4c	**Parks, Mesa Verde**, *Sept. 25*	2.25
		Mesa Verde, Colo., *(51,882)*	2.75
744	5c	**Parks, Yellowstone**, *July 30*	2.25
		Yellowstone, Wyo., *(87,000)*	2.50
745	6c	**Parks, Crater Lake**, *Sept. 5*	3.00
		Crater Lake, Ore., *(45,282)*	3.25
746	7c	**Parks, Arcadia**, *Oct. 2*	3.00
		Bar Harbor, Maine *(51,312)*	3.25
747	8c	**Parks, Zion**, *Sept. 18*	3.25
		Zion, Utah, *(43,650)*	3.75
748	9c	**Parks, Glacier Park**, *Aug. 27*	3.50
		Glacier Park, Mont., *(52,626)*	3.75
749	10c	**Parks, Smoky Mountains**, *Oct. 8*	6.00
		Sevierville, Tenn., *(39,000)*	7.50

Imperf

750	3c	**American Philatelic Society**, sheet of 6, *Aug. 28*, Atlantic City, N.J.	40.00
750a		**A.P.S.**, single, *Aug. 28*, Atlantic City, N.J. *(40,000)*	3.25
		Washington, D.C., *Sept. 4*	2.00
751	1c	**Trans-Mississippi Philatelic Expo.**, sheet of 6, *Oct. 10*, Omaha, Neb.	35.00
751a	1c	**Trans-Miss. Phil. Expo.**, Omaha, Neb., *Oct. 10 (125,000)*, strip of 3	3.25
		Washington, D.C., *Oct. 15*	2.00

1935

SPECIAL PRINTING
Nos. 752-771 issued Mar. 15

752	3c	**Peace Commemoration**	5.00
753	3c	**Byrd**	6.00
754	3c	**Mothers of America**	6.00
755	3c	**Wisconsin Tercentenary**	6.00
756	1c	**Parks, Yosemite**, strip of 3	6.00
757	2c	**Parks, Grand Canyon**, pair	6.00
758	3c	**Parks, Mount Rainier**	6.00
759	4c	**Parks, Mesa Verde**	6.50
760	5c	**Parks, Yellowstone**	6.50
761	6c	**Parks, Crater Lake**	6.50
762	7c	**Parks, Acadia**	6.50
763	8c	**Parks, Zion**	7.50
764	9c	**Parks, Glacier Park**	7.50
765	10c	**Parks, Smoky Mountains**	7.50
766a	1c	**Century of Progress**, strip of 3	5.50
		Pane of 25	250.00
767a	3c	**Century of Progress**	5.50
		Pane of 25	250.00
768a	3c	**Byrd**	6.50
		Pane of 6	250.00
769a	1c	**Parks, Yosemite**, strip of 3	4.00
		Pane of 6	250.00
770a	3c	**Parks, Mount Rainier**	5.00
		Pane of 6	250.00
771	16c	**Airmail Special Delivery**	12.50

> **Catalogue values from this point to No. 986 are for addressed covers with the most common cachets.**

772	3c	**Connecticut Tercentenary**, *Apr. 26*, Hartford, Conn. *(217,800)*	14.00
		Washington, D.C., *Apr. 27*	2.25
773	3c	**California Exposition**, *May 29*, San Diego, Cal. *(214,042)*	14.00
		Washington, D.C., *May 31*	1.50
774	3c	**Boulder Dam**, *Sept. 30*, Boulder City, Nev. *(166,180)*	15.00
		Washington, D.C., *Oct. 1*	2.00
775	3c	**Michigan Centenary**, *Nov. 1*, Lansing, Mich. *(176,962)*	15.00
		Washington, D.C., *Nov. 2*	1.50

1936

776	3c	**Texas Centennial**, *Mar. 2*, Gonzales, Texas *(319,150)*	20.00
		Washington, D.C., *Mar. 3*	2.00
777	3c	**Rhode Island Tercentenary**, *May 4*, Providence, R.I. *(245,400)*	12.50
		Washington, D.C., *May 5*	2.25
778		**TIPEX** souvenir sheet, *May 9 (297,194)* New York, N.Y. (TIPEX cancellation)	14.00
		Washington, D.C., *May 11*	3.50
782	3c	**Arkansas Centennial**, *June 15*, Little Rock, Ark. *(376,693)*	13.00
		Washington, D.C., *June 16*	1.25
783	3c	**Oregon Territory Centennial**, *July 14*, Astoria, Ore. *(91,110)*	10.00
		Daniel, Wyo. *(67,013)*	10.00
		Lewiston, Ida., *(86,100)*	10.00
		Missoula, Mont., *(59,883)*	11.00
		Walla Walla, Wash., *(106,150)*	9.00
		Washington, D.C., *July 15*	1.25
784	3c	**Susan B. Anthony**, *Aug. 26 (178,500)*	15.00

1936-37

785	1c	**Army**, *Dec. 15, 1936*, strip of 3	8.00
786	2c	**Army**, *Jan. 15, 1937*, pair	8.00
787	3c	**Army**, *Feb. 18, 1937*	8.00
788	4c	**Army**, *Mar. 23, 1937*	8.00
789	5c	**Army**, *May 26, 1937*, West Point, N.Y., *(160,000)*	8.00
		Washington, D.C., *May 27*	4.00
790	1c	**Navy**, *Dec. 15, 1936*, strip of 3	8.00
791	2c	**Navy**, *Jan. 15, 1937*, pair	8.00
792	3c	**Navy**, *Feb. 18, 1937*	8.00
793	4c	**Navy**, *Mar. 23, 1937*	8.00
794	5c	**Navy**, *May 26, 1937*, Annapolis, Md., *(202,806)*	8.00
		Washington, D.C., *May 27*	4.00

Covers for #785 & 790 total 390, 749; #786 & 791 total 292,570; #787 & 792 total 320,888; #788 & 793 total 331,000.

1937

795	3c	**Ordinance of 1787**, *July 13* Marietta, Ohio *(130,531)*	9.00
		New York, N.Y. *(125,134)*	9.00
		Washington, D.C., *July 14*	1.25
796	5c	**Virginia Dare**, *Aug. 18*, Manteo, N.C. *(226,730)*	11.00
797	10c	**Souvenir Sheet**, *Aug. 26*, Asheville, N.C. *(164,215)*	11.00
798	3c	**Constitution**, *Sept. 17*, Philadelphia, Pa. *(281,478)*	9.00
799	3c	**Hawaii**, *Oct. 18*, Honolulu, Hawaii *(320,334)*	11.00
800	3c	**Alaska**, *Nov. 12*, Juneau, Alaska *(230,370)*	10.00
801	3c	**Puerto Rico**, *Nov. 25*, San Juan, P.R. *(244,054)*	10.00
802	3c	**Virgin Islands**, *Dec. 15*, Charlotte Amalie, V.I. *(225,469)*	10.00

1938

PRESIDENTIAL ISSUE

803	½c	**Franklin**, *May 19*, Philadelphia, Pa. *(224,901)*, block of 6	3.50
804	1c	**G. Washington**, *Apr. 25 (124,037)*, strip of 3	3.50
804b		Booklet pane of 6, *Jan. 27, 1939*	12.50
805	1½c	**M. Washington**, *May 5 (128,339)*, pair	3.50
806	2c	**J. Adams**, *June 3 (127,806)*, pair	3.50
806b		Booklet pane of 6, *Jan. 27, 1939*	15.00
807	3c	**Jefferson**, *June 16 (118,097)*	3.50
807a		Booklet pane of 6, *Jan. 27, 1939*	17.50
808	4c	**Madison**, *July 1 (118,765)*	3.50
809	4½c	**White House**, *July 11 (115,820)*	3.50
810	5c	**Monroe**, *July 21 (98,282)*	3.50
811	6c	**J.Q. Adams**, *July 28 (97,428)*	3.50
812	7c	**Jackson**, *Aug. 4 (98,414)*	3.50
813	8c	**Van Buren**, *Aug. 11 (94,857)*	3.50
814	9c	**W.H. Harrison**, *Aug. 18 (91,229)*	3.50
815	10c	**Tyler**, *Sept. 2 (83,707)*	3.50
816	11c	**Polk**, *Sept. 8 (63,966)*	5.00
817	12c	**Taylor**, *Sept. 14 (62,935)*	5.00
818	13c	**Fillmore**, *Sept. 22 (58,965)*	5.00
819	14c	**Pierce**, *Oct. 6 (49,819)*	5.00
820	15c	**Buchanan**, *Oct. 13 (52,209)*	5.00
821	16c	**Lincoln**, *Oct. 20 (59,566)*	7.00
822	17c	**A. Johnson**, *Oct. 27 (55,024)*	6.00
823	18c	**Grant**, *Nov. 3 (53,124)*	6.00
824	19c	**Hayes**, *Nov. 10 (54,124)*	6.00
825	20c	**Garfield**, *Nov. 10 (51,971)*	7.00
826	21c	**Arthur**, *Nov. 22 (44,367)*	7.00
827	22c	**Cleveland**, *Nov. 22 (44,358)*	8.00
828	24c	**B. Harrison**, *Dec. 2 (46,592)*	8.00
829	25c	**McKinley**, *Dec. 2 (45,691)*	8.00
830	30c	**T. Roosevelt**, *Dec. 8 (43,528)*	9.00
831	50c	**Taft**, *Dec. 8 (41,984)*	12.50
832	$1	**Wilson**, purple & black, *Aug. 29 (24,618)*	50.00
832c		red violet & black, *Aug. 31, 1954 (20,202)*	25.00
833	$2	**Harding**, *Sept. 29 (19,895)*	100.00
834	$5	**Coolidge**, *Nov. 17 (15,615)*	175.00

1938

835	3c	**Constitution**, *June 21*, Philadelphia, Pa. *(232,873)*	15.00
836	3c	**Swedes and Finns**, *June 27*, Wilmington, Del. *(225,617)*	15.00
837	3c	**Northwest Sesqui.**, *July 15*, Marietta, Ohio *(180,170)*	15.00
838	3c	**Iowa**, *Aug. 24*, Des Moines, Iowa *(209,860)*	15.00

1939

COIL STAMPS
Perf. 10 Vertically

839	1c	**G. Washington**, *Jan. 20*, strip of 3	5.00
840	1½c	**M. Washington**, *Jan. 20*, pair	5.00
841	2c	**J. Adams**, *Jan. 20*, pair	5.00
842	3c	**Jefferson**, *Jan. 20*	5.00
843	4c	**Madison**, *Jan. 20*	5.00
844	4½c	**White House**, *Jan. 20*	5.00
845	5c	**Monroe**, *Jan. 20*	5.00
846	6c	**J.Q. Adams**, *Jan. 20*	6.50
847	10c	**Tyler**, *Jan. 20*	9.00
		839-847 on one cover, *Jan. 20*	45.00

Perf. 10 Horizontally

848	1c	Strip of 3, *Jan. 27*	5.00
849	1½c	Pair, *Jan. 27*	5.00
850	2c	Pair, *Jan. 27*	5.00
851	3c	*Jan. 27*	5.50
		848-851 on one cover, *Jan. 27*	25.00

1939

852　3c **Golden Gate Expo,** *Feb. 18,* San Francisco, Cal. *(352,165)* ... 16.00
853　3c **N.Y. World's Fair,** *Apr. 1,* New York, N.Y. *(585,565)* ... 20.00
854　3c **Washington Inauguration,** *Apr. 30,* New York, N.Y. *(395,644)* ... 17.50
855　3c **Baseball Centennial,** *June 12,* Cooperstown, N.Y. *(398,199)* ... 40.00
856　3c **Panama Canal,** *Aug. 15,* U.S.S. Charleston, Canal Zone *(230,974)* ... 18.00
857　3c **Printing Tercentenary,** *Sept. 25,* New York, N.Y. *(295,270)* ... 15.00
858　3c **50th Statehood Anniversary,** Bismarck, N.D. *Nov. 2 (142,106)* ... 12.50
　　　　Pierre, S.D., *Nov. 2 (150,429)* ... 12.50
　　　　Helena, Mont., *Nov. 8 (130,273)* ... 12.50
　　　　Olympia, Wash., *Nov. 11 (150,429)* ... 12.50

1940

FAMOUS AMERICANS

859　1c **Washington Irving,** *Jan. 29,* Tarrytown, N.Y. *(170,969),* strip of 3 ... 4.50
860　2c **James Fenimore Cooper,** *Jan. 29,* Cooperstown, N.Y. *(154,836),* pair ... 3.00
861　3c **Ralph Waldo Emerson,** *Feb. 5,* Boston, Mass. *(185,148)* ... 3.00
862　5c **Louisa May Alcott,** *Feb. 5,* Concord, Mass. *(134,325)* ... 4.00
863　10c **Samuel L. Clemens,** *Feb. 13,* Hannibal, Mo. *(150,492)* ... 8.00
864　1c **Henry W. Longfellow,** *Feb. 16,* Portland, Me. *(160,508),* strip of 3 ... 3.00
865　2c **John Greenleaf Whittier,** *Feb. 16,* Haverhill, Mass. *(148,423),* pair ... 3.00
866　3c **James Russell Lowell,** *Feb. 20,* Cambridge, Mass. *(148,735)* ... 3.00
867　5c **Walt Whitman,** *Feb. 20,* Camden, N.J. *(134,185)* ... 4.00
868　10c **James Whitcomb Riley,** *Feb. 24,* Greenfield, Ind. *(131,760)* ... 6.00
869　1c **Horace Mann,** *Mar. 14,* Boston, Mass. *(186,854),* strip of 3 ... 3.00
870　2c **Mark Hopkins,** *Mar. 14,* Williamstown, Mass. *(140,286),* pair ... 3.00
871　3c **Charles W. Eliot,** *Mar. 28,* Cambridge, Mass. *(155,708)* ... 3.00
872　5c **Frances E. Willard,** *Mar. 28,* Evanston, Ill. *(140,483)* ... 4.00
873　10c **Booker T. Washington,** *Apr. 7,* Tuskegee Institute, Ala. *(163,507)* ... 10.00
874　1c **John James Audubon,** *Apr. 8,* St. Francisville, La. *(144,123),* strip of 3 ... 3.00
875　2c **Dr. Crawford W. Long,** *Apr. 8,* Jefferson, Ga. *(158,128),* pair ... 3.00
876　3c **Luther Burbank,** *Apr. 17,* Santa Rosa, Cal. *(147,033)* ... 3.00
877　5c **Dr. Walter Reed,** *Apr. 17 (154,464)* ... 4.00
878　10c **Jane Addams,** *Apr. 26,* Chicago, Ill. *(132,375)* ... 6.00
879　1c **Stephen Collins Foster,** *May 3,* Bardstown, Ky. *(183,461),* strip of 3 ... 3.00
880　2c **John Philip Sousa,** *May 3 (131,422),* pair ... 4.00
881　3c **Victor Herbert,** *May 13,* New York, N.Y. *(168,200)* ... 3.00
882　5c **Edward A. MacDowell,** *May 13,* Peterborough, N.H. *(135,155)* ... 4.00
883　10c **Ethelbert Nevin,** *June 10,* Pittsburgh, Pa. *(121,951)* ... 6.00
884　1c **Gilbert Stuart,** *Sept. 5,* Narragansett, R.I. *(131,965),* strip of 3 ... 3.00
885　2c **James A. McNeill Whistler,** *Sept. 5,* Lowell, Mass. *(130,962),* pair ... 3.00
886　3c **Augustus Saint-Gaudens,** *Sept. 16,* New York, N.Y. *(138,200)* ... 3.00
887　5c **Daniel Chester French,** *Sept. 16,* Stockbridge, Mass. *(124,608)* ... 4.00
888　10c **Frederic Remington,** *Sept. 30,* Canton, N.Y. *(116,219)* ... 7.00
889　1c **Eli Whitney,** *Oct. 7,* Savannah, Ga. *(140,868),* strip of 3 ... 3.00
890　2c **Samuel F.B. Morse,** *Oct. 7,* New York, N.Y. *(135,388),* pair ... 3.00
891　3c **Cyrus Hall McCormick,** *Oct. 14,* Lexington, Va. *(137,415)* ... 3.00
892　5c **Elias Howe,** *Oct. 14,* Spencer, Mass. *(126,334)* ... 4.00
893　10c **Alexander Graham Bell,** *Oct. 28,* Boston, Mass. *(125,372)* ... 10.00

1940

894　3c **Pony Express,** *Apr. 3,* St. Joseph, Mo. *(194,589)* ... 12.00
　　　　Sacramento, Cal. *(160,849)* ... 12.00
895　3c **Pan American Union,** *Apr. 14 (182,401)* ... 9.50
896　3c **Idaho Statehood,** *July 3,* Boise, Idaho *(156,429)* ... 9.50
897　3c **Wyoming Statehood,** *July 10* Cheyenne, Wyo. *(156,709)* ... 9.50
898　3c **Coronado Expedition,** *Sept. 7,* Albuquerque, N.M. *(161,012)* ... 9.50
899　1c **Defense,** *Oct. 16,* strip of 3 ... 7.00
900　2c **Defense,** *Oct. 16,* pair ... 7.00
901　3c **Defense,** *Oct. 16* ... 7.00
　　　　899-901 on one cover ... 12.00

First day cancel was applied to 450,083 covers bearing one or more of Nos. 899-901.

902　3c **Thirteenth Amendment,** *Oct. 20,* World's Fair, N.Y. *(156,146)* ... 10.00

1941

903　3c **Vermont Statehood,** *Mar. 4,* Montpelier, Vt. *(182,423)* ... 10.00

MacArthur, W. Va.
Apr 15, 1942
First Day Cover

Covers exist with this cancellation. "First Day" refers to the first day of the new name of the town, previously known as Hollywood, W. Va.

1942

904　3c **Kentucky Statehood,** *June 1,* Frankfort, Ky. *(155,730)* ... 10.00
905　3c **"Win the War",** *July 4 (191,168)* ... 10.00
906　5c **Chinese Resistance,** *July 7,* Denver, Colo. *(168,746)* ... 12.00

1943-44

907　2c **Allied Nations,** *Jan. 14, 1943 (178,865),* pair ... 6.00
908　1c **Four Freedoms,** *Feb. 12, 1943 (193,800),* strip of 3 ... 6.00
909　5c **Poland,** *June 22, 1943,* Chicago, Ill. *(88,170)* ... 6.00
　　　　Washington, D.C. *(136,002)* ... 5.00
910　5c **Czechoslovakia,** *July 12, 1943 (145,112)* ... 4.00
911　5c **Norway,** *July 27, 1943 (155,054)* ... 4.00
912　5c **Luxemburg,** *Aug. 10, 1943 (166,367)* ... 4.00
913　5c **Netherlands,** *Aug. 24, 1943 (148,763)* ... 4.00
914　5c **Belgium,** *Sept. 14, 1943 (154,220)* ... 4.00
915　5c **France,** *Sept. 28, 1943 (163,478)* ... 4.00
916　5c **Greece,** *Oct. 12, 1943 (166,553)* ... 4.00
917　5c **Yugoslavia,** *Oct. 26, 1943 (161,835)* ... 4.00
918　5c **Albania,** *Nov. 9, 1943 (162,275)* ... 4.00
919　5c **Austria,** *Nov. 23, 1943 (172,285)* ... 4.00
920　5c **Denmark,** *Dec. 7, 1943 (173,784)* ... 4.00
921　5c **Korea,** *Nov. 2, 1944 (192,860)* ... 5.00

1944

922　3c **Railroad,** *May 10,* Ogden, Utah *(151,324)* ... 10.00
　　　　Omaha, Neb. *(171,000)* ... 10.00
　　　　San Francisco, Cal. *(125,000)* ... 10.00
923　3c **Steamship,** *May 22,* Kings Point, N.Y. *(152,324)* ... 9.00
　　　　Savannah, Ga. *(181,472)* ... 9.00
924　3c **Telegraph,** *May 24 (141,907)* ... 9.00
　　　　Baltimore, Md. *(136,480)* ... 9.00
925　3c **Philippines,** *Sept. 27 (214,865)* ... 9.00
926　3c **Motion Picture,** *Oct. 31,* Hollywood, Cal. *(190,660)* ... 10.00
　　　　New York, N.Y. *(176,473)* ... 9.00

1945

927　3c **Florida,** *Mar. 3,* Tallahassee, Fla. *(228,435)* ... 9.00
928　5c **United Nations Conference,** *Apr. 25,* San Francisco, Cal. *(417,450)* ... 10.00
929　3c **Iwo Jima,** *July 11 (391,650)* ... 15.00

1945-46

930　1c **Roosevelt,** *July 26, 1945,* Hyde Park, N.Y. *(390,219),* strip of 3 ... 5.00
931　2c **Roosevelt,** *Aug. 24, 1945,* Warm Springs, Ga. *(426,142),* pair ... 5.00
932　3c **Roosevelt,** *June 27, 1945 (391,650)* ... 5.00
933　5c **Roosevelt,** *Jan. 30, 1946 (466,766)* ... 5.00

1945

934　3c **Army,** *Sept. 28 (392,300)* ... 11.00
935　3c **Navy,** *Oct. 27,* Annapolis, Md. *(460,352)* ... 11.00
936　3c **Coast Guard,** *Nov. 10* New York, N.Y. *(405,280)* ... 11.00
937　3c **Alfred E. Smith,** *Nov. 26* New York, N.Y. *(424,950)* ... 3.00
938　3c **Texas,** *Dec. 29,* Austin, Tex. *(397,860)* ... 9.00

1946

939　3c **Merchant Marine,** *Feb. 26 (432,141)* ... 9.00
940　3c **Veterans of WWII,** *May 9 (492,786)* ... 11.00
941　3c **Tennessee,** *June 1, 1946,* Nashville, Tenn. *(463,512)* ... 4.00
942　3c **Iowa,** *Aug. 3,* Iowa City, Iowa *(517,505)* ... 4.00
943　3c **Smithsonian,** *Aug. 10 (402,448)* ... 4.00
944　3c **Kearny Expedition,** *Oct. 16,* Santa Fe, N.M. *(384,300)* ... 4.00

1947

945　3c **Thomas A. Edison,** *Feb. 11,* Milan, Ohio *(632,473)* ... 5.00
946　3c **Joseph Pulitzer,** *Apr. 10,* New York, N.Y. *(580,870)* ... 4.00
947　3c **Stamp Centenary,** *May 17,* New York, N.Y. *(712,873)* ... 4.00
948　5c and 10c **Centenary Exhibition Sheet,** *May 19,* New York, N.Y. *(502,175)* ... 4.50
949　3c **Doctors,** *June 9,* Atlantic City, N.J. *(508,016)* ... 9.00
950　3c **Utah,** *July 24,* Salt Lake City, Utah *(456,416)* ... 3.00
951　3c **"Constitution,"** *Oct. 21,* Boston, Mass. *(683,416)* ... 9.00
952　3c **Everglades Park,** *Dec. 5,* Florida City, Fla. *(466,647)* ... 3.00

1948

953　3c **Carver,** *Jan. 5,* Tuskegee Institute, Ala. *(402,174)* ... 3.00
954　3c **California Gold,** *Jan. 24,* Coloma, Calif. *(526,154)* ... 4.00
955　3c **Mississippi Territory,** *Apr. 7,* Natchez, Miss. *(434,804)* ... 2.00

956　3c **Four Chaplains,** *May 28 (459,070)* ... 10.00
957　3c **Wisconsin Centennial,** *May 29,* Madison, Wis. *(470,280)* ... 3.00
958　5c **Swedish Pioneers,** *June 4* Chicago, Ill. *(364,318)* ... 4.00
959　3c **Women's Progress,** *July 19,* Seneca Falls, N.Y. *(401,923)* ... 3.00
960　3c **William Allen White,** *July 31,* Emporia, Kans. *(385,648)* ... 2.50
961　3c **U.S.-Canada Friendship,** *Aug. 2,* Niagara Falls, N.Y. *(406,467)* ... 3.00
962　3c **Francis Scott Key,** *Aug. 9,* Frederick, Md. *(505,930)* ... 2.50
963　3c **Salute to Youth,** *Aug. 11 (347,070)* ... 2.50
964　3c **Oregon Territory Establishment,** *Aug. 14,* Oregon City, Ore. *(365,898)* ... 3.00
965　3c **Harlan Fiske Stone,** *Aug. 25,* Chesterfield, N.H. *(362,170)* ... 2.50
966　3c **Palomar Observatory,** *Aug. 30,* Palomar Mountain, Calif. *(401,365)* ... 5.00
967　3c **Clara Barton,** *Sept. 7,* Oxford, Mass. *(362,000)* ... 4.00
968　3c **Poultry Industry,** *Sept. 9,* New Haven, Conn. *(475,000)* ... 3.00
969　3c **Gold Star Mothers,** *Sept. 21 (386,064)* ... 2.00
970　3c **Fort Kearny,** *Sept. 22,* Minden, Neb. *(429,633)* ... 2.00
971　3c **Volunteer Firemen,** *Oct. 4,* Dover, Del. *(399,630)* ... 10.00
972　3c **Indian Centennial,** *Oct. 15,* Muskogee, Okla. *(459,528)* ... 3.50
973　3c **Rough Riders,** *Oct. 27,* Prescott, Ariz. *(399,198)* ... 2.50
974　3c **Juliette Low,** *Oct. 29,* Savannah, Ga. *(476,573)* ... 8.00
975　3c **Will Rogers,** *Nov. 4,* Claremore, Okla. *(450,350)* ... 2.50
976　3c **Fort Bliss,** *Nov. 5,* El Paso, Tex. *(421,000)* ... 5.00
977　3c **Moina Michael,** *Nov. 9,* Athens, Ga. *(374,090)* ... 2.50
978　3c **Gettysburg Address,** *Nov. 19,* Gettysburg, Pa. *(511,990)* ... 2.75
979　3c **American Turners Society,** *Nov. 20,* Cincinnati, Ohio *(434,090)* ... 2.00
980　3c **Joel Chandler Harris,** *Dec. 9,* Eatonton, Ga. *(426,199)* ... 2.25

1949

981　3c **Minnesota Territory,** *Mar. 3,* St. Paul, Minn. *(458,750)* ... 2.25
982　3c **Washington and Lee University,** *Apr. 12,* Lexington, Va. *(447,910)* ... 2.25
983　3c **Puerto Rico Election,** *Apr. 27,* San Juan, P.R. *(390,416)* ... 2.25
984　3c **Annapolis, Md.,** *May 23,* Annapolis, Md. *(441,802)* ... 3.00
985　3c **G.A.R.,** *Aug. 29,* Indianapolis, Ind. *(471,696)* ... 3.25
986　3c **Edgar Allan Poe,** *Oct. 7,* Richmond, Va. *(371,020)* ... 4.00

> Catalogue values from this point to the end of the section are for unaddressed covers with the most common cachets.

1950

987　3c **American Bankers Assoc.,** *Jan. 3,* Saratoga Springs, N.Y. *(388,622)* ... 2.75
988　3c **Samuel Gompers,** *Jan. 27 (332,023)* ... 1.75

National Capital Sesquicentennial

989　3c **Freedom,** *Apr. 20 (371,743)* ... 1.50
990　3c **Executive,** *June 12 (376,789)* ... 1.50
991　3c **Judicial,** *Aug. 2 (324,007)* ... 1.50
992　3c **Legislative,** *Nov. 22 (352,215)* ... 1.50
993　3c **Railroad Engineers,** *Apr. 29,* Jackson, Tenn. *(420,830)* ... 4.00
994　3c **Kansas City Centenary,** *June 3,* Kansas City, Mo. *(405,390)* ... 1.50
995　3c **Boy Scouts,** *June 30,* Valley Forge, Pa. *(622,972)* ... 12.00
996　3c **Indiana Territory Sesquicentennial,** *July 4,* Vincennes, Ind. *(359,643)* ... 1.75
997　3c **California Statehood,** *Sept. 9,* Sacramento, Cal. *(391,919)* ... 2.50

1951

998　3c **United Confederate Veterans,** *May 30,* Norfolk, Va. *(374,235)* ... 3.00
999　3c **Nevada Centennial,** *July 14,* Genoa, Nev. *(336,890)* ... 1.50
1000　3c **Landing of Cadillac,** *July 24,* Detroit, Mich. *(323,094)* ... 1.50
1001　3c **Colorado Statehood,** *Aug. 1,* Minturn, Colo. *(311,568)* ... 1.50
1002　3c **American Chemical Society,** *Sept. 4,* New York, N.Y. *(436,419)* ... 1.75
1003　3c **Battle of Brooklyn,** *Dec. 10,* Brooklyn, N.Y. *(420,000)* ... 1.50

1952

1004　3c **Betsy Ross,** *Jan. 2,* Philadelphia, Pa. *(314,312)* ... 1.50
1005　3c **4-H Club,** *Jan. 15,* Springfield, Ohio *(383,290)* ... 3.25
1006　3c **B. & O. Railroad,** *Feb. 28,* Baltimore, Md. *(441,600)* ... 4.50
1007　3c **American Automobile Association,** *Mar. 4,* Chicago, Ill. *(520,123)* ... 1.75
1008　3c **NATO,** *Apr. 4 (313,518)* ... 1.50
1009　3c **Grand Coulee Dam,** *May 15,* Grand Coulee, Wash. *(341,680)* ... 1.50

1010 3c **Lafayette,** *June 13,* Georgetown, S.C. *(349,102)* 1.50
1011 3c **Mt. Rushmore Memorial,** *Aug. 11,* Keystone, S.D. *(337,027)* 1.50
1012 3c **Civil Engineers,** *Sept. 6,* Chicago, Ill. *(318,483)* 1.50
1013 3c **Service Women,** *Sept. 11* (308,062) 1.75
1014 3c **Gutenberg Bible,** *Sept. 30* (387,078) 1.50
1015 3c **Newspaper Boys,** *Oct. 4,* Philadelphia, Pa. *(626,000)* 1.50
1016 3c **Red Cross,** *Nov. 21,* New York, N.Y. *(439,252)* 2.00

1953
1017 3c **National Guard,** *Feb. 23* (387,618) 2.00
1018 3c **Ohio Sesquicentennial,** *Mar. 2,* Chillicothe, Ohio *(407,983)* 1.50
1019 3c **Washington Territory,** *Mar. 2,* Olympia, Wash. *(344,047)* 1.50
1020 3c **Louisiana Purchase,** *Apr. 30,* St. Louis, Mo. *(425,600)* 1.50
1021 5c **Opening of Japan,** *July 14* (320,541) 1.75
1022 3c **American Bar Association,** *Aug. 24,* Boston, Mass. *(410,036)* 8.00
1023 3c **Sagamore Hill,** *Sept. 14,* Oyster Bay, N.Y. *(379,750)* 1.50
1024 3c **Future Farmers,** *Oct. 13,* Kansas City, Mo. *(424,193)* 1.50
1025 3c **Trucking Industry,** *Oct. 27,* Los Angeles, Calif. *(875,021)* 1.50
1026 3c **Gen. G.S. Patton, Jr.,** *Nov. 11,* Fort Knox, Ky. *(342,600)* 5.00
1027 3c **New York City,** *Nov. 20,* New York, N.Y. *(387,914)* 1.50
1028 3c **Gadsden Purchase,** *Dec. 30,* Tucson, Ariz. *(363,250)* 1.50

1954
1029 3c **Columbia University,** *Jan. 4,* New York, N.Y. *(550,745)* 1.50

1954-67
LIBERTY ISSUE
1030a ½c **Franklin,** *Oct. 20, 1955* (223,122), block of 6 .... 1.00
1031b 1c **Washington,** *Aug. 26, 1954,* Chicago, Ill. *(272,581),* strip of 3 .... 1.00
1031A 1¼c **Palace of Governors,** *June 17, 1960,* Santa Fe, N.M., strip of 3 .... 1.00
  1031A and 1054A on one cover 1.50

First day cancel was applied to 501,848 covers bearing one or more of Nos. 1031A, 1054A.

1032 1½c **Mt. Vernon,** *Feb. 22, 1956,* Mount Vernon, Va. *(270,109),* pair 1.00
1033 2c **Jefferson,** *Sept. 15, 1954,* San Francisco, Cal. *(307,300),* pair 1.00
1034 2½c **Bunker Hill,** *June 17, 1959,* Boston, Mass. *(315,060),* pair 1.00
1035e 3c **Statue of Liberty,** *June 24, 1954,* Albany, N.Y. *(340,001)* 1.00
1035a   Booklet pane of 6, *June 30, 1954* 3.50
1035b   3c Tagged, *July 6, 1966* 40.00
1036c 4c **Lincoln,** *Nov. 19, 1954,* New York, N.Y. *(374,064)* 1.50
1036a   Booklet pane of 6, *July 31, 1958,* Wheeling, W. Va. *(135,825)* 4.00
1036b   4c Tagged, *Nov. 2, 1963* 50.00

No. 1036b was supposed to have been issued at Dayton Nov. 2, but a mix-up delayed its issuance there until Nov. 4. About 510 Covers received the Nov. 2 cancellation.

1037 4½c **Hermitage,** *Mar. 16, 1959,* Hermitage, Tenn. *(320,000)* 1.00
1038 5c **Monroe,** *Dec. 2, 1954,* Fredericksburg, Va. *(255,650)* 1.00
1039a 6c **T. Roosevelt,** *Nov. 18, 1955,* New York, N.Y. *(257,551)* 1.00
1040 7c **Wilson,** *Jan. 10, 1956,* Staunton, Va. *(200,111)* 1.00
1041 8c **Statue of Liberty** (flat plate), *Apr. 9, 1954* 1.00
1041B 8c **Statue of Liberty** (rotary press), *Apr. 9, 1954* 1.00

First day cancellation was applied to 340,077 covers bearing one or more of Nos. 1041-1041B.

1042 8c **Statue of Liberty** (Giori press), *Mar. 22, 1958,* Cleveland, O. *(223,899)* 1.00
1042A 8c **Pershing,** *Nov. 17, 1961,* New York, N.Y. *(321,031)* 1.25
1043 9c **Alamo,** *June 14, 1956,* San Antonio, Texas *(207,086)* 1.50
1044 10c **Independence Hall,** *July 4, 1956,* Philadelphia, Pa. *(220,930)* 1.00
1044d   10c Tagged, *July 6, 1966* 40.00
1044A 11c **Statue of Liberty,** *June 15, 1961* *(238,905)* 1.25
1044Ac   11c Tagged, *Jan. 11, 1967* 40.00
1045 12c **B. Harrison,** *June 6, 1959,* Oxford, O. *(225,869)* 1.25
1045a   12c Tagged, *May 6, 1968* 40.00
1046 15c **Jay,** *Dec. 12, 1958* (205,680) 1.25
1046a   15c Tagged, *July 6, 1966* 40.00
1047 20c **Monticello,** *Apr. 13, 1956,* Charlottesville, Va. *(147,860)* 1.25
1048 25c **Revere,** *Apr. 18, 1958,* Boston, Mass. *(196,530)* 1.25
1049a 30c **Lee,** *Sept. 21, 1955,* Norfolk, Va. *(120,166)* 2.00
1050a 40c **Marshall,** *Sept. 24, 1955,* Richmond, Va. *(113,972)* 2.00
1051a 50c **Anthony,** *Aug. 25, 1955,* Louisville, Ky. *(110,220)* 6.00

1052a $1 **Henry,** *Oct. 7, 1955,* Joplin, Mo. *(80,191)* 15.00
1053 $5 **Hamilton,** *Mar. 19, 1956,* Paterson, N.J. *(34,272)* 50.00

1954-73
COIL STAMPS
1054c 1c **Washington,** *Oct. 8, 1954,* Baltimore, Md. *(196,318),* strip of 3 .... 1.00
1054A 1¼c **Palace of Governors,** *June 17, 1960,* Santa Fe, N.M., strip of 3 .... 1.00
1055d 2c **Jefferson,** *Oct. 22, 1954,* St. Louis, Mo. *(162,050),* pair 1.00
1055a   2c Tagged, *May 6, 1968,* pair 32.50
1056 2½c **Bunker Hill,** *Sept. 9, 1959,* Los Angeles, Calif. *(198,680),* pair 2.00
1057c 3c **Statue of Liberty,** *July 20, 1954* *(137,139)* 1.00
1058 4c **Lincoln,** *July 31, 1958,* Mandan, N.D. *(184,079)* 1.50
1059 4½c **Hermitage,** *May 1, 1959,* Denver, Colo. *(202,454)* 1.75
1059A 25c **Revere,** *Feb. 25, 1965,* Wheaton, Md. *(184,954)* 1.25
1059Ab   25c Tagged, *Apr. 3, 1973,* New York, N.Y. 40.00

1954
1060 3c **Nebraska Territory,** *May 7,* Nebraska City, Neb. *(401,015)* 1.00
1061 3c **Kansas Territory,** *May 31,* Fort Leavenworth, Kans. *(349,145)* 1.00
1062 3c **George Eastman,** *July 12,* Rochester, N.Y. *(630,448)* 1.00
1063 3c **Lewis & Clark Expedition,** *July 28,* Sioux City, Iowa *(371,557)* 2.00

1955
1064 3c **Pennsylvania Academy of the Fine Arts,** *Jan. 15,* Philadelphia, Pa. *(307,040)* 1.00
1065 3c **Land Grant Colleges,** *Feb. 12,* East Lansing, Mich. *(419,241)* 1.25
1066 8c **Rotary International,** *Feb. 23,* Chicago, Ill. *(350,625)* 3.00
1067 3c **Armed Forces Reserve,** *May 21* *(300,436)* 1.25
1068 3c **New Hampshire,** *June 21,* Franconia, N.H. *(330,630)* 2.00
1069 3c **Soo Locks,** *June 28,* Sault Sainte Marie, Mich. *(316,616)* 1.00
1070 3c **Atoms for Peace,** *July 28* (351,940) 1.00
1071 3c **Fort Ticonderoga,** *Sept. 18,* Fort Ticonderoga, N.Y. *(342,946)* 1.00
1072 3c **Andrew W. Mellon,** *Dec. 20* (278,897) 1.00

1956
1073 3c **Benjamin Franklin,** *Jan. 17,* Philadelphia, Pa. *(351,260)* 1.25
1074 3c **Booker T. Washington,** *Apr. 5,* Booker T. Washington Birthplace, Va. *(272,659)* 2.00
1075 11c **FIPEX Souvenir Sheet,** *Apr. 28,* New York, N.Y. *(429,327)* 5.00
1076 3c **FIPEX,** *Apr. 30,* New York, N.Y. *(526,090)* 1.00
1077 3c **Wildlife (Turkey),** *May 5,* Fond du Lac, Wis. *(292,121)* 1.75
1078 3c **Wildlife (Antelope),** *June 22,* Gunnison, Colo. *(294,731)* 1.75
1079 3c **Wildlife (Salmon),** *Nov. 9,* Seattle, Wash. *(346,800)* 1.75
1080 3c **Pure Food and Drug Laws,** *June 27,* Washington, D.C. *(411,761)* 1.00
1081 3c **Wheatland,** *Aug. 5,* Lancaster, Pa. *(340,142)* 1.00
1082 3c **Labor Day,** *Sept. 3,* Camden, N.J. *(338,450)* 1.00
1083 3c **Nassau Hall,** *Sept. 22,* Princeton, N.J. *(350,756)* 1.00
1084 3c **Devils Tower,** *Sept. 24,* Devils Tower, Wyo. *(285,090)* 1.25
1085 3c **Children,** *Dec. 15* (305,125) 1.00

1957
1086 3c **Alexander Hamilton,** *Jan. 11,* New York, N.Y. *(305,117)* 1.00
1087 3c **Polio,** *Jan. 15* (307,630) 1.50
1088 3c **Coast & Geodetic Survey,** *Feb. 11,* Seattle, Wash. *(309,931)* 1.00
1089 3c **Architects,** *Feb. 23,* New York, N.Y. *(368,840)* 1.25
1090 3c **Steel Industry,** *May 22,* New York, N.Y. *(473,284)* 1.00
1091 3c **Naval Review,** *June 10,* U.S.S. Saratoga, Norfolk, Va. *(365,933)* 1.25
1092 3c **Oklahoma Statehood,** *June 14,* Oklahoma City, Okla. *(327,172)* 1.00
1093 3c **School Teachers,** *July 1,* Philadelphia, Pa. *(357,986)* 2.00
  (Spelling error) Philadelpia 8.00
1094 4c **Flag,** *July 4* (523,879) 1.00
1095 3c **Shipbuilding,** *Aug. 15,* Bath, Maine *(347,432)* 1.25
1096 8c **Ramon Magsaysay,** *Aug. 31* (334,558) 1.50
1097 3c **Lafayette Bicentenary,** *Sept. 6,* Easton, Pa. *(260,421)* 1.00
  Fayetteville, N.C. *(230,000)* 1.00
  Louisville, Ky. *(207,856)* 1.00
1098 3c **Wildlife (Whooping Cranes),** *Nov. 22,* New York, N.Y. *(162,050)* 1.25
  New Orleans, La. *(154,327)* 1.25
  Corpus Christi, Tex. *(280,990)* 1.25
1099 3c **Religious Freedom,** *Dec. 27,* Flushing, N.Y. *(357,770)* 1.00

1958
1100 3c **Gardening-Horticulture,** *Mar. 15,* Ithaca, N.Y. *(451,292)* 1.00
1104 3c **Brussels Exhibition,** *Apr. 17,* Detroit, Mich. *(428,073)* 1.00
1105 3c **James Monroe,** *Apr. 28,* Montross, Va. *(326,988)* 1.00
1106 3c **Minnesota Statehood,** *May 11,* Saint Paul, Minn. *(475,552)* 1.00
1107 3c **International Geophysical Year,** *May 31,* Chicago, Ill. *(397,000)* 1.00
1108 3c **Gunston Hall,** *June 12,* Lorton, Va. *(349,801)* 1.00
1109 3c **Mackinac Bridge,** *June 25,* Mackinac Bridge, Mich. *(445,605)* 1.00
1110 4c **Simon Bolivar,** *July 24* 1.50
1111 8c **Simon Bolivar,** *July 24* 2.25
  1110-1111 on one cover 2.00

First day cancellation was applied to 708, 777 covers bearing one or more of Nos. 1110-1111.

1112 4c **Atlantic Cable,** *Aug. 15,* New York, N.Y. *(365,072)* 1.00

1958-59
1113 1c **Lincoln Sesquicentennial,** *Feb. 12, 1959,* Hodgenville, Ky. *(379,862)* block of four 2.50
1114 3c **Lincoln Sesquicentennial,** *Feb. 27, 1959,* New York, N.Y. *(437,737)* 2.50
1115 4c **Lincoln-Douglas Debates,** *Aug. 27, 1958,* Freeport, Ill. *(373,063)* 2.50
1116 4c **Lincoln Sesquicentennial,** *May, 30, 1959* *(894,887)* 2.50

1958
1117 4c **Lajos Kossuth,** *Sept. 19* 1.25
1118 8c **Lajos Kossuth,** *Sept. 19* 1.50
  1117-1118 on one cover 2.25

First day cancellation was applied to 722,188 covers bearing one or more of Nos. 1117-1118.

1119 4c **Freedom of Press,** *Sept. 22,* Columbia, Mo. *(411,752)* 1.00
1120 4c **Overland Mail,** *Oct. 10,* San Francisco, Cal. *(352,760)* 1.00
1121 4c **Noah Webster,** *Oct. 16,* West Hartford, Conn. *(364,608)* 1.00
1122 4c **Forest Conservation,** *Oct. 27,* Tucson, Ariz. *(405,959)* 1.00
1123 4c **Fort Duquesne,** *Nov. 25,* Pittsburgh, Pa. *(421,764)* 1.00

1959
1124 4c **Oregon Statehood,** *Feb. 14,* Astoria, Ore. *(452,764)* 1.00
1125 4c **San Martin,** *Feb. 25* 1.50
1126 8c **San Martin,** *Feb. 25* 2.25
  1125-1126 on one cover 2.00

First day cancellation was applied to 910,208 covers bearing one or more of No. 1125-1126.

1127 4c **NATO,** *Apr. 1* (361,040) 1.25
1128 4c **Arctic Exploration,** *Apr. 6,* Cresson, Pa. *(397,770)* 1.00
1129 8c **World Trade,** *Apr. 20* (503,618) 1.00
1130 4c **Silver Centennial,** *June 8,* Virginia City, Nev. *(337,233)* 1.00
1131 4c **St. Lawrence Seaway,** *June 26,* Massena, N.Y. *(543,211)* 1.25
1132 4c **Flag** (49 stars), *July 4,* Auburn, N.Y. *(523,773)* 1.00
1133 4c **Soil Conservation,** *Aug. 26,* Rapid City, S.D. *(400,613)* 1.00
1134 4c **Petroleum Industry,** *Aug. 27,* Titusville, Pa. *(801,859)* 1.50
1135 4c **Dental Health,** *Sept. 14,* New York, N.Y. *(649,813)* 3.50
1136 4c **Reuter,** *Sept. 29* 1.25
1137 8c **Reuter,** *Sept. 29* 1.50
  1136-1137 on one cover 2.25

First day cancellation was applied to 1,207,933 covers bearing one or more of Nos. 1136-1137.

1138 4c **Dr. Ephraim McDowell,** *Dec. 3,* Danville, Ky. *(344,603)* 1.25

1960-61
1139 4c **Washington "Credo,"** *Jan. 20, 1960,* Mount Vernon, Va. *(438,335)* 1.25
1140 4c **Franklin "Credo,"** *Mar. 31, 1960,* Philadelphia, Pa. *(497,913)* 1.25
1141 4c **Jefferson "Credo,"** *May 18, 1960,* Charlottesville, Va. *(454,903)* 1.25
1142 4c **Francis Scott Key "Credo,"** *Sept. 14, 1960,* Baltimore, Md. *(501,129)* 1.25
1143 4c **Lincoln "Credo,"** *Nov. 19, 1960,* New York, N.Y. *(467,780)* 1.50
1144 4c **Patrick Henry "Credo,"** *Jan. 11, 1961,* Richmond, Va. *(415,252)* 1.25

1960
1145 4c **Boy Scouts,** *Feb. 8* (1,419,955) 4.00
1146 4c **Olympic Winter Games,** *Feb. 18,* Olympic Valley, Calif. *(516,456)* 1.25
1147 4c **Masaryk,** *Mar. 7* 1.25
1148 8c **Masaryk,** *Mar. 7* 1.50
  1147-1148 on one cover 2.25

First day cancellation was applied to 1,710,726 covers bearing one or more of Nos. 1147-1148.

1149 4c **World Refugee Year,** *Apr. 7* (413,298) 1.00
1150 4c **Water Conservation,** *Apr. 18* (648,988) 1.00
1151 4c **SEATO,** *May 31* (514,926) 1.00
1152 4c **American Woman,** *June 2* (830,385) 1.25

No.	Description	Price
1153	4c **50-Star Flag,** *July 4*, Honolulu, Hawaii *(820,900)*	1.00
1154	4c **Pony Express Centennial,** *July 19*, Sacramento, Calif. *(520,223)*	1.75
1155	4c **Employ the Handicapped,** *Aug. 28*, New York, N.Y. *(439,638)*	1.50
1156	4c **World Forestry Congress,** *Aug. 29*, Seattle, Wash. *(350,848)*	1.00
1157	4c **Mexican Independence,** *Sept. 16*, Los Angeles, Calif. *(360,297)*	1.00
1158	4c **U.S.-Japan Treaty,** *Sept. 28 (545,150)*	1.00
1159	4c **Paderewski,** *Oct. 8*	1.25
1160	8c **Paderewski,** *Oct. 8*	1.50
	1159-1160 on one cover	2.25

First day cancellation was applied to 1,057,438 covers bearing one or more of Nos. 1159-1160.

1161	4c **Robert A. Taft,** *Oct. 10*, Cincinnati, Ohio *(312,116)*	1.00
1162	4c **Wheels of Freedom,** *Oct. 15*, Detroit, Mich. *(380,551)*	1.00
1163	4c **Boys' Clubs,** *Oct. 18*, New York, N.Y. *(435,009)*	1.00
1164	4c **Automated P.O.,** *Oct. 20*, Providence, R.I. *(458,237)*	1.00
1165	4c **Mannerheim,** *Oct. 26*	1.25
1166	8c **Mannerheim,** *Oct. 26*	1.50
	1165-1166 on one cover	2.25

First day cancellation was applied to 1,168,770 covers bearing one or more of Nos. 1165-1166.

1167	4c **Camp Fire Girls,** *Nov. 1*, New York, N.Y. *(324,944)*	3.00
1168	4c **Garibaldi,** *Nov. 2*	1.25
1169	8c **Garibaldi,** *Nov. 2*	1.50
	1168-1169 on one cover	2.25

First day cancellation was applied to 1,001,490 covers bearing one or more of Nos. 1168-1169.

1170	4c **Senator George,** *Nov. 5*, Vienna, Ga. *(278,890)*	1.00
1171	4c **Andrew Carnegie,** *Nov. 25*, New York, N.Y. *(318,180)*	1.00
1172	4c **John Foster Dulles,** *Dec. 6 (400,055)*	1.00
1173	4c **Echo I,** *Dec. 15 (583,747)*	2.50

1961-65
1174	4c **Gandhi,** *Jan. 26, 1961*	1.25
1175	8c **Gandhi,** *Jan. 26, 1961*	1.75
	1174-1175 on one cover	2.50

First day cancellation was applied to 1,013,515 covers bearing one or more of Nos. 1174-1175.

1176	4c **Range Conservation,** *Feb. 2, 1961*, Salt Lake City, Utah *(357,101)*	1.00
1177	4c **Horace Greeley,** *Feb. 3, 1961*, Chappaqua, N.Y. *(359,205)*	1.00
1178	4c **Fort Sumter,** *Apr. 12, 1961*, Charleston, S.C. *(602,599)*	4.00
1179	4c **Battle of Shiloh,** *Apr. 7, 1962*, Shiloh, Tenn. *(526,062)*	4.00
1180	4c **Battle of Gettysburg,** *July 1, 1963*, Gettysburg, Pa. *(600,205)*	4.00
1181	5c **Battle of Wilderness,** *May 5, 1964*, Fredericksburg, Va. *(450,904)*	4.00
1182	5c **Appomattox,** *Apr. 9, 1965*, Appomattox, Va. *(653,121)*	4.00

1961
1183	4c **Kansas Statehood,** *May 10*, Council Grove, Kansas *(480,561)*	1.00
1184	4c **Senator Norris,** *July 11 (482,875)*	1.00
1185	4c **Naval Aviation,** *Aug. 20*, San Diego, Calif. *(416,391)*	1.50
1186	4c **Workmen's Compensation,** *Sept. 4*, Milwaukee, Wis. *(410,236)*	1.00
1187	4c **Frederic Remington,** *Oct. 4 (723,443)*	1.25
1188	4c **China Republic,** *Oct. 10 (463,900)*	5.50
1189	4c **Naismith-Basketball,** *Nov. 6*, Springfield, Mass. *(479,917)*	7.50
1190	4c **Nursing,** *Dec. 28 (964,005)*	10.00

1962
1191	4c **New Mexico Statehood,** *Jan. 6*, Sante Fe, N.M. *(365,330)*	2.00
1192	4c **Arizona Statehood,** *Feb. 14*, Phoenix, Ariz. *(508,216)*	1.75
1193	4c **Project Mercury,** *Feb. 20*, Cape Canaveral, Fla. *(3,000,000)*	3.00
	Any other city	5.00
1194	4c **Malaria Eradication,** *Mar. 30 (554,175)*	1.00
1195	4c **Charles Evans Hughes,** *Apr. 11 (544,424)*	1.00
1196	4c **Seattle World's Fair,** *Apr. 25*, Seattle, Wash. *(771,856)*	1.25
1197	4c **Louisiana Statehood,** *Apr. 30*, New Orleans, La. *(436,681)*	1.00
1198	4c **Homestead Act,** *May 20*, Beatrice, Nebr. *(487,450)*	1.00
1199	4c **Girl Scouts,** *July 24*, Burlington, Vt. *(634,347)*	5.00
1200	4c **Brien McMahon,** *July 28*, Norwalk, Conn. *(384,419)*	1.00
1201	4c **Apprenticeship,** *Aug. 31 (1,003,548)*	1.00
1202	4c **Sam Rayburn,** *Sept. 16*, Bonham, Texas *(401,042)*	1.50
1203	4c **Dag Hammarskjold,** *Oct. 23*, New York, N.Y. *(500,683)*	1.00
1203a	4c **Dag Hammarskjold,** original yellow inverted, *Oct. 23*, New York, N.Y.	3,000.
1204	4c **Hammarskjold,** yellow inverted, *Nov. 16*, (about *75,000)*	5.00
1205	4c **Christmas,** *Nov. 1*, Pittsburgh, Pa. *(491,312)*	1.10

| 1206 | 4c **Higher Education,** *Nov. 14 (627,347)* | 1.25 |
| 1207 | 4c **Winslow Homer,** *Dec. 15*, Gloucester, Mass. *(498,866)* | 1.25 |

1963-66
| 1208 | 5c **Flag,** *Jan. 9, 1963 (696,185)* | 1.00 |
| 1208a | 5c **Tagged,** *Aug. 25, 1966* | 30.00 |

1962-66
REGULAR ISSUE
1209	1c **Jackson,** *Mar. 22, 1963*, New York, N.Y. *(392,363)*, block of 5 or 6	1.00
1209a	1c **Tagged,** *July 6, 1966*, block of 5 or 6	30.00
1213	5c **Washington,** *Nov. 23, 1962*, New York, N.Y. *(360,531)*	1.00
1213a	Booklet pane of 5 + label, *Nov. 23, 1962*, New York, N.Y. *(111,452)*	4.00
1213b	5c **Tagged,** *Oct. 28, 1963*, Dayton, Ohio (about *15,000)*	30.00
1213c	Booklet pane of 5 + label, tagged, *Oct. 28, 1963*, Dayton, Ohio Washington, D.C. *(750)*	100.00 / 110.00
1225	1c **Jackson,** Coil, *May 31, 1963*, Chicago, Ill. *(238,952)*, pair and strip of 3	1.00
1225a	Coil, tagged, *July 6, 1966*, pair and strip of 3	30.00
1229	5c **Washington,** Coil, *Nov. 23, 1962*, New York, N.Y. *(184,627)*	1.00
1229a	5c Coil, tagged, *Oct. 28, 1963*, Dayton, Ohio (about *2,000)*	30.00

1963
1230	5c **Carolina Charter,** *Apr. 6*, Edenton, N.C. *(426,200)*	1.00
1231	5c **Food for Peace,** *June 4 (624,342)*	1.00
1232	5c **West Virginia Statehood,** *June 20*, Wheeling, W. Va. *(413,389)*	1.00
1233	5c **Emancipation Proclamation,** *Aug. 16*, Chicago, Ill. *(494,886)*	1.75
1234	5c **Alliance for Progress,** *Aug. 17 (528,095)*	1.00
1235	5c **Cordell Hull,** *Oct. 5* Carthage, Tenn. *(391,631)*	1.00
1236	5c **Eleanor Roosevelt,** *Oct. 11 (860,155)*	1.25
1237	5c **Science,** *Oct. 14 (504,503)*	1.25
1238	5c **City Mail Delivery,** *Oct. 26 (544,806)*	1.25
1239	5c **Red Cross,** *Oct. 29 (557,678)*	2.00
1240	5c **Christmas,** *Nov. 1*, Santa Claus, Ind. *(458,619)*	1.25
1240a	5c **Christmas,** tagged, *Nov. 2*, (about *500)*	60.00

Note below No. 1036b also applies to No. 1240a.

| 1241 | 5c **Audubon,** *Dec. 7*, Henderson, Ky. *(518,855)* | 1.25 |

1964
1242	5c **Sam Houston,** *Jan. 10*, Houston, Tex. *(487,986)*	1.75
1243	5c **Charles Russell,** *Mar. 19*, Great Falls, Mont. *(658,745)*	1.25
1244	5c **N.Y. World's Fair,** *Apr. 22*, World's Fair, N.Y. *(1,656,346)*	2.00
1245	5c **John Muir,** *Apr. 29*, Martinez, Calif. *(446,925)*	1.50
1246	5c **John F. Kennedy,** *May 29*, Boston, Mass. *(2,003,096)*	3.00
	Any other city	5.00
1247	5c **New Jersey Tercentenary,** *June 15*, Elizabeth, N.J. *(526,879)*	1.00
1248	5c **Nevada Statehood,** *July 22*, Carson City, Nev. *(584,973)*	1.00
1249	5c **Register & Vote,** *Aug. 1 (533,439)*	1.25
1250	5c **Shakespeare,** *Aug. 14*, Stratford, Conn. *(524,053)*	2.00
1251	5c **Drs. Mayo,** *Sept. 11*, Rochester, Minn. *(674,846)*	3.00
1252	5c **American Music,** *Oct. 15*, New York, N.Y. *(466,107)*	1.50
1253	5c **Homemakers,** *Oct. 26*, Honolulu, Hawaii *(435,392)*	1.00
1257b	5c **Christmas,** *Nov. 9*, Bethlehem, Pa. 1254-1257, any single	3.00 / 1.00
1257c	5c **Tagged,** *Nov. 10*, Dayton, O. 1254a-1257a, any single	57.50 / 30.00

First day cancellation was applied to 794,900 covers bearing Nos. 1254-1257 in singles or multiples and at Dayton to about 2,700 covers bearing Nos. 1254a-1257a in singles or multiples.

1258	5c **Verrazano-Narrows Bridge,** *Nov. 21*, Staten Island, N.Y. *(619,780)*	1.00
1259	5c **Fine Arts,** *Dec. 2 (558,046)*	1.00
1260	5c **Amateur Radio,** *Dec. 15*, Anchorage, Alaska *(452,255)*	5.00

1965
1261	5c **Battle of New Orleans,** *Jan. 8*, New Orleans, La. *(466,029)*	1.00
1262	5c **Physical Fitness-Sokol,** *Feb. 15 (864,848)*	1.25
1263	5c **Cancer Crusade,** *Apr. 1 (744,485)*	2.50
1264	5c **Churchill,** *May 13*, Fulton, Mo. *(773,580)*	2.50
1265	5c **Magna Carta,** *June 15*, Jamestown, Va. *(479,065)*	1.00
1266	5c **Intl. Cooperation Year,** *June 26*, San Francisco, Cal. *(402,925)*	1.00
1267	5c **Salvation Army,** *July 2*, New York, N.Y. *(634,228)*	3.00
1268	5c **Dante,** *July 17*, San Francisco, Cal. *(424,893)*	1.00
1269	5c **Herbert Hoover,** *Aug. 10*, West Branch, Iowa *(698,182)*	1.00

1270	5c **Robert Fulton,** *Aug. 19*, Clermont, N.Y. *(550,330)*	1.00
1271	5c **Florida Settlement,** *Aug. 28*, St. Augustine, Fla. *(465,000)*	1.00
1272	5c **Traffic Safety,** *Sept. 3*, Baltimore, Md. *(527,075)*	1.00
1273	5c **Copley,** *Sept. 17 (613,484)*	1.00
1274	11c **Intl. Telecommunication Union,** *Oct. 6 (332,818)*	1.10
1275	5c **Adlai Stevenson,** *Oct. 23*, Bloomington, Ill. *(755,656)*	1.00
1276	5c **Christmas,** *Nov. 2*, Silver Bell, Ariz. *(705,039)*	1.00
1276a	5c **Tagged,** *Nov. 15*, (about *300)*	50.00

1965-78
PROMINENT AMERICANS ISSUE
1278	1c **Jefferson,** *Jan. 12, 1968*, Jeffersonville, Ind., block of 5 or 6	1.00
1278a	Booklet pane of 8, *Jan. 12, 1968*, Jeffersonville, Ind.	2.50
1278b	Booklet pane of 4 + 2 labels, *May 10, 1971*	11.50

First day cancellation was applied to 655,680 covers bearing one or more of Nos. 1278, 1278a and 1299.

1279	1¼c **Gallatin,** *Jan. 30, 1967*, Gallatin, Mo. *(439,010)*	1.00
1280	2c **Wright,** *June 8, 1966*, Spring Green, Wis. *(460,427)*	1.00
1280a	Booklet pane of 5 + label, *Jan. 8, 1968*, Buffalo, N.Y. *(147,244)*	3.50
1280c	Booklet pane of 6, *May 7, 1971*, Spokane, Wash.	15.00
1281	3c **Parkman,** *Sept. 16, 1967*, Boston, Mass. *(518,355)*	1.00
1282	4c **Lincoln,** *Nov. 19, 1965*, New York, N.Y. *(445,629)*	1.50
1282a	4c Tagged, *Dec. 1, 1965*, Dayton, O. (about *2,000)* Washington, D.C. *(1,200)*	30.00 / 32.50
1283	5c **Washington,** *Feb. 22, 1966*, *(525,372)*	1.00
1283a	5c Tagged, *Feb. 23, 1966*, (about *900)* Dayton, Ohio (about *200)*	30.00 / 75.00
1283B	5c **Washington,** Redrawn, *Nov. 17, 1967*, New York, N.Y. *(328,983)*	1.00
1284	6c **Roosevelt,** *Jan. 29, 1966*, Hyde Park, N.Y. *(448,631)*	1.00
1284a	6c Tagged, *Dec. 29, 1966*	40.00
1284b	Booklet pane of 8, *Dec. 28, 1967*	2.75
1284c	Booklet pane of 5 + label, *Jan. 9, 1968*	100.00
1285	8c **Einstein,** *Mar. 14, 1966*, Princeton, N.J. *(366,803)*	3.00
1285a	8c Tagged, *July 6, 1966*	40.00
1286	10c **Jackson,** *Mar. 15, 1967*, Hermitage, Tenn. *(255,945)*	1.00
1286A	12c **Ford,** *July 30, 1968*, Greenfield Village, Mich. *(342,850)*	1.50
1287	13c **Kennedy,** *May 29, 1967*, Brookline, Mass. *(391,195)*	1.75
1288	15c **Holmes,** type I, *Mar. 8, 1968*, *(322,970)*	1.00
1288B	15c **Holmes** from bklt., *June 14, 1978*, Boston, Mass.	1.00
1288Bc	Booklet pane of 8	3.00

First day cancellation was applied to 387,119 covers bearing one or more of Nos. 1288B and 1305E.

1289	20c **Marshall,** *Oct. 24, 1967*, Lexington, Va. *(221,206)*	1.10
1289a	20c Tagged, *Apr. 3, 1973*, New York, N.Y.	40.00
1290	25c **Douglass,** *Feb. 14, 1967* *(213,730)*	2.50
1290a	25c Tagged, *Apr. 3, 1973*, New York, N.Y.	45.00
1291	30c **Dewey,** *Oct. 21, 1968*, Burlington, Vt. *(162,790)*	1.75
1291a	30c Tagged, *Apr. 3, 1973*, New York, N.Y.	45.00
1292	40c **Paine,** *Jan. 29, 1968*, Philadelphia, Pa. *(157,947)*	1.75
1292a	40c Tagged, *Apr. 3, 1973*, New York, N.Y.	45.00
1293	50c **Stone,** *Aug. 13, 1968*, Dorchester, Mass. *(140,410)*	2.50
1293a	50c Tagged, *Apr. 3, 1973*, New York, N.Y.	45.00
1294	$1 **O'Neill,** *Oct. 16, 1967*, New London, Conn. *(103,102)*	6.00
1294a	$1 Tagged, *Apr. 3, 1973*, New York, N.Y.	60.00
1295	$5 **Moore,** *Dec. 3, 1966*, Smyrna, Del. *(41,130)*	40.00
1295a	$5 Tagged, *Apr. 3, 1973*, New York, N.Y.	120.00

First day cancellation was applied to 17,533 covers bearing one or more of Nos. 1059b, 1289a, 1290a, 1291a, 1292a, 1293a, 1294a and 1295a.

COIL STAMPS
| 1297 | 3c **Parkman,** *Nov. 4, 1975*, Pendleton, Ore. *(166,798)* | 1.00 |
| 1298 | 6c **Roosevelt,** Perf. 10 Horiz., *Dec. 28, 1967* | 1.00 |

First day cancellation was applied to 312,330 covers bearing one or more of Nos. 1298 and 1284b.

1299	1c **Jefferson,** *Jan. 12, 1968*, Jeffersonville, Ind., pair and strip of 3	1.00
1303	4c **Lincoln,** *May 28, 1966*, Springfield, Ill. *(322,563)*	1.50
1304	5c **Washington,** *Sept. 8, 1966*, Cincinnati, O. *(245,400)*	1.00

1305	6c	**Roosevelt,** Perf. 10 vert., *Feb. 28, 1968 (317,199)*	1.00
1305E	15c	**Holmes,** type I, *June 14, 1978,* Boston, Mass.	1.00
1305C	$1	**O'Neill,** *Jan. 12, 1973,* Hempstead, N.Y. *(121,217)*	4.00

1966

1306	5c	**Migratory Bird Treaty,** *Mar. 16,* Pittsburgh, Pa. *(555,485)*	1.75
1307	5c	**Humane Treatment of Animals,** *Apr. 9,* New York, N.Y. *(524,420)*	1.25
1308	5c	**Indiana Statehood,** *Apr. 16,* Corydon, Ind. *(575,557)*	1.00
1309	5c	**Circus,** *May 2,* Delavan, Wis. *(754,076)*	2.00
1310	5c	**SIPEX,** *May 21 (637,802)*	1.00
1311	5c	**SIPEX, souvenir sheet,** *May 23 (700,882)*	1.10
1312	5c	**Bill of Rights,** *July 1,* Miami Beach, Fla. *(562,920)*	1.75
1313	5c	**Polish Millennium,** *July 30 (715,603)*	1.50
1314	5c	**Natl. Park Service,** *Aug. 25,* Yellowstone National Park, Wyo. *(528,170)*	1.00
1314a	5c	Tagged, *Aug. 26*	35.00
1315	5c	**Marine Corps Reserve,** *Aug. 29 (585,923)*	1.50
1315a	5c	Tagged, *Aug. 29*	35.00
1316	5c	**Gen. Fed. of Women's Clubs,** *Sept. 12,* New York, N.Y. *(383,334)*	1.25
1316a	5c	Tagged, *Sept. 13*	35.00
1317	5c	**Johnny Appleseed,** *Sept. 24,* Leominster, Mass. *(794,610)*	1.50
1317a	5c	Tagged, *Sept. 26*	35.00
1318	5c	**Beautification of America,** *Oct. 5 (564,440)*	1.00
1318a	5c	Tagged, *Oct. 5*	35.00
1319	5c	**Great River Road,** *Oct. 21,* Baton Rouge, La. *(330,933)*	1.00
1319a	5c	Tagged, *Oct. 22*	35.00
1320	5c	**Savings Bond-Servicemen,** *Oct. 26,* Sioux City, Iowa *(444,421)*	1.00
1320a	5c	Tagged, *Oct. 27*	35.00
1321	5c	**Christmas,** *Nov. 1,* Christmas, Mich. *(537,650)*	1.00
1321a	5c	Tagged, *Nov. 2*	35.00
1322	5c	**Mary Cassatt,** *Nov. 17 (593,389)*	1.00
1322a	5c	Tagged, *Nov. 17*	35.00

1967

1323	5c	**National Grange,** *Apr. 17 (603,460)*	1.00
1324	5c	**Canada Centenary,** *May 25,* Montreal, Canada *(711,795)*	1.00
1325	5c	**Erie Canal,** *July 4,* Rome, N.Y. *(784,611)*	1.00
1326	5c	**Search for Peace-Lions,** *July 5,* Chicago, Ill. *(393,197)*	1.00
1327	5c	**Thoreau,** *July 12,* Concord, Mass. *(696,789)*	1.00
1328	5c	**Nebraska Statehood,** *July 29,* Lincoln, Nebr. *(1,146,957)*	1.00
1329	5c	**Voice of America,** *Aug. 1 (455,190)*	2.00
1330	5c	**Davy Crockett,** *Aug. 17,* San Antonio, Tex. *(462,291)*	1.25
1331a	5c	**Space Accomplishments,** *Sept. 29,* Kennedy Space Center, Fla. *(667,267)*	8.00
		1331-1332, any single	3.00
1333	5c	**Urban Planning,** *Oct. 2 (389,009)*	1.00
1334	5c	**Finland Independence,** *Oct. 6,* Finland, Minn. *(408,532)*	1.00
1335	5c	**Thomas Eakins,** *Nov. 2 (648,054)*	1.40
1336	5c	**Christmas,** *Nov. 6,* Bethlehem, Ga. *(462,118)*	1.25
1337	5c	**Mississippi Statehood,** *Dec. 11,* Natchez, Miss. *(379,612)*	1.00

1968-71

1338	6c	**Flag** (Giori), *Jan. 24, 1968 (412,120)*	1.00
1338A	6c	**Flag coil,** *May 30, 1969,* Chicago, Ill. *(248,434)*	1.00
1338D	6c	**Flag** (Huck) *Aug. 7, 1970 (365,280)*	1.00
1338F	6c	**Flag,** *May 10, 1971*	1.00
1338G	8c	**Flag coil,** *May 10, 1971*	1.00

First day cancellation (May 10) was applied to 235,543 covers bearing one or more of Nos. 1338F-1338G.

1968

1339	6c	**Illinois Statehood,** *Feb. 12,* Shawneetown, Ill. *(761,640)*	1.00
1340	6c	**HemisFair'68,** *Mar. 30,* San Antonio, Tex. *(469,909)*	1.00
1341	$1	**Airlift,** *Apr. 4,* Seattle, Wash. *(105,088)*	7.00
1342	6c	**Youth-Elks,** *May 1,* Chicago, Ill. *(354,711)*	1.00
1343	6c	**Law and Order,** *May 17 (407,081)*	2.50
1344	6c	**Register and Vote,** *June 27 (355,685)*	1.00
1354a	6c	**Historic Flag series of 10,** *July 4,* Pittsburgh, Pa. *(2,924,962)*	15.00
		1345-1354, any single	3.00
1355	6c	**Disney,** *Sept. 11,* Marceline, Mo. *(499,505)*	25.00
1356	6c	**Marquette,** *Sept. 20,* Sault Ste. Marie, Mich. *(379,710)*	1.00
1357	6c	**Daniel Boone,** *Sept. 26,* Frankfort, Ky. *(333,440)*	1.25
1358	6c	**Arkansas River,** *Oct. 1,* Little Rock, Ark. *(358,025)*	1.00
1359	6c	**Leif Erikson,** *Oct. 9,* Seattle, Wash. *(376,565)*	1.00
1360	6c	**Cherokee Strip,** *Oct. 15,* Ponca, Okla. *(339,330)*	1.00
1361	6c	**John Trumbull,** *Oct. 18,* New Haven, Conn. *(278,285)*	2.00

1362	6c	**Waterfowl Conservation,** *Oct. 24,* Cleveland, Ohio, *(349,719)*	1.25
1363	6c	**Christmas,** tagged, *Nov. 1 (739,055)*	1.25
1363a	6c	Untagged, *Nov. 2*	10.00
1364	6c	**American Indian,** *Nov. 4 (415,964)*	1.25

1969

1368a	6c	**Beautification of America,** *Jan. 16 (1,094,184)*	4.00
		1365-1368, any single	1.00
1369	6c	**American Legion,** *Mar. 15 (632,035)*	1.00
1370	6c	**Grandma Moses,** *May 1 (367,880)*	1.50
1371	6c	**Apollo 8,** *May 5,* Houston, Texas *(908,634)*	2.25
1372	6c	**W.C. Handy,** *May 17,* Memphis, Tenn. *(398,216)*	2.25
1373	6c	**California Bicentenary,** *July 16,* San Diego, Calif. *(530,210)*	1.00
1374	6c	**J.W. Powell,** *Aug. 1,* Page, Ariz. *(434,433)*	1.00
1375	6c	**Alabama Statehood,** *Aug. 2,* Huntsville, Ala. *(485,801)*	1.00
1379a	6c	**Botanical Congress,** *Aug. 23,* Seattle, Wash. *(737,935)*	5.00
		1376-1379, any single	1.50
1380	6c	**Dartmouth Case,** *Sept. 22,* Hanover, N.H. *(416,327)*	1.00
1381	6c	**Professional Baseball,** *Sept. 24,* Cincinnati, Ohio *(414,942)*	12.00
1382	6c	**Intercollegiate Football,** *Sept. 26,* New Brunswick, N.J. *(414,860)*	6.50
1383	6c	**Dwight D. Eisenhower,** *Oct. 14,* Abilene, Kans. *(1,009,560)*	1.00
1384	6c	**Christmas,** *Nov. 3,* Christmas, Fla. *(555,500)*	1.25
1385	6c	**Hope for Crippled,** *Nov. 20,* Columbus, Ohio *(342,676)*	1.25
1386	6c	**William M. Harnett,** *Dec. 3,* Boston, Mass. *(408,860)*	1.00

1970-74

1390a	6c	**National History,** *May 6, 1970,* New York, N.Y. *(834,260)*	4.00
		1387-1390, any single	1.50
1391	6c	**Maine Statehood,** *July 9, 1970,* Portland, Maine, *(472,165)*	2.75
1392	6c	**Wildlife Conservation,** *July 20, 1970,* Custer, S.D. *(309,418)*	1.00
1393	6c	**Eisenhower,** *Aug. 6, 1970*	1.00
1393a		Booklet pane of 8	3.00
1393b		Booklet pane of 5 + label	1.50

First day cancellations were applied to 823,540 covers bearing one or more of Nos. 1393 and 1401.

1393D	7c	**Franklin,** *Oct. 20, 1972,* Philadelphia, Pa. *(309,276)*	1.00
1394	8c	**Eisenhower** (multi), *May 10, 1971*	1.00
1395	8c	**Eisenhower** (claret), *May 10, 1971*	1.00
1395a		Booklet pane of 8	2.50
1395b		Booklet pane of 6	2.50
1395c		Booklet pane of 4 + 2 labels, *Jan. 28, 1972,* Casa Grande, Ariz.	2.25
1395d		Booklet pane of 7 + label, *Jan. 28, 1972,* Casa Grande, Ariz.	2.25

First day cancellations were applied to 813,947 covers bearing one or more of Nos. 1394, 1395 and 1402. First day cancellations were applied to 181,601 covers bearing one or more of Nos. 1395c or 1395d.

1396	8c	**Postal Service Emblem,** *July 1, 1971, any city* (est. 16,300,000)	1.00

First day cancels from over 16,000 different cities are known. Some are rare.

1397	14c	**Fiorello H. LaGuardia,** *Apr. 24, 1972,* New York, N.Y. *(180,114)*	1.00
1398	16c	**Ernie Pyle,** *May 7, 1971 (444,410)*	1.50
1399	18c	**Elizabeth Blackwell,** *Jan. 23, 1974,* Geneva, N.Y. *(217,938)*	1.25
1400	21c	**Amadeo Giannini,** *June 27, 1973,* San Mateo, Calif. *(282,520)*	1.50
1401	6c	**Eisenhower coil,** *Aug. 6, 1970*	1.00
1402	8c	**Eisenhower coil,** *May 10, 1971*	1.00

1970

1405	6c	**Edgar Lee Masters,** *Aug. 22,* Petersburg Ill. *(372,804)*	1.00
1406	6c	**Woman Suffrage,** *Aug. 26,* Adams, Mass. *(508,142)*	1.00
1407	6c	**South Carolina Anniv.,** *Sept. 12,* Charleston, S.C. *(533,000)*	1.00
1408	6c	**Stone Mt. Memorial,** *Sept. 19,* Stone Mountain, Ga. *(538,546)*	1.00
1409	6c	**Fort Snelling,** *Oct. 17,* Fort Snelling, Minn. *(497,611)*	1.00
1413a	6c	**Anti-Pollution,** *Oct. 28,* San Clemente, Calif. *(1,033,147)*	4.00
		1410-1413, any single	1.25
1414	6c	**Christmas** (Nativity), *Nov. 5*	1.25
1414a	6c	Precanceled, *Nov. 5*	7.50
1418b	6c	**Christmas,** *Nov. 5*	5.50
		1415-1418, any single	1.50
		1414-1418 on one cover	8.50
1418c	6c	Precanceled, *Nov. 5*	15.00
		1415a-1418a, any single	5.00
		1414a-1418a on one cover	30.00

First day cancellation was applied to 2,014,450 covers bearing one or more of Nos. 1414-1418 or 1414a-1418a.

1419	6c	**United Nations,** *Nov. 20,* New York, N.Y. *(474,070)*	1.50
1420	6c	**Pilgrims' Landing,** *Nov. 21,* Plymouth, Mass. *(629,850)*	1.00
1421	6c	**Disabled Veterans,** *Nov. 24,* Cincinnati, Ohio, or Montgomery, Ala.	2.00

1422	6c	**U.S. Servicemen,** *Nov. 24,* Cincinnati, Ohio, or Montgomery, Ala.	2.00
1421a			

First day cancellation was applied to 476,610 covers at Cincinnati and 336,417 at Montgomery, each cover bearing one or more of Nos. 1421-1422.

1971

1423	6c	**Wool Industry,** *Jan. 19,* Las Vegas, Nev. *(379,911)*	1.00
1424	6c	**MacArthur,** *Jan. 26,* Norfolk, Va. *(720,035)*	2.00
1425	6c	**Blood Donor,** *Mar. 12,* New York, N.Y. *(644,497)*	1.00
1426	8c	**Missouri Sesquicentennial,** *May 8,* Independence, Mo. *(551,000)*	1.00
1430a	8c	**Wildlife Conservation,** *June 12,* Avery Island, La. *(679,483)*	3.00
		1427-1430, any single	1.25
1431	8c	**Antarctic Treaty,** *June 23 (419,200)*	1.00
1432	8c	**American Revolution Bicentennial,** *July 4 (434,930)*	1.00
1433	8c	**John Sloan,** *Aug. 2,* Lock Haven, Pa. *(482,265)*	1.00
1434a	8c	**Space Achievement Decade,** *Aug. 2,* Kennedy Space Center, Fla. *(1,403,644)*	2.00
		Houston, Texas *(811,560)*	2.00
		Huntsville, Ala. *(524,000)*	2.00
1436	8c	**Emily Dickinson,** *Aug. 28,* Amherst, Mass. *(498,180)*	1.00
1437	8c	**San Juan,** *Sept. 12,* San Juan, P.R. *(501,668)*	1.00
1438	8c	**Drug Abuse,** *Oct. 4,* Dallas, Texas *(425,330)*	1.00
1439	8c	**CARE,** *Oct. 27,* New York, N.Y. *(402,121)*	1.00
1443a	8c	**Historic Preservation,** *Oct. 29,* San Diego, Calif. *(783,242)*	3.00
		1440-1443, any single	1.25
1444	8c	**Christmas** (religious), *Nov. 10*	1.25
1445	8c	**Christmas** (secular), *Nov. 10*	1.25
		1444-1445 on one cover	2.00

First day cancellation was applied to 348,038 covers with No. 1444 and 580,062 with No. 1445.

1972

1446	8c	**Sidney Lanier,** *Feb. 3,* Macon Ga. *(394,800)*	1.00
1447	8c	**Peace Corps,** *Feb. 11 (453,660)*	1.00
1451a	2c	**National Parks Centennial,** *Apr. 5,* Hatteras, N.C., block of 4 *(505,697)*	3.00
1452	6c	**National Parks,** *June 26,* Vienna, Va. *(403,396)*	1.00
1453	8c	**National Parks,** *Mar. 1,* Yellowstone National Park, Wyo. Washington, D.C. *(847,500)*	1.00
1454	15c	**National Parks,** *July 28,* Mt. McKinley National Park, Alaska *(491,456)*	1.00
1455	8c	**Family Planning,** *Mar. 18,* New York, N.Y. *(691,385)*	1.00
1459a	8c	**Colonial Craftsmen** (Rev. Bicentennial), *July 4,* Williamsburg, Va. *(1,914,976)*	2.50
		1456-1459, any single	1.00
1460	6c	**Olympics,** *Aug. 17*	1.00
1461	8c	**Winter Olympics,** *Aug. 17*	1.00
1462	15c	**Olympics,** *Aug. 17*	1.00
		1460-1462 and C85 on one cover	2.00

First day cancellation was applied to 971,536 covers bearing one or more of Nos. 1460-1462 and C85.

1463	8c	**P.T.A.,** *Sept. 15,* San Francisco, Cal. *(523,454)*	1.00
1467a	8c	**Wildlife,** *Sept. 20,* Warm Springs, Ore. *(733,778)*	3.00
		1464-1467, any single	1.50
1468	8c	**Mail Order,** *Sept. 27,* Chicago, Ill. *(759,666)*	1.00
1469	8c	**Osteopathy,** *Oct. 9,* Miami, Fla. *(607,160)*	1.50
1470	8c	**Tom Sawyer,** *Oct. 13,* Hannibal, Mo. *(459,013)*	2.00
1471	8c	**Christmas** (religious), *Nov. 9*	1.00
1472	8c	**Christmas** (secular), *Nov. 9*	1.00
		1471-1472 on one cover	2.00

First day cancellation was applied to 713,821 covers bearing one or more of Nos. 1471-1472.

1473	8c	**Pharmacy,** *Nov. 10,* Cincinnati, Ohio *(804,320)*	8.00
1474	8c	**Stamp Collecting,** *Nov. 17,* New York, N.Y. *(434,680)*	1.25

1973

1475	8c	**Love,** *Jan. 26,* Philadelphia, Pa. *(422,492)*	2.00
1476	8c	**Pamphleteer** (Rev. Bicentennial), *Feb. 16,* Portland, Ore. *(431,784)*	1.00
1477	8c	**Broadside** (Rev. Bicentennial), *Apr. 13,* Atlantic City, N.J. *(423,437)*	1.00
1478	8c	**Post Rider** (Rev. Bicentennial), *June 22,* Rochester, N.Y. *(586,850)*	1.00
1479	8c	**Drummer** (Rev. Bicentennial), *Sept. 28,* New Orleans, La. *(522,427)*	1.00
1483a	8c	**Boston Tea Party** (Rev. Bicentennial), *July 4,* Boston, Mass. *(897,870)*	3.00
		1480-1483, any single	1.00
1484	8c	**George Gershwin,** *Feb. 28,* Beverly Hills, Calif. *(448,814)*	1.00
1485	8c	**Robinson Jeffers,** *Aug. 13,* Carmel, Calif. *(394,261)*	1.00
1486	8c	**Henry O. Tanner,** *Sept. 10,* Pittsburgh, Pa. *(424,065)*	2.50

1487	8c	**Willa Cather**, *Sept. 20*, Red Cloud, Nebr. *(435,784)*	1.00
1488	8c	**Nicolaus Copernicus**, *Apr. 23* *(734,190)*	1.50
1498a	8c	**Postal People**, *Apr. 30*, any city	5.00
		1489-1498, any single	1.00

First day cancellation was applied at Boston to 1,205,212 covers bearing one or more of Nos. 1489-1498. Cancellations at other cities unrecorded.

1499	8c	**Harry S Truman**, *May 8*, Independence, Mo. *(938,636)*	1.50
1500	6c	**Electronics**, *July 10*, New York, N.Y.	1.00
1501	8c	**Electronics**, *July 10*, New York, N.Y.	1.00
1502	15c	**Electronics**, *July 10*, New York, N.Y.	1.00
		1500-1502 and C86 on one cover	4.00

First day cancellation was applied to 1,197,700 covers bearing one or more of Nos. 1500-1502 and C86.

1503	8c	**Lyndon B. Johnson**, *Aug. 27*, Austin, Texas *(701,490)*	1.00

1973-74

1504	8c	**Angus Cattle**, *Oct. 5, 1973*, St. Joseph, Mo. *(521,427)*	1.00
1505	10c	**Chautauqua**, *Aug. 6, 1974*, Chautauqua, N.Y. *(411,105)*	1.00
1506	10c	**Wheat**, *Aug. 16, 1974*, Hillsboro, Kans. *(468,280)*	1.00
1507	8c	**Christmas (religious)**, *Nov. 7, 1973*	1.00
1508	8c	**Christmas (secular)**, *Nov. 7, 1973*	1.00
		1507-1508 on one cover	1.10

First day cancellation was applied to 807,468 covers bearing one or both of Nos. 1507-1508.

1509	10c	**Crossed Flags**, *Dec. 8, 1973*, San Francisco, Calif.	1.00

First day cancellation was applied to 341,528 covers bearing one or more of Nos. 1509 and 1519.

1510	10c	**Jefferson Memorial**, *Dec. 14, 1973*	1.00
1510b		Booklet pane of 5 + label	2.25
1510c		Booklet pane of 8	2.50
1510d		Booklet pane of 6, *Aug. 5, 1974*, Oakland, Calif.	3.00

First day cancellation was applied to 686,300 covers bearing one or more of Nos. 1510, 1510b, 1510c, 1520.

1511	10c	**Zip Code**, *Jan. 4, 1974 (335,220)*	1.00
1518	6.3c	**Bell Coil**, *Oct. 1, 1974 (221,141)*	1.00
1519	10c	**Crossed Flags coil**, *Dec. 8, 1973*, San Francisco, Calif.	1.00
1520	10c	**Jefferson Memorial coil**, *Dec. 14, 1973*	1.00

1974

1525	10c	**Veterans of Foreign Wars**, *Mar. 11 (543,598)*	1.50
1526	10c	**Robert Frost**, *Mar. 26*, Derry, N.H. *(500,425)*	1.00
1527	10c	**EXPO '74**, *Apr. 18*, Spokane, Wash. *(565,548)*	1.00
1528	10c	**Horse Racing**, *May 4*, Louisville, Ky. *(623,983)*	3.00
1529	10c	**Skylab**, *May 14*, Houston, Tex. *(972,326)*	1.50
1537a	10c	**UPU Centenary**, *June 6 (1,374,765)*	4.00
		1530-1537, any single	1.00
1541a	10c	**Mineral Heritage**, *June 13*, Lincoln, Neb. *(865,368)*	2.75
		1538-1541, any single	1.00
1542	10c	**Kentucky Settlement**, *June 15*, Harrodsburg, Ky. *(478,239)*	1.00
1546a	10c	**Continental Congress** (Rev. Bicentennial), *July 4*, Philadelphia, Pa. *(2,124,957)*	2.75
		1543-1546, any single	1.00
1547	10c	**Energy Conservation**, *Sept. 23*, Detroit, Mich. *(587,210)*	1.00
1548	10c	**Sleepy Hollow**, *Oct. 10*, North Tarrytown, N.Y. *(514,836)*	3.00
1549	10c	**Retarded Children**, *Oct. 12*, Arlington Tex. *(412,882)*	1.00
1550	10c	**Christmas (Religious)**, *Oct. 23*, New York, N.Y. *(634,990)*	1.00
1551	10c	**Christmas (Currier & Ives)**, *Oct. 23*, New York, N.Y. *(634,990)*	1.00
		1550-1551 on one cover	1.10
1552	10c	**Christmas (Dove)**, *Nov. 15*, New York, N.Y. *(477,410)*	1.50

1975

1553	10c	**Benjamin West**, *Feb. 10*, Swarthmore, Pa. *(465,017)*	1.00
1554	10c	**Paul L. Dunbar**, *May 1*, Dayton, Ohio *(397,347)*	1.50
1555	10c	**D.W. Griffith**, *May 27*, Beverly Hills, Calif. *(424,167)*	1.00
1556	10c	**Pioneer-Jupiter**, *Feb. 28*, Mountain View, Calif. *(594,896)*	1.25
1557	10c	**Mariner 10**, *Apr. 4*, Pasadena, Calif. *(563,636)*	1.25
1558	10c	**Collective Bargaining**, *Mar. 13 (412,329)*	1.00
1559	8c	**Sybil Ludington** (Rev. Bicentennial), *Mar. 25*, Carmel, N.Y. *(394,550)*	1.00
1560	10c	**Salem Poor** (Rev. Bicentennial), *Mar. 25*, Cambridge, Mass. *(415,565)*	1.50
1561	10c	**Haym Salomon** (Rev. Bicentennial), *Mar. 25*, Chicago, Ill. *(442,630)*	1.00
1562	18c	**Peter Francisco** (Rev. Bicentennial), *Mar. 25*, Greensboro, N.C. *(415,000)*	1.00
1563	10c	**Lexington-Concord** (Rev. Bicentennial), *Apr. 19*, Lexington, Mass., or Concord, Mass, *(975,020)*	1.00

1564	10c	**Bunker Hill** (Rev. Bicentennial), *June 17*, Charlestown, Mass. *(557,130)*	1.00
1568a	10c	**Military Services** (Rev. Bicentennial), *July 4 (1,134,831)*	2.50
		1565-1568, any single	1.00
1569a	10c	**Apollo-Soyuz**, *July 15*, Kennedy Space Center, Fla. *(1,427,046)*	5.00
		1569-1570, any single	3.00
1571	10c	**International Women's Year**, *Aug. 26*, Seneca Falls, N.Y. *(476,769)*	1.00
1575a	10c	**Postal Service Bicentenary**, *Sept. 3*, Philadelphia, Pa. *(969,999)*	2.50
		1572-1575, any single	1.00
1576	10c	**World Peace through Law**, *Sept. 29 (386,736)*	1.25
1577a	10c	**Banking-Commerce**, *Oct. 6*, New York, N.Y. *(555,580)*	1.75
		1577-1578, any single	1.00
1579	(10c)	**Christmas (religious)**, *Oct. 14*	1.00
1580	(10c)	**Christmas (secular)**, *Oct. 14*	1.00
		1579-1580 on one cover	2.00

First day cancellation was applied to 730,079 covers bearing one or more of Nos. 1579-1580.

1975-79

AMERICANA ISSUE

1581	1c	**Inkwell**, *Dec. 8, 1977*, St. Louis, Mo., multiple for 1st class rate	1.00
1582	2c	**Speaker's Stand**, *Dec. 8, 1977*, St. Louis, Mo., multiple for 1st class rate	1.00
1584	3c	**Ballot Box**, *Dec. 8, 1977*, St. Louis, Mo., multiple for 1st class rate	1.00
1585	4c	**Books and Eyeglasses**, *Dec. 8, 1977*, St. Louis, Mo., multiple for 1st class rate	1.00

First day cancellation was applied to 530,033 covers bearing one or more of Nos. 1581-1582, 1584-1585.

1590	9c	**Capitol Dome**, from bklt., *Mar. 11, 1977*, New York, N.Y., plus postage for 1st class rate	1.00
1591	9c	**Capitol Dome**, *Nov. 24, 1975 (190,117)*, multiple for 1st class rate	1.00
1592	10c	**Justice**, *Nov. 17, 1977*, New York, N.Y. *(359,050)*, multiple for 1st class rate	1.00
1593	11c	**Printing Press**, *Nov. 13, 1975*, Philadelphia, Pa. *(217,755)*, multiple for 1st class rate	1.00
1594	12c	**Torch**, *Apr. 8, 1981*, Dallas, TX, multiple for 1st class rate	1.00

First day cancellation was applied to 280,930 covers bearing one or more of Nos. 1594 and 1816.

1595	13c	**Liberty Bell**, *Oct. 31, 1975*, Cleveland, Ohio *(256,734)*	1.00
1595a		Booklet pane of 6	2.00
1595b		Booklet pane of 7 + label	2.75
1595c		Booklet pane of 8	2.50
1595d		Booklet pane of 5 + label, *Apr. 2, 1976*, Liberty, Mo.	2.25
1596	13c	**Eagle and Shield**, *Dec. 1, 1975*, Juneau, Alaska *(418,272)*	1.00
1597	15c	**Flag**, *June 30*, Baltimore, Md.	1.00
1598	15c	**Flag**, from bklt., *June 30, 1978*, Baltimore, Md.	1.00
1598a		Booklet pane of 8	2.50

First day cancellation was applied to 315,359 covers bearing one or more of Nos. 1597, 1598, and 1618C.

1599	16c	**Statue of Liberty**, *Mar. 31, 1978*, New York, N.Y.	1.00
1603	24c	**Old North Church**, *Nov. 14, 1975*, Boston, Mass. *(208,973)*	1.00
1604	28c	**Fort Nisqually**, *Aug. 11, 1978*, Tacoma, Wash. *(159,639)*	1.00
1605	29c	**Sandy Hook Lighthouse**, *Apr. 14, 1978*, Atlantic City, N.J. *(193,476)*	1.50
1606	30c	**Schoolhouse**, *Aug. 27, 1979*, Devils Lake, N.D. *(186,882)*	1.25
1608	50c	**Betty Lamp**, *Sept. 11, 1979*, San Juan, P.R. *(159,540)*	1.50
1610	$1	**Rush Lamp**, *July 2, 1979*, San Francisco, Calif. *(255,575)*	3.00
1611	$2	**Kerosene Lamp**, *Nov. 16, 1978*, New York, N.Y. *(173,596)*	5.00
1612	$5	**Railroad Lantern**, *Aug. 23, 1979*, Boston, Mass. *(129,192)*	12.50

COIL STAMPS

1613	3.1c	**Guitar**, *Oct. 25, 1979*, Shreveport, La. *(230,403)*	1.00
1614	7.7c	**Saxhorns**, *Nov. 20, 1976*, New York, N.Y. *(285,290)*	1.00
1615	7.9c	**Drum**, *Apr. 23, 1976*, Miami, Fla. *(193,270)*	1.00
1615C	8.4c	**Piano**, *July 13, 1978*, Interlochen, Mich. *(200,392)*	1.00
1616	9c	**Capitol Dome**, *Mar. 5, 1976*, Milwaukee, Wis. *(128,171)*	1.00
1617	10c	**Justice**, *Nov. 4, 1977*, Tampa, Fla. *(184,954)*	1.00
1618	13c	**Liberty Bell**, *Nov. 25, 1975*, Allentown, Pa. *(320,387)*	1.00
1618C	15c	**Flag**, *June 30, 1978*, Baltimore, Md.	1.00
1619	16c	**Statue of Liberty**, *Mar. 31, 1978*, New York, N.Y.	1.00

First day cancellation was applied to 376,338 covers bearing one or more of Nos. 1599 and 1619.

1975

1622	13c	**13-Star Flag**, *Nov. 15*, Philadelphia, Pa.	1.00
1623	13c	**Flag over Capitol**, *Mar. 11*, New York, N.Y.	1.50
1623a		Booklet pane of 8, perf 11 (1 #1590 +7 #1623)	25.00
1623Bc		Booklet pane of 8, perf. 10x9¾ (1 #1590A + 7 #1623B)	15.00

First day cancellation was applied to 242,208 covers bearing Nos. 1623, 1623a, 1623B or 1623Bc.

1625	13c	**13-Star Flag coil**, *Nov. 15*, Philadelphia, PA	1.00

First day cancellation was applied to 362,959 covers bearing one or more of Nos. 1622 and 1625.

1976

1631a	13c	**Spirit of '76**, *Jan. 1*, Pasadena, CA *(1,013,067)*	2.00
		1629-1631, any single	1.25
1632	13c	**Interphil '76**, *Jan. 17*, Philadelphia, Pa. *(519,902)*	1.00
1682a	13c	**State Flags**, *Feb. 23*	27.50
		1633-1682, any single	1.50
1683	13c	**Telephone**, *Mar. 10*, Boston, Mass. *(662,515)*	1.00
1684	13c	**Commercial Aviation**, *Mar. 19*, Chicago Ill. *(631,555)*	1.50
1685	13c	**Chemistry**, *Apr. 6*, New York, N.Y. *(557,600)*	1.50

Bicentennial Souvenir Sheets of 5

1686	13c	**Surrender of Cornwallis**, *May 29*, Philadelphia, Pa.	7.50
1687	18c	**Declaration of Independence**, *May 29*, Philadelphia, Pa.	7.50
1688	24c	**Declaration of Independence**, *May 29*, Philadelphia, Pa.	7.50
1689	31c	**Washington at Valley Forge**, *May 29*, Philadelphia, Pa.	7.50

First day cancellation was applied to 879,890 covers bearing singles, multiples or complete sheets of Nos. 1686-1689.

1690	13c	**Franklin**, *June 1*, Philadelphia, Pa. *(588,740)*	1.00
1694a	13c	**Declaration of Independence**, *July 4*, Philadelphia, Pa. *(2,093,880)*	2.00
		1691-1694, any single	1.00
1698a	13c	**Olympic Games**, *July 16*, Lake Placid, N.Y. *(1,140,189)*	2.00
		1695-1698, any single	1.00
1699	13c	**Clara Maass**, *Aug. 18*, Belleville, N.J. *(646,506)*	2.50
1700	13c	**Adolph S. Ochs**, *Sept. 18*, New York, N.Y. *(582,580)*	1.00
1701	13c	**Christmas (religious)**, *Oct. 27*, Boston, Mass. *(540,050)*	1.00
1702	13c	**Christmas (secular)**, *Oct. 27*, Boston, Mass. *(181,410)*	1.00
1703	13c	**Christmas (secular)**, block tagged, *Oct. 27*, Boston, Mass. *(330,450)*	1.00
		1701 and 1702 or 1703 on one cover	1.25

1977

1704	13c	**Washington at Princeton**, *Jan. 3*, Princeton, N.J. *(695,335)*	1.00
1705	13c	**Sound Recording**, *Mar. 23 (632,216)*	1.25
1709a	13c	**Pueblo Art**, *Apr. 13*, Santa Fe, N.M. *(1,194,554)*	2.00
		1706-1709, any single	1.00
1710	13c	**Lindbergh Flight**, *May 20*, Roosevelt Sta., N.Y. *(3,985,989)*	3.50
1711	13c	**Colorado Statehood**, *May 21*, Denver, Colo. *(510,880)*	1.00
1715a	13c	**Butterflies**, *June 6*, Indianapolis, Ind. *(1,218,278)*	2.00
		1712-1715, any single	2.00
1716	13c	**Lafayette's Landing**, *June 13*, Charleston, S.C. *(514,506)*	1.00
1720a	13c	**Skilled Hands**, *July 4*, Cincinnati, Ohio *(1,263,568)*	2.00
		1717-1720, any single	1.00
1721	13c	**Peace Bridge**, *Aug. 4*, Buffalo, N.Y. *(512,995)*	1.00
1722	13c	**Battle of Oriskany**, *Aug. 6*, Utica, N.Y. *(605,906)*	1.00
1723a	13c	**Energy Conservation**, *Oct. 20 (410,299)*	1.50
		1723-1724, any single	1.25
1725	13c	**Alta California**, *Sept. 9*, San Jose, Calif. *(709,457)*	1.00
1726	13c	**Articles of Confederation**, *Sept. 30*, York, Pa. *(605,455)*	1.00
1727	13c	**Talking Pictures**, *Oct. 6*, Hollywood, Calif. *(570,195)*	1.50
1728	13c	**Surrender at Saratoga** *Oct. 7*, Schuylerville, N.Y. *(557,529)*	1.00
1729	13c	**Christmas (Valley Forge)**, *Oct. 21*, Valley Forge, Pa. *(583,139)*	1.00
1730	13c	**Christmas (mailbox)**, *Oct. 21*, Omaha, Nebr. *(675,786)*	1.00

1978

1731	13c	**Carl Sandburg**, *Jan. 6*, Galesburg, Ill. *(493,826)*	1.00
1732a	13c	**Captain Cook**, *Jan. 20*, Honolulu, Hawaii, or Anchorage, Alaska	1.75
		1732-1733, any single	1.25

First day cancellation was applied to 823,855 covers at Honolulu, and 672,804 at Anchorage, each cover bearing one or both of Nos. 1732-1733.

1734	13c	**Indian Head Penny**, *Jan. 11*, Kansas City, Mo. *(512,426)*	1.00

1978-80

REGULAR ISSUE

1735	(15c)	**"A" Eagle,** *May 22,* Memphis, Tenn.	1.00
1736	(15c)	**"A" Eagle,** bklt. single *May 22,* Memphis, Tenn.	1.00
1736a		Booklet pane of 8	2.50
1737	15c	**Roses,** *July 11,* Shreveport, La. *(445,003)*	1.00
1737a		Booklet pane of 8	2.50
1742a	15c	**Windmills Booklet pane of 10,** *Feb. 7, 1980,* Lubbock, TX	3.50
		1738-1742, any single	1.00
1743	15c	**"A" Eagle coil,** *May 22,* Memphis, Tenn.	1.00

First day cancellation was applied to 689,049 covers bearing one or more of Nos. 1735, 1736 and 1743. First day cancellation was applied to 708,411 covers bearing one or more of Nos. 1738-1742a.

1978

1744	13c	**Harriet Tubman,** *Feb. 1 (493,495)*	1.75
1748a	13c	**American Quilts,** *Mar. 8,* Charleston, W.Va.	2.00
		1745-1748, any single	1.00

First day cancellation was applied to 1,081,827 covers bearing one or more of Nos. 1745-1748.

1752a	13c	**American Dance,** *Apr. 26,* New York, N.Y. *(1,626,493)*	2.00
		1749-1752, any single	1.00
1753	13c	**French Alliance,** *May 4,* York, Pa. *(705,240)*	1.00
1754	13c	**Papanicolaou,** *May 18 (535,584)*	1.00
1755	13c	**Jimmie Rodgers,** *May 24,* Meridian, Miss. *(599,287)*	1.00
1756	15c	**George M. Cohan,** *July 3,* Providence, R.I. *(740,750)*	1.25
1757	15c	**CAPEX souv. sheet,** *June 10,* Toronto, Canada *(1,994,067)*	2.75
1758	15c	**Photography,** *June 26,* Las Vegas, Nev. *(684,987)*	1.00
1759	15c	**Viking Missions,** *July 20,* Hampton, Va. *(805,051)*	1.00
1763a	15c	**American Owls,** *Aug. 26,* Fairbanks, Alas. *(1,690,474)*	2.00
		1760-1763, any single	1.25
1767a	15c	**American Trees,** *Oct. 9,* Hot Springs National Park, Ark. *(1,139,100)*	2.00
		1764-1767, any single	1.25
1768	15c	**Christmas (Madonna),** *Oct. 18 (553,064)*	1.00
1769	15c	**Christmas (Hobby Horse),** *Oct. 18,* Holly, Mich. *(603,008)*	1.00

1979-80

1770	15c	**Robert Kennedy,** *Jan. 12 (624,582)*	1.50
1771	15c	**Martin L. King,** *Jan. 13,* Atlanta, Ga. *(726,149)*	2.00
1772	15c	**Year of Child,** *Feb. 15,* Philadelphia, Pa. *(716,782)*	1.00
1773	15c	**John Steinbeck,** *Feb. 27,* Salinas, Calif. *(709,073)*	1.00
1774	15c	**Albert Einstein,** *Mar. 4,* Princeton, N.J. *(641,423)*	3.50
1778a	15c	**Toleware,** *Apr. 19,* Lancaster, Pa. *(1,581,962)*	2.00
		1775-1778, any single	1.00
1782a	15c	**American Architecture,** *June 4,* Kansas City, Mo. *(1,219,258)*	2.00
		1779-1782, any single	1.00
1786a	15c	**Endangered Flora,** *June 7,* Milwaukee, Wis. *(1,436,268)*	2.00
		1783-1786, any single	1.00
1787	15c	**Guide Dogs,** *June 15,* Morristown, N.J. *(588,826)*	1.25
1788	15c	**Special Olympics,** *Aug. 9,* Brockport, N.Y. *(651,344)*	1.25
1789	15c	**John Paul Jones,** *Sept. 23,* Annapolis, Md.	1.50
1789A	15c	**John Paul Jones,** *Sept. 23,* Annapolis, Md.	1.50

Total for 1789 and 1789A is 587,018.

1790	10c	**Olympic Javelin,** *Sept. 5,* Olympia, Wash. *(305,122)*	1.00
1794a	15c	**Olympics 1980,** *Sept. 28,* Los Angeles, Calif. *(1,561,366)*	2.00
		1791-1794, any single	1.25
1798b	15c	**Winter Olympics,** *Feb. 1, 1980,* Lake Placid, N.Y. *(1,166,302)*	2.00
		1795-1798, any single	1.25

1979

1799	15c	**Christmas (Madonna),** *Oct. 18 (686,990)*	1.25
1800	15c	**Christmas (Santa Claus),** *Oct. 18,* North Pole, Alaska *(511,829)*	1.25
		1799-1800, both stamps issued *Oct. 18*	2.00
1801	15c	**Will Rogers,** *Nov. 4,* Claremore, Okla. *(1,643,151)*	1.50
1802	15c	**Viet Nam Veterans,** *Nov. 11,* Arlington, VA *(445,934)*	3.25

1980

1803	15c	**W.C. Fields,** *Jan. 29,* Beverly Hills, CA *(633,303)*	2.00
1804	15c	**Benjamin Banneker,** *Feb. 15,* Annapolis, MD *(647,126)*	2.00
1810a	15c	**Letter Writing,** *Feb. 25 (1,083,360)*	2.50
		1805-1810, any single	1.00

1980-81

DEFINITIVES

1811	1c	**Quill Pen,** coil, *Mar. 6, 1980,* New York, NY *(262,921)*	1.00
1813	3.5c	**Violins,** coil, *June 23, 1980,* Williamsburg, PA	1.00

FD cancel was applied to 716,988 covers bearing Nos. 1813 or U590.

1816	12c	**Torch,** coil, *Apr. 8, 1981,* Dallas, TX	1.00
1818	(18c)	**"B" Eagle,** *Mar. 15, 1981,* San Francisco, CA	1.25

FD cancel was applied to 511,688 covers bearing one or more of Nos. 1818-1820, U592 or UX88.

1819	(18c)	**"B" Eagle,** bklt. single, *Mar. 15, 1981,* San Francisco, CA	1.00
1819a		Booklet pane of 8	3.00
1820	(18c)	**"B" Eagle,** coil, *Mar. 15, 1981,* San Francisco, CA	1.00

1980

1821	15c	**Frances Perkins,** *Apr. 10 (678,966)*	1.00
1822	15c	**Dolley Madison,** *May 20 (331,048)*	1.00
1823	15c	**Emily Bissell,** *May 31,* Wilmington, DE *(649,509)*	1.00
1824	15c	**Helen Keller, Anne Sullivan,** *June 27,* Tuscumbia, AL *(713,061)*	1.25
1825	15c	**Veterans Administration,** *July 21 (634,101)*	1.50
1826	15c	**Bernardo de Galvez,** *July 23,* New Orleans, LA *(658,061)*	1.00
1830a	15c	**Coral Reefs,** *Aug. 26,* Charlotte Amalie, VI *(1,195,126)*	2.00
		1827-1830, any single	1.00
1831	15c	**Organized Labor,** *Sept. 1 (759,973)*	1.00
1832	15c	**Edith Wharton,** *Sept. 5,* New Haven, CT *(633,917)*	1.00
1833	15c	**Education,** *Sept. 12,* Franklin, MA *(672,592)*	1.50
1837a	15c	**Indian Masks,** *Sept. 25,* Spokane, WA *(2,195,136)*	2.00
		1834-1837, any single	1.00
1841a	15c	**Architecture,** *Oct. 9,* New York, NY *(2,164,721)*	1.75
		1838-1841, any single	1.00
1842	15c	**Christmas (Madonna),** *Oct. 31 (718,614)*	1.25
1843	15c	**Christmas (Toys),** *Oct. 31,* Christmas, MI *(755,108)*	1.25

1980-85

GREAT AMERICANS ISSUE

1844	1c	**Dorothea Dix,** *Sept. 23, 1983,* Hampden, ME *(164,140)*	1.00
1845	2c	**Igor Stravinsky,** *Nov. 18, 1982,* New York, NY *(501,719)*	1.00
1846	3c	**Henry Clay,** *July 13, 1983 (204,320)*	1.00
1847	4c	**Carl Schurz,** *June 3, 1983,* Watertown, WI *(165,010)*	1.00
1848	5c	**Pearl Buck,** *June 25, 1983,* Hillsboro, WV *(231,852)*	1.00
1849	6c	**Walter Lippman,** *Sept. 19, 1985,* Minneapolis, MN *(371,990)*	1.00
1850	7c	**Abraham Baldwin,** *Jan. 25, 1985,* Athens, GA *(402,285)*	1.25
1851	8c	**Henry Knox,** *July 25, 1985,* Thomaston, ME *(315,937)*	1.00
1852	9c	**Sylvanus Thayer,** *June 7, 1985,* Braintree, MA *(345,649)*	1.25
1853	10c	**Richard Russell,** *May 31, 1984,* Winder, GA *(183,581)*	1.00
1854	11c	**Alden Partridge,** *Feb. 12, 1985,* Northfield, VT *(442,311)*	1.25
1855	13c	**Crazy Horse,** *Jan. 15, 1982,* Crazy Horse, SD	1.50
1856	14c	**Sinclair Lewis,** *Mar. 21, 1985,* Sauk Centre, MN *(308,612)*	1.00
1857	17c	**Rachel Carson,** *May 28, 1981,* Springdale, PA *(273,686)*	1.00
1858	18c	**George Mason,** *May 7, 1981,* Gunston Hall, VA *(461,937)*	1.00
1859	19c	**Sequoyah,** *Dec. 27, 1980,* Tahlequah, OK *(241,325)*	1.25
1860	20c	**Ralph Bunche,** *Jan. 12, 1982,* New York, NY	1.75
1861	20c	**Thomas H. Gallaudet,** *June 10, 1983,* West Hartford, CT *(261,336)*	1.25
1862	20c	**Harry S Truman,** *Jan. 26, 1984 (267,631)*	1.25
1863	22c	**John J. Audubon,** *Apr. 23, 1985,* New York, NY *(516,249)*	1.25
1864	30c	**Frank Laubach,** *Sept. 2, 1984,* Benton, PA *(118,974)*	1.25
1865	35c	**Charles Drew,** *June 3, 1981 (383,882)*	1.75
1866	37c	**Robert Millikan,** *Jan. 26, 1982,* Pasadena, CA	1.25
1867	39c	**Grenville Clark,** *Mar. 20, 1985,* Hanover, NH *(297,797)*	1.25
1868	40c	**Lillian Gilbreth,** *Feb. 24, 1984,* Montclair, NJ *(110,588)*	1.50
1869	50c	**Chester W. Nimitz,** *Feb. 22, 1985,* Fredericksburg, TX *(376,166)*	2.00

1981

1874	15c	**Everett Dirksen,** *Jan. 4,* Pekin, IL *(665,755)*	1.00
1875	15c	**Whitney M. Young,** *Jan. 30,* New York, NY *(963,870)*	1.75
1879a	18c	**Flowers,** *Apr. 23,* Fort Valley, GA *(1,966,599)*	2.50
		1876-1879, any single	1.00

1980-81

DEFINITIVES

1889a	18c	**Animals Booklet pane of 10,** *May 14,* Boise, ID	5.00
		1880-1889, any single	1.00
1890	18c	**Flag-Anthem (grain),** *Apr. 24,* Portland, ME	1.00
1891	18c	**Flag-Anthem (sea),** *Apr. 24,* Portland, ME	1.50
1892	6c	**Star Circle,** *Apr. 24,* Portland, ME	1.00
1893	18c	**Flag-Anthem (mountain),** *Apr. 24,* Portland, ME	1.00
1893a		Booklet pane of 8 (2 #1892, 6 #1893)	2.50

FDC cancel was applied to 691,526 covers bearing one or more of Nos. 1890-1893 & 1893a.

1894	20c	**Flag-Court,** *Dec. 17*	1.00
1895	20c	**Flag-Court,** coil, *Dec. 17*	1.00
1896	20c	**Flag-Court,** perf. 11x10½, *Dec. 17 (185,543)*	1.00
1896a		Booklet pane of 6	6.00
1896b		Booklet pane of 10, *June 1, 1982*	10.00

First day cancellations were applied to 598,169 covers bearing one or more of Nos. 1894-1896.

1981-84

TRANSPORTATION ISSUE

1897	1c	**Omnibus,** *Aug. 19, 1983,* Arlington, VA *(109,463)*	1.00
1897A	2c	**Locomotive,** *May 20, 1982,* Chicago, IL *(290,020)*	1.50
1898	3c	**Handcar,** *Mar. 25, 1983,* Rochester, NY *(77,900)*	1.00
1898A	4c	**Stagecoach,** *Aug. 19, 1982,* Milwaukee, WI *(152,940)*	1.00
1899	5c	**Motorcycle,** *Oct. 10, 1983,* San Francisco, CA *(188,240)*	2.00
1900	5.2c	**Sleigh,** *Mar. 21, 1983,* Memphis, TN *(141,979)*	1.00
1901	5.9c	**Bicycle,** *Feb. 17, 1982,* Wheeling, WV *(814,419)*	1.50
1902	7.4c	**Baby Buggy,** *Apr. 7, 1984,* San Diego, CA	1.00
1903	9.3c	**Mail Wagon,** *Dec. 15, 1981,* Shreveport, LA *(199,645)*	1.00
1904	10.9c	**Hansom,** *Mar. 26, 1982,* Chattanooga, TN	1.00
1905	11c	**Railroad Caboose,** *Feb. 3, 1984,* Chicago, IL *(172,753)*	1.50
1906	17c	**Electric Auto,** *June 25, 1982,* Greenfield Village, MI *(239,458)*	1.00
1907	18c	**Surrey,** *May 18, 1981,* Notch, MO *(207,801)*	1.00
1908	20c	**Fire Pumper,** *Dec. 10, 1981,* Alexandria, VA *(304,668)*	2.00
1909	$9.35	**Eagle,** *Aug. 12, 1983,* Kennedy Space Center, FL *(77,858)*	50.00
1909a		Booklet pane of 3	125.00

1981

1910	18c	**Red Cross,** *May 1 (874,972)*	2.00
1911	18c	**Savings & Loan,** *May 8,* Chicago, IL *(740,910)*	1.00
1919a	18c	**Space Achievement,** *May 21,* Kennedy Space Center, FL *(7,027,549)*	3.00
		1912-1919, any single	1.00
1920	18c	**Professional Management,** *June 18,* Philadelphia, PA *(713,096)*	1.00
1924a	18c	**Wildlife Habitats,** *June 26,* Reno, NV *(2,327,609)*	2.50
		1921-1924, any single	1.00
1925	18c	**Year of Disabled,** *June 29,* Milford, MI *(714,244)*	1.00
1926	18c	**Edna St. V. Millay,** *July 10,* Austerlitz, NY *(725,978)*	1.00
1927	18c	**Alcoholism,** *Aug. 19 (874,972)*	3.00
1931a	18c	**Architecture,** *Aug. 28,* New York, NY *(1,998,208)*	2.50
		1928-1931, any single	1.00
1932	18c	**Babe Zaharias,** *Sept. 22,* Pinehurst, NC	6.50
1933	18c	**Bobby Jones,** *Sept. 22,* Pinehurst, NC	10.00
		1932-1933, both stamps issued *Sept. 22,* Pinehurst, NC	12.50

First day cancel was applied to 1,231,543 covers bearing one or more of Nos. 1932-1933.

1934	18c	**Frederic Remington,** *Oct. 9,* Oklahoma City, OK *(1,367,099)*	1.25
1935	18c	**James Hoban,** *Oct. 13*	1.00
1936	20c	**James Hoban,** *Oct. 13*	1.00
		1935-1936, both stamps issued *Oct. 13*	2.50

FD cancel was applied to 635,012 covers bearing Nos. 1935-1936.

1938a	18c	**Yorktown-Va. Capes Battle,** *Oct. 16,* Yorktown, VA *(1,098,278)*	1.50
		1937-1938, any single	1.00
1939	(20c)	**Christmas (Madonna),** *Oct. 28,* Chicago, IL *(481,395)*	1.00
1940	(20c)	**Christmas (Teddy Bear),** *Oct. 28,* Christmas Valley, OR *(517,898)*	1.00
1941	20c	**John Hanson,** *Nov. 5,* Frederick, MD *(605,616)*	1.00
1945a	20c	**Desert Plants,** *Dec. 11,* Tucson, AZ *(1,770,187)*	2.50
		1942-1945, any single	1.00

REGULAR ISSUE

1946	(20c)	**"C" Eagle,** *Oct. 11,* Memphis, TN	1.00
1947	(20c)	**"C" Eagle,** coil, *Oct. 11,* Memphis, TN	1.00

1948	(20c) **"C" Eagle,** bklt. single, *Oct. 11,* Memphis, TN	1.00
1948a	Booklet pane of 10	3.50

First day cancellations were applied to 304,404 covers bearing one or more of Nos. 1946-1948.

1982

1949	20c **Bighorn,** *Jan. 8,* Bighorn, MT	1.25
1949a	Booklet pane of 10	6.00
1950	20c **F.D. Roosevelt,** *Jan. 30,* Hyde Park, NY	1.00
1951	20c **Love,** *Feb. 1,* Boston, MA *(325,727)*	1.00
1952	20c **Washington,** *Feb. 22,* Mt. Vernon, VA	1.25
2002b	20c **Birds-Flowers,** perf 10½x11¼ *Apr. 14,* Washington, DC, or State Capital 1953-2002, any single	30.00 1.25
2002Ac	20c **Birds-Flowers,** perf 11¼x11 *Apr. 14,* Washington, DC, or State Capital 1953A-2002A, any single	— —
2003	20c **U.S.-Netherlands,** *Apr. 20*	1.00
2004	20c **Library of Congress,** *Apr. 21*	1.00
2005	20c **Consumer Education,** *Apr. 27*	1.00
2009a	20c **Knoxville Fair,** *Apr. 29,* Knoxville, TN 2006-2009, any single	2.50 1.00
2010	20c **Horatio Alger,** *Apr. 30,* Willow Grove, PA	1.00
2011	20c **Aging,** *May 21,* Sun City, AZ	1.00
2012	20c **Barrymores,** *June 8,* New York, NY	1.00
2013	20c **Dr. Mary Walker,** *June 10,* Oswego, NY	1.00
2014	20c **Peace Garden,** *June 30,* Dunseith, ND	1.00
2015	20c **America's Libraries,** *July 13,* Philadelphia, PA	1.00
2016	20c **Jackie Robinson,** *Aug. 2,* Cooperstown, NY	6.00
2017	20c **Touro Synagogue,** *Aug. 22,* Newport, RI *(517,264)*	1.50
2018	20c **Wolf Trap Farm Park,** *Sept. 1,* Vienna, VA *(704,361)*	1.00
2022a	20c **Architecture,** *Sept. 30 (1,552,567)* 2019-2022, any single	2.50 1.00
2023	20c **St. Francis,** *Oct. 7,* San Francisco, CA *(530,275)*	1.25
2024	20c **Ponce de Leon,** *Oct. 12,* San Juan, PR *(530,275)*	1.00
2025	13c **Puppy, Kitten,** *Nov. 3,* Danvers, MA *(239,219)*	1.25
2026	20c **Christmas (Madonna),** *Oct. 28 (462,982)*	1.00
2030a	20c **Christmas (Children),** *Oct. 28,* Snow, OK *(676,950)* 2027-2030, any single	2.50 1.00

1983

2031	20c **Science & Industry,** *Jan. 19,* Chicago, IL *(526,693)*	1.00
2035a	20c **Balloons,** *Mar. 31,* Albuquerque, NM or Washington, DC *(989,305)* 2032-2035, any single	2.50 1.00
2036	20c **U.S.-Sweden,** *Mar. 24,* Philadelphia, PA *(526,373)*	1.00
2037	20c **Civilian Conservation Corps.,** *Apr. 5,* Luray, VA *(483,824)*	1.00
2038	20c **Joseph Priestley,** *Apr. 13,* Northumberland, PA *(673,266)*	1.00
2039	20c **Voluntarism,** *Apr. 20 (574,708)*	1.00
2040	20c **U.S.-Germany,** *Apr. 29,* Germantown, PA *(611,109)*	1.00
2041	20c **Brooklyn Bridge,** *May 17,* Brooklyn, NY *(815,085)*	1.75
2042	20c **TVA,** *May 18,* Knoxville, TN *(837,588)*	1.00
2043	20c **Physical Fitness,** *May 14,* Houston, TX *(501,336)*	1.25
2044	20c **Scott Joplin,** *June 9,* Sedalia, MO *(472,667)*	1.75
2045	20c **Medal of Honor,** *June 7 (1,623,995)*	5.50
2046	20c **Babe Ruth,** *July 6,* Chicago, IL *(1,277,907)*	5.00
2047	20c **Nathaniel Hawthorne,** *July 8,* Salem, MA *(442,793)*	1.00
2051a	13c **Summer Olympics,** *July 28,* South Bend, IN *(909,332)* 2048-2051, any single	2.50 1.25
2052	20c **Treaty of Paris,** *Sept. 2 (651,208)*	1.00
2053	20c **Civil Service,** *Sept. 9 (422,206)*	1.00
2054	20c **Metropolitan Opera,** *Sept. 14,* New York, NY *(807,609)*	1.50
2058a	20c **American Inventors,** *Sept. 21 (1,006,516)* 2055-2058, any single	2.50 1.00
2062a	20c **Streetcars,** *Oct. 8,* Kennebunkport, ME *(1,116,909)* 2059-2062, any single	2.50 1.00
2063	20c **Christmas (Madonna),** *Oct. 28 (361,874)*	1.00
2064	20c **Christmas (Santa),** *Oct. 28,* Santa Claus, IN *(388,749)*	1.00
2065	20c **Martin Luther,** *Nov. 11 (463,777)*	1.50

1984

2066	20c **Alaska Statehood,** *Jan. 3,* Fairbanks, AK *(816,591)*	1.00
2070a	20c **Winter Olympics,** *Jan. 6,* Lake Placid, NY *(1,245,807)* 2067-2070, any single	2.50 1.00
2071	20c **Federal Deposit Ins. Corp.,** *Jan. 12 (536,329)*	1.00
2072	20c **Love,** *Jan. 31 (327,727)*	1.00

2073	20c **Carter Woodson,** *Feb. 1 (387,583)*	1.75
2074	20c **Soil & Water Conservation,** *Feb. 6,* Denver, CO *(426,101)*	1.00
2075	20c **Credit Union Act,** *Feb. 10,* Salem, MA *(523,583)*	1.00
2079a	20c **Orchids,** *Mar. 5,* Miami, FL *(1,063,237)* 2076-2079, any single	2.50 1.00
2080	20c **Hawaii Statehood,** *Mar. 12,* Honolulu, HI *(546,930)*	1.00
2081	20c **National Archives,** *Apr. 16 (414,415)*	1.00
2085a	20c **Olympics 1984,** *May 4,* Los Angeles, CA *(1,172,313)* 2082-2085, any single	2.50 1.25
2086	20c **Louisiana Exposition,** *May 11,* New Orleans, LA *(467,408)*	1.00
2087	20c **Health Research,** *May 17,* New York, NY *(845,007)*	1.00
2088	20c **Douglas Fairbanks,** *May 23,* Denver CO *(547,134)*	1.00
2089	20c **Jim Thorpe,** *May 24,* Shawnee, OK *(568,544)*	3.00
2090	20c **John McCormack,** *June 6,* Boston, MA *(464,117)*	1.00
2091	20c **St. Lawrence Seaway,** *June 26,* Massena, NY *(550,173)*	1.00
2092	20c **Waterfowl Preservation Act,** *July 2,* Des Moines, IA *(549,388)*	1.00
2093	20c **Roanoke Voyages,** *July 13,* Manteo, NC *(443,725)*	1.00
2094	20c **Herman Melville,** *Aug. 1,* New Bedford, MA *(378,293)*	1.75
2095	20c **Horace A. Moses,** *Aug. 6,* Bloomington, IN *(459,386)*	1.00
2096	20c **Smokey Bear,** *Aug. 13,* Capitan, NM *(506,833)*	4.00
2097	20c **Roberto Clemente,** *Aug. 17,* Carolina, PR *(547,387)*	9.00
2101a	20c **Dogs,** *Sept. 7,* New York, NY *(1,157,373)* 2098-2101, any single	3.00 1.50
2102	20c **Crime Prevention,** *Sept. 26 (427,564)*	1.25
2103	20c **Hispanic Americans,** *Oct. 31 (416,796)*	1.75
2104	20c **Family Unity,** *Oct. 1,* Shaker Heights, OH *(400,659)*	1.00
2105	20c **Eleanor Roosevelt,** *Oct. 11,* Hyde Park, NY *(479,919)*	1.00
2106	20c **Nation of Readers,** *Oct. 16 (437,559)*	1.00
2107	20c **Christmas (Madonna),** *Oct. 30 (386,385)*	1.00
2108	20c **Christmas (Santa),** *Oct. 30,* Jamaica, NY *(430,843)*	1.00
2109	20c **Vietnam Veterans' Memorial,** *Nov. 10 (434,489)*	5.00

1985

2110	22c **Jerome Kern,** *Jan. 23,* New York, NY *(503,855)*	1.00

REGULAR ISSUE

2111	(22c) **"D" Eagle,** *Feb. 1,* Los Angeles, CA	1.00
2112	(22c) **"D" Eagle, coil,** *Feb. 1,* Los Angeles, CA	1.00
2113	(22c) **"D" Eagle, bklt. single,** *Feb. 1,* Los Angeles, CA	1.00
2113a	Booklet pane of 10	7.50

First Day cancel was applied to 513,027 covers bearing one or more of Nos. 2111-2113.

2114	22c **Flag over Capitol Dome,** *Mar. 29*	1.00
2115	22c **Flag over Capitol Dome, coil,** *Mar. 29*	1.00
2115b	Inscribed "T" at bottom, *May 23, 1987,* Secaucus, NJ	1.00

First Day Cancel was applied to 268,161 covers bearing one or more of Nos. 2114-2115.

2116	22c **Flag Over Capitol Dome, bklt.** single, *Mar. 29,* Waubeka, WI *(234,318)*	1.00
2116a	Booklet pane of 5	3.50
2121a	22c **Seashells Booklet pane of 10,** *Apr. 4,* Boston, MA *(426,290)* 2117-2121, any single	7.50 1.00
2122	$10.75 **Eagle and Half Moon,** type I, *Apr. 29,* San Francisco, CA *(93,154)*	50.00
2122a	Booklet pane of 3	125.00
2122b	Type II, *June 19, 1989*	350.00
2122c	Booklet pane of 3, type II	700.00

TRANSPORTATION ISSUE
1985-87

2123	3.4c **School Bus,** *June 8, 1985,* Arlington, VA *(131,480)*	1.00
2124	4.9c **Buckboard,** *June 21, 1985,* Reno, NV	1.00
2125	5.5c **Star Route Truck,** *Nov. 1, 1986,* Fort Worth, TX *(136,021)*	1.00
2126	6c **Tricycle,** *May 6, 1985,* Childs, MD *(151,494)*	1.25
2127	7.1c **Tractor,** *Feb. 6, 1987,* Sarasota, FL *(167,555)*	1.00
2127a	7.1c **Tractor,** Zip+4 precancel, untagged, *May 26, 1989,* Rosemont, IL *(202,804)*	5.00
2128	8.3c **Ambulance,** *June 21, 1986,* Reno, NV	1.00

First day cancel was applied to 338,765 covers bearing one or more of Nos. 2124 and 2128.

2129	8.5c **Tow Truck,** *Jan. 24, 1987,* Tucson, AZ *(224,285)*	1.25
2130	10.1c **Oil Wagon,** *Apr. 18, 1985,* Oil Center, NM	1.25
2130a	10.1c **"Bulk Rate Carrier Route Sort"** precancel, *June 27, 1988 (136,428)*	1.25
2131	11c **Stutz Bearcat,** *June 11, 1985,* Baton Rouge, LA *(135,037)*	1.25
2132	12c **Stanley Steamer,** *Apr. 2, 1985,* Kingfield, ME *(173,998)*	1.25
2133	12.5c **Pushcart,** *Apr. 18, 1985,* Oil Center, NM	1.25

First day cancel was applied to 319,953 covers bearing one or more of Nos. 2130 and 2133.

2134	14c **Ice Boat,** *Mar. 23, 1985,* Rochester, NY *(324,710)*	1.25
2135	17c **Dog Sled,** *Aug. 20, 1986,* Anchorage, AK	1.50
2136	25c **Bread Wagon,** *Nov. 22, 1986,* Virginia Beach, VA *(151,950)*	1.25

1985

2137	22c **Mary McLeod Bethune,** *Mar. 5 (413,244)*	1.50
2141a	22c **Duck Decoys,** *Mar. 22,* Shelburne, VT *(932,249)* 2138-2141, any single	2.50 1.00
2142	22c **Winter Special Olympics,** *Mar. 25,* Park City, UT *(253,074)*	1.00
2143	22c **Love,** *Apr. 17,* Hollywood, CA *(283,072)*	1.00
2144	22c **Rural Electrification Administration,** *May 11,* Madison, SD *(472,895)*	1.00
2145	22c **AMERIPEX '86,** *May 25,* Rosemont, IL *(457,038)*	1.00
2146	22c **Abigail Adams,** *June 14,* Quincy, MA *(491,026)*	1.00
2147	22c **Frederic Auguste Bartholdi,** *July 18,* New York, NY *(594,896)*	1.00
2149	18c **George Washington, Washington Monument,** *Nov. 6 (376,238)*	1.00
2150	21.1c **Envelopes,** *Oct. 22 (119,941)*	1.00
2152	22c **Korean War Veterans,** *July 26 (391,754)*	3.00
2153	22c **Social Security Act,** *Aug. 14,* Baltimore, MD *(265,143)*	1.00
2154	22c **World War I Veterans,** *Aug. 26,* Milwaukee, WI	1.50
2158a	22c **Horses,** *Sept. 25,* Lexington, KY *(1,135,368)* 2155-2158, any single	2.50 1.50
2159	22c **Public Education in America,** *Oct. 1,* Boston, MA *(356,030)*	1.00
2163a	22c **International Youth Year,** *Oct. 7,* Chicago, IL *(1,202,541)* 2160, 2162-2163, any single 2161	2.50 1.00 2.00
2164	22c **Help End Hunger,** *Oct. 15 (299,485)*	1.00
2165	22c **Christmas (Madonna & Child),** *Oct. 30,* Detroit, MI	1.00
2166	22c **Christmas (Poinsettia),** *Oct. 30,* Nazareth, MI *(524,929)*	1.00

1986

2167	22c **Arkansas Statehood,** *Jan. 3,* Little Rock, AR *(364,729)*	1.00

GREAT AMERICANS ISSUE
1986-94

2168	1c **Margaret Mitchell,** *June 30, 1986,* Atlanta, GA *(316,764)*	2.00
2169	2c **Mary Lyon,** *Feb. 28, 1987,* South Hadley, MA *(349,831)*	1.00
2170	3c **Dr. Paul Dudley White,** *Sept. 15, 1986*	1.00
2171	4c **Father Flanagan,** *July 14, 1986,* Boys Town, NE *(367,883)*	1.25
2172	5c **Hugo Black,** *Feb. 27, 1986 (303,012)*	1.00
2173	5c **Luis Munoz Marin,** *Feb. 18, 1990,* San Juan, PR *(269,618)*	1.00
2175	10c **Red Cloud,** *Aug. 15, 1987,* Red Cloud, NE *(300,472)*	1.50
2176	14c **Julia Ward Howe,** *Feb. 12, 1987,* Boston, MA *(454,829)*	1.00
2177	15c **Buffalo Bill Cody,** *June 6, 1988* Cody, WY *(356,395)*	2.00
2178	17c **Belva Ann Lockwood,** *June 18, 1986,* Middleport, NY *(249,215)*	1.00
2179	20c **Virginia Apgar,** *Oct. 24, 1994,* Dallas, TX *(28,461)*	1.00
2180	21c **Chester Carlson,** *Oct. 21, 1988,* Rochester, NY *(288,073)*	1.00
2181	23c **Mary Cassatt,** *Nov. 4, 1988,* Philadelphia, PA *(322,537)*	1.00
2182	25c **Jack London,** *Jan. 11, 1986,* Glen Ellen, CA *(358,686)*	1.50
2182a	Booklet pane of 10, *May 3, 1988,* San Francisco, CA	6.00
2183	28c **Sitting Bull,** *Sept. 14, 1989,* Rapid City, SD *(126,777)*	1.75
2184	29c **Earl Warren,** *Mar. 9, 1992 (175,517)*	1.25
2185	29c **Thomas Jefferson,** *Apr. 13, 1993,* Charlottesville, VA *(202,962)*	1.25
2186	35c **Dennis Chavez,** *Apr. 3, 1991,* Albuquerque, NM *(285,570)*	1.25
2187	40c **Claire Chennault,** *Sept. 6, 1990,* Monroe, LA *(186,761)*	2.00
2188	45c **Harvey Cushing,** *June 17, 1988,* Cleveland, OH *(135,140)*	1.25
2189	52c **Hubert Humphrey,** *June 3, 1991,* Minneapolis, MN *(93,391)*	1.40

2190	56c	**John Harvard**, *Sept. 3, 1986*, Cambridge, MA	2.50
2191	65c	**Hap Arnold**, *Nov. 5, 1988*, Gladwyne, PA *(129,829)*	2.50
2192	75c	**Wendell Willkie**, *Feb. 18, 1992*, Bloomington, IN *(47,086)*	2.50
2193	$1	**Dr. Bernard Revel**, *Sept. 23, 1986*, New York, NY	5.00
2194	$1	**Johns Hopkins**, *June 7, 1989*, Baltimore, MD *(159,049)*	3.00
2195	$2	**William Jennings Bryan**, *Mar. 19, 1986*, Salem, IL *(123,430)*	6.00
2196	$5	**Bret Harte**, *Aug. 25, 1987*, Twain Harte, CA *(111,431)*	15.00
2197	25c	**Jack London**, bklt. single, *May 3, 1988*, San Francisco, CA	1.00
2197a		Booklet pane of 6	4.00

First day cancel was applied to 94,655 covers bearing one or more of Nos. 2183a, 2197, and 2197a.

1986

2201a	22c	**Stamp Collecting Booklet pane of 4**, *Jan. 23*, State College, PA	4.00
		2198-2201, any single	1.00

First day cancellation was applied to 675,924 covers bearing one or more of Nos. 2198-2201a.

2202	22c	**Love**, *Jan. 30*, New York, NY	1.00
2203	22c	**Sojourner Truth**, *Feb. 4*, New Paltz, NY *(342,985)*	1.75
2204	22c	**Republic of Texas**, *Mar. 2*, San Antonio, TX *(380,450)*	1.75
2209a	22c	**Fish Booklet pane of 5**, *Mar. 21*, Seattle, WA	5.00
		2205-2209, any single	1.25

First day cancellation was applied to 988,184 covers bearing one or more of Nos. 2205-2209a.

2210	22c	**Public Hospitals**, *Apr. 11*, New York, NY *(403,665)*	1.00
2211	22c	**Duke Ellington**, *Apr. 29*, New York, NY *(397,894)*	2.25
2216	22c	**Presidents Souvenir Sheet of 9 (Washington-Harrison)**, *May 22*, Chicago, IL	4.50
2217	22c	**Presidents Souvenir Sheet of 9 (Tyler-Grant)**, *May 22*, Chicago, IL	4.50
2218	22c	**Presidents Souvenir Sheet of 9 (Hayes-Wilson)**, *May 22*, Chicago, IL	4.50
2219	22c	**Presidents Souvenir Sheet of 9 (Harding-Johnson)**, *May 22*, Chicago, IL	4.50
		2216a-2219g, 2219i, any single	1.50
		2219h	2.50

First day cancellation was applied to 9,009,599 covers bearing one or more of Nos. 2216-2219, 2216a-2219i.

2223a	22c	**Polar Explorers**, *May 28*, North Pole, AK *(760,999)*	3.75
		2220-2223, any single	1.25
2224	22c	**Statue of Liberty**, *July 4*, New York, NY *(1,540,308)*	1.25

1986-87

TRANSPORTATION ISSUE

2225	1c	**Omnibus**, *Nov. 26, 1986 (57,845)*	1.00
2226	2c	**Locomotive**, *Mar. 6, 1987*, Milwaukee, WI *(169,484)*	1.50

1986

2238a	22c	**Navajo Art**, *Sept. 4*, Window Rock, AZ *(1,102,520)*	2.00
		2235-2238, any single	1.00
2239	22c	**T.S. Eliot**, *Sept. 26*, St. Louis, MO *(304,764)*	1.00
2243a	22c	**Woodcarved Figurines**, *Oct. 1* *(629,399)*	2.00
		2240-2243, any single	1.00
2244	22c	**Christmas (Madonna)**, *Oct. 24 (467,999)*	1.00
2245	22c	**Christmas (Winter Village)**, *Oct. 24*, Snow Hill, MD *(504,851)*	1.00

1987

2246	22c	**Michigan Statehood Sesquicent.**, *Jan. 26*, Lansing, MI *(379,117)*	1.00
2247	22c	**Pan American Games**, *Jan. 29*, Indianapolis, IN *(344,731)*	1.00
2248	22c	**Love**, *Jan. 30*, San Francisco, CA *(333,329)*	1.00
2249	22c	**Pointe du Sable**, *Feb. 20*, Chicago, IL *(313,054)*	1.50
2250	22c	**Enrico Caruso**, *Feb. 27*, New York, NY *(389,834)*	1.00
2251	22c	**Girl Scouts of America**, *Mar. 12 (556,391)*	2.50

1987-88

TRANSPORTATION ISSUE

2252	3c	**Conestoga Wagon**, *Feb. 29, 1988*, Conestoga, PA *(155,203)*	1.00
2253	5c	**Milk Wagon**, *Sept. 25, 1987*, Indianapolis, IN	1.00

First day cancel was applied to 162,571 covers bearing one or more of Nos. 2253 and 2262.

2254	5.3c	**Elevator**, *Sept. 16, 1988*, New York, NY *(142,705)*	1.00
2255	7.6c	**Carretta**, *Aug. 30, 1988*, San Jose, CA *(140,024)*	1.00
2256	8.4c	**Wheelchair**, *Aug. 12, 1988*, Tucson, AZ *(136,337)*	1.00

2257	10c	**Canal Boat**, *Apr. 11, 1987*, Buffalo, NY *(171,952)*	1.00
2258	13c	**Police Patrol Wagon**, *Oct. 29, 1988*, Anaheim, CA *(132,928)*	1.50
2259	13.2c	**Railway Coal Car**, *July 19, 1988*, Pittsburgh, PA *(123,965)*	1.00
2260	15c	**Tugboat**, *July 12, 1988*, Long Beach, CA *(134,926)*	1.00
2261	16.7c	**Popcorn Wagon**, *July 7, 1988*, Chicago, IL *(117,908)*	1.00
2262	17.5c	**Racing Car**, *Sept. 25, 1987*, Indianapolis, IN	1.25
2263	20c	**Cable Car**, *Oct. 28, 1988*, San Francisco, CA *(150,068)*	1.00
2264	20.5c	**Fire Engine**, *Sept. 28, 1988*, San Angelo, TX *(123,043)*	1.50
2265	21c	**Railway Mail Car**, *Aug. 16, 1988*, Santa Fe, NM *(124,430)*	1.00
2266	24.1c	**Tandem Bicycle**, *Oct. 26, 1988*, Redmond, WA *(138,593)*	1.50

1987

2274a	22c	**Special Occasions Booklet pane of 10**, *Apr. 20*, Atlanta, GA	5.00
		2267-2274, any single	1.00

First day cancellation was applied to 1,588,129 covers bearing one or more of Nos. 2267-2274a.

2275	22c	**United Way**, *Apr. 28 (556,391)*	1.00

1987-89

2276	22c	**Flag and Fireworks**, *May 9, 1987* Denver, CO *(398,855)*	1.00
2276a		Booklet pane of 20, *Nov. 30, 1987*	8.00
2277	(25c)	**"E" Earth**, *Mar. 22, 1988*	1.25
2278	25c	**Flag and Clouds**, *May 6, 1988*, Boxborough, MA *(131,265)*	1.25
2279	(25c)	**"E" Earth**, coil, *Mar. 22, 1988*	1.25
2280	25c	**Flag over Yosemite**, large block tagging, *May 20, 1988*, Yosemite, CA *(144,339)*	1.25
2280a	25c	Prephosphored paper, *Feb. 14, 1989*, Yosemite, CA *(118,874)*	1.25
2281	25c	**Honey Bee**, *Sept. 2, 1988*, Omaha, NE *(122,853)*	1.25
2282	(25c)	**"E" Earth**, bklt. single, *Mar. 22, 1988*	1.25
2282a		Booklet pane of 10	6.00

First day cancel was applied to 363,639 covers bearing one or more of Nos. 2277, 2279 and 2282.

2283	25c	**Pheasant**, *Apr. 29, 1988*, Rapid City, SD *(167,053)*	1.25
2283a		Booklet pane of 10	6.00
2285b	25c	**Grosbeak & Owl, booklet pane of 10** *May 28, 1988*, Arlington, VA	6.00
		2284-2285, any single	1.25

First day cancel was applied to 272,359 covers bearing one or more of Nos. 2284 and 2285.

2285A	25c	**Flag and Clouds**, bklt. single, *July 5, 1988 (117,303)*	1.00
2285Ac		Booklet pane of 6	4.00
2335a	22c	**American Wildlife**, *June 13, 1987*, Toronto, Canada	50.00
		2286-2335, any single	1.50

1987-90   RATIFICATION OF THE CONSTITUTION

2336	22c	**Delaware**, *July 4, 1987*, Dover, DE *(505,770)*	1.50
2337	22c	**Pennsylvania**, *Aug. 26, 1987*, Harrisburg, PA *(367,184)*	1.50
2338	22c	**New Jersey**, *Sept. 11, 1987*, Trenton, NJ *(432,899)*	1.50
2339	22c	**Georgia**, *Jan. 6, 1988*, Atlanta, GA *(467,804)*	1.50
2340	22c	**Connecticut**, *Jan. 9, 1988*, Hartford, CT *(379,706)*	1.50
2341	22c	**Massachusetts**, *Feb. 6, 1988*, Boston, MA *(412,616)*	1.50
2342	22c	**Maryland**, *Feb. 15, 1988*, Annapolis, MD *(376,403)*	1.50
2343	25c	**South Carolina**, *May 23, 1988*, Columbia, SC *(322,938)*	1.50
2344	25c	**New Hampshire**, *June 21, 1988*, Concord, NH *(374,402)*	1.50
2345	25c	**Virginia**, *June 25, 1988*, Williamsburg, VA *(474,079)*	1.50
2346	25c	**New York**, *July 26, 1988*, Albany, NY *(385,793)*	1.50
2347	25c	**North Carolina**, *Aug. 22, 1989*, Fayetteville, NC *(392,953)*	1.50
2348	25c	**Rhode Island**, *May 29, 1990*, Pawtucket, RI *(305,566)*	1.50

1987

2349	22c	**U.S.-Morocco Diplomatic Relations Bicent.**, *July 17 (372,814)*	1.00
2350	22c	**William Faulkner**, *Aug. 3*, Oxford, MS *(480,024)*	1.00
2354a	22c	**Lacemaking**, *Aug. 14*, Ypsilanti, MI	2.50
		2351-2354, any single	1.00
2359a	22c	**Drafting of Constitution Bicent. Booklet pane of 5**, *Aug. 28*	4.00
		2355-2359, any single	1.25

First day cancellation was applied to 1,008,799 covers bearing one or more of Nos. 2355-2359a.

2360	22c	**Signing of Constitution Bicent.**, *Sept. 17*, Philadelphia, PA *(719,975)*	1.25
2361	22c	**Certified Public Accounting**, *Sept. 21*, New York, NY *(362,099)*	7.50

2366a	22c	**Locomotives booklet pane of 5**, *Oct. 1*, Baltimore, MD	3.00
		2362-2366, any single	1.25

First day cancellation was applied to 976,694 covers bearing one or more of Nos. 2362-2366a.

2367	22c	**Christmas (Madonna)**, *Oct. 23 (320,406)*	1.25
2368	22c	**Christmas (Ornaments)**, *Oct. 23*, Holiday-Anaheim, CA *(375,858)*	1.25

1988

2369	22c	**Winter Olympics, Calgary**, *Jan. 10*, Anchorage, AK *(395,198)*	1.00
2370	22c	**Australia Bicentennial**, *Jan. 26 (523,465)*	1.75
2371	22c	**James Weldon Johnson**, *Feb. 2*, Nashville, TN *(465,282)*	1.75
2375a	22c	**Cats**, *Feb. 5*, New York, NY *(872,734)*	4.50
		2372-2375, any single	2.00
2376	22c	**Knute Rockne**, *Mar. 9*, Notre Dame, IN *(404,311)*	4.00
2377	25c	**Francis Ouimet**, *June 13*, Brookline, MA *(383,168)*	4.50
2378	25c	**Love**, *July 4*, Pasadena, CA *(399,038)*	1.00
2379	45c	**Love**, *Aug. 8*, Shreveport, LA *(121,808)*	1.25
2380	25c	**Summer Olympics, Seoul**, *Aug. 19*, Colorado Springs, CO *(402,616)*	1.25
2385a	25c	**Automobiles booklet pane of 5**, *Aug. 25*, Detroit, MI	4.00
		2381-2385, any single	1.25

First day cancel was applied to 875,801 covers bearing one or more of Nos. 2381-2385a.

2389a	25c	**Antarctic Explorers**, *Sept. 14 (720,537)*	3.00
		2386-2389, any single	1.25
2393a	25c	**Carousel Animals**, *Oct. 1*, Sandusky, OH *(856,380)*	4.00
		2390-2393, any single	1.50
2394	$8.75	**Express Mail**, *Oct. 4*, Terre Haute, IN *(66,050)*	27.50
2396a	25c	**Special Occasions (Happy Birthday, Best Wishes)**, *Oct. 22*, King of Prussia, PA	4.00
		2395-2396, any single	1.25
2398a	25c	**Special Occasions (Thinking of You, Love You)**, *Oct. 22*, King of Prussia, PA	4.00
		2397-2398, any single	1.25

First day cancel was applied to 126,767 covers bearing one or more of Nos. 2395-2398, 2396a, 2398a.

2399	25c	**Christmas (Madonna)**, *Oct. 20 (247,291)*	1.25
2400	25c	**Christmas (Contemporary)**, *Oct. 20*, Berlin, NH *(412,213)*	1.25

1989

2401	25c	**Montana**, *Jan. 15*, Helena, MT *(353,319)*	1.25
2402	25c	**A. Philip Randolph**, *Feb. 3*, New York, NY *(363,174)*	1.75
2403	25c	**North Dakota**, *Feb. 21*, Bismarck, ND *(306,003)*	1.00
2404	25c	**Washington Statehood**, *Feb. 22*, Olympia, WA *(445,174)*	1.00
2409a	25c	**Steamboats Booklet pane of 5**, *Mar. 3*, New Orleans, LA	3.00
		2405-2409, any single	1.25

First day cancel was applied to 981,674 covers bearing one or more of Nos. 2405-2409a.

2410	25c	**World Stamp Expo**, *Mar. 16*, New York, NY *(296,310)*	1.00
2411	25c	**Arturo Toscanini**, *Mar. 25*, New York, NY *(309,441)*	1.00

1989-90

BRANCHES OF GOVERNMENT

2412	25c	**House of Representatives**, *Apr. 4, 1989 (327,755)*	1.50
2413	25c	**Senate**, *Apr. 6, 1989 (341,288)*	1.50
2414	25c	**Executive Branch**, *Apr. 16, 1989* Mount Vernon, VA *(387,644)*	1.50
2415	25c	**Supreme Court**, *Feb. 2, 1990 (233,056)*	1.50

1989

2416	25c	**South Dakota**, *May 3*, Pierre, SD *(348,370)*	1.00
2417	25c	**Lou Gehrig**, *June 10*, Cooperstown, NY *(694,227)*	4.00
2418	25c	**Ernest Hemingway**, *July 17*, Key West, FL *(345,436)*	1.25
2419	$2.40	**Moon Landing**, *July 20 (208,982)*	7.50
2420	25c	**Letter Carriers**, *Aug. 30*, Milwaukee, WI *(372,241)*	1.25
2421	25c	**Bill of Rights**, *Sept. 25*, Philadelphia, PA *(900,384)*	1.00
2425a	25c	**Dinosaurs**, *Oct. 1*, Orlando, FL *(871,634)*	3.00
		2422-2425, any single	1.50
2426	25c	**Southwest Carved Figure**, *Oct. 12*, San Juan, PR *(215,285)*	1.00
2427	25c	**Christmas (Madonna)**, *Oct. 19 (395,321)*	1.00
2427a		Booklet pane of 10	6.00
2428	25c	**Christmas (Sleigh with Presents)**, *Oct. 19*, Westport, CT	1.00

2429	25c **Christmas (Sleigh with Presents)** **from bklt.,** *Oct. 19,* Westport, CT	1.00	
2429a	Booklet pane of 10	6.00	

First day cancel was applied to 345,931 covers bearing one or more of Nos. 2428-2429a.

2431	25c **Eagle and Shield,** *Nov. 10,* Virginia Beach, VA	1.25	
2433	90c **World Stamp Expo '89 Souvenir Sheet,** *Nov. 17 (281,725)*	7.00	
2437a	25c **Classic Mail Transportation,** *Nov. 19 (916,389)*	2.50	
	2434-2437, any single	1.25	
2438	25c **Classic Mail Transportation Souvenir Sheet,** *Nov. 28 (241,634)*	3.00	

1990

2439	25c **Idaho Statehood,** *Jan. 6,* Boise, ID *(252,493)*	1.25	
2440	25c **Love,** *Jan. 18,* Romance, AR	1.25	
2441	25c **Love, from bklt.,** *Jan. 18,* Romance, AR	1.00	
2441a	Booklet pane of 10	6.00	

First day cancel was applied to 257,788 covers bearing one or more of Nos. 2440-2441a.

2442	25c **Ida B. Wells,** *Feb. 1,* Chicago, IL *(229,226)*	2.00	
2443	15c **Beach Umbrella,** *Feb. 3,* Sarasota, FL	1.25	
2443a	Booklet pane of 10	4.25	

First day cancel was applied to 72,286 covers bearing one or more of Nos. 2443-2443a.

2444	25c **Wyoming Statehood,** *Feb. 23,* Cheyenne, WY *(317,654)*	1.00	
2448a	25c **Classic Films,** *Mar. 23,* Hollywood, CA *(863,079)*	5.00	
	2445-2448, any single	2.50	
2449	25c **Marianne Moore,** *Apr. 18,* Brooklyn, NY *(390,535)*	1.25	

1990-95

TRANSPORTATION COILS

2451	4c **Steam Carriage,** *Jan. 25, 1991,* Tucson, AZ *(100,393)*	1.25	
2452	5c **Circus Wagon,** engraved, *Aug. 31, 1990,* Syracuse, NY *(71,806)*	1.50	
2452B	5c **Circus Wagon,** photogravure, *Dec. 8, 1992,* Cincinnati, OH	1.50	
2452D	5c **Circus Wagon,** with cent sign, photogravure, *Mar. 20, 1995,* Kansas City MO *(20,835)*	2.00	
2453	5c **Canoe,** engraved, *May 25, 1991,* Secaucus, NJ *(108,634)*	1.25	
2454	5c **Canoe,** photogravure, *Oct. 22, 1991,* Secaucus, NJ	1.25	
2457	10c **Tractor Trailer,** engr., *May 25, 1991,* Secaucus, NJ *(84,717)*	1.25	
2458	10c **Tractor Trailer,** photo., *May 25, 1994,* Secaucus, NJ *(15,431)*	1.25	
2463	20c **Cog Railway,** *June 9, 1995,* Dallas, TX *(28,883)*	1.25	
2464	23c **Lunch Wagon,** *Apr. 12, 1991,* Columbus, OH *(115,830)*	1.25	
2466	32c **Ferry Boat,** *June 2, 1995,* McLean VA	1.25	

First day cancellation was applied to 59,100 covers bearing one or more of Nos. 2466, 2492.

2468	$1 **Seaplane,** *Apr. 20, 1990* Phoenix, AZ *(244,775)*	3.00	

1990

2474a	25c **Lighthouses booklet pane of 5,** *Apr. 26*	4.00	
	2470-2474, any single	1.50	

First day cancel was applied to 805,133 covers bearing one or more of Nos. 2470-2474a.

2475	25c **Flag,** *May 18,* Seattle, WA *(97,567)*	1.00	

1990-95

FLORA AND FAUNA ISSUE

2476	1c **Kestrel,** *June 22,* Aurora, CO *(77,781)*	1.00	
2477	1c **Kestrel, with cent sign,** *May 10, 1995* Aurora, CO *(21,767)*	1.00	
2478	3c **Eastern Bluebird,** *June 22,* Aurora, CO *(76,149)*	1.00	
2479	19c **Fawn,** *Mar. 11 (100,212)*	1.00	
2480	30c **Cardinal,** *June 22,* Aurora, CO *(101,290)*	1.25	
2481	45c **Pumpkinseed Sunfish,** *Dec. 2, 1992 (38,696)*	1.75	
2482	$2 **Bobcat,** *June 1,* Arlington, VA *(49,660)*	5.00	
2483	20c **Blue Jay,** booklet single, *June 15, 1995,* Kansas City MO	1.25	

First day cancellation was applied to 16,847 covers bearing one or more of Nos. 2483, 2483a.

2484	29c **Wood Duck,** black denomination bklt. single, *Apr. 12,* Columbus, OH	1.00	
2484a	Booklet pane of 10	4.00	
2485	29c **Wood Duck,** red denomination bklt. single, *Apr. 12,* Columbus, OH	1.00	
2485a	Booklet pane of 10	4.00	

First day cancel was applied to 205,305 covers bearing one or more of Nos. 2484-2485, 2484a-2485a.

2486	29c **African Violet,** *Oct. 8, 1993,* Beaumont, TX	1.00	
2486a	Booklet pane of 10	4.00	

First day cancellation was applied to 40,167 covers bearing one or more of Nos. 2486-2486a.

2487	32c **Peach,** booklet single, *July 8, 1995,* Reno NV	1.50	
2488	32c **Pear,** booklet single, *July 8, 1995,* Reno NV	1.50	

First day cancellation was applied to 71,086 covers bearing one or more of Nos. 2487-2488, 2488a, 2493-2495A.

2488a	Booklet pane, 5 each #2488-2489	7.50	
2489	29c **Red Squirrel,** self-adhesive, *June 25, 1993* Milwaukee, WI *(48,564)*	1.25	
2490	29c **Red Rose,** self-adhesive, *Aug. 19, 1993* Houston, TX *(37,916)*	1.25	
2491	29c **Pine Cone,** self-adhesive, *Nov. 5, 1993* Kansas City, MO *(110,924)*	1.25	
2492	32c **Pink Rose,** self-adhesive, *June 2, 1995,* McLean VA	1.25	

First day cancel was applied to 59,100 covers bearing one or more of Nos. 2466, 2492.

2493	32c **Peach,** self-adhesive, *July 8, 1995,* Reno NV	1.25	
2494	32c **Pear,** self-adhesive, *July 8, 1995,* Reno NV	1.25	
2495	32c **Peach,** self-adhesive, serpentine die cut vert., *July 8, 1995,* Reno NV	1.25	
2495A	32c **Pear,** self-adhesive, serpentine die cut vert., *July 8, 1995,* Reno NV	1.25	

First day cancellation was applied to 71,086 covers bearing one or more of Nos. 2487-2488, 2488a, 2493-2495A.

1990

2500a	25c **Olympians,** *July 6,* Minneapolis, MN *(1,143,404)*	4.00	
	2496-2500, any single	1.25	
2505a	25c **Indian Headdresses, booklet pane of 10** *Aug. 17,* Cody, WY	6.00	
	2501-2505, any single	1.25	

First day cancel was applied to 979,580 covers bearing one or more of Nos. 2501-2505a.

2507a	25c **Micronesia, Marshall Islands,** *Sept. 28 (343,816)*	2.00	
	2506-2507, any single	1.25	
2511a	25c **Sea Creatures,** *Oct. 3,* Baltimore, MD *(706,047)*	3.00	
	2508-2511, any single	1.25	
2512	25c **Grand Canyon,** *Oct. 12,* Grand Canyon, AZ *(164,190)*	1.75	
2513	25c **Dwight D. Eisenhower,** *Oct. 13,* Abilene, KS *(487,988)*	1.50	
2514	25c **Christmas (traditional),** *Oct. 18*	1.25	
2514a	Booklet pane of 10	6.00	

First day cancel was applied to 378,383 covers bearing one or more of Nos. 2514-2514a.

2515	25c **Christmas (secular),** *Oct. 18,* Evergreen, CO	1.25	
2516	25c **Christmas (secular),** *Oct. 18,* Evergreen, CO	1.00	
2516a	Booklet pane of 10	6.00	

First day cancel was applied to 230,586 covers bearing one or more of Nos. 2515-2516a.

1991-94

2517	(29c) **"F" Flower,** *Jan. 22, 1991 (106,698)*	1.25	
2518	(29c) **"F" Flower,** coil, *Jan. 22, 1991 (39,311)*	1.25	
2519	(29c) **"F" Flower,** bklt. single (bullseye perf. 11.2), *Jan. 22, 1991*	1.00	
2519a	Booklet pane of 10	7.25	
2520	(29c) **"F" Flower,** bklt. single (perf. 11), *Jan. 22, 1991*	1.25	
2520a	Booklet pane of 10	8.00	

First day cancel was applied to 32,971 covers bearing one or more of Nos. 2519-2520, 2519a-2520a.

2521	(4c) **Makeup Stamp,** *Jan. 22, 1991 (51,987)*	1.25	
2522	(29c) **"F" Flag,** *Jan. 22, 1991 (48,821)*	1.25	
2523	29c **Flag over Mt. Rushmore,** engraved, *Mar. 29, 1991* Mt. Rushmore, SD *(233,793)*	1.25	
2523A	29c **Flag over Mt. Rushmore,** photogravure, *July 4, 1991* Mt. Rushmore, SD *(80,662)*	1.25	
2524	29c **Flower,** *Apr. 5, 1991,* Rochester, NY *(132,233)*	1.00	
2525	29c **Flower,** roulette 10 coil, *Aug. 16, 1991,* Rochester, NY *(144,750)*	1.00	
2526	29c **Flower,** perf. 10 coil, *Mar. 3, 1992,* Rochester, NY *(35,877)*	1.00	
2527	29c **Flower,** bklt. single, *Apr. 5, 1991,* Rochester, NY	1.00	
2527a	Booklet pane of 10	4.00	

First day cancel was applied to 16,975 covers bearing one or more of Nos. 2527-2527a.

2528	29c **Flag and Olympic Rings,** bklt. single, *Apr. 21, 1991,* Atlanta, GA	1.25	
2528a	Booklet pane of 10	5.00	

First day cancel was applied to 319,488 covers bearing one or more of Nos. 2528-2528a.

2529	19c **Fishing Boat,** two loops, *Aug. 8, 1991 (82,698)*	1.50	

2529C	19c **Fishing Boat,** one loop, *June 25, 1994,* Arlington, VA *(14,538)*	1.50	
2530	19c **Balloon,** *May 17, 1991,* Denver, CO	1.25	
2530a	Booklet pane of 10	5.00	

First day cancel was applied to 96,351 covers bearing one or more of Nos. 2530-2530a.

2531	29c **Flags on Parade,** *May 30, 1991,* Waterloo, NY *(104,046)*	1.00	
2531A	29c **Liberty Torch,** *June 25, 1991,* New York, NY *(68,456)*	1.25	

1991-95

2532	50c **Switzerland,** *Feb. 22,* Washington, DC *(316,017)*	1.40	
2533	29c **Vermont,** *Mar. 1,* Bennington, VT *(308,105)*	1.50	
2534	29c **Savings Bonds,** *Apr. 30,* Washington, DC *(341,955)*	1.25	
2535	29c **Love,** *May 9,* Honolulu, HI *(336,132)*	1.25	
2536	29c **Love,** bklt. single, *May 9,* Honolulu, HI	1.25	
2536a	Booklet pane of 10	5.00	

First day cancel was applied to 43,336 covers bearing one or more of Nos. 2536-2536a.

2537	52c **Love,** *May 9,* Honolulu, HI *(90,438)*	1.25	
2538	29c **William Saroyan,** *May 22,* Fresno, CA *(334,373)*	1.50	
2539	$1 **Eagle & Olympic Rings,** *Sept. 29,* Orlando, FL *(69,241)*	2.25	
2540	$2.90 **Eagle & Olympic Rings,** *July 7,* San Diego, CA *(79,555)*	5.50	
2541	$9.95 **Eagle & Olympic Rings,** *June 16,* Sacramento, CA *(68,657)*	15.00	
2542	$14 **Eagle,** *Aug. 31,* Hunt Valley, MD *(54,727)*	27.50	
2543	$2.90 **Futuristic Space Shuttle,** *June 3, 1993,* Kennedy Space Center, FL *(36,359)*	6.00	
2544	$3 **Space Shuttle Challenger,** *June 22, 1995* Anaheim CA *(16,502)*	6.00	
2544A	$10.75 **Space Shuttle Endeavour,** *Aug. 4, 1995* Irvine CA *(10,534)*	15.00	

1991

2549	29c **Fishing Flies booklet pane of 5,** *May 31,* Cuddebackville, NY *(1,045,726)*	3.00	
	2545-2549, any single	1.25	
2550	29c **Cole Porter,** *June 8,* Peru, IN *(304,363)*	1.25	
2551	29c **Desert Storm/ Desert Shield,** *July 2*	2.50	
2552	29c **Desert Storm/ Desert Shield,** bklt. single, *July 2*	2.50	
2552a	Booklet pane of 5	5.00	

First day cancel was applied to 860,455 covers bearing one or more of Nos. 2551-2552, 2552a.

2557a	29c **Summer Olympics,** *July 12,* Los Angeles, CA *(886,984)*	3.00	
	2553-2557, any single	1.25	
2558	29c **Numismatics,** *Aug. 13,* Chicago, IL *(288,519)*	1.25	
2559	29c **World War II block of 10,** *Sept. 3,* Phoenix, AZ *(1,832,967)*	7.00	
	2559a-2559j, any single	2.00	
2560	29c **Basketball,** *Aug. 28,* Springfield, MA *(295,471)*	2.25	
2561	29c **District of Columbia,** *Sept. 7 (299,989)*	1.25	
2566a	29c **Comedians booklet pane of 10,** *Aug. 29,* Hollywood, CA	3.00	
	2562-2566, any single	1.25	

First day cancel was applied to 954,293 covers bearing one or more of Nos. 2562-2566a.

2567	29c **Jan Matzeliger,** *Sept. 15,* Lynn, MA *(289,034)*	1.75	
2577a	29c **Space Exploration booklet pane of 10,** *Oct. 1,* Pasadena, CA	5.00	
	2568-2577, any single	1.25	

First day cancel was applied to 1,465,111 covers bearing one or more of Nos. 2568-2577a.

2578	(29c) **Christmas (religious),** *Oct. 17,* Houston, TX	1.25	
2579	(29c) **Christmas (secular),** *Oct. 17,* Santa, ID *(169,750)*	1.25	
2581b	(29c) **Christmas booklet pane of 4,** *Oct. 17,* Santa, ID	2.50	
	2580-2581, any single	1.25	
2582	(29c) **Christmas,** bklt. single, *Oct. 17,* Santa, ID	1.25	
2582a	Booklet pane of 4	2.50	
2583	(29c) **Christmas,** bklt. single, *Oct. 17,* Santa, ID	1.25	
2583a	Booklet pane of 4	2.50	
2584	(29c) **Christmas,** bklt. single, *Oct. 17,* Santa, ID	1.25	
2584a	Booklet pane of 4	2.50	
2585	(29c) **Christmas,** bklt. single, *Oct. 17,* Santa, ID	1.25	
2585a	Booklet pane of 4	2.50	

First day cancel was applied to 168,794 covers bearing one or more of Nos. 2580-2585, 2581b, 2582a, 2583a, 2584a and 2585a.

1991-95

2587	32c **James K. Polk,** *Nov. 2, 1995,* Columbia TN *(189,429)*	1.25	
2590	$1 **Surrender of Gen. John Burgoyne,** *May 5, 1994,* New York, NY *(379,629)*	2.50	

2592	$5	**Washington & Jackson,** *Aug. 19, 1994,* Pittsburgh, PA *(16,303)*	12.50
2593	29c	**Pledge of Allegiance,** black denomination, *Sept. 8, 1992,* Rome, NY	1.25
2593a		Booklet pane of 10	5.00

First day cancel was applied to 61,464 covers bearing one or more of Nos. 2593-2593a.

2595	29c	**Eagle & Shield,** brown denomination, *Sept. 25, 1992,* Dayton, OH	1.50
2596	29c	**Eagle & Shield,** green denomination, *Sept. 25, 1992,* Dayton, OH	1.50
2597	29c	**Eagle & Shield,** red denomination, *Sept. 25, 1992,* Dayton, OH	1.50

First day cancel was applied to 65,822 covers bearing one or more of Nos. 2595-2597.

2598	29c	**Eagle,** *Feb. 4, 1994,* Sarasota, FL *(67,300)*	1.25
2599	29c	**Statue of Liberty,** *June 24, 1994,* Haines City, FL *(39,810)*	1.25
2602	(10c)	**Eagle & Shield,** Bulk Rate USA, *Dec. 13, 1991,* Kansas City, MO *(21,176)*	1.25
2603	(10c)	**Eagle & Shield,** USA Bulk Rate, *May 29, 1993,* Secaucus, NJ	1.25
2604	(10c)	**Eagle & Shield,** gold eagle, *May 29, 1993,* Secaucus, NJ	1.25

First day cancellation was applied to 36,444 covers bearing one or more of Nos. 2603-2604.

2605	23c	**Flag,** *Sept. 27, 1991*	1.25
2606	23c	**Reflected Flag,** *July 21, 1992,* Kansas City, MO *(35,673)*	1.25
2607	23c	**Reflected Flag,** 7mm "23," *Oct. 9, 1992,* Kansas City, MO	1.25
2608	23c	**Reflected Flag,** 8 ½mm "First Class" *May 14, 1993,* Denver, CO *(15,548)*	1.25
2609	29c	**Flag over White House,** *Apr. 23, 1992 (56,505)*	1.25

1992

2615a	29c	**Winter Olympics,** *Jan. 11,* Orlando, FL *(1,062,048)*	3.50
		2611-2615, any single	1.25
2616	29c	**World Columbian Stamp Expo,** *Jan. 24,* Rosemont, IL *(309,729)*	1.25
2617	29c	**W.E.B. Du Bois,** *Jan. 31,* Atlanta, GA *(196,219)*	1.75
2618	29c	**Love,** *Feb. 6,* Loveland, CO *(218,043)*	1.25
2619	29c	**Olympic Baseball,** *Apr. 3,* Atlanta, GA *(105,996)*	2.00
2623a	29c	**Voyages of Columbus,** *Apr. 24,* Christiansted, VI	2.75
		2620-2623, any single	1.25

First day cancellation was applied to 509,270 covers bearing one or more of Nos. 2620-2623a.

2624		**First Sighting of Land Souvenir Sheet of 3,** *May 22,* Chicago, IL	3.50
2624a	1c		1.50
2624b	4c		1.50
2624c	$1		2.50
2625		**Claiming a New World Souvenir Sheet of 3,** *May 22,* Chicago, IL	9.00
2625a	2c		1.50
2625b	3c		1.50
2625c	$4		8.00
2626		**Seeking Royal Support Souvenir Sheet of 3,** *May 22,* Chicago, IL	3.00
2626a	5c		1.50
2626b	30c		1.50
2626c	50c		2.00
2627		**Royal Favor Restored Souvenir Sheet of 3,** *May 22,* Chicago, IL	7.50
2627a	6c		1.50
2627b	8c		1.50
2627c	$3		7.50
2628		**Reporting Discoveries Souvenir Sheet of 3,** *May 22,* Chicago, IL	8.50
2628a	10c		1.50
2628b	15c		1.50
2628c	$2		5.00
2629	$5	**Christopher Columbus Souvenir Sheet,** *May 22,* Chicago, IL	12.50

First day cancel was applied to 211,142 covers bearing one or more of Nos. 2624-2629.

2630	29c	**New York Stock Exchange,** *May 17,* New York, NY *(261,897)*	2.50
2634a	29c	**Space Accomplishments,** *May 29,* Chicago, IL	2.75
		2631-2634, any single	1.50

First day cancellation was applied to 277,853 covers bearing one or more of Nos. 2631-2634a.

2635	29c	**Alaska Highway,** *May 30,* Fairbanks, AK *(186,791)*	1.25
2636	29c	**Kentucky,** *June 1,* Danville, KY *(251,153)*	1.25
2641a	29c	**Summer Olympics,** *June 11,* Baltimore, MD *(713,942)*	3.00
		2637-2641, any single	1.25
2646a	29c	**Hummingbirds booklet pane of 5,** *June 15*	3.00
		2642-2646, any single	1.25

First day cancel was applied to 995,278 covers bearing one or more of Nos. 2642-2646a.

2696a	29c	**Wildflowers,** *July 24,* Columbus, OH	30.00
		2647-2696, any single	1.25

First day cancellation was applied to 3,693,972 covers bearing one or more of Nos. 2647-2696a.

2697	29c	**World War II block of 10,** *Aug. 17,* Indianapolis, IN *(1,734,880)*	7.00
		2697a-2697j, any single	2.00

First day cancellation was applied to 1,734,880 covers bearing one or more of Nos. 2697, 2697a-2697j.

2698	29c	**Dorothy Parker,** *Aug. 22,* West End, NJ *(266,323)*	1.50
2699	29c	**Theodore von Karman,** *Aug. 31 (256,986)*	1.50
2703a	29c	**Minerals,** *Sept. 17*	2.75
		2700-2703, any single	1.25

First day cancellation was applied to 681,416 covers bearing one or more of Nos. 2700-2703.

2704	29c	**Juan Rodriguez Cabrillo,** *Sept. 28,* San Diego, CA *(290,720)*	1.25
2709a	29c	**Wild Animals booklet pane of 5,** *Oct. 1,* New Orleans, LA	3.25
		Any other city	4.00
		2705-2709, any single	1.25

First day cancel was applied to 604,205 New Orleans covers bearing one or more of Nos. 2705-2709a.

2710	29c	**Christmas (religious),** *Oct. 22*	1.25
2710a		Booklet pane of 10	7.25

First day cancel was applied to 201,576 covers bearing one or more of Nos. 2710-2710a.

2714a	29c	**Christmas (secular),** *Oct. 22,* Kansas City, MO	2.75
		2711-2714, any single	1.25
2718a	29c	**Christmas (secular) booklet pane of 4,** *Oct. 22,* Kansas City, MO	2.75
		2715-2718, any single	1.25

First day cancel was applied to 461,937 covers bearing one or more of Nos. 2711-2714, 2715-2718 and 2718a.

2719	29c	**Christmas (secular),** self-adhesive, *Oct. 28,* New York, NY *(48,873)*	1.25
2720	29c	**Chinese New Year,** *Dec. 30,* San Francisco, CA *(138,238)*	2.25

1993

2721	29c	**Elvis (Presley),** *Jan. 8,* Memphis, TN, AM cancellation, *(4,452,815)*	2.00
		Any city, PM cancellation	3.00
2722	29c	**Oklahoma!,** *Mar. 30,* Oklahoma City, OK *(283,837)*	1.25
2723	29c	**Hank Williams,** perf 10, *June 9,* Nashville, TN	1.25
2723A	29c	**Hank Williams,** perf 11.2x11.5, *June 9,* Nashville, TN	—

First day cancel was applied to 311,106 covers bearing one or more of Nos. 2723-2723A.

2730a	29c	**Rock & Roll/Rhythm & Blues Musicians,** *June 16,* Cleveland OH or Santa Monica CA	5.00
		Any other city	5.00
		2724-2730, any single	1.25
		Any single, any other city	1.25

Value for No. 2730a is also for any se-tenant configuration of seven different stamps.

First day cancel was applied to 540,809 covers bearing one or more of Nos. 2724-2730a, 2731-2737b.

2737a	29c	**Rock & Roll/Rhythm & Blues Musicians booklet pane of 8,** *June 16,* Cleveland, OH or Santa Monica CA	5.25
		Any other city	5.25
		2731-2737, any single	1.25
		Any single, any other city	1.25
2737b	29c	**Rock & Roll/Rhythm & Blues Musicians booklet pane of 4,** *June 16,* Cleveland, OH or Santa Monica CA	2.75
		Any other city	2.75

For first day cancellation quantities, see No. 2730a.

2745a	29c	**Space Fantasy booklet pane of 5,** *Jan. 25,* Huntsville, AL	3.25
		2741-2745, any single	1.25

First day cancel was applied to 631,203 covers bearing one or more of Nos. 2741-2745a.

2746	29c	**Percy Lavon Julian,** *Jan. 29,* Chicago, IL *(120,877)*	1.75
2747	29c	**Oregon Trail,** *Feb. 12,* Salem, OR *(436,550)*	1.25

No. 2747 was also available on the first day of issue in 36 cities along the route of the Oregon Trail.

2748	29c	**World University Games,** *Feb. 25,* Buffalo, NY *(157,563)*	1.50
2749	29c	**Grace Kelly,** *Mar. 24,* Beverly Hills, CA *(263,913)*	3.00
2753a	29c	**Circus,** *Apr. 6*	3.00
		2750-2753, any single	1.50

First day cancel was applied to 676,927 covers bearing one or more of Nos. 2750-2753a.

2754	29c	**Cherokee Strip Land Run,** *Apr. 17,* Enid, OK *(260,118)*	1.25
2755	29c	**Dean Acheson,** *Apr. 21,* *(158,783)*	1.25
2759a	29c	**Sporting Horses,** *May 1,* Louisville, KY	4.00
		2756-2759, any single	2.00

First day cancel was applied to 448,059 covers bearing one or more of Nos. 2756-2759a.

2764a	29c	**Garden Flowers booklet pane of 5,** *May 15,* Spokane, WA	3.00
		2760-2764, any single	1.50

First day cancel was applied to 492,578 covers bearing one or more of Nos. 2760-2764a.

2765	29c	**World War II block of 10,** *May 31,*	7.00
		2765a-2765j, any single	2.00

First day cancel was applied to 543,511 covers bearing one or more of Nos. 2765, 2765a-2765j.

2766	29c	**Joe Louis,** *June 22,* Detroit, MI *(229,272)*	3.00
2770a	29c	**Broadway Musicals booklet pane of 4,** *July 14,* New York, NY	3.50
		2767-2770, any single	1.25

First day cancel was applied to 308,231 covers bearing one or more of Nos. 2767-2770a.

2774a	29c	**Country Music,** *Sept. 25,* Nashville, TN	3.00
		2771-2774, any single	1.25
2778a	29c	**Country Music booklet pane of 4,** *Sept. 25,* Nashville, TN	3.00
		2775-2778, any single	1.25

First day cancel was applied to 362,904 covers bearing one or more of Nos. 2771-2774a, 2775-2778a.

2782a	29c	**National Postal Museum,** *July 30*	2.75
		2779-2782, any single	1.25

First day cancel was applied to 371,115 covers bearing one or more of Nos. 2779-2782a.

2784a	29c	**Deafness/Sign Language,** *Sept. 20,* Burbank, CA	2.50
		2783-2784, any single	1.50

First day cancel was applied to 112,350 covers bearing one or more of Nos. 2783-2784a.

2788a	29c	**Classic Books,** *Oct. 23,* Louisville, KY	2.75
		2785-2788, any single	1.25

First day cancel was applied to 269,457 covers bearing one or more of Nos. 2785-2788a.

2789	29c	**Christmas (religious),** *Oct. 21,* Raleigh, NC	1.25
2790	29c	**Christmas (religious),** booklet single, *Oct. 21,* Raleigh, NC	1.25
2790a		Booklet pane of 4	2.50

First day cancellation was applied to 155,192 covers bearing one or more of Nos. 2789-2790a.

2794a	29c	**Christmas (secular),** sheet stamps, *Oct. 21,* New York, NY	2.75
		2791-2794, any single	1.25
2798a	29c	**Christmas (secular) booklet pane of 10,** *Oct. 21,* New York, NY	6.50
2798b	29c	**Christmas (secular) booklet pane of 10,** *Oct. 21,* New York, NY	6.50
		2795-2798, any single	1.25
2799	29c	**Christmas (snowman),** large self-adhesive, *Oct. 28,* New York, NY	1.25
2800	29c	**Christmas (soldier),** self-adhesive, *Oct. 28,* New York, NY	1.25
2801	29c	**Christmas (jack-in-the-box),** self-adhesive, *Oct. 28,* New York, NY	1.25
2802	29c	**Christmas (reindeer),** self-adhesive, *Oct. 28,* New York, NY	1.25
		2799-2802 on one cover	2.50
2803	29c	**Christmas (snowman),** small self-adhesive, *Oct. 28,* New York, NY	1.25

First day cancel was applied to 384,262 covers bearing one or more of Nos. 2791-2794a, 2795-2798b, 2799-2803.

2804	29c	**Mariana Islands,** *Nov. 4,* Saipan, MP *(157,410)*	1.25
2805	29c	**Columbus' Landing in Puerto Rico,** *Nov. 19,* San Juan, PR *(222,845)*	1.25
2806	29c	**AIDS Awareness,** *Dec. 1,* New York, NY	2.00
2806a		Booklet single, perf. 11 vert.	2.00
2806b		Booklet pane of 5	4.00

First day cancellation was applied to 209,200 covers bearing one or more of Nos. 2806-2806b.

1994

2811a	29c	**Winter Olympics,** *Jan. 6,* Salt Lake City, UT	3.00
		2807-2811, any single	1.25

First day cancellation was applied to 645,636 covers bearing one or more of Nos. 2807-2811a.

2812	29c	**Edward R. Murrow,** *Jan. 21,* Pullman, WA *(154,638)*	1.25
2813	29c	**Love,** self-adhesive, *Jan. 27,* Loveland, OH *(125,146)*	1.25
2814	29c	**Love,** booklet single, *Feb. 14,* Niagara Falls, NY	1.25
2814a		Booklet pane of 10	6.50
2814C	29c	**Love,** *June 11,* Niagara Falls, NY *(42,109)*	1.25
2815	52c	**Love,** *Feb. 14,* Niagara Falls, NY	1.50
2816	29c	**Dr. Allison Davis,** *Feb. 1,* Williamstown, MA *(162,404)*	2.00
2817	29c	**Chinese New Year,** *Feb. 5,* Pomona, CA *(148,492)*	2.00
2818	29c	**Buffalo Soldiers,** *Apr. 22,* Dallas, TX *(107,223)*	3.00

No. 2818 was also available on the first day of issue in forts in Kansas, Texas and Arizona.

| 2828a | 29c | **Silent Screen Stars,** *Apr. 27,* San Francisco, CA | 6.50 |
| | | 2819-2828, any single | 1.50 |

First day cancellation was applied to 591,251 covers bearing one or more of Nos. 2819-2828a.

| 2833a | 29c | **Garden Flowers booklet pane of 5,** *Apr. 28,* Cincinnati, OH | 3.25 |
| | | 2829-2833, any single | 1.25 |

First day cancellation was applied to 153,069 covers bearing one or more of Nos. 2829-2833a.

2834	29c	**World Cup Soccer,** *May 26,* New York, NY	2.00
2835	40c	**World Cup Soccer,** *May 26,* New York, NY	2.00
2836	50c	**World Cup Soccer,** *May 26,* New York, NY	2.00

First day cancellation was applied to 443,768 covers bearing one or more of Nos. 2834-2836.

2837		**World Cup Soccer souvenir sheet of 3,** *May 26,* New York, NY *(59,503)*	4.00
2838	29c	**World War II block of 10,** *June 6,* USS Normandy	7.00
		2838a-2838j, any single	2.00

No. 2838 was also available on the first day of issue in 13 other locations.

First day cancellation was applied to 744,267 covers bearing one or more of Nos. 2838, 2838a-2838j.

2839	29c	**Norman Rockwell,** *July 1,* Stockbridge, MA *(232,076)*	1.25
2840	50c	**Norman Rockwell Souvenir Sheet of 4,** *July 1,* Stockbridge, MA	3.50
		2840a-2840d, any single	1.50

First day cancellation was applied to 19,734 covers bearing one or more of Nos. 2840-2840d.

| 2841 | 29c | **Moon Landing Sheet of 12,** *July 20,* | 6.50 |
| | | 2841a, single stamp | 2.00 |

First day cancellation was applied to 303,707 covers bearing one or more of Nos. 2841-2841a.

2842	$9.95	**Moon Landing,** *July 20 (11,463)*	25.00
2847a	29c	**Locomotives booklet pane of 5,** *July 28,* Chama, NM	5.00
		2843-2847, any single	1.75

First day cancellation was applied to 169,016 covers bearing one or more of Nos. 2843-2847a.

2848	29c	**George Meany,** *Aug. 16 (172,418)*	1.25
2853a	29c	**American Music Series,** *Sept. 1,* New York, NY	4.50
		2849-2853, any single	1.50

First day cancellation was applied to 156,049 covers bearing one or more of Nos. 2849-2853a.

| 2861a | 29c | **American Music Series,** *Sept. 17,* Greenville MS | 6.00 |
| | | 2854-2861, any single | 1.25 |

First day cancellation was applied to 483,737 covers bearing one or more of Nos. 2854-2861a.

Nos. 2854-2861 were available on the first day in 9 other cities.

2862	29c	**James Thurber,** *Sept. 10,* Columbus OH *(39,064)*	1.25
2866a	29c	**Wonders of the Sea,** *Oct. 3,* Honolulu HI	2.75
		2863-2866, any single	1.25

First day cancellation was applied to 284,678 covers bearing one or more of Nos. 2863-2866a.

| 2868a | 29c | **Cranes,** *Oct. 9,* | 2.50 |
| | | 2867-2868, any single | 1.25 |

First day cancellation was applied to 202,955 covers bearing one or more of Nos. 2867-2868a, 24,942 with the People's Republic of China stamps.

2869	29c	**Legends of the West Pane of 20,** *Oct. 18,* Laramie WY *(429,680)*	15.00
		Tucson, AZ *(220,417)*	15.00
		Lawton, OK *(191,393)*	15.00
		2869a-2869t, any single, any city	2.25

First day cancellation was applied to covers bearing one or more of Nos. 2869-2869t.

2871	29c	**Christmas (religious),** perf 11¼, *Oct. 20 (155,192)*	1.25
2871A	29c	**Christmas (religious),** perf 9¾x11, *Oct. 20 (155,192)*	1.25
2872	29c	**Christmas (stocking),** *Oct. 20,* Harmony MN	1.25
2873	29c	**Christmas (Santa Claus),** self-adhesive, *Oct. 20,* Harmony MN	1.25
2874	29c	**Christmas (cardinal),** small self-adhesive, *Oct. 20,* Harmony MN	1.25

First day cancellation was applied to 132,005 covers bearing one or more of Nos. 2872, 2872a, 2873, 2874.

2875	$2	**Bureau of Printing and Engraving Souvenir sheet,** *Nov. 3,* New York, NY *(13,126)*	25.00
2875a	$2	Single stamp	7.00
2876	29c	**Chinese New Year (Boar),** *Dec. 30,* Sacramento CA	1.75
2877	(3c)	**Dove, bright blue,** *Dec. 13*	1.25
2878	(3c)	**Dove, dark blue,** *Dec. 13*	1.25
2879	(20c)	**G, black,** *Dec. 13*	1.25
2880	(20c)	**G, red,** *Dec. 13*	1.25
2881	(32c)	**G, black,** *Dec. 13*	1.25
2881a		Booklet pane of 10	6.75
2882	(32c)	**G, red,** *Dec. 13*	1.25
2883	(32c)	**G, black,** *Dec. 13*	1.25
2883a		Booklet pane of 10	6.75

2884	(32c)	**G, black,** *Dec. 13*	1.25
2884a		Booklet pane of 10	6.75
2885	(32c)	**G, red,** *Dec. 13*	1.25
2885a		Booklet pane of 10	6.75
2886	(32c)	**G, gray, blue, light blue, red & black,** self-adhesive, *Dec. 13*	1.25
2887	(32c)	**G, black, blue & red,** self-adhesive, *Dec. 13*	1.25
2888	(25c)	**G, black,** coil, *Dec. 13*	1.25
2889	(32c)	**G, black,** coil, *Dec. 13*	1.25
2890	(32c)	**G, blue,** coil, *Dec. 13*	1.25
2891	(32c)	**G, red,** coil, *Dec. 13*	1.25
2892	(32c)	**G, red,** rouletted coil, *Dec. 13*	1.25

Originally, No. 2893 (the 5c green Non-profit Presort G rate stamp) was only available through the Philatelic Fullfillment Center after their announcement 1/12/95. Requests for first day cancels received a 12/13/94 cancel, even though they were not available on that date. Value, $1.25.

First day cancellation was applied to 338,107 covers bearing one or more of Nos. 2877-2893(?), and U633-U634.

| 2897 | 32c | **Flag Over Porch,** *May 19,* Denver CO | 1.25 |

First day cancellation was applied to 66,609 covers bearing one or more of Nos. 2897, 2913-2914, 2916 and possibly, 2920.

1995-98

| 2902 | (5c) | **Butte,** coil, *Mar. 10,* State College PA | 1.25 |

First day cancellation was applied to 80,003 covers bearing one or more of Nos. 2902, 2905, and U635-U636.

| 2902B | (5c) | **Butte,** self-adhesive coil, *June 15, 1996,* San Antonio TX | 1.25 |

First day cancellation was applied to 87,400 covers bearing one or more of Nos. 2902B, 2904A, 2906, 2910, 2912A, 2915B.

| 2903 | (5c) | **Mountain,** purple & multi coil, *Mar. 16, 1996* San Jose CA | 1.25 |
| 2904 | (5c) | **Mountain,** blue & multi coil, *Mar. 16,1996* San Jose CA | 1.25 |

First day cancellation was applied to 28,064 covers bearing one or more of Nos. 2903-2904.

| 2904A | (5c) | **Mountain,** purple & multi self-adhesive coil, *June 15, 1996,* San Antonio TX | 1.25 |

First day cancellation was applied to 87,400 covers bearing one or more of Nos. 2902B, 2904A, 2906, 2910, 2912A, 2915B.

2904B	(5c)	**Mountain,** purple & multi self-adhesive coil, inscription outlined, *Jan. 24, 1997,* Tucson, AZ	1.25
2905	(10c)	**Auto,** coil, *Mar. 10,* State College PA	1.25
2906	(10c)	**Auto,** self-adhesive coil, *June 15, 1996* San Antonio TX	1.25

First day cancellation was applied to 87,400 covers bearing one or more of Nos. 2902B, 2904A, 2906, 2910, 2912A, 2915B.

| 2907 | (10c) | **Eagle & Shield,** USA Bulk Rate self-adhesive coil, *May 21, 1996* | 1.25 |

First day cancellation was applied to 54,102 covers bearing one or more of Nos. 2907, 2915A, 2915C, 2921.

| 2908 | (15c) | **Auto tail fin (dark orange yellow),** coil, *Mar. 17,* New York NY | 1.25 |
| 2909 | (15c) | **Auto tail fin (buff),** coil, *Mar. 17,* New York, NY | 1.25 |

First day cancellation was applied to 93,770 covers bearing one or more of Nos. 2908-2909, 2911-2912, 2919.

| 2910 | (15c) | **Auto tail fin (buff),** self-adhesive coil, *June 15, 1996,* San Antonio TX | 1.25 |

First day cancellation was applied to 87,400 covers bearing one or more of Nos. 2902B, 2904A, 2906, 2910, 2915B.

| 2911 | (25c) | **Juke box,** coil, *Mar. 17,* New York NY | 1.25 |
| 2912 | (25c) | **Juke box,** coil, *Mar. 17,* New York NY | 1.25 |

First day cancellation was applied to 93,770 covers bearing one or more of Nos. 2908-2909, 2911-2912, 2919.

| 2912A | (25c) | **Juke box,** self-adhesive coil, bright orange red & multi, microperfs, *June 15, 1996,* New York NY | 1.25 |

First day cancellation was applied to 87,400 covers bearing one or more of Nos. 2902B, 2904A, 2906, 2910, 2912A, 2915B.

2912B	(25c)	**Juke box,** self-adhesive coil, dark red & multi, *Jan. 24, 1997,* Tucson, AZ	1.25
2913	32c	**Flag Over Porch,** coil, *May 19,* Denver CO	1.25
2914	32c	**Flag Over Porch,** coil, *May 19,* Denver CO	1.25
2915	32c	**Flag Over Porch,** self-adhesive, die cut 8.7 vert., *Apr. 18*	1.25
2915A	32c	**Flag Over Porch,** self-adhesive, die cut 9.8 vert., 11 teeth, *May 21, 1996*	1.25
2915B	32c	**Flag Over Porch,** self-adhesive die cut 11.5 vert., *June 15, 1996,* San Antonio TX	1.25

First day cancellation was applied to 87,400 covers bearing one or more of Nos. 2902B, 2904A, 2906, 2910, 2912A, 2915B.

| 2915C | 32c | **Flag Over Porch,** self-adhesive, die cut 10.9, *May 21, 1996* | 2.00 |

| 2915D | 32c | **Flag Over Porch,** self-adhesive coil, self-adhesive die cut 9.8 vert., 9 teeth, *Jan. 24, 1997,* Tucson, AZ | 1.25 |

First day cancellation was applied to 56,774 covers bearing one or more of Nos. 2904B, 2912B, 2915D and 2921b.

2916	32c	**Flag Over Porch,** booklet single, *May 19,* Denver CO	1.25
2916a		Booklet pane of 10	7.50
2919	32c	**Flag Over Field,** self-adhesive, *Mar. 17,* New York NY	1.25

First day cancellation was applied to 93,770 covers bearing one or more of Nos. 2908-2909, 2911-2912, 2919.

| 2920 | 32c | **Flag Over Porch,** self-adhesive, *Apr. 18* | 1.25 |

First day cancellation was applied to 66,609 covers bearing one or more of Nos. 2897, 2913-2914, 2916 and possibly, 2920.
First day cancellation was applied to 57,639 covers bearing one or more of Nos. 2920d, 3030, 3044.

| 2921 | 32c | **Flag Over Porch,** self-adhesive, booklet stamp, die cut 9.8 on 2 or 3 sides, *May 21, 1996* | 1.25 |

First day cancellation was applied to 54,102 covers bearing one or more of Nos. 2907, 2915A, 2915C, 2921.

GREAT AMERICANS ISSUE

2933	32c	**Milton Hershey,** *July 11,* Hershey PA *(121,228)*	1.25
2934	32c	**Cal Farley,** *Apr. 26, 1996,* Amarillo TX *(109,440)*	1.25
2935	32c	**Henry Luce,** *Apr. 3, 1998,* New York NY *(76,982)*	1.25
2936	32c	**Wallace,** *July 16, 1998,* Pleasantville NY *(72,183)*	1.25
2938	46c	**Ruth Benedict,** *Oct. 20,* Virginia Beach VA *(24,793)*	1.40
2940	55c	**Alice Hamilton,** *July 11,* Boston MA *(24,225)*	1.40
2941	55c	**Justin Morrill,** *July 17, 1999* Strafford VT *(19,699)*	1.40
2942	77c	**Mary Breckinridge,** *Nov. 9, 1998* Troy, NY	1.75

First day cancellation was applied to 121,662 covers bearing one or more of Nos. 2942, 3257-3261, 3263-3269.

| 2943 | 78c | **Alice Paul,** *Aug. 18,* Mount Laurel NJ *(25,071)* | 1.75 |

1995

| 2948 | (32c) | **Love,** *Feb. 1,* Valentines VA | 1.50 |
| 2949 | (32c) | **Love,** self-adhesive, *Feb. 1,* Valentines VA | 1.50 |

First day cancellation was applied to 70,778 covers bearing one or more of Nos. 2948, 2949.

2950	32c	**Florida Statehood,** *Mar. 3,* Tallahassee FL *(167,499)*	1.25
2954a	32c	**Earth Day,** *Apr. 20*	2.75
		2951-2954, any single	1.25

First day cancellation was applied to 328,893 covers bearing one or more of Nos. 2951-2954, 2954a.

2955	32c	**Richard Nixon,** *Apr. 26,* Yorba Linda CA *(377,605)*	1.25
2956	32c	**Bessie Coleman,** *Apr. 27,* Chicago IL *(299,834)*	1.75
2957	32c	**Love,** *May 12,* Lakeville PA	1.25
2958	55c	**Love,** *May 12,* Lakeville PA	1.25
2959	32c	**Love,** booklet single, *May 12,* Lakeville PA	1.25
2959a		Booklet pane of 10	7.50
2960	55c	**Love,** self-adhesive, *May 12,* Lakeville PA	1.40

First day cancellation was applied to 273,350 covers bearing one or more of Nos. 2957-2959, 2959a, and U637.

| 2965a | 32c | **Recreational Sports,** *May 20,* Jupiter FL | 3.25 |
| | | 2961-2965, any single | 1.50 |

First day cancellation was applied to 909,807 covers bearing one or more of Nos. 2961-2965, 2965a.

2966	32c	**Prisoners of War & Missing in Action,** *May 29 (231,857)*	2.50
2967	32c	**Marilyn Monroe,** *June 1,* Universal City CA *(703,219)*	3.25
		Any other city	2.00
2968	32c	**Texas Statehood,** *June 16,* Austin TX *(177,550)*	1.75
2973a	32c	**Great Lakes Lighthouses booklet pane of 5,** *June 17,* Cheboygan MI	5.00
		2969-2973, any single	2.00

First day cancellation was applied to 626,055 covers bearing one or more of Nos. 2969-2973, 2973a.

2974	32c	**UN, 50th Anniv.,** *June 26,* San Francisco CA *(160,383)*	1.50
2975	32c	**Civil War pane of 20,** *June 29,* Gettysburg PA	16.00
		Any other city	16.00
		2975a-2975t, any single, Gettysburg PA	2.00
		Any other city	1.75

First day cancellation was applied to 1,950,134 covers bearing one or more of Nos. 2975, 2975a-2975t, and UX200-UX219.

| 2979a | 32c | **Carousel Horses,** *July 21,* Lahaska PA | 3.25 |
| | | 2976-2979, any single | 1.25 |

First day cancellation was applied to 479,038 covers bearing one or more of Nos. 2976-2979, 2979a.

2980	32c **Woman Suffrage,** *Aug. 26 (196,581)*		1.25
2981	32c **World War II block of 10,** *Sept. 2,* Honolulu HI		7.00
	2981a-2981j, any single		2.00

First day cancellation was applied to 1,562,094 covers bearing one or more of Nos. 2981, 2981a-2981j.

2982	32c **American Music Series,** *Sept. 1,* New Orleans LA *(258,996)*		1.75
2992a	32c **American Music Series,** *Sept. 16,* Monterey CA		6.50
	2983-2992, any single		1.50

First day cancellation was applied to 629,956 covers bearing one or more of Nos. 2983-2992, 2992a.

2997a	32c **Garden Flowers booklet pane of 5,** *Sept. 19,* Encinitas CA		4.00
	2993-2997, any single		1.25

First day cancellation was applied to 564,905 covers bearing one or more of Nos. 2993-2997, 2997a.

2998	60c **Eddie Rickenbacker,** *Sept. 25,* Columbus OH *(24,283)*		1.75
2999	32c **Republic of Palau,** *Sept. 29,* Agana GU *(157,377)*		1.25
3000	32c **Comic Strips Pane of 20,** *Oct. 1,* Boca Raton FL		13.00
	3000a-3000t, any single		2.00

First day cancellation was applied to 1,362,990 covers bearing one or more of Nos. 3000, 3000a-3000t.

3001	32c **US Naval Academy,** *Oct. 10,* Annapolis, MD *(222,183)*		2.00
3002	32c **Tennessee Williams,** *Oct. 13,* Clarksdale MS *(209,812)*		1.25
3003	32c **Christmas, Madonna,** perf 11.2, *Oct. 19*		1.25
3003A	32c **Christmas, Madonna,** perf 9.8x10.9, *Oct. 19*		1.25
3003Ab	Booklet pane of 10		7.25

First day cancellation was applied to 223,301 covers bearing one or more of Nos. 3003, 3003A-3003Ab.

3007a	32c **Christmas (secular) sheet,** *Sept. 30,* North Pole NY		3.25
	3004-3007, any single		1.25
3007b	32c **Booklet pane of 10, 3 #3004,** etc.		7.25
3007c	32c **Booklet pane of 10, 2 #3004,** etc.		7.25

First day cancellation was applied to 487,816 covers bearing one or more of Nos. 3004-3007, 3007a.

3008-3011	32c **Christmas (secular) self-adhesive booklet stamps,** *Sept. 30,* North Pole NY		3.25
	3008-3011, any single		1.25
3012	32c **Angel,** *Oct. 19,* Christmas FL		1.25
3013	32c **Children sledding,** *Oct. 19,* Christmas FL		1.25

First day cancellation was applied to 77,675 covers bearing one or more of Nos. 3012, 3013, 3018.

3014-3017	32c **Self-adhesive coils,** *Sept. 30,* North Pole NY		2.50
	3014-3017, any single		1.25
3018	32c **Self-adhesive coil,** *Oct. 19,* Christmas FL		1.25

First day cancellation was applied to 77,675 covers bearing one or more of Nos. 3012, 3013, 3018.

3023a	32c **Antique Automobiles,** *Nov. 3,* New York NY		3.00
	3019-3023, any single		1.25

First day cancellation was applied to 757,003 covers bearing one or more of Nos. 3019-3023, 3023a.

1996

3024	32c **Utah Statehood Cent.,** *Jan. 4,* Salt Lake City UT *(207,089)*		1.25
3029a	32c **Garden Flowers booklet pane,** *Jan. 19,* Kennett Square PA		3.50
	3025-3029, any single		1.25

First day cancellation was applied to 876,176 covers bearing one or more of Nos. 3025-3029, 3029a.

3030	32c **Love self-adhesive,** *Jan. 20,* New York NY		1.25

First day cancellation was applied to 57,639 covers bearing one or more of Nos. 2920d, 3030, 3044.

1996-2000

FLORA AND FAUNA

3031	1c **Kestrel,** *Nov. 19, 1999,* New York, NY *(14,431)*		1.50
3032	2c **Red-headed woodpecker,** *Feb. 2,* Sarasota FL *(37,319)*		1.25
3033	3c **Eastern Bluebird,** *Apr. 3 (23,405)*		1.25
3036	$1 **Red Fox,** *Aug. 14, 1998*		3.50

First day cancellation was applied to 46,557 covers bearing one or more of Nos. 3228-3229, 3036.

3044	1c **American Kestrel, coil,** *Jan. 20,* New York NY		1.25

First day cancellation was applied to 57,639 covers bearing one or more of Nos. 2920d, 3030, 3044.

3045	2c **Red-Headed Woodpecker,** *June 22, 1999 (14,377)*		1.25

3048	20c **Blue Jay, booklet stamp, self-adhesive,** *Aug. 2,* St. Louis MO		1.25

First day cancellation was applied to 32,633 covers bearing one or more of Nos. 3048, 3053.

3049	32c **Yellow Rose, booklet stamp, self-adhesive,** *Oct. 24,* Pasadena, CA *(7,849)*		1.25
3050	20c **Ring-necked Pheasant, booklet stamp, self-adhesive,** *July 31, 1998* Somerset NJ		1.25

First day cancellation was applied to 32,220 covers bearing one or more of Nos. 3050, 3055.

3052	33c **Coral Pink Rose,** serpentine die cut 11½x11¼, *Aug. 13, 1999,* Indianapolis, IN		1.25
3052E	33c **Coral Pink Rose,** serpentine die cut 10¾x10½, *Apr. 7, 2000,* New York, NY *(18,199)*		1.25
3053	20c **Blue Jay, coil, self-adhesive,** *Aug. 2,* St. Louis MO		1.25
3054	32c **Yellow Rose, self-adhesive,** *Aug. 1, 1997,* Falls Church VA *(20,029)*		1.25
3055	20c **Ring-necked Pheasant, coil, self-adhesive,** *July 31, 1998* Somerset NJ		1.25

First day cancellation was applied to 32,220 covers bearing one or more of Nos. 3050, 3055.

1996

3058	32c **Ernest E. Just,** *Feb. 1 (191,360)*		1.75
3059	32c **Smithsonian, 150th anniv.,** *Feb. 7,* *(221,399)*		1.25
3060	32c **Chinese New Year,** *Feb. 8,* San Francisco CA *(237,451)*		1.75
3064a	32c **Pioneers of Communication,** *Feb. 22,* New York NY		2.50
	3061-3064, any single		1.25

First day cancellation was applied to 567,205 covers bearing one or more of Nos. 3061-3064, 3064a.

3065	32c **Fulbright Scholarships,** *Feb. 28,* Fayetteville AR *(227,330)*		1.25
3066	50c **Jacqueline Cochran,** *Mar. 9,* Indio CA *(30,628)*		1.75
3067	32c **Marathon,** *Apr. 11,* Boston MA *(177,050)*		2.00
3068	32c **Olympics, pane of 20,** *May 2*		13.00
	3068a-3068t, any single		1.25
	Atlanta, GA		—

Washington DC first day cancellation was applied to 1,807,316 covers bearing one or more of Nos. 3068, 3068a-3068t. Atlanta was also an official first day city, and covers postmarked there are scarce.

3069	32c **Georgia O'Keeffe,** *May 23,* Santa Fe NM *(200,522)*		1.50
3070	32c **Tennessee Statehood, Bicen.,** *May 31,* Knoxville, Memphis or Nashville TN		1.25
3071	32c **Tennessee, self-adhesive,** *May 31,* Knoxville, Memphis or Nashville TN		1.25

First day cancellation was applied to 217,281 covers bearing one or more of Nos. 3070-3071.

3076a	32c **American Indian Dances, strip of 5,** *June 7,* Oklahoma City OK		2.75
	3072-3076, any single		1.25

First day cancellation was applied to 653,057 covers bearing one or more of Nos. 3072-3076, 3076a.

3080a	32c **Prehistoric Animals,** *June 8,* Toronto, Canada		2.75
	3077-3080, any single		1.50

First day cancellation was applied to 485,929 covers bearing one or more of Nos. 3077-3080, 3080a.

3081	32c **Breast Cancer Awareness,** *June 15 (183,896)*		1.25
	Any other city		1.25
3082	32c **James Dean,** *June 24,* Burbank CA *(263,593)*		2.00
3086a	32c **Folk Heroes,** *July 11,* Anaheim CA		2.75
	3083-3086, any single		1.25

First day cancellation was applied to 739,706 covers bearing one or more of Nos. 3083-3086, 3086a.

3087	32c **Centennial Olympic Games,** *July 19,* Atlanta GA *(269,056)*		1.25
3088	32c **Iowa Statehood, 150th Anniv.,** *Aug. 1,* Dubuque IA		1.25
3089	32c **Iowa Statehood, self-adhesive** *Aug. 1,* Dubuque IA		1.25
	3088, 3089, both stamps issued *Aug. 1,* Dubuque, IA		1.75

First day cancellation was applied to 215,181 covers bearing one or more of Nos. 3088-3089.

3090	32c **Rural Free Delivery,** *Aug. 7,* Charleston WV *(192,070)*		1.25
3091-3095	32c **Riverboats,** *Aug. 22,* Orlando FL		3.50

	3091-3095, any single		1.25
3095b	32c **Riverboats, special die cutting,** *Aug. 22,* Orlando FL		3.50

First day cancellation was applied to 770,384 covers bearing one or more of Nos. 3091-3095, 3095b.

3099a	32c **Big Band Leaders,** *Sept. 11,* New York NY		3.25
	3096-3099, any single		1.25

First day cancellation was applied to 1,235,166 covers bearing one or more of Nos. 3096-3103, 3099a, 3103a.

3103a	32c **Songwriters,** *Sept. 11,* New York NY		3.25
	3100-3103, any single		1.25

First day cancellation was applied to 1,235,166 covers bearing one or more of Nos. 3096-3103, 3099a, 3103a.

3104	23c **F. Scott Fitzgerald,** *Sept. 27,* St. Paul MN *(150,783)*		1.25
3105	32c **Endangered Species,** *Oct. 2,* San Diego CA		7.50
	3105a-3105o, any single		1.25

First day cancellation was applied to 941,442 covers bearing one or more of Nos. 3105, 3105a-3105o.

3106	32c **Computer Technology,** *Oct. 8,* Aberdeen Proving Ground MD *(153,688)*		1.75
3107	32c **Christmas Madonna,** *Nov. 1,* Richmond VA		1.25

First day cancellation was applied to 164,447 covers bearing one or more of Nos. 3107, 3112.

3111a	32c **Christmas (secular),** *Oct. 8,* North Pole AK		2.75
	3108-3111, any single		1.25

First day cancellation was applied to 884,339 covers bearing one or more of Nos. 3108-3111, 3111a, 3113-3117.

3112	32c **As No. 3107, self-adhesive,** *Nov. 1,* Richmond VA		1.25
3113-3116	32c **Christmas (secular), self-adhesive,** *Oct. 8,* North Pole AK		3.25
	3113-3116, any single		1.25
3117	32c **Skaters, self-adhesive,** *Oct. 8,* North Pole AK		1.25

First day cancellation was applied to 884,339 covers bearing one or more of Nos. 3108-3111, 3111a, 3113-3117.

3118	32c **Hanukkah,** *Oct. 22 (179,355)*		1.75
3119	50c **Cycling,** *Nov. 1,* New York NY		4.00
	3119a-3119b, any single		2.00

First day cancellation was applied to 290,091 covers bearing one or more of Nos. 3119, 3119a-3119b.

1997

3120	32c **Chinese New Year,** *Jan. 5,* Honolulu *(233,638)*		1.75
3121	32c **Benjamin O. Davis, Sr.,** *Jan. 28 (166,527)*		1.75
3122	32c **Statue of Liberty, self-adhesive,** *Feb. 1,* San Diego CA *(40,003)*		1.25
3123	32c **Love, Swans, self-adhesive,** *Feb. 4,* Los Angeles CA		1.25
3124	55c **Love, Swans, self-adhesive,** *Feb. 4,* Los Angeles CA		1.50

First day cancellation was applied to 257,380 covers bearing one or more of Nos. 3123-3124.

3125	32c **Helping Children Learn, self-adhesive** *Feb. 18 (175,410)*		1.25
3126	32c **Merian Botanical Prints, Citron, etc., self-adhesive, die cut 10.9x10.2,** *Mar. 3*		1.25
3127	32c **Merian Botanical Prints, Pineapple, etc., self-adhesive, die cut 10.9x10.2,** *Mar. 3*		1.25
3128	32c **Merian Botanical Prints, Citron, etc., self-adhesive, die cut 11.2x10.8,** *Mar. 3*		1.25
3128a	32c **Merian Botanical Prints, Citron, etc., self-adhesive, die cut mixed perf,** *Mar. 3*		1.25
3129	32c **Merian Botanical Prints, Pineapple, etc., self-adhesive, die cut 11.2x10.8,** *Mar. 3*		1.25
3129a	32c **Merian Botanical Prints, Pineapple, etc., self-adhesive, die cut mixed perf,** *Mar. 3*		1.25

First day cancellation was applied to 336,897 covers bearing one or more of Nos. 3126-3129, 3128a-3129a.

3131a	32c **Pacific 97,** *Mar. 13,* New York NY		2.00
	3130-3131, any single		1.50

First day cancellation was applied to 371,908 covers bearing one or more of Nos. 3130-3131, 3131a.

3132	(25c) **Juke Box, self-adhesive** *Mar. 14,* New York NY		1.25
3133	32c **Flag over Porch, Self-adhesive** *Mar. 14,* New York NY		1.25

First day cancellation was applied to 26,0820 covers bearing one or more of Nos. 3132-3133.

3134	32c **Thornton Wilder,** *Apr. 17,* Hamden CT *(157,299)*		1.25

3135	32c	**Raoul Wallenberg,** Apr. 24 (168,668)	2.00
3136	32c	**Dinosaurs, pane of 15** May 1, Grand Junction CO	7.50
		3136a-3136o, any single	1.25

First day cancellation was applied to 1,782,1221 covers bearing one or more of Nos. 3136, 3136a-3136o.

3137a	32c	**Bugs Bunny,** May 22, Burbank CA (378,142)	2.00
3139	50c	**Pacific 97, Franklin, pane of 12** May 29, San Francisco CA	12.00
		3139a, single	2.00
3140	60c	**Pacific 97,, pane of 12,** May 30, San Francisco CA	12.00
		3140a, single	2.00

First day cancellation was applied to 328,401 covers bearing one or more of Nos. 3139-3140, 3139a-3140b.

3141	32c	**Marshall Plan,** June 4, Cambridge MA (157,622)	1.50
3142	32c	**Classic American Aircraft,** July 19, Dayton OH	10.00
		3142a-3142t, any single	1.25

First day cancellation was applied to 1,413,833 covers bearing one or more of Nos. 3142, 3142a-3142t.

3146a	32c	**Football Coaches** July 25, Canton OH	3.00
		3143-3146, any single	1.75

First day cancellation was applied to 586,946 covers bearing one or more of Nos. 3143-3146.

3147	32c	**Bear Bryant,** Aug. 5, Green Bay WI (119,428)	1.75
3148	32c	**Pop Warner,** Aug. 7, Tuscaloosa AL (23,858)	1.75
3149	32c	**Vince Lombardi,** Aug. 8, Philadelphia PA (37,839)	1.75
3150	32c	**George Halas,** Aug. 16, Chicago IL (26,760)	1.75
3151	32c	**American Dolls,** July 28, Anaheim CA	8.00
		3151a-3151o, any single	1.25

First day cancellation was applied to 831,359 covers bearing one or more of Nos. 3151, 3151a-3151o.

3152	32c	**Humphrey Bogart,** July 31, Los Angeles CA (220,254)	2.00
3153	32c	**"The Star and Stripes Forever,"** Aug. 21, Milwaukee WI (36,666)	1.25
3157a	32c	**Opera Singers,** Sept. 10, New York NY	2.75
		3154-3157, any single	1.25

First day cancellation was applied to 386,689 covers bearing one or more of Nos. 3154-3157.

3165a	32c	**Classical Composers and Conductors,** Sept. 12, Cincinnati OH	5.25
		3158-3165, any single	1.25

First day cancellation was applied to 424,344 covers bearing one or more of Nos. 3158-3165.

3166	32c	**Padre Felix Varela,** Sept. 15, Miami FL (120,079)	1.25
3167	32c	**Department of the Air Force,** Sept. 18 (178,519)	1.50
3172a	32c	**Classic Movie Monsters,** Sept. 30, Universal City CA	3.75
		3168-3172, any single	1.50

First day cancellation was applied to 476,993 covers bearing one or more of Nos. 3168-3172.

3173	32c	**First Supersonic Flight,** Oct. 14, Edwards AFB CA (173,778)	1.50
3174	32c	**Women in Military Service,** Oct. 18 (106,121)	1.75
3175	32c	**Kwanzaa,** Oct. 22, Los Angeles CA (92,489)	1.75
3176	32c	**Christmas Madonna,** Oct. 27 (35,809)	1.25
3177	32c	**Holly,** Oct. 30, New York NY (87,332)	1.25
3178	$3	**Mars Pathfinder,** Dec. 10 Pasadena CA (11,699)	9.00

1998

3179	32c	**Chinese New Year,** Jan. 5, Seattle WA (234,269)	1.75
3180	32c	**Alpine Skiing,** Jan. 22, Salt Lake City UT (196,504)	1.25
3181	32c	**Madam C. J. Walker,** Jan. 28, Indianapolis IN (146,348)	1.75

1998-2000

CELEBRATE THE CENTURY

3182	32c	**1900s,** Feb. 3 (11,699)	8.50
		3182a-3182o, any single	1.50
3183	32c	**1910s,** Feb. 3	8.50
		3183a-3183o, any single	1.50

First day cancellation was applied to 3,896,387 covers bearing one or more of Nos. 3182-3182o, 3183-3183o.

3184	32c	**1920s,** May 28	8.50
		3184a-3184o, any single	1.75

First day cancellation was applied to 1,057,909 covers bearing one or more of Nos. 3184-3184o.

3185	32c	**1930s,** Sept. 10, Cleveland OH	8.50
		3185a-3185o, any single	1.75

First day cancellation was applied to 999,017 covers bearing one or more of Nos. 3185-3185o.

3186	33c	**1940s,** Feb. 18, 1999, Dobbins AFB GA	8.50
		3186a-3186o, any single	1.75

First day cancellation was applied to 1,459,138 covers bearing one or more of Nos. 3186-3186o.

3187	33c	**1950s,** May 26, 1999, Springfield MA	8.50
		3187a-3187o, any single	1.75

First day cancellation was applied to 1,454,906 covers bearing one or more of Nos. 3187-3187o.

3188	33c	**1960s,** Sept. 17, 1999, Green Bay, WI	8.50
		3188a-3188o, any single	1.75

First day cancellation was applied to 1,252,243 covers bearing one or more of Nos. 3188-3188o.

3189	33c	**1970s,** Nov. 18, 1999, New York, NY	8.50
		3189a-3189o, any single	1.75

First day cancellation was applied to 894,084 covers bearing one or more of Nos. 3189-3189o.

3190	33c	**1980s,** Jan. 12, 2000, Kennedy Space Center, FL	8.50
		3190a-3190o, any single	1.75
3191	33c	**1990s,** May 2, 2000, Escondido, CA	8.50
		3191a-3191o, any single	1.75

First day cancellation was applied to 1,172,962 covers bearing one or more of Nos. 3191-3190o.

1998

3192	32c	**"Remember the Maine,"** Feb. 15, Key West FL (161,657)	1.75
3193-3197	32c	**Flowering Trees,** Mar. 19, New York NY	3.75
		3193-3197, any single	1.50

First day cancellation was applied to 666,199 covers bearing one or more of Nos. 3193-3197.

3202a	32c	**Alexander Calder,** Mar. 25	3.75
		3198-3202, any single	1.50

First day cancellation was applied to 588,887 covers bearing one or more of Nos. 3198-3202, 3202a.

3203	32c	**Cinco de Mayo,** Apr. 16, San Antonio TX (144,443)	1.25
3204a	32c	**Sylvester & Tweety,** Apr. 27, New York NY (213,839)	1.25
3206	32c	**Wisconsin Statehood,** May 29, Madison WI (130,810)	1.25

1998-99

3207	(5c)	**Wetlands,** June 5, McLean VA	1.25
3207A	(5c)	**Wetlands, Serpentine die cut,** Dec. 14	1.25
3208	(25c)	**Diner,** June 5, McLean VA	1.25

First day cancellation was applied to 35,333 covers bearing one or more of Nos. 3207, 3208; 13,378 covers bearing one of more of Nos. 3207A, 3270-3271.

3208A	(25c)	**Diner, Serpentine die cut,** June 5 (13,984)	1.25

1998

1898 TRANS-MISSISSIPPI STAMPS, CENT.

3209		**Sheet of 9,** June 18, Anaheim CA	6.50
3209a	1c		1.50
3209b	2c		1.50
3209c	4c		1.50
3209d	5c		1.50
3209e	8c		1.50
3209f	10c		1.50
3209g	50c		2.00
3209h	$1		2.50
3209i	$2		4.50
3210	$1	**Sheet of 9,** June 18, Anaheim CA	15.00

First day cancellation was applied to 203,649 covers bearing one or more of Nos. 3209-3210, 3209a-3209i.

1998

3211	32c	**Berlin Airlift,** June 26, Berlin, Germany (137,894)	1.50
3215a	32c	**Folk Musicians,** June 26	3.25
		3212-3215, any single	1.25

First day cancellation was applied to 341,015 covers bearing one or more of Nos. 3212-3215, 3215a.

3219a	32c	**Gospel Music,** July 15, New Orleans LA	3.25
		3216-3219, any single	1.25

First day cancellation was applied to 330,533 covers bearing one or more of Nos. 3216-3219, 3219a.

3220	32c	**Spanish Settlement of the Southwest,** July 11, Española NM (122,182)	1.25
3221	32c	**Stephen Vincent Benét,** July 22, Harpers Ferry WV (107,412)	1.25

3225a	32c	**Tropical Birds,** July 29, Ponce PR	3.00
		3222-3225, any single	1.25

First day cancellation was applied to 371,354 covers bearing one or more of Nos. 3222-3225, 3225a.

3226	32c	**Alfred Hitchcock,** Aug. 3, Los Angeles CA (140,628)	1.50
3227	32c	**Organ & Tissue Donation,** Aug. 5, Columbus OH (110,601)	1.25
3228	(10c)	**Modern Bicycle, Serpentine die cut,** Aug. 14	1.25
3229	(10c)	**Modern Bicycle,** Aug. 14	1.25

First day cancellation was applied to 46,557 covers bearing one or more of Nos. 3228-3229, 3036.

3230-3234	32c	**Bright Eyes,** Aug. 20, Boston MA	3.25
		3230-3234, any single	1.75

First day cancellation was applied to 394,280 covers bearing one or more of Nos. 3230-3234.

3235	32c	**Klondike Gold Rush Cent.,** Aug. 21, Nome or Skagway AK (123,559)	1.50
3236	32c	**American Art, pane of 20,** Aug. 27, Santa Clara CA	9.00
		3236a-3236t, any single	1.25

First day cancellation was applied to 924,031 covers bearing one or more of Nos. 3236, 3236a-3236t.

3237	32c	**American Ballet,** Sept. 16, New York NY (133,034)	1.25
3242a	32c	**Space Discovery,** Oct. 1, Kennedy Space Center FL	3.75
		3238-3242, any single	1.25

First day cancellation was applied to 399,807 covers bearing one or more of Nos. 3238-3242, 3242a.

3243	32c	**Giving & Sharing,** Oct. 7, Atlanta GA (124,051)	1.25
3244	32c	**Christmas, Madonna,** Oct. 15 (105,835)	1.25
3245-3248	32c	**Christmas, Secular,** Oct. 15, Christmas MI	3.25
		3245-3248, any single	1.25
3249-3252	32c	**Christmas, Secular, size: 23x30mm,** Oct. 15, Christmas MI	3.00
		3249-3252, any single	1.25

First day cancellation was applied to 328,199 covers bearing one or more of Nos. 3245-3252.

3257	(1c)	**Weather Vane, white USA,** Nov. 9, Troy NY	1.25
3258	(1c)	**Weather Vane, pale blue USA,** Nov. 9, Troy NY	1.25
3259	22c	**Uncle Sam,** Nov. 9, Troy NY	1.25
3260	(33c)	**Uncle Sam's Hat,** Nov. 9, Troy NY	1.25
3261	$3.20	**Space Shuttle Landing,** Nov. 9,	5.00
3262	$11.75	**Piggyback Space Shuttle,** Nov. 9, New York NY (3,703)	25.00
3263	22c	**Uncle Sam, coil,** Nov. 9, Troy NY	1.25
3264	(33c)	**Uncle Sam's Hat, coil,** Nov. 9, Troy NY	1.25
3265	(33c)	**Uncle Sam's Hat, self-adhesive coil, die cut 9.9, round corners,** Nov. 9, Troy NY	1.25
3266	(33c)	**Uncle Sam's Hat, self-adhesive coil, die cut 9.9, square corners,** Nov. 9, Troy NY	1.50
3267	(33c)	**Uncle Sam's Hat, self-adhesive booklet single, die cut 9.9** Nov. 9, Troy NY	1.25
3268	(33c)	**Uncle Sam's Hat, self-adhesive booklet single, die cut 11.2x11.1** Nov. 9, Troy NY	1.25
3269	(33c)	**Uncle Sam's Hat, self-adhesive booklet single, die cut 8** Nov. 9, Troy NY	1.25

First day cancellation was applied to 121,662 covers bearing one or more of Nos. 2942, 3257-3261, 3263-3269.

3270	(10c)	**Eagle & Shield, Presorted Std.,** Dec. 14	
3271	(10c)	**Eagle & Shield, Presorted Std., self-adhesive, Serpentine die cut,** Dec. 14	1.25

First day cancellation was applied to 13,378 covers bearing one of more of Nos. 3207A, 3270-3271.

1999

3272	33c	**Chinese New Year,** Jan. 5, Los Angeles CA (151,436)	1.75
3273	33c	**Malcolm X,** Jan. 20, New York NY (107,226)	2.00
3274	33c	**Love,** Jan. 28, Loveland CO	1.25
3275	55c	**Love,** Jan. 28, Loveland CO	1.50

First day cancellation was applied to 189,331 covers bearing one or more of Nos. 3274, 3275, UX300.

3276	33c	**Hospice Care,** Feb. 9, Largo FL (136,976)	1.25
3277	33c	**Flag & City,** Feb. 25, Orlando FL	1.25
3278	33c	**Flag & City, self-adhesive, die cut 11.1** Feb. 25, Orlando FL	1.25

3279	33c	**Flag & City, self-adhesive, die cut 9.8** *Feb. 25,* Orlando FL	1.25
3280	33c	**Flag & City, coil, perf. 9.9 vert.** *Feb. 25,* Orlando FL	1.25
3281	33c	**Flag & City, self-adhesive coil, die cut 9.8 vert, square corners,** *Feb. 25,* Orlando FL	1.25
3282	33c	**Flag & City, self-adhesive coil, die cut 9.8 vert., round corners,** *Feb. 25,* Orlando FL	1.25

First day cancellation was applied to 88,569 covers bearing one of more of Nos. 3277-3282.

3283	33c	**Flag & Blackboard, self-adhesive, die cut 7.9,** *Mar. 13 (26,067)*	1.25
3286	33c	**Irish Immigration,** *Feb. 26,* Boston MA *(127,213)*	1.50
3287	33c	**Lunt & Fontanne,** *Mar. 2,* New York NY *(120,423)*	1.25
3292a	33c	**Arctic Animals,** *Mar. 12,* Barrow AK	3.25
		3288-3292, any single	1.25

First day cancellation was applied to 476,863 covers bearing one of more of Nos. 3288-3292, 3292a.

3293	33c	**Sonoran Desert, Pane of 10,** *Apr. 6,* Tucson AZ	6.75
		3293a-3293j, any single	1.25

First day cancellation was applied to 410,985 covers bearing one of more of Nos. 3293-3293j.

3294-3297	33c	**Christmas Berries, die cut 11.2x11.7** *Apr. 10,* Ponchatoula LA	3.25
		3294-3297, any single	1.25
		3297e, dated 2000, *Mar. 15, 2000,* Ponchatoula LA	3.25
		3294a-3296a, 3297c, any single	1.25
3298-3301	33c	**Christmas Berries, die cut 9.5x10** *Apr. 10,* Ponchatoula LA	3.25
		3298-3301, any single	1.25
3302-3305	33c	**Christmas Berries, die cut 8.5 vert.** *Apr. 10,* Ponchatoula LA	3.25
		3302-3305, any single	1.25

First day cancellation was applied to 101,344 covers bearing one of more of Nos. 3294-3305.

3306a	33c	**Daffy Duck,** *Apr. 16,* Los Angeles CA	1.50

First day cancellation was applied to 177,988 covers bearing one of more of Nos. 3306-3307c, UX304.

3308	33c	**Ayn Rand,** *Apr. 22,* New York NY *(123,660)*	2.50
3309	33c	**Cinco de Mayo,** *Apr. 27,* San Antonio TX *(20,904)*	1.25
3310-3313	33c	**Tropical Flowers,** *May 1,* Honolulu HI	3.25
		3310-3313, any single	1.25

First day cancellation was applied to 311,495 covers bearing one of more of Nos. 3310-3313, 3313a, 3313b.

3314	33c	**Bartram,** *May 18,* Philadelphia PA *(110,381)*	1.25
3315	33c	**Prostate Cancer Awareness,** *July 22,* Austin TX *(113,299)*	1.25
3316	33c	**California Gold Rush,** *June 18,* Sacramento CA *(123,648)*	1.25
3317-3320	33c	**Aquarium Fish,** *June 24,* Anaheim CA	3.25
		3317-3320, any single	1.25

First day cancellation was applied to 301,719 covers bearing one of more of Nos. 3317-3320, 3320a-3320c.

3321-3324	33c	**Extreme Sports,** *June 25,* San Francisco CA	3.00
		3321-3324, any single	1.25

First day cancellation was applied to 278,068 covers bearing one of more of Nos. 3321-3324, 3324a.

3328a	33c	**American Glass,** *June 29,* Corning NY	3.00
		3325-3328, any single	1.25

First day cancellation was applied to 272,792 covers bearing one of more of Nos. 3325-3328, 3328a.

3329	33c	**James Cagney,** *July 22,* Burbank CA *(135,867)*	1.75
3330	55c	**"Billy" Mitchell,** *July 30,* Milwaukee WI	1.50

First day cancellation was applied to 42,144 covers bearing one of more of Nos. 3330, C134.

3331	33c	**Honoring Those Who Served,** *Aug. 16,* Kansas City MO *(130,306)*	2.00
3332	45c	**Universal Postal Union,** *Aug. 25,* Beijing, China *(20,371)*	1.25
3337a	33c	**Famous Trains,** *Aug. 26,* Cleveland, OH	3.75
		any other city	3.75
		#3333-3337, any single, Cleveland, OH	1.50
		#3333-3337, any single, any other city	1.50

First day cancellation was applied to 518,446 covers bearing one of more of Nos. 3333-3337, 3337a, UX307-UX311a.

3338	33c	**Frederick Law Olmsted,** *Sept. 12,* Boston, MA *(109,735)*	1.25
3344a	33c	**Hollywood Composers,** *Sept. 16,* Los Angeles, CA	3.75
		#3339-3344, any single, Los Angeles, CA	1.25

First day cancellation was applied to 287,407 covers bearing one of more of Nos. 3339-3344, 3344a.

3350a	33c	**Broadway Songwriters,** *Sept. 21,* New York, NY	3.75
		#3345-3350, any single, New York, NY	1.25

First day cancellation was applied to 284,840 covers bearing one of more of Nos. 3345-3350, 3350a.

3351	33c	**Insects & Spiders,** *Oct. 1,* Indianapolis, IN	10.00
		#3351a-3351t, any single	1.25

First day cancellation was applied to 773,590 covers bearing one of more of Nos. 3351-3351t.

3352	33c	**Hanukkah,** *Oct. 8,* Washington, DC	1.50
3353	22c	**Uncle Sam perforated coil,** *Oct. 8,* Washington, DC	1.25

First day cancellation was applied to 44,534 covers bearing one of more of Nos. 3352-3353, O157.

3354	33c	**NATO,** *Oct. 13,* Brussels, Belgium *(110,415)*	1.50
3355	33c	**Christmas Madonna,** *Oct. 20,* Washington, DC *(110,460)*	1.25
3356-3359	33c	**Christmas Deer, narrow frame (sheet),** *Oct. 20,* Rudolph, WI	3.00
		3356-3359, any single	1.25
3360-3363	33c	**Christmas Deer, thick frame (booklet),** *Oct. 20,* Rudolph, WI	3.00
		3360-3363, any single	1.25
3364-3367	33c	**Christmas Deer, smaller size (booklet),** *Oct. 20,* Rudolph, WI	3.00
		3364-3367, any single	1.25

First day cancellation was applied to 239,350 covers bearing one of more of Nos. 3356-3367, 3359a, 3363a, 3367a-3367c.

3368	33c	**Kwanzaa,** *Oct. 29,* Los Angeles, CA *(20,493)*	1.75
3369	33c	**Year 2000,** *Dec. 27,* Washington, DC *(145,928)*	1.75

2000

3370	33c	**Chinese New Year,** *Jan. 6,* San Francisco, CA *(155,586)*	1.75
3371	33c	**Patricia Roberts Harris,** *Jan. 27,* Washington, DC *(82,211)*	1.75
3372	33c	**Los Angeles Class Submarine, with microprinting,** *Mar. 27,* Groton, CT	1.50
3373	22c	**S Class Submarine,** *Mar. 27,* Groton, CT	1.50
3374	33c	**Los Angeles Class Submarine, no microprinting,** *Mar. 27,* Groton, CT	1.50
3375	55c	**Ohio Class Submarine,** *Mar. 27,* Groton, CT	1.75
3376	60c	**USS Holland,** *Mar. 27,* Groton, CT	1.75
3377	$3.20	**Gato Class Submarine,** *Mar. 27,* Groton, CT	6.00
		3377a, Booklet pane of 5, #3373-3377, either selvage	8.00

First day cancellation was applied to 265,226 covers bearing one of more of Nos. 3372-3377, 3377a.

3378	33c	**Pacific Coast Rain Forest Pane of 10,** *Mar. 29,* Seattle, WA	6.75
		3378a-3378j, any single	1.25

First day cancellation was applied to 435,549 covers bearing one of more of Nos. 3378-3378j.

3383a	33c	**Louise Nevelson,** *Apr. 6,* New York, NY	3.25
		3379-3383, any single	1.25

First day cancellation was applied to 389,200 covers bearing one of more of Nos. 3379-3383, 3383a.

3388a	33c	**Hubble Space Telescope,** *Apr. 10,* Greenbelt, MD	3.25
		3384-3388, any single	1.25

First day cancellation was applied to 411,449 covers bearing one of more of Nos. 3384-3388, 3388a.

3389	33c	**American Samoa,** *Apr. 17,* Pago Pago, AS *(107,346)*	1.25
3390	33c	**Library of Congress,** *Apr. 24,* Washington, DC *(115,679)*	1.25
3391a	33c	**Road Runner & Wile E. Coyote,** *Apr. 26,* Phoenix, AZ	1.25

First day cancellation was applied to 154,903 covers bearing one of more of Nos. 3391-3392, 3391a-3391c, 3392a-3392c.

3396a	33c	**Distinguished Soldiers,** *May 3,* Washington, DC	3.25
		Any other city	3.25
		3393-3396, any single, Washington, DC	1.50
		Any other city	1.25

First day cancellation was applied to 322,278 covers bearing one of more of Nos. 3393-3396, 3396a.

3397	33c	**Summer Sports,** *May 5,* Spokane, WA *(110,768)*	1.25
3398	33c	**Adoption,** *May 10,* Beverly Hills, CA	1.25

First day cancellation was applied to 137,903 covers bearing one of more of Nos. 3398, UX315.

3402a	33c	**Youth Team Sports,** *May 27,* Lake Buena Vista, FL	3.25
		3399-3402, any single	1.25

First day cancellation was applied to 309,349 covers bearing one of more of Nos. 3399-3402, 3402a.

3403	33c	**The Stars and Stripes, pane of 20,** *June 14,* Baltimore, MD	10.00
		3403a-3403t, any single	1.25

First day cancellation was applied to 1,121,071 covers bearing one of more of Nos. 3403-3403t.

3404-3407	33c	**Berries, die cut 8½ horiz.,** *June 16,* Buffalo, NY	3.25
		3404-3707, any single	1.25

First day cancellation was applied to 35,671 covers bearing one of more of Nos. 3404-3407, 3407a.

3408	33c	**Legends of Baseball, pane of 20,** *July 6,* Atlanta, GA	10.00
		3408a-3708t, any single	1.75

First day cancellation was applied to 1,214,413 covers bearing one of more of Nos. 3408-3408t.

3409	60c	**Probing the Vastness of Space,** *July 10,* Anaheim, CA	6.00
		3409a-3409f, any single	1.50

First day cancellation was applied to 296,252 covers bearing one of more of Nos. 3409-3409f.

3410	$1	**Exploring the Solar System,** *July 11,* Anaheim, CA	9.00
		3410a-3410e, any single	2.00

First day cancellation was applied to 49,500 covers bearing one of more of Nos. 3410-3410e.

3411	$3.20	**Escaping the Gravity of Earth,** *July 9,* Anaheim, CA	9.50
		3411a-3411b, any single	3.75

First day cancellation was applied to 22,321 covers bearing one of more of Nos. 3411-3411b.

3412	$11.75	**Space Achievement and Exploration,** *July 7,* Anaheim, CA *(12,070)*	17.50
3413	$11.75	**Landing on the Moon,** *July 8,* Anaheim, CA *(11,639)*	17.50
3414-3417	33c	**Stampin' The Future,** *July 13,* Anaheim, CA	3.25
		3414-3417, any single	1.25

First day cancellation was applied to 294,434 covers bearing one of more of Nos. 3414-3417, 3417a.

Distinguished Americans Issue 2000-2009

3420	10c	**Joseph W. Stilwell,** *Aug. 24,* Providence, RI *(21,669)*	1.50
3422	23c	**Wilma Rudolph, litho. & engr.** *July 14, 2004,* Sacramento, CA	1.25
3426	33c	**Claude Pepper,** *Sept. 7,* Washington, DC *(60,689)*	1.25
3427	58c	**Margaret Chase Smith,** *June 13, 2007,* Washington, DC	2.40
3427A	59c	**James A. Michener,** *May 12, 2008,* Washington, DC	2.40
3428	63c	**Dr. Jonas Salk,** *Mar. 8,* Washington, DC	2.50
		Any other city	2.50
3430	75c	**Harriet Beecher Stowe,** *June 13, 2007* Washington, DC	2.75
3431	76c	**Hattie Caraway,** *Feb. 21, 2001,* Little Rock, AR	1.75
3432A	76c	**Edward Trudeau,** *May 12, 2008,* Washington, DC	2.75
3432B	78c	**Mary Lasker,** *May 15, 2009,* Washington, DC	2.75
3433	83c	**Edna Ferber,** *July 29, 2002,* Appleton, WI	1.75
3435	87c	**Dr. Albert Sabin,** *Mar. 8,* Washington, DC	3.00
		Any other city	3.00
3436	23c	**Wilma Rudolph, litho. booklet stamp** *July 14, 2004,* Sacramento, CA	1.25
3438	33c	**California Statehood,** *Sept. 8,* Sacramento, CA *(119,729)*	1.25
3443a	33c	**Deep Sea Creatures,** *Oct. 2,* Monterey, CA	3.75
		#3439-3443, any single	1.25

First day cancellation was applied to 385,406 covers bearing one of more of Nos. 3439-3443, 3443a.

3444	33c	**Thomas Wolfe,** *Oct. 3,* Asheville, NC *(112,293)*	1.25
3445	33c	**White House,** *Oct. 18,* Washington, DC *(135,844)*	1.25
3446	33c	**Edward G. Robinson,** *Oct. 24,* Los Angeles, CA *(120,125)*	1.75
3447	(10c)	**New York Public Library Lion,** *Nov. 9,* New York, NY *(18,477)*	1.25
3448	(34c)	**Flag Over Farm, perf,** *Dec. 15,* Washington, DC	1.25
3449	(34c)	**Flag Over Farm, litho. self-adhesive,** *Dec. 15,* Washington, DC	1.25
3450	(34c)	**Flag Over Farm, photo. self-adhesive,** *Dec. 15,* Washington, DC	1.25
3451	(34c)	**Statue of Liberty, booklet stamp,** *Dec. 15,* Washington, DC	1.25
3452	(34c)	**Statue of Liberty perforated coil,** *Dec. 15,* Washington, DC	1.25

3453	(34c)	**Statue of Liberty self-adhesive coil,** *Dec. 15,* Washington, DC	1.25
3454-3457	(34c)	**Flowers, booklet stamps die cut 10¼x10¾,** *Dec. 15,* Washington, DC	3.25
		3454-3457, any single	1.25
3458-3461	(34c)	**Flowers, booklet stamps die cut 11½x11¾,** *Dec. 15,* Washington, DC	3.25
		3458-3461, any single	1.25
3462-3465	(34c)	**Flowers, coil stamps,** *Dec. 15,* Washington, DC	3.25
		3462-3465, any single	1.25

First day cancellation was applied to 178,635 covers bearing one or more of Nos. 3448-3465, 3450a, 3451a-3451d, 3457a-3457e, 3461a-3461c, 3465a.

2001

3466	34c	**Statue of Liberty coil (rounded corners),** *Jan. 7,* Washington, DC	1.25
3467	21c	**American Buffalo, perforated sheet stamp,** *Sept. 20,* Washington, DC	1.25
3468	21c	**American Buffalo, perforated sheet stamp,** *Feb. 22,* Wall, SD	1.25
3468A	23c	**George Washington, sheet stamp,** *Sept. 20,* Washington, DC	1.25
3469	34c	**Flag Over Farm, perforated sheet stamp,** *Feb. 7,* New York, NY	1.25
3470	34c	**Flag Over Farm, self-adhesive sheet stamp,** *Mar. 6,* Lincoln, NE	1.25
3471	55c	**Eagle,** *Feb. 22,* Wall, SD	1.50
3471A	57c	**Eagle,** *Sept. 20,* Washington, DC	1.50
3472	$3.50	**Capitol Dome,** *Jan. 29,* Washington, DC	6.25
3473	$12.25	**Washington Monument,** *Jan. 29,* Washington, DC	15.00
3475	21c	**American Buffalo coil stamp,** *Feb. 22,* Wall, SD	1.25
3475A	23c	**George Washington, coil stamp,** *Sept. 20,* Washington, DC	1.25
3476	34c	**Statue of Liberty, perforated coil stamp,** *Feb. 7,* New York, NY	1.25
3477	34c	**Statue of Liberty coil stamp (right angle corners),** *Feb. 7,* New York, NY	1.25
3478-3481	34c	**Flower coil stamps,** *Feb. 7,* New York, NY	3.25
		3478-3481, any single	1.25

Serpentine Die Cut 11¼

3482	20c	**George Washington booklet stamp,** *Feb. 22,* Wall, SD	1.25

Serpentine Die Cut 10½x11¼

3483	21c	**George Washington booklet stamp,** *Feb. 22,* Wall, SD	1.25
3484	21c	**American Buffalo, booklet stamp, serp. die cut 11¼,** *Sept. 20,* Washington, DC	1.25
3484A	21c	**American Buffalo, booklet stamp, serp. die cut 10½x11¼,** *Sept. 20,* Washington, DC	*1.25*
3485	34c	**Statue of Liberty booklet stamp,** *Feb. 7,* New York, NY	1.25
3487-3490	34c	**Flower booklet stamps,** *Feb. 7,* New York, NY	3.25
		3487-3490, any single	1.25
3491-3492	34c	**Apple & Orange booklet stamps,** *Feb. 7,* Lincoln, NE	2.25
		3491-3492, any single	1.25
3495	34c	**Flag Over Farm, booklet stamp,** *Dec. 17,* Washington, DC	1.25
3496	(34c)	**Love Letter,** *Jan. 19,* Tucson, AZ	1.25
3497	34c	**Love Letters,** *Feb. 14,* Lovejoy, GA	1.25

Serpentine Die Cut 11½x10¾

3498	34c	**Love Letters, die cut 11½x10¾,** *Feb. 14,* Lovejoy, GA	1.25
3499	55c	**Love Letter,** *Feb. 14,* Lovejoy, GA	1.50
3500	34c	**Chinese New Year,** *Jan. 20,* Oakland, CA	1.75
3501	34c	**Roy Wilkins,** *Jan. 24,* Minneapolis, MN	1.25
3502	34c	**American Illustrators pane of 20,** *Feb. 1,* New York, NY	9.50
		3502a-3502t, any single	1.25
3503	34c	**Diabetes Awareness,** *Mar. 16,* Boston, MA	1.25
3504	34c	**Nobel Prize Centenary,** *Mar. 22,* Washington, DC	1.50
3505		**Pan-American Inverts Pane,** *Mar. 29,* New York, NY	6.00
3505a	1c		1.25
3505b	2c		1.25
3505c	4c		1.25
3505d	80c		1.75
3506	34c	**Great Plains Prairie Pane of 10,** *Apr. 19,* Lincoln, NE	7.00
3507	34c	**Peanuts,** *May 17,* Santa Rosa, CA	1.50
3508	34c	**Honoring Veterans,** *May 23,* Washington, DC	2.00
		Any other city	1.25
3509	34c	**Frida Kahlo,** *June 21,* Phoenix, AZ	1.25
3519a	34c	**Legendary Playing Fields,** *June 27,* New York, NY, Boston, MA, Chicago, IL or Detroit, MI	6.50
		3510-3519, any single, New York, NY, Boston, MA, Chicago, IL or Detroit, MI	1.50

3520	(10c)	**Atlas Statue,** *June 29,* New York, NY	1.25
3521	34c	**Leonard Bernstein,** *July 10,* New York, NY	1.25
3522	(15c)	**Woody Wagon,** *Aug. 3,* Denver, CO	1.25
3523	34c	**Lucille Ball,** *Aug. 6,* Los Angeles, CA	2.00
3527a	34c	**Amish Quilts,** *Aug. 9,* Nappanee, IN	3.25
		3524-3527, any single	1.25
3531a	34c	**Carniverous Plants,** *Aug. 23,* Des Plaines, IL	3.25
		3528-3531, any single	1.25
3532	34c	**Eid** *Sept. 1,* Des Plaines, IL	1.25
3533	34c	**Enrico Fermi,** *Sept. 29,* Chicago, IL	1.25
3534a	34c	**That's All Folks!,** *Oct. 1,* Beverly Hills, CA	1.25

First day cancellation was applied to 151,009 covers bearing one or more of Nos. 3534-3535, 3534a-3534c, 3535a-3535c.

3536	34c	**Christmas, Madonna,** *Oct. 10,* Philadelphia, PA	1.25
3537-3540	34c	**Christmas, Santas, black inscriptions, large date** *Oct. 10,* Santa Claus, IN	3.25
		3537-3540, any single	1.25
		3537a-3540a, small date (from booklet)	3.25
		3537a-3540a, any single	1.25
3541-3544	34c	**Christmas, Santas, green and red inscriptions,** *Oct. 10,* Santa Claus, IN	3.25
		3541-3544, any single	1.25
3545	34c	**James Madison,** *Oct. 18,* New York, NY	1.25
3546	34c	**Thanksgiving,** *Oct. 19,* Dallas, TX	1.25
3547	34c	**Hanukkah,** *Oct. 21,* New York, NY	1.25
3548	34c	**Kwanzaa,** *Oct. 21,* New York, NY	1.25
3549	34c	**United We Stand,** *Oct. 24,* Washington, DC	1.50

First day cancellation was applied to 451,053 covers bearing one or more of Nos. 3549, 3550, 3550A.

3549B	34c	**United We Stand,** serpentine die cut 10½x10¾ booklet stamp *Oct. 24,* Washington, DC	

2002

3552-3555	34c	**Winter Sports,** *Jan. 8,* Park City, UT	3.25
		3552-3555, any single	1.25
3556	34c	**Mentoring a Child,** *Jan. 10,* Annapolis, MD	1.25
3557	34c	**Langston Hughes,** *Feb. 1,* New York, NY	1.25
3558	34c	**Happy Birthday,** *Feb. 8,* Riverside, CA	1.25
3559	34c	**Chinese New Year,** *Feb. 11,* New York, NY	1.50
3560	34c	**U.S. Military Academy Bicent.,** *Mar. 16,* West Point, NY	1.75
3610a	34c	**Greetings from America Pane,** *Apr. 4,* New York, NY	32.50
		3561-3610, Any single, New York, NY	1.25
		3610a, Any other city	32.50
		3561-3610, Any single, any other city	1.50
		3561-3610, any state capital	2.50
3611	34c	**Longleaf Pine Forest Pane of 10,** *Apr. 26,* Tallahassee, FL	7.00
		3611a-3611j, any single	1.25
3612	5c	**Toleware Coffeepot,** *May 31,* McLean, VA	1.25
3613	3c	**Litho. Star sheet stamp,** *June 7,* Washington, DC	1.25
		Any other city	1.25
3614	3c	**Photo. Star sheet stamp,** *June 7,* Washington, DC	1.25
		Any other city	1.25
3615	3c	**Star coil stamp,** *June 7,* Washington, DC	1.25
3616	23c	**George Washington,** water-activated gum sheet stamp, *June 7,* Washington, DC	1.00
3617	23c	**George Washington,** gray green coil stamp, *June 7,* Washington, DC	1.00
3618	23c	**George Washington,** booklet stamp, serp. die cut 11¼ on 3 sides, *June 7,* Washington, DC	1.00
3620	(37c)	**Flag,** water-activated gum sheet stamp, *June 7,* Washington, DC	1.25
		Any other city	1.25
3621	(37c)	**Flag,** self-adhesive sheet stamp, serp. die cut 11¼x11, *June 7,* Washington, DC	1.25
		Any other city	1.25
3622	(37c)	**Flag,** coil stamp, *June 7,* Washington, DC	1.25
		Any other city	1.25
3623	(37c)	**Flag,** booklet stamp, serp. die cut 11¼ on 2, 3 or 4 sides, *June 7,* Washington, DC	1.25
3624	(37c)	**Flag,** booklet stamp, serp. die cut 10½x10¾ on 2 or 3 sides, *June 7,* Washington, DC	1.25
		Any other city	1.25
3625	(37c)	**Flag,** booklet stamp, serp. die cut 8 on 2, 3 or 4 sides, *June 7,* Washington, DC	1.25
		Any other city	1.25

3626-3629	(37c)	**Antique Toys,** booklet stamps, *June 7,* Washington, DC	3.25
		Any other city	3.25
		3626-3629, any single	1.25
		3626-3629, any single, any other city	1.25
3629F	37c	**Flag,** perf. 11¼, *Nov. 24,* Washington, DC	1.25
3630	37c	**Flag,** self-adhesive sheet stamp, serp. die cut 11¼x11, *June 7,* Washington, DC	1.25
		Any other city	1.25
3631	37c	**Flag,** water-activated gum coil stamp, *June 7,* Washington, DC	1.25
3632	37c	**Flag,** self-adhesive coil stamp, serp. die cut 10 vert., *June 7,* Washington, DC	1.25
3632A	37c	**Flag coil, lacking star points at top** *Aug. 7, 2003* Columbus, OH	—
3633	37c	**Flag,** self-adhesive coil stamp, serp. die cut 8½ vert., *June 7,* Washington, DC	1.25
3634	37c	**Flag,** self-adhesive booklet stamps, serp. die cut 11 on 3 sides, *June 7,* Washington, DC	1.25
3635	37c	**Flag,** booklet stamp, serp. die cut 11¼ on 2, 3 or 4 sides, *June 7,* Washington, DC	1.25
3636	37c	**Flag,** booklet stamp, serp. die cut 10½x10¾ on 2 or 3 sides, *June 7,* Washington, DC	1.25
3637	37c	**Flag,** booklet stamp, serp. die cut 8 on 2, 3 or 4 sides, *Feb. 4, 2003* Washington, DC	1.25
3638-3641	37c	**Antique Toys coil stamps,** *July 26,* Rochester, NY	3.25
		3638-3641, any single	1.25
3642-3645	37c	**Antique Toys booklet stamps,** *July 26,* Rochester, NY	3.25
		3642-3645, any single	1.25
3642a-3645f	37c	**Antique Toys,** booklet stamps, serp. die cut 11x11¼ on 2 or 3 sides, *Sept. 3,* Washington, DC	3.25
		3642a-3645f, any single	1.25
3646	60c	**Coverlet Eagle,** *July 12,* Oak Brook, IL	1.50
3647	$3.85	**Jefferson Memorial,** *July 30,* Washington, DC	7.00
		Any other city	7.00
3648	$13.65	**Capitol Dome,** *July 30,* Washington, DC	25.00
		Any other city	25.00
3649	37c	**Masters of American Photography,** *June 13,* San Diego, CA	10.00
		3649a-3649t, any single	1.25
3650	37c	**John James Audubon,** *June 27,* Santa Clara, CA	1.25
3651	37c	**Harry Houdini,** *July 3,* New York, NY	1.50
3652	37c	**Andy Warhol,** *Aug. 9,* Pittsburgh, PA	1.25
3653-3656	37c	**Teddy Bears,** *Aug. 15,* Atlantic City, NJ	3.25
		3653-3656, any single	1.25
3657	37c	**Love,** *Aug. 16,* Atlantic City, NJ	1.25
3658	60c	**Love,** *Aug. 16,* Atlantic City, NJ	1.50
3659	37c	**Ogden Nash,** *Aug. 19,* Baltimore, MD	1.25
3660	37c	**Duke Kahanamoku,** *Aug. 24,* Honolulu, HI	1.25
3661-3664	37c	**American Bats,** *Sept. 13,* Austin, TX	3.25
		3661-3664, any single	1.25
3665-3668	37c	**Women in Journalism,** *Sept. 14,* Fort Worth, TX	3.25
		3665-3668, any single	1.25
3669	37c	**Irving Berlin,** *Sept. 15,* New York, NY	1.25
3670-3671	37c	**Neuter and Spay,** *Sept. 20,* Washington, DC	2.25
		Any other city	2.25
		3670-3671, either single, Washington, DC	1.25
		3670-3671, either single, any other city	1.25
3672	37c	**Hanukkah,** *Oct. 10,* Washington, DC	1.25
3673	37c	**Kwanzaa,** *Oct. 10,* Washington, DC	1.25
3674	37c	**Eid,** *Oct. 10,* Washington, DC	1.25
3675	37c	**Christmas Madonna,** design size 19x27mm,*Oct. 10,* Chicago, IL	1.25
3676-3679	37c	**Christmas Snowmen,** serp. die cut 11 (sheet stamps), *Oct. 28,* Houghton, MI	3.25
		3676-3679, any single	1.25
3680-3683	37c	**Christmas Snowmen,** serp. die cut 8½ vert. (coil stamps), *Oct. 28,* Houghton, MI	3.25
		3680-3683, any single	1.25
3684-3687	37c	**Christmas Snowmen,** serp. die cut 10¾x11 on 2 or 3 sides (large booklet stamps), *Oct. 28,* Houghton, MI	3.25
		3684-3687, any single	1.25
3688-3691	37c	**Christmas Snowmen,** serp. die cut 11 on 2 or 3 sides (small booklet stamps), *Oct. 28,* Houghton, MI	3.25
		3688-3691, any single	1.25

3692	37c **Cary Grant,** *Oct. 15,* Los Angeles, CA	1.75
3693	(5c) **Sea Coast,** *Oct. 21,* Washington, DC	1.25
3694	37c **Hawaiian Missionary Stamps sheet,** *Oct. 24,* New York, NY	4.00
	3694a-3694d, any single	1.25
3695	37c **Happy Birthday,** *Oct. 25,* New York, NY	1.25

2002

3745a	37c **Greetings From America,** *Oct. 25,* New York, NY	35.00
	3696-3745, any single	1.25
	3696-3745, any state capital	1.50

2003

3746	37c **Thurgood Marshall,** *Jan. 7,* Washington, DC	1.25
3747	37c **Chinese New Year,** *Jan. 15,* Chicago, IL	1.50
3748	37c **Zora Neale Hurston,** *Jan. 24,* Eatonville, FL	1.25

American Design Series 2003-08

3749	1c **Tiffany Lamp,** *Mar. 16, 2007,* New York, NY	2.00
3749A	1c **Tiffany Lamp,** *Mar. 7, 2008,* New York, NY	2.00
3750	2c **Navajo Necklace,** *Aug. 20, 2004,* Indianapolis, IN	1.25
3751	2c **Navajo Necklace,** photo., serpentine die cut 11¼x11½, *Dec. 8, 2005,* Washington, DC	2.00
	Any other city	2.00
3752	2c **Navajo Necklace,** litho., serpentine die cut 11¼x11, *Dec. 8, 2005,* Washington, DC	2.00
	Any other city	2.00
3753	2c **Navajo Necklace,** litho., serpentine die cut 11¼x10¾, microprinting at left, *May 12, 2007,* Washington, DC	2.00
3754	3c **Silver Coffeepot,** *Mar. 16, 2007,* New York, NY	2.00
3755	4c **Chippendale Chair,** *Mar. 5, 2004,* New York, NY	1.25
3756	5c **Toleware, serpentine die cut 11¼x11¾,** *June 25, 2004,* Santa Clara, CA	1.25
3757	10c **American Clock,** *Jan. 24, 2003,* Tucson, AZ	1.25
3758	1c **Tiffany Lamp Coil,** *Mar. 1, 2003,* Biloxi, MS	1.25
3758A	1c **Tiffany Lamp,** litho. coil stamp, *June 7, 2008,* McLean, VA	2.10
3759	3c **Silver Coffeepot Coil,** *Sept. 16, 2005,* Milwaukee, WI	2.00
3761	4c **Chippendale Chair coil,** *July 19, 2007,* Washington, DC	2.00
3762	10c **American Clock Coil,** *Aug. 4, 2006,* Independence, OH	2.00
3763	10c **American Clock coil,** litho., *July 15, 2008,* Washington, DC	2.00

American Culture Series

3766	$1 **Wisdom,** *Feb. 28,* Biloxi, MS	2.50
3769	(10c) **New York Public Library Lion,** perf. 10 vert., *Feb. 4,* Washington, DC	1.25
3771	80c **Special Olympics,** *Feb. 13,* Chicago, IL	1.75
3772	37c **American Filmmaking: Behind the Scenes Pane of 10,** *Feb. 25,* Beverly Hills, CA	7.25
	3772a-3772j, any single	1.25
3773	37c **Ohio Statehood Bicentennial,** *Mar. 1,* Chillicothe, OH	1.25
3774	37c **Pelican Island National Wildlife Refuge, Cent.,** *Mar. 14,* Sebastian, FL	1.25
3775	(5c) **Sea Coast,** perf. 9¾ vert. *Mar. 19,* Washington, DC	1.25
3776-3780	37c **Old Glory,** *Apr. 3,* New York, NY	4.00
	3776-3780, any single	1.25
3781	37c **Cesar E. Chavez,** *Apr. 23,* Los Angeles, CA	1.25
3782	37c **Louisiana Purchase, Bicent.,** *Apr. 30,* New Orleans, LA	1.25
3783	37c **First Flight,** *May 22,* Dayton, OH or Kill Devil Hills, NC	1.25
3784	37c **Purple Heart,** *May 30,* Mount Vernon, VA	1.50
3784A	37c **Purple Heart, serpentine die cut 10¾x10¼,** *Aug. 1,* Somerset, NJ	—
3786	37c **Audrey Hepburn,** *June 11,* Los Angeles, CA	1.75
3787-3791	37c **Southeastern Lighthouses,** *June 13,* Tybee Island, GA	4.00
	3787, 3788a, 3789-3791, Tybee Island, GA	4.00
	3787-3791, 3788a, any single	1.50
3792-3801	(25c) **Eagle coils,** *June 26,* Santa Clara, CA	6.00
	3792-3801, any single	1.25
3792a-3801b	(25c) **Eagle coil dated "2005",** *Aug. 5,* Grand Rapids, MI	6.00
	3792a-3801b, any single	1.25
3802	37c **Arctic Tundra,** *July 2,* Fairbanks, AK	7.50
	3802a-3802j, any single	1.25
3803	37c **Korean War Veterans Memorial,** *July 27,* Washington, DC	2.00

3804-3807	37c **Mary Cassatt booklet stamps,** *Aug. 7,* Columbus, OH	3.25
	3804-3807, any single	1.25
3808-3811	37c **Early Football Heroes,** *Aug. 8,* South Bend, IN	3.25
	3808-3811, any single	1.25
3812	37c **Roy Acuff,** *Sept. 13,* Nashville, TN	1.25
3813	37c **District of Columbia,** *Sept. 23,* Washington, DC	1.25
3814-3818	37c **Reptiles and Amphibians,** *Oct. 7,* San Diego, CA	4.00
	3814-3818, any single, San Diego, CA	1.25
3820	37c **Christmas Madonna,** design size 19½x28mm, *Oct. 23,* New York, NY	1.25
3821-3824	37c **Christmas Music Makers (sheet stamps),** serp. die cut 11x11¼, *Oct. 23,* New York, NY	3.25
	3821-3824, any single	1.25
3825-3828	37c **Christmas Music Makers (vending machine booklet stamps),** serp. die cut 11¾x11 on 3 sides, *Oct. 23,* New York, NY	3.25
	3825-3828, any single	1.25
3829	37c **Snowy Egret coil,** *Oct. 24,* New York, NY	1.25

2004

3830	37c **Snowy Egret booklet stamp,** *Jan. 30,* Norfolk, VA	1.25
3831	37c **Pacific Coral Reef,** *Jan. 2,* Honolulu, HI	7.50
	3831a-3831j, any single	1.25
3832	37c **Chinese New Year,** *Jan. 13,* San Francisco, CA	1.50
3833	37c **Love Candy Hearts,** *Jan. 14,* Revere, MA	1.25
3834	37c **Paul Robeson,** *Jan. 20,* Princeton, NJ	1.25
3835	37c **Theodor Seuss Geisel (Dr. Seuss),** *Mar. 2,* La Jolla, CA	1.25
3836	37c **Flowers,** *Mar. 4,* New York, NY	1.25
3837	60c **Flowers,** *Mar. 4,* New York, NY	1.50
3838	37c **U.S. Air Force Academy,** *Apr. 1,* Colorado Springs, CO	1.50
3839	37c **Henry Mancini,** *Apr. 13,* Los Angeles, CA	1.25
3840-3843	37c **American Choreographers,** *May 4,* Newark, NJ	3.25
	3840-3843, any single	1.25
3844-3853	(25c) **Eagle coils,** perf. 9¾ vert. *May 12,* Washington, DC	6.00
	3844-3853, any single	1.25
3854	37c **Lewis & Clark,** *May 14,* Astoria, OR	1.75
	Atchison, KS	1.75
	Great Falls, MT	1.75
	Hartford, IL	1.75
	Ilwaco, WA	1.75
	Orofino, ID	1.75
	Omaha, NE	1.75
	Pierre, SD	1.75
	Sioux City, IA	1.75
	St. Charles, MO	1.75
	Washburn, ND	1.75
3855-3856	37c **Lewis & Clark booklet stamps,** *May 14,* Astoria, OR	2.75
	Atchison, KS	2.75
	Great Falls, MT	2.75
	Hartford, IL	2.75
	Ilwaco, WA	2.75
	Orofino, ID	2.75
	Omaha, NE	2.75
	Pierre, SD	2.75
	Sioux City, IA	2.75
	St. Charles, MO	2.75
	Washburn, ND	2.75
	3855-3856, any single, any of the aforementioned 11 cities	1.40
3857-3861	37c **Isamu Noguchi,** *May 18,* Long Island City, NY	4.00
	3857-3861, any single	1.25
3862	37c **National World War II Memorial,** *May 29,* Washington, DC	1.75
	Any other city	1.75
3863	37c **Summer Olympics,** *June 9,* Philadelphia, PA	1.25
3864	(5c) **Sea Coast coil with black 2004 date,** *June 11,* Washington, DC	1.25
3865-3868	37c **Disney Characters,** *June 23,* Anaheim, CA	3.25
	3865-3868, any single	1.25
3869	37c **U.S.S. Constellation,** *June 30,* Baltimore, MD	1.25
3870	37c **R. Buckminster Fuller,** *July 12,* Stanford, CA	1.25
3871	37c **James Baldwin,** *July 23,* New York, NY	1.25
3872	37c **Martin Johnson Heade,** *Aug. 12,* Sacramento, CA	1.25
3873	37c **Art of the American Indian pane of 10,** *Aug. 21,* Santa Fe, NM	7.00
	3873a-3873j, any single, Santa Fe, NM	1.25
3876	37c **John Wayne,** *Sept. 9,* Los Angeles, CA	2.00
3877	37c **Sickle Cell Disease,** *Sept. 29,* Atlanta, GA	1.25
3878	37c **Cloudscapes,** *Oct. 4,* Milton, MA	9.00
	3878a-3878o any single	1.25
3879	37c **Christmas Madonna,** *Oct. 14,* New York, NY	1.25
3880	37c **Hanukkah,** *Oct. 15,* New York, NY	1.25
3881	37c **Kwanzaa,** *Oct. 16,* Chicago, IL	1.25
3882	37c **Moss Hart,** *Oct. 25,* New York, NY	1.25

3883-3886	37c **Christmas Santa Ornaments,** serpentine die cut 11½x11, *Nov. 16,* New York, NY	3.25
	3883-3886, any single	1.25
3887-3890	37c **Christmas Santa Ornaments,** serpentine die cut 10¼x10¾ on 2 or 3 sides, *Nov. 16,* New York, NY	3.25
	3887-3890, any single	1.25
3891-3894	37c **Christmas Santa Ornaments,** serpentine die cut 8 on 2, 3 or 4 sides, *Nov. 16,* New York, NY	3.25
	3891-3894, any single	1.25

2005

3895	37c **Chinese New Year double-sided pane,** *Jan. 6,* Honolulu, HI	20.00
	3895a-3895l, any single	1.25
3896	37c **Marian Anderson,** *Jan. 27,* Washington, DC	1.25
3897	37c **Ronald Reagan,** *Feb. 9,* Simi Valley, CA	2.00
	Any other city	1.50
3898	37c **Love,** *Feb. 18,* Atlanta, GA	1.25
3899	37c **Northeast Deciduous Forest,** *Mar. 3,* New York, NY	7.50
	3899a-3899j, any single	1.25
3900-3903	37c **Spring Flowers,** *Mar. 15,* Chicago, IL	3.25
	3900-3903, any single	1.25
3904	37c **Robert Penn Warren,** *Apr. 22,* Guthrie, KY	1.25
3905	37c **Yip Harburg,** *Apr. 28,* New York, NY	1.25
3906-3909	37c **American Scientists,** *May 4,* New Haven, CT	3.25
	3906-3909, any single	1.25
3910	37c **Modern American Architecture,** *May 19,* Las Vegas NV	9.00
	Any other city	9.00
	3910a-3910l, any single, Las Vegas, NV	1.25
	3910a-3910l, any single, any other city	1.25
3911	37c **Henry Fonda,** *May 20,* Los Angeles, CA	1.25
3912-3915	37c **Disney Characters,** *June 30,* Anaheim, CA	3.25
	3912-3915, any single	1.25
3916-3925	37c **Advances in Aviation,** *July 29,* Oshkosh, WI	7.50
	July 29, Vienna, VA	7.50
	3916-3925, any single, Oshkosh, WI	1.50
	3916-3925, any single, Vienna, VA	1.50
3926-3929	37c **Rio Grande Blankets,** *July 30,* Santa Fe, NM	3.25
	3926-3929, any single	1.25
3930	37c **Presidential Libraries Act, 50th Anniv.,** *Aug. 4,* Grand Rapids, MI	1.25
	Abilene, KS	1.50
	Ann Arbor, MI	1.25
	Atlanta, GA	1.25
	Austin, TX	1.25
	Boston, MA	1.50
	College Station, TX	1.25
	Hyde Park, NY	1.50
	Independence, MO	1.50
	Little Rock, AR	1.25
	Simi Valley, CA	1.50
	West Branch, IA	1.25
	Yorba Linda, CA	1.25
3931-3935	37c **Sporty Cars of the 1950s,** *Aug. 20,* Detroit, MI	5.00
	3931-3935, any single	2.00
3936	37c **Arthur Ashe,** *Aug. 27,* Flushing, NY	2.00
3937	37c **To Form a More Perfect Union pane of 10,** *Aug. 30,* Washington, DC	8.75
	Greensboro, NC	8.75
	Jackson, MS	8.75
	Little Rock, AR	8.75
	Memphis, TN	8.75
	Montgomery, AL	8.75
	Selma, AL	8.75
	Topeka, KS	8.75
	Any other city	8.75
	3937a-3937j, any single, Washington, DC	2.00
	3937a-3937j, any single, Greensboro, NC	2.00
	3937a-3937j, any single, Jackson, MS	2.00
	3937a-3937j, any single, Little Rock, AR	2.00
	3937a-3937j, any single, Memphis, TN	2.00
	3937a-3937j, any single, Montgomery, AL	2.00
	3937a-3937j, any single, Selma, AL	2.00
	3937a-3937j, any single, Topeka, KS	2.00
	3937a-3937j, any single, any other city	2.00
3938	37c **Child Health,** *Sept. 7,* Philadelphia, PA	2.00
	Any other city	2.00
3939-3942	37c **Let's Dance,** *Sept. 17,* New York, NY	4.25
	Miami, FL	4.25
	3939-3942, any single, New York, NY	2.00
	3939-3942, any single, Miami, FL	2.00

3943	37c **Greta Garbo**, *Sept. 23*, New York, NY	2.00
3944	37c **Jim Henson and the Muppets**, *Sept. 28*, North Hollywood, CA	9.25
	3944a-3944k, any single	2.00
3945-3948	37c **Constellations**, *Oct. 3*, Bloomfield Hills, MI	4.25
	3945-3948, any single	2.00
3949-3952	37c **Christmas Cookies**, serpentine die cut 10¾x11, *Oct. 20*, New York, NY	4.25
	Minneapolis, MN	4.25
	3949-3952, any single, New York, NY	2.00
	3949-3952, any single, Minneapolis, MN	2.00
3953-3956	37c **Christmas Cookies**, convertible booklet stamps, serpentine die cut 10¾x11 on 2 or 3 sides, *Oct. 20*, New York, NY	4.25
	Minneapolis, MN	4.25
	3949-3952, any single, New York, NY	2.00
	3949-3952, any single, Minneapolis, MN	2.00
3957-3960	37c **Christmas Cookies**, vending machine booklet stamps, serpentine die cut 10½x10¾, *Oct. 20*, New York, NY	4.25
	Minneapolis, MN	4.25
	3949-3952, any single, New York, NY	2.00
	3949-3952, any single, Minneapolis, MN	2.00
3961-3964	37c **Distinguished Marines**, *Nov. 10*, Washington, DC	4.25
	Oceanside, CA	4.25
	Any other city	4.25
	3961-3964, any single, Washington, DC	2.00
	3961-3964, any single, Oceanside, CA	2.00
	3961-3964, any single, any other city	2.00
3965	(39c) **Flag and Statue of Liberty**, perf. 11¼, *Dec. 8*, Washington, DC	2.00
	Any other city	2.00
3966	(39c) **Flag and Statue of Liberty**, self-adhesive, serpentine die cut 11¼x11, *Dec. 8*, Washington, DC	2.00
	Any other city	2.00
3967	(39c) **Flag and Statue of Liberty**, coil stamp, perf. 9¾ vert., *Dec. 8*, Washington, DC	2.00
	Any other city	2.00
3968	(39c) **Flag and Statue of Liberty**, self-adhesive coil stamp, photo., serpentine die cut 8½ vert., *Dec. 8*, Washington, DC	2.00
	Any other city	2.00
3969	(39c) **Flag and Statue of Liberty**, self-adhesive coil stamp, photo., serpentine die cut 10¼ vert., *Dec. 8*, Washington, DC	2.00
	Any other city	2.00
3970	(39c) **Flag and Statue of Liberty**, self-adhesive coil stamp, litho., serpentine die cut 9½ vert., *Dec. 8*, Washington, DC	2.00
3972	(39c) **Flag and Statue of Liberty**, self-adhesive booklet stamp with bright blue spot over date, photo., serpentine die cut 11¼x10¾ on 2 or 3 sides, *Dec. 8*, Washington, DC	2.00
	Any other city	2.00
3973	(39c) **Flag and Statue of Liberty**, self-adhesive booklet stamp, serpentine die cut 10¼x10¾, *Dec. 8*, Washington, DC	2.00
	Any other city	2.00

Although No. 3973 has an issue date of Dec. 8, it was not known to have been available until January 2006.

3974	(39c) **Flag and Statue of Liberty**, self-adhesive booklet stamp with dark blue spot over date, litho., serpentine die cut 11¼x11 on 2 or 3 sides, *Dec. 8*, Washington, DC	2.00
3975	(39c) **Flag and Statue of Liberty**, self-adhesive booklet stamp, photo., serpentine die cut 8 on 2, 3 or 4 sides, *Dec. 8*, Washington, DC	2.00
	Any other city	2.00

2006

3976	(39c) **Birds**, self-adhesive booklet stamp, *Jan. 3*, Washington, DC	2.00
	Any other city	2.00
3978	39c **Flag and Statue of Liberty**, self-adhesive, *Apr. 8*, Washington, DC	2.00
	Any other city	2.00
3979	39c **Flag and Statue of Liberty**, coil stamp, perf. 10 vert., *Mar. 8*, Washington, DC	2.00
	Any other city	2.00
3980	39c **Flag and Statue of Liberty**, self-adhesive coil stamp, serpentine die cut 11 vert. with rounded corners, *Jan. 9*, Washington, DC	2.00
	Any other city	2.00
3981	39c **Flag and Statue of Liberty**, self-adhesive coil stamp, serpentine die cut 9½ vert., *Apr. 8*, Washington, DC	2.00
	Any other city	2.00

3985b	39c **Flag and Statue of Liberty**, photo., serpentine die cut 11.1 on 2 or 3 sides, *Nov. 8*, Washington, DC	2.00
3987-3994	39c **Children's Book Animals**, *Jan. 10*, Findlay, OH	7.50
	3987-3994, any single	2.00
3999	39c **2006 Winter Olympics**, *Jan. 11*, Colorado Springs, CO	2.00
3996	39c **Hattie McDaniel**, *Jan. 25*, Beverly Hills, CA	2.00
3997	39c **Chinese New Year pane**, *Jan. 29*, Washington, DC	10.50
	3997a-3997l, any single	2.00
3998	39c **Wedding Dove**, *Mar. 1*, New York, NY	2.00
3999	63c **Wedding Dove**, *Mar. 1*, New York, NY	2.50
4000	24c **Common Buckeye Butterfly**, perf. 11¼, *Mar. 8*, Washington, DC	2.00
	Any other city	2.00
4001	24c **Common Buckeye Butterfly**, self-adhesive, serpentine die cut 11, *Mar. 8*, Washington, DC	2.00
	Any other city	2.00
4001a	24c **Common Buckeye Butterfly**, self-adhesive booklet pane stamp, serpentine die cut 10¾x11¼, *Mar. 8*, Washington, DC	2.00
	Any other city	2.00
4002	24c **Common Buckeye Butterfly**, self-adhesive coil stamp, serpentine die cut 8½ horiz., *Mar. 8*, Washington, DC	2.00
	Any other city	2.00
4003-4007	39c **Crops of the Americas**, self-adhesive coil stamps, *Mar. 16*, New York, NY	5.25
	4003-4007, any single	2.00
4008-4012	39c **Crops of the Americas**, self-adhesive booklet stamps, serpentine die cut 10¾x10½ on 2 or 3 sides, *Mar. 16*, New York, NY	5.25
	4008-4012, any single	2.00
4013-4017	39c **Crops of the Americas**, self-adhesive booklet stamps, serpentine die cut 10¾x11¼ on 2 or 3 sides, *Mar. 16*, New York, NY	5.25
	4013-4017, any single	2.00
4018	$4.05 **X-Plane**, *Mar. 17*, New York, NY	8.00
	Any other city	8.00
4019	$14.40 **X-Plane**, *Mar. 17*, New York, NY	27.50
	Any other city	27.50
4020	39c **Sugar Ray Robinson**, *Apr. 7*, New York, NY	2.00
4021-4024	39c **Benjamin Franklin**, *Apr. 7*, Philadelphia, PA	4.50
	4021-4024, any single	2.00
4025-4028	39c **Disney Characters**, *Apr. 21*, Orlando, FL	4.50
	4025-4028, any single	2.00
4029	39c **Birds**, self-adhesive booklet stamp, *May 1*, Washington, DC	2.00
4030	39c **Katherine Anne Porter**, *May 15*, Kyle, TX	2.00
4031	39c **Amber Alert**, *May 25*, Arlington, TX	2.00
	Washington, DC	2.00
4032	39c **Purple Heart**, *May 26*, Washington, DC	2.00
4072a	39c **Wonders of America**, *May 27*, Washington, DC	32.50
	4033-4072, any single, Washington, DC	2.00
	4072a, any other city	32.50
	4033-4072, any single, any other city	2.75
4073	39c **Samuel de Champlain**, self-adhesive stamp, *May 28*, Washington, DC	2.00
	Ticonderoga, NY	2.00
	Annapolis Royal, Nova Scotia, Canada	2.00
4074	**Samuel de Champlain**, souvenir sheet, *May 28*, Washington, DC	4.75
	Ticonderoga, NY	4.75
	Annapolis Royal, Nova Scotia, Canada	4.75
4075	**Washington 2006 World Philatelic Exhibition**, souvenir sheet, *May 29*, Washington, DC	16.00
4075a	$1	3.25
4075b	$2	5.25
4075c	$5	10.00
4076	39c **Distinguished American Diplomats**, souvenir sheet, *May 30*, Washington, DC	6.00
	4076a-4076f, any single	2.00
4077	39c **Judy Garland**, *June 10*, New York, NY	2.25
4078	39c **Ronald Reagan**, *June 14*, Simi Valley, CA	2.00
4079	39c **Happy Birthday**, *June 23*, Santa Clara, CA	2.00
4080-4083	39c **Baseball Sluggers**, *July 15*, Bronx, NY	4.50
	4080-4083, any single	2.00
4084	39c **DC Comics Superheroes**, *July 20*, San Diego, CA	16.00
	4084a-4084t, any single	2.00
4085-4088	39c **Motorcycles**, *Aug. 7*, Sturgis, SD	4.50
	4085-4088, any single, Sturgis, SD	2.00
4089-4098	39c **Quilts of Gee's Bend**, *Aug. 24*, Chicago, IL	8.00
	4089-4098, any single, Chicago, IL	2.00
4099	39c **Southern Florida Wetland**, *Oct. 4*, Naples, FL	9.00

	4099a-4099j, any single	2.00
4100	39c **Christmas Madonna**, *Oct. 17*, Denver, CO	2.00
4101-4104	39c **Christmas Snowflakes**, denominations higher than year date, serpentine die cut 11¼x11, *Oct. 5*, New York, NY	4.50
	4101-4104, any single	2.00
4105-4108	39c **Christmas Snowflakes**, denominations even with year date, serpentine die cut 11¼x11½ on 2 or 3 sides, *Oct. 5*, New York, NY	4.50
	4105-4108, any single	2.00
4109-4112	39c **Christmas Snowflakes**, denominations even with year date, serpentine die cut 11¼x11 on 2 or 3 sides, *Oct. 5*, New York, NY	4.50
	4109-4112, any single	2.00
4113-4116	39c **Christmas Snowflakes**, denominations even with year date, serpentine die cut 8 on 2, 3 or 4 sides, *Oct. 5*, New York, NY	4.50
	4113-4116, any single	2.00
4117	39c **Eid**, *Oct. 6*, New York, NY	2.00
4118	39c **Hanukkah**, *Oct. 6*, New York, NY	2.00
4119	39c **Kwanzaa**, *Oct. 6*, New York, NY	2.00

2007-09

4120	39c **Ella Fitzgerald**, *Jan. 10*, New York, NY	2.00
4121	39c **Oklahoma Statehood**, *Jan. 11*, Oklahoma City, OK	2.00
4122	39c **Love**, self-adhesive booklet stamp, *Jan. 13*, Hershey, PA	2.00
4123	84c **International Polar Year**, *Feb. 21*, Fairbanks, AK	4.75
	4123a-4123b, either single	3.00
4124	39c **Henry Wadsworth Longfellow**, *Mar. 15*, New York, NY	2.00
4125	(41c) **Liberty Bell**, self-adhesive booklet stamp, large microprinting, 16mm bell, serpentine die cut 11¼x10¾, *Apr. 12*, Philadelphia, PA	2.10
4125b	(42c) **Forever**, dated "2008," *Aug. 22, 2008*, Falls Church, VA	2.10
4126	(41c) **Liberty Bell**, self-adhesive booklet stamp, small microprinting, 16mm bell, serpentine die cut 11¼x10¾, *Apr. 12*, Philadelphia, PA	2.10
4126b	(42c) **Forever**, dated "2008," *Aug. 22, 2008*, Falls Church, VA	2.10
4127	(41c) **Liberty Bell**, self-adhesive booklet stamp, medium microprinting, 15mm bell, serpentine die cut 11¼x10¾, *Apr. 12*, Philadelphia, PA	2.10
4127d	(42c) **Forever**, dated "2008," *May 12, 2008*, Washington, DC	2.10
4127f	(42c) **Forever**, small "2008" date, *Oct. 25, 2008*, New York, NY	2.10
4127i	(44c) **Forever**, dated "2009" in copper, *May 15, 2009*, Washington, DC	2.10
4128	(41c) **Liberty Bell**, self-adhesive booklet stamp, large microprinting, 16mm bell, serpentine die cut 8, *Apr. 12*, Philadelphia, PA	2.10
4128b	(42c) **Forever**, dated "2009," *Feb. 24*, Washington, DC	2.10
4129	(41c) **Flag**, perf. 11¼, *Apr. 12*, Washington, DC	2.10
4130	(41c) **Flag**, self-adhesive, serpentine die cut 11¼x10¾, *Apr. 12*, Washington, DC	2.10
4131	(41c) **Flag**, coil stamp, perf. 9¾ vert., *Apr. 12*, Washington, DC	2.10
4132	(41c) **Flag**, self-adhesive coil stamp, serpentine die cut 9½ vert., *Apr. 12*, Washington, DC	2.10
4133	(41c) **Flag**, self-adhesive coil stamp, serpentine die cut 11 vert., perpendicular corners, *Apr. 12*, Washington, DC	2.10
4134	(41c) **Flag**, self-adhesive coil stamp, serpentine die cut 8½ vert., *Apr. 12*, Washington, DC	2.10
4135	(41c) **Flag**, self-adhesive coil stamp, serpentine die cut 11 vert., rounded corners, *Apr. 12*, Washington, DC	2.10
4136	41c **Settlement of Jamestown**, *May 11*, Jamestown, VA	2.10
4137	26c **Florida Panther**, perf. 11¼x11 *May 12*, Washington, DC	2.10
4138	17c **Bighorn Sheep**, self-adhesive, serpentine die cut 11, *May 14*, Washington, DC	2.10
4139	26c **Florida Panther**, self-adhesive, serpentine die cut 11¼x11, *May 12*, Washington, DC	2.10
4140	17c **Bighorn Sheep**, self-adhesive coil, serpentine die cut 11 vert., *May 21*, Washington, DC	2.10
4141	26c **Florida Panther**, self-adhesive coil, serpentine die cut 11 vert., *May 12*, Washington, DC	2.10
4142	26c **Florida Panther**, self-adhesive booklet stamp, serpentine die cut 11¼x11 on 3 sides, *May 12*, Washington, DC	2.10
4143	39c **Star Wars**, *May 25*, Los Angeles, CA	12.50
	4143a-4143o, any single	2.10

4144	$4.60 **Air Force One,** *June 13,* Washington, DC	9.25	
4145	$16.25 **Marine One,** *June 13,* Washington, DC	32.50	
4146-4150	41c **Pacific Lighthouses,** *June 21,* Westport, WA	5.50	
	4146-4150, any single	2.10	
4151	41c **Wedding Heart,** *June 27,* Washington, DC	2.10	
4152	58c **Wedding Heart,** *June 27,* Washington, DC	2.40	
4153-4156	41c **Pollination,** type I, *June 29,* Washington, DC	4.50	
	4153-4156, type I, any single	2.10	
	4153a-4156a, type II	4.50	
	4153a-4156a, type II, any single	2.10	
4157	(10c) **Patriotic Banner coil,** serpentine die cut 11 vert., *July 4,* Washington, DC	2.00	
4158	(10c) **Patriotic Banner coil,** serpentine die cut 11 ½ vert., *July 4,* Washington, DC	2.00	
4159	41c **Marvel Comics Superheroes,** *July 26,* San Diego, CA	17.00	
	4159a-4159t, any single	2.10	
4160-4163	41c **Vintage Mahogany Speedboats,** *Aug. 4,* Clayton, NY	4.50	
	4160-4163, any single	2.10	
4164	41c **Purple Heart,** *Aug. 7,* Washington, DC	2.10	
4165	41c **Louis Comfort Tiffany,** *Aug. 9,* Portland, OR	2.10	
4166-4175	41c **Flowers,** self-adhesive stamps, *Aug. 10,* Portland, OR	8.25	
	4166-4175, any single	2.10	
4176-4185	41c **Flowers,** self-adhesive booklet stamps, *Aug. 10,* Portland, OR	8.25	
	4176-4185, any single	2.10	
4186	41c **Flag,** self-adhesive coil stamp with microprinting on right side of flagpole, serpentine die cut 9 ½ vert., *Aug. 15,* Washington, DC	2.10	
4187	41c **Flag,** self-adhesive coil stamp with microprinting on left side of flagpole, serpentine die cut 9 ½ vert., *Aug. 15,* Washington, DC	2.10	
4188	41c **Flag,** self-adhesive coil stamp with perpendicular corners, serpentine die cut 8 ½ vert., *Aug. 15,* Washington, DC	2.10	
4189	41c **Flag,** self-adhesive coil stamp with rounded corners, serpentine die cut 11 vert., *Aug. 15,* Washington, DC	2.10	
4190	41c **Flag,** self-adhesive booklet stamp with microprinting on right side of flagpole, *Aug. 15,* Washington, DC	2.10	
4191	41c **Flag,** self-adhesive booklet stamp with microprinting on left side of flagpole, *Aug. 15,* Washington, DC	2.10	
4192-4195	41c **Disney Characters,** *Aug. 16,* Orlando, FL	4.50	
	4192-4195, any single	2.10	
4196	41c **Celebrate,** *Aug. 17,* Stamford, CT	2.10	
4197	41c **James Stewart,** *Aug. 17,* Universal City, CA	2.10	
4198	41c **Alpine Tundra,** *Aug. 28,* Estes Park, CO	8.25	
	4198a-4198j, any single	2.10	
4199	41c **Gerald R. Ford,** *Aug. 31,* Grand Rapids, MI	2.10	
	Rancho Mirage, CA	2.10	
4200	41c **Jury Duty,** *Sept. 12,* New York, NY	2.10	
4201	41c **Mendez v. Westminster,** *Sept. 14,* Santa Ana, CA	2.10	
4202	41c **Eid,** *Sept. 28,* Washington, DC	2.10	
4203-4204	41c **Auroras,** *Oct. 1,* Washington, DC	3.00	
	4203-4204, any single	2.10	
4205	41c **Yoda,** *Oct. 25,* New York, NY	2.10	
4206	41c **Christmas Madonna,** *Oct. 25,* New York, NY	2.10	
4207-4210	41c **Christmas Knits,** serpentine die cut 10 ¾, *Oct. 25,* New York, NY	4.50	
	4207-4210, any single	2.10	
4211-4214	41c **Christmas Knits,** serpentine die cut 11 ¼x11 on 2 or 3 sides, *Oct. 25,* New York, NY	4.50	
	4211-4214, any single	2.10	
4215-4218	41c **Christmas Knits,** serpentine die cut 8 on 2, 3 or 4 sides, *Oct. 25,* New York, NY	4.50	
	4215-4218, any single	2.10	
4219	41c **Hanukkah,** *Oct. 26,* New York, NY	2.10	
4220	41c **Kwanzaa,** *Oct. 26,* New York, NY	2.10	

2008

4221	41c **Chinese New Year,** *Jan. 9,* San Francisco, CA	2.10	
4222	41c **Charles W. Chesnutt,** *Jan. 31,* Cleveland, OH	2.10	
4223	41c **Marjorie Kinnan Rawlings,** *Feb. 21,* Hawthorne, FL	2.10	
4224-4227	41c **American Scientists,** *Mar. 6,* New York, NY	4.50	
	4224-4227, any single	2.10	
4228-4231	42c **Flags,** coil stamps, perf. 10 vert., *Apr. 18,* Washington, DC	4.75	
	4228-4231, any single	2.10	
4232-4235	42c **Flags,** self-adhesive coil stamps, serpentine die cut 9 ½ vert., *Apr. 18,* Washington, DC	4.75	

	4232-4235, any single	2.10	
4236-4239	42c **Flags,** self-adhesive coil stamps, serpentine die cut 11 vert. with perpendicular corners, *Apr. 18,* Washington, DC	4.75	
	4236-4239, any single	2.10	
4240-4243	42c **Flags,** self-adhesive coil stamps, serpentine die cut 8 ½ vert., *Apr. 18,* Washington, DC	4.75	
	4240-4243, any single	2.10	
4244-4247	42c **Flags,** self-adhesive coil stamps, serpentine die cut 11 vert. with rounded corners, *Apr. 18,* Washington, DC	4.75	
	4244-42471, any single	2.10	
4248-4252	42c **American Journalists,** *Apr. 22,* Washington, DC	5.50	
	4248-4252, any single	2.10	
4253-4257	27c **Tropical Fruit,** serpentine die cut 11 ¼x10 ¾, *Apr. 25,* Burlingame, CA	4.00	
	4253-4257, any single	1.75	
4258-4262	27c **Tropical Fruit,** self-adhesive coil stamps, serpentine die cut 8 ½ vert., *Apr. 25,* Burlingame, CA	4.00	
	4258-4262, any single	1.75	
4263	42c **Purple Heart,** perf. 11 ¼, *Apr. 30,* Washington, DC	2.10	
4264	42c **Purple Heart,** self-adhesive, serpentine die cut 11 ¼x10 ¾, *Apr. 30,* Washington, DC	2.10	
4265	42c **Frank Sinatra,** *May 13,* New York, NY	2.25	
	Las Vegas, NV	2.10	
4266	42c **Minnesota Statehood, 150th Anniv.,** *May 17,* St. Paul, MN	2.10	
4267	62c **Dragonfly,** *May 19,* Washington, DC	2.50	
4268	$4.80 **Mount Rushmore,** *June 6,* McLean, VA	9.75	
4269	$16.50 **Hoover Dam,** *June 20,* Washington, DC	33.00	
4270	42c **Love,** *June 10,* Washington, DC	2.10	
4271	42c **Wedding Heart,** *June 10,* Washington, DC	2.10	
4272	59c **Wedding Heart,** *June 10,* Washington, DC	2.40	
4273-4282	42c **Flags of Our Nation,** *June 14,* Washington, DC	8.50	
	4273-4282, any single	2.10	
4283-4292	42c **Flags of Our Nation,** *Sept. 2,* Washington, DC	8.50	
	4283-4292, any single	2.10	
4333	42c **Charles and Ray Eames,** *June 17,* Santa Monica, CA	13.50	
	4333a-4333p, any single	2.10	
4334	42c **Summer Olympics,** *June 19,* Philadelphia, PA	2.10	
4335	42c **Celebrate,** *July 10,* Washington, DC	2.10	
4336-4340	42c **Vintage Black Cinema,** *July 16,* Newark, NJ	5.50	
	4336-4340, any single	2.10	
4341	42c **Take Me Out to the Ballgame, Cent.,** *July 16,* Washington, DC	2.10	
4342-4345	42c **Disney Characters,** *Aug. 7,* Anaheim, CA	4.75	
	4342-4345, any single	2.10	
4346	42c **Albert Bierstadt,** *Aug. 14,* Hartford, CT	2.10	
4347	42c **Sunflower,** *Aug. 15,* Hartford, CT	2.10	
4348	(5c) **Sea Coast coil with 2008 date,** litho., *Sept. 5,* Washington, DC	2.10	
4349	42c **Latin Jazz,** *Sept. 8,* Washington, DC	2.10	
4350	42c **Bette Davis,** *Sept. 18,* Boston, MA	2.10	
4351	42c **Eid,** *Sept. 23,* Washington, DC	2.10	
4352	42c **Great Lakes Dunes,** *Oct. 2,* Empire, MI	8.50	
	4352a-4352j, any single	2.10	
4353-4357	42c **Automobiles of the 1950s,** *Oct. 3,* Carlisle, PA	5.50	
	4353-4357, any single	2.10	
4358	42c **Alzheimer's Disease Awareness,** *Oct. 17,* Morgantown, WV	2.10	
4359	42c **Christmas Madonna,** *Oct. 23,* New York, NY	2.10	
4360-4363	42c **Christmas Nutcrackers,** serpentine die cut 10 ¾x11 on 2 or 3 sides, *Oct. 23,* New York, NY	4.75	
	4360-4363, any single	2.10	
4364-4367	42c **Christmas Nutcrackers,** serpentine die cut 11 ¼x11 on 2 or 3 sides, *Oct. 23,* New York, NY	4.75	
	4364-4367, any single	2.10	
4368-4371	42c **Christmas Nutcrackers,** serpentine die cut 8 on 2, 3 or 4 sides, *Oct. 23,* New York, NY	4.75	
	4368-4371, any single	2.10	
4372	42c **Hanukkah,** *Oct. 24,* New York, NY	2.10	
4373	42c **Kwanzaa,** *Oct. 24,* New York, NY	2.10	

2009

4374	42c **Alaska Statehood,** *Jan. 3,* Anchorage, AK	2.10	
4375	42c **Chinese New Year,** *Jan. 8,* New York, NY	2.10	
4376	42c **Oregon Statehood,** *Jan. 14,* Portland, OR	2.10	
4377	42c **Edgar Allan Poe,** *Jan. 16,* Richmond, VA	2.10	
4378	$4.95 **Redwood Forest,** *Jan. 16,* San Diego, CA	10.00	

4379	$17.50 **Old Faithful,** *Jan. 16,* San Diego, CA	35.00	
4380-4383	42c **Abraham Lincoln,** *Feb. 9,* Springfield, IL	4.75	
	4380-4383, any single	2.10	
4384	42c **Civil Rights Pioneers,** *Feb. 21,* New York, NY	6.25	
	4384a-4384b, any single	2.10	
4385	(10c) **Patriotic Banner coil,** perf. 9 ¾ vert., *Feb. 24,* Washington, DC	2.10	
4386	61c **Richard Wright,** *Apr. 9,* Chicago, IL	2.50	
4387	28c **Polar Bear,** serpentine die cut 11 ¼x11, *Apr. 16,* New York, NY	2.10	
4388	64c **Dolphin,** *June 12,* Washington, DC	2.50	
4389	28c **Polar Bear coil,** serpentine die cut 8 ½ vert., *Apr. 16,* New York, NY	2.10	
4390	44c **Purple Heart,** *Apr. 28,* Washington, DC	2.10	
4391	44c **Flag,** coil stamp, perf. 9 ¾ vert., *May 1,* Washington, DC	2.10	
4392	44c **Flag,** litho. self-adhesive coil stamp, serpentine die cut 11 vert. with perpendicular corners, *May 8,* Washington, DC	2.10	
4393	44c **Flag,** litho. self-adhesive coil stamp, serpentine die cut 9 ½ vert., *May 8,* Washington, DC	2.10	
4394	44c **Flag,** photo. self-adhesive coil stamp, serpentine die cut 8 ½ vert., *May 8,* Washington, DC	2.10	
4395	44c **Flag,** photo. self-adhesive coil stamp, serpentine die cut 11 vert. with rounded corners, *May 1,* Washington, DC	2.10	
4396	44c **Flag,** self-adhesive booklet stamp, serpentine die cut 11 ¼x10 ¾ on 3 sides, *June 5,* McLean, VA	2.10	
4397	44c **Wedding Rings,** *May 1,* Washington, DC	2.10	
4398	61c **Wedding Cake,** *May 1,* Washington, DC	2.50	
4399-4403	44c **The Simpsons,** *May 7,* Los Angeles, CA	5.75	
	4399-4403, any single	2.10	
4404-4405	44c **Love (King and Queen of Hearts),** *May 8,* Washington, DC	3.00	
	4404-4405, either single	2.10	
4406	44c **Bob Hope,** *May 29,* San Diego, CA	2.10	
4407	44c **Celebrate,** *June 10,* Washington, DC	2.10	
4408	44c **Anna Julia Cooper,** *June 11,* Washington, DC	2.10	

SEMI-POSTAL FIRST DAY COVERS

1998

B1	32c +8c **Breast Cancer,** *July 29,* Washington, DC (51,775)	2.00	

2002

B2	(34c+11c) **Heroes of 2001,** *June 7,* New York, NY	3.00	
	Any other city	2.00	

2003

B3	(37c+8c) **Stop Family Violence,** *Oct. 8,* Washington, DC	1.60	
	Any other city	1.60	

AIR POST FIRST DAY COVERS

1918
C1   6c **orange,** *Dec. 10*   *25,000.*
C2   16c **green,** *July 11*   *32,500.*
C3   24c **carmine rose & blue,** *May 13*   *27,500.*

1923
C4   8c **dark green,** *Aug. 15*   400.00
C5   16c **dark blue,** *Aug. 17*   600.00
C6   24c **carmine,** *Aug. 21*   750.00

1926-27
C7   10c **dark blue,** *Feb. 13, 1926*   70.00
        Chicago, Ill.   85.00
        Detroit, Mich.   85.00
        Cleveland, Ohio   130.00
        Dearborn, Mich.   130.00
C8   15c **olive brown,** *Sept. 18, 1926*   85.00
C9   20c **yellow green,** *Jan. 25, 1927*   100.00
        New York, N.Y.   125.00
C10   10c **dark blue,** *June 18, 1927*   25.00
        St. Louis, Mo.   25.00
        Little Falls, Minn.   35.00
        Detroit, Mich.   35.00
C10a   Booklet pane of 3, *May 26, 1928*   875.00
        Cleveland Midwestern Philatelic Sta.
        cancel   800.00
        C10a & 645 on one cover, Washing-
        ton, D.C.   1,000.

1928-30
C11   5c **carmine & blue,** *July 25, 1928,*
        pair   50.00
C12   5c **violet,** *Feb. 10, 1930*   12.00
C13   65c **green,** *Apr. 19, 1930*   1,200.
C14 $1.30 **brown,** *Apr. 19, 1930*   1,100.
C15 $2.60 **blue,** *Apr. 19, 1930*   1,200.
        C13-C15 on one cover   15,000.

Values are for first day covers flown on Zeppelin flights with appropriate markings. Non-flown covers sell for less.

1931-33
C16   5c **violet,** *Aug. 19, 1931*   175.00
C17   8c **olive bister,** *Sept. 26, 1932*   15.00
C18   50c **green,** *Oct. 2, 1933,* New York, N.Y.
        (3,500)   200.00
        Akron, Ohio, *Oct. 4*   300.00
        Washington, D.C., *Oct. 5*   275.00
        Miami, Fla., *Oct. 6*   150.00
        Chicago, Ill., *Oct. 7*   250.00

1934-37
C19   6c **dull orange,** *June 30, 1934,* Balti-
        more, Md.   *190.00*
        New York, N.Y.   *800.00*
        Brooklyn, N.Y.   *1,200.*
        San Francisco, Calif.   *1,500.*
        Washington, D.C., *July 1*   10.00

> **Catalogue values for Nos. C20-C45 are for addressed covers with the most common cachets.**

C20   25c **blue,** *Nov. 22, 1935 (10,910)*   40.00
        San Francisco, Cal. *(15,000)*   35.00
C21   20c **green,** *Feb. 15, 1937*   45.00
C22   50c **carmine,** *Feb. 15, 1937*   50.00
        C21-C22 on one cover   100.00

First day covers of Nos. C21 and C22 total 40,000.

1938-39
C23   6c **dark blue & carmine,** *May 14, 1938,*
        Dayton, Ohio *(116,443)*   15.00
        St. Petersburg, Fla. *(95,121)*   15.00
        Washington, D.C., *May 15*   3.50
C24   30c **dull blue,** *May 16, 1939,* New York,
        N.Y. *(68,634)*   47.50

1941-44
C25   6c **carmine,** *June 25, 1941 (99,986)*   3.75
C25a   Booklet pane of 3, *Mar. 18, 1943*   25.00
C26   8c **olive green,** *Mar. 21, 1944 (147,484)*   3.75
C27   10c **violet,** *Aug. 15, 1941,* Atlantic City,
        N.J. *(87,712)*   8.00
C28   15c **brown carmine,** *Aug. 19, 1941,* Balti-
        more, Md. *(74,000)*   10.00
C29   20c **bright green,** *Aug. 27, 1941,* Phila-
        delphia, Pa. *(66,225)*   12.50
C30   30c **blue,** *Sept. 25, 1941,* Kansas City,
        Mo. *(57,175)*   20.00
C31   50c **orange,** *Oct. 29, 1941,* St. Louis, Mo.
        (54,580)   40.00

1946-48
C32   5c **carmine,** *Sept. 25, 1946*   2.00

First day covers of Nos. C32 & UC14 total 396,669.

C33   5c **carmine,** *Mar. 26, 1947 (342,634)*   2.00
C34   10c **black,** *Aug. 30, 1947 (265,773)*   2.00
C35   15c **bright blue green,** *Aug. 20, 1947,* New
        York, N.Y. *(230,338)*   1.75
C36   25c **blue,** *July 30, 1947,* San Francisco, Cal.
        (201,762)   2.25

C37   5c **carmine, coil,** *Jan. 15, 1948 (192,084)*   1.75
C38   5c **New York City,** *July 31, 1948,* New
        York, N.Y. *(371,265)*   1.75

1949
C39   6c **carmine,** *Jan. 18 (266,790)*   1.50
C39a   Booklet pane of 6, *Nov. 18, 1949,*
        New York, N.Y.   10.00
C40   6c **Alexandria Bicentennial,** *May 11,* Al-
        exandria, Va. *(386,717)*   1.50
C41   6c **carmine coil,** *Aug. 25 (240,386)*   1.25
C42   10c **U.P.U.,** *Nov. 18,* New Orleans, La.
        (270,000)   1.75
C43   15c **U.P.U.,** *Oct. 7,* Chicago, Ill. *(246,833)*   2.75
C44   25c **U.P.U.,** *Nov. 30,* Seattle, Wash.
        (220,215)   3.75
C45   6c **Wright Brothers,** *Dec. 17,* Kitty
        Hawk, N.C. *(378,585)*   2.75

> **Catalogue values from this point to the end of the section are for unaddressed covers with the most common cachets.**

1952-59
C46   80c **Hawaii,** *Mar. 26, 1952,* Honolulu, Ha-
        waii, *(89,864)*   20.00
C47   6c **Powered Flight,** *May 29, 1953,* Day-
        ton, Ohio *(359,050)*   1.50
C48   4c **bright blue,** *Sept. 3, 1954,* Philadel-
        phia, Pa. *(295,720)*   1.00
C49   6c **Air Force,** *Aug. 1, 1957 (356,683)*   2.75
C50   5c **red,** *July 31, 1958,* Colorado Springs,
        Colo. *(207,954)*   1.00
C51   7c **blue,** *July 31, 1958,* Philadelphia, Pa.
        (204,401)   1.00
C51a   Booklet pane of 6, San Antonio, Tex.
        (119,769)   9.00
C52   7c **blue coil,** *July 31, 1958,* Miami, Fla.
        (181,603)   1.00
C53   7c **Alaska Statehood,** *Jan. 3, 1959,* Ju-
        neau, Alaska *(489,752)*   1.50
C54   7c **Balloon Jupiter,** *Aug. 17, 1959,* La-
        fayette, Ind. *(383,556)*   1.75
C55   7c **Hawaii Statehood,** *Aug. 21, 1959,*
        Honolulu, Hawaii *(533,464)*   1.00
C56   10c **Pan American Games,** *Aug. 27,*
        1959, Chicago, Ill. *(302,306)*   1.00

1959-66
C57   10c **Liberty Bell,** *June 10, 1960,* Miami,
        Fla. *(246,509)*   1.50
C58   15c **Statue of Liberty,** *Nov. 20, 1959,*
        New York, N.Y. *(259,412)*   2.00
C59   25c **Abraham Lincoln,** *Apr. 22, 1960,*
        San Francisco, Cal. *(211,235)*   1.50
C59a   25c Tagged, *Dec. 29, 1966 (about 3,000)*   50.00
C60   7c **carmine,** *Aug. 12, 1960,* Arlington,
        Va. *(247,190)*   1.00
C60a   Booklet pane of 6, *Aug. 19, 1960,* St.
        Louis, Mo. *(143,363)*   8.00
C61   7c **carmine coil,** *Oct. 22, 1960,* Atlantic
        City, N.J. *(197,995)*   1.00

1961-67
C62   13c **Liberty Bell,** *June 28, 1961,* New
        York, N.Y. *(316,166)*   1.00
C62a   13c Tagged, *Feb. 15, 1967*   50.00
C63   15c **Redrawn Statue of Liberty,** *Jan. 13,*
        1961, Buffalo, N.Y. *(192,976)*   1.00
C63a   15c Tagged, *Jan. 11, 1967*   50.00
C64   8c **carmine,** *Dec. 5, 1962 (288,355)*   1.00
C64b   Booklet pane of 5 + label *(146,835)*   3.50
C64a   8c Tagged, *Aug. 1, 1963,* Dayton, Ohio
        (262,720)   2.00
C65   8c **carmine coil,** *Dec. 5, 1962 (220,173)*   1.00

1963-69
C66   15c **Montgomery Blair,** *May 3, 1963,*
        Silver Spring, Md. *(260,031)*   1.50
C67   6c **Bald Eagle,** *July 12, 1963,* Boston,
        Mass. *(268,265)*   1.00
C67a   6c Tagged, *Feb. 15, 1967*   50.00
C68   8c **Amelia Earhart,** *July 24, 1963,*
        Atchison, Kan. *(437,996)*   4.00
C69   6c **Robert H. Goddard,** *Oct. 5, 1964,*
        Roswell, N.M. *(421,020)*   3.00
C70   8c **Alaska Purchase,** *Mar. 30, 1967,*
        Sitka, Alaska *(554,784)*   1.50
C71   20c **Audubon,** *Apr. 26, 1967,* Audubon
        (Station of N.Y.C.), N.Y. *(227,930)*   2.00
C72   10c **carmine,** *Jan. 5, 1968,* San Francis-
        co, Cal.   1.00
C72b   Booklet pane of 8   3.75
C72c   Booklet pane of 5 + label, slogan 4
        Jan. 6, 1968   125.00
        With slogan 5   110.00
C73   10c **carmine coil,** *Jan. 5, 1968,* San
        Francisco, Cal.   1.00
C74   10c **Air Mail Service,** *May 15, 1968*
        (521,084)   1.50

C75   20c **USA and Jet,** *Nov. 22, 1968,* New
        York, N.Y. *(276,244)*   1.25
C76   10c **Moon Landing,** *Sept. 9, 1969*
        (8,743,070)   5.00

1971-73
C77   9c **red,** *May 15, 1971,* Kitty Hawk, N.C.   1.00

First day cancellation was applied to 379,442 covers of Nos. C77 and UXC10.

C78   11c **carmine,** *May 7, 1971,* Spokane,
        Wash.   1.00
C78a   Booklet pane of 4 + 2 labels   2.25
C79   13c **carmine,** *Nov. 16, 1973,* New York,
        N.Y. *(282,550)*   1.00
C79a   Booklet pane of 5 + label, *Dec. 27,*
        1973, Chicago, Ill.   2.25

First day cancellation was applied to 464,750 covers of Nos. C78, C78a and C82, and to 204,756 covers of Nos. C79a and C83.

C80   17c **Statue of Liberty,** *July 13, 1971,*
        Lakehurst, N.J. *(172,269)*   1.50
C81   21c **USA and Jet,** *May 21, 1971 (293,140)*   1.00
C82   11c **carmine coil,** *May 7, 1971,* Spokane,
        Wash.   1.00
C83   13c **carmine coil,** *Dec. 27, 1973,* Chicago,
        Ill.   1.00
C84   11c **National Parks Centennial,** *May 3,*
        1972, Honaunau, Hawaii *(364,816)*   1.00
C85   11c **Olympics,** *Aug. 17, 1972*   1.00

First day cancellation was applied to 971,536 covers of Nos. 1460-1462 and C85.

C86   11c **Electronics,** *July 10, 1973,* New York,
        N.Y.   1.00

First day cancellation was applied to 1,197,700 covers of Nos. 1500-1502 and C86.

1974-79
C87   18c **Statue of Liberty,** *Jan. 11, 1974,*
        Hempstead, N.Y. *(216,902)*   1.25
C88   26c **Mt. Rushmore,** *Jan. 2, 1974,* Rapid
        City, S.D. *(210,470)*   2.00
C89   25c **Plane and Globes,** *Jan. 2, 1976,* Hon-
        olulu, Hawaii   1.00
C90   31c **Plane, Globes and Flag,** *Jan. 2, 1976,*
        Honolulu, Hawaii   1.25
C92a   31c **Wright Brothers,** *Sept. 23, 1978,* Day-
        ton, Ohio   4.00
        C91-C92, any single   3.00
C94a   21c **Octave Chanute,** *Mar. 29, 1979,*
        Chanute, Kan. *(459,235)*   4.00
        C93-C94, any single   3.00
C96a   25c **Wiley Post,** *Nov. 20, 1979,* Oklahoma
        City, Okla.   4.00
        C95-C96, any single   3.00
C97   31c **Olympics,** *Nov. 1, 1979,* Colorado
        Springs, CO   1.50

1980
C98   40c **Philip Mazzei,** *Oct. 13*   1.50
C99   28c **Blanche Stuart Scott,** *Dec. 30,* Ham-
        mondsport, NY *(238,502)*   1.50
C100   35c **Glenn Curtiss,** *Dec. 30,* Hammond-
        sport, NY *(208,502)*   1.50

1983
C104a   28c **Olympics,** *June 17,* San Antonio, TX
        (901,028)   3.75
        C101-C104, any single   1.75
C108a   40c **Olympics,** *Apr. 8,* Los Angeles, CA
        (1,001,657)   5.00
        C105-C108, any single   1.75
C112a   35c **Olympics,** *Nov. 4,* Colorado Springs,
        CO *(897,729)*   4.50
        C109-C112, any single   1.75

1985
C113   33c **Alfred V. Verville,** *Feb. 13,* Garden
        City, NY   1.50
C114   39c **Lawrence & Elmer Sperry,** *Feb. 13,*
        Garden City, NY   1.50

First day cancel was applied to 429,290 covers bearing one more of Nos. C113-C114.

C115   44c **Transpacific Air Mail,** *Feb. 15,* San
        Francisco, CA *(269,229)*   1.75

A total of 269,229 first day cancels were applied for Nos. C115 and UXC22.

C116   44c **Junipero Serra,** *Aug. 22,* San Diego,
        CA *(254,977)*   2.00

1988
C117   44c **Settling of New Sweden,** *Mar. 29,*
        Wilmington, DE *(213,445)*   1.50
C118   45c **Samuel P. Langley,** *May 14,* San Die-
        go, CA   1.50
C119   36c **Igor Sikorsky,** *June 23,* Stratford, CT
        (162,986)   2.50

1989
C120   45c **French Revolution,** *July 14 (309,975)*   1.50
C121   45c **Southeast Carved Figure,** *Oct. 12,*
        San Juan, PR *(93,569)*   1.50

C125a	45c	**Future Mail Transportation,** *Nov. 27* (765,479)	6.50
		C122-C125, any single	1.75
C126	45c	**Future Mail Transportation Souvenir Sheet,** *Nov. 24 (257,826)*	6.50

1990

| C127 | 45c | **Tropical Coast,** *Oct. 12,* Grand Canyon, AZ (137,068) | 1.50 |

1991

C128	50c	**Harriet Quimby,** *Apr. 27,* Plymouth, MI	1.50
C129	40c	**William T. Piper,** *May 17,* Denver, CO	1.50
C130	50c	**Antarctic Treaty,** *June 21*	1.50
C131	50c	**Bering Land Bridge,** *Oct. 12,* Anchorage, AK	1.50

1999

C133	48c	**Niagara Falls,** *May 12,* Niagara Falls, NY (20,878)	1.75
C134	40c	**Rio Grande,** *July 30,* Milwaukee, WI	2.00
		any other city	2.00

First day cancel was applied to 42,144 covers bearing one more of Nos. 3330, C134.

| C135 | 60c | **Grand Canyon,** *Jan. 20,* Grand Canyon, AZ (64,282) | 2.00 |

2001

C136	70c	**Nine-mile Prairie,** *Mar. 6,* Lincoln, NE	2.00
C137	80c	**Mt. McKinley,** *Apr. 17,* Fairbanks, AK	2.00
C138	60c	**Acadia National Park,** *May 30,* Bar Harbor, ME	2.00

2006

C139	63c	**Bryce Canyon National Park,** *Feb. 24,* St. Louis, MO	2.50
		Any other city	2.50
C140	75c	**Great Smoky Mountains National Park,** *Feb. 24,* St. Louis, MO	2.75
		Any other city	2.75
C141	84c	**Yosemite National Park,** *Feb. 24,* St. Louis, MO	3.00
		Any other city	3.00

2007

| C142 | 69c | **Okefenokee Swamp,** *June 1,* McLean, VA | 2.60 |
| C143 | 90c | **Hagatña Bay,** *June 1,* Barrigada, GU | 3.00 |

2008

C144	72c	**13-Mile Woods, New Hampshire,** *May 16,* Rochester, NY	2.75
C145	94c	**Trunk Bay, St. John, Virgin Islands,** *May 16,* Rochester, NY	3.25
		St. John, VI	3.25

2009

| C146 | 79c | **Zion National Park,** *June 28,* Washington, DC | 3.00 |
| C147 | 98c | **Grand Teton National Park,** *June 28,* Washington, DC | 3.25 |

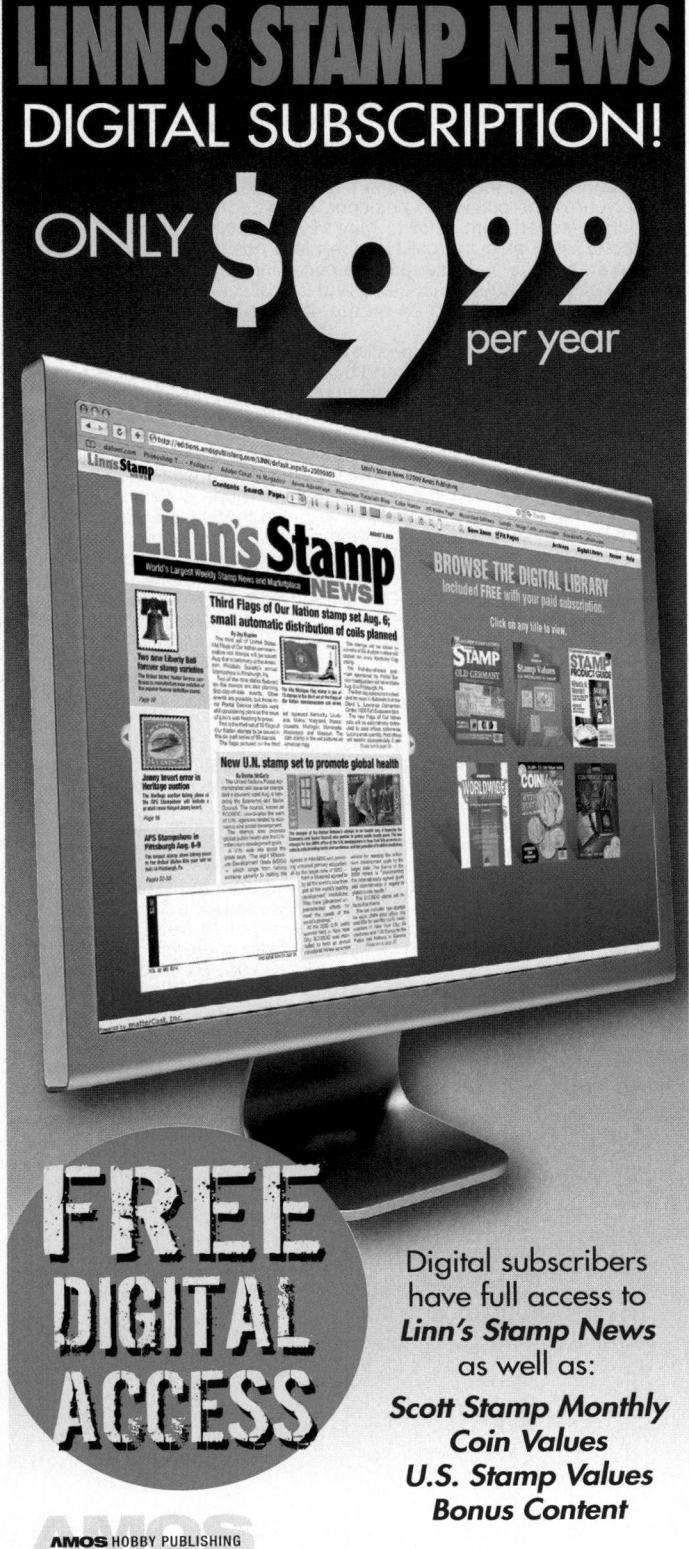

BOOKLETS: PANES & COVERS

Most booklet panes issued before 1962 consist of a vertical block of 6 stamps perforated vertically through the center. The panes are perforated horizontally on all but the bottom edge and the top of the selvage tab. The selvage top, the two sides and the bottom are straight edged. Exceptions for panes issued before 1962 are the 1917 American Expeditionary Forces panes (30 stamps); Lindbergh and 6¢ 1943 air mails (3), and the Savings Stamps (10). Since 1962, panes have been issued with 3 to 20 stamps and various configurations. They have included one or more labels and two or more stamps se-tenant.

Flat plate booklet panes, with the exceptions noted above, were made from specially designed plates of 180 or 360 subjects. They are collected in plate positions. There are nine collectible positions on the 180-subject plate and 12 on the 360-subject plate.

Rotary booklet panes issued from 1926 to May 1978 (except for Nos. 1623a and 1623Bc) were made from specially designed plates of 180, 320, 360, and 400 subjects. They also are collected in plate positions. There are five collectible positions on the 360-subject plates which were printed before electric eye plates came into use, and 18 collectible positions on the Type II "new design" 360-subject rotary plates. There are 17 collectible positions in the rotary air mail 180-subject plate, and 21 collectible positions in the Type IV "modified design" 360-subject plate. There are 13 collectible positions on the 320-subject plates and 24 on the 400 subject plates. There are five collectible positions on Defense and War Savings 300-subject plates.

The generally accepted methods of designating pane positions as illustrated and explained hereafter are those suggested by George H. Beans in the May 1913 issue of "Everybody's Philatelist" and by B. H. Mosher in his monograph "Discovering U.S. Rotary Pane Varieties 1926-78." Some collectors seek all varieties possible, but the majority collect unused (A) panes and plate number (D) panes from flat plate issues, and plain panes and panes with electric eye bars and electric eye dashes, where available, from rotary plates.

Starting in 1977, BEP made two major changes in booklet production. Printing of panes was gradually moved from rotary plates to sleeves for modern high speed presses. Also, booklet production was transferred to Goebel booklet-forming machines. These changes virtually eliminated collectible pane positions for several years. However, beginning with No. BK156 (No. 2276a), BEP and other printers began placing printing process control marks in pane tabs. As a result, specialist booklet pane collectors actively resumed collecting pane positions. Collectible positions on these issues are not shown in this catalogue but can be found in the United States Stamp Society's Research Paper No. 2 "Folded Style Checklist," Michael O. Perry, editor. Also, because of the requirements of the Goebel machine, the subject size of printing plates or sleeves varied widely. For these reasons, plate layouts are not shown for each issue. The plate layout for No. 1288c and the sleeve layout for No. 1623a are shown as typical.

The following panes, issued after Mar. 11, 1977, were printed from pairs of rotary plates and assembled into booklets on the Goebel machine: Nos. 1288c, 1742a, 1819a, 1889a, and 1949a. One pane in 12 of those issues may have a join line along either long side of the pane, creating three collectible positions: no join line, join line top (or right) and join line bottom (or left). Except for Nos. 1736a and 2276a, all other booklet panes issued from Mar. 11, 1977 on were printed from intaglio sleeves, gravure cylinders, and/or offset plates.

At least one pane in every booklet produced on the BEP's Goebel machines contains two register marks in the tab: a cross register line (CRL) 1.5mm wide which runs across the width of the tab and a length register mark (LRM), typically 1.5x5mm, usually placed above the right hand (or top) stamp of the pane. Nos. 1623a and 1623Bc were regularly issued with the LRM over either stamp. Some examples of Nos. 1893a, 2121a and 3003Ab were issued with the LRM over the left stamp.

Starting with No. 1889a (except for No. 1948a), plate numbers (1 to 5 digits) were placed in the tab, normally over the left stamp. On booklets containing Nos. 1889a, 1949a and 2113a, the plate number is supposed to be on the top pane, the second pane not having a number. All subsequent multi-pane booklets have the plate number on each pane. Some multi-pane booklets contain panes with different plate numbers. The booklet value is determined by the top pane.

Most recent booklets have been printed by contractors other than the BEP so markings may differ or be absent.

Panes in all booklets assembled on the Goebel machine will be folded at least once. **Repeated handling of booklets with folded panes may cause the panes to fall apart.**

Booklet panes with tabs attached to the cover by adhesive instead of staples are valued on the basis of the tab intact. Minor damage on the back of the tab due to removal from the booklet does not affect the value. Some of these panes were furnished to first day cover processors unfolded and not pasted into covers. Around 1989, these panes were available to collectors through the Philatelic Agency.

All panes from 1967 to date are tagged, unless otherwise stated.

Dr. William R. Bush, Morton Dean Joyce, Robert E. Kitson, Richard F. Larkin, Dr. Robert Marks, Bruce H. Mosher, Michael O. Perry, the United States Stamp Society (formerly the Bureau Issues Association), and the Booklet Collectors Club helped the editors extensively in compiling the listings and preparing the illustrations of booklets, covers and plate layouts.

180-SUBJECT PLATE — 9 Collectible Positions

Beginning at upper left and reading from left to right, the panes are designated from 1 to 30. All positions not otherwise identifiable are designated by the letter A: Pane 1A, 2A, 3A, 4A, etc.
The identifiable positions are as follows:
A — The ordinary booklet pane without distinguishing features. Occurs in Position 1, 2, 3, 4, 8, 9, 10, 21, 22, 23, 24, 27, 28, 29, 30.
B — Split arrow and guide line at right. Occurs in Position 5 only.
C — Split arrow and guide line at left. Occurs in Position 6 only.
D — Plate number pane. Occurs in Position 7 only.
E — Guide line pane showing horizontal guide line between stamps 1-2 and 3-4 of the pane. Occurs in Positions 11, 12, 13, 14, 17, 18, 19, and 20.
F — Guide line through pane and at right. Occurs in Position 15 only.
G — Guide line through pane and at left. Occurs in Position 16 only.
H — Guide line at right. Occurs in Position 25 only.
I — Guide line at left. Occurs in Position 26 only.
Only positions B, F and H or C, G and I may be obtained from the same sheet, depending on whether the knife which separated the panes fell to right or left of the line. Side arrows, bottom arrows, or bottom plate numbers are seldom found because the margin of the sheets is usually cut off, as are the sides and bottom of each pane. In the illustrations, the dotted lines represent the rows of perforations, the unbroken lines represents the knife cut.

360-SUBJECT PLATE — 12 Collectible Positions

As with the 180-Subject Sheets, the position of the various panes is indicated by numbers beginning in the upper left corner with the No. 1 and reading from left to right to No. 60.

The identifiable positions are as follows:

A — The ordinary booklet pane without distinguishing features. Occurs in Positions 1, 2, 3, 4, 8, 9, 10, 11, 12, 13, 14, 17, 18, 19, 20, 41, 42, 43, 44, 47, 48, 49, 50, 51, 52, 53, 54, 57, 58, 59, and 60.

B — Split arrow and guide line at right. Occurs in Position 5 only.
C — Split arrow and guide line at left. Occurs in Position 6 only.
D — Plate number pane. Occurs in Position 7 only.
E, F, G — Do not occur in the 360-Subject Plate.
H — Guide line at right. Occurs in Positions 15, 45, and 55.
I — Guide line at left. Occurs in Positions 16, 46, and 56.
J — Guide line at bottom. Occurs in Positions 21, 22, 23, 24, 27, 28, 29 and 30.
K — Guide line at right and bottom. Occurs in Position 25 only.
L — Guide line at left and bottom. Occurs in Position 26 only.
M — Guide line at top. Occurs in Positions 31, 32, 33, 34, 37, 38, 39 and 40.
N — Guide line at top and right. Occurs in Position 35 only.
O — Guide line at top and left. Occurs in Position 36 only.

Only one each of Positions B or C, K, L, N or O; four positions of H or I, and eight or nine positions of J or M may be obtained from each 360 subject sheet, depending on whether the knife fell to the right or left, top or bottom of the guide lines.

Because the horizontal guide line appears so close to the bottom row of stamps on panes Nos. 21 to 30, Positions M, N, and O occur with great deal less frequency than Positions J, K and L.

The 360-Subject Rotary Press Plate (before Electric Eye) Position A only

The 360-Subject Rotary Press Plate — Electric Eye

A modified design was put into use in 1956. The new plates have 20 frame bars instead of 17.

The A.E.F. Plate — 360-Subject Flat Plate — 8 Collectible Positions (See listings)

The 320-Subject Plate

400-Subject Plate — The 300-Subject plate with double labels has the same layout.

1 A	2 A	3 A	4 A	5 B	6 C	7 A	8 A	9 A	10 A
11 A	12 A	13 A	14 A	15 H	16 I	17 A	18 A	19 A	20 A
21 J	22 J	23 J	24 J	25 K	26 L	27 J	28 J	29 J	30 J
31 M	32 M	33 M	34 M	35 N	36 O	37 M	38 M	39 M	40 M
41 A	42 A	43 A	44 A	45 H	46 I	47 A	48 A	49 A	50 A
51 A	52 A	53 A	54 A	55 H	56 I	57 A	58 A	59 A	60 A

Lindbergh Booklet Plate-180 Subjects — 11 Collectible Positions

Airmail 180-Subject Rotary Press Plate — Electric Eye

Plate Sizes: No. 1288Bc to date.

Since 1978 numerous plate sizes from 78 to 1080 subjects have been used. Because plate size is not relevant to collecting these panes, we are not including this information in the catalogue.

BOOKLET PANES

Values for both unused and used booklet panes are for complete panes with selvage, and for panes of six unless otherwise stated. Panes in booklets are Never Hinged. Values for stapled booklets are for those with creasing along the lines of the staples. Values for booklets which were glued shut are for opened booklets without significant damage to the cover.

See other notes in the introduction to this section.

BOOKLET COVERS

Front covers of booklets of postage and airmail issues are illustrated and numbered.

Included are the Booklet Cover number (BC2A); and the catalogue numbers of the Booklet Panes (300b, 331a). The text of the inside and or back covers changes. Some modern issues have minor changes on the front covers also. When more than one combination of covers exists, the number of possible booklets is noted in parentheses after the booklet listing. Booklet covers that have no card stock color given are white.

Washington — A88

Wmk. 191 Horizontally or Vertically

1900-03			*Perf. 12*
279Bj A88 2c **red,** horizontal wmk., *Apr. 18*		500.	*1,250.*
light red		500.	
orange red, *1902*		500.	
Never hinged		1,000.	
With plate number (D)		1,350.	*3,000.*

Never hinged		2,150.	
279Bk A88 2c **red,** vertical watermark		500.	*1,250.*
Never hinged		1,000.	
With plate number (D)		1,350.	
Never hinged		2,150.	

360- (horiz. wmk.) and 180- (vert. wmk.) subject plates. All plate positions exist, except J, K, and L, due to the horizontal guide line being placed too far below stamps to appear on the upper panes.

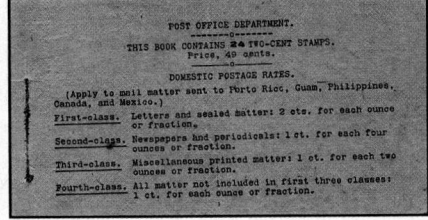

279Bj-279Bk — BC1

1900-03

Text only cover

25c booklet contains 2 panes of six 2c stamps.
49c booklet contains 4 panes of six 2c stamps.
97c booklet contains 8 panes of six 2c stamps.

Booklets sold for 1c more than the face value of the stamps.

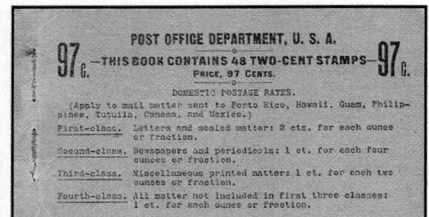

279Bj, 279Bk, 301c, 319, 332a — BC2B

1900-08
Text cover with price added in upper corners

25c booklets contain 4 panes of six 1c stamps or 2 panes of six 2c stamps.
49c booklet contains 4 panes of six 2c stamps.
97c booklet contains 8 panes of six 2c stamps.

Booklets

BK1	BC1	25c	black, cream	—
BK2	BC1	25c	black, buff	6,000.
BK3	BC1	49c	green, cream	—
BK4	BC1	49c	black, buff	—
BK5	BC1	97c	red, cream	—
BK6	BC1	97c	black, gray	—
BK7	BC2B	25c	black, cream (3)	7,000.
BK8	BC2B	49c	black, buff (3)	—
BK9	BC2B	97c	black, gray (3)	15,000.

Nos. BK1-BK6 and one type each of Nos. BK7-BK9 exist with specimen overprints handstamped on cover and individual stamps.

All covers of BK7-BK9 exist with "Philippines" overprint in 50mm or 48mm.

Franklin — A115

1903-07   Wmk. 191 Vertically

300b	A115	1c blue green, Mar. 6, 1907	600.	12,500.
		Never hinged	1,150.	
		With plate number (D)	1,300.	
		Never hinged	2,250.	
		With plate number 3472 over left stamp (D)	4,000.	

180-Subject Plates only. All plate positions exist.

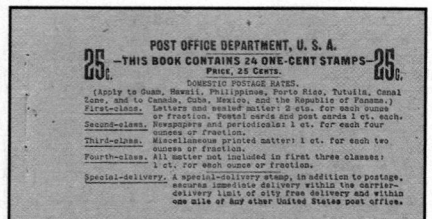

300b, 331a — BC2A

1900-08
Text cover with price added in upper corners

25c booklets contain 4 panes of six 1c stamps or 2 panes of six 2c stamps.
49c booklet contains 4 panes of six 2c stamps.

Booklet

BK10	BC2A	25c	black, green (6)	6,500.

Washington — A116

301c	A116	2c carmine, Jan. 24, 1903	500.	4,500.
		Never hinged	950.	
		With plate number (D)	1,500.	5,250.
		Never hinged	2,500.	

180-Subject Plates only. All plate positions exist.

Booklets

BK11	BC2B	25c	black, cream	3,000.
BK12	BC2B	49c	black, buff	4,000.
BK13	BC2B	97c	black, gray	—

Washington — A129

1903   Wmk. 191 Vertically

319g	A129	2c carmine, type I, Dec. 3, 1903	125.00	550.00
		Never hinged	240.00	
		With plate number (D)	275.00	850.00
		Never hinged	500.00	
		Wmk. horizontal	4,000.	
		Never hinged	6,500.	
		With Plate number (D)	9,500.	
319n	A129	2c carmine rose (I)	250.00	650.00
		Never hinged	450.00	
		With plate number (D)	425.00	950.00
		Never hinged	725.00	
319p	A129	2c scarlet (I)	185.00	575.00
		Never hinged	350.00	
		With plate number (D)	350.00	900.00
		Never hinged	625.00	
319h	A129	2c carmine, type II, 1907	900.00	
		Never hinged	1,500.	
		With plate number (D)	1,500.	
		Never hinged	2,500.	
319q	A129	2c lake (II)	300.00	750.00
		Never hinged	575.00	
		With plate number (D)	550.00	
		Never hinged	900.00	

180-Subject Plates only. All plate positions exist.

Booklets

BK14	BC2B	25c	black, cream (11)	1,100.
BK15	BC2A	49c	black, buff (11)	1,350.
BK16	BC2A	49c	black, pink	2,500.
BK17	BC2B	97c	black, gray (11)	3,250.

Booklet Covers

When more than one combination of covers exists, the number of possible booklets is noted in parentheses after the booklet listing.

Franklin — A138

1908   Wmk. 191 Vertically

331a	A138	1c green, Dec. 1908	160.00	450.00
		Never hinged	285.00	
		With plate number (D)	240.00	
		Never hinged	400.00	

180- and 360-Subject Plates. All plate positions exist.
No. 331 exists in horizontal pair, imperforate between, a variety resulting from booklet experiments. Not regularly issued. Value, unused $2,500.

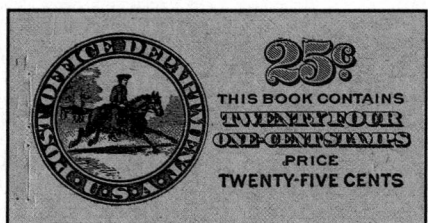

331a, 332a, 374a, 375a, 405b, 406a — BC3

1908-12   Postrider

25c booklet contains 4 panes of six 1c stamps.
25c booklet contains 2 panes of six 2c stamps.
49c booklet contains 4 panes of six 2c stamps.
97c booklet contains 8 panes of six 2c stamps.

Booklets

BK18	BC2A	25c	black, green (3)	2,000.
BK19	BC3	25c	black, green	2,250.

Washington — A139

332a	A139	2c carmine, Nov. 16, 1908	135.00	400.00
		Never hinged	230.00	
		With plate number (D)	175.00	
		Never hinged	300.00	

180- and 360-Subject Plates. All plate positions exist.

Booklets

BK20	BC2B	25c	black, cream (2)	1,250.
BK21	BC2A	49c	black, buff (2)	2,750.
BK22	BC2A	49c	black, pink	2,750.
BK23	BC2B	97c	black, gray (3)	3,000.
BK24	BC3	25c	black, cream	1,250.
BK25	BC3	49c	black, pink	2,500.
BK26	BC3	97c	black, gray	3,000.

1910 — Wmk. 190 Vertically — Perf. 12

374a	A138	1c **green**, *Oct. 7, 1910*	225.00	300.00
		Never hinged	375.00	
		With plate number (D)	300.00	
		Never hinged	475.00	

360-Subject Plates only. All plate positions exist.

Booklet

BK27	BC3	25c **black**, *green* (2)	2,000.

375a	A139	2c **carmine**, *Nov. 30, 1910*	125.00	200.00
		Never hinged	200.00	
		With plate number (D)	170.00	
		Never hinged	290.00	

360-Subject Plates only. All plate positions exist.

Booklets

BK28	BC3	25c **black**, *cream* (2)	900.00
BK29	BC3	49c **black**, *pink* (2)	2,500.
BK30	BC3	97c **black**, *gray* (2)	3,000.

Washington — A140

1912 — Wmk. 190 Vertically

405b	A140	1c **green**, *Feb. 8, 1912*	65.00	75.00
		Never hinged	110.00	
		With plate number (D)	80.00	
		Never hinged	140.00	

360-Subject Plates only. All plate positions exist.

405b, 424d, 462a, 498e, 632a, 804b — BC4A

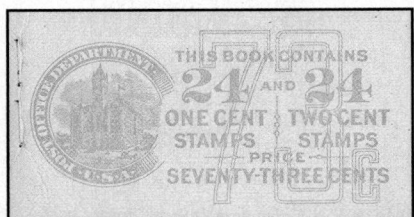

405b, 424d, 462a, 498e, 552a, 632a — BC4B

1912-39 — Washington P.O.

Price of booklet in large numerals behind contents information

25c booklet contains 4 panes of six 1c stamps.
73c booklet contains 4 panes of six 1c stamps and 4 panes of six 2c stamps.
97c booklet contains 16 panes of six 1c stamps.

Ordinary Booklets

BK31	BC3	25c **black**, *green* (2)	1,000.
BK32	BC4A	25c **green**, *green* (3)	1,250.
BK33	BC4A	97c **green**, *lavender*	1,750.

Combination Booklet

BK34	BC4B	73c **red**, 4 #405b + 4 #406a	3,000.

Washington — A140

406a	A140	2c **carmine**, *Feb. 8, 1912*	65.00	90.00
		Never hinged	110.00	
		With plate number (D)	80.00	
		Never hinged	140.00	

360-Subject Plates only. All plate positions exist.

406a, 425e, 463a, 499e, 554c, 583a, 632a, 634d, 804b, 806b — BC5A

1912-39 — Small Postrider

Large background numerals

25c booklets contain 4 panes of six 1c stamps or 2 panes of six 2c stamps.
49c booklet contains 4 panes of six 2c stamps.
97c booklets contain 16 panes of six 1c stamps or 8 panes of six 2c stamps.

Ordinary Booklets

BK35	BC3	25c **black**, *cream* (2)	825.00
BK36	BC3	49c **black**, *pink* (2)	1,500.
BK37	BC3	97c **black**, *gray* (2)	2,000.
BK38	BC5A	25c **red**, *buff* (3)	1,000.
BK39	BC5A	49c **red**, *pink* (3)	1,750.
BK40	BC5A	97c **red**, *blue*, (3)	2,250.

Combination Booklet

See No. BK34.

1914 — Wmk. 190 Vertically — Perf. 10

424d	A140	1c **green**	5.25	7.50
		Never hinged	8.75	
		Double transfer, Plate 6363	—	—
		With plate number (D)	14.00	
		Never hinged	22.50	
		Cracked plate	—	
e.		As "d," imperf.	2,000.	
		With plate number (D)	—	

360-Subject Plates only. All plate positions exist.
All known examples of No. 424e are without gum.

Ordinary Booklets

BK41	BC4A	25c **green**, *green* (3)	300.00
BK42	BC4A	97c **green**, *lavender* (2)	135.00

Combination Booklet

BK43	BC4B	73c **red**, 4 #424d + 4 #425e (3)	300.00

425e	A140	2c **carmine**, *Jan. 6, 1914*	17.50	25.00
		Never hinged	30.00	
		With plate number (D)	42.50	
		Never hinged	70.00	

360-Subject Plates only. All plate positions exist.

Ordinary Booklets

BK44	BC5A	25c **red**, *buff* (3)	500.00
BK45	BC5A	49c **red**, *pink* (3)	1,000.
BK46	BC5A	97c **red**, *blue* (3)	1,250.

Combination Booklet

See No. BK43.

1916 — Unwmk. — Perf. 10

462a	A140	1c **green**, *Oct. 15, 1916*	9.50	12.50
		Never hinged	16.00	
		Cracked plate at right	225.00	
		Never hinged	325.00	
		Cracked plate at left	310.00	

		Never hinged	425.00
		With plate number (D)	25.00
		Never hinged	37.50

360-Subject Plates only. All plate positions exist.

Ordinary Booklets

BK47	BC4A	25c **green**, *green*	650.00
BK48	BC4A	97c **green**, *lavender*	500.00

Combination Booklets

BK49	BC4B	73c **red**, 4 #462a + 4 #463a (2)	900.00

463a	A140	2c **carmine**, *Oct. 8, 1916*	110.00	110.00
		Never hinged	180.00	
		With plate number (D)	150.00	
		Never hinged	240.00	

360-Subject Plates only. All plate positions exist.

Ordinary Booklets

BK50	BC5A	25c **red**, *buff*	950.00
BK51	BC5A	49c **red**, *pink*	1,500.
BK52	BC5A	97c **red**, *blue*	2,500.

Combination Booklets

See No. BK49.

1917-18 — Unwmk. — Perf. 11

498e	A140	1c **green**, *Apr. 6, 1917*	2.50	2.00
		Never hinged	4.25	
		Double transfer	—	—
		With plate number (D)	6.00	2.00
		Never hinged	9.00	

360-Subject Plates only. All plate positions exist.

498e, 552a — BC6A

1917-23   Oval designs
25c booklet contains 4 panes of six 1c stamps.

Ordinary Booklets

BK53	BC4A	25c **green,** *green* (2)	300.00	
BK54	BC4A	97c **green,** *lavender* (4)	85.00	
BK55	BC6A	25c **green,** *green* (5)	120.00	

Combination Booklets

BK56	BC4B	73c **red,** 4 #498e + 4 #499e (4)	80.00	
BK57	BC4B	73c **red,** 4 #498e + 4 #554c (3)	100.00	

Washington — A140

A.E.F. Panes of 30

1917, Aug.

498f	A140	1c **green** (pane of 30)	1,150.
		Never hinged	1,800.

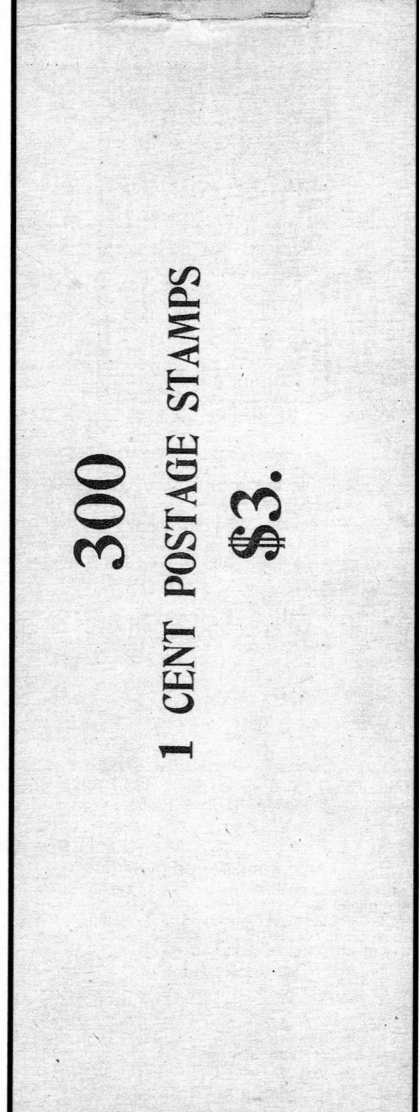

498f, 499f — BC7

Illustration reduced.

A.E.F.

1917
$3 booklet contains 10 panes of thirty 1c stamps.
$6 booklet contains 10 panes of thirty 2c stamps.

Booklets sold for face value.

Booklet

BK64	BC7	$3 **black,** *green*	25,000.

499e	A140	2c **rose,** type I, *Mar. 31, 1917*	4.00	*2.50*
		Never hinged	6.75	
		With plate number (D)	7.00	*2.25*
		Never hinged	10.00	

360-Subject Plates only. All plate positions exist.

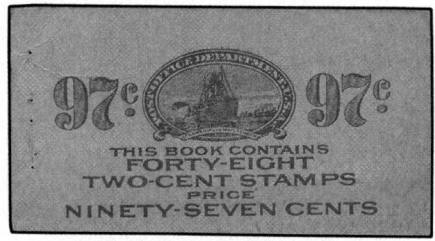

499e, 554c, 583a, 634d — BC6C

1917-27   Oval designs
97c booklet contains 8 panes of six 2c stamps.

Ordinary Booklets

BK58	BC5A	25c **red,** *buff* (5)	250.00
BK59	BC5A	49c **red,** *pink* (4)	400.00
BK60	BC5A	97c **red,** *blue* (3)	750.00
BK61	BC6C	97c **red,** *blue* (2)	1,250.

Combination Booklets

See No. BK56.

499f	A140	2c **rose,** (pane of 30) type I	28,000.	—
		Never hinged	38,000.	

Booklet

BK65	BC7	$6 **black,** *pink*	

No examples of No. BK65 are known. The number and description are provided only for specialist reference.

Nos. 498f and 499f were for use of the American Expeditionary Force in France.

They were printed from the ordinary 360-Subject Plates, the sheet being cut into 12 leaves of 30 stamps each in place of 60 leaves of 6 stamps each, and, of course, the lines of perforations changed accordingly.

The same system as used for designating plate positions on the ordinary booklet panes is used for designating the war booklet, only each war booklet pane is composed of 5 ordinary panes. Thus, No. W1 booklet pane would be composed of positions 1, 2, 3, 4, and 5 of an ordinary pane, etc.

The A. E. F. booklet panes were bound at side margins which accounts for side arrows sometimes being found on positions W5 and W6. As the top and bottom arrows were always removed when the sheets were cut, positions W1 and W2 cannot be distinguished from W7 and W8. Cutting may remove guidelines on these, but identification is possible by wide bottom margins. Positions W3 and W4 cannot be distinguished from W9 and W10.

There are thus just 8 collectible positions from the sheet as follows:

W1 or W7 Narrow top and wide bottom margins. Guide line at right.

W2 or W8 As W1, but guide line at left.

W3 or W9 Approximately equal top and bottom margins. Guide line at right.

W4 or W10 As W3, but guide line at left.

W5 Narrow bottom margin showing guideline very close to stamps. Wide top margin. Guide line at right. Pane with extra long tab may show part of split arrow at left.

W6 As W5, but guide line at left, split arrow at right. Guide line at left and at bottom. Arrow at lower right may or may not show.

W11 Narrow bottom and wide top margins. Guide line at right. Siderographer initials on left tab.

W12 Narrow bottom and wide top margins. Guide line at left. Finisher initials on right tab.

Washington — A140

501b	A140	3c **violet,** type I, *Oct. 17, 1917*	75.00	*60.00*
		Never hinged	125.00	
		With plate number (D)	105.00	
		Never hinged	160.00	

360-Subject Plates only. All plate positions exist.

501b, 502b — BC6B

1917-18   **Oval designs**

37c booklet contains 2 panes of six 3c stamps.

Booklet

BK62	BC6B	37c **violet,** *sage*		500.00
502b	A140	3c **violet,** type II, *Mar. 1918*	60.00	*55.00*
		Never hinged	100.00	
		With plate number (D)	77.50	
		Never hinged	120.00	

360-Subject Plates only. All plate positions exist.

Booklet

BK63	BC6B	37c **violet,** *sage*	235.00

Franklin — A155

1923			**Unwmk.**		**Perf. 11**
552a	A155	1c **deep green,** *Aug. 1923*		7.50	*4.00*
		Never hinged		12.50	
		With plate number (D)		13.00	
		Never hinged		21.00	

360-Subject Plates only. All plate positions exist.

Ordinary Booklets

BK66	BC6A	25c **green,** *green* (2)	75.00
BK67	BC4A	97c **green,** *lavender* (3)	650.00

Combination Booklet

BK68	BC4B	73c **white,** *red,* 4 #552a + 4 #554c (3)	85.00

Washington — A157

554c	A157	2c **carmine**		7.00	*3.00*
		Never hinged		12.00	
		With plate number (D)		12.00	
		Never hinged		20.00	

360-Subject Plates only. All plate positions exist.

Ordinary Booklets

BK69	BC5A	25c **red,** *buff* (3)	400.00
BK70	BC5A	49c **red,** *pink* (3)	950.00
BK71	BC6C	97c **red,** *blue* (3)	1,500.

Combination Booklets

See Nos. BK57 and BK68.

ROTARY PRESS PRINTINGS

Two experimental plates were used to print No. 583a. At least one guide line pane (H) is known from these plates. The rest of rotary press booklet panes were printed from specially prepared plates of 360-subjects in arrangement as before, but without the guide lines and the plate numbers are at the sides instead of at the top as on the flat plates.

The only varieties possible are the ordinary pane (A) and partial plate numbers appearing at the right or left of the upper or lower stamps of a booklet pane when the trimming of the sheets is off center. The note

---

applies to Nos. 583a, 632a, 634d, 720b, 804b, 806b and 807a, before Electric Eyes.

1926			**Perf. 10**	
583a	A157	2c **carmine,** *Aug. 1926*	95.00	*150.00*
		Never hinged	175.00	

Ordinary Booklets

BK72	BC5A	25c **red,** *buff* (3)	*725.00*
BK73	BC5A	49c **red,** *pink*	1,000.
BK74	BC6C	97c **red,** *blue*	1,250.

1927			**Perf. 11x10½**	
632a	A155	1c **green,** *Nov. 2, 1927*	5.00	*4.00*
		Never hinged	8.00	

Ordinary Booklets

BK75	BC5A	25c **green,** *green* (3)	65.00
BK76	BC4A	97c **green,** *lavender*	600.00
BK77	BC5A	97c **green,** *lavender*	—

632a, 804b — BC5D

1927-39   **Small Postrider**

Large background numerals

73c booklet contains 4 panes of six 1c stamps and 4 panes of six 2c stamps.

Combination Booklets

BK78	BC4B	73c **red,** 4 #632a + 4 #634d	—
BK79	BC5D	73c **red,** 4 #632a + 4 #634d (2)	90.00
634d	A157	2c **carmine,** type I, *Feb. 25, 1927*	1.50	*1.50*
		Never hinged	2.50	

Ordinary Booklets

BK80	BC5A	25c **red,** *buff* (2)	10.00
a.		With experimental cellophane interleaving	1,500.
BK81	BC5A	49c **red,** *pink* (2)	15.00
BK82	BC5A	97c **red,** *blue* (3)	50.00
BK83	BC6C	97c **red,** *blue*	900.00

Combination Booklets

See Nos. BK78 and BK79.

56,000 booklets of BK80a were produced in 1928 using .00125 inch thick cellophane interleaving. Scarce, as few were saved.

Varieties

634e	A157	2c **carmine lake,** type I	625.00
		Never hinged	1,250.

Booklet

BK82a	BC5A	97c **red,** *blue,* containing 8 panes of No. 634e	10,000.

Washington — A226

1932				
720b	A226	3c **deep violet,** *July 25, 1932*	35.00	*12.50*
		Never hinged	60.00	

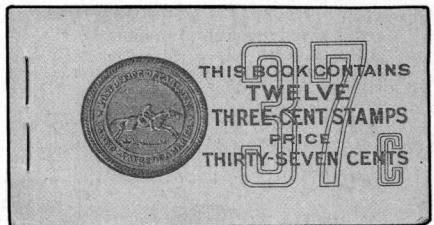

720b, 806b, 807a, 1035a — BC9A

1932-54   **Post Office Seal**

Large background numerals

25c booklet contains 2 panes of six 2c stamps.
37c booklet contains 2 panes of six 3c stamps.
49c booklet contains 4 panes of six 2c stamps.
73c booklets contain 4 panes of six 3c stamps or 4 panes of six 1c stamps and 4 panes of six 2c stamps.

Ordinary Booklets

BK84	BC9A	37c **violet,** *buff* (2)	135.00
a.		With experimental cellophane interleaving	1,750.
BK85	BC9A	73c **violet,** *pink* (2)	375.00

30,000 booklets of No. BK84a were made with .001 inch thick cellophane interleaving, similar to but thinner than the experimental interleaving used for No. BK80a. Poor handling qualities during booklet assembly plus higher cost prevented wider use. Placed on sale in Wash. D.C. post office in Sept., 1936. Extremely scarce, as few were saved.

> **Catalogue values for unused panes in this section, from this point to the end, are for Never Hinged items.**

Washington — A276

In 1942 plates were changed to the Type II "new design" and the E. E. marks may appear at the right or left margins of panes of Nos. 804b, 806b and 807a. Panes printed from E. E. plates have 2½mm vertical gutter; those from pre-E. E. plates have 3mm vertical gutter.

1939-42			**Perf. 11x10½**	
804b	A276	1c 3mm vert. gutter, *Jan. 27, 1939*	4.00	*.85*

Ordinary Booklets

BK86	BC5A	25c **green,** *green*	75.00
BK87	BC5A	97c **green,** *lavender*	*450.00*
BK88	BC4A	97c **green,** *lavender*	—

Combination Booklet

BK89	BC5D	73c **red,** 4 #804b + 4 #806b	135.00
804b	A276	1c 2½mm vert. gutter, *Apr. 14, 1942*	2.00	*.50*

Ordinary Booklets

BK90	BC5A	25c **green,** *green*	8.25
BK91	BC5A	97c **green,** *lavender*	450.00

804b, 806b — BC9E

1939   **Post Office Seal**
Large background numerals
73c booklets contain 4 panes of six 3c stamps or 4 panes of six 1c stamps and 4 panes of six 2c stamps.

Combination Booklets

BK92	BC5D	73c	**red**, 4 #804b + 4 #806b	30.00	
BK93	BC9E	73c	**red**, 4 #804b + 4 #806b	37.50	

Adams — A278

806b	A278	2c 3mm vert. gutter, *Jan. 27, 1939*	22.50	2.50

Ordinary Booklets

BK94	BC5A	97c **red**, *blue*	375.00

Combination Booklet

See No. BK89.

806b	A278	2c 2½mm vert. gutter, *Apr. 25, 1942*	5.50	1.00

Ordinary Booklets

BK95	BC5A	97c **red**, *blue*	1,250.
BK96	BC5A	25c **red**, *buff*	19.00
BK97	BC9A	25c **red**, *buff*	90.00
BK98	BC5A	49c **red**, *pink*	45.00
BK99	BC9A	49c **red**, *pink*	75.00

Combination Booklets

See Nos. BK92 and BK93.

Jefferson — A279

807a	A279	3c 3mm vert. gutter, *Jan. 27, 1939*	30.00	3.25

Booklets

BK100	BC9A	37c **violet**, *buff*	85.00
BK101	BC9A	73c **violet**, *pink*	750.00

807a	A279	3c 2½mm vert. gutter, *Mar. 6, 1942*	8.50	2.00

Booklets

BK102	BC9A	37c **violet**, *buff* (3)	22.50
BK103	BC9A	73c **violet**, *pink* (3)	47.50

Variety

807d	A279	As "a," imperf between vert.	—

Statue of Liberty — A482

1954-58   *Perf. 11x10½*

1035a	A482	3c pane of 6, *June 30, 1954*	4.00	1.25
1035f		Dry printing	5.00	1.50

Booklets

BK104	BC9A	37c **violet**, *buff*, with #1035a	22.50
a.		With #1035f	27.50
BK105	BC9A	73c **violet**, *pink*, with #1035a	27.50
a.		With #1035f	32.50

Variety

1035g		As "a," vert. imperf. betwn.	—

Lincoln — A483

1036a	A483	4c pane of 6, *July 31, 1958*	2.75	1.25

1036a — BC9F

1036a — BC9G

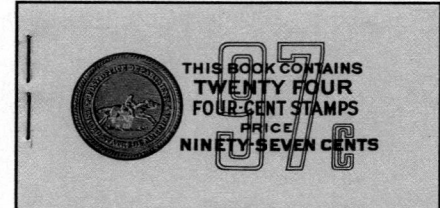

1036a — BC9H

1958

97c booklet contains 4 panes of six 4c stamps.

Booklets

BK106	BC9F	97c on 37c **violet**, *buff*	60.00
BK107	BC9G	97c on 73c **violet**, *pink*	30.00
BK108	BC9H	97c **blue**, *yellow*	150.00
BK109	BC9H	97c **blue**, *pink* (3)	18.00
a.		With experimental silicone interleaving	150.00

Variety

1036d	A483	As "a," imperf. horiz.	—

Washington (Slogan 1) — A650

Slogan 2

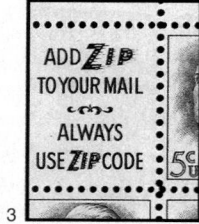

Slogan 3

1962-64   *Perf. 11x10½*
Plate of 300 stamps, 60 labels

1213a	A650	5c pane of 5+label, slogan 1, *Nov. 23, 1962*	7.00	4.00
		With slogan 2, *1963*	16.00	7.00
		With slogan 3, *1964*	3.00	2.00

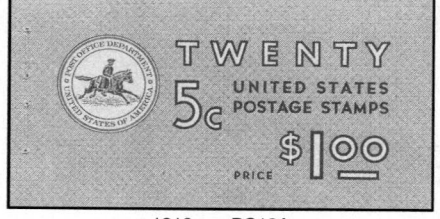

1213a — BC12A

1962-63   **Small Postrider**
$1 booklet contains 4 panes of five 5c stamps.

1213a, 1213c — BC13A

1963-64   **Mr. Zip**
$1 booklet contains 4 panes of five 5c stamps.

Booklets

BK110	BC12A	$1 **blue**, slogan 1	30.00	
BK111	BC12A	$1 **blue**, slogan 2	110.00	
BK112	BC13A	$1 **blue**, slogan 2	90.00	
BK113	BC13A	$1 **blue**, slogan 3 (3)	15.00	

1213c	A650	As No. 1213a, tagged, slogan 2, *Oct. 28, 1963*	60.00	*10.00*
		With slogan 3, *1964*	2.25	*1.50*

Booklets

BK114	BC13A	$1 **blue**, slogan 2	240.00	
BK115	BC13A	$1 **blue**, slogan 3 (4)	10.50	

Jefferson — A710

1967-78   **Perf. 11x10½**

1278a	A710	1c pane of 8, shiny gum, *Jan. 12, 1968*	1.00	*.75*
		Dull gum	2.00	

Combination Booklets

See Nos. BK116, BK117B, BK118 and BK119.

Variety

1278e	A710	As "a," dull gum, tagging omitted		*75.00*

Jefferson — A710

1278b	A710	1c pane of 4+2 labels, slogans 5 & 4, *May 10, 1971*	.80	.60

Combination Booklet

See No. BK122.

Wright — A712

Slogan 4

Slogan 5

1280a	A712	2c pane of 5+label, slogan 4, *Jan. 8, 1968*	1.25	.80
		With slogan 5	1.25	.80

Combination Booklets

See Nos. BK117 and BK120.

1280c	A712	2c pane of 6, shiny gum, *May 7, 1971*	1.00	.75
		Dull gum	1.10	

Combination Booklets

See Nos. BK127 and BKC22.

The 1c and 6c panes of 8, Nos. 1278a and 1284b, were printed from 320-subject plates and from 400-subject plates, both with electric eye markings. The 2c and 6c panes of 5 stamps plus label, Nos. 1280a and 1284c, were printed from 360-subject plates.

An experimental moisture-resistant gum was used on 1,000,000 panes of No. 1278a and 4,000,000 of No. 1393a released in March, 1971. This dull finish gum shows no breaker ridges. The booklets lack interleaving. This gum was also used for Nos. 1395c, 1395d, 1288c and all engraved panes from No. 1510b on unless noted.

Roosevelt — A716

Perf. 10½x11

1284b	A716	6c pane of 8, *Dec. 28, 1967*	1.50	1.00

1278a, 1284b, 1393a — BC14A

1967-70
$2 booklet contains 4 panes of eight 6c stamps and 1 pane of eight 1c stamps.

Combination Booklet

BK116	BC14A	$2 **brown**, 4 #1284b (6c)+1 #1278a(1c)(2)	7.75	

Variety

1284e	A716	6c As "b," tagging omitted	*50.00*	—

Combination Booklet

BK116a	BC14A	$2 **brown**, 4 #1284e (6c) + 1 #1278a (1c)	250.00	

Roosevelt — A716

1284c	A716	6c pane of 5+label, slogan 4, *Jan. 9, 1968*	1.50	1.00
		With slogan 5	1.50	1.00

1278a, 1280a, 1284c, 1393b, 1395b — BC15

1968-71
$1 booklets contain 2 panes of six 8c stamps and 1 pane of four 1c stamps, or 3 panes of five 6c stamps and 1 pane of five 2c stamps.

Combination Booklet

BK117	BC15	$1 **brown**, 3 #1284c (6c) + 1 #1280a (2c) (2)	7.00	

No. BK117 contains panes with slogan 4, slogan 5 or combinations of 4 and 5.

Oliver Wendell Holmes
— A720

Perf. 10

1288Bc	A720	15c pane of 8, *June 14, 1978*	2.80	1.75

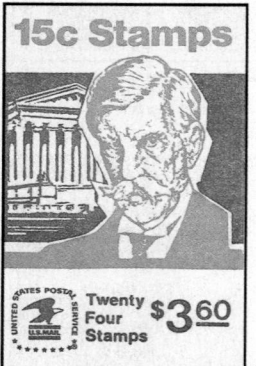

1288Bc — BC23

1978
$3.60 booklet contains 3 panes of eight 15c stamps.

Booklet

BK117A	BC23	$3.60 **red & light blue**, no P#	8.75	

Varieties

1288Be	A720	As "c," vert. imperf. btwn.	*1,750.*	
1288Bi	A720	As "c," tagging omitted	85.00	50.00

Eisenhower — A815

Plate of 400 subjects for No. 1393a.

1970 Tagged   Perf. 11x10½

1393a	A815	6c pane of 8, shiny gum, *Aug. 6*	1.50	.75
		Dull gum	1.90	

1278a, 1393a, 1395a — BC16

1970-71   Eisenhower
$2 booklet contains 4 panes of eight 6c stamps and 1 pane of eight 1c stamps.
$1.92 booklet contains 3 panes of eight 8c stamps.

Combination Booklets

BK117B	BC14A	$2 **blue**, 4 #1393a (6c) + 1 #1278a (1c)	9.00
BK118	BC16	$2 **blue**, 4 #1393a (6c) + 1 #1278a (1c) (2)	7.25
BK119	BC16	$2 **blue**, dull gum, 4 #1393a (6c) + 1 #1278a (1c) (2)	8.75

Varieties

1393h	A815	6c As "a," tagging omitted, shiny gum	250.00	—
		Dull gum		

Eisenhower — A815

Plate of 300 stamps and 60 labels for No. 1393b.

1393b	A815	6c pane of 5+label, slogan 4, *Aug. 6*	1.50	.75
		With slogan 5	1.50	.75

Combination Booklet

BK120	BC15	$1 **blue**, 3 #1393b (6c) + 1 #1280a (2c)	6.00

No. BK120 contains panes with slogan 4, slogan 5 or combinations of 4 and 5.

Eisenhower — A815a

1971-72   Shiny Gum   Perf. 11x10½

1395a	A815a	8c **deep claret**, pane of 8, *May 10, 1971*	1.80	1.25

Booklet

BK121	BC16	$1.92 **claret** (2)	6.50

Variety

1395f		As "a," tagging omitted	—	—

Eisenhower — A815a

1395b	A815a	8c pane of 6, *May 10, 1971*	1.25	1.10

Combination Booklet

BK122	BC15	$1 **claret**, 2 #1395b (8c) + 1 #1278b (1c) (2)	4.00

Variety

1395g		As "b," tagging omitted	40.00	—

Slogans 6 and 7

Eisenhower — A815a

Dull Gum

1395c	A815a	8c pane of 4 + 2 labels, slogans 6 and 7, *Jan. 28, 1972*	1.65	1.00
1395d	A815a	8c pane of 7 + label, slogan 4, *Jan. 28, 1972*	1.90	1.10
		With slogan 5	1.90	1.10

1395c, 1395d — BC17A

1972   Postal Service Emblem
$2 booklet contains 3 panes of seven 8c stamps and 1 pane of four 8c stamps.

Combination Booklet

BK123	BC17A	$2 **claret**, *yellow*, 3 #1395d + 1 #1395c	7.75

Varieties

1395h		As "c," tagging omitted	40.00	—
1395i		As "d," tagging omitted	—	—

Plate of 400 subjects for No. 1395a. Plate of 360 subjects for No. 1395b. Plate of 300 subjects (200 stamps and 100 double-size labels) for No. 1395c. Plate of 400 subjects (350 stamps and 50 labels) for No. 1395d.

A pane of No. 1395d is known with a foldover resulting in a vertical pair of stamp and label, imperf between.

No. BK123 exists with covers printed on both thin and thick card stock.

Booklet Covers
When more than one combination of covers exists, the number of possible booklets is noted in parentheses after the booklet listing.

Jefferson Memorial (Slogan 8) — A924

1973-74   **Perf. 11x10½**
1510b A924   10c pane of 5 + label, slogan 8, *Dec. 14, 1973*   1.65   .90

1510b — BC17B

1973   **Postal Service Emblem**
$1 booklet contains 2 panes of five 10c stamps.

Booklet
BK124 BC17B $1 **red & blue**   3.75

Jefferson Memorial — A924

1510c A924   10c pane of 8, *Dec. 14, 1973*   1.65   1.00

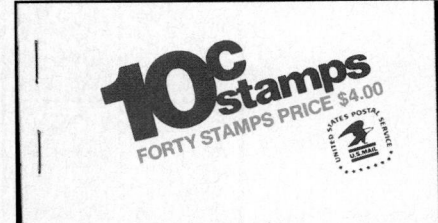

1510c — BC17C

1973   **Postal Service Emblem**
$4 booklet contains 5 panes of eight 10c stamps.

Booklet
BK125 BC17C $4 **red & blue**   8.50

Jefferson Memorial — A924

1510d A924   10c pane of 6, *Aug. 5, 1974*   5.25   1.75

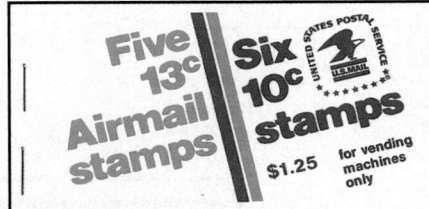

1510d, C79a — BC17D

1974   **Postal Service Emblem**
$1.25 booklet contains 1 pane of five 13c stamps and 1 pane of six 10c stamps.

Combination Booklet
BK126 BC17D $1.25 **red & blue**, 1 #1510d (10c) + 1 #C79a (13c)   7.25

No. BK125 exists with covers printed on both thin and thick card stock.

Variety
1510h   As "c," tagging omitted   —

1975-78   **Perf. 11x10½**
1595a A998   13c pane of 6, *Oct. 31, 1975*   2.25   1.00

1595a, 1595d, 1280c — BC19A

1975-76
90c booklet contains 1 pane of six 13c stamps and 1 pane of six 2c stamps.
$1.30 booklet contains 2 panes of five 13c stamps.

Combination Booklet
BK127 BC19A   90c **red & blue**, 1 #1595a (13c) + 1 #1280c (2c) (2)   3.25

Variety
1595h   As "a," miscut and inserted upside down into booklet cover, imperf below bottom stamps and with "tab" at bottom   —

Liberty Bell — A998

1595b A998   13c pane of 7 + label, slogan 8, *Oct. 31, 1975*   2.25   1.00
1595c A998   13c pane of 8, *Oct. 31, 1975*   2.25   1.00

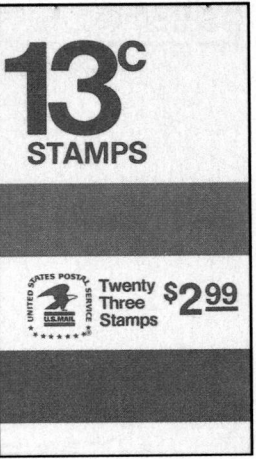

1595b, 1595c — BC19B

1975

$2.99 booklet contains 2 panes of eight 13c stamps and 1 pane of seven 13c stamps.

Combination Booklet

BK128 BC19B $2.99 **red & blue,** 2 #1595c (13c) + 1 #1595b (13c) (2)   7.75

No. BK128 exists with covers printed on both thin and thick card stock.

Liberty Bell (Slogan 9) — A998

1595d A998   13c pane of 5 + label, slogan 9, *Apr. 2, 1976*   1.75   1.00

Booklet

BK129 BC19A $1.30 **red & blue**   4.00

Fort McHenry Flag (15 Stars) — A1001

1977-78   **Perf. 11x10½**

1598a A1001   15c pane of 8, *June 30, 1978*   4.25   .80

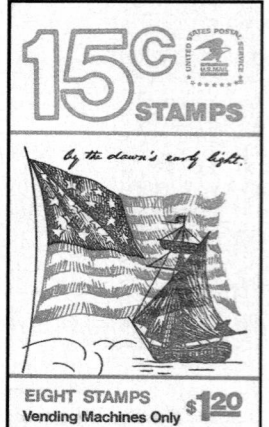

1598a — BC21

1978

$1.20 booklet contains 1 pane of eight 15c stamps.

Booklet

BK130 BC21 $1.20 **red & light blue,** no P#   4.50

1623a — A994, A1018a

1623a A1018a   Pane of 8 (1 #1590 + 7 #1623), *Mar. 11, 1977*   2.25   1.25

1623a — BC20

1977

$1 booklet contains 1 pane of one 9c stamp and seven 13c stamps.

Booklet

BK131 BC20 $1 **red & light blue,** no P# (3)   2.50

Variety

1623g   As "a," tagging omitted   —

Booklet

BK131a BC20 $1 with #1623g   —

Perf. 10x9¾

1623Bc A1018a   Pane of 8 (1 #1590A + 7 #1623B), *Mar. 11, 1977*   22.50   —

Booklet

BK132 BC20 $1 **red & light blue,** no P# (2)   23.00

1736a — A1124

1978   **Tagged**   **Perf. 11x10½**

1736a A1124 A pane of 8, *May 22*   2.50   1.50

1736a — BC24

BC24 illustration reduced.

1978

$3.60 booklet contains 3 panes of eight A (15c) stamps.

Booklet

BK133 BC24 $3.60 **deep orange**   7.75

No. BK133 exists with covers printed on both thin and thick card stock.

Variety

1736b   As "a," tagging omitted   —

1737a — A1126

Perf. 10

1737a A1126 15c pane of 8, *July 11* 2.50 1.50

1737a — BC22

1978
$2.40 booklet contains 2 panes of eight 15c stamps.

Booklet
BK134 BC22 $2.40 **rose red & yel grn,** no
P# 5.25

Varieties
1737c As "a," imperf. *2,200.*
1737d As "a," tagging omitted *50.00* —

Windmills — A1127-A1131

1980 **Perf. 11**
1742a A1127 15c pane of 10, *Feb. 7* 3.50 3.00

1742a — BC25

1980
$3 booklet contains 2 panes of ten 15c stamps.

Booklet
BK135 BC25 $3 **light blue & dark blue,**
blue, no P# 7.50

1819a — A1207

1981
1819a A1207 B pane of 8, *Mar. 15* 3.75 2.25

1819a — BC26

1981
$4.32 booklet contains 3 panes of eight B (18c) stamps.

Booklet
BK136 BC26 $4.32 **dull violet,** no P# 11.75

1889a — A1267-
A1276

1889a A1267 18c pane of 10, *May 14* 8.50 6.00

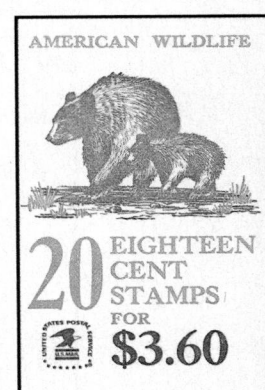

1889a — BC28

1981
$3.60 booklet contains 2 panes of ten 18c stamps.

Booklet
BK137 BC28 $3.60 **gray & olive,** P#1-10 17.50
P#11-13 40.00
P#14-16 35.00

1893a — A1279-A1280

1893a   A1279   Pane of 8 (2 #1892, 6 #1893), *Apr. 24*   3.00   2.50

1893a — BC27

1981

$1.20 booklet contains 1 pane of two 6c and six 18c stamps.

Booklet

BK138   BC27 $1.20 **blue & red,** P#1   3.25

Varieties

1893b   As "a," vert. imperf. btwn.   70.00
1893d   As "a," tagging omitted   —

Booklets

BK138a   BC27 $1.20 With No. 1893b, P#1   70.00
BK138b   BC27 $1.20 With No. 1893d, P#1   —

1896a — A1281

1981-83

1896a   A1281   20c pane of 6, small block tagging, *Dec. 17, 1981*   3.00   2.25
                Scored perforations   3.00   2.25

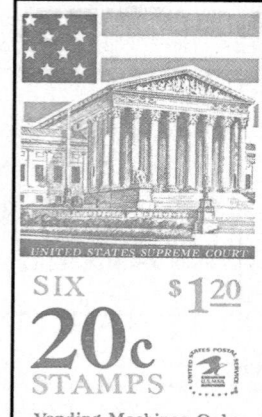

1896a — BC29

1982

$1.20 booklet contains 1 pane of six 20c stamps.

Booklet

BK139   BC29 $1.20 **blue & red,** P#1 (2)   3.25

1896b — A1281

1896b   A1281   20c pane of 10, *June 1, 1982*   5.25   3.25

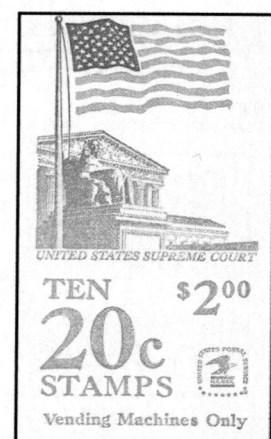

1896b — BC29A

1982

$2 booklet contains 1 pane of ten 20c stamps.

Booklet

BK140   BC29A $2 **blue & red,** P#1 (4)   5.50
                      P#4   47.50

1896e   A1281   20c pane of 10, large block tagging, *Nov. 17, 1983*   5.25   3.25
                Scored perforations   5.25   3.25

1896b — BC29B

1983

$4 booklet contains 2 panes of ten 20c stamps.

Booklet

BK140A   BC29B $4 **blue & red,** *Nov. 17, 1983,* P#2   11.00
                      P#3   17.50

P#4   260.00

Variety

1896f   As "a," tagging omitted   —   —

The small block tagging is 16x18mm (Nos. 1896a-1896b).
The large block tagging is 18x21mm (No. 1896e).

Booklet Covers

When more than one combination of covers exists, the number of possible booklets is noted in parentheses after the booklet listing.

1909a — A1296

1983

1909a   A1296 $9.35 pane of 3, *Aug. 12*   60.00   —

1909a — BC31

1983

$28.05 booklet contains 1 pane of three $9.35 stamps.

Booklet

BK140B BC31   28.05 **blue & red**, P#1111   62.50

1948a — A1333

1981

1948a   A1333   C pane of 10, *Oct. 11*   4.50   3.25

1948a
—
BC26A

1981

$4 booklet contains 2 panes of ten C (20c) stamps.

Booklet

BK141 BC26A $4 **brown**, *blue*, no P#   10.00

1949a — A1334

1982

1949a   A1334   20c pane of 10, type I,
                        Jan. 8   5.50   2.50
1949d   As "a," type II   14.00   —

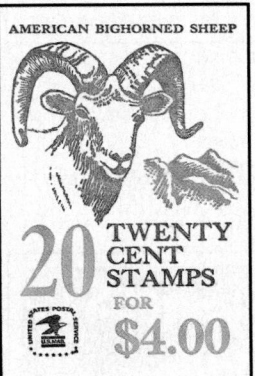

1949a — BC30

1982

$4 booklet contains 2 panes of ten 20c stamps.

Booklets

BK142 BC30 $4 **blue & yellow
                        green**, P#1-6, 9-10   16.00
                        P#11, 12, 15   40.00
                        P#14   30.00
                        P#16   75.00
                        P#17-19   55.00
                        P#20, 22-24   100.00
                        P#21, 28, 29   350.00
                        P#25-26   150.00
    a.   Type II, P#34   22.00

Varieties

1949b   As "a," vert. imperf. btwn.   95.00
1949f   As "a," tagging omitted   50.00   —

Booklets

BK142b   As BK142, with 2 #1949b   190.00
BK142c   As BK142, with 2 #1949f, P#4, 5,
                6, 19   100.00

Stamps in No. 1949a are 18¾mm wide and have overall tagging. Stamps in No. 1949d are 18½mm wide and have block tagging.

Plate number does not always appear on top pane in Nos. BK142, BK142a. These booklets sell for more, except P#14 and 15.

Booklet cover BC30 comes in blue & yellow green and in blue & olive green. Both are equally common.

2113a — A1497

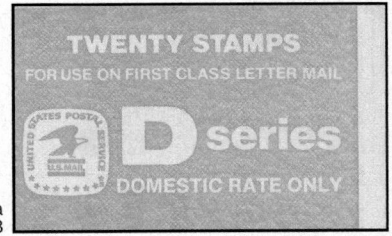

2113a
BC26B

1985

$4.40 booklet contains 2 panes of ten D (22c) stamps.

Booklet

BK143 BC26B $4.40 **green**, P#1, 3, 4   17.00
                        P#2   500.00

Variety

2113b   As "a," imperf. between, horiz.   —

Plate number does not always appear on top pane in No. BK143. No. BK143 is known with no plate number on top pane and plate number 1, 2, 3 or 4 on bottom pane. These booklets sell for more except P#4. No. BK143 with P#2 on bottom is rare; value, $2,100.

2116a — A1499

1985
2113a A1497 D pane of 10 *Feb. 1*   8.50   3.00

Perf. 11

Perf. 10 Horiz.

2116a A1499 22c pane of 5, *Mar. 29*   2.50   1.25
                    Scored perforations   2.50

2116a — BC33C

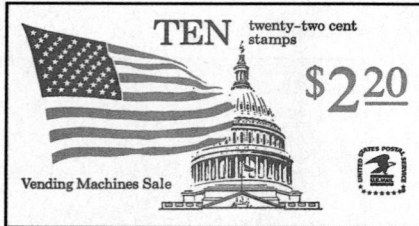

2116a — BC32

1985
$1.10 booklet contains one pane of five 22c stamps.
$2.20 booklet contains two panes of five 22c stamps.

Booklets
BK144 BC33C $1.10 **blue & red,** P#1, 3
(2)
BK145 BC32 $2.20 **blue & red,** P#1, 3   2.75
(2)   5.25

2121a — A1500-
A1504

Perf. 10
2121a   A1500   22c pane of 10, *Apr. 4*   4.00   3.00

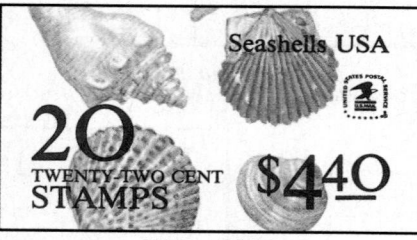

2121a — BC33A

Many different seashell configurations are possible on BC33A. Seven adjacent covers are necessary to show all 25 shells.

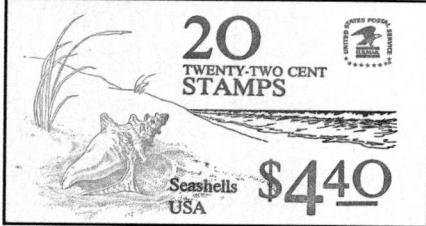

2121a — BC33B

1985
$4.40 booklet contains two panes of ten 22c stamps.

Booklets
BK146 BC33A $4.40 **multicolored,** P#1, 3   8.50
P#2   10.00
BK147 BC33B $4.40 **brown & blue,** P#1,
3, 5, 6, 7, 10   8.50
P#8   10.00

Varieties
2121b   As "a," violet omitted on both Nos.
2120   475.00
2121c   As "a," vert. imperf. btwn.   450.00
2121d   As "a," imperf.   —

2122a — A1505

1985-89   **Perf. 10 Vert.**
2122a A1505 10.75 type I, pane of 3, *Apr.*
29, 1985   60.00   —

2122a — BC31A

1985
$32.25 booklet contains 1 pane of three $10.75 stamps.

Booklet
BK148 BC31A 32.25 **multicolored,**
P#11111   62.50
2122c A1505 10.75 type II, pane of 3,
June 19, 1989   65.00   —

2122c — BC31B

1989
$32.25 booklet contains 1 pane of three $10.75 stamps.

Booklet
BK149 BC31B 32.25 **blue & red,** P#22222
(2)   67.50

2182a — A1564

1988   **Perf. 11**
2182a A1564 25c pane of 10, *May 3*   5.00   3.75

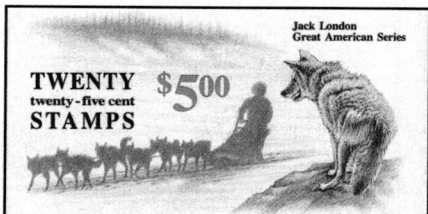

2182a — BC43

1988
$5 booklet contains two panes of ten 25c stamps.

Booklet
BK150 BC43 $5 **multicolored,** P#1-2   10.50

Varieties
2182c   As "a," tagging omitted   —
2182e   As "a," all color omitted on right stamps   —
Booklet
BK150a BC43 $5 As BK150, with
#2182c   —

2197a — A1564

Perf. 10 on 2 or 3 Sides
2197a A1564 25c pane of 6, *May 3*   3.30   2.50

2197a — 43BCA

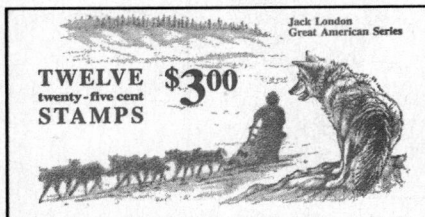

2197a — BC43B

1988
$1.50 booklet contains one pane of six 25c stamps.
$3 booklet contains two panes of six 25c stamps.

Booklets

BK151	BC43A	$1.50 **blue & brown**, P#1		3.30
BK152	BC43B	$3 **brown & blue**, P#1		6.60

BK151 and BK152 exist with covers printed on both thin and thick card stock.

Variety

2197c	A1564	25c As "a," tagging omitted		50.00

Booklet

BK151a	BC43A	$1.50 As BK151, with #2197c	57.50

2201a — A1581-A1584

1986

2201a	A1581	22c pane of 4, *Jan. 23*	2.00	1.75

STAMP COLLECTING USA • AMERIPEX 86

The International Stamp Show at Chicago May 22 – June 1, 1986, will admit the bearer of this booklet cover free of charge.

Eight 22 cent stamps — $1.76

2201a — BC34

1986
$1.76 booklet contains 2 panes of four 22c stamps.

Booklet

BK153	BC34	$1.76 **purple & black**, P#1	4.00

Varieties

2201b	As "a," black omitted on Nos. 2198, 2201	47.50
2201c	As "a," blue (litho.) omitted on Nos. 2198-2200	2,250.
2201d	As "a," buff (litho.) omitted	—

Booklets

BK153a	BC34	$1.76 As No. BK153, with 2 #2201b	110.00
BK153b	BC34	$1.76 As No. BK153, with 2 #2201c	5,000.

2209a — A1588-A1592

2209a	A1588	22c pane of 5, *Mar. 21*	6.00	2.75

FISH USA

10 twenty-two cent stamps **$2.20**

2209a — BC35

1986
$2.20 booklet contains 2 panes of five 22c stamps.

Booklet

BK154	BC35	$2.20 **blue green and red**, P#11111, 22222	12.50

2274a — A1637-A1644

1987

2274a	A1637	22c pane of 10, *Apr. 20*	10.00	5.00

FOR 22 CENTS, YOU CAN ADD ONE OF THESE GREETINGS TO A LETTER TO ANYONE IN THE UNITED STATES, CANADA OR MEXICO.

Get Well!
Thank You!
Best Wishes!
Keep in Touch!
Love You, Dad!
Happy Birthday!
Congratulations!
Love You, Mother!

10 TWENTY-TWO CENT U.S. POSTAGE STAMPS $2.20

2274a — BC36

1987
$2.20 booklet contains 1 pane of ten 22c stamps.

Booklet

BK155	BC36	$2.20 **blue & red**, P#111111, 222222	12.50

2276a — A1646

Perf. 11

2276a A1646 22c pane of 20, *Nov. 30* 8.50 —

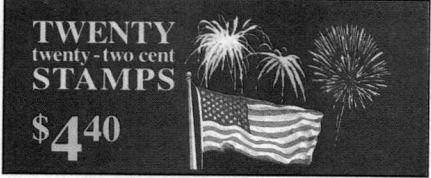

2276a — BC39

Illustration reduced.

1987
$4.40 booklet contains one pane of twenty 22c stamps.

Booklet

BK156	BC39	$4.40 **multicolored,** no P#	9.00	
		P#1111, 2222	12.00	
		P#2122	19.00	

Varieties

2276b As "a," vert. pair, imperf. between *1,500.*
2276c As "a," miscut and inserted upside down into booklet cover, imperf. between stamps and right selvage. —

No. 2276a was made from sheets of No. 2276 which had alternating rows of perforations removed and the right sheet margins trimmed off.

2282a — A1647

1988
Perf. 10
2282a A1647 E pane of 10, *Mar. 22* 6.50 3.50
Scored perforations 6.50 —

2282a — BC40

1988
$5 booklet contains two panes of ten E stamps.

Booklet

BK157	BC40	$5 **blue,** P#1111, 2222	13.00	
		P#2122	15.00	

2283a — A1649a

Perf. 11

2283a A1649a 25c pane of 10, *Apr. 29* 6.00 3.50

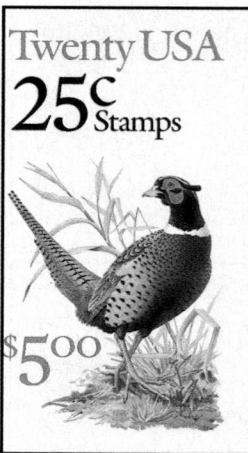

2283a,
2283c — BC41

1988
$5 booklet contains two panes of ten 25c stamps.

Booklet

BK158	BC41	$5 **multicolored,** P#A1111	12.00	

2283c — A1649a

Color Change

2283c A1649a 25c red removed from sky, pane of 10 65.00 —

Booklet

BK159	BC41	$5 **multicolored,** P#A3111, A3222	125.00	

2285b — A1649b-
A1649c

Perf. 10

2285b A1649b 25c pane of 10, *May 28* 5.00 3.50

2285b — BC45

1988
$5 booklet contains two panes of ten 25c stamps.

Booklet

BK160 BC45 **$5 red & black,** P#1111, 1112,
1211, 1433, 1434, 1734,
2121, 2321, 3333, 5955 (2)   12.00
P#1133, 2111, 2122, 2221,
2222, 3133, 3233, 3412,
3413, 3422, 3521, 4642,
4644, 4911, 4941   20.00
P#1414   95.00
P#1634, 3512   50.00
P#3822   40.00
P#5453   165.00

No. BK160 exists with two cover types: one with one bud at end of flowering branch, and one (shown) with two buds. Two-bud cover only contains panes with P# 1111, 1211, 2122 or 2222. One-bud cover contains panes with all listed plate numbers.

2285Ac — A1648

2285Ac A1648   25c pane of 6, *July 5*   3.00   2.00

2285Ac — BC46

1988
$3 booklet contains two panes of six 25c stamps.

Booklet

BK161 BC46 $3 **blue & red,** P#1111   6.00

2359a — A1719-A1723

1987
2359a A1719   22c pane of 5, *Aug. 28*   4.50   2.25

We the People $4.40 Twenty 22-cent stamps USA

2359a — BC37

1987
$4.40 booklet contains four panes of five 22c stamps.

Booklet

BK162 BC37 $4.40 **red & blue,** P#1111,
1112   18.00

2366a — A1726-
A1730

2366a A1726   22c pane of 5, *Oct. 1*   2.75   2.50

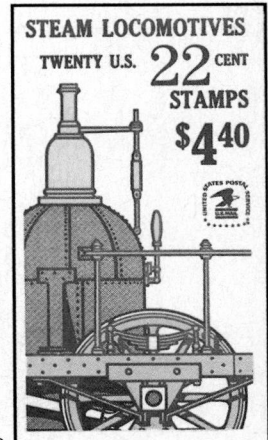

2366a — BC38

1987
$4.40 booklet contains four panes of five 22c stamps.

Booklet

BK163 BC38 $4.40 **black & yellow,** P#1, 2   11.00

2385a — A1745-A1749

1988
2385a   A1745   25c pane of 5, *Aug. 25*   6.00   3.50

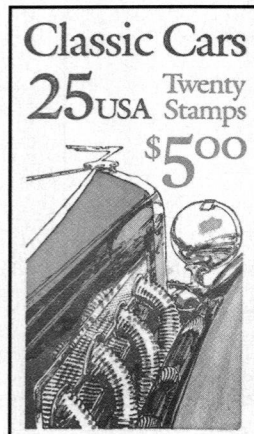

2385a — BC47

1988
$5 booklet contains four panes of five 25c stamps.
Booklet
BK164   BC47 $5 **black & red,** P#1   25.00

2396a — A1759-A1760

2398a — A1761-A1762

Perf. 11

2396a   A1759   25c pane of 6, *Oct. 22*   3.50   3.25
2398a   A1761   25c pane of 6, *Oct. 22*   3.50   3.25

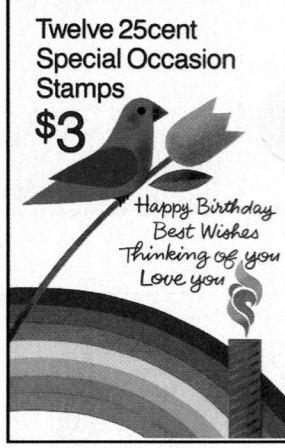

2396a,
2398a — BC48

1988
$3 booklet contains two panes of six 25c stamps.
Combination Booklet
BK165   BC48 $3 **multicolored,** 1
#2396a, 1 #2398a,
P#A1111 (2)   7.00

Varieties
2398b   As "a," imperf. horiz.   —
2398c   As "a," imperf   —

One example of a mint, never-hinged and never-folded pane of No. 2396a is recorded. A second example of a never-folded pane of No. 2396a exists uncancelled, affixed to a USPS souvenir page. Examples of No. 2398a in mint, never-hinged, never-folded condition also are recorded (very scarce).

2409a — A1769-
A1773

1989   **Perf. 10**
2409a   A1769   25c pane of 5, *Mar. 3*   2.50   1.75
Never folded pane, P#1   8.00
P#2   20.00

2409a — BC49

1989
$5 booklet contains four panes of five 25c stamps.
Booklet
BK166   BC49 $5 **blue & black,** P#1, 2   10.00

Variety
2409b   As "a," tagging omitted   —

2427a — A1791

Perf. 11½

2427a	A1791	25c pane of 10, *Oct. 19*		5.00	3.50
		Never folded pane, P#1		10.00	

2427a — BC50

1989
$5 booklet contains two panes of ten 25c stamps.

Booklet

BK167	BC50	$5 multicolored, P#1	10.00	

Variety

2427c	As "a," imperf	—

2429a — A1792

2429a	A1792	25c pane of 10, *Oct. 19*	5.00	3.50

	Never folded pane, P#1111	17.50

2429a — BC51

Illustration reduced.

1989
$5 booklet contains two panes of ten 25c stamps.

Booklet

BK168	BC51	$5 multicolored, P#1111, 2111	10.00	

Varieties

2429c	As "a," imperf between	—
2429d	As "a," red omitted	3,500.

2431a — A1793

2431a — BC52

1989
$5 fold-it-yourself booklet contains eighteen self-adhesive 25c stamps.

Self-adhesive   *Die cut*

2431a	A1793	25c pane of 18, *Nov. 10*, P#A1111	11.00	

By its nature, No. 2431a constitutes a complete booklet. Blue & red peelable paper backing is booklet cover (BC52). Sold for $5.

2441a — A1800

1990   *Perf. 11½*

2441a	A1800	25c pane of 10, *Jan. 18*	5.00	3.50
		Never folded pane, P#1211	20.00	

2441a — BC53

Illustration reduced.

1990
$5 booklet contains two panes of ten 25c stamps.

Booklet

BK169	BC53	$5 multicolored, P#1211	10.50	
		P#2111	20.00	
		P#2211	30.00	
		P#2222	17.50	

Variety

2441c	As "a," bright pink omitted	1,500.

Panes exist containing both normal and bright pink omitted stamps. Value is less than that of No. 2441c.

2443a — A1802

Perf. 11

2443a	A1802	15c pane of 10, *Feb. 3*	3.00	2.00

Never folded pane,
P#111111   9.00

2443a — BC54

1990
$3 booklet contains two panes of ten 15c stamps.

Booklet
BK170 BC54 $3 **multi,** P#111111   6.00
                P#221111   10.00
Variety
2443c   As "a," blue omitted   *1,250.*

2474a — A1829-A1833

Perf. 10
2474a A1829 25c pane of 5, *Apr. 26*   9.50 2.00
              Never folded pane,
              P#1, 3, 5   10.00
              P#2   12.00
              P#4   —

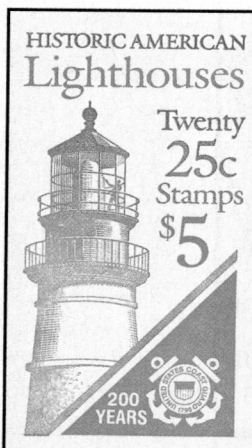

2474a — BC55

1990
$5 booklet contains four panes of five 25c stamps.

Booklet
BK171 BC55 $5 **blue & red,** P#1-5 (2)   38.00
Variety
2474b   As "a," white omitted 100.00 —
Booklet
BK171a   As No. BK171, with 4
             No. 2474b   400.00

2483a — A1847

1991-95
2483a A1847 20c **multicolored,** pane of 10, *June
              15, 1995,*   5.25 2.25
              Never folded pane, P#S1111   6.25

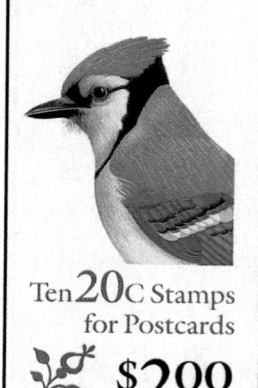

2483a — BC56

1995
$2 booklet contains one pane of 10 20c stamps.

Booklet
BK172 BC56 $2 **multicolored,**
             P#S1111   5.25
Variety
2483b   As "a," imperf   —

2484a — A1848

Perf. 10
2484a A1848 29c **black & multi,** overall
              tagging, pane of 10,
              Apr. 12, 1991   6.00 3.75
              Never folded pane,
              P#1111   9.50
2484e A1848 29c **black & multi,**
              prephosphored coated
              paper with surface tag-
              ging showing a solid ap-
              pearance, pane of 10,
              1992   6.00 3.75

2484a, 2485a — BC57

Illustration reduced.

1991-92
$2.90 booklet contains one pane of 10 29c stamps.
$5.80 booklet contains two panes of 10 29c stamps.

Booklets
BK173 BC57 $2.90 **black & green,** with
              No. 2484e, P#4444   6.25
BK174 BC57 $5.80 **black & red,** P#1111,
              2222   12.00
              P#1211   125.00
              P#3222, 3333   20.00
BK174a   As No. BK174, with 2
              #2484e, P#2122,
              2222, 3222, 3333   17.50
              P#3221   100.00
              P#3331   —
              P#4444   15.00
Varieties
2484c   As "a," imperf horiz.   950.00
2484g   As "a," imperf between
              and with natural
              straight edge at top or
              bottom   —

2485a — A1848

Perf. 11
2485a A1848 29c **red & multi,** pane of
              10, *Apr. 12, 1991*   6.00 4.00
              Never folded pane,
              P#K11111   12.50
Booklet
BK175 BC57 $5.80 **black & multi,**
              P#K11111   13.00

2486a — A1849

2486a A1849 29c pane of 10, *Oct. 8, 1993* 6.00 4.00
              Never folded pane,
              P#K1111   6.75

2486a — BC58

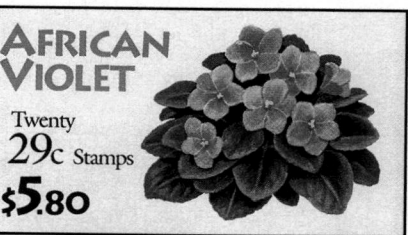

2486a — BC58A

1993

$2.90 booklet contains one pane of 10 29c stamps.
$5.80 booklet contains two panes of 10 29c stamps.

Booklets

BK176	BC58	$2.90	**multicolored,** P#K1111	6.25
BK177	BC58A	$5.80	**multicolored,** P#K1111	12.50

2488a — A1850-
A1851

2488a	A1850	32c	**multicolored,** pane of 10, *July 8, 1995*	6.50	4.25
			Never folded pane, P# 11111	7.25	

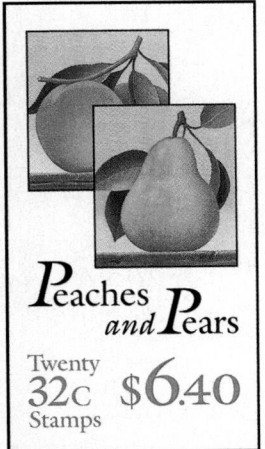

2488a — BC59

1995

$6.40 booklet contains two panes of 10 32c stamps.

Booklet

BK178	BC59	$6.40	**multicolored,** P#11111	13.00

• D2 133 Self-adhesive stamps • DO NOT WET • Peel here to fold •

2489a — A1852

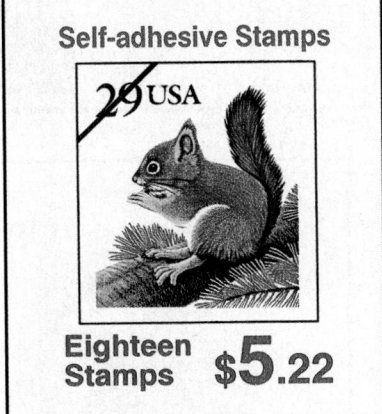

2489a
BC60

1993

$5.22 fold-it-yourself booklet contains 18 self-adhesive 29c stamps.

	Self-Adhesive			***Die Cut***
2489a	A1852	29c pane of 18, *June 25, 1993,* P#D11111, D22211		12.00
		P#D22221, D22222, D23133		14.50

By its nature, No. 2489a constitutes a complete booklet (BC60). The peelable backing serves as a booklet cover.

Variety

2489b	As "a," die cutting omitted	—

S 1 1 1   • Peel here to fold • Self-adhesive stamps • DO NOT WET

2490a — A1853

2490a
BC61

1993

$5.22 fold-it-yourself booklet contains 18 self-adhesive 29c stamps.

	Self-Adhesive		***Die Cut***
2490a	A1853	29c pane of 18, *Aug. 19, 1993,* P#S111	12.00

By its nature, No. 2490a constitutes a complete booklet (BC61). The peelable backing, of which two types are known, serves as a booklet cover.

2491a — A1854

2492a — A1853

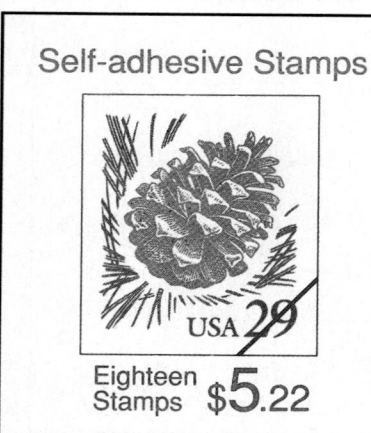

Self-adhesive Stamps

Eighteen Stamps $5.22

2491a — BC61A

1993

$5.22 fold-it-yourself booklet contains 18 self-adhesive stamps.

Self-Adhesive		*Die Cut*
2491a A1854 29c pane of 18, *Nov. 5, 1993,*		
P#B3-11, 13-14, 16	11.00	
P#B1	17.50	
P#B2, 12, 15	15.00	

By its nature, No. 2491a constitutes a complete booklet (BC61A). The peelable backing serves as a booklet cover.

Twenty
Self-adhesive Stamps

$6.40

2492a — BC61B

1995

$6.40 fold-it-yourself booklet contains 20 self-adhesive 32c stamps.

Serpentine Die Cut 11.3x11.7 on 2, 3 or 4 Sides
Self-Adhesive

2492a A1853 32c pane of 20 + label, *June 2, 1995,* P#S111, S112, S333, prephosphored coated paper	13.00

2492b	A1853 32c pane of 15 + label, *1996*	9.75
2492e	A1853 32c pane of 14, *1996*	21.00
2492f	A1853 32c pane of 16, *1996*	21.00

By its nature, No. 2492a is a complete booklet (BC61B). The peelable backing serves as a booklet cover.

Nos. 2492a and 2492b exist on two types of surface-tagged paper that exhibit either a solid or grainy solid appearance. Values are the same. Nos. 2492e and 2492f have only tagging with a solid appearance.

Nos. 2492a and 2492b come either with no die cutting on the label or with die cutting.

No. 2492e contains blocks of 4, 6 and 4 stamps. No. 2492f contains blocks of 6, 6 and 4 stamps. The blocks are on rouletted backing paper. The peel-a-way strips that were between the blocks have been removed to fold the pane.

Booklets
See note before No. BK243.

BK178A	BC126 $4.80 **blue**, No. 2492b (5) (solid tagging)	10.00
g.	As No. BK178A, pane with grainy solid tagging	10.00
BK178B	BC126 $4.80 **blue**, No. 2492f with bottom right stamp removed (solid tagging)	40.00
h.	As No. BK178B, pane with grainy solid tagging	40.00
BK178C	BC126 $9.60 **blue**, 2 #2492b, No P# (3) (grainy solid tagging only)	20.00
BK178D	BC126 $9.60 **blue**, 2 panes of #2492f ea with a stamp removed from either the top or bottom row, No P# (3) (grainy solid tagging only)	45.00

Combination Booklets
See note before No. BK243.

BK178E	BC126 $9.60 **blue**, 1 ea #2492e, 2492f, no P# (3) (solid tagging only)	47.50
BK178F	BC126 $9.60 **blue**, #2492b, 2492f with bottom right stamp removed, no P# (grainy solid tagging only)	*225.00*

No. BK178A was issued wrapped in cellophane and not wrapped in cellophane. The two cellophane-wrapped versions are scarcer.

No. BK178E was sold wrapped in cellophane with the contents of the booklet listed on a label. Three versions exist. No. 2492f is affixed to the booklet cover, and No. 2492e is loose.

The panes of #2492f with one stamp removed that are contained in Nos. BK178B, BK178D and BK178F cannot be made from No. 2492b, a pane of 15 + label. The label is located in the sixth or seventh row of the pane and is sometimes die cut. The panes with one stamp removed all have the stamp removed from the top or bottom row of the pane.

Variety

2492d	As "a," 2 stamps and parts of 7 others printed on backing liner	—

2494a — A1850-A1851

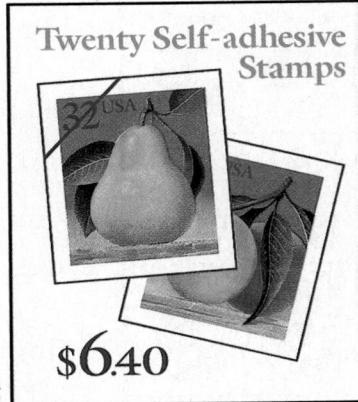

2494a
BC61C

1995
$6.40 fold-it-yourself booklet contains 20 self-adhesive 32c stamps.

Serpentine Die Cut 8.8

2494a	A1850	32c pane of 20+label, *July 8, 1995,* P# list 1		13.00
		P# list 2		18.00
		P#V11132, V33353		15.00
		P#V33323		25.00
		P#V11232		—

By its nature, No. 2494a is a complete booklet (BC61C). The peelable backing serves as a booklet cover. It comes either with no die cutting on the label or with die cutting.

List 1 — P#V11111, V11122, V12132, V12211, V12221, V22212, V22222, V33142, V33243, V33333, V33343, V33363, V44424, V44434, V45434, V45464, V54365, V54565, V55365, V55565.
List 2 — P#V11131, V12131, V12232, V22221, V33143, V33453.

2505a — A1860-A1864

1990   *Perf. 11*
2505a A1860 25c pane of 10, *Aug. 17*   15.00   7.50
              Never folded pane, P#1-2   20.00

2505a — BC62

1990
$5 booklet contains two panes of 10 25c stamps.

Booklet
BK179	BC62	$5 multicolored, P#1, 2		30.00

Varieties
2505b		As "a," black (engr.) omitted	*3,500.*
2505d		As "a," horiz. imperf.	—

2514b — A1873

1990   *Perf. 11½*
2514b A1873 25c pane of 10, *Oct. 18*   5.00 3.25
              Never folded pane   12.50

2514a — BC63

1990
$5 booklet contains two panes of 10 25c stamps.

Booklet
BK180	BC63	$5 multicolored, P#1		10.00

2516a — A1874

1990   *Perf. 11½x11*
2516a A1874 25c pane of 10, *Oct. 18*   5.00   3.25
                  Never folded pane, P#1211   15.00

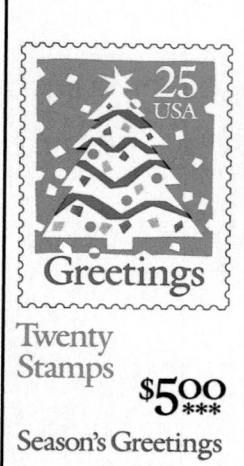

2516a — BC64

1990
$5 booklet contains two panes of 10 25c stamps.

Booklet
BK181 BC64 $5 **multicolored,** P#1211   11.00
                P#1111   —

2519a — A1875

1991   *Perf. 11.2* **Bullseye**
2519a A1875   F pane of 10, *Jan. 22*   6.50   4.50

2519a,
2520a — BC65

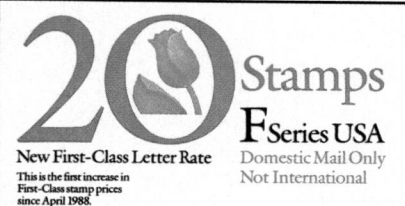

2519a, 2520a — BC65A

1991
$2.90 booklet contains one pane of 10 F stamps.
$5.80 booklet contains two panes of 10 F stamps.

Booklets
BK182 BC65   ($2.90) **yellow & multi,** P#2222   6.50
BK183 BC65A ($5.80) **grn, red & blk,** P#1111,
                  2121, 2222   13.00
                  P#1222, 2111, 2212   25.00

2520a — A1875

                                        Perf. 11
2520a A1875   F pane of 10, *Jan. 22*   18.00   4.50
                   Never folded pane,
                   P#K1111   —
                        Booklet
BK184 BC65 ($2.90) like #BK182, **grn, red &**
                  blk, P#K1111   18.00
                        Varieties
2520b   As "a," imperf. horiz.   —
2520c   Horiz. pair, imperf be-
                    tween, in error booklet
                    pane of 12 stamps   *500.00*
No. 2520c is from a paper foldover before perforating.

2527a — A1879

                                        Perf. 11
2527a A1879   29c pane of 10, *Apr. 5*   6.00   3.50
                   Never folded pane,
                   P#K1111   8.00

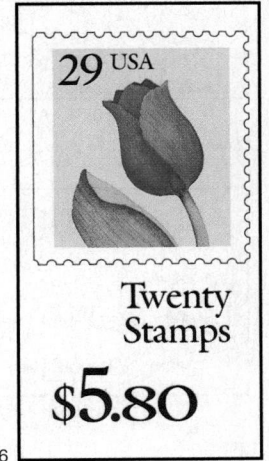

2527a — BC66

1991
$2.90 booklet contains one pane of 10 29c stamps.

Booklet

BK185	BC66	$5.80	multicolored, P#K1111, K2222, K3333	12.00

Varieties

2527d	As "a," imperf horiz.	*750.00*
2527e	As "a," imperf vert.	—

2528a — A1880

Perf. 11

2528a	A1880	29c pane of 10, *Apr. 21*	6.00	3.50
		Never folded pane	7.00	

2528a — BC67

2528a — BC67A

1991
$2.90 booklet contains one pane of 10 29c stamps.

Booklets

BK186	BC67	$2.90	black & mul-ticolored, P#K11111	5.75
BK186A	BC67A	$2.90	red & multicolored, P#K11111 (2)	6.75

Booklet Covers
When more than one combination of covers exists, the number of possible booklets is noted in parentheses after the booklet listing.

2530a — A1882

Perf. 10

2530a	A1882	19c pane of 10, *May 17*	4.00	2.75
		Never folded pane, P#1111	5.00	

2530a — BC68

1991
$3.80 booklet contains two panes of 10 19c stamps.

Booklet

BK187	BC68	$3.80	black & blue, P#1111, 2222	8.00
			P#1222	32.50

Peel here and Fold • Self-adhesive stamps • DO NOT WET • © USPS 1991

2531Ab — A1884

Self-adhesive Stamps

Convenient: No Licking!

Strong Adhesive: Stays on Envelopes!

Easy to Use: No Tearing!

Eighteen Stamps

2531Ae — BC68B

1991-92
$5.22 fold-it-yourself booklet contains 18 self-adhesive 29c stamps.

Self-Adhesive
Die Cut
2531Ab A1884   29c pane of 18, prephosphored coated paper with surface tagging showing a solid appearance, *June 25,* no P#   11.00

By its nature, No. 2531Ab constitutes a complete booklet (BC68A). The peelable backing serves as a booklet cover.

Variety
2531Ae   As "b," overall tagging (BC68B), *1992*   11.00

2536a — A1890

1991   *Perf. 11*
2536a A1890   29c pane of 10, *May 9*   6.00   3.50
Never folded pane, P#1111, 1112   8.25

 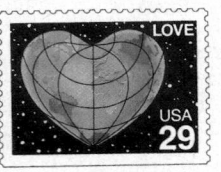

2536a — BC69

1991
$5.80 booklet contains two panes of 10 29c stamps.

Booklet
BK188 BC69 $5.80 **multicolored,** P#1111, 1112   12.00
P#1113, 1123, 2223   16.00
P#1212   42.50

2549a — A1899-A1903

                            Perf. 11
2549a A1899   29c pane of 5, *May 31*   12.50   3.50
Never folded pane, P#A23133, A23213   15.00

P#A11111, A22122, A22132, A33213   —
P#A23124   45.00
P#A32225, A33233   27.50

2549a — BC70

1991
$5.80 booklet contains four panes of 5 29c stamps.

Booklet
BK189 BC70 $5.80 **multicolored,** P#A22122, A23123, A23124, A33235, A44446, A45546, A45547   50.00
P#A11111, A22133, A23133, A23213   57.50
P#A22132, A32224, A32225, A33233   52.50
P#A31224   75.00

No. BK189 exists assembled from panes with different plate numbers.
P#33213 has yet to be found as top pane in booklets.

2552a — A1905

                            Perf. 11
2552a A1905   29c pane of 5, *July 2*   3.00   2.25
Never folded pane, P#A11121111   4.75

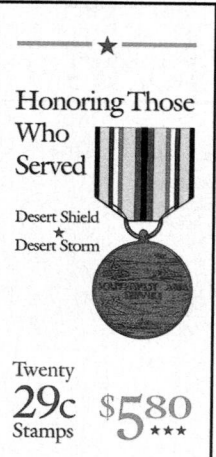

2552a — BC71

1991
$5.80 booklet contains four panes of 5 29c stamps.

Booklet
BK190 BC71 $5.80 **multicolored,** P#A11111111, A11121111   12.00

2566a — A1916-A1920

2566a A1916   29c pane of 10, *Aug. 29*   10.00   5.00
Never folded pane, P#1   11.50

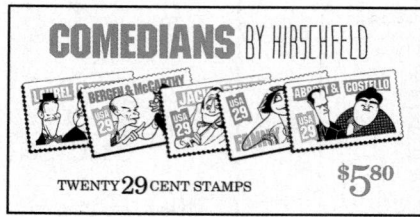

2566a — BC72

1991
$5.80 booklet contains two panes of ten 29c stamps.

Booklet
BK191 BC72 $5.80 **scar, blk & brt vio,** P#1, 2   21.00

Variety
2566b   As "a," scar & brt violet (engr.) omitted   *550.00*

2577a — A1922-A1931

2577a A1922   29c pane of 10, *Oct. 1*   11.00   4.50
Never folded pane, P#111111   14.50

2577a — BC73

1991
$5.80 booklet contains two panes of 10 29c stamps.

Booklet
BK192 BC73 $5.80 **blue, black & red,** P#111111   22.50
P#111112   26.50

2578a — A1933

2578a	A1933	(29c) pane of 10, *Oct. 17*	6.00	3.25
		Never folded pane	8.00	

2578a — BC74

1991
($5.80) booklet contains two panes of 10 (29c) stamps.

Booklet
BK193 BC74 ($5.80) **multicolored,** P#1   12.00

2581b — A1934

2582a — A1935

2583a — A1936

2584a — A1937

2585a — A1938

2581b	A1934	(29c) pane, 2 each, #2580, 2581, *Oct. 17*	11.00	1.25
		Never bound pane, P#A11111	12.00	
2582a	A1935	(29c) pane of 4, *Oct. 17*	2.40	1.25
		Never bound pane, P#A11111	3.50	
2583a	A1936	(29c) pane of 4, *Oct. 17*	2.40	1.25
		Never bound pane, P#A11111	3.50	
2584a	A1937	(29c) pane of 4, *Oct. 17*	2.40	1.25
		Never bound pane, P#A11111	3.50	
2585a	A1938	(29c) pane of 4, *Oct. 17*	2.40	1.25
		Never bound pane, P#A11111	3.50	

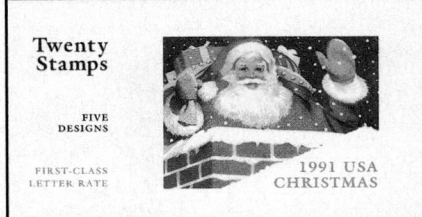

2581b, 2582a-2585a — BC75

1991
($5.80) booklet contains five panes of 4 (29c) stamps.

Combination Booklet
BK194 BC75   ($5.80) **multicolored,** 1
each #2581b,
2582a-2585a,
P#A11111, A12111   20.00

Nos. 2581b-2585a are unfolded panes.
Imperf examples of Nos. 2582a-2585a are printer's waste.

2593a — A1946

				Perf. 10
1992-94				
2593a	A1946	29c **black & multi,** pane of 10, *Sept. 8*	6.00	4.25
		Never folded pane, P#1111	8.00	

2593a — BC76

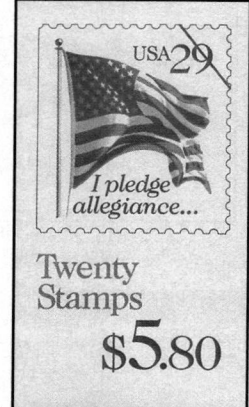

2593a — BC76A

1992
$2.90 booklet contains one pane of 10 29c stamps.
$5.80 booklet contains two panes of 10 29c stamps.

Booklets

BK195	BC76	$2.90 **blue & red,** P#1111, 2222	6.00
BK196	BC76A	$5.80 **blue & red,** P#1111, 2222	12.00
		P#1211, 2122	—

Perf. 11x10

2593Bc	A1946	29c **black & multi,** pane of 10, shiny gum, *1993*	17.00	7.50
		Low gloss gum	35.00	

Booklet

BK197	BC76A	$5.80 **blue & red,** P#1111, 1211, 2122, 2222, 2232, 3333	35.00
		P#2232, low gloss gum	70.00
		P#2333	250.00
		P#3333, low gloss gum	140.00
		P#4444, low gloss gum	125.00

2594a — A1946

2594a	A1946	29c **red & multi,** pane of 10, *1993*	6.50	4.25
		Never folded pane, P# K1111	8.00	

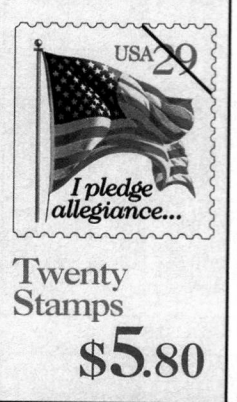

2594a — BC76B

2594a — BC76C

1993-94
$2.90 booklet contains one pane of 10 29c stamps.
$5.80 booklet contains two panes of 10 29c stamps.

Booklet

BK198	BC76B	$2.90 **black, red & blue,** P#K1111	6.00
BK199	BC76C	$5.80 **multicolored,** *1994,* P#K1111	13.50

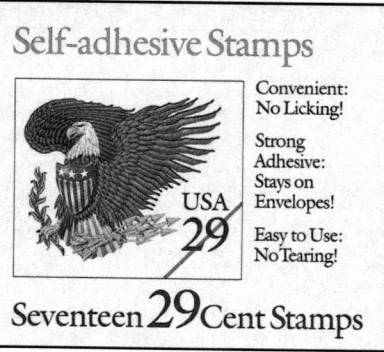

2595a — A1947

2595a — BC77

1992
$5 fold-it-yourself booklet contains 17 self-adhesive 29c stamps.

No. BC77 for Nos. 2595a, 2596a and 2597a differs in size and style of type as well as location of UPC labels.

Self-adhesive
Die Cut

2595a	A1947	29c **brown & multi,** pane of 17 + label, *Sept. 25,* P#B1111-1, B1111-2, B2222-1, B2222-2, B3333-1, B3333-3, B3434-1, B3434-3, B4444-1	13.00	
		P#B4344-1, B4444-3	15.00	
		P#B4344-3	*200.00*	

Variety

2595d		As "a," no die cutting	1,150.
2596a	A1947	29c **green & multi,** pane of 17 + label, *Sept. 25, 1992,* P#D11111, D21221, D22322, D32322, D32332, D43352, D43452, D43453, D54563, D54573, D65784	12.00
		P#D54571, D54673, D61384	15.00
		P#D32342, D42342	35.00
		P#D54561	25.00
2597a	A1947	29c **red & multi,** pane of 17 + label, *Sept. 25,* P#S1111	10.50

By their nature, Nos. 2595a-2597a constitute complete booklets (BC77). A peelable paper backing serves as a booklet cover for each. No. 2595a has a black and multicolored backing with serifed type. No. 2596a has a blue and multicolored backing. No. 2597a has a black and multicolored backing with unserifed type.

2598a — A1950

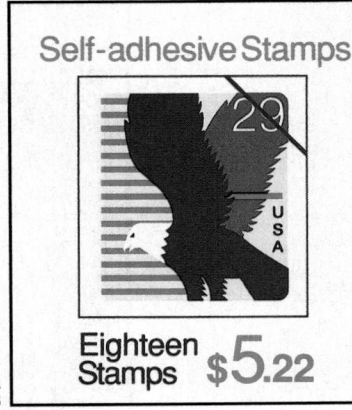

2598a
BC78

1994
$5.22 fold-it-yourself booklet contains 18 self-adhesive 29c stamps.

	Self-Adhesive	**Die Cut**
2598a	A1950 29c pane of 18, *Feb. 4, 1994,* P#M111, M112	11.00

By its nature, No. 2598a constitutes a complete booklet (BC78). The peelable backing serves as a booklet cover.

2599a — A1951

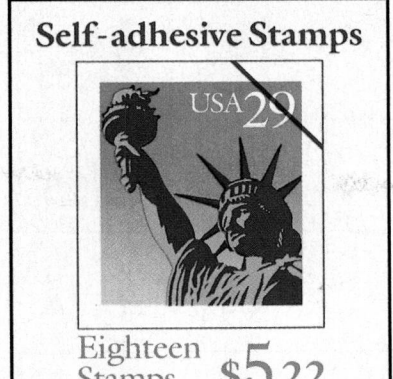

2599a
— BC79

1994
$5.22 fold-it-yourself booklet contains 18 self-adhesive 29c stamps.

	Self-Adhesive	**Die Cut**
2599a	A1951 29c pane of 18, *June 24, 1994,* P#D1111, D1212	11.00

By its nature, No. 2599a constitutes a complete booklet (BC79). The peelable backing serves as a booklet cover.

2646a — A1994-A1998

1992
2646a A1994 29c pane of 5, *June 15* 3.00 2.50
Never folded pane,
P#A2212112, A2212122,
A2222222 4.00
P#A1111111, A2212222 10.00

Imperforate panes are proofs.

Hummingbirds

Five Different Designs

Twenty 29c Stamps $5.80

2646a — BC80

1992
$5.80 booklet contains four panes of 5 29c stamps.

Booklet
BK201 BC80 $5.80 **multicolored,**
P#A1111111, A2212112,
A2212222, A2222222 12.00
P#A2212122 18.00

K1111

Giraffe

Giant Panda

Flamingo

King Penguins

White Bengal Tiger

2709a — A2057-A2061

2709a A2057 29c pane of 5, *Oct. 1* 3.25 2.25
Never folded pane 4.25

Wild Animals
Five Different Designs

Twenty 29c Stamps $5.80

2709a — BC83

1992
$5.80 booklet contains four panes of 5 29c stamps.

	Booklet	
BK202	BC83 $5.80 **multicolored,** P#K1111	12.00
	Variety	
2709b	As "a," imperf.	*2,250.*

2710a — A2062

| 2710a | A2062 | 29c pane of 10, *Oct. 22* | 6.00 | 3.50 |
| | | Never folded pane, P#1 | 7.00 | |

2710a — BC83A

1992
$5.80 booklet contains two panes of 10 29c stamps.

Booklet
BK202A BC83A $5.80 **multicolored**, P#1   12.00

2718a — A2063-A2066

2718a	A2063	29c pane of 4, *Oct. 22*	3.50	1.25
		Never bound pane, P#A111111, A222222	4.50	
		P#A112211	—	

2718a — BC84

1992
$5.80 booklet contains five panes of 4 29c stamps.

Booklet
BK203 BC84 $5.80 **multi**, P#A111111, A112211, A222222   19.00

Imperfs and part-perfs of No. 2718a are proofs.

2719a — A2064

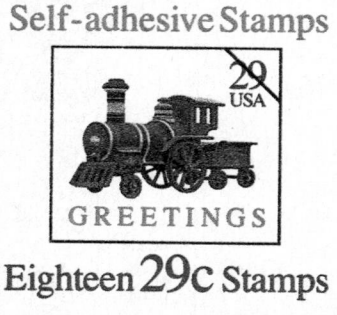

2719a BC85

1992
$5.22 fold-it-yourself booklet contains 18 self-adhesive 29c stamps.

Self-Adhesive
Die Cut

| 2719a | A2064 | 29c **multicolored**, pane of 18, *Oct. 29*, P#V11111 | 11.00 |

By its nature, No. 2719a constitutes a complete booklet (BC85). The peelable paper backing serves as a booklet cover.

2737a — A2071, A2075-A2077

Tab format on No. 2737a is similar to that shown for No. 2737b.

1993

2737a	A2071	29c pane of 8, 2 #2731, 1 each #2732-2737, *June 16*	5.00	2.25
		Never folded pane, P#A22222	6.25	
		P#A13113	—	
2737b	A2071	29c pane of 4, #2731, 2735-2737 + tab, *June 16*	2.40	1.50
		Never folded pane, P#A22222	3.50	
		P#A13113	—	

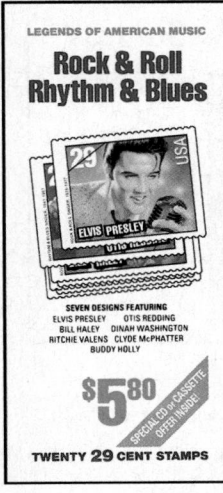

2737a, 2737b — BC86

1993
$5.80 booklet contains one pane of four 29c
stamps and two panes of eight 29c stamps.

Combination Booklet

BK204 BC86 $5.80 **multicolored**, 2 #2737a + 1
#2737b, P#A11111,
A22222 12.50
P#A13113, A44444 15.00

No. 2737b without tab is indistinguishable from broken No.
2737a.
Never folded panes of No. 2737a with P#A11111 exist missing the bottom stamp (found in some USPS mint sets).
No. BK204 exists assembled from panes with different plate
numbers.
Imperforate panes of Nos. 2737a and 2737b are proofs.

2745a — A2086-A2090

2745a A2086 29c pane of 5, *Jan. 25* 3.00 2.25
Never folded pane, P#1111,
1211 4.00
P#2222 6.50

Half of the printing of No. 2745a shows a part of No. 2745 on
the left side of the selvage tab. Values, same.

2745a — BC89

1993
$5.80 booklet contains four panes of 5 29c stamps.

Booklet

BK207 BC89 $5.80 **multi**, P#1111, 1211, 2222 12.00

2764a — A2105-A2109

2764a A2105 29c pane of 5, *May 15* 3.75 2.25
Never folded pane, P#1 4.75

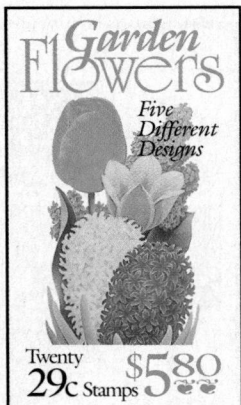

2764a — BC90

1993
$5.80 booklet contains four panes of 5 29c stamps.

Booklet

BK208 BC90 $5.80 **multicolored**, P#1, 2 15.00

Varieties

2764b As "a," black (engr.) omitted *175.00*
2764c As "a," imperf. *1,000.*

Booklet

BK208a As #BK208, with 4 #2764b *850.00*

2770a — A2069, A2112-
A2114

2770a A2069 29c pane of 4, *July 14* 2.75 2.25
Never folded pane,
P#A11111, A11121,
A22222 3.75

Imperforate panes are proofs.

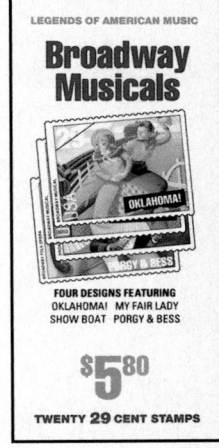

2770a — BC91

1993
$5.80 booklet contains five panes of 4 29c stamps.

Booklet

BK209 BC91 $5.80 **multicolored**, P#A11111,
A11121, A22222, A23232,
A23233 12.00

2778a — A2070,
A2115-A2117

2778a A2070 29c pane of 4, *Sept. 25, 1993* 2.50 2.00
Never folded pane,
P#A222222 3.50

Imperforate panes are proofs.

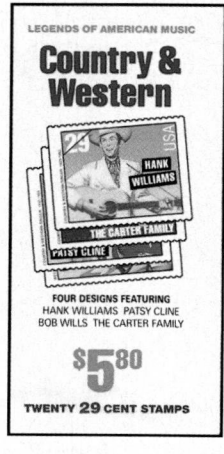

2778a — BC92

1993
$5.80 booklet contains five panes of 4 29c stamps.

Booklet

BK210 BC92 $5.80 **multicolored,** P#A111111,
A222222, A333333,
A422222
P#A333323 — 11.00

2790a — A2128

2790a A2128 29c pane of 4, *Oct. 21, 1993* 2.40 1.75
Never bound pane,
P#K111111, K133333,
K144444, 3.50
P#K255555 *85.00*

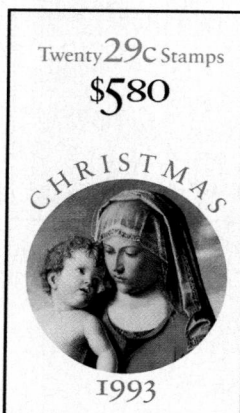

2790a — BC93

1993
$5.80 booklet contains five panes of 4 29c stamps.

Booklet

BK211 BC93 $5.80 **multicolored,** P#K111111,
K133333, K144444,
K255555, K266666 12.00
P#K222222 35.00

Variety

2790c As "a," imperf. —

2798a — A2129-
A2132

2798a A2129 29c pane of 10, 3 each
#2795-2796, 2 each
#2797-2798, *Oct. 21,
1993* 8.50 4.00
Never folded pane,
P#111111 10.00

2798b A2129 29c pane of 10, 3 each
#2797-2798, 2 each
#2795-2796, *Oct. 21,
1993* 8.50 4.00
Never folded pane,
P#111111 10.00

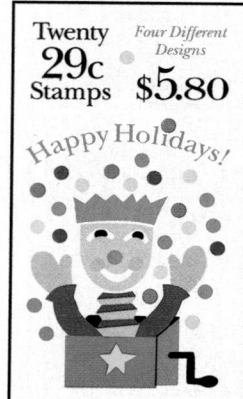

2798a — BC94

1993
$5.80 booklet contains two panes of 10 29c
stamps.

Combination Booklet

BK212 BC94 $5.80 **multicolored,** 1 each
#2798a, 2798b, P#111111,
222222 19.00
On No. 2798b the plate number appears close to the top row
of perfs. Different selvage markings can be found there.

2802a — A2129-A2132

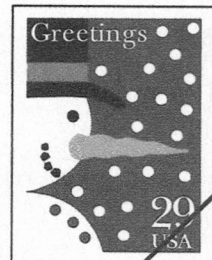

2802a — BC95

1993
$3.48 fold-it-yourself booklet contains 12 self-adhesive
29c stamps.

		Self-Adhesive	*Die Cut*
2802a A2129 29c pane of 12, 3 each #2799-
2802, *Oct. 28, 1993,*
P#V1111111, V2221222,
V2222112, V2222122,
V2222221, V2222222 8.00
P#V3333333 10.00

2803a — A2131

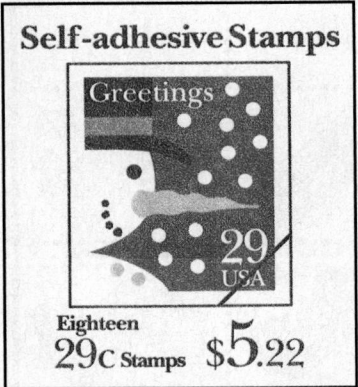

Self-adhesive Stamps

Greetings 29 USA

Eighteen
29c Stamps $5.22

2803a
BC96

1993
$5.22 fold-it-yourself booklet contains 18 self-adhesive 29c stamps.

2803a A2131 29c pane of 18, *Oct. 28, 1993*,
P#V1111 11.00
P# V2222 14.00

By their nature, Nos. 2802a-2803a constitute complete booklets (BC95-BC96). The peelable backing serves as a booklet cover.

2806b — A2135

2806b A2135 29c pane of 5, *Dec. 1, 1993* 3.50 2.00
Never folded pane, P#K111 4.50

AIDS AWARENESS

Ten 29c Stamps $2.90

2806b — BC97

1993
$2.90 booklet contains two panes of 5 29c stamps.

Booklet
BK213 BC97 $2.90 **black & red**, P#K111 7.00

B 33 4 • Peel here to fold • Self-adhesive stamps • DO NOT WET • 11

2813a — A2142

Self-adhesive Stamps

LOVE USA 2⅝

Eighteen Stamps $5.22

2813a
BC98

1994
$5.22 fold-it-yourself booklet contains 18 self-adhesive 29c stamps.

1994	Self-Adhesive	Die Cut
2813a A2142 29c pane of 18, *Jan. 27*, P#, see list		11.00
P#B111-5, B333-14		*75.00*
P#B121-5, B444-7, B444-8, B444-9, B444-14		14.00
P#B333-5, B333-7, B333-8		22.50
P#B334-11		*750.00*
P#B344-11		50.00
P#B434-10		100.00

By its nature, No. 2813a constitutes a complete booklet (BC98). The peelable backing serves as a booklet cover.

List — #B111-1, B111-2, B111-3, B111-4, B221-5, B222-4, B222-5, B222-6, B333-9, B333-10, B333-11, B333-12, B333-17, B344-12, B344-13, B444-10, B444-13, B444-15, B444-16, B444-17, B444-18, B444-19, B555-20, B555-21

A11111

2814a — A2143

2814a A2143 29c pane of 10, *Feb. 14, 1994* 6.00 3.50
Never folded pane, P#A11111 7.50

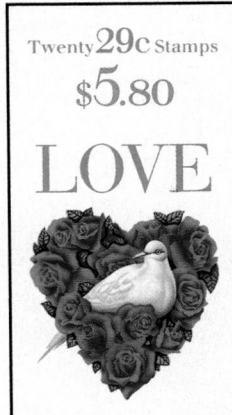

Twenty 29c Stamps $5.80

LOVE

2814a — BC99

1994
$5.80 booklet contains two panes of 10 29c stamps.

Booklet
BK214 BC99 $5.80 **multicolored**, P#A11111, A11311, A12112, A21222, A22122, A22322 11.00
P#A12111, A12211, A12212, A21311 25.00
P#A22222 16.00

2833a — A2158-A2162

2833a A2158 29c pane of 5, *Apr. 28, 1994* 3.00 2.25
Never folded pane, P#2 3.50

2833a — BC100

1994
$5.80 booklet contains four panes of 5 29c stamps.

Booklet

BK215 BC100 $5.80 **multicolored**, P#1, 2   12.00

Varieties

2833b	As "a," imperf	*800.00*
2833c	As "a," black (engr.) omitted	*225.00*
2833d	As "a," tagging omitted	—

Booklet

BK215a	As #BK215, with 4 #2833c	*1,050.*

2847a — A2171-A2175

2847a	A2171	29c pane of 5, *July 28, 1994*	3.50	2.00
		Never folded pane	4.50	

American Steam Locomotives
Five Different Designs
Twenty **29c Stamps**
$5.80

2847a — BC101

1994
$5.80 booklet contains four panes of 5 29c stamps.

Booklet

BK216 BC101 $5.80 **multicolored**, P#S11111   14.00

Variety

2847b	As "a," imperf	*2,500.*

2871Ab — A2200

2871Ab	A2200	29c pane of 10, *Oct. 20, 1994*	6.25	3.50
		Never folded pane, P#1, 2	7.00	

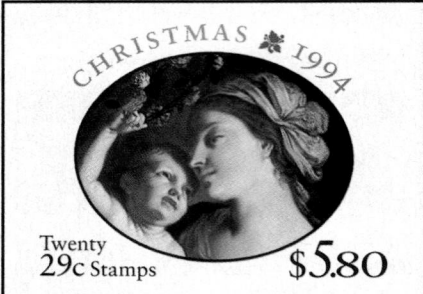

2871Ab — BC102

1994
$5.80 booklet contains two panes of 10 29c stamps.

Booklet

BK217 BC102 $5.80 **multicolored**, P#1, 2   12.50

2872a — A2201

2872a	A2201	29c pane of 20, *Oct. 20, 1994*	12.50	4.00
		Never folded pane, P#P11111, P22222, P44444	14.00	
		P#P33333	—	

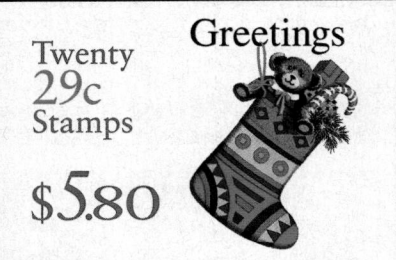

2872a — BC103

1994
$5.80 booklet contains one pane of 20 29c stamps.

Booklet
BK218 BC103 $5.80 **multicolored,** P#P11111,
P22222, P33333, P44444 12.50

2873a — A2202

2873a — BC104

1994
$3.48 fold-it-yourself booklet contains 12 self-adhesive
29c stamps.

2873a A2202 29c pane of 12, *Oct. 20, 1994,*
P#V1111 8.50

By its nature, No. 2873a constitutes a complete booklet
(BC104). The peelable backing serves as a booklet cover.

2874a — A2203

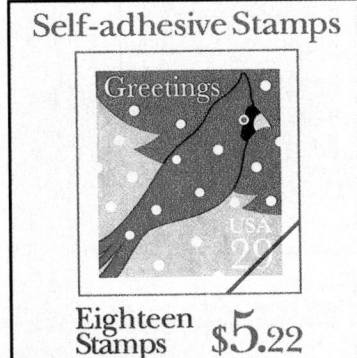

2874a
BC105

1994
$5.22 fold-it-yourself booklet contains 18 self-adhesive
29c stamps.

2874a A2203 29c pane of 18, *Oct. 20, 1994,*
P#V1111, V2222 11.00

By its nature, No. 2874a constitutes a complete booklet
(BC105). The peelable backing serves as a booklet cover.

2881a — A2208

1994   *Perf. 11.2x11.1*
2881a A2208 (32c) **black "G" & multi,** pane
of 10, *Dec. 13, 1994* 12.50 5.00

2881a, 2883a, 2884a,
2885a — BC106

1994
($3.20) booklet contains one pane of 10 G stamps.
($6.40) booklet contains two panes of 10 G stamps.

No. BC106 was printed by three different manufacturers in
either two- or four-color formats, with G in different colors and
with other minor design differences.

Booklet
BK219 BC106 ($3.20) **pale blue & red,**
P#1111 12.50

Perf. 10x9.9
2883a A2208 (32c) **black "G" & multi,**
pane of 10, *Dec. 13,*
1994 6.50 3.75

Booklets
BK220 BC106 ($3.20) **pale blue & red,**
P#1111, 2222 6.50
BK221 BC106 ($6.40) **blue & red,** P#1111,
2222 13.00

Perf. 10.9
2884a A2208 (32c) **blue "G" & multi,** pane
of 10, *Dec. 13, 1994* 6.50 3.75

Booklet
BK222 BC106 ($6.40) **blue "G" & multi,**
P#A1111, A1211,
A2222, A3333, A4444 13.00

No. BK222 exists with panes that have different plate
numbers.

Variety
2884b   As "a," imperf. *1,700.*

Perf. 11x10.9

2885a	A2208	(32c) **red "G" & multi,** pane of 10, *Dec. 13, 1994*	9.00	4.50

Booklet

BK223	BC106	($6.40) **red "G" & multi,** P#K1111	19.00

2886a — A2208b

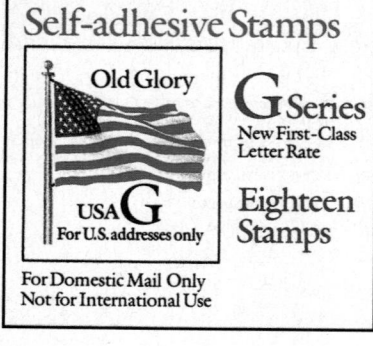

2886a, 2887a BC107

1994

($5.76) fold-it-yourself booklet contains 18 self-adhesive G stamps.

		Self-Adhesive	*Die Cut*
2886a	A2208b	(32c) **gray, blue, light blue, red & black,** pane of 18, *Dec. 13, 1994,* P#V11111, V22222	14.00
2887a	A2208c	(32c) **black, blue & red,** pane of 18, *Dec. 13, 1994,* no P#	13.50

By their nature, Nos. 2886a and 2887a constitute complete booklets (BC107). The peelable backing serves as a booklet cover. The backing on No. 2886a contains a UPC symbol, while the backing on No. 2887a does not.

2916a — A2212

Perf. 10.8x9.8

2916a	A2212	32c **blue, tan, brown, red & light blue,** pane of 10, *May 19, 1995*	6.50	3.25
		Never folded pane, P#11111	7.25	

2916a — BC108

1995

$3.20 booklet contains one pane of 10 32c stamps.
$6.40 booklet contains two panes of 10 32c stamps.

Booklets

BK225	BC108	$3.20 **blue & red,** P#11111, 22222, 33332		6.50
		P#23222, 44444		—
BK226	BC108	$6.40 **multicolored,** P#11111, 22222, 23222, 33332, 44444		13.00

Variety

2916b	As "a," imperf.	—

2919a — A2230

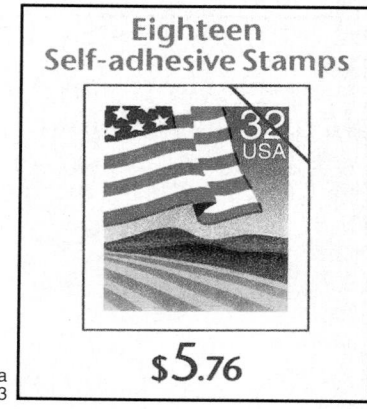

2919a BC113

1995

$5.76 fold-it-yourself booklet contains 18 self-adhesive 32c stamps.

		Self-Adhesive	*Die Cut*
2919a	A2230	32c pane of 18, *Mar. 17, 1995,* P#V1111, V1311, V1433, V2222, V2322	12.00
		P#V2111	45.00

By its nature No. 2919a is a complete booklet (BC113). The peelable backing serves as a booklet cover.

2920a — A2212

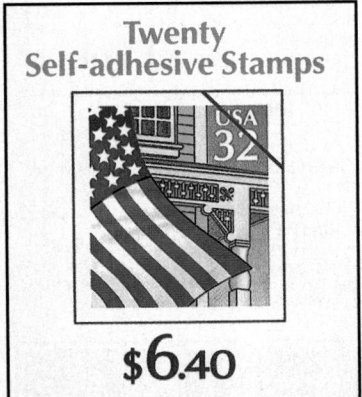

Twenty Self-adhesive Stamps

$6.40

2920a
BC114

1995
$6.40 fold-it-yourself booklet contains 20 self-adhesive 32c stamps.

Serpentine Die Cut 8.7 on 2 or 3 Sides
Self-Adhesive
2920a A2212 32c pane of 20 + label, large date, *Apr. 18, 1995* (see List 1) 13.00
P#V23422 25.00
P#V23522 40.00
P#V57663 —

2920c A2212 32c pane of 20 + label, small date, *Apr. 18, 1995,* P#V11111 120.00
Variety
2920g As "a," partial pane of 10, 3 stamps and parts of 7 stamps printed on backing liner —

By their nature Nos. 2920a, 2920c are complete booklets (BC114). The rouletted peelable backing, of which two types are known, serves as a booklet cover.
Date on No. 2920a is nearly twice as large as date on No. 2920c.
No. 2920a comes either with no die cutting on the label or with die cutting.
List 1 — P#V12211, V12212, V12312, V12321, V12322, V12331, V13322, V13831, V13834, V13836, V22211, V23322, V23432, V34743, V34745, V36743, V42556, V45554, V56663, V56665, V56763, V65976, V78989.

2920f — A2212

Serpentine Die Cut 8.7
Self-Adhesive
2920f A2212 32c pane of 15 + label 10.00
2920h A2212 32c pane of 15, see note, *1996* 50.00
Booklets
BK226A BC126 $4.80 **blue,** 1 #2920f, no P# (4) 10.00
BK226B BC126 $4.80 **blue,** 1 #2920h, no P# (3) 75.00
BK227 BC126 $9.60 **blue,** 2 #2920f (3) 18.00

No. 2920h is a pane of 16 with one stamp removed. The missing stamp is the lower right stamp in the pane or (more rarely) the upper left stamp. No. 2920h cannot be made from No. 2920f, a pane of 15 + label. The label is located in the sixth or seventh row of the pane and is die cut. If the label is removed, an impression of the die cutting appears on the backing paper.
Nos. BK226A-B and BK227 are makeshift vending machine booklets. See note before No. BK243.

2920De — A2212

Serpentine Die Cut 11.3
Self-Adhesive
2920De A2212 32c pane of 10, *Jan. 20, 1996* 8.00

By its nature No. 2920De is a complete booklet (BC114). The rouletted peelable backing serves as a booklet cover.
Below is a list of known plate numbers. Some numbers may be scarcer than the value indicated in the listing.
No. 2920De — P#V11111, V12111, V23222, V31121, V32111, V32121, V44322, V44333, V44444, V55555, V66666, V66886, V67886, V68886, V68896, V76989, V77666, V77668, V77766, V77776, V78698, V78886, V78896, V78898, V78986, V78989, V89999.

2921a — A2212

Serpentine Die Cut 9.8
Self-Adhesive

2921a	A2212	32c pane of 10, dated red "1996," *May 21, 1996*		9.00
		Never folded pane, P#21221, 22221, 22222		10.50
2921c	A2212	32c pane of 10, dated red "1997," *Jan. 24, 1997*		12.00
		Never folded pane, P#11111		14.00
2921d	A2212	32c pane of 5 + label, dated red "1997," *Jan. 24, 1997*		7.00
		Never folded pane, P#11111		8.50

Combination Booklet

BK227A BC108 $4.80 **multicolored,** 1 ea #2921c-2921d P#11111   19.00

No. BK227A is only source of No. 2921c with P# above right column of stamps and no length register marks or cross register lines in selvage tab.

Booklets

BK228 BC108 $6.40 **blue, red & black,** 2 #2921a (5)   18.00

Known numbers for BK228: P#11111, 13111, 21221, 22221, 22222, 44434, 44444, 55555, 55556, 66666, 77777, 88788, 88888, 99999. Some numbers may be scarcer than the value indicated in the listing.

No. BK228 is only source of No. 2921a, which has P# above left column of stamps and no length register marks or cross register lines in selvage tab.

BK228A BC108 $9.60 **multicolored,** 3 #2921c, P#11111   22.50

No. BK228A is only source of No. 2921c with P# above left column of stamps and length register marks and cross register lines in selvage tab.

Variety

2921e   As "a," die cutting omitted   200.00

Booklet

BK228b   As #BK228, with 2 #2921e, P#11111, 13111   400.00

2949a — A2264

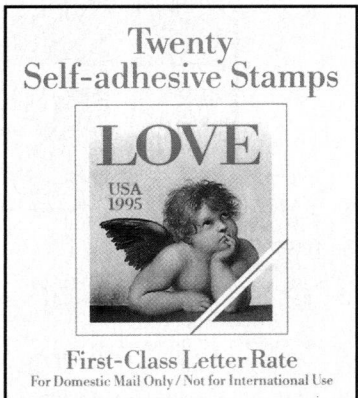

2949a BC115

1995
($6.40) fold-it-yourself booklet contains 20 self-adhesive non-denominated 32c stamps.

		Self-Adhesive	*Die Cut*	
2949a	A2264	(32c) pane of 20 + label, *Feb. 1, 1995,* P#B1111-1, B2222-1, B2222-2, B3333-2		13.00

By its nature, No. 2949a is a complete booklet (BC115). The peelable backing serves as a booklet cover.

Variety

2949c   As "a," red (engr.) omitted   5,500.

2959a — A2272

Perf. 9.8x10.8

2959a	A2272	32c pane of 10, *May 12, 1995*		6.50	3.25
		Never folded pane		6.75	

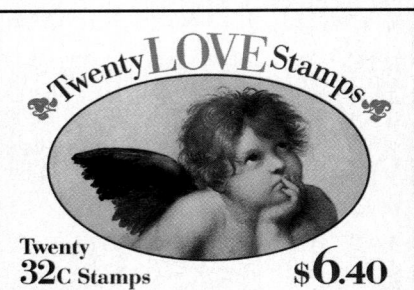

2959a — BC116

1995
$6.40 booklet contains two panes of 10 32c stamps.

Booklet

BK229 BC116 $6.40 **multicolored,** P#1   13.00

2960a — A2274

2960a — BC117

1995
$11 fold-it-yourself booklet contains 20 self-adhesive 55c stamps.

		Self-Adhesive	*Die Cut*	
2960a	A2274	55c pane of 20 + label, *May 12, 1995,* P#B1111-1, B2222-1		22.50

By its nature, No. 2960a is a complete booklet (BC117). The peelable backing serves as a booklet cover. It comes either with no die cutting on the label or with die cutting.

2973a — A2283-A2287

2973a	A2283	32c pane of 5, *June 17, 1995*		6.25	3.00
		Never folded pane		6.75	

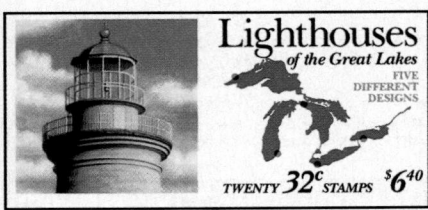

2973a — BC118

1995

$6.40 booklet contains four panes of 5 32c stamps.

Booklet

BK230   BC118 $6.40 **multicolored,** P#S11111   25.00

2997a — A2306-A2310

2997a	A2306	32c pane of 5, *Sept. 19, 1995*	3.25	2.25
		Never folded pane	4.25	

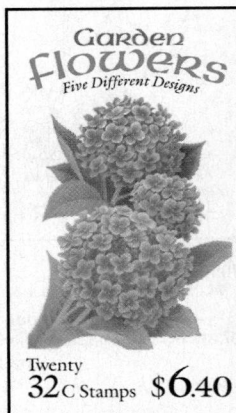

2997a — BC119

1995

$6.40 booklet contains four panes of 5 32c stamps.

Booklet

BK231   BC119 $6.40 **multicolored,** P#2   13.00

Variety

2997b	As "a," imperf.	2,750.

3003Ab — A2316

3003Ab	A2316	32c pane of 10, *Oct. 19, 1995*	6.50	4.00
		Never folded pane	7.50	

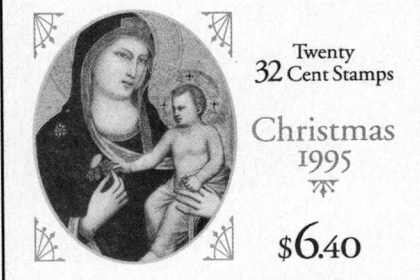

3003b — BC120

1995

$6.40 booklet contains two panes of 10 32c stamps.

Booklet

BK232   BC120 $6.40 **multicolored,** P#1   13.00

3007b — A2317-A2320

3007b	A2317	32c pane of 10, 3 each #3004-3005, 2 each #3006-3007, *Sept. 30, 1995*	8.00	4.00
		Never folded pane, P#P1111	9.00	
3007c	A2317	32c pane of 10, 2 each #3004-3005, 3 each #3006-3007, *Sept. 30, 1995*	8.00	4.00
		Never folded pane, P#P1111	9.00	

Variety

3007e	As "b," miscut and inserted upside down into booklet cover, with full bottom selvage	—

3007b-3007c — BC121

1995

$6.40 booklet contains two panes of 10 32c stamps

Combination Booklet

BK233   BC121 $6.40 **multicolored,** 1 each #3007b, 3007c, P#P1111, P2222   14.00

3011a — A2317-A2320

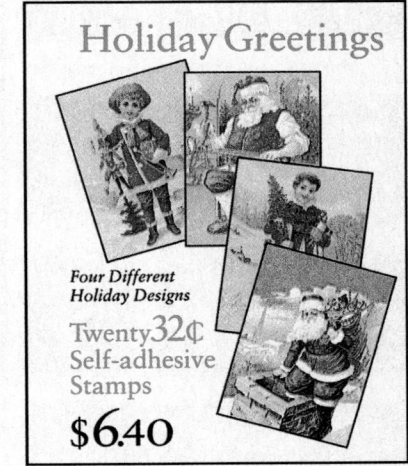

3011a — BC122

1995

$6.40 fold-it-yourself booklet contains 20 self-adhesive 32c stamps

Serpentine Die Cut

3011a	A2317	32c pane of 20 +label, *Sept. 30, 1995,* P#V1111, V1211, V3233, V3333, V4444	19.00
		P#V1212	26.00

By its nature, No. 3011a is a complete booklet (BC122). The peelable backing serves as a booklet cover.

3012a — A2321

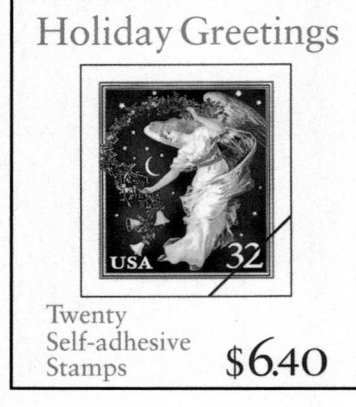

Holiday Greetings

Twenty Self-adhesive Stamps $6.40

3012a
BC123

1995
$6.40 fold-it-yourself booklet contains 20 self-adhesive 32c stamps

Serpentine Die Cut

3012a	A2321	32c pane of 20 + label, *Oct. 19, 1995,* P#B1111, B2222, B3333		13.00

By its nature, No. 3012a is a complete booklet (BC123). The peelable backing serves as a booklet cover.

No. 3012a comes either with no die cutting on the label (1995 printing) or with die cutting from the 1996 printing.

3012c	A2321	32c pane of 15 + label, *1996,* no P#		13.00

3012d	A2321	32c pane of 15, see note, *1996*		30.00

Booklets

BK233A	BC126	$4.80 **blue,** #3012c (2)	13.00
BK233B	BC126	$4.80 **blue,** #3012d	—
BK233C	BC126	$9.60 **blue** 2 #3012c (3)	26.00
BK233D	BC126	$9.60 **blue,** 2 #3012d, no P# (3)	60.00
f.		As No. BK233D, but one pane is of 16 stamps (thus 31 stamps in the booklet) (error)	—

Combination Booklet

BK233E	BC126	$9.60 **blue,** 1 ea #3012c, 3012d (2)	80.00

No. 3012d is a pane of 16 with one stamp removed. The missing stamp can be from either row 1, 2, 3, 7 or 8. No. 3012d cannot be made from No. 3012c, a pane of 15 + label. The label is die cut. If the label is removed, an impression of the die cutting appears on the backing paper.

Nos. BK233A-E are makeshift vending machine booklets. See note before No. BK243.

3013a — A2322

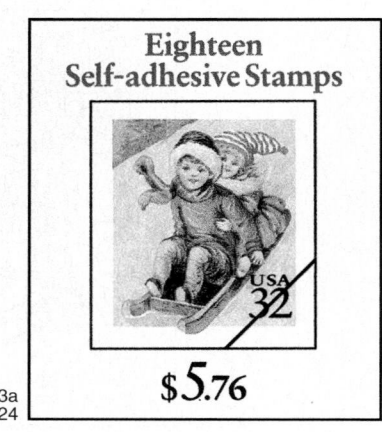

Eighteen Self-adhesive Stamps

$5.76

3013a
BC124

1995
$5.76 fold-it-yourself booklet contains 18 self-adhesive 32c stamps

---

Die Cut

3013a	A2322	32c Pane of 18, *Oct. 19, 1995,* P#V1111		12.00

Variety

3013b		As "a," tagging omitted	—

By its nature, No. 3013a is a complete booklet (BC124). The peelable backing serves as a booklet cover.

3029a — A2329-A2333

3029a	A2329	32c pane of 5, *Jan. 19, 1996*	3.75	2.50
		Never folded pane	4.25	

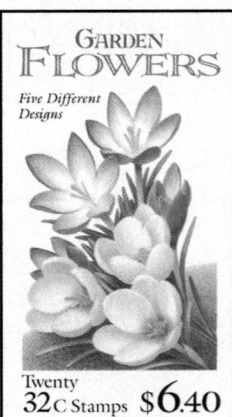

GARDEN FLOWERS

Five Different Designs

Twenty 32C Stamps $6.40

3029a — BC125

1996
$6.40 booklet contains four panes of 5 32c stamps

Booklet

BK234	BC125	$6.40 **multicolored,** P#1	15.00

Variety

3029b		As "a," imperf.	—

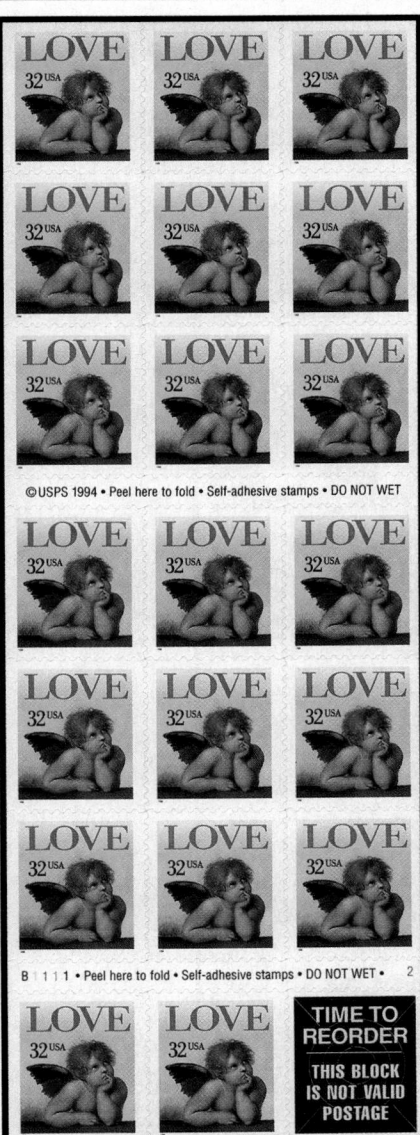

3030a — A2334

Serpentine Die Cut 11.3x11.7

3030a A2334 32c pane of 20+label, *Jan. 20, 1996*   13.00

By its nature, No. 3030a is a complete booklet (BC115). The peelable backing serves as a booklet cover.
P#B1111-1, B1111-2, B2222-1, B2222-2.

Variety

3030g As "a," stamps 1-5 with double impression of red (engr. "Love").   —

3030b A2334 32c pane of 15 + label, *1996*   10.00

Booklet

BK235 BC126 $4.80 **blue**, #3030b (4)   10.00
BK236 BC126 $9.60 **blue**, 2 #3030b (3)   18.00

3048a — A1847

3048a-3048c — BC128

1996
$2.00 fold-it-yourself booklet contains 10 self-adhesive 20c stamps
$2.00 booklet contains 10 self-adhesive 20c stamps

Serpentine Die Cut 10.4x10.8

3048a A1847 20c pane of 10, *Aug. 2, 1996*, P#S1111, S2222   4.00

By is nature, No. 3048a is a complete booklet (BC128). The peelable backing serves as a booklet cover.

3048b, 3048c — A1847

3048b A1847 20c Booklet pane of 4   *25.00*
3048c A1847 20c Booklet pane of 6   *40.00*

Nos. 3048b-3048c are from the vending machine booklet No. BK237 that has a glue strip at the top edge of the top pane, the peelable strip removed and the rouletting line 2mm lower than on No. 3048a when the panes are compared with the bottoms aligned.

Combination Booklet

BK237 BC128 $2.00 **multicolored**, 1 ea #3048b, 3048c, P#S1111, S2222   *75.00*

3049a — A1853

Serpentine Die Cut 11.3x11.7

3049a A1853 32c pane of 20 + label, *Oct. 24, 1996*, P#S1111, S2222   13.00

By its nature, No. 3049a is a complete booklet (BC61B). The peelable backing, of which three types are known, serves as a booklet cover.

3049b, 3049c, 3049d — A1853

3049b A1853 32c pane of 4, *Dec. 1996*, no P#   2.60
3049c A1853 32c pane of 5 + label, *Dec. 1996*, P#S1111   3.50
3049d A1853 32c pane of 6, *Dec. 1996*, without P#   4.00

3049b, 3049c, 3049d — BC129

1996
$4.80 booklet contains 15 self-adhesive 32c stamps
$9.60 booklet contains 30 self-adhesive 32c stamps

Combination Booklet

BK241 BC129 $4.80 **multicolored**, 1 ea
#3049b-3049d, P#S1111   10.25

Booklet

BK242 BC129 $9.60 **multicolored**, 5 #3049d, P#S1111   20.00

The backing on Nos. BK241-BK242 is rouletted between each pane.

The plate # single in No. 3049c from No. BK241 is on the lower left stamp. In No. 3049d from BK242, P# single is the lower right stamp on the bottom pane of the booklet.

Variety

3049d Pane of 6 containing P# single   6.00

3050a, 3050c — A2350

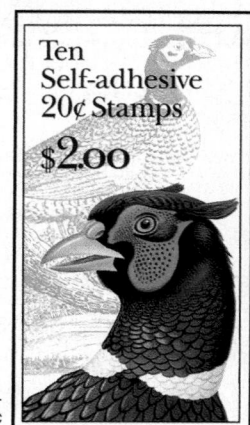

3050a, 3050c, 3051Ab-
3051Ac
BC130

1998
$2.00 fold-it-yourself booklet contains 10 self-adhesive 20c stamps
$2.00 booklet contains 10 self-adhesive 20c stamps

1998   *Serpentine Die Cut 11.2*
3050a A2350 20c pane of 10, *July 31, 1998*, P#V1111, V2222, V2232, V3233   6.00
P#V2342, V2343, V3232   11.00

Serpentine Die Cut 11

3050c A2350 20c pane of 10, *July 31, 1998*,
P#V2333, V2342, V2343,
V3232, V3243, V3333
P#V2232, V2332 .... 12.50

By their nature Nos. 3050a and 3050c are complete booklets (BC130). The peelable backing serves as a booklet cover. All stamps in Nos. 3050a and 3050c are upright.

3051Ab, 3051Ac —
A2350

Serpentine Die Cut 10½x11 on 3 Sides (#3051), 10.6x10.4 on 3 sides (#3051A)

1999

Self-Adhesive

3051Ab A2350 20c pane, 4 #3051, 1 #3051A
turned sideways at top,
July 1999 .... 9.00
3051Ac A2350 20c pane, 4 #3051, 1 #3051A
turned sideways at bottom, *July 1999* 9.00

Booklet

BK242A BC130 $2.00 **multicolored,** #3051Ab,
3051Ac, P#V1111, *July
1999* 19.00

3052a-3052c —
A2351

Serpentine Die Cut 11½x11¼

3052a A2351 33c pane of 4, no P# 3.60
3052b A2351 33c pane of 5 + label, no P# ... 4.50
3052c A2351 33c pane of 6 .... 5.50

3052a-3052c —
BC131A

1999
$4.95 booklet contains 15 self-adhesive 33c stamps + label

Combination Booklet

BK242B BC131A $4.95 **multicolored,** 1 each
#3052a-3052c, P#S111,
Aug. 13, 1999 .... 13.75

No. BK242B has a self-adhesive strip on #3052b that adheres to the plastic-coated peelable backing of #3052a when the booklet is closed. When the booklet is opened, this strip is sticky and may adhere firmly to mounts, album pages, etc. Removal of this strip will damage the backing paper of #3052b.

Plate numbers for No. BK242B are on backing paper below bar code.

3052d — A2351

3052d — BC131

1999
$6.60 fold-it-yourself booklet contains 20 self-adhesive 33c stamps + label

3052d A2351 33c pane of 20 + label, P#S111,
S222 .... 17.50

No. 3052d is a complete booklet (BC131). The peelable backing serves as a booklet cover.

3052Ef — A2351

Serpentine Die Cut 10¾x10½ on 2 or 3 Sides

2000

3052Ef A2351 33c pane of 20, *Apr. 7, 2000*,
P#S111, S222, S333 .... 16.00

By its nature, No. 3052Ef is a complete booklet. Eight stamps and the booklet cover (similar to BC131) are printed on one side of the peelable backing and twelve stamps plus P# appear on the other side of the backing.

Variety

3052Eh As "f," all 12 stamps on one side with
black ("33 USA," etc.) omitted .... —

3071a — A2370

3089a — A2387

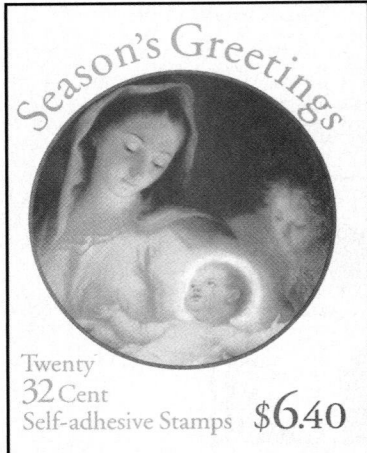

3112a
BC134

1996
$6.40 fold-it-yourself booklet contains 20 self-adhesive
32c stamps

Serpentine Die Cut 10 on 2, 3 or 4 Sides

3112a A2405 32c pane of 20 + label, *Nov. 1,*
1996   15.00
Variety
3112c   As "a," die cutting omitted   —
By its nature No. 3112a is a complete booklet (BC134). The
peelable backing serves as a booklet cover.
Below is a list of known plate numbers. Some numbers may
be scarcer than the value indicated in the listing.
P#1111-1, 1211-1, 2212-1, 2222-1, 2323-1, 3323-1, 3333-1,
3334-1, 4444-1, 5544-1, 5555-1, 5556-1, 5556-2, 5656-2, 6656-
2, 6666-1, 6666-2, 6766-1, 7887-1, 7887-2, 7888-2, 7988-2.

3116a — A2406-2409

Twenty
Self-adhesive Stamps

$6.40

UNITED STATES
POSTAL SERVICE
We Deliver For You.

3071a — BC127

1996
$6.40 fold-it-yourself booklet contains 20 self-adhesive
32c stamps

Serpentine Die Cut 9.9x10.8

3071a A2370 32c pane of 20, *May 31, 1996,*
P#S11111   15.00
By its nature, No. 3071a is a complete booklet (BC127). The
peelable backing serves as a booklet cover.

Twenty
Self-adhesive Stamps

$6.40

UNITED STATES
POSTAL SERVICE
We Deliver For You.

3089a — BC133

1996
$6.40 fold-it-yourself booklet contains 20 self-adhesive
32c stamps

Serpentine Die Cut 11.6x11.4

3089a A2387 32c pane of 20, *Aug. 1, 1996,*
P#B1111   14.00
By its nature, No. 3089a is a complete booklet (BC133). The
peelable backing serves as a booklet cover.

3112a — A2405

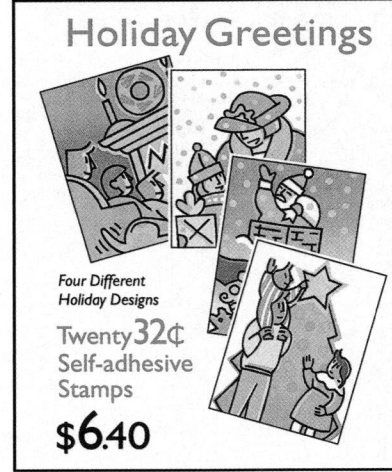

3116a — BC135

1996
$6.40 fold-it-yourself booklet contains 20 self-adhesive
32c stamps

Serpentine Die Cut 11.8x11.5 on 2, 3 or 4 Sides

3116a A2406 32c pane of 20 + label, *Oct.*
8, 1996, P#B1111,
B2222, B3333   15.00
Variety
3116d   As "a," die cutting omitted   *2,100.*
By its nature No. 3116a is a complete booklet (BC135). The
peelable backing serves as a booklet cover.

3117a — A2410

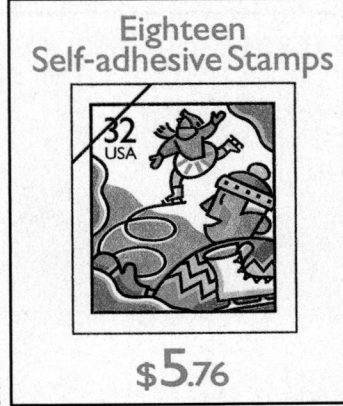

Eighteen
Self-adhesive Stamps

$5.76

3117a
BC136

1996
$5.76 fold-it-yourself booklet contains 18 self-adhesive 32c stamps

Die Cut

3117a A2410 32c pane of 18, *Oct. 8, 1996,*
P#V1111, V2111 .... 12.00

By its nature No. 3117a is a complete booklet (BC136). The peelable backing serves as a booklet cover.

MAKESHIFT VENDING MACHINE BOOKLETS

The booklets listed below were released in 1996 to meet the need for $4.80 and $9.60 vending machine booklets. The booklets consist of blocks of sheet stamps folded and affixed to a standard cover (BC126) with a spot of glue.

The cover varies from issue to issue in the line of text on the front that indicates the number of stamps contained in the booklet and in the four lines of text on the back that describe the contents of the booklet and list the booklet's item number. Due to the folding required to make stamps fit within the covers, the stamp blocks may easily fall apart when booklets are opened. Stamps may also easily detach from booklet cover.

Front

Now you can order stamps by phone:
1•800•STAMP•24
(1•800•782•6724)

Call toll free:
24 hours per day,
7 days per week

Fifteen Stamps (15)
15-32¢ Love Cherubs PSA
Item No. 3627
Value $4.80

Back — BC126

1996
$4.80 booklet contains 15 32c stamps
$9.60 booklet contains 30 32c stamps

A number of different stamps have been sold in BC126. The text on the front and back changes to describe the contents of the booklet. The enclosed stamps are affixed to the cover with a spot of glue.

1996

Booklets

BK243	BC126	$4.80 **blue,** 15 #2897 (32c Flag Over Porch)	11.00
BK244	BC126	$4.80 **blue,** 15 #2957 (32c Cherub/Love)	11.00
BK245	BC126	$4.80 **blue,** 15 #3024 (32c Utah)	12.50
BK246	BC126	$4.80 **blue,** 15 #3065 (32c Fulbright Scholarships)	11.00
BK247	BC126	$4.80 **blue,** 15 #3069 (32c Georgia O'Keeffe)	11.00
BK248	BC126	$4.80 **blue,** 15 #3070 (32c Tennessee)	11.00
BK249	BC126	$4.80 **blue,** 3 #3076a (32c Indian Dances)	11.00
BK250	BC126	$4.80 **blue,** 15 #3082 (32c James Dean)	13.50
BK251	BC126	$4.80 **blue,** 15 (#3083-3086) (32c Folk Heroes)	11.00
BK252	BC126	$4.80 **blue,** 15 #3087 (32c Olympic Centennial)	15.00
BK253	BC126	$4.80 **blue,** 15 #3088 (32c Iowa)	11.00
BK254	BC126	$9.60 **blue,** 30 #3090 (32c Rural Free Delivery)	22.50
BK255	BC126	$4.80 **blue,** 3 #3095a (32c Riverboats)	12.50
BK256	BC126	$4.80 **blue,** #3105a-3105o (32c Endangered Species)	11.00

BK257	BC126	$4.80 **blue,** 15 #3107 (32c Madonna Christmas)	11.00
BK258	BC126	$4.80 **blue,** 15 #3118 (32c Hanukkah)	11.00

The contents of #BK251 may vary.
See Nos. BK178A-BK178F, BK226A-BK226B, BK227, BK233A-BK233E, BK235-BK236, BK266-BK269, BK272-BK274, BK277-BK278.

3122a — A1951

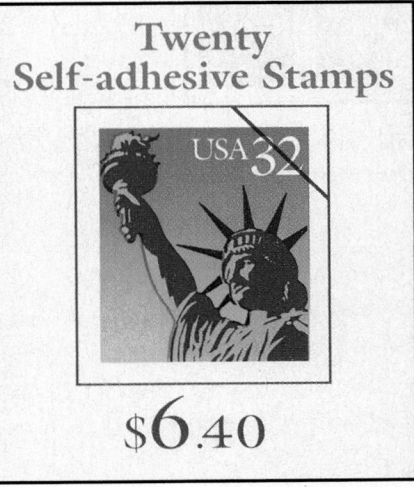

Twenty
Self-adhesive Stamps

$6.40

3122a — BC79A

1997
$6.40 fold-it-yourself booklet contains 20 self-adhesive
32c stamps

1997

Serpentine Die Cut 11

3122a	A1951	32c pane of 20 + label, *Feb. 1,* P#V1111, V1211, V1311, V2122, V2222, V2311, V2331, V3233, V3333, V3513, V4532	14.00

Variety

3122h	As "a," die cutting omitted	—

By its nature, No. 3122a is a complete booklet (BC79A). The peelable backing, of which two types are known, serves as a booklet cover.

3122b-3122d — A1951

3122b	A1951	32c pane of 4, *Feb. 1,* no P#	2.80
3122c	A1951	32c pane of 5 + label, *Feb. 1,* P#V1111	3.75
3122d	A1951	32c pane of 6, *Feb. 1,* without P#	4.25

3122b-3122d — BC79B

1997
$4.80 fold-it-yourself booklet contains 15 self-adhesive
32c stamps
$9.60 fold-it-yourself booklet contains 30 self-adhesive
32c stamps

Combination Booklet

BK259	BC79B $4.80 **multicolored,** 1 ea #3122b-3122d, P#V1111		11.00

Booklet

BK260	BC79B $9.60 **multicolored,** 5 #3122d, P#V1111		21.50

The backing on Nos. BK259-BK260 is rouletted between each pane.

Variety

3122d	pane of 6 containing P# single	6.00

The plate # single in No. 3122c is the lower left stamp and should be collected unused with the reorder label to its right to differentiate it from the plate # single in No. 3122d which is the lower left stamp in the bottom pane of the booklet and should be collected with a normal stamp adjoining it at right. In used condition, these plate # singles are indistinguishable.

Serpentine Die Cut 11.5x11.8 on 2, 3 or 4 Sides

3122Ef	A1951	32c pane of 20 + label, P#V1111, V1211, V2122, V2222	40.00

By its nature, No. 3122Ef is a complete booklet (BC79A). The peelable backing serves as a booklet cover.

3122Eg	A1951	32c pane of 6, *1997,* without plate # single	9.00

Booklet

BK260A	BC79B $9.60 **multicolored,** 5 #3122Eg, P#V1111		50.00

Variety

3122Eg	pane of 6 containing P# single	13.50

The plate # single in No. 3122Eg from No. BK260A is the lower left stamp in the bottom pane of the booklet.

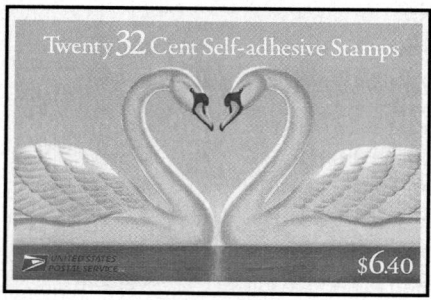

3123a — A2415

Twenty 32 Cent Self-adhesive Stamps
$6.40

3123a — BC137

1997
$6.40 fold-it-yourself booklet contains 20 self-adhesive
32c stamps

1997

Serpentine Die Cut 11.8x11.6 on 2, 3 or 4 Sides

3123a	A2415	32c pane of 20 + label, *Feb. 4,* P#B1111, B2222, B3333, B4444, B5555, B6666, B7777	13.00

Varieties

3123c	As "a," die cutting omitted	1,350.
3123d	As "a," black omitted	—

3124a — A2416

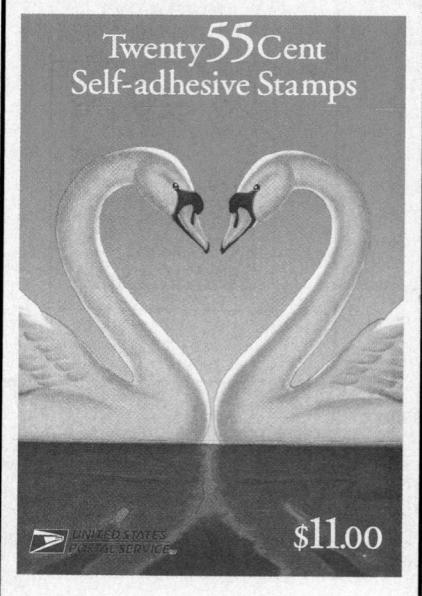

Twenty 55 Cent Self-adhesive Stamps
$11.00

3124a — BC137A

1997
$11 fold-it-yourself booklet contains 20 self-adhesive 55c
stamps

Serpentine Die Cut 11.6x11.8 on 2, 3 or 4 Sides

3124a	A2416	55c pane of 20 + label, *Feb. 4,* P#B1111, B2222, B3333, B4444	22.00

By their nature, Nos. 3123a-3124a are complete booklets (BC137 and BC137A). The peelable backing serves as a booklet cover.

3127a — A2418-A2419

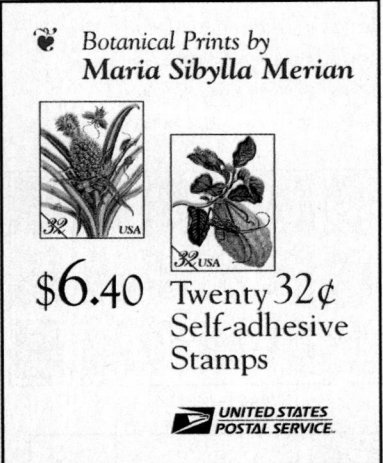

$6.40

Botanical Prints by
Maria Sibylla Merian

Twenty 32¢
Self-adhesive
Stamps

UNITED STATES POSTAL SERVICE.

3127a
BC138

1997
$6.40 fold-it-yourself booklet contains 20 32c stamps

Serpentine Die Cut 10.9x10.2 on 2, 3 or 4 Sides
1997
3127a   A2418   32c pane of 20 + label, 10 ea
         #3126-3127, *Mar. 3,*
         P#S11111, S22222,
         S33333   13.00

By its nature, No. 3127a is a complete booklet (BC138). The peelable backing serves as a booklet cover.

3128b, 3129b —
A2418-A2419

3128b   A2418   32c pane of 5, 2 ea #3128-
         3129, 1 #3128a, *Mar. 3,*
         no P# or P#S11111   7.00
3129b   A2419   32c pane of 5, 2 ea #3128-
         3129, 1 #3129a, *Mar. 3,*
         no P#   9.00

Botanical Prints by
Maria Sibylla Merian

$4.80 Fifteen 32¢
Self-adhesive
Stamps

UNITED STATES POSTAL SERVICE.

3128b, 3129b —
BC138A

1997
$4.80 booklet contains 15 32c stamps
Combination Booklet
BK261 BC138A $4.80 2 #3128b, 1 #3129b,
         P#S11111   25.00

In No. BK261, No. 3128b at top has no plate #, while the No. 3128b at bottom has a plate # in the selvage.

3176a — A2459

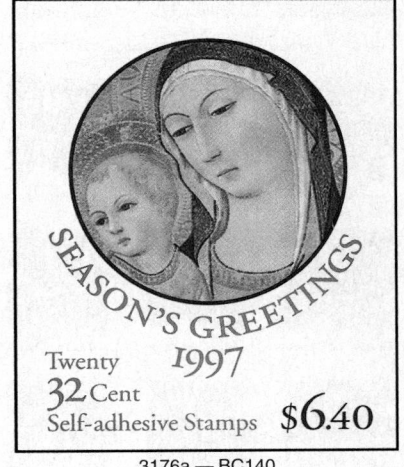

SEASON'S GREETINGS
Twenty *1997*
32 Cent
Self-adhesive Stamps $6.40

3176a — BC140

1997
$6.40 fold-it-yourself booklet contains 20 self-adhesive
    32c stamps

Serpentine Die Cut 9.9 on 2, 3 or 4 Sides
1997, Oct. 27   **Tagged**
3176a A2459   32c pane of 20 + label, P#1111,
         2222, 3333   13.00

By its nature, No. 3176a is a complete booklet (BC140). The peelable backing serves as a booklet cover.

3177a — A2460

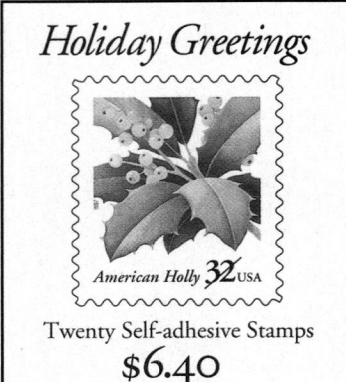

Holiday Greetings

American Holly 32USA

Twenty Self-adhesive Stamps
$6.40

3177a
BC141

1997
$6.40 fold-it-yourself booklet contains 20 self-adhesive
32c stamps

Serpentine Die Cut 11.2x11.6 on 2, 3 or 4 Sides
1997, Oct. 30   **Tagged**
Self-Adhesive
3177a   A2460   32c pane of 20 + label,
                       P#B1111, B2222,
                       B3333   13.00
By its nature No. 3177a is a complete booklet (BC141). The
peelable backing serves as a booklet cover.

3177b-3177d — A2460

3177b	A2460	32c Booklet pane of 4, no P#	2.60
3177c	A2460	32c Booklet pane of 5 + label, no P#	3.25
3177d	A2460	32c Booklet pane of 6, no P# or P#B1111	3.90

Holiday Greetings

American Holly 32USA

Fifteen
Self-adhesive Stamps
$4.80

3177b-3177d —
BC141A

1997
$4.80 booklet contains 15 self-adhesive 32c stamps

$9.60 booklet contains 30 self-adhesive 32c stamps

Combination Booklet
BK264   BC141A $4.80 **black & green,** 1 ea
                              #3177b-3177d,
                              P#B1111   9.75
Booklet
BK265   BC141A $9.60 **black & green,** 5
                              #3177d, P#B1111   20.00
Panes in Nos. BK264-BK265 are separated by rouletting
between each pane.

MAKESHIFT VENDING MACHINE BOOKLETS
See note before No. BK243.
1997
BK266   BC126 $4.80 #3151a-3151o (32c
                                 Dolls)   9.00
BK267   BC126 $4.80 15 #3152 (32c Humphrey
                                 Bogart)   9.00
BK268   BC126 $4.80 15 #3153 (32c Stars &
                                 Stripes)   9.00
BK269   BC126 $4.80 3 ea #3168-3172 (32c
                                 Movie Monsters)   9.00

3244a — A2524

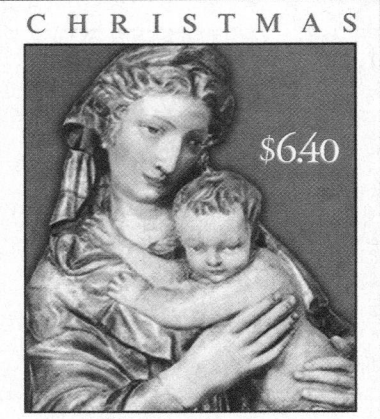

CHRISTMAS

$6.40

Twenty 32¢ Self-adhesive Stamps

3244a — BC142

1998
$6.40 fold-it-yourself booklet contains 20 self-adhesive
32c stamps

Serpentine Die Cut 10.1x9.9 on 2, 3 or 4 Sides
1998, Oct. 15   **Tagged**
3244a   A2524   32c pane of 20 + label,
                       P#11111, 22222, 33333   13.00
No. 3244a is a complete booklet (BC142). The peelable backing serves as a booklet cover.

3248a-3248c — BC143

1998
  $4.80 booklet contains 15 self-adhesive 32c stamps

Combination Booklet

BK270 BC143 $4.80 **multi**, 1 each #3248a-
3248c, P#B111111   *100.00*

Varieties

3248d	A2525	32c As "a," die cutting omitted	—
3248e	A2525	32c As "b," die cutting omitted	—
3248f	A2525	32c As "c," die cutting omitted	—

3252c, 3252e — A2525-A2528

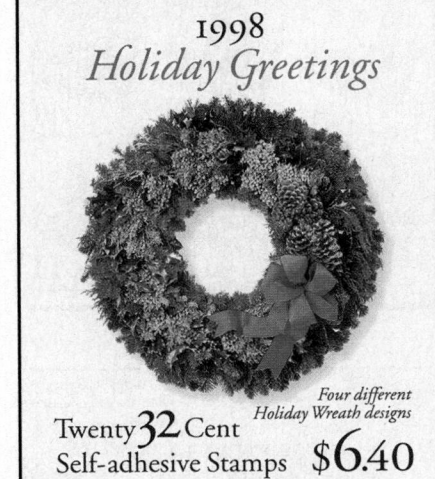

3252c, 3252e — BC143A

1998
  $6.40 fold-it-yourself booklet contains 20 self-adhesive
  32c stamps

Serpentine Die Cut 11.4x11.5 on 2, 3 or 4 Sides

3252c	A2525	32c pane of 20, 5 each #3249-3252 + label, P#B222222, B333333, B444444, B555555	35.00

Serpentine Die Cut 11.7x11.6 on 2, 3 or 4 Sides

3252e	A2525	32c pane of 20, 5 each #3249a-3252a + label, P#B111111, B222222	35.00

Nos. 3252c and 3252e are complete booklets (BC143A). The
peelable backing serves as a booklet cover.

Variety

3252i	As "c," die cutting omitted	—

3267a — A2531

Serpentine Die Cut 9.9 on 2 or 3 Sides
1998, Nov. 9

3267a	A2531	(33c) pane of 10	7.50

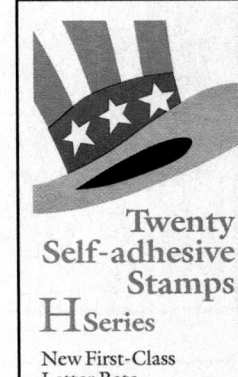

3267a, 3268a — BC144

1998
  ($6.60) booklet contains 20 self-adhesive (33c) stamps
  ($3.30) fold-it-yourself booklet (#3268a) contains 10 self-
  adhesive (33c) stamps

Booklet

BK271 BC144 ($6.60) **multi**, 2 #3267a,
P#1111, 2222, 3333   15.00

3248a-3248c —
A2525-A2528

Serpentine Die Cut 11.3x11.6 on 2, or 3 Sides

1998, Oct. 15			**Tagged**
3248a	A2525	32c pane of 4, #3245-3248, no P#	25.00
3248b	A2525	32c pane of 5, #3245-3246, 3248, 2 #3247 + label, no P#	32.50
3248c	A2525	32c pane of 6, #3247-3248, 2 each #3245-3246, P#B111111	40.00

3268c — A2531

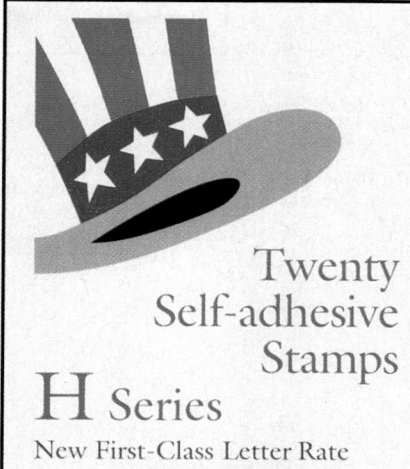

Twenty
Self-adhesive
Stamps
H Series
New First-Class Letter Rate

3268c — BC144A

1998

($6.60) fold-it-yourself booklet contains 20 self-adhesive (33c) stamps

Die cut 11¼ on 3 sides (No. 3268a), 11 on 2, 3 or 4 Sides (No. 3268c)

3268a	A2531	(33c) pane of 10, P#V1111, V1211, V2211, V2222	7.50
3268c	A2531	(33c) pane of 20 + label, P#V1111, V1112, V1113, V1213, V1222, V2113, V2122, V2213, V2223	15.00
		P# V1122, V2222	21.00

3269a — A2531

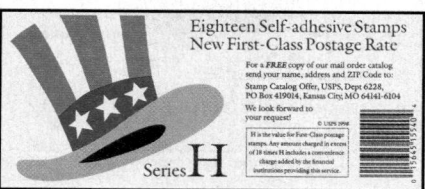

3269a — BC144B

1998

($5.94) fold-it-yourself booklet contains 18 self-adhesive (33c) stamps

Die Cut 8

3269a	A2531	(33c) pane of 18, P#V1111	12.00

Nos. 3268a, 3268c, 3269a are complete booklets (BC144, BC144A, BC144B). The peelable backing serves as a booket cover.

MAKESHIFT VENDING MACHINE BOOKLETS

See note before No. BK243.

1998

BK272	BC126	$4.80	15 (#3222-3225) (32c Tropical Birds)	9.00
BK273	BC126	$4.80	15 #3237 (32c Ballet)	9.00
BK274	BC126	$4.80	3 #3242a (32c Space Discovery)	9.00

Configuration of stamps in #BK272 may vary.

3274a — A2537

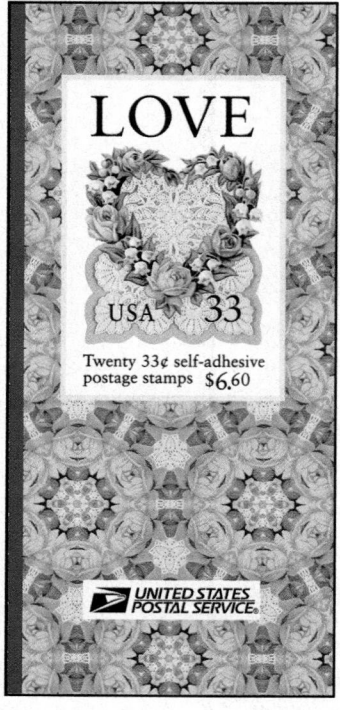

3274a
BC145

1999

$6.60 Fold-it-yourself booklet contains 20 self-adhesive 33c stamps

	Tagged		**Die Cut**
3274a	A2537 33c pane of 20, *Jan. 28, 1999*		13.00

No. 3274a is a complete booklet (BC145). The peelable backing serves as a booklet cover.

Below is a list of known plate numbers. Some numbers may be scarcer than the value indicated in the listing.

P#V1111, V1112, V1117, V1118, V1211, V1212, V1213, V1233, V1313, V1314, V1333, V1334, V1335, V2123, V2221, V2222, V2223, V2424, V2425, V2426, V2324, V3123, V3124, V3125, V3133, V3134, V3323, V3327, V3333, V3334, V3336, V4549, V5650.

Variety

3274c	As "a," die cutting omitted	1,250.

3278a-3278c — A2540

Serpentine Die Cut 11 on 2, 3 or 4 Sides

1999			Tagged
	Self-Adhesive		
3278a	A2540	33c pane of 4, no P#	2.60
3278b	A2540	33c pane of 5 + label, P#V1111, V1112, V1121, V1122, V1212, V2212	3.25
3278c	A2540	33c pane of 6, no P#	3.90

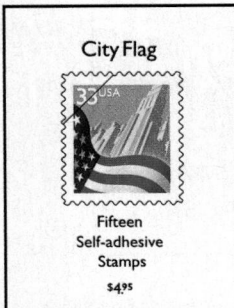

3278a-3278c — BC146

1999
$4.95 booklet contains 15 self-adhesive 33c stamps

COMBINATION BOOKLET

BK275 BC146 $4.95 **multi,** 1 each #3278a-
3278c, P#V1111,
V1112, V1121, V1122,
V1212, V2212 10.00

The plate # single in No. 3278b from No. BK275 is the lower left stamp in the bottom pane of the booklet.

3278d, 3278j — A2540

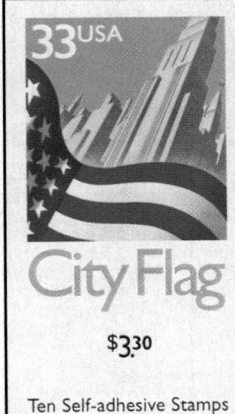

3278d — BC146A

1999
$3.30 Fold-it-yourself booklet contains 10 self-adhesive 33c stamps

3278d A2540 33c pane of 10, P#V1112, V1113, V2322, V2324, V3433, V3434, V3545 12.50
P#V1111 —

3278e, 3278Fg — A2540

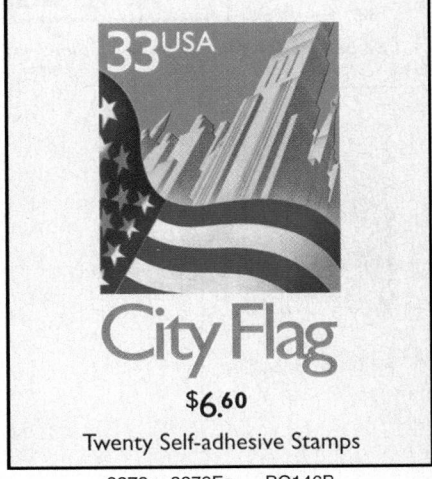

3278e, 3278Fg — BC146B

1999
$6.60 Fold-it-yourself booklet contains 20 self-adhesive 33c stamps

3278e	A2540	33c pane of 20 + label, P#V1111, V1211, V2122, V2222, V2223, V3333, V4444	17.00
		P#V8789	

Nos. 3278d-3278e are complete booklets (BC146A, BC146B). The peelable backing serves as a booklet cover.

Serpentine Die Cut 11½x11¾ on 2, 3 or 4 Sides
3278Fg	A2540	33c pane of 20 + label	22.50

No. 3278Fg is a complete booklet. The peelable backing serves as a booklet cover and is similar to BC146B.
Below is a list of known plate numbers. Some numbers may be scarcer than the value indicated in the listing.
P# V1111, V1131, V2222, V2223, V2227, V2243, V2323, V2423, V2443, V3333, V4444, V5428, V5445, V5446, V5576, V5578, V6423, V6456, V6546, V6556, V6575, V6576, V7567, V7663, V7667, V7676, V8789.

Serpentine Die Cut 11¼
3278j	A2540	33c pane of 10, P#V1111, V1112, V2222	30.00
		P#V1113, V2322	40.00

By its nature No. 3278j is a complete booklet. The peelable backing serves as a booklet cover and is similar to BC146A.

3279a — A2540

Serpentine Die Cut 9.8 on 2 or 3 Sides
3279a	A2540	33c pane of 10	8.50

3279a — BC146C

1999
$6.60 Booklet contains 20 self-adhesive 33c stamps

BOOKLET
BK276	BC146C	$6.60 multi, 2 #3279a, P#1111, 1121	17.00

Variety
3278h		As "e," die cutting omitted	—

3283a — A2541

Classroom Flag

Eighteen Self-adhesive Stamps

$5.94

3283a — BC147

1999
$5.94 fold-it-yourself booklet contains 18 self-adhesive 33c stamps

Serpentine Die Cut 7.9 on 2, 3 or 4 Sides
Tagged
3283a	A2541	33c pane of 18, P#V1111	12.00

No. 3283a is a complete booklet (BC147). The peelable backing serves as a booklet cover.

3297b — A2550-A2553

Fruit Berries

20 SELF-ADHESIVE STAMPS $6.60

3297b
BC148

1999
$6.60 fold-it-yourself booklet contains 20 self-adhesive 33c stamps + label

Serpentine Die Cut 11¼x11½ on 2, 3 or 4 Sides
1999-2000   **Tagged**
Self-Adhesive
3297b	A2550	33c pane of 20, 5 ea #3294-3297 + label	17.00

No. 3297b is a complete booklet (BC148). The peelable backing serves as a booklet cover.
P#B1111, B1112, B2211, B2222, B3331, B3332, B3333, B4444, B5555.

3297d, BC148A —
A2550–A2553

Serpentine Die Cut 11¼x11½ on 2 or 3 Sides

3297d A2550 33c pane of 20, 5 #3297e +
              label, *Mar. 15, 2000,*
              P#B1111   25.00

By its nature, No. 3297d is a double-sided complete booklet. Eight stamps and the booklet cover (BC148A) plus P# are printed on one side of the peelable backing and 12 stamps are printed on the other side of the backing.

3301a-3301c — A2550–A2553

Serpentine Die Cut 9½x10 on 2 or 3 sides

3301a A2550 33c pane of 4, no P#   3.60
3301b A2550 33c pane of 5 + label, no P# 4.50
3301c A2550 33c pane of 6, P#B1111,
              B1112, B2212, B2222   5.50
              P#B2221   —

3301a-3301c —
BC148B

1999
$4.95 booklet contains 15 self-adhesive 33c stamps + label

COMBINATION BOOKLET

BK276A BC148B $4.95 **multicolored,** 1 each
               #3301a-3301c, P# see
               3301c   14.00

3313b, BC149 — A2556–A2559

Serpentine Die Cut 10.9 on 2 or 3 Sides
1999   **Tagged**
3313b A2556 33c pane of 20, all P# (see below)
              except P#S22444   13.00
              P#S22444   —

By its nature, No. 3313b is a complete booklet. Eight stamps and the booklet cover (BC149) plus P# are printed on one side of the peelable backing and 12 stamps are printed on the other side of the backing.
P#S11111, S22222, S22244, S22344, S22444, S22452, S22462, S23222, S24222, S24224, S24242, S24244, S24422, S24442, S24444, S26462, S32323, S32333, S32444, S33333, S44444, S45552, S46654, S55452, S55552, S56462, S62544, S62562, S64452, S64544, S65544, S65552, S66462, S66544, S66552, S66562, S66652.

3355a, BC150 — A2599

1999, Oct. 20   **Serpentine Die Cut 11¼**
                           Self-Adhesive
3355a A2599 33c pane of 20, P#B1111,
              B2222, B3333   20.00

No. 3355a is a complete booklet. Eight stamps and the booklet cover (BC150) plus P# are printed on one side of the peelable backing and 12 stamps are printed on the other side of the backing.

3363a — A2600

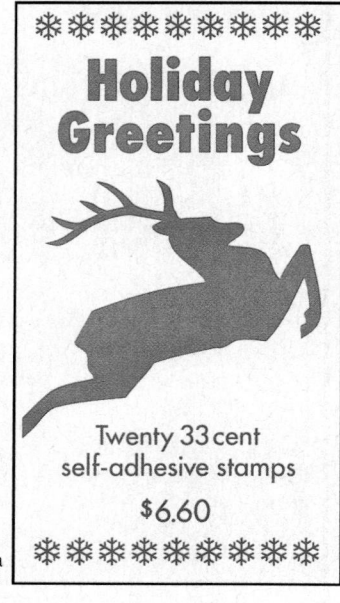

3363a
BC151

1999
$6.60 fold-it-yourself booklet contains 20 self-adhesive
33c stamps

1999, Oct. 20   *Serpentine Die Cut 11¼*
Self-Adhesive

3363a   A2600   33c pane of 20, P#B111111,
B222222, B333333,
B444444, B555555,
B666666, B777777,
B888888, B999999,
B000000, BAAAAAA,
BBBBBBB   32.50

No. 3363a is a complete booklet (BC151). The peelable backing serves as a booklet cover.

Variety
3363d   As "a," die cutting omitted   —

3367a-3367c —
A2600

Serpentine Die Cut 11½x11¼ on 2 or 3 sides
Stamp Size: 21x19mm

3367a   A2600   33c pane of 4, no P#   9.00
3367b   A2600   33c pane of 5 + label, no P#   11.25
3367c   A2600   33c pane of 6, P#B111111,
B222222   13.50

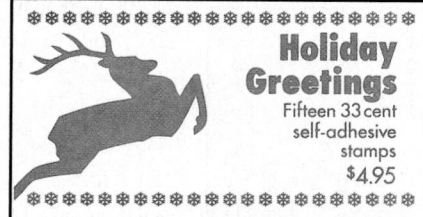

3367a-3367c — BC152

1999
$4.95 fold-it-yourself booklet contains 15 self-adhesive
33c stamps

COMBINATION BOOKLET
BK276B BC152 $4.95 **green & gold,** 1 each
#3367a-3367c, P# see
3367c   35.00

MAKESHIFT VENDING MACHINE BOOKLETS
See note before No. BK243.
1999
BK277   BC126 $4.95 4 each #3325, 3327-
3328, 3 #3326 (33c
American Glass)   11.00
BK278   BC126 $4.95 3 each #3333-3337 (33c
Famous Trains)   11.00

3377a — A2604-A2608

Selvage 1

THE SUBMARINE STAMPS
U.S. Navy Submarines
A Century of Service to America

USS **Holland,** the U.S. Navy's
first submarine, was
purchased in 1900.

S-class submarines
were designed during WWI.

Gato class submarines
played a key role in
the destruction of Japanese
maritime power in the
Pacific during WWII.

Los Angeles class
attack submarines, armed with
"smart" torpedoes and cruise
missiles, are nuclear powered.

Ohio class submarines—also
nuclear powered—carry more
than half of America's strategic
weapons, making them a vital part
of America's nuclear deterrence.

Selvage 2

2000, Mar. 27   *Perf. 11*
3377a   pane of 5 with selvage 1   25.00   —
With selvage 2   25.00   —

3377a — BC153

2000
$9.80 booklet contains 2 panes of one 22c, 33c, 55c, 60c and $3.20 stamps and 6 leaves of text.

Booklet

BK279 BC153 $9.80 **multicolored,** no P#   50.00

No. BK279 contains one pane with selvage 1 and one pane with selvage 2.

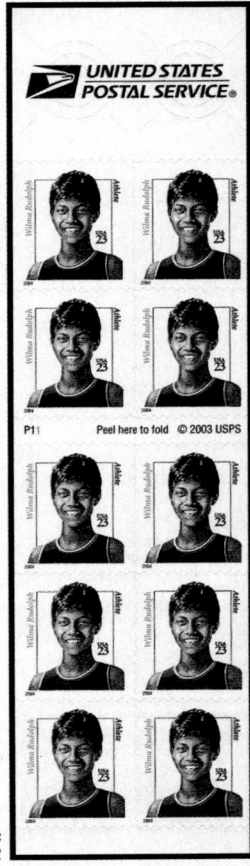

3436a, 3436b, 3436c
— A2652

Serpentine Die Cut 11¼x10¾ on 3 Sides

2004, July 14   Litho.

Self-Adhesive

3436a A2652 23c pane of 4, no P#   1.80
3436b A2652 23c pane of 6, no P#   2.70
3436c A2652 23c pane of 10, P#P11   4.50

3436a, 3436b,
3436c — BC153A

2004
$2.30 booklet contains 10 self-adhesive 23c stamps
$2.30 fold-it-yourself booklet contains 10 self-adhesive 23c stamps

COMBINATION BOOKLET

BK279A BC153A $2.30 **multi,** #3436a-3436b, no P#   4.50

By its nature, No. 3436c is a complete booklet (BC153A). The peelable backing serves as a booklet cover. No. BK279A lacks the self-adhesive panel that covers the rouletting. The backing

on No. 3436b has a different product code (672900) than that found on the lower portion of No. 3436c (673000).

Variety

3436d A2652 23c As "c," die cutting omitted —

3450a — A2678

3450a
BC154

2000
$6.12 fold-it-yourself booklet contains 18 self-adhesive (34c) stamps

2000   *Serpentine Die Cut 8 on 2, 3 or 4 Sides*
Self-Adhesive

3450a A2678 (34c) pane of 18, P#V1111, Dec. 15   16.00

No. 3450a is a complete booklet (BC154). The peelable backing serves as a booklet cover.

3451a — A2679

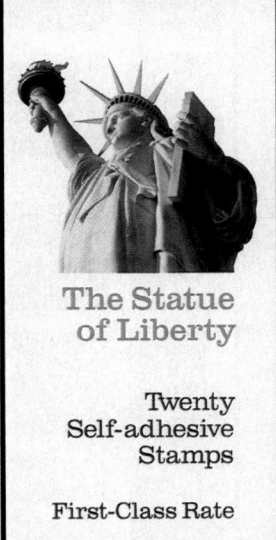

3451a — BC155

2000
$6.80 fold-it-yourself booklet contains 20 self-adhesive (34c) stamps

Serpentine Die Cut 11 on 2, 3 or 4 Sides
2000, Dec. 15
Self-Adhesive

3451a A2679 (34c) pane of 20, P#V1111, V2222   14.00

No. 3451a is a complete booklet (BC155). The peelable backing serves as a booklet cover.

3451b-3451c — A2679

3451b A2679 (34c) pane of 4, without plate # 3.00
3451c A2679 (34c) pane of 6, no P# 5.75

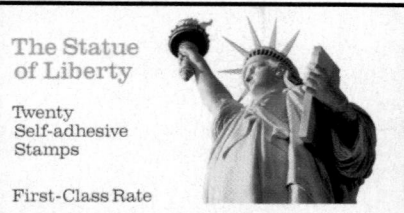

3451b, 3451c — BC156

2000

$6.80   booklet contains 20 self-adhesive (34c) stamps

COMBINATION BOOKLET

BK280 BC156 ($6.80) **multicolored,** 1 #3451b
without P#, 1 #3451b
with P#V1111 or V2222,
2 #3451c 20.00

The plate # on No. 3451b from No. BK280 is on the lower right stamp of the right pane of 4 of the booklet.

Varieties

3451b   pane of 4, containing P#
single 4.50
3451d   As "a," die cutting omitted ...... —

3457b-3457d —
A2681-A2684

Serpentine Die Cut 10½x10¾ on 2 or 3 Sides (#3454-3457), 11½x11¾ on 2 or 3 sides (#3458-3461)

2000

Self-Adhesive

3457b A2681 (34c) pane of 4, #3454-3457, *Dec. 15* 4.00
3457c A2681 (34c) pane of 6, #3456, 3457, 2 each #3454-3455, no P#, *Dec. 15* 6.00
3457d A2681 (34c) pane of 6, #3454, 3455, 2 each #3456-3457, no P#, *Dec. 15* 6.00

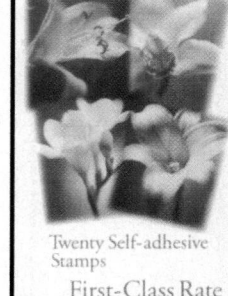

3457b-3457d — BC158

2000

$6.80   booklet contains 20 self-adhesive (34c) stamps

COMBINATION BOOKLET

BK281 BC158 ($6.80) **multicolored,** #3457c,
3457d, 2 #3457b,
P#S1111 .... 22.50

P# on No. BK281 is on the backing paper of the top pane of No. 3457b.

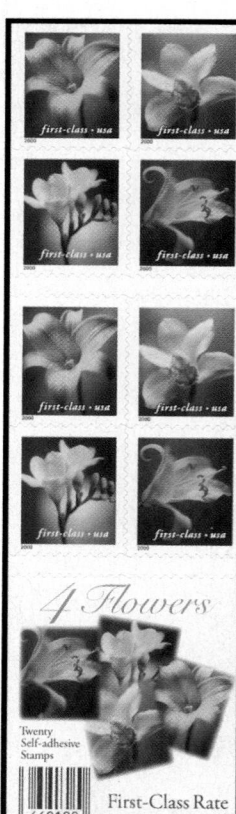

3457e, BC157 —
A2681-A2684

3457e A2681   (34c) pane of 20, 5 each #
3454-3457, P#S1111,
Dec. 15 .... 20.00

No. 3457e is a complete booklet. Eight stamps and the booklet cover (BC157) are printed on one side of the peelable backing and 12 stamps plus P# are printed on the other side of the backing.

3461b A2681   pane of 20, 2 each
                  #3461a, 3 each #3457a,
                  #S1111, *Dec. 15*   36.50
3461c A2681   pane of 20, 2 each
                  #3457a, 3 each #3461a,
                  #S1111, *Dec. 15*   45.00

Nos. 3461b and 3461c are complete booklets. Two blocks of four with the same gauge die cutting and the booklet cover (BC157) are printed on one side of the peelable backing and three blocks of four with the other gauge die cutting plus P# are printed on the other side of the backing.

3482a, 3483c, 3483f
— A2686

3482a, 3483c,
3483f — BC159

2001
   $2 fold-it-yourself booklet contains 10 self-adhesive 20c stamps
   $2 booklet contains 10 self-adhesive 20c stamps

Serpentine Die Cut 11¼x11 on 3 Sides
2001, Feb. 22
Self-Adhesive
3482a A2686 20c pane of 10, P#P1, P2, P3   4.50

3482b, 3483c —
A2686

3482b A2686 20c pane of 4, P#P1, P2, P3   1.80
3482c A2686 20c pane of 6, no P#   2.70
COMBINATION BOOKLET
BK281A BC159 $2 **multicolored**, #3482b-
                  3482c, P#P1, P2, P3   4.50

No. BK281A has slightly smaller cover (BC159) than No. 3482a and lacks self-adhesive panel that covers the rouletting.

3483a A2686 20c pane of 4, 2 #3482 at L, 2
                  #3483 at R, P#P1, P2, P3   12.00
3483b A2686 20c pane of 6, 3 #3482 at L, 3
                  #3483 at R, no P#   20.00
3483c A2686 20c pane of 10, 5 #3482 at L, 5
                  #3483 at R, P#P1, P2, P3   25.00
3483d A2686 20c pane of 4, 2 #3483 at L, 2
                  #3282 at R, P#P1, P2, P3   12.00
3483e A2686 20c pane of 6, 3 #3483 at L, 3
                  #3282 at R, no P#   20.00
3483f A2686 20c pane of 10, 5 #3483 at L, 5
                  #3282 at R, P#P1, P2, P3   25.00

Nos. 3482a, 3483c and 3483f are complete booklets (BC159) and include a self-adhesive panel that covers the rouletting. The peelable backing, which is slightly longer than that on Nos. BK282 and BK282A, serves as a booklet cover.

COMBINATION BOOKLETS
BK282 BC159 $2 **multicolored**, #3483a-
                  3483b, P#P1, P2, P3   32.50
BK282A BC159 $2 **multicolored**, #3483d-
                  3483e, P#P1, P2, P3   32.50

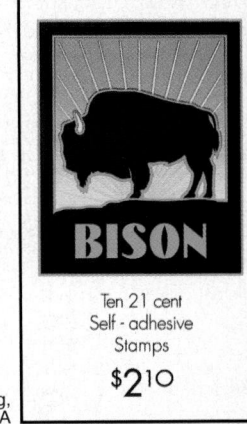

3484d, 3484Ag,
3484Aj — BC159A

2001
   $2.10 fold-it-yourself booklet contains 10 self-adhesive 21c stamps
   $2.10 booklet contains 10 self-adhesive 21c stamps

Serpentine Die Cut 11¼ on 3 Sides
2001, Sept. 20
Self-Adhesive
3484b A2687 21c pane of 4, P#P111111,
                  P333333, P444444   2.00
3484c A2687 21c pane of 6, no P#   3.00

COMBINATION BOOKLET
BK282B BC159A $2.10 **multi**, #3484b-3484c,
                  P#P111111, P333333,
                  P444444   5.00

3484b, 3484c —
A2687

3484d, 3484Ag,
3484Aj — A2687

3485a — A2689

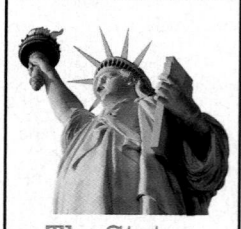

The Statue
of Liberty

Ten **34** cent
Self-adhesive
Stamps
$340

3485a — BC160

3485b — A2689

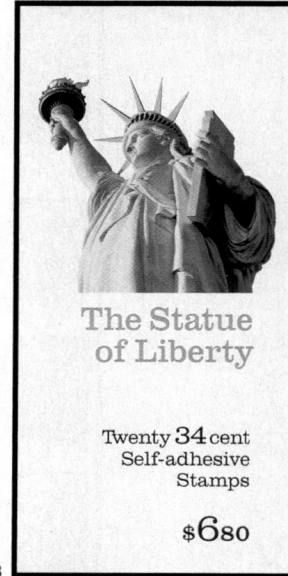

The Statue
of Liberty

Twenty **34** cent
Self-adhesive
Stamps

$680

3485b — BC160B

3484d	A2687	21c pane of 10, P#P111111, P222222, P333333, P444444, P555555	5.00

Serpentine Die Cut 10½x11¼ on 3 Sides

3484Ae	A2687	21c pane of 4, 2 #3484 at L, 2# 3484A at R, P#P111111, P333333, P444444	12.00
3484Af	A2687	21c pane of 6, 3 #3484 at L, 3# 3484A at R, no P#	20.00
3484Ag	A2687	21c pane of 10, 5 #3484 at L, 5# 3484A at R, P#P111111, P222222, P333333, P444444, P555555	30.00
3484Ah	A2687	21c pane of 4, 2 #3484A at L, 2# 3484 at R, P#P111111, P333333, P444444	12.00
3484Ai	A2687	21c pane of 6, 3 #3484A at L, 3# 3484 at R, no P#	20.00
3484Aj	A2687	21c pane of 10, 5 #3484A at L, 5# 3484 at R, P#P111111, P222222, P333333, P444444, P555555	30.00

COMBINATION BOOKLETS

| BK282C | BC159A | $2.10 **multi**, #3484Ae-3484Af, P#P111111, P333333, P444444 | 32.50 |
| BK282D | BC159A | $2.10 **multi**, #3484Ah-3484Ai, P#P111111, P333333, P444444 | 32.50 |

Nos. 3484d, 3484Ag and 3484Aj are complete booklets (BC159A). The peelable backing serves as a booklet cover. Nos. BK282B-BK282D lack self-adhesive panel that covers the rouletting. Nos. BK282B-BK282D have a small 662900 UPC code on cover back, while Nos. 3484d, 3484Ag and 3484Aj have a large 662800 UPC code on cover back.

2001
$3.40 fold-it-yourself booklet contains 10 self-adhesive 34c stamps

**2001, Feb. 7   *Serpentine Die Cut 11 on 3 Sides
Self-Adhesive***

| 3485a | A2689 | 34c pane of 10, P#V1111, V1221 | 7.00 |

2001
$6.80 fold-it-yourself booklet contains 20 self-adhesive 34c stamps

| 3485b | A2689 | 34c pane of 20, P#V1111, V1211, V1221, V2111, V2112, V2121, V2122, V2212, V2222 | 14.00 |

Nos. 3485a-3485b are complete booklets (BC160 and BC160B). The peelable backing serves as a booklet cover.

3485c, 3485d —
A2689

| 3485c | A2689 | 34c pane of 4, without P# | 3.00 |
| 3485d | A2689 | 34c pane of 6, no P# | 4.50 |

The Statue
of Liberty

Twenty 34 cent
Self-adhesive
Stamps

$6.80

3485c, 3485d — BC160A

2001
$6.80 booklet contains 20 self-adhesive 34c
stamps

COMBINATION BOOKLET

BK283 BC160A $6.80 **multicolored,** 1 #3485c
with P#, 1 #3485c with-
out P#, 2 3485d,
P#V1111, V1122, V2212,
V2222   15.00
P#V1112, V1121   —

The plate # on No. 3485c from No. BK283 is on the lower
right stamp of the right pane of 4 of the booklet.

Varieties

3485c   Pane of 4 containing P#V1111, V1122,
V2212, V2222
Pane of 4 containing P#V1112, V1121   4.00
—
3485f   As "b," die cutting omitted   —

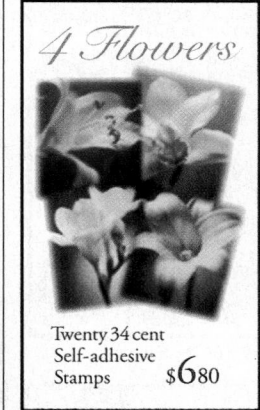

3490b, 3490c, 3490d
— A2690-A2693

Serpentine Die Cut 10½ x 10¾ on 2 or 3 Sides
2001, Feb. 7

Self-Adhesive

3490b   34c pane of 4   3.00
3490c   34c pane of 6, #3489-3490, 2 each
#3487-3488   4.50

3490d   34c pane of 6, #3487-3488, 2 each
#3489-3490   4.50

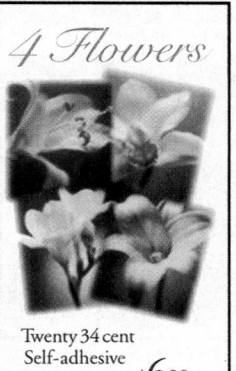

4 Flowers

Twenty 34 cent
Self-adhesive
Stamps $6.80

3490b, 3490c,
3490d — BC162

2001
$6.80 booklet contains 20 self-adhesive 34c
stamps

COMBINATION BOOKLET

BK284 BC162 $6.80 **multicolored,** #3490c-
3490d, 2 #3490b,
P#S1111   15.00

P# on No. BK284 is on the backing paper of the bottom pane
of No. 3490b.

$6.80 *4 Flowers*

Twenty 34 cent
Self-adhesive Stamps
© 2000 USPS

0 669200 7

3490e, BC161 —
A2690-A2693

3490e   34c pane of 20, 5 #3490a,
P#S1111, S2222   15.00

No. 3490e is a complete booklet with 12 stamps plus P# on
one side and eight stamps plus booklet cover (BC161) on the
other side. The peelable backing serves as a booklet cover.

3492b — A2694-A2695

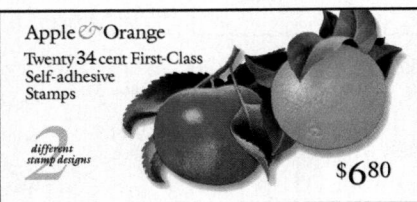

Apple & Orange

Twenty 34 cent First-Class
Self-adhesive
Stamps

2 different stamp designs

$6.80

3492b — BC163

2001
$6.80 fold-it-yourself booklet contains 20 self-adhesive 34c stamps

Serpentine Die Cut 11¼ on 2, 3 or 4 sides
2001, Mar. 6
Self-Adhesive
3492b   34c pane of 20, 10 each #3491-3492,
          P# B1111, B2222, B3333,
          B4444, B5555, B6666, B7777   14.00

No. 3492b is a complete booklet (BC163). The peelable backing serves as a booklet cover.

Varieties
3492e   As "b," die cutting omitted   —
3492f   As "b," right four stamps yellow omitted   —

3494b, 3494c, 3494d
— A2694-A2695

2001, May   *Serpentine Die Cut 11½x10¾*
Self-Adhesive
3494b   34c pane of 4, 2 each #3493-3494,
          without P#   5.00
3494c   34c pane of 6, 3 each #3493-3494,
          #3493 at UL, no P#   7.50
3494d   34c pane of 6, 3 each #3493-3494,
          #3494 at UL, no P#   7.50

Apple & Orange

Twenty 34 cent
Self-adhesive
Stamps

$6.80

2 different stamp designs

3494b, 3494c,
3494d — BC163A

2001
$6.80 booklet contains 20 self-adhesive 34c stamps

COMBINATION BOOKLET
BK284A BC163A $6.80 **multi,** #3494c, 3494d,
          2 #3494b, P#B1111   25.00

The plate # on No. 3494b from No. BK284A is on bottom left stamp in the bottom pane of the booklet.

Variety
3494b   Pane of 4 with P#B1111   6.50

3495a —
A2688

3495a —
BC163B

2001
$6.12 booklet contains 18 self-adhesive 34c
stamps

Serpentine Die Cut 8 on 2, 3 or 4 Sides
2001, Dec. 17
Self-Adhesive

3495a   34c pane of 18, #V1111   18.00
Nos. 3495a is a complete booklet (BC163B). The peelable
backing serves as a booklet cover.

3496a — A2699

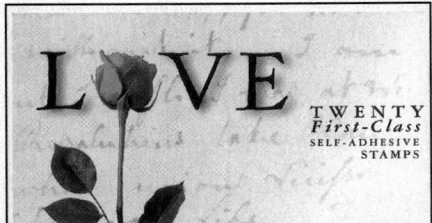

3496a — BC164

2001
$6.80 fold-it-yourself booklet contains 20 self-ad-
hesive (34c) stamps

2001   Serpentine Die Cut 11¼ on 2, 3, or 4 Sides
Self-Adhesive

3496a   A2699 (34c) pane of 20, P#B1111,
B2222, *Jan. 19*   18.00
No. 3496a is a complete booklet (BC164). The peelable back-
ing serves as a booklet cover.

3497a — A2700

3497a — BC165

2001
$6.80 fold-it-yourself booklet contains 20 self-ad-
hesive 34c stamps

2001   Serpentine Die Cut 11¼ on 2, 3 or 4 Sides
Self-Adhesive

3497a   A2700 34c pane of 20, P#B1111, B2222,
B3333, B4444, B5555, *Feb.
14*   18.00
No. 3497a is a complete booklet (BC165). The peelable backing serves as a booklet cover.

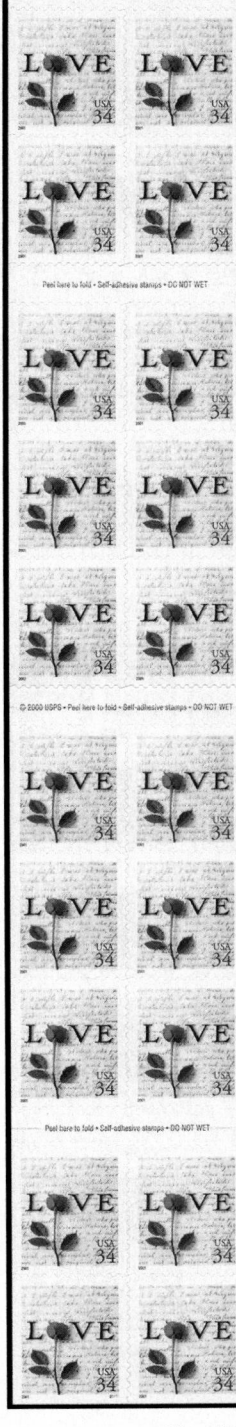

3498a, 3498b —
A2700

Size: 18x21mm
Serpentine Die Cut 11½x10¾

3498a   A2700 34c pane of 4, without P#, *Feb.
14*   4.00
3498b   A2700 34c pane of 6, no P#, *Feb. 14*   6.00

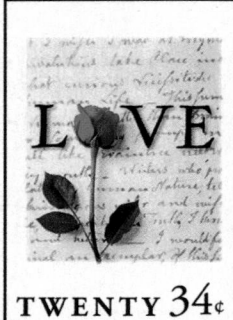

3498a,
3498b — BC166

2001

$6.80 booklet contains 20 self-adhesive 34c stamps

COMBINATION BOOKLET

BK285 BC166 $6.80 **multicolored,** 2 each
#3498a-3498b, P#B1111   22.50

The plate # on No. 3498a from No. BK285 is on bottom left stamp in the bottom pane of the booklet.

Variety

3498a   pane of 4, containing P#B1111   6.00

3536a — A2737

3536a — BC167

2001

$6.80 fold-it-yourself booklet contains 20 self-adhesive 34c stamps

Serpentine Die Cut 11½ on 2, 3 or 4 Sides
2001, Oct. 10

Self-Adhesive

3536a   A2737   34c pane of 20, P#B1111   15.00

No. 3536a is a complete booklet (BC167). The peelable backing serves as a booklet cover.

Holiday Greetings

$6.80

3540d, 3540g, BC168
— A2738-A2741

Serpentine Die Cut 10¾x11 on 2 or 3 Sides

3540d   A2738   34c pane of 20, small date, 5
#3540c + label, P#S1111   16.50
3540g   A2738   34c pane of 20, large date, 5
#3540f + label, P#S3333,
S4444   40.00

Nos. 3540d and 3540g are complete booklets with 12 stamps plus P# on one side and eight stamps plus booklet cover (BC168) on the other side. The peelable backing serves as a booklet cover.

3544b, 3544c, 3544d
— A2738-A2741

Green Denomination
Stamp Size: 21x18½mm
Serpentine Die Cut 11 on 2 or 3 sides

3544b   A2738   34c pane of 4, #3541-3544   2.80
3544c   A2738   34c pane of 6, #3543-3544, 2
#3541-3542   4.25
3544d   A2738   34c pane of 6, #3541-3542, 2
#3543-3544   4.25

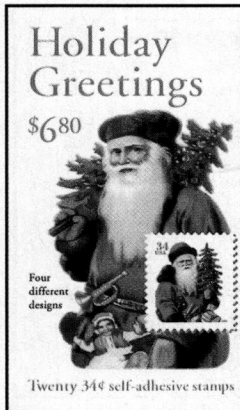

3544b, 3544c,
3544d — BC169

2001
$6.80 booklet contains 20 self-adhesive 34c
stamps

COMBINATION BOOKLET
BK286 BC169 $6.80 **multi,** #3544c-3544d, 2
#3544b, P#V1111   14.00

P# on No. BK286 is on the backing paper of the bottom pane
of No. 3544b.

3549a — A2744

3549a — BC170

2001
$6.80 booklet contains 20 self-adhesive 34c
stamps

Serpentine Die Cut 11¼ on 2, 3 or 4 Sides
2001, Oct. 24
Self-Adhesive
3549a A2744 34c Pane of 20, P#B1111,
B2222, B3333, B4444   15.00

No. 3549a is a complete booklet (BC170). The peelable backing serves as a booklet cover.

3549Bc, 3549Bd —
A2744

Serpentine Die Cut 10½x10¾ on 2 or 3 Sides
2002, Jan.
Self-Adhesive
3549Bc A2744 34c pane of 4   3.60
3549Bd A2744 34c pane of 6   5.40

3549Bc,
3549Bd — BC171

2002
$6.80 booklet contains 20 self-adhesive 34c
stamps

COMBINATION BOOKLET
BK287 BC171 $6.80 **multi,** 2 each #3549Bc,
3549Bd, P#S1111   18.00

P# on No. BK287 is on the backing paper of the lower example of No. 3549Bd.

3549Be, BC172 —
A2744

3549Be A2744   34c pane of 20, P#S1111   18.00

No. 3549Be is a complete booklet with 12 stamps plus P# on
one side and eight stamps plus booklet cover (BC172) on the
other side. The peelable backing serves as a booklet cover.

Washington Type of 2002

3618a, 3618b —
A2686

Serpentine Die Cut 11¼x11 on 3 Sides
2002, June 7

Self-Adhesive

3618a	A2686	23c pane of 4, P#P1, P2, P3	2.00
3618b	A2686	23c pane of 6, no P#	3.00

3618c, 3619e,
3619f — BC173

2002
$2.30 booklet contains 10 self-adhesive 23c stamps

COMBINATION BOOKLET

BK288 BC173 $2.30 **multi,** #3618a-3618b, P#P1, P2, P4   5.00

No. BK288 has a 671800 UPC code on cover back, while No. 3618c has a 671000 UPC code on cover back.

3618c — A2686

3618c A2686 23c pane of 10, P#P1, P2, P3   4.50

No. 3618c is a complete booklet and includes a self-adhesive panel that covers the rouletting. The peelable backing (BC173), which is slightly longer than on No. BK288, serves as a booklet cover.

Washington Type of 2002
Serpentine Die Cut 10½x11 on 3 Sides
2002, June 7

Self-Adhesive

3619a	A2686	23c pane of 4, 2 #3619 at L, 2 #3618 at R, P#P1, P2, P3	9.00
3619b	A2686	23c pane of 6, 3 #3619 at L, 3 #3618 at R, no P#	14.00
3619c	A2686	23c pane of 4, 2 #3618 at L, 2 #3619 at R, P#P1, P2, P4	9.00
3619d	A2686	23c pane of 6, 3 #3618 at L, 3 #3619 at R, no P#	14.00

COMBINATION BOOKLETS

BK289	BC173 $2.30 **multi,** #3619a-3619b, P#P1, P2, P4		23.00
BK289A	BC173 $2.30 **multi,** #3619c-3619d, P#P1, P2, P4		23.00

Serpentine Die Cut 10½x11 on 3 Sides
Self-Adhesive

3619e	A2686	23c pane of 10, 5 #3619 at L, 5 #3618 at R, P#P1, P2, P3	21.00
3619f	A2686	23c pane of 10, 5 #3618 at L, 5 #3619 at R, P#P1, P2, P3	21.00

Nos. 3619e and 3619f are complete booklets and include a self-adhesive panel that covers the rouletting. The peelable backing (BC173), which is slightly longer than those on Nos. BK289 and BK289A, serves as a booklet cover.

3623a — A2807

3623a — BC174

2002
$7.40 fold-it-yourself booklet contains 20 self-adhesive (37c) stamps

Serpentine Die Cut 11¼ on 2, 3 or 4 Sides
2002, June 7   **Litho.**
Self-Adhesive

3623a	A2807	(37c) pane of 20, P#B1111, B2222, B3333	15.00

No. 3623a is a complete booklet (BC174). The peelable backing serves as a booklet cover.

3624a, 3624b —
A2807

Serpentine Die Cut 10½x10¾ on 2 or 3 Sides
2002, June 7 Photo.
Self-Adhesive
3624a A2807 (37c) pane of 4, no P# 3.00
3624b A2807 (37c) pane of 6 4.50

3624c, BC176 —
A2807

Serpentine Die Cut 10½x10¾ on 2 or 3 Sides
3624c A2807 (37c) pane of 20, P#S1111 15.00

No. 3624c is a complete booklet with 12 stamps plus P# on one side and eight stamps plus booklet cover (BC176) on the other side. The peelable backing serves as a booklet cover.

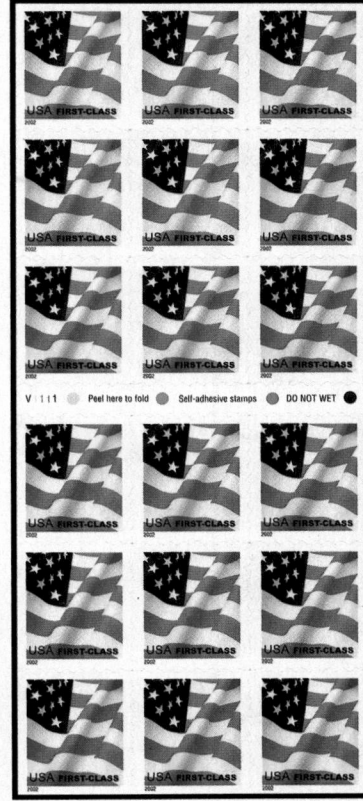

3624a, 3624b — BC175

2002
$7.40 booklet contains 20 self-adhesive (37c) stamps

COMBINATION BOOKLET
BK290 BC175 ($7.40) **multi,** 2 each #3624a, 3624b, P#S11111 15.00

Plate number on No. BK290 is on the backing paper of the lower example of No. 3624b.

3625a —
A2807

3625a
BC177

2002
$6.66 fold-it-yourself booklet contains 18 self-adhesive (37c) stamps

Serpentine Die Cut 8 on 2, 3 or 4 Sides
2002, June 7 Photo.
Self-Adhesive
3625a A2807 (37c) pane of 18, P#V1111 13.50

No. 3625a is a complete booklet (BC177). The peelable backing serves as a booklet cover.

3629b, 3629c, 3629d
— A2808-A2811

Serpentine Die Cut 11 on 2 or 3 Sides

2002, June 7			Photo.

Self-Adhesive

3629b	A2808 (37c) pane of 4, #3626-3629, no P#		
			3.00
3629c	A2808 (37c) pane of 6, #3627, 3629, 2 each #3626, 3628, no P#		
			4.50
3629d	A2808 (37c) pane of 6, #3626, 3628, 2 each #3627, 3629, no P#		
			4.50

3629b, 3629c, 3629d — BC178

2002

$7.40 booklet contains 20 self-adhesive (37c) stamps

COMBINATION BOOKLET

BK291 BC178 ($7.40) **multi,** #3629c-3629d, 2
#3629b, no P#   15.00

3629e — A2808-A2811

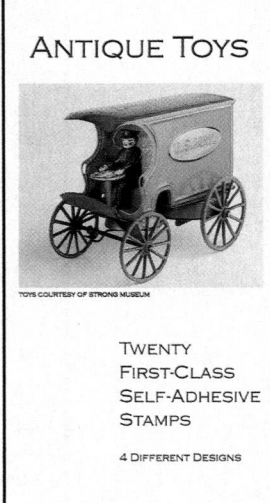

3629e — BC179

2002

$7.40 fold-it-yourself booklet contains 20 self-adhesive (37c) stamps

Serpentine Die Cut 11 on 2, 3 or 4 Sides

3629e	A2808 (37c) pane of 20, 5 each #3626-3629, P#V1111, V1112, V2222	
		15.00

No. 3629e is a complete booklet (BC179). The peelable backing serves as a booklet cover.

3634a — A2812

3634a — BC180

2002

$3.70 fold-it-yourself booklet contains 10 self-adhesive 37c stamps

Serpentine Die Cut 11.1 on 3 Sides

2002, June 7		Photo.

Self-Adhesive

3634a	A2812 37c pane of 10, P#V1111	7.50

No. 3634a is a complete booklet (BC180). The peelable backing serves as a booklet cover.

3634c, 3634d —
A2812

Serpentine Die Cut 11 on 2 or 3 Sides
2003, Nov.   Photo.

Self-Adhesive
3634c A2812 37c pane of 4 #3634b, no P#   3.00
3634d A2812 37c pane of 6 #3634b   4.50

3634c, 3634d —
BC180A

2002
$7.40 booklet contains 20 self-adhesive 37c stamps.

COMBINATION BOOKLET
BK291A BC180A $7.40 **multi,** 2 each #3634c,
3634d, P#V1111   15.00
Plate number on No. BK291A is on the backing paper of the
lower example of No. 3634d.

2002(?)   *Serpentine Die Cut 11.3 on 3 Sides*
Self-Adhesive
Photo.
3634f A2812   37c pane of 10, P#V1111   8.50
No. 3634f is a complete booklet (BC180). The peelable back-
ing serves as a booklet cover.

3635a — A2812

3635a — BC181

2002
$7.40 fold-it-yourself booklet contains 20 self-ad-
hesive 37c stamps
Serpentine Die Cut 11¼ on 2, 3 or 4 Sides
2002, June 7   Litho.
Self-Adhesive
3635a A2812 37c pane of 20, P#B1111, B2222,
B3333, B4444, B5555,
B6666, B7777   15.00
No. 3635a is a complete booklet (BC181). The peelable back-
ing serves as a booklet cover.

3636a, 3636b —
A2812

Serpentine Die Cut 10½x10¾ on 2 or 3 Sides
2002, June 7   Photo.

Self-Adhesive
3636a A2812 37c pane of 4, no P#   3.00
3636b A2812 37c pane of 6   4.50

3636a, 3636b — BC182

2002
$7.40 fold-it-yourself booklet contains 20 self-adhesive 37c stamps

COMBINATION BOOKLET
BK291B BC182 $7.40 **multi,** 2 each #3636a, 3636b, P#S11111   15.00

Plate number on No. BK291B is on the backing paper of the lower example of No. 3636b.

3636c, BC183 — A2812

Serpentine Die Cut 10½x10¾ on 2 or 3 Sides
2002, June 7   Photo.
Self-Adhesive
3636c A2812 37c pane of 20, P#S1111, S2222, S3333, S4444, S5555   15.00

No. 3636c is a complete booklet with 12 stamps plus P# on one side and eight stamps plus booklet cover (BC183) on the other side. The peelable backing serves as a booklet cover.

Variety
3636f   As "c," 11 stamps and part of 12th stamp on reverse printed on backing liner, the 8 stamps on front side imperf   —

Serpentine Die Cut 11¼x11 on 2 or 3 Sides
2004, July   Photo.
Self-Adhesive
3636De A2812 37c pane of 20, P#V1111, V1112, V2222   22.50

No. 3636De is a complete booklet with 12 stamps plus P# on one side and eight stamps plus booklet cover (BC183) on the other side. The peelable backing serves as a booklet cover.

3637a — A2812

3637a—BC184

2003
$6.66 fold-it-yourself booklet contains 18 self-adhesive 37c stamps

Serpentine Die Cut 8 on 2, 3 or 4 Sides
2003, Feb. 4   Photo.
Self-Adhesive
3637a A2812 37c pane of 18, #V1111   13.50

No. 3637a is a complete booklet (BC184). The peelable backing serves as a booklet cover.

3645b, 3645c, 3645d — A2813-A2816

Serpentine Die Cut 11 on 2 or 3 Sides
2002, July 26   Photo.
Self-Adhesive
3645b A2813 37c pane of 4, #3642-3645, no P#   3.00
3645c A2813 37c pane of 6, #3643, 3645, 2 each #3642, 3644, no P#   4.50
3645d A2813 37c pane of 6, #3642, 3644, 2 each #3643, 3645   4.50

3645b, 3645c, 3645d — BC185

2002
$7.40 booklet contains 20 self-adhesive 37c stamps

COMBINATION BOOKLET
BK292 BC185 $7.40 **multi**, #3645c-3645d, 2 #3645b, P#V1111   15.00

Plate number on No. BK292 is on the backing paper of No. 3645d.

3645e — A2813-A2816

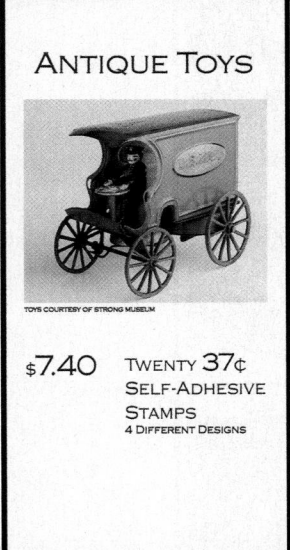

3645e — BC186

2002
$7.40 fold-it-yourself booklet contains 20 self-adhesive 37c stamps

Serpentine Die Cut 11 on 2, 3 or 4 Sides
2002
3645e A2813 37c pane of 20, 5 each #3642-3645, P#V1111, V1112, V2221, V2222   15.00

No. 3645e is a complete booklet (BC186). The peelable backing serves as a booklet cover.

3645h, BC179A — A2813-A2816

Serpentine Die Cut 11x11¼ on 2 or 3 Sides
2003, Sept. 3   **Photo.**
Self-Adhesive
3645h A2813 37c pane of 20, P#V1111   15.00

No. 3645h is a complete double-sided booklet. Eight stamps and the booklet cover (BC179A) are printed on one side of the peelable backing paper, and 12 stamps plus P# appear on the other side of the backing paper.

3657a — A2828

3657a — BC187

2002
$7.40 fold-it-yourself booklet contains 20 self-adhesive 37c stamps

Serpentine Die Cut 11 on 2, 3 or 4 Sides
2002, Aug. 16   **Litho.**
Self-Adhesive
3657a A2828 37c pane of 20, P#B11111, B22222, B33333, B44444, B55555, B66666, B77777   15.00

No. 3657a is a complete booklet (BC187). The peelable backing serves as a booklet cover.

Variety
3657b As "a," silver ("Love 37 USA") missing on top five stamps (CM)   750.00

3675a — A2843

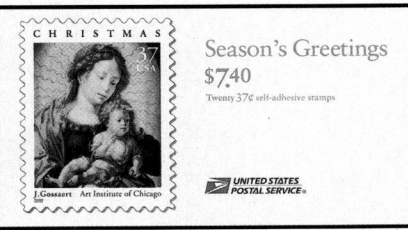

3675a — BC188

2002
$7.40 fold-it-yourself booklet contains 20 self-adhesive 37c stamps

Serpentine Die Cut 11x11¼ on 2, 3 or 4 Sides
2002, Oct. 10
Self-Adhesive
3675a A2843 37c pane of 20, P#B1111, B2222   15.00

No. 3675a is a complete booklet (BC188). The peelable backing serves as a booklet cover.

3687b, BC189 — A2844-A2847

Serpentine Die Cut 10¾ on 2 or 3 Sides
2002, Oct. 28
Self-Adhesive
3687b A2844 37c Pane of 20, P#S111, S1113, S2222, S4444   25.00

No. 3687b is a complete booklet with 12 stamps plus P# on one side and eight stamps plus booklet cover (BC189) on the other side. The peelable backing serves as a booklet cover.

3691b, 3691c, 3691d
— A2848-A2851

Serpentine Die Cut 11 on 2 or 3 Sides

3691b	A2848	37c Pane of 4, #3688-3691		4.00
3691c	A2848	37c Pane of 6, #3690-3691, 2		
		each #3688-3689, no P#		6.00
3691d	A2848	37c Pane of 6, #3688-3689, 2		
		each #3690-3691		6.00

3691b, 3691c,
3691d — BC190

2002
    $7.40 booklet contains 20 self-adhesive 37c
    stamps

COMBINATION BOOKLET

BK293 BC190 $7.40 **multi,** #3691c, 3691d, 2
    #3691b, P#V1111   22.50

    Plate number on No. BK293 is on the backing paper of the
upper example of No. 3691b.

3780b — A2883-A2887

Backing 1

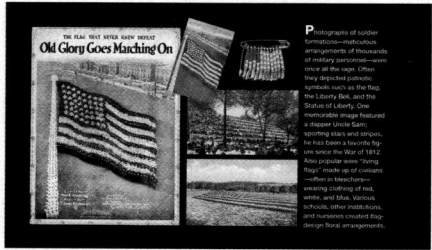

Backing 2

2003, Apr. 3   Litho.   Serpentine Die Cut 10x9¾
Self-Adhesive

3780b	A2883	37c Pane of 2 #3780a with backing 1	7.50
		With backing 2	7.50

3780b — BC191

2003
    $7.40 booklet contains 20 self-adhesive stamps

Booklet

BK294 BC191 $7.40 **multi,** no P#   15.00

    No. BK294 contains one No. 3780b with backing 1 and one
No. 3780b with backing 2.

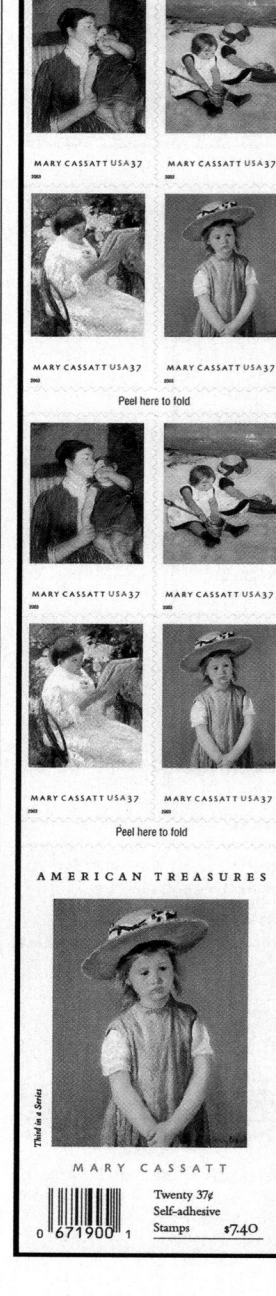

3807b, BC193 —
A2902-A2905

Serpentine Die Cut 10¾ on 2 or 3 Sides
2003, Aug. 7 Photo.

Self-Adhesive

3807b A2902 37c pane of 20, 5 #3807a,
P#S11111 15.00

No. 3807b is a complete double-sided booklet. Eight stamps and the booklet cover (BC193) are printed on one side of the peelable backing paper and 12 stamps plus P# are printed on the other side of the backing paper.

3820a, BC194 — A2843

Serpentine Die Cut 11x11¼ on 2 or 3 Sides
2003, Oct. 23

Self-Adhesive
Size: 28x19½mm

3820a A2843 37c pane of 20, P#P1111 15.00

No. 3820a is a complete double-sided booklet. Eight stamps, P# and the booklet cover (BC194) are printed on one side of the peelable backing paper, and 12 stamps plus P# are printed on the other side of the backing paper.

On one version of this pane (shown), an incorrect bar code was printed over with white ink, mostly covering the incorrect code, and the correct bar code was then added. This version is much scarcer; value $30.

3824b, BC195 —
A2917-A2920

Serpentine Die Cut 11¾x11 on 2 or 3 Sides
2003, Oct. 23

Self-Adhesive

3824b A2917 37c Pane of 20, 5 each #3821-
3824, P#S1111, S2222 16.00

No. 3824b is a complete double-sided booklet. Eight stamps plus P# and the booklet cover (BC195) are printed on one side

---

of the peelable backing paper, and 12 stamps plus P# are printed on the other side of the backing paper.

3828b, 3828c, 3828d
— A2921-A2924

Serpentine Die Cut 10½x10¾ on 2 or 3 Sides

3828b A2921 37c Pane of 4, #3825-3828, no P# 4.00
3828c A2921 37c Pane of 6, #3827-3828, 2
each #3825-3828, no P# 6.00
3828d A2921 37c Pane of 6, #3825-3826, 2
each #3827-3828,
P#S111111 6.00

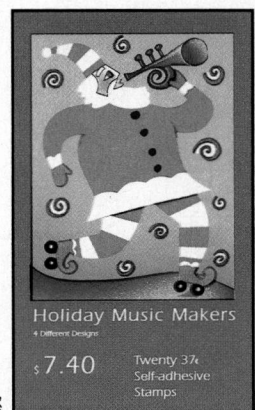

3828b, 3828c,
3828d — BC196

2003
$7.40 booklet contains 20 self-adhesive 37c stamps

COMBINATION BOOKLET

BK296 BC196 $7.40 **multi,** #3828c, 3828d, 2
each #3828b, P#S11111 20.00

Plate number on No. BK296 is printed on the backing paper of No. 3828d.

3830a — A2925

3830a — BC197

2004
$7.40 fold-it-yourself booklet contains 20 self-adhesive 37c stamps

Serpentine Die Cut 11½x11 on 2, 3 or 4 Sides
2004, Jan. 30 Litho.

Self-Adhesive

3830a A2925 37c pane of 20, P#P11111,
P22222 15.00

No. 3830a is a complete booklet (BC197). The peelable backing serves as a booklet cover.

Variety

3830c As "a," die cutting omitted —

Serpentine Die Cut 11½x11 on 2, 3 or 4 Sides
2005? Photo.

Self-Adhesive
With "USPS" Microprinted on Bird's Breast

3830De A2925 37c pane of 20, P#P33333,
P44444, P55555 120.00

No. 3830De is a complete booklet (BC197). The peelable backing serves as a booklet cover.

Variety

3830Dg As "e," die cutting omitted —

3833a — A2928

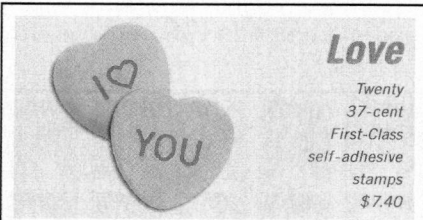

3833a — BC198

2004
$7.40 fold-it-yourself booklet contains 20 self-adhesive 37c stamps

Serpentine Die Cut 10¾ on 2, 3 or 4 Sides
2004, Jan. 14   **Photo.**
Self-Adhesive
3833a A2928 37c pane of 20, P#V1111   15.00
  No. 3833a is a complete booklet (BC198). The peelable backing serves as a booklet cover.

3836a — A2931

3836a — BC199

2004
$7.40 booklet contains 20 self-adhesive stamps

Serpentine Die Cut 10¾ on 2, 3 or 4 Sides
2004, Mar. 4   **Litho.**
Self-Adhesive
3836a A2931 37c pane of 20, #P22222   15.00
  No. 3836a is a complete booklet (BC199). The peelable backing serves as a booklet cover.

3856b — A2940-A2941

Backing 1

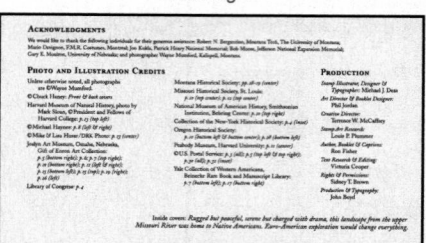

Backing 2

Serpentine Die Cut 10½x10¾
2004, May 14   **Litho. & Engr.**
Self-Adhesive
3856b A2940 37c Pane, 5 each #3855-3856 with
      backing 1   9.00
      With backing 2   9.00

3856b — BC200

2004
$8.95 booklet contains 20 self-adhesive stamps
Booklet
BK297 BC200 $8.95 **multi**, no P#   18.00
  No. BK297 contains one No. 3856b with backing 1 and one No. 3856b with backing 2.

3872a, BC201 — A2956

Serpentine Die Cut 10¾ on 2 or 3 Sides
2004, Aug. 12   **Photo.**
Self-Adhesive
3872a A2956 37c pane of 20, P#S1111   15.00
  No. 3872a is a complete booklet with 12 stamps plus P# on one side and eight stamps plus booklet cover (BC201) on the other side. The peelable backing serves as a booklet cover.

3879a, BC202 — A2961

Serpentine Die Cut 10¾x11 on 2 or 3 Sides
2004, Oct. 14   **Litho.**
Self-Adhesive
3879a A2961 37c pane of 20, P#P1111   15.00
  No. 3879a is a complete booklet with 12 stamps plus P# on one side and eight stamps plus P# and a label that serves as a booklet cover (BC202) on the other side.
Variety
3879b As "a," die cutting omitted   —

3886b, BC203
—A2965-A2968

Serpentine Die Cut 11½x11 on 2 or 3 Sides
2004, Nov. 16   **Photo.**
Self-Adhesive
3886b A2965 37c pane of 20, 5 #3886a,
P#S1111   18.00

No. 3886b is a complete double-sided booklet. Eight stamps and the booklet cover (BC203) are on one side of the peelable backing paper and 12 stamps plus P# are on the other side of the backing paper.

3890b, 3890c, 3890d
— A2969-A2972

Serpentine Die Cut 10¼x10¾ on 2 or 3 Sides
3890b A2969 37c pane of 4 #3887-3890, no P#   3.60
3890c A2969 37c pane of 6 #3889-3890, 2 each
#3887-3888, no P#   5.50
3890d A2969 37c pane of 6 #3887-3888, 2 each
#3889-3890, P#S11111   5.50

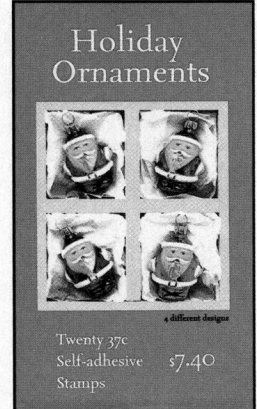

3890b, 3890c,
3890d — BC204

2004
$7.40 booklet contains 20 self-adhesive 37c stamps

COMBINATION BOOKLET
BK298 BC204 $7.40 **multi,** #3890c, 3890d, 2
#3890b, P#S1111   19.00

Plate number on No. BK298 is printed on the backing paper of No. 3890d.

3894b — A2969-A2972

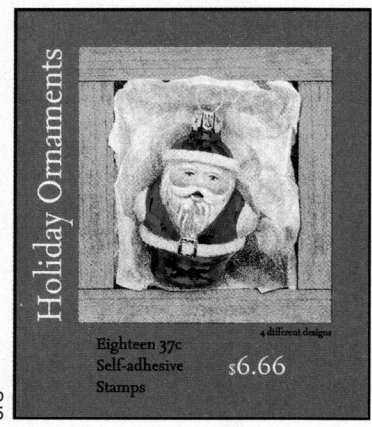

3894b
BC205

2004

$6.66 fold-it-yourself booklet contains 18 self-adhesive 37c stamps

Serpentine Die Cut 8 on 2, 3 or 4 Sides

3894b   A2969   37c pane of 18, 6 each #3891,
    3893, 3 each #3892, 3894,
    P#V11111   20.00

No. 3894b is a complete booklet (BC205). The peelable backing serves as a booklet cover.

3898a — A2975

3898a — BC206

2005

$7.40 booklet contains 20 self-adhesive stamps

Serpentine Die Cut 10¾x11 on 2, 3 or 4 Sides
2005, Feb. 18   **Photo.**
Self-Adhesive

3898a   A2975   37c pane of 20, #V1111, V1112   15.00

No. 3898a is a complete booklet (BC206). The peelable backing serves as a booklet cover.

3903b, BC207 — A2977-A2980

Serpentine Die Cut 10¾ on 2 or 3 Sides
2005, Mar. 15   **Litho.**
Self-Adhesive

3903b   A2977   37c pane of 20, P#P1111   17.00

Variety

3903c   As "b," die cutting omitted on
        side with eight stamps   —

No. 3903b is a complete booklet with 12 stamps plus P# on one side and eight stamps plus P# and a label that serves as a booklet cover (BC207) on the other side.

3929b, BC208 — A3003-A3006

Serpentine Die Cut 10¾ on 2 or 3 Sides
2005, July 30   **Litho.**
Self-Adhesive

3929b   A3003   37c pane of 20, P#P1111   15.00

No. 3929b is a complete booklet with 12 stamps plus two P# on one side and eight stamps plus a label that serves as a booklet cover (BC208) on the other side.

3935b, BC209 — A3008-A3012

Serpentine Die Cut 10¾ on 2 or 3 Sides
2005, Aug. 20   **Litho.**
Self-Adhesive

3935b   A3008   37c pane of 20, P#P1111   16.00

No. 3935b is a complete booklet with 12 stamps (2 each #3931, 3933, 3935, and 3 each #3932, 3934) plus P# on one side and eight stamps (1 each #3932, 3934, and 2 each #3931, 3933, 3935) plus a label that serves as the booklet cover (BC209) on the other side.

3956b, BC210 — A3026-A3029

Serpentine Die Cut 10¾x11 on 2 or 3 Sides
2005, Oct. 20   **Photo.**
Self-Adhesive

3956b   A3026   37c pane of 5 #3956a, P#S1111   15.00

No. 3956b is a complete double-sided booklet. Eight stamps and the booklet cover (BC210) are on one side of the peelable backing paper and 12 stamps plus P# are on the other side of the backing.

3960b, 3960c, 3960d
— A3030-A3033

Serpentine Die Cut 10½x10¾ on 2 or 3 Sides

3960b   A3030   37c pane of 4 #3957-3960   6.00
3960c   A3030   37c pane of 6 #3959-3960, 2 each
        #3957-3958, no P#   9.00

3960d A3030 37c pane of 6 #3957-3958, 2 each
　　　　#3959-3960, no P#　　9.00

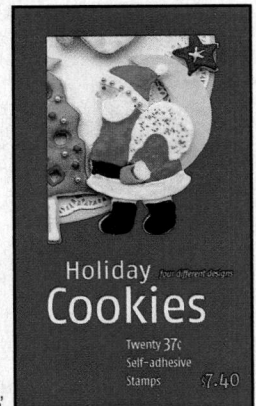

3960b, 3960c,
3960d — BC211

2005
　$7.40 booklet contains 20 self-adhesive 37c
　stamps

COMBINATION BOOKLET
BK299 BC211 $7.40 **multi**, #3960c, 3960d, 2
　　　　#3960b, P#S1111　　30.00

　Plate number on No. BK299 is printed on the backing paper
of the lower example of No. 3960b.

3966a, 3972a, 3973a,
BC212 — A3038

Serpentine Die Cut 11¼x11 on 2 or 3 Sides
2005, Dec. 8　　　　　　　　**Litho.**
　　　　Self-Adhesive
3966a A3038 (39c) pane of 20, P#P1111　　16.00
　　　　Variety
3966b　As "a," die cutting omitted　　—
　　　　Photo.
Serpentine Die Cut 11¼x10¾ on 2 or 3 Sides
3972a A3038 (39c) pane of 20, P#V1111　　16.00
Serpentine Die Cut 10¼x10¾ on 2 or 3 Sides
3973a A3038 (39c) pane of 20, P#S1111　　16.00

　Nos. 3966a, 3972a and 3973a are complete double-sided
booklets. Eight stamps and the booklet cover (BC212) are on
one side of the peelable backing paper and 12 stamps plus P#
are on the other side of the backing paper. On No. 3966a, the
stamps on one side are upside-down with relation to the stamps
on the other side. On Nos. 3972a and 3973a the stamps are all
aligned the same on both sides.

3974a, 3974b —
A3038

Serpentine Die Cut 11¼x11 on 2 or 3 Sides
　　　　Litho.
3974a A3038 (39c) pane of 4　　　3.20
3974b A3038 (39c) pane of 6, no P#　　4.80

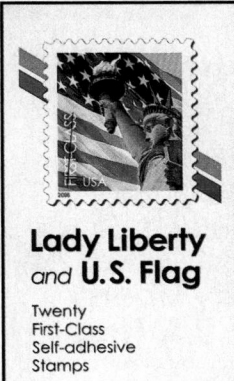

3974a, 3974b — BC213

2005
　($7.80) booklet contains 20 self-adhesive (39c)
　stamps

COMBINATION BOOKLET
BK300 BC213 ($7.80) **multi**, 2 each #3974a,
　　　　3974b, P#S1111　　16.00

　Plate number on No. BK300 is printed on the backing paper
of the upper example of No. 3974a.

3975a — A3038

444

3975a
BC214

2005
   ($7.02) fold-it-yourself booklet contains 18 self-
adhesive (39c) stamps

Serpentine Die Cut 8 on 2, 3 or 4 Sides
Photo.

3975a A3038 (39c) pane of 18, P#V1111   14.50
   No. 3975a is a complete booklet (BC214). The peelable backing serves as a booklet cover.

3976a — A3039

3976a — BC215

2006
   ($7.80) fold-it-yourself booklet contains 20 self-
adhesive (39c) stamps

Serpentine Die Cut 11 on 2, 3 or 4 Sides
2006, Jan. 3   **Photo.**

Self-Adhesive

3976a A3039 (39c) pane of 20, P#V11111   18.00
   No. 3976a is a complete booklet (BC215). The peelable backing serves as a booklet cover.

3978a — A3040

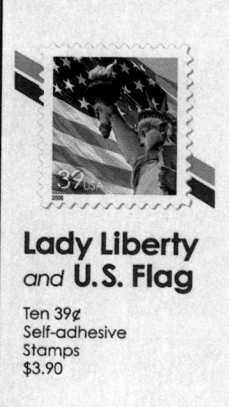

3978a — BC216

2006
   $3.90 fold-it-yourself booklet contains 10 self-ad-
hesive 39c stamps

Serpentine Die Cut 11¼x10¾ on 3 Sides
2006, Apr. 8   **Litho.**

Self-Adhesive

3978a A3040 39c pane of 10, P#P1111   8.00
   No. 3978a is a complete booklet (BC216). The peelable backing serves as a booklet cover.

3978b, 3985a, BC217
— A3040

Serpentine Die Cut 11¼x10¾ on 2 or 3 Sides
2006, Apr. 8   **Litho.**

Self-Adhesive

3978b A3040 39c pane of 20, P#P1111   16.00
Variety
3978c   As "b," die cutting omitted on the side
   with eight stamps   —
   No. 3978b is a complete booklet with 12 stamps plus P# on
one side and eight stamps plus a label that serves as the
booklet cover (BC217) on the other side.

**Flag and Statue of Liberty (No. 3978b) Type of
2006**

Serpentine Die Cut 11¼x10¾ on 2 or 3 Sides
2006, Apr. 8   **Photo.**

Self-Adhesive
Without Microprinting

3985a A3040 39c pane of 20, #V1111   16.00
   No. 3985a is a complete booklet with 12 stamps plus P# on
one side and eight stamps plus a label that serves as the
booklet cover (BC217) on the other side. The fonts of the UPC
code on the booklet cover for No. 3985a differ from those used
on No. 3978b.

3985c, 3985d — A3040

Serpentine Die Cut 11.1 on 2 or 3 Sides

2006, Nov. 8   **Photo.**

Self-Adhesive

3985c	A3040	39c pane of 4	3.20
3985d	A3040	39c pane of 6, no P#	4.80

Lady Liberty *and* U.S. Flag

Twenty 39¢
Self-adhesive
Stamps
$7.80

3985c,
3985d — BC216A

2006

$7.80 fold-it-yourself booklet contains 20 self-adhesive 39c stamps

COMBINATION BOOKLET

BK300A	BC216A	$7.80 **multi,** 2 each #3985c,		
		3985d P#V11111	16.00

Plate number on No. BK300A is printed on the backing paper of the lower example of No. 3985c.

3998a — A3051

3998a — BC218

2006

$7.80 booklet contains 20 self-adhesive 39c stamps

Serpentine Die Cut 10¾x11 on 2, 3 or 4 Sides

2006, Mar. 1   **Litho.**

Self-Adhesive

3998a	A3051	39c pane of 20, #P1	16.00

Variety

3998b	As "a," die cutting omitted	—

No. 3998a is a complete booklet (BC218). The peelable backing serves as a booklet cover.

3999a — A3051-A3052

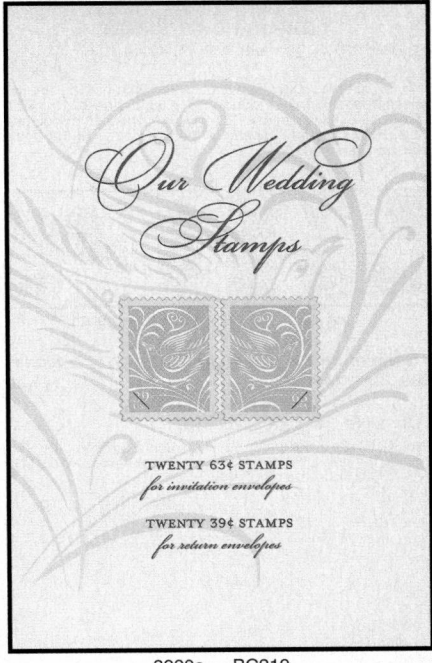

Our Wedding Stamps

TWENTY 63¢ STAMPS
for invitation envelopes

TWENTY 39¢ STAMPS
for return envelopes

3999a — BC219

2006

$20.40 booklet contains 20 self-adhesive 39c stamps and 20 self-adhesive 63c stamps

Serpentine Die Cut 10¾x11

3999a		Pane of 40 (20 each #3998-3999),	
		#P11	45.00

No. 3999a is a complete booklet (BC219). The peelable backing serves as a booklet cover.

4001b — A3053

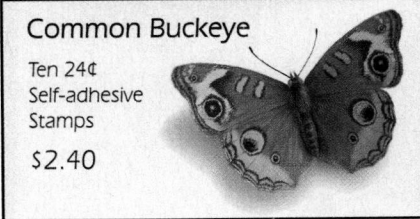

Common Buckeye

Ten 24¢
Self-adhesive
Stamps

$2.40

4001b — BC220

2006

$2.40 fold-it-yourself booklet contains 10 self-adhesive 24c stamps

Serpentine Die Cut 10¾x11¼

2006, Mar. 8   **Photo.**

Self-Adhesive

4001b A3053 24c pane of 10 #4001a, P#V1111   5.00

No. 4001b is a complete booklet (BC220). The peelable backing paper serves as a booklet cover. No. 4001b was sold flat. It has a self-adhesive panel that covers the rouletting on the inside of the booklet cover that is not found in BK301. Three large cuts of rouletting separate the two halves of the booklet cover on No. 4001b.

4001c, 4001d — A3053

4001c A3053 24c pane of 4 #4001a, P#V1111   2.00
4001d A3053 24c pane of 6 #4001a, no P#   3.00

COMBINATION BOOKLET

BK301 BC220 $2.40 **multi**, #4001c, 4001d,
           P#V1111   5.00

No. BK301 was sold glued shut. When the booklet is opened, the self-adhesive panel found on the right side of No. 4001d sticks to the left side of 4001c, as shown in the illustration above. Fine rouletting separates the two halves of the booklet cover on No. BK301.

4012b, BC221 — A3054-A3058

Serpentine Die Cut 10¾x10½ on 2 or 3 Sides

2006, Mar. 16   **Photo.**

Self-Adhesive

4012b A3054 39c pane of 20, P#S1111   16.00

No. 4012b is a complete booklet with 12 stamps plus P# on one side and eight stamps plus a label that serves as a booklet cover (BC221) on the other side.

4016a, 4017b, 4017c,
4017d — A3054-
A3058

Serpentine Die Cut 10¾x11¼ on 2 or 3 Sides

Litho.

4016a	A3054	39c pane of 4, #4013-4016, no P#	3.60
4017b	A3054	39c pane of 4, #4013-4015, 4017, no P#	3.60
4017c	A3054	39c pane of 6, #4013-4016, 2 #4017, no P#	5.50
4017d	A3054	39c pane of 6, #4013-4015, 4017, 2 #4016, no P#	5.50

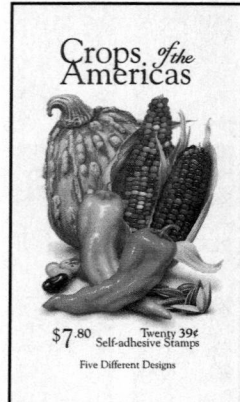

4016a, 4017b, 4017c,
4017d — BC222

2006

$7.80 booklet contains 20 self-adhesive 39c stamps

COMBINATION BOOKLET

BK302 BC222 $7.80 **multi**, #4016a, 4017b,
          4017c, 4017d, no P#   18.50

4029a — A3070

4029a — BC223

2006

$7.80 fold-it-yourself booklet contains 20 self-adhesive 39c stamps

Serpentine Die Cut 11 on 2, 3 or 4 Sides

2006, May 1   **Photo.**

Self-Adhesive

4029a A3070 39c pane of 20, P#V11111   16.00

No. 4029a is a complete booklet (BC223). The peelable backing serves as a booklet cover.

4098b, BC224 — A3127-A3136

Serpentine Die Cut 10¾ on 2 or 3 Sides

2006, Aug. 24   **Photo.**

Self-Adhesive

4098b A3127 39c pane of 20, P#S11111   20.00

No. 4098b is a complete booklet with 12 stamps (1 each #4090-4093, 4095-4098, and 2 each #4089, 4094) plus P# on one side and eight stamps (1 each #4090-4093, 4095-4098) plus a label that serves as the booklet cover (BC224) on the other side.

4100a, BC225 — A3138

Serpentine Die Cut 10¾x11 on 2 or 3 Sides

2006 **Litho.**

Self-Adhesive

4100a A3138 39c pane of 20, P#P1111, *Oct. 17* 16.00

No. 4100a is a complete double-sided booklet with 12 stamps plus P# on one side of the peelable backing and eight stamps plus P# and the label that serves as a booklet cover (BC225) on the other side of the backing.

4108b, BC226 — A3139-A3142

Serpentine Die Cut 11¼x11½ on 2 or 3 Sides

4108b A3139 39c pane of 20, P#S1111, *Oct. 5* 16.00

No. 4108b is a complete double-sided booklet. Eight stamps and the label that serves as a booklet cover (BC226) are on one side of the peelable backing and 12 stamps plus P# are on the other side of the backing.

4112b, 4112c, 4112d — A3139-A3142

Serpentine Die Cut 11¼x11 on 2 or 3 Sides

4112b A3139 39c pane of 4, #4109-4112 *Oct. 5* 3.60
4112c A3139 39c pane of 6, #4111-4112, 2 each #4109-4110, no P#, *Oct. 5* 5.50
4112d A3139 39c pane of 6, #4109-4110, 2 each #4111-4112, *Oct. 5* 5.50

4112b, 4112c, 4112d — BC227

2006

$7.80 booklet contains 20 self-adhesive 39c stamps

COMBINATION BOOKLET

BK303 BC227 $7.80 **multi,** #4112c, 4112d, 2 #4112b, P#S1111 18.50

Plate number on No. BK303 is printed on the backing paper of No. 4112d.

4116b — A3139-A3142

Snowflakes

Four different designs

Eighteen 39¢ Self-adhesive Stamps

$7.02

4116b
BC228

2006
$7.02 fold-it-yourself booklet contains 18 self-adhesive 39c stamps

Serpentine Die Cut 8 on 2, 3 or 4 Sides
Photo.

4116b A3139 39c pane of 18, 4 each #4114, 4116, 5 each #4113, 4115, P#V1111, Oct. 5 ..... 20.00

No. 4116b is a complete booklet (BC228). The peelable backing serves as a booklet cover.

4122a — A3145

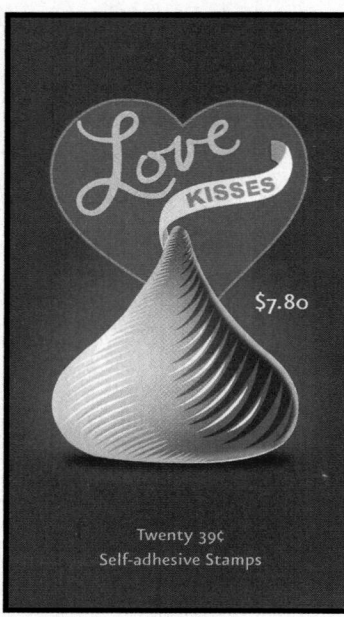

Love
KISSES

$7.80

Twenty 39¢ Self-adhesive Stamps

4122a
BC229

2007
$7.80 fold-it-yourself booklet contains 20 self-adhesive 39c stamps

Serpentine Die Cut 10¾x11 on 2, 3 or 4 Sides
2007, Jan. 13   **Photo.**
Self-Adhesive

4122a A3145 39c pane of 20 ..... 16.00

No. 4122a is a complete booklet (BC229). The peelable backing serves as a booklet cover. The plate number (V1111) is printed on the rear cover of the booklet.

4125a, 4125c, 4126a, 4126c, 4127a, 4127e, 4127j, BC230 — A3148

Serpentine Die Cut 11¼x10¾ on 2 or 3 Sides
2007, Apr. 12   **Photo.**
Self-Adhesive
Large Microprinting, Bell 16mm Wide

4125a A3148 (41c) pane of 20, P#V11111 ..... 17.00
4125c A3148 (42c) pane of 20 #4125b, P#V11111 ..... 17.00

Litho.
Small Microprinting, Bell 16mm Wide

4126a A3148 (41c) pane of 20, P#P11111 ..... 17.00
4126c A3148 (42c) pane of 20 #4126b, P#P11111 ..... 17.00

Medium Microprinting, Bell 15mm Wide

4127a A3148 (41c) pane of 20, P#S11111, "2007" year date 18.00
4127e A3148 (42c) pane of 20, P#S11111, "2008" year date 18.00
4127j A3148 (44c) pane of 20, P#S11111, "2009" year date in copper 18.00

Varieties

4125d As "c," copper ("FOREVER") omitted ..... —
4125e As "c," copper ("FOREVER") omitted on side with 12 stamps, copper splatters on side with 8 stamps ..... —

Nos. 4125a, 4125c, 4126a, 4126c, 4127a, 4127e, and 4127j are complete double-sided booklets with 12 stamps plus P# on one side of the peelable backing and eight stamps and a label that serves as a booklet cover (BC230) on the other side of the backing. Stamps on Nos. 4125c and 4126c are dated "2008" instead of "2007." On Nos. 4125c and 4126c, the bar code number found on the booklet cover was changed to "06777005."

No. 4127a and its varieties exist on two types of surface-tagged paper that exhibit either an uneven or solid or appearance, as follows: tagging on No. 4127a appears uneven, tagging on Nos. 4127e and 4127j appears solid. Additionally, a version of No. 4127e exists that has tagging with a solid appearance on the front side with eight stamps and tagging with an uneven appearance on the side with 12 stamps. Values are the same.

No. BC230 was printed by three different manufacturers with differences in the fonts used in the UPC code.

4127b, 4127c — A3148

Medium Microprinting, Bell 15mm Wide

4127b A3148 (41c) pane of 4 #4127, P#S11111 ..... 3.60
4127c A3148 (41c) pane of 6 #4127, no P# 5.50
4127g A3148 (42c) pane of 4 #4127f, P#S11111 ..... 3.60
4127h A3148 (42c) pane of 6 #4127f, no P# 5.50

No. 4127f has a smaller "2008" date. The "2008" date on No. 4127d is the same size as the "2007" date on No. 4127.

4127b, 4127c, 4127g,
4127h — BC231

2007
$8.20 booklet contains 20 self-adhesive (41c)
stamps

COMBINATION BOOKLETS

BK304 BC231 ($8.20) **multi,** 2 each #4127b,
4127c, P#S11111 .... 18.00
BK304a BC231 ($8.40) **multi,** 2 each #4127g,
4127h, P#S11111 .... 18.00

Plate number on No. BK304 is printed on the backing of the
lower example of No. 4127b. On No. BK304a, plate number
appears on the backing of the lower example of No. 4127g.

4128a —
A3148

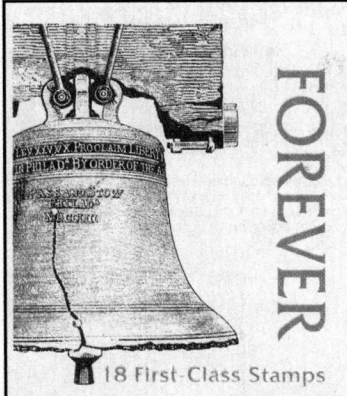

4128a
BC232

2007
$7.38 fold-it-yourself booklet contains 18 self-ad-
hesive (41c) stamps

Serpentine Die Cut 8 on 2, 3 or 4 Sides
Large Microprinting, Bell 16mm Wide
Photo.

4128a A3148 (41c) pane of 18 ('07) 15.50
4128c A3148 (41c) pane of 18 #4128b,
P#V11111 ('09) 15.50

Nos. 4128a and 4128c are complete booklets (BC232). The
peelable backing serves as a booklet cover.

Two versions of No. 4128a exist. The original issue has
P#V11 on the backing paper, while a second printing has
P#V22222 on the peelable strip on the front.

On No. 4128c, the bar code number found on the booklet
cover was changed to "05733002."

4142a — A3152

4142a — BC233

2007
$2.60 fold-it-yourself booklet contains 10 self-ad-
hesive 26c stamps

Serpentine Die Cut 11¼x11 on 3 Sides
2007, May 12 Photo.

Self-Adhesive

4142a A3152 26c pane of 10, P#V11111 .... 5.50

No. 4142a is a complete booklet (BC233). The peelable backing serves as a booklet cover.

4151a — A3161

4151a — BC234

2007
$8.20 fold-it-yourself booklet contains 20 self-ad-
hesive 41c stamps

Serpentine Die Cut 10¾ on 2, 3 or 4 Sides
2007, June 27 Litho.

Self-Adhesive

4151a A3161 41c pane of 20 .... 17.00

No. 4151a is a complete booklet (BC234). The peelable backing, which has a plate number (P11111), serves as a booklet
cover.

4156d, BC235 — A3163-A3166

Serpentine Die Cut 11 on 2 or 3 Sides
2007, June 29   Litho.
Self-Adhesive
4156d A3163 41c pane of 20, 3 each #4153-
            4156, 2 each #4153a-4156a,
            P#P1111   17.00
   No. 4156d is a complete double-sided booklet with 12 stamps
(2 each #4153-4156, 1 each 4153a-4156a) on one side of the
peelable backing and eight stamps plus P# and the label that
serves as a booklet cover (BC235) on the other side of the
backing.

4165a, BC236 — A3173

Serpentine Die Cut 10¾ on 2 or 3 Sides
2007, Aug. 9   Litho.
Self-Adhesive
4165a A3173 41c pane of 20, #P11111   17.00
   No. 4165a is a complete double-sided booklet with 12 stamps
on one side and eight stamps plus P# and a label that serves as
the booklet cover (BC236) on the other side.

4185a, BC237 — A3174-A3183

Serpentine Die Cut 11¼x11½ on 2 or 3 Sides
2007, Aug. 10   Photo.
Self-Adhesive
4185a 41c pane of 20, 2 each #4176-4185,
          P#V1111   17.00
Variety
4185b As "a," die cutting missing on Nos.
          4178 and 4183 on side with eight
          stamps (PS)   —
   No. 4185a is a complete double-sided booklet with 12 stamps
(2 each #4176-4177, and 1 each #4178-4185) plus P# on one
side and eight stamps (#4178-4185) plus a label (BC237) that
serves as the booklet cover on the other side.

4190a—A3184

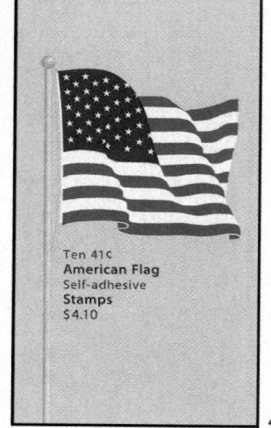

4190a — BC238

2007
   $4.10 fold-it-yourself booklet contains 10 self-ad-
   hesive 41c stamps

Serpentine Die Cut 11¼x10¾ on 3 Sides
2007, Aug. 15   Litho.
Self-Adhesive
**With "USPS" Microprinted on Right Side of
Flagpole**
4190a 41c pane of 10, P#P11111   8.50
   By its nature, No. 4190a is a complete booklet (BC238). The
peelable backing serves as a booklet cover.

4191a, BC239 — A3184

**Serpentine Die Cut 11¼x10¾ on 2 or 3 Sides
With "USPS" Microprinted on Left Side of
Flagpole**
4191a 41c pane of 20, P#S11111   17.00
   No. 4191a is a complete double-sided booklet with 12 stamps
plus P# on one side of the peelable backing and eight stamps
plus a label (BC239) that serves as the booklet cover on the
other side.

4206a, BC240 — A3198

Serpentine Die Cut 10¾x11 on 2 or 3 Sides
2007, Oct. 25   Litho.
Self-Adhesive
4206a A3198 41c pane of 20, P#P1111   17.00
   No. 4206a is a complete double-sided booklet with 12 stamps
on one side of the peelable backing and eight stamps plus P#
and the label that serves as a booklet cover (BC240) on the
other side of the backing.

4210b, BC241 — A3199-A3202

Serpentine Die Cut 10¾ on 2 or 3 Sides
4210b 41c pane of 20, P#S1111   17.00
   No. 4210b is a complete double-sided booklet. Eight stamps
(two each #4207-4210) plus P# and the label that serves as a
booklet cover (BC241) are on one side of the peelable backing
and 12 stamps (three each #4207-4210) are on the other side
of the backing.

4214b, 4214c, 4214d — A3203-A3206

Serpentine Die Cut 11¼x11 on 2 or 3 Sides

4214b	41c pane of 4, #4211-4214	3.40
4214c	41c pane of 6, #4213-4214, 2 each	
	#4211-4212, no P#	5.10
4214d	41c pane of 6, #4211-4212, 2 each	
	#42131-4214, no P#	5.10

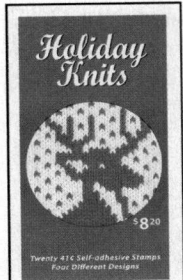

4214b, 4214c, 4214d — BC242

2007
$8.20 booklet contains 20 self-adhesive 41c stamps

COMBINATION BOOKLET

BK305 BC242 $8.20 **multi**, #4214c, 4214d, 2
#4214b, P#S1111   17.00

On No. BK305, plate number appears on the backing of the lower example of No. 4214b.

4218b — A3203-A3206

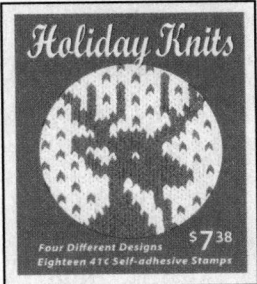

4218b — BC243

2007
$7.38 fold-it-yourself booklet contains 18 self-adhesive 41c stamps

Serpentine Die Cut 8 on 2, 3 or 4 Sides
Photo.

4218b   41c pane of 18, 4 each #4215, 4218, 5
each #4216, 4217, P#V1111   15.50

No. 4218b is a complete booklet (BC243). The peelable backing serves as a booklet cover.

4270a — A3233

4270a — BC244

2008
$8.40 fold-it-yourself booklet contains 20 self-adhesive 42c stamps

Serpentine Die Cut 10¾ on 2, 3 or 4 Sides
2008, June 10   Photo.

Self-Adhesive

4270a A3233   42c pane of 20, P#V1111   17.00

No. 4270a is a complete booklet (BC244). The peelable backing serves as a booklet cover.

4271a — A3234

4271a — BC245

2008
$8.40 fold-it-yourself booklet contains 20 self-adhesive 42c stamps

Serpentine Die Cut 10¾ on 2, 3 or 4 Sides
2008, June 10   Litho.

Self-Adhesive

4271a A3234   42c pane of 20   17.00

No. 4271a is a complete booklet (BC245). The peelable backing, which has a plate number (P1111), serves as a booklet cover.

4346a, BC246 — A3308

Serpentine Die Cut 11 on 2 or 3 Sides
2008, Aug. 14   **Litho.**
Self-Adhesive

4346a A3308 42c pane of 20, P#S1111   17.00

No. 4346a is a complete booklet with 12 stamps plus P# on one side and eight stamps plus booklet cover (BC246) on the other side. The peelable backing serves as a booklet cover.

4347a, BC247 —
A3309

Serpentine Die Cut 11¼x10¾ on 2 or 3 Sides
2008, Aug. 15   **Litho.**
Self-Adhesive

4347a A3309 42c pane of 20, P#P1111   17.00

No. 4347a is a complete booklet with 12 stamps plus P# on one side and eight stamps plus booklet cover (BC247) on the other side. The peelable backing serves as a booklet cover.

4359a, BC248 — A3319

Serpentine Die Cut 10¾x11 on 2 or 3 Sides
2008, Oct. 23   **Litho.**
Self-Adhesive

4359a A3319 42c pane of 20, P#P11111   17.00

No. 4359a is a complete double-sided booklet with 12 stamps on one side of the peelable backing and eight stamps plus P# and the label that serves as a booklet cover (BC248) on the other side of the backing.

4363b, BC249 — A3320-A3323

Serpentine Die Cut 10¾x11 on 2 or 3 Sides
2008, Oct. 23
Self-Adhesive

4363b   42c pane of 20, P#S11111   17.00

No. 4363b is a complete double-sided booklet. Eight stamps (two each #4360-4363) plus P# and the label that serves as a booklet cover (BC249) are on one side of the peelable backing and 12 stamps (three each #4360-4363) are on the other side of the backing.

4367b, 4367c, 4367d
— A3324-A3327

Serpentine Die Cut 11¼x11 on 2 or 3 Sides
2008, Oct. 23
Self-Adhesive

4367b	42c pane of 4, #4364-4367, no P#	3.40
4367c	42c pane of 6, #4366-4367, 2 each	
	#4364-4365, no P#	5.10
4367d	42c pane of 6, #4364-4365, 2 each	
	#4366-4367, no P#	5.10

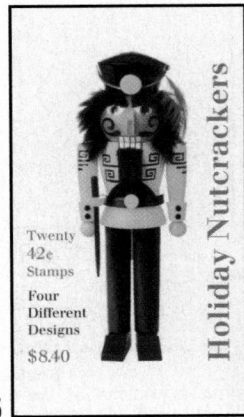

4367b, 4367c,
4367d — BC250

$8.40 booklet contains 20 self-adhesive 42c
stamps

COMBINATION BOOKLET

BK306 BC250 $8.40 **multi,** #4367c, 4367d, 2
#4367b, P#S11111   17.00

On No. BK306, plate number appears on the backing of the
lower example of No. 4367b.

4371b — A3324-A3327

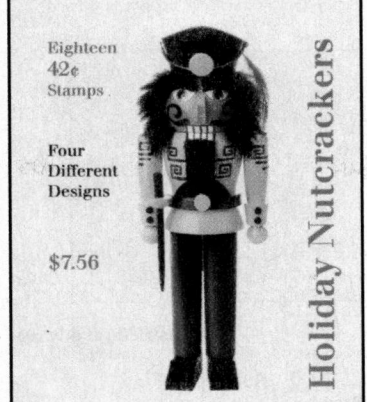

4371b
BC251

2008
$7.56 fold-it-yourself booklet contains 18 self-ad-
hesive 42c stamps

Serpentine Die Cut 8 on 2, 3 or 4 Sides
Photo.

4371b   42c pane of 18, 5 each #4368-4369, 4
each #4370-4371, P#V1111   15.50

No. 4371b is a complete booklet (BC251). The peelable backing serves as a booklet cover.

4396a—A3342

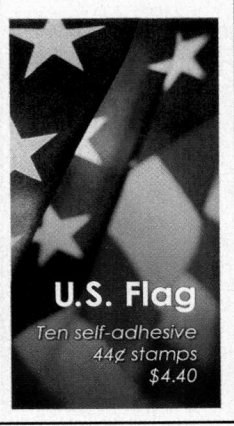

4396a — BC252

2009
$4.40 fold-it-yourself booklet contains 10 self-adhesive
44c stamps

Serpentine Die Cut 11¼x10¾ on 3 Sides
2009, June 5   **Photo.**
Self-Adhesive

4396a A3342 44c pane of 10, #V1111   9.00

By its nature, No. 4396a is a complete booklet (BC252). The
peelable backing serves as a booklet cover.

4403b — A3345-A3349

4403b — BC253

2009
$8.80 fold-it-yourself booklet contains 20 self-adhesive
44c stamps

Serpentine Die Cut 10¾ on 2, 3 or 4 Sides
2009, May 7   **Litho.**
4403b   44c pane of 20, 4 each #4399-4403, no
P# (4)   18.00

No. 4403b is a complete booklet (BC253). The peelable backing, which has a plate number (S11111), serves as a booklet
cover. The four different booklet covers show #4399 (shown
above), #4400 and 4403, #4401, and #4402.

4405b — A3350-A3351

4405b — BC254

2009
$8.80 fold-it-yourself booklet contains 20 self-ad-
hesive 44c stamps

Serpentine Die Cut 10¾ on 2, 3 or 4 Sides
2009, May 8   **Litho.**
4405b   44c pane of 20, 10 each #4404-4405,
          no P#   18.00

No. 4405b is a complete booklet (BC254). The peelable backing, which has a plate number (V11111), serves as a booklet
cover.

AIR POST BOOKLET PANES

C10a — AP6

FLAT PLATE PRINTING

1928   **Perf. 11**
C10a   AP6   10c **dark blue**, *May 26*   80.00   *65.00*
              Never hinged   130.00
              Tab at bottom

No. C10a was printed from specially designed 180-subject
plates arranged exactly as a 360-subject plate-each pane of
three occupying the relative position of a pane of six in a 360-
subject plate. Plate numbers appear at the sides, therefore
Position D does not exist except partially on panes which have

---

been trimmed off center. All other plate positions common to a
360-subject plate are known.

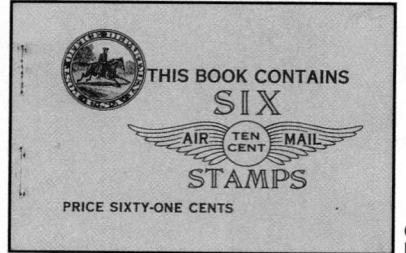

C10a
BC8

1928   **Postrider and Wings**
61c booklet contains 2 panes of three 10c stamps.

Booklet
BKC1   BC8   61c **blue**   275.00
       Tab at bottom, one pane in complete
       booklet   *13,500.*

> **Catalogue values for unused panes in this
> section, from this point to the end, are for Never
> Hinged items.**

C25a — AP17

ROTARY PRESS PRINTINGS

1943
C25a   AP17   6c **carmine**, *Mar. 18*   5.00   1.50
180-Subject Plates Electric Eye Convertible.

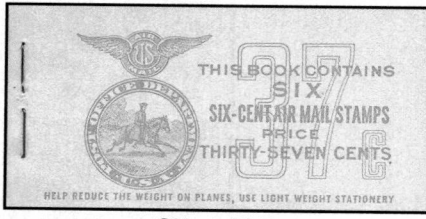

C25a — BC10

Large background numerals
1943   **Postrider and Wings**
37c booklet contains 2 panes of three 6c stamps.
73c booklet contains 4 panes of three 6c stamps.

Booklets
BKC2   BC10   37c **red**   11.00
BKC3   BC10   73c **red**   22.50

C39a — AP19

1949   **Perf. 10½x11**
C39a   AP19   6c **carmine**, *Nov. 18*   10.00   5.00
C39c   Dry printing   25.00   —

C39a — BC11A

1949   **U.S. Airmail Wings**
The 73c and 85c booklets were the last sold for 1c over face
value.
73c booklet contains 2 panes of six 6c stamps.

Booklets
BKC4   BC11A   73c **red**, with #C39a (3)   25.00
BKC4a   BC11A   73c **red**, with #C39c   60.00

C51a — AP33

1958
C51a   AP33   7c **blue**, *July 31*   9.00   7.00

C51a — BC11B

C51a, C60a — BC11C

1958-60   **U.S. Airmail Wings**
The 73c and 85c booklets were the last sold for 1c over face
value.
85c booklet contains 2 panes of six 7c stamps.

Booklets
BKC5   BC11B   85c on 73c **red**   22.50
BKC6   BC11C   85c **blue**   19.00

1960
C60a   AP33   7c **carmine**, *Aug. 19*   10.00   8.00
Booklets
BKC7   BC11C   85c **blue**   21.00
BKC8   BC11C   85c **red**   25.00

C64b — AP42

1962-64
C64b AP42 8c **carmine**, pane of 5 + label, slogan 1, *Dec. 5, 1962* 7.00 3.00
With slogan 2, *1963* 60.00 5.00
With slogan 3, *1964* 13.00 2.50

C64b, C64c — BC11D

C64b, C64c — BC11E

1962-64   **U.S. Airmail Wings**
80c booklet contains 2 panes of five 8c stamps.
$2 booklet contains 5 panes of five 8c stamps.

C64b, C64c — BC13B

1963-64   **Mr. Zip**
$2 booklet contains 5 panes of five 8c stamps.

Booklets (No. C64b)
BKC9 BC11D 80c **black**, *pink*, slogan 1 22.50
BKC10 BC11E $2 **red**, *pink*, slogan 1 35.00
BKC11 BC11D 80c **black**, *pink*, slogan 3 (2) 30.00
BKC12 BC11E $2 **red**, *pink*, slogan 2 300.00
BKC13 BC13B $2 **red**, *pink*, slogan 2 350.00
BKC14 BC13B $2 **red**, slogan 3 3,500.
BKC15 BC13B $2 **red**, *pink*, slogan 3 100.00

Fake examples of No. BKC14, such as booklets containing panes with extra staple holes, having obvious signs of being restapled and/or containing panes from two or more booklets, are known in the marketplace. Expertization by competent authorities is strongly recommended.

C64c AP42 As No. C64b, tagged, slogan 3, *1964* 2.00 .75
Plate of 360 subjects (300 stamps, 60 labels).

Booklets (No. C64c)
BKC16 BC11D 80c **black** (2) 50.00
BKC17 BC11D 80c **black**, *pink* 700.00
BKC18 BC13B $2 **red**, *pink* 325.00
BKC19 BC13B $2 **red** (3) 13.00

C72b — AP49

1968-73   *Perf. 11x10½*
C72b AP49 10c **carmine**, pane of 8, *Jan. 5, 1968* 2.00 .75

1968
$4 booklet contains 5 panes of eight 10c stamps.

Booklet
BKC20 BC14B $4 **red** (2) 12.00

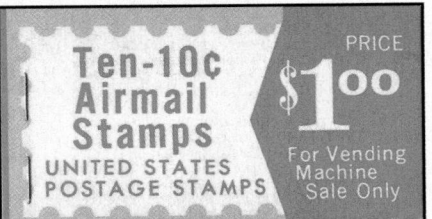

C72c — AP49

C72c AP49 10c **carmine**, pane of 5 + label, slogan 4, *Jan. 6, 1968* 3.75 .75
With slogan 5 3.75 .75

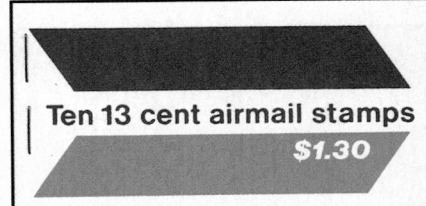

C72c — BC15A

1968
$1 booklet contains 2 panes of five 10c stamps.

Booklet
BKC21 BC15A $1 **red** (2) 8.00

Variety
C72f As "b," tagging omitted —

C78a — AP54

C78a AP54 11c **carmine**, pane of 4 + 2 labels, slogans 5 & 4, *May 7, 1971* 1.25 .75

C78a, 1280c — BC15B

1971
$1 booklet contains 2 panes of four 11c stamps and 1 pane of six 2c stamps.

Combination Booklet
BKC22 BC15B $1 **red**, 2 #C78a + 1 #1280c (2) 3.75

C79a — AP55

C79a AP55 13c **carmine**, pane of 5 + label, slogan 8, *Dec. 27, 1973* 1.50 .75

C79a — BC18

1973
$1.30 booklet contains 2 panes of five 13c stamps.

Booklet
BKC23 BC18 $1.30 **blue & red** (2) 3.25
Combination Booklet
See No. BK126.

No. C72b, the 8-stamp pane, was printed from 320-subject plate and from 400-subject plate; No. C72c, C78a and C79a from 360-subject plates.

COMPUTER VENDED POSTAGE STAMPS

Unlike meters, except for the limits of the service requested, computer vended postage stamps are usable from any post office at any date.

Self-service user-interactive mailing system machines which vended computer-printed postage were in service and available to the general public at the Martin Luther King, Jr., Station of the Washington, DC, Post Office, and at the White Flint Mall in Kensington, MD, until May 7, 1990.

Machines were also available for use by delegates to the 20th Universal Postal Congress at the Washington Convention Center between Nov. 13 and Dec. 14, 1989. These machines, Washington Nos. 11 and 12, were not readily accessible by the general public.

A variety of services were available by using the machines, which could weigh items to be sent, determine postage rates through the connected computer, permit the customer to cancel the transaction or continue with it and generate a postage stamp, a label and a receipt. The stamps produced were valid only for domestic postage.

A tagged orange strip runs along the left side of the stamp. The requested mail service is in a double line box.

The denomination is in the upper box at right under "U.S. Postage." The date of the transaction is below the denomination. Next to the date is a number which indicates the item number within the transaction. The maximum number of items per transaction may be five.

Above the post office location is a box at right which gives the machine number, followed by the transaction or serial number. Stamps from the same transaction, which are generated and printed at the same time, will have the same transaction number, but different item numbers, even if different mail services are requested. Transaction numbers go back to 00001 every time the machine is reset. Below this is the weight of the item to be mailed.

Along with each stamp generated came an unattached label with one of three slogan types: "We Deliver. . .," used from September to November, "We Deliver. . . / United States Postal Service," used thereafter, and "Developed by / Technology Resource Department," used only on Machine 11 during its limited use.

Listings and values are for the basic denominations of the five postal services, though others are known or possible (45c, 65c, 85c for first class over 1 oz., $1.10 for certified first class, $3.25 for priority mail, $8.50 for express mail to post office boxes, parcel post weight and zone variations, etc.). Values for used copies are for those with a regular cancellation.

A total of 3,000 unused sets of five different service stamps and unused sets of two 25c (Nos. 02501-12500) first class stamps furnished to the Philatelic Agency have a first day date and serial numbers with the final three digits matching. First day dates Nos. 00101-02500 were sold over the counter at post offices.

Stamps were intended to be dispensed individually. The height of the stamps produced differs from machine to machine. Unsevered strips of stamps are known, as are unsevered strips of a slogan and one or more stamps. Printing varieties such as squeezes (more than one impression condensed on to one stamp) and stretches (impression stretched out so that a complete impression will not fit on the paper) also are known.

Issues starting with No. 31 will be explained with the listings.

CVP1

CVP2

1989, Aug. 23   **Tagged**   *Guillotined*
Self-Adhesive
Washington, DC, Machine 82

CVP1   CVP1   25c **First Class,** any date other than first day   6.00   —
   a.   First day dated, serial Nos. 12501-15500   4.50   —
   b.   First day dated, serial Nos. 00001-12500   4.50   —
    On cover with first day cancel   150.00
   c.   First day dated, over No. 27500   —   —
    On cover with first day cancel   150.00
CVP2   CVP1 $1 **Third Class,** any date other than first day   —   —
   a.   First day dated, serial Nos. 24501-27500   —   —
   b.   First day dated, over No. 27500   —   —
CVP3   CVP2 $1.69 **Parcel Post,** any date other than first day   —   —
   a.   First day dated, serial Nos. 21501-24500   —   —
   b.   First day dated, over No. 27500   —   —
CVP4   CVP1 $2.40 **Priority Mail,** any date other than first day   —   —
   a.   First day dated, serial Nos. 18501-21500   —   —
   b.   Priority Mail ($2.74), with bar code (CVP2)   100.00
   c.   First day dated, over No. 27500   —   —
    On cover with first day cancel or verifying receipt   500.00
CVP5   CVP1 $8.75 **Express Mail,** any date other than first day   —   —
   a.   First day dated, serial Nos. 15501-18500   —   —
   b.   First day dated, over No. 27500   —   —
    On cover with first day cancel or verifying receipt   —
    Nos. 1a-5a (5)   82.50

Washington, DC, Machine 83

CVP6   CVP1   25c **First Class,** any date other than first day   6.00   —
   a.   First day dated, serial Nos. 12501-15500   4.50   —
   b.   First day dated, serial Nos. 00001-12500   4.50   —
    On cover with first day cancel   150.00
   c.   First day dated, over No. 27500   —   —
    On cover with first day cancel   150.00
   Error dates 11/17/90 and 11/18/90 exist.
CVP7   CVP1 $1 **Third Class,** any date other than first day   —   —
   a.   First day dated, serial Nos. 24501-27500   —   —
   b.   First day dated, over No. 27500   —   —
CVP8   CVP2 $1.69 **Parcel Post,** any date other than first day   —   —
   a.   First day dated, serial Nos. 21501-24500   —   —
   b.   First day dated, over No. 27500   —   —
CVP9   CVP1 $2.40 **Priority Mail,** any date other than first day   —   —
   a.   First day dated, serial Nos. 18501-21500   —   —
   b.   First day dated, over No. 27500   —   —
    On cover with first day cancel or verifying receipt   500.00
   Error date 11/17/90 exists.
   c.   Priority Mail ($2.74), with bar code (CVP2)   100.00
   Error date 11/18/90 exists.
CVP10   CVP1 $8.75 **Express Mail,** any date other than first day   —   —
   a.   First day dated, serial Nos. 15501-18500   —   —
   b.   First day dated, over No. 27500   —   —
    On cover with first day cancel or verifying receipt   —
    Nos. 6a-10a (5)   57.50
   Error date 11/17/90 exists.

1989, Sept. 1   **Kensington, MD, Machine 82**
CVP11   CVP1   25c **First Class,** any date other than first day   6.00   —
   a.   First day dated, serial Nos. 12501-15500   4.50   —
   b.   First day dated, serial Nos. 00001-12500   4.50   —
    On cover with first day cancel   100.00
   c.   First day dated, over No. 27500   —   —
    On cover with first day cancel   100.00
CVP12   CVP1 $1 **Third Class,** any date other than first day   —   —
   a.   First day dated, serial Nos. 24501-27500   —   —
   b.   First day dated, over No. 27500   —   —
CVP13   CVP2 $1.69 **Parcel Post,** any date other than first day   —   —
   a.   First day dated, serial Nos. 21501-24500   —   —
   b.   First day dated, over No. 27500   —   —
CVP14   CVP1 $2.40 **Priority Mail,** any date other than first day   —   —
   a.   First day dated, serial Nos. 18501-21500   —   —
   b.   First day dated, over No. 27500   —   —

---

   c.   Priority Mail ($2.74), with bar code (CVP2)   100.00
CVP15   CVP1 $8.75 **Express Mail,** any date other than first day   —   —
   a.   First day dated, serial Nos. 15501-18500   —   —
   b.   First day dated, over No. 27500   —   —
    Nos. 11a-15a (5)   57.50   —
    Nos. 1b, 11b (2)   9.00   —

Kensington, MD, Machine 83

CVP16   CVP1   25c **First Class,** any date other than first day   6.00   —
   a.   First day dated, serial Nos. 12501-15500   4.50   —
   b.   First day dated, serial Nos. 00001-12500   4.50   —
   c.   First day dated, over No. 27500   —   —
    On cover with first day cancel   100.00
CVP17   CVP1 $1 **Third Class,** any date other than first day   —   —
   a.   First day dated, serial Nos. 24501-27500   —   —
   b.   First day dated, over No. 27500   —   —
CVP18   CVP2 $1.69 **Parcel Post,** any date other than first day   —   —
   a.   First day dated, serial Nos. 21501-24500   —   —
   b.   First day dated, over No. 27500   —   —
CVP19   CVP1 $2.40 **Priority Mail,** any date other than first day   —   —
   a.   First day dated, serial Nos. 18501-21500   —   —
   b.   First day dated, over No. 27500   —   —
   c.   Priority Mail ($2.74), with bar code (CVP2)   100.00
CVP20   CVP1 $8.75 **Express Mail,** any date other than first day   —   —
   a.   First day dated, serial Nos. 15501-18500   —   —
   b.   First day dated, over No. 27500   —   —
    Nos. 16a-20a (5)   57.50   —
    Nos. 6b, 16b (2)   9.00   —

Unsevered pairs and single with advertising label exist for most, if not all, of the machine vended items from Kensington machine #83. Other combinations also exist.

1989, Nov.   **Washington, DC, Machine 11**
CVP21   CVP1   25c **First Class**   150.00
   a.   First Class, with bar code (CVP2)   —

Stamps in CVP1 design with $1.10 denominations exist (certified first class).

CVP22   CVP1 $1 **Third Class**   500.00
CVP23   CVP2 $1.69 **Parcel Post**   500.00

CVP24 CVP1 $2.40 **Priority Mail**   500.00
   a.   Priority Mail ($2.74), with bar
      code (CVP2)   —
CVP25 CVP1 $8.75 **Express Mail**   500.00
   No. 21 dated Nov. 30 known on cover, Nos. 24-25 known
dated Dec. 2.

Washington, DC, Machine 12

CVP26 CVP1 25c **First Class**   150.00
   A $1.10 certified First Class stamp, dated Nov. 20, exists on
cover.

CVP27 CVP1 $1 **Third Class**   —
   A $1.40 Third Class stamp of type CVP2, dated Dec. 1 is
known on a Dec. 2 cover.

CVP28 CVP2 $1.69 **Parcel Post**   —
CVP29 CVP1 $2.40 **Priority Mail**   —
   a.   Priority Mail ($2.74), with bar
      code (CVP2)   —
CVP30 CVP1 $8.75 **Express Mail**   —
   Nos. 29-30 known dated Dec. 1. An $8.50 Express Mail
stamp, dated Dec. 2, exists on cover.

CVP3 — Type I   CVP3 — Type II

Denomination printed by ECA GARD Postage and Mailing
Center machines.

COIL STAMPS

1992, Aug. 20   Engr.   Tagged   *Perf. 10 Horiz.*
CVP31 CVP3 29c **red & blue**, type I,
   prephosphored paper
   (solid tagging), dull gum   .75   .25
   Pair   1.50
   P# strip of 5, P#1   9.00
   P# single, #1   5.50
  a. 29c Type I, prephosphored paper
   (mottled tagging), shiny gum   .75   .25
   Pair   1.50   —
   P# strip of 5, P#1   9.00
   P# single, #1   5.50
   First day cover, Oklahoma
   City, OK   1.25
  b. 32c Type II, prephosphored paper
   (solid tagging), dull gum, *Nov.*
   1994   .90   .40
   Pair   1.80
   P# strip of 5, P#1   50.00
   P# single, #1   5.50
  c. 32c Type II, prephosphored paper
   (mottled tagging), shiny gum   1.00   .40
   Pair   2.00
   P# strip of 5, P#1   8.75
   P# single, #1   8.00

   Types I and II differ in style of asterisk, period between dollar
and cent figures and font used for figures, as shown in
illustrations.
   No. 31 was available at five test sites in the Southern Maryland, Miami, Oklahoma City, Detroit and Santa Ana, CA, divisions. They were produced for use in ECA GARD Postage and
Mailing Center (PMC) machines which can produce denominations from 1c through $99.99.
   For Nos. 31-31a, the 29c value is listed because it was the
current first class rate and was the only value available through
the USPS Philatelic Sales Division. The most common denomination available other than 29c is 1c (value 20c) because these
were made in quantity, by collectors and dealers, between plate
number strips. Later the machines were adjusted to provide
only 19c and higher value stamps.
   For Nos. 31b-31c, the 32c value is listed because it was the
first class rate in effect for the majority of the period the stamps
were in use.

CVP4

Denominations printed by Unisys PMC machines.

1994, Feb. 19   Photo.   Tagged   *Perf. 9.9 Vert.*
CVP32 CVP4 29c **dark red & dark blue**   .70   .35
   Pair   1.40
   P# strip of 5, #A11   8.00
   P# single, #A11   5.50
   First day cover, Merrifield,
   VA (26,390)   1.25

   No. 32 was available at six test sites in northern Virginia. It
was produced for use in machines which can produce values
from 19c to $99.99. See note following No. 31.
   For No. 32, the 29c value has been listed because it was the
first class rate in effect at the time the stamp was issued.

1996, Jan. 26   Photo.   Tagged   *Perf. 9.9 Vert.*
CVP33 CVP4 32c **bright red & blue**, "1996"
   below design   .70   .25
   Pair   1.40
   P# strip of 5, same, #11   8.00
   P# single, #11   6.00

   Letters in "USA" on No. 33 are thicker than on No. 32. Numerous other design differences exist in the moire pattern and in
the bunting. No. 33 has "1996" in the lower left corner; No. 32
has no date.
   For No. 33, the 32c value has been listed because it was the
first class rate in effect at the time the stamp was issued.

CVP5

Illustration reduced.

1999   Tagged   *Die Cut*
Self-Adhesive
CVP34 CVP5 33c **black**   50.00
   On cover   75.00
  a. "Priority Mail" under encryption at LL   —
  b. "Express Mail" under encryption at
   LL   —

   No. CVP34 was available from 15 NCR Automated Postal
Center machines located in central Florida. Machines could
produce values in any denomination required. The backing
paper is taller and wider than the stamp.
   Sales of No. CVP34 were discontinued in 2000 or 2001.

CVP6

Illustration reduced.

1999, May 7   Tagged   *Die Cut*
Self-Adhesive
Size: 77½x39mm
Microprinting Above Red Orange Line
CVP35 CVP6 33c **black & red orange**, control
   numbers only at LL, square
   corners   190.00   —
   Round corners   13.50   —
  a. "Priority Mail" at LL, square corners   150.00   —
   Round corners   —
  b. "Priority Mail AS" and text string at
   LL, square corners   150.00   —

No Microprinting Above Red Orange Line
CVP36 CVP6 33c **black & red orange**, control
   numbers only at LL, square
   corners   190.00   —
   Round corners   10.00   —
  a. "Priority Mail" at LL, square corners   125.00   —
   Round corners   —
  b. "Priority Mail AS" and text string at
   LL, square corners   125.00   —
   Round corners   —

Size: 73½x42mm
CVP37 CVP6 33c **black & pink**, control numbers only at LL   3.75   —
  a. "Priority Mail" at LL   5.00   —
  b. "Priority Mail AS" and text string at LL   5.00   —

   Nos. CVP35-CVP37 were available from 18 IBM Neopost
machines located in central Florida. The backing paper is taller
than the stamp. Any denomination could be printed up to
$99.99.

Simplypostage.com — CVP8

2001

Self-Adhesive
Serpentine Die Cut 8 at Right
Eagle and Stars Background
CVP39 CVP8 34c **black, blue & orange**, *2001*   —
   On cover   75.00
   Pane of 4   —
CVP40 CVP8 34c **black, blue & orange**, with
   control number at UL, *2001*   —
   On cover   75.00
   Pane of 4   —

Flag Background
CVP41 CVP8 34c **black, blue & orange**, with
   control number at UL, *2001*   —
   On cover   150.00
   Pane of 4   —
CVP42 CVP8 34c **black, blue & orange**, with
   control number at LL, *2001*   20.00
   On cover   150.00
   Pane of 4   80.00

   Customers could print up to five panes of Nos. CVP39-
CVP42 in each transaction. Panes were consecutively numbered identifying the total number of stamps and panes in each
transaction.

Neopostage.com — CVP9

2002, June -2003   *Serpentine Die Cut 8¾ at Right*
Self-Adhesive
CVP43 CVP9 21c **black, blue & orange**, *June*
   2002   —   —
   On cover   —
  a. Booklet pane of 10   —
CVP44 CVP9 23c **black, blue & orange**, *June*
   2002   —   —
   On cover   —
  a. Booklet pane of 10   —
CVP45 CVP9 34c **black, blue & orange**, *June*
   2002   —   —
   On cover   —
  a. Booklet pane of 10   —
CVP46 CVP9 37c **black, blue & orange**, *July*
   1, 2003   —   —
   On cover   —
  a. Booklet pane of 10   —
CVP47 CVP9 50c **black, blue & orange**, *July*
   1, 2003   —   —
   On cover   —
  a. Booklet pane of 10   —
CVP48 CVP9 60c **black, blue & orange**, *July*
   1, 2003   —   —
   On cover   —
  a. Booklet pane of 10   —
CVP49 CVP9 70c **black, blue & orange**, *July*
   1, 2003   —   —
   On cover   —
  a. Booklet pane of 10   —
CVP50 CVP9 80c **black, blue & orange**, *July*
   1, 2003   —   —
   On cover   —
  a. Booklet pane of 10   —
CVP51 CVP9 $3.50 **black, blue & orange**, *June*
   2002   —   —
   On cover   —
  a. Booklet pane of 1   —
  b. Booklet pane of 2   —
  c. Booklet pane of 5   —
  d. Booklet pane of 10   —
CVP52 CVP9 $3.85 **black, blue & orange**, *July*
   1, 2003   —   —
   On cover   —
  a. Booklet pane of 1   —
  b. Booklet pane of 2   —
  c. Booklet pane of 5   —
  d. Booklet pane of 10   —
CVP53 CVP9 $13.65 **black, blue & orange**, *July*
   1, 2003   —   —
   On cover   —
  a. Booklet pane of 1   —
  b. Booklet pane of 2   —
  c. Booklet pane of 5   —
  d. Booklet pane of 10   —

   Nos. CVP43-CVP53 were printed only with the stated values.
   A 57c denomination (pane of 10) and $12.45 denomination
(pane of 1) exist, but may have been produced at a site not
accessible by the public.
   While the name on Nos. CVP39-CVP42 reads simplypos-
tage.com and the name on Nos. CVP43-CVP53 reads neopos-
tage.com, both were products of Neopost.

CVP10

IBM Pitney Bowes — CVP11

Illustrations reduced.

2004, Apr. 14   Die Cut
Self-Adhesive

CVP54	CVP10	37c **black & pink**		5.75	—
a.		"First Class Mail" under encryption at LL		2.50	—
b.		"Priority Mail" under encryption at LL		2.50	—
c.		"Parcel Post" under encryption at LL		2.50	—
d.		"International" under encryption at LL		2.50	—
CVP55	CVP11	37c **black**, "US Postage" under encryption at LL		2.50	—
a.		"First Class Mail" under encryption at LL		—	—
b.		"Priority Mail" under encryption at LL		—	—
c.		"Parcel Post" under encryption at LL		—	—
d.		"International" under encryption at LL		—	—

Nos. CVP54-CVP55 could be printed in any denomination up to $99.99.

CVP12

IBM Pitney Bowes — CVP13

Illustrations reduced.

2004, Nov. 19   Die Cut
Self-Adhesive

CVP56	CVP12	37c **black & pink**		2.50	.25
a.		"Priority" under denomination		3.00	—
b.		"Parcel Post" under denomination		3.00	—
c.		"Express" under denomination		3.00	—
CVP57	CVP13	37c **black & pink**		1.00	.25
a.		"Priority" under denomination		1.25	—
b.		"Parcel Post" under denomination		1.25	—
c.		"Express" under denomination		1.25	—
d.		"Int Air LP" under denomination		1.25	—
e.		"FCM Letter" under denomination		1.25	—
f.		"FCM Flat" under denomination		1.25	—
g.		"FCM Parcel" under denomination		1.25	—
h.		"FCM Intl" under denomination, "IM" and numbers under encryption		1.25	—
i.		"FCM Lg Env" under denomination		1.25	—
j.		"PM Fr Env" under denomination, "PM" and numbers under encryption		1.25	—
k.		"PM Fr Box" under denomination, "PM" and numbers under encryption		1.25	—
l.		"PM Lfr Box" under denomination, "PM" and numbers under encryption		1.25	—
m.		"Exp Fr Env" under denomination, "EM" and numbers under encryption		1.25	—
n.		"FCMI Ltr" under denomination, "IM" and numbers under encryption		1.25	—
o.		"FCMI L Env" under denomination, "IM" and numbers under encryption		1.25	—

Nos. CVP56-CVP57 could be printed in any denomination. Catalogue values for CVP56a-CVP56c and CVP57a-CVP57o are for stamps with low denominations. Stamps with denominations appropriate to the service described are valued correspondingly higher.

Nos. CVP57e-CVP57h issued May 2007; No. CVP57i issued Sept. 2007; Nos. CVP57j-CVP57m issued 2008; Nos. CVP57n-CVP57o, May 2008.

Under the encryption No. CVP57 has "FC" and numbers; on No. CVP57a, "PM" and numbers; on No. CVP57b, "PP" and numbers; on No. CVP57c, "EM" and numbers; and on No. CVP57d, "IM" and numbers.

Blank Under Denomination
"IM" and Numbers Under Encryption

CVP58	CVP13	60c **black & pink**		3.00	.50
CVP59	CVP13	80c **black & pink**		3.75	.50

"PM" and Numbers Under Encryption

CVP60	CVP13	$3.85 **black & pink**		15.00	.50

"EM" and Numbers Under Encryption

CVP61	CVP13	$13.65 **black & pink**		42.50	1.00

"IB" and Numbers Under Encryption

CVP62	CVP13	$1 **black & pink**		4.00	.25

Nos. CVP58-CVP61 could only be printed in denominations listed. No. CVP62 could be printed in any denomination above 99c. As of May 12, 2008, it was possible to create stamps with "IB" and numbers under encryption in any denomination. The computer software was later changed to once again only permit stamps of certain denominations to be created with "IB" and numbers under the encryption.

IBM Pitney Bowes Type of 2004
2006 ?   Die Cut
Self-Adhesive
Blank Under Denomination
"IM" and Numbers Under Encryption

CVP63	CVP13	48c **black & pink**		1.25	.40
CVP64	CVP13	63c **black & pink**		1.50	.50
CVP65	CVP13	84c **black & pink**		2.00	.50

"PM" and Numbers Under Encryption

CVP66	CVP13	$4.05 **black & pink**		9.50	.50
CVP66A	CVP13	$8.10 **black & pink**		16.50	1.00

"EM" and Numbers Under Encryption

CVP67	CVP13	$14.40 **black & pink**		30.00	1.00

Nos. CVP63-CVP67 could only be printed in denominations listed.

IBM Pitney Bowes — CVP14

Illustration reduced.

2006   Die Cut
Self-Adhesive
No Inscription Under Encryption
Serial Number to Right of "APC"
"Ship To:" Above Destination City

CVP69	CVP14	39c **black**		2.25	.25
a.		"Priority" under denomination		2.25	—
b.		"Parcel Post" under denomination		2.25	—
c.		"Express" under denomination		2.25	—
d.		"FCM Flat" under denomination		1.25	—
e.		"FCM Parcel" under denomination		1.25	—
f.		"FCM Lg Env" under denomination		1.25	—
g.		**PM Fr Env" under denomination		1.25	—
h.		"PM Fr Box" under denomination		1.25	—
i.		"PM Lfr Box" under denomination		1.25	—
j.		"Exp Fr Env" under denomination		1.25	—

Nos. CVP69-CVP69j could be printed in any denomination. Catalogue values are for stamps with low denominations. Stamps with denominations appropriate to the service described are valued correspondingly higher.

Nos. CVP69d-CVP69e issued May 2007; No. CVP69f issued Sept. 2007; Nos. CVP69g-CVP69j issued 2008.

IBM Pitney Bowes Type of 2004
2006(?)-07   Die Cut
Self-Adhesive
Blank Under Denomination
"IB" and Numbers Under Encryption

CVP70	CVP13	39c **black & pink**		1.00	.50
CVP71	CVP13	41c **black & pink**		1.00	.50
CVP72	CVP13	69c **black & pink**		1.40	.70

"IM" and Numbers Under Encryption

CVP73	CVP13	61c **black & pink**		1.25	.50
CVP74	CVP13	90c **black & pink**		1.90	.95

Nos. CVP70-CVP74 could only be printed in the denominations listed.

Nos. CVP71-CVP74 issued May, 2007. No. CVP70 was issued before the May rate change. As of May 12, 2008, it was possible to create stamps with "IB" and numbers under encryption in any denomination. The computer software was later changed to once again only permit stamps of certain denominations to be created with "IB" and numbers under the encryption. No. CVP70 was available for sale from Nov. 2006 to May 13, 2007. Nos. CVP71-CVP72 were available for sale from May 14, 2007 to May 11, 2008.

Pitney Bowes — CVP15

Illustration reduced.

2006, Dec.   Die Cut
Self-Adhesive

CVP75	CVP15	41c **black & pink**		—	—
a.		"Mailed From Zip Code ..." on bottom line		.20	—
b.		"Postcard" on bottom line		.55	—
c.		"First Class Mail Intl" on bottom line		1.25	—

d.	"Parcel Post" on bottom line	7.50	—
e.	"Priority" on bottom line	9.25	—
f.	"Express Mail" on bottom line	33.00	—

No. CVP75 was put into service at large companies and universities in Dec. 2006, with the majority of the machines not being available to the general public. Information about this stamp was not made available until 2007. Other rates and inscriptions might be available.

Nos. CVP75a could be printed in any denomination. Nos. CVP75b-CVP75f could be printed only in pre-programmed denominations based on the current rates for the service, or in any denominations at or above the minimum rates for the service. Values are for stamps with low denominations. A stamp with "First Class" on the bottom line has been reported but has not been seen by the editors. Inscriptions generated by the software may vary from machine to machine depending on when the software was installed.

IBM Pitney Bowes Type of 2004

2008, May   *Die Cut*

Self-Adhesive
Blank Under Denomination
"IM" and Numbers Under Encryption

CVP76	CVP13	94c	black & pink	2.00	.60
CVP77	CVP13	$1.20	black & pink	2.40	1.25

Nos. CVP76-CVP77 could only be printed in the denominations listed.

IBM — CVP16

Illustration reduced.

2008, June 4   *Die Cut With Rounded Corners*
Self-Adhesive

CVP78	CVP16	42c	black & pink	—	—

Die Cut With Perpendicular Corners

CVP79	CVP16	42c	black & pink	—	—
a.		Pane of 6			—
b.		Pane of 7			—
c.		Pane of 8			—
d.		Pane of 9			—
e.		Pane of 10			—

Nos. CVP78-CVP79 were made available during a pilot study to evaluate a new IBM kiosk at Schaumburg, IL. No. CVP78 could be printed in any denomination from 1c to $25. Because each kiosk transaction was limited to $100, No. CVP79e could only be bought with stamps denominated from 1c to $10. Individual panes with 6, 7, 8, 9 or 10 stamps could be purchased as long as the total face value of the pane did not exceed $100. Stamps denominated from $10.01 to $16.66 could only be purchased in panes containing fewer than 10 stamps. Stamps denominated from $16.67 to $25 could only be purchased as a single stamp.

Machine Set-up Test Labels

Test labels were generated when machines were activated. They were not intended for public distribution.

Other samples, advertizing labels, proofs, etc. exist.

POSTAL CARDS

On July 5, 1990 the first of a number of "Postal Buddy" machines was placed in service at the Merrifield, VA post office. The machine printed out numerous items such as address labels (including monogram if you wished), fax labels, "penalty" cards, denominated postal cards, etc. Certain services were free, such as the penalty card mailed to your post office for change of address. The 15-cent denominated card cost 33-cents each and could be used to notify others of address change, meeting notices, customized messages, etc. Borders, messages, backs are different. The cards also came in sheets of 4.

These machines were tested in at least 30 locations in Virginia, including 16 post offices.

Denominated Postal Cards

10005-90-198-022

Number under design includes machine number, year, date (1 through 366) and transaction number.

1990, July 5

CVUX1	15c		6.00	*10.00*
	First day cancel, Merrifield, VA *(6,500)*			5.00

1991, Feb. 3

CVUX2	19c		3.00	*8.00*
	First day cancel, any location			35.00

Number under design includes ZIP Code of the originating machine (22033 in illustration), machine number (101), last digit of year, numbers of month and day (21203 for Dec. 3, 1992) and transaction number (041).

1992, Nov. 13

CVUX3	19c		6.00	*15.00*
	First day dated, Reston or Chantilly, VA			25.00

A total of 171 machines were used in the greater Washington, DC area including locations in Virginia and Maryland (109), the greater San Diego area (59), and in Denver (3). The machine numbers (011, 012, 021, 101, 111, 121, 131) when combined with the zip code created unique identification numbers for each machine.

No. 3 is known also on fluorescent paper. Two different designs on back known for each paper type.

The contract for Postal Buddy machines was canceled Sept. 16, 1993. After the contract was canceled, the Postal Buddy Corporation sold remaining stocks of card stock to the public with both reverse designs imprinted. By using this stock and a high quality copier, very dangerous counterfeits can be created. The duplication of numbers in the transaction line will be one indicator.

PERSONAL COMPUTER POSTAGE

Personal computer postage, approved by the US Postal Service, was created by subscribing to Stamps.com, an internet website. Customers ordered self-adhesive labels showing vignettes, but lacking any franking value. The franking value portion of the stamps could be printed at the customer's convenience at any computer with an internet connection, using the customer's access codes. Any postage printed would be charged against the customer's account.

Stamps with major listings could be printed in any denomination up to $999.99. Stamps with minor listings could only be printed in denominations calculated by the weight of the piece being mailed. Denominations for minor listings can range from 23c to $133.20. Customers could print the franking value portion of the stamps on whatever they put into their printer, be it envelopes, plain gummed labels or regular paper, but these listings are limited to items on the self-adhesive labels shown, which have tagging that allows the mail the stamp is on to go through the mail stream smoothly.

Neopost

CVPA1

2000   *Serpentine Die Cut 8*
Self-Adhesive

1CVP1	CVPA1	33c	black, yellow & pink	—	—
		On cover			—
		Pane of 10			—

Stamps.com

Flag and Star — CVPA1a

2002, July   *Serpentine Die Cut 5¾ at Left*
"Stamps.com" in Lower Case Letters
Identification Code Below Zip Code

1CVP2	CVPA1a	37c	black, blue & orange, no mail class inscribed	7.00	3.00
		On cover			4.00
		Sheet of 25		175.00	

Identification Code Above Zip Code

1CVP2A	CVPA1a	37c	black, blue & orange	4.00	3.00
		On cover			3.50
		Sheet of 25		100.00	
a.		"First Class" below "US Postage"		2.75	2.00
b.		"Priority" below "US Postage"		8.25	2.50
c.		"Express" below "US Postage"		25.00	5.00
d.		"Media Mail" below "US Postage"		7.75	2.50
e.		"Parcel Post" below "US Postage"		7.75	2.50
f.		"Bound Printed Matter" below "US Postage"		7.75	2.50
g.		"BPM" below "US Postage"		7.75	2.50

See Nos. 1CVP9, 1CVP21.

Later versions of the Stamps.com software allow any denomination to be printed, as well as additional or different mail-class inscriptions, on any basic stamp except for No. 1CVP2.

Values for Nos. 1CVP2A and 1CVP3-1CVP42 are for items appropriate to the service described. Stamps with denominations far lower than those appropriate to the service are valued correspondingly lower.

The software changes allow Nos. 1CVP2A and 1CVP3-1CVP37 to be printed with the mail-class inscriptions described for Nos. 1CVP38f-1CVP38p.

Later software changes allow Nos. 1CVP2A, 1CVP3-1CVP42 and 1CVP51-1CVP58 to be printed with mail-class inscriptions "Library Mail," "Intl. First Class," "Intl Priority," "Intl Express," and "M-Bag" with any denomination.

Love — CVPA2

2002 *Serpentine Die Cut 5¾ at Left*
1CVP3 CVPA2 37c **black, blue & orange** ... 4.00 4.00
　On cover ... 5.00
　Sheet of 25 ... 100.00
a. "First Class" below "US Postage" ... 2.75 2.00
b. "Priority" below "US Postage" ... 8.25 2.50
c. "Express" below "US Postage" ... 25.00 5.00
d. "Media Mail" below "US Postage" ... 7.75 2.50
e. "Parcel Post" below "US Postage" ... 7.75 2.50
f. "Bound Printed Matter" below "US Postage" ... 7.75 2.50
g. "BPM" below "US Postage" ... 7.75 2.50

Statue of Liberty and Flag — CVPA3

Liberty Bell and Flag — CVPA4

Eagle and Flag — CVPA5

George Washington and Flag — CVPA6

Capitol Building and Flag — CVPA7

2003, June *Serpentine Die Cut 5¾ at Left*
1CVP4 CVPA3 37c **black, blue & orange** ... 3.50 2.00
　On cover ... 3.00
a. "First Class" below "US Postage" ... 3.25 2.00
b. "Priority" below "US Postage" ... 8.00 1.00
c. "Express" below "US Postage" ... 25.00 3.00
d. "Media Mail" below "US Postage" ... 7.50 1.00
e. "Parcel Post" below "US Postage" ... 7.50 1.00
f. "Bound Printed Matter" below "US Postage" ... 7.50 1.00
g. "BPM" below "US Postage" ... 7.50 1.00
1CVP5 CVPA4 37c **black, blue & orange** ... 3.50 2.00
　On cover ... 3.00
a. "First Class" below "US Postage" ... 3.25 2.00
b. "Priority" below "US Postage" ... 8.00 1.00
c. "Express" below "US Postage" ... 25.00 3.00
d. "Media Mail" below "US Postage" ... 7.50 1.00
e. "Parcel Post" below "US Postage" ... 7.50 1.00
f. "Bound Printed Matter" below "US Postage" ... 7.50 1.00
g. "BPM" below "US Postage" ... 7.50 1.00
1CVP6 CVPA5 37c **black, blue & orange** ... 3.50 2.00
　On cover ... 3.00
a. "First Class" below "US Postage" ... 3.25 2.00
b. "Priority" below "US Postage" ... 8.00 1.00
c. "Express" below "US Postage" ... 25.00 3.00
d. "Media Mail" below "US Postage" ... 7.50 1.00
e. "Parcel Post" below "US Postage" ... 7.50 1.00
f. "Bound Printed Matter" below "US Postage" ... 7.50 1.00
g. "BPM" below "US Postage" ... 7.50 1.00
1CVP7 CVPA6 37c **black, blue & orange** ... 3.50 2.00
　On cover ... 3.00
a. "First Class" below "US Postage" ... 3.25 .20
b. "Priority" below "US Postage" ... 8.00 1.00
c. "Express" below "US Postage" ... 25.00 3.00
d. "Media Mail" below "US Postage" ... 7.50 1.00
e. "Parcel Post" below "US Postage" ... 7.50 1.00
f. "Bound Printed Matter" below "US Postage" ... 7.50 1.00
g. "BPM" below "US Postage" ... 7.50 1.00
1CVP8 CVPA7 37c **black, blue & orange** ... 3.50 2.00
　On cover ... 3.00
a. "First Class" below "US Postage" ... 3.25 .20
b. "Priority" below "US Postage" ... 8.00 1.00
c. "Express" below "US Postage" ... 25.00 3.00
d. "Media Mail" below "US Postage" ... 7.50 1.00
e. "Parcel Post" below "US Postage" ... 7.50 1.00
f. "Bound Printed Matter" below "US Postage" ... 7.50 1.00
g. "BPM" below "US Postage" ... 7.50 1.00
h. Strip of 5, #1CVP4-1CVP8 ... 17.50

Flag and Star Type of 2002 Redrawn With "Stamps.com" in Upper Case Letters
2003, June *Serpentine Die Cut 5¾ at Left*
Identification Code Above Zip Code
1CVP9 CVPA1a 37c **black, blue & orange,** "US Postage" only ... 3.00 1.50
　On cover ... 2.50
　Sheet of 25 ... 75.00
a. "First Class" below "US Postage" ... 2.00 .20
b. "Priority" below "US Postage" ... 8.00 1.00
c. "Express" below "US Postage" ... 25.00 3.00
d. "Media Mail" below "US Postage" ... 7.50 1.00
e. "Parcel Post" below "US Postage" ... 7.50 1.00
f. "Bound Printed Matter" below "US Postage" ... 7.50 1.00
g. "BPM" below "US Postage" ... 7.50 1.00

Snowman — CVPA8

Snowflakes CVPA9

Holly — CVPA10

Dove — CVPA11

Gingerbread Man and Candy — CVPA12

2003, Dec.   *Serpentine Die Cut 4½ at Left*

1CVP10	CVPA8 37c **black, blue & orange**	3.00	1.50
	On cover		2.50
a.	"First Class" below "US Postage"	2.00	1.00
b.	"Priority" below "US Postage"	8.00	1.00
c.	"Express" below "US Postage"	25.00	3.00
d.	"Media Mail" below "US Postage"	7.50	1.00
e.	"Parcel Post" below "US Postage"	7.50	1.00
f.	"Bound Printed Matter" below "US Postage"	7.50	1.00
g.	"BPM" below "US Postage"	7.50	1.00
1CVP11	CVPA9 37c **black, blue & orange**	3.00	1.50
	On cover		2.50
a.	"First Class" below "US Postage"	2.00	1.00
b.	"Priority" below "US Postage"	8.00	1.00
c.	"Express" below "US Postage"	25.00	3.00
d.	"Media Mail" below "US Postage"	7.50	1.00
e.	"Parcel Post" below "US Postage"	7.50	1.00
f.	"Bound Printed Matter" below "US Postage"	7.50	1.00
g.	"BPM" below "US Postage"	7.50	1.00
1CVP12	CVPA10 37c **black, blue & orange**	3.00	1.50
	On cover		2.50
a.	"First Class" below "US Postage"	2.00	1.00
b.	"Priority" below "US Postage"	8.00	1.00
c.	"Express" below "US Postage"	25.00	3.00
d.	"Media Mail" below "US Postage"	7.50	1.00
e.	"Parcel Post" below "US Postage"	7.50	1.00
f.	"Bound Printed Matter" below "US Postage"	7.50	1.00
g.	"BPM" below "US Postage"	7.50	1.00
1CVP13	CVPA11 37c **black, blue & orange**	3.00	1.50
	On cover		2.50
a.	"First Class" below "US Postage"	2.00	1.00
b.	"Priority" below "US Postage"	8.00	1.00
c.	"Express" below "US Postage"	25.00	3.00
d.	"Media Mail" below "US Postage"	7.50	1.00
e.	"Parcel Post" below "US Postage"	7.50	1.00
f.	"Bound Printed Matter" below "US Postage"	7.50	1.00
g.	"BPM" below "US Postage"	7.50	1.00
1CVP14	CVPA12 37c **black, blue & orange**	3.00	1.50
	On cover		2.50
a.	"First Class" below "US Postage"	2.00	1.00
b.	"Priority" below "US Postage"	8.00	1.00
c.	"Express" below "US Postage"	25.00	3.00
d.	"Media Mail" below "US Postage"	7.50	1.00
e.	"Parcel Post" below "US Postage"	7.50	1.00
f.	"Bound Printed Matter" below "US Postage"	7.50	1.00
g.	"BPM" below "US Postage"	7.50	1.00
h.	Strip of 5, #1CVP10-1CVP14	12.50	

Mailbox — CVPA13

2004, Mar.   *Serpentine Die Cut 6½ at Left*

1CVP15	CVPA13 37c **black, blue & orange**	25.00	15.00
	On cover		35.00
a.	"First Class" below "US Postage"	25.00	15.00
b.	"Priority" below "US Postage"	—	—
c.	"Express" below "US Postage"	—	—
d.	"Media Mail" below "US Postage"	—	—
e.	"Parcel Post" below "US Postage"	—	—
f.	"Bound Printed Matter" below "US Postage"	—	—
g.	"BPM" below "US Postage"	—	—

Blank sheets of No. 1CVP15 were sent free of charge to those who responded to special Stamps.com promotions which offered a fixed amount of free postage as an enticement to new subscribers. The franking portion of the stamps could only be applied after subscribing.

George Washington CVPA14

Thomas Jefferson — CVPA15

Abraham Lincoln — CVPA16

Theodore Roosevelt — CVPA17

John F. Kennedy — CVPA18

2004, Apr.   *Serpentine Die Cut 6½ at Left*

1CVP16	CVPA14 37c **black, blue & orange**	2.00	1.00
	On cover		2.50
a.	"First Class" below "US Postage"	1.10	.75
b.	"Priority" below "US Postage"	5.00	2.50
c.	"Express" below "US Postage"	20.00	5.00

d.	"Media Mail" below "US Postage"	5.00	2.50
e.	"Parcel Post" below "US Postage"	5.00	2.50
f.	"Bound Printed Matter" below "US Postage"	5.00	2.50
g.	"BPM" below "US Postage"	5.00	2.50
1CVP17	CVPA15 37c **black, blue & orange**	2.00	1.00
	On cover		2.50
a.	"First Class" below "US Postage"	1.10	.75
b.	"Priority" below "US Postage"	5.00	2.50
c.	"Express" below "US Postage"	20.00	5.00
d.	"Media Mail" below "US Postage"	5.00	2.50
e.	"Parcel Post" below "US Postage"	5.00	2.50
f.	"Bound Printed Matter" below "US Postage"	5.00	2.50
g.	"BPM" below "US Postage"	5.00	2.50
1CVP18	CVPA16 37c **black, blue & orange**	2.00	1.00
	On cover		2.50
a.	"First Class" below "US Postage"	1.10	.75
b.	"Priority" below "US Postage"	5.00	2.50
c.	"Express" below "US Postage"	20.00	5.00
d.	"Media Mail" below "US Postage"	5.00	2.50
e.	"Parcel Post" below "US Postage"	5.00	2.50
f.	"Bound Printed Matter" below "US Postage"	5.00	2.50
g.	"BPM" below "US Postage"	5.00	2.50
1CVP19	CVPA17 37c **black, blue & orange**	2.00	1.00
	On cover		2.50
a.	"First Class" below "US Postage"	1.10	.75
b.	"Priority" below "US Postage"	5.00	2.50
c.	"Express" below "US Postage"	20.00	5.00
d.	"Media Mail" below "US Postage"	5.00	2.50
e.	"Parcel Post" below "US Postage"	5.00	2.50
f.	"Bound Printed Matter" below "US Postage"	5.00	2.50
g.	"BPM" below "US Postage"	5.00	2.50
1CVP20	CVPA18 37c **black, blue & orange**	2.00	1.00
	On cover		2.50
a.	"First Class" below "US Postage"	1.10	.75
b.	"Priority" below "US Postage"	5.00	2.50
c.	"Express" below "US Postage"	20.00	5.00
d.	"Media Mail" below "US Postage"	5.00	2.50
e.	"Parcel Post" below "US Postage"	5.00	2.50
f.	"Bound Printed Matter" below "US Postage"	5.00	2.50
g.	"BPM" below "US Postage"	5.00	2.50
h.	Horiz. strip of 5, #1CVP16-1CVP20	10.00	

Flag and Star Type of 2002 Redrawn With Orange Stars and Text at Left

2004, Apr.   *Serpentine Die Cut 6½ at Left*
"Stamps.com" in Upper Case Letters
Identification Code Above Zip Code

1CVP21	CVPA1a 37c **black, blue & orange**	2.00	1.00
	On cover		2.50
	Sheet of 25	50.00	
a.	"First Class" below "US Postage"	1.35	.75
b.	"Priority" below "US Postage"	6.00	2.50
c.	"Express" below "US Postage"	22.50	5.00
d.	"Media Mail" below "US Postage"	6.00	2.50
e.	"Parcel Post" below "US Postage"	6.00	2.50
f.	"Bound Printed Matter" below "US Postage"	6.00	2.50
g.	"BPM" below "US Postage"	6.00	2.50

Bicycling — CVPA19

Running — CVPA20

Swimming
CVPA21

Boxing — CVPA22

Equestrian
CVPA23

Basketball
CVPA24

Judo — CVPA25

Soccer — CVPA26

Gymnastics
CVPA27

Tennis — CVPA28

2004, Apr.　　　　*Serpentine Die Cut 6½ at Left*

1CVP22	CVPA19 37c **black, blue & orange**		3.00	2.00
	On cover			3.00
a.	"First Class" below "US Postage"		2.50	1.50
b.	"Priority" below "US Postage"		8.00	1.00
c.	"Express" below "US Postage"		25.00	3.00
d.	"Media Mail" below "US Postage"		7.50	1.00
e.	"Parcel Post" below "US Postage"		7.50	1.00
f.	"Bound Printed Matter" below "US Postage"		7.50	1.00
g.	"BPM" below "US Postage"		7.50	1.00
1CVP23	CVPA20 37c **black, blue & orange**		3.00	2.00
	On cover			3.00
a.	"First Class" below "US Postage"		2.50	1.50
b.	"Priority" below "US Postage"		8.00	1.00
c.	"Express" below "US Postage"		25.00	3.00
d.	"Media Mail" below "US Postage"		7.50	1.00
e.	"Parcel Post" below "US Postage"		7.50	1.00
f.	"Bound Printed Matter" below "US Postage"		7.50	1.00
g.	"BPM" below "US Postage"		7.50	1.00
1CVP24	CVPA21 37c **black, blue & orange**		3.00	2.00
	On cover			3.00
a.	"First Class" below "US Postage"		2.50	1.50
b.	"Priority" below "US Postage"		8.00	1.00
c.	"Express" below "US Postage"		25.00	3.00
d.	"Media Mail" below "US Postage"		7.50	1.00
e.	"Parcel Post" below "US Postage"		7.50	1.00
f.	"Bound Printed Matter" below "US Postage"		7.50	1.00
g.	"BPM" below "US Postage"		7.50	1.00
1CVP25	CVPA22 37c **black, blue & orange**		3.00	2.00
	On cover			3.00
a.	"First Class" below "US Postage"		2.50	1.50
b.	"Priority" below "US Postage"		8.00	1.00
c.	"Express" below "US Postage"		25.00	3.00
d.	"Media Mail" below "US Postage"		7.50	1.00
e.	"Parcel Post" below "US Postage"		7.50	1.00
f.	"Bound Printed Matter" below "US Postage"		7.50	1.00
g.	"BPM" below "US Postage"		7.50	1.00
1CVP26	CVPA23 37c **black, blue & orange**		3.00	2.00
	On cover			3.00
a.	"First Class" below "US Postage"		2.50	1.50
b.	"Priority" below "US Postage"		8.00	1.00
c.	"Express" below "US Postage"		25.00	3.00
d.	"Media Mail" below "US Postage"		7.50	1.00
e.	"Parcel Post" below "US Postage"		7.50	1.00
f.	"Bound Printed Matter" below "US Postage"		7.50	1.00

g.	"BPM" below "US Postage"		7.50	1.00
h.	Horiz. strip of 5, #1CVP22-1CVP26		15.00	
1CVP27	CVPA24 37c **black, blue & orange**		3.00	2.00
	On cover			3.00
a.	"First Class" below "US Postage"		2.50	1.50
b.	"Priority" below "US Postage"		8.00	1.00
c.	"Express" below "US Postage"		25.00	3.00
d.	"Media Mail" below "US Postage"		7.50	1.00
e.	"Parcel Post" below "US Postage"		7.50	1.00
f.	"Bound Printed Matter" below "US Postage"		7.50	1.00
g.	"BPM" below "US Postage"		7.50	1.00
1CVP28	CVPA25 37c **black, blue & orange**		3.00	2.00
	On cover			3.00
a.	"First Class" below "US Postage"		2.50	1.50
b.	"Priority" below "US Postage"		8.00	1.00
c.	"Express" below "US Postage"		25.00	3.00
d.	"Media Mail" below "US Postage"		7.50	1.00
e.	"Parcel Post" below "US Postage"		7.50	1.00
f.	"Bound Printed Matter" below "US Postage"		7.50	1.00
g.	"BPM" below "US Postage"		7.50	1.00
1CVP29	CVPA26 37c **black, blue & orange**		3.00	2.00
	On cover			3.00
a.	"First Class" below "US Postage"		2.50	1.50
b.	"Priority" below "US Postage"		8.00	1.00
c.	"Express" below "US Postage"		25.00	3.00
d.	"Media Mail" below "US Postage"		7.50	1.00
e.	"Parcel Post" below "US Postage"		7.50	1.00
f.	"Bound Printed Matter" below "US Postage"		7.50	1.00
g.	"BPM" below "US Postage"		7.50	1.00
1CVP30	CVPA27 37c **black, blue & orange**		3.00	2.00
	On cover			3.00
a.	"First Class" below "US Postage"		2.50	1.50
b.	"Priority" below "US Postage"		8.00	1.00
c.	"Express" below "US Postage"		25.00	3.00
d.	"Media Mail" below "US Postage"		7.50	1.00
e.	"Parcel Post" below "US Postage"		7.50	1.00
f.	"Bound Printed Matter" below "US Postage"		7.50	1.00
g.	"BPM" below "US Postage"		7.50	1.00
1CVP31	CVPA28 37c **black, blue & orange**		3.00	2.00
	On cover			3.00
a.	"First Class" below "US Postage"		2.50	1.50
b.	"Priority" below "US Postage"		8.00	1.00
c.	"Express" below "US Postage"		25.00	3.00
d.	"Media Mail" below "US Postage"		7.50	1.00
e.	"Parcel Post" below "US Postage"		7.50	1.00
f.	"Bound Printed Matter" below "US Postage"		7.50	1.00
g.	"BPM" below "US Postage"		7.50	1.00
h.	Horiz. strip of 5, #1CVP27-1CVP31		15.00	

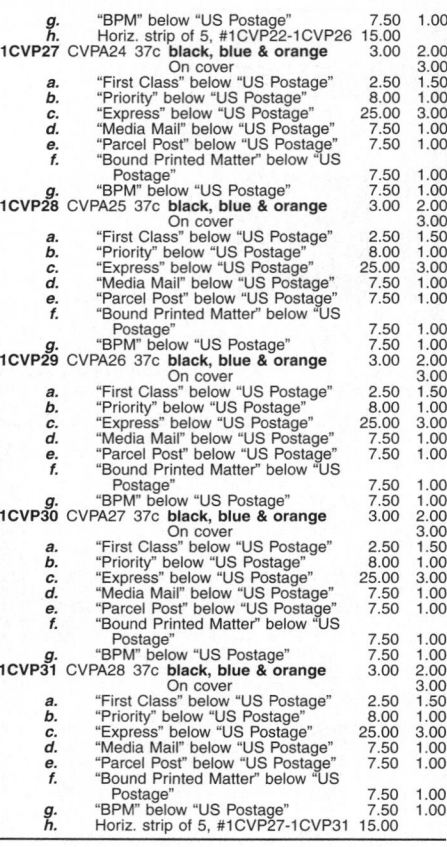

The item pictured above was produced by Stamps.com for a special promotional mailing of its own and was not made available unused to customers.

Leaning Tower of
Pisa — CVPA29

Sphinx and Pyramids — CVPA30

Sydney Opera House — CVPA31

Mayan Pyramid — CVPA32

Asian Temple — CVPA33

2004, July   *Serpentine Die Cut 6½ at Left*

1CVP32	CVPA29 37c **black, blue & orange**		3.00	2.00
	On cover			3.00
a.	"First Class" below "US Postage"		2.30	1.50
b.	"Priority" below "US Postage"		8.00	1.00
c.	"Express" below "US Postage"		25.00	3.00
d.	"Media Mail" below "US Postage"		7.50	1.00
e.	"Parcel Post" below "US Postage"		7.50	1.00
f.	"Bound Printed Matter" below "US Postage"		7.50	1.00
g.	"BPM" below "US Postage"		7.50	1.00
1CVP33	CVPA30 37c **black, blue & orange**		3.00	2.00
	On cover			3.00
a.	"First Class" below "US Postage"		2.30	1.50
b.	"Priority" below "US Postage"		8.00	1.00
c.	"Express" below "US Postage"		25.00	3.00
d.	"Media Mail" below "US Postage"		7.50	1.00
e.	"Parcel Post" below "US Postage"		7.50	1.00
f.	"Bound Printed Matter" below "US Postage"		7.50	1.00
g.	"BPM" below "US Postage"		7.50	1.00
1CVP34	CVPA31 37c **black, blue & orange**		3.00	2.00
	On cover			3.00
a.	"First Class" below "US Postage"		2.30	1.50
b.	"Priority" below "US Postage"		8.00	1.00
c.	"Express" below "US Postage"		25.00	3.00
d.	"Media Mail" below "US Postage"		7.50	1.00
e.	"Parcel Post" below "US Postage"		7.50	1.00

f.	"Bound Printed Matter" below "US Postage"		7.50	1.00
g.	"BPM" below "US Postage"		7.50	1.00
1CVP35	CVPA32 37c **black, blue & orange**		3.00	2.00
	On cover			3.00
a.	"First Class" below "US Postage"		2.30	1.50
b.	"Priority" below "US Postage"		8.00	1.00
c.	"Express" below "US Postage"		25.00	3.00
d.	"Media Mail" below "US Postage"		7.50	1.00
e.	"Parcel Post" below "US Postage"		7.50	1.00
f.	"Bound Printed Matter" below "US Postage"		7.50	1.00
g.	"BPM" below "US Postage"		7.50	1.00
1CVP36	CVPA33 37c **black, blue & orange**		3.00	2.00
	On cover			3.00
a.	"First Class" below "US Postage"		2.30	1.50
b.	"Priority" below "US Postage"		8.00	1.00
c.	"Express" below "US Postage"		25.00	3.00
d.	"Media Mail" below "US Postage"		7.50	1.00
e.	"Parcel Post" below "US Postage"		7.50	1.00
f.	"Bound Printed Matter" below "US Postage"		7.50	1.00
g.	"BPM" below "US Postage"		7.50	1.00
h.	Strip of 5, #1CVP32-1CVP36		15.00	

Computer and Letters — CVPA34

2005, Mar.   *Serpentine Die Cut 6½ at Left*

1CVP37	CVPA34 37c **black, blue & orange**		25.00	15.00
	On cover			75.00
a.	"First Class" below "US Postage"		25.00	15.00
b.	"Priority" below "US Postage"		—	—
c.	"Express" below "US Postage"		—	—
d.	"Media Mail" below "US Postage"		—	—
e.	"Parcel Post" below "US Postage"		—	—
f.	"Bound Printed Matter" below "US Postage"		—	—
g.	"BPM" below "US Postage"		—	—

Blank sheets of No. 1CVP37 were sent free of charge to those who responded to special Stamps.com promotions which offered a fixed amount of free postage as an enticement to new subscribers. The franking portion of the stamps could only be applied after subscribing.

Logo — CVPA35

2005, Aug.   *Die Cut Perf. 6½ at Left*

1CVP38	CVPA35 37c **black, blue & orange**		1.00	.30
	On cover			2.50
a.	"Priority" below "US Postage"		8.00	1.00
b.	"Express" below "US Postage"		25.00	3.00
c.	"Media Mail" below "US Postage"		7.50	1.00
d.	"Parcel Post" below "US Postage"		7.50	1.00
e.	"BPM" below "US Postage"		7.50	1.00
f.	"Aerogramme" below "US Postage"		1.40	1.00
g.	"Intl Air Letter" below "US Postage"		1.25	1.00
h.	"Intl Eco Letter" (Economy Letter Mail) below "US Postage"		5.50	1.00
i.	"GXG" (Global Express Guaranteed) below "US Postage"		50.00	6.00
j.	"EMS" (Global Express Mail) below "US Postage"		32.50	4.00
k.	"GPM" (Global Priority Mail) below "US Postage"		8.00	1.00
l.	"Intl Air Parcel" (Air Parcel Post) below "US Postage"		26.00	3.00
m.	"Intl Eco Parcel" (Economy Parcel Post) below "US Postage"		32.50	4.00
n.	"M-Bag (Air)" below "US Postage"		35.00	5.00
o.	"M-Bag (Economy)" below "US Postage"		18.00	3.00
p.	"Mat for Blind" below "US Postage"		.20	—

Values for lettered varieties on Nos. 1CVP38 are based on the prices set as the minimum values for each service classification in the software available at the time the stamps were issued. In mid-December 2005, the software was changed to allow for a 1c minimum value for any of these lettered varieties. In 2006, No. 1CVP38 was made available on a coil roll.

Snowman — CVPA36

Candy Cane — CVPA37

Dove — CVPA38

Stylized Christmas Tree and Window — CVPA39

2005, Nov.   *Die Cut Perf. 6 at Right*

1CVP39	CVPA36 37c **multicolored**		1.60	.20
	On cover			2.50
a.	"Priority" below "US Postage"		8.00	1.00
b.	"Express" below "US Postage"		25.00	3.00
c.	"Media Mail" below "US Postage"		7.50	1.00
d.	"Parcel Post" below "US Postage"		7.50	1.00
e.	"BPM" below "US Postage"		7.50	1.00
f.	"Aerogramme" below "US Postage"		1.40	1.00
g.	"Intl Air Letter" below "US Postage"		1.25	1.00
h.	"Intl Eco Letter" (Economy Letter Mail) below "US Postage"		5.50	1.00
i.	"GXG" (Global Express Guaranteed) below "US Postage"		50.00	6.00
j.	"EMS" (Global Express Mail) below "US Postage"		32.50	4.00
k.	"GPM" (Global Priority Mail) below "US Postage"		8.00	1.00
l.	"Intl Air Parcel" (Air Parcel Post) below "US Postage"		26.00	3.00
m.	"Intl Eco Parcel" (Economy Parcel Post) below "US Postage"		32.50	4.00
n.	"M-Bag (Air)" below "US Postage"		35.00	5.00
o.	"M-Bag (Economy)" below "US Postage"		18.00	3.00
p.	"Mat for Blind" below "US Postage"		.20	—
1CVP40	CVPA37 37c **multicolored**		1.60	.20
	On cover			2.50
a.	"Priority" below "US Postage"		8.00	1.00
b.	"Express" below "US Postage"		25.00	3.00
c.	"Media Mail" below "US Postage"		7.50	1.00
d.	"Parcel Post" below "US Postage"		7.50	1.00
e.	"BPM" below "US Postage"		7.50	1.00
f.	"Aerogramme" below "US Postage"		1.40	1.00
g.	"Intl Air Letter" below "US Postage"		1.25	1.00
h.	"Intl Eco Letter" (Economy Letter Mail) below "US Postage"		5.50	1.00
i.	"GXG" (Global Express Guaranteed) below "US Postage"		50.00	6.00
j.	"EMS" (Global Express Mail) below "US Postage"		32.50	4.00
k.	"GPM" (Global Priority Mail) below "US Postage"		8.00	1.00
l.	"Intl Air Parcel" (Air Parcel Post) below "US Postage"		26.00	3.00
m.	"Intl Eco Parcel" (Economy Parcel Post) below "US Postage"		32.50	4.00
n.	"M-Bag (Air)" below "US Postage"		35.00	5.00
o.	"M-Bag (Economy)" below "US Postage"		18.00	3.00
p.	"Mat for Blind" below "US Postage"		.20	—

1CVP41 CVPA38 37c **multicolored** ... 1.60 .20
    On cover ... 2.50
   a.   "Priority" below "US Postage" ... 8.00 1.00
   b.   "Express" below "US Postage" ... 25.00 3.00
   c.   "Media Mail" below "US Postage" ... 7.50 1.00
   d.   "Parcel Post" below "US Postage" ... 7.50 1.00
   e.   "BPM" below "US Postage" ... 7.50 1.00
   f.   "Aerogramme" below "US Postage" ... 1.40 1.00
   g.   "Intl Air Letter" below "US Postage" ... 1.25 1.00
   h.   "Intl Eco Letter" (Economy Letter Mail) below "US Postage" ... 5.50 1.00
   i.   "GXG" (Global Express Guaranteed) below "US Postage" ... 50.00 6.00
   j.   "EMS" (Global Express Mail) below "US Postage" ... 32.50 4.00
   k.   "GPM" (Global Priority Mail) below "US Postage" ... 8.00 1.00
   l.   "Intl Air Parcel" (Air Parcel Post) below "US Postage" ... 26.00 3.00
   m.   "Intl Eco Parcel" (Economy Parcel Post) below "US Postage" ... 32.50 4.00
   n.   "M-Bag (Air)" below "US Postage" ... 35.00 5.00
   o.   "M-Bag (Economy)" below "US Postage" ... 18.00 3.00
   p.   "Mat for Blind" below "US Postage" ... .20 —
1CVP42 CVPA39 37c **multicolored** ... 1.60 .20
    On cover ... 2.50
   a.   "Priority" below "US Postage" ... 8.00 1.00
   b.   "Express" below "US Postage" ... 25.00 3.00
   c.   "Media Mail" below "US Postage" ... 7.50 1.00
   d.   "Parcel Post" below "US Postage" ... 7.50 1.00
   e.   "BPM" below "US Postage" ... 7.50 1.00
   f.   "Aerogramme" below "US Postage" ... 1.40 1.00
   g.   "Intl Air Letter" below "US Postage" ... 1.25 1.00
   h.   "Intl Eco Letter" (Economy Letter Mail) below "US Postage" ... 5.50 1.00
   i.   "GXG" (Global Express Guaranteed) below "US Postage" ... 50.00 6.00
   j.   "EMS" (Global Express Mail) below "US Postage" ... 32.50 4.00
   k.   "GPM" (Global Priority Mail) below "US Postage" ... 8.00 1.00
   l.   "Intl Air Parcel" (Air Parcel Post) below "US Postage" ... 26.00 3.00
   m.   "Intl Eco Parcel" (Economy Parcel Post) below "US Postage" ... 32.50 4.00
   n.   "M-Bag (Air)" below "US Postage" ... 35.00 5.00
   o.   "M-Bag (Economy)" below "US Postage" ... 18.00 3.00
   p.   "Mat for Blind" below "US Postage" ... .20 —
   q.   Vert. strip, 2 each #1CVP39-1CVP42 ... 6.00

Values for lettered varieties on Nos. 1CVP39-1CVP42 are based on the prices set as the minimum values for each service classification in the software available at the time the stamps were issued. In mid-December 2005, the software was changed to allow for a 1c minimum value for any of these lettered varieties.

Endicia.com

CVPA40

CVPA41

2005-06   *Serpentine Die Cut 10¼*
1CVP43 CVPA40 24c **black & bright rose** ... 10.00 4.00
   a.   39c "First Class" under "US Postage" ... 2.00 .50
   b.   63c "Intl. Mail" under "US Postage" ... 3.25 2.50
   c. $4.05 "Priority Mail" under "US Postage" ... 12.00 2.50

Coil Stamps
Serpentine Die Cut 10½x10¼ on 2 Sides
1CVP44 CVPA41 24c **black & pink** ... 11.00 4.00
   a.   39c "First Class" under "US Postage" ... 2.25 .50

   b.   63c "Intl. Mail" under "US Postage" ... 3.50 2.50
   c. $4.05 "Priority Mail" under "US Postage" ... 12.50 2.50

Issued: Nos. 1CVP43, Nov. 2005; Nos. 1CVP44, Jan. 2006.
Originally, face values of 2c, 52c, 63c, 87c, $1.11, $1.35, $1.59, $1.83, $2.07, $2.31, $2.55, $2.79, $3.03, and $3.27 could also be printed on stamps with the "First class" inscription. Additionally, an 84c face value could be printed on stamps with the "Intl. Mail" inscription, and a $8.10 face value could be printed on stamps with the "Priority Mail" inscription. Values for Nos. 1CVP43-1CVP44 are for stamps with the listed face values and mail-class inscription. Values for stamps with lower or higher face values are correspondingly lower or higher.
In 2007, software changes permitted Nos. 1CVP43 and 1CVP44 to be printed with mail class inscriptions "Media Mail," "BPM," "Parcel Post," "Library Mail," and "Express Mail," as well as any face value for any mail-class inscription.
Nos. 1CVP43 and 1CVP44 printed after the software changes are inscribed "First Class" under "US Postage" and sell for considerably less than the values shown. Stamps printed before the software changes are inscribed "Postcard" under "US Postage," as shown in the illustrations.

Stamps.com

Flag and Mount Rushmore — CVPA42

Flag and Eagle — CVPA43

Flag and Statue of Liberty — CVPA44

Flag and Liberty Bell — CVPA45

2006, Mar.   *Die Cut Perf. 6 at Right*
1CVP51 CVPA42 39c **multicolored** ... .80 .20
    On cover ... 2.50
1CVP52 CVPA43 39c **multicolored** ... .80 .20
    On cover ... 2.50
1CVP53 CVPA44 39c **multicolored** ... .80 .20
    On cover ... 2.50
1CVP54 CVPA45 39c **multicolored** ... .80 .20
    On cover ... 2.50
   a.   Vert. strip of 8, 2 each #1CVP51-1CVP54 ... 8.00

Other service inscriptions with any possible face value can be printed on Nos. 1CVP51-1CVP54.

Stamps.com

Leaning Tower of Pisa — CVPA46

Taj Mahal — CVPA47

Eiffel Tower — CVPA48

Parthenon — CVPA49

2006   *Die Cut Perf 6 at Right*
1CVP55 CVPA46 39c **black** ... .80 .20
    On cover ... 2.50

Serial Number Under Encryption
APC
1CVP56 CVPA47 39c **black** ... .80 .20
    On cover ... 2.50
1CVP57 CVPA48 39c **multicolored** ... .80 .20
    On cover ... 2.50
1CVP58 CVPA49 39c **multicolored** ... .80 .20
    On cover ... 2.50
   a.   Vert. strip, 2 each #1CVP55-1CVP58 ... 8.00

With the introduction of the new software in December 2005, any stamp could have any denomination above 1c, and any service classification.

Pitney Bowes Stamp Expressions

CVPA50

Illustration reduced.

2006   *Die Cut Perf. 6 Horiz.*
Inscribed "pitneybowes.com/se" at Right
1CVP59 CVPA50 39c **black** + label ... 1.35 .80
    On cover ... 4.00

The stamp and label are separated by vertical roulettes. Users could create their own label images on the Pitney Bowes Stamp Expressions website (which required approval of the image from Pitney Bowes before it could be used), or download various pre-approved label images from the website into their personal computers. Stamps could be printed without label images. Stamps were printed on rolls of tagged thermal paper from a device that could be operated without a direct connection to the personal computer. See No. 1CVT1.

Stamps.com

CVPA51

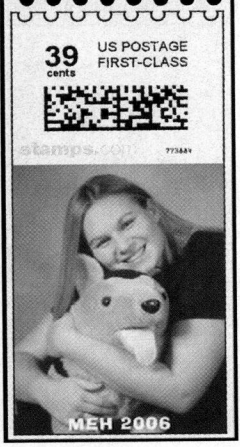

Personalizable Images — CVPA52

Illustration CVPA51 is reduced.

2006, Sept.   *Die Cut Perf. 6 at Right*

1CVP60	CVPA51	39c	multicolored	1.50	.95
			On cover	4.50
1CVP61	CVPA52	39c	multicolored	1.50	.95
			On cover	4.50

Users could requisition sheets of Nos. 1CVP60 and 1CVP61 with images of their choice from Stamps.com at $4.99 per sheet of 24. Priority and Express service classifications could also be printed on Nos. 1CVP60-1CVP61 with any denomination. Stamps exist with slightly larger die cutting (60x30mm and 30x60mm) in both squared and rounded corners. The denomination type shown on Nos. 1CVP60-1CVP61 can be placed on label types CVPA36-CVPA39, CVPA42-CVPA49, CVPA53-CVPA60 and any later stamps.com labels of this size.

Autumn Leaves — CVPA53

Pumpkins — CVPA54

Basket of Apples, Sheaf of Wheat, Falling Leaves and Pumpkins — CVPA55

Leaves and Carved Pumpkin — CVPA56

2006   *Die Cut Perf. 6 at Right*

1CVP62	CVPA53	39c	multicolored	1.25	.20
			On cover		2.50
1CVP63	CVPA54	39c	multicolored	1.25	.20
			On cover		2.50
1CVP64	CVPA55	39c	multicolored	1.25	.20
			On cover		2.50
1CVP65	CVPA56	39c	multicolored	1.25	.20
			On cover		2.50
a.		Vert. strip, 2 each #1CVP62-1CVP65		10.00	

See note after No. 1CVP58.

"Season's Greetings" — CVPA57

Christmas Trees — CVPA58

Snowman — CVPA59

Dove — CVPA60

2006   *Die Cut Perf. 6 at Right*

1CVP66	CVPA57	39c	multicolored	1.25	.20
			On cover		2.50
1CVP67	CVPA58	39c	multicolored	1.25	.20
			On cover		2.50
1CVP68	CVPA59	39c	multicolored	1.25	.20
			On cover		2.50
1CVP69	CVPA60	39c	multicolored	1.25	.20
			On cover		2.50
a.		Vert. strip, 2 each #1CVP66-1CVP69		10.00	

See note after No. 1CVP58.

COMPUTER VENDED POSTAGE TEST STAMPS
Pitney Bowes Stamp Expressions

CVT1

Illustration reduced.

2006   *Die Cut Perf. 6 Horiz.*
Inscribed "pbstampexpressions.com" at Right

1CVT1	CVT1	39c	black + label	5.00	—
			On cover		—

No. 1CVT1 were produced only by beta testers of the Pitney Bowes Stamp Expressions system, and as such were not available to normal subscribers to the system. Examples are known to have passed through the mail. Notes concerning No. 1CVP59 apply to No. 1CVT1.

NON-PERSONALIZABLE POSTAGE

These stamps, approved by the USPS, were non-personalizable stamps that could be purchased directly from private manufacturers, which shipped them to the customer. Other non-personalizable stamps have been created by a variety of companies, all sold at excessive amounts over face value as "collectibles". Such items are not listed here. Most items created that sold for excessive amounts over face value have vignettes that are licensed images, usually depicting sport team emblems or other sports-related themes, or celebrities.

Personalized postage stamps, first available in 2004, created by a variety of different companies, and heretofore listed with Scott numbers having a "2CVP" prefix, are no longer listed. Personalized stamps, though valid for postage, are not sold at any U.S. Postal Service post office. They are available only by on-line ordering through the company's website. Stamps are only available from the companies in full panes of 20. Each pane is sold at a significant premium above the stated face value to cover the costs of personalization, shipping and handling.

In recent years, there has been a steadily increasing number of private companies, either directly licensed by the USPS or created as spinoff companies of these licensees, creating distinctly different personalized stamps. None of the companies has issued fewer than seven stamps for each rate change, with one issuing as many as 42 different stamps. Because mailing rates set by the USPS are expected to change yearly, the collective output of distinctly different, rate-based stamps from these various companies likely will increase. There are no restrictions in place to prevent more firms from bringing personalized stamps to the marketplace, or to keep stamp producers from offering even more customer options. Some personalized stamps do not differ in any appreciable manner from some of the non-personalizable stamps sold as collectibles and not listed here.

Stamps.com

CVPC1

CVPC2

2007, May			*Die Cut*	
Self-Adhesive				
3CVP1	CVPC1 2c **black & gray**		.20	.20
a.	Inscribed "US Postag"		—	—
Die Cut Perf. 5¼ at Right				
3CVP2	CVPC2 2c **multicolored**		.20	.20
a.	Tagged		1.40	1.40

2008			*Die Cut*	
3CVP3	CVPC1 1c **black & gray**		.20	.20

No. 3CVP1 was printed in sheets of 40 stamps. Stamps with serial numbers ending in "06" are No. 3CVP1a. Sheets were sold for face value plus a shipping charge and were obtainable through the stamps.com website.

No. 3CVP2 was printed in sheets of 20. Full sheets were given free of charge to first-time stamps.com customers, but the full sheets were available for sale to other customers at face value plus a shipping charge through the stamps.com website.

VENDING & AFFIXING MACHINE PERFORATIONS

Imperforate sheets of 400 were first issued in 1906 on the request of several makers of vending and affixing machines. The machine manufacturers made coils from the imperforate sheets and applied various perforations to suit the particular needs of their machines. These privately applied perforations were used for many years and form a chapter of postal history.

Unused values are for pairs, used values for singles. Used multiples are highly valued, with prices often equalling or exceeding those for unused pairs or strips. "On cover" values are for single stamps used commercially in the proper period when known that way. Several, primarily the Alaska-Yukon and Hudson-Fulton commemoratives, are known almost exclusively on covers from contemporaneous stamp collectors and stamp dealers. Virtually all are rare and highly prized by specialists.

The 2mm and 3mm spacings refer only to the 1908-10 issues. (See note following No. 330 in the Postage section.) Values for intermediate spacings would roughly correspond to the lower-valued of the two listed spacings. Guide line pairs of 1906-10 issues have 2mm spacing except the Alaska-Yukon and Hudson-Fulton issues, which have 3mm spacing. Scott Nos. 408-611 have 3mm spacing, except the "A" plates which have 2¾mm spacing and Scott No. 577, which has both 2¾mm and 3mm spacing. (All spacing measurements are approximate.)

Spacing on paste-up pairs is not a factor in valuing them. Because they were joined together by hand, many different spacings can occur, from less than 2mm to more than 3mm.

Perfins listed here are punched into the stamp just before being affixed to an envelope. The most common pattern consisted of a 7mm square made up of nine holes. Pins would be removed to create special perfins for each company using the machines. The catalogue value is for the most common perfin pattern on each stamp.

* — Many varieties are suspected or known to have been perforated for philatelic purposes and not actually used in machines. These are indicated by an asterisk before the number. Several of these privately applied perforation varieties exist in blocks, which were not produced in the regular course of business. They are generally valued at a premium over the multiple of the coil pairs contained, with an additional premium for plate numbers attached.

Counterfeits are prevalent, especially of items having a basic imperf. variety valued far lower than the vending machine coil.

The Vending and Affixing Machine Perforations Committee of the Bureau Issues Association (now the United States Stamp Society) and William R. Weiss, Jr., compiled these listings.

The Attleboro Stamp Co.
See following U.S. Automatic Vending Company.

THE BRINKERHOFF COMPANY
Sedalia, Mo., Clinton, Iowa
Manufacturers of Vending Machines

Perforations Type I

Stamps were cut into strips and joined before being perforated.

Type IIa — One knife cut.
Type IIb — Two knife cuts.

Perforations Type II, 2 Holes

The Type II items listed below are without knife cuts and did not pass through the vending machine. Types IIa and IIb (illustrated above) have knife cuts, applied by the vending machine, to help separate the stamps.

Perforations Type I

Scott	Denom	Description	Unused Pair	Used Single
On Issue of 1906-08				
314	1c	blue green	200.00	30.00
		Guide line pair	375.00	
320	2c	carmine	225.00	30.00
		Guide line pair	425.00	
		Pasteup pair	320.00	
*320a	2c	lake	170.00	25.00
		Guide line pair	325.00	
		Pasteup pair	240.00	
On Issue of 1908-09				
*343	1c	green	120.00	20.00
		Guide line pair	300.00	
		Pasteup pair	230.00	
*344	2c	carmine	105.00	20.00
		On cover		1,650.
		Guide line pair	210.00	—
		Pasteup pair	185.00	
*345	3c	deep violet	140.00	—
		Guide line pair	275.00	
*346	4c	orange brown	160.00	120.00
		Guide line pair	285.00	
		Pasteup pair	210.00	
*347	5c	blue	300.00	80.00
		On cover		3,250.
		Guide line pair	500.00	
On Lincoln Issue of 1909				
*368	2c	carmine, coiled endwise	170.00	175.00
		Guide line pair	320.00	
On Alaska-Yukon Issue of 1909				
*371	2c	carmine, coiled sideways	575.00	—
		Guide line pair	1,000.	
On Issue of 1910				
*383	1c	green	200.00	
		Guide line pair		
On Issue of 1912				
*408	1c	green	32.50	15.00
		On cover		800.00
		Guide line pair	65.00	

Perforations Type II, 2 Holes

Scott	Type	Denom	Description	Unused Pair	Used Single
			Pasteup pair	52.50	
*409		2c	carmine	32.50	15.00
			On cover		1,100.
			Guide line pair	65.00	
			Pasteup pair	52.50	
On Issue of 1906-08					
314	*II	1c	blue green	95.00	12.50
			On cover		850.00
	IIa	1c	blue green	80.00	12.50
			Guide line pair	160.00	
	*IIb	1c	blue green	425.00	—
			Pasteup pair	725.00	
320	*II	2c	carmine	200.00	65.00
			On cover		700.00
			Pasteup pair	320.00	
	IIa	2c	carmine	40.00	12.50
			On cover		575.00
			Guide line pair	115.00	
320a	*II	2c	lake	200.00	65.00
			On cover		575.00
	IIa	2c	lake	85.00	12.50
			On cover		575.00
			Guide line pair	170.00	
			Pasteup pair	95.00	
	*IIb	2c	lake	340.00	75.00
On Issue of 1908-09					
343	*II	1c	green	65.00	
			On cover		700.00
			Guide line pair	110.00	
	IIa	1c	green	19.00	3.25
			On cover		700.00
			Pasteup pair	32.50	
	IIb	1c	green	32.50	
			On cover		850.00
			Pasteup pair	55.00	
344	*II	2c	carmine	75.00	
			On cover, pair		700.00
			Guide line pair	160.00	
			Pasteup pair	125.00	
	IIa	2c	carmine	19.00	3.25
			Guide line pair	37.50	
			On cover		800.00
	IIb	2c	carmine	26.00	6.50
			Guide line pair	75.00	
			Pasteup pair	57.50	
345	*II	3c	deep violet	105.00	12.50
			Guide line pair	260.00	
	*IIa	3c	deep violet	85.00	12.50
			On cover		1,650.
			Guide line pair	170.00	
	*IIb	3c	deep violet	275.00	
346	*II	4c	orange brown	150.00	
			Guide line pair	275.00	
	*IIa	4c	orange brown	130.00	50.00
			On cover		1,350.
			Guide line pair	240.00	
			Pasteup pair	200.00	
	*IIb	4c	orange brown	150.00	50.00
			On cover		1,650.
347	*II	5c	blue	240.00	
			Guide line pair	400.00	
	*IIa	5c	blue	140.00	100.00
			On cover		3,500.
			Pasteup pair	210.00	
	*IIb	5c	blue	180.00	
			Pasteup pair	350.00	
On Lincoln Issue of 1909					
368	*II	2c	carmine	75.00	
			On cover		1,150.
			Guide line pair	150.00	
	IIa	2c	carmine	75.00	14.00
			On cover		1,350.
			Guide line pair	250.00	
	IIb	2c	carmine	210.00	22.50
			On cover		1,700.
			Guide line pair	425.00	
On Alaska-Yukon Issue of 1909					
371	*II	2c	carmine, coiled sideways	160.00	100.00
			On cover		1,150.
			Guide line or pasteup pair	325.00	
	II	2c	carmine, coiled endwise	650.00	
			Guide line pair	1,275.	
	IIa	2c	carmine, coiled sideways	170.00	45.00
			On cover		850.00
			Guide line pair	325.00	
			Pasteup pair	260.00	
On Hudson-Fulton Issue of 1909					
373	*II	2c	carmine, coiled sidewise	260.00	
			Guide line or pasteup pair	475.00	
On Issue of 1910					
383	*II	1c	green	37.50	
			Guide line pair	75.00	
	IIa	1c	green	45.00	9.00
			On cover		925.00
	IIb	1c	green	90.00	50.00
			On cover		1,150.
			Guide line pair	170.00	
384	*II	2c	carmine	37.50	
			On cover		850.00
			Guide line pair	70.00	
	IIa	2c	carmine	115.00	
			On cover		1,150.
			Pasteup pair	185.00	
	IIb	2c	carmine	65.00	9.00
			On cover		1,700.
			Guide line pair	185.00	
			Pasteup pair	130.00	
On Issue of 1912					
408	*II	1c	green	95.00	
			On cover		925.00
			Guide line pair	150.00	
			Pasteup pair	115.00	
	*IIa	1c	green	115.00	

Type				Unused Pair	Used Single
	IIb	1c	Guide line pair	210.00	
			green	24.00	5.50
			On cover		925.00
409	*II	2c	Guide line pair	47.50	
			carmine	70.00	
			On cover		925.00
			Guide line pair	140.00	
			Pasteup pair	130.00	
	*IIa	2c	carmine	270.00	—
			On cover		925.00
			Guide line pair	475.00	
	IIb	2c	carmine	32.50	5.50
			On cover		700.00
			Guide line pair	57.50	

THE FARWELL COMPANY

Chicago, Ill.

A wholesale dry goods firm using Schermack (Mailometer) affixing machines. In 1911 the Farwell Company began to make and perforate their own coils. These were sometimes wrongly called "Chambers" perforations.

Type A

Type B

Stamps were perforated in sheets, then cut into strips and coiled. Blocks exist.

The following listings are grouped according to the number of holes, further divided into two types of spacing, narrow and wide.

The type symbols (3A2) indicate 3 holes over 2 holes with narrow, type A, spacing between groups.

Types A and B occurred in different rows on the same sheet. Left margin or pasteup stamps sometimes show different perforation type on the two sides.

Commercial usages of Farwell perforations are generally, but not always, on printed Farwell Co. corner card covers.

				Unused Pair Spacing 2mm	3mm	Used Single
Group I, no spacing						
On Issue of 1910						
384		2c	carmine, 7 holes	2,650.	2,650.	950.00
			On cover			5,000.
384		2c	carmine, 6 holes	4,250.	4,250.	2,250.
			On cover			5,000.

Type						
Group 2, two and three holes						
On Issue of 1910						
383	2B3	1c	green	400.00	650.00	200.00
	3A2	1c	green	400.00	650.00	
			On cover			—
			Guide line pair	700.00		
384	2A3	2c	carmine	290.00	500.00	200.00
			On cover			1,100.
			Guide line pair	1,000.	1,050.	
			Pasteup pair		850.00	
	2B3	2c	carmine	650.00	725.00	225.00
			On cover			
			Pasteup pair		1,050.	
	3A2	2c	carmine	450.00	500.00	210.00
			On cover			1,700.
			Guide line pair	800.00		
	3B2	2c	carmine	400.00	400.00	300.00
			Guide line pair	850.00		
Group 3, three and four holes						
On Issue of 1910						
383	3B4	1c	green	325.00	325.00	200.00
			Pasteup pair	650.00		
	4B3	1c	green	450.00	450.00	200.00
384	3B4	2c	carmine	600.00	600.00	260.00
			On cover			

Type						
			Guide line pair	850.00		
4B3	2c		carmine	850.00	850.00	400.00
			On cover			800.00
			Guide line pair	—		
4A3	2c		Carmine	—		
Group 4, four and four holes						
On Issue of 1908-09						
343	*A	1c	green	240.00		
	*B	1c	green	240.00		
			On cover			575.00
344	*A	2c	carmine	240.00	375.00	
	*B	2c	carmine	185.00	170.00	115.00
On Lincoln Issue of 1909						
368	*A	2c	carmine	850.00	850.00	
	*B	2c	carmine	850.00	850.00	
On Issue of 1910						
383	A	1c	green	67.50	62.50	60.00
			Guide line pair	140.00		
	B	1c	green	67.50	57.50	—
			On cover			290.00
			Guide line pair	140.00		
384	A	2c	carmine	75.00	67.50	25.00
			Guide line pair	150.00		
	B	2c	carmine	75.00	67.50	17.50
			On cover			350.00
			Guide line pair	150.00		
			Pasteup pair	160.00		
On Issue of 1912						
408	A	1c	green	37.50		2.75
			On cover			425.00
			Guide line pair	67.50		
	B	1c	green	37.50		2.75
			On cover			250.00
			Guide line pair	67.50		
409	A	2c	carmine	32.50		2.75
			On cover			60.00
	B	2c	carmine	32.50		2.75
			On cover			60.00
			Guide line pair	62.50		
On Issue of 1916-17						
482	A	2c	carmine	425.00		60.00
			On cover			1,250.
			Guide line pair	750.00		
			Pasteup pair	650.00		
	B	2c	carmine	450.00		60.00
			On cover			1,250.
			Guide line pair	800.00		
Group 5, four and five holes						
On Issue of 1910						
383	4A5	1c	green	700.00	650.00	—
			Guide line pair	1,250.		
384	4A5	2c	carmine	850.00	750.00	—
			Guide line pair	1,600.		
On Issue of 1912						
408	4A5	1c	green	1,150.		
			Guide line pair	2,100.		
	*5A4	1c	green	1,150.		
			Guide line pair	2,100.		
409	*4A5	2c	carmine	1,150.		—
			Guide line or pasteup pair	2,100.		
	*5A4	2c	carmine	1,150.		
			Guide line pair	2,100.		

INTERNATIONAL VENDING MACHINE CO.

Baltimore, Md.

Similar to the Government Coil stamp #322, but approximately perf. 12½ with somewhat inconsistent spacing.

On Issue of 1906-08				
320		2c	carmine	2,500.
320b		2c	scarlet	2,500.
On Issue of 1908-09				
343		1c	green	2,900.
344		2c	carmine	1,150.
345		3c	deep violet	1,150.
346		4c	orange brown	—
347		5c	blue	6,000.

THE MAILOMETER COMPANY

Detroit, Mich.

Formerly the Schermack Mailing Machine Co., then Mail-om-eter Co., and later the Mail-O-Meter Co. Their round-hole perforations were developed in an attempt to get the Bureau of Engraving and Printing to adopt a larger perforation for coil stamps.

Perforations Type I

Used experimentally in Detroit and Chicago in August, 1909. Later used regularly in the St. Louis branch.

Two varieties exist: six holes 1.95mm in diameter spaced an average 1.2mm apart with an overall length of 17.7mm, and six holes 1.95mm in diameter spaced an average 1.15mm apart with an overall length of 17.45mm.

To date, only the 17.7mm length perfs. have been found on commercial covers.

				Unused Pair Spacing 2mm	3mm	Used Single
On Issue of 1906-08						
*320		2c	carmine	475.00		
*320a		2c	lake	375.00		
			Guide line pair	850.00		
*320b		2c	scarlet	350.00		
On Issue of 1908-09						
343		1c	green	47.50	52.50	25.00
			On cover			575.00
			Guide line pair	75.00		
344		2c	carmine	42.50	47.50	5.00
			On cover, St. Louis			80.00
			On cover, Detroit or Chicago			1,400.
			On cover, Washington, D.C.			2,000.
			Guide line pair	90.00		
			With perforated control mark, single			100.00
			Same, on cover			450.00
345		3c	deep violet	67.50		20.00
			Guide line pair	135.00		
346		4c	orange brown	135.00	95.00	40.00
			Guide line pair	260.00		
347		5c	blue	150.00		40.00
			Guide line pair	260.00		
On Lincoln Issue of 1909						
*368		2c	carmine	190.00	135.00	110.00
			Guide line or pasteup pair	375.00		
On Alaska-Yukon Issue of 1909						
*371		2c	carmine		230.00	110.00
			Guide line pair		425.00	
On Hudson-Fulton Issue of 1909						
*373		2c	carmine		220.00	100.00
			Guide line pair		425.00	
On Issue of 1910						
383		1c	green	45.00	40.00	3.50
			On cover			—
			Guide line pair	85.00		
384		2c	carmine	57.50	47.50	5.00
			On cover			80.00
			Guide line pair	105.00		
On Issue of 1912						
*408		1c	green		26.00	4.50
			Guide line pair		50.00	
*409		2c	carmine		26.00	4.50
			Guide line pair		50.00	

Perforations Type II

Used experimentally: Chicago, 1909; Detroit, 1911. Perforation holes 1.95mm in diameter.

				Unused Pair Spacing 2mm	3mm	Used Single
On Issue of 1906-08						
*320		2c	carmine	750.00		
*320b		2c	scarlet	1,050.		
			Guide line pair	1,500.		
On Issue of 1908-09						
343		1c	green	67.50	67.50	15.00
			Guide line pair	135.00		
344		2c	carmine	80.00	80.00	15.00
			On cover			5,750.
			Guide line pair	160.00		
*345		3c	deep violet	290.00		70.00
			Pasteup pair	425.00		
*346		4c	orange brown	425.00	320.00	
*347		5c	blue	650.00		
On Lincoln Issue of 1909						
*368		2c	carmine	650.00	600.00	

On Alaska-Yukon Issue of 1909
| *371 | 2c | carmine | | | 700.00 |

On Hudson-Fulton Issue of 1909
| *373 | 2c | carmine | | | 400.00 |
| | | Guide line or pasteup pair | | | 700.00 |

On Issue of 1910
383	1c	green	160.00	160.00	27.50
		Guide line or pasteup pair	320.00		
384	2c	carmine	170.00	160.00	55.00
		On cover			4,500.

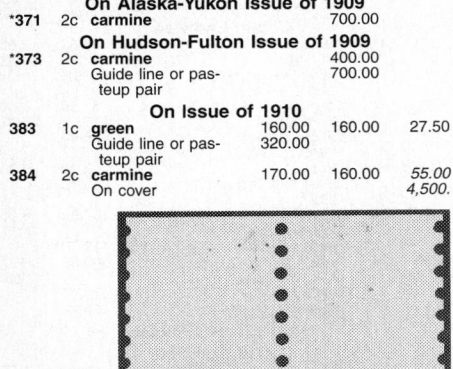

Perforations Type III

Used experimentally in Detroit in 1910. Perforation holes 1.8mm in diameter.

On Issue of 1906-08
| *320 | 2c | carmine | 850.00 |
| *320b | 2c | scarlet | 950.00 |

On Issue of 1908-09
343	1c	green	180.00	180.00
		Guide line pair	360.00	
344	2c	carmine	230.00	230.00
		Guide line pair	475.00	
		Pasteup pair	425.00	
*345	3c	deep violet	320.00	
		Guide line pair	575.00	
		Pasteup pair	1,200.	
*346	4c	orange brown	450.00	375.00
		Pasteup pair	650.00	
*347	5c	blue	750.00	
		Pasteup pair		1,150.

On Lincoln Issue of 1909
| *368 | 2c | carmine | 340.00 | 290.00 | 100.00 |
| | | Pasteup pair | 500.00 | | |

On Alaska-Yukon Issue of 1909
| *371 | 2c | carmine | 800.00 |

On Hudson-Fulton Issue of 1909
| *373 | 2c | carmine | 750.00 |
| | | Guide line pasteup pair | 1,475. |

Perforations Type IV

Used in St. Louis branch office. Blocks exist but were not regularly produced or issued.

On Issue of 1906-08
*320	2c	carmine	230.00		80.00
		Guide line pair	475.00		
		Pasteup pair	425.00		
*320b	2c	scarlet	160.00		65.00
		Guide line pair	525.00		

On Issue of 1908-09
343	1c	green	47.50	42.50	9.00
		Guide line pair	100.00		
		Pasteup pair	95.00		
344	2c	carmine	57.50	47.50	9.00
		On cover			
		Guide line or pasteup pair	105.00		
345	3c	deep violet	110.00		
		Guide line or pasteup pair	225.00		
346	4c	orange brown	175.00	150.00	
		Guide line pair	340.00		
347	5c	blue	210.00		55.00
		Guide line pair	400.00		

On Lincoln Issue of 1909
| *368 | 2c | carmine | 110.00 | 110.00 | 27.50 |
| | | Guide line or pasteup pair | 210.00 | | |

On Alaska-Yukon Issue of 1909
*371	2c	carmine	340.00
		Guide line pair	600.00
		Pasteup pair	600.00

On Hudson-Fulton Issue of 1909
*373	2c	carmine	340.00
		On cover	
		Guide line pair	550.00

On Issue of 1910
383	1c	green	15.00	10.50	2.25
		On cover			225.00
		Guide line pair	24.00		
384	2c	carmine	26.50	24.00	1.25
					90.00
		On cover			
		Guide line pair	42.50		

On Issue of 1912
408	1c	green	7.50	1.25
				65.00
		On cover		
		Guide line or pasteup pair	11.50	
409	2c	carmine	8.50	.75
				35.00
		On cover		
		Guide line pair	15.00	
		Pasteup pair	14.00	

On Issue of 1916-17
481	1c	green	—
482	2c	carmine	115.00	65.00
				300.00
		On cover		
		Guide line pair	210.00	
		Pasteup pair	240.00	
483	3c	violet, type I	160.00	65.00
				425.00
		On cover		
		Guide line pair	320.00	
		Pasteup pair	240.00	

THE SCHERMACK COMPANY

Detroit, Mich.

These perforations were developed by the Schermack Mailing Machine Co. before it became the Mailometer Co. The Type III perforation was used in the company's affixing machines from 1908 through 1927 or 1928.

Perforations Type I. Eight Holes

Perforated in sheets, then cut into strips and coiled.

| | | | Unused Pair Spacing | | Used |
			2mm	3mm	Single
On Issue of 1906-08					
314	1c	blue green	160.00		100.00
		Guide line pair	320.00		
		*Seven holes	1,050.		
		*Pasteup pair	1,400.		
		*Six holes	950.00		
		Guide line pair	2,400.		
320	2c	carmine	135.00		55.00
					2,250.
		On cover			
		Guide line pair	250.00		
		Seven holes	1,150.		300.00
					8,750.
		On cover			
		Guide line pair	1,600.		
		Pasteup pair	1,150.		
		*Six holes	1,050.		
		Guide line pair	2,350.		
*320a	2c	lake	375.00		110.00
		*Seven holes	650.00		
		Guide line pair	1,600.		
		*Six holes	1,300.		
*320b	2c	scarlet, six holes	1,600.		
*315	5c	blue			
On Issue of 1908-09					
*343	1c	green	260.00	—	80.00
		Guide line pair	1,050.		
*344	2c	carmine	1,050.		
		Guide line pair	1,500.		
*345	3c	deep violet	1,500.		
		Guide line pair	1,850.		
*346	4c	orange brown	650.00	—	
		Guide line pair	650.00		
*347	5c	blue	650.00		
		Guide line pair	650.00		
On Lincoln Issue of 1909					
*368	2c	carmine	210.00	240.00	80.00
		Guide line pair	375.00		
		*Seven holes	1,200.		—
		*Six holes	1,050.		—

| | | | Unused Pair Spacing | | Used |
			2mm	3mm	Single
		Guide line pair			1,600.

Perforations Type II

Cut into strips and joined before being perforated.

			Unused		Used
On Issue of 1906-08					
314	1c	blue green	320.00		80.00
		On cover			2,000.
		Guide line pair	525.00		
320	2c	carmine	160.00		55.00
		Guide line pair	290.00		
*320a	2c	lake	275.00		100.00
		Guide line pair	475.00		
*315	5c	blue	11,500.		1,750.
On Issue of 1908-09					
*343	1c	green	650.00	675.00	
		Guide line pair	1,100.		
*344	2c	carmine	650.00	625.00	
		Guide line pair	1,150.		
*345	3c	deep violet	650.00		
		Guide line pair	1,150.		
*346	4c	orange brown	850.00		—
		Guide line pair	1,500.		
*347	5c	blue	800.00		
		Guide line pair	1,600.		
On Lincoln Issue of 1909					
*368	2c	carmine	160.00	140.00	65.00
		Guide line pair	290.00		
On Issue of 1910					
*383	1c	green	—		
		Guide line or pasteup pair			
*384	2c	carmine	—		—

Existance of genuine examples of Nos. 383-384 has been questioned.

Perforations Type III

Blocks exist but were not regularly produced or issued.

| | | | Unused Pair Spacing | | Used |
			2mm	3mm	Single
On Issue of 1906-08					
314	1c	blue green	11.50		2.25
		On cover			140.00
		Guide line pair	24.00		
		Pasteup pair	20.00		
		With both Type I (eight holes) and Type III perfs			—
320	2c	carmine, type I	17.00		5.50
		On cover			90.00
		Guide line pair	32.50		
		With both Type I (eight holes) and Type III perfs			—
320a	2c	lake, type II	24.00		2.75
		On cover			80.00
		Guide line pair	47.50		
		Pasteup pair	42.50		
		With perforated control mark, single			
		With both Type I (seven holes) and Type III perfs			
*320b	2c	scarlet, type I	24.00		5.50
		On cover			
		Guide line pair	42.50		
320c	2c	carmine rose, type I	57.50		
320d	2c	carmine, type II, single	130.00		
		On cover			675.00
		Pair	240.00		
		Guide line pair	475.00		
314A	4c	brown, single	90,000.		50,000.
		Pair	225,000.		
		On cover			140,000.
		Guide line pair	375,000.		
*315	5c	blue	4,750.		

On Issue of 1908-09

			Spacing 2mm	3mm	Used Single
343	1c	green	5.75	6.75	1.25
		On cover			27.50
		Guide line or pasteup pair	10.50		
		With perforated control mark, single			50.00
		Same, on cover			500.00
344	2c	carmine	5.75	6.75	1.25
		On cover			20.00
		Guide line or pasteup pair	10.50		
		With perforated control mark, single			50.00
		Same, on cover			500.00
345	3c	deep violet	24.00	*160.00*	12.50
		On cover			—
		Guide line pair	52.50		
		Pasteup pair	52.50		
		With perforated control mark, single			900.00
		Same, on cover			*8,000.*
346	4c	orange brown	35.00	22.50	17.50
		On cover			*3,250.*
		Guide line or pasteup pair	57.50		
		With perforated control mark, single			*1,500.*
		On cover			*10,000.*
347	5c	blue	57.50		17.50
		On cover			*2,500.*
		Guide line pair	105.00		

On Lincoln Issue of 1909

			2mm	3mm	Used Single
368	2c	carmine	67.50	52.50	12.50
		On cover			*190.00*
		Guide line or pasteup pair	135.00		

On Alaska-Yukon Issue of 1909

			2mm	3mm	Used Single
*371	2c	carmine		90.00	
		On cover			*4,500.*
		Guide line or pasteup pair		170.00	

On Hudson-Fulton Issue of 1909

			2mm	3mm	Used Single
*373	2c	carmine		110.00	
		Guide line or pasteup pair		210.00	

On Issue of 1910

			2mm	3mm	Used Single
383	1c	green	4.75	3.40	1.25
		On cover			22.50
		Guide line or pasteup pair	9.25		
		With perforated control mark, single			40.00
		Same, on cover			400.00

Earliest documented use: Feb. 8, 1911.

			2mm	3mm	Used Single
384	2c	carmine	10.50	8.25	1.25
		On cover			22.50
		Guide line pair	17.00		
		With perforated control mark, single			40.00
		Same, on cover			400.00

On Issue of 1912

			2mm	3mm	Used Single
408	1c	green	2.40		.60
		On cover			22.50
		Guide line or pasteup pair	4.75		
		With perforated control mark, single			47.50
		Same, on cover			350.00
409	2c	carmine	2.40		.50
		On cover			22.50
		Guide line or pasteup pair	4.75		
		Aniline ink ("pink back")			—
		With perforated control mark, single			47.50
		Same, on cover			350.00
		Single stamp in pasteup with strip of three No. TD14a test stamps		*6,000.*	

Earliest documented use: Mar. 21, 1912.

On Issue of 1916-17

			2mm	3mm	Used Single
481	1c	green	3.50		.40
		On cover			22.50
		Guide line or pasteup pair	6.75		
482	2c	carmine, type I	4.25		.60
		On cover			20.00
		Guide line or pasteup pair	9.00		
		Aniline ink ("pink back")			—

Earliest documented use: Dec. 16, 1916.

			2mm	3mm	Used Single
482A	2c	deep rose, type Ia, single			*65,000.*
		Pair			*140,000.*
		On cover			*70,000.*
483	3c	violet, type I	11.50		2.75
		On cover			100.00
		Guide line or pasteup pair	20.00		

Earliest documented use: Nov 2, 1917.

			2mm	3mm	Used Single
484	3c	violet, type II	17.00		4.50
		On cover			100.00
		Guide line or pasteup pair		32.50	

Earliest documented use: April 5, 1918.

On Issue of 1918-20

			2mm	3mm	Used Single
531	1c	green		16.00	4.50
		On cover			110.00
		Guide line or pasteup pair		32.50	
532	2c	carmine, type IV		42.50	3.50
		On cover			80.00
		Guide line or pasteup pair		85.00	
		Pasteup strip of 4, left pair No. 532, right pair No. 482		*2,000.*	

Earliest documented use: April 28, 1920.

			2mm	3mm	Used Single
533	2c	carmine, type V		375.00	45.00
		On cover			275.00
		Guide line or pasteup pair		*1,050.*	
534	2c	carmine, type Va		27.50	2.25
		On cover			100.00
		Guide line or pasteup pair		57.50	
534A	2c	carmine, type VI		47.50	4.50
		On cover			80.00
		Guide line or pasteup pair		95.00	

Earliest documented use: Aug. 31, 1920.

			2mm	3mm	Used Single
534B	2c	carmine, type VII		*1,275.*	85.00
		On cover			450.00
		Guide line or pasteup pair		*2,100.*	
535	3c	violet, type IV		21.00	3.50
		On cover			80.00
		Guide line or pasteup pair		42.50	

On Issue of 1923-26

			2mm	3mm	Used Single
575	1c	green		*210.00*	6.75
		Unused single		25.00	
		On cover			*425.00*
		Guide line or pasteup pair		*400.00*	
		Precanceled		4.75	1.25
		On cover, precanceled			*115.00*
576	1½c	yellow brown		24.00	4.50
		On cover			*225.00*
		Guide line or pasteup pair		42.50	
		Precanceled		4.75	1.00
		On cover, precanceled			*85.00*
577	2c	carmine	29.00	24.00	1.25
		On cover			22.50
		Guide line or pasteup pair	52.50	42.50	

On Harding Issue of 1923

			2mm	3mm	Used Single
611	2c	black		100.00	17.50
		On cover			*8,250.*
		Guide line or pasteup pair		170.00	

U.S. AUTOMATIC VENDING COMPANY

New York, N.Y.

Separations Type I

Cut into strips and joined before being perforated.
Two varieties exist: 15½ and 16mm between notches of the perforations.

On Issue of 1906-08
Coiled Endwise

			Unused Pair	Used Single
314	1c	blue green	52.50	12.50
		On cover		*2,100.*
		Guide line or pasteup pair	100.00	
320	2c	carmine	47.50	9.00
		On cover		*4,000.*
		Guide line pair	95.00	
		Pasteup pair	85.00	
*320a	2c	lake	105.00	9.00
		Guide line or pasteup pair	210.00	
320b	2c	scarlet	57.50	8.00
		On cover		*4,000.*
		Guide line pair	115.00	
315	5c	blue	800.00	*2,000.*
		On cover		*11,500.*
		Guide line pair	*2,650.*	
		Pasteup pair	*2,900.*	

On Issue of 1908-09
Coiled Endwise

			Unused Pair	Used Single
343	1c	green	11.50	1.75
		On cover		110.00
		On postcard		50.00
		Guide line or pasteup pair	23.50	
344	2c	carmine	9.50	1.75
		On cover		110.00
		Guide line or pasteup pair	19.00	
*345	3c	deep violet	35.00	9.00
		On cover		*575.00*
		Guide line or pasteup pair	67.50	
*346	4c	orange brown	52.50	10.00
		Guide line or pasteup pair	110.00	
347	5c	blue	95.00	45.00
		On cover		*2,500.*
		On cover (pair) with No. 373 USAV type II pair		*7,500.*
		Guide line or pasteup pair	185.00	

On Lincoln Issue of 1909

			Unused Pair	Used Single
368	2c	carmine, coiled endwise	42.50	8.00
		On cover		*2,000.*
		First day cover, *Feb. 12, 1909*		*14,500.*
		Guide line or pasteup pair	85.00	

On Alaska-Yukon Issue of 1909

			Unused Pair	Used Single
*371	2c	carmine, coiled sideways	85.00	12.50
		On cover		*575.00*
		Guide line pair	160.00	
		Type Ia, No T. and B. margins	150.00	17.50
		Type Ia, Guide line or pasteup pair	240.00	

Type Ia stamps are a deep shade and have a misplaced position dot in the "S" of "Postage." Beware of trimmed copies of No. 371 type I.

On Issue of 1910

			Unused Pair	Used Single
383	1c	green	6.75	2.75
		On cover		110.00
		On postcard		40.00
		Guide line or pasteup pair	11.50	
*384	2c	carmine	24.00	5.00
		Guide line or pasteup pair	42.50	

On Issue of 1912

			Unused Pair	Used Single
*408	1c	green	11.50	2.25
		Guide line pair	20.00	
*409	2c	carmine	15.00	4.50
		Guide line or pasteup pair	24.00	

Separations Type II

Similar to Type I but with notches farther apart and a longer slit. Cut into strips and joined before being perforated.

On Issue of 1906-08
Coiled Sideways

			Spacing 2mm	3mm	Used Single
*314	1c	blue green	52.50		9.00
		On cover			
		Guide line or pasteup pair	87.50		
*320	2c	carmine	92.50		
		Guide line pair	130.00		
*320b	2c	scarlet	62.50		5.50
		Guide line pair	105.00		

			Unused Pair Spacing		Used Single
			2mm	3mm	
*315	5c	blue	1,500.		
		Guide line pair	2,650.		

On Issue of 1908-09

343	1c	green	15.00		3.50
		On cover			1,150.
		Guide line or pasteup pair	24.00		
344	2c	carmine	17.00		
		On cover			2,800.
		Guide line pair	27.50		
*345	3c	deep violet	67.50		—
		Guide line pair	115.00		
*346	4c	orange brown	100.00	87.50	
		Guide line pair	170.00		
*347	5c	blue	200.00		
		Guide line pair	320.00		

On Lincoln Issue of 1909

368	2c	carmine	105.00	92.50	22.50
		Guide line pair	185.00		

On Alaska-Yukon Issue of 1909

*371	2c	carmine	80.00		40.00
		On cover			575.00
		Guide line or pasteup pair	140.00		

On Hudson-Fulton Issue of 1909

*373	2c	carmine	85.00		17.50
		On cover			2,250.
		Guide line or pasteup pair	160.00		

See No. 347 USAV type I for combination cover.

On Issue of 1910

383	1c	green	17.00	13.00	
		On cover			1,150.
		Guide line pair	29.00		
384	2c	carmine	24.00	17.00	
		On cover			2,750.
		Guide line pair	42.50		

On Issue of 1912

408	1c	green	11.50		2.25
		On cover			1,700.
		Guide line pair	20.00		
409	2c	carmine	17.00		4.50
		Guide line pair	27.50		

Perforations
Type III

Cut into strips and joined before being perforated.

On Issue of 1906-08

*314	1c	blue green	57.50		12.50
		Guide line pair	105.00		
*320	2c	carmine	105.00		
*320b	2c	scarlet	67.50		12.50
		Guide line pair	115.00		
*315	5c	blue	1,275.		
		Guide line or pasteup pair	2,650.		

On Issue of 1908-09

343	1c	green	29.00	26.50	5.50
		Guide line or pasteup pair	47.50		
344	2c	carmine	29.00	37.50	5.50
		Guide line pair	47.50		
*345	3c	deep violet	115.00		
		Guide line pair	200.00		
*346	4c	orange brown	115.00	105.00	14.00
		Guide line pair	200.00		
*347	5c	blue	150.00		
		Guide line pair	270.00		

On Lincoln Issue of 1909

*368	2c	carmine	75.00	62.50	19.00
		Guide line pair	130.00		
		Experimental perf. 12.3	3,400.		
		Guide line pair	5,750.		

On Alaska-Yukon Issue of 1909

*371	2c	carmine	95.00		19.00
		On cover			—
		Guide line or pasteup pair	150.00		

On Hudson-Fulton Issue of 1909

*373	2c	carmine	105.00		19.00
		On cover			—
		Guide line or pasteup pair	150.00		

On Issue of 1910

383	1c	green	16.00	14.00	2.75
		Guide line pair	26.50		
384	2c	carmine	19.00	16.00	2.75
		Guide line pair	29.00		

On Issue of 1912

408	1c	green	10.50		
		Guide line pair	17.00		
409	2c	carmine	19.00		

		Guide line pair	26.50	
		Pasteup pair	26.50	

On 1914 Rotary Press Coil

459	2c	carmine	27,500.	11,500.

This firm also produced coil strips of manila paper, folded so as to form small "pockets", each "pocket" containing one 1c stamp and two 2c stamps, usually imperforate but occasionally with either government or U.S.A.V. private perforations. The manila "pockets" were perforated type II, coiled sidewise. They fit U.S.A.V. ticket vending machines. Multiples exist.

Values are for "pockets" with known combinations of stamps, listed by basic Scott Number. Other combinations exist, but are not listed due to the fact that the stamps may have been added at a later date.

Pocket Type 1 (1908)
("Patents Pending" on front and green advertising on reverse)

Type 1-1	314 + 320	2,900.
Type 1-2	314 + 320b	2,900.

Pocket Type 2 (1909)
("Patents Applied For" Handstamped in greenish blue)

Type 2-1	343 + 371	1,600.
Type 2-2	343 + 372	950.
Type 2-3	343 (USAV Type I) + 371	2,100.
Type 2-4	343 + 375	950.

Pocket Type 3 (1909)
("Patents Pending" printed in red)

Type 3-1	347 + 371	1,050.
Type 3-1A	343 + 372	1,050.
Type 3-2	343 + 373	850.
Type 3-3	343 + 375	850.
Type 3-4	383 + 406	850.

Pocket Type 4 (1909)
(No printing on front, serial number on back)

Type 4-1	343 + 344	320.
Type 4-2	343 + 368	320.
Type 4-3	343 + 371	320.
Type 4-4	383 + 344	320.
Type 4-5	383 (USAV Type II) + 344	320.
Type 4-6	383 + 384	320.
Type 4-7	383 + 406	320.

THE ATTLEBORO STAMP COMPANY

Attleboro, Mass.

This Company used an affixing machine to stamp its newsletters during the summer and fall of 1909.

Nos. 343-344

No. 371

			Unused Pair	Used Single
On Issue of 1908-09			1,500.	1,000.
343	1c	green		
		On Attleboro Philatelist wrapper		5,500.
		On cover		20,000.
		Guide line or pasteup pair	2,650.	
344	2c	carmine	45,000.	

The No. 344 pair is unique.

On Alaska-Yukon Issue of 1909

371	2c	carmine, coiled sidewise	3,650.	1,100.
		Guide line or pasteup pair	5,750.	—
		On wrapper or cover	9,000.	

IMPERFORATE FLAT PLATE COIL STAMPS

These flat plate imperforate coil stamps were made from imperforate sheets of the regular issues, and were issued in coils of 500 or 1,000. The numbers assigned below are those of the regularly issued imperforate sheet stamps to which "H" or "V" has been added to indicate that the stamps are coiled horizontally (side by side), or vertically (top to bottom). These coil stamps are virtually indistinguishable from the corresponding imperforate sheet stamps, although they can be authenticated, particularly when in strips of four or longer. Many genuine imperforate coil stamps bear authenticating signatures of contemporaneous experts.

Values for stamps on cover are for single stamps.

FLAT PLATE PRINTING

1908 — Wmk. 191 — Imperf.

```
314V A115 1c blue green, pair, never
    hinged                        —       —
    Strip of 4                    —
    Guide line pair               —
    Guide line strip of 4         —
```

The Philatelic Foundation has certified one unused No. 314V pair (with coil leader strip attached). The existence of any of the other listed items has been questioned by specialists. The editors would like to see certified evidence of the other listings.

```
314H A115 1c blue green, pair   2,100.     —
    Never hinged                3,750.
    On cover                              1,300.
    Pair on cover                         2,000.
    Strip of 4                    —
    Never hinged                8,000.
    Guide line pair             5,000.
    Guide line strip of 4       8,000.
    Pasteup pair                3,500.
    Never hinged                5,500.
    Pasteup strip of 4          5,000.
    Never hinged                8,000.
```

Earliest documented use: Mar. 9, 1908.

```
320V A129 2c carmine, pair      1,500.     —
    On cover                              3,000.
    Strip of 4                    —        —
    Guide line pair               —
    Guide line strip of 4         —
```

Earliest documented use: Apr. 9, 1908.

```
320H A129 2c carmine, pair       500.00    —
    Strip of 4                    —        —
    Guide line pair               —
    Guide line strip of 4         —
```

Earliest documented use: Sept. 17, 1908.

1908-10 — Imperf.

```
343V A138 1c green, pair         25.00    8.50
    Never hinged                 40.00
    On cover                              10.00
    Strip of 4                   60.00     —
    Guide line pair              60.00
    Guide line strip of 4        85.00
    Pasteup pair                 50.00
```

Earliest documented use: May 24, 1910.

```
343H A138 1c green, pair         50.00     —
    Never hinged                 80.00
    Strip of 4                  120.00     —
    Guide line pair             100.00
    Guide line strip of 4       250.00
    Pasteup pair                 80.00
344V A139 2c carmine, pair       30.00    25.00
    Never hinged                 50.00
    On cover                              15.00
    Strip of 4                   75.00     —
    Guide line pair              60.00
    Guide line strip of 4       105.00
    Pasteup pair                 60.00
    Foreign entry, design of 1c 2,500.   3,000.
    Never hinged                3,500.
```

Earliest documented use: Oct. 13, 1909.

```
344H A139 2c carmine, pair (2mm spacing) 35.00  25.00
    Never hinged                 55.00
    On cover                               —
    Strip of 4                   90.00
    Guide line pair              80.00
    Guide line strip of 4       140.00
    Pasteup pair                 60.00
    Pair (3mm spacing)           40.00     —
    Strip of 4                  100.00
    Guide line pair              85.00     —
    Guide line strip of 4       150.00
```

Earliest documented use: March 23, 1909.

```
345H A140 3c deep violet, type I, pair     —
346V A140 4c orange brown, pair  160.00
    Never hinged                250.00
    Strip of 4                  375.00     —
    Never hinged                650.00
    Guide line pair             325.00    75.00
    Guide line strip of 4       700.00
    Pasteup pair                250.00
```

Earliest documented use: Feb. 18, 1911.

```
347V A140 5c blue, pair         175.00     —
    Never hinged                275.00
    On cover                               —
    Strip of 4                  425.00     —
    Never hinged                700.00
    Guide line pair             375.00     —
    Guide line strip of 4       600.00
```

Earliest documented use: April 17, 1909.

1909 — Imperf.

```
368V A141 2c carmine, Lincoln, pair  200.00   —
    Never hinged                300.00
    On cover                               —
    Strip of 4                  500.00     —
    Never hinged                750.00
    Guide line pair             400.00
    Never hinged                650.00
    Guide line strip of 4       800.00     —
    Never hinged               1,250.
    Pasteup pair                300.00
    Never hinged                475.00
```

Earliest documented use: Feb. 12, 1909.

```
368H A141 2c carmine, Lincoln, pair  275.00   —
    Never hinged                450.00
    On cover                               —
    Strip of 4                  700.00     —
    Never hinged               1,050.
    Guide line pair             525.00
    Never hinged                900.00
    Guide line strip of 4       900.00     —
    Pasteup pair                425.00
    Never hinged                650.00
```

Earliest documented use: Dec. 9, 1909.

1910 — Wmk. 190 — Imperf.

```
383V A138 1c green, pair         12.00     —
    Never hinged                 20.00
    On cover                               6.00
    Strip of 4                   27.50     —
    Guide line pair              25.00
    Never hinged                 40.00
    Guide line strip of 4        60.00
    Never hinged                 95.00
    Pasteup pair                 20.00
    Never hinged                 35.00
    Double transfer                        —
```

Earliest documented use: Apr. 13, 1911.

```
383H A138 1c green, pair (2mm spacing) 17.50  —
    Never hinged                 28.00
    Strip of 4                   42.50     —
    Never hinged                 65.00
    Guide line pair              35.00     —
    Never hinged                 55.00
    Guide line strip of 4        65.00     —
    Never hinged                110.00
    Pasteup pair                 30.00
    Pair (3mm spacing)           17.50
    Never hinged                 28.00
    Strip of 4                   42.50
    Never hinged                 65.00
    Guide line pair              35.00
    Never hinged                 55.00
    Guide line strip of 4        65.00
    Never hinged                110.00
384V A139 2c carmine, pair       14.00
    Never hinged                 24.00
    On cover                               7.00
    Strip of 4                   30.00
    Guide line pair              30.00
    Guide line strip of 4        55.00
    Pasteup pair                 22.50
    Foreign entry, design of 1c 1,500.
```

Earliest documented use: Oct. 21, 1910.

```
384H A139 2c carmine, pair (2mm spacing) 27.50  —
    Never hinged                 45.00
    Strip of 4                   70.00
    Guide line pair              60.00
    Guide line strip of 4       105.00
    Pasteup pair                 50.00
    Pair (3mm spacing)           25.00     —
    Strip of 4                   70.00
    Guide line pair              55.00
    Guide line strip of 4       100.00
```

Earliest documented use: Mar. 9, 1912.

1912 — Wmk. 190 — Imperf.

```
408V A140 1c green, pair          4.00
    Never hinged                  7.00
    On cover                               —
    Strip of 4                    8.50
    Guide line pair               9.00
    Guide line strip of 4        14.00
    Pasteup pair                  7.00
```

Earliest documented use: May 17, 1912.

```
408H A140 1c green, pair          5.00
    Never hinged                  8.00
    Strip of 4                   12.00
    Guide line pair              10.00
    Guide line strip of 4        17.50
409V A140 2c carmine, pair        4.00
    Never hinged                  7.00
    Strip of 4                    9.00
    Never hinged                 15.00
    Guide line pair               8.00
    Never hinged                 15.00
    Guide line strip of 4        14.00
    Pasteup pair                  7.00
```

Earliest documented use: May 29, 1912.

```
409H A140 2c carmine, pair        6.00
    Never hinged                 10.00
    Strip of 4                   14.00
    Guide line pair               9.00
    Never hinged                 16.00
    Guide line strip of 4        15.00
    Pasteup pair                  7.00
    Double transfer               7.00
```

Earliest documented use: Dec. 17, 1914.

COMMEMORATIVE STAMPS, QUANTITIES ISSUED

Quantities issued fall into four categories. First are stamps where reasonably accurate counts are made of the number of stamps sold.

Second are stamps where the counts are approximations of the number sold.

Third are stamps where the count is of quantities shipped to post offices and philatelic sales units, but no adjustments are made for returned or destroyed stamps.

Fourth are stamps for which the quantity printed is furnished but no other adjustments are made.

Occasionally more accurate figures are determined. In these cases the quantities here will be adjusted. For example, it is now known that while 2,000,000 sets of the Voyages of Columbus souvenir sheets were printed, the number sold was 1,185,170 sets.

Scott No.	Quantity	Scott No.	Quantity	Scott No.	Quantity
230	449,195,550	675	980,000	783	74,407,450
231	1,464,588,750	676	850,000	784	269,522,200
232	11,501,250	677	1,480,000	785	105,196,150
233	19,181,550	678	530,000	786	93,848,500
234	35,248,250	679	1,890,000	787	87,741,150
235	4,707,550	680	29,338,274	788	35,794,150
236	10,656,550	681	32,680,900	789	36,839,250
237	16,516,950	682	74,000,774	790	104,773,450
238	1,576,950	683	25,215,574	791	92,054,550
239	617,250	688	25,609,470	792	93,291,650
240	243,750	689	66,487,000	793	34,552,950
241	55,050	690	96,559,400	794	36,819,050
242	45,550	702	99,074,600	795	84,825,250
243	27,650	703	25,006,400	796	25,040,400
244	26,350	704	87,969,700	797	5,277,445
245	27,350	705	1,265,555,100	798	99,882,300
285	70,993,400	706	304,926,800	799	78,454,450
286	159,720,800	707	4,222,198,300	800	77,004,200
287	4,924,500	708	456,198,500	801	81,292,450
288	7,694,180	709	151,201,300	802	76,474,550
289	2,927,200	710	170,565,100	835	73,043,650
290	4,629,760	711	111,739,400	836	58,564,368
291	530,400	712	83,257,400	837	65,939,500
292	56,900	713	96,506,100	838	47,064,300
293	56,200	714	75,709,200	852	114,439,600
294	91,401,500	715	147,216,000	853	101,699,550
295	209,759,700	716	51,102,800	854	72,764,550
296	5,737,100	717	100,869,300	855	81,269,600
297	7,201,300	718	168,885,300	856	67,813,350
298	4,921,700	719	52,376,100	857	71,394,750
299	5,043,700	724	49,949,000	858	66,835,000
323	79,779,200	725	49,538,500	859	56,348,320
324	192,732,400	726	61,719,200	860	53,177,110
325	4,542,600	727	73,382,400	861	53,260,270
326	6,926,700	728	348,266,800	862	22,104,950
327	4,011,200	729	480,239,300	863	13,201,270
328	77,728,794	730 (sheet of 25)	456,704	864	51,603,580
329	149,497,994	730a	11,417,600	865	52,100,510
330	7,980,594	731 (sheet of 25)	441,172	866	51,666,580
367	148,387,191	731a	11,029,300	867	22,207,780
368	1,273,900	732	1,978,707,300	868	11,835,530
369	637,000	733	5,735,944	869	52,471,160
370	152,887,311	734	45,137,700	870	52,366,440
371	525,400	735 (sheet of 6)	811,404	871	51,636,270
372	72,634,631	735a	4,868,424	872	20,729,030
373	216,480	736	46,258,300	873	14,125,580
397 & 401	334,796,926	737	193,239,100	874	59,409,000
398 & 402	503,713,086	738	15,432,200	875	57,888,600
399 & 403	29,088,726	739	64,525,400	876	58,273,180
400 & 404	16,968,365	740	84,896,350	877	23,779,000
537	99,585,200	741	74,400,200	878	15,112,580
548	137,978,207	742	95,089,000	879	57,322,790
549	196,037,327	743	19,178,650	880	58,281,580
550	11,321,607	744	30,980,100	881	56,398,790
610	1,459,487,085	745	16,923,350	882	21,147,000
611	770,000	746	15,988,250	883	13,328,000
612	99,950,300	747	15,288,700	884	54,389,510
614	51,378,023	748	17,472,600	885	53,636,580
615	77,753,423	749	18,874,300	886	55,313,230
616	5,659,023	750 (sheet of 6)	511,391	887	21,720,580
617	15,615,000	750a	3,068,346	888	13,600,580
618	26,596,600	751 (sheet of 6)	793,551	889	47,599,580
619	5,348,800	751a	4,761,306	890	53,766,510
620	9,104,983	752	3,274,556	891	54,193,580
621	1,900,983	753	2,040,760	892	20,264,580
627	307,731,900	754	2,389,288	893	13,726,580
628	20,280,500	755	2,294,948	894	46,497,400
629	40,639,485	756	3,217,636	895	47,700,000
630 (sheet of 25)	107,398	757	2,746,640	896	50,618,150
643	39,974,900	758	2,168,088	897	50,034,400
644	25,628,450	759	1,822,684	898	60,943,700
645	101,330,328	760	1,724,576	902	44,389,550
646	9,779,896	761	1,647,696	903	54,574,550
647	5,519,897	762	1,682,948	904	63,558,400
648	1,459,897	763	1,638,644	906	21,272,800
649	51,342,273	764	1,625,224	907	1,671,564,200
650	10,319,700	765	1,644,900	908	1,227,334,200
651	16,684,674	766 (pane of 25)	98,712	909	19,999,646
654	31,679,200	766a	2,467,800	910	19,999,646
655	210,119,474	767 (pane of 25)	85,914	911	19,999,646
656	133,530,000	767a	2,147,850	912	19,999,646
657	51,451,880	768 (pane of 6)	267,200	913	19,999,646
658	13,390,000	768a	1,603,200	914	19,999,646
659	8,240,000	769 (pane of 6)	279,960	915	14,999,646
660	87,410,000	769a	1,679,760	916	14,999,646
661	2,540,000	770 (pane of 6)	215,920	917	14,999,646
662	2,290,000	770a	1,295,520	918	14,999,646
663	2,700,000	771	1,370,560	919	14,999,646
664	1,450,000	772	70,726,800	920	14,999,646
665	1,320,000	773	100,839,600	921	14,999,646
666	1,530,000	774	73,610,650	922	61,303,000
667	1,130,000	775	75,823,900	923	61,001,450
668	2,860,000	776	124,324,500	924	60,605,000
669	8,220,000	777	67,127,650	925	50,129,350
670	8,990,000	778 (sheet of 4)	2,809,039	926	53,479,400
671	73,220,000	778a	2,809,039	927	61,617,350
672	2,110,000	778b	2,809,039	928	75,500,000
673	1,600,000	778c	2,809,039	929	137,321,000
674	1,860,000	778d	2,809,039	930	128,140,000
		782	72,992,650	931	67,255,000

Scott No.	Quantity	Scott No.	Quantity	Scott No.	Quantity
932	133,870,000	1079	109,275,000	1199	126,515,000
933	76,455,400	1080	112,932,200	1200	130,960,000
934	128,357,750	1081	125,475,000	1201	120,055,000
935	138,863,000	1082	117,855,000	1202	120,715,000
936	111,616,700	1083	122,100,000	1203	121,440,000
937	308,587,700	1084	118,180,000	1204	40,270,000
938	170,640,000	1085	100,975,000	1205	861,970,000
939	135,927,000	1086	115,299,450	1206	120,035,000
940	260,339,100	1087	186,949,627	1207	117,870,000
941	132,274,500	1088	115,235,000	1230	129,945,000
942	132,430,000	1089	106,647,500	1231	135,620,000
943	139,209,500	1090	112,010,000	1232	137,540,000
944	114,684,450	1091	118,470,000	1233	132,435,000
945	156,540,510	1092	102,230,000	1234	135,520,000
946	120,452,600	1093	102,410,000	1235	131,420,000
947	127,104,300	1094	84,054,400	1236	133,170,000
948	10,299,600	1095	126,266,000	1237	130,195,000
949	132,902,000	1096	39,489,600	1238	128,450,000
950	131,968,000	1097	122,990,000	1239	118,665,000
951	131,488,000	1098	174,372,800	1240	1,291,250,000
952	122,362,000	1099	114,365,000	1241	175,175,000
953	121,548,000	1100	122,765,200	1242	125,995,000
954	131,109,500	1104	113,660,200	1243	128,025,000
955	122,650,000	1105	120,196,580	1244	145,700,000
956	121,953,500	1106	120,805,200	1245	120,310,000
957	115,250,000	1107	125,815,200	1246	511,750,000
958	64,198,500	1108	108,415,200	1247	123,845,000
959	117,642,500	1109	107,195,200	1248	122,825,000
960	77,649,600	1110	115,745,280	1249	453,090,000
961	113,474,500	1111	39,743,640	1250	123,245,000
962	120,868,500	1112	114,570,200	1251	123,355,000
963	77,800,500	1113	120,400,200	1252	126,970,000
964	52,214,000	1114	91,160,200	1253	121,250,000
965	53,958,100	1115	114,860,200	1254-1257	1,407,760,000
966	61,120,010	1116	126,500,000	1258	120,005,000
967	57,823,000	1117	120,561,280	1259	125,800,000
968	52,975,000	1118	44,064,576	1260	122,230,000
969	77,149,000	1119	118,390,200	1261	115,695,000
970	58,332,000	1120	125,770,200	1262	115,095,000
971	56,228,000	1121	114,114,280	1263	119,560,000
972	57,832,000	1122	156,600,200	1264	125,180,000
973	53,875,000	1123	124,200,200	1265	120,135,000
974	63,834,000	1124	120,740,200	1266	115,405,000
975	67,162,200	1125	133,623,280	1267	115,855,000
976	64,561,000	1126	45,569,088	1268	115,340,000
977	64,079,500	1127	122,493,280	1269	114,840,000
978	63,388,000	1128	131,260,200	1270	116,140,000
979	62,285,000	1129	47,125,200	1271	116,900,000
980	57,492,610	1130	123,105,000	1272	114,085,000
981	99,190,000	1131	126,105,050	1273	114,880,000
982	104,790,000	1132	209,170,000	1274	26,995,000
983	108,805,000	1133	120,835,000	1275	128,495,000
984	107,340,000	1134	115,715,000	1276	1,139,930,000
985	117,020,000	1135	118,445,000	1306	116,835,000
986	122,633,000	1136	111,685,000	1307	117,470,000
987	130,960,000	1137	43,099,200	1308	123,770,000
988	128,478,000	1138	115,444,000	1309	131,270,000
989	132,090,000	1139	126,470,000	1310	122,285,000
990	130,050,000	1140	124,560,000	1311	14,680,000
991	131,350,000	1141	115,455,000	1312	114,160,000
992	129,980,000	1142	122,060,000	1313	128,475,000
993	122,315,000	1143	120,540,000	1314	119,535,000
994	122,170,000	1144	113,075,000	1315	125,110,000
995	131,635,000	1145	139,325,000	1316	114,853,200
996	121,860,000	1146	124,445,000	1317	124,290,000
997	121,120,000	1147	113,792,000	1318	128,460,000
998	119,120,000	1148	44,215,200	1319	127,585,000
999	112,125,000	1149	113,195,000	1320	115,875,000
1000	114,140,000	1150	121,805,000	1321	1,173,547,420
1001	114,490,000	1151	115,353,000	1322	114,015,000
1002	117,200,000	1152	111,080,000	1323	121,105,000
1003	116,130,000	1153	153,025,000	1324	132,045,000
1004	116,175,000	1154	119,665,000	1325	118,780,000
1005	115,945,000	1155	117,855,000	1326	121,985,000
1006	112,540,000	1156	118,185,000	1327	111,850,000
1007	117,415,000	1157	112,260,000	1328	117,225,000
1008	2,899,580,000	1158	125,010,000	1329	111,515,000
1009	114,540,000	1159	119,798,000	1330	114,270,000
1010	113,135,000	1160	42,696,000	1331-1332	120,865,000
1011	116,255,000	1161	106,610,000	1333	110,675,000
1012	113,860,000	1162	109,695,000	1334	110,670,000
1013	124,260,000	1163	123,690,000	1335	113,825,000
1014	115,735,000	1164	123,970,000	1336	1,208,700,000
1015	115,430,000	1165	124,796,000	1337	113,330,000
1016	136,220,000	1166	42,076,800	1339	141,350,000
1017	114,894,600	1167	116,210,000	1340	144,345,000
1018	118,706,000	1168	126,252,000	1342	147,120,000
1019	114,190,000	1169	42,746,400	1343	130,125,000
1020	113,990,000	1170	124,117,000	1344	158,700,000
1021	89,289,600	1171	119,840,000	1345-1354	228,040,000
1022	114,865,000	1172	117,187,000	1355	153,015,000
1023	115,780,000	1173	124,390,000	1356	132,560,000
1024	115,244,600	1174	112,966,000	1357	130,385,000
1025	123,709,600	1175	41,644,200	1358	132,265,000
1026	114,789,600	1176	110,850,000	1359	128,710,000
1027	115,759,600	1177	98,616,000	1360	124,775,000
1028	116,134,600	1178	101,125,000	1361	128,295,000
1029	118,540,000	1179	124,865,000	1362	142,245,000
1060	115,810,000	1180	79,905,000	1363	1,410,580,000
1061	113,603,700	1181	125,410,000	1364	125,100,000
1062	128,002,000	1182	112,845,000	1365-1368	192,570,000
1063	116,078,150	1183	106,210,000	1369	148,770,000
1064	116,139,800	1184	110,810,000	1370	139,475,000
1065	120,484,800	1185	116,995,000	1371	187,165,000
1066	53,854,750	1186	121,015,000	1372	125,555,000
1067	176,075,000	1187	111,600,000	1373	144,425,000
1068	125,944,400	1188	110,620,000	1374	135,875,000
1069	122,284,600	1189	109,110,000	1375	151,110,000
1070	133,638,850	1190	145,350,000	1376-1379	159,195,000
1071	118,664,600	1191	112,870,000	1380	129,540,000
1072	112,434,000	1192	121,820,000	1381	130,925,000
1073	129,384,550	1193	289,240,000	1382	139,055,000
1074	121,184,600	1194	120,155,000	1383	150,611,200
1075	2,900,731	1195	124,595,000	1384	1,709,795,000
1076	119,784,200	1196	147,310,000	1385	127,545,000
1077	123,159,400	1197	118,690,000	1386	145,788,800
1078	123,138,800	1198	122,730,000	1387-1390	201,794,200

Scott No.	Quantity	Scott No.	Quantity	Scott No.	Quantity
1391	171,850,000	1690	164,890,000	2031	118,555,000
1392	142,205,000	1691-1694	208,035,000	2032-2035	226,128,000
1405	137,660,000	1695-1698	185,715,000	2036	118,225,000
1406	135,125,000	1699	130,592,000	2037	114,290,000
1407	135,895,000	1700	158,332,800	2038	165,000,000
1408	132,675,000	1701	809,955,000	2039	120,430,000
1409	134,795,000	1702-1703	963,370,000	2040	117,025,000
1410-1413	161,600,000	1704	150,328,000	2041	181,700,000
1414-1414a	683,730,000	1705	176,830,000	2042	114,250,000
1415-1418,		1706-1709	195,976,000	2043	111,775,000
1415a-1418a	489,255,000	1710	208,820,000	2044	115,200,000
1419	127,610,000	1711	192,250,000	2045	108,820,000
1420	129,785,000	1712-1715	219,830,000	2046	184,950,000
1421-1422	134,380,000	1716	159,852,000	2047	110,925,000
1423	136,305,000	1717-1720	188,310,000	2048-2051	395,424,000
1424	134,840,000	1721	163,625,000	2052	104,340,000
1425	130,975,000	1722	156,296,000	2053	114,725,000
1426	161,235,000	1723-1724	158,676,000	2054	112,525,000
1427-1430	175,679,600	1725	154,495,000	2055-2058	193,055,000
1431	138,700,000	1726	168,050,000	2059-2062	207,725,000
1432	138,165,000	1727	156,810,000	2063	715,975,000
1433	152,125,000	1728	153,736,000	2064	848,525,000
1434-1435	176,295,000	1729	882,260,000	2065	165,000,000
1436	142,845,000	1730	921,530,000	2066	120,000,000
1437	148,755,000	1731	156,560,000	2067-2070	319,675,000
1438	139,080,000	1732-1733	202,155,000	2071	103,975,000
1439	130,755,000	1744	156,525,000	2072	554,675,000
1440-1443	170,208,000	1745-1748	165,182,400	2073	120,000,000
1444	1,074,350,000	1749-1752	157,598,400	2074	106,975,000
1445	979,540,000	1753	102,856,000	2075	107,325,000
1446	137,355,000	1754	152,270,000	2076-2079	306,912,000
1447	150,400,000	1755	94,600,000	2080	120,000,000
1448-1451	172,730,000	1756	151,570,000	2081	108,000,000
1452	104,090,000	1757	15,170,400	2082-2085	313,350,000
1453	164,096,000	1758	161,228,000	2086	130,320,000
1454	53,920,000	1759	158,880,000	2087	120,000,000
1455	153,025,000	1760-1763	186,550,000	2088	117,050,000
1456-1459	201,890,000	1764-1767	168,136,000	2089	115,725,000
1460	67,335,000	1768	963,120,000	2090	116,600,000
1461	179,675,000	1769	916,800,000	2091	120,000,000
1462	46,340,000	1770	159,297,600	2092	123,575,000
1463	180,155,000	1771	166,435,000	2093	120,000,000
1464-1467	198,364,800	1772	162,535,000	2094	117,125,000
1468	185,490,000	1773	155,000,000	2095	117,225,000
1469	162,335,000	1774	157,310,000	2096	95,525,000
1470	162,789,950	1775-1778	174,096,000	2097	119,125,000
1471	1,003,475,000	1779-1782	164,793,600	2098-2101	216,260,000
1472	1,017,025,000	1783-1786	163,055,000	2102	120,000,000
1473	165,895,000	1787	161,860,000	2103	108,140,000
1474	166,508,000	1788	165,775,000	2104	117,625,000
1475	320,055,000	1789	160,000,000	2105	112,896,000
1476	166,005,000	1790	67,195,000	2106	116,500,000
1477	163,050,000	1791-1794	186,905,000	2107	751,300,000
1478	159,005,000	1795-1798	208,295,000	2108	786,225,000
1479	147,295,000	1799	873,710,000	2109	105,300,000
1480-1483	196,275,000	1800	931,880,000	2110	124,500,000
1484	139,152,000	1801	161,290,000	2137	120,000,000
1485	128,048,000	1802	172,740,000	2138-2141	300,000,000
1486	146,008,000	1803	168,995,000	2142	120,580,000
1487	139,608,000	1804	160,000,000	2143	729,700,000
1488	159,475,000	1805-1810	232,134,000	2144	124,750,000
1489-1498	486,020,000	1821	163,510,000	2145	203,496,000
1499	157,052,800	1822	256,620,000	2146	126,325,000
1500	53,005,000	1823	95,695,000	2147	130,000,000
1501	159,775,000	1824	153,975,000	2152	119,975,000
1502	39,005,000	1825	160,000,000	2153	120,000,000
1503	152,624,000	1826	103,850,000	2154	119,975,000
1504	145,840,000	1827-1830	204,715,000	2155-2158	147,940,000
1505	151,335,000	1831	166,545,000	2159	120,000,000
1506	141,085,000	1832	163,310,000	2160-2163	130,000,000
1507	885,160,000	1833	160,000,000	2164	120,000,000
1508	939,835,000	1834-1837	152,404,000	2165	759,200,000
1525	143,930,000	1838-1841	152,420,000	2166	757,600,000
1526	145,235,000	1842	692,500,000	2198-2201	67,996,800
1527	135,052,000	1843	718,715,000	2202	947,450,000
1528	156,750,000	1874	160,155,000	2203	130,000,000
1529	164,670,000	1875	159,505,000	2204	136,500,000
1530-1537	190,156,800	1876-1879	210,633,000	2205-2209	219,990,000
1538-1541	167,212,800	1910	165,175,000	2210	130,000,000
1542	156,265,000	1911	107,240,000	2211	130,000,000
1543-1546	195,585,000	1912-1919	337,819,000	2216	5,825,050
1547	148,850,000	1920	99,420,000	2217	5,825,050
1548	157,270,000	1921-1924	178,930,000	2218	5,825,050
1549	150,245,000	1925	100,265,000	2219	5,825,050
1550	835,180,000	1926	99,615,000	2220-2223	130,000,000
1551	882,520,000	1927	97,535,000	2224	220,725,000
1552	213,155,000	1928-1931	167,308,000	2235-2238	240,525,000
1553	156,995,000	1932	101,625,000	2239	131,700,000
1554	146,365,000	1922	99,170,000	2240-2243	240,000,000
1555	148,805,000	1934	101,155,000	2244	690,100,000
1556	173,685,000	1935	101,200,000	2245	882,150,000
1557	158,600,000	1936	167,360,000	2246	167,430,000
1558	153,355,000	1937-1938	162,420,000	2247	166,555,000
1559	63,205,000	1939	597,720,000	2248	811,560,000
1560	157,865,000	1940	792,600,000	2249	142,905,000
1561	166,810,000	1941	167,130,000	2250	130,000,000
1562	44,825,000	1942-1945	191,560,000	2251	149,980,000
1563	144,028,000	1950	163,939,200	2267-2274	610,425,000
1564	139,928,000	1952	180,700,000	2275	156,995,000
1565-1568	179,855,000	1953-2002	666,950,000	2286-2335	645,975,000
1569-1570	161,863,200	2003	109,245,000	2336	166,725,000
1571	145,640,000	2004	112,535,000	2337	186,575,000
1572-1575	168,655,000	2006-2009	124,640,000	2338	184,325,000
1576	146,615,000	2010	107,605,000	2339	165,845,000
1577-1578	146,196,000	2011	173,160,000	2340	155,170,000
1579	739,430,000	2012	107,285,000	2341	102,100,000
1580	878,690,000	2013	109,040,000	2342	103,325,000
1629-1631	219,455,000	2014	183,270,000	2343	162,045,000
1632	157,825,000	2015	169,495,000	2344	153,295,000
1633-1682	436,005,000	2016	164,235,000	2345	160,245,000
1683	159,915,000	2017	110,130,000	2346	183,290,000
1684	156,960,000	2018	110,995,000	2347	179,800,000
1685	158,470,000	2019-2022	165,340,000	2348	164,130,000
1686	1,990,000	2023	174,180,000	2349	157,475,000
1687	1,983,000	2024	110,261,000	2350	156,225,000
1688	1,953,000	2026	703,295,000	2351-2354	163,980,000
1689	1,903,000	2027-2030	788,880,000	2355-2359	584,340,000

Scott No.	Quantity	Scott No.	Quantity	Scott No.	Quantity
2360	168,995,000	2749	172,870,000	3090	134,000,000
2361	163,120,000	2753a	65,625,000	3095a	32,000,000
2362-2366	394,776,000	2754	110,000,000	3099a	23,025,000
2367	528,790,000	2755	115,870,000	3103a	23,025,000
2368	978,340,000	2759a	40,000,000	3104	300,000,000
2369	158,870,000	2764a	199,784,500	3105	14,910,000
2370	145,560,000	2765	120,000,000	3106	93,612,000
2371	97,300,000	2766	160,000,000	3107	243,575,000
2372-2375	158,556,000	2770a	128,735,000	3111a	56,479,000
2376	97,300,000	2774a	25,000,000	3112	847,750,000
2377	153,045,000	2778a	170,000,000	3116a	451,312,500
2378	841,240,000	2782a	37,500,000	3117	495,504,000
2379	169,765,000	2784a	41,840,000	3118	103,520,000
2380	157,215,000	2788a	37,550,000	3120	106,000,000
2381-2385	635,238,000	2804	88,300,000	3121	112,000,000
2386-2389	162,142,500	2805	105,000,000	3123	1,660,000,000
2390-2393	305,015,000	2806	100,000,000	3124	814,000,000
2395-2398	480,000,000	2806a	250,000,000	3125	122,000,000
2399	821,285,000	2811a	35,800,000	3131a	65,000,000
2400	1,030,850,000	2812	150,500,000	3134	97,500,000
2401	165,495,000	2813	357,949,584	3135	96,000,000
2402	151,675,000	2814	830,000,000	3136	14,600,000
2403	163,000,000	2814C	300,000,000	3137	37,800,000
2404	264,625,000	2815	274,800,000	3138	118,000
2405-2409	204,984,000	2816	155,500,000	3139	593,775
2410	103,835,000	2817	105,000,000	3140	592,849
2411	152,250,000	2818	185,500,000	3141	45,250,000
2412	138,760,000	2828a	18,600,000	3142	8,050,000
2413	137,985,000	2833a	166,000,000	3146a	22,500,000
2414	138,580,000	2834	201,000,000	3147	20,000,000
2415	150,545,000	2835	300,000,000	3148	20,000,000
2416	164,680,000	2836	269,370,000	3149	10,000,000
2417	262,755,000	2837	60,000,000	3150	10,000,000
2418	191,755,000	2838	120,600,000	3151	7,000,000
2420	188,400,000	2839	209,000,000	3152	195,000,000
2421	191,860,000	2840	20,000,000	3153	323,000,000
2422-2425	406,988,000	2841	12,958,000	3157a	21,500,000
2426	137,410,000	2842	100,500,000	3158-3161	12,900,000
2427	913,335,000	2847a	159,200,000	3162-3165	8,600,000
2428	900,000,000	2848	150,500,000	3166	25,250,000
2429	399,243,000	2853a	35,436,000	3167	45,250,000
2433	2,017,225	2854	24,986,000	3172a	36,250,000
2434-2437	163,824,000	2855	24,986,000	3173	173,000,000
2438	2,047,200	2856	24,986,000	3174	37,000,000
2439	173,000,000	2857	19,988,800	3175	133,000,000
2440	886,220,000	2858	19,988,800	3176	882,500,000
2441	995,178,000	2859	19,988,800	3177	1,621,465,000
2442	153,125,000	2860	19,988,800	3178	15,000,000
2444	169,495,000	2861	19,988,800	3179	51,000,000
2445-2448	176,808,000	2862	150,750,000	3180	80,000,000
2449	150,000,000	2866a	56,475,000	3181	45,000,000
2470-2474	733,608,000	2868a	77,748,000	3182	12,533,000
2496-2500	178,587,500	2869	20,000,000	3183	12,533,000
2501-2505	619,128,000	2870	150,186	3184	12,533,000
2506-2507	151,430,000	2871	518,500,000	3185	12,533,000
2508-2511	278,264,000	2872	602,500,000	3186	12,533,000
2512	143,995,000	2873	236,997,600	3187	12,533,000
2513	142,692,000	2874	45,000,000	3188	8,000,000
2514	728,919,000	2875	5,000,000	3189	6,000,000
2515	599,400,000	2876	80,000,000	3190	6,000,000
2516	320,304,000	2948	214,700,000	3191	8,250,000
2532	103,648,000	2949	1,220,970,000	3192	30,000,000
2533	179,990,000	2950	94,500,000	3193-3197	250,000,000
2534	150,560,000	2954a	50,000,000	3198-3202	80,000,000
2538	161,498,000	2955	80,000,000	3203	85,000,000
2545-2549	744,918,000	2956	97,000,000	3204	39,600,000
2550	149,848,000	2957	315,000,000	3205	650,000
2551	200,003,000	2958	300,000,000	3206	32,000,000
2552	200,000,000	2965a	30,000,000	3209	2,200,000
2553-2557	170,025,600	2966	125,000,000	3210	2,200,000
2558	150,310,000	2967	400,000,000	3211	30,000,000
2560	149,810,000	2968	99,424,000	3212-3215	45,000,000
2561	149,260,000	2973a	120,240,000	3216-3219	45,000,000
2562-2566	699,978,000	2974	60,000,000	3220	46,300,000
2567	148,973,000	2975	300,000,000	3221	30,000,000
2577a	33,394,800	2979a	62,500,000	3222-3225	70,000,000
2615a	32,000,000	2980	105,000,000	3226	65,000,000
2616	148,665,000	2981	100,000,000	3227	50,000,000
2617	149,990,000	2982	150,000,000	3230-3234	180,000,000
2618	835,000,000	2983-2992	15,000,000	3235	28,000,000
2619	160,000,000	2992	15,000,000	3236	4,000,000
2623a	40,005,000	2997a	200,000,000	3237	130,750,000
2624	1,185,170	2998	300,000,000	3238-3242	185,000,000
2625	1,185,170	2999	85,000,000	3243	50,000,000
2626	1,185,170	3000	300,000,000	3244	925,200,000
2627	1,185,170	3001	80,000,000	3245-3248	116,760,000
2628	1,185,170	3002	80,000,000	3249-3252	991,750,000
2629	1,185,170	3003	300,000,000	3272	51,000,000
2630	148,000,000	3007a	75,000,000	3273	100,000,000
2634a	37,315,000	3008	350,495,000	3274	1,000,000,000
2635	146,610,000	3009	350,495,000	3275	
2636	160,000,000	3010	350,495,000	3276	100,000,000
2641a	32,000,000	3011	350,495,000	3286	40,400,000
2646a	87,728,000	3013	90,000,000	3287	42,500,000
2696a	11,000,000	3023a	30,000,000	3288-3292	73,155,000
2697	12,000,000	3024	120,000,000	3293	10,000,000
2698	105,000,000	3029a	160,000,000	3306	42,700,000
2699	142,500,000	3030	2,550,000,000	3307	500,000
2703a	36,831,000	3058	92,100,000	3308	42,500,000
2704	85,000,000	3059	115,600,000	3309	105,000,000
2709a	80,000,000	3060	93,150,000	3310-3313	1,500,000,000
2720	105,000,000	3064a	23,292,500	3314	145,375,000
2721	517,000,000	3065	111,000,000	3315	78,100,000
2722	150,000,000	3066	314,175,000	3316	89,270,000
2723	152,000,000	3067	209,450,000	3317-3320	141,175,000
2730a	14,285,715	3068	16,207,500	3321-3324	151,976,000
2731	98,841,000	3069	156,300,000	3325-3328	116,083,500
2732	32,947,000	3070	100,000,000	3329	75,500,000
2733	32,947,000	3071	60,120,000	3330	100,750,000
2734	32,947,000	3076a	27,850,000	3331	101,800,000
2735	65,894,000	3080a	22,218,000	3332	43,150,000
2736	65,894,000	3081	95,600,000	3333-3337	120,000,000
2737	65,894,000	3082	300,000,000	3338	42,500,000
2745a	140,000,000	3086a	23,681,250	3339-3344	42,500,000
2746	105,000,000	3087	133,613,000	3345-3350	42,500,000
2747	110,000,000	3088	103,400,000	3351	4,235,000
2748	110,000,000	3089	60,000,000	3352	65,000,000

Scott No.	Quantity
3354	44,600,000
3355	1,555,560,000
3356-3359	116,500,000
3360-3363	1,785,060,000
3364-3367	118,125,000
3368	95,000,000
3369	120,000,000

Quantities for Nos. 3370-on, and for Nos. 3190, 3191 and 3236, are for quantities ordered.

Scott No.	Quantity
3370	56,000,000
3371	150,000,000
3372	65,150,000
3373-3377	15,000,000
3378	10,000,000
3379-3383	55,000,000
3384-3388	105,350,000
3389	16,000,000
3390	55,000,000
3391	30,000,000
3392	236,000
3393-3396	55,000,000
3397	90,600,000
3398	200,000,000
3399-3402	88,000,000
3403	4,000,000
3408	11,250,000
3409	1,695,000
3410	1,695,000
3411	1,695,000
3412	1,695,000
3413	1,695,000
3414-3417	100,000,000
3438	53,000,000
3439-3443	85,000,000
3444	53,000,000
3445	125,000,000
3446	52,000,000
3496	500,000,000
3497	1,500,000,000
3498	80,000,000
3499	180,000,000
3500	55,000,000
3501	200,000,000
3502	125,000,000
3503	100,000,000
3504	35,000,000
3505	1,598,000
3506	8,960,000
3507	125,000,000
3508	200,000,000
3509	55,000,000
3510-3519	125,000,000
3521	55,000,000
3523	110,000,000
3524-3527	96,000,000
3528-3531	100,000,000
3532	75,000,000
3533	30,000,000
3534a	275,000,000
3535	236,000
3536	800,000,000
3537-3540	125,000,000
3537a-3540a	1,500,000,000
3541-3544	201,000,000
3545	32,000,000
3546	69,000,000
3547	49,000,000
3548	40,000,000
3551	100,000,000
3552-3555	80,000,000
3556	125,000,000
3557	120,000,000
3558	75,000,000
3559	70,000,000
3560	55,000,000
3561-3610	200,000,000
3611	7,000,000
3649	3,000,000
3650	70,000,000
3651	61,000,000
3652	61,000,000
3653-3656	200,000,000
3657	1,500,000,000
3658	150,000,000
3659	75,000,000
3660	62,800,000
3661-3664	111,000,000
3665-3668	61,000,000
3669	61,000,000
3670-3671	200,000,000
3672	35,000,000
3673	40,000,000
3674	35,000,000
3675	739,200,000
3676-3679	125,000,000
3680-3683	300,000,000
3684-3687	1,705,000,000
3688-3691	200,000,000
3692	80,000,000
3694	1,610,000
3695	50,000,000
3696-3745	200,000,000
3746	150,000,000
3747	70,000,000
3748	70,000,000
3771	60,000,000
3772	7,000,000
3773	50,000,000
3774	55,000,000
3776-3780	60,000,000
3781	75,000,000
3782	54,000,000
3783	85,000,000
3786	80,000,000
3787-3791	125,000,000

Scott No.	Quantity
3802	6,000,000
3803	86,800,000
3804-3807	778,800,000
3808-3811	70,000,000
3812	52,000,000
3813	72,000,000
3814-3818	80,000,000
3820	700,000,000
3821-3824	1,875,000,000
3825-3828	200,990,000
3831	7,600,000
3832	80,000,000
3833	750,000,000
3834	130,000,000
3835	172,000,000
3836	750,000,000
3837	150,000,000
3838	60,000,000
3839	80,000,000
3840-3843	57,000,000
3854	62,200,000
3855-3856	20,000,000
3857-3861	57,000,000
3862	96,400,000
3863	71,800,000
3865-3868	284,000,000
3869	45,800,000
3870	60,000,000
3871	50,000,000
3872	794,000,000
3873	8,700,000
3876	100,000,000
3877	96,400,000
3878	8,336,000
3879	776,400,000
3881	60,000,000
3882	45,000,000
3883-3886	125,000,000
3887-3890	200,990,000
3891-3894	270,000,000
3895	4,500,000
3896	150,000,000
3897	170,000,000
3898	1,500,000,000
3899	5,600,000
3900-3903	790,000,000
3904	45,000,000
3905	40,000,000
3906-3909	50,000,000
3910	5,000,000
3911	65,000,000
3912-3915	215,000,000
3916-3925	110,000,000
3926-3929	420,000,000
3930	40,000,000
3931-3935	640,000,000
3936	75,000,000
3937	5,000,000
3938	65,000,000
3939-3942	70,000,000
3943	40,000,000
3944	21,000,000
3945-3948	70,000,000
3949-3952	200,000,000
3953-3956	800,000,000
3957-3960	100,000,000
3961-3964	60,000,000
3976	600,000,000
3987-3994	192,000,000
3995	60,000,000
3996	150,000,000
3997	5,000,000
3998-3999	200,000,000
4020	100,000,000
4021-4024	40,000,000
4025-4028	175,000,000
4029	400,000,000
4030	30,000,000
4031	80,000,000
4032	50,000,000
4033-4072	204,000,000
4073	40,000,000
4074	1,000,000
4075	3,000,000
4076	3,000,000
4077	75,000,000
4078	50,000,000
4079	60,000,000
4080-4083	200,000,000
4084	12,500,000
4085-4088	85,000,000
4089-4098	500,000,000
4099	5,000,000
4100	700,000,000
4101-4104	200,000,000
4105-4108	1,515,000,000
4109-4112	100,000,000
4113-4116	54,000,000
4117	35,000,000
4118	40,000,000
4119	40,000,000
4120	150,000,000
4121	25,000,000
4122	300,000,000
4123	2,000,000
4124	30,000,000
4136	60,000,000
4143	30,000,000
4146-4150	175,000,000
4151	500,000,000
4152	200,000,000
4153-4156	420,000,000
4153a-4156a	280,000,000
4159	12,500,000
4160-4163	36,000,000
4165	500,000,000
4192-4195	200,000,000

Scott No.	Quantity
4196	60,000,000
4197	55,000,000
4198	5,000,000
4199	80,000,000
4200	40,000,000
4201	40,000,000
4202	40,000,000
4203-4204	80,000,000
4205	100,000,000
4206	700,000,000
4207-4210	1,700,000,000
4211-4214	80,900,000
4215-4218	88,200,000
4219	50,000,000
4220	50,000,000

AIR POST STAMPS

Cat. No.	Quantity
C1	3,395,854
C2	3,793,887
C3	2,134,888
C4	6,414,576
C5	5,309,275
C6	5,285,775
C7	42,092,800
C8	15,597,307
C9	17,616,350
C10	20,379,179
C11	106,887,675
C12	97,641,200
C13	93,536
C14	72,428
C15	61,296
C16	57,340,050
C17	76,648,803
C18	324,070
C19	302,205,100
C20	10,205,400
C21	12,794,600
C22	9,285,300
C23	349,946,500
C24	19,768,150
C25	4,746,527,700
C26	1,744,878,650
C27	67,117,400
C28	78,434,800
C29	42,359,850
C30	59,880,850
C31	11,160,600
C32	864,753,100
C33	971,903,700
C34	207,976,550
C35	756,186,350
C36	132,956,100
C37	33,244,500
C38	38,449,100
C39	5,070,095,200
C40	75,085,000
C41	260,307,500
C42	21,061,300
C43	36,613,100
C44	16,217,100
C45	80,405,000
C46	18,876,800
C47	78,415,000
C48	50,483,977
C49	63,185,000
C50	72,480,000
C51	1,326,960,000
C52	157,035,000
C53	90,055,200
C54	79,290,000
C55	84,815,000
C56	38,770,000
C57	39,960,000
C58	98,160,000
C59	
C60	1,289,460,000
C61	87,140,000
C62	
C63	
C64	
C65	
C66	42,245,000
C67	
C68	63,890,000
C69	62,255,000
C70	55,710,000
C71	+ 50,000,000
C72	
C73	
C74	+ 60,000,000
C75	
C76	152,364,800
C77	
C78	
C79	
C80	
C81	
C82	
C83	
C84	78,210,000
C85	96,240,000
C86	58,705,000
C87	
C88	
C89	
C90	
C91-C92	
C93-C94	
C95-C96	

Cat. No.	Quantity	Cat. No.	Quantity	Cat. No.	Quantity
C97		C121	39,325,000	C136	85,000,000
C101-C104	+ 165,000,000	C122-C125	106,360,000	C137	85,000,000
C105-C108	+ 165,000,000	C126	1,944,000	C138	100,000,000
C109-C112	+ 175,000,000	C127	48,000,000	C139	145,000,000
C113	98,600,000	C128	250,000,000	C140	100,000,000
C114	110,475,000	C129	182,400,000	C141	100,000,000
C115	167,625,000	C130	113,000,000	C142	100,000,000
C116	45,700,000	C131	15,260,000	C143	100,000,000
C117	22,975,000	C132	100,000,000		
C118	201,150,000	C133	100,750,000	+ Quantity ordered printed.	
C119	111,550,000	C134	100,750,000		
C120	38,532,000	C135	+ 100,800,000		

CARRIERS' STAMPS

The term "Carriers' Stamps" is applied to certain stamps of the United States used to defray delivery to a post office on letters going to another post office, and for collection and delivery in the same city (local letters handled only by the carrier department). A less common usage was for a collection fee from the addressee at the post office ("drop letters"). During the period when these were in use, the ordinary postage fee defrayed the carriage of mail matter from post office to post office only.

In many of the larger cities the private ("Local") posts delivered mail to the post office or to an addressee in the city direct for a fee of 1 or 2 cents (seldom more), and adhesive stamps were often employed to indicate payment. (See introduction to "Local Stamps" section.)

Carrier service dates back at least to 1689 when the postmaster of Boston was instructed "to receive all letters and deliver them at 1d." In 1794, the law allowed a penny post to collect 2 cents in cash for the delivery of a letter. As these early fees were paid in cash, little evidence survives.

In 1851 the Federal Government, under the acts of 1825 and 1836, began to deliver letters in many cities and so issued Carriers' stamps for local delivery service. This Act of Congress of March 3, 1851, effective July 1, 1851 (succeeding Act of 1836), provided for the collecting and delivering of letters to the post office by carriers, "for which not exceeding 1 or 2 cents shall be charged."

Carriers' stamps were issued under the authority of, or derived from, the postmaster general. The "General Issues" (Nos. LO1-LO2) were general issues of which No. LO2 was valid for postage at face value, and No. LO1 at the value set upon sale, in any post office. They were issued under the direct authority of the postmaster general. The "City Carrier Department" were valid in the city in which they were issued either directly by or sanctioned by the local postmaster under authority derived from the postmaster general.

These "General" and "City Carrier Department" Carriers' stamps prepaid the fees of official letter carriers who were appointed by the postmaster general and were under heavy bond to the United States for the faithful performance of their duties. Some of the letter carriers received fixed salaries from the government. Others were paid from the fees received for the delivery and collection of letters carried by them. After discontinuance of carrier fees on June 30, 1863, all carriers of the United States Post Office were government employees, paid by salary at a yearly rate.

Some Carriers' stamps are often found on cover with the regular government stamps and have the official post office cancellation applied to them as well. Honour's City Express and the other Charleston, S.C., Carrier stamps almost always have the stamp uncanceled or canceled with pen, or less frequently pencil.

Unless indicated otherwise, values for Carriers' stamps on cover are for covers having the stamp tied by a handstamped cancellation. Carriers' stamps, either uncanceled or pen-canceled, **on covers to which they apparently belong**, also are valued where possible. For covers with stamps canceled by pen or pencil with initials or name of carrier, as sometimes seen on No. LO2 from Washington, and on Baltimore carrier stamps, the premium is 75% of the on-cover value.

All Carriers' stamps are imperforate and on wove paper, either white or colored through, unless otherwise stated.

Counterfeits exist of many Carriers' stamps.

GENERAL ISSUE CARRIER STAMPS

Franklin — OC1

Eagle — OC2

Engraved and printed by Toppan, Carpenter, Casilear & Co. Plate of 200 subjects divided into two panes of 100 each, one left, one right.

1851, Sept.   Unwmk.   *Imperf.*

LO1 OC1 (1c) **dull blue** (shades), rose	6,500.	7,500.
On cover from Philadelphia		17,500.
On cover from New York		30,000.
On cover from New Orleans with 3c #10 (a 2nd #LO1 removed)		30,000.
Pair	18,000.	18,000.
Strip of 3	26,500.	26,000.
Major plate crack		
Major plate crack, on cover		60,000.
Corner plate cracks (91L)	—	—
Double transfer	—	—
Double transfer, on cover		30,000.

Earliest known use: Oct. 28, 1851.

Cancellations

Red star (Philadelphia)	7,500.
Blue town (Philadelphia)	+1,000.
Red town (New York)	+1,000.
Black town (New York), unique	+4,000.
Blue grid (New York)	—

Black grid (New York)	—
Black grid (New Orleans)	—
Green grid (New Orleans)	+6,000.

Of the entire issue of 310,000 stamps, 250,000 were sent to New York, 50,000 to New Orleans, 10,000 to Philadelphia. However, the quantity sent to each city is not indicative of proportionate use. More appear to have been used in Philadelphia than in the other two cities. The use in all three cities was notably limited.

No. LO1, major plate crack on cover, is unique. The double transfer on cover also is unique, as is the unused pair.

U.S.P.O. Despatch

Engraved and printed by Toppan, Carpenter, Casilear & Co. Plate of 200 subjects divided into two panes of 100 each, one upper, one lower.

1851, Nov. 17   Unwmk.   *Imperf.*

LO2 OC2 1c **blue** (shades)	50.00	*80.00*
On cover, used alone	500.00	
On cover, precanceled	600.00	
On cover, pair or 2 singles	1,500.	
On cover with block of 3, 1c #9		4,500.
On cover with 3c #11		400.
On cover with 3c #25		—
On cover with 3c #26		600.
On cover with strip of 3, 3c #26		—
On cover with 5c #30A and 10c #32		33,000.
On cover, tied by town handstamp, with 3c #65 (Washington, D.C.)		4,500.
On 3c envelope #U1, #LO2 pen canceled		—
On 3c envelope #U2, tied by handstamp		—
On 3c envelope #U2, #LO2 pen canceled		—
On 3c envelope #U10, not canceled, with certicate		500.00
Pair	80.00	400.00
Pair on cover (Cincinnati)		1,250.
Block of 4	300.00	

Margin block of 8, imprint	850.00	
Double transfer	—	—
Double transfer on cover	—	—

Earliest known use: Jan. 3, 1852.

Cancellations

Red star	80.
Philadelphia	+50.
Cincinnati	+200.
Black grid	—
Blue grid	+300.
Red grid	+300.
Black town	+5.
Blue town	+100.
Red town	+300.
Kensington, Pa. (red)	—
Kensington, Pa. red "3c"	—
Washington, D.C.	+1,000.
Blue squared target	—
Red squared target	—
Railroad	—
Black carrier (Type C32)	—
Red carrier (Type C32)	—
Carrier's initial, manuscript	—

Earliest known use: Jan. 3, 1852. Used principally in Philadelphia, Cincinnati, Washington, D.C., and Kensington, Pa.

GOVERNMENT REPRINTS

Printed by the Continental Bank Note Co. (first and second printings) and American Bank Note Co. (third printing).

First reprinting-10,000 stamps of each design, on May 19, 1875 (all sold).

Second reprinting-10,000 stamps of each design, on Dec. 22, 1875 (all sold).

Third reprinting of Franklin stamp - 1881 (2,110 sold).

Third reprinting of Eagle stamp - 1881 (9,680 sold).

The first reprinting of the Franklin stamp was on the rose paper of the original, obtained from Toppan, Carpenter, Casilear & Co. Two batches of ink were used, both darker than the original. The second reprinting was on rose paper using ink that fluoresces green. The third reprinting was on much thicker, paler paper in an indigo color. All of these differ under ultraviolet light. The design of the reprints is not as distinct as the original design and may appear a bit "muddy" in the lathework above the vignette.

The first two reprintings of 10,000 each of the Eagle stamp are on the same hard white paper used for special printings of the postage issue. Stamps from the second reprinting were printed with ink that fluoresces green. Stamps from the third reprinting are on thick wove paper using ink that does not fluoresce. Reprints may be differentiated from the originals under ultraviolet light by the whiteness of the paper. Nos. LO3-LO6 are ungummed, Nos. LO1-LO2 have brown gum. No. LO1 was printed on a somewhat yellowish paper.

1875

Franklin Reprints
Imperf

LO3	OC1	(1c)	**blue**, *rose*	50.
		indigo, *rose*	70.
		Block of 4	225.
		Margin block of 4, imprint	—
		Corner plate cracks (91L)	100.
		Short transfer	—

Perf. 12

LO4	OC1	(1c)	**blue**	16,000.
		Pair	35,000.

No. LO4 is valued in the grade of average to fine.

Eagle Reprints
Imperf.

LO5	OC2	1c	**blue**	25.
		Block of 4	125.
		Margin block of 8, imprint & Pl.#	—

Perf. 12

LO6	OC2	1c	**blue**	175.
		Block of 4	1,000.
		Margin block of 8, imprint & Pl.#	12,500.

CITY CARRIER DEPARTMENT STAMPS

All are imperforate.

Baltimore, Md.

C1

1850-55   Typo.   Settings of 10 (2x5) varieties

1LB1	C1	1c	**red** (shades), *bluish*	180.	160.
		On cover, tied by handstamp			1,000.
		On cover with 1c #9			
		On cover (tied) with 3c #11			500.
		On cover (tied) with 3c #11A			500.
1LB2	C1	1c	**blue** (shades), *bluish*	200.	150.
		On cover, tied			1,000.
		On cover (tied) with 3c #11			500.
		On cover, uncanceled, with 3c #11A			225.
a.		Bluish laid paper			
1LB3	C1	1c	**blue** (shades)	160.	100.
		On cover, tied by handstamp			1,500.
		On cover, tied by ms.			250.
		Block of 4		1,000.	
a.		Laid paper		200.	150.
		On cover, tied by handstamp			1,000.
b.		Block of 14 containing three tete-beche gutter pairs (unique)		6,000.	
1LB4	C1	1c	**green**		1,000.
		On cover, tied by handstamp			5,000.
		On cover, not tied			1,200.
		On cover with 1c #7, tied by handstamp			2,250.
		On cover, not tied, with 3c #10A			2,000.
		On cover with 3c #11, ms. tied			—
		On 3c envelope #U10			3,500.
		Pair			5,000.
1LB5	C1	1c	**red**	2,250.	1,750.
		On cover, tied by handstamp			4,500.
		On cover, not tied			3,000.
		On cover (tied) with 3c #11			5,000.

The No. 1LB4 pair is the unique multiple of this stamp.

Cancellations on Nos. 1LB1-1LB5:

Black grid	—
Blue grid	—
Black cross	—
Black town	—
Blue town	+100.
Black numeral	—
Blue numeral	—
Black pen	—

C2

1856					Typo.
1LB6	C2	1c	**blue** (shades)	130.	90.
		On cover			400.
		On cover with 3c #11			1,000.
		On cover with 3c #25 (both tied)			1,350.
		On cover with 3c #26			1,250.
		On cover with 3c #26A			—
1LB7	C2	1c	**red** (shades)	130.	90.
		On cover			300.
		On cover (tied) with 3c #25			350.
		On cover (tied) with 3c #26			350.
		On 3c envelope #U9, tied			300.
		On 3c envelope #U10, tied			350.
		Block of 4		850.	

C3

Plate of 10 (2x5); 10 Varieties

The sheet consisted of at least four panes of 10 placed horizontally, the two center panes tete beche. This makes possible five horizontal tete beche gutter pairs.

1857					Typo.
1LB8	C3	1c	**black** (shades)	65.	50.
		On cover, tied by handstamp			125.
		On cover, tied by handstamp, to Germany			3,750.
		On cover (tied) with 3c #26			225.
		On 3c envelope #U9, tied			225.
		On 3c envelope #U10, tied			225.
		On 3c envelope #U27, tied			250.
		Strip of 3 (not tied), on cover			4,000.
		Block of 4		275.	
		Pane of 10		1,000.	
		Tete beche gutter pair		650.	
a.		"SENT," Pos. 7	100.		75.
		On cover, tied by handstamp			175.
		On cover (tied) with 3c #26			250.
		On 3c envelope #U9, tied			250.
		On 3c envelope #U10, tied			250.
b.		Short rays, Pos. 2	100.		75.
		On cover (tied) with 3c #26			600.

Cancellations

Black pen (or pencil)	20.00
Blue town	+2.50
Black town	+2.50
Black Steamship	

1LB9	C3	1c	**red** (shades)	100.	90.
		On cover			175.
		On cover (tied) with 3c #26			300.
		On 3c envelope #U9			325.
		On 3c envelope #U10			325.
		Block of 6		2,750.	
a.		"SENT," Pos. 7	140.		110.
		On cover (tied) with 3c #26			500.
b.		Short rays, Pos. 2	140.		110.
c.		As "b," double impression			800.

The block of 6 of No. 1LB9 is the only recorded multiple of this stamp.

Cancellations on Nos. 1LB6-1LB7, 1LB9:

Black town	—
Blue town	—
Blue numeral	—
Black pen	—
Carrier's initial, manuscript	+25.

Boston, Mass.

C6

Several Varieties

1849-50			Pelure Paper		Typeset
3LB1	C6	1c	**blue**	375.	180.
		On cover, tied by handstamp			300.
		On cover, uncanceled			150.
		On cover with 5c #1			4,000.
		On cover with two 5c #1			8,750.
		On cover with 3c #10			450.
a.		Wrong ornament at left			400.
		On cover, not tied			—

Cancellations

Red town	—
Red grid	—
Black ornate double oval	—
Black "Penny Post Paid" in 3-bar circle	—

C7

1851   Typeset

Several Varieties
Wove Paper Colored Through

3LB2	C7	1c	**blue** (shades), *slate*	190.	100.
		On cover			220.
		On cover with 5c #1			12,500.
		On cover with 3c #10			500.
		On cover with 3c #11			325.
		On 3c envelope #U2, #U5 or #U9			350.
		Tete beche gutter pair		600.	

Cancellations on Nos. 3LB2:

Black small fancy circle	—
Black diamond grid	+100.00
Red town	—
Black grid	—
Black PAID	—
Black crayon	—
Red small fancy circle	+50.00
Red diamond grid	+100.00
Black railroad	—
Black hollow star	—
Black pencil	—
Red crayon	—
Black "Penny Post Paid" in 3-bar circle	—
Red "Penny Post Paid" in 3-bar circle	—

Charleston, S. C.

John H. Honour was appointed a letter carrier at Charleston, in 1849, and engaged his brother-in-law, E. J. Kingman, to assist him. They separated in 1851, dividing the carrier business of the city between them. At the same time Kingman was appointed a letter carrier. In March, 1858, Kingman retired, being replaced by Joseph G. Martin. In the summer of 1858, John F. Steinmeyer, Jr., was added to the carrier force. When Honour retired in 1860, John C. Beckman was appointed in his place.

Each of these carriers had stamps prepared. These stamps were sold by the carriers. The Federal Government apparently encouraged their use.

Honour's City Express

C8

1849	Typo.		Wove Paper Colored Through	
4LB1	C8	2c	**black**, *brown rose*	10,000.
		Cut to shape	4,000.	4,000.
		On cover, not canceled, with certificate		17,000.
		On cover, cut to shape, tied, with 10c #2		40,000.
4LB2	C8	2c	**black**, *yellow*, cut to shape		—
		On cover, not tied, with certificate		12,500.
		On cover, cut to shape, uncanceled		—
		On cover, rectangular-cut, tied, with 10c #2		—

Cancellations on Nos. 4LB1-4LB2: Red grid, red town, red crayon.

No. 4LB1 unused is a unique uncanceled stamp on piece. The used cut-to-shape stamp is also unique. Additionally, each of the listed covers bearing No. 4LB1 is unique.

Four examples of No. 4LB2 are recorded, each listing above being unique.

4LB2A C8   2c **black**, *bluish gray*, on cover, cut to shape   —

No. 4LB2A is unique.

C10

1854		Wove Paper	Typeset
4LB3	C10	2c **black**	1,500.
		On cover, tied by pen cancel	3,000.
		On cover with 3c #11, tied	4,000.
		On cover with 3c #11, not tied	3,250.

Cancellations

Black town	—
Blue town	—
Black pen	—
Black pencil	—
Brown "PAID"	—
Initial "H"	—

C11

Several Varieties

1849-50		Wove Paper Colored Through		Typeset
4LB5	C11	2c **black**, *bluish*, pelure	750.	500.
		On cover (not tied)		3,500.
		On cover with pair 5c #1b		—
		On cover with two 5c #1b		—
		On cover (tied) with 3c #11		4,500.
a.		"Ceuts"	5,750.	
4LB7	C11	2c **black**, *yellow*	750.	1,000.
		On cover, tied by hand-stamp		9,000.
		On cover, not canceled		2,000.
a.		"Ccnts," ms. tied on cover		14,500.

No. 4LB5a is unique. It is without gum and is valued thus. No. 4LB7a also is unique.

The varieties of type C11 on bluish wove (thicker) paper and pink, pelure paper are not believed genuine.

Cancellation Nos. 4LB5, 4LB7:

Red town	—
Black pen	—
Red pen	—
Red crayon	—

C13

C15

 (Honour's Penny Post PAID) — C14

Several varieties of each type

1851-58		Wove Paper Colored Through		Typeset
4LB8	C13	2c **black**, *bluish*	350.	175.
		On cover, tied by hand-stamp		700.
		On cover, not tied		300.
		On cover, tied, with 3c #10		1,500.
		On cover, tied, with 3c #11		1,500.
		On cover, tied, with 3c #26		1,500.
		Pair		1,500.
a.		Period after "PAID"	500.	250.
		On cover		650.
		On cover, ms. tied, with 3c #11		750.
b.		"Cens"	700.	900.
		On cover, ms. tied, with 3c #11		3,250.
c.		"Conours" and "Bents"		
4LB9	C13	2c **black**, *bluish*, pelure	850.	950.
4LB10	C13	2c **black**, *pink*, pelure, on cover		7,000.
		On cover with 3c #11		
4LB11	C14 (2c)	**black**, *bluish*	—	375.
		On cover, tied by hand-stamp, with 3c #11		12,500.

		On cover, ms. tied, with 3c #11		3,000.
		On 3c envelope #U10, tied		1,500.
		On cover, tied, to foreign destination (Ireland), unique		25,000.
4LB12	C14 (2c)	**black**, *bluish*, pelure		
4LB13	C15 (2c)	**black**, *bluish* ('58)	750.	400.
		On cover with 3c #11, Aiken, S.C. postmark, tied by handstamp (unique)		6,000.
		On cover with 3c #26, tied by pen cancel		4,500.
		Horiz. pair		3,500.
a.		Comma after "PAID"	1,100.	
b.		No period after "Post"	1,400.	

The pair of No. 4LB13 is the unique multiple of this stamp. A 2c of design C13 exists on pink pelure paper. It is believed not to have been issued by the post, but to have been created later and perhaps accidentally.

Cancellations on Nos. 4LB8-4LB13

Black town	—
Blue town	—
Red town	—
Black pen	—
Black pencil	—
Red crayon	—
Brown cork initial "H"	—

Kingman's City Post

C16

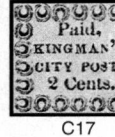
C17

Several varieties of each

1851(?)-58(?)		Wove Paper Colored Through		Typeset
4LB14	C16	2c **black**, *bluish*	1,400.	900.
		Vert. pair, ms. tied, on Valentine cover		6,000.
		On cover with 3c #11		7,000.
		On cover with 3c #26		6,000.
a.		"Kingman's" erased		5,000.
4LB15	C17	2c **black**, *bluish*	800.	800.
		On cover		—
		Vertical pair		—
		Horiz. pair, not tied, on Valentine cover		8,750.
		Vertical strip of 3 uncanceled, on cover		22,500.
a.		"Kingman's" erased, on cover with 3c #11, tied by pen cancel (unique)		4,500.

The No. 4LB14 pair on cover is the only recorded multiple of this stamp.

The 4LB15 pair and strip of 3 actually are uncanceled on covers and are valued thus. The horiz. pair on cover is ms. canceled.

Cancellations on Nos. 4LB14-4LB15: Black town, black pen.

Martin's City Post

C18

Several varieties

1858		Wove Paper Colored Through	Typeset
4LB16	C18	2c **black**, *bluish*	8,000.

Beckman's City Post

Same as C19, but inscribed "Beckmann's City Post."

1860			
4LB17	C19	2c **black**, on cover	

No. 4LB17 is unique. It is on cover with 3c No. 26, both tied by black circle townmark: "CHARLESTON, S.C. JUN 18, 1860".

Steinmeyer's City Post

C19

C20

Several varieties of Type C19
Type C20 printed from plate of 10 (2x5) varieties

1859		Wove Paper Colored Through		Typeset
4LB18	C19	2c **black**, *bluish*	21,000.	
		On cover, uncanceled		—
4LB19	C20	2c **black**, *bluish*	4,500.	—
4LB20	C20	2c **black**, *pink*	200.	—
		Block of 4	850.	
		Sheet of 10	2,250.	

4LB21	C20	2c **black**, *yellow*	200.	
		Block of 4	850.	
		Sheet of 10	2,250.	

Sheets of 10 of Nos. 4LB20-4LB21 exist signed by J.F. Steinmeyer Jr. These sell for about 50% more than the unsigned sheets.

Two examples of No. 4LB18 are known on cover, both uncanceled.

Cancellation on Nos. 4LB19-4LB21: Black pen.

Cincinnati, Ohio
Williams' City Post

Organized by C. C. Williams, who was appointed and commissioned by the Postmaster General.

C20a

1854		Wove Paper		Litho.
9LB1	C20a	2c **brown**	—	4,000.
		On cover, tied by hand-stamp		—
		On cover, tied by pen cancel		4,500.
		On cover with 1c #9		7,500.
		Pair	7,500.	

Cancellations

Red squared target	—
Black pen	—
Blue company circle	—

Fraser & Co.

Local stamps of designs L146-L147 were carrier stamps when used on cover between Feb. 3, 1848 and June 30, 1849.

Cleveland, Ohio
Bishop's City Post.

Organized by Henry S. Bishop, "Penny Postman" who was appointed and commissioned by the Postmaster General.

C20b

C20c

1854		Wove Paper		Litho.
10LB1	C20b	blue	5,000.	4,000.
		On cover, tied by hand-stamp		15,000.
		Pair on cover, canceled by pencil, with 3c #11, with certificate		17,000.

Vertically Laid Paper

10LB2	C20c	2c **black**, *bluish*	4,000.	7,000.
		On cover		—
		Pair		—
		Pair on cover, canceled by pencil, with 3c #11		14,000.

Cancellations on #10LB1-10LB2

Red town	—
Red boxed numeral	—
Black pen	—
Black pencil	—

No. 10LB2 unused is unique. It is cut in at bottom and without gum, and is valued thus.

Louisville, Ky.

Carrier Service was first established by the Louisville Post Office about 1854, with one carrier. David B. Wharton, appointed a carrier in 1856, issued an adhesive stamp in 1857, but as he was soon thereafter replaced in the service, it is believed that few, if any, of these stamps were used. Brown & McGill, carriers who succeeded Wharton, issued stamps in April, 1858.

Wharton's U.S.P.O. Despatch

C21

Sheet of 50 subjects in two panes of 25 (5x5) each, one upper, one lower

1857			Lithographed by Robyn & Co.
5LB1	C21	(2c)	bluish green (shades)	125.
			Block of 4	650.
			Pane of 25	3,250.
			Sheet of 50	7,000.

Brown & McGill's U. S. P. O. Despatch

C22

1858			Litho. by Hart & Maypother		
5LB2	C22	(2c)	blue (shades)	250.	750.
			On cover, not tied, with 3c #26		750.
			On cover with 3c #26, tied by handstamp		6,250.
			Block of 4	1,250.	
5LB3	C22	(2c)	black	4,500.	15,000.

The value for No. 5LB3 used refers to the finer of the two known used (canceled) examples; it is on a piece with a 3c #26.

Cancellations on Nos. 5LB2-5LB3: Blue town, black pencil.

New York, N. Y.
UNITED STATES CITY DESPATCH POST

By an order made on August 1, 1842, the Postmaster General established a carrier service in New York known as the "United States City Despatch Post." Local delivery service had been authorized by the Act of Congress of July 2, 1836.

Greig's City Despatch Post was sold to the U. S. P. O. Department and on August 16, 1842, began operation as the "United States City Despatch Post" under the superintendence of Alexander M. Greig who was appointed a U. S. letter carrier for that purpose.

The Greig circular introducing this service stated that letter boxes had been placed throughout the city, that letters might be sent prepaid or collect, and that registry service was available for an extra 3 cents.

The City Despatch Post stamps were accepted for the service of the United States City Despatch Post. The stamps thus used bear the cancellation of the New York Post Office, usually "U.S." in an octagon which served to indicate that the carrier service was now a government operation (no longer a private local post) as well as a cancellation.

Some examples are canceled by a circular date stamp reading "U.S. CITY DESPATCH POST" or, infrequently, a New York town postmark. When canceled "FREE" in frame they were used as local stamps. See No. 40L1 in Locals section.

No. 6LB3 was the first stamp issued by authority of the U.S.P.O. Department. The 3c denomination included 1 cent in lieu of drop letter postage until June 30, 1845, and the maximum legal carrier fee of 2 cents. Service was discontinued late in November, 1846.

C23   C24

Engraved and printed by Rawdon, Wright & Hatch.

Plate of 42 (6x7) subjects
Wove Paper Colored Through

1842				
6LB1	C23	3c	black, grayish	2,000.
			On cover, tied by handstamp	11,500.
			On cover, not tied	10,000.
			On cover, not tied, with Aug. 16 (1842) cancel, First day of government carrier service	100,000.

Cancellations

Red "U.S" in octagon	2,000.
Red circle "U.S. City Despatch Post"	—
Red town	—

Used examples which do not bear the official cancellation of the New York Post Office and unused examplesd are classed as Local stamps. See No. 40L1.

Wove Paper (unsurfaced) Colored Through
Engraved plate of 50 in two panes of 25

1842-45					
6LB2	C24	3c	black, rosy buff	2,500.	
6LB3	C24	3c	black, light blue	550.	500.
			On cover, tied by handstamp		2,000.
			On cover, not tied		750.00
			Pair	2,250.	
6LB4	C24	3c	black, green	11,500.	

Some authorities consider No. 6LB2 to be an essay, and No. 6LB4 a color changeling.

Glazed Paper, Surface Colored

6LB5	C24	3c	black, blue green (shades)	200.	175.
			On cover, tied by handstamp		600.
			Five on cover		20,000.
			Pair		400.
			Strip of 3		650.
			Strip of 4		800.
			Strip of 5		—
			Ribbed paper		—
			Double transfer		—
a.			Double impression		1,500.
b.			3c black, blue	650.	300.
			On cover		750.
			Strip of 3 + single on cover		14,000.
			Strip of 3	2,500.	
			Block of 12	23,000.	
c.			As "b," double impression		850.
d.			3c black, green	1,000.	900.
			On cover		750.
			Five examples on cover		45,000.
e.			As "d," double impression		—
			On cover		—

Cancellations

Red curved PAID	—
Red "U.S City Despatch Post"	—
Red "U.S" in octagon	—
Red New York	—
Red double line circle "U.S. City Despatch Post"	—

No. 6LB5 has been noted on cover with the 5c New York signed "R.H.M.," No. 9X1d.

6LB6	C24	3c	black, pink, on cover front	14,500.

No. 6LB6 is unique.

C25

1846
No. 6LB5 Surcharged in Red

6LB7	C25	2c on 3c	black, bluish green, on cover, not tied, with certificate	70,000.

The City Dispatch 2c red formerly listed as No. 6LB8 is now listed under Local Stamps as No. 160L1.

U.S. MAIL

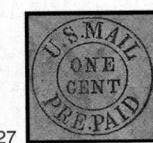

C27

Issued by the Postmaster at New York, N.Y.

1849			Wove Paper, Colored Through		Typo.
6LB9	C27	1c	black, rose	100.	100.
			On cover, tied by handstamp		350.
			On cover with 5c #1		2,000.
			Pair	250.	
			Block of 4	600.	

1849-50			**Glazed Surface Paper**		
6LB10	C27	1c	black, yellow	100.	100.
			On cover, tied by handstamp		350.
			On cover with 5c #1		1,500.
			Pair	250.	
			Block of 4	600.	
6LB11	C27	1c	black, buff	100.	100.
			On cover		250.
			On cover, not tied, with 5c #1, with certificate		3,000.
a.			Pair, one stamp sideways	2,850.	

Cancellations on #6LB9-6LB11

Red town	—
Red grid	—
Red "PAID"	+50.
Black numeral in circle	—
Red "N.Y. U.S. CITY MAIL" in circle	+150.
Black pen	—
Black pencil	—

Philadelphia, Pa.

C28

Several Varieties
Thick Wove Paper Colored Through

1849-50					Typeset
7LB1	C28	1c	black, rose (with "L P")	450.	
			On cover, tied by handstamp		3,000.
			On cover, not canceled		2,000.
			On cover with 5c #1		—
7LB2	C28	1c	black, rose (with "S")	3,000.	
			On cover, not canceled		4,500.
7LB3	C28	1c	black, rose (with "H")	275.	
			On cover, tied by handstamp		3,750.
			On cover, not canceled		1,000.
			On cover with 5c #1		3,500.
7LB4	C28	1c	black, rose (with "L S")	400.	500.
			On cover, not canceled		3,000.
7LB5	C28	1c	black, rose (with "J J")	7,500.	
			On cover with 5c #1, uncanceled		70,000.

The unique used No. 7LB5 in an uncanceled stamp on a cover front.

C29

			Several Varieties		
7LB6	C29	1c	black, rose	300.	250.
			On cover, tied by handstamp		2,500.
			On cover, uncanceled		500.00
7LB7	C29	1c	black, blue, glazed	1,000.	
			On cover, tied by handstamp		6,500.
			On cover, uncanceled		1,250.
			On cover with 5c #1		3,500.
7LB8	C29	1c	black, vermilion, glazed	700.	
			On cover, tied by handstamp		1,500.
			On cover, uncanceled		900.
			On cover with 5c dark brown #1a, uncanceled		12,500.
			On cover with 5c orange brown #1b, uncanceled		21,000.
7LB9	C29	1c	black, yellow, glazed	2,750.	2,250.
			On cover, not canceled		4,000.
			On cover with 3c #10, uncanceled		2,000.

Cancellations on Nos. 7LB1-7LB9: Normally these stamps were left uncanceled on the letter, but occasionally were accidentally tied by the Philadelphia town postmark which was normally struck in blue ink.

A 1c black on buff (unglazed) of type C29 is believed to be a color changeling.

C30

Settings of 25 (5x5) varieties (Five basic types)

1850-52				Litho.
7LB11	C30	1c **gold,** *black,* glazed	175.	110.
		On cover, tied by hand- stamp		600.
		On cover, uncanceled		325.
		On cover (tied) with 5c #1		3,500.
		On cover (tied) with 3c #10		800.
		On cover (uncanceled) with 3c #10		250.
		Block of 19	8,250.	
7LB12	C30	1c **blue**	400.	275.
		On cover, tied by hand- stamp		1,250.
		On cover, not tied		400.
		On cover (tied) with 3c #10		1,750.
		On cover (tied) with 3c #11		1,250.
		Pair		1,600.
7LB13	C30	1c **black**	750.	550.
		On cover, tied by hand- stamp		2,500.
		On cover, uncanceled		1,250.
		On cover (tied) with 3c #10		
		On cover (not tied) with 3c #11		3,250.

Cancellations on #7LB11-7LB13
Red star		—
Red town		—
Blue town		—

C31

Handstamped
7LB14	C31	1c **blue,** *buff*		3,250.

No. 7LB14 was handstamped on coarse dark buff paper on which rectangles in the approximate size of the type C31 handstamp had been ruled in pencil. The stamps so produced were later cut out and show traces of the adjoining handstamp markings as well as parts of the penciled rectangle. Some uncanceled examples exist on covers.

1855(?)				
7LB16	C31	1c **black**		5,000.
		On cover with strip of 3, 1c #9		—
		On cover with 3c 1851 stamp removed, tied by handstamp		7,000.

C32

1856(?)			Handstamped	
7LB18	C32	1c **black**	1,250.	2,000.
		Paper showing blue plate imprint		4,000.
		On cover (cut diamond- shaped) with pair 1c #7 and single 1c #9		—
		On cover with strip of 3, 1c #7		17,000.
		On cover with 3c #11		9,500.
		On 3c envelope #U5		—
		On 3c envelope #U10, not canceled		9,000.

Cancellations on #7LB16, 7LB18
Black circled grid		—
Black town		—

Nos. 7LB16 and 7LB18 were handstamped on the sheet margins of U.S. 1851 1c stamps, cut out and used as adhesives. The paper therefore has some surface bluing, and some stamps show parts of the plate imprint.

Values are for stamps cut square unless otherwise mentioned.

ENVELOPES
Handstamps of types C31 and C32 were also used to make stamped envelopes and letter sheets or circulars. These same types were also used as postmarks or cancellations in the same period.

A handstamp similar to C32, but with "U.S.P. DESPATCH" in serif capitals, is believed to have been used only as a postmark.

Type C31 exists struck in blue or red, type C32 in blue, black or red. When found on cover, on various papers, struck alone, they are probably postmarks and not prepaid stamped envelopes. As such, these entire covers, depending upon the clarity of the handstamp and the general attractiveness of the letter are valued between $400 and $800.

When found on envelopes with the Carrier stamp canceled by a handstamp (such as type C31 struck in blue on a buff envelope canceled by the red solid star cancellation) they can be regarded as probably having been sold as prepaid envelopes. Value approximately $3,000.

Labels of these designs are believed by most specialists not to be carrier stamps. Those seen are uncanceled, either off cover or affixed to stampless covers of the early 1850s. Some students believe they should be given carrier status.

St. Louis, Mo.

C36   C37

Illustrations enlarged to show details of the two types (note upper corners especially). Sizes of actual designs are 17 1/2x22mm.

1849		White Wove Paper Two Types		Litho.
8LB1	C36	2c **black**	7,000.	3,000.
8LB2	C37	2c **black**	6,000.	—

Cancellation on Nos. 8LB1-8LB2: Black town.

C38

1857				Litho.
8LB3	C38	2c **blue**		22,500.
		On cover, tied by hand- stamp		55,000.
		On Valentine cover, ms. cancel, not tied		35,000.

The used example off cover is unique. Four covers are recorded.

Cancellations on No. 8LB3: Black boxed "1ct," "Paid" in arc, black pen.

LOCAL STAMPS

This listing of Local stamps includes stamps issued by Local Posts (city delivery), Independent Mail Routes and Services, Express Companies and other private posts which competed with, or supplemented, official services.

The Independent Mail Routes began using stamps early in 1844 and were put out of business by an Act of March, 1845, which became effective July 1, 1845. By this Act, the Government reduced the zones to two, reduced the rates to 5c and 10c and applied them to weight instead of the number of sheets of paper which composed a letter.

Most of the Local Posts still in business were forced to discontinue service by an Act of 1861, except Boyd's and Hussey's which were able to continue about 20 years longer because of the particular nature of their business. Other posts appeared illegally and sporadically after 1861 and were quickly suppressed.

City posts generally charged 1c to deliver a letter to the Post Office (usually the letter bore a government stamp as well) and 2c for intracity delivery (such letters naturally bore only local stamps). These usages are not catalogued separately because the value of a cover is determined as much by its attractiveness as its franking, rarity being the basic criterion.

Only a few Local Posts used special handstamps for canceling. The stamps frequently were left uncanceled, were canceled by pen, or less often by pencil. **Unless indicated otherwise, values for stamps on cover are for covers having the stamp tied by a handstamped cancellation, either private or governmental.** Local stamps, either uncanceled or pen canceled, **on covers to which they apparently belong**, also are valued where possible.

The absence of any specific cancellation listed indicates that no company handstamp is known so used, and that the canceling, if any, was done by pen, pencil or government handstamp. Local stamps used on letters directed out of town (and consequently bearing government stamps) sometimes, because of their position, are tied together with the government stamp by the cancellation used to cancel the latter.

Values for envelopes are for entires unless specifically mentioned.

All Local stamps are imperforate and on wove paper, either white or colored through, unless otherwise stated.

Counterfeits exist of many Local stamps, but most of these are crude reproductions and would deceive only the novice.

Adams & Co.'s Express, California

This post started in September, 1849, operating only on the Pacific Coast.

D. H. Haskell, Manager

L1   L2

Nos. 1L2-1L5 Printed in Sheets of 40 (8x5).

1854   **Litho.**

1L1 L1 25c	**black,** *blue*	2,750.	—
	On cover		—
1L2 L2 25c	**black** (initials in black)	75.00	—
	Block of 4	375.00	
	Sheet of 40	—	
a.	Initials in red		—
b.	Without initials		—

Cancellation (1L1-1L2): Black Express Co.
Nos. 1L1-1L2 were the earliest adhesive franks issued west of the Mississippi River.
No. 1L2 usually bear manuscript control markings "LR" for Louis Reed or less commonly "ICW" for Isaiah C. Wood.

Glazed Surface Cardboard

1L3 L2 25c	**black,** *pink*	30.00
	Block of 4	160.00
	Sheet of 40	2,000.
	Retouched flaw above LR "25"	100.00

No. 1L3 was probably never placed in use as a postage stamp.

L3

Overprinted in red "Over our California lines only"

1L4 L3 25c **black** (with initials "LR" or "ICW")   750.00   —

L4   L5

1L5 L4 25c	**black** (black surcharge)	4,000.	—
1L6 L5 25c	**black**	3,000.	
	Pair	7,500.	

The pair of No. 1L6 is unique.

NEWSPAPER STAMP

L6

1LP1 L6	**black,** *claret*	—	2,000.

Cancellation: Blue company oval.

ENVELOPES

L6a   L6b

Typo.

1LU1 L6a	25c **blue** (cut square)	—	15,000.
1LU2 L6a	25c **black,** on U.S. #U9	—	—
1LU3 L6b	50c **black,** on U.S. #U9	2,500.	2,500.
1LU4 L6b	50c **black,** *buff*	—	15,000.

Nos. 1LU2 and 1LU3 exist cut out and apparently used as adhesives.
Cancellation: Blue company oval.

Adams' City Express Post, New York, N.Y.

L7   L7a

L8

1850-51			**Typo.**
2L2 L7	2c **black,** *buff*	5,000.	2,250.
	On cover, canceled, not tied, with certificate		10,000.
2L3 L7a	1c **black,** *gray*		
2L4 L8	2c **black,** *gray*	450.00	450.00
	On cover, tied by handstamp		5,500.
2L5 L8	2c **blue,**		
	On cover, pen cancel		7,500.

Nos. 2L3-2L4 were reprinted in black on white wove paper. Some students claim that a 1c in blue on white wove paper exists as originals.

Allen's City Dispatch, Chicago, Ill.

Established by Edwin Allen for intracity delivery of letters and circulars. The price of the stamps is believed to have been determined on a quantity basis. Uncanceled and canceled remainders were sold to collectors after suppression of the post in February, 1883.

L9

1882	**Typo.**		**Perf. 10**
	Sheet of 100 (10x10)		
3L1 L9	**pink**	7.50	25.00
	On cover		900.00
	Block of 4	40.00	
a.	Horizontal pair, imperf. between		—
3L2 L9	**black**	12.50	100.00
	On cover, tied by handstamp		1,500.
	Block of 4	55.00	
a.	Horizontal pair, imperf. between		—
3L3 L9	**red,** *yellow*	.75	20.00
	On cover, tied by handstamp		900.00

	Block of 4	*3.25*
a.	Imperf., pair	*150.00*
b.	Horizontal pair, imperf. between	—
3L4 L9	**blackish purple**	120.00

Cancellations: Violet company oval, violet "eagle."

American Express Co., New York, N.Y.

Believed by some researchers to have been established by Smith & Dobson in 1856, and short-lived.

L10

Typeset
Glazed Surface Paper

4L1 L10	2c **black**, *green*	9,000.

American Letter Mail Co.

Lysander Spooner established this independent mail line operating to and from New York, Philadelphia and Boston.

L12   L13

1844   Engr.

Sheet of 20 (5x4)

5L1 L12	5c **black,** thin paper (2nd printing)	7.50	*35.00*
	Thick paper (1st printing)	35.00	*50.00*
	On cover, tied		*750.00*
	On cover, not tied		*450.00*
	Pair on cover		*1,000.*
	Pair on cover, tied by handstamp, with # 96L3a, ms. tied		*10,000.*
	Block of 4, thin paper	40.00	
	Sheet of 20, thin paper	225.00	

No. 5L1 has been extensively reprinted in several colors, distinguishable by the rust marks on the plate, which were mostly removed from the margins and gutters between stamps but remain within the stamp designs. Cancellations: Red dotted star (2 types). Red "PAID," black brush, red brush.

Engr.

5L2 L13	**black,** *gray*	150.00	*250.00*
	On cover, tied by handstamp		*1,000.*
	On cover, ms. tied		*500.00*
	On cover, not tied		*350.00*
	Pair on cover, tied by ms.		*1,200.*
	Vertical strip of 4		*3,000.*
	Block of 4		*4,000.*
5L3 L13	**blue,** *gray*	2,000.	*1,750.*
	On cover, uncanceled, with certificate		*11,000.*
	On cover, not tied, with certificate		*5,000.*
	On cover, tied by ms.		*12,000.*

Cancellations: Red "PAID," red company oval.

A. W. Auner's Despatch Post, Philadelphia, Pa.

L13a

1851   Typeset

Cut to shape

154L1 L13a	**black,** *grayish*	9,000.
	On cover, not tied, with certificate	*16,500.*

Nos. 154L1 unused and on cover are each unique.

Baker's City Express Post, Cincinnati, Ohio

L14

1849

6L1 L14	2c **black**, *pink*	2,250.
	On cover, uncanceled, with certificate	*12,500.*

Bank & Insurance Delivery Office or City Post
See Hussey's Post.

Barnard's Cariboo Express, British Columbia

The adhesives were used on British Columbia mail and the post did not operate in the United States, so the formerly listed PAID and COLLECT types are omitted. This company had an arrangement with Wells, Fargo & Co. to exchange mail at San Francisco.

Barnard's City Letter Express, Boston, Mass.

Established by Moses Barnard

L19

1845

7L1 L19	**black**, *yellow*, glazed paper	1,250.	*1,000.*
	On cover, not canceled		*3,000.*
7L2 L19	**red**	1,000.	
	On cover, ms. cancel, not tied, with certificate		*5,000.*

No. 7L2 unused and on cover are each unique.

Barr's Penny Dispatch, Lancaster, Pa.

Established by Elias Barr.

L19a   L20

1855

Five varieties of each   Typeset

8L1 L19a	**red**	1,000.	*1,000.*
	On cover, ms. tied		*5,000.*
	On cover, ms. cancel, not tied, with certificate		*2,000.*
8L2 L20	**black**, *green*	300.	*250.*
	On cover, uncanceled		*900.*
	On cover with 3c #11		—
	Pair		*750.*

Bayonne City Dispatch, Bayonne City, N.J.

Organized April 1, 1883, to carry mail, with three daily deliveries. Stamps sold at 80 cents per 100.

L21

1883   Electrotyped

Sheet of 10

9L1 L21	1c **black**	200.	*275.*
	On cover, tied by handstamp		*750.*
	On cover with 1c #183 & 2c #206		*2,750.*
	On cover with 3c #207		*1,600.*

Cancellation: Purple concentric circles.

ENVELOPE

1883, May 15   Handstamped

9LU1 L21	1c **purple**, *amber*	175.	*1,000.*

Bentley's Dispatch, New York, N.Y.

Established by H. W. Bentley, who acquired Cornwell's Madison Square Post Office, operating until 1856, when the business was sold to Lockwood. Bentley's postmark was double circle handstamp.

L22   L22a

1856(?)   Glazed Surface Paper

10L1 L22	**gold**	9,000.	*9,000.*
10L2 L22a	**gold**		*7,500.*
	Pair		*10,000.*

Two unused examples of No. 10L1 are known, while the used example is unique.

Cancellation: Black "PAID."

Berford & Co.'s Express, New York, N.Y.

Organized by Richard G. Berford and Loring L. Lombard. Carried letters, newspapers and packages by steamer to Panama and points on the West Coast, North and South America. Agencies in West Indies, West Coast of South America, Panama, Hawaii, etc.

L23

1851

11L1 L23	3c **black**	5,000.	*7,000.*
	On cover, not canceled		—
11L2 L23	6c **green**	—	—
	On cover, tied		*5,000.*
11L3 L23	10c **violet**	5,000.	
	On cover, not canceled		*5,000.*
	Four cut to shape on cover		*15,000.*
	Pair	—	
a.	Horiz. tete beche pair		
	On cover with normal pair		*50,000.*
	Two tete beche pair on cover		*75,000.*
11L4 L23	25c **red**	17,000.	
	On cover with #11L1 & 2 #11L2		*75,000.*

Values of cut to shape stamps are about half of those quoted.
No. 11L4 unused and on cover are each unique.
Cancellation: Red "B & Co. Paid" (sometimes impressed without ink). Dangerous counterfeits exist of Nos. 11L1-11L4.

Bicycle Mail Route, California

During the American Railway Union strike, Arthur C. Banta, Fresno agent for Victor bicycles, established this post to carry mail from Fresno to San Francisco and return, employing messengers on bicycles. The first trip was made from Fresno on July 6, 1894. Service was discontinued on July 18 when the strike ended. In all, 380 letters were carried. Stamps were used on covers with U.S. Government adhesive stamps and on stamped envelopes.

L24

Printed from single die. Sheet of six.
Error of spelling "SAN FRANSISCO"

1894		Typo.		Rouletted 10	
12L1	L24	25c green		150.	200.
		On cover			2,750.
		Block of 4		700.	
		Pane of 6		1,750.	

L25

Retouched die. Spelling error corrected.

12L2	L25	25c green	30.	75.
		On cover		1,500.
		On cover with No. 220, both tied		2,000.
		Block of 4	125.	
		Pane of 6	250.	
a.		"Horiz." pair, imperf. "vert"		75.
		As "a," pane of 6		—

ENVELOPES

12LU1	L25	25c brown, on 2c No. U311	200.	1,750.
12LU2	L25	25c brown, on 2c No. U312	200.	1,750.

Cancellation: Two black parallel bars 2mm apart.
Stamps and envelopes were reprinted from the defaced die.

Bigelow's Express, Boston, Mass.

Authorities consider items of this design to be express company labels rather than stamps.

Bishop's City Post, Cleveland, Ohio
See Carriers' Stamps, Nos. 10LB1-10LB2.

Blizzard Mail

Organized March, 1888, to carry mail to New York City during the interruption of U.S. mail by the Blizzard of 1888. Used March 12-16.

L27

1888, Mar. 12		Quadrille Paper		Typo.
163L1	L27	5c black	3,750.	
a.		"CETNS" instead of "CENTS"	—	
b.		Tete beche pair		

D.O. Blood & Co., Philadelphia, Pa.
I. Philadelphia Despatch Post

Operated by Robertson & Co., predecessor of D.O. Blood & Co.

L28

L29

Initialed "R & Co."

1842			Handstamped
		Cut to Shape	
15L1	L28	3c red, bluish	1,500.
		On cover, not tied	8,500.
15L2	L28	3c black	1,500.
		On cover, not tied, with certificate	15,000.

Cancellations on Nos. 15L1-15L2: Red "3," red pattern of segments.

With or without shading in background.
Initialed "R & Co"

1843			Litho.
15L3	L29	(3c) black, grayish	750.
		On cover, tied by handstamp	12,500.
		On cover, tied by ms. cancel	5,000.
		On cover, not tied, with certificate	3,500.
a.		Double impression	

Cancellation on No. 15L3: Red "3"
The design shows a messenger stepping over the Merchants' Exchange Building, which then housed the Government Post Office, implying that the private post gave faster service.
See illustration L161 for similar design.

II. D.O. Blood & Co.
Formed by Daniel Otis Blood and Walter H. Blood in 1845. Successor to Philadelphia Despatch Post which issued Nos. 15L1-15L3.

L30

Initialed "Dob & Cos" or "D.O.B. & Co."

1845			
		Shading in background	
15L4	L30	(3c) black, grayish	600.
		On cover, tied by handstamp	6,000.
		On cover, not tied	1,500.

L32

1846				
15L5	L31	(2c) black	125.	250.
		On cover		
		On cover, not tied, with certificate		800.
		Block of 4	475.	
		Pane of 12	5,500.	

1847				
15L6	L32	(2c) black	—	200.
		On cover		
		On cover, not tied, with certificate		1,250.
		On cover, not tied, with 5c #1		—

Cancellations on Nos. 15L4-15L6: Black dot pattern, black cross, red "PAID."
Dangerous counterfeits exist of Nos. 15L3-15L6.

L33

L34

L35

1846-47				
15L7	L33	(2c) black	175.00	350.00
		On cover, tied by handstamp		1,750.
		On cover, cut to shape, tied by handstamp		1,100.
		On cover, not tied		750.00
15L8	L34	(2c) black	110.00	75.00
		On cover, tied by handstamp		950.00
		On cover, uncanceled		500.00
		On cover, uncanceled, with 5c #1		2,000.
15L9	L35	(2c) black	100.00	60.00
		On cover, tied by handstamp		1,500.
		On cover, uncanceled, with 5c #1		2,000.
		On cover, not tied		500.00
		Block of 4		

Values for Nos. 15L7-15L9 cut to shape are half of those quoted.

"On cover" listings of Nos. 15L7-15L9 are for stamps tied by government town postmarks, either Philadelphia, or rarely Baltimore.

L36

L37

1848				
15L10	L36	(2c) black & blue	350.00	500.00
		On cover, tied by handstamp		2,250.
		On cover, not tied		1,750.
		On cover, not canceled		1,000.
		On cover, with 5c #1		
		Pair	1,300.	

15L11 L37 (2c) **black,** *pale green*   325.00   325.00
  On cover, tied by handstamp   *2,000.*
  On cover, not tied   *1,500.*
    Cancellation: Black grid.

L38

L39

L40

L41

1848-54
15L12 L38 (2c) **gold,** *black,* glazed   *110.00*   100.00
  On cover, tied by handstamp   *500.00*
  On cover, acid tied   *200.00*
  On cover, uncanceled, with
    5c #1   *2,000.*
15L13 L39 1c **bronze,** *black,* glazed ('50)   25.00   12.50
  On cover, tied by handstamp   *225.00*
  On cover, acid tied   *75.00*
  On cover, acid tied, with 5c
    #1   *2,000.*
  On cover, acid tied, with pair
    of 5c #1b   —
  On cover with 10c #2   —
  On cover, acid tied, with
    three 1c #7   *1,100.*
  On cover, tied, with 3c #10   *1,000.*
  Block of 4   150.00
  Pane of 24   *1,250.*
15L14 L40 (1c) **bronze,** *lilac* ('54)   4.25   2.50
  On cover, tied by handstamp   *200.00*
  On cover, acid tied   *30.00*
  On cover, acid tied, with 1c
    #9   *300.00*
  On cover with 3c #11   *375.00*
  On cover, acid tied, with 10c
    #14   *1,500.*
  On cover, tied by hand-
    stamp, with 1c #24 and
    three 3c #26   *1,150.*
  On cover, tied by hand-
    stamp, with 3c #26   *200.00*
  On cover, acid tied, with 3c
    #64b   *250.00*
  On cover, acid tied, with 3c
    #65   *225.00*
  Block of 4   50.00
  Pane of 25   *750.00*
   a.   Laid paper   —
   b.   Tete beche pair   —
15L15 L40 (1c) **blue & pink,** *bluish* ('53)   22.50   12.50
  On cover, tied by handstamp   *200.00*
  On cover, acid tied   *50.00*
  On cover, acid tied, with 1c
    #7 and three 3c #11   *1,000.*
  Block of 4   80.00
  Pane of 25   *1,250.*
   a.   Laid paper   35.00   —
  Block of 4   150.00
15L16 L40 (1c) **bronze,** *black,* glazed ('54)   30.00   25.00
  On cover, tied by handstamp   *225.00*
  On cover, acid tied   *75.00*
  On cover, acid tied by hand-
    stamp, with 3c #11   *275.00*
15L17 L41 (2c) **bronze,** *black,* glazed   35.00   20.00
  On cover, tied by handstamp   *225.00*
  On cover, acid tied   *75.00*
  On cover, acid or hand-
    stamp tied, with 5c #1   *1,250.*
  On cover, not tied, with 5c
    #1   *750.*
  On cover, handstamp tied,
    with pair of 5c #1a   *11,000.*
  On cover, acid or hand-
    stamp tied, with 10c #2   *5,000.*

D.O. Blood & Co. reduced the cost for mailing letters from 2c to 1c as of Jan. 8, 1849, in anticipation of the government carrier rate reduction. As a result, Nos. 15L12 and 15L17 could be purchased for 1c after this date.
  Cancellations: Black grid (No. 15L12, 15L17). Nos. 15L13-15L16 were almost always canceled with an acid which discolored both stamp and cover.

III. Blood's Penny Post

Blood's Penny Post was acquired by the general manager, Charles Kochersperger, in 1855, when Daniel O. Blood died.

Henry Clay — L42

1855   **Engr. by Draper, Welsh & Co.**
15L18 L42 (1c) **black**   35.00   10.00
  On cover   *150.00*
  On cover, tied by hand-
    stamp, with 3c #11   *400.00*
  On cover, not tied, with 1c
    #24   *900.00*
  On cover, tied by hand-
    stamp, with 1c #24 and 3c
    #26   *2,000.*
  On cover, tied by hand-
    stamp, with 3c #26   *350.00*
  On 3c entire #U9   *300.00*
  Block of 4   175.00

Cancellations: Black or red circular "Blood's Penny Post," black "1" in frame, red "1" in frame.

ENVELOPES

L42A

L43

L44

1848-60   **Embossed**
15LU1   L42A   **albino embossing,** *white*   —
15LU1A L42A   **albino embossing,** *buff*   —   4,000.
15LU1B L43   **red,** *white*   75.00   100.00
  a.   **Pink,** *white*   100.00
15LU2   L43   **red,** *buff*   —   150.00
15LU3   L44   **red,** *white*   75.00   160.00
15LU4   L44   **red,** *buff*   75.00   125.00

One example of No. 15LU1 is recorded, uncanceled, with the embossed stamp cut out and reattached. Two examples of No. 15LU1A are recorded, canceled by the "Blood's Despatch/28 So. Sixth" handstamp.

L45

15LU5   L45   **red,** *white*   35.00   75.00
  Used with 3c #11   *350.00*
  Used with 3c #26   *350.00*
  b.   Impressed on US Env. #U9   *250.00*
  c.   Impressed on US Env. #U1   *300.00*
  d.   Impressed on US Env. #U3   *500.00*
  e.   Impressed on US Env. #U2   *275.00*
15LU6   L45   **red,** *amber*   35.00   100.00
15LU6A L45   **red,** *buff*   350.00
  Used with 10c #2   —
  Used with three 1c #9   —
  Used with 3c #11   —

Laid Paper

15LU7   L45   **red,** *white*   35.00   125.00
  Used with acid tied #15L14   *200.00*
  a.   Impressed on US env. #U9   —
  a.   Impressed on US env. #U2   *300.00*
15LU8   L45   **red,** *amber*   35.00   125.00
  Used with 3c No. 25   *200.00*
15LU9   L45   **red,** *buff*   35.00   250.00
  Used with 3c No. 26A   —
15LU10 L45   **red,** *blue*   6,500.

Nos. 15LU1-15LU9 exist in several envelope sizes. No. 15LU6A exists in many shades, from buff to brown, as a result of various printings and changes over time.
  Cancellations: Black grid (Nos. 15LU1-15LU4), black company circle (2 sizes and types). When on government envelope, the Blood stamp was often left uncanceled.

Bouton's Post, New York, N.Y.
I. Franklin City Despatch Post

Organized by John R. Bouton

L46

1847   **Glazed Surface Paper**   **Typo.**
16L1 L46 (2c) **black,** *green*   7,500.
  a.   "Bouton" in blk. ms. vert. at side   7,000.
  On cover   *14,000.*

II. Bouton's Manhattan Express
Acquired from William V. Barr

L47

1847   **Typo.**
17L1 L47   2c **black,** *pink*   4,000.
  Cut to shape   900.
  On cover, uncanceled   *4,500.*

III. Bouton's City Dispatch Post
(Sold to Swarts' in 1849.)

Corner
Leaves — L48

Corner Dots — L49

Design: Zachary Taylor

1848   **Litho.**
18L1 L48   2c **black**   —   600.
  On cover   *2,000.*
  On cover with 5c #1   *27,500.*
  On cover with 10c #2   *50,000.*
18L2 L49   2c **black,** *gray blue*   —   250.
  On cover, tied by handstamp   600.
  On cover tied by Swarts'
    handstamp   *1,000.*
  On cover with 5c #1   *25,000.*
  On cover with 10c #2   *7,500.*

Cancellations on Nos. 18L1-18L2: Red "PAID BOUTON."

Boyce's City Express Post, New York, N.Y.

L50

Center background has 17 parallel lines

1852   **Glazed Surface Paper**   **Typo.**
19L1 L50   2c **black,** *green*   1,500.   1,000.
  Cut to shape   850.00
  On cover, tied by manu-
    script cancel   *4,000.*
  On cover, uncanceled   *1,500.*

Boyd's City Express, New York, N.Y.

Boyd's City Express, as a post, was established by John T. Boyd, on June 17, 1844. In 1860 the post was briefly operated by John T. Boyd, Jr., under whose management No. 20L15 was issued.
  For about six months in 1860 the post was suspended. It was then sold to William and Mary Blackham who resumed operation on Dec. 24, 1860.
  The Blackham issues began with No. 20L16. Boyd's had arrangements to handle local delivery mail for Pomeroy, Letter Express, Brooklyn City Express Post, Staten Island Express Post and possibly others.

L51

Designs L51-L56, L59-L60 have a rectangular frame of fine lines surrounding the design.

1844		Glazed Surface Paper		Litho.
20L1 L51	2c **black,** *green*			*1,000.*
	On cover			*4,000.*
	On cover, not tied, with #117L4			*7,000.*

Cancellation: Red "FREE."

L52

L53

L54

Plain background. Map on globe.

1844				Litho.
20L2 L52	2c **black,** *yellow green*			175.00
	On cover			*450.00*

Cancellation: Red "FREE."

Plain background. Only globe shaded.

1845				Engr.
20L3 L53	2c **black,** *bluish green*		—	250.00
	On cover			*500.00*

Cancellation: Red "FREE."

Inner oval frame of two thin lines. Netted background, showing but faintly on late impressions.

1845				Engr.
20L4 L54	2c **black,** *green*		—	15.00
	On cover, tied by handstamp			250.00
	On cover, not tied			75.00
	On cover, tied, with 5c U.S. Postmaster Provisional #9X1, on cover front			—
	On cover, tied, with 5c #1			*5,000.*
	On cover, not tied, with 5c #1			*1,500.*
	Double transfer			35.00
a.	Diagonal half used as 1c on cover			*2,300.*

Cancellations: Red "FREE." Black grid.
The 20L4 and 9X1 on cover front is the only recorded usage of a local stamp and a Postmaster Provisional.

1848				
20L5 L54	2c **gold,** *cream*		600.00	600.00
	On cover, not tied			*1,750.*
	On cover, cut to shape, not tied			*750.00*

Designs L54-L59 (except No. 20L23) were also obtainable die cut. An extra charge was made for such stamps. In general, genuine Boyd die-cuts sell for 75% of rectangular cut stamps. Stamps hand cut to shape are worth much less.

L55

L56

L57

No period after "CENTS." Inner oval frame has heavy inner line.

1848				Engr.
20L7 L55	2c **black,** *green* (glazed)		10.00	15.00
	On cover, tied by handstamp			175.00
	On cover, tied by handstamp, with 5c #1			*3,250.*
	On cover with 3c #10			—
	On cover, tied, with 3c #11			275.00
	Block of 4		40.00	
	Partially erased transfer			—
	On cover			—
a.	2c **black,** *yellow green*			15.00
	On cover			135.00

Cancellation: Black grid.
No. 20L7a is on unglazed surface-colored paper.

Period after "CENTS." Inner frame as in L55.

1852				Litho.
20L8 L56	2c **black,** *green*		25.00	35.00
	On cover			150.00
	Vert. strip of 3 on cover			300.00
20L9 L56	2c **gold,**		12.50	80.00
	On cover, tied by handstamp			750.00
	On cover with 3c #11			*1,250.*
	Block of 4		80.00	

Cancellations on Nos. 20L8-20L9: Black cork. Black "PAID J.T.B."
No. 20L8 was reprinted in 1862 on unglazed paper, and about 1880 on glazed paper without rectangular frame.

1854

Period after "CENTS." Inner oval frame has heavy outer line. Eagle's tail pointed. Upper part of "2" open, with heavy downstroke at left shorter than one at right. "2C" closer than "T2."

20L10 L57	2c **black,** *green*		32.50	25.00
	On cover, tied by handstamp			200.00

Cancellation: Black "PAID J.T.B."

L58

L59

1855   Unglazed Paper Colored Through   Typo.

Outer oval frame of three lines, outermost heavy. Solid background.

20L11 L58	2c **black,** *olive green*		65.00	90.00
	On cover, tied by handstamp			350.00

1856

20L12 L58	2c **brick red,** *white*		50.00	45.00
	On cover, tied by handstamp			500.00
20L13 L58	2c **dull orange,** *white*		50.00	45.00
	On cover			400.00
a.	Printed on both sides			—

Cancellation on Nos. 20L11-20L13: Black "PAID J.T.B."
Nos. 20L11-20L13 were reprinted in the 1880's for sale to collectors. They were printed from a new small plate of 25 on

lighter weight paper and in colors of ink and paper lighter than the originals.

1857   Glazed Surface Paper   Litho.

Similar to No. 20L10, but eagle's tail square. Upper part of "2" closed (in well printed specimens) forming a symmetrical "o" with downstrokes equal. "T2" closer than "2C."

20L14 L59	2c **black,** *green*		12.50	25.00
	On cover			125.00
	On cover, tied by handstamp, with 3c #26			—
	Pair on cover			—
	Block of 4		65.00	
a.	Serrate perf.			—

The serrate perf. is probably of private origin.
No. 20L15 was made by altering the stone of No. 20L14, and many traces of the "S" of "CENTS" remain.

1860

20L15 L59	1c **black,** *green*		1.00	50.00
	On cover, tied by handstamp			400.00
	Block of 4		7.50	
a.	"CENTS" instead of "CENT"			450.00
	On cover			450.00

Cancellation on Nos. 20L14-20L15: Black "PAID J.T.B."

L60

L61

Center dots before "POST" and after "CENTS."

1861

20L16 L60	2c **black,** *red*		7.50	20.00
	On cover, tied by handstamp			200.00
	Block of 4		37.50	
a.	Tete beche pair		45.00	
20L17 L60	1c **black,** *lilac*		12.50	17.50
	On cover, tied by handstamp			250.00
	On cover, tied by handstamp, with 3c #26			200.00
	On cover, tied by handstamp, with 3c #65			500.00
	Block of 4		50.00	
a.	"CENTS" instead of "CENT"		50.00	75.00
	Two on cover (No. 20L17a)			—
b.	"1" inverted			—
20L18 L60	1c **black,** *blue gray*		22.50	35.00
	On cover, tied by handstamp			250.00
	On cover, tied by handstamp, with 3c #26			225.00
	On cover, tied by handstamp, with 3c #65			225.00
	Block of 4		90.00	
a.	"CENTS" instead of "CENT"		75.00	90.00
	On cover			250.00
	On cover, tied by handstamp, with 1c #24 and three 3c #26			*2,000.*
b.	"1" inverted			—

Cancellations on Nos. 20L16-20L18: Black or blue company oval, black company circle, black or blue "PAID" in circle.

1861

20L19 L60	2c **gold,**			*250.00*
	Block of 4			—
a.	Tete beche pair			—
20L20 L60	2c **gold,** *green*			20.00
	Block of 4			—
a.	Tete beche pair			—
20L21 L60	2c **gold,** *dark blue*			12.50
	On cover, tied by handstamp			*150.00*
	Block of 4			—
a.	Tete beche pair			*300.00*
20L22 L60	2c **gold,** *crimson*			25.00
a.	Tete beche pair			—

1866   Typo.

20L23 L58	2c **black,** *red*		7.50	25.00
	On cover, tied by handstamp			250.00
	Block of 4		37.50	
a.	Tete beche pair		55.00	

Cancellations: Black company, black "PAID" in circle.
No. 20L23 was reprinted from a new stone on paper of normal color. See note after No. 20L13.

1866   Typo.

No period or center dots.

20L24 L61	1c **black,** *lilac*		30.00	65.00
	On cover, tied by handstamp			500.00
	Block of 4			—

20L25 L61   1c **black,** *blue*   6.00   *50.00*
       On cover, tied by handstamp   *500.00*
       Block of 4   30.00

Cancellation on Nos. 20L24-20L25: Black company.
Reprints exist of Nos. 20L24 and 20L25. Originals of No. 20L24 are grayish black on glazed paper, while the reprints are deep black on unglazed paper. Reprints of No. 20L25 are identical to the originals, and it is customary to regard stamps with original gum as originals and those without gum as reprints.

Boyd's City Dispatch
(Change in Name)

L62

1874   **Glazed Surface Paper**   **Litho.**
20L26 L62   2c **light blue**   35.00   40.00
       On cover   —
       Block of 4   —

A unique sheet of 100 exists. It demonstrates 10 transfer types (2x5) repeated ten times to produce the printing stone. The same stone was modified to produce Nos. 20L30-20L36.
The 2c black on wove paper, type L62, is a cut-out from the Bank Notices Nos. 20LUX1, 20LUX2, or 20LUX3.

Surface Colored Paper
20L28 L62   2c **black,** *red*   —
20L29 L62   2c **blue,** *red*   *250.00*

The adhesives of type L62 were made from the third state of the envelope die.
Nos. 20L28 and 20L29 are color trials, possibly used postally.

L63   L64

1877   **Litho.**
20L30 L63   2c **lilac,** *roseate*   —
Laid Paper
20L31 L63   2c **lilac,** *roseate*   —
Wove Paper
Perf. 12½
20L32 L63   2c **lilac,** *roseate*   27.50   25.00
       On cover   *200.00*
   a.   2c **lilac,** *grayish*   27.50   25.00
Laid Paper
20L33 L63   2c **lilac,** *roseate*   25.00
   a.   2c **lilac,** *grayish*
Glazed Surface Paper
20L34 L63   2c **brown,** *yellow*   35.00   35.00
       On cover, tied by handstamp   —
   a.   Imperf. horizontally   —

1877   **Laid Paper**   **Perf. 11, 12, 12½**
20L35 L64 (1c) **violet,** *lilac*   15.00   17.50
       On cover, tied by handstamp   *450.00*
   a.   (1c) **red lilac,** *lilac*   27.50   27.50
   b.   (1c) **gray lilac,** *lilac*   17.50   17.50
   c.   Vert. pair, imperf. horiz.   400.00
20L36 L64 (1c) **gray,** *roseate*   15.00   15.00
       On cover, tied by handstamp   *325.00*
   a.   (1c) **gray,** *grayish*   15.00

Cancellations on Nos. 20L30-20L36: Black "PAID" in circle. Purple company oval.

Boyd's Dispatch
(Change in Name)

Mercury Series — Type I — L65

Printed in sheets of 100.
Inner frame line at bottom broken below foot of Mercury. Printed by C.O. Jones.

1878   **Litho.**   **Wove Paper**   *Imperf.*
20L37 L65   **black,** *pink*   *400.00 300.00*
Surface Colored Wove Paper
20L38 L65   **black,** *orange red*   *750.00 500.00*
20L39 L65   **black,** *crimson*   *450.00 300.00*
Laid Paper
20L40 L65   **black,** *salmon*   *450.00*
20L41 L65   **black,** *lemon*   *450.00 400.00*
20L42 L65   **black,** *lilac pink*   *450.00*

Nos. 20L37-20L42 are color trials, some of which may have been used postally.

Surface Colored Paper
Perf. 12
20L43 L65   **black,** *crimson*   60.00   50.00
       On cover, tied by handstamp   *300.00*
   a.   **black,** *dull brown red*   40.00   40.00
       On cover, tied by handstamp   *300.00*
20L43A L65   **black,** *orange red*   150.00 150.00
       On cover, tied by handstamp   *1,000.*

Cancellations on Nos. 20L37-20L43A: Black "PAID" in circle. Purple company oval.

Wove Paper
Perf. 11, 11½, 12, 12½ and Compound
20L44 L65 (1c) **black,** *pink*   1.50   2.50
       On cover   *200.00*
   a.   Horizontal pair, imperf. between   —

1879   **Perf. 11, 11½, 12**
20L45 L65 (1c) **black,** *blue*   10.00   15.00
       On cover, tied by handstamp   *200.00*
20L46 L65 (1c) **blue,** *blue*   27.50   32.50
       On cover, tied by handstamp   *400.00*

1880   **Perf. 11, 12, 13½**
20L47 L65 (1c) **black,** *lavender*   8.00   20.00
       On cover, tied by handstamp   *300.00*
       Block of 4   50.00
   a.   Horizontal pair, imperf. between   *400.00*
20L48 L65 (1c) **blue,** *lavender*   —

1881   **Laid Paper**   **Perf. 12, 12½, 14**
20L49 L65 (1c) **black,** *pink*   350.00
       On cover, tied by handstamp   *600.00*

1880
20L50 L65 (1c) **black,** *lilac pink*   7.00   25.00
       On cover, tied by handstamp   *325.00*

Mercury Series — Type II — L65a — 20L51   Mercury Series — Type III — L65b — 20L55

No break in frame, the great toe raised, other toes touching line.
Printed by J. Gibson

1881   **Wove Paper**   **Perf. 12, 16 & Compound.**
20L51 L65a (1c) **black,** *blue*   35.00   30.00
20L52 L65a (1c) **black,** *pink*   75.00   75.00
       On cover, tied by handstamp   *400.00*
Laid Paper
20L53 L65a (1c) **black,** *pink*   7.50   7.50
       On cover, tied by handstamp   *125.00*
20L54 L65a (1c) **black,** *lilac pink*   12.50   10.00
       On cover   *200.00*

No break in frame, the great toe touching.
Printed by the "Evening Post"

Perf. 10, 11½, 12, 16 & Compound

1882   **Wove Paper**
20L55 L65b (1c) **black,** *blue*   4.00   10.00
       On cover, tied by handstamp   *225.00*
       Pair on cover   *225.00*
20L56 L65b (1c) **black,** *pink*   .40   1.50
       On cover, tied by handstamp   *100.00*
       Block of 4   2.00

Cancellations on Nos. 20L44-20L56: black or purple company ovals of various types, purple company circle, purple "SPECIAL," purple Maltese cross.

ENVELOPES
Boyd's City Post

L66

Imprinted in upper right corner.
Used envelopes show Boyd's handstamps.

1864   **Diagonally Laid Paper**   **Embossed**
20LU1 L66   **red**   175.00
20LU2 L66   **red,** *amber*   90.00
20LU3 L66   **red,** *yellow*   —
20LU4 L66   **blue**   175.00
20LU5 L66   **blue,** *amber*   175.00
20LU6 L66   **blue,** *yellow*   —

Several shades of red and blue.

20LU7 L66   **deep blue,** *orange,* cut
       square   600.00
       Entire   *5,500.*

Reprinted on pieces of white, fawn and oriental buff papers, vertically, horizontally or diagonally laid.

Wove Paper
20LU8 L66   **red,** *cream*   175.00
20LU9 L66   **red,** *orange*   — *2,500.*
20LU10 L66   **blue,** *cream*   —
20LU11 L66   **blue,** *orange*   —
       Impression at upper left   *4,000.*
20LU11A L66   **blue,** *amber*   —

Boyd's City Dispatch

L67a   L67b

L67a. Lines and letters sharp and clear. Trefoils at sides pointed and blotchy, middle leaf at right long and thick at end.
L67b. Lines and letters thick and rough. Lobes of trefoils rounded and definitely outlined. Stamp impressed normally in upper right corner of envelope; L67b rarely in upper left.

1867   **Diagonally Laid Paper**   **Typo.**
20LU12 L67 2c **red** (a) (b)   — *800.00*
20LU13 L67 2c **red,** *amber* (b)   — *300.00*
20LU14 L67 2c **red,** *cream* (b)   — *300.00*
   a.   On horiz. laid paper   —
20LU15 L67 2c **red,** *yellow* (a) (b)   — *300.00*
20LU16 L67 2c **red,** *orange* (b)   — *300.00*
   a.   Stamp impressed at upper left   —
Wove Paper
20LU17 L67 2c **red** (a) (b)   — *300.00*
20LU18 L67 2c **red,** *cream* (a) (b)   — *300.00*
20LU19 L67 2c **red,** *yellow* (a)   —
20LU20 L67 2c **red,** *orange* (a) (b)   —
20LU21 L67 2c **red,** *blue* (a) (b)   500.00 *400.00*

Design as Type L62
First state of die, showing traces of old address.

1874

Diagonally Laid Paper
20LU22 L62 2c **red,** *amber*   *200.00*
20LU23 L62 2c **red,** *cream*   *200.00*
Wove Paper
20LU24 L62 2c **red,** *amber*   *200.00*
20LU25 L62 2c **red,** *yellow*   *200.00*

Second state of die, no traces of address.

1875

Diagonally Laid Paper

20LU26	L62	2c **red**, *amber*		1,250.
20LU27	L62	2c **red**, *cream*	—	375.00

Wove Paper

20LU28	L62	2c **red**, *amber*		450.00

L68   L69

1877

Laid Paper

20LU29	L68	2c **red**, *amber*		800.00

Stamp usually impressed in upper left corner of envelope.

1878

Diagonally Laid Paper

20LU30	L69	(1c) **red**, *amber*	—	650.00

Wove Paper

20LU31	L69	(1c) **red**, *cream*	—	
20LU32	L69	(1c) **red**, *yellow*	—	

Boyd's Dispatch

Mercury Series —   Mercury Series —
Type IV — L70   Type V — L71

Mercury Series–Type IV

Shading omitted in banner. No period after "Dispatch." Short line extends to left from great toe.

1878

Diagonally Laid Paper

20LU33	L70	**black**	40.00	100.00
20LU34	L70	**black**, *amber*		80.00
20LU35	L70	**black**, *cream*	50.00	100.00
20LU36	L70	**red**		50.00
20LU37	L70	**red**, *amber*	35.00	45.00
20LU38	L70	**red**, *cream*	35.00	80.00
20LU39	L70	**red**, *yellow green*		—
20LU40	L70	**red**, *orange*		350.00
20LU41	L70	**red**, *fawn*		—

Wove Paper

20LU42	L70	**red**	—	800.00

Mercury Series–Type V

Colorless crosshatching lines in frame work. Very little shading on arms and legs.

1878

Diagonally Laid Paper

20LU43	L71	**red**	—	450.00
20LU44	L71	**red**, *cream*	25.00	50.00

Wove Paper

20LU44A	L71	**red**		1,000.

Boyd's Bank Notices
IMPORTERS' AND TRADERS'
NATIONAL BANK OF NEW YORK

No. 20LUX9a

1874-83

Incomplete Year Date ("187 "), Card Stock

20LUX1	L62	(2c) **black**, 155x100mm	250.00

Complete Year Date, Medium Wove Paper

20LUX2	L62	2c **black**, 157x104mm (1875)	—
20LUX3	L62	2c **black**, 152x104mm (1876)	250.00
20LUX4	L68	2c **black**, 154x105mm (1876)	—
20LUX5	L68	2c **black**, 156x108mm (1877)	400.00
20LUX6	L69	(1c) **black**, 156x108mm (1878)	—
a.		Four officers in masthead instead of three	—
20LUX7	L70	(1c) **black**, 158x110mm (1879)	250.00
20LUX8	L70	(1c) **black**, large year date and city, 158x110mm (1879)	250.00
20LUX9	L70	(1c) **black**, 149x102mm (1880)	75.00
a.		Three officers in masthead instead of four, 156x112mm	400.00
20LUX10	L70	(1c) **black**, 149x102mm (1881)	
a.		Four officers in masthead instead of three	
20LUX11	L71	(1c) **black**, 152x106mm (1883)	—

Sizes of these cards may vary by up to two millimeters in either dimension from the measurements shown.

Nos. 20LUX5 and 20LUX9 exist on paper with a papermaker's watermark. Nos. 20LUX6, 20LUX9 and 20LUX10 may be found with either three or four bank officers listed in the masthead. The major number is the card that was issued first. No. 20LUX11 is known only unused, and may be a remainder that was printed but not used.

NATIONAL PARK BANK
Medium Wove Paper

1881 (?)

20LUX12	L71	(1c) **black**, 122x63mm ('83)	300.00

No postmarks or cancellations were used on Bank Notices. Boyd's sometimes added the recipient's address in pencil.

FLEISCHMANN'S MODEL BAKERY
Card Stock

1879

20LUX13	L69	(1c) **black**, 130x75mm	3,000.

This card is imprinted "Fleischmann's Model Bakery."

Bradway's Despatch, Millville, N.J.
Operated by Isaac Bradway

L72

1857   **Typo.**

21L1	L72	**gold**, *lilac,* on cover, not tied, with certificate	9,250.
		On cover, not tied, with 3c #11, with certificate	12,000.

Brady & Co., New York, N.Y.

Operated by Abner S. Brady at 97 Duane St. Successor to Clark & Co.

L73

1857   **Typo.**

22L1	L73	1c **red**, *yellow*	1,000.	1,000.
		On cover, tied by company handstamp		22,000.
		On cover, tied by "PAID" handstamp		10,000.

Cancellations: Blue boxed "PAID," blue company oval. *Reprints exist.*

No. 22L1 tied on corner by company handstamp is unique. Three covers recorded with stamp tied by "PAID."

Brady & Co.'s Penny Post, Chicago, Ill.

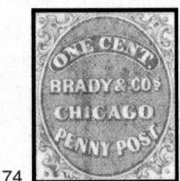

L74

1860(?)   **Litho.**

23L1	L74	1c **violet**	650.00	—

The authenticity of this stamp has not been fully established.

Brainard & Co.

Established by Charles H. Brainard in 1844, operating between New York, Albany and Troy, Exchanged mail with Hale & Co. by whom Brainard had been employed.

L75

1844   **Typo.**

24L1	L75	**black**	1,000.	1,250.
		On cover, two stamps tied		—
		On cover, tied by pen cancel		2,500.
		On cover, not tied		2,000.
		On cover, cut to shape, not tied		1,750.
24L2	L75	**blue**	1,000.	1,250.
		On cover, not tied		4,500.

Nos. 21L1-24L2 cut to shape are one half of values quoted.

Brigg's Despatch, Philadelphia, Pa.

Established by George W. Briggs

L76   L77

1847

25L1	L76	(2c) **black**, *yellow buff*	1,000.
		On cover, not tied, with certificate	11,500.
25L2	L76	(2c) **black**, *blue,* cut to shape	7,500.

No. 25L2 is unique. It is on cover, manuscript "X" cancel, genuine, but Philatelic Foundation has declined to give an opinion as to whether the stamp originated on the cover.

1848

25L4	L77	(2c) **gold**, *yellow,* glazed	5,500.
		On cover, not tied	—
25L5	L77	(2c) **gold**, *black,* glazed	4,000.
		On cover	—
25L6	L77	(2c) **gold**, *pink*	—

No. 25L4 used and on cover are each unique.

Handstamps formerly illustrated as types L78 and L79 are included in the section "Local Handstamped Covers" at the end of the Local Stamp listings. They were used as postmarks and there is no evidence that any prepaid handstamped envelopes or letter sheets were ever sold.

Broadway Post Office, New York, N.Y.

Started by James C. Harriott in 1848. Sold to Dunham & Lockwood in 1855.

L80

1849(?)   **Typo.**

26L1	L80	(1c)	**gold**, *black*, glazed	1,000.	1,250.
			Cut to shape		250.
			On cover		—
			Pair (tied) on cover		—

1851(?)

26L2	L80	(1c)	**black**	250.	400.
			On cover		1,500.
			On cover, cut to shape, tied		
			by handstamp		1,000.
			On cover with 3c #11		2,750.
			Pair	1,000.	1,000.
			Pair on part of cover		1,500.
			Block of 4		1,750.

Cancellation: Black oval "Broadway City Express Post-Office 2 Cts."

Bronson & Forbes' City Express Post, Chicago, Ill.

Operated by W.H. Bronson and G.F. Forbes.

L81

1855   **Typo.**

27L1	L81		**black**, *green*	600.	2,000.
			On cover		—
			On cover, tied by handstamp,		
			with 3c #11		14,000.
27L2	L81		**black**, *lilac*		3,500.

Cancellation: Black circle "Bronson & Forbes' City Express Post" (2 types).
No. 27L2 is unique.

Brooklyn City Express Post, Brooklyn, N.Y.

According to the foremost students of local stamps, when this concern was organized its main asset was the business of Kidder's City Express Post, of which Isaac C. Snedeker was the proprietor.

L82   L83

1855-64   **Glazed Surface Paper**   **Typo.**

28L1	L82	1c	**black**, *blue* (shades)	25.00	80.00
			On cover, tied by handstamp		400.00
			Block of 4	125.00	
a.			Tete beche pair	80.00	
28L2	L82	1c	**black**, *green*	20.00	50.00
			On cover, tied by handstamp		350.00
			On cover, tied by handstamp,		
			with 3c #65		1,250.
			Block of 4	100.00	
a.			Tete beche pair	125.00	
28L3	L83	2c	**black**, *crimson*	60.00	70.00
			On cover, tied by handstamp		400.00
			Block of 4	300.00	
28L4	L83	2c	**black**, *pink*	17.50	100.00
			On cover, tied by handstamp		550.00
			On cover, tied by handstamp,		
			with 3c #65		1,750.
			Block of 4	100.00	
a.			Tete beche pair	60.00	
28L5	L83	2c	**black**, *dark blue*	50.00	90.00
			On cover, tied by handstamp		500.00
			On cover, tied by handstamp,		
			with 3c #11		500.00
			Block of 4	250.00	

No. 28L5 has frame (dividing) lines around design.

28L6	L83	2c	**black**, *orange*	—	—
			On cover		—
a.			Tete beche pair		—

Unsurfaced Paper Colored Through

28L7	L83	2c	**black**, *pink*	300.00	750.00

Cancellations: Black ring, red "PAID."

Reprints exist of Nos. 28L1-28L4, 28L6.

Browne & Co.'s City Post Office, Cincinnati, Ohio

Operated by John W.S. Browne

L84   L85

1852-55   **Litho.**

29L1	L84	1c	**black** (Brown & Co.)	175.	150.
			On cover, tied by handstamp		1,000.
			On cover with 3c #11		2,750.
			Pair	450.	
29L2	L85	2c	**black** (Brown & Co.)	175.	175.
			On cover, tied by handstamp		5,000.
			On cover with 3c #11A		4,500.
			Pair	575.	

Cancellations: Black, blue or red circle "City Post*," red, bright blue or dull blue circle "Browne & Co. City Post Paid."

Browne's Easton Despatch, Easton, Pa.

Established by William J. Browne

L87   L88

1857   **Glazed Surface Paper**   **Typeset**

30L1	L87	2c	**black**, *red*	—	5,000.
30L2	L88	2c	**black**, *red*		

George Washington — L89

           Wove Paper   **Engr.**

30L3	L89	2c	**black**	750.	1,000.
			Pair	1,600.	
			Block of 6	5,750.	

The No. 30L3 block of 6 is the only reported block of this stamp. Three pairs are reported.

Cancellation on No. 30L3: Black oval "Browne's Despatch Easton Pa."

Brown's City Post, New York, N.Y.

Established by stamp dealer William P. Brown for philatelic purposes.

L86

1877   **Glazed Surface Paper**   **Typo.**

31L1	L86	1c	**black**, *bright red*	200.00	275.00
			On cover, tied by handstamp		2,250.
31L2	L86	1c	**black**, *yellow*	200.00	275.00
			On cover, tied by handstamp		1,000.
31L3	L86	1c	**black**, *green*	200.00	275.00
			On cover, tied by handstamp		1,000.
31L4	L86	1c	**black**, *violet*	200.00	275.00
			On cover, tied by handstamp		2,250.

31L5	L86	1c	**black**, *vermilion*	200.00	275.00
			On cover, tied by handstamp		500.00

Cancellation: Black and purple circle "Brown's Despatch Paid."

Bury's City Post, New York, N.Y.

L90   L91

1857   **Embossed without color**

32L1	L90	1c	*blue*		8,000.

               Handstamped

32L2	L91		**black**, *blue*		—

Bush's Brooklyn City Express, Brooklyn, N.Y.

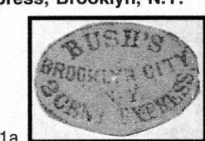

L91a

1848(?)   **Cut to shape**   **Handstamped**

157L1	L91a	2c	**red**, *green*, glazed		27,500.

No. 157L1 is unique. It is uncanceled on a large piece.
See Bush handstamp in Local Handstamped Covers section.

California City Letter Express Co., San Francisco, Calif.

Organized by J.W. Hoag, proprietor of the Contra-Costa Express, for local delivery. Known also as the California Letter Express Co.

L92

L93

L93a

1862-66   **Typeset**

33L1	L92	10c	**red**	—	—
			On cover, not tied		7,500.
			On cover, not tied, with		
			10c #68, with certificate		23,000.
33L2	L92	10c	**blue**		
			On cover, not tied, with		
			certificate		16,500.
33L3	L92	10c	**green**	5,500.	
			On cover, uncanceled, with		
			certificate		18,000.
33L4	L93	10c	**red**		
33L5	L93	10c	**blue**		14,000.
33L6	L93	10c	**green**	19,000.	

On cover, not tied, with
certificate 31,000.

No side ornaments, "Hoogs & Madison's" in one line

33L7a	L93a	10c **red**		1,200.
		On cover, not tied, with certificate		19,000.
33L8a	L93a	10c **blue**	4,000.	
		On cover, not tied, with 10c #68, with certificate		55,000.

Nos. 33L1 unused, 33L1 on cover with #68, 33L3 on cover, 33L6 unused, 33L6 on (patriotic) cover, 33L7 used, 33L7 on cover, 33L8 unused and 33L8 on cover with #68 each are unique. The other varieties of Nos. 33L1-33L8 are all rare.

California Penny Post Co.

Established in 1855 by J. P. Goodwin and partners. At first confined its operations to San Francisco, Sacramento, Stockton and Marysville, but branches were soon established at Benicia, Coloma, Nevada, Grass Valley and Mokelumne Hill. Operation was principally that of a city delivery post, as it transported mail to the General Post Office and received mail for local delivery. Most of the business of this post was done by means of prepaid envelopes.

L94

L94a

L95

L95a

1855				Litho.
34L1	L94	2c **blue**	700.	750.
		On cover		20,000.
		Block of 4	3,000.	
34L1A	L94a	3c **blue**		850.
34L2	L95	5c **blue**	250.	425.
		On cover		1,250.
		Block of 4	750.	
34L3	L95a	10c **blue**	475.	—
		On cover		3,000.

Cancellation: Blue circle "Penny Post Co."
Only one example of No. 34L1 on cover is recorded. The stamp is tied by manuscript cancel. Three examples of No. 34L1A are recorded, each uncanceled on cover.

L96

34L4	L96	5c **blue**	600.	1,750.
		On cover		3,000.
		On cover, uncanceled, with 10c #14		55,000.
		Strip of 3	3,500.	

The strip of 3 of No. 34L4 has faults but is unique. Value is for strip in faulty condition.

ENVELOPES

L97

1855-59				
34LU1	L97	2c **black**, *white*	200.	900.
		With 1c #9		
		With 3c #11		9,000.
		With 10c #14		11,000.
a.		Impressed on 3c US env. #U10	250.	1,000.
34LU2	L97	5c **blue**, *blue*	200.	900.
34LU3	L97	5c **black**, *buff*	200.	900.
a.		Impressed on 3c US env. #U10		1,500.
34LU4	L97	7c **black**, *orange buff*	—	
a.		Impressed on 3c US env. #U10		

L98

34LU6	L98	7c **vermilion** on 3c US env. #U9	200.00	1,000.
34LU7	L98	7c **vermilion** on 3c US env. #U10	225.00	1,750.

L98A

34LU8	L98A	5c **black**, *white*	150.	1,200.
34LU9	L98A	5c **black**, *buff*	150.	1,200.
		On cover, with 3c #11		3,500.
a.		Impressed on 3c US env. #U10		1,250.
34LU10	L98A	7c **black**, *white*	150.	1,000.
		On cover, with 3c #11		1,750.
a.		Impressed on 3c US env. #U9		1,750.
34LU11	L98A	7c **black**, *buff*	150.00	1,100.
a.		Impressed on 3c US env. #U10		1,500.
34LU11C	L98A	**black**, *buff*, "Collect Penny Postage" (no denomination)	250.	1,500.
		On cover, with 3c #11		

L98B

34LU11B	L98B	7c **black** on 3c US env. #U10	250.	1,400.
34LU12	L98B	7c **black** on 3c US env. #U9	250.	4,500.

OCEAN PENNY POSTAGE.
PAID 5.

L98C

34LU13	L98C	5c **black**, *buff*	—	—

CALIFORNIA
Penny Postage.
PAID 7

L98D

34LU13A	L98D	5c **black**, *buff*		
34LU14	L98D	7c **black**, *buff*	300.	3,000.
		With 3c #11		5,000.
34LU15	L98D	7c **black** on 3c US env. #U9	350.	2,500.
34LU16	L98D	7c **black** on 3c US env. #U10		

The non-government envelopes of types L97, L98A, L98C and L98D bear either 1c No. 9 or 3c No. 11 adhesives. These

adhesives are normally canceled with the government postmark of the town of original mailing. Values are for covers of this kind. The U.S. adhesives are seldom canceled with the Penny Post cancellation. When they are, the cover sells for more.
At least eight different varieties of the 34LU14 are known with different printed instructions/addresses, some with room to add U.S. postage.

Carnes' City Letter Express, San Francisco, Calif.

Established by George A. Carnes, former P.O. clerk.

L99

L100

1864				Typo.
35L1	L99	(5c) **rose**	175.	300.
		On cover, tied		15,000.
		Block of 4	750.	

Cancellations: Black dots. Blue dots. Blue "Paid." Blue oval "Wm. A. Frey."
See illustration L206

Overprinted "X" in Blue

35L2	L99	10c **rose**	200.00

Litho.

35L3	L100	5c **bronze**	125.00
a.		Tete beche pair	300.00
35L4	L100	5c **gold**	125.00
a.		Tete beche pair	300.00
35L5	L100	5c **silver**	125.00
a.		Tete beche pair	300.00
35L6	L100	5c **black**	125.00
a.		Tete beche pair	300.00
35L7	L100	5c **blue**	100.00
a.		Tete beche pair	250.00
35L8	L100	5c **red**	125.00
a.		Tete beche pair	300.00

Printed in panes of 18 (3x6) from three settings of 6 (3x2), with the bottom setting inverted, creating three tete-beche pairs.

G. Carter's Despatch, Philadelphia, Pa.
Operated by George Carter

L101

1849-51				
36L1	L101	2c **black**	—	100.00
		On cover, tied by pen cancel		225.00
		On cover, with 5c #1		300.00
a.		Vertically ribbed paper	—	140.00
		On cover, tied by pen cancel		300.00

No. 36L1 exists on paper with a blue, red or maroon wash. The origin and status are unclear.
Cancellation: Black circle "Carter's Despatch."

ENVELOPE

L102

36LU1	L102	**blue**, *buff*	1,000.
		Cut to shape	150.
		On cover with 3c No. 10	3,250.
		On cover with 3c No. 11	1,750.

Cheever & Towle, Boston, Mass.
Sold to George H. Barker in 1851

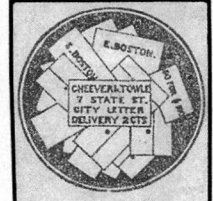

L104

1849(?)

37L1	L104	2c **blue**	600.	350.
		Cut to shape		125.
		On cover, tied by hand- stamp		7,000.
		On cover, not tied		1,500.
		On cover, not tied, cut to shape		500.

Cancellation: Red oval "Towle's City Despatch Post 7 State Street."

Chicago Penny Post, Chicago, Ill.

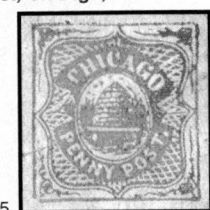

L105

1862   **Typo.**

38L1	L105	(1c) **orange brown**	800.	1,250.
		On cover, serrated perfora- tions		5,000.

Reprints exist.

Cancellation: Black circle "Chicago Penny Post A. E. Cooke Sup't."

Cincinnati City Delivery, Cincinnati, Ohio

Operated by J. Staley, who also conducted the St. Louis City Delivery Co. He established the Cincinnati post in January, 1883. The government suppressed both posts after a few weeks. Of the 25,000 Cincinnati City Delivery stamps printed, about 5,000 were sold for postal use. The remainders, both canceled and uncanceled, were sold to collectors.

L106

1883   **Typo.**   **Perf. 11**

39L1	L106	(1c) **carmine**	2.50	12.50
		On cover		300.00
a.		Imperf., pair	—	—

Cancellation: Purple target.

City Despatch Post, New York, N.Y.

The City Despatch Post was started Feb. 1, 1842, by Alexander M. Greig and Henry T. Windsor. Greig's Post extended to 23rd St. Its operations were explained in a circular which throws light on the operations of all Local Posts:

New York City Despatch Post, Principal Office, 46 William Street.

"The necessity of a medium of communication by letter from one part of the city to another being universally admitted, and the Penny Post, lately existing having been relinquished, the opportunity has been embraced to reorganize it under an entirely new proprietary and management, and upon a much more comprehensive basis, by which Despatch, Punctuality and Security-those essential elements of success-may at once be attained, and the inconvenience now experienced be entirely removed."

"**** Branch Offices-Letter boxes are placed throughout every part of the city in conspicuous places; and all letters deposited therein not exceeding two ounces in weight, will be punctually delivered three times a day *** at three cents each."

"**** Post-Paid Letters.-Letters which the writers desire to send free, must have a free stamp affixed to them. An ornamental stamp has been prepared for this purpose *** 36 cents per dozen or 2 dolls. 50c per hundred. ****"

"No money must be put in boxes. All letters intended to be sent forward to the General Post Office for the inland mails must have a free stamp affixed to them."

"Unpaid Letters.-Letters not having a free stamp will be charged three cents, payable by the party to whom they are addressed, on delivery."

"Registry and Despatch.-A Registry will be kept for letters which it may be wished to place under special charge. Free stamps must be affixed for such letters for the ordinary postage, and three cents additional be paid (or an additional fee stamp be affixed), for the Registration."

NOTE: The word "Free," as used in this circular, should be read as "Prepaid." Likewise, the octagonal "FREE" cancellation should be taken to mean "Prepaid" (that is, "Free" of further charge).

The City Despatch Post was purchased by the United States Government and ceased to operate as a private carrier on August 15, 1842. It was replaced by the "United States City Despatch Post" which began operation on August 16, 1842, as a Government carrier.

No. 40L1 was issued by Alexander M. Greig; No. 40L2 and possibly No. 40L3 by Abraham Mead; Nos. 40L4-40L8 probably by Charles Cole.

L106a   Cancellation

Plate of 42 (6x7) subjects

This was the first adhesive stamp used in the United States. This stamp was also used as a carrier stamp. See No. 6LB1.

1842, Feb. 1

40L1	L106a	3c **black**, *grayish*	375.	275.
		On cover, tied by hand- stamp		2,500.
		On cover, not tied		1,100.
		First day cover		25,000.
		Pair	850.	
		Block of 4	1,900.	
		Sheet of 42	27,500.	

No. 40L1 was used until Aug. 16, 1842, the first day of operation of the U.S. City Despatch Post. The latest recorded No. 40L1 cover is dated Aug. 13, 1842.

Cancellations: Red framed "FREE" (see illustration above), red circle "City Despatch Post" (2 types).

Die reprints of No. 40L1 were made in 1892 on grayish white, orange, red and green surface-colored papers. It is believed that only four carrier sets were made. Value, each reprint $500.

1846

Glazed Surface Paper

40L2	L106a	2c **black**, *green*	200.00	150.00
		On cover, tied by hand- stamp		750.00
		On cover, not tied		400.00

1847

40L3	L106a	2c **black**, *pink*		2,250.
		On cover, not tied, with cer- tificate		9,000.

Cancellations: Red framed "FREE," black framed "FREE," red circle "City Despatch Post."

L107

Similar to L106a with "CC" at sides.

1847-52

40L4	L107	2c **black**, *green glazed*	350.	200.
		On cover, tied by hand- stamp		1,500.
		On cover, not tied		600.
a.		"C" at right inverted	3,500.	
b.		"C" at left sideways		—
		On cover, tied by hand- stamp		—
c.		"C" at right only		—

Some students think No. 40L4c may have just a badly worn sideways "C" at left.

40L5	L107	2c **black**, *grayish*		500.
		On cover, tied by hand- stamp		850.
a.		"C" at right inverted		—
b.		"C" at left sideways		—
c.		"C" in ms. between "Two" and "Cents"		1,000.
d.		"C" at left sideways plus "C" in ms. between "Two" and "Cents"		1,900.
		On cover, tied by hand- stamp		4,000.
40L6	L107	2c **black**, *vermilion glazed*	450.	300.

		On cover, tied by hand- stamp		1,500.
a.		"C" at right inverted		4,500.
b.		"C" at left sideways		
		On cover, tied by hand- stamp		5,750.
		On cover, not tied		4,750.
40L8	L107	2c **black**, *yellowish buff* ('52)	—	—
a.		"C" at right inverted		—
b.		"C" at left sideways		12,000.

An uncanceled copy of No. 40L8 exists on cover.

Cancellations: Red framed "FREE," black framed "FREE," black "PAID," red "PAID," red circle company, black grid of 4 short parallel bars.

Each of the No. 40L6b covers are unique as listed.

City Dispatch, New York, N.Y.

L107a

1846   **Typo.**

160L1	L107a	2c **red**	3,000.	4,000.
		On cover		—
		Vertical pair	19,000.	

The unique vertical pair is the only reported multiple of No. 160L1.

Cancellation: Red "PAID."

City Dispatch, Philadelphia, Pa.

Justice — L108

1860   **Thick to Thin Wove Paper**   **Litho.**

41L1	L108	1c **black**	7.50	50.00
		On cover, tied by hand- stamp		500.00
		Block of 4	55.00	

Cancellations: Black circle "Penny Post Philada.," black circled grid of X's.

City Dispatch, St. Louis, Mo.

L109

Initials in black ms.

1851   **Litho.**

42L1	L109	2c **black**, *blue*		40,000.

No. 42L1 used is unique. A second example, on cover, is recorded.

City Dispatch Post Office, New Orleans, La.

Stamps sold at 5c each, or 30 for $1.

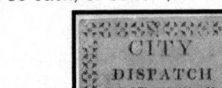

L110

1847   **Glazed Surface Paper**   **Typeset**

43L1	L110	(5c) **black**, *green*	6,000.	
		On cover		—
43L2	L110	(5c) **black**, *pink*	6,000.	
		On cover, not canceled		—

City Express Post, Philadelphia, Pa.

L111   L112

184-(?)   **Typeset**

44L1 L111   2c **black,** on cover, uncanceled, with certificate   11,000.
44L2 L112   (2c) **black,** *pink*   10,000.
    On cover, uncanceled, with
    certificate   20,000.
44L3 L112   (2c) **red,** *yellow,* on cover, uncanceled   30,000.

One example recorded of Nos. 44L1 and 44L3. Six No. 44L2 recorded, five of these uncanceled on covers. See illustration L8.

City Letter Express Mail, Newark, N.J.

Began business under the management of Augustus Peck at a time when there was no free city delivery in Newark.

L113

1856   **Litho.**
45L1 L113   1c **red**   350.00   500.00
    Cut to shape   100.00
    On cover   —
    On cover, cut to shape, tied
    by handstamp, with 3c
    #11   17,000.
45L2 L113   2c **red,** on cover, cut to shape,
    uncanceled, with certifi-
    cate   11,000.

On No. 45L2, the inscription reads "City Letter/Express/City Delivery" in three lines across the top. The example on cover is unique.

City Mail Co., New York, N.Y.

There is evidence that Overton & Co. owned this post.

L114

1845
46L1 L114   (2c) **black,** *grayish*   1,500.   1,500.
    On cover, not tied, with
    certificate   8,000.

Cancellation: Red "PAID."

City One Cent Dispatch, Baltimore, Md.

L115

1851
47L1 L115   1c **black,** *pink* (on cover)   —

Clark & Co., New York, N.Y.

(See Brady & Co.)

L116

1857   **Typo.**
48L1 L116   1c **red,** *yellow*   600.   900.
    On cover   2,500.

Cancellation: Blue boxed "PAID."

Clark & Hall, St. Louis, Mo.

Established by William J. Clark and Charles F. Hall.

L117

Several varieties

1851   **Typeset**
49L1 L117   1c **black,** *pink,* on cover, uncanceled, with certificate   19,000.

Clarke's Circular Express, New York, N.Y.

Established by Marion M. Clarke

George
Washington — L118

Impression handstamped through inked ribbon.
Cut squares from envelopes or wrappers.

1865-68(?)
50LU1 L118   **blue,** wove paper   5,750.
    a.   Diagonally laid paper   4,500.
50LU2 L118   **black,** diag. laid paper   5,750.

No. 50LU1 unused is unique.

Cancellation: Blue dated company circle.

Clinton's Penny Post, Philadelphia, Pa.

L118a

Typo.
161L1 L188a   (1c) **black**   22,500.

Cook's Dispatch, Baltimore, Md.

Established by Isaac Cook

L119

1853
51L1 L119   (1c) **green,** *white*   4,000.   3,000.
    Cut to shape   1,500.
    On cover   —

Cancellation: Red straight-line "I cook."

Cornwell's Madison Square Post Office, New York, N.Y.

Established by Daniel H. Cornwell. Sold to H.W. Bentley.

L120

1856   **Typo.**
52L1 L120   (1c) **red,** *blue*   1,500.   —
52L2 L120   (1c) **red**   250.   600.
    On cover, tied by hand-
    stamp   10,000.
    Pair   —

Cancellation: Black oval "Cornwall's Madison Square Post Office." Covers also bear black boxed "Paid Swarts."

Cressman & Co.'s Penny Post, Philadelphia, Pa.

L121

1856
     Glazed Surface Paper
53L1 L121   (1c) **gold,** *black*   350.   350.
    On cover, tied   1,500.
    Pair   1,200.
53L2 L121   (1c) **gold,** *lilac,* on cover, acid
    tied   25,000.

The vertical pair of No. 53L1 is unique. No. 53L2 also is unique.

Cancellation: Acid. (See D.O. Blood & Co. Nos. 15L13-15L16.)

Crosby's City Post, New York, N.Y.

Established by Oliver H. Crosby. Stamps printed by J.W. Scott & Co.

L123

1870   **Typo.**
     Printed in sheets 25 (5x5), imprint at left.
54L1 L123   2c **carmine** (shades)   1.00   50.00
    On cover, tied by hand-
    stamp   750.00
    Pair   —
    Sheet of 25   50.00

Cancellation: Black oval "Crosby's City Post."

Cummings' City Post, New York, N.Y.

Established by A. H. Cummings.

L124

1844   **Glazed Surface Paper**   **Typo.**
55L1 L124   2c **black,** *rose*   1,000.
    On cover, tied, with certifi-
    cate   5,000.
    On cover, not tied, with cer-
    tificate   —
55L2 L124   2c **black,** *green*   650.
    On cover   2,500.
55L3 L124   2c **black,** *yellow*   750.
    On cover, tied by hand-
    stamp   2,000.
    On cover, not tied, with cer-
    tificate   1,400.

Cancellations: Red boxed "FREE," red boxed "PAID AHC," black cork (3 types).

L125

55L4 L125   2c **black,** *green*   750.00   750.00
55L5 L125   2c **black,** *olive*   750.00   750.00

L126

55L7 L126   2c **black,** *vermilion*   8,250.

On cover, uncanceled, with
    certificate   22,000.

As L124, but "Cummings" erased on cliche
55L8 L124 2c **black**, *vermilion*   —
    Nos. 55L7 on cover and 55L8 each are unique.

Cutting's Despatch Post, Buffalo, N.Y.

Established by Thomas S. Cutting

L127

Cut to shape

1847
Glazed Surface Paper
56L1 L127 2c **black**, *vermilion*   —
    On cover, cut to shape, un-
    canceled, with certificate   22,000.

Davis's Penny Post, Baltimore, Md.

Established by William D. Davis and brother.

L128

1856   **Typeset**
57L1 L128 (1c) **black**, *lilac*   2,750.
    On cover, tied by hand-
    stamp   12,500.
a.   "Pennq," pos. 2   8,250. 8,250.
    Cancellation: Red company circle.

Deming's Penny Post, Frankford, Pa.

Established by Sidney Deming

L129

1854   **Litho.**
58L1 L129 (1c) **black**, *grayish*   5,750.
    On cover, with 3c #11   18,000.

Douglas' City Despatch, New York, N.Y.

Established by George H. Douglas

L130   L131

Printed in sheets of 25

1879   **Typo.**   **Perf. 11**
59L1 L130 (1c) **pink**   10.00   15.00
    On cover   300.00
a.   Imperf.   30.00   —
59L2 L130 (2c) **blue**   10.00   15.00
    On cover, tied by hand-
    stamp   500.00
a.   Imperf.   50.00   —
b.   Printed on both sides   —
    Printed in sheets of 50 (10x5).

Perf. 11, 12 & Compound
59L3 L131 1c **vermilion**   15.00   35.00
    On cover   325.00
a.   Imperf.   1.00   —
59L4 L131 1c **orange**   25.00   50.00
    On cover, tied by hand-
    stamp   600.00
59L5 L131 1c **blue**   30.00   50.00
    On cover   300.00
a.   Imperf.   1.00   —
59L6 L131 1c **slate blue**   20.00   25.00
a.   Imperf.   7.50   —
    Cancellations on Nos. 59L1-59L6: Ornate purple design, pur-
ple circular design composed of bars and wedges.

Imperforates are believed to be remainders sold by the
printer.

Dupuy & Schenck, New York, N.Y.

Established by Henry J. Dupuy and Jacob H.
Schenck, formerly carriers for City Despatch Post and
U. S. City Despatch Post.

Beehive — L132

1846-47   **Engr.**
60L1 L132 (1c) **black**, glazed paper 175.   300.
    On cover, tied by hand-
    stamp   1,750.
    On cover, tied by ms.   1,250.
60L2 L132 (1c) **black**, *gray*   175.   300.
    On cover, tied by hand-
    stamp   1,500.
    On cover, tied by pen can-
    cel   1,000.
    On cover, not tied   450.
    Cancellation: Red "PAID."

Eagle City Post, Philadelphia, Pa.

Established by W. Stait, an employee of Adams'
Express Co.

L133

Black manuscript "WS" on used examples

1847   **Pelure Paper**   **Typeset**
61L1 L133 (2c) **black**, *grayish* 14,000. 10,000.
    Cut to shape, on cover   —
    No. 61L1 unused is unique. Value reflects a 1997 auction
sale.

L134   L135

Two types: 39 and 46 points around circle

1846   **Litho.**
61L2 L134 (2c) **black**   125.00 250.00
    On cover, tied by hand-
    stamp   1,500.
    On cover, not tied   1,000.
    Block of 4   600.00
a.   Tete beche pair   500.00
    Block of 18, containing 4
    tete beche pairs   4,000.
    Paper varies in thickness.
    Five types identified of Nos. 61L3-61L4.

1850
61L3 L135 (1c) **red**, *bluish* 225.00 225.00
    On cover, not tied, with cer-
    tificate   1,750.
61L4 L135 (1c) **blue**, *bluish* 175.00 250.00
    On cover, tied by hand-
    stamp   6,500.
    On cover, not tied   400.00
    Block of 4   1,150.
    Cancellations on Nos. 61L2-61L4: Red "PAID" in large box,
red circular "Stait's at Adams Express."

East River Post Office, New York, N. Y.

Established by Jacob D. Clark and Henry Wilson in
1850, and sold to Sigmund Adler in 1852.

L136

1852   **Typo.**
62L1 L136 (1c) **black**, *rose* (on cover)   —

L137   L138

1852-54   **Litho.**
62L3 L137 (1c) **black**, *green*, glazed 1,000.
    On cover, not tied   —

1855
62L4 L138 (1c) **black**, *green*, glazed 250.00 250.00
    On cover   800.00
    On cover, not tied   400.00
    Vertical pair   2,500.
    The unique No. 62L4 pair is the only recorded multiple of any
of the East River Post Office stamps.

Eighth Avenue Post Office, New York, N.Y.

L139

1852   **Typo.**
63L1 L139 **red**, on cover   19,000.
    One example known, uncanceled on cover.

Empire City Dispatch, New York, N.Y.

Established by J. Bevan & Son and almost immediately suppressed by the Government.

L140

1881   **Typo.**   **Laid Paper**   **Perf. 12**
64L1 L140 **black**, *green*   1.50
    Block of 4   7.50
a.   Imperf.
b.   Horiz. pair, imperf. btwn.   85.00
c.   Vert. pair, imperf. btwn.   85.00

Essex Letter Express, New York, N.Y.

L141

1856   **Glazed Surface Paper**   **Typo.**
65L1 L141 2c **black**, *red*   1,250.
    Though uncanceled examples exist affixed to covers, some
authorities doubt that No. 65L1 was placed in use.

Faunce's Penny Post, Atlantic City, N.J.

Established in 1884 by Ancil Faunce to provide local
delivery of letters to and from the post office. Discontinued in 1887.

L141a

1885   **Die cut**
152L1 L141a (1c) **black**, *red*   325.   350.
                    On cover   1,500.

Jabez Fearey & Co.'s Mustang Express, Newark, N.J.

Established by Jabez Fearey, Local Agent of the Pacific & Atlantic Telegraph Co.

L142

1887 (?)   **Glazed Surface Paper**   **Typeset**
66L1 L142 **black**, *red*   275.00
                    On cover   —

Some authorities consider this item to be an express company label rather than a stamp.

Fiske & Rice

Authorities consider items of this design to be express company labels rather than stamps.

Floyd's Penny Post, Chicago, Ill.

Established by John R. Floyd early in 1860, operated by him until June 20, 1861, then continued by Charles W. Mappa.

John R. Floyd — L144

1860   **Typo.**
68L1 L144 (1c) **blue** (shades)   125.
                    On cover, tied by
                    handstamp   1,000.
                    On cover with 3c #26   1,500.
                    On cover with 3c #65   1,500.
                    Pair   275.
                    Strip of 4   1,250.
68L2 L144 (1c) **brown**   500.   1,000.
                    On cover   4,250.
68L3 L144 (1c) **green**   4,500.   3,250.
                    On cover
                    On 3c pink entire   20,000.

Cancellations: Black circle "Floyd's Penny Post Chicago," black circle "Floyd's Penny Post" and sunburst, black or blue oval "Floyd's Penny Post Chicago."

Franklin City Despatch Post, N.Y.

(See Bouton's Manhattan Express.)

Frazer & Co., Cincinnati, Ohio.

Established by Hiram Frazer. Stamps used while he was a Cincinnati letter carrier. Stamps of designs L146 and L147 were carrier stamps when used on cover between Feb. 3, 1848 and June 30, 1849.

L145

Cut to shape

1845
Glazed Surface Paper
69L1 L145 2c **black**, *green*, on cover   —

L146   L147

1845-51   **Wove Paper**   **Litho.**
69L2 L146 2c **black**, *pink*   —   3,500.
                    On cover, ms. tied   6,750.
69L3 L146 2c **black**, *green*   2,500.   2,750.
                    On 1847 cover, tied by
                    handstamp   11,000.
                    On cover, not tied   3,500.
69L4 L146 2c **black**, *yellow*   2,500.   2,500.
69L5 L146 2c **black**, *grayish*   2,500.   2,500.
                    On cover, tied by hand-
                    stamp   7,000.

Two stamps of type L146 show manual ms. erasure of "& Co."

1848-51
69L6 L147 2c **black**, *rose*   2,750.
                    On 1848 cover, not tied,
                    with certificate   6,500.
69L7 L147 2c **black**, *blue* (shades)   3,500.   2,000.
69L8 L147 2c **black**, *yellow*   2,750.
                    On 1848 part-printed notice   7,500.

Hiram Frazer was a government letter carrier until June 5, 1849. Therefore, any usage before that date is a government-carrier usage, not a local-post usage.

Freeman & Co.'s Express, New York, N.Y.

L147a

1855 (?)   **Litho.**
164L1 L147a (25c) **blue**   3,500.
                    On cover, not tied, with
                    certificate   —

Friend's Boarding School, Barnesville, Ohio.

(Barclay W. Stratton, Supt.)

On Nov. 6, 1877 the school committee decided to charge the students one cent for each letter carried to or from the post office, one and a half miles away. Adhesive labels were prepared and sold for one cent each. Their sale and use continued until 1884.

L147b — Type I

L147b — Type II

L147b — Type III

Three main types and sizes of frame

1877   **Typo.**
151L1 L147b (1c) **black**   175.00   —
                    On cover, uncanceled, af-
                    fixed to backflap   400.00

                    On cover, tied by hand-
                    stamp, with 3c #158   2,400.
                    On cover, tied by hand-
                    stamp, with 2c #210   2,750.

No. 151L1 was usually affixed to the back of the envelope and left uncanceled.

Gahagan & Howe City Express, San Francisco, Calif.

Established by Dennis Gahagan and C. E. B. Howe, as successors to John C. Robinson, proprietor of the San Francisco Letter Express. Sold in 1865 to William E. Loomis, who later purchased the G. A. Carnes business. Loomis used the adhesive stamps and handstamps of these posts, changing the Carnes stamp by erasing his name.

L148

L149

1849-70   **Typeset**
70L1 L148 5c **light blue**   1,200.   800.
70L2 L149 (5c) **blue**   150.   400.
  a.   Tete beche pair   450.
                    Sheet of 20, with 4 tete
                    beche pairs   —

Sheets of No. 70L2 contain five vertical rows of 4, the first two rows being reversed against the others, making horizontal tete beche pairs with wide margins between. The pairs were not evenly locked up in the form. There are five different types of No. 70L2.

L150

70L3 L150 (5c) **black**   40.00   45.00
                    Pair   100.00
                    Strip of 3   175.00

                    Overprinted "X" in Blue
70L4 L150 10c **black**   1,500.

Cancellations: Blue or black oval "Gahagan & Howe," blue or black oval "San Francisco Letter Express" and horseman (Robinson), blue or black oval "PAID" (Loomis).

Glen Haven Daily Mail, Glen Haven, N.Y.

Glen Haven was located at the head of Skaneateles Lake, Cayuga County, N.Y., until 1910 when the City of Syracuse, having purchased the land for reservoir purposes, razed all the buildings.

Glen Haven, by 1848, had become a famous Water Cure resort, with many sanitariums conducted there. The hamlet had a large summer colony interested in dress reform under the leadership of Amelia Jenks Bloomer; also antislavery, and other reform movements.

A local post was established by the hotel and sanitarium managements for their guests' convenience to deliver mail to the U.S. post offices at Homer or Scott, N.Y. The local stamps were occasionally pen canceled. They are known tied to cover with the Homer or Scott town postmark when the local stamp was placed adjacent to the government stamp and received the cancellation accidentally. The local stamps are only known used in conjunction with government stamps.

L151   L152

1854-58   Typeset
Several varieties of each
71L1	L151	1c **black**, *dark green*	1,000.	
a.		"Gien" instead of "Glen"	3,500.	
		On cover, uncanceled, with 3c #26, with certificate		6,250.

No. 71L1a unused (actually uncanceled on piece) and on cover with #26 each are unique.

Glazed Surface Paper
71L2	L152	1c **black**, *green*	500.	500.
		On cover		2,000.
		On cover, tied by handstamp. with 3c #11		3,750.

Links at corners — L153

Varying ornaments at corners — L153a

Several varieties of each
Glazed Surface Paper
71L3	L153	1c **black**, *green*	200.	225.
		On cover		2,000.
		On cover, tied by handstamp, with 3c #11		1,750.
		On cover, not tied, with 3c #11		500.
		Pair	700.	
71L4	L153a	1c **black**, *green*	300.	350.
		On cover		1,000.
		On 3c entire #U9, tied by handstamp		1,000.
		"Block" of 3	900.00	

The strip of 3 of No. 71L4 is the only known multiple of any Glen Haven stamp. It has faults and is valued thus.

Gordon's City Express, New York, N. Y.
Established by Samuel B. Gordon

L154

1848-52		**Typo.**	**Surface Colored Paper**	
72L1	L154	2c **black**, *vermilion*	7,000.	
		On cover, uncanceled, with certificate		15,000.
72L2	L154	2c **black**, *green*	150.	175.
		On cover, tied by handstamp		950.

Glazed Surface Paper
72L3	L154	2c **black**, *green*	125.	200.
		On cover, not tied		650.

Cancellation: Small black or red "PAID."

Grafflin's Baltimore Despatch, Baltimore, Md.
Established by Joseph Grafflin; operated from Apr. 1, 1855, until June 30, 1863

L155

1856				**Litho.**
73L1	L155	1c **black**	200.	350.
		On cover, tied by handstamp		4,000.
		On cover, tied by handstamp, with 3c #11		4,500.
		Block of 4	1,050.	

Originals show traces of a fine horizontal line through tops of most of the letters in "BALTIMORE."

Guy's City Despatch, Philadelphia, Pa.
Established by F. A. Guy, who employed 8 carriers.

L156

Sheets of 25 (5x5)
1879		**Typo.**	**Perf. 11, 12, 12½**	
74L1	L156	(1c) **pink**	30.00	35.00
		On cover, tied by handstamp		800.00
		Block of 4	150.00	
a.		Imperf., pair		—
74L2	L156	(1c) **blue**	45.00	60.00
		On cover, tied by handstamp		1,500.
		Block of 4	225.00	
a.		Imperf., pair		—
b.		(1c) **Ultramarine**	75.00	100.00

Cancellation: Purple company oval.

Guy's City Despatch was in operation from April to June, 1879. When Guy's was suppressed, the remainders were sold to a New York stamp dealer.

Hackney & Bolte Penny Post, Atlantic City, N.J.
Established in 1886 by Evan Hackney and Charles Bolte to provide delivery of mail to and from the post office. Discontinued in 1887.

L156a

Die cut
153L1	L156a	(1c) **black**, *red*	250.	375.
		On cover		1,500.
		On cover, tied by handstamp, with 2c #210		4,500.

Hale & Co.
Established by James W. Hale at New York, N.Y., to carry mail to points in New England, New York State, Philadelphia and Baltimore. Stamps sold at 6 cents each or "20 for $1.00."

L157

L158

Printed in sheets of 20 (5x4)
Pelure paper was used for initial printings, with medium wove paper used subsequently.

1844				**Typo.**
75L1	L157	(6c) **light blue** (shades)	65.00	40.00
		Cut to shape		17.50
		On cover, tied by handstamp		500.00
		Cut to shape on cover, tied by handstamp		200.00
		Pair on cover, not tied		800.00
		Strip of 3 on cover, tied by handstamp		7,000.
		Strip of 3 on cover, not tied		2,750.
a.		Pelure paper		
75L2	L157	(6c) **red**, *bluish*	300.00	300.00
		Cut to shape		75.00
		On cover, tied by handstamp		2,500.
		On cover, tied by pencil cancel		1,500.
		On cover, not tied		500.00
		Cut to shape on cover, tied by handstamp		1,000.
		Pair on cover		
		Ms. "23 State," cut to shape		1,900.
		On cover		4,500.
a.		Pelure paper		

Two covers recorded showing the manuscript change of address.

Same Handstamped in Black or Red, "City Despatch Office, 23 State St."
75L3	L157	(6c) **red**, *bluish* (Bk), cut to shape		2,000.
		Pair, partly cut to shape		44,000.
75L4	L157	(6c) **blue** (R), cut to shape		2,000.

No. 75L3 single and pair each are unique.
No. 75L3 and 75L4 represent the first handstamped overprints in philately.

Same as Type L157 but street address omitted
75L5	L158	(6c) **blue** (shades)	40.00	20.00
		Cut to shape		5.00
		On cover, tied by handstamp		450.00
		On cover, not tied		300.00
		Cut to shape on cover, tied by handstamp		300.00
		Pair on cover, tied by handstamp		900.00
		Strip of 3 on cover, not tied		—
		Pair	500.00	
		Block of 9	—	
		Block of 15	9,500.	
		Sheet of 20 (5x4)	17,000.	
		Ms. "23 State St.," on cover, tied by handstamp		7,500.

Cancellations on Nos. 75L1-75L5: Large red "PAID," red, black or blue oval "Hale & Co." (several types and cities), small red ornamental framed box (several types), red negative monogram "WE," magenta ms. "NB" (New Bedford).
The No. 75L5 sheet of 20 is unique.

Same as Type L158 Handstamped in Red "Office / 23 State St"
75L6	L158	(6c) **blue**, on cover		—

No. 75L6 is unique.

Hall & Mills' Despatch Post, New York, N.Y.
Established by Gustavus A. Mills and A. C. Hall.

L159

Several Varieties
1847		**Glazed Surface Paper**		**Typeset**
76L1	L159	(2c) **black**, *green*	300.	300.
		On cover, tied by handstamp		2,500.
		On cover with 5c #1		2,500.

T.A. Hampton City Despatch, Philadelphia, Pa.

L159a

L159b

Several Varieties of L159a

1847		Cut to shape		Typeset
77L1	L159a (2c)	black		1,500.
		On cover, tied by hand- stamp		14,000.
		On cover, uncanceled, with certificate		5,000.
77L2	L159b	black		—
		On cover		13,000.

Only one cover known with No. 77L1 tied by handstamp. Five or six covers are known with stamp uncanceled.

Two covers known with No. 77L2, each with stamp canceled, not tied. May 23 cover with certificate is valued above. Second cover is undated Valentine cover.

A handstamp similar to type L159b with denomination "2cts" or "3c" instead of "PAID." in center has been used as a postmark.

Hanford's Pony Express, New York, N.Y.

Established by John W. Hanford.

L160

1845		Glazed Surface Paper		Typo.
78L1	L160 2c	black, orange yellow (shades)	400.	400.
		Cut to shape		60.
		On cover, tied by handstamp		2,250.
		On cover, not tied		1,250.

Cancellation: Small red "PAID."

The handstamp in black or red formerly listed as Nos. 78LU1-78LU6 is illustrated in the Local Handstamped Covers section. It was used as a postmark and there is no evidence that any prepaid handstamped envelopes or lettersheets were ever sold.

George S. Harris City Despatch Post, Philadelphia, Pa.

L160a

L160b

1847 (?)			Typeset
79L1	L160a (2c)	black, on cover	—
79L2	L160b	black, on cover	30,000.

One example each known of Nos. 79L1-79L2, each uncanceled on cover, No. 79L2 with certificate.

Hartford, Conn. Mail Route

L161

Plate of 12 (6x2) varieties

1844		Glazed Surface Paper		Engr.
80L1	L161 (5c)	black, yellow	1,250.	2,000.
		On cover, not canceled		11,000.
		On cover, not tied		11,000.
		Pair		5,000.
		Pair on cover, not canceled		32,500.
80L3	L161	black, pink		3,500.

Chemically affected examples of No. 80L1 appear as buff, and of No. 80L3 as salmon.

Cancellations are usually initials or words ("S," "W," "South," etc.) in black ms. This may indicate destination or routing.

Hill's Post, Boston, Mass.

Established by Oliver B. Hill

L162

1849				Typo.
81L1	L162	1c black, rose, on cover, tied by handstamp		7,500.
		On cover, canceled but not tied, with certificate		6,500.

Only one No. 81L1 tied to cover recorded. Six covers recorded bearing No. 80L1 not tied, all but one of those also uncanceled.

A. M. Hinkley's Express Co., New York, N.Y.

Organized by Abraham M. Hinkley, Hiram Dixon and Hiram M. Dixon, in 1855, and business transferred to the Metropolitan Errand & Carrier Express Co. in same year.

L163

Sheets of 64 (8x8)

1855				Litho.
82L1	L163	1c red, bluish		650.00
		Block of 4		—
a.		Tete-beche pair		—

It is doubtful that No. 82L1 was ever placed in use. Only one example of No. 82L1a is recorded. It is contained in a block of 16 of No. 82L1.

Reprints exist on white paper somewhat thicker than the originals.

Homan's Empire Express, New York, N.Y.

Established by Richard S. Homan

L164

Several varieties

1852				Typeset
83L1	L164	black, yellow		—
a.		"1" for "I" in "PAID"		9,750.

No. 83L1a is unique. It is affixed to a cover front, uncanceled, with certificate.

Hopedale Penny Post, Milford, Mass.

Hopedale was a large farm community southwest of Milford, Mass. The community meeting of Feb. 2, 1849, voted to arrange for regular transportation of mail to the nearest post office, which was at Milford, a mile and a half distant, at a charge of 1c a letter. A complete history of this community may be found in "The Hopedale Community," published in 1897.

Rayed asterisks in corners — L165

Plain asterisks in corners — L166

Several varieties of Types L165-L166

1849		Glazed Surface Paper		Typeset
84L1	L165 (1c)	black, pink	800.00	800.00
		On cover with 3c #11, handstamp tied		3,750.
		On cover with 3c #11A, not canceled		1,000.
84L2	L166 (1c)	black, pink	1,000.	1,000.

Types L165 and L166 probably were printed together in a single small plate.

L167

		Wove Paper		Typo.
84L3	L167 (1c)	black, yellow		2,400.
		Cut to shape	900.	
		On cover		—
84L4	L167 (1c)	black, pink	600.	600.
		Pair	4,500.	

The No. 84L4 pair is unique, defective at top. It is the only recorded multiple of any Hopedale Penny Post issue.

J. A. Howell's City Despatch, Philadelphia, Pa.

L167a

184?			Typo.
165L1	L167a	black	—

Hoyt's Letter Express, Rochester, N.Y.

David Hoyt, agent at Rochester for the express company of Livingston, Wells & Pomeroy, operated a letter and package express by boats on the Genesee Canal between Dansville, N.Y., and Rochester, where connection was also made with Pomeroy's Letter Express.

L168

Several varieties

1844		Glazed Surface Paper		Typeset
85L1	L168 (5c)	black, vermilion		4,000.
a.		"Lettcr" instead of "Letter"		
		Pair, #85L1, 85L1a, on cov- er front		—

Humboldt Express, Nevada

A branch of Langton's Pioneer Express, connecting with the main line of Pioneer Express at Carson City, Nevada, and making tri-weekly trips to adjacent points.

L169

1863				Litho.
86L1	L169	25c brown	1,750.	1,250.
		Pair		2,750.
		On cover (U.S. Envelopes Nos. U34 or U35)		—
		On cover with 3c #65		40,000.

Cancellations: Blue oval "Langton's Pioneer Express Unionville." Red "Langton & Co."

Hussey's Post, New York, N.Y.

Established by George Hussey.
Reprints available for postage are so described.

L170

L171

1854				Litho.
87L1	L170 (1c)	blue		500.
		On cover, tied by hand- stamp		—
		On cover, with U.S. 3c (#11)		2,750.

1856

87L2	L171	(1c)	black	300.	200.
			On cover, tied by hand-stamp		1,850.
87L3	L171	(1c)	red		200.
			On cover, tied by hand-stamp		750.

Cancellation on Nos. 87L1-87L3: Black "FREE."

L172   L173

1858

87L4	L172	1c	brown red	45.	125.
			On cover, tied by hand-stamp		450.
			Pair on cover		1,000.
87L5	L172	1c	black	175.	—
			On cover		—
			Block of 4		—
			Strip of 7		—

Cancellation on Nos. 87L4-87L5: Black circle "1ct PAID HUSSEY 50 Wm. ST," date in center.
The No. 87L5 block of 4 and strip of 7 are unique.

1858

87L6	L173	(1c)	black	5.00	—
			On cover		—
87L7	L173	(1c)	rose red	5.00	—
			On cover		—
			Sheet of 46	350.00	
87L8	L173	(1c)	red	60.00	—
			On cover		—
			Sheet of 46		—

Type L173 was printed in sheets of 46: 5 horizontal rows of 8, one row of 6 sideways at bottom. Type L173 saw little, if any, commercial use and was probably issued mainly for collectors. Covers exist, many with apparently contemporaneous corner cards. On-cover stamps bear a black HUSSEY'S POST hand-stamp, but most if not all of Nos. 87L6-87L8 were canceled after the post ceased to operate.

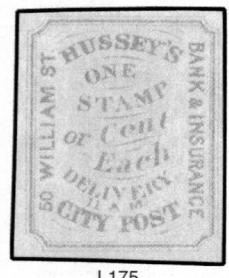

L174   L175

1858

87L9	L174	(1c)	blue	**Typo.**	
				5.00	

1859

87L10	L175	1c	rose red	**Litho.**	
				15.00	40.00
			On cover, tied by hand-stamp		400.00

No. 87L10 in orange red is not known to have been placed in use.
Cancellations: Black "FREE," black company circle "1 CT PAID HUSSEY 50 WM ST.," no date in center (smaller than cancel on Nos. 87L4-87L5).

87L11	L175	1c	lake	—	
87L12	L175	1c	black	—	

L176   L177

1862

87L13	L176	1c	black	25.00	
87L14	L176	1c	blue	15.00	25.00
			On cover, tied by hand-stamp		600.00
87L15	L176	1c	green	20.00	
			On cover		450.00
87L16	L176	1c	red	30.00	
87L17	L176	1c	red brown	30.00	
87L18	L176	1c	brown	30.00	
87L19	L176	1c	lake	—	
87L20	L176	1c	purple	30.00	
87L21	L176	1c	yellow	30.00	

Similar to L174 but has condensed "50" and shows a short flourish line over the "I" of "DELIVERY."
Printed in sheets of 49

1862

87L22	L177	(1c)	blue	3.00	25.00
			On cover		

L178   Similar to L171, but no dots in corners — L179

Printed in sheets of 30

1863

87L23	L178	(1c)	blue	7.50	
87L24	L179	(1c)	black	5.00	
			Sheet of 30	225.00	
87L25	L179	(1c)	red	6.50	
			Sheet of 30	250.00	
			On cover with 6c #115		12,500.

See No. 87L52.

L180   L182

87L26	L180	1c	brown red	5.00	25.00
			Block of 4	25.00	
			On cover, tied by hand-stamp		450.00

A so-called "reprint" of No. 87L26, made for J. W. Scott, has a colored flaw extending diagonally upward from the "I" in "CITY."
Reprints of types L173, L174, L178, L179 and L180 were made in 1875-76 on thicker paper in approximately normal colors and were available for postage.

1863

Dated 1863

87L27	L182	1c	blue	20.00	
			Cut to shape	12.50	
			On cover, tied by hand-stamp		500.00
87L28	L182	1c	green	27.50	
			Cut to shape	14.00	
			On cover, tied by hand-stamp		550.00
87L29	L182	1c	yellow	25.00	
			Cut to shape	12.50	
			On cover, tied by hand-stamp		500.00
87L30	L182	1c	brown	27.50	
			Cut to shape	14.00	
87L31	L182	1c	red brown	30.00	
			Cut to shape	15.00	
87L32	L182	1c	red	27.50	
			Cut to shape	14.00	
87L33	L182	1c	black	40.00	
			Cut to shape	20.00	
87L34	L182	1c	violet	40.00	
			Cut to shape	20.00	
87L35	L182	2c	brown	40.00	75.00
			Cut to shape	20.00	
			On cover, tied by hand-stamp		650.00

The 2c blue dated 1863 exists only as a counterfeit.

1865

Dated 1865

87L38	L182	2c	blue	35.00	45.00
			On cover, tied by hand-stamp		475.00

1867

Dated 1867

87L39	L182	2c	blue	45.00	40.00
			On cover, tied by hand-stamp		450.00

1868

Dated 1868

87L40	L182	2c	blue	40.00	65.00
			On cover, tied by hand-stamp		500.00

1869

Dated 1870

87L41	L182	2c	blue	45.00	70.00
			On cover, tied by hand-stamp		500.00

1871

Dated 1871

87L42	L182	2c	blue	40.00	65.00
			On cover, tied by hand-stamp		750.00

L183   L184

1872

Wove Paper

87L43	L183		black	5.00	20.00
			On cover, tied by hand-stamp		300.00
			Pair on cover, tied by hand-stamp		1,500.
87L44	L183		red lilac	9.00	40.00
			On cover, tied by hand-stamp		300.00
87L45	L183		blue	6.00	40.00
			On cover, tied by hand-stamp		300.00
			Pair on cover, tied by hand-stamp		750.00
87L46	L183		green	10.00	45.00
			On cover, tied by hand-stamp		300.00

Sheets contain four panes of 28 each. Double periods after "A.M." on two stamps in two panes, and on four stamps in the other two panes.
Covers show postmark reading: "HUSSEY'S SPECIAL-MESSENGER EXPRESS-PAID-54 PINE ST."

1872

Thick Laid paper

87L47	L184		black	10.00	35.00
			On cover		—
			Block of 4	45.00	
87L48	L184		yellow	17.50	65.00
87L49	L184		red brown	17.50	50.00
			On cover		200.00
87L50	L184		red	17.50	40.00
			On cover		—

L185   L186

1873

Thin Wove Paper

87L51	L185	2c	black	75.00	150.00
			On cover, tied by hand-stamp		500.00

A reprint of No. 87L51, believed to have been made for J. W. Scott, shows a 4mm break in the bottom frameline under "54."

Type of 1863

1875

Thick Wove Paper

87L52	L179	(1c)	blue	750.00

1875

L186 in imitation of L180, but no corner dots, "S" for "$," etc.

87L53	L186	1c	black	2.00

Some authorities believe Nos. 87L52-87L53 are imitations made from new stones. Attributed to J. W. Scott.

"Copyright 1877" — L188

L188a

1877

Thick Wove Paper

87L55	L188	black	175.00	—
		On cover		600.00

Error of design, used provisionally. Stamp was never copyrighted. Printed singly.

87L56	L188a	black	350.00	

Thin Wove Paper

87L57	L188a	blue	45.00	
87L58	L188a	rose	30.00	
		On cover		—

Perf. 12½

87L59	L188a	blue	3.00	10.00
		On cover		250.00
a.		Imperf. horizontally, pair	—	
87L60	L188a	rose	3.00	10.00
		On cover		250.00

"TRADE MARK" small — L189

"TRADE MARK" medium — L190

"TRADE MARK" larger, touching "s" of "Easson." — L191

1878

Wove Paper — Perf. 11, 11½, 11x12, 12

87L61	L189	blue	15.00	50.00
		On cover, tied by handstamp		150.00
87L62	L189	carmine	12.50	40.00
		On cover, tied by handstamp		200.00
87L63	L189	black	100.00	

Nos. 87L61-87L63 exist imperforate.

Perf. 11, 12, 12½, 14, 16 and Compound

87L64	L190	blue	5.00	17.50
		On cover, tied by handstamp		200.00

87L65	L190	red	5.00	10.00
		On cover, tied by handstamp		150.00
87L66	L190	black		—

The existence of No. 87L66 either perforated or as an imperf reprint has been questioned by specialists. The editors would like to see authenticated evidence of its existence.

Nos. 87L64-87L65 imperf. are reprints.

1879 — **Perf. 11, 12, and Compound**

87L67	L191	blue	3.00	10.00
		On cover, tied by handstamp		300.00

1880 — **Imperf.**

87L70	L191	blue	4.00	10.00
		On cover, tied by handstamp		450.00
87L71	L191	red	5.00	75.00
87L72	L191	black	4.00	

The authenticity of Nos. 87L70-87L72 has not been fully established.

L192

Two types of L192:
I. Imprint "N. F. Seebeck, 97 Wall St. N. Y." is in lower tablet below "R Easson, etc."
II. Imprint in margin below stamp.

1880 — **Glazed Surface Wove Paper** — **Perf. 12**

87L73	L192	brown, type I	10.00	20.00
		On cover, tied by handstamp		250.00
		Block of 4	—	
a.		Type II	3.00	5.00
		On cover, tied by handstamp		250.00
b.		Horiz. pair, imperf. between	50.00	
c.		Imperf., pair, type I	50.00	
87L74	L192	ultramarine, type I	12.50	25.00
		On cover, tied by handstamp		350.00
a.		Imperf., pair	—	
		Imperf (single) on cover		135.00
b.		Deep blue, type II	40.00	
87L75	L192	red, type II	1.50	3.50
		On cover, tied by handstamp		175.00
		Block of 4	6.50	
a.		Imperf, single on cover		150.00
b.		Horiz. pair, imperf between	—	

1882 — **Perf. 16, 12x16**

87L76	L192	brown, type I	12.50	30.00
		On cover, tied by handstamp		125.00
87L77	L192	ultramarine, type I	10.00	20.00
		On cover, tied by handstamp		125.00

Cancellations: Violet 3-ring target, violet ornamental "T." Imperf. impressions of Type I in various colors, on horizontally laid paper, ungummed, are color trials.

SPECIAL DELIVERY STAMPS

L181

Typographed; Numerals Inserted Separately

1863 — **Glazed Surface Paper**

87LE1	L181	5c	black, vermilion	2.00	17.50
			On cover, tied by handstamp		325.00
87LE2	L181	10c	gold, green	2.50	20.00
			On cover, tied by handstamp		325.00
87LE3	L181	15c	gold, black	3.50	27.50
			On cover, tied by handstamp		325.00
			On cover with 1c #87L10, tied by handstamps		—
87LE4	L181	20c	black	2.00	17.50
			On cover, tied by handstamp		325.00
87LE5	L181	25c	gold, blue	4.00	40.00
			On cover, tied by handstamp		325.00
87LE6	L181	30c	black, vermilion	—	
87LE7	L181	50c	black, green	—	

Nos. 87LE1-87LE7 on cover show Hussey handstamp cancellations in various types.

Nos. 87LE4 and 87LE5 are on unglazed paper, the latter surface colored. Ten minor varieties of each value, except the 30c and 50c, which have the figures in manuscript. Printed in

two panes of 10, certain values exist in horizontal cross-gutter tete beche pairs.

Originals of the 5c to 20c have large figures of value. The 25c has condensed figures with decimal point. Reprints exist with both large and condensed figures. Reprints of the 25c also exist with serifs on large figures.

Most of the Hussey adhesives are known on cover, tied with Hussey Express postmarks. Many of these were canceled after the post ceased to operate as a mail carrier. "On cover" values are for original stamps used while the post was operating.

LETTERSHEETS AND WRAPPERS (No. 87LUP2)

L192a   L192b

1856 — **Handstamped** — **Inscribed: "82 Broadway"**

87LUP1	L192a	black	—	500.

1858 — **Inscribed: "50 William St. Basement"**

87LUP2	L192b	black, manila	—	600.
		With 1c #87L3, tied by handstamp		1,250.
87LUP3	L192b	black	—	650.
		With 1c #87L2, tied by handstamp		2,750.
		With 1c #87L3, tied by handstamp		1,750.

Nos. 87LUP1 and 87LUP3 appear on papers of various colors.

Jefferson Market P. O., New York, N. Y.

Established by Godfrey Schmidt

L193

1850 — **Glazed Surface Paper** — **Litho.**

88L1	L193	(2c)	black, pink	9,750.	
88L2	L193	(2c)	black, blue	—	
			On cover, tied by handstamp		—
			On cover, not tied		3,500.

Four examples recorded of No. 88L1, all unused. Five No. 88L2 recorded, all on covers (two with stamp tied by handstamp).

Jenkins' Camden Dispatch, Camden, N. J.

Established by Samuel H. Jenkins and continued by William H. Jenkins.

George Washington — L194

There are two types of design L194.

1853-54 — **Litho.**

89L1	L194	black (fine impression) (1854)	350.	450.
		Block of 9	7,500.	
		On cover, not tied		900.
		On cover, tied by ms., with certificate		3,000.

George Washington — L194a

Typo. from Woodcut

89L2	L194a	black, yellow (coarse impression) (1853)	3,000.	
		On cover, tied by ms., with certificate		6,500.

L195

Typeset

89L3 L195　1c **black,** *grayish* (1853)　　　　　　—
　　　　　　On cover, tied by ms.　　　　　17,500.

　　No. 89L3 was probably the first stamp issued by Jenkins. Each of the four known examples is of a different type. One exampled is unused; three are recorded on cover (one of which is uncanceled).

Johnson & Co.'s City Despatch Post, Baltimore, Md.

Operated by Ezekiel C. Johnson, letter carrier

L196

1848　　　　　　　　　　　　　　**Typeset**
90L1 L196　2c **black,** *lavender,* on cover,
　　　　　　　　uncanceled　　　　　22,500.

　　Two recorded examples of No. 90L1, each uncanceled on cover.

Jones' City Express, Brooklyn, N. Y.

George Washington — L197

1845　　　　**Glazed Surface Paper**　　**Engr.**
91L1 L197　2c **black,** *pink*　　　1,000.　1,500.
　　　　　　On cover, not tied, with certifi-
　　　　　　cate　　　　　　　　3,000.

　　Cancellation: Red oval "Boyd's City Express Post."

Kellogg's Penny Post & City Despatch, Cleveland, Ohio

L198

1853　　　　　　　　　　　　　**Typo.**
92L1 L198　(1c) **vermilion**　　　　　1,750.
　　　　　On cover, tied by handstamp　　—
　　　　　On cover, tied by handstamp,
　　　　　with 3c #11, with certificate　42,500.
　　　　　On cover, not tied, with 3c #11,
　　　　　with certificate　　　　15,000.
　　　　　On 3c entire #U2, tied by
　　　　　handstamp　　　　　　9,000.

　　Cancellation: Black grid.

Kidder's City Express Post, Brooklyn, N.Y.

　　In 1847, Henry A. Kidder took over the post of Walton & Co., and with the brothers Isaac C. Snedeker and George H. Snedeker increased its scope. In 1851, the business was sold to the Snedekers. It was operated under the old name until 1853 when the Brooklyn City Express Post was founded.

L199

Stamps bear black manuscript "I S" control in two styles.

1847　　　**Glazed Surface Paper**　　**Typo.**
93L1 L199　2c **black,** *blue* (shades)　750.　500.
　　　　　On cover, tied by handstamp　6,000.
　　　　　On cover, not tied　　　　4,500.
　　　　　Block of 4　　　　　3,500.

　　Cancellation: Red "PAID."

Reprinted on green paper.

Kurtz Union Despatch Post, New York, N.Y.

L200

Typeset; "T" in Black Ms.

1853

Glazed Surface Paper

94L1 L200　2c **black,** *green*　　　3,500.

Langton & Co.
(See Humboldt Express.)

Ledger Dispatch, Brooklyn, N.Y.

　　Established by Edwin Pidgeon. Stamps reported to have been sold at 80 cents per 100. Suppressed after a few months.

L201

1882　　　**Typo.**　　**Rouletted 12 in color**
95L1 L201　**rose** (shades)　　300.　600.
　　　　　Block of 4　　　　1,500.

Letter Express

　　Established by Henry Wells. Carried mail for points in Western New York, Chicago, Detroit and Duluth.

L202　　　　　　　　L203

1844　　**Glazed Surface Paper**　　**Typo.**
96L1 L202　5c **black,** *pink*　　300.00　200.00
　　　　　On cover, tied by ms. can-
　　　　　cel　　　　　　　　1,000.
　　　　　On cover, not tied　　　500.00
　　　　　Pair on cover, tied by
　　　　　handstamp　　　　　3,500.
　　　　　Pair on cover, tied by ms.
　　　　　cancel　　　　　　　2,000.
　　　　　Pair on cover, not tied　1,000.
　　　　　Pair　　　　　700.00　450.00
　　　　　Block of 10　28,500.
96L2 L202　5c **black,** *green*　　—　500.00
　　　　　On cover, tied by ms. can-
　　　　　cel　　　　　　　　5,000.
　　　　　On cover, not tied　　　3,500.
　　　　　Pair　　　　　　　　1,500.
96L3 L203　10c **black,** *pink*　　—　500.00
　　　　　On cover, tied by ms. can-
　　　　　cel　　　　　　　　2,000.
　　　　　On cover, not tied　　　1,500.
　　　　　Pair　　　　　1,500.　1,500.
　　　　　Strip of 3　　　　　9,250.
　　a.　Bisect on cover, tied by ms. cancel　—
　　　　　Bisect on cover, un-
　　　　　canceled　　　　　2,500.

　　No. 96L3a was sold as a horizontal or vertical bisect. It is known used singly for 5c (rare), or as two bisects for 10c (extremely rare). Stamps are known almost exclusively tied with black ms. "X" covering the cut, and can be authenticated by experts.
　　The block of 10 of No. 96L1 is the only block recorded of any Letter Express issue. Value represents actual auction sale price in 1999.

L204

96L4 L204　10c **black,** *scarlet*　　—　2,500.
　　　　　On cover, tied by ms. cancel,
　　　　　with certificate　　　　9,250.
　　a.　Tete beche pair, one stamp a horiz.
　　　　　bisect, on piece　　　　8,750.

　　Cancellations: Red large partly boxed "PAID," red boxed "Boyd's City Express Post."

Locomotive Express Post

L205

1847 (?)　　　　　　　　**Handstamped**
97L1 L205　**black**　　　　　　　　—

Wm. E. Loomis Letter Express, San Francisco, Calif.

　　William E. Loomis established this post as the successor to the Gahagan & Howe City Express, which he bought in 1865. He continued to use the Gahagan & Howe stamps unchanged. Later Loomis bought Carnes' City Letter Express. He altered the Carnes stamp by erasing "CARNES)" from the plate and adding the address below the oval: "S.E. cor. Sans'e & Wash'n."

L206

1868　　　　　　　　　　　　**Typo.**
98L1 L206　(5c) **rose**　　　300.00　650.00
　　　　　On cover, tied by ms.　　4,250.

　　Cancellation: Blue "PAID."

McGreely's Express, Alaska

　　Established in 1898 by S. C. Marcuse to carry letters and packages by motorboat between Dyea and Skagway, Alaska.

L208

1898　　　　**Typo.**　　　　**Perf. 14**
155L1 L208　25c **blue**　　　　　50.00
　　　　　Block of 4　　　　　250.00

　　The status of No. 155L1 is questioned.

McIntire's City Express Post, New York, N.Y.

Established by William H. McIntire

Mercury — L207

1859   **Litho.**
99L1 L207 2c **pink**   10.00 *100.00*
      Block of 4   75.00
      On cover, tied by handstamp   *3,250.*
a.   Period after CENTS omitted   —
Cancellation: Black oval "McIntire's City Express Post Paid."

McMillan's City Dispatch Post, Chicago, Ill.

L208a

1855   **Typeset**
100L1 L208a **black,** *rose*   *25,000.*
      No. 100L1 is unique.

Mac & Co's Dispatch, Fallsington-Morrisville, Pa.

L208b

                  Typo.
166L1 L208b 1c **black,** on 3c entire #U1,
      uncanceled, with certifi-
      cate   *17,500.*
      No. 166L1 is unique.

Magic Letter Express, Richmond, Va.
Established by Evans, Porter & Co.

L209   L209a

1865   **Typo.**
101L1 L209   1c **black,** on cover, not tied
      by cancel   *40,000.*
101L2 L209a 2c **black,** *brown*   *14,000.*
101L3 L209a 5c **black,** *brown*   — *8,000.*
      Nos. 101L1-101L2 each are unique.

Mason's New Orleans City Express, New Orleans, La.
J. Mason, proprietor

L210

1850-57   **Typeset**
102L1 L210 ½c **black,** *blue* (value changed
      to "1" in black ms.)   *12,500.*
      On cover, tied
102L2 L210 2c **black,** *yellow*   — *3,000.*
      On cover, tied by hand-
      stamp   *10,000.*
      Cancellations: Red grid, small red circle "Mason's City Express."

Mearis' City Despatch Post, Baltimore, Md.
Established by Malcom W. Mearis

L211

L212

Black ms. initials "M W M" control on all stamps

1846   **Typeset**
103L1 L211 1c **black,** *gray*   — —
      On cover, tied by hand-
      stamp   *22,000.*
103L2 L212 1c **black,** *gray*   —
103L3 L212 2c **black,** *gray*   —
      On cover, uncancelled, with
      certificate   *15,000.*
a.   Horiz. pair, #103L2-103L3   —
      Two types of No. 103L3.

L213

Two types of each.
103L4 L213 1c **black,** *gray*   —
103L5 L213 2c **black,** *gray*   —
a.   Horiz. pair, #103L4-103L5   —

L214

103L6 L214 1c **black,** *gray*   *11,000.*
      No. 103L6 is unique; tied on small piece by handstamp.
      Corner ornaments of Nos. 103L1-103L6 differ on each stamp. All varieties of Nos. 103L1-103L6 contained in one plate.

Menant & Co.'s Express, New Orleans, La.

L215

1853 (?)   **Typo.**
104L1 L215 2c **dark red**   *15,000.*
      Only four examples are known. Two have Philatelic Foundation Certificates. All four have faults, and the stamp is valued thus.
      Reprints are fairly common and are orange red, not dark red.

Mercantile Library Association, New York, N.Y.
      Stamps paid for special delivery service of books ordered from the library, and of forms especially provided to subscribers. The forms bore a government stamp on the outside, a library stamp inside.

L216

1870-75   **Litho.**
105L1 L216 5c **black,** *maroon*   250. *350.*
105L2 L216 5c **black,** *yellow*   350. *500.*
a.   With delivery check attached at right   1,150.
105L3 L216 5c **blue**   350. *500.*
      Pair, on postal card   *1,400.*
105L5 L216 6c **black,** *maroon*   2,250.
105L6 L216 10c **black,** *yellow*   500. *750.*
      No. 105L5 is slightly larger than the 5c and 10c stamps.
      The stamps "on cover" are affixed to cutouts from order blanks showing order number, title of book desired, and subscriber's name and address. When canceled, the stamps and order blanks show a dull blue double-lined oval inscribed "MERCANTILE LIBRARY ASSOCIATION" and date in center. The

---

stamps are really more a form of receipt for a prepaid parcel delivery service than postage stamps.

POSTAL CARD
Printed on U.S. Postal Card, First Issue
105LUX1 L216 10c **yellow**   *3,500.*
      No. 105LUX1 is unique.

Messenkope's Union Square Post Office, New York, N.Y.
      Established by Charles F. Messenkope in 1849 and sold to Joseph E. Dunham in 1850.

L217

1849   **Glazed Surface Paper**   **Litho.**
106L1 L217 (1c) **black,** *green*   90. *90.*
      On cover, tied by hand-
      stamp   *500.*
      Two singles on cover (2c
      rate), tied by handstamp   *3,000.*
      Pair on cover (2c rate), tied
      by handstamp   *3,000.*
      On cover with 5c #1   *3,000.*
      On cover, tied by hand-
      stamp, with 3c #10   *1,500.*
      On cover, tied by hand-
      stamp, with 3c #11   *2,000.*
      On cover with 3c #26   *1,000.*
      Strip of 3   400.
106L2 L217 (2c) **black,** *pink*   — —
      On cover   —
      Some examples of No. 106L1 are found with "MESSENKOPES" crossed through in black ms. in an apparent attempt (by Dunham?) to obliterate it.
      Cancellations: Red "PAID," red oval "DUNHAMS UNION SQUARE POST OFFICE," red grid of dots.

Metropolitan Errand and Carrier Express Co., New York, N.Y.
      Organized Aug. 1, 1855, by Abraham M. Hinkley, Hiram Dixon, and others.

L218

L219

Printed in sheets of 100 (10x10), each stamp separated by thin ruled lines.

1855   **Thin to Medium Wove Paper**   **Engr.**
107L1 L218 1c **red orange** (shades)   20.00 *25.00*
      Cut to shape   5.00 *4.00*
      On cover, tied by hand-
      stamp   *600.00*
      On cover, cut to shape, tied
      by handstamp   *150.00*
      On cover, cut to shape, with
      3c #11   *900.00*
      Pair   35.00
      Pair on cover, tied by hand-
      stamp
      Pair on cover, uncanceled   *1,000.*
      Block of 4   90.00
107L2 L218 5c **red orange**   225.00
      Cut to shape   60.00
107L3 L218 10c **red orange**   300.00
      Cut to shape   60.00
107L4 L218 20c **red orange**   325.00
      Cut to shape   60.00
      Cancellations: Black, blue or green boxed "PAID."
      The imprint "Baldwin, Bald & Cousland New York" appears in the bottom margin of the two stamps at the bottom right of the sheets.

Nos. 107L1-107L4 have been extensively reprinted in brown and in blue on paper much thicker than the originals.

ENVELOPE
Embossed
Wide Diagonally Laid Paper

107LU1 L219 2c **red**, *amber*, entire 125.00 —

No. 107LU1 has been reprinted on amber wove, diagonally laid or horizontally laid paper with narrow lines. The embossing is sharper than on the original.

Metropolitan Post Office, New York, N.Y.

Established by Lemuel Williams who later took William H. Laws as a partner.

L220

L221

L222

L223

Nos. 108L1-108L5 were issued die cut.

1852-53		**Glazed Surface Paper**	**Embossed**	
108L1	L220	(2c) **red** (L. Williams)	550.	550.
		On cover, tied by pencil, with certificate		—
		On cover, tied by blue ms., with two 3c #11 and strip of 3 12c #17		—
108L2	L221	(2c) **red** (address and name erased)	1,000.	1,000.
		On cover, uncanceled, with certificate		5,500.
108L3	L222	(2c) **red**	275.	350.
		On cover, tied by handstamp		3,750.
108L3A	L222	(2c) **blue**	600.	700.
		On cover, tied by handstamp		7,500.
		On cover, tied by handstamp, with 3c #11		8,250.
		Wove Paper		
108L4	L223	1c **red**	75.	90.
		On cover		300.
		On cover, tied by handstamp, with 3c #11		1,500.
		On cover, cut to shape, no tied, with 3c #11A		500.
108L5	L223	1c **blue**	600.	100.
		Cut to shape	400.	
		On cover		350.
		On cover, cut to shape, tied by handstamp, with 3c #11		300.
		On cover, tied by handstamp, with 3c #26		700.

Cancellations: Black circle "METROPOLITAN P. O.," black boxed "PAID W. H. LAWS," black smudge.

G. A. Mills' Despatch Post, New York, N.Y.

Established by Gustavus A. Mills at 6 Wall St., succeeding Hall & Mills.

L224

Several varieties

1847		**Glazed Surface Paper**	**Typeset**	
109L1	L224	(2c) **black**, *green*	500.	500.
		On cover, uncanceled		1,400.

Moody's Penny Dispatch, Chicago, Ill.
Robert J. Moody, proprietor

"CHICAGO"
8mm — L225

Several varieties

1856		**Glazed Surface Paper**	**Typeset**	
110L1	L225	(1c) **black**, *red*,	1,750.	1,750.
		On cover, tied by handstamp, with 3c #11		16,000.
		On cover with three 1c #9		70,000.
		Vert. strip of 3 showing 3 varieties: period, colon, comma after "Dispatch"	18,000.	6,000.
a.		"CHICAGO" sans serif and 12½mm	18,000.	2,750.
b.		"Henny" instead of "Penny," on cover, tied by handstamp, with 3c #11		45,000.

Cancellations: Blue circle "Moody's Despatch."
The vertical strip of 3, the cover with the three 1c stamps and No. 110L1b, are each unique.

Morton's Post, Philadelphia, Pa.

L225a

167L1	L225a	2c **black**, *grayish*, on cover, uncanceled, with certificate		14,000.

No. 167L1 is unique.

New York City Express Post, New York, N.Y.

L226

Several varieties

1847		**Glazed Surface Paper**	**Engr.**	
111L1	L226	2c **black**, *green*	1,200.	1,500.
		Cut to shape	400.	450.
		On cover, not tied		1,750.
		On cover, tied by handstamp		4,000.
		On cover, cut to shape, tied by handstamp		2,000.
		Wove Paper		
111L2	L226	2c **orange**	—	—
		On cover		8,000.

One Cent Despatch, Baltimore, Md., Washington, D.C.

Established by J.H. Wiley to deliver mail in Washington, Georgetown and Baltimore. Made as many as five deliveries daily at 1 cent if prepaid, or 2 cents payable on delivery.

L227

L228

Two types:
I. Courier's letter points to "O" of "ONE."
II. Letter points to "N" of "ONE."

1856		**Washington, D.C.**	**Litho.**	
		Inscribed at bottom "Washington City"		
112L1	L227	1c **violet**	225.	150.
		On cover, tied by handstamp		750.
		On cover, tied by handstamp, with 3c #11		1,500.
		On cover, tied, with 10c #15		5,500.
		On 3c entire #U1, tied by handstamp		750.
		Horiz. pair, types I & II		1,250.

Baltimore, Maryland
No name at bottom

112L2	L228	1c **red**	450.	250.
		On cover, tied by handstamp		1,750.
		On cover with 3c #11		2,250.

The No. 112L1 pair is the unique multiple of either One Cent Despatch stamp.

Cancellation on Nos. 112L1-112L2: Black circle "City Despatch."

Overton & Co.

Carried mail principally between New York and Boston; also to Albany. Stamps sold for 6c each, 20 for $1.

L229

1844				
113L1	L229	(6c) **black**, *greenish*	400.	400.
		On cover, tied by ms.		5,000.
		On cover, not tied		2,250.
		Pair		850.
a.		"FREE" printed below design		1,750.
		On cover		4,000.
		Pair on cover, not tied, with certificate		18,500.

Cancellation: Black "PAID." Red "Cd."

Penny Express Co.

Little information is available on this post, but a sheet is known carrying the ms. initials of Henry Reed of the Holladay staff. The post was part of the Holladay Overland Mail and Express Co. system.

In 1866 in the West the "short-bit" or 10 cents was the smallest currency generally used. The word "penny" is believed to refer to the "half-bit" or 5 cents (nickel).

L230

Printed in sheets of 32 (8x4)

1866			**Litho.**	
114L1	L230	5c **black**	400.00	
		Pair	850.00	
a.		Sheet of 32 initialed "HR," black ms., original gum	7,000.	
114L2	L230	5c **blue**	15.00	
		Block of 4	65.00	
		Sheet of 32, no gum	650.00	
114L3	L230	5c **red**	15.00	
		Block of 4	65.00	
		Sheet of 32, no gum	650.00	

Nos. 114L1-114L3 lack gum and probably were never placed in use.

Philadelphia Despatch Post, Philadelphia, Pa.
See D.O. Blood & Co.
Pinkney's Express Post, New York, N.Y.

L231

1851		**Glazed Surface Paper**	**Typo.**	
115L1	L231	2c **black**, *green*	1,400.	
		Cut to shape	800.	
		On cover, tied by ms., with certificate		4,500.
		On cover, uncanceled, with certificate		9,000.
		On cover, uncanceled, cut to shape, with certificate		3,500.

On the cover with No. 115L1 tied, the stamp is faulty. It is valued thus.

Pips Daily Mail, Brooklyn, N.Y.

L232

1862 (?)					**Litho.**
116L1	L232	1c	**black**	400.	
116L2	L232	1c	**black,** *buff*	375.	2,250.
116L3	L232	1c	**black,** *yellow*	250.	
116L4	L232	1c	**black,** *dark blue*	800.	
116L5	L232	1c	**black,** *rose*	300.	
			Block of 4	—	

No. 116L2 used is unique.

Pomeroy's Letter Express.

Established in 1844 by George E. Pomeroy. Carried mail principally to points in New York State. Connected with Letter Express for Western points.

L233

Engraved by John E. Gavit, Albany, N.Y. (Seen as "GAVIT" in bottom part of stamp). Sheets of 40 (8x5).

1844

Surface Colored Wove Paper
Value Complete ("20 for $1")

117L1	L233	5c	**black,** *greenish yellow, dull yellow*	6.50	65.00
			On cover, tied by ms.		1,000.
			On cover, handstamp cancel		1,000.
			Pair		250.00
			Pair on cover		3,500.
			Block of 4	40.00	

Value Incomplete ("20 for $-")

117L2	L233		**black,** *greenish yellow, dull yellow*	750.	1,500.
			On cover, tied by ms.		5,000.
			On cover, handstamp cancel, not tied		4,500.
			On cover, ms. cancel, not tied		3,500.
			On cover, with No. 117L1		—

Value Complete ("20 for $1")
Thick Wove Paper

117L2A	L233	5c	**black,** *buff,* without gum	—	
117L2B	L233	5c	**black,** *yellow, buff tint on back,* without gum	5.00	
			Sheet of 40	300.00	
117L2C	L233	6c	**black,** *yellow (colored through),* without gum	5.00	
a.		5c	**black,** *orange yellow (colored through),* with gum	10.00	

No. 117L2A may be a proof impression. Nos. 117L2B-117L2Ca may be remainders or reprints.

Thin Bond Paper

117L3	L233	5c	**blue** *(shades)*	150.00	500.00
			On cover, not tied		2,000.
			On cover, tied by pen cancel		2,500.
			Pair on cover, not tied		6,000.
117L4	L233	5c	**black**	5.00	150.00
			On cover		1,500.
			Pair on cover, red "Paid" cancel		7,500.
			Strip of 4 on cover		5,000.
			Block of 4	30.00	
			Sheet of 40, without gum	350.00	
117L5	L233	5c	**red** *(shades)*	5.00	300.00
			On cover, not tied		3,500.
			Strip of 3 on cover		8,500.
			Block of 4	25.00	
			Sheet of 40	300.00	
117L6	L233	5c	**lake**	—	750.00
			On cover, tied by ms.		1,500.
			Pair on cover		
			On cover, handstamp cancel		6,000.

Cancellations: Large red partly boxed "PAID" (Nos. 117L1, 117L6), red "Cd" (Nos. 117L1-117L2, 117L4); stamps are considered "tied to cover" by this "Cd" when the impression shows through the letter paper.
Remainders of Nos. 117L1, 117L3, 117L4 and 117L5 are plentiful in unused condition, including multiples and sheets. A

5c chocolate brown and a 5c bright yellow were prepared but not issued. No. 117L2 was never remaindered.

Thin Pelure Paper

117L7	L233	5c	**deep blue** *(shades)*	—	—
			Pair on cover, not tied		2,500.
117L8	L233	5c	**black**	—	—
			Pair		—
117L9	L233	5c	**chocolate brown**	—	—

5c stamps on a medium, fibrous paper in orange, deep blue, black, red and brown exist. It is believe that stamps on this paper come from remainders of a printing that was prepared but never issued. They may also be reprints.

P. O. Paid, Philadelphia, Pa.
See note in Carriers' Stamps Section.

Price's City Express, New York, N.Y.

L235   L236

1857-58		**Glazed Surface Paper**			**Litho.**
119L1	L235	2c	**black,** *vermilion*	275.	
			On cover, tied by handstamp		5,000.
			On cover, ms. tied		900.
			On cover, not tied, with certificate		750.
			On cover, tied by handstamp, with 3c #26		—
119L2	L235	2c	**black,** *green*	250.	
			Cut to shape		85.
1858					
			Sheets of 108 (12x9)		
119L3	L236	2c	**black,** *green*	5.00	150.00
			On cover		
			Block of 4	27.50	

Cancellation on #119L3: Black oval "Price's City Express."

Price's Eighth Avenue Post Office, New York, N.Y.

Established by James Price at 350 Eighth Avenue, in 1854, and sold to Russell in the same year.

L237

1854					**Litho.**
120L1	L237	(2c)	**red,** *bluish*	600.00	
			On cover, uncanceled, with certificate		7,500.

Priest's Despatch, Philadelphia, Pa.
Established by Solomon Priest

L238   L239

1851		**Glazed Surface Paper**			**Typo.**
121L1	L238	(2c)	**silver,** *vermilion*	2,250.	
121L2	L238	(2c)	**gold,** *dark blue*	500.	
			Wove Paper		
121L2A	L238	(2c)	**bronze,** *bluish*	500.	1,000.
121L3	L238	(2c)	**black,** *yellow*	500.	
			On cover, uncanceled, with 3c #11, with certificate		5,500.
121L4	L238	(2c)	**black,** *rose*	500.	
			On cover, uncanceled with certificate		2,000.
121L5	L238	(2c)	**black,** *blue*	1,000.	
121L6	L239	(2c)	**black,** *yellow*	500.	
			On cover, uncanceled, with certificate		1,500.
			On cover, uncanceled, with 3c #11, with certificate		4,500.
121L7	L239	(2c)	**black,** *blue*	750.	

			On cover, uncanceled, with certificate		3,250.
121L8	L239	(2c)	**black,** *rose*	500.	
121L9	L239	(2c)	**black,** *emerald,* uncanceled, on cover		6,500.

No. 121L9 is believed to be unique.

Prince's Letter Dispatch, Portland, Maine

Established by J. H. Prince of Portland. Mail carried nightly by messenger travelling by steamer to Boston. Stamp engraved by Lowell of Lowell & Brett, Boston, his name appearing in the design below the steamship.

L240

Printed in sheets of 40 (5x8)

1861					**Litho.**
122L1	L240		**black**	7.50	125.00
			On cover, tied by handstamp		5,000.
			On cover, uncanceled, with certificate		—
			On cover, tied by handstamp, with 3c #65		8,000.
			On cover, tied by handstamp, with 3c #94		5,000.
			Block of 4	40.00	
			Sheet of 40	550.00	

Cancellations: Black, blue or red Boston datestamps, blue company serrated oval, black "Boston & Portland/Express/11 State Street, Boston/34 Exchange Street, Portland" framed ribbon-marker handstamp.

Private Post Office, San Francisco, Calif.
ENVELOPES

L241

(Illustration reduced size.)

Impressed on U.S. Envelopes, 1863-64 Issue

1864					**Typo.**
123LU1	L241	15c	**blue,** *orange* (on US #U56)		600.00
123LU2	L241	15c	**blue,** *buff* (on US #U54)		600.00
a.		15c	**blue** (on US #U58)	700.00	4,750.
b.		15c	**blue,** *buff* (on US #U59)		600.00
123LU3	L241	25c	**blue,** *buff* (on US #U54)		600.00

Providence Despatch, Providence, R.I.

L242

1849					**Typeset**
124L1	L242		**black**		2,000.

Public Letter Office, San Francisco, Calif.
ENVELOPES

L243

Illustration reduced.

Impressed on U.S. Envelopes, 1863-64 Issue

1864					**Typeset**
125LU1	L243		**black**	400.00	
125LU2	L243		**blue**	400.00	
125LU3	L243	15c	**blue**	450.00	5,000.
125LU4	L243	25c	**blue**	450.00	

The Private Post Office of San Francisco changed its name to Public Post Office sometime in 1864. The office address was the same for both, 5 Kearny St.

Reed's City Despatch Post, San Francisco, Calif.

Pioneer San Francisco private post. Also serving Adams & Co. for city delivery.

 L244

1853-54 **Glazed Surface Paper** **Litho.**
126L1 L244 **black**, *green*, on cover, tied by handstamp —
126L2 L244 **black**, *blue*, on cover, un-canceled 27,500.

No. 126L1 is unique. Two No. 126L2 recorded, each uncanceled on cover.

Cancellation: Blue double-circle "Adams & Co. San Francisco."

Ricketts & Hall, Baltimore, Md.

L244a

1857 **Cut to shape** **Typo.**
127L1 L244a 1c **red**, *bluish* — 9,000.
On cover —

Of the seven recorded examples of No. 127L1, three have been cut to shape removing the outer address circle, including the unique unused stamp. One of the three examples on cover has had the outer address circle removed.

Robison & Co., Brooklyn, N.Y.

 L245

1855-56 **Typo.**
128L1 L245 1c **black**, *blue* 4,750. 4,750.
On cover, tied 7,000.

Cancellation: Blue "PAID."

Roche's City Dispatch, Wilmington, Del.

L246

1850 **Glazed Surface Paper** **Typo.**
129L1 L246 (2c) **black**, *green* 2,250.
Cut to shape 1,750.
On cover, uncanceled, with certificate 8,250.
On cover, cut to shape, un-canceled, with certificate 3,500.

A black negative handstamp similar to type L246 served solely as a postmark and no evidence exists that any prepaid handstamped envelopes or lettersheets were ever sold.

Rogers' Penny Post, Newark, N.J.

Established by Alfred H. Rogers, bookseller, at 194 Broad St., Newark, N.J.

 L246a

Cut to shape

1856 **Glazed Surface Paper** **Handstamped**
162L1 L246a (1c) **black**, *green* 30,000.

No. 162L1 is unique. It is on a tiny piece. Value represents 2000 auction sale price.

See Rogers' handstamp in Local Handstamp Covers section.

Russell 8th Ave. Post Office, New York, N.Y.

(See Price's Eighth Avenue Post Office.)

L247

1854-58 **Wood Engraving**
130L1 L247 (2c) **blue**, *rose* 600. 500.
On cover, uncanceled, with certificate —
On cover, tied by hand-stamp 27,500.
On cover, tied with 3c #11
130L2 L247 (2c) **black**, *yellow* 750. 650.
On cover, tied 5,000.
On cover, uncanceled, with 3c #11, with certificate 9,250.
130L3 L247 (2c) **red**, *bluish* 900. 750.
On cover, tied by hand-stamp 8,250.
On cover, not tied, with 3c #11, with certificate 5,750.
130L4 L247 (2c) **blue green**, *green* 3,000.

No. 130L4 used is unique. It is damaged and is valued thus.

St. Louis City Delivery Company, St. Louis, Mo.

(See Cincinnati City Delivery.)

L249

1883 **Typo.** **Perf. 12**
131L1 L249 (1c) **red** 4.00 7.50
Block of 4 17.50
On cover, tied by hand-stamp 2,750.
a. Imperf., pair —
b. Horiz. pair, imperf between 350.00

Cancellation: Purple target.

Smith & Stephens' City Delivery, St. Louis, Mo.

L284

Typeset
158L1 L284 1c **black**, *pale rose*, on cover, tied by ms. cancel 25,000.

No. 158L1 is unique.

Smith's City Express Post, New York, N.Y.

Successor to the American Express Co.

L284a

Typeset
Glazed Surface Paper
168L1 L284a 2c **black**, *green* —

Spaulding's Penny Post, Buffalo, N.Y.

 L283 L283a

1848-49
156L1 L283 2c **vermilion** 40,000.
156L2 L283a 2c **carmine** 40,000.
On cover —

Nos. 156L1 unused, 156L2 unused and 156L2 on cover each are unique.
A No. 156L1 on cover, uncanceled, was reported but has not been seen.

Spence & Brown Express Post, Philadelphia, Pa.

L285

L286

(Illustrations reduced size.)

1847 (?) **Typeset**
159L1 L285 2c **black**, *bluish* 10,000. 11,500.

One each recorded of No. 159L1 unused and used.

1848 **Litho.**
159L2 L286 (2c) **black** 1,500. —
On cover, tied by ms. 33,000.
Block of 4 6,500.

No. 159L2 on cover is unique.

Squier & Co. City Letter Dispatch, St. Louis, Mo.

(Jordan & Co.)

This post began to operate as a local carrier on July 6, 1859 and was discontinued in the early part of 1860. Squier & Co. used imperforate stamps; their successors (Jordan & Co.) about Jan. 1 1860, used the roulettes.

L248

1859 **Litho.** **Imperf.**
132L1 L248 1c **green** 150. 175.
On cover 1,500.
On cover, tied by hand-stamp, with 3c #26 4,000.
On cover, tied by ms., with 3c #26 1,000.
On cover, uncanceled, with 3c #26 600.
Block of 4 750.

1860 **Rouletted 19**
132L2 L248 1c **rose brown** 280. 280.
On cover 1,000.
On cover, with 3c #26, each tied by handstamps (unique) 11,500.
132L3 L248 1c **brownish purple** 280. 280.

132L4	L248	1c	**green**		280.	1,000. 350.
			On cover			1,000.
			On cover, tied by hand- stamp, with 3c #26			5,000.

Cancellation: Black circle "Jordan's Penny Post Saint Louis."

Staten Island Express Post, Staten Island, N. Y.

Established by Hagadorn & Co., with office at Stapleton, Staten Island. Connected with Boyd for delivery in New York City.

L250

1849   **Typo.**

133L1	L250	3c	**vermilion**	1,400.	1,100.
			On cover, tied by ms.		4,750.
			On cover, not tied		3,500.
			On cover, uncanceled, with certificate		3,250.
133L2	L250	6c	**vermilion**, on cover		—

Stringer & Morton's City Despatch, Baltimore, Md.

According to an advertisement in the Baltimore newspapers, dated October 19, 1850, this post aimed to emulate the successful posts of other cities, and divided the city into six districts, with a carrier in each district. Stamps were made available throughout the city.

L251

1850   **Glazed Surface Paper**

| 134L1 | L251 | (1c) | **gold**, black | 500. | — |
| | | | On cover, uncanceled | | 650. |

Cancellation: Black circle "Baltimore City Despatch & Express Paid."

Sullivan's Dispatch Post, Cincinnati, Ohio

L252

1853   **Glazed Surface Paper**   **Litho.**

| 135L1 | L252 | (2c) | **black**, green, uncanceled,
on cover | | — |

Wove Paper

135L2	L252	(2c)	**bluish black**, uncanceled, on magazine, with certifi- cate		40,000.
135L3	L252	(2c)	**green**	60,000.	
			On cover		—

Nos. 135L1-135L2 are either die cut octagonally or cut round. They do not exist cut square.

Each listed Sullivan Post item is unique. Additionally, a second No. 135L2 on magazine is in the Smithsonian Institution collection.

Swarts' City Dispatch Post, New York, N.Y.

Established by Aaron Swarts, at Chatham Square, in 1847, becoming one of the largest local posts in the city.

The postmarks of Swarts' Post Office are often found on stampless covers, as this post carried large quantities of mail without using adhesive stamps.

Zachary Taylor
L253

George
Washington
L254

1849-53   **Glazed Surface Paper**   **Litho.**

136L1	L253	(2c)	**black**, light green	—	175.00
			On cover, tied by hand- stamp		450.00
			On cover, not tied		300.00
			On cover, tied, with 5c #1		45,000.
			On cover with 3c #10		450.00
136L2	L253	(2c)	**black**, dark green	—	135.00
			On cover, tied by hand- stamp		375.00

Wove Paper

136L3	L253	(2c)	**pink**	—	35.00
			On cover, tied by hand- stamp		500.00
			On cover with 5c #1		—
136L4	L253	(2c)	**red** (shades)	20.00	20.00
			On cover, tied by hand- stamp		600.00
			On cover, not tied		450.00
			On cover with 5c #1		5,000.
			On cover, tied by hand- stamp, with 3c #11		650.00
			Block of 4	85.00	
			Sheet of 25	600.00	
136L5	L253	(2c)	**pink**, blue	—	60.00
			On cover, tied by hand- stamp		375.00
136L6	L253	(2c)	**red**, blue	—	60.00
			On cover, tied by hand- stamp		400.00
136L7	L253	(2c)	**black**, blue gray	200.00	150.00
			On cover, tied by hand- stamp		400.00
			On cover, uncanceled		225.00
136L8	L253	(2c)	**blue**	—	200.00
			On cover, tied by hand- stamp		1,250.
136L9	L254	(1c)	**red**	—	40.00
			On cover, tied by hand- stamp		350.00
			On cover, tied by hand- stamp, with 3c #11A		450.00
136L10	L254	(1c)	**pink**	—	30.00
			On cover, tied by hand- stamp		250.00
			On cover, tied by hand- stamp, with 3c #11		800.00
			On cover, tied by hand- stamp, with 3c #26		350.00
136L11	L254	(1c)	**red**, bluish	—	100.00
			On cover		500.00
136L12	L254	(1c)	**pink**, bluish	—	100.00
			On cover		450.00

Bouton's Stamp with Red ms. "Swarts" at Top

136L13	L49	2c	**black**, gray blue	500.	550.
			On cover, tied by hand- stamp		1,500.
			On cover, not tied		600.

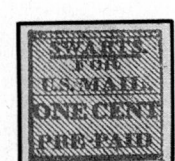
L255

Printed in sheets of 25 (5x5). Five minor varieties, the stamps in each vertical row being identical.

136L14	L255	1c	**blue**	15.	60
			On cover, tied by hand- stamp		175.
			On cover, tied by hand- stamp, with 3c #11A		225.
			Block of 4	65.	
a.			Thin paper	8.00	
			Block of 4	35.	
			Sheet of 25	225.00	
136L15	L255	1c	**red**	—	500.
			On cover, tied by hand- stamp		1,000.
			On cover with 3c #10		1,650.
			On cover, tied by hand- stamp, with 3c #11A		4,000.
136L16	L255	1c	**red**, bluish	—	135.
			On cover, tied by hand- stamp		1,000.
136L17	L255	1c	**black**, on cover, tied by handstamp		20,000.

Nos. 136L3-136L4, 136L9-136L10, 136L14-136L15 have been reprinted.

Cancellations: Red boxed "PAID" (mostly on Nos. 136L1-136L8, 136L13), black boxed "PAID SWARTS" (mostly on Nos. 136L6-136L12), black oval "Swarts Post Office Chatham Square" (Nos. 136L9-136L12), black oval "Swarts B Post Chatham Square," black grids (5-bar rectangle, 6-bar circle, solid star, hollow star, star in circle, etc.). Other handstamp postmarks of the post have been found as cancellations. Government town postmarks exist on almost all Swarts stamps.

Teese & Co. Penny Post, Philadelphia, Pa.

L256

Printed in sheet of 200 divided into two panes of 100. Each pane includes setting of 20, repeated 5 times. Vertical or horizontal tete beche pairs appear twice in each setting. Twenty varieties.

1852   **Wove Paper**   **Litho.**

137L1	L256	(1c)	**blue**, bluish	20.00	125.00
			On cover, tied by hand- stamp		3,000.
			On cover, tied by hand- stamp, with 3c #11A		2,250.
			Block of 4	90.00	
a.			Tete beche pair	100.00	

Telegraph Despatch P. O., Philadelphia, Pa.

L257

1848

138L1	L257	1c	**black**, yellowish		2,750.
			On cover, tied by ms., with certificate		15,000.
			On cover, not tied, with certificate		5,500.
138L2	L257	2c	**black**, yellowish, on cover with 5c #1		21,000.

The 2c differs in design, including the address, "Office No. 6 Sth 8 St" at bottom.
One example known of No. 138L2.

Third Avenue Post Office, New York, N.Y.

Established by S. Rothenheim, a former carrier for Boyd's City Express. All stamps were cut to shape by hand before being sold and exist only in that form.

L258

1855   **Glazed Surface Paper**   **Handstamped**

139L1	L258	2c	**black**, green	500.	500.
			On cover, uncanceled		1,250.
			On cover, uncanceled, with 3c #11, with certificate		1,600.
139L1A	L258	2c	**blue**, green, on cover, un- canceled, with certificate		2,250.
139L2	L258	2c	**black**, maroon	3,250.	2,250.

Unsurfaced Paper colored through

139L3	L258	2c	**black**, yellow		2,250.
			On cover, uncanceled, with 3c #11, with certificate		3,000.
139L4	L258	2c	**black**, blue		—
			On cover, uncanceled, with 3c #11, with certificate		11,000.
139L5	L258	2c	**black**, brown	2,250.	
139L6	L258	2c	**black**, buff	2,500.	
139L7	L258	2c	**black**, pink	5,250.	
			On cover, uncanceled, with 3c #11		6,500.
139L8	L258	2c	**black**, green	4,150.	2,200.

Nos. 139L1A, 139L2, 139L4 on cover, 139L7-139L8 unused and 139L8 used are each unique.

Cancellation on No. 139L1: Black "PAID."

Union Post, New York, N.Y.

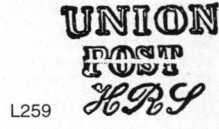
L259

1846   **Handstamped**

Thick Glazed Surface Paper

140L3	L259		**blue**, green ("UNOIN")	3,000.	
140L4	L259		**red**, blue ("UNION")	2,000.	
			On cover		—

Type L259 was used also as a postmark, usually struck in blue.

Union Square Post Office, New York, N.Y.

Established by Joseph E. Dunham about 1850. In 1851 Dunham acquired Messenkope's Union Square Post Office, operating the combined posts until 1854 or 1855. The business was sold in 1855 to Phineas C. Godfrey.

L259a · L260

Printed in sheets of 120 (6x20)

1852					Typo.
141L1	L259a	1c	**black,** *dark green*	9.00	45.00
			On cover, tied by hand-stamp		900.00
			On cover, tied by hand-stamp, with 3c #11A		1,250.
			On cover, not tied, with 3c #11A		750.00
			Block of 4	45.00	
141L2	L259a	1c	**black,** *light apple green*	40.00	75.00
			On cover, tied by hand-stamp		700.00
			On cover, tied by hand-stamp, with 3c #11		1,500.
			On cover, cut to shape, tied by handstamp, with 3c #11		200.00
141L3	L260	2c	**black,** *rose*	3.50	3,000.
			On cover		3,500.
			Block of 4	17.50	

Used stamps must bear handstamp cancels.

Walton & Co.'s City Express, Brooklyn, N.Y.

Operated by Wellington Walton.

L261

1846			**Glazed Surface Paper**		Litho.
142L1	L261	2c	**black,** *pink*	700.	900.
			On cover, tied by ms.		—
			On cover, ms. cancel, not tied, with certificate		16,000.
			On cover, handstamp can-cel, not tied		—
			On cover, cut to shape, tied by handstamp, with certificate		4,500.
			On cover, cut to shape, handstamp cancel, not tied, with certificate		6,000.

Cancellations: Black "PAID / W. W." Black oblong quad (ties stamp "through" to cover).

Wells, Fargo and Co.

Wells, Fargo & Company entered the Western field about July 1, 1852, to engage in business on the Pacific Coast, and soon began to acquire other express businesses, eventually becoming the most important express company in its territory.

The Central Overland, California and Pikes Peak Express Company, inaugurated in 1860, was the pioneer Pony Express system and was developed to bring about quicker communication between the extreme portions of the United States. Via water the time was 28 to 30 days, with two monthly sailings, and by the overland route the time was 28 days. In 1860 the pioneer Pony Express carried letters only, reducing the time for the 2,100 miles (St. Joseph to San Francisco) to about 12 days. The postage rate was originally $5 the half-ounce.

About April 1, 1861, Wells, Fargo & Company became agents for the Central Overland, California and Pikes Peak Express Company and issued $2 red and $4 green stamps.

During the July 1 to Oct. 24, 1861, period of use of Nos. 143L3-143L6, Wells, Fargo & Co. was under contract with the U.S. government, so stamps used during this period are technically official issues authorized by Congress.

The rates were cut in half about July 1, 1861, and new stamps were issued: the $1 red, $2 green and $4 black, and the $1 garter design.

The revival of the Pony Express in 1862, known as the "Virginia City Pony" resulted in the appearance of the "cents" values, first rate.

Advertisement in the Placerville newspaper, Aug. 7, 1862: "Wells, Fargo & Co.'s Pony Express. On and after Monday, the 11th inst., we will run a Pony Express Daily between Sacramento and Virginia City, carrying letters and exchange papers, through from San Francisco in 24 hours, Sacramento in 15 hours and Placerville in 10 hours. Rates: All letters to be

enclosed in our franks, and TEN CENTS PREPAID, in addition, for each letter weighing half an ounce or less, and ten cents for each additional half-ounce."

Wells, Fargo & Company used various handstamps to indicate mail transit. These are illustrated and described in the handbook, "Wells, Fargo & Co.'s Handstamps and Franks" by V. M. Berthold, published by Scott Stamp & Coin Co., Ltd. (out of print). The history of the Pony Express, a study of the stamps and reprints, and a survey of existing covers are covered in "The Pony Express," by M. C. Nathan and Winthrop S. Boggs, published by the Collectors Club, 22 E. 35th., New York, N.Y. 10016.

Wells Fargo stamps of types L262 and L264 were lithographed by Britton & Rey, San Francisco. Type L263 was printed by George F. Nesbitt, New York.

L262 · Front hoof missing

The $2 and $4 stamps were printed from plates of 20 (5x4), while the $1 was printed from a plate of 40 (8x5), and divided into two panes of 20 (4x5) each.

1861			**(April to July 1)**		Litho.
143L1	L262	$2	**red**	175.	800.
			On US envelope #U10		—
			On US envelope #U16		12,500.
			On US envelope #U17		12,500.
			On US envelope #U18		12,500.
			On US envelope #U32		15,000.
			On US envelope #U32 (patriotic cover)		100,000.
			On US envelope #U33		17,500.
			On US envelope #U65		—
143L2	L262	$4	**green**	300.	1,250.
			Block of 4	9,000.	
			On US envelope #U33		—

The No. 143L2 block is the only recorded $4 block.

1861			**(July 1 to Nov.)**		
143L3	L262	$1	**red**	90.	750.
			Block of 4	750.	
			Sheet of 40	7,000.	
			On US envelope #U11		—
			On US envelope #U15		9,000.
			On US envelope #U17		9,000.
			On US envelope #U32		10,000.
			On US envelope #U33		10,000.
			On US envelope #U35		9,000.
			On US envelope #U40		10,000.
			On US envelope #U41		9,000.
			Front hoof missing (9R)	1,250.	6,000.
143L4	L262	$2	**green**	250.	1,750.
			Block of 4	1,200.	
			On US envelope #U41		50,000.
143L5	L262	$4	**black**	175.	6,000.
			Block of 4		—
			On cover to Wash., D.C., tied by handstamp		350,000.

Cancellations: Blue, black or magenta express company. *Nos. 143L1-143L5 and 143L7-143L9 were reprinted in 1897. The reprints are retouched. Shades vary from originals. Originals and reprints are fully described in "The Pony Express," by M. C. Nathan and W. S. Boggs (Collectors Club).*

L263

Printed in sheets of 20 (5x4). One example recorded with Nesbitt imprint (pos. 18).

1861			**Thin Wove Paper**		
143L6	L263	$1	**blue**	800.	1,250.
			Strip of 3		—
			On 10c US env. #U40		75,000.
			On 10c US env. #U40 with 10c #35, tied		185,000.

No. 143L6 apparently used only from east to west. Most counterfeits have a horizontal line bisecting the shield. Some genuine stamps have a similar line drawn in with blue or red ink. Value for genuine with line, $300.

L264

Printed in sheets of 40 (8x5), four panes of 10, each pane 2x5.

1862-64					
143L7	L264	10c	**brown** (shades)	50.	150.
			Pair	125.	500.
			Block of 4	500.	
			On US envelope #U26		5,000.
			On US envelope #U32		3,500.
			On US envelope #U34		4,500.
			On US envelope #U35		4,000.
			On cover with 3c #65		—
143L8	L264	25c	**blue**	75.	140.
			Pair	175.	
			Block of 4	500.	
			On plain cover		2,250.
			Strip of 3 on cover		—
			On US envelope #U10		—
			On US envelope #U26		2,000.
			On US envelope #U34		4,500.
			On US envelope #U35		4,000.
143L9	L264	25c	**red**	30.	80.
			Pair	80.	
			Block of 4	225.	
			Sheet of 40	4,500.	
			On US envelope #U9		—
			On US envelope #U10		5,000.
			On US envelope #U34		5,000.
			On US envelope #U34 with 3c #65		13,500.
			On US envelope #U35		5,000.
			Pair on US envelope #U35		9,000.
			On US envelope #U59		2,750.

Cancellations on Nos. 143L7-143L9: Blue or black express company, black town.

NEWSPAPER STAMPS

L265

L266

L267

L268

L269

L270

1861-70

143LP1	L265	**black**	*1,250.*	—
		On cover, uncanceled, with certificate		*7,500.*
143LP2	L266	**blue**	*1,250.*	
143LP3	L267	**blue**	20.00	75.00
		Pair	100.00	
		Block of 4	—	
		Sheet of 50	—	
a.		Thin paper	40.00	100.00
143LP4	L268	**blue**	50.00	

Rouletted 10

143LP5	L267	**blue**	25.00	*125.00*
		On wrapper		*1,500.*
		Pair	55.00	
		Block of 4	125.00	
a.		Thin paper	—	
143LP6	L267	**blue**	22.50	
a.		Tete beche pair	350.00	

Design L267 was printed in sheets of 50 (5x10).

1883-88   *Perf. 11, 12, 12½*

143LP7	L268	**blue**	12.50	*25.00*
143LP8	L269	**blue**	25.00	*35.00*
143LP9	L270	**blue**	3.50	*5.00*
		Double transfer		
		On wrapper		*2,400.*
		Strip of 3 on wrapper		—
a.		Vertical pair, imperf. between	125.00	
b.		Horiz. strip of 3, imperf. vert. between all stamps, natural straight edge at right	350.00	

FOR PUBLISHERS' USE

L271

1876   **Typo.**

143LP10	L271	**blue**	8.50	*25.00*
		Pair	17.50	*60.00*
		Block of 4	45.00	
		Sheet of 50	—	
		On wrapper		*1,750.*
		On wrapper with #143LP9		—

Cancellation: Blue company.

ENVELOPES

1862

143LU1	L264	**10c red**	—	*1,250.*
		On US envelope #U34		*3,000.*
143LU2	L264	**10c blue**	—	
		On US envelope #U34		*9,500.*
143LU3	L264	**25c red**	700.00	
		On "Gould & Curry" overall advertising env.	700.00	
		On US envelope #U34	950.00	

Westervelt's Post, Chester, N.Y.

Operated by Charles H. Westervelt. Rate was 1 cent for letters and 2 cents for packages carried to the post office. Local and government postage required prepayment.

L273

Several varieties

1863 (?)   **Typeset**

144L1	L273	**(1c) black,** *buff*	35.00	
		On cover		*650.*
		On cover, tied by hand-stamp, with 3c #65		*1,000.*
		Sheet of 6	*675.00*	
144L2	L273	**black,** *lavender*	40.00	—
		On cover		

Indian Chief — L274

General U. S. Grant — L275

Six varieties

1864 (?)   **Typeset**

144L9	L274	**(1c) red,** *pink*	75.00	
		On cover		*650.00*
		On cover, tied by hand-stamp, with 3c #65		*3,000.*

Six varieties

1865   **Typo.**

144L29	L275	**2c black,** *yellow*	35.00	—
144L30	L275	**2c black,** *gray green*	40.00	—
144L40	L275	**2c red,** *pink*	40.00	—

All of the Westervelt stamps are believed to have a philatelic flavor, although it is possible that Nos. 144L1-144L2 were originally issued primarily for postal purposes. It is possible that Nos. 144L9, 144L29-144L30 and 144L40 were used in the regular course of business, particularly No. 144L9.

However, the large number of varieties on various colors of paper, which exist both as originals as well as contemporaneous and near-contemporaneous reprints, are believed to have been produced solely for sale to collectors. Design L275 was certainly issued primarily for sale to collectors. Many of the unlisted colors in all three types exist only as reprints. Forgeries of all three designs also exist.

L276

ENVELOPES
Impressed at top left

1865   **Typo.**

144LU1	L276	**red,** *white*	—	
144LU2	L276	**red brown,** *orange*	—	*250.00*
144LU3	L276	**black,** *bluish*	—	
144LU4	L276	**black,** *buff*	—	
144LU5	L276	**black,** *white*	—	

It is possible that Nos. 114LU1-144LU5 were corner cards and had no franking value.

Westtown, Westtown, Pa.

The Westtown School at Westtown, Pa., is the oldest of the secondary schools in America, managed by the Society of Friends. It was established in 1799. In 1853 the school authorities decided that all outgoing letters carried by stage should pay a fee of 2 cents. Prepaid stamps were placed on sale at the school. Stamps were usually affixed to the reverse of the letter sheets or envelopes.

At first, letters were usually mailed at West Chester, Pa. After March 4, 1859, letters were sent from Street Road Post Office, located at the railroad station. Later this became the Westtown Post Office. The larger stamp was the first used. The smaller stamp came into use about 1867.

L277 — Type I

L277 — Type III

L277a — Type V

L277 — Type II

L277 — Type IV

L277a — Type VI

L277a — Type VII

1853-67(?)   **Litho.**

145L1	L277	**(2c) gold**	45.	—
		On front of cover, tied with 3c #11		*4,500.*
		On front of cover, uncanceled, with 1c #9		*1,000.*
		On front of cover, uncanceled, with 3c #11		*150.*
		On front of cover, uncanceled, with 3c #26a		*200.*
145L2	L277a	**(2c) gold**	30.	
		On cover		*400.*
		On cover, tied by hand-stamp, with 3c #158		*2,250.*
		Block of 4	*400.*	
		Block of 6	*1,000.*	
a.		Tete beche pair	*300.*	

No. 145L1 in red brown is a fake.

Whittelsey's Express, Chicago, Ill.
Operated by Edmund A. and Samuel M. Whittelsey

George Washington — L278

1857   **Typo.**

146L1	L278	**2c red**	*2,000.*	*6,000.*
		Block of 11	*20,000.*	

Cancellation: Blue oval "Whittelsey's Express."

Williams' City Post, Cincinnati, Ohio.
See Carriers' Stamps, No. 9LB1.

Wood & Co. City Despatch, Baltimore, Md.
Operated by W. Wood

L280

1856   **Typeset**

148L1	L280	**(1c) black,** *yellow,* on cover, ms. cancel, not tied, with certificate		*13,000.*
		On printed matter, tied by ms.		*7,500.*
		On 3c red entire #U10, tied by ms., with certificate		*14,500.*

W. Wyman, Boston, Mass.
Established to carry mail between Boston and New York

L281

1844   **Litho.**

149L1	L281	**5c black**	—	*750.00*
		On cover, tied by ms., Wyman handstamp		*3,500.*
		On cover, tied by ms., Overton handtsamp		*10,000.*
		On cover, not tied		*1,750.*

No. 149L1 may have been sold singly at 6 cents each.

Zieber's One Cent Dispatch, Pittsburgh, Pa.

L282

1851   **Typeset**
150L1   L282   1c **black**, *gray blue*   20,000.
       On cover, acid cancel, with   —
       3c #10

    No. 150L1 used and on cover are each unique.

         Cancellation: Acid

For Local #151L1 see **Friend's Boarding School.**
For Local #152L1 see **Faunce's Penny Post.**

For Local #153L1 see **Hackney & Bolte Penny Post.**
For Local #154L1 see **A. W. Auner's Despatch Post.**
For Local #155L1 see **McGreely's Express.**
For Local #156L1-156L2 see **Spaulding's Penny Post.**
For Local #157L1 see **Bush's Brooklyn City Express.**
For Local #158L1 see **Smith & Stephens City Delivery.**
For Local #159L1-159L2 see **Spence & Brown Express Post.**
For Local #160L1 see **City Dispatch, New York City.**
For Local #161L1 see **Clinton's Penny Post.**

For Local #162L1 see **Rogers' Penny Post.**
For Local #163L1 see **Blizzard Mail.**
For Local #164L1 see **Freeman & Co.'s Express, New York City.**
For Local #165L1 see **J. A. Howell's City Despatch.**
For Local #166L1 see **Mac & Co's Dispatch.**
For Local #167L1 see **Morton's Post.**
For Local #168L1 see **Smith's City Express Post.**

LOCAL HANDSTAMPED COVERS

In 1835-1860 when private companies carried mail, many of them used handstamps on the covers they carried. Examples of these handstamps are shown on this and following pages.

Accessory Transit Co. of Nicaragua

Blue or Black

Red, Black or Blue

A sub-variety shows "Leland" below "MAILS" in lower right corner.

                          Red or Blue

1853

Barker's City Post, Boston, Mass.

Black

1855-59

Also known with "10" instead of "34" Court Square.

E. N. Barry's Despatch Post, New York, N.Y.

Black

1852

Bates & Co., New Bedford, Mass.
(Agent for Hale & Co. at New Bedford)

Red

1845

Branch Post Office, New York, N. Y.
(Swarts' Chatham Square Post Office)

Red

1847

Brigg's Despatch, Philadelphia, Pa.

Black

1848

Bush's Brooklyn City Express, Brooklyn, N. Y.

Red

1848

Cover shows red PAID.

Central Post Office, New York, N.Y.

Black

1856

Cover shows black PAID.

City Despatch Post, New York, N. Y.
(Used by Mead, successor to United States City Despatch Post.)

Black

1848

City Dispatch Post, Baltimore, Md.

Red

1846-47

City Despatch & Express, Baltimore, Md.

Black

1850

Cole's City Despatch P. O., New York, N. Y.
(Used by Cole with some of the City Despatch Post stamps.)

Black or Red

1848-50

Dunhams Post Office, New York, N. Y.
(See Union Square Post Office).

Red

1850-52

Gay, Kinsley & Co., Boston, Mass.
(A package express)

Red

Hanford's Pony Express Post, New York, N.Y.

Black or Red

1845-51

Hartford Penny Post, Hartford, Conn.

Black

1852-61

Hudson Street Post Office, New York, N. Y.

Red

1850

Cover shows red PAID.

Jones & Russell's Pikes Peak Express Co.,
Denver, Colo.

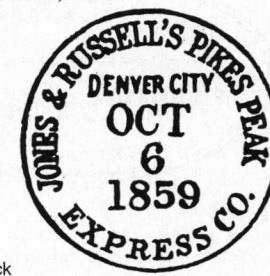

Black

1859-60

Kenyon's Letter Office, 91 Wall St., New York City

Red

1846-60

Letter Express, San Francisco, Cal.
(See Gahagan & Howe, San Francisco, Cal.)

Blue

1865-66

Libbey & Co.'s City Post, Boston, Mass.

**LIBBEY & CO'S
CITY POST.
10 COURT SQUARE**   Black or Red

1852

Cover has 3c 1851 postmarked Boston, Mass.

Manhattan Express, New York, N. Y.
(W. V. Barr. See Bouton's Manhattan Express.)

Red

1847

New York Penny Post,
New York, N. Y.

Black or Red

1840-41

Also known with hour indicated.

Noisy Carriers, San Francisco, Cal.

Blue or
Green

Blue

Black or Red

Black, Blue or
Green

Black

Black
or
Blue

1853-56

Northern Liberties News Rooms, Philadelphia,
Pa.
(Actually a carrier marking mechanically applied.)

Black

Black

1835-36

Overton & Co.'s City Mail,
New York, N. Y.

Red

1844-45

Pony Express

1860
Blue or Red

1861
Blue (Enlarged)

1860-61
Black or Carmine

1853-56
Blue or Red

1860-61
Black or Green

Red

California Pony Express

1860
Blue

Rogers' Penny Post, Newark, N. J.

1856
Black

Spark's Post Office, New York, N. Y.

1848
Red, Green, Blue or Black

Spaulding's Penny Post, Buffalo, N. Y.

1848
Black

from

St. Joseph, Mo.	Black or Green
Denver City, K. T.	Black
Leavenworth City, K. T.	Black
San Francisco, Cal.	Blue

Spence & Brown Express Post, Philadelphia, Pa.

1848
Black

Stait's Despatch Post, Philadelphia, Pa.
(Eagle City Post)

1850-51
Red or Black

1850-55
Red

Stone's City Post, New York, N. Y.

1858-59
Red

J. W. Sullivan's Newspaper Office,
San Francisco, Cal.

1854-55
Black or Red

Towle & Co. Letter Delivery, Boston, Mass.

1847
Red

Towle's City Dispatch Post, Boston, Mass.

Red

1849

Towle's City Post, Boston, Mass.

(Also 10
Court Sq.)
Red

1849-50

Cover shows PAID.

STAMPED ENVELOPES AND WRAPPERS

Fine-Very Fine →

THE
SCOTT
CATALOGUE
VALUES
CUT SQUARES
IN THIS GRADE

Very Fine →

Extremely Fine →

  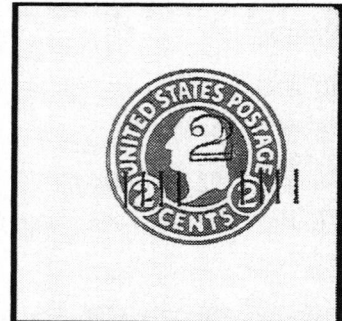

VALUES

Values for cut squares and most entires are for examples in the grade of very fine. Very fine cut squares will have the design well centered within moderately large margins. The margins on 20th century cut squares should be at least ¼ inch on the cut sides unless indicated otherwise. Cut squares of modern issues should show full tagging bars when they exist. An illustrated grading guide is shown above. These examples are computer-manipulated images made from single digitized master illustrations. Selected issues from both the 19th and 20th centuries are shown in the grades of fine-very fine, very fine and extremely fine. In addition to margin size, collectors are reminded that very fine cut squares (and entires) also will possess a fresh appearance and be free from defects.

Precanceled cut squares must include the entire precancellation. Values for unused entires are for those without printed or manuscript address, and for the most popular sizes. In a number of cases the larger envelopes are less expensive than the values shown here, for example, Nos. U348-U351. Values for letter sheets and wrappers are for folded entires. Unfolded examples sell for more.

"Full corner" cut squares include both back and side flaps. These items generally command a premium of 25% or more above the cut square values shown here, which are not for "full corners."

A plus sign (+) before a Catalogue number indicates that the item was not regularly issued and is not known used.

Envelopes are not available before the First day of issue so most cachets are applied after the envelope has been canceled. First day covers are valued uncacheted. First day covers prior to Nos. U532, UC18 and UO73 are addressed. Minimum values are $1 through 1986, and $1.25 after.

PRECANCELED CUT SQUARES

Precanceled envelopes do not normally receive another cancellation. Since the lack of a cancellation makes it impossible to distinguish between cut squares from used and unused envelopes, they are valued here as used only. Precanceled entires are valued mint and used since entires will show evidence of usage.

HISTORY

STAMPED ENVELOPES were first issued on July 1, 1853. They have always been made by private contractors, after public bidding, usually at four-year intervals. They have always been sold to the public at postage value plus cost of manufacture. They have appeared in many sizes and shapes, made of a variety of papers, with a number of modifications.

George F. Nesbitt & Co. made the government envelopes during the 1853-70 period. The Nesbitt seal or crest on the tip of the top flap was officially ordered discontinued July 7, 1853.

Watermarks in envelope paper, illustrated in this introduction, were mandatory from their first appearance in 1853 and lasted until the manila newspaper wrappers were discontinued in October 1934. The envelope contractor, due to inability to obtain watermarked Manila paper, was permitted to buy unwatermarked stock in the open market, a procedure that accounts for the wide range of shades and weights in this paper, including glazed and unglazed brown (kraft) paper. No. U615, and other unwatermarked envelopes that follow will be so noted in the listings. Diagonally laid paper has been used for some envelopes beginning with Scott U571.

A few stamped envelopes, in addition to the Manila items noted above, have been found without watermarks or with unauthorized watermarks. Such unusual watermarks or lack of watermarks are errors, bidders' samples or "specimen" envelopes, and most of them are quite rare.

Watermarks usually have been changed with every four-year contract, and thus serve to identify the envelope contractor, and since 1911, the manufacturer of the paper.

Envelope paper watermarks can be seen by spreading the envelope open and holding it against the light.

COLORS IN ENVELOPE PAPER

Stamped envelopes usually have been supplied in several colors and qualities of paper, some of which blend into each other and require study for identification. The following are the principal colors and their approximate years of use for stamped envelopes and wrappers:

Amber: 1870-1920 and 1929-1943; in two qualities; a pale yellow color; its intentional use in the Nesbitt series is doubtful.

Amber-Manila: 1886-98; same as Manila-amber.

Blue: 1874-1943; usually in two qualities; light and dark shades.

Buff: 1853-70; called cream, 1870-78; and oriental buff, 1886-1920; varies widely in shades.

Canary: 1873-78; another designation given to lemon.

Cream: 1870-78; see buff; second quality in 1c and 2c envelopes.

Fawn: 1874-86; very dark buff, almost light chocolate.

Lemon: 1873-78; Post Office official envelopes only, same as canary.

Manila: 1861-1934; second quality envelopes 1886-1928, and most wrappers; light and dark shades 1920-34; also kraft colored paper in later years.

Manila-Amber: 1886-98; amber shade of Manila quality.

Orange: 1861-83; second and third qualities only.

Oriental Buff: 1886-1920; see buff.

White: 1853-date; two qualities 1915-date; three qualities 1915-25; many shades including ivory, light gray, and bluish; far more common than any other color of paper. Envelopes that have no paper color given are white.

Laid paper was used almost exclusively from 1853 to 1915, but there were a few exceptions, mostly in the Manila papers. Wove paper has been the rule since 1915.

EMBOSSING AND PRINTING DIES

Until the modern era, stamped envelopes were always embossed, with the colorless areas slightly raised above the colored (or printed) flat background. While this process was not made mandatory in the original act, custom and tradition firmly established this policy. In 1977, No. U584 became the first envelope to have no embossing. Since 1977, most envelopes are not embossed. Embossing is an unusual procedure, seldom seen in other printed matter. Embossed impressions without color and those where lines are raised are not unusual. The method of making envelope embossings has few counterparts in the typographic industries, and hence is not well understood, even by stamp collectors.

Three types of dies are used, closely interrelated in their derivation, MASTER dies, HUB dies and WORKING (or PRINTING) dies. These types and the ways in which they are made, have undergone many changes with the years, and some of the earlier techniques are unrecorded and rather vague. No attempt will be made to describe other than the present day-methods. As an aid to clarity, the design illustrated herewith is the interlocked monogram "US," within a single circular border. Dies with curved faces for rotary printing are used extensively, as well as with straight faces for flat printing; only the latter will be described, since the basic principles are the same for both.

Figure 1

Master Die for Envelope Stamps
Colorless Lines are Recessed Below the Printing Surface.

It Reads Backward.

The MASTER die (Figure 1) is engraved on the squared end of a small soft steel cylinder, before hardening. The lines that are to remain colorless are cut or engraved into the face of this die, leaving the flat area of the face to carry the printing ink. The monogram is reversed, reading backward, as with any printing type or plate. Instead of engraving, a master die may be made by transfer under heavy pressure, usually for some modification in design, in which case it is called a sub-master or supplementary-master die. Sub-master dies are sometimes made without figures of value, when the balance of the design is as desired, and only the figures of value engraved by hand. Various other combinations of transfer and engraving are known, always resulting in a reversed design, with recessed lines and figures, from which proofs can be pulled, and which accurately represents the printing surface that is desired in the eventual working die. The soft steel of a master die, after engraving and transferring is completed, is hardened by heat treatments before it can be used for making hubs.

Figure 2

Hub Die for Envelope Stamps
Colorless Lines Protrude above the Surface.
The Monogram Reads Forward.

The HUB die (Figure 2), also called HOB die, is made from soft steel by transfer under pressure from the hardened master or sub-master die, which serves as a matrix or pattern. Since it is a transfer from the master die, the colorless lines protrude from the surface and it reads forward. This transfer impression of the hub die is made in a depression at the end of a sturdy cylinder, as it is subject to extremely hard service in making many working dies.

Figure 3

Pressure Transfer From Master Die to Hub Die
Above, Hardened Steel Master Die with Recessed Monogram.

Below, Soft Steel Hub Die Blank.

Figure 3 shows the relative position of the hardened steel master die as it enters the depression in the soft steel hub die blank. Some surplus metal may be squeezed out as the master die is forced into the hub blank, and require removal, leading to possible minor differences between the hub and master dies. At the completion of the pressure transfer the engraver may need to touch up the protruding surfaces to eliminate imperfections, to make letters and figures more symmetrical, and to improve the facial lines of the bust.

A hub die may be made by normal transfer, as above, the figures of value then ground off, and thus be ready for use in making a sub-master die without figures of value, and in which the figures of value may be engraved or punched. Since a hub die may be used to make a hundred or more working dies, it must be exceedingly sturdy and withstand terrific punishment without damage. Duplicate hub dies are frequently made from master dies, as stand-bys or reserves. After completion, hub dies are hardened. Hub dies cannot be engraved, nor can proof impressions be taken from them.

Figure 4

Working or Printing Die for Envelope Stamps
An exact Replica of the Master Die, except for size and shape of shank, which is designed for Printers} lock-up.

It Reads Backward.

The WORKING, or PRINTING, die (Figure 4) is like the type or plate that printers use, and may be thin to clamp to a base block, or type-high with square sides to lock in a printer's form. Its face reads backward, i.e., in reverse, and it is an exact replica of the master die as well as an exact matrix of the hub die.

Figure 5

Pressure Transfer from Hub to Working Die
Above, Soft Steel Blank for Working Die.

Below, Hardened Steel Hub Die with Protruding Lines.

The process of pressure transfer is shown in Figure 5. where the soft steel blank of the working die is entering the depression on the top end of the hardened hub die, In fact the pressure transfer of working dies from hub dies closely resembles that of minting coins, and many of these envelope stamp dies are made at the United States Mint in Philadelphia.

In some cases even working dies may be made without figures of value, and the figures of value individually engraved thereon. This is known to be the case in Die B of the 6c orange airmail stamped envelope die, where the size and position of the "6" has eleven variations.

There are some known instances, as in the case of the 4c and 5c envelopes dies of 1903 and 1907, where the engraved master dies were used as printing dies, since the anticipated demand did not justify the expense of making hub dies.

While working envelope dies are heat treated to the hardest temper known, they do wear down eventually to a point where impressions deteriorate and are unsatisfactory, due to shallow recesses or to broken areas, and such dies are destroyed. In many cases these printing dies can be reworked, or deepened, by annealing the steel, touching up the lines or busts by hand engraving to restore the letters or renew the facial contour lines, and then rehardened for subsequent use. This recutting is the principal cause for minor die varieties in envelope stamps. When working dies are no longer useful, they are mutilated and eventually melted down into scrap metal.

The average "life" (in number of good impressions obtained) of a hardened steel working die, as used in envelope printing and embossing machines is around 30,000,000 on flat bed presses, and 43,000,000 on rotary presses. With a production of stamped envelopes of approximately 2 billion annually, 60 to 75 working dies are worn out each year, and require replacement with new dies or a reworking of old dies. Some 200 to 250 working dies can be in constant use, since most envelope printing presses are set up for a special size, type or value, and few can be operated continuously at maximum capacity.

Master and hub dies of obsolete envelope issues are kept in the vaults of the Bureau of Engraving and printing in Washington, as are the original dies of adhesive stamps, revenue paper, government securities and paper currency.

PRINTING ENVELOPE STAMPS
Embossed envelope stamps are not printed against a rigid flat platen, as is the normal printed page, but against a somewhat flexible or resilient platen or make-ready (Figure 6). This resilient platen is hard enough to produce a clear full impression from the ink on the face of the working die, and soft enough to push the paper into the uninked recesses that correspond to the engraved lines cut into the master die. The normal result is raised lines or embossments without ink or color, standing out in relief against an inked or colored background. The method differs from the usual embossing technique, where rigid dies are used on both sides of the paper, as in notarial seals. The use of the resilient platen in envelope embossing permits far higher operating speeds than can be obtained with rigid embossing dies, without the need of such accurate register between the printing surface and the platen.

Figure 6

Printing Process for Embossed
A. Working Die, Carrying ink on its surface.

B. Resilient Platen, or Make-ready, Pushing Paper into uninked recesses, so that lines of Embossed Monogram receive no color.

C. Paper of Envelope Blank, after Printing and Embossing. Heavy line shows deposit of ink on surface of paper, but Embossed Lines are not inked.

D. Front view of Embossed impression.

When these recessed lines in a working die become filled with ink or other foreign material, the paper is not pushed in, the plugged area receives ink, and the corresponding colorless line does not appear on the stamp. This accounts for missing letters, lines or figures, and is a printing error, not a die variety.

An ALBINO impression is where two or more envelope blanks are fed into the printing press. The one adjacent to the printing die receives the color and the embossing, while the others are embossed only. Albinos are printing errors and are sometimes worth more than normal, inked impressions. Because of the nature of the printing process, many albinos were produced, and most collectors will not pay much, or any, premium for most of them. Albinos of earlier issues, canceled while current, are scarce.

Before January 1, 1965, stamped envelopes were printed by two processes: (1.) The rotary, with curved dies, on Huckins and Harris presses. (2.) The flat process, with straight dies, as illustrated, on the O'Connell-type press, which is a redesigned Hartford press. The flat bed presses include a gumming and folding attachment, while the rotary presses, running at higher speeds, require separate folding machines.

Different master dies in every denomination are required for Huckins, Harris and flat bed presses. This difference gives rise to most of the major die varieties in envelope stamps.

Web-fed equipment which converts paper from a roll into finished envelopes in a continuous operation has produced envelopes starting with Nos. U547 and UC37. Albino impressions do not occur on envelopes produced by web-fed equipment.

Some authorities claim that Scott U37, U48, U49, U110, U124, U125, U130, U133A, U137A, U137B, U137C, W138, U140A, U145, U162, U178A, U185, U220, U285, U286, U298, U299, UO3, UO32, UO38, UO45 and UO45A (with plus sign + before number), were not regularly issued and are not known to have been used.

Wrappers are listed with envelopes of corresponding design, and are numbered with the prefix "W" instead of "U."

ENVELOPE WATERMARKS

Watermark Illustrations 5, 6, 17 and 18 are condensed. Watermark 4 was intended for Official (Post Office Dept.) envelopes, but some leftover paper was also used for regular envelopes. Watermarks 9 and 10 (penalty) paper was never intended for public sale, but some manila/amber manila paper envelopes were released due to factory paper mixups. Watermarks 17-18 were the last laid paper watermarks; watermarks 19-21 the first wove paper watermarks. Beginning with No. U615, unwatermarked paper was used for some issues. Beginning with No. U625, unwatermarked paper was used for all issues.

Wmks. 1 (1853-70) & 2 (1870-78)

Wmk. 3 (1876)

Wmk. 4 (1877-82)

Wmk. 5 (1878-82)

Wmk. 6 (1882-86)

Wmks. 7 (1886-90) & 8 (1890-94)

Wmks. 9 (1886-87) & 10 (1886-99)

Wmk. 11 (1893)

Wmks. 12 (1894-98) & 13 (1899-1902)

Wmks. 14 (1903-07) & 15 (1907-11)

Wmks. 15A (1907-11) & 16 (1911-15)

USSE   US-SE
1911   1911

Wmks. 17 & 18 (1911-15)

Wmk. 19, 20 & 21 (1915-19)

Wmks. 22 & 23 (1919-20)

Wmks. 24 & 25 (1921-24)

Wmks. 26 & 27 (1925-28)

Wmks. 28 & 28A (1929-32)

Wmks. 29, 30 & 30A (1929-32)

Wmks. 31, 32, 33 (1933-36)

Wmks. 35 & 36 (1937-40)

Wmks. 38 & 39 (1941-44)

Wmks. 40 & 41 (1945-48)

Wmks. 42 & 43 (1949-52)

Wmks. 44 & 45 (1953-56)

Wmk. 46 (1957-60)

Wmks. 47 & 48 (1961-88)

Wmks. 49 & 50 (1965-92)

Letter Sheet (1886-94)

Official Envelopes (1991)

Washington — U1

"THREE" in short label with curved ends; 13mm wide at top. Twelve varieties.

U2

"THREE" in short label with straight ends; 15½mm wide at top. Three varieties.

U3

"THREE" in short label with octagonal ends. Two varieties.

U4

"THREE" in wide label with straight ends; 20mm wide at top.

U5

"THREE" in medium wide label with curved ends; 14½mm wide at top. Ten varieties. A sub-variety shows curved lines at either end of label omitted; both T's have longer cross stroke; R is smaller (20 varieties).

U6

Four varieties.

U7

"TEN" in short label; 15½mm wide at top.

U8

"TEN" in wide label; 20mm wide at top.

Printed by George F. Nesbitt & Co., New York, N.Y.

1853-55
On Diagonally Laid Paper (Early printings of No. U1 on Horizontally Laid Paper)

U1	U1	3c	red	400.00	35.00
			Entire	2,250.	45.00
U2	U1	3c	**red,** *buff*	125.00	35.00
			Entire	1,000.	30.00
U3	U2	3c	red	1,200.	50.00
			Entire	6,000.	100.00
U4	U2	3c	**red,** *buff*	400.00	42.50
			Entire	2,750.	100.00
U5	U3	3c	**red** ('54)	6,250.	550.00
			Entire	*37,500.*	900.00
U6	U3	3c	**red,** *buff* ('54)	4,750.	75.00
			Entire	—	150.00
U7	U4	3c	red	5,500.	150.00
			Entire	—	300.00
U8	U4	3c	**red,** *buff*	8,750.	175.00
			Entire	—	300.00
U9	U5	3c	**red** ('54)	50.00	4.00
			Entire	150.00	9.00
U10	U5	3c	**red,** *buff* ('54)	25.00	4.00
			Entire	75.00	6.00
U11	U6	6c	red	300.00	90.00
			Entire	425.00	175.00
U12	U6	6c	**red,** *buff*	140.00	90.00
			Entire	450.00	200.00
U13	U6	6c	green	400.00	150.00
			Entire	700.00	225.00
U14	U6	6c	**green,** *buff*	250.00	125.00
			Entire	450.00	225.00
U15	U7	10c	**green** ('55)	550.00	100.00
			Entire	950.00	150.00
U16	U7	10c	**green,** *buff* ('55)	200.00	85.00
			Entire	500.00	150.00
a.		10c	**pale green,** *buff*	150.00	65.00
			Entire	425.00	125.00
U17	U8	10c	**green** ('55)	475.00	140.00
			Entire	900.00	225.00
a.		10c	**pale green**	350.00	125.00
			Entire	700.00	200.00
U18	U8	10c	**green,** *buff* ('55)	400.00	90.00
			Entire	600.00	175.00
a.		10c	**pale green,** *buff*	375.00	90.00
			Entire	650.00	175.00

Nos. U9, U10, U11, U12, U13, U14, U17, and U18 have been reprinted on white and buff papers, wove or vertically laid, and are not known entire. The originals are on diagonally laid paper. Value, set of 8 reprints on laid, $225. Reprints on wove sell for more.

Franklin — U9

Period after "POSTAGE." (Eleven varieties.)

Franklin — U10

Bust touches inner frame-line at front and back.

Franklin — U11

No period after "POSTAGE." (Two varieties.)

Washington — U12

Nine varieties of type U12.

Envelopes are on diagonally laid paper.

Wrappers on vertically or horizontally laid paper, or on unwatermarked wove paper (Nos. W22, W25)

Wrappers of the 1 cent denomination were authorized by an Act of Congress, February 27, 1861, and were issued in October, 1861. These were suspended in 1863, and their use resumed in June, 1864.

1860-61

W18B	U9	1c	**blue** ('61)		5,750.
U19	U9	1c	**blue**, *buff*	40.00	15.00
			Entire	90.00	32.50
W20	U9	1c	**blue**, *buff* ('61)	70.00	50.00
			Entire	125.00	75.00
W21	U9	1c	**blue**, *manila* ('61)	60.00	45.00
			Entire	125.00	100.00
U21A	U9	1c	**blue**, *orange*, entire		2,750.
W22	U9	1c	**blue**, *orange* ('61)		4,250.
			Entire		8,000.
U23	U10	1c	**blue**, *orange*	750.00	350.00
			Entire	1,000.	500.00
U24	U11	1c	**blue**, *amber*	375.00	110.00
			Entire	750.00	225.00
W25	U11	1c	**blue**, *manila* ('61)	7,500.	2,000.
			Entire	20,000.	5,750.
U26	U12	3c	**red**	35.00	20.00
			Entire	60.00	32.50
U27	U12	3c	**red**, *buff*	26.00	13.00
			Entire	45.00	22.50
U28	U12 + U9	3c + 1c	**red & blue**	325.00	225.00
			Entire	825.00	400.00
U29	U12 + U9	3c + 1c	**red & blue**, *buff*	325.00	250.00
			Entire	825.00	450.00
U30	U12	6c	**red**	3,500.	1,500.
			Entire	4,000.	
U31	U12	6c	**red**, *buff*	4,000.	1,400.
			Entire	6,000.	15,000.
U32	U12	10c	**green**	1,650.	425.00
			Entire	14,000.	650.00
U33	U12	10c	**green**, *buff*	1,650.	375.00
			Entire	4,500.	550.00

Nos. U26, U27, U30 to U33 have been reprinted on the same vertically laid paper as the reprints of the 1853-55 issue, and are not known entire. Value, Nos. U26-U27, $160; Nos. U30-U33, $100.

Washington — U13

17 varieties for Nos. U34-U35; 2 varieties for No. U36.

Washington — U14

Washington — U15

Washington — U16

Envelopes are on diagonally laid paper.

U36 and U45 come on vertically or horizontally laid paper. U36 appeared in August, 1861, and was withdrawn in 1864. Total issue 211,800.

1861

U34	U13	3c	**pink**	32.50	6.00
			Entire	62.50	13.00
U35	U13	3c	**pink**, *buff*	37.50	7.50
			Entire	62.50	13.00
U36	U13	3c	**pink**, *blue* (Letter Sheet)	77.50	60.00
			Entire	225.00	140.00
+U37	U13	3c	**pink**, *orange*	5,500.	
			Entire	8,000.	
U38	U14	6c	**pink**	125.00	80.00
			Entire	210.00	190.00
U39	U14	6c	**pink**, *buff*	70.00	62.50
			Entire	225.00	160.00
U40	U15	10c	**yellow green**	47.50	30.00
			Entire	82.50	60.00
a.		10c	**blue green**	47.50	30.00
			Entire	82.50	60.00
U41	U15	10c	**yellow green**, *buff*	47.50	30.00
			Entire	82.50	52.50
a.		10c	**blue green**, *buff*	47.50	30.00
			Entire	82.50	52.50
U42	U16	12c	**red & brown**, *buff*	275.00	200.00
			Entire	550.00	650.00
a.		12c	**lake & brown**, *buff*	1,400.	
U43	U16	20c	**red & blue**, *buff*	275.00	225.00
			Entire	550.00	1,250.
U44	U16	24c	**red & green**, *buff*	250.00	225.00
			Entire	700.00	1,500.
a.		24c	**lake & green**, *salmon*	325.00	225.00
			Entire	850.00	1,750.
U45	U16	40c	**black & red**, *buff*	450.00	400.00
			Entire	950.00	4,500.

Nos. U38 and U39 have been reprinted on the same papers as the reprints of the 1853-55 issue, and are not known entire. Value, set of 2 reprints, $60.

Jackson — U17

"U.S. POSTAGE" above. Downstroke and tail of "2" unite near the point (seven varieties).

Jackson — U18

"U.S. POSTAGE" above. The downstroke and tail of the "2" touch but do not merge.

Jackson — U19

"U.S. POST" above. Stamp 24-25mm wide (Sixteen varieties).

Jackson — U20

"U.S. POST" above. Stamp 25½-26¼mm wide. (Twenty-five varieties.)

Envelopes are on diagonally laid paper.
Wrappers on vertically or horizontally laid paper.

1863-64

U46	U17	2c	**black**, *buff*	60.00	24.00
			Entire	85.00	37.50
W47	U17	2c	**black**, *dark manila*	100.00	65.00
			Entire	120.00	90.00
+U48	U18	2c	**black**, *buff*	3,250.	
			Entire	6,250.	
+U49	U18	2c	**black**, *orange*	2,900.	
			Entire	5,750.	
U50	U19	2c	**black**, *buff* ('64)	19.00	9.50
			Entire	42.50	21.00
W51	U19	2c	**black**, *buff* ('64)	500.00	275.00
			Entire	800.00	400.00
U52	U19	2c	**black**, *orange* ('64)	19.00	9.50
			Entire	37.50	18.00
W53	U19	2c	**black**, *dark manila* ('64)	52.50	40.00
			Entire	175.00	140.00
U54	U20	2c	**black**, *buff* ('64)	19.00	9.50
			Entire	39.00	16.00
W55	U20	2c	**black**, *buff* ('64)	105.00	65.00
			Entire	160.00	120.00
U56	U20	2c	**black**, *orange* ('64)	22.00	8.50
			Entire	34.00	16.00
W57	U20	2c	**black**, *light manila* ('64)	24.00	14.00
			Entire	37.50	24.00

Washington — U21

79 varieties for Nos. U58-U61; 2 varieties for Nos. U63-U65.

Washington — U22

1864-65

U58	U21	3c	**pink**	12.00	1.60
			Entire	20.00	3.25
U59	U21	3c	**pink**, *buff*	12.00	1.25
			Entire	20.00	3.00
U60	U21	3c	**brown** ('65)	75.00	40.00
			Entire	140.00	125.00
U61	U21	3c	**brown**, *buff* ('65)	60.00	30.00
			Entire	125.00	80.00
U62	U21	6c	**pink**	110.00	29.00
			Entire	190.00	85.00
U63	U21	6c	**pink**, *buff*	55.00	27.50
			Entire	110.00	50.00
U64	U21	6c	**purple** ('65)	70.00	26.00
			Entire	100.00	55.00
U65	U21	6c	**purple**, *buff* ('65)	60.00	20.00
			Entire	80.00	55.00
U66	U22	9c	**lemon**, *buff* ('65)	450.00	250.00
			Entire	625.00	1,000.
U67	U22	9c	**orange**, *buff* ('65)	160.00	90.00
			Entire	225.00	275.00
a.		9c	**orange yellow**, *buff*	160.00	90.00
			Entire	225.00	275.00
U68	U22	12c	**brown**, *buff* ('65)	300.00	300.00
			Entire	600.00	1,200.
U69	U22	12c	**red brown**, *buff* ('65)	150.00	55.00
			Entire	200.00	360.00
U70	U22	18c	**red**, *buff* ('65)	100.00	95.00
			Entire	200.00	800.00
U71	U22	24c	**blue**, *buff* ('65)	100.00	95.00
			entire	225.00	750.00
U72	U22	30c	**green**, *buff* ('65)	130.00	80.00
			Entire	200.00	1,500.
a.		30c	**yellow green**, *buff*	125.00	80.00
			Entire	200.00	1,500.
U73	U22	40c	**rose**, *buff* ('65)	125.00	250.00
			Entire	350.00	2,000.

Printed by George H. Reay, Brooklyn, N. Y.
The engravings in this issue are finely executed.

Franklin — U23

Bust points to the end of the "N" of "ONE."

Jackson — U24

Bust narrow at back. Small, thick figures of value.

Washington — U25

Queue projects below bust.

Lincoln — U26

Neck very long at the back.

Stanton — U27

Bust pointed at the back; figures "7" are normal.

Jefferson — U28

Queue forms straight line with the bust.

Clay — U29

Ear partly concealed by hair, mouth large, chin prominent.

Webster — U30

Has side whiskers.

Scott — U31

Straggling locks of hair at top of head; ornaments around the inner oval end in squares.

Hamilton — U32

Back of bust very narrow, chin almost straight; labels containing figures of value are exactly parallel.

Perry — U33

Front of bust very narrow and pointed; inner lines of shields project very slightly beyond the oval.

1870-71

U74	U23	1c	**blue**	45.00	30.00
			Entire	80.00	45.00
a.		1c	**ultramarine**	72.50	35.00
			Entire	140.00	60.00
U75	U23	1c	**blue**, *amber*	37.50	27.50
			Entire	60.00	40.00
a.		1c	**ultramarine**, *amber*	70.00	30.00
			Entire	100.00	55.00
U76	U23	1c	**blue**, *orange*	21.00	15.00
			Entire	37.50	22.50
W77	U23	1c	**blue**, *manila*	45.00	37.50
			Entire	82.50	70.00
U78	U24	2c	**brown**	42.50	16.00
			Entire	60.00	22.50
U79	U24	2c	**brown**, *amber*	22.50	10.00
			Entire	42.50	17.50
U80	U24	2c	**brown**, *orange*	13.00	6.50
			Entire	18.00	11.00
W81	U24	2c	**brown**, *manila*	29.00	22.50
			Entire	62.50	57.50
U82	U25	3c	**green**	8.50	1.00
			Entire	17.00	4.00
a.		3c	**brown** (error), entire	*9,000.*	

U83	U25	3c	**green**, *amber*	7.25	2.00
			Entire	18.00	5.00
U84	U25	3c	**green**, *cream*	11.00	4.50
			Entire	17.00	10.00
U85	U26	6c	**dark red**	32.50	16.00
			Entire	60.00	21.00
a.		6c	**vermilion**	32.50	16.00
			Entire	75.00	20.00
U86	U26	6c	**dark red**, *amber*	50.00	20.00
			Entire	80.00	30.00
a.		6c	**vermilion**, *amber*	50.00	20.00
			Entire	80.00	30.00
U87	U26	6c	**dark red**, *cream*	50.00	25.00
			Entire	80.00	30.00
a.		6c	**vermilion**, *cream*	40.00	20.00
			Entire	80.00	30.00
U88	U27	7c	**vermilion**, *amber* ('71)	70.00	190.00
			Entire	90.00	900.00
U89	U28	10c	**olive black**	975.00	900.00
			Entire	1,350.	1,250.
U90	U28	10c	**olive black**, *amber*	975.00	900.00
			Entire	1,350.	*1,250.*
U91	U28	10c	**brown**	92.50	72.50
			Entire	140.00	125.00
U92	U28	10c	**brown**, *amber*	110.00	52.50
			Entire	140.00	125.00
a.		10c	**dark brown**, *amber*	110.00	75.00
			Entire	140.00	125.00
U93	U29	12c	**plum**	125.00	82.50
			Entire	240.00	*450.00*
U94	U29	12c	**plum**, *amber*	140.00	110.00
			Entire	240.00	*650.00*
U95	U29	12c	**plum**, *cream*	275.00	225.00
			Entire	350.00	
U96	U30	15c	**red orange**	85.00	85.00
			Entire	175.00	
a.		15c	**orange**	85.00	
			Entire	175.00	
U97	U30	15c	**red orange**, *amber*	200.00	*300.00*
			Entire	375.00	
a.		15c	**orange**, *amber*	200.00	
			Entire	375.00	
U98	U30	15c	**red orange**, *cream*	400.00	400.00
			Entire	450.00	
a.		15c	**orange**, *cream*	350.00	
			Entire	450.00	
U99	U31	24c	**purple**	150.00	150.00
			Entire	200.00	
U100	U31	24c	**purple**, *amber*	250.00	*325.00*
			Entire	425.00	
U101	U31	24c	**purple**, *cream*	325.00	*500.00*
			Entire	525.00	
U102	U32	30c	**black**	80.00	110.00
			Entire	300.00	*750.00*
U103	U32	30c	**black**, *amber*	300.00	*500.00*
			Entire	750.00	
U104	U32	30c	**black**, *cream*	300.00	*500.00*
			Entire	475.00	
U105	U33	90c	**carmine**	175.00	*350.00*
			Entire	250.00	
U106	U33	90c	**carmine**, *amber*	350.00	*1,000.*
			Entire	1,000.	*4,500.*
U107	U33	90c	**carmine**, *cream*	200.00	*2,500.*
			Entire	500.00	*5,000.*

Printed by Plimpton Manufacturing Co.

U34

Bust forms an angle at the back near the frame. Lettering poorly executed. Distinct circle in "O" of "Postage."

U35

Lower part of bust points to the end of the "E" in "ONE." Head inclined downward.

U36

Bust narrow at back. Thin numerals. Head of "P" narrow. Bust broad at front, ending in sharp corners.

U37

Bust broad. Figures of value in long ovals.

U38

Similar to U37 but the figure "2" at the left touches the oval.

U39

Similar to U37 but the "O" of "TWO" has the center netted instead of plain and the "G" of "POSTAGE" and the "C" of "CENTS" have diagonal crossline.

U40

Bust broad: numerals in ovals short and thick.

U41

Similar to U40 but the ovals containing the numerals are much heavier. A diagonal line runs from the upper part of the "U" to the white frame-line.

U42

Similar to U40 but the middle stroke of "N" in "CENTS" is as thin as the vertical strokes.

U43

Bottom of bust cut almost semi-circularly.

U44

Thin lettering, long thin figures of value.

U45

Thick lettering, well-formed figures of value, queue does not project below bust.

U46

Top of head egg-shaped; knot of queue well marked and projects triangularly.

Taylor — U47

Die 1 — Figures of value with thick, curved tops.

Die 2 — Figures of value with long, thin tops.

U48

Neck short at back.

U49

Figures of value turned up at the ends.

U50

Very large head.

U51

Knot of queue stands out prominently.

U52

Ear prominent, chin receding.

U53

No side whiskers, forelock projects above head.

U54

Hair does not project; ornaments around the inner oval end in points.

U55

Back of bust rather broad, chin slopes considerably; labels containing figures of value are not exactly parallel.

U56

Front of bust sloping; inner lines of shields project considerably into the inner oval.

1874-86

U108	U34	1c **dark blue**	210.00	70.00
		Entire	275.00	110.00
a.		1c **light blue**	210.00	70.00

		Entire	275.00	125.00
U109	U34	1c **dark blue**, *amber*	190.00	75.00
		Entire	210.00	140.00
+U110	U34	1c **dark blue**, *cream*	1,750.	
U111	U34	1c **dark blue**, *orange*	25.00	17.50
		Entire	35.00	25.00
a.		1c **light blue**, *orange*	25.00	17.50
		Entire	35.00	25.00
W112	U34	1c **dark blue**, *manila*	72.50	42.50
		Entire	110.00	75.00
U113	U35	1c **light blue**	2.00	1.00
		Entire	3.00	1.10
a.		1c **dark blue**	9.00	7.50
		Entire	29.00	20.00
U114	U35	1c **light blue**, *amber*	4.00	4.00
		Entire	8.25	6.00
a.		1c **dark blue**, *amber*	20.00	10.00
		Entire	30.00	20.00
U115	U35	1c **blue**, *cream*	5.25	4.50
		Entire	10.50	6.50
a.		1c **dark blue**, *cream*	20.00	8.50
		Entire	32.50	20.00
U116	U35	1c **light blue**, *orange*	.80	.40
		Entire	1.25	1.00
a.		1c **dark blue**, *orange*	4.50	2.50
		Entire	16.00	8.00
U117	U35	1c **light blue**, *blue* ('80)	8.50	5.25
		Entire	13.50	9.00
U118	U35	1c **light blue**, *fawn* ('79)	8.50	5.25
		Entire	15.00	10.00
U119	U35	1c **light blue**, *manila* ('86)	9.00	3.25
		Entire	17.00	5.00
W120	U35	1c **light blue**, *manila*	1.60	1.10
		Entire	2.75	1.75
a.		1c **dark blue**, *manila*	9.00	8.00
		Entire	16.00	15.00
U121	U35	1c **light blue**, *amber manila* ('86)	19.00	10.00
		Entire	29.00	20.00
U122	U36	2c **brown**	160.00	60.00
		Entire	175.00	85.00
U123	U36	2c **brown**, *amber*	72.50	40.00
		Entire	125.00	70.00
+U124	U36	2c **brown**, *cream*	1,250.	
+U125	U36	2c **brown**, *orange*	25,000.	
		Entire	45,000.	
W126	U36	2c **brown**, *manila*	175.00	85.00
		Entire	300.00	160.00
W127	U36	2c **vermilion**, *manila*	3,250.	250.00
		Entire	4,750.	5,000.
U128	U37	2c **brown**	65.00	35.00
		Entire	110.00	75.00
U129	U37	2c **brown**, *amber*	90.00	45.00
		Entire	125.00	77.50
+U130	U37	2c **brown**, *cream*	50,000.	
W131	U37	2c **brown**, *manila*	20.00	17.00
		Entire	29.00	26.00
U132	U38	2c **brown**	82.50	29.00
		Entire	130.00	80.00
U133	U38	2c **brown**, *amber*	525.00	70.00
		Entire	675.00	140.00
+U133A	U38	2c **brown**, *cream*	100,000.	
U134	U39	2c **brown**	1,500.	160.00
		Entire	2,250.	300.00
U135	U39	2c **brown**, *amber*	525.00	140.00
		Entire	750.00	160.00
U136	U39	2c **brown**, *orange*	57.50	29.00
		Entire	87.50	37.50
W137	U39	2c **brown**, *manila*	80.00	40.00
		Entire	125.00	55.00
+U137A	U39	2c **vermilion**	40,000.	
+U137B	U39	2c **vermilion**, *amber*	40,000.	
+U137C	U39	2c **vermilion**, *orange*	100,000.	
+W138	U39	2c **vermilion**, *manila*	32,500.	
U139	U40	2c **brown** ('75)	62.50	37.50
		Entire	82.50	47.50
U140	U40	2c **brown**, *amber* ('75)	97.50	62.50
		Entire	140.00	77.50
+U140A	U40	2c **reddish brown**, *orange* ('75)	25,000.	
		Entire	40,000.	
W141	U40	2c **brown**, *manila* ('75)	37.50	27.50
		Entire	45.00	32.50
U142	U40	2c **vermilion** ('75)	10.00	5.00
		Entire	14.00	7.50
a.		2c **pink**	10.00	5.00
		Entire	14.00	7.50
U143	U40	2c **vermilion**, *amber* ('75)	10.00	4.50
		Entire	13.00	5.75
U144	U40	2c **vermilion**, *cream* ('75)	21.00	7.50
		Entire	26.00	12.50
+U145	U40	2c **vermilion**, *orange* ('75)	50,000.	
U146	U40	2c **vermilion**, *blue* ('80)	140.00	40.00
		Entire	220.00	140.00
U147	U40	2c **vermilion**, *fawn* ('75)	11.00	5.00
		Entire	17.00	7.00
W148	U40	2c **vermilion**, *manila* ('75)	4.75	3.75
		Entire	9.00	6.50
U149	U41	2c **vermilion** ('78)	62.50	32.50
		Entire	95.00	45.00
a.		2c **pink**	62.50	35.00
		Entire	95.00	45.00
U150	U41	2c **vermilion**, *amber* ('78)	42.50	17.50
		Entire	62.50	22.50
U151	U41	2c **vermilion**, *blue* ('80)	14.00	10.00
		Entire	21.00	15.00
a.		2c **pink**, *blue*	15.00	10.00

		Entire	17.50	12.50
U152	U41	2c **vermilion**, *fawn* ('78)	15.00	4.75
		Entire	20.00	9.50
U153	U42	2c **vermilion** ('76)	85.00	30.00
		Entire	115.00	40.00
U154	U42	2c **vermilion**, *amber* ('76)	350.00	90.00
		Entire	450.00	175.00
W155	U42	2c **vermilion**, *manila* ('76)	24.00	11.00
		Entire	47.50	20.00
U156	U43	2c **vermilion** ('81)	1,750.	175.00
		Entire	3,750.	500.00
U157	U43	2c **vermilion**, *amber* ('81)	57,500.	35,000.
		Entire	110,000.	
W158	U43	2c **vermilion**, *manila* ('81)	110.00	62.50
		Entire	190.00	175.00
U159	U44	3c **green**	40.00	11.50
		Entire	62.50	17.50
U160	U44	3c **green**, *amber*	37.50	10.50
		Entire	65.00	20.00
U161	U44	3c **green**, *cream*	42.50	15.00
		Entire	70.00	30.00
+U162	U44	3c **green**, *blue*	125,000.	
U163	U45	3c **green**	1.50	.30
		Entire	4.25	2.25
U164	U45	3c **green**, *amber*	1.60	.70
		Entire	4.25	2.00
U165	U45	3c **green**, *cream*	9.50	6.50
		Entire	19.00	9.00
U166	U45	3c **green**, *blue*	8.50	6.25
		Entire	17.00	11.00
U167	U45	3c **green**, *fawn* ('75)	5.25	3.50
		Entire	9.25	5.00
U168	U46	3c **green** ('81)	1,500.	80.00
		Entire	5,000.	275.00
U169	U46	3c **green**, *amber*	700.00	125.00
		Entire	975.00	300.00
U170	U46	3c **green**, *blue* ('81)	12,500.	3,250.
		Entire	20,000.	4,750.
U171	U46	3c **green**, *fawn* ('81)	45,000.	3,250.
		Entire		14,000.
U172	U47	5c **blue**, die 1 ('75)	15.00	11.00
		Entire	21.00	16.00
U173	U47	5c **blue**, die 1, *amber* ('75)	15.00	12.50
		Entire	21.00	17.00
U174	U47	5c **blue**, die 1, *cream* ('75)	125.00	47.50
		Entire	190.00	95.00
U175	U47	5c **blue**, die 1, *blue* ('75)	40.00	19.00
		Entire	57.50	27.50
U176	U47	5c **blue**, die 1, *fawn* ('75)	175.00	70.00
		Entire	300.00	
U177	U47	5c **blue**, die 2 ('75)	14.00	10.00
		Entire	20.00	18.00
U178	U47	5c **blue**, die 2, *amber* ('75)	12.00	10.00
		Entire	21.00	19.00
+U178A	U47	5c **blue**, die 2, *cream* ('76)	14,000.	
		Entire	22,500.	
U179	U47	5c **blue**, die 2, *blue* ('75)	32.50	13.50
		Entire	47.50	30.00
U180	U47	5c **blue**, die 2, *fawn* ('75)	140.00	47.50
		Entire	240.00	140.00
U181	U48	6c **red**	10.00	6.75
		Entire	15.00	12.50
a.		6c **vermilion**	10.00	6.75
		Entire	15.00	12.50
U182	U48	6c **red**, *amber*	15.00	6.75
		Entire	24.00	15.00
a.		6c **vermilion**, *amber*	15.00	6.75
		Entire	24.00	15.00
U183	U48	6c **red**, *cream*	55.00	17.50
		Entire	87.50	40.00
a.		6c **vermilion**, *cream*	55.00	17.50
		Entire	87.50	40.00
U184	U48	6c **red**, *fawn* ('75)	24.00	13.50
		Entire	35.00	29.00
+U185	U49	7c **vermilion**	1,250.	
U186	U49	7c **vermilion**, *amber*	175.00	75.00
		Entire	210.00	
U187	U50	10c **brown**	45.00	22.50
		Entire	65.00	
U188	U50	10c **brown**, *amber*	82.50	35.00
		Entire	160.00	
U189	U51	10c **chocolate** ('75)	8.00	4.25
		Entire	13.00	9.25
a.		10c **bister brown**	9.00	5.25
		Entire	13.00	10.50
b.		10c **yellow ocher**	4,500.	
		Entire	8,500.	
U190	U51	10c **chocolate**, *amber* ('75)	9.00	7.25
		Entire	14.50	11.50
a.		10c **bister brown**, *amber*	9.00	7.75
		Entire	14.50	11.50
b.		10c **yellow ocher** *amber*	3,500.	
		Entire	6,500.	
U191	U51	10c **brown**, *oriental buff* ('86)	20.00	8.75
		Entire	22.50	11.50
U192	U51	10c **brown**, *blue* ('86)	20.00	8.75
		Entire	22.50	15.00
a.		10c **gray black**, *blue*	18.00	8.25
		Entire	21.00	15.00
b.		10c **red brown**, *blue*	18.00	8.25
		Entire	21.00	15.00
U193	U51	10c **brown**, *manila* ('86)	19.00	10.00
		Entire	24.00	16.00
a.		10c **red brown**, *manila*	19.00	10.00

		Entire	24.00	16.00
U194	U51	10c **brown**, *amber manila* ('86)	21.00	9.00
		Entire	27.50	17.50
	a.	10c **red brown**, *amber manila*	21.00	9.00
		Entire	27.50	17.50
U195	U52	12c **plum**	300.00	100.00
		Entire	650.00	
U196	U52	12c **plum**, *amber*	275.00	175.00
		Entire	350.00	
U197	U52	12c **plum**, *cream*	225.00	150.00
		Entire	950.00	
U198	U53	15c **orange**	55.00	40.00
		Entire	92.50	55.00
U199	U53	15c **orange**, *amber*	160.00	100.00
		Entire	300.00	
U200	U53	15c **orange**, *cream*	700.00	350.00
		Entire	1,000.	
U201	U54	24c **purple**	190.00	175.00
		Entire	250.00	
	a.	Printed on both sides, one inverted and overlapping, cut to shape	450.00	
U202	U54	24c **purple**, *amber*	200.00	125.00
		Entire	260.00	
U203	U54	24c **purple**, *cream*	190.00	125.00
		Entire	750.00	
U204	U55	30c **black**	65.00	27.50
		Entire	90.00	65.00
U205	U55	30c **black**, *amber*	80.00	65.00
		Entire	140.00	*250.00*
U206	U55	30c **black**, *cream* ('75)	500.00	375.00
		Entire	800.00	
U207	U55	30c **black**, *oriental buff* ('81)	120.00	82.50
		Entire	180.00	
U208	U55	30c **black**, *blue* ('81)	125.00	82.50
		Entire	200.00	
U209	U55	30c **black**, *manila* ('81)	100.00	80.00
		Entire	200.00	
U210	U55	30c **black**, *amber manila* ('86)	200.00	115.00
		Entire	235.00	
U211	U56	90c **carmine** ('75)	115.00	85.00
		Entire	160.00	95.00
U212	U56	90c **carmine**, *amber* ('75)	225.00	300.00
		Entire	275.00	
U213	U56	90c **carmine**, *cream* ('75)	1,650.	
		Entire	3,500.	
U214	U56	90c **carmine**, *oriental buff* ('86)	200.00	275.00
		Entire	400.00	300.00
U215	U56	90c **carmine**, *blue* ('86)	250.00	275.00
		Entire	325.00	325.00
U216	U56	90c **carmine**, *manila* ('86)	180.00	250.00
		Entire	275.00	275.00
U217	U56	90c **carmine**, *amber manila* ('86)	180.00	*200.00*
		Entire	250.00	*275.00*

Note: No. U206 has watermark #2; No. U207 watermark #6 or #7. No U213 has watermark #2; No. U214 watermark #7. These envelopes cannot be positively identified except by the watermark.

U57

Single line under "POSTAGE."

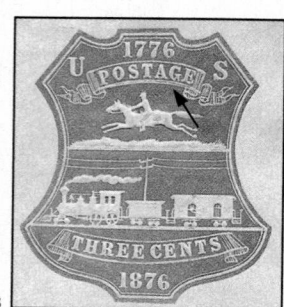

U58

Double line under "POSTAGE."

1876
Printed by Plimpton Manufacturing Co.

U218	U57	3c **red**	52.50	25.00
		Entire	77.50	50.00
U219	U57	3c **green**	45.00	17.50
		Entire	65.00	40.00
U220	U58	3c **red**	*42,500.*	
		Entire	*60,000.*	
U221	U58	3c **green**	52.50	25.00
		Entire	85.00	50.00

Garfield — U59

1882-86
Printed by Plimpton Manufacturing Co. and Morgan Envelope Co.

U222	U59	5c **brown**	5.75	3.00
		Entire	10.50	7.00
U223	U59	5c **brown**, *amber*	6.00	3.50
		Entire	11.00	8.50
U224	U59	5c **brown**, *oriental buff* ('86)	140.00	75.00
		Entire	200.00	
U225	U59	5c **brown**, *blue*	82.50	35.00
		Entire	125.00	75.00
U226	U59	5c **brown**, *fawn*	375.00	
		Entire	525.00	

Washington — U60

1883, October

U227	U60	2c **red**	4.50	2.25
		Entire	10.00	3.00
	a.	2c **brown** (error), entire	*10,000.*	
U228	U60	2c **red**, *amber*	6.00	2.75
		Entire	11.00	6.00
U229	U60	2c **red**, *blue*	8.50	5.00
		Entire	13.00	8.00
U230	U60	2c **red**, *fawn*	9.25	5.25
		Entire	15.00	7.00

Washington — U61

Wavy lines fine and clear.

1883, November
Four Wavy Lines in Oval

U231	U61	2c **red**	5.50	2.50
		Entire	10.00	4.00
U232	U61	2c **red**, *amber*	6.50	3.75
		Entire	12.00	5.75
U233	U61	2c **red**, *blue*	11.00	7.50
		Entire	19.00	10.00
U234	U61	2c **red**, *fawn*	8.00	4.75
		Entire	12.00	6.00
W235	U61	2c **red**, *manila*	22.50	6.25
		Entire	32.50	12.50

U62

Retouched die. Wavy lines thick and blurred.

1884, June

U236	U62	2c **red**	14.50	4.00
		Entire	22.50	7.75
U237	U62	2c **red**, *amber*	17.50	10.00
		Entire	27.50	11.00
U238	U62	2c **red**, *blue*	29.00	12.00
		Entire	40.00	15.00
U239	U62	2c **red**, *fawn*	25.00	11.00
		Entire	35.00	12.50

U63

3½ links over left "2."

U240	U63	2c **red**	100.00	47.50
		Entire	160.00	72.50
U241	U63	2c **red**, *amber*	1,000.	325.00
		Entire	2,750.	750.00
U242	U63	2c **red**, *fawn*	*37,500.*	
		Entire	*55,000.*	

U64

2 links below right "2."

U243	U64	2c **red**	140.00	75.00
		Entire	175.00	100.00
U244	U64	2c **red**, *amber*	350.00	100.00
		Entire	500.00	125.00
U245	U64	2c **red**, *blue*	500.00	210.00
		Entire	650.00	225.00
U246	U64	2c **red**, *fawn*	450.00	200.00
		Entire	700.00	275.00

U65

Round "O" in "TWO." White lines above "WO" of "TWO" joined to form thick white dash.

U247	U65	2c **red**	3,500.	500.00
		Entire	4,500.	*1,250.*
U248	U65	2c **red**, *amber*	5,250.	750.00
		Entire	8,000.	*1,650.*
U249	U65	2c **red**, *fawn*	1,400.	500.00
		Entire	2,250.	*750.00*

Jackson, Die 1 — U66

Die 1
—
Numeral
at left
is
2¾mm
wide.

Die 2
—
Numeral
at left
is
3¼mm
wide

1883-86

U250	U66	4c **green,** die 1	4.00	3.50
		Entire	6.50	6.00
U251	U66	4c **green,** die 1, *amber*	5.00	3.50
		Entire	7.50	5.25
U252	U66	4c **green,** die 1, *oriental buff* ('86)	13.00	9.00
		Entire	18.00	12.50
U253	U66	4c **green,** die 1, *blue* ('86)	13.00	6.50
		Entire	18.00	8.00
U254	U66	4c **green,** die 1, *manila* ('86)	16.00	7.50
		Entire	21.00	15.00
U255	U66	4c **green,** die 1, *amber manila* ('86)	24.00	10.00
		Entire	32.50	15.00
U256	U66	4c **green,** die 2	11.00	5.00
		Entire	19.00	6.75
U257	U66	4c **green,** die 2, *amber*	15.00	7.00
		Entire	25.00	10.00
U258	U66	4c **green,** die 2, *manila* ('86)	15.00	7.50
		Entire	25.00	12.50
U259	U66	4c **green,** die 2, *amber manila* ('86)	15.00	7.50
		Entire	25.00	12.50

1884, May

U260	U61	2c **brown**	19.00	5.75
		Entire	21.00	9.00
U261	U61	2c **brown,** *amber*	19.00	6.50
		Entire	21.00	7.50
U262	U61	2c **brown,** *blue*	23.00	10.00
		Entire	29.00	14.00
U263	U61	2c **brown,** *fawn*	18.50	9.25
		Entire	20.00	12.50
W264	U61	2c **brown,** *manila*	19.00	11.50
		Entire	26.00	19.00

1884, June

Retouched Die

U265	U62	2c **brown**	20.00	6.50
		Entire	27.50	12.00
U266	U62	2c **brown,** *amber*	67.50	40.00
		Entire	75.00	50.00
U267	U62	2c **brown,** *blue*	25.00	9.00
		Entire	32.50	15.00
U268	U62	2c **brown,** *fawn*	18.00	11.00
		Entire	22.50	15.00
W269	U62	2c **brown,** *manila*	30.00	15.00
		Entire	35.00	24.00

2 Links Below Right "2"

U270	U64	2c **brown**	140.00	50.00
		Entire	175.00	110.00
U271	U64	2c **brown,** *amber*	500.00	110.00
		Entire	600.00	350.00
U272	U64	2c **brown,** *fawn*	10,000.	3,000.
		Entire	12,000.	4,000.

Round "O" in "Two"

U273	U65	2c **brown**	300.00	110.00
		Entire	400.00	200.00
U274	U65	2c **brown,** *amber*	300.00	110.00
		Entire	400.00	190.00
U275	U65	2c **brown,** *blue*		20,000.
		Entire		47,500.
U276	U65	2c **brown,** *fawn*	1,000.	700.00
		Entire	1,550.	900.00

Washington — U67

Extremity of bust below the queue forms a point.

U68

Extremity of bust is rounded. Similar to U61. Two wavy lines in oval.

1884-86

U277	U67	2c **brown**	.50	.20
		Entire	1.00	.40
a.		2c **brown lake,** die 1	22.50	21.00
		Entire	27.50	26.00
U278	U67	2c **brown,** *amber*	.65	.50
		Entire	1.75	.75
a.		2c **brown lake,** *amber*	35.00	25.00
		Entire	42.50	32.50
U279	U67	2c **brown,** *oriental buff* ('86)	5.00	2.10
		Entire	7.50	3.00
U280	U67	2c **brown,** *blue*	3.00	2.10
		Entire	4.50	3.50
U281	U67	2c **brown,** *fawn*	4.00	2.40
		Entire	5.75	4.00
U282	U67	2c **brown,** *manila* ('86)	13.00	4.00
		Entire	17.50	6.50
W283	U67	2c **brown,** *manila*	8.00	5.00
		Entire	11.00	6.50
U284	U67	2c **brown,** *amber manila* ('86)	9.00	5.75
		Entire	15.00	7.00
+U285	U67	2c **red**	775.00	
		Entire	1,650.	
+U286	U67	2c **red,** *blue*	325.00	
		Entire	375.00	
W287	U67	2c **red,** *manila*	150.00	
		Entire	210.00	
U288	U68	2c **brown**	325.00	50.00
		Entire	825.00	150.00
U289	U68	2c **brown,** *amber*	18.00	13.00
		Entire	24.00	17.00
U290	U68	2c **brown,** *blue*	1,250.	300.00
		Entire	2,400.	450.00
U291	U68	2c **brown,** *fawn*	35.00	22.50
		Entire	45.00	27.50
W292	U68	2c **brown,** *manila*	25.00	19.00
		Entire	35.00	22.50

Gen. U.S. Grant — US1

1886

Printed by American Bank Note Co.
Issued August 18, 1886. Withdrawn June 30, 1894.
Letter Sheet, 160x271mm
Stamp in upper right corner
Creamy White Paper

U293	US1	2c **green,** entire	30.00	20.00

Perforation varieties:

83 perforations at top	30.00	20.00
42 perforations at top	65.00	30.00
33 perforations at top	65.00	30.00

All with 41 perforations at top

Inscribed: Series 1	30.00	20.00
Inscribed: Series 2	30.00	20.00
Inscribed: Series 3	30.00	20.00
Inscribed: Series 4	30.00	20.00
Inscribed: Series 5	30.00	20.00
Inscribed: Series 6	30.00	20.00
Inscribed: Series 7	30.00	20.00
No inscription, continuous side perforations	30.00	20.00
No inscription, interrupted side perforations	30.00	20.00

Franklin — U69

Washington — U70

Bust points between third and fourth notches of inner oval "G" of "POSTAGE" has no bar.

U71

Bust points between second and third notches of inner oval; "G" of "POSTAGE" has a bar; ear is indicated by one heavy line; one vertical line at corner of mouth.

U72

Frame same as U71; upper part of head more rounded; ear indicated by two curved lines with two locks of hair in front; two vertical lines at corner of mouth.

Jackson — U73

Grant — U74

There is a space between the beard and the collar of the coat. A button is on the collar.

U75

The collar touches the beard and there is no button.

1887-94

Printed by Plimpton Manufacturing Co. and Morgan Envelope Co., Hartford, Conn.; James Purcell, Holyoke, Mass.

U294	U69	1c **blue**	.55	.20
		Entire	1.00	.50
U295	U69	1c **dark blue** ('94)	8.00	2.50
		Entire	11.00	6.50
U296	U69	1c **blue**, *amber*	3.50	1.25
		Entire	6.00	3.50
U297	U69	1c **dark blue**, *amber* ('94)	47.50	22.50
		Entire	57.50	27.50
+U298	U69	1c **blue**, *oriental buff*	15,000.	
		Entire	20,000.	
+U299	U69	1c **blue**, *blue*	20,000.	
		Entire	30,000.	
U300	U69	1c **blue**, *manila*	.65	.35
		Entire	1.25	.75
W301	U69	1c **blue**, *manila*	.45	.30
		Entire	1.25	.60
U302	U69	1c **dark blue**, *manila* ('94)	30.00	12.50
		Entire	37.50	20.00
W303	U69	1c **dark blue**, *manila* ('94)	17.50	10.00
		Entire	25.00	15.00
U304	U69	1c **blue**, *amber manila*	12.50	5.00
		Entire	17.50	7.50
U305	U70	2c **green**	19.00	10.50
		Entire	35.00	15.00
U306	U70	2c **green**, *amber*	45.00	17.50
		Entire	55.00	22.50
U307	U70	2c **green**, *oriental buff*	97.50	35.00
		Entire	125.00	50.00
U308	U70	2c **green**, *blue*	20,000.	1,250.
		Entire		22,000.
U309	U70	2c **green**, *manila*	17,500.	750.00
		Entire	25,000.	1,050.
U310	U70	2c **green**, *amber manila*	40,000.	1,250.
		Entire	—	3,500.
U311	U71	2c **green**	.35	.20
		Entire	.75	.25
a.		2c **dark green** ('94)	.50	.30
		Entire	1.10	.85
U312	U71	2c **green**, *amber*	.45	.20
		Entire	.80	.30
a.		Double impression	—	
b.		2c **dark green**, *amber* ('94)	.60	.35
		Entire	1.10	.85
U313	U71	2c **green**, *oriental buff*	.60	.25
		Entire	1.20	.40
a.		2c **dark green**, *oriental buff* ('94)	2.00	1.00
		Entire	4.00	4.00
U314	U71	2c **green**, *blue*	.65	.30
		Entire	1.25	.40
a.		2c **dark green** *blue* ('94)	.85	.40
		Entire	1.75	1.50
U315	U71	2c **green**, *manila*	2.00	.50
		Entire	3.00	1.00
a.		2c **dark green** *manila* ('94)	2.75	.75
		Entire	4.00	1.50
W316	U71	2c **green**, *manila*	4.00	2.50
		Entire	11.00	7.00
U317	U71	2c **green**, *amber manila*	3.00	1.90
		Entire	6.00	3.00
a.		2c **dark green**, *amber manila* ('94)	4.00	3.00
		Entire	7.50	4.00
U318	U72	2c **green**	150.00	12.50
		Entire	200.00	45.00
U319	U72	2c **green**, *amber*	200.00	25.00
		Entire	275.00	50.00
U320	U72	2c **green**, *oriental buff*	200.00	40.00
		Entire	275.00	70.00
U321	U72	2c **green**, *blue*	200.00	65.00
		Entire	325.00	82.50
U322	U72	2c **green**, *manila*	275.00	65.00
		Entire	325.00	110.00
U323	U72	2c **green**, *amber manila*	500.00	100.00
		Entire	700.00	175.00
U324	U73	4c **carmine**	3.25	2.00
		Entire	6.00	2.10
a.		4c **lake**	3.50	2.00
		Entire	7.00	3.75
b.		4c **scarlet** ('94)	3.50	2.00
		Entire	7.00	3.75
U325	U73	4c **carmine**, *amber*	3.75	3.50
		Entire	7.50	4.00
a.		4c **lake**, *amber*	3.75	3.50
		Entire	7.75	4.00
b.		4c **scarlet**, *amber* ('94)	4.00	3.75
		Entire	8.00	4.25
U326	U73	4c **carmine**, *oriental buff*	8.00	3.50
		Entire	16.00	6.25
a.		4c **lake**, *oriental buff*	8.00	3.50
		Entire	16.00	6.25
U327	U73	4c **carmine**, *blue*	6.50	4.00
		Entire	13.00	7.00
a.		4c **lake**, *blue*	6.50	4.00
		Entire	13.00	6.00
U328	U73	4c **carmine**, *manila*	9.00	7.00
		Entire	13.00	7.50
a.		4c **lake**, *manila*	9.00	6.00
		Entire	13.00	7.50
b.		4c **pink**, *manila*	15.00	10.00
		Entire	21.00	12.50
U329	U73	4c **carmine**, *amber manila*	7.50	3.25

		Entire	13.50	5.00
a.		4c **lake**, *amber manila*	7.50	3.25
		Entire	13.50	5.00
b.		4c **pink**, *amber manila*	16.00	10.00
		Entire	22.50	12.50
U330	U74	5c **blue**	4.00	4.00
		Entire	8.00	11.00
U331	U74	5c **blue**, *amber*	5.50	2.50
		Entire	10.50	14.00
U332	U74	5c **blue**, *oriental buff*	6.00	4.00
		Entire	17.00	18.00
U333	U74	5c **blue**, *blue*	10.50	6.00
		Entire	17.00	15.00
U334	U75	5c **blue** ('94)	27.50	12.50
		Entire	42.50	22.50
U335	U75	5c **blue**, *amber* ('94)	15.00	7.50
		Entire	23.00	40.00
U336	U55	30c **red brown**	60.00	47.50
		Entire	70.00	475.00
a.		30c **yellow brown**	60.00	47.50
		Entire	70.00	475.00
b.		30c **chocolate**	60.00	47.50
		Entire	70.00	475.00
U337	U55	30c **red brown**, *amber*	60.00	47.50
		Entire	70.00	475.00
a.		30c **yellow brown**, *amber*	60.00	47.50
		Entire	70.00	475.00
b.		30c **chocolate**, *amber*	60.00	47.50
		Entire	70.00	475.00
U338	U55	30c **red brown**, *oriental buff*	60.00	47.50
		Entire	70.00	475.00
a.		30c **yellow brown**, *oriental buff*	60.00	47.50
		Entire	70.00	475.00
U339	U55	30c **red brown**, *blue*	60.00	47.50
		Entire	70.00	475.00
a.		30c **yellow brown**, *blue*	60.00	47.50
		Entire	70.00	475.00
U340	U55	30c **red brown**, *manila*	60.00	47.50
		Entire	70.00	475.00
a.		30c **brown**, *manila*	60.00	47.50
		Entire	70.00	475.00
U341	U55	30c **red brown**, *amber manila*	60.00	47.50
		Entire	70.00	475.00
a.		30c **yellow brown**, *amber manila*	60.00	47.50
		Entire	70.00	475.00
U342	U56	90c **purple**	77.50	90.00
		Entire	125.00	1,050.
U343	U56	90c **purple**, *amber*	92.50	90.00
		Entire	140.00	1,050.
U344	U56	90c **purple**, *oriental buff*	92.50	90.00
		Entire	150.00	1,050.
U345	U56	90c **purple**, *blue*	92.50	90.00
		Entire	150.00	1,050.
U346	U56	90c **purple**, *manila*	100.00	92.50
		Entire	160.00	1,050.
U347	U56	90c **purple**, *amber manila*	100.00	92.50
		Entire	160.00	1,050.

Columbus and Liberty — U76

Four dies were used for the 1c, 2c and 5c:
1 — Meridian behind Columbus' head. Period after "CENTS" and "AMERICA" appears on 1c, 2c and 5c.
2 — No meridian. With periods. Appears on 1c, 2c and 5c.
3 — With meridian. No periods. Appears on 1c, 2c and 10c.
4 — No meridian. No periods. Appears on 2c.

1893

U348	U76	1c **deep blue**	2.25	1.25
		Entire	3.00	1.50
		Entire, Expo. station machine cancel		100.00
		Entire, Expo. station duplex handstamp cancel		250.00
U349	U76	2c **violet**	1.75	.50
		Entire	3.50	.60
		Entire, Expo. station machine cancel		40.00
		Entire, Expo. station duplex handstamp cancel		85.00
a.		2c **dark slate** (error)	2,500.	
		Entire	5,000.	
U350	U76	5c **chocolate**	8.50	7.50
		Entire	13.00	10.00
		Entire, Expo. station machine cancel		150.00
		Entire, Expo. station duplex handstamp cancel		250.00
a.		5c **slate brown** (error)	850.00	950.00
		Entire	1,200.	1,400.
U351	U76	10c **slate brown**	35.00	30.00
		Entire	70.00	60.00

Entire, Expo. station machine cancel		250.00
Entire, Expo. station duplex handstamp cancel		450.00

Franklin — U77

Washington — U78

Bust points to first notch of inner oval and is only slightly concave below.

U79

Bust points to middle of second notch of inner oval and is quite hollow below. Queue has ribbon around it.

U80

Same as die 2, but hair flowing. No ribbon on queue.

Lincoln — U81

Bust pointed but not draped.

U82

Bust broad and draped.

U83

Head larger, inner oval has no notches.

Grant — U84

Similar to design of 1887-95 but smaller.

1899

U352	U77	1c	**green**	1.10	.20
			Entire	2.75	.50
U353	U77	1c	**green**, *amber*	5.50	1.50
			Entire	9.00	2.75
U354	U77	1c	**green**, *oriental buff*	14.50	2.75
			Entire	19.00	3.75
U355	U77	1c	**green**, *blue*	14.50	7.50
			Entire	19.00	12.50
U356	U77	1c	**green**, *manila*	2.50	.95
			Entire	6.50	2.00
W357	U77	1c	**green**, *manila*	2.75	1.10
			Entire	9.00	4.00
U358	U78	2c	**carmine**	3.00	1.75
			Entire	8.00	3.25
U359	U78	2c	**carmine**, *amber*	25.00	15.00
			Entire	32.50	21.00
U360	U78	2c	**carmine**, *oriental buff*	26.00	12.50
			Entire	35.00	15.00
U361	U78	2c	**carmine**, *blue*	65.00	35.00
			Entire	77.50	50.00
U362	U79	2c	**carmine**	.35	.20
			Entire	.65	.30
a.		2c	**dark lake**	30.00	30.00
			Entire	37.50	35.00
U363	U79	2c	**carmine**, *amber*	2.00	.20
			Entire	3.00	.60
U364	U79	2c	**carmine**, *oriental buff*	1.20	.20
			Entire	3.00	.60
U365	U79	2c	**carmine**, *blue*	1.50	.55
			Entire	3.50	2.00
W366	U79	2c	**carmine**, *manila*	9.00	3.25
			Entire	15.00	7.50
U367	U80	2c	**carmine**	6.00	2.75
			Entire	11.00	6.75
U368	U80	2c	**carmine**, *amber*	11.00	6.75
			Entire	15.00	12.00
U369	U80	2c	**carmine**, *oriental buff*	27.50	12.50
			Entire	32.50	20.00
U370	U80	2c	**carmine**, *blue*	12.50	10.00
			Entire	26.00	15.00
U371	U81	4c	**brown**	20.00	13.00
			Entire	30.00	18.00
U372	U81	4c	**brown**, *amber*	20.00	13.00
			Entire	32.50	24.00
U373	U82	4c	**brown**	10,000.	1,250.
			Entire	15,000.	
U374	U83	4c	**brown**	15.00	8.00
			Entire	29.00	12.50
U375	U83	4c	**brown**, *amber*	65.00	25.00
			Entire	80.00	40.00
W376	U83	4c	**brown**, *manila*	20.00	10.00
			Entire	35.00	25.00
U377	U84	5c	**blue**	13.00	10.00
			Entire	18.00	17.00
U378	U84	5c	**blue**, *amber*	17.00	10.50
			Entire	25.00	18.00

Franklin — U85

Washington — U86

"D" of "UNITED" contains vertical line at right that parallels the left vertical line. One short and two long vertical lines at the right of "CENTS."

Grant — U87

Lincoln — U88

1903
Printed by Hartford Manufacturing Co., Hartford, Conn.

U379	U85	1c	**green**	.80	.20
			Entire	1.25	.35
U380	U85	1c	**green**, *amber*	16.00	2.00
			Entire	22.50	2.50
U381	U85	1c	**green**, *oriental buff*	19.00	2.50
			Entire	26.00	3.00
U382	U85	1c	**green**, *blue*	24.00	2.50
			Entire	35.00	3.00
U383	U85	1c	**green**, *manila*	4.50	.90
			Entire	6.00	1.25
W384	U85	1c	**green**, *manila*	3.00	.40
			Entire	5.00	.80
U385	U86	2c	**carmine**	.50	.20
			Entire	.95	.35
a.		2c	**pink**	2.00	1.50
			Entire	3.00	2.00
b.		2c	**red**	2.00	1.50
			Entire	3.00	2.00
U386	U86	2c	**carmine**, *amber*	2.50	.20
			Entire	4.00	.80
a.		2c	**pink**, *amber*	5.50	3.00
			Entire	7.50	4.00
b.		2c	**red**, *amber*	14.00	7.00
			Entire	20.00	10.00
U387	U86	2c	**carmine**, *oriental buff*	2.25	.30
			Entire	3.50	.35
a.		2c	**pink**, *oriental buff*	3.50	2.00
			Entire	5.00	3.00
b.		2c	**red**, *oriental buff*	4.00	2.25
			Entire	5.50	3.25
U388	U86	2c	**carmine**, *blue*	2.00	.50
			Entire	3.00	.60
a.		2c	**pink**, *blue*	22.50	14.00
			Entire	30.00	18.00
b.		2c	**red**, *blue*	22.50	14.00
			Entire	30.00	18.00
W389	U86	2c	**carmine**, *manila*	21.00	10.00
			Entire	27.50	15.00
U390	U87	4c	**chocolate**	22.50	12.50
			Entire	32.50	15.00
U391	U87	4c	**chocolate**, *amber*	24.00	12.50
			Entire	35.00	15.00
W392	U87	4c	**chocolate**, *manila*	25.00	12.50
			Entire	50.00	40.00
U393	U88	5c	**blue**	24.00	12.50
			Entire	35.00	17.50
U394	U88	5c	**blue**, *amber*	24.00	12.50
			Entire	35.00	20.00

U89

Re-cut die — "D" of "UNITED" is well rounded at right. The three lines at the right of "CENTS" and at the left of "TWO" are usually all short; the lettering is heavier and the ends of the ribbons slightly changed.

1904
Re-cut Die

U395	U89	2c	**carmine**	.75	.20
			Entire	1.75	.45
a.		2c	**pink**	5.50	2.50

U396	U89	2c	**carmine**, *amber*	9.00	1.00
			Entire	14.00	2.00
a.		2c	**pink**, *amber*	11.00	3.00
U397	U89	2c	**carmine**, *oriental buff*	6.00	1.10
			Entire	8.50	1.50
a.		2c	**pink**, *oriental buff*	7.50	2.75
U398	U89	2c	**carmine**, *blue*	4.50	.90
			Entire	6.00	1.40
a.		2c	**pink**, *blue*	6.00	2.50
W399	U89	2c	**carmine**, *manila*	16.00	10.00
			Entire	35.00	25.00
a.		2c	**pink**, *manila*	27.50	17.50
			Entire	70.00	85.00

Franklin — U90

U90 Die 1

U90 Die 2

U90 Die 3

U90 Die 4

Die 1 — Wide "D" in "UNITED."
Die 2 — Narrow "D" in "UNITED."
Die 3 — Wide "S-S" in "STATES" (1910).
Die 4 — Sharp angle at back of bust, "N" and "E" of "ONE" are parallel (1912).

1907-16
Printed by Mercantile Corp. and Middle West Supply Co., Dayton, Ohio

U400	U90	1c	**green**, die 1	.35	.20
			Entire	.60	.30
a.			Die 2	.85	.25
			Entire	1.25	.45
b.			Die 3	.85	.35
			Entire	1.40	.65
c.			Die 4	.90	.30
			Entire	1.40	.45
U401	U90	1c	**green**, *amber*, die 1	2.10	.40
			Entire	2.75	.60
a.			Die 2	2.60	.70
			Entire	3.50	.80
b.			Die 3	3.25	.75
			Entire	4.00	.80
c.			Die 4	2.10	.65
			Entire	4.00	2.00
U402	U90	1c	**green**, *oriental buff*, die 1	10.50	1.00
			Entire	13.50	5.00
a.			Die 2	13.00	1.50
			Entire	18.50	1.75
b.			Die 3	15.50	1.50
			Entire	21.00	2.50
c.			Die 4	10.50	1.50
			Entire	13.50	2.25
U403	U90	1c	**green**, *blue*, die 1	10.50	1.50
			Entire	13.50	2.25
a.			Die 2	13.00	3.00
			Entire	16.50	4.00
b.			Die 3	12.50	3.00
			Entire	16.00	7.00
c.			Die 4	9.50	1.25
			Entire	13.50	3.00
U404	U90	1c	**green**, *manila*, die 1	3.50	1.90
			Entire	6.00	2.75
a.			Die 3	4.50	3.00
			Entire	7.00	4.50
W405	U90	1c	**green**, *manila*, die 1	1.00	.25
			Entire	2.25	1.00
a.			Die 2	65.00	25.00
			Entire	90.00	30.00
b.			Die 3	12.00	4.00
			Entire	36.00	25.00
c.			Die 4	90.00	—
			Entire	—	—

Washington — U91 —
brown red

U91 Die 1 — carmine

U91 Die 2

U91 Die 3

U91 Die 4

U91 Die 5

U91 Die 6

U91 Die 7

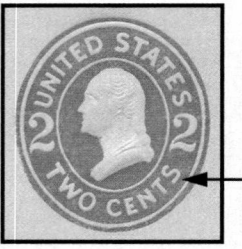

U91 Die 8

Die 1 — Oval "O" in "TWO" and "C" in "CENTS." Front of bust broad.

Die 2 — Similar to 1 but hair re-cut in two distinct locks at top of head.

Die 3 — Round "O" in "TWO" and "C" in "CENTS," coarse lettering.

Die 4 — Similar to 3 but lettering fine and clear, hair lines clearly embossed. Inner oval thin and clear.

Die 5 — All "S's" wide (1910).

Die 6 — Similar to 1 but front of bust narrow (1913).

Die 7 — Similar to 6 but upper corner of front of bust cut away (1916).

Die 8 — Similar to 7 but lower stroke of "S" in "CENTS" is a straight line. Hair as in Die 2 (1916).

U406	U91	2c **brown red,** die 1	1.00	.20
		Entire	2.75	.30
a.	Die 2		45.00	7.00
		Entire	100.00	50.00
b.	Die 3		.90	.20
		Entire	2.75	1.00
U407	U91	2c **brown red,** *amber,* die 1	6.50	2.00
		Entire	9.00	5.00
a.	Die 2		375.00	65.00
		Entire	600.00	200.00
b.	Die 3		4.50	1.25
		Entire	7.00	1.90
U408	U91	2c **brown red,** *oriental buff,* die 1	8.75	1.50
		Entire	12.00	3.75
a.	Die 2		375.00	125.00
		Entire	450.00	300.00
b.	Die 3		7.50	2.50
		Entire	11.00	5.00
U409	U91	2c **brown red,** *blue,* die 1	5.75	2.00
		Entire	8.00	3.75
a.	Die 2		390.00	200.00
		Entire	750.00	500.00
b.	Die 3		5.75	1.75
		Entire	8.00	3.50
W410	U91	2c **brown red,** *manila,* die 1	42.50	32.50
		Entire	55.00	42.50
U411	U91	2c **carmine,** die 1	.35	.20
		Entire	1.25	.35
a.	Die 2		.90	.20
		Entire	2.25	1.50
b.	Die 3		.80	.35
		Entire	1.50	.50
c.	Die 4		.65	.20
		Entire	1.25	.35
d.	Die 5		.65	.30
		Entire	1.75	.50
e.	Die 6		.60	.20
		Entire	1.50	.30
f.	Die 7		42.50	25.00
		Entire	55.00	30.00
g.	Die 8		42.50	25.00
		Entire	55.00	30.00
h.	#U411 with added impression of #U400, entire		475.00	
i.	#U411 with added impression of #U416a, entire		475.00	
k.	As No. U411, double impression, entire		—	
U412	U91	2c **carmine,** *amber,* die 1	.30	.20
		Entire	1.10	.20
a.	Die 2		2.10	.25
		Entire	5.00	3.00
b.	Die 3		2.25	.45
		Entire	3.00	.75
c.	Die 4		.55	.25
		Entire	1.25	.40
d.	Die 5		.90	.35
		Entire	1.50	.55
e.	Die 6		.70	.35
		Entire	1.10	.50
f.	Die 7		37.50	25.00
		Entire	50.00	32.50
U413	U91	2c **carmine,** *oriental buff,* die 1	.55	.20

		Entire	.75	.25
a.	Die 2		2.25	.45
		Entire	5.00	3.75
b.	Die 3		9.00	3.00
		Entire	15.00	5.50
c.	Die 4		.55	.20
		Entire	1.25	.40
d.	Die 5		3.50	1.25
		Entire	5.00	3.25
e.	Die 6		.70	.35
		Entire	1.25	.55
f.	Die 7		105.00	45.00
		Entire	135.00	62.50
g.	Die 8		32.50	22.50
		Entire	50.00	27.50
U414	U91	2c **carmine,** *blue,* die 1	.60	.20
		Entire	1.40	.25
a.	Die 2		2.25	.35
		Entire	5.50	5.00
b.	Die 3		2.75	.60
		Entire	4.00	.70
c.	Die 4		.70	.25
		Entire	1.25	.45
d.	Die 5		2.25	.30
		Entire	3.00	.40
e.	Die 6		.65	.30
		Entire	1.10	.40
f.	Die 7		42.50	25.00
		Entire	50.00	35.00
g.	Die 8		42.50	25.00
		Entire	50.00	35.00
W415	U91	2c **carmine,** *manila,* die 1	5.00	2.00
		Entire	8.00	4.75
a.	Die 2		5.50	1.25
		Entire	8.00	4.50
b.	Die 5		5.50	2.50
		Entire	8.00	3.00
c.	Die 7		130.00	97.50
		Entire	175.00	125.00

U90 4c Die 1

U90 4c Die 2

Die 1 — "F" close to (1mm) left "4."
Die 2 — "F" far from (1¾mm) left "4."

U416	U90	4c **black,** die 2	6.00	3.00
		Entire	11.00	5.00
a.	Die 1		6.00	3.00
		Entire	11.00	5.00
U417	U90	4c **black,** *amber,* die 2	7.50	2.50
		Entire	12.00	4.00
a.	Die 1		7.50	2.50
		Entire	12.00	4.00

Die 1 — Tall
"F" in "FIVE"

Die 2 —
Short "F" in
"FIVE"

Die 1 — Tall "F" in "FIVE."
Die 2 — Short "F" in "FIVE."

U418	U91	5c **blue,** die 2	7.00	2.25
		Entire	13.50	6.50
a.	Die 1		7.00	2.25
		Entire	13.50	6.50
b.	5c **blue,** *buff,* die 2 (error)		3,000.	
c.	5c **blue,** *blue,* die 2 (error)		3,000.	
d.	As "c," die 1 (error), entire		6,500.	
U419	U91	5c **blue,** *amber,* die 2	16.50	11.00
		Entire	22.50	13.00
a.	Die 1		16.50	11.00
		Entire	22.50	13.00

On July 1, 1915 the use of laid paper was discontinued and wove paper was substituted. Nos. U400 to W405 and U411 to U419 exist on both papers; U406 to W410 come on laid only. Nos. U429 and U430 exist on laid paper.

Franklin — U92

Die 1   Die 2

Die 3   Die 4   Die 5

(The 1c and 4c dies are the same except for figures of value.)
Die 1 — UNITED nearer inner circle than outer circle.
Die 2 — Large U; large NT closely spaced.
Die 3 — Knob of hair at back of neck. Large NT widely spaced.
Die 4 — UNITED nearer outer circle than inner circle.
Die 5 — Narrow oval C, (also O and G).

Printed by Middle West Supply Co. and International Envelope Corp., Dayton, Ohio.

1915-32

U420	U92	1c	**green,** die 1 ('17)	.25	.20
			Entire	.40	.20
a.	Die 2			150.00	55.00
			Entire, size 8	200.00	70.00
b.	Die 3			.35	.20
			Entire	.50	.25
c.	Die 4			.55	.40
			Entire	.80	.50
d.	Die 5			.45	.35
			Entire	.75	.45
U421	U92	1c	**green,** *amber,* die 1 ('17)	.55	.30
			Entire	.80	.45
a.	Die 2			500.00	175.00
			Entire, size 8	700.00	200.00
b.	Die 3			1.40	.65
			Entire	2.00	.95
c.	Die 4			1.90	.85
			Entire	2.50	1.25
d.	Die 5			1.10	.55
			Entire	1.75	.80
U422	U92	1c	**green,** *oriental buff,* die 1 ('17)	2.40	.90
			Entire	3.25	1.40
a.	Die 4			5.50	1.25
			Entire	8.00	2.75
U423	U92	1c	**green,** *blue,* die 1 ('17)	.50	.35
			Entire	1.00	.50
a.	Die 3			.80	.45
			Entire	1.25	.70
b.	Die 4			1.40	.65
			Entire	2.50	.95
c.	Die 5			.85	.35
			Entire	1.60	.65
U424	U92	1c	**grn,** *manila* (unglazed), die 1 ('16)	7.50	4.00
			Entire	9.00	5.00
W425	U92	1c	**grn,** *manila* (unglazed), die 1 ('16)	.30	.20
			Entire	1.00	.20
a.	Die 3			190.00	125.00
			Entire	250.00	140.00
U426	U92	1c	**green,** (glazed) *brown,* die 1 ('20)	45.00	15.00
			Entire	55.00	17.50
W427	U92	1c	**green,** (glazed) *brown,* die 1 ('20)	65.00	30.00
			Entire	75.00	*40.00*
U428	U92	1c	**green,** (unglazed) *brown,* die 1 ('20)	16.50	7.50
			Entire	24.00	9.00
W428A	U92	1c	**green,** (unglazed) *brown,* die 1 ('20), entire		*3,000.*

All manila envelopes of circular dies are unwatermarked. Manila paper, including that of Nos. U424 and W425, exists in many shades.

Washington — U93

Die 1

Die 2

Die 3

Die 4

Die 5

Die 6

Die 7

Die 8

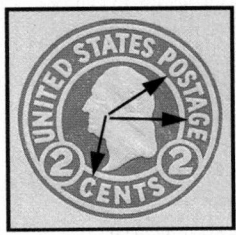

Die 9

(The 1½c, 2c, 3c, 5c, and 6c dies are the same except for figures of value.)
Die 1 — Letters broad. Numerals vertical. Large head (9¼mm). from tip of nose to back of neck. E closer to inner circle than N of cents.
Die 2 — Similar to 1; but U far from left circle.
Die 3 — Similar to 2; but all inner circles very thin (Rejected die).
Die 4 — Large head as in Die 1. C of CENTS close to circle. Baseline of right numeral "2" slants downward to right. Left numeral "2" is larger.
Die 5 — Small head (8¾mm) from tip of nose to back of neck. T and S of CENTS close at bottom.
Die 6 — Similar to 5; but T and S of CENTS far apart at bottom. Left numeral slopes to right.
Die 7 — Large head. Both numerals slope to right. Clean cut lettering. All letters T have short top strokes.
Die 8 — Similar to 7; but all letters T have long top strokes.
Die 9 — Narrow oval C (also O and G).

U429	U93	2c	**carmine,** die 1, *Dec. 20, 1915*	.25	.20
			Entire	.40	.20
a.	Die 2			16.00	7.00
			Entire	25.00	10.00
b.	Die 3			47.50	50.00
			Entire	100.00	200.00
c.	Die 4			32.50	15.00
			Entire	45.00	20.00
d.	Die 5			.55	.35
			Entire	1.00	.45
e.	Die 6			.65	.30
			Entire	1.25	.60
f.	Die 7			.70	.25
			Entire	1.25	.75
g.	Die 8			.50	.20
			Entire	1.00	.50
h.	Die 9			.50	.20
			Entire	1.00	.45
i.			2c **green** (error), die 1, entire	*14,000.*	
j.			#U429 with added impression of #U420	1,100.	
			Entire	1,500.	
k.			#U429 with added impression of #U416a, entire	1,000.	
l.			#U429 with added impression of #U400, entire	1,000.	
m.			#U429, double impression, entire	1,750.	
U430	U93	2c	**carmine,** *amber,* die 1 ('16)	.30	.20
			Entire	.50	.20
a.	Die 2			21.00	12.50
			Entire	30.00	15.00
b.	Die 4			52.50	25.00
			Entire	70.00	30.00
c.	Die 5			1.60	.35
			Entire	2.25	.60
d.	Die 6			1.25	.40
			Entire	2.25	.75
e.	Die 7			.75	.35
			Entire	1.75	.95
f.	Die 8			.70	.30
			Entire	1.10	.45
g.	Die 9			.65	.20
			Entire	1.10	.35
U431	U93	2c	**carmine,** *oriental buff,* die 1 ('16)	2.25	.65
			Entire	4.75	1.40
a.	Die 2			210.00	75.00
			Entire	275.00	*100.00*
b.	Die 4			77.50	60.00
			Entire	100.00	75.00
c.	Die 5			3.50	2.00
			Entire	6.00	2.75
d.	Die 6			3.50	2.00
			Entire	7.00	2.75
e.	Die 7			3.50	2.00
			Entire	6.00	3.25
U432	U93	2c	**carmine,** *blue,* die 1 ('16)	.30	.20
			Entire	.60	.20
b.	Die 2			42.50	25.00
			Entire	60.00	35.00
c.	Die 3			165.00	90.00

d.	Die 4	Entire	225.00	*400.00*
		Entire	67.50	50.00
e.	Die 5		100.00	55.00
		Entire	1.10	.30
f.	Die 6		2.00	.75
		Entire	1.10	.40
g.	Die 7		2.00	.60
		Entire	.85	.35
h.	Die 8		1.75	.65
		Entire	.65	.25
i.	Die 9		1.50	.50
		Entire	1.00	.30
j.	2c purple (error), die 9		2.75	.55

U432A   U93   2c **car**, *manila*, die 7, unwatermarked, entire   *55,000.*

W433	U93	2c **carmine**, *manila*, die 1 ('16)	.25	.20
		Entire	.50	.30
W434	U93	2c **carmine**, (glazed) *brown* ('20), die 1	97.50	50.00
		Entire	125.00	60.00
W435	U93	2c **carmine** (unglazed) *brown*, die 1 ('20)	97.50	50.00
		Entire	125.00	60.00
U436	U93	3c **purple**, die 1 ('32)	.30	.20
		Entire	.55	.25
a.		3c **dark violet**, die 1 ('17)	.60	.20
		Entire	1.00	.25
b.		3c **dark violet**, die 5 ('17)	1.75	.75
		Entire	3.25	.90
c.		3c **dark violet**, die 6 ('17)	2.10	1.40
		Entire	3.25	1.50
d.		3c **dark violet**, die 7 ('17)	1.50	.95
		Entire	3.00	1.00
e.		3c **purple**, die 7 ('32)	.70	.30
		Entire	1.75	.75
f.		3c **purple**, die 9 ('32)	.45	.20
		Entire	.60	.30
g.		3c **carmine** (error), die 1	42.50	30.00
		Entire	65.00	45.00
h.		3c **carmine** (error), die 5	37.50	30.00
		Entire	60.00	45.00
i.		#436 with added impression of #U420, entire	900.00	
j.		#436 with added impression of #U429, entire	900.00	950.00
k.		As "f," double impression, preprinted, entire	—	
U437	U93	3c **purple**, *amber*, die 1 ('32)	.35	.20
		Entire	.60	.35
a.		3c **dark violet**, die 1 ('17)	5.50	1.25
		Entire	9.00	2.25
b.		3c **dark violet**, die 5 ('17)	8.50	2.50
		Entire	12.00	3.00
c.		3c **dark violet**, die 6 ('17)	8.50	2.50
		Entire	12.00	3.00
d.		3c **dark violet**, die 7 ('17)	8.50	2.25
		Entire	12.00	2.50
e.		3c **purple**, die 7 ('32)	.75	.20
		Entire	1.25	.50
f.		3c **purple**, die 9 ('32)	.55	.20
		Entire	1.00	.30
g.		3c **carmine** (error), die 5	500.00	350.00
		Entire	525.00	*325.00*
h.		3c **black** (error), die 1	200.00	—
		Entire	300.00	
U438	U93	3c **dark violet**, *oriental buff*, die 1 ('17)	27.50	1.65
		Entire	35.00	2.00
a.	Die 5		27.50	1.65
		Entire	35.00	2.00
b.	Die 6		37.50	3.50
		Entire	50.00	4.50
c.	Die 7		37.50	3.50
		Entire	50.00	7.75
U439	U93	3c **purple**, *blue*, die 1 ('32)	.35	.20
		Entire	.75	.25
a.		3c **dark violet**, die 1 ('17)	8.50	2.00
		Entire	15.00	6.00
b.		3c **dark violet**, die 5 ('17)	9.50	6.00
		Entire	15.00	7.50
c.		3c **dark violet**, die 6 ('17)	9.50	6.00
		Entire	15.00	7.50
d.		3c **dark violet**, die 7 ('17)	12.50	6.00
		Entire	18.50	7.50
e.		3c **purple**, die 7 ('32)	.75	.25
		Entire	1.50	.50
f.		3c **purple**, die 9 ('32)	.60	.20
		Entire	1.50	.45
g.		3c **carmine** (error), die 5	375.00	300.00
		Entire	475.00	*725.00*
U440	U92	4c **black**, die 1 ('18)	2.00	.60
		Entire	3.50	2.00
a.		With added impression of 2c carmine (#U429), die 1, entire	450.00	
U441	U92	4c **black**, *amber*, die 1 ('18)	3.00	.85
		Entire	5.00	2.00
U442	U92	4c **black**, *blue*, die 1 ('21)	3.50	.85
		Entire	6.00	1.75
U443	U93	5c **blue**, die 1 ('18)	3.50	2.75
		Entire	6.00	3.25
U444	U93	5c **blue**, *amber*, die 1 ('18)	4.50	1.60
		Entire	7.00	3.50
U445	U93	5c **blue**, *blue*, die 1 ('21)	4.25	3.25
		Entire	8.50	4.25

For 1½c and 6c see Nos. U481-W485, U529-U531.

Surcharged Envelopes

The provisional 2c surcharges of 1920-21 were made at central post offices with canceling machines using slugs provided by the Post Office Department.

Double or triple surcharge listings of 1920-25 are for specimens with surcharge directly or partly upon the stamp.

Surcharged on 1874-1920 Envelopes indicated by Numbers in Parentheses

Surcharged

Type 1

1920-21

Surcharged in Black

U446	U93	2c on 3c **dark vio** (U436a, die 1)	16.00	10.00
		Entire	25.00	12.50
a.		On No. U436b (die 5)	16.00	10.00
		Entire	25.00	12.50
b.		As "a," double surcharge	150.00	

Surcharged

Type 2

Rose Surcharge

U447	U93	2c on 3c **dark vio** (U436a, die 1)	10.00	6.50
		Entire	17.50	8.50
b.		On No. U436c (die 6)	13.00	8.50
		Entire	27.50	10.00

Black Surcharge

U447A	U92	2c on 1c **green** (U420, die 1) Entire	*1,500.*	
U447C	U93	2c on 2c **carmine** (U429, die 1) Entire	*50,000.*	
U447D	U93	2c on 2c **carmine**, *amber* (U430, die 1)	—	
U448	U93	2c on 3c **dark vio** (U436a, die 1)	2.75	2.00
		Entire	4.00	2.50
a.		On No. U436b (die 5)	2.75	2.00
		Entire	4.00	2.50
b.		On No. U436c (die 6)	3.50	2.00
		Entire	5.00	2.50
c.		On No. U436d (die 7)	2.75	2.00
		Entire	4.00	2.50
U449	U93	2c on 3c **dark violet**, *amber* (U437a, die 1)	7.50	6.00
		Entire	10.00	7.50
a.		On No. U437b (die 5)	13.00	7.50
		Entire	17.50	10.00
b.		On No. U437c (die 6)	9.50	6.00
		Entire	13.50	7.50
c.		On No. U437d (die 7)	8.50	6.50
		Entire	12.00	8.00
U450	U93	2c on 3c **dark violet**, *oriental buff* (U438, die 1)	20.00	15.00
		Entire	25.00	18.00
a.		On No. U438a (die 5)	20.00	15.00
		Entire	25.00	18.00
b.		On No. U438b (die 6)	20.00	15.00
		Entire	25.00	18.00
c.		On No. U438c (die 7)	135.00	90.00
		Entire	175.00	125.00
U451	U93	2c on 3c **dark violet**, *blue* (U439a, die 1)	16.00	10.50
		Entire	22.50	11.50
b.		On No. U439b (die 5)	16.00	10.50
		Entire	22.50	11.50
c.		On No. U439c (die 6)	16.00	10.50
		Entire	22.50	11.50
d.		On No. U439d (die 7)	29.00	22.50
		Entire	42.50	27.50

Type 2 exists in three city sub-types.

Surcharged

Type 3

Bars 2mm apart, 25 to 26mm in length

U451A	U90	2c on 1c **green** (U400, die 1)	*30,000.*	
		Entire	—	
U452	U92	2c on 1c **green** (U420, die 1)	*3,750.*	
		Entire	*4,250.*	
a.		On No. U420b (die 3)	*3,750.*	
		Entire	*4,250.*	
b.		As No. U452, double surcharge	*4,500.*	
		Entire	*5,000.*	
U453	U91	2c on 2c **car** (U411b, die 3)	*5,000.*	
		Entire	*8,000.*	
a.		On No. U411 (die 1)	*5,000.*	
		Entire	*8,000.*	
U453B	U91	2c on 2c **carmine**, *blue* (U414e, die 6)	*3,000.*	
		Entire	*3,750.*	
U453C	U91	2c on 2c **carmine**, *oriental buff* (U413e, die 6)	*2,500.*	*750.00*
		Entire	*3,250.*	
d.		On No. U413 (die 1)	*2,500.*	
		Entire	*3,250.*	
U454	U93	2c on 2c **car** (U429e, die 6)	150.00	
		Entire	200.00	
a.		On No. U429 (die 1)	350.00	
		Entire	400.00	
b.		On No. U429d (die 5)	500.00	
		Entire	650.00	
c.		On No. U429f (die 7)	150.00	
		Entire	200.00	
U455	U93	2c on 2c **carmine**, *amber* (U430, die 1)	*2,250.*	
		Entire	*4,250.*	
a.		On No. U430d (die 6)	*2,250.*	
		Entire	*4,250.*	
b.		On No. U430e (die 7)	*2,250.*	
		Entire	*4,250.*	
U456	U93	2c on 2c **carmine**, *oriental buff* (U431a, die 2)	350.00	
		Entire	400.00	
a.		On No. U431c (die 5)	350.00	
		Entire	600.00	
b.		On No. U431e (die 7)	850.00	
		Entire	900.00	
c.		As No. U456, double surcharge	750.00	
U457	U93	2c on 2c **carmine**, *blue* (U432f, die 6)	400.00	
		Entire	450.00	
a.		On No. U432e (die 5)	400.00	
		Entire	550.00	
b.		On No. U432g (die 7)	800.00	
		Entire	850.00	
U458	U93	2c on 3c **dark vio** (U436a, die 1)	.55	.35
		Entire	.80	.45
a.		On No. U436b (die 5)	.55	.40
		Entire	.80	.50
b.		On No. U436c (die 6)	.55	.35
		Entire	.80	.45
c.		On No. U436d (die 7)	.55	.35
		Entire	.80	.45
d.		As #U458, double surcharge	25.00	7.50
		Entire	35.00	10.00
e.		As #U458, triple surcharge	110.00	
		Entire	160.00	
f.		As #U458, dbl. surch., 1 in **magenta**	110.00	
		Entire	150.00	
g.		As #U458, dbl. surch., types 2 & 3	140.00	
		Entire	190.00	
h.		As "a," double surcharge	27.50	15.00
		Entire	37.50	20.00
i.		As "a," triple surcharge	110.00	
		Entire	160.00	
j.		As "a," double surch., both **magenta**	110.00	
		Entire	150.00	
k.		As "b," double surcharge	25.00	8.00
		Entire	35.00	11.00
l.		As "c," double surcharge	25.00	8.00
		Entire	35.00	11.00
m.		As "c," triple surcharge	110.00	
		Entire	150.00	
n.		Double impression of indicia, single surcharge, entire	—	
U459	U93	2c on 3c **dark violet**, *amber* (U437c, die 6)	3.25	1.00
		Entire	5.00	1.75
a.		On No. U437a (die 1)	4.25	1.00
		Entire	6.00	1.75
b.		On No. U437b (die 5)	4.25	1.00
		Entire	6.00	1.75
c.		On No. U437d (die 7)	3.25	1.00

d.	As #U459, double surcharge	Entire	6.00	1.75
		Entire	35.00	
		Entire	50.00	
e.	As "a," double surcharge		35.00	
		Entire	50.00	
f.	As "b," double surcharge		35.00	
		Entire	50.00	
g.	As "b," double surcharge, types 2 & 3		125.00	
		Entire	175.00	
h.	As "c," double surcharge		35.00	
		Entire	50.00	

U460 U93 2c on 3c **dark violet**, *oriental buff* (U438a, die 5)

			4.00	2.00
		Entire	5.00	2.50
a.	On No. U438 (die 1)		4.00	2.00
		Entire	5.00	2.50
b.	On No. U438b (die 6)		4.25	2.00
		Entire	6.00	2.50
c.	As #U460, double surcharge		20.00	
		Entire	30.00	
d.	As "a," double surcharge		20.00	
		Entire	30.00	
e.	As "b," double surcharge		20.00	
		Entire	30.00	
f.	As "b," triple surcharge		150.00	
		Entire	250.00	

U461 U93 2c on 3c **dark violet**, *blue* (U439a, die 1)

			6.50	1.00
		Entire	9.00	1.50
a.	On No. U439b (die 5)		6.50	1.00
		Entire	9.00	1.50
b.	On No. U439c (die 6)		6.50	1.00
		Entire	9.00	1.50
c.	On No. U439d (die 7)		13.50	2.00
		Entire	20.00	3.00
d.	As #U461, double surcharge		20.00	
		Entire	30.00	
e.	As "a," double surcharge		20.00	
		Entire	30.00	
f.	As "b," double surcharge		20.00	
		Entire	30.00	
g.	As "c," double surcharge		20.00	
		Entire	30.00	

U462 U87 2c on 4c **chocolate** (U390)

		625.00	260.00
Entire		900.00	500.00

U463 U87 2c on 4c **chocolate**, *amber* (U391)

		1,250.	350.00
Entire		1,600.	500.00

U463A U90 2c on 4c **black** (U416, die 2)

		1,400.	400.00
Entire		2,000.	

U464 U93 2c on 5c **blue** (U443)

	1,400.	
Entire	2,000.	

Type 3 exists in 11 city sub-types.

Surcharged

Type 4

Bars 1 mm apart, 21 to 23 mm in length

U465 U92 2c on 1c **green** (U420, die 1)

	1,400.	
	2,250.	
a. On No. U420b (die 3)	1,750.	
	2,500.	

U466 U91 2c on 2c **car** (U411e, die 6)

	15,000.	
	27,500.	

The existence of No. U466 as a cut square has been questioned by specialists.

U466A U93 2c on 2c **carmine** (U429, die 1)

	900.00	
Entire	1,600.	
c. On No. U429d (die 5)	1,000.	
Entire	1,750.	
d. On No. U429e (die 6)	1,000.	
Entire	1,750.	
e. On No. U429f (die 7)	1,000.	
Entire	1,750.	

U466B U93 2c on 2c **carmine**, *amber* (U430)

	15,000.	
	27,500.	

U466C U93 2c on 2c **carmine**, *oriental buff* (U431), entire —

U466D U25 2c on 3c **green**, die 2 (U82)

	7,500.

U467 U45 2c on 3c **green**, die 2 (U163)

	425.00
Entire	550.00

U468 U93 2c on 3c **dark vio** (U436, die 1)

		.70	.45
	Entire	1.00	.75
a.	On No. U436b (die 5)	.70	.50
	Entire	1.00	.75
b.	On No. U436c (die 6)	.70	.50
	Entire	1.00	.75
c.	On No. U436d (die 7)	.70	.50
	Entire	1.00	.75
d.	As #U468, double surcharge	20.00	
	Entire	30.00	
e.	As #U468, triple surcharge	100.00	

		Entire	150.00	
f.	As #U468, dbl. surch., types 2 & 4		125.00	
		Entire	175.00	
g.	As "a," double surcharge		20.00	
		Entire	30.00	
h.	As "b," double surcharge		20.00	
		Entire	30.00	
i.	As "c," double surcharge		20.00	
		Entire	30.00	
j.	As "c," triple surcharge		100.00	
		Entire	150.00	
k.	As "c," inverted surcharge		75.00	
		Entire	125.00	
l.	2c on 3c **carmine** (error), (U436h)		650.00	
		Entire	800.00	
m.	As #U468, triple surcharge, one inverted, entire	700.00		

U469 U93 2c on 3c **dark violet**, *amber* (U437a, die 1)

			3.75	2.25
		Entire	5.00	2.75
a.	On No. U437b (die 5)		3.75	2.25
		Entire	5.00	2.75
b.	On No. U437c (die 6)		3.75	2.25
		Entire	5.00	2.75
c.	On No. U437d (die 7)		3.75	2.25
		Entire	5.00	2.75
d.	As #U469, double surcharge		30.00	
		Entire	40.00	
e.	As "a," double surcharge		30.00	
		Entire	40.00	
f.	As "a," double surcharge, types 2 & 4		100.00	
		Entire	150.00	
g.	As "b," double surcharge		30.00	
		Entire	40.00	
h.	As "c," double surcharge		30.00	
		Entire	40.00	

U470 U93 2c on 3c **dark violet**, *oriental buff* (U438, die 1)

			6.00	2.50
		Entire	10.00	4.00
a.	On No. U438a (die 5)		6.00	2.50
		Entire	10.00	4.00
b.	On No. U438b (die 6)		6.00	2.50
		Entire	10.00	4.00
c.	On No. U438c (die 7)		42.50	32.50
		Entire	70.00	45.00
d.	As #U470, double surcharge		25.00	
		Entire	35.00	
e.	As #U470, double surch., types 2 & 4		100.00	
		Entire	150.00	
f.	As "a," double surcharge		25.00	
		Entire	35.00	
g.	As "b," double surcharge		25.00	
		Entire	35.00	

U471 U93 2c on 3c **dark violet**, *blue* (U439a, die 1)

			7.50	1.75
		Entire	13.00	3.50
a.	On No. U439b (die 5)		7.50	1.75
		Entire	13.00	3.50
b.	On No. U439c (die 6)		7.50	1.75
		Entire	13.00	3.50
c.	On No. U439d (die 7)		10.50	6.00
		Entire	22.50	10.00
d.	As #U471, double surcharge		30.00	
		Entire	40.00	
e.	As #U471, double surch., types 2 & 4		175.00	
		Entire	250.00	
f.	As "a," double surcharge		30.00	
		Entire	40.00	
g.	As "b," double surcharge		30.00	
		Entire	40.00	

U471A U83 2c on 4c **brown**, (U374), entire

	625.00

U472 U87 2c on 4c **chocolate** (U390)

		15.00	8.00
	Entire	27.50	14.00
a.	Double surcharge	150.00	

U473 U87 2c on 4c **chocolate**, *amber* (U391)

	17.00	10.00
Entire	27.50	13.50

Type 4 exists in 30 city sub-types.

Surcharged

Double Surcharge, Type 4 and 1c as above

U474 U93 2c on 1c on 3c **dark violet** (U436a, die 1)

	300.	
	400.	
a.	On No. U436b (die 5)	400.
	Entire	575.
b.	On No. U436d (die 7)	900.
	Entire	1,150.

U475 U93 2c on 1c on 3c **dark violet**, *amber* (U437a, die 1)

	300.
Entire	475.

Surcharged

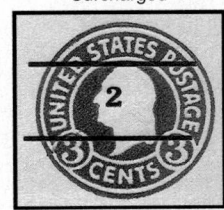

U476 U93 2c on 3c **dark violet**, *amber* (U437a, die 1)

		300.
	Entire	475.
a.	On No. U437c (die 6)	750.
	Entire	1,000.
b.	As #U476, double surcharge	—

Surcharged at Duncan, OK.

Surcharged

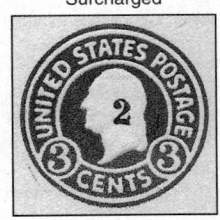

U477 U93 2c on 3c **dark vio** (U436a, die 1)

		140.
	Entire	190.
a.	On No. U436b (die 5)	275.
	Entire	325.
b.	On No. U436c (die 6)	275.
	Entire	325.
c.	On No. U436d (die 7)	275.
	Entire	325.

U478 U93 2c on 3c **dark violet**, *amber* (U437a, die 1)

		350.
	Entire	450.

Surcharged at Frederick, OK.

Handstamped Surcharged in Black or Violet

U479 U93 2c on 3c **dark violet** (Bk) (U436a, die 1)

		300.	—
	Entire	550.	
a.	On No. U436b (die 5)	750.	
	Entire	1,100.	
b.	On No. U436d (die 7)	450.	
	Entire	550.	

U480 U93 2c on 3c **dark violet** (V) (U436d, die 7)

		6,000.
	Entire	8,000.
a.	Double overprint	

Expertization by competent authorities is required for Nos. U476-U480.

Surcharged at Daytona, FL (#U479) and Orlando Beach, FL (#U480).

1925

Type of 1916-32 Issue

U481 U93 1½c **brown**, die 1, *Mar. 19*

		.25	.20
	Entire	.60	.20
	Entire, 1st day cancel	60.00	
a.	Die 8	.70	.25
	Entire	1.00	.50
b.	1½c **purple**, die 1 (error) ('34)	95.00	—
	Entire	125.00	

U482 U93 1½c **brown**, die 1, *amber*

		.95	.40
	Entire	1.60	.60
a.	Die 8	1.90	.75
	Entire	2.50	.80

U483 U93 1½c **brown**, die 1, *blue*

		1.60	.95
	Entire	2.50	1.25
a.	Die 8	2.40	1.25
	Entire	3.25	1.40

U484 U93 1½c **brown**, die 1, *manila*

	6.50	3.00
Entire	12.00	6.00

W485 U93 1½c **brown**, die 1, *manila* .85 .20
    Entire 2.00 .45
  a. With added impression of #W433 120.00

The manufacture of newspaper wrappers was discontinued in 1934.

New rates on printed matter effective Apr. 15, 1925, resulted in revaluing some of the current envelopes.

Under the caption "Revaluation of Surplus Stocks of the 1 cent envelopes," W. Irving Glover, Third Assistant Postmaster-General, distributed through the Postal Bulletin a notice to postmasters authorizing the surcharging of envelopes under stipulated conditions.

Surcharging was permitted "at certain offices where the excessive quantities of 1 cent stamped envelopes remained in stock on April 15, 1925."

Envelopes were revalued by means of post office canceling machines equipped with special dies designed to imprint "1 ½" in the center of the embossed stamp and four vertical bars over the original numerals "1" in the lower corners.

Postmasters were notified that the revaluing dies would be available for use only in the International and "Universal" Model G machines and that the overprinting of surplus envelopes would be restricted to post offices having such canceling equipment available.

Envelopes of Preceding Issues Surcharged

Provisional surcharges exist for California cities Santa Rosa and Santa Ana. These were unauthorized but served postal duty. All are scarce. Expertization recommended.

1925

On Envelopes of 1887

U486 U71 1½c on 2c **green** (U311) 900.
    Entire 1,300.
U487 U71 1½c on 2c **green**, *amber* (U312) 1,400.
    Entire 1,850.

On Envelopes of 1899

U488 U77 1½c on 1c **green** (U352) 675.
    Entire 1,000.
U489 U77 1½c on 1c **green**, *amber* (U353) 125. 60.
    Entire 200. 90.

On Envelopes of 1907-16

U490 U90 1½c on 1c **green** (U400, die 1) 6.75 3.50
    Entire 11.00 5.50
  a. On No. U400a (die 2) 18.00 9.00
    Entire 22.50 12.00
  b. On No. U400b (die 3) 42.50 17.50
    Entire 55.00 22.50
  c. On No. U400c (die 4) 10.00 2.50
    Entire 14.00 4.00
U491 U90 1½c on 1c **green**, *amber* (U401c, die 4) 8.00 2.25
    Entire 12.50 4.50
  a. On No. U401 (die 1) 12.50 2.50
    Entire 17.50 6.00
  b. On No. U401a (die 2) 120.00 65.00
    Entire 140.00 95.00
  c. On No. U401b (die 3) 52.50 30.00
    Entire 70.00 40.00
U492 U90 1½c on 1c **green**, *oriental buff* (U402a, die 2) 500.00 150.00
    Entire 700.00 175.00
  a. On No. U402c (die 4) 1,200. 250.00
    Entire 1,500. 300.00
U493 U90 1½c on 1c **grn**, *blue* (U403c, die 4) 125.00 65.00
    Entire 160.00 70.00
  a. On No. U403a (die 2) 125.00 67.50
    Entire 160.00 90.00
U494 U90 1½c on 1c **grn**, *manila* (U404, die 1) 400.00 100.00
    Entire 550.00 150.00
  a. On No. U404a (die 3) 1,250.
    Entire 1,500.

On Envelopes of 1916-20

U495 U92 1½c on 1c **green** (U420, die 1) .80 .25
    Entire 1.10 .45
  a. On No. U420a (die 2) 85.00 52.50
    Entire 125.00 90.00
  b. On No. U420b (die 3) 2.10 .70
    Entire 3.00 .85
  c. On No. U420c (die 4) 2.10 .85
    Entire 3.00 1.15
  d. As #U495, double surcharge 10.00 3.00

    Entire 15.00 5.00
  e. As "b," double surcharge 10.00 3.00
    Entire 15.00 5.00
  f. As "c," double surcharge 10.00 3.00
    Entire 15.00 5.00
U496 U92 1½c on 1c **grn**, *amber* (U421, die 1) 21.00 12.50
    Entire 30.00 15.00
  a. On No. U421b (die 3) 600.00
    Entire 700.00
  b. On No. U421c (die 4) 21.00 12.50
    Entire 30.00 15.00
U497 U92 1½c on 1c **green**, *oriental buff* (U422, die 1) 3.75 1.90
    Entire 7.00 2.25
  a. On No. U422b (die 4) 67.50
    Entire 100.00
U498 U92 1½c on 1c **grn**, *blue* (U423c, die 4) 1.60 .75
    Entire 2.50 1.00
  a. On No. U423 (die 1) 2.75 1.50
    Entire 4.50 2.00
  b. On No. U423b (die 3) 2.10 1.50
    Entire 3.50 2.00
U499 U92 1½c on 1c **green**, *manila* (U424) 14.00 6.00
    Entire 20.00 7.00
U500 U92 1½c on 1c **green**, *brown* (unglazed) (U428) 85.00 30.00
    Entire 100.00 35.00
U501 U92 1½c on 1c **green**, *brown* (glazed) (U426) 85.00 30.00
    Entire 100.00 35.00
U502 U93 1½c on 2c **carmine** (U429, die 1) 300.00 —
    Entire 500.00 —
  a. On No. U429d (die 5) 400.00
    Entire 575.00
  b. On No. U429f (die 7) 400.00
    Entire 575.00
  c. On No. U429e (die 6) 425.00
  d. On No. U429g (die 8) 550.00
U503 U93 1½c on 2c **carmine**, *oriental buff* (U431c, die 5) 300.00 —
    Entire 525.00 —
  a. Double surcharge
  b. Double surcharge, one inverted 700.00
U504 U93 1½c on 2c **car**, *blue* (U432, die 1) 450.00 —
    Entire 525.00 —
  a. On No. U432g (die 7) 450.00
    Entire 525.00

On Envelopes of 1925

U505 U93 1½c on 1½c **brown** (U481, die 1) 500.00 —
    Entire 650.00
  a. On No. U481a (die 8) 500.00
    Entire 650.00
  b. As No. U505, double surcharge, entire —
U506 U93 1½c on 1½c **brown**, *blue* (U483a, die 8) 500.00
    Entire 650.00
  a. On No. U483 (die 1) 500.00

The paper of No. U500 is not glazed and appears to be the same as that used for the wrappers of 1920.
Type 8 exists in 20 city sub-types.

Surcharged

Black Surcharge
On Envelopes of 1887

U507 U69 1½c on 1c **blue** (U294) 3,250.
    Entire 4,000.
U507A U69 1½c on 1c **blue**, *amber* (U296) —
U507B U69 1½c on 1c **blue**, *manila* (U300) 5,000.
    Entire 6,500.

On Envelope of 1899

U508 U77 1½c on 1c **green**, *amber* (U353) 70.00
    Entire 100.00

On Envelopes of 1903

U508A U85 1½c on 1c **green** (U379) 4,750.
    Entire 6,750.
U509 U85 1½c on 1c **green**, *amber* (U380) 16.00 10.00
    Entire 30.00 15.00
  a. Double surcharge 75.00
    Entire 100.00
U509B U85 1½c on 1c **green**, *oriental buff* (U381) 60.00 40.00
    Entire 75.00 50.00

On Envelopes of 1907-16

U510 U90 1½c on 1c **green** (U400, die 1) 2.90 1.25
    Entire 5.00 1.50
  b. On No. U400a (die 2) 9.50 4.00

    Entire 13.50 6.00
  c. On No. U400b (die 3) 37.50 8.00
    Entire 50.00 11.00
  d. On No. U400c (die 4) 4.25 1.25
    Entire 8.00 2.00
  e. As No. U510, double surcharge 25.00
    Entire 50.00
U511 U90 1½c on 1c **green**, *amber* (U401, die 1) 250.00 100.00
    Entire 375.00 150.00
U512 U90 1½c on 1c **green**, *oriental buff* (U402, die 1) 9.00 4.00
    Entire 16.50 6.50
  a. On No. U402c (die 4) 21.00 14.00
    Entire 30.00 17.00
U513 U90 1½c on 1c **grn**, *blue* (U403, die 1) 6.50 4.00
    Entire 10.00 5.00
  a. On No. U403c (die 4) 6.50 4.00
    Entire 10.00 5.00
U514 U90 1½c on 1c **green**, *manila* (U404, die 1) 34.00 9.00
    Entire 45.00 22.50
  a. On No. U404a (die 3) 77.50 37.50
    Entire 100.00 45.00

On Envelopes of 1916-20

U515 U92 1½c on 1c **green** (U420, die 1) .40 .20
    Entire .75 .30
  a. On No. U420a (die 2) 21.00 15.00
    Entire 30.00 20.00
  b. On No. U420b (die 3) .40 .20
    Entire .75 .30
  c. On No. U420c (die 4) .40 .20
    Entire .75 .30
  d. As #U515, double surcharge 10.00
    Entire 15.00
  e. As #U515, inverted surcharge 20.00
    Entire 30.00
  f. As #U515, triple surcharge 20.00
    Entire 30.00
  g. As #U515, dbl. surch., one invtd., entire —
  h. As "b," double surcharge 10.00
    Entire 15.00
  i. As "b," inverted surcharge 20.00
    Entire 30.00
  j. As "b," triple surcharge 30.00
    Entire 40.00
  k. As "c," double surcharge 10.00
    Entire 15.00
  l. As "c," inverted surcharge 20.00
    Entire 30.00
U516 U92 1½c on 1c **green**, *amber* (U421c, die 4) 50.00 25.00
    Entire 65.00 35.00
  a. On No. U421 (die 1) 55.00 30.00
    Entire 70.00 40.00
U517 U92 1½c on 1c **green**, *oriental buff* (U422, die 1) 6.25 1.25
    Entire 9.00 1.50
  a. On No. U422a (die 4) 7.25 1.50
    Entire 10.00 2.00
U518 U92 1½c on 1c **green**, *blue* (U423b, die 4) 5.50 1.25
    Entire 8.00 1.50
  a. On No. U423 (die 1) 7.75 2.50
    Entire 11.00 3.00
  b. On No. U423a (die 3) 27.50 7.50
    Entire 40.00 9.00
  c. As "a," double surcharge 30.00
    Entire 42.50
U519 U92 1½c on 1c **green**, *manila* (U424, die 1) 32.50 10.00
    Entire 45.00 12.50
  a. Double surcharge 100.00
U520 U93 1½c on 2c **car** (U429, die 1) 350.00 —
    Entire 500.00 —
  a. On No. U429d (die 5) 350.00
    Entire 500.00
  b. On No. U429e (die 6) 350.00
    Entire 500.00
  c. On No. U429f (die 7) 400.00
    Entire 550.00
U520D U93 1½c on 2c **car**, *amber* (U430c, die 5), entire —
U520E U92 1½c on 2c **black**, (U440, die 1), entire —

Magenta Surcharge

U521 U92 1½c on 1c **green** (U420b, die 3), *Oct. 22, 1925* 4.75 3.50
    Entire 7.00 5.50
    Entire, 1st day cancel, Washington, D.C. 100.00
  a. Double surcharge 75.00
    Entire 125.00

Sesquicentennial Exposition Issue

150th anniversary of the Declaration of Independence.

Liberty Bell — U94

Die 1. The center bar of "E" of "postage" is shorter than top bar.
Die 2. The center bar of "E" of "postage" is of same length as top bar.

1926, July 27

U522	U94	2c **carmine**, die 1		1.10	.50
		Entire		1.60	.95
a.		Die 2		7.00	3.75
		Entire		11.00	5.50
		Entire, die 2, 1st day cancel, Washington, D.C.			32.50
		Entire, die 2, 1st day cancel, Philadelphia			27.50

Washington Bicentennial Issue

200th anniversary of the birth of George Washington.

Mount Vernon — U95

2c Die 1 — "S" of "Postage" normal.
2c Die 2 — "S" of "Postage" raised.

1932

U523	U95	1c **olive green**, *Jan. 1*		1.00	.80
		Entire		1.50	1.75
		Entire, 1st day cancel			18.00
U524	U95	1½c **chocolate**, *Jan. 1*		2.00	1.50
		Entire		2.75	2.50
		Entire, 1st day cancel			18.00
U525	U95	2c **carmine**, die 1, *Jan. 1*		.40	.20
		Entire		.50	.25
		Entire, 1st day cancel			16.00
a.		2c **carmine**, die 2		70.00	20.00
		Entire		85.00	27.50
b.		2c **carmine**, *blue*, die 1 (error) entire		40,000.	
U526	U95	3c **violet**, *June 16*		2.00	.35
		Entire		2.50	.40
		Entire, 1st day cancel			18.00
U527	U95	4c **black**, *Jan. 1*		18.00	*20.00*
		Entire		22.50	*35.00*
		Entire, 1st day cancel			30.00
U528	U95	5c **dark blue**, *Jan. 1*		4.00	3.50
		Entire		4.75	4.75
		Entire, 1st day cancel			20.00
		Nos. U523-U528 (6)		27.40	26.35

1932, Aug. 18

Type of 1916-32 Issue

U529	U93	6c **orange**, die 7		6.00	4.00
		Entire		9.50	7.50
		Entire, 1st day cancel, Los Angeles			20.00
U530	U93	6c **orange**, *amber*, die 7		12.00	10.00
		Entire		15.00	12.50
		Entire, 1st day cancel, Los Angeles			20.00
U531	U93	6c **orange**, *blue*, die 7		12.00	10.00
		Entire		15.00	12.50
		Entire, 1st day cancel			20.00

Franklin — U96

Die 1	Die 2

Die 3

Die 1 — Short (3½mm) and thick "I" in thick circle.
Die 2 — Tall (4½mm) and thin "1" in thin circle; upper and lower bars of E in ONE long and 1mm from circle.
Die 3 — As in Die 2, but E normal and 1½mm from circle.

Printed by International Envelope Corp.

1950

U532	U96	1c **green**, die 1, *Nov. 16*		5.00	1.75
		Entire		8.00	2.25
		Entire, 1st day cancel, NY, NY			1.00
a.		Die 2		6.50	3.00
		Entire		11.00	3.75
b.		Die 3		6.50	3.00
		Entire		11.00	3.75
		Precanceled, die 3			1.25
		Entire, precanceled, die 3		2.50	1.50

Washington — U97

Die 1

Die 2

Die 3

Die 4

Die 1 — Thick "2" in thick circle; toe of "2" is acute angle.
Die 2 — Thin "2" in thin circle; toe of "2" is almost right angle; line through left stand of "N" in UNITED and stand of "E" in POSTAGE goes considerably below tip of chin; "N" of UNITED is tall; "O" of TWO is high.
Die 3 — Figure "2" as in Die 2. Short UN in UNITED thin crossbar in A of STATES.
Die 4 — Tall UN in UNITED; thick crossbar in A of STATES; otherwise like Die 3.

U533	U97	2c **carmine**, die 3		.75	.25
		Entire		1.25	.35
a.		Die 1, *Nov. 17*		.85	.30
		Entire		1.50	.45
		Entire, 1st day cancel, NY, NY			1.00
b.		Die 2		1.50	.85
		Entire		2.00	.95
c.		Die 4		1.40	.60
		Entire		1.60	.65

Die 1	Die 2

Die 3

Die 4	Die 5

Die 1 — Thick and tall (4½mm) "3" in thick circle; long top bars and short stems in T's of STATES.
Die 2 — Thin and tall (4½mm) "3" in medium circle; short top bars and long stems in T's of STATES.
Die 3 — Thin and short (4mm) "3" in thin circle; lettering wider than Dies 1 and 2; line from left stand of N to stand of E is distinctly below tip of chin.
Die 4 — Figure and letters as in Die 3. Line hits tip of chin; short N in UNITED and thin crossbar in A of STATES.
Die 5 — Figure, letter and chin line as in Die 4; but tall N in UNITED and thick crossbar in A of STATES.

U534	U97	3c **dark violet**, die 4		.40	.20
		Entire		.50	.25
a.		Die 1, *Nov. 18*		2.00	.70
		Entire		2.50	1.20
		Entire, 1st day cancel, NY, NY			1.00
b.		Die 2, *Nov. 19*		.80	.50
		Entire		1.60	.55
		Entire, 1st day cancel, NY, NY			4.00
c.		Die 3		.60	.25
		Entire		1.10	.45
d.		Die 5		.80	.45
		Entire		1.25	.65

Washington — U98

1952

U535	U98	1½c **brown**		5.00	3.50
		Entire		6.00	4.25
		Precanceled			1.25
		Entire, precanceled		2.50	1.50

Die 1

Die 2

Die 3

Benjamin Franklin —
U99

George
Washington — U100

Die 2

Die 3

Die 1 — Head high in oval (2mm below T of STATES). Circle near (1mm) bottom of colored oval.

Die 2 — Head low in oval (3mm). Circle 1½mm from edge of oval. Right leg of A in POSTAGE shorter than left. Short leg on P.

Die 3 — Head centered in oval (2½mm). Circle as in Die 2. Legs of A of POSTAGE about equal. Long leg on P.

Die 1

Die 1 — Center bar of E of POSTAGE is above the middle. Center bar of E of STATES slants slightly upward. Nose sharper, more pointed. No offset ink specks inside envelope on back of die impression.

Die 2 — Center bar of E of POSTAGE in middle. P of POST-AGE has short stem. Ink specks on back of die impression.

Die 3 — Fl of FIVE closer than Die 1 or 2. Second T of STATES seems taller than ES. Ink specks on back of die impression.

1962

U544	U102	5c **dark blue,** die 2, *Nov. 19,*			
		1962		.85	.20
		Entire		1.10	.30
		Entire, 1st day cancel, Springfield, Ill. *(163,258)*			1.50
a.		Die 1		.85	.25
		Entire		1.10	.30
b.		Die 3		.90	.35
		Entire		1.20	.40
c.		Die 2 with albino impression of 4c (#U536), entire		85.00	—
d.		Die 3 with albino impression of 4c (#U536), entire		85.00	—
e.		Die 3 on complete impression of 4c (#U536), cut square		60.00	

No. U536 Surcharged in Green at left of Stamp

a

Two types of surcharge:

Type I — "U.S. POSTAGE" 18½mm high. Serifs on cross of T both diagonal. Two lines of shading in C of CENT.

Type II — "U.S. POSTAGE" 17½mm high. Right serif on cross of T is vertical. Three shading lines in C.

1962

U545	U96	4c + 1c **red vio.,** die 1, type I, *Nov. 1962*		1.40	*1.25*
		Entire		1.60	*2.50*
a.		Type II		1.40	*1.25*
		Entire		1.60	*2.50*

1958

U536	U96	4c **red violet,** die 1, *July 31*		.80	.20
		Entire		1.00	.25
		Entire, 1st day cancel, Montpelier, Vt. *(163,746)*			1.00
a.	Die 2			1.00	.20
		Entire		1.30	.25
b.	Die 3			1.00	.20
		Entire		1.30	.25

Nos. U429, U429f, U429h, U533, U533a-U533c
Surcharged in Red at Left of Stamp

b

1958

U537	U93	2c + 2c **carmine,** die 1		3.25	1.50
		Entire		4.50	15.00
a.	Die 7			10.00	7.00
		Entire		14.00	15.00
b.	Die 9			5.00	50.00
		Entire		7.50	15.00
U538	U97	2c + 2c **carmine,** die 1		.80	1.25
		Entire		1.25	25.00
a.	Die 2			.80	1.25
		Entire		2.00	50.00
b.	Die 3			.70	1.25
		Entire		2.00	25.00
c.	Die 4			.80	1.25
		Entire		1.50	25.00

Nos. U436a, U436e-U436f, U534, U534b-U534d
Surcharged in Green at Left of Stamp

a

U539	U93	3c + 1c **purple,** die 1		15.00	11.00
		Entire		17.50	—
a.	Die 7			12.00	9.00
		Entire		15.00	—
b.	Die 9			25.00	15.00
		Entire		35.00	—
U540	U97	3c + 1c **dark violet,** die 3		.50	1.00
		Entire		.60	2.00
a.	Die 2			3,500.	—
		Entire			
b.	Die 4			.75	1.00
		Entire		.90	2.00
c.	Die 5			.75	1.00
		Entire		1.00	2.00

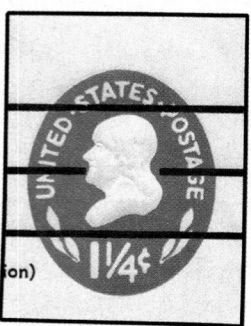
Die 2

Dies of 1¼c

Die 1 — The "4" is 3mm high. Upper leaf in left cluster is 2mm from "U."

Die 2 — The "4" is 3½mm high. Leaf clusters are larger. Upper leaf at left is 1mm from "U."

1960

U541	U99	1¼c **turquoise,** die 1, *June 25, 1960*		.75	.50
		Entire		.90	.55
		Entire, 1st day cancel, Birmingham, Ala. *(211,500)*			1.00
		Precanceled			.20
		Entire, precanceled		.45	.45
a.	Die 2, precanceled				1.00
		Entire, precanceled		2.00	2.00
U542	U100	2½c **dull blue,** *May 28, 1960*		.90	.50
		Entire		1.00	.60
		Entire, 1st day cancel, Chicago, Ill. *(196,977)*			1.00
		Precanceled			.25
		Entire, precanceled		.75	.55

Pony Express Centennial Issue

Pony Express
Rider — U101

White Outside, Blue Inside.

1960

U543	U101	4c **brown,** *July 19, 1960*		.60	.30
		Entire		.75	.40
		Entire, 1st day cancel, St. Joseph, Mo. *(407,160)*			1.00

Die 1

Abraham
Lincoln — U102

New York World's Fair Issue

Issued to publicize the New York World's Fair, 1964-65.

Globe with
Satellite
Orbit — U103

1964

U546	U103	5c **maroon,** *Apr. 22, 1964*		.60	.40
		Entire		.75	.50
		Entire, 1st day cancel World's Fair, N.Y. *(466,422)*			1.00

Precanceled cut squares

Precanceled envelopes do not normally receive another cancellation. Since the lack of a cancellation makes it impossible to distinguish between cut squares from used and unused envelopes, they are valued here as used only.

Liberty Bell — U104

Old Ironsides — U105

Eagle — U106

Head of Statue of
Liberty — U107

Printed by the United States Envelope Company, Williamsburg, Pa. Designed (6c) by Howard C. Mildner and (others) by Robert J. Jones.

1965-69

U547	U104	1¼c **brown**, *Jan. 6, 1965*		.20
		Entire	.90	2.00
		Entire, 1st day cancel, Washington, D.C.		1.00
U548	U104	1⁹⁄₁₀c **brown**, *Mar. 26, 1968*		.20
		Entire	1.00	2.00
		Entire, 1st day cancel, Springfield, Mass. (134,832)		1.00
U548A	U104	1⁹⁄₁₀c **orange**, *June 16, 1969*		.20
		Entire	1.00	2.00
		Entire, 1st day cancel, Washington, D.C.		1.00
b.		1⁹⁄₁₀c **brown (error)**, entire	—	
U549	U105	4c **bright blue**, *Jan. 6, 1965*	1.00	.20
		Entire	1.00	.20
		Entire, 1st day cancel, Washington, D.C.		1.00
U550	U106	5c **bright purple**, *Jan. 5, 1965*	.80	.20
		Entire	.90	.25
		Entire, 1st day cancel, Williamsburg, Pa. (246,496)		1.00
a.		Bar tagged, *Aug. 15, 1967*	4.00	1.00
		Entire	5.00	5.00
		Entire, tagged, 1st day cancel		3.50
b.		orange-red (air post) instead of yellow-green tagging, entire	—	

Tagged

U551	U107	6c **light green**, *Jan. 4, 1968*	.75	.20
		Entire	.85	.25
		Entire, 1st day cancel, New York, N.Y. (184,784)		1.25

First day covers of the 1¼c and 4c total 451,960.

Nos. U549-U550 Surcharged Types "b" and "a" in Red or Green at Left of Stamp

1968, Feb. 5

U552	U105	4c + 2c **bright blue** (R)	3.75	2.00
		Entire	4.00	2.50
		Entire, 1st day cancel		6.00
U553	U106	5c + 1c **bright purple** (G)	3.50	2.75
		Entire	4.00	3.25
		Entire, 1st day cancel		6.00
a.		Tagged	3.00	2.75
		Entire	4.00	3.25
		Entire, 1st day cancel		6.00

Tagged

Envelopes from No. U554 onward are tagged, except for bulk-rate and non-profit envelopes, which are untagged. The tagging element is in the ink through No. 608 unless otherwise noted. From No. 611 on, envelopes have bar or block tagging unless otherwise noted.

Herman Melville Issue

Issued to honor Herman Melville (1819-1891), writer, and the whaling industry.

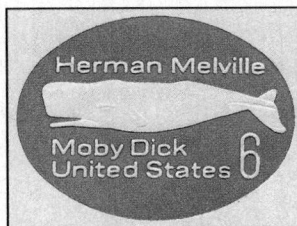

Moby
Dick — U108

1970, Mar. 7

U554	U108	6c **blue**	.50	.20
		Entire	.60	.25
		Entire, 1st day cancel, New Bedford, Mass. (433,777)		1.50

Youth Conference Issue

Issued to publicize the White House Conference on Youth, Estes Park, Colo., Apr. 18-22.

Conference Emblem Symbolic of Man's Expectant Soul and of Universal Brotherhood
U109

Printed by United States Envelope Company, Williamsburg, Pa. Designed by Chermayeff and Geismar Associates.

1971, Feb. 24

U555	U109	6c **light blue**	.75	.20
		Entire	.85	.40
		Entire, 1st day cancel, Washington, D.C. (264,559)		1.00

Liberty Bell Type of 1965 and U110

Eagle — U110

Printed by the United States Envelope Co., Williamsburg, Pa. Designed (8c) by Bradbury Thompson.

1971

U556	U104	1⁷⁄₁₀c **deep lilac**, untagged, *May 10*		.20
		Entire	.30	.20
		Entire, 1st day cancel, Baltimore, Md. (150,767)		1.00
U557	U110	8c **ultramarine**, *May 6*	.40	.20
		Entire	.50	.25
		Entire, 1st day cancel, Williamsburg, Pa. (193,000)		1.00

Nos. U551 and U555 Surcharged in Green at Left of Stamp

1971, May 16

U561	U107	6c + (2c) **light green**	1.00	1.25
		Entire	1.10	2.50
		Entire, 1st day cancel, Washington, D.C.		2.50
U562	U109	6c + (2c) **light blue**	2.00	2.50
		Entire	2.50	3.00
		Entire, 1st day cancel, Washington, D.C.		3.00

Bowling Issue

Issued as a salute to bowling and in connection with the 7th World Tournament of the International Bowling Federation, Milwaukee, Wis.

Bowling Ball and Pin — U111

Designed by George Giusti.

1971, Aug. 21

U563	U111	8c **rose red**	.70	.20
		Entire	.80	.20
		Entire, 1st day cancel, Milwaukee, Wis. (281,242)		1.00

Aging Conference Issue

White House Conference on Aging, Washington, D.C., Nov. 28-Dec. 2, 1971.

Conference Symbol — U112

Designed by Thomas H. Geismar.

1971, Nov. 15

U564	U112	8c **light blue**	.50	.20
		Entire	.65	.20
		Entire, 1st day cancel, Washington, D.C. (125,000)		1.00

International Transportation Exhibition Issue

U.S. International Transportation Exhibition, Dulles International Airport, Washington, D.C., May 27-June 4.

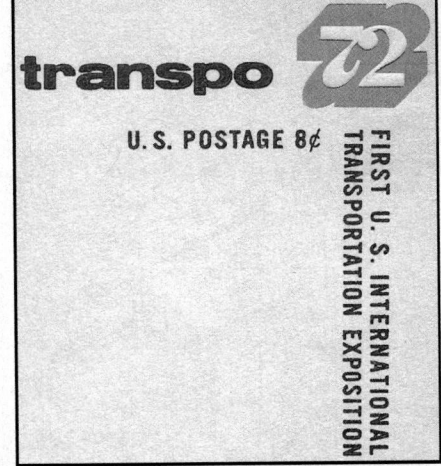

Transportation Exhibition Emblem — U113

Emblem designed by Toshihiki Sakow.

1972, May 2

U565	U113	8c **ultramarine & rose red**	.50	.20
		Entire	.75	.25
		Entire, 1st day cancel, Washington, D.C.		1.00

No. U557 Surcharged Type "b" (like Nos. U537-U538) in Ultramarine at Left of Stamp

1973, Dec. 1

U566	U110	8c + 2c **brt. ultramarine**	.40	1.25
		Entire	.50	2.50
		Entire, 1st day cancel, Washington, D.C.		1.50

Liberty
Bell — U114

1973, Dec. 5

U567	U114	10c **emerald**	.40	.20
		Entire	.50	.20
		Entire, 1st day cancel, Phila-		
		delphia, Pa. *(142,141)*		1.00

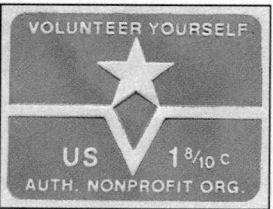

"Volunteer
Yourself" — U115

Designed by Norman Ives.

1974, Aug. 23

Untagged

U568	U115	1⁸⁄₁₀c **blue green**		.20
		Entire	.75	2.00
		Entire, 1st day cancel, Cincin-		
		nati, Ohio		1.00

Tennis Centenary Issue

Centenary of tennis in the United States.

Tennis Racquet — U116

Designed by Donald Moss.

1974, Aug. 31   **Block Tagged**

U569	U116	10c **yellow, brt. blue & light green**	.65	.20
		Entire	.80	.25
		Entire, 1st day cancel, Forest		
		Hills, N.Y. *(245,000)*		1.25

Bicentennial Era Issue

The
Seafaring
Tradition —
Compass
Rose
U118

The American Homemaker — Quilt Pattern — U119

The American Farmer — Sheaf of Wheat — U120

The American Doctor — Mortar — U121

The American Craftsman — Tools, c. 1750 — U122

Designs (in brown on left side of envelope): 10c, Norwegian sloop Restaurationen. No. U572, Spinning wheel. No. U573, Plow. No. U574, Colonial era medical instruments and bottle. No. U575, Shaker rocking chair.
Designed by Arthur Congdon.

1975-76   **Diagonally Laid Paper**   **Embossed**

U571	U118	10c **brown & blue,** *light brown,* *Oct. 13, 1975*	.30	.20
		Entire	.45	.20
		Entire, 1st day cancel, Minne-		
		apolis, Minn. *(255,304)*		1.00
a.		Brown ("10c/USA," etc.) omitted, entire	*150.00*	
U572	U119	13c **brown & blue green,** *light* *brown, Feb. 2, 1976*	.35	.20
		Entire	.55	.20
		Entire, 1st day cancel, Biloxi,		
		Miss. *(196,647)*		1.00
a.		Brown ("13c/USA," etc.) omitted, entire	*150.00*	
U573	U120	13c **brown & bright green,** *light* *brown, Mar. 15, 1976*	.35	.20
		Entire	.55	.20
		Entire, 1st day cancel, New Or-		
		leans, La. *(214,563)*		1.00
a.		Brown ("13c/USA," etc.) omitted, entire	*150.00*	
U574	U121	13c **brown & orange,** *light brown,* *June 30, 1976*	.35	.20
		Entire	.55	.20
		Entire, 1st day cancel, Dallas,		
		Texas		1.50
a.		Brown ("13c/USA," etc.) omitted, entire	*150.00*	
U575	U122	13c **brown & carmine,** *lt. brown,* *Aug. 6, 1976*	.35	.20
		Entire	.55	.20
		Entire, 1st day cancel, Han-		
		cock, Mass.		1.00
a.		Brown ("13c/USA," etc.) omitted, entire	*150.00*	
		Nos. U571-U575 (5)	1.70	1.00

Liberty Tree,
Boston,
1646
U123

Designed by Leonard Everett Fisher.

1975, Nov. 8   **Embossed**

U576	U123	13c **orange brown**	.30	.20
		Entire	.40	.20
		Entire, 1st day cancel, Memphis,		
		Tenn. *(226,824)*		1.00

Star and
Pinwheel — U124

U125

U126

Eagle — U127

Uncle
Sam — U128

Designers: 2c, Rudolph de Harak. 2.1c, Norman Ives. 2.7c, Ann Sforza Clementino. 15c, George Mercer.

1976-78   **Embossed**

U577	U124	2c **red,** untagged, *Sept. 10, 1976*		.20
		Entire	.70	1.50
		Entire, 1st day cancel, Hemp-		
		stead, N.Y. *(81,388)*		1.00
U578	U125	2.1c **green,** untagged, *June 3, 1977*		.20
		Entire	.85	2.00
		Entire, 1st day cancel, Houston,		
		Tex. *(120,280)*		1.00
U579	U126	2.7c **green,** untagged, *July 5, 1978*		.20
		Entire	1.00	1.50
		Entire, 1st day cancel, Raleigh,		
		N.C. *(92,687)*		1.00
U580	U127	(15c) **orange,** *May 22, 1978*	.40	.20
		Entire	.55	.75
		Entire, 1st day cancel, Memphis,		
		Tenn.		1.00
U581	U128	15c **red,** ink tagged, *June 3, 1978*	.40	.20
		Entire	.55	.60
		Entire, 1st day cancel, Williams-		
		burg, Pa. *(176,000)*		1.00
a.		Bar tagged	7.00	—

Bicentennial Issue

Centennial
Envelope,
1876 — U129

1976, Oct. 15   **Embossed**
U582 U129 13c **emerald**   .35   .20
Entire   .45   .20
Entire, 1st day cancel, Los Ange-
les, Cal. (277,222)   1.00

Golf Issue

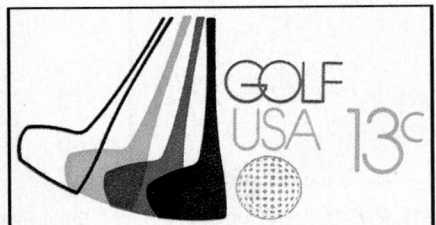

Golf Club in Motion and Golf Ball — U130

Designed by Guy Salvato.

1977, Apr. 7   **Photogravure and Embossed**
U583 U130 13c **black, blue & yellow green**   .70   .20
Entire   .80   1.00
Entire, 1st day cancel, Augusta,
Ga. (252,000)   1.50
a.   Black omitted, entire   650.00
b.   Black & blue omitted, entire   650.00
c.   Black, blue & yellow green omitted, en-
tire   600.00
On No. U583c, the embossing is present.

Energy Issue

Conservation and development of national resources.

"Conservation"
U131

"Development"
U132

Designed by Terrance W. McCaffrey.

1977, Oct. 20   **Embossed**
Bar Tagged
U584 U131 13c **black, red & yellow**   .45   .20
Entire   .55   .20
Entire, 1st day cancel, Ridley
Park, Pa.   1.00
a.   Red & yellow omitted, entire   250.00
b.   Yellow omitted, entire   175.00
c.   Black omitted, entire   175.00
d.   Black & red omitted, entire   400.00
U585 U132 13c **black, red & yellow**   .45   .20
Entire   .55   .20
Entire, 1st day cancel, Ridley
Park, Pa.   1.00
First day cancellation applied to 353,515 of Nos. U584 and
U585.

Olive Branch and Star — U133

Designed by George Mercer.

1978, July 28   **Embossed**
Black Surcharge
U586 U133 15c on 16c **blue**   .40   .20
Entire   .55   1.00
Entire, 1st day cancel, Williamsburg, Pa. (193,153)   1.00
a.   Surcharge omitted, entire   375.00   1,000.
b.   Surcharge on No. U581, entire   100.00   260.00
c.   As "a," with surcharge printed on
envelope flap   175.00   —
d.   Surcharge inverted (in lower left corner), entire   450.00   —

Auto Racing Issue

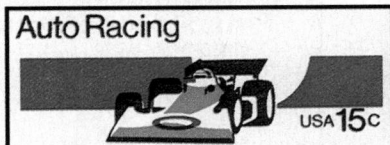

Indianapolis 500 Racing Car — U134

Designed by Robert Peak.

1978, Sept. 2   **Embossed**
U587 U134 15c **red, blue & black**   .45   .20
Entire   .60   1.00
Entire, 1st day cancel, Ontario,
Cal. (209,147)   1.75
a.   Black omitted, entire   120.00
b.   Black & blue omitted, entire   450.00
c.   Red omitted, entire   120.00
d.   Red & blue omitted, entire   550.00

No. U576 Surcharged Like No. U586

1978, Nov. 28   **Embossed**
U588 U123 15c on 13c **orange brown**   .40   .20
Entire   .55   .20
Entire, 1st day cancel, Williamsburg, Pa. (137,500)   1.00
a.   Surcharge inverted (in lower left corner),
entire   —

U135

Weaver Violins — U136

U137

Eagle — U138

U139

Eagle — U140

1979, May 18   **Untagged**   **Embossed**
U589 U135 3.1c **ultramarine**   .50
Entire   .25   1.50
Entire, 1st day cancel, Denver,
Colo. (117,575)   1.00

1980, June 23   **Untagged**   **Embossed**
U590 U136 3.5c **purple**   .50
Entire   .30   1.50
Entire, 1st day cancel, Williams-
burg, Pa.   1.00
a.   3.5c **violet**, tagged (in ink), error of color
and tagging using ink intended for No.
U592   —   —

1982, Feb. 17   **Untagged**   **Embossed**
U591 U137 5.9c **brown**   .50
Entire   .30   1.50
Entire, 1st day cancel, Wheeling,
WV   1.00

1981, Mar. 15   **Embossed**
U592 U138 (18c) **violet**   .45   .25
Entire   .55   .30
Entire, 1st day cancel, Memphis,
TN (179,171)   1.00

1981, Apr. 2   **Embossed**
U593 U139 18c **dark blue**   .45   .25
Entire   .55   .30
Entire, 1st day cancel, Star City,
IN (160,439)   1.00

1981, Oct. 11   **Embossed**
U594 U140 (20c) **brown**   .45   .25
Entire   .55   .30
Entire, 1st day cancel, Memphis,
TN (304,404)   2.00

Veterinary Medicine Issue

Seal of
Veterinarians
U141

Design at left side of envelope shows 5 animals and bird in
brown, "Veterinary Medicine" in gray.
Designed by Guy Salvato.

1979, July 24   **Embossed**
U595 U141 15c **brown & gray**   .50   .20
     Entire   .90   1.00
     Entire, 1st day cancel, Seattle,
       WA *(209,658)*   1.00
   a.   Gray omitted, entire   *1,000.*
   b.   Brown omitted, entire   *1,000.*
   c.   Gray & brown omitted, entire   *450.00*
     On No. 595c, the embossing of the seal is present.

Olympic Games Issue
22nd Olympic Games, Moscow, July 19-Aug. 3, 1980.

U142

     Design (multicolored on left side of envelope) shows two soccer players with ball.
     Designed by Robert M. Cunningham.

1979, Dec. 10   **Embossed**
U596 U142 15c **red, green & black**   .60   .20
     Entire   .70   1.00
     Entire, 1st day cancel, East
       Rutherford, NJ *(179,336)*   1.00
   a.   Red & green omitted, tagging omitted,
       entire   *225.00*
   b.   Black omitted, tagging omitted, entire   *225.00*
   c.   Black & green omitted, entire   *225.00*
   d.   Red omitted, tagging omitted, entire   *400.00*
     No. U596c exists with a portion of the green present in the Olympics 1980 design at the lower left corner of the envelope.

Highwheeler Bicycle — U143

     Design (blue on left side of envelope) shows racing bicycle.
     Designed by Robert Hallock.

1980, May 16   **Embossed**
U597 U143 15c **blue & rose claret**   .40   .20
     Entire   .55   .20
     Entire, 1st day cancel, Balti-
       more, MD *(173,978)*   1.25
   a.   Blue ("15c USA") omitted, entire   *100.00*

Yacht — U144

     Designed by Cal Sachs.

1980, Sept. 15   **Embossed**
U598 U144 15c **blue & red**   .40   .20
     Entire   .65   .20
     Entire, 1st day cancel, Newport,
       RI *(192,220)*   1.00

Italian Honeybee and Orange Blossoms U145

     Bee and petals colorless embossed.
     Designed by Jerry Pinkney.

1980, Oct. 10   **Photogravure and Embossed**
U599 U145 15c **brown, green & yellow**   .35   .20
     Entire   .50   .20
     Entire, 1st day cancel, Paris, IL
       (202,050)   1.00
   a.   Brown ("USA 15c") omitted, entire   *125.00*
   b.   Green omitted, entire   —
     No. U599b also has almost all of the brown color missing.

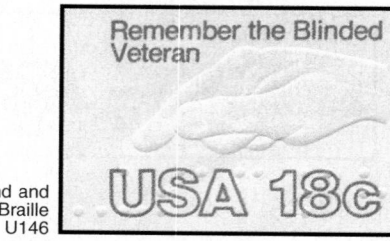

Hand and Braille U146

     Hand and braille colorless embossed.
     Designed by John Boyd.

1981, Aug. 13   **Embossed**
U600 U146 18c **blue & red**   .45   .20
     Entire   .55   .25
     Entire, 1st day cancel, Arling-
       ton, VA *(175,966)*   1.00
   a.   Blue omitted, entire   *350.00*
   b.   Red omitted, entire   *250.00*

Capitol Dome — U147

1981, Nov. 13   **Embossed**
U601 U147 20c **deep magenta, ink** tagged   .45   .20
     Entire   .55   .20
     Entire, 1st day cancel, Los Ange-
       les, CA   1.00
   a.   Bar tagged   4.50   1.50

U148

     Designed by Bradbury Thompson.

1982, June 15   **Embossed**
U602 U148 20c **dark blue, black & magenta**   .45   .20
     Entire   .55   .20
     Entire, 1st day cancel, Wash-
       ington, DC *(163,905)*   1.00
   a.   Dark blue omitted, entire   *400.00*
   b.   Dark blue & magenta omitted, entire   —

U149

     Designed by John Boyd.

1982, Aug. 6   **Embossed**
U603 U149 20c **purple & black**   .75   .20
     Entire   1.00   .20
     Entire, 1st day cancel, Wash-
       ington, DC *(110,679)*   1.25
   a.   Black omitted, entire   —
   b.   Purple omitted, entire   *425.00*

U150

1983, Mar. 21   **Untagged**   **Embossed**
U604 U150 5.2c **orange**   .20
     Entire   .50   1.00
     Entire, 1st day cancel, Memphis,
       TN *(141,979)*   1.00

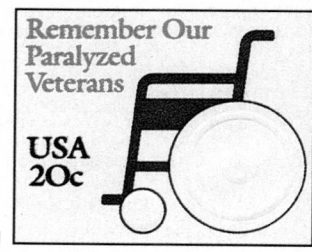

U151

1983, Aug. 3   **Embossed**
U605 U151 20c **red, blue & black**   .45   .20
     Entire   .55   .20
     Entire, 1st day cancel, Port-
       land, OR *(21,500)*   1.00
   a.   Red omitted, entire   *350.00*
   b.   Blue omitted, entire   *350.00*
   c.   Red & black omitted, entire   *150.00*
   d.   Blue & black omitted, entire   *150.00*
   e.   Black omitted, entire   *375.00*

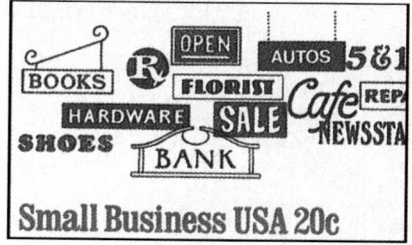

U152

     Designed by Peter Spier and Pat Taylor.
     Design shows storefronts at lower left. Stamp and design continue on back of envelope.

1984, May 7
U606 U152 20c **multi**   .50   .20
     Entire   .60   .20
     Entire, 1st day cancel, Washing-
       ton, DC *(77,665)*   1.00

U153

Designed by Bradbury Thompson.

1985, Feb. 1   **Embossed**
U607 U153 (22c) **deep green**   .55   .30
    Entire   .65   .40
    Entire, 1st day cancel, Los An-
    geles, CA   1.00

American
Buffalo
U154

Designed by George Mercer.

1985, Feb. 25   **Embossed**
U608 U154 22c **violet brown**, ink tagged   .55   .20
    Entire   .65   .20
    Entire, 1st day cancel, Bison,
    SD *(105,271)*   1.00
   a.   Untagged, 3 precancel lines, un-
     watermarked, *Nov. 1, 1986*   .20
     Entire   .60   .20
   b.   Bar tagged   2.00   1.00
     Entire   10.00   1.25
   c.   As "b," tagging omitted   —   1.25
Original printings of No. U608 were printed with luminescent
ink. later printings have a luminescent vertical bar to the left of
the stamp.

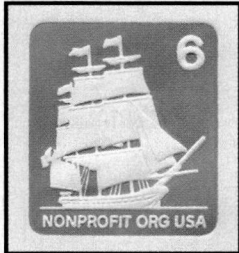

Frigate U.S.S.
Constitution — U155

Designed by Cal Sacks.

1985, May 3   **Untagged**   **Embossed**
U609 U155 6c **green blue**   .20
    Entire   .35   1.00
    Entire, 1st day cancel, Boston,
    MA *(170,425)*   1.25

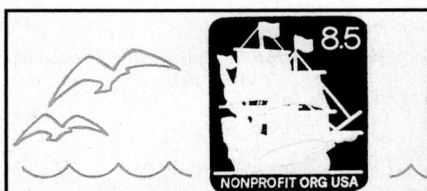

The Mayflower — U156

Designed by Robert Brangwynne.

1986, Dec. 4   **Untagged**   **Embossed**
          Precanceled
U610 U156 8.5c **black & gray**   .20
    Entire   .45   .30
    Entire, 1st day cancel, Plymouth,
    MA *(105,164)*   1.00

Stars
U157

Designed by Joe Brockert.

1988, Mar. 26   **Typo. & Embossed**
U611 U157 25c **dark red & deep blue**   .60   .20
    Entire   .70   .25
    Entire, 1st day cancel, Star, MS
    (29,393)   1.25
   a.   Dark red (25) omitted, tagging omitted,
     entire   75.00   —
   b.   Tagging omitted, entire   14.00
   c.   Dark red (25) omitted, tagging not omit-
     ted   —

U.S. Frigate Constellation — U158

Designed by Jerry Dadds.

1988, Apr. 12   **Untagged**   **Typo. & Embossed**
          Precanceled
U612 U158   8.4c **black & bright blue**   .20
    Entire   .40   1.00
    Entire, 1st day cancel, Balti-
    more, MD *(41,420)*   1.25
   a.   Black omitted, entire   800.00

Snowflake — U159

Designed by Randall McDougall. "Holiday Greetings!"
inscribed in lower left.

1988, Sept. 8   **Typo.**
U613 U159 25c **dark red & green**   1.00   20.00
    Entire   1.50   50.00
    Entire, 1st day cancel, Snow-
    flake, AZ *(32,601)*   1.25

Stars
U160

Designed by Joe Brockert. "Philatelic Mail" and asterisks in
dark red below vignette; continuous across envelope face and
partly on reverse.

1989, Mar. 10   **Typo.**
U614 U160 25c **dark red & deep blue**   .50   .25
    Entire   .60   .30
    Entire, 1st day cancel, Cleveland,
    OH   1.25
   a.   Tagging omitted, entire   —
    No. U614 was issued only in No. 9 size.

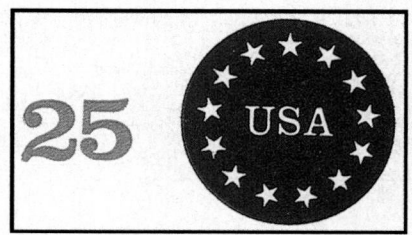

Stars — U161

Designed by Joe Brockert.

1989, July 10   **Typo.**   **Unwmk.**
U615 U161 25c **dark red & deep blue**   .50   .25
    Entire   .60   .30
    Entire, 1st day cancel, Washing-
    ton, DC *(33,461)*   1.25
   a.   Dark red omitted, entire   —
Lined with a blue design to provide security for enclosures.
Issued only in No. 9 size.

Love!
U162

Designed by Tim Girvin. Light blue lines printed diagonally
over the entire surface of the envelope.

1989, Sept. 22   **Litho. & Typo.**   **Unwmk.**
U616 U162 25c **dark red & bright blue**   .50   *.75*
    Entire   .60   *.85*
    Entire, 1st day cancel, Mc-
    Lean, VA *(69,498)*   1.25
   a.   Dark red and bright blue omitted, en-
     tire   175.00
   b.   Bright blue omitted, entire   —
No. U616 has light blue lines printed over the entire surface of
the envelope. Issued only in No. 9 size.

Shuttle Docking at Space Station — U163

Designed by Richard Sheaff.

1989, Dec. 3   **Typo.**   **Unwmk.**
         Die Cut
U617 U163 25c **ultramarine**   .90   .60
    Entire   1.00   1.00
    Entire, 1st day cancel, Wash-
    ington, DC   1.25
   a.   Ultramarine omitted, entire   550.00
    A hologram, visible through the die cut window to the right of
"USA 25," is affixed to the inside of the envelope.
Available only in No. 9 size.
See Nos. U625, U639.

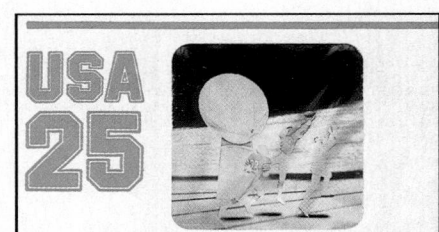

Vince Lombardi Trophy, Football Players — U164

Designed by Bruce Harman.

1990, Sept. 9   Typo.   Unwmk.   Die Cut

U618 U164 25c **vermilion**	.90	.60
Entire	1.00	.70
Entire, 1st day cancel, Green Bay, WI *(54,589)*		1.25

A hologram, visible through the die cut window to the right of "USA 25," is affixed to the inside of the envelope. Issued only in No. 10 size.

Star — U165

Designed by Richard Sheaff.

1991, Jan. 24   Typo. & Embossed   Wmk.

U619 U165 29c **ultramarine & rose**	.60	.30
Entire	.70	.35
Entire, unwatermarked, *May 1, 1992*	.70	.35
Entire, 1st day cancel, Washington, DC *(33,025)*		1.25
a. Ultramarine omitted, entire	600.00	
b. Rose omitted, entire	375.00	

Unwatermarked envelopes are on recycled paper, were issued May 1, 1992, and have a "recycled" imprint under the flap.
See No. U623.

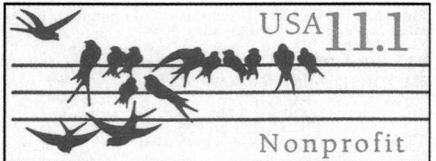

Birds — U166

Designed by Richard Sheaff
Stamp and design continue on back of envelope. Illustration reduced.

1991, May 3   Typo.   Wmk.
Untagged, Precanceled

U620 U166 11.1c **blue & red**		.50
Entire	.55	1.00
Entire, 1st day cancel, Boxborough, MA *(20,720)*		1.25
Entire, unwatermarked, *May 1, 1992*	.60	.25

Unwatermarked envelopes are on recycled paper, were issued May 1, 1992, and have a "recycled" imprint under the flap.

Love — U167

Designed by Salahattin Kanidinc.

1991, May 9   Litho.   Unwmk.

U621 U167 29c **light blue, purple & bright rose**	.60	.60
Entire	.70	.70
Entire, 1st day cancel, Honolulu, HI *(40,110)*		1.25
a. Bright rose omitted, entire	500.00	

Unwatermarked envelopes on recycled paper were issued May 1, 1992, and have a "recycled" imprint under the flap. Envelopes on recycled paper show more gray in the paper, and "29/USA" is in a lighter shade of purple.

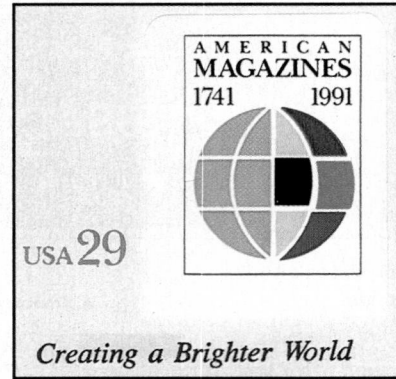

Magazine Industry, 250th Anniv. — U168

Designed by Bradbury Thompson.

1991, Oct. 7   Photo. & Typo.   Unwmk.

U622 U168 29c **multicolored**	.60	.50
Entire	.70	1.50
Entire, 1st day cancel, Naples, FL *(26,020)*		1.25

The photogravure vignette, visible through the die cut window to the right of "USA 29," is affixed to the inside of the envelope. Issued only in No. 10 size.

Star
U169

Designed by Richard Sheaff.
Stamp and design continue on back of envelope.

1991, July 20   Typo.

U623 U169 29c **ultra & rose**	.60	.30
Entire	.70	.35
Entire, 1st day cancel, Washington, DC *(16,038)*		1.25
a. Ultra omitted, entire	575.00	
b. Rose omitted, entire	250.00	

Lined with a blue design to provide security for enclosures. Unwatermarked envelopes are on recycled paper, were issued May 1, 1992, and have a "recycled" imprint under the flap. Issued only in No. 9 size. Value $1.50.

Country Geese U170

Designed by Marc Zaref.

1991, Nov. 8   Litho. & Typo.   Wmk.

U624 U170 29c **blue gray & yellow**	.60	.60
Entire	.70	.70
Entire, 1st day cancel, Virginia Beach, VA *(21,031)*		1.25
Entire, unwatermarked, *May 1, 1992*	1.00	.70

Unwatermarked envelopes are on recycled paper were issued May 1, 1992, and have a "recycled" imprint under the flap.

Space Shuttle Type of 1989

Designed by Richard Sheaff.

1992, Jan. 21   Typo.   Unwmk.   Die Cut

U625 U163 29c **yellow green**	.90	.50
Entire	1.00	.60
Entire, 1st day cancel, Virginia Beach, VA *(37,646)*		1.25

A hologram, visible through the die cut window to the right of "USA 29," is affixed to the inside of the envelope. Examples on recycled paper were issued May 1, 1992 and have a "recycled" imprint under the flap. Issued only in No. 10 size. Value $1.25.

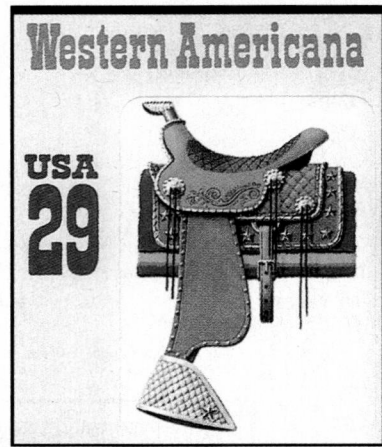

U171

Designed by Harry Zelenko.

1992, Apr. 10   Typo. & Litho.   Die Cut

U626 U171 29c **multicolored**	.60	.90
Entire	.70	1.75
Entire, 1st day cancel, Dodge City, KS *(34,258)*		1.25

The lithographed vignette, visible through the die cut window to the right of "USA 29," is affixed to the inside of the envelope. Issued only in the No. 10 size.

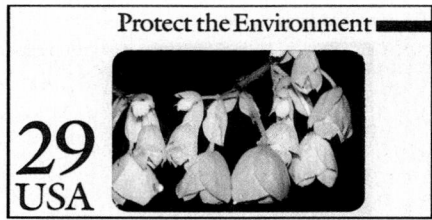

Hillebrandia — U172

Designed by Joseph Brockert. Illustration reduced.

1992, Apr. 22

U627 U172 29c **multicolored**	.60	.30
Entire	.70	1.75
Entire, 1st day cancel, Chicago, IL *(29,432)*		1.25

The lithographed vignette, visible through the die cut window to the right of "29 USA," is affixed to the inside of the envelope. Inscribed "Save the Rain Forests" in the lower left. Issued only in the No. 10 size.

Star — U173

Designed by Joseph Brockert.

1992, May 19   Typo. & Embossed   Precanceled
Untagged

U628 U173 19.8c **red & blue**		.40
Entire	.60	1.00
Entire, 1st day cancel, Las Vegas, NV *(18,478)*		1.25

Issued only in No. 10 size.

U174

Designed by Richard Sheaff. Illustration reduced.

1992, July 22   **Typo.**
U629 U174   29c   **red & blue**   .60   .30
Entire   .70   .35
Entire, 1st day cancel, Washington, DC *(28,218)*   1.25

U175

Designed by Nancy Krause. Illustration reduced.

1993, Oct. 2   **Typo. & Litho.**   ***Die Cut***
U630 U175   29c   **multicolored**   1.00   *1.00*
Entire   1.25   *1.75*
Entire, 1st day cancel, King of Prussia, PA *(6,511)*   1.25

The lithographed vignette, visible through the die cut window to the right of "USA 29," is affixed to the inside of the envelope. Issued only in the No. 10 size.

U176

Designed by Richard Sheaff.

1994, Sept. 17   **Typo. & Embossed**
U631 U176   29c   **brown & black**   .60   *.90*
Entire   .70   *1.50*
Entire, 1st day cancel, Canton, OH *(28,977)*   1.25
a.   Black ("29/USA") omitted, entire   *375.00*
Issued only in No. 10 size.

Liberty Bell — U177

Designed by Richard Sheaff.

1995, Jan. 3   **Typo. & Embossed**
U632 U177   32c   **greenish blue & blue**   .65   .30
Entire   .75   .40
Entire, 1st day cancel, Williamsburg, PA   1.25
a.   Greenish blue omitted, entire   *450.00*
b.   Blue ("USA 32") omitted, entire   *150.00*

First day cancellation was applied to 54,102 of Nos. U632, UX198.
See No. U638.

Spiral Heart — U181

Designed by Uldis Purins.

Design sizes: 49x38mm (#U633), 53x44mm (U634). Stamp and design continue on back of envelope.

1995   **Typo.**
U633 U178   (32c)   **blue & red**   1.00   *.90*
Entire, #6¾   1.25   1.00
U634 U178   (32c)   **blue & red**   1.00   *.90*
Entire, #10   1.25   1.00
a.   Red & tagging omitted, entire   *500.00*
b.   Blue omitted, entire   *500.00*

Originally, Nos. U633-U634 were only available through the Philatelic Fullfillment Center after their announcement 1/12/95. Envelopes submitted for first day cancels received a 12/13/94 cancel, even though they were not available on that date.

U179

Design size: 58x25mm. Stamp and design continue on back of envelope.
Designed by Douglas Smith.

1995, Mar. 10   **Precanceled, Untagged**   **Typo.**
U635 U179   (5c)   **green & red brown**   .50
Entire   .55   *1.00*
Entire, 1st day cancel, State College, PA   1.25

Graphic Eagle — U180

Designed by Uldis Purins.

1995, Mar. 10   **Precanceled, Untagged**   **Typo.**
U636 U180   (10c)   **dark carmine & blue**   .20
Entire   .30   *1.50*
Entire, 1st day cancel, State College, PA   1.25
Issued only in No. 10 size.

1995, May 12   **Typo.**
U637 U181   32c   **red**, *light blue*   .65   .30
Entire   .75   .60
Entire, 1st day cancel, Lakeville, PA   1.25
a.   Red omitted, entire   —

On No. U637a, the red "RECYCLED" and recycling symbol appear on the bottom backflap.

Liberty Bell Type

1995, May 16   **Typo.**
U638 U177   32c   **greenish blue & blue**   .65   .30
Entire   .70   .35
Entire, 1st day cancel, Washington, DC   1.25
a.   Greenish blue omitted, entire   —

No. U638 was printed on security paper and was issued only in No. 9 size.

Space Shuttle Type of 1989

Designed by Richard Sheaff.

1995, Sept. 22   **Typo.**   ***Die Cut***
U639 U163   32c   **carmine rose**   .65   .35
Entire   .70   .40
Entire, 1st day cancel, Milwaukee, WI   1.25

A hologram, visible through the die cut window to the right of "USA 32," is affixed to the inside of the envelope. No. U639 was issued only in No. 10 size.

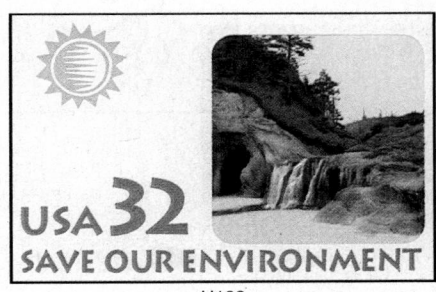

U182

Designed by Richard Sheaff.

1996, Apr. 20   **Typo. & Litho.**   ***Die Cut***
U640 U182   32c   **multicolored**   .60   .30
Entire   .70   .35
Entire, 1st day cancel, Chicago, IL *(9,921)*   1.25

The lithographed vignette, visible through the die cut window to the right of "USA 32c," is affixed to the inside of the envelope. Issued only in the No. 10 size.

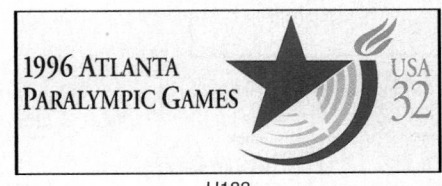

U183

Designed by Brad Copeland. Illustration reduced.

1996, May 2
U641 U183   32c   **multicolored**   .60   .30
Entire   .70   .35
Entire, 1st day cancel, Washington, DC   1.25
a.   Blue & red omitted, entire   —
b.   Blue & gold omitted, entire   *675.00*
c.   Red omitted, entire   —
d.   Black & red omitted, entire   *450.00*
e.   Blue omitted, entire   —

U184   U184a

Designer by Richard Sheaff.

1999, Jan. 11   **Typo. & Embossed**
U642 U184   33c   **yellow, blue & red**, tagging bar to left of design   .65   .30
Entire   .80   .40
Entire, 1st day cancel, Washington, DC   1.25
a.   Tagging bar to right of design   3.00   .30
Entire   3.50   .40
b.   As "a," blue omitted, entire   —
c.   As "a," yellow omitted, entire   —
d.   As "a," yellow and blue omitted, entire   —
e.   As "a," blue and red omitted, entire   —
f.   As "a," all colors omitted, entire   —

Earliest documented use of No. U642a, 10/12/99.
On No. U642f, the distinctive tagging bar is present. Expertization is required.

1999, Jan. 11   **Typo.**
U643 U184a   33c   **blue & red**   .65   .30
Entire   .80   .40
Entire, 1st day cancel, Washington, DC   1.25
a.   Tagging bar to right of design   .65   .30
Entire   .80   .40
Issued only in No. 9 size.

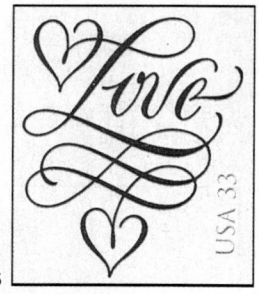

U185

Designed by Julian Waters.

1999, Jan. 28   **Litho.**
U644 U185 33c **violet**   .65 .30
        Entire   .80 .40
        Entire, 1st day cancel, Love-
          land, CO   1.25
  a.   Tagging bar to right of design   .65 .30
        Entire   .80 .40

Lincoln — U186

Designed by Richard Sheaff.

1999, June 5   **Typo. & Litho.**
U645 U186 33c **blue & black**   .65 .30
        Entire   .80 .40
        Entire, 1st day cancel,
          Springfield, IL   1.25

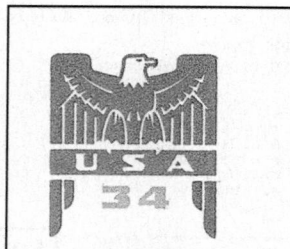

Eagle — U187

Designed by Michael Doret.

2001, Jan. 7   **Typo.**
U646 U187 34c **blue gray & gray**   .65 .30
        Entire   .85 .40
        Entire, 1st day cancel,
          Washington, DC   1.25
  a.   Blue gray omitted, entire   275.00
        Many color shades known.
All No. U646 were printed on recycled paper. It was also
produced using a different blue-gray recycled paper starting in
2002.

Lovebirds
U188

Designed by Robert Brangwynne.

2001, Feb. 14   **Litho.**
U647 U188 34c **rose & dull violet**   .65 .30
        Entire   .85 .40
        Entire, 1st day cancel,
          Lovejoy, GA   1.25

Community Colleges, Cent. — U189

Designed by Howard Paine.

2001, Feb. 20   **Typo.**
U648 U189 34c **dark blue & orange brown** .65 .30
        Entire   .85 .40
        Entire, 1st day cancel, Joliet, IL   1.25

Ribbon Star — U190

Designed by Terrence W. McCaffrey.

2002, June 7   **Typo.**
U649 U190 37c **red, blue & gray**   .75 .35
        Entire   .90 .45
        Entire, 1st day cancel, Washing-
          ton, DC   1.25
        Entire, 1st day cancel, any other
          city   1.25
  a.   Gray omitted, entire   —
  b.   Blue and gray omitted, entire   —
All No. U649 were printed on recycled paper. It was also
produced using a different blue-gray recycled paper starting in
2002.

**Type of 1995 Inscribed "USA / Presorted /
Standard"**
Designed by Uldis Purins.

2002, Aug. 8   **Untagged**
                Precanceled
U650 U180 (10c) **dark carmine & blue**   .20
        Entire   .75 1.50
        Entire, 1st day cancel, Washington, DC   1.25
        Issued only in No. 10 size.

Nurturing Love — U191

Designed by Craig Frazier.

2003, Jan. 25   **Typo.**
U651 U191 37c **olive green & yellow orange** .75 .35
        Entire   .90 .45
        Entire, 1st day cancel, Tucson, AZ   1.25
  a.   Tagging omitted, entire   —

Jefferson Memorial Type
Designed by Derry Noyes.

2003, Dec. 29   **Typo.**
U652 A2818 $3.85 **multicolored**   14.00 6.25
        Entire   15.00 7.00
        Entire, 1st day cancel, Wash-
          ington, DC   5.75
On No. U652, the stamp indicia is printed on the flap of the
envelope.

Disney Type of 2004
Designed by David Pacheco.

2004, June 23   **Litho.**
U653 A2949 37c **multicolored**   2.50 2.10
        Entire   2.50 2.50
        Entire, 1st day cancel,
          Anaheim, CA   2.50
U654 A2950 37c **multicolored**   2.50 2.10
        Entire   2.50 2.50
        Entire, 1st day cancel,
          Anaheim, CA   2.50
U655 A2951 37c **multicolored**   2.50 2.10
        Entire   2.50 2.50
        Entire, 1st day cancel,
          Anaheim, CA   2.50
  a.   All color missing on reverse, entire   —
U656 A2952 37c **multicolored**   2.50 2.10
        Entire   2.50 2.50
        Entire, 1st day cancel,
          Anaheim, CA   2.50
  a.   Booklet of 12 letter sheets, 3 each
          #U653-U656   30.00
        No. U656a sold for $14.95.

White Lilacs and Pink Roses Type of 2004
Designed by Richard Sheaff.

2005, Mar. 3   **Litho.**
U657 A2931 37c **multicolored**   2.50 2.50
        First day cancel, New York, NY   2.50
        No. U657 was sold in pads of 12 for $14.95.

Computer-generated Study of an X-Plane — U192

2006, Jan. 5   **Typo.**   **Unwmk.**
U658 U192 $4.05 **multicolored**   8.25 6.50
        Entire   8.50 7.25
        Entire, 1st day cancel, Kansas
          City, MO   6.50

Benjamin
Franklin — U193

Designed by Richard Sheaff.

2006, Jan. 9   **Typo.**   **Unwmk.**
U659 U193 39c **blue green & black**   .80 .40
        Entire   .95 .50
        Entire, 1st day cancel, Washing-
          ton, DC   1.25
        Entire, 1st day cancel, any other
          city   1.25
  a.   All color omitted, entire   —
On No. 659a, the tagging bar and the blue green printing on
the reverse are present.

Air Force
One — U194

Designed by Phil Jordan.

2007, May 6   **Typo.**   **Unwmk.**
U660 U194 $4.60 **multicolored**   9.25 7.00
        Entire   10.00 7.50
        Entire, 1st day cancel, Kansas
          City, MO   9.25
No. U660 was sold only in packs of 5, 10 or 25 envelopes.

Marine One — U195

Designed by Phil Jordan.

2007, May 6		Typo.		Unwmk.	
U661	U195	$16.25 **multicolored**		33.00	17.00
		Entire		33.00	19.00
		Entire, 1st day cancel, Kansas City, MO			33.00

No. U661 was sold only in packs of three envelopes, with each envelope having a different Star Wars character (Darth Vader, Yoda, or Obi-wan Kenobi) on the back of the envelope. Values for entires are for any envelope back.

Horses — U196

illustration reduced. Designed by Tom Engeman.

2007, May 12		Typo.		Unwmk.	
U662	U196	41c **reddish brown & black**		.85	.40
		Entire		1.00	.50
		Entire, 1st day cancel, Washington, DC			2.10

Elk U197

Designed by Carl T. Herrman.

2008, May 2		Typo.		Unwmk.	
U663	U197	42c **green & black**, tagging bar 20mm tall, Ashton-Potter printing		.85	.40
a.		Tagging bar 26mm tall, Westvaco printing		.85	.40
		Entire, Westvaco printing		1.00	.50
		Entire, Ashton-Potter printing		1.00	.50
		Entire, 1st day cancel, Washington, DC			2.10
b.		Tagging bar 19mm tall		.85	.40
		Entire, Ashton-Potter litho. printing		1.00	.50
		Entire, Ashton-Potter litho. printing, 1st day cancel, Hartford, CT			2.10

No. U663 was printed by National Envelope for Ashton-Potter (USA) Ltd. No. U663a was printed by Westvaco. Envelopes printed by Westvaco have copyright and recycled content text, found on the envelope's back, in black. These features are in green on Ashton-Potter envelopes. All Westvaco envelopes have pointed flaps, while the Ashton-Potter envelopes have flaps with curved ends.

No. U663b was printed by Ashton-Potter (USA) Ltd. The lithographed impressions of No. U663b are slightly sharper (some tree branches are slightly thinner and more distinct) than the typographed impressions on Nos. U663 and U663a, but because of the nature of the design are nonetheless difficult to distinguish without measuring the tagging bar. Entires of No. U663b have the recycling emblem on the back of the envelope at the right side of the paper content statement. On No. U663 the recycling emblem is in the lower left corner.

Mount Rushmore U198

Designed by Carl T. Herrman.

2008, May 12		Typo.		Unwmk.	
U664	U198	$4.80 **multicolored**		9.75	7.00
		Entire		9.75	7.00
		Entire, 1st day cancel, Kansas City, MO			9.75

No. U664 was sold only in packs of 5, 10 or 25 envelopes.

Sunflower Type of 2008

Designed by Derry Noyes.

2008, Aug. 15		Litho.		Unwmk.	
U665	A3309	42c **multicolored**		3.00	3.00
		First day cancel, Hartford, CT			4.25

No. U665 was sold in packs of 10 for $14.95.

Redwood Forest Type of 2009

Designed by Carl T. Herrman.

2009, Jan. 16		Typo.		Unwmk.	
U666	A3332	$4.95 **multicolored**		10.00	7.50
		First day cancel, Kansas City, MO			10.00

No. U666 was sold only in packs of 5.

Liberty Bell U199

Designed by Terrence W. McCaffrey.

2009, May 11		Litho.		Unwmk.	
U667	U199	(44c) **multicolored**		.90	.90
		Entire		1.10	1.10
		Entire, 1st day cancel, Kansas City, MO			2.40

No. U667 had a franking value of 44c on the day of issue and will be valid for the one ounce first class postage rate after any new rates go into effect. The envelope was created primarily for customers desiring a printed return address on the envelope, and was not sold individually. Water-activated gum envelopes sold in boxes of 50 for $26.80 and boxes of 500 for $247. Self-adhesive envelopes in boxes of 50 for $31.80 and boxes of 500 for $262. A pack of 18 envelopes containing one example of each of the twelve different envelope styles of No. UX667 and the six different self-adhesive envelope styles of No. UX668 was sold for the convenience of collectors for $10.92.

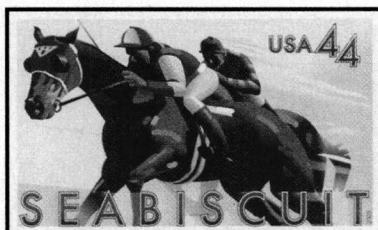

Racehorse Seabiscuit — U200

Designed by John Mattos. Printed by Ashton-Potter (USA) Ltd.

2009, May 11		Litho.		Unwmk.	
U668	U200	44c **multicolored**		.90	.45
		Entire		1.10	.55
		Entire, 1st day cancel, Kansas City, MO			2.40
a.		As #U668, typographed, *June 1*		.90	.45
		Typographed, entire		1.10	.55
		Entire, 1st day cancel, Kansas City, MO			2.40

No. U668 self-adhesive flap envelopes were not sold individually, but were sold in boxes and packs like No. U667.

No. U668a was printed by National Envelope. The screened blue dots cover the entire area between the "S" and the "C" on No. U668, but appear more random on No. U668a. The pattern of blue dots running towards the shoulder under the head and neck of the horse is long and distinct on No. U668, but barely noticeable, with only a few dots showing, on No. U668a.

AIR POST STAMPED ENVELOPES AND AIR LETTER SHEETS

All envelopes have carmine and blue borders, unless noted. There are seven types of borders:

Carmine Diamond in Upper Right Corner.

a — Diamonds measure 9 to 10mm paralled to edge of envelope and 11 to 12mm along oblique side (with top flap open). Sizes 5 and 13 only.

b — Like "a" except diamonds measure 7 to 8mm along oblique side (with top flap open). Sizes 5 and 13 only.

c — Diamonds measure 11 to 12mm parallel to edge of envelope. Size 8 only.

Blue Diamond in Upper Right Corner.

d — Lower points of top row of diamonds point to left. Size 8 only.

e — Lower points of top row of diamonds point to right. Size 8 only.

Diamonds Omitted in Upper Right Corner (1965 Onward)

f — Blue diamond above at left of stamp.

g — Red diamond above at left of stamp.

UC1

5c — Vertical rudder is not semi-circular but slopes down to the left. The tail of the plane projects into the G of POSTAGE. Border types a, b, c, d and e.

UC2

Die 2 (5c and 8c): Vertical rudder is semi-circular. The tail of the plane touches but does not project into the G of POSTAGE. Border types b, d, and e for the 5c; b and d for the 8c.

Die 2 (6c) — Same as UC2 except three types of numeral.

2a — The numeral "6" is 6½mm wide.

2b — The numeral "6" is 6mm wide.

2c — The numeral "6" is 5½mm wide.

Eleven working dies were used in printing the 6c. On each, the numeral "6" was engraved by hand, producing several variations in position, size and thickness.

Nos. UC1 and UC2 occur with varying size blue blobs, caused by a shallow printing die. They are not constant.

Border types b and d for dies 2a and 2b; also without border (June 1944 to Sept. 1945) for. dies 2a, 2b and 2c.

Die 3 (6c): Vertical rudder leans forward. S closer to O than to T of POSTAGE. E of POSTAGE has short center bar. Border types b and d, also without border.

No. UC1 with 1933 and 1937 watermarks and No. UC2 with 1933 watermark were issued in Puerto Rico.

No. UC1 in blue black, with 1925 watermark #26 and border type a, is a proof.

1929-44

UC1	UC1	5c **blue,** *Jan. 12, 1929*	3.50	2.00
		Entire, border a or b	4.75	2.25
		Entire, border c, d or e	8.50	5.75
		First day cancel, border a, entire		40.00
		1933 wmk. #33, border d, entire	750.00	750.00
		1933 wmk. #33, border b, entire	—	—
		1937 wmk. #36, border d, entire	—	2,500.
		1937 wmk. #36, border b, entire	—	—
		Bicolored border omitted, entire	1,300.	
a.		Orange and blue border, type b	375.00	450.00
UC2	UC2	5c **blue,** die 2	12.00	5.00
		Entire, border b	14.00	6.50
		Entire, border e	21.00	12.50
		1929 wmk. #28, border d, entire	—	1,500.
		1933 wmk. #33, border b, entire	650.00	—

	1933 wmk. #33, border d, entire	325.00	—
UC3	UC2 6c **orange**, die 2a, *July 1, 1934*	1.50	.40
	Entire, bicolored border	1.75	.60
	Entire, without border	2.50	1.25
	Entire, 1st day cancel		14.00
a.	With added impression of 3c purple (#U436a), entire without border	*4,000.*	
UC4	UC2 6c **orange**, die 2b ('41)	3.00	2.00
	Entire, bicolored border, 1941 wmk. #39	60.00	20.00
	Entire, without border	4.50	2.00
UC5	UC2 6c **orange**, die 2c ('44)	.75	.30
	Entire	1.00	.45
UC6	UC2 6c **orange**, die 3 ('42)	1.00	.35
	Entire, bicolored border	1.50	.75
	Entire, without border	2.50	.90
	Entire, carmine of border omitted	*4,000.*	
	Double impression, entire	400.00	
a.	6c orange, *blue*, die 3 (error) Entire, without border	*3,500.*	*2,400.*
UC7	UC2 8c **olive green**, die 2, *Sept. 26, 1932*	13.00	3.50
	Entire, bicolored border	17.50	15.00
	Entire, 1st day cancel		11.00

Surcharged in black on envelopes indicated by number in parenthesis

1945

UC8	U93 6c on 2c **carmine** (U429, die 1)	1.25	.65
	Entire	1.60	1.00
a.	On U429f, die 7	2.25	1.50
	Entire	3.00	2.00
b.	On U429g, die 8	1.90	1.10
	Entire	3.00	1.75
c.	On U429h, die 9	11.00	7.50
	Entire	16.00	11.00
d.	6c on 1c green (error) (U420)	*1,750.*	
	Entire	*2,500.*	
e.	6c on 3c dk violet (error) (U436a)	*2,000.*	
	Entire	*4,000.*	
f.	6c on 3c dk violet (error), *amber* (U437a)	*3,000.*	
	Entire	*3,500.*	
g.	6c on 3c violet (error) (U526)	*3,000.*	
	Entire	*7,000.*	
UC9	U95 6c on 2c **carmine** (U525)	65.00	35.00
	Entire	90.00	45.00

Ten surcharge varieties are found on Nos. UC8-UC9.

Surcharged in Black on 6c Air Post Envelopes without borders

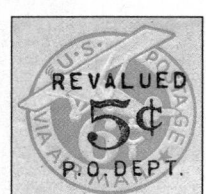

1946

UC10	UC2 5c on 6c **orange**, die 2a	3.00	1.50
	Entire	5.75	2.50
	First day of rate, *Oct. 1, 1946*, entire		100.00
a.	Double surcharge	75.00	
UC11	UC2 5c on 6c **orange**, die 2b	10.00	5.50
	Entire	11.00	7.00
	First day of rate, *Oct. 1, 1946*, entire		150.00
UC12	UC2 5c on 6c **orange**, die 2c	.75	.50
	Entire	1.25	.60
	First day of rate, *Oct. 1, 1946*, entire		75.00
a.	Double surcharge	75.00	300.00
UC13	UC2 5c on 6c **orange**, die 3	.80	.60
	Entire	1.00	.75
	First day of rate, *Oct. 1, 1946*, entire		75.00
a.	Double surcharge	75.00	50.00
UC13B	U93 5c on 6c (UC8a), entire	—	
	First day of rate, *Oct. 1, 1946*, entire		—

The 6c borderless envelopes and the revalued envelopes were issued primarily for use to and from members of the armed forces. The 5c rate came into effect Oct. 1, 1946.
Ten surcharge varieties are found on Nos. UC10-UC13.

DC-4
Skymaster — UC3

Envelopes with borders types b and d.
Die 1 — The end of the wing at the right is a smooth curve. The juncture of the front end of the plane and the engine forms an acute angle. The first T of STATES and the E's of UNITED STATES lean to the left.
Die 2 — The end of the wing at the right is a straight line. The juncture of the front end of the plane and the engine is wide open. The first T of STATES and the E's of UNITED STATES lean to the right.

1946

UC14	UC3 5c **carmine**, die 1, *Sept. 25, 1946*	.85	.25
	Entire, bicolored border	1.10	.40
	Entire, 1st day cancel		1.50
	Entire, bicolored border omitted	—	
UC15	UC3 5c **carmine**, die 2	.85	.25
	Entire, bicolored border	1.10	.40

No. UC14, printed on flat bed press, measures 21½mm high. No. UC15, printed on rotary press, measures 22mm high. See No. UC18.

DC-4 Skymaster — UC4

1947-55   Typographed, Without Embossing
Letter Sheets for Foreign Postage

UC16	UC4 10c **bright red**, *pale blue*, "Air Letter" on face, 2-line inscription on back, entire	8.50	10.00
	Entire, 1st day cancel, *Apr. 29, 1947*		2.00
	Die cutting reversed, entire	110.00	
UC16a	UC4 10c **bright red**, *pale blue*, Sept. 1951, "Air Letter" on face, 4-line inscription on back, entire	17.50	14.00
	Die cutting reversed, entire	275.00	
b.	10c **chocolate**, *pale blue*, entire	450.00	
UC16c	UC4 10c **bright red**, *pale blue*, Nov. 1953, "Air Letter" and "Aerogramme" on face, 4-line inscription on back, entire	45.00	12.50
	Die cutting reversed, entire	150.00	
UC16d	UC4 10c **bright red**, *pale blue*, 1955, "Air Letter" and "Aerogramme" on face, 3-line inscription on back, entire	9.00	8.00
	Die cutting reversed, entire	60.00	
	Dark blue (inscriptions & border diamonds) omitted	—	
	Die cutting omitted	—	

Printed on protective tinted paper containing colorless inscription,
UNITED STATES FOREIGN AIR MAIL multiple, repeated in parallel vertical or horizontal lines.

Postage Stamp Centenary Issue

Centenary of the first postage stamps issued by the United States Government.

Washington and Franklin, Early and Modern Mail-carrying Methods — UC5

Two dies: Rotary, design measures 22¼mm high; and flat bed press, design 21¾mm high.

1947, May 21   Embossed
For Domestic Postage

UC17	UC5 5c **carmine** (rotary)	.50	.30
	Entire, bicolored border b	.60	.40
	Entire, 1st day cancel, NY, NY		1.25
a.	Flat plate printing	.50	.30
	Entire	.60	.40

Type of 1946

Type I: 6's lean to right.
Type II: 6's upright.

1950

UC18	UC3 6c **carmine**, type I, *Sept. 22, 1950*	.40	.25
	Entire, bicolored border	.60	.30
	Entire, 1st day cancel, Philadelphia		1.00
a.	Type II	.75	.25
	Entire	1.00	.30

Several other types differ slightly from the two listed.

Nos. UC14, UC15, UC18 Surcharged in Red at Left of Stamp

1951

UC19	UC3 6c on 5c **carmine**, die 1	.85	1.00
	Entire	1.25	*1.25*
UC20	UC3 6c on 5c **carmine**, die 2	.85	1.00
	Entire	1.25	*1.25*
a.	6c on 6c **carmine** (error) entire	*1,500.*	
b.	Double surcharge	975.00	—

To qualify as No. UC20b, both surcharges must be to the left of the indicia.

Nos. UC14 and UC15 Surcharged in Red at Left of Stamp

1952

UC21	UC3 6c on 5c **carmine**, die 1	27.50	17.50
	Entire	35.00	22.50
a.	Double surcharge, entire		—
UC22	UC3 6c on 5c **carmine**, die 2, *Aug. 29, 1952*	4.25	2.50
	Entire	10.00	4.25
	Entire, 1st day cancel, Norfolk, Va.		25.00
a.	Double surcharge	200.00	
b.	Triple surcharge, entire	—	

To qualify as Nos. UC22a or UC22b, all surcharges must be to the left of the indicia.

Same Surcharge in Red on No. UC17

UC23	UC5 6c on 5c **carmine**	1,500.	
	Entire	2,000.	

The 6c on 4c black (No. U440) is believed to be a favor printing.

Fifth International Philatelic Exhibition Issue

FIPEX, the Fifth International Philatelic Exhibition, New York, N.Y., Apr. 28-May 6, 1956.

Eagle in Flight — UC6

1956, May 2

UC25	UC6 6c **red**	.75	.50
	Entire	1.00	.80
	Entire, 1st day cancel, New York, N.Y. *(363,239)*		1.25

Two types exist, differing slightly in the clouds at top.

Skymaster Type of 1946

1958, July 31

UC26	UC3 7c **blue**	.65	.50
	Entire	1.00	.55
	Entire, 1st day cancel, Dayton, O. *(143,428)*		1.00

Nos. UC3-UC5, UC18 and UC25 Surcharged in
Green at Left of Stamp

1958

UC27	UC2	6c + 1c **orange**, die 2a	350.00	250.00
		Entire, without border	375.00	600.00
		Entire, with border	8,000.	
UC28	UC2	6c + 1c **orange**, die 2b	80.00	80.00
		Entire, without border	110.00	250.00
UC29	UC2	6c + 1c **orange**, die 2c	45.00	50.00
		Entire	50.00	110.00
UC30	UC3	6c + 1c **carmine**, type I	1.00	.50
		Entire	1.25	.65
a.		Type II	1.00	.50
		Entire	1.25	.65
UC31	UC6	6c + 1c **red**	1.00	.50
		Entire	1.40	.85

Jet Airliner — UC7

Letter Sheet for Foreign Postage

Type I: Back inscription in 3 lines.
Type II: Back inscription in 2 lines.

1958-59 Typographed, Without Embossing

UC32	UC7	10c **blue & red**, *blue,* II, *May, 1959,* entire	6.00	5.00
b.		Red omitted, II, entire	850.00	
c.		Blue omitted, II, entire	850.00	
UC32a	UC7	10c **blue & red**, *blue,* I, *Sept. 12, 1958,* entire	10.00	5.00
		Entire, 1st day cancel, St. Louis, Mo. *(92,400)*		1.25
		Die cutting reversed, entire	75.00	
d.		Red omitted, I, entire	1,000.	

Silhouette of Jet Airliner —
UC8

1958, Nov. 21 Embossed

UC33	UC8	7c **blue**	.60	.25
		Entire	.70	.30
		Entire, 1st day cancel, New York, N.Y. *(208,980)*		1.00

1960, Aug. 18

UC34	UC8	7c **carmine**	.60	.25
		Entire	.70	.30
		Entire, 1st day cancel, Portland, Ore. *(196,851)*		1.00

Jet Airliner and
Globe — UC9

Letter Sheet for Foreign Postage
Typographed, Without Embossing

1961, June 16

UC35	UC9	11c **red & blue**, *blue,* entire	3.00	*3.50*
		Entire, 1st day cancel, Johnstown, Pa. *(163,460)*		1.00
		Die cutting reversed, entire	35.00	
a.		Red omitted, entire	1,000.	
b.		Blue omitted, entire	1,100.	

Jet Airliner — UC10

1962, Nov. 17 Embossed

UC36	UC10	8c **red**	.55	.20
		Entire	.75	.30
		Entire, 1st day cancel, Chantilly, Va. *(194,810)*		1.00

Jet Airliner — UC11

1965-67

UC37	UC11	8c **red**, *Jan. 7*	.45	.20
		Entire, border "f"	.60	.30
		Entire, border "g"	*22.50*	
		Entire, 1st day cancel, Chicago, Ill. *(226,178)*		1.00
a.		Tagged, *Aug. 15, 1967*	3.75	.30
		Entire	5.50	.75
		Tagged, 1st day cancel		3.50

No. UC37a has a 8x24mm panel at left of stamp that glows
orange red under ultraviolet light.

Pres. John F.
Kennedy and
Jet Plane
UC12

Letter Sheets for Foreign Postage
Typographed, Without Embossing

1965, May 29

UC38	UC12	11c **red & dark blue**, *blue,* entire	3.25	*4.00*
		Entire, 1st day cancel, Boston, Mass. *(337,422)*		1.50
		Die cutting reversed, entire	40.00	

1967, May 29

UC39	UC12	13c **red & dark blue**, *blue,* entire	3.25	*4.00*
		Entire, 1st day cancel, Chicago, Ill. *(211,387)*		1.50
		Die cutting reversed, entire	100.00	
a.		Red omitted, entire	750.00	
b.		Dark blue omitted, entire	500.00	

Jet Liner — UC13

Designed by Robert J. Jones.

1968, Jan. 8 Tagged Embossed

UC40	UC13	10c **red**	.50	.20
		Entire	.80	.20
		Entire, 1st day cancel, Chicago, Ill. *(157,553)*		1.00

No. UC37 Surcharged in Red at Left of Stamp

1968, Feb. 5

UC41	UC11	8c + 2c **red**	.65	.20
		Entire	.90	.50
		Entire, 1st day cancel, Washington, D.C.		8.00

Human Rights Year Issue

Issued for International Human Rights Year, and to
commemorate the 20th anniversary of the United
Nations' Declaration of Human Rights.

Globes and Flock of Birds — UC14

Printed by Acrovure Division of Union-Camp Corporation,
Englewood, N.J. Designed by Antonio Frasconi.

Letter Sheet for Foreign Postage

1968, Dec. 3 Tagged Photo.

UC42	UC14	13c **gray, brown, orange & black**, *blue,* entire	8.00	5.00
		Entire, 1st day cancel, Washington, D.C. *(145,898)*		1.25
		Die cutting reversed, entire	75.00	
a.		Orange omitted, entire	1,000.	
b.		Brown omitted, entire	375.00	
c.		Black omitted, entire	—	

No. UC42 has a luminescent panel ⅜x1 inch on the right
globe. The panel glows orange red under ultraviolet light.

Jet Plane — UC15

Printed by United States Envelope Co., Williamsburg, Pa.
Designed by Robert Geissmann.

1971, May 6 Embossed (Plane)
Center Circle Luminescent

UC43	UC15	11c **red & blue**	.50	*.90*
		Entire	.60	*1.00*
		Entire, 1st day cancel, Williamsburg, Pa. *(187,000)*		1.00

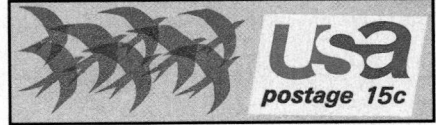

Birds in Flight — UC16

Printed by Bureau of Engraving and Printing. Designed by
Soren Noring.

Letter Sheet for Foreign Postage

1971 Tagged Photo.

UC44	UC16	15c **gray, red, white & blue**, *blue,* entire, *May 28*	1.50	*3.00*
		Entire, 1st day cancel, Chicago, Ill. *(130,669)*		1.25
		Die cutting reversed, entire	30.00	
a.		"AEROGRAMME" added to inscription, entire, *Dec. 13*	1.50	*3.00*
		Entire, 1st day cancel, Philadelphia, Pa.		1.25
		Die cutting reversed, entire	30.00	

Folding instructions (2 steps) in capitals on No. C44; (4 steps)
in upper and lower case on No. UC44a.
On Nos. UC44-UC44a the white rhomboid background of
"USA postage 15c" is luminescent. No. UC44 is inscribed: "VIA
AIR MAIL-PAR AVION". "postage 15c" is in gray. See No.
UC46.

No. UC40 Surcharged in Green at Left of Stamp

1971, June 28   **Embossed**
UC45 UC13 10c + (1c) **red**   1.50   .20
    Entire   1.90   .50
    Entire, 1st day cancel, Washing-
    ton, D.C.   8.00

HOT AIR BALLOONING CHAMPIONSHIPS ISSUE

Hot Air Ballooning World Championships, Albuquerque, N.M., Feb. 10-17, 1973.

Design: Three balloons and cloud at left in address section; no birds beside stamp. Inscribed "INTERNATIONAL HOT AIR BALLOONING." "postage 15c" in blue.
Printed by Bureau of Engraving and Printing. Designed by Soren Noring (vignette) and Esther Porter (balloons).

Letter Sheet for Foreign Postage

1973, Feb. 10   **Tagged**   **Photo.**
UC46 UC16 15c **red, white & blue**, *blue*, entire   1.00 .40
    Entire, 1st day cancel, Albuquer-
    que, N.M. (210,000)   1.00

Folding instructions as on No. UC44a. See notes after No. UC44.

Bird in
Flight — UC17

1973, Dec. 1   **Luminescent Ink**
UC47 UC17 13c **rose red**   .30   .20
    Entire   .40   .20
    Entire, 1st day cancel, Memphis,
    Tenn. (132,658)   1.00

UC18

Printed by the Bureau of Engraving and Printing. Designed by Bill Hyde.

Letter Sheet for Foreign Postage.

1974, Jan. 4   **Tagged**   **Photo.**
UC48 UC18 18c **red & blue**, *blue*, entire   1.00 2.00
    Entire, 1st day cancel, Atlanta,
    Ga. (119,615)   1.00
    Die cutting reversed, entire   —
a. Red omitted, entire   —

25TH ANNIVERSARY OF NATO ISSUE

UC19

Design: "NATO" and NATO emblem at left in address section.
Printed by Bureau of Engraving and Printing. Designed by Soren Noring.

Letter Sheet for Foreign Postage

1974, Apr. 4   **Tagged**   **Photo.**
UC49 UC19 18c **red & blue**, *blue*, entire   1.00 .40
    Entire, 1st day cancel, Washing-
    ton, D.C.   1.00

UC20

Printed by Bureau of Engraving and Printing. Designed by Robert Geissmann.

Letter Sheet for Foreign Postage

1976, Jan. 16   **Tagged**   **Photo.**
UC50 UC20 22c **red & blue**, *blue*, entire   1.00 1.50
    Entire, 1st day cancel, Tempe,
    Ariz. (118,303)   1.00
    Die cutting reversed, entire   15.00
a. Red color missing due to foldover and
    die cutting   —

"USA" — UC21

Printed by Bureau of Engraving and Printing. Designed by Soren Noring.

Letter Sheet for Foreign Postage

1978, Nov. 3   **Tagged**   **Photo.**
UC51 UC21 22c **blue**, *blue*, entire   1.00 .25
    Entire, 1st day cancel, St. Pe-
    tersburg, Fla. (86,099)   1.00
    Die cutting reversed, entire   25.00

22nd OLYMPIC GAMES, MOSCOW, JULY 19-AUG. 3, 1980.

UC22

Design (multicolored in bottom left corner) shows discus thrower.
Printed by Bureau of Engraving and Printing. Designed by Robert M. Cunningham.

Letter Sheet for Foreign Postage

1979, Dec. 5   **Tagged**   **Photo.**
UC52 UC22 22c **red, black & green**, *bluish*, en-
    tire   1.50 .25
    Entire, 1st day cancel, Bay
    Shore, N.Y.   1.00

"USA" — UC23

Design (brown on No. UC53, green and brown on No. UC54): lower left, Statue of Liberty. Inscribed "Tour the United States." Folding area shows tourist attractions.
Printed by Bureau of Engraving and Printing. Designed by Frank J. Waslick.

Letter Sheet for Foreign Postage

1980, Dec. 29   **Tagged**   **Photo.**
UC53 UC23 30c **blue, red & brown**, *blue*, entire   .85 1.50
    Entire, 1st day cancel, San
    Francisco, CA   1.25
    Die cutting reversed, entire   20.00
a. Red (30) omitted, entire   70.00

1981, Sept. 21   **Tagged**   **Photo.**
UC54 UC23 30c **yellow, magenta, blue &**
    black, *blue*, entire   .65 1.00
    Entire, 1st day cancel, Honolu-
    lu, HI   1.25
    Die cutting reversed, entire   20.00

UC24

Design: "Made in USA . . . world's best buys!" on flap, ship, tractor in lower left. Reverse folding area shows chemicals, jet silhouette, wheat, typewriter and computer tape disks. Printed by Bureau of Engraving and Printing.
Designed by Frank J. Waslick.

Letter Sheet for Foreign Postage

1982, Sept. 16   **Tagged**   **Photo.**
UC55 UC24 30c **multi**, *blue*, entire   .80 2.75
    Entire, 1st day cancel, Seattle,
    WA   1.25
    Die cutting reversed, entire   —

WORLD COMMUNICATIONS YEAR

World Map Showing Locations of Satellite Tracking Stations — UC25

Design: Reverse folding area shows satellite, tracking station.
Printed by Bureau of Engraving and Printing.
Designed by Esther Porter.

Letter Sheet for Foreign Postage

1983, Jan. 7   **Tagged**   **Photo.**
UC56 UC25 30c **multi**, *blue*, entire   .90 5.00
    Entire, 1st day cancel,
    Anaheim, CA   1.25
    Die cutting reversed, entire   25.00

1984 OLYMPICS

UC26

Indicia in black, multicolor design of woman equestrian at lower left with montage of competitive events on reverse folding area.
Printed by the Bureau of Engraving & Printing.
Designed by Bob Peak.

Letter Sheet for Foreign Postage

1983, Oct. 14   **Tagged**   **Photo.**
UC57 UC26 30c **black & multi**, *light blue*, entire   .85 3.00
    Entire, 1st day cancel, Los Ange-
    les, CA   1.25
    Die cutting reversed, entire   —

WEATHER SATELLITES, 25TH ANNIV.

Landsat
Infrared and
Thermal
Mapping
Bands
UC27

Design: Landsat orbiting the earth at lower left with three Landsat photographs on reverse folding area. Inscribed: "Landsat views the Earth."
Printed by the Bureau of Engraving & Printing.
Designed by Esther Porter.

Letter Sheet for Foreign Postage

1985, Feb. 14		Tagged	Photo.
UC58 UC27 36c **multi**, *blue*, entire		.85	3.00
Entire, 1st day cancel, Goddard Flight Center, MD		1.40	
Die cutting reversed, entire	30.00		

NATIONAL TOURISM WEEK

Urban Skyline — UC28

Design: Inscribed "Celebrate America" at lower left and "Travel. . . the perfect freedom" on folding area. Skier, Indian chief, cowboy, jazz trumpeter and pilgrims on reverse folding area.
Printed by the Bureau of Engraving & Printing.
Designed by Dennis Luzak.

Letter Sheet for Foreign Postage

1985, May 21		Tagged	Photo.
UC59 UC28 36c **multi**, *blue*, entire		.85	3.00
Entire, 1st day cancel, Washington, DC		1.40	
Die cutting reversed, entire	25.00		
a. Black omitted, entire		950.00	—

MARK TWAIN AND HALLEY'S COMET

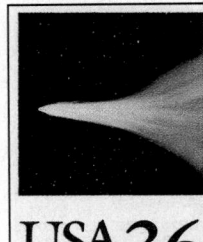

Comet Tail Viewed from Space — UC29

Design: Portrait of Twain at lower left and inscribed "I came in with Halley's Comet in 1835. It is coming again next year, and I expect to go out with it. It will be the greatest disappointment of my life if I don't go out with Halley's Comet." "1835 . Mark Twain . 1910 . Halley's Comet . 1985" and Twain, Huckleberry Finn, steamboat and comet on reverse folding areas.
Printed by the Bureau of Engraving & Printing.
Designed by Dennis Luzak.

Letter Sheet for Foreign Postage

1985, Dec. 4		Tagged	Photo.
UC60 UC29 36c **multi**, entire		1.00	4.00
Entire, 1st day cancel, Hannibal, MO		2.00	
Die cutting reversed, entire	25.00		

UC30

Printed by the Bureau of Engraving & Printing.

Letter Sheet for Foreign Postage

1988, May 9		Litho.	Tagged
UC61 UC30 39c **multi**, entire		1.00	2.25
Entire, 1st day cancel, Miami, FL (27,446)		1.60	
a. Tagging bar to left of design ('89)		.95	1.50

On No. UC61, the tagging bar is between "USA" and "39."

MONTGOMERY BLAIR, POSTMASTER GENERAL 1861-64

Blair and Pres. Abraham Lincoln — UC31

Design: Mail bags and "Free city delivery," "Railway mail service" and "Money order system" at lower left. Globe, locomotive, bust of Blair, UPU emblem and "The Paris conference of 1863, initiated by Postmaster General Blair, led, in 1874, to the founding of the Universal Postal Union" contained on reverse folding area.
Printed by the Bureau of Engraving & Printing.
Designed by Ned Seidler.

Letter Sheet for Foreign Postage

1989, Nov. 20		Litho.	Tagged
UC62 UC31 39c **multicolored**, entire		1.00	10.00
Entire, 1st day cancel, Washington, DC		1.75	
a.	Double impression	—	
b.	Triple impression	—	
c.	Quadruple impression	—	

UC32

Designed by Bradbury Thompson.
Printed by the Bureau of Engraving and Printing.

Letter Sheet for Foreign Postage

1991, May 17		Litho.	Tagged
UC63 UC32 45c **gray, red & blue**, *blue*, entire		1.00	1.50
a. White paper		1.00	1.50
Entire, 1st day cancel, Denver, CO (19,941)		1.40	

Thaddeus Lowe (1832-1913), Balloonist — UC33

Designed by Davis Meltzer.
Printed by the Bureau of Engraving & Printing.

Letter Sheet for Foreign Postage

1995, Sept. 23		Litho.	Tagged
UC64 UC33 50c **multicolored**, *blue*, entire		1.25	2.25
Entire, 1st day cancel, Tampa, FL		1.25	

Voyageurs Natl. Park, Minnesota UC34

Designed by Phil Jordan.

Printed by Bureau of Engraving & Printing.

Letter Sheet for Foreign Postage

1999, May 15		Litho.	Tagged
UC65 UC34 60c **multicolored**, *blue*, entire		1.25	2.25
Entire, 1st day cancel, Denver, CO		1.50	

OFFICIAL ENVELOPES & WRAPPERS

By the Act of Congress, January 31, 1873, the franking privilege of officials was abolished as of July 1, 1873 and the Postmaster General was authorized to prepare official envelopes. At the same time official stamps were prepared for all Departments. Department envelopes became obsolete July 5, 1884. After that, government offices began to use franked envelopes of varied design. These indicate no denomination and lie beyond the scope of this Catalogue.

Post Office Department

UO1

Numeral 9mm high.

UO2

Numeral 9mm high.

UO3

Numeral 9½mm high.

Printed by George H. Reay, Brooklyn, N.Y.

1873					
UO1	UO1	2c **black**, *lemon*		24.00	10.00
		Entire		35.00	15.00
UO2	UO2	3c **black**, *lemon*		16.00	6.50
		Entire		30.00	11.00
+UO3	UO2	3c **black**		42,500.	

				Entire	57,000.	
UO4	UO3	6c	**black,** *lemon*		26.00	16.00
				Entire	35.00	22.50

The No. UO3 entire is unique. It has a tear through the stamp that has been professionally repaired. Value based on auction sale in 1999.

UO4

Numeral 9¼mm high.

UO5

Numeral 9¼mm high.

UO6

Numeral 10½mm high.

Printed by Plimpton Manufacturing Co., Hartford, Conn.

1874-79

UO5	UO4	2c	**black,** *lemon*		10.50	4.25
				Entire	15.00	7.00
UO6	UO4	2c	**black**		140.00	35.00
				Entire	190.00	55.00
UO7	UO5	3c	**black,** *lemon*		3.25	.85
				Entire	4.25	1.50
UO8	UO5	3c	**black**		3,000.	1,200.
				Entire	5,750.	
UO9	UO5	3c	**black,** *amber*		150.00	40.00
				Entire	175.00	60.00
UO10	UO5	3c	**black,** *blue*		45,000.	
				Entire	50,000.	
UO11	UO5	3c	**blue,** *blue* ('75)		45,000.	
				Entire	50,000.	
UO12	UO6	6c	**black,** *lemon*		16.00	6.50
				Entire	26.00	12.50
UO13	UO6	6c	**black**		3,000.	2,100.
				Entire	5,750.	

Fakes exist of Nos. UO3, UO8 and UO13.

Postal Service

UO7

1877

UO14	UO7		**black**		7.00	4.50
				Entire	12.00	6.00
UO15	UO7		**black,** *amber*		250.00	50.00
				Entire	900.00	65.00
UO16	UO7		**blue,** *amber*		210.00	40.00
				Entire	900.00	65.00
UO17	UO7		**blue,** *blue*		9.00	6.75
				Entire	13.50	10.50

War Department

Franklin — UO8

Bust points to the end of "N" of "ONE".

Jackson — UO9

Bust narrow at the back.

Washington — UO10

Queue projects below the bust.

Lincoln — UO11

Neck very long at the back.

Jefferson — UO12

Queue forms straight line with bust.

Clay — UO13

Ear partly concealed by hair, mouth large, chin prominent.

Webster — UO14

Has side whiskers.

Scott — UO15

Hamilton — UO16

Back of bust very narrow; chin almost straight; the labels containing the letters "U S" are exactly parallel.

Printed by George H. Reay.

1873

UO18	UO8	1c	**dark red**		700.00	300.00
				Entire	1,200.	325.00
WO18A	UO8	1c	**dark red,** *manila*		—	
UO19	UO9	2c	**dark red**		2,250.	400.00
				Entire	3,000.	
UO20	UO10	3c	**dark red**		72.50	42.50
				Entire	100.00	70.00
UO21	UO10	3c	**dark red,** *amber*		40,000.	
				Entire	50,000.	
UO22	UO10	3c	**dark red,** *cream*		1,000.	300.00
				Entire	1,200.	350.00
UO23	UO11	6c	**dark red**		325.00	100.00
				Entire	425.00	250.00
UO24	UO11	6c	**dark red,** *cream*		8,000.	425.00
				Entire	10,000.	3,500.
UO25	UO12	10c	**dark red**		17,500.	2,250.
				Entire	27,500.	4,000.
UO26	UO13	12c	**dark red**		175.00	50.00
				Entire	250.00	—
UO27	UO14	15c	**dark red**		160.00	55.00
				Entire	210.00	375.00
UO28	UO15	24c	**dark red**		175.00	50.00
				Entire	225.00	1,250.
UO29	UO16	30c	**dark red**		550.00	150.00
				Entire	725.00	500.00

1873

UO30	UO8	1c	**vermilion**		200.00	
				Entire	400.00	
WO31	UO8	1c	**vermilion,** *manila*		20.00	14.00
				Entire	35.00	25.00
+UO32	UO9	2c	**vermilion**		500.00	
				Entire	25,000.	
WO33	UO9	2c	**vermilion,** *manila*		225.00	
				Entire	375.00	
UO34	UO10	3c	**vermilion**		100.00	40.00
				Entire	175.00	125.00
UO35	UO10	3c	**vermilion,** *amber*		125.00	
				Entire	375.00	
UO36	UO10	3c	**vermilion,** *cream*		17.00	12.50
				Entire	40.00	26.00
UO37	UO11	6c	**vermilion**		100.00	
				Entire	175.00	
+UO38	UO11	6c	**vermilion,** *cream*		575.00	
				Entire	27,500.	
UO39	UO12	10c	**vermilion**		350.00	
				Entire	450.00	
UO40	UO13	12c	**vermilion**		175.00	
				Entire	225.00	
UO41	UO14	15c	**vermilion**		300.00	
				Entire	3,000.	
UO42	UO15	24c	**vermilion**		450.00	
				Entire	650.00	
UO43	UO16	30c	**vermilion**		500.00	
				Entire	625.00	

UO17

Bottom serif on "S" is thick and short; bust at bottom below hair forms a sharp point.

UO18

Bottom serif on "S" is thick and short; front part of bust is rounded.

UO19

Bottom serif on "S" is short; queue does not project below bust.

UO20

Neck very short at the back.

UO21

Knot of queue stands out prominently.

UO22

Ear prominent, chin receding.

UO23

Has no side whiskers; forelock projects above head.

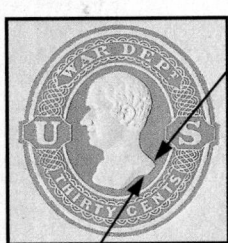

UO24

Back of bust rather broad; chin slopes considerably; the label containing letters "U S" are not exactly parallel.

Printed by Plimpton Manufacturing Co.

1875

UO44	UO17	1c **red**	190.00	85.00
		Entire	250.00	175.00
+UO45	UO17	1c **red,** *amber*	1,000.	
+UO45A	UO17	1c **red,** *orange*	37,500.	
WO46	UO17	1c **red,** *manila*	4.50	2.75
		Entire	9.50	6.50
UO47	UO18	2c **red**	140.00	
		Entire	190.00	
UO48	UO18	2c **red,** *amber*	37.50	17.50
		Entire	45.00	27.50
UO49	UO18	2c **red,** *orange*	70.00	17.50
		Entire	80.00	30.00
WO50	UO18	2c **red,** *manila*	120.00	50.00
		Entire	225.00	—
UO51	UO19	3c **red**	17.50	10.00
		Entire	22.50	17.50
UO52	UO19	3c **red,** *amber*	22.50	10.00
		Entire	30.00	16.00
UO53	UO19	3c **red,** *cream*	7.00	3.75
		Entire	10.00	6.50
UO54	UO19	3c **red,** *blue*	4.00	2.75
		Entire	6.00	4.50
UO55	UO19	3c **red,** *fawn*	6.50	2.75
		Entire	11.50	4.00
UO56	UO20	6c **red**	65.00	30.00
		Entire	100.00	
UO57	UO20	6c **red,** *amber*	95.00	40.00
		Entire	125.00	
UO58	UO20	6c **red,** *cream*	225.00	85.00
		Entire	575.00	
UO59	UO21	10c **red**	250.00	80.00
		Entire	300.00	—
UO60	UO21	10c **red,** *amber*	1,250.	
		Entire	1,650.	
UO61	UO22	12c **red**	65.00	40.00
		Entire	190.00	*250.00*
UO62	UO22	12c **red,** *amber*	800.00	
		Entire	950.00	
UO63	UO22	12c **red,** *cream*	700.00	
		Entire	950.00	
UO64	UO23	15c **red**	250.00	140.00
		Entire	300.00	—
UO65	UO23	15c **red,** *amber*	950.00	
		Entire	1,200.	
UO66	UO23	15c **red,** *cream*	775.00	
		Entire	1,000.	
UO67	UO24	30c **red**	190.00	140.00
		Entire	225.00	—
UO68	UO24	30c **red,** *amber*	925.00	
		Entire	2,400.	
UO69	UO24	30c **red,** *cream*	950.00	
		Entire	1,350.	

POSTAL SAVINGS ENVELOPES

Issued under the Act of Congress, approved June 25, 1910, in lieu of penalty or franked envelopes. Unused remainders, after mid-October 1914, were overprinted with the Penalty Clause. Regular stamped envelopes, redeemed by the Government, were also overprinted for official use.

UO25

1911

UO70	UO25	1c **green**	85.00	25.00
		Entire	125.00	42.50
UO71	UO25	1c **green,** *oriental buff*	250.00	75.00
		Entire	300.00	90.00
UO72	UO25	2c **carmine**	13.50	4.00
		Entire	22.50	12.00
a.		2c **carmine,** *manila* (error)	1,750.	1,000.
		Entire	2,500.	1,400.

Tagged
Envelopes from No. UO73 onward are tagged unless otherwise noted.

OFFICIAL MAIL

Great
Seal — UO26

1983, Jan. 12   **Typo. & Embossed**
UO73 UO26 20c **blue,** entire   1.25   *30.00*
     First day cancel, Washington,
     DC   1.00

UO27

1985, Feb. 26   **Typo. & Embossed**
UO74 UO27 22c **blue,** entire   1.00   *30.00*
     First day cancel, Washington,
     DC   1.00

UO28

1987, Mar. 2   **Typo.**
UO75 UO28 22c **blue,** entire   1.25   *35.00*
     First day cancel, Washington,
     DC   1.00

Used exclusively to mail U.S. Savings Bonds.

UO29

1988, Mar. 22   **Typo.**
UO76 UO29 (25c) **black & blue,** entire   1.75   *35.00*
     First day cancel, Washington,
     DC   1.25

Used exclusively to mail U.S. Savings Bonds.

UO30

UO31

1988, Apr. 11   Typo. & Embossed
UO77 UO30 25c **black & blue,** entire   .85 *25.00*
             First day cancel, Washington,
             DC   1.25
   a.   Denomination & lettering as on No.
             UO78, entire   5.00 *20.00*

Typo.
UO78 UO31 25c **black & blue,** entire   1.25 *35.00*
             First day cancel, Washington,
             DC *(12,017)*   1.25
   a.   Denomination & lettering as on No.
             UO77, entire   1.00 *35.00*

No. UO78 used exclusively to mail U.S. Savings Bonds.
First day cancellations applied to 12,017 of Nos. UO77,
UO78.

Used Values

Postally used examples of Nos. UO79-UO82, UO91-
UO93 seldom or never appear in the marketplace and
thus cannot be valued. The editors would like to see
examples of these used envelopes.

1990, Mar. 17   Typo.
Stars and "E Pluribus Unum" illegible. "Official" is 13mm,
"USA" is 16mm long.
UO79 UO31 45c **black & blue,** entire   1.25   —
             First day cancel, Springfield,
             VA *(5,956)*   1.50   —
UO80 UO31 65c **black & blue,** entire   1.75   —
             First day cancel, Springfield,
             VA *(6,922)*   2.25

Used exclusively to mail U.S. passports.

UO32

Stars and "E Pluribus Unum" clear and sharply printed. "Official" is 14½mm, "USA" is 17mm long.

1990, Aug. 10   Litho.
UO81 UO32 45c **black & blue,** entire   1.25   —
             First day cancel, Washing-
             ton, DC *(7,160)*   1.50   —
UO82 UO32 65c **black & blue,** entire   1.75   —
             First day cancel, Washing-
             ton, DC *(6,759)*   2.25

Used exclusively to mail U.S. passports.

UO33

1991, Jan. 22   Typo.   Wmk.
UO83 UO33 (29c) **black & blue,** entire   1.25 *35.00*
             First day cancel, Washington,
             DC *(30,549)*   1.25

Used exclusively to mail U.S. Savings Bonds.

UO34

1991, Apr. 6   Wmk.   Litho. & Embossed
UO84 UO34 29c **black & blue,** entire   .75 *20.00*
             First day cancel, Oklahoma
             City, OK *(27,841)*   1.25
             Entire, unwatermarked, *May 1,*
             1992   .75   —

Unwatermarked envelopes on recycled paper were issued
May 1, 1992, and have a "recycled" imprint under the flap.

UO35

1991, Apr. 17   Typo.   Wmk.
UO85 UO35 29c **black & blue,** entire   .70 *20.00*
             First day cancel, Washington,
             DC *(25,563)*   1.25
             Entire, unwatermarked, *May 1,*
             1992   .70   —

Used exclusively to mail U.S. Savings Bonds.
Unwatermarked envelopes on recycled paper were issued May
1, 1992, and have a "recycled" imprint under the flap.

Consular Service,
Bicent. — UO36

Designed by Zebulon Rogers. Quotation from O. Henry on
flap.

1992, July 10   Litho.   Unwmk.
UO86 UO36 52c **blue & red,** entire   5.00 *125.00*
             First day cancel, Washington,
             DC *(30,374)*   2.25
   a.   52c blue & red, *blue-white,* entire   1.50 *125.00*
UO87 UO36 75c **blue & red,** entire   10.00 *125.00*
             First day cancel, Washington,
             DC *(25,995)*   3.25
   a.   75c blue & red, *blue-white,* entire   2.50 *125.00*

Used exclusively to mail U.S. passports.
Available only in 4⅝ inch x 8⅞ inch size with self-adhesive
flap.
Original issues have "USPS copyright" on left under flap. Re-
issues (Nos. UO86a and UO87a) have it at right.

UO37

1995-99   Typo. & Embossed   Unwmk.
UO88 UO37 32c **blue & red,** entire, *May 9,*
             1995   .80 *20.00*
             First day cancel, Washington,
             DC   1.25
UO89 UO37 33c **blue & red,** entire, *Feb. 22,*
             1999   .70 *20.00*
             First day cancel, Washington,
             DC   1.25

Type of 1995
2001, Feb. 27   Typo. & Embossed   Unwmk.
UO90 UO37 34c **blue & red,** entire   .85 *20.00*
             First day cancel, Washington,
             DC   1.25

Type of 1995
2002, Aug. 2   Typo. & Embossed   Unwmk.
UO91 UO37 37c **blue & red,** type I, entire   .90
             First day cancel, Washington, DC   1.25
             First day cancel, any other city   1.25
   a.   Type II, entire, *Aug. 2, 2002*   .90

Type I has 29x28mm blue panel, top of "USA" even with the
bottom of the eagle's neck and is made with "100% recycled
paper" as noted on reverse. Type II has a 27½x27½mm blue
panel, top of "USA" even with the highest arrow, and has no
mention of "100% recycled paper" on reverse.

Type of 1995
2006, Jan. 9   Typo. & Embossed   Unwmk.
UO92 UO37 39c **blue & red,** entire   .95
             Entire, 1st day cancel, Washing-
             ton, DC   1.25
             Entire, 1st day cancel, any other
             city   1.25

Type of 1995
2007, May 12   Typo. & Embossed   Unwmk.
UO93 UO37 41c **blue & red,** entire   1.00
             Entire, 1st day cancel, Washing-
             ton, DC   2.10

Type of 1995
2008, June 20   Typo.   Unwmk.
UO94 UO37 42c **blue & red,** entire   1.00 .50
             Entire, 1st day cancel, Washing-
             ton, DC   2.10

POSTAL CARDS

Values are for unused cards as sold by the Post Office, without printed or written address or message, and used cards with Post Office cancellation, when current. Used cards with postage added to meet higher rates sell for less. Used cards for international rates are for proper usage. Those used domestically sell for less.

The "Preprinted" values are for unused cards with printed or written address or message.

Starting with No. UX21, all postal cards have been printed by the Government Printing Office.

Nos. UX1-UX48 are typographed; others are lithographed (offset) unless otherwise stated.

Numerous printing varieties exist. Varieties of surcharged cards include (a) inverted surcharge at lower left, (b) double surcharge, one inverted at lower left, (c) surcharge in other abnormal positions, including back of card. Such surcharge varieties command a premium.

Colored cancellations sell for more than black in some instances. **All values are for entire cards.**

As of Jan. 1, 1999, postal cards were sold individually for 1c over face value. Currently, they are sold for 2c over face value.

See Computer Vended Postage section for "Postal Buddy" cards.

Since 1875 it has been possible to purchase some postal cards in sheets for multiple printing, hence pairs, strips and blocks are available. Some sheets have been cut up so that cards exist with stamp inverted, in center of card, two on one card, in another corner, etc. These are only curiosities and of minimal value.

Liberty — PC1

Wmk. Large "U S P O D" in Monogram, (90x60mm)

1873, May   Size: 130x76mm
UX1 PC1 1c **brown,**   400.00   25.00
     Preprinted   70.00
     First day cancel, Boston, New
     York or Washington   12,000.

One card is documented canceled May 10 in Owensboro, Ky.; another May 11 in Providence, R.I.; and another May 12 in Springfield, Mass.

Wmk. Small "U S P O D" in Monogram, (53x36mm)

1873, July 6
UX3 PC1 1c **brown,** buff   85.00   3.50
     Preprinted   22.50
   a.   Without watermark   800.00

The watermarks on Nos. UX1, UX3 and UX4 are found in normal position, inverted, reversed, and inverted and reversed. They are often very dim, especially on No. UX4. Values listed are for clear watermarks.

No. UX3a is not known unused. Cards offered as such are either unwatermarked proofs, or have partial or vague watermarks. See No. UX65.

Liberty — PC2

Inscribed: "WRITE THE ADDRESS . . ."
1875   **Wmk. Small "U S P O D" in Monogram**
UX4 PC2 1c **black,** buff, Sept. 28   4,000.   350.

     Preprinted   750.
        Unwmk.
UX5 PC2 1c **black,** buff, Sept. 30   82.50   .45
     Preprinted   7.00
For other postal card of type PC2 see No. UX7.

Liberty — PC3

For International Use

1879, Dec. 1
UX6 PC3 2c **blue,** buff   35.00   25.00
     Preprinted   11.50
   a.   2c **dark blue,** buff   35.00   25.00
     Preprinted   11.50
     See Nos. UX13 and UX16.

Design of PC2, Inscribed "NOTHING BUT THE ADDRESS."

1881, Oct. 17 (?)
UX7 PC2 1c **black,** buff   70.00   .40
     Preprinted   6.50
   a.   23 teeth below "ONE CENT"   1,350.   65.00
     Preprinted   225.00
   b.   Printed on both sides   1,000.   750.00

Jefferson — PC4

1885, Aug. 24
UX8 PC4 1c **brown,** buff   55.00   1.25
     Preprinted   10.00
   c.   1c **dark chocolate,** buff   350.00   65.00
     Preprinted   75.00
   d.   Double impression   7,500.
   e.   Double impression, one inverted   9,500.
   f.   Printed on both sides   —
   g.   "M" in double frame above "O" of
     "POSTAL"   —

Card was printed in many shades of brown ink.
Earliest documented use: Aug. 29, 1885.

PC5

Head of Jefferson facing right, centered on card.

1886, Dec 1
UX9 PC5 1c **black,** buff   25.00   .55
     Preprinted   1.75
   a.   1c **black,** dark buff   75.00   5.00
     Preprinted   20.00
   b.   Double impression
   c.   Double impression, one inverted   13,250.
   d.   1c **black,** salmon pink   2,000.   3,250.
   e.   Triple impression   3,000.

Grant — PC6

1891, Dec. 16   Size: 155x95mm
UX10 PC6 1c **black,** buff   47.50   1.50
     Preprinted   7.50
   a.   Double impression, one inverted   4,000.
   b.   Double impression   1,250.
   c.   Triple impression, one inverted   7,000.
   d.   Quintuple impression, three in-
     verted   5,750.

     Two types exist of No. UX10.
Earliest documented use: Dec. 23, 1891.

        Size: 117x75mm
UX11 PC6 1c **blue,** grayish white   22.50   3.00
     Preprinted   5.00
   b.   Double impression, one inverted   8,000.
Cards printed in black instead of blue are invariably proofs.
Earliest documented use: Dec. 21, 1891.

PC7

Head of Jefferson facing left.
Small wreath and name below.
Size: 140x89mm

1894, Jan. 2
UX12 PC7 1c **black,** buff   45.00   .65
     Preprinted   2.25
   a.   Double impression   —

Two types exist of No. UX12: flat bed printing and rotary press printing.

For International Use

1897, Jan. 25   Design of PC3
        Size: 140x89mm
UX13 PC3 2c **blue,** cream   240.00   85.00
     Preprinted   85.00

     Earliest documented use: Apr. 17, 1897.

PC8

Head same as PC7. Large wreath and name below.

1897, Dec. 1
Size: 139x82mm
UX14 PC8 1c **black,** *buff*   40.00   .45
       Preprinted   2.75
a.   Double impression, one inverted   11,500.   8,750.
       Preprinted   —
b.   Printed both sides   —
       Preprinted   3,000.
c.   Double impression   —
       Preprinted   —
d.   **Black,** *salmon pink,* preprinted   1,500.

John Adams — PC9

1898
Size: 126x74mm
UX15 PC9   1c **black,** *buff, Mar. 31*   47.50   15.00
       Preprinted   12.50
Design same as PC3, without frame around card.
For International Use
Size: 140x82mm
UX16 PC3   2c **black,** *buff*   15.00   *17.00*
       Preprinted   5.00

McKinley — PC10

1902
UX17 PC10 1c **black,** *buff*   9,000.
       Preprinted   3,500. 3,750.
     Earliest documented use; May 27, 1902.

McKinley — PC11

1902
UX18 PC11 1c **black,** *buff*   17.50   .35
       Preprinted   1.75
    Earliest documented use; July 14, 1902.
Two types exist of Nos. UX18-UX20.

McKinley — PC12

1907
UX19 PC12 1c **black,** *buff*   45.00   .50
       Preprinted   2.25
    Earliest documented use; June 28, 1907.

Same design, correspondence space at left
1908, Jan. 2
UX20 PC12 1c **black,** *buff*   57.50   4.25
       Preprinted   8.50

PC13

McKinley, background shaded.

1910
UX21 PC13 1c **blue,** *bluish*   105.00   13.00
       Preprinted   17.50
a.   1c **bronze blue,** *bluish*   400.00   100.00
       Preprinted   150.00
b.   Double impression   1,200.
       Preprinted   —
c.   Triple impression   2,500.
d.   Double impression, one inverted   —
e.   Four arcs above and below "IS" of
       inscription to left of stamp im-
       pression are pointed   2,250.   600.00
       Preprinted   900.00
A No. UX21 card exists with Philippines No. UX11 printed on
the back.

PC14

Same design, white background.

1910, Apr. 13
UX22 PC14 1c **blue,** *bluish*   20.00   .35
       Preprinted   2.00
a.   Double impression   750.00
b.   Triple impression   3,000.   3,250.
c.   Triple impression, one inverted   —
d.   Quintuple impression   6,000.
        See No. UX24.

PC15

Head of Lincoln, solid background.

1911, Jan. 21
Size: 127x76mm
UX23 PC15 1c **red,** *cream*   11.00   5.50
       Preprinted   3.50
a.   Triple impression
b.   Double impression   7,250.
        See No. UX26.

       Design same as PC14
1911, Aug. 10   **Size: 140x82mm**
UX24 PC14 1c **red,** *cream*   11.00   .35
       Preprinted   1.25
a.   Double impression
b.   Triple impression   —
Copies with 1920 2-line surcharge are considered favor items.

Grant — PC16

1911, Oct. 27
For International Use
Size: 140x82mm
UX25 PC16 2c **red,** *cream*   1.50   *20.00*
       Preprinted   .65
a.   Double impression   —
       For surcharge see No. UX36.

1913, July 29
Size: 127x76mm
UX26 PC15 1c **green,** *cream*   13.00   7.50
       Preprinted   2.50

Jefferson — PC17

Die I — End of queue small, sloping sharply downward to
right.

Die II (re-cut) — End of queue large and rounded.

1914-16
Size: 140x82mm

UX27	PC17 1c **green**, *buff*, die I,			
	June 4	.25	.25
	Preprinted	.20	
a.	1c **green**, *cream*	5.00	.65
	Preprinted	1.25	
b.	Double impression	2,500.	
e.	Triple impression	5,500.	
f.	Quadruple impression	6,500.	

On gray, rough surfaced card

UX27C	PC17 1c **green**, die I, *1916*	4,000.	250.00
	Preprinted	400.00	
UX27D	PC17 1c **dark green**, die II,		
	Dec. 22, 1916	24,000.	160.00
	Preprinted	375.00	

For surcharges see Nos. UX39 and UX41.

Lincoln — PC19

1917, Mar. 14
Size: 127x76mm

UX28	PC19 1c **green**, *cream*	.60	.30
	Preprinted	.30	
a.	1c **green**, *dark buff*	1.50	.60
	Preprinted	.50	
b.	Double impression	—	
	Preprinted	2,250.	

No. UX28 was printed also on light buff and canary. See No. UX43. For surcharges see Nos. UX40 and UX42.

Jefferson — PC20

Die I — Rough, coarse impression. End of queue slopes sharply downward to right. Left basal ends of "2" form sharp points.

Size: 140x82mm

Die II — Clear fine lines in hair. Left basal ends of "2" form balls.

1917-18

UX29	PC20 2c **red**, *buff*, die I, *Oct. 22*	42.50	2.10
	Preprinted	6.50	
a.	2c **lake**, *cream*, die I	50.00	4.00
	Preprinted	9.00	
c.	2c **vermilion**, *buff*, die I	925.00	75.00
	Preprinted	70.00	
UX30	PC20 2c **red**, *cream*, die II, *Jan. 23,*		
	1918	30.00	1.60
	Preprinted	4.50	

2c Postal Cards of 1917-18 Revalued

Surcharged in one line by canceling machine at Washington, DC

1920, Apr.

UX31	PC20 1c on 2c **red**, *cream*, die II	4,250.	4,500.
	Preprinted	2,600.	

Surcharged in two lines by canceling machine (46 Types)

UX32	PC20 1c on 2c **red**, *buff*, die I	52.50	12.50
	Preprinted	15.00	
a.	1c on 2c **vermilion**, *buff*	150.00	60.00
	Preprinted	60.00	
b.	Double surcharge	150.00	100.00
	Preprinted	100.00	
c.	Double surcharge, one inverted, both in normal position on stamp	—	—
	Preprinted	—	
d.	Double surcharge, one inverted at lower left	65.00	30.00
	Preprinted	30.00	
e.	Triple surcharge	—	
	Preprinted	—	
f.	Inverted surcharge at lower left	65.00	30.00
	Preprinted	30.00	
UX33	PC20 1c on 2c **red**, *cream*, die II	13.00	2.00
	Preprinted	2.50	
a.	Inverted surcharge, on stamp	150.00	200.00
	Preprinted	—	
b.	Double surcharge	150.00	175.00
	Preprinted	50.00	
c.	Double surcharge, one inverted, both in normal position on stamp	350.00	
d.	Triple surcharge	375.00	
e.	Double surcharge, one inverted at lower left	30.00	25.00
	Preprinted	20.00	
f.	Inverted surcharge at lower left	30.00	30.00
	Preprinted	20.00	
g.	Triple surcharge, one inverted at lower left	—	
	Preprinted	—	

Double and triple surcharges on Nos. UX32 and UX33 generally sell for less than above values if one or more of the surcharges is not on the stamp.

Surcharged in Two Lines by Press Printing
1920

UX34	PC20 1c on 2c **red**, *buff*, die I	800.00	52.50
	Preprinted	125.00	
a.	Double surcharge	1,000.	
UX35	PC20 1c 2c **red**, *cream*, die II	225.00	37.50
	Preprinted	55.00	
a.	Double surcharge, one inverted at lower left	—	

Surcharges were prepared from (a) special dies fitting International and Universal post office canceling machines (Nos. UX31-UX33), and (b) printing press dies (Nos. UX34-UX35). There are 38 canceling machine types on Die I, and 44 on Die II. There are two printing press types of each die.

UX36	PC16 1c on 2c **red**, *cream* (#UX25)	57,500.

Unused examples of No. UX36 (New York surcharge) were probably made by favor. Used examples of No. UX36 (Los Angeles surcharge, three to four examples used in Long Beach are recorded) are unquestionably authentic. Surcharges on other numbers exist, but their validity is doubtful.

McKinley — PC21

1926, Feb. 1
For International Use

UX37	PC21 3c **red**, *buff*	4.50	15.00
	Preprinted	1.75	
	First day cancel, Washington, DC		200.00
a.	3c **red**, *yellow*	6.00	15.00
	Preprinted	1.75	
b.	Double impression	5,000.	

Franklin — PC22

1951, Nov. 16

UX38	PC22 2c **carmine rose**, *buff*	.35	.25
	Preprinted	.25	
	First day cancel		1.00
a.	Double impression	500.00	
b.	2c **carmine rose**, *dark buff*, (error)	700.00	
c.	2c **lake**, *buff*,	35.00	25.00
d.	Indicia omitted (inscriptions normal)	1,000.	

No. UX38b was printed on spacer paper used for counting. For surcharge see No. UX47.

Nos. UX27 and UX28 Surcharged by Canceling Machine at Left of Stamp in Light Green

1952

UX39	PC17 2c on 1c **green**, *buff*, *Jan. 1*	.50	.35
	Preprinted	.25	
	First day cancel, any city		12.00
a.	Surcharged vertically, reading down	8.00	10.00
	Preprinted	3.00	
b.	Double surcharge	20.00	25.00
c.	Double surcharge, one inverted at lower left	20.00	25.00
d.	Inverted surcharge at lower left	12.00	12.00
e.	Triple surcharge	—	—
f.	Triple surcharge, one inverted at lower left	—	—
g.	Surcharge black (error), entire	3,000.	
UX40	PC19 2c on 1c **green**, *cream*, *Mar. 22*	.65	.45
	Preprinted	.40	
	First day cancel, Washington, D.C.		22.50
a.	Surcharged vertically, reading down	7.00	5.50
	Preprinted	4.00	
b.	Double surcharge	240.00	
c.	Double surcharge, one inverted at lower left	275.00	
d.	Inverted surcharge at lower left	200.00	

Nos. UX27 and UX28 with Similar Surcharge Typographed at Left of Stamp in Dark Green.

1952

UX41	PC17 2c on 1c **green**, *buff*	5.00	2.00
	Preprinted	1.75	
a.	Inverted surcharge at lower left	85.00	125.00
	Preprinted	45.00	
b.	Double surcharge	—	—
UX42	PC19 2c on 1c **green**, *cream*	5.00	2.50
	Preprinted	3.00	
a.	Surcharged by offset lithography	5.00	2.50
b.	Surcharged on back	300.00	

Type of 1917

1952, July 31
Size: 127x76mm

UX43	PC19 2c **carmine**, *buff*	.30	1.00
	Preprinted	.20	
	First day cancel		1.00

Torch and Arm of Statue of Liberty — PC23

Fifth International Philatelic Exhibition (FIPEX), New York City, Apr. 28-May 6, 1956.

1956, May 4
UX44 PC23 2c **deep carmine & dark violet blue,** *buff* .25 1.00
   First day cancel, New York,
   NY *(537,474)* 1.00
a. Dark violet blue omitted 525.00 600.00
b. Double impression of dark violet blue 40.00 —
c. Double impression of deep carmine 40.00 30.00
d. Double impression of deep carmine & dark violet blue 650.00
e. Double impression of deep carmine, dark violet blue omitted —
f. 2c **rose pink & dark violet blue,** *buff* 100.00 75.00
g. As "f," dark violet blue omitted 750.00
h. 2c **pink & dark violet blue,** *buff* 750.00 750.00
i. As "h," double impression of dark violet blue —

Statue of Liberty
PC24   PC25

For International Use

1956, Nov. 16
UX45 PC24 4c **deep red & ultramarine,** *buff* 1.50 90.00
   First day cancel, New York, NY
   (129,841) 1.00
   See No. UY16.

1958, Aug. 1
UX46 PC25 3c **purple,** *buff* .50 .20
   First day cancel, Philadelphia, Pa. *(180,610)* 1.00
a. "N GOD WE TRUST" 12.00 25.00
   First day cancel, Philadelphia, Pa. 175.00
b. Double impression 250.00
c. Double impression one inverted 4,500.
d. Precanceled with 3 printed purple lines, 1961 4.25 2.50
e. Indicia omitted (inscription normal) 1,000.
f. 3c **purple,** *dark buff* (error) 900.00

On No. UX46d, the precanceling lines are incorporated with the design. The earliest documented postmark on this experimental card is Oct. 31, 1961. UX46f was printed on spacer paper used for counting.
See No. UY17.

No. UX38 Surcharged by Canceling Machine at Left of Stamp in Black

1958
UX47 PC22 2c + 1c **carmine rose,** *buff* 235.00 700.00
a. Surcharge inverted at lower left 500.00

The surcharge was applied to 750,000 cards for the use of the General Electric Co., Owensboro, Ky. A variety of the surcharge shows the D of PAID beneath the N of ADDITIONAL. All known examples of No. UX47 have a printed advertisement on the back and a small punch hole near lower left corner.
Used value is for commercially used card.

Lincoln
PC26

1962, Nov. 19
Precanceled with 3 printed red violet lines
UX48 PC26 4c **red violet** .50 .20
   First day cancel, Springfield, IL
   (162,939) 1.25
a. Tagged, *June 25, 1966* .60 .20
b. Inscription omitted
   First day cancel, Bellevue, OH 30.00

No. UX48a was printed with luminescent ink.
See note on Luminescence in "Information for Collectors."
See No. UY18.

Used values are for contemporaneous usage without additional postage applied. Used values for international-rate cards are for proper usage.

Map of Continental United States — PC27

Designed by Suren H. Ermoyan

For International Use

1963, Aug. 30
UX49 PC27 7c **blue & red** 4.00 65.00
   First day cancel, New York, NY 1.00
a. Blue omitted 7,500.

First day cancellation was applied to 270,464 of Nos. UX49 and UY19. See Nos. UX54, UX59, UY19-UY20.

Flags and Map of U.S.
PC28

175th anniv. of the U.S. Customs Service.

Designed by Gerald N. Kurtz

1964, Feb. 22
Precanceled with 3 printed blue lines
UX50 PC28 4c **red & blue** .50 1.00
   First day cancel, Washington, DC *(313,275)* 1.00
a. Blue omitted 650.00
b. Red omitted —
c. Double red impression 650.00

Americans "Moving Forward" (Street Scene) — PC29

Issued to publicize the need to strengthen the US Social Security system. Released in connection with the 15th conf. of the Intl. Social Security Association at Washington, DC.

Designed by Gerald N. Kurtz

1964, Sept. 26
Precanceled with a blue and 2 red printed lines
UX51 PC29 4c **dull blue & red** .40 1.00
   First day cancel, Washington, D.C. *(293,650)* 1.00
a. Red omitted —
b. Dull blue omitted 650.00 650.00

Coast Guard Flag — PC30

175th anniv. of the U.S. Coast Guard.

Designed by Muriel R. Chamberlain

1965, Aug. 4
Precanceled with 3 printed red lines
UX52 PC30 4c **blue & red** .30 1.00
   First day cancel, Newburyport, Mass. *(338,225)* 1.25
a. Blue omitted —

Crowd and Census Bureau Punch Card — PC31

Designed by Emilio Grossi

1965, Oct. 21
Precanceled with 3 bright blue printed lines
UX53 PC31 4c **bright blue & black** .30 1.00
   First day cancel, Philadelphia, Pa. *(275,100)* 1.00

Map Type of 1963
For International Use

1967, Dec. 4
UX54 PC27 8c **blue & red** 4.50 65.00
   First day cancel, Washington, DC 1.00

First day cancellation was applied to 268,077 of Nos. UX54 and UY20.

Lincoln
PC33

Designed by Robert J. Jones

Luminescent Ink

1968, Jan. 4
Precanceled with 3 printed green lines
UX55 PC33 5c **emerald** .30 .60
   First day cancel, Hodgenville, Ky. 1.25
a. Double impression —

First day cancellation was applied to 274,000 of Nos. UX55 and UY21.

Woman Marine, 1968, and Marines of Earlier Wars — PC34

25th anniv. of the Women Marines.

Designed by Muriel R. Chamberlain

1968, July 26
UX56 PC34 5c **rose red & green** .35 1.00
   First day cancel, San Francisco, Cal. *(203,714)* 1.25

Tagged

Postal cards from No. UX57 onward are either tagged or printed with luminescent ink unless otherwise noted.

Weather Vane — PC35

Centenary of the Army's Signal Service, the Weather Services (Weather Bureau).

Designed by Robert Geissmann

1970, Sept. 1
UX57 PC35 5c **blue, yellow, red & black**   .30   1.00
  First day cancel, Fort Myer, Va. *(285,800)*   1.00
 a. Yellow & black omitted   1,250. 900.00
 b. Blue omitted   1,000. 5,000.
 c. Black omitted   1,250. 850.00

Paul Revere — PC36

Issued to honor Paul Revere, Revolutionary War patriot.

Designed by Howard C. Mildner after statue near Old North Church, Boston

1971, May 15
Precanceled with 3 printed brown lines
UX58 PC36 6c **brown**   .30   1.00
  First day cancel, Boston, Mass.   1.00
 a. Double impression   1,400.

First day cancellation was applied to 340,000 of Nos. UX58 and UY22.

Map Type of 1963
For International Use

1971, June 10
UX59 PC27 10c **blue & red**   4.50   65.00
  First day cancel, New York, NY   1.00

First day cancellation was applied to 297,000 of Nos. UX59 and UXC11.

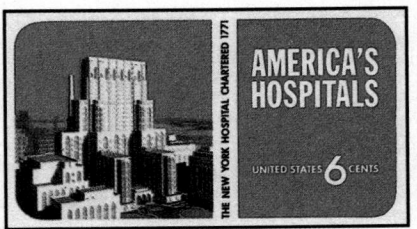

New York Hospital, New York City — PC37

Issued as a tribute to America's hospitals in connection with the 200th anniversary of New York Hospital.

Designed by Dean Ellis

1971, Sept. 16
UX60 PC37 6c **blue & multicolored**   .30   1.00
  First day cancel, New York, NY *(218,200)*   1.00
 a. Blue & yellow omitted   1,000.
 b. Yellow omitted   500.00
 c. Red & black omitted   —
 d. Red omitted   —
 e. Tagging omitted   150.00
 f. Black omitted   3,500.

No. UX60f is significantly miscut, with only a small portion of the indicia present at the center top. The black vertical inscription line at the center is missing.

U.S.F. Constellation — PC38

Monument Valley — PC39

Gloucester, Mass. — PC40

Tourism Year of the Americas.

Designed by Melbourne Brindle

1972, June 29
  Size: 152½x108½mm
UX61 PC38 6c **black,** U.S.F. Constellation, *buff* (Yosemite, Mt. Rushmore, Niagara Falls, Williamsburg on back)   .85   10.00
  First day cancel, any city   1.25
 a. Address side blank   300.00
 b. Reverse blank   —   750.00
 c. Tagging omitted   200.00
UX62 PC39 6c **black,** Monument Valley, *buff* (Monterey, Redwoods, Gloucester, U.S.F. Constellation on back)   .40   10.00
  First day cancel, any city   1.25
 a. Black omitted on back   —
 b. Orange omitted on back   —
 c. Reverse blank   350.00
 d. Tagging omitted   200.00
UX63 PC40 6c **black,** Gloucester, *buff* (Rodeo, Mississippi Riverboat, Grand Canyon, Monument Valley on back)   .40   6.00
  First day cancel, any city   1.25
 a. Black inverted   —
 b. Reverse blank   500.00
 c. Tagging omitted   —
 d. Back inverted to the front   1,000.
  Nos. UX61-UX63,UXC12-UXC13 (5)   3.15   176.00

Nos. UX61-UX63, UXC12-UXC13 went on sale throughout the United States. They were sold as souvenirs without postal validity at Belgica Philatelic Exhibition in Brussels and were displayed at the American Embassies in Paris and Rome. This is reflected in the first day cancel.

Varieties of the pictorial back printing include: black omitted (UX62), black and pale salmon omitted (UX63), and back inverted in relation to address side (UX63).

Used value for No. UX61b is for a copy that is canceled but unaddressed.

John Hanson — PC41

Designed by Thomas Kronen after statue by Richard Edwin Brooks in Maryland Capitol

1972, Sept. 1
Precanceled with 3 printed blue lines.
UX64 PC41 6c **blue**   .50   1.00
  First day cancel, Baltimore, MD   1.00
 a. Coarse paper   .75   1.25

Liberty Type of 1873
Centenary of first U.S. postal card.

1973, Sept. 14
UX65 PC1 6c **magenta**   .25   1.00
  First day cancel, Washington, D.C. *(289,950)*   1.00
 a. Tagging omitted   —
 b. Tagging inverted at lower left —

Samuel Adams — PC42

Designed by Howard C. Mildner

1973, Dec. 16
Precanceled with 3 printed orange lines
UX66 PC42 8c **orange**   .50   1.00
  First day cancel, Boston, Mass. *(147,522)*   1.00
 a. Coarse paper   .75   1.00
 b. Double impression   1,200.

Ship's Figurehead, 1883 — PC43

Design is after a watercolor by Elizabeth Moutal of the oak figurehead by John Rogerson from the barque Edinburgh.

1974, Jan. 4
For International Use
UX67 PC43 12c **multicolored**   .35   50.00
  First day cancel, Miami, Fla. *(138,500)*   1.00
 a. Yellow omitted   1,000.
 b. Tagging omitted   300.00

Charles Thomson — PC44

John Witherspoon — PC45

Caesar Rodney — PC46

Designed by Howard C. Mildner

1975-76
    Precanceled with 3 printed emerald lines
UX68 PC44 7c **emerald**, *Sept. 14, 1975*   .30   10.00
        First day cancel, Bryn
          Mawr, Pa.   1.00
    Precanceled with 3 printed brown lines
UX69 PC45 9c **yellow brown**, *Nov. 10,*
      1975   .30   *1.00*
        First day cancel,
          Princeton, N.J.   1.00
    Precanceled with 3 printed blue lines
UX70 PC46 9c **blue**, *July 1, 1976*   .30   *1.00*
        First day cancel, Dover,
          Del.   1.00
    a.   Double impression   4,500.
    First day cancellation applied to 231,919 of Nos. UX68 and UY25; 254,239 of Nos. UX69 and UY26; 304,061 of Nos. UX70 and UY27.

Federal Court House, Galveston, Texas — PC47

The Court House, completed in 1861, is on the National Register of Historic Places.

Designed by Donald Moss

1977, July 20
UX71 PC47 9c **multicolored**   .25   *1.00*
        First day cancel, Galves-
          ton, Tex. *(245,535)*   1.00
    a.   Black Omitted   6,000.
    b.   Tagging omitted   150.00

Nathan Hale PC48

Designed by Howard C. Mildner

1977, Oct. 14
    Precanceled with 3 printed green lines
UX72 PC48 9c **green**   .25   *1.00*
        First day cancel, Coventry,
          Conn.   1.00
    a.   Cent sign missing after "9"   125.00
    b.   Double impression   275.00
    First day cancellation applied to 304,592 of Nos. UX72 and UY28.
    Approximately 400 examples are recorded of No. UX72a. The variety also exists on fluorescent stock (18 recorded). Value thus is 7 times the listed value.

Cincinnati Music Hall — PC49

Centenary of Cincinnati Music Hall, Cincinnati, Ohio.

Designed by Clinton Orlemann

1978, May 12
UX73 PC49 10c **multicolored**   .30   *1.00*
        First day cancel,
          Cincinnati, O.
          (300,000)   1.75

John Hancock — PC50

Designed by Howard Behrens

1978
    Precanceled with 3 printed brown orange lines.
UX74 PC50 (10c) **brown orange**, *May 19*   .30 *1.00*
        First day cancel, Quincy, Mass.
          (299,623)   1.00
    Inscribed "U.S. Postage 10¢"
UX75 PC50 10c **brown orange**, *June 20*   .30 *1.00*
        First day cancel, Quincy, Mass.
          (187,120)   1.00

Coast Guard Cutter Eagle — PC51

Designed by Carl G. Evers

        For International Use
1978, Aug. 4
UX76 PC51 14c **multicolored**   .40 *35.00*
        First day cancel, Seattle, Wash.
          (196,400)   1.00

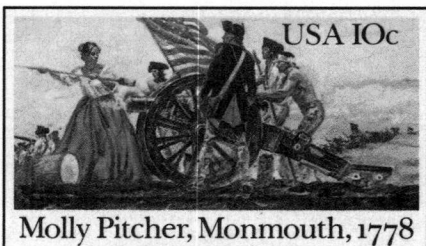

Molly Pitcher Firing Cannon at Monmouth — PC52

Bicentennial of Battle of Monmouth, June 28, 1778, and to honor Molly Pitcher (Mary Ludwig Hays).

Designed by David Blossom

1978, Sept. 8   **Litho.**
UX77 PC52 10c **multicolored**   .30 *1.60*
        First day cancel, Freehold, N.J.
          (180,280)   1.00

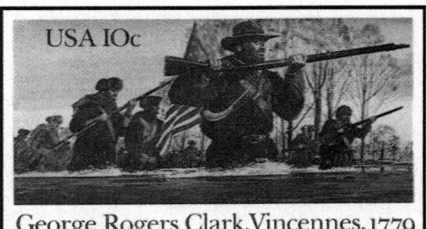

Clark and his Frontiersmen Approaching Fort Sackville — PC53

Bicentenary of capture of Fort Sackville from the British by George Rogers Clark.

Designed by David Blossom

1979, Feb. 23   **Litho.**
UX78 PC53 10c **multicolored**   .30 *1.50*
        First day cancel, Vincennes, Ind.   1.00
    a.   Yellow omitted   —

Gen. Casimir Pulaski — PC54

Bicentenary of the death of Gen. Casimir Pulaski (1748-1779), Polish nobleman who served in American Revolutionary Army.

1979, Oct. 11   **Litho.**
UX79 PC54 10c **multicolored**   .30 *1.50*
        First day cancel, Savannah. GA
          (210,000)   1.00

        Olympic Games Issue

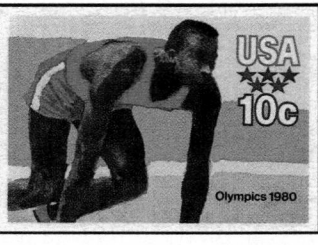

Sprinter PC55

22nd Olympic Games, Moscow, July 19-Aug. 3, 1980.

Designed by Robert M. Cunningham

1979, Sept. 17   **Litho.**
UX80 PC55 10c **multicolored**   .60 *1.50*
        First day cancel, Eugene,
          Ore.   1.00
    a.   Tagging omitted   200.00 *300.00*

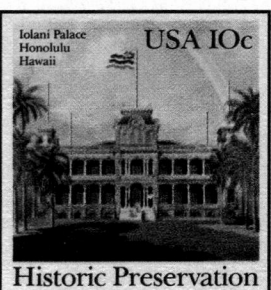

Iolani Palace, Honolulu — PC56

1979, Oct. 1   **Litho.**
UX81 PC56 10c **multicolored**   .30 *1.50*
        First day cancel, Honolulu, HI
          (242,804)   1.00
    a.   Tagging omitted   —

Women's Figure Skating PC57

13th Winter Olympic Games, Lake Placid, N.Y., Feb. 12-24.

Designed by Robert M. Cunningham

For International Use

1980, Jan. 15			**Litho.**
UX82 PC57 14c **multicolored**		.60	25.00
a.	Double impression of tagging bar, one at left	—	
	First day cancel, Atlanta, GA (160,977)		1.00

Salt Lake Temple, Salt Lake City — PC58

1980, Apr. 5			**Litho.**
UX83 PC58 10c **multicolored**		.25	1.50
	First day cancel, Salt Lake City, UT (325,260)		1.00
a.	Tagging omitted	300.00	

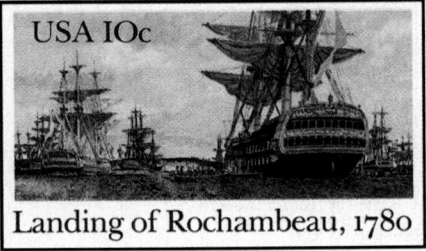

Rochambeau's Fleet — PC59

Count Jean-Baptiste de Rochambeau's landing at Newport, R.I. (American Revolution) bicentenary.

Designed by David Blossom

1980, July 11			**Litho.**
UX84 PC59 10c **multicolored**		.25	1.50
	First day cancel, Newport, R.I. (180,567)		1.00
a.	Front normal, black & yellow on back		
b.	Magenta & blue omitted	4,000.	

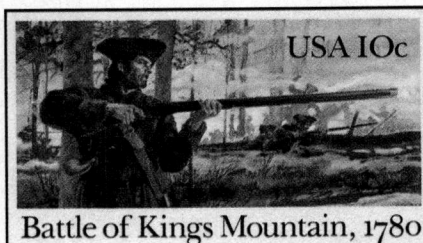

Whig Infantrymen — PC60

Bicentenary of the Battle of Kings Mountain (American Revolution).

Designed by David Blossom

1980, Oct. 7			**Litho.**
UX85 PC60 10c **multicolored**		.25	1.50
	First day cancel, Kings Mountain, NC (136,130)		1.00

Golden Hinde — PC61

300th anniv. of Sir Francis Drake's circumnavigation (1578-1580).

Designed by Charles J. Lundgren

For International Use

1980, Nov. 21			
UX86 PC61 19c **multicolored**		.75	35.00
	First day cancel, San Rafael, CA (290,547)		1.00

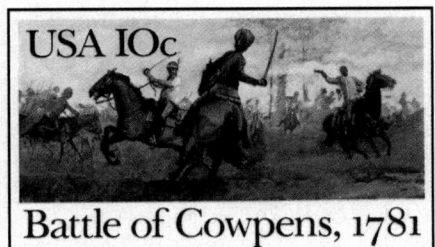

Cols. Washington and Tarleton — PC62

Bicentenary of the Battle of Cowpens (American Revolution).

Designed by David Blossom

1981, Jan. 17			
UX87 PC62 10c **multicolored**		.25	17.50
	First day cancel, Cowpens, SC (160,000)		1.00

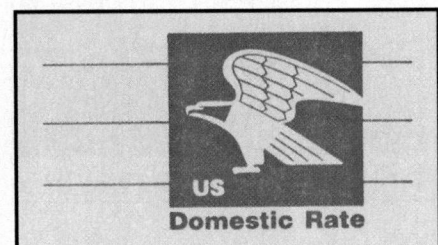

Eagle — PC63

1981, Mar. 15			
Precanceled with 3 printed violet lines			
UX88 PC63 (12c) **violet**		.35	.65
	First day cancel, Memphis, TN		1.00

See No. 1818, FDC section.

Isaiah Thomas — PC64

Designed by Chet Jezierski

1981, May 5	**Precanceled with 3 printed lines**		
UX89 PC64 12c **light blue**		.30	.75
	First day cancel, Worcester, MA (185,610)		1.00

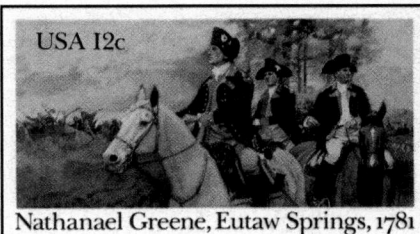

PC65

Bicentenary of the Battle at Eutaw Springs (American Revolution)

Designed by David Blossom

1981, Sept. 8			**Litho.**
UX90 PC65 12c **multicolored**		.30	22.50
	First day cancel, Eutaw Springs, SC (115,755)		1.00
a.	Red & yellow omitted	2,900.	

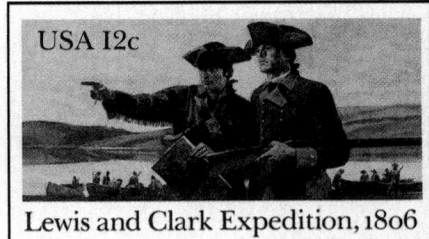

PC66

Designed by David Blossom

1981, Sept. 23			
UX91 PC66 12c **multicolored**		.30	30.00
	First day cancel, Saint Louis, MO		1.00

Robert Morris — PC67

1981

Precanceled with 3 printed lines			
UX92 PC67 (13c) **buff**, *Oct. 11*		.30	.60
	First day cancel, Memphis, TN		1.00

See No. 1946, FDC section.

Inscribed: U.S. Postage 13¢			
UX93 PC67 13c **buff**, *Nov. 10*		.30	.60
	First day cancel, Philadelphia, PA		1.00
a.	Buff omitted	500.00	

On No. UX93a, the copyright symbol and "1981" in buff is present at the lower left corner of the card.

General Francis Marion (1732?-1795) — PC68

Designed by David Blossom

1982, Apr. 3			**Litho.**
UX94 PC68 13c **multicolored**		.30	1.00
	First day cancel, Marion, SC (141,162)		1.00

La Salle claims Louisiana, 1682

Rene Robert Cavelier, Sieur de la Salle (1643-1687) — PC69

Designed by David Blossom

1982, Apr. 7   **Litho.**
UX95   PC69   13c **multicolored**   .30   *1.00*
     First day cancel, New Orleans,
     LA   1.00

PC70

Designed by Melbourne Brindle

1982, June 18   **Litho.**
UX96   PC70   13c **brown, red & cream,** *buff*   .30   *1.00*
     First day cancel, Philadel-
     phia, PA   1.00
   a.   Brown & cream omitted   *750.00*

PC71

Designed by Clint Orlemann

1982, Oct. 14   **Litho.**
UX97   PC71   13c **multicolored**   .30   *1.00*
     First day cancel, St. Louis, MO   1.00

Landing of Oglethorpe, Georgia, 1733

Gen. Oglethorpe Meeting Chief Tomo-Chi-Chi of the Yamacraw — PC72

Designed by David Blossom

1983, Feb. 12   **Litho.**
UX98   PC72   13c **multicolored**   .30   *1.00*
     First day cancel, Savannah,
     GA *(165,750)*   1.00

PC73

Designed by Walter Brooks

1983, Apr. 19   **Litho.**
UX99   PC73   13c **multicolored**   .30   *1.00*
     First day cancel, Washington,
     DC *(125,056)*   1.00

Olympics 84, Yachting — PC74

Designed by Bob Peak

1983, Aug. 5   **Litho.**
UX100   PC74   13c **multicolored**   .30   *1.00*
     First day cancel, Long
     Beach, CA *(132,232)*   1.00
   a.   Yellow & red omitted   *5,500.*   —
     Preprinted   *5,000.*

Ark and Dove, Maryland, 1634

The Ark and the Dove — PC75

Designed by David Blossom

1984, Mar. 25   **Litho.**
UX101   PC75   13c **multicolored**   .30   *1.00*
     First day cancel, St. Clement's
     Island, MD *(131,222)*   1.00

Runner Carrying Olympic Torch — PC76

Designed by Robert Peak

1984, Apr. 30   **Litho.**
UX102   PC76   13c **multicolored**   .30   *1.25*
     First day cancel, Los Ange-
     les, CA *(110,627)*   1.00
   a.   Black & yellow inverted   *5,250.*
   b.   Tagging omitted   *350.00*

Frederic Baraga, Michigan, 1835

Father Baraga and Indian Guide in Canoe — PC77

Designed by David Blossom

1984, June 29   **Litho.**
UX103   PC77   13c **multicolored**   .30   *1.00*
     First day cancel, Marquette, MI
     (100,156)   1.00

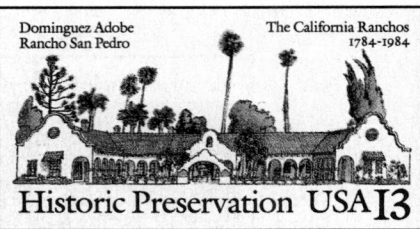

Historic Preservation USA 13

Dominguez Adobe at Rancho San Pedro — PC78

Designed by Earl Thollander

1984, Sept. 16   **Litho.**
UX104   PC78   13c **multicolored**   .30   *1.00*
     First day cancel, Compton,
     CA *(100,545)*   1.00
   a.   Black & blue omitted   *1,500.*
   b.   Tagging omitted   —

Charles Carroll (1737-1832) — PC79

Designed by Richard Sparks

1985
     Precanceled with 3 printed lines
UX105   PC79   (14c) **pale green,** *Feb. 1*   .45   *.65*
     First day cancel, New Carroll-
     ton, MD *(135,642)*   1.00
     Inscribed: USA 14
UX106   PC79   14c **pale green,** *Mar. 6*   .45   *.55*
     First day cancel, Annapolis,
     MD *(111,122)*   1.00

Clipper Flying Cloud — PC80

Designed by Richard Schlecht

     For International Use
1985, Feb. 27   **Litho.**
UX107   PC80   25c **multicolored**   .70   *22.50*
     First day cancel, Salem, MA
     (95,559)   1.25

     No. UX107 was sold by the USPS at CUP-PEX 87, Perth, Western Australia, with a cachet honoring CUP-PEX 87 and the America's Cup race. Value $2.

George Wythe (1726-1806) — PC81

Designed by Chet Jezierski from a portrait by John Fergusson.

1985, June 20
Precanceled with 3 printed lines
UX108 PC81 14c **bright apple green** .30 .75
    First day cancel, Williamsburg,
    VA *(133,334)* 1.00
  a.   Indicia missing —
On No. UX108a, the left precancel, "George Wythe" and the copyright symbol are normal.

Settling of Connecticut, 1636

Arrival of Thomas Hooker and Hartford Congregation — PC82

Settlement of Connecticut, 350th Anniv.

Designed by David Blossom

1986, Apr. 18 Litho.
UX109 PC82 14c **multicolored** .30 1.50
    First day cancel, Hartford, CT
    (76,875) 1.00

Stamp Collecting — PC83

Designed by Ray Ameijide

1986, May 23 Litho.
UX110 PC83 14c **multicolored** .30 1.25
    First day cancel, Chicago, IL
    (75,548) 1.00
No. UX110 was sold by the USPS at "najubria 86" with a show cachet. Value: unused, $6; used, $20.

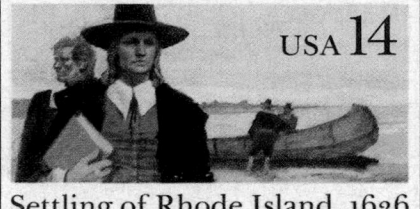

Settling of Rhode Island, 1636

Roger Williams (1603-1683), Clergyman, Landing at Providence — PC85

Settling of Rhode Island, 350th Anniv.

Designed by David Blossom

1986, June 26 Litho.
UX112 PC85 14c **multicolored** .30 1.50
    First day cancel, Providence, RI
    (54,559) 1.00

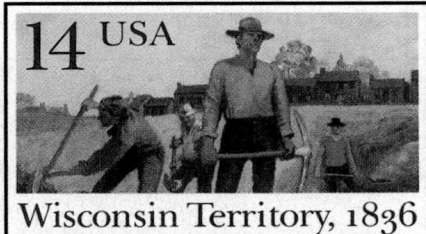

Wisconsin Territory, 1836

Miners, Shake Rag Street Housing — PC86

Wisconsin Territory Sesquicentennial.

Designed by David Blossom

1986, July 3 Litho.
UX113 PC86 14c **multicolored** .30 1.00
    First day cancel, Mineral
    Point, WI *(41,224)* 1.00
  a.   Tagging omitted 200.00

National Guard Heritage, 1636-1986

The First Muster, by Don Troiani — PC87

Designed by Bradbury Thompson

1986, Dec. 12 Litho.
UX114 PC87 14c **multicolored** .30 1.25
    First day cancel, Boston, MA
    (72,316) 1.00

PC88

The self-scouring steel plow invented by blacksmith John Deere in 1837 pictured at lower left.

Designed by William H. Bond

1987, May 22 Litho.
UX115 PC88 14c **multicolored** .30 1.25
    First day cancel, Moline, IL
    (160,009) 1.00

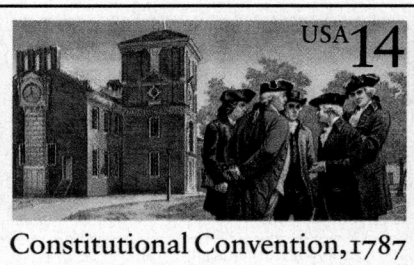

Constitutional Convention, 1787

Convening of the Constitutional Convention, 1787 — PC89

George Mason, Gouverneur Morris, James Madison, Alexander Hamilton and Charles C. Pinckney are listed in the lower left corner of the card.

Designed by David K. Stone

1987, May 25 Litho.
UX116 PC89 14c **multicolored** .30 .75
    First day cancel, Philadel-
    phia, PA *(138,207)* 1.00
  a.   Double black and blue, with first
    day cancel 650.00

Stars and Stripes — PC90

Designed by Steven Dohanos

1987, June 14 Litho.
UX117 PC90 14c **black, blue & red** .30 .60
    First day cancel, Baltimore,
    MD 1.00
  a.   Double impression of tagging bar 175.00
No. UX117 was sold by the USPS at Cologne, Germany, with a cachet for Philatelia'87. Value $2.

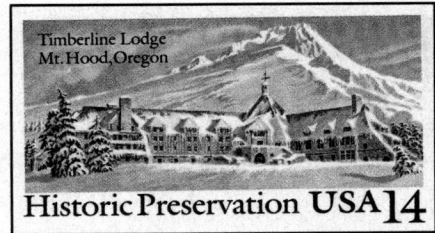

Take Pride in America — PC91

Designed by Lou Nolan

1987, Sept. 22 Litho.
UX118 PC91 14c **multicolored** .30 1.25
    First day cancel, Jackson, WY
    (47,281) 1.00

Timberline Lodge, 50th Anniversary — PC92

Designed by Walter DuBois Richards

1987, Sept. 28 Litho.
UX119 PC92 14c **multicolored** .30 1.25
    First day cancel, Timberline, OR
    (63,595) 1.25

Francis Vigo, Vincennes, 1779

Francis Vigo (1747-1836) — PC84

Designed by David Blossom

1986, May 24 Litho.
UX111 PC84 14c **multicolored** .30 1.25
    First day cancel, Vincennes, IN
    (100,141) 1.00

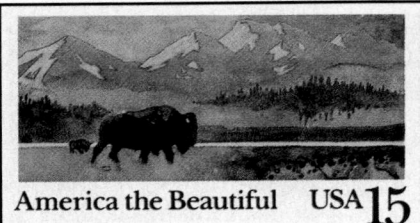

American Buffalo and Prairie — PC93

Designed by Bart Forbes

1988, Mar. 28		**Litho.**
UX120 PC93 15c **multicolored**	.30	.60
First day cancel, Buffalo, WY (52,075)		1.00

a.	Black omitted	1,750.
b.	Printed on both sides	475.00
c.	Front normal, blue & black on back	600.00
d.	Black & magenta omitted	1,500.
e.	Black, yellow, blue & tagging omitted	1,000.
f.	Black, blue & tagging omitted	1,250.
g.	Black, magenta, yellow & tagging omitted	1,250.
h.	Double black impression	—
i.	Triple black impression	—
j.	Double black and blue impression	—
k.	Double magenta & blue, and triple black impression	—

Tagged

Postal cards from No. UX57 onward are either tagged or printed with luminescent ink unless otherwise noted.

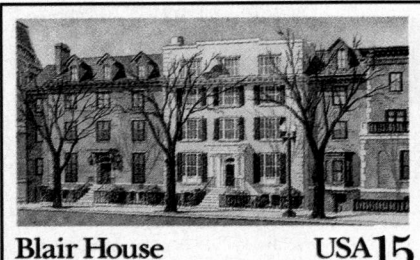

PC94

Designed by Pierre Mion

1988, May 4		**Litho.**
UX121 PC94 15c **multicolored**	.30	1.00
First day cancel, Washington, DC (52,188)		1.00

Yorkshire, Squarerigged Packet — PC95

Inscribed: Yorkshire, Black Ball Line, Packet Ship, circa 1850 at lower left.

Designed by Richard Schlect

For International Use

1988, June 29		**Litho.**
UX122 PC95 28c **multicolored**	.60	20.00
First day cancel, Mystic, CT (46,505)		1.00

a.	Black & blue omitted	850.00
b.	Black, blue, yellow & tagging omitted	1,250.
c.	Black, magenta & tagging omitted	1,000.
d.	Black, magenta, yellow & tagging omitted	1,000.
e.	Black & tagging omitted	2,000.

Harvesting Corn Fields — PC96

Iowa Territory Sesquicentennial.

Designed by Greg Hargreaves

1988, July 2		**Litho.**
UX123 PC96 15c **multicolored**	.30	1.00
First day cancel, Burlington, IA (45,565)		1.00

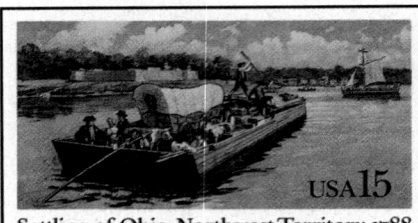

Flatboat Ferry Transporting Settlers Down the Ohio River — PC97

Bicentenary of the settlement of Ohio, the Northwest Territory. Design at lower left shows map of the eastern United States with Northwest Territory highlighted.

Designed by James M. Gurney and Susan Sanford

1988, July 15		**Litho.**
UX124 PC97 15c **multicolored**	.30	1.00
First day cancel, Marietta, OH (28,778)		1.00

a.	Black, blue, yellow & tagging omitted	1,150.
b.	Black, magenta & tagging omitted	750.00
c.	Blue, black & tagging omitted	900.00
d.	Black & tagging omitted	2,000.
e.	Black, magenta, yellow & tagging omitted	1,500.

PC98

Designed by Robert Reynolds

1988, Sept. 20		**Litho.**
UX125 PC98 15c **multicolored**	.30	1.00
First day cancel, San Simeon, CA (84,786)		1.00

a.	Black, magenta & tagging omitted	750.00
b.	Black, blue, yellow & tagging omitted	2,000.
c.	Black, magenta, yellow & tagging omitted	1,000.
d.	Black & tagging omitted	2,000.
e.	Black, blue & tagging omitted	1,000.

Pressman, New Yorker Reading Newspaper, 1787 — PC99

Designed by Roy Andersen

1988, Oct. 27		**Litho.**
UX126 PC99 15c **multicolored**	.30	1.00
First day cancel, New York, NY (37,661)		1.00

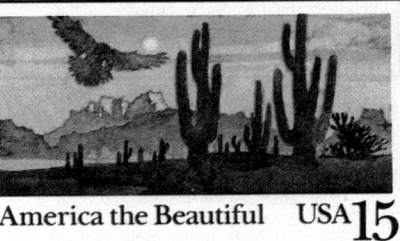

Red-tailed Hawk and Sonora Desert at Sunset — PC100

Designed by Bart Forbes

1989, Jan. 13		**Litho.**
UX127 PC100 15c **multicolored**	.30	1.00
First day cancel, Tucson, AZ (51,891)		1.00

Healy Hall, Georgetown University — PC101

Designed by John Morrell. Inscription at lower left: "Healy Hall / Georgetown / Washington, DC / HISTORIC PRESERVATION."

1989, Jan. 23		**Litho.**
UX128 PC101 15c **multicolored**	.30	1.00
First day cancel, Washington, DC (54,897)		1.00

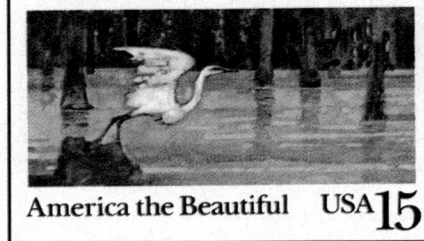

Great Blue Heron, Marsh — PC102

Designed by Bart Forbes

1989, Mar. 17		**Litho.**
UX129 PC102 15c **multicolored**	.30	1.00
First day cancel, Okefenokee, GA (58,208)		1.25

Settling of Oklahoma — PC103

Designed by Bradbury Thompson

1989, Apr. 22		**Litho.**
UX130 PC103 15c **multicolored**	.30	1.00
First day cancel, Guthrie, OK (68,689)		

Used values are for contemporaneous usage without additional postage applied. Used values for international-rate cards are for proper usage.

America the Beautiful USA **21**

Canada Geese and Mountains — PC104

Designed by Bart Forbes

1989, May 5   Litho.   For Use to Canada
UX131 PC104 21c **multicolored**   .50 *20.00*
First day cancel, Denver, CO
(59,303)   1.25

America the Beautiful USA **15**

Seashore — PC105

Designed by Bart Forbes

1989, June 17   Litho.
UX132 PC105 15c **multicolored**   .30 *1.00*
First day cancel, Cape Hatter-
as, NC *(67,073)*   1.25

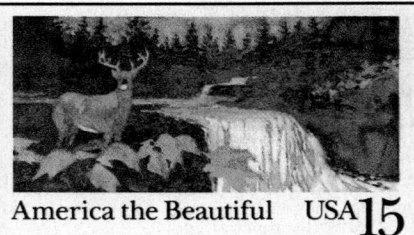

America the Beautiful USA **15**

PC106

Designed by Bart Forbes

1989, Aug. 26   Litho.
UX133 PC106 15c **multicolored**   .30 *1.00*
First day cancel, Cherokee,
NC *(67,878)*   1.25

Jane Addams' Hull House Community Center 1889, Chicago — PC107

Designed by Michael Hagel

1989, Sept. 16   Litho.
UX134 PC107 15c **multicolored**   .30 *1.00*
First day cancel, Chicago, IL
(53,773)   1.00

America the Beautiful USA **15**

Aerial View of Independence Hall, Philadelphia — PC108

Designed by Bart Forbes

1989, Sept. 25   Litho.
UX135 PC108 15c **multicolored**   .30 *1.00*
First day cancel, Philadelphia,
PA *(61,659)*   1.00
See No. UX139.

America the Beautiful USA **15**

Inner Harbor, Baltimore — PC109

Designed by Bart Forbes

1989, Oct. 7   Litho.
UX136 PC109 15c **multicolored**   .30 *1.00*
First day cancel, Baltimore,
MD *(58,746)*   1.00
See No. UX140.

America the Beautiful USA **15**

59th Street Bridge, New York City — PC110

Designed by Bart Forbes

1989, Nov. 8   Litho.
UX137 PC110 15c **multicolored**   .30 *1.00*
First day cancel, New York, NY
(48,044)   1.00
See No. UX141.

America the Beautiful USA **15**

West Face of the Capitol, Washington D.C. — PC111

Designed by Bart Forbes

1989, Nov. 26   Litho.
UX138 PC111 15c **multicolored**   .30 *1.00*
First day cancel, Washington,
DC   1.00
See No. UX142.

1989, Dec. 1   Litho.
Designed by Bart Forbes. Issued in sheets of 4 + 2 inscribed labels picturing 20th UPU Congress or World Stamp Expo '89 emblems, and rouletted 9½ on 2 or 3 sides.
UX139 PC108 15c **multicolored**   3.25 *4.00*
First day cancel, Washing-
ton, DC   1.00
UX140 PC109 15c **multicolored**   3.25 *4.00*
First day cancel, Washing-
ton, DC   1.00
UX141 PC110 15c **multicolored**   3.25 *4.00*
First day cancel, Washing-
ton, DC   1.00
UX142 PC111 15c **multicolored**   3.25 *4.00*
First day cancel, Washing-
ton, DC   1.00
  a. Sheet of 4, #UX139-UX142   14.00
        Nos. UX135-UX142 (8)   14.20 *20.00*

Unlike Nos. UX135-UX138, Nos. UX139-UX142 do not contain inscription and copyright symbol at lower left. Order on sheet is Nos. UX140, UX139, UX142, UX141.

Most copies of No. UX142a and UX139 are bent at the upper right corner.

15 USA

The White House — PC112

USA **15**

Jefferson Memorial — PC113

Designed by Pierre Mion. Space for message at left.

1989   Litho.
UX143 PC112 15c **multicolored,** *Nov. 30*   1.50 *2.50*
First day cancel, Washington,
DC   2.00
UX144 PC113 15c **multicolored,** *Dec. 2*   1.50 *2.00*
First day cancel, Washington,
DC   2.00

Nos. UX143-UX144 sold for 50c each. Illustrations of the buildings without denominations are shown on the back of the card.

USA **15**

Rittenhouse Paper Mill, Germantown, PA — PC114

Designed by Harry Devlin.

1990, Mar. 13   Litho.
UX145 PC114 15c **multicolored**   .30 *1.00*
First day cancel, New York, NY
(9,866)   1.00

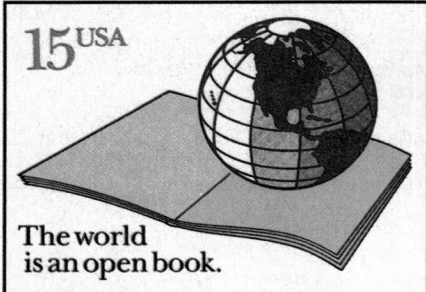

World Literacy Year — PC115

Designed by Joe Brockert.

1990, Mar. 22   **Litho.**
UX146 PC115 15c **multicolored**   .30 *.90*
     First day cancel, Washington,
     DC *(11,163)*   1.00

PC116

Designed by Bradbury Thompson. Inscription in upper left corner: "Fur Traders Descending the Missouri / George Caleb Bingham, 1845 / Metropolitan Museum of Art".

1990, May 4   **Litho.**
UX147 PC116 15c **multicolored**   1.50 *2.50*
     First day cancel, St. Louis, MO
     (13,632)   2.00

No. UX147 sold for 50c and shows more of the painting without the denomination on the back.

PC117

Designed by Frank Constantino. Inscription at lower left: "HISTORIC PRESERVATION SERIES / Isaac Royall House, 1700s / Medford, Massachusetts / National Historic Landmark".

1990, June 16   **Litho.**
UX148 PC117 15c **multicolored**   .30 *1.00*
     First day cancel, Medford, MA
     (21,708)   1.00

Quadrangle, Stanford University — PC119

Designed by Jim M'Guinness.

1990, Sept. 30   **Litho.**
UX150 PC119 15c **multicolored**   .30 *1.00*
     First day cancel, Stanford, CA
     (28,430)   1.00

Constitution Hall, Washington, DC — PC120

Designed by Pierre Mion. Inscription at upper left: "Washington: Constitution Hall (at right)/ Memorial Continental Hall (reverse side) / Centennial, Daughters of the American Revolution".

1990, Oct. 11   **Litho.**
UX151 PC120 15c **multicolored**   1.50 *2.00*
     First day cancel, Washington,
     DC *(33,254)*   2.00

No. UX151 sold for 50c.

Chicago Orchestra Hall — PC121

Designed by Michael Hagel. Inscription at lower left: "Chicago: Orchestra Hall / HISTORIC PRESERVATION / Chicago Symphony Orchestra / Centennial, 1891-1991".

1990, Oct. 19   **Litho.**
UX152 PC121 15c **multicolored**   .30 *1.00*
     First day cancel, Chicago, IL
     (28,546)   1.00

PC122

Designed by Richard Sheaff.

1991, Jan. 24   **Litho.**
UX153 PC122 19c **rose, ultramarine & black**   .40 *.75*
     First day cancel, Washington,
     DC *(26,690)*   1.00

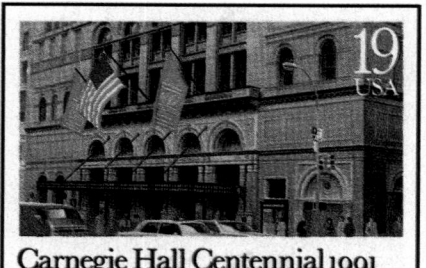

PC123

Designed by Howard Koslow.

1991, Apr. 1   **Litho.**
UX154 PC123 19c **multicolored**   .40 *1.00*
     First day cancel, New York, NY
     (27,063)   1.00

Old Red, University of Texas Medical Branch, Galveston, Cent. — PC124

Designed by Don Adair.

1991, June 14   **Litho.**
UX155 PC124 19c **multicolored**   .40 *1.00*
     First day cancel, Galveston,
     TX *(24,308)*   1.00

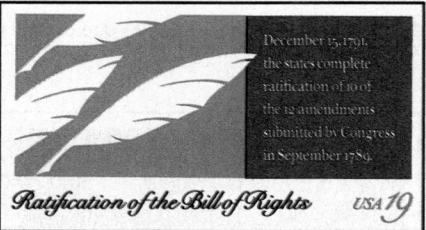

Ratification of the Bill of Rights, Bicent. — PC125

Designed by Mark Zaref.

1991, Sept. 25   **Litho.**
UX156 PC125 19c **red, blue & black**   .40 *.90*
     First day cancel, Richmond,
     VA *(27,457)*   1.00

Main Building, University of Notre Dame PC126

Designed by Frank Costantino. Inscription at lower left: Notre Dame / Sesquicentennial / 1842-1992.

1991, Oct. 15   **Litho.**
UX157 PC126 19c **multicolored**   .40 *1.00*
     First day cancel, Notre
     Dame, IN *(34,325)*   1.00

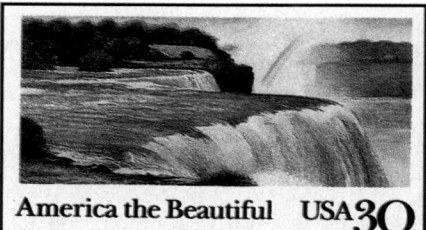

Niagara Falls — PC127

Designed by Wendell Minor.

1991, Aug. 21   **Litho.**
For Use to Canada & Mexico
UX158 PC127 30c **multicolored**   .75 *13.00*
     First day cover, Niagara
     Falls, NY *(29,762)*   1.25

Tagged
Postal cards from No. UX57 onward are either tagged or printed with luminescent ink unless otherwise noted.

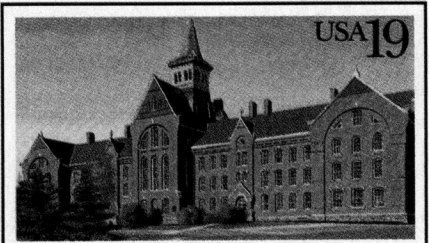

The Old Mill — PC128

Designed by Harry Devlin. Inscription at lower left: The Old Mill / University of Vermont / Bicentennial.

1991, Oct. 29   **Litho.**
UX159 PC128 19c **multicolored**   .40 *1.00*
    First day cancel, Burlington,
    VT *(23,965)*   1.00

Wadsworth Atheneum, Hartford, CT — PC129

Designed by Frank Costantino. Inscription at lower left: Wadsworth Atheneum / Hartford, Connecticut / 150th Anniversary / 1842-1992.

1992, Jan. 16   **Litho.**
UX160 PC129 19c **multicolored**   .40 *1.00*
    First day cancel, Hartford, CT
    (41,499)   1.00

Cobb Hall, University of Chicago — PC130

Designed by Michael P. Hagel. Inscription at lower left: Cobb Hall / The University of Chicago / Centennial Year, 1991-1992.

1992, Jan. 23   **Litho.**
UX161 PC130 19c **multicolored**   .40 *1.00*
    First day cancel, Chicago, IL
    (27,150)   1.00

Waller Hall, Willamette University — PC131

Designed by Bradbury Thompson. Inscription at lower left: Waller Hall / Salem, Oregon / Willamette University / Sesquicentennial / 1842-1992.

1992, Feb. 1   **Litho.**
UX162 PC131 19c **multicolored**   .40 *1.00*
    First day cancel, Salem, OR
    (28,463)   1.00

PC132

Designed by Dennis Simon. Space for message at left. Inscription at upper left: "At right: The Reliance, USA 1903 / Reverse: The Ranger, USA 1937."

1992, May 6   **Litho.**
UX163 PC132 19c **multicolored**   1.75 *3.00*
    First day cancel, San Diego,
    CA *(19,944)*   2.00

No. UX163 sold for 50 cents.

PC133

Designed by Ken Hodges.

1992, May 9   **Litho.**
UX164 PC133 19c **multicolored**   .40 *1.00*
    First day cancel, Stevenson,
    WA *(32,344)*   1.00

Ellis Island Immigration Museum — PC134

Designed by Howard Koslow. Inscription at lower left: "Ellis Island / Centennial 1992."

1992, May 11   **Litho.**
UX165 PC134 19c **multicolored**   .40 *1.00*
    First day cancel, Ellis Island,
    NY *(38,482)*   1.00

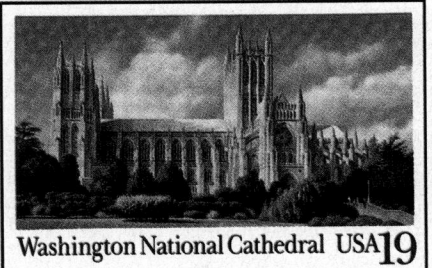

PC135

Designed by Howard Koslow.

1993, Jan. 6   **Litho.**
UX166 PC135 19c **multicolored**   .40 *1.00*
    First day cancel, Washington,
    DC *(8,315)*   1.00

PC136

Designed by Pierre Mion.

1993, Feb. 8   **Litho.**
UX167 PC136 19c **multicolored**   .40 *1.00*
    First day cancel, Williamsburg,
    VA *(9,758)*   1.00

Opening of Holocaust Memorial Museum — PC137

Designed by Tom Engeman. Space for message at left. Inscription at upper left: "Washington, DC: / United States / Holocaust Memorial Museum."

1993, Mar. 23   **Litho.**
UX168 PC137 19c **multicolored**   1.75 *3.00*
    First day cancel, Washington,
    DC *(8,234)*   2.00

No. UX168 sold for 50c, and shows aerial view of museum on the back.

PC138

Designed by Michael Hagel.

1993, June 13   **Litho.**
UX169 PC138 19c **multicolored**   .40 *.90*
    First day cancel, Fort Recovery, OH *(8,254)*   1.00

PC139

Designed by Robert Timberlake.

1993, Sept. 14   **Litho.**
UX170 PC139 19c **multicolored**   .40 *1.00*
    First day cancel, Chapel Hill,
    NC *(7,796)*   1.00

PC140

Designed by Frank Constantino.

1993, Sept. 17 Litho.
UX171 PC140 19c **multicolored** .40 *.90*
First day cancel, Worcester,
MA *(4,680)* 1.00

PC141

Designed by Michael Hagel.

1993, Oct. 9 Litho.
UX172 PC141 19c **multicolored** .40 *.90*
First day cancel, Jacksonville,
IL *(5,269)* 1.00

PC142

Designed by Harry Devlin.

1993, Oct. 14 Litho.
UX173 PC142 19c **multicolored** .40 *.90*
First day cancel, Brunswick,
ME *(33,750 est.)* 1.00

PC143

Designed by Michael Hagel.

1994, Feb. 12 Litho.
UX174 PC143 19c **multicolored** .40 *.90*
First day cancel, Springfield, IL
(26,164) 1.00

PC144

Designed by Michael Hagel.

1994, Mar. 11 Litho.
UX175 PC144 19c **multicolored** .40 *.90*
First day cancel, Springfield,
OH *(20,230)* 1.00

PC145

Designed by William Matthews.

1994, Aug. 11 Litho.
UX176 PC145 19c **multicolored** .40 *1.00*
First day cancel, Chinle, AZ
(19,826) 1.00

St. Louis Union Station — PC146

Designed by Harry Devlin.

1994, Sept. 3 Litho.
UX177 PC146 19c **multicolored** .40 *1.00*
First day cancel, St. Louis, MO
(38,881) 1.00

Legends of the West Type
Designed by Mark Hess.

1994, Oct. 18 Litho.
UX178 A2197 19c Home on the Range 1.10 *3.00*
UX179 A2197 19c Buffalo Bill 1.10 *3.00*
UX180 A2197 19c Jim Bridger 1.10 *3.00*
UX181 A2197 19c Annie Oakley 1.10 *3.00*
UX182 A2197 19c Native American Culture 1.10 *3.00*
UX183 A2197 19c Chief Joseph 1.10 *3.00*
UX184 A2197 19c Bill Pickett (revised) 1.10 *3.00*
UX185 A2197 19c Bat Masterson 1.10 *3.00*
UX186 A2197 19c John Fremont 1.10 *3.00*
UX187 A2197 19c Wyatt Earp 1.10 *3.00*
UX188 A2197 19c Nellie Cashman 1.10 *3.00*
UX189 A2197 19c Charles Goodnight 1.10 *3.00*
UX190 A2197 19c Geronimo 1.10 *3.00*
UX191 A2197 19c Kit Carson 1.10 *3.00*
UX192 A2197 19c Wild Bill Hickok 1.10 *3.00*
UX193 A2197 19c Western Wildlife 1.10 *3.00*
UX194 A2197 19c Jim Beckwourth 1.10 *3.00*
UX195 A2197 19c Bill Tilghman 1.10 *3.00*
UX196 A2197 19c Sacagawea 1.10 *3.00*
UX197 A2197 19c Overland Mail 1.10 *3.00*
Nos. UX178-UX197 (20) 22.00
First day cancel, #UX178-UX197, any
card, Tucson, AZ, Lawton, OK or
Laramie, WY *(10,000 USPS est.)* 1.50
Nos. UX178-UX197 sold in packages of 20 different for $7.95.

Red Barn — PC147

Designed by Wendell Minor.

1995, Jan. 3 Litho.
UX198 PC147 20c **multicolored** .40 *.60*
First day cancel, Williams-
burg, PA 1.00

First day cancellation was applied to 54,102 of Nos. U632, UX198.

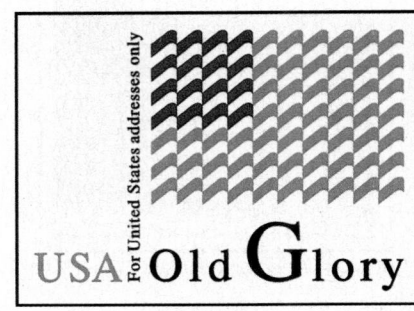

PC148

1995 Litho.
UX199 PC148 (20c) **black, blue & red** 3.25 *2.50*

No. UX199 was only available through the Philatelic Fulfillment Center after its announcement 1/12/95. Cards submitted for first day cancels received a 12/13/94 cancel, even though they were not available on that date.

Civil War Types
Designed by Mark Hess.

1995, June 29 Litho.
UX200 A2289 20c Monitor & Virginia 1.75 *3.00*
UX201 A2289 20c Robert E. Lee 1.75 *3.00*
UX202 A2289 20c Clara Barton 1.75 *3.00*
UX203 A2289 20c Ulysses S. Grant 1.75 *3.00*
UX204 A2289 20c Battle of Shiloh 1.75 *3.00*
UX205 A2289 20c Jefferson Davis 1.75 *3.00*
UX206 A2289 20c David Farragut 1.75 *3.00*
UX207 A2289 20c Frederick Douglass 1.75 *3.00*
UX208 A2289 20c Raphael Semmes 1.75 *3.00*
UX209 A2289 20c Abraham Lincoln 1.75 *3.00*
UX210 A2289 20c Harriet Tubman 1.75 *3.00*
UX211 A2289 20c Stand Watie 1.75 *3.00*
UX212 A2289 20c Joseph E. Johnston 1.75 *3.00*
UX213 A2289 20c Winfield Hancock 1.75 *3.00*
UX214 A2289 20c Mary Chesnut 1.75 *3.00*
UX215 A2289 20c Battle of Chancellorsville 1.75 *3.00*
UX216 A2289 20c William T. Sherman 1.75 *3.00*
UX217 A2289 20c Phoebe Pember 1.75 *3.00*
UX218 A2289 20c Stonewall Jackson 1.75 *3.00*
UX219 A2289 20c Battle of Gettysburg 1.75 *3.00*
Nos. UX200-UX219 (20) 35.00
First day cancel, any card,
Gettysburg, PA 1.50
First day cancel, any card,
any other city 1.50

Nos. UX200-UX219 sold in packages of 20 different for $7.95.

PC148a

For International Use

1995, Aug. 24 Litho.
UX219A PC148a 50c **multicolored** 1.25 *9.00*
First day cancel, St. Louis,
MO *(6,008)* 1.25

PC149

Designed by Richard Sheaff.

1995, Sept. 3   **Litho.**
UX220 PC149 20c **multicolored**   .40   .75
          First day cancel, Hunt Valley,
             MD *(5,281)*   1.00

Comic Strip Types
Designed by Carl Herrman.

1995, Oct. 1   **Litho.**
UX221 A2313 20c The Yellow Kid   2.50 3.00
UX222 A2313 20c Katzenjammer Kids   2.50 3.00
UX223 A2313 20c Little Nemo in Slumberland 2.50 3.00
UX224 A2313 20c Bringing Up Father   2.50 3.00
UX225 A2313 20c Krazy Kat   2.50 3.00
UX226 A2313 20c Rube Goldberg's Inventions 2.50 3.00
UX227 A2313 20c Toonerville Folks   2.50 3.00
UX228 A2313 20c Gasoline Alley   2.50 3.00
UX229 A2313 20c Barney Google   2.50 3.00
UX230 A2313 20c Little Orphan Annie   2.50 3.00
UX231 A2313 20c Popeye   2.50 3.00
UX232 A2313 20c Blondie   2.50 3.00
UX233 A2313 20c Dick Tracy   2.50 3.00
UX234 A2313 20c Alley Oop   2.50 3.00
UX235 A2313 20c Nancy   2.50 3.00
UX236 A2313 20c Flash Gordon   2.50 3.00
UX237 A2313 20c Li'l Abner   2.50 3.00
UX238 A2313 20c Terry and the Pirates   2.50 3.00
UX239 A2313 20c Prince Valiant   2.50 3.00
UX240 A2313 20c Brenda Starr Reporter   2.50 3.00
          Nos. UX221-UX240 (20)   50.00
          First day cancel, any card,
             Boca Raton, FL   1.50
Nos. UX221-UX240 sold in packages of 20 different for $7.95.

Winter Scene — PC150

1996, Feb. 23   **Litho.**
UX241 PC150 20c **multicolored**   .40   .75
          First day cancel, Watertown,
             NY *(11,764)*   1.00

Summer Olympics Type
Designed by Richard Waldrep.

1996, May 2   **Litho.**
                  Size: 150x108mm
UX242 A2368 20c Men's cycling   2.75 3.00
UX243 A2368 20c Women's diving   2.75 3.00
UX244 A2368 20c Women's running   2.75 3.00
UX245 A2368 20c Men's canoeing   2.75 3.00
   a.   Tagging omitted
UX246 A2368 20c Decathlon (javelin)   2.75 3.00
   a.   Inverted impression of entire address
                side, men's cycling picture on re-
                verse   350.00
UX247 A2368 20c Women's soccer   2.75 3.00
UX248 A2368 20c Men's shot put   2.75 3.00
UX249 A2368 20c Women's sailboarding   2.75 3.00
UX250 A2368 20c Women's gymnastics   2.75 3.00
UX251 A2368 20c Freestyle wrestling   2.75 3.00
UX252 A2368 20c Women's softball   2.75 3.00
UX253 A2368 20c Women's swimming   2.75 3.00
UX254 A2368 20c Men's sprints   2.75 3.00
UX255 A2368 20c Men's rowing   2.75 3.00
UX256 A2368 20c Beach volleyball   2.75 3.00
UX257 A2368 20c Men's basketball   2.75 3.00
UX258 A2368 20c Equestrian   2.75 3.00
UX259 A2368 20c Men's gymnastics   2.75 3.00
UX260 A2368 20c Men's swimming   2.75 3.00

UX261 A2368 20c Men's hurdles   2.75 3.00
   a.   Booklet of 20 postal cards, #UX242-
                UX261   55.00
          First day cancel, any card,
             Washington, DC   1.50
First day cancels of Nos. UX242-UX261 were available as
sets from the US Postal Service. Unused sets of Nos. UX242-
UX261 were not available from the US Philatelic Fullfillment
Center for several months after the "official" first day. No.
UX261a sold for $12.95.

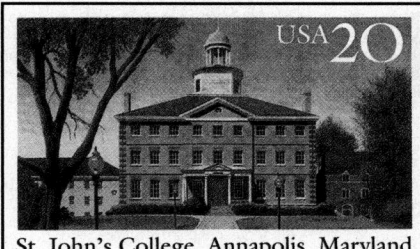

PC151

Designed by Harry Devlin.

1996, June 1   **Litho.**
UX262 PC151 20c **multicolored**   .50   .75
          First day cancel, Annapolis,
             MD *(8,793)*   1.00

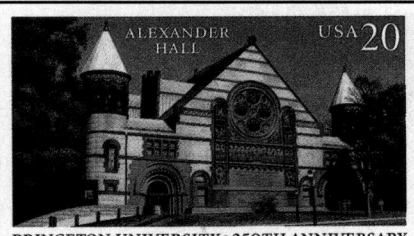

PC152

Designed by Howard Koslow.

1996, Sept. 20   **Litho.**
UX263 PC152 20c **multicolored**   .50   .75
          First day cancel, Princeton, NJ
             (11,621)   1.00

Endangered Species Type
Designed by James Balog.

1996, Oct. 2   **Litho.**
UX264 A2403 20c Florida panther   3.50 2.50
UX265 A2403 20c Black-footed ferret   3.50 2.50
UX266 A2403 20c American crocodile   3.50 2.50
UX267 A2403 20c Piping plover   3.50 2.50
UX268 A2403 20c Gila trout   3.50 2.50
UX269 A2403 20c Florida manatee   3.50 2.50
UX270 A2403 20c Schaus swallowtail butterfly 3.50 2.50
UX271 A2403 20c Woodland caribou   3.50 2.50
UX272 A2403 20c Thick-billed parrot   3.50 2.50
UX273 A2403 20c San Francisco garter snake 3.50 2.50
UX274 A2403 20c Ocelot   3.50 2.50
UX275 A2403 20c Wyoming toad   3.50 2.50
UX276 A2403 20c California condor   3.50 2.50
UX277 A2403 20c Hawaiian monk seal   3.50 2.50
UX278 A2403 20c Brown pelican   3.50 2.50
   a.   Booklet of 15 cards, #UX264-UX278 55.00
          First day cancel, #UX264-UX278,
             any card, San Diego, CA *(5,000)*   1.75
Nos. UX264-UX278 were issued bound three-to-a-page in a
souvenir booklet that was sold for $11.95.

Love (Swans) Type
Designed by Supon Design.

1997, Feb. 4   **Litho.**
UX279 A2415 20c multicolored   .80 2.50
Stamp Designs Depicted on Reverse of Card
             Scott 2814   2.50 2.50
             Scott 2815   2.50 2.50
             Scott 3123   2.50 2.50
             Scott 3124   2.50 2.50
             Sheet of 4, #2814-2815, 3123-3124 10.00
             Scott 2202   7.50 2.50
             Scott 2248   7.50 2.50
             Scott 2440   7.50 2.50
             Scott 2813   7.50 2.50
             Sheet of 4, #2202, 2248, 2440, 2813 30.00
No. UX279 was sold in sets of 3 sheets of 4 picture postal
cards with 8 different designs for $6.95 (two sheets of #2814-
2815, 3123-3124 and one sheet of #2202, 2248, 2440, 2813).
The cards are separated by microperfs. The picture side of
each card depicted a previously released Love stamp design
without the inscriptions and value.

First day cancels were not available on Feb. 4. It was
announced after Feb. 4 that collectors could purchase the cards
and send them to the U.S.P.S. for First Day cancels.

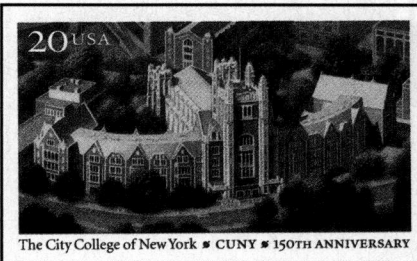

PC153

Designed by Howard Koslow.

1997, May 7   **Litho.**
UX280 PC153 20c **multicolored**   .50   .75
          First day cancel, New York,
             NY *(9,576)*   1.00

Bugs Bunny Type
Designed by Warner Bros.

1997, May 22   **Litho.**
UX281 A2425 20c **multicolored**   1.25 2.00
          First day cancel, Burbank, CA   1.75
   a.   Booklet of 10 cards   12.50
          No. UX281a sold for $5.95.
First day cancellations applied to 378,142 of Nos. UX281 and
3138.

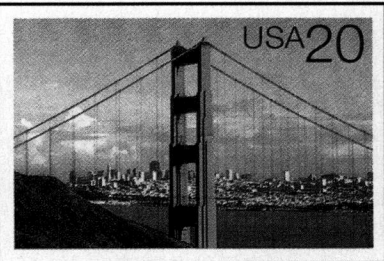

Golden Gate in Daylight — PC154

Golden Gate at Sunset — PC155

Designed by Carol Simowitz.

1997, June 2   **Litho.**
UX282 PC154 20c **multicolored,** *June 2*   .40   .80
          First day cancel, San Francis-
             co, CA   1.25
            For International Use
UX283 PC155 50c **multicolored,** *June 3*   1.10 5.00
          First day cancel, San Francis-
             co, CA   2.00
First day cancellation was applied to 21,189 of Nos. UX282-
UX283.

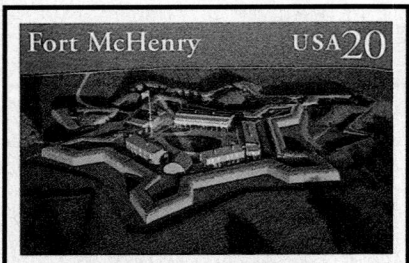

PC156

Designed by Richard Sheaff.

1997, Sept. 7   Litho.
UX284   PC156   20c   **multicolored**   .40   *.75*
     First day cancel, Baltimore,
     MD *(9,611)*   1.00

Similar to Classic Movie Monsters with 20c Denomination
Designed by Derry Noyes.

1997, Sept. 30   Litho.
UX285   A2451   20c   Phantom of the Opera   1.60   *2.00*
UX286   A2452   20c   Dracula   1.60   *2.00*
UX287   A2453   20c   Frankenstein's Monster   1.60   *2.00*
UX288   A2454   20c   The Mummy   1.60   *2.00*
UX289   A2455   20c   The Wolf Man   1.60   *2.00*
   a.   Booklet of 20 cards, 4 each #UX285-
     UX289   32.00
     First day cancel, #UX285-
     UX289, any card, Universal
     City, CA   1.75

Nos. UX285-UX289 were issued bound in a booklet of 20 cards containing four of each card. Booklet was sold in package for $5.95.

PC157

Designed by Howard Paine.

1998, Apr. 20   Litho.
UX290   PC157   20c   **multicolored**   .50   *.75*
     First day cancel, University,
     MS *(22,276)*   1.00

Similar to Sylvester & Tweety with 20c Denomination
Designed by Brenda Guttman.

1998, Apr. 27   Litho.
UX291   A2487   20c   **multicolored**   1.40   *2.00*
     First day cancel, New York,
     NY   1.75
   a.   Booklet of 10 cards   14.00

No. UX291a sold for $5.95.
First day cancellations applied to 231,839 of Nos. UX291, 3204 and 3205.

PC158

Designed by Phil Jordan.

1998, May 1   Litho.
UX292   PC158   20c   **multicolored**   .50   *.75*
     First day cancel, Philadelphia,
     PA *(13,853)*   1.00

Similar to Tropical Birds with 20c Denomination and No Inscription
Designed by Phil Jordan.

1998, July 29   Litho.
UX293   A2503   20c   Antillean euphonia   1.00   *1.75*
UX294   A2504   20c   Green-throated carib   1.00   *1.75*
UX295   A2505   20c   Crested honeycreeper   1.00   *1.75*
UX296   A2506   20c   Cardinal honeyeater   1.00   *1.75*
   a.   Booklet of 20 cards, 5 ea #UX293-
     UX296   20.00
     First day cancel, #UX293-
     UX296, any card, Ponce PR   1.75

Nos. UX293-UX296 were issued bound in a booklet of 20 cards containing five of each card. Illustration of the stamp without denomination is shown on the back of each card. Booklet was sold in packages for $6.95.

American Ballet Type
Designed by Derry Noyes.

1998, Sept. 16   Litho.
UX297   A2517   20c   **multicolored**   1.25   *1.40*
   a.   Booklet of 10 cards   12.50
     First day cancel, New York,
     NY   1.75

No. UX297a was sold for $5.95.

PC159

Designed by Richard Sheaff.

1998, Oct. 3   Litho.
UX298   PC159   20c   **multicolored**   .50   *.75*
     First day cancel, Boston, MA
     (14,812)   1.00

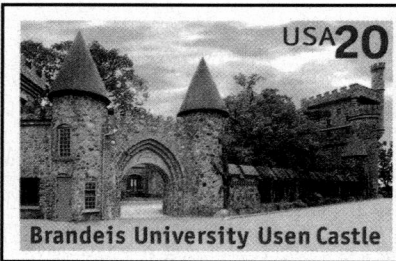

PC160

Designed by Richard Sheaff.

1998, Oct. 17   Litho.
UX299   PC160   20c   **multicolored**   .50   *.75*
     First day cancel, Waltham, MA
     (14,137)   1.00

Love Type
Designed by John Grossman, Holly Sudduth

1999, Jan. 28   Litho.
UX300   A2537   20c   **multicolored**   1.25   *1.50*
     First day cancel, Loveland, CO   1.00

No. UX300 was sold in packs containing 5 sheets of 4 cards for $6.95.

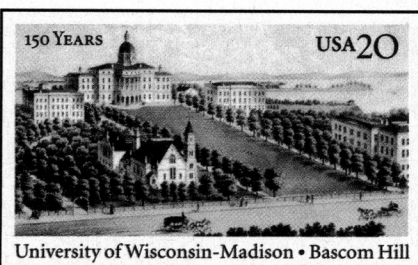

PC161

Designed by Carl Herrman.

1999, Feb. 5   Litho.
UX301   PC161   20c   **multicolored**   .50   *.75*
     First day cancel, Madison, WI
     (12,582)   1.00

PC162

Designed by Derry Noyes.

1999, Feb. 11   Litho.
UX302   PC162   20c   **multicolored**   .50   *.75*
     First day cancel, Lexington, VA
     (17,556)   1.00

PC163

Designed by Richard Sheaff.

1999, Mar. 11   Litho.
UX303   PC163   20c   **red & black**   .50   *.75*
     First day cancel, Newport, RI
     (13,649)   1.00

Daffy Duck Type
Designed by Ed Wieczyk.

1999, Apr. 16   Litho.
UX304   A2554   20c   **multicolored**   1.40   1.40
     First day cancel, Los Angeles,
     CA   1.40
   a.   Booklet of 10 cards   14.00

No. UX304a sold for $6.95.
First day cancellation was applied to 177,988 of UX304, 3306 and 3307.

PC164

Designed by Richard Sheaff.

1999, May 14   Litho.
UX305   PC164   20c   **multicolored**   .50   *.75*
     First day cancel, Mount
     Vernon, VA *(14,642)*   1.00

Block Island Lighthouse — PC165

Designed by Derry Noyes.

					Litho.
1999, July 24					**Litho.**
UX306	PC165	20c	multicolored	.40	.75
		First day cancel, Block Island, RI (12,694)			1.25

Famous Trains Type

Designed by Howard Paine.

					Litho.
1999, Aug. 26					**Litho.**
UX307	A2583	20c	Super Chief	1.50	1.50
UX308	A2582	20c	Hiawatha	1.50	1.50
UX309	A2579	20c	Daylight	1.50	1.50
UX310	A2580	20c	Congressional	1.50	1.50
UX311	A2581	20c	20th Century Limited	1.50	1.50
a.		Booklet of 20 cards, 4 ea #UX307-UX311			25.00
		First day cancel, #UX307-UX311, any card, Cleveland, OH			1.75
		First day cancel, #UX307-UX311, any card, any other city			1.75

Nos. UX307-UX311 were issued bound in a booklet of 20 cards containing four of each card. Booklet sold for $6.95.

PC166

Designed by Ethel Kessler.

					Litho.
2000, Feb. 28					**Litho.**
UX312	PC166	20c	multicolored	.40	.75
		First day cancel, Salt Lake City, UT (14,230)			1.00

PC167

Designed by Richard Sheaff.

					Litho.
2000, Mar. 18					**Litho.**
UX313	PC167	20c	multicolored	.40	.75
		First day cancel, Nashville, TN (12,690)			1.00

Road Runner & Wile E. Coyote Type

Designed by Ed Wleczyk, Warner Bros.

					Litho.
2000, Apr. 26					**Litho.**
UX314	A2622	20c	multicolored	1.40	1.40
		First day cancel, Phoenix, AZ			1.40
a.		Booklet of 10 cards			14.00

No. UX314a sold for $6.95.
First day cancellation was applied to 154,903 of UX314 and 3391.

Adoption Type

Designed by Greg Berger.

					Litho.
2000, May 10					**Litho.**
UX315	A2628	20c	multicolored	1.40	1.50
		First day cancel, Beverly Hills, CA			1.40
a.		Booklet of 10 cards			14.00

No. UX315a sold for $6.95. The design, without denominations, is shown on the back of the card.
First day cancellation was applied to 137,903 of UX315 and 3398.

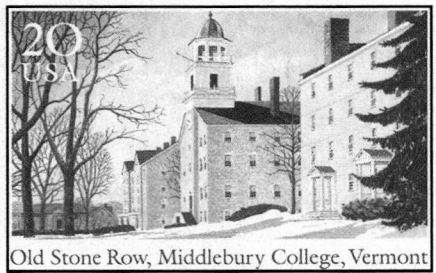

PC168

Designed by Howard Paine.

					Litho.
2000, May 19					**Litho.**
UX316	PC168	20c	multicolored	.40	.50
		First day cancel, Middlebury, VT (13,586)			1.00

Stars and Stripes Type

Designed by Richard Sheaff.

					Litho.
2000, June 14					**Litho.**
UX317	A2633	20c	Sons of Liberty Flag, 1775	2.00	2.00
UX318	A2633	20c	New England Flag, 1775	2.00	2.00
UX319	A2633	20c	Forster Flag, 1775	2.00	2.00
UX320	A2633	20c	Continental Colors, 1776	2.00	2.00
a.		Sheet of 4 cards, #UX317-UX320			8.00
UX321	A2633	20c	Francis Hopkinson Flag, 1777	2.00	2.00
UX322	A2633	20c	Brandywine Flag, 1777	2.00	2.00
UX323	A2633	20c	John Paul Jones Flag, 1779	2.00	2.00
UX324	A2633	20c	Pierre L'Enfant Flag, 1783	2.00	2.00
a.		Sheet of 4 cards, #UX321-UX324			8.00
UX325	A2633	20c	Indian Peace Flag, 1803	2.00	2.00
UX326	A2633	20c	Easton Flag, 1814	2.00	2.00
UX327	A2633	20c	Star-Spangled Banner, 1814	2.00	2.00
UX328	A2633	20c	Bennington Flag, c. 1820	2.00	2.00
a.		Sheet of 4 cards, #UX325-UX328			8.00
UX329	A2633	20c	Great Star Flag, 1837	2.00	2.00
UX330	A2633	20c	29-Star Flag, 1847	2.00	2.00
UX331	A2633	20c	Fort Sumter Flag, 1861	2.00	2.00
UX332	A2633	20c	Centennial Flag, 1876	2.00	2.00
a.		Sheet of 4 cards, #UX329-UX332			8.00
UX333	A2633	20c	38-Star Flag, 1877	2.00	2.00
UX334	A2633	20c	Peace Flag, 1891	2.00	2.00
UX335	A2633	20c	48-Star Flag, 1912	2.00	2.00
UX336	A2633	20c	50-Star Flag, 1960	2.00	2.00
a.		Sheet of 4 cards, #UX333-UX336			8.00
		First day cancel, any card, Baltimore, MD			.90
		Nos. UX317-UX336 (20)		40.00	40.00

Nos. UX320a, UX324a, UX328a, UX332a and UX336a were sold together in a package for $8.95. Microperforations are between individual cards on each sheet. Illustrations of the flags, without denominations, are shown on the back of the cards.

Legends of Baseball Type

Designed by Phil Jordan.

					Litho.
2000, July 6					**Litho.**
UX337	A2638	20c	Jackie Robinson	1.50	1.50
UX338	A2638	20c	Eddie Collins	1.50	1.50
UX339	A2638	20c	Christy Mathewson	1.50	1.50
UX340	A2638	20c	Ty Cobb	1.50	1.50
UX341	A2638	20c	George Sisler	1.50	1.50
UX342	A2638	20c	Rogers Hornsby	1.50	1.50
UX343	A2638	20c	Mickey Cochrane	1.50	1.50
UX344	A2638	20c	Babe Ruth	1.50	1.50
UX345	A2638	20c	Walter Johnson	1.50	1.50
UX346	A2638	20c	Roberto Clemente	1.50	1.50
UX347	A2638	20c	Lefty Grove	1.50	1.50
UX348	A2638	20c	Tris Speaker	1.50	1.50
UX349	A2638	20c	Cy Young	1.50	1.50
UX350	A2638	20c	Jimmie Foxx	1.50	1.50
UX351	A2638	20c	Pie Traynor	1.50	1.50
UX352	A2638	20c	Satchel Paige	1.50	1.50
UX353	A2638	20c	Honus Wagner	1.50	1.50
UX354	A2638	20c	Josh Gibson	1.50	1.50
UX355	A2638	20c	Dizzy Dean	1.50	1.50
UX356	A2638	20c	Lou Gehrig	1.50	1.50
a.		Booklet of 20 cards, #UX337-UX356			30.00
		First day cancel, any card, Atlanta, GA			.90

No. UX356a sold for $8.95.

Christmas Deer Type of 1999

Designed by Tom Nikosey.

					Litho.	Rouletted on 2 sides
2000, Oct. 12					**Litho.**	**Rouletted on 2 sides**
UX357	A2600	20c	gold & blue	1.25	1.25	
UX358	A2600	20c	gold & red	1.25	1.25	
UX359	A2600	20c	gold & purple	1.25	1.25	
UX360	A2600	20c	gold & green	1.25	1.25	
a.		Sheet of 4, #UX357-UX360			5.00	
		First day cancel, any card, Rudolph, WI			1.75	

Nos. UX357-UX360 were sold in packs containing five No. UX360a for $8.95.

PC169

Designed by Derry Noyes.

					Litho.
2001, Mar. 30					**Litho.**
UX361	PC169	20c	multicolored	.40	.75
		First day cancel, New Haven, CT			1.00

PC170

Designed by Ethel Kessler.

					Litho.
2001, Apr. 26					**Litho.**
UX362	PC170	20c	multicolored	.40	.75
		First day cancel, Columbia, SC			1.00

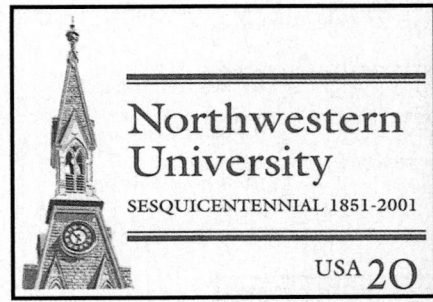

PC171

Designed by Howard Paine.

					Litho.
2001, Apr. 28					**Litho.**
UX363	PC171	20c	multicolored	.40	.75
		First day cancel, Evanston, IL			1.00

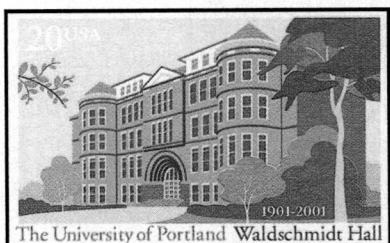

PC172

Designed by Richard Sheaff.

					Litho.
2001, May 1					**Litho.**
UX364	PC172	20c	multicolored	.40	.75
		First day cancel, Portland, OR			1.00

Legendary Playing Fields Type with 21c Denomination
Designed by Phil Jordan.

2001, June 27   **Litho.**
UX365 A2712 21c Ebbets Field 2.00 2.00
UX366 A2713 21c Tiger Stadium 2.00 2.00
UX367 A2714 21c Crosley Field 2.00 2.00
UX368 A2715 21c Yankee Stadium 2.00 2.00
UX369 A2716 21c Polo Grounds 2.00 2.00
UX370 A2717 21c Forbes Field 2.00 2.00
UX371 A2718 21c Fenway Park 2.00 2.00
UX372 A2719 21c Comiskey Park 2.00 2.00
UX373 A2720 21c Shibe Park 2.00 2.00
UX374 A2721 21c Wrigley Field 2.00 2.00
  a. Booklet of 10 cards, #UX365-UX374 22.50
     First day cancel, any card,
     New York, NY, Boston, MA,
     Chicago, IL, or Detroit MI 1.00

No. UX374a sold for $6.95.

White Barn — PC173

Designed by Derry Noyes.

2001, Sept. 20   **Litho.**
UX375 PC173 21c multicolored .45 .75
     First day cancel, Washington,
     DC 1.00

That's All Folks! Type
Designed by Ed Wleczyk, Warner Bros.

2001, Oct. 1   **Litho.**
UX376 A2736 21c multicolored 1.50 1.50
     First day cancel, Beverly Hills,
     CA 1.50
  a. Booklet of 10 cards 15.00

No. UX376a sold for $7.25.

Christmas Type
Designed by Richard Sheaff.

2001, Oct. 10   **Litho.**   *Rouletted on 2 Sides*
UX377 A2740 21c multicolored 1.25 1.25
     First day cancel, Santa Claus,
     IN 1.25
UX378 A2741 21c multicolored 1.25 1.25
     First day cancel, Santa Claus,
     IN 1.25
UX379 A2738 21c multicolored 1.25 1.25
     First day cancel, Santa Claus,
     IN 1.25
UX380 A2739 21c multicolored 1.25 1.25
     First day cancel, Santa Claus,
     IN 1.25
  a. Sheet of 4, #UX377-UX380 5.00

Packages of 5 No. UX380a sold for $9.25.

Carlsbad Caverns National Park — PC174

Designed by Carl Herrman.

2002, June 7   **Litho.**
UX381 PC174 23c multicolored .50 .75
     First day cancel, Carlsbad,
     NM 1.00
     First day cancel, any other
     city 1.00

Teddy Bears Type
Designed by Margaret Bauer.

2002, Aug. 15   **Litho.**   *Rouletted on 2 Sides*
UX382 A2827 23c Ideal Bear, c. 1905 1.25 1.25
     First day cancel, Atlantic City, NJ 1.25
UX383 A2826 23c Gund Bear, c. 1948 1.25 1.25
     First day cancel, Atlantic City, NJ 1.25

UX384 A2824 23c Bruin Bear, c. 1907 1.25 1.25
     First day cancel, Atlantic City, NJ 1.25
UX385 A2825 23c "Stick" Bear, 1920s 1.25 1.25
     First day cancel, Atlantic City, NJ 1.25
  a. Sheet of 4, #UX382-UX385 5.50

Packages of 5 No. UX385a sold for $9.25.

Christmas Snowmen Type
Designed by Derry Noyes.

2002, Oct. 28   **Litho.**   *Rouletted on 2 Sides*   **Design Size: 28x38mm**
UX386 A2844 23c multicolored 1.25 1.25
     First day cancel, Houghton, MI 1.00
UX387 A2845 23c multicolored 1.25 1.25
     First day cancel, Houghton, MI 1.00
UX388 A2846 23c multicolored 1.25 1.25
     First day cancel, Houghton, MI 1.00
UX389 A2847 23c multicolored 1.25 1.25
     First day cancel, Houghton, MI 1.00
  a. Sheet of 4, #UX386-UX389 5.00

Packages of 5 #UX389a sold for $9.75.

Old Glory Type
Designed by Richard Sheaff.

2003, Apr. 3   **Litho.**   *Rouletted on 1 Side*
UX390 A2883 23c multicolored 1.25 1.25
     First day cancel, New York, NY 1.00
UX391 A2884 23c multicolored 1.25 1.25
     First day cancel, New York, NY 1.00
UX392 A2885 23c multicolored 1.25 1.25
     First day cancel, New York, NY 1.00
UX393 A2886 23c multicolored 1.25 1.25
     First day cancel, New York, NY 1.00
UX394 A2887 23c multicolored 1.25 1.25
     First day cancel, New York, NY 1.00
  a. Booklet of 20 cards, 4 each #UX390-UX394 25.00

No. UX394a sold for $9.75.

Southeastern Lighthouses Type
Designed by Howard E. Paine.

2003, June 13   **Litho.**   *Rouletted on 1 Side*
UX395 A2893 23c multicolored 1.25 1.25
     First day cancel, Tybee Island, GA 1.00
UX396 A2894 23c multicolored 1.25 1.25
     First day cancel, Tybee Island, GA 1.00
UX397 A2895 23c multicolored 1.25 1.25
     First day cancel, Tybee Island, GA 1.00
UX398 A2896 23c multicolored 1.25 1.25
     First day cancel, Tybee Island, GA 1.00
UX399 A2897 23c multicolored 1.25 1.25
     First day cancel, Tybee Island, GA 1.00
  a. Booklet of 20 cards, 4 each #UX395-UX399 25.00

No. UX399a sold for $9.75.

Ohio University, 200th Anniv. — PC175

Designed by Tom Engemann.

2003, Oct. 10   **Litho.**
UX400 PC175 23c multicolored .50 .75
     First day cancel, Athens, OH 1.00

Christmas Music Makers Type
Designed by Ethel Kessler.

2003, Oct. 23   **Litho.**   *Rouletted on 2 Sides*
UX401 A2917 23c multicolored 1.10 1.10
     First day cancel, New York, NY 1.00
UX402 A2918 23c multicolored 1.10 1.10
     First day cancel, New York, NY 1.00
UX403 A2919 23c multicolored 1.10 1.10
     First day cancel, New York, NY 1.00
UX404 A2920 23c multicolored 1.10 1.10
     First day cancel, New York, NY 1.00
  a. Sheet of 4, #UX401-UX404 4.50

Packages of 5 #UX404a sold for $9.75.

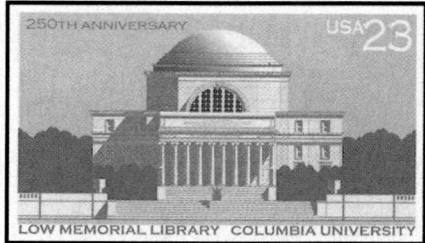

Columbia University, 250th Anniv. — PC176

Designed by Tom Engeman.

2004, Mar. 25   **Litho.**
UX405 PC176 23c multicolored .50 .75
     First day cancel, New York, NY 1.00

Harriton House, Bryn Mawr, PA, Bicent. PC177

Designed by Carl T. Herrman.

2004, June 10   **Litho.**
UX406 PC177 23c multicolored .50 .75
     First day cancel, Bryn Mawr, PA 1.00

Disney Type of 2004
Designed by David Pacheco.

2004, June 23   **Litho.**
UX407 A2950 23c multicolored 1.25 1.25
     First day cancel, Anaheim, CA 1.00
UX408 A2951 23c multicolored 1.25 1.25
     First day cancel, Anaheim, CA 1.00
UX409 A2949 23c multicolored 1.25 1.25
     First day cancel, Anaheim, CA 1.00
UX410 A2952 23c multicolored 1.25 1.25
     First day cancel, Anaheim, CA 1.00
  a. Booklet of 20 cards, 5 each #UX407-UX410 25.00

No. UX410a sold for $9.75.

Art of the American Indian Type of 2003
Designed by Richard Sheaff.

2004, Aug. 21   **Litho.**   *Rouletted on 1 Side*
UX411 A2957 23c Mimbres bowl 1.25 1.25
     First day cancel, Santa Fe, NM 1.00
UX412 A2957 23c Kutenai parfleche 1.25 1.25
     First day cancel, Santa Fe, NM 1.00
UX413 A2957 23c Tlingit sculptures 1.25 1.25
     First day cancel, Santa Fe, NM 1.00
UX414 A2957 23c Ho-Chunk bag 1.25 1.25
     First day cancel, Santa Fe, NM 1.00
UX415 A2957 23c Seminole doll 1.25 1.25
     First day cancel, Santa Fe, NM 1.00
UX416 A2957 23c Mississippian effigy 1.25 1.25
     First day cancel, Santa Fe, NM 1.00
UX417 A2957 23c Acoma pot 1.25 1.25
     First day cancel, Santa Fe, NM 1.00
UX418 A2957 23c Navajo weaving 1.25 1.25
     First day cancel, Santa Fe, NM 1.00
UX419 A2957 23c Seneca carving 1.25 1.25
     First day cancel, Santa Fe, NM 1.00
UX420 A2957 23c Luiseño basket 1.25 1.25
     First day cancel, Santa Fe, NM 1.00
  a. Booklet of 20 cards, 2 each #UX411-UX420 25.00

No. UX420a sold for $9.75.

Cloudscapes Type
Designed by Howard E. Paine.

2004, Oct. 4   **Litho.**   *Rouletted at Left*
UX421 A2960 23c Cirrus radiatus 1.25 1.25
     First day cancel, Milton, MA 1.00
UX422 A2960 23c Cirrostratus fibratus 1.25 1.25

	First day cancel, Milton, MA			1.00
UX423	A2960 23c Cirrocumulus undulatus		1.25	1.25
	First day cancel, Milton, MA			1.00
UX424	A2960 23c Cumulonimbus mammatus		1.25	1.25
	First day cancel, Milton, MA			1.00
UX425	A2960 23c Cumulonimbus incus		1.25	1.25
	First day cancel, Milton, MA			1.00
UX426	A2960 23c Altocumulus stratiformis		1.25	1.25
	First day cancel, Milton, MA			1.00
UX427	A2960 23c Altostratus translucidus		1.25	1.25
	First day cancel, Milton, MA			1.00
UX428	A2960 23c Altocumulus undulatus		1.25	1.25
	First day cancel, Milton, MA			1.00
UX429	A2960 23c Altocumulus castellanus		1.25	1.25
	First day cancel, Milton, MA			1.00
UX430	A2960 23c Altocumulus lenticularis		1.25	1.25
	First day cancel, Milton, MA			1.00
UX431	A2960 23c Stratocumulus undulatus		1.25	1.25
	First day cancel, Milton, MA			1.00
UX432	A2960 23c Stratus opacus		1.25	1.25
	First day cancel, Milton, MA			1.00
UX433	A2960 23c Cumulus humilis		1.25	1.25
	First day cancel, Milton, MA			1.00
UX434	A2960 23c Cumulus congestus		1.25	1.25
	First day cancel, Milton, MA			1.00
UX435	A2960 23c Cumulonimbus with tornado		1.25	1.25
	First day cancel, Milton, MA			1.00
a.	Booklet of 20, #UX421-UX422, UX425, UX427, UX429, UX431-UX435, 2 each #UX423-UX424, UX426, UX428, UX430			25.00

No. UX435a sold for $9.75.

Disney Type of 2005
Designed by David Pacheco.

2005, June 30		**Litho.**		
UX436	A2989 23c multicolored		1.10	1.10
	First day cancel, Anaheim, CA			1.00
UX437	A2990 23c multicolored		1.10	1.10
	First day cancel, Anaheim, CA			1.00
UX438	A2991 23c multicolored		1.10	1.10
	First day cancel, Anaheim, CA			1.00
UX439	A2992 23c multicolored		1.10	1.10
	First day cancel, Anaheim, CA			1.00
a.	Booklet of 20 cards, 5 each #UX436-UX439			22.50

No. UX439a sold for $9.75.

Sporty Cars Type of 2005
Designed by Art M. Fitzpatrick.

2005, Aug. 20		**Litho.**	**Rouletted at Left**	
UX440	A3012 23c 1955 Ford Thunderbird		1.00	1.00
	First day cancel, Detroit, MI			1.75
UX441	A3011 23c 1952 Nash Healey		1.00	1.00
	First day cancel, Detroit, MI			1.75
UX442	A3010 23c 1953 Chevrolet Corvette		1.00	1.00
	First day cancel, Detroit, MI			1.75
UX443	A3008 23c 1953 Studebaker Starliner		1.00	1.00
	First day cancel, Detroit, MI			1.75
UX444	A3009 23c 1954 Kaiser Darrin		1.00	1.00
	First day cancel, Detroit, MI			1.75
a.	Booklet of 20 cards, 4 each #UX440-UX444			20.00

No. UX444a sold for $9.75.

Let's Dance Type
Designed by Ethel Kessler.

2005, Sept. 17		**Litho.**	**Rouletted at Left**	
UX445	A3018 23c Cha cha cha		1.00	1.00
	First day cancel, New York, NY			1.75
	First day cancel, Miami, FL			1.75
UX446	A3019 23c Mambo		1.00	1.00
	First day cancel, New York, NY			1.75
	First day cancel, Miami, FL			1.75
UX447	A3017 23c Salsa		1.00	1.00
	First day cancel, New York, NY			1.75
	First day cancel, Miami, FL			1.75
UX448	A3016 23c Merengue		1.00	1.00
	First day cancel, New York, NY			1.75
	First day cancel, Miami, FL			1.75
a.	Booklet of 20, 5 each #UX445-UX448			20.00

No. UX448a sold for $9.75.

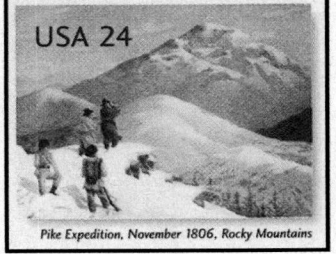

Zebulon Pike Expedition at Pikes Peak, Bicent. PC178

Designed by Carl Herrman.

2006, Jan. 9			**Litho.**	
UX449	PC178 24c multicolored		.55	*.90*
	First day cancel, Washington, DC			1.75
	First day cancel, any other city			1.75

Disney Type of 2006
Designed by David Pacheco.

2006, Apr. 21		**Litho.**	**Rouletted at Left**	
UX450	A3066 24c multicolored		1.00	1.00
	First day cancel, Orlando, FL			1.75
UX451	A3067 24c multicolored		1.00	1.00
	First day cancel, Orlando, FL			1.75
UX452	A3069 24c multicolored		1.00	1.00
	First day cancel, Orlando, FL			1.75
UX453	A3068 24c multicolored		1.00	1.00
	First day cancel, Orlando, FL			1.75
a.	Booklet of 20, 5 each #UX450-UX4538			20.00

No. UX453a sold for $9.75.

Baseball Sluggers Type of 2006
Designed by Phil Jordan.

2006, July 15		**Litho.**	**Rouletted at Left**	
UX454	A3121 24c Mickey Mantle		1.25	1.25
	First day cancel, Bronx, NY			1.75
UX455	A3118 24c Roy Campanella		1.25	1.25
	First day cancel, Bronx, NY			1.75
UX456	A3119 24c Hank Greenberg		1.25	1.25
	First day cancel, Bronx, NY			1.75
UX457	A3120 24c Mel Ott		1.25	1.25
	First day cancel, Bronx, NY			1.75
a.	Booklet of 20 cards, 5 each #UX454-UX457			25.00

No. UX457a sold for $9.95.

DC Comics Superheroes Type of 2006
Designed by Carl T. Herrman.

2006, July 20		**Litho.**	**Rouletted at Left**	
UX458	A3122 24c Superman cover		1.50	1.50
	First day cancel, San Diego, CA			1.75
UX459	A3122 24c Superman		1.50	1.50
	First day cancel, San Diego, CA			1.75
UX460	A3122 24c Batman cover		1.50	1.50
	First day cancel, San Diego, CA			1.75
UX461	A3122 24c Batman		1.50	1.50
	First day cancel, San Diego, CA			1.75
UX462	A3122 24c Wonder Woman cover		1.50	1.50
	First day cancel, San Diego, CA			1.75
UX463	A3122 24c Wonder Woman		1.50	1.50
	First day cancel, San Diego, CA			1.75
UX464	A3122 24c Green Lantern cover		1.50	1.50
	First day cancel, San Diego, CA			1.75
UX465	A3122 24c Green Lantern		1.50	1.50
	First day cancel, San Diego, CA			1.75
UX466	A3122 24c Green Arrow cover		1.50	1.50
	First day cancel, San Diego, CA			1.75
UX467	A3122 24c Green Arrow		1.50	1.50
	First day cancel, San Diego, CA			1.75
UX468	A3122 24c The Flash cover		1.50	1.50
	First day cancel, San Diego, CA			1.75
UX469	A3122 24c The Flash		1.50	1.50
	First day cancel, San Diego, CA			1.75
UX470	A3122 24c Plastic Man cover		1.50	1.50
	First day cancel, San Diego, CA			1.75
UX471	A3122 24c Plastic Man		1.50	1.50
	First day cancel, San Diego, CA			1.75
UX472	A3122 24c Aquaman cover		1.50	1.50
	First day cancel, San Diego, CA			1.75
UX473	A3122 24c Aquaman		1.50	1.50
	First day cancel, San Diego, CA			1.75
UX474	A3122 24c Supergirl cover		1.50	1.50
	First day cancel, San Diego, CA			1.75
UX475	A3122 24c Supergirl		1.50	1.50
	First day cancel, San Diego, CA			1.75
UX476	A3122 24c Hawkman cover		1.50	1.50
	First day cancel, San Diego, CA			1.75
UX477	A3122 24c Hawkman		1.50	1.50
	First day cancel, San Diego, CA			1.75
a.	Booklet of 20 cards, #UX458-UX477			30.00

No. UX477a sold for $9.95.

Southern Florida Wetland Type of 2006
Designed by Ethel Kessler.

2006, Oct. 4		**Litho.**	**Rouletted on 1 Side**	
UX478	A3137 39c Snail kite		4.00	4.00
	First day cancel, Naples, FL			2.00
UX479	A3137 39c Cape Sable seaside sparrow		4.00	4.00
	First day cancel, Naples, FL			2.00
a.	Sheet of 2, #UX478-UX479		8.00	
UX480	A3137 39c Wood storks		4.00	4.00
	First day cancel, Naples, FL			2.00
UX481	A3137 39c Florida panther		4.00	4.00
	First day cancel, Naples, FL			2.00
a.	Sheet of 2, #UX480-UX481		8.00	
UX482	A3137 39c Bald eagle		4.00	4.00
	First day cancel, Naples, FL			2.00
UX483	A3137 39c White ibis		4.00	4.00
	First day cancel, Naples, FL			2.00
a.	Sheet of 2, #UX482-UX483		8.00	
UX484	A3137 39c American crocodile		4.00	4.00
	First day cancel, Naples, FL			2.00
UX485	A3137 39c Everglades mink		4.00	4.00
	First day cancel, Naples, FL			2.00
a.	Sheet of 2, #UX484-UX485		8.00	
UX486	A3137 39c Roseate spoonbills		4.00	4.00
	First day cancel, Naples, FL			2.00
UX487	A3137 39c American alligator		4.00	4.00
	First day cancel, Naples, FL			2.00
a.	Sheet of 2, #UX486-UX487		8.00	
	Nos. UX478-UX487 (10)		40.00	40.00

Packet of 10 cards sold for $7.95.

Pineapple — PC179

Designed by Ethel Kessler.

2007, May 12			**Litho.**	
UX488	PC179 26c multicolored		.60	*1.00*
	First day cancel, Washington, DC			1.75

Star Wars Type of 2007
Designed by Terrence McCaffrey and William J. Gicker, Jr..

2007, May 27		**Litho.**	**Rouletted at Left**	
UX489	A3153 26c Darth Vader		1.75	1.75
	First day cancel, Los Angeles, CA			3.00
UX490	A3153 26c Luke Skywalker		1.75	1.75
	First day cancel, Los Angeles, CA			3.00
UX491	A3153 26c C-3PO		1.75	1.75
	First day cancel, Los Angeles, CA			3.00
UX492	A3153 26c Queen Padmé Amidala		1.75	1.75
	First day cancel, Los Angeles, CA			3.00
UX493	A3153 26c Millennium Falcon		1.75	1.75
	First day cancel, Los Angeles, CA			3.00
UX494	A3153 26c Emperor Palpatine		1.75	1.75
	First day cancel, Los Angeles, CA			3.00
UX495	A3153 26c Anakin Skywalker and Obi-Wan Kenobi		1.75	1.75
	First day cancel, Los Angeles, CA			3.00
UX496	A3153 26c Obi-Wan Kenobi		1.75	1.75
	First day cancel, Los Angeles, CA			3.00
UX497	A3153 26c Boba Fett		1.75	1.75
	First day cancel, Los Angeles, CA			3.00
UX498	A3153 26c Darth Maul		1.75	1.75
	First day cancel, Los Angeles, CA			3.00
UX499	A3153 26c Yoda		1.75	1.75
	First day cancel, Los Angeles, CA			3.00
UX500	A3153 26c Princess Leia and R2-D2		1.75	1.75
	First day cancel, Los Angeles, CA			3.00
UX501	A3153 26c Chewbacca and Han Solo		1.75	1.75
	First day cancel, Los Angeles, CA			3.00
UX502	A3153 26c X-wing Starfighter		1.75	1.75
	First day cancel, Los Angeles, CA			3.00
UX503	A3153 26c Stormtroopers		1.75	1.75
	First day cancel, Los Angeles, CA			3.00
a.	Booklet of 15, #UX489-UX503		26.00	

No. UX503a sold for $12.95.

Pacific Lighthouses Type of 2007
Designed by Howard E. Paine.

2007, June 21 — Litho. — Rouletted at Left

UX504	A3158	26c Grays Harbor Lighthouse	1.25	1.25
		First day cancel, Westport, WA		2.50
UX505	A3157	26c Five Finger Lighthouse	1.25	1.25
		First day cancel, Westport, WA		2.50
UX506	A3159	26c Umpqua River Lighthouse	1.25	1.25
		First day cancel, Westport, WA		2.50
UX507	A3156	26c Diamond Head Lighthouse	1.25	1.25
		First day cancel, Westport, WA		2.50
UX508	A3160	26c St. George Reef Lighthouse	1.25	1.25
		First day cancel, Westport, WA		2.50
a.		Booklet of 20, 4 each #UX504-UX508	26.00	

No. UX503a sold for $12.95.

Marvel Comics Superheroes Type of 2006
Designed by Carl T. Herrman.

2007, July 26 — Litho. — Rouletted at Left

UX509	A3168	26c Spider-Man	1.25	1.25
		First day cancel, San Diego, CA		1.75
UX510	A3168	26c The Hulk	1.25	1.25
		First day cancel, San Diego, CA		1.75
UX511	A3168	26c Sub-Mariner	1.25	1.25
		First day cancel, San Diego, CA		1.75
UX512	A3168	26c The Thing	1.25	1.25
		First day cancel, San Diego, CA		1.75
UX513	A3168	26c Captain America	1.25	1.25
		First day cancel, San Diego, CA		1.75
UX514	A3168	26c Silver Surfer	1.25	1.25
		First day cancel, San Diego, CA		1.75
UX515	A3168	26c Spider-Woman	1.25	1.25
		First day cancel, San Diego, CA		1.75
UX516	A3168	26c Iron Man	1.25	1.25
		First day cancel, San Diego, CA		1.75
UX517	A3168	26c Elektra	1.25	1.25
		First day cancel, San Diego, CA		1.75
UX518	A3168	26c Wolverine	1.25	1.25
		First day cancel, San Diego, CA		1.75
UX519	A3168	26c Spider-Man cover	1.25	1.25
		First day cancel, San Diego, CA		1.75
UX520	A3168	26c Incredible Hulk cover	1.25	1.25
		First day cancel, San Diego, CA		1.75
UX521	A3168	26c Sub-Mariner cover	1.25	1.25
		First day cancel, San Diego, CA		1.75
UX522	A3168	26c Fantastic Four cover	1.25	1.25
		First day cancel, San Diego, CA		1.75
UX523	A3168	26c Captain America cover	1.25	1.25
		First day cancel, San Diego, CA		1.75
UX524	A3168	26c Silver Surfer cover	1.25	1.25
		First day cancel, San Diego, CA		1.75
UX525	A3168	26c Spider-Woman cover	1.25	1.25
		First day cancel, San Diego, CA		1.75
UX526	A3168	26c Iron Man cover	1.25	1.25
		First day cancel, San Diego, CA		1.75
UX527	A3168	26c Elektra cover	1.25	1.25
		First day cancel, San Diego, CA		1.75
UX528	A3168	26c X-Men cover	1.25	1.25
		First day cancel, San Diego, CA		1.75
a.		Booklet of 20 cards, #UX509-UX528	26.00	

No. UX528a sold for $12.95.

Disney Characters Type of 2007
Designed by David Pacheco.

2007, Aug. 16 — Litho. — Rouletted at Left

UX529	A3185	26c Mickey Mouse	1.25	1.25
		First day cancel, Orlando, FL		2.50
UX530	A3186	26c Peter Pan and Tinker Bell	1.25	1.25
		First day cancel, Orlando, FL		2.50
UX531	A3187	26c Dumbo and Timothy Mouse	1.25	1.25
		First day cancel, Orlando, FL		2.50
UX532	A3188	26c Aladdin and Genie	1.25	1.25
		First day cancel, Orlando, FL		2.50
a.		Booklet of 20, 5 each #UX529-UX532	26.00	

No. UX503a sold for $12.95.

Mount St. Mary's University, Bicent. PC180

Designed by Richard Sheaff.

2008, Apr. 26 — Litho.

UX533	PC180	27c multicolored	.60	1.00
		First day cancel, Emmitsburg, MD		1.75

Corinthian Column From Capitol Building — PC181

Designed by Gerald Gallo.

2008, May 12 — Litho.

UX534	PC181	27c multicolored	.60	1.00
		First day cancel, Washington, DC		1.75

Disney Characters Type of 2008
Designed by David Pacheco.

2008, Aug. 7 — Litho. — Rouletted at Left

UX535	A3305	27c Steamboat Willie	1.40	1.40
		First day cancel, Anaheim, CA		2.60
UX536	A3304	27c Pongo and Pup	1.40	1.40
		First day cancel, Anaheim, CA		2.60
UX537	A3306	27c Princess Aurora, Flora, Fauna, Merryweather	1.40	1.40
		First day cancel, Anaheim, CA		2.60
UX538	A3307	27c Mowgli and Baloo	1.40	1.40
		First day cancel, Anaheim, CA		2.60
a.		Booklet of 20, 5 each #UX535-UX538	28.00	

No. UX538a sold for $13.95.

Great Lakes Dunes Type of 2006
Designed by Ethel Kessler.

2008, Oct. 2 — Litho. — Rouletted on 1 Side

UX539	A3312	42c Vesper sparrow	1.90	1.90
UX540	A3312	42c Piping plover	1.90	1.90
a.		Sheet of 2, #UX539-UX540	4.00	
UX541	A3312	42c Eastern hognose snake	1.90	1.90
UX542	A3312	42c Common mergansers	1.90	1.90
a.		Sheet of 2, #UX541-UX542	4.00	
UX543	A3312	42c Piping plover nestlings	1.90	1.90
UX544	A3312	42c Red fox	1.90	1.90
a.		Sheet of 2, #UX543-UX544	4.00	
UX545	A3312	42c Tiger beetle	1.90	1.90
UX546	A3312	42c White-footed mouse	1.90	1.90
a.		Sheet of 2, #UX545-UX546	4.00	
UX547	A3312	42c Spotted sandpiper	1.90	1.90
UX548	A3312	42c Red admiral butterfly	1.90	1.90
a.		Sheet of 2, #UX547-UX548	4.00	
		First day cancel, any card, Empire, MI		3.00
Nos. UX539-UX548 (10)			19.00	19.00

Packet of 10 cards sold for $8.95.

Automobiles of the 1950s Type of 2008
Designed by Carl T. Herrman.

2008, Oct. 3 — Litho. — Rouletted at Left

UX549	A3316	27c 1957 Lincoln Premiere	1.40	1.40
UX550	A3317	27c 1957 Chrysler 300C	1.40	1.40
UX551	A3313	27c 1959 Cadillac Eldorado	1.40	1.40
UX552	A3314	27c 1957 Studebaker Golden Hawk	1.40	1.40
UX553	A3315	27c 1957 Pontiac Safari	1.40	1.40
a.		Booklet of 20, 4 each #UX549-UX553	28.00	
		First day cancel, any card, Carlisle, PA		2.60

No. UX553a sold for $13.95.

Miami University (Oxford, Ohio), Bicent. PC182

Designed by Howard E. Paine

2009, Feb. 17 — Litho.

UX554	PC182	27c multicolored	.60	.60
		First day cancel, Oxford, OH		1.75

White, Orange and White Koi — PC183

Black, Red and White Koi — PC184

Designed by Ethel Kessler.

2009, Apr. 17 — Litho.

UX555	PC183	28c multicolored	.65	.65
		First day cancel, New York, NY		1.90
UX556	PC184	28c multicolored	.65	.65
		First day cancel, New York, NY		1.90

Nos. UX555 and UX556 were also printed in uncut sheets of 40 cards (20 of each) on a rougher stock and having a background dot pattern that differs from the cut cards.

The Simpsons Type of 2009
Designed by Matt Groening.

2009, May 7 — Litho. — Rouletted at Left

UX557	A3345	28c Homer Simpson	1.50	1.50
UX558	A3346	28c Marge Simpson	1.50	1.50
UX559	A3347	28c Bart Simpson	1.50	1.50
UX560	A3348	28c Lisa Simpson	1.50	1.50
UX561	A3349	28c Maggie Simpson	1.50	1.50
a.		Booklet of 20, 4 each #UX557-UX561	30.00	
		First day cancel, any card, Los Angeles, CA		2.75

No. UX561a sold for $14.95.

PAID REPLY POSTAL CARDS

These are sold to the public as two unsevered cards, one for message and one for reply. These are listed first as unsevered cards and then as severed cards. Values are for:

Unused cards (both unsevered and severed) without printed or written address or message.

Unsevered cards sell for a premium if never folded.

Used unsevered cards, Message Card with Post Office cancellation and Reply Card uncanceled (from 1968 value is for a single used severed card); and used severed cards with cancellation when current.

Used values for International Paid Reply Cards are for proper usage. Those domestically used or with postage added sell for less than the unused value.

"Preprinted," unused cards (both unsevered and severed) with printed or written address or message. Used value applies after 1952.

First day cancel values are for cards without cachets.

PM1

Head of Grant, card framed.
PR1 inscribed "REPLY CARD."

1892, Oct. 25   **Size: 140x89mm**
UY1 PM1+PR1 1c +1c **black,** *buff,* unsevered   40.00   9.00
    Preprinted   15.00
a.   Message card printed on both
    sides, reply card blank   250.00 750.00
b.   Message card blank, reply card
    printed on both sides   300.00
c.   Cards joined at bottom   200.00 100.00
    Preprinted   100.00
m.   PM1 Message card detached   6.00   1.75
    Preprinted   3.00
r.   PR1 Reply card detached   6.00   1.75
    Preprinted   3.00

For other postal cards of types PM1 and PR1 see No. UY3.

Liberty — PM2

PR2 inscribed "REPLY CARD."

1893, Mar. 1   **For International Use**
UY2 PM2+PR2 2c +2c **blue,** *grayish white,*
unsevered   22.50   20.00
    Preprinted   12.50
a.   2c+2c **dark blue,** *grayish white,* unsevered   22.50   20.00
    Preprinted   12.50
b.   Message card printed on both
    sides, reply card blank   500.00
c.   Message card blank, reply card
    printed on both sides   —
d.   Message card normal, reply card
    blank   300.00
m.   PM2 Message card detached   5.00   6.00
    Preprinted   2.50
r.   PR2 Reply card detached   5.00   6.00
    Preprinted   2.50

For other postal cards of types PM2 and PR2 see No. UY11.

**Design same as PM1 and PR1, without frame
around card**

1898, Sept.
     Size: 140x82mm
UY3 PM1+PR1 1c +1c **black,** *buff,* unsevered   67.50   12.50
    Preprinted   12.50
a.   Message card normal, reply card
    blank   400.00
b.   Message card printed on both
    sides, reply card blank   450.00
c.   Message card blank, reply card
    printed on both sides   400.00
d.   Message card without "Detach an-
    nexed card/for answer"   250.00 150.00
    Preprinted   —
e.   Message card blank, reply card nor-
    mal   250.00
f.   Message card normal, reply card
    double impression, preprinted   *825.00*
m.   PM1 Message card detached   12.50   2.50
    Preprinted   6.00
r.   PR1 Reply card detached   12.50   2.50
    Preprinted   6.00

PR3

PM3 pictures Sherman.

1904, Mar, 31
UY4 PM3+PR3 1c +1c **black,** *buff,* unsevered   57.50   6.50
    Preprinted   10.00
a.   Message card normal, reply card
    blank   275.00
b.   Message card printed on both
    sides, reply card blank   *950.00*
c.   Message card blank, reply card nor-
    mal   275.00
d.   Message card blank, reply card
    printed on both sides   — 175.00
    Preprinted   200.00
m.   PM3 Message card detached   9.00   1.10
    Preprinted   4.00
r.   PR3 Reply card detached   9.00   1.10
    Preprinted   4.00

PM4

PR4 pictures Martha Washington.

Double frame line around instructions

1910, Sept. 14
UY5 PM4+PR4 1c +1c **blue,** *bluish,* unsevered   175.00   25.00
    Preprinted   40.00
a.   Message card normal, reply card
    blank   325.00 *750.00*
m.   PM4 Message card detached   15.00   3.75
    Preprinted   9.00
r.   PR4 Reply card detached   15.00   3.75
    Preprinted   9.00

1911, Oct. 27
UY6 PM4+PR4 1c +1c **green,** *cream,* unsevered   175.00   25.00
    Preprinted   60.00
a.   Message card normal, reply card
    blank   —
m.   PM4 Message card detached   22.50   6.50
    Preprinted   12.50
r.   PR4 Reply card detached   22.50   6.50
    Preprinted   12.50

Single frame line around instructions

1915, Sept. 18
UY7 PM4+PR4 1c +1c **green,** *cream,* unsevered   1.50   .50
    Preprinted   .60
a.   1c+1c **dark green,** *buff,* unsevered   1.50   .50
    Preprinted   .60
b.   Message card normal, reply card
    blank   —
m.   PM4 Message card detached   .30   .20
    Preprinted   .20
r.   PR4 Reply card detached   .30   .20
    Preprinted   .20
s.   As "a," missing Reply indicia   2,000.
    See No. UY13.

PR5

PM5 pictures George Washington.

1918, Aug. 2
UY8 PM5+PR5 2c +2c **red,** *buff,* unsevered   90.00 40.00
    Preprinted   30.00
m.   PM5 Message card detached   20.00   7.50
    Preprinted   10.00
r.   PR5 Reply card detached   20.00   7.50
    Preprinted   10.00

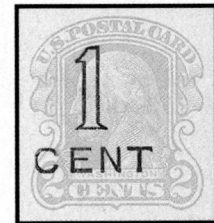

Same Surcharged

Fifteen canceling machine types

1920, Apr.
UY9 PM5+PR5 1c on 2c+1c on 2c **red,**
buff, unsevered   22.50   11.00
    Preprinted   10.00
a.   Message card normal, reply card
    no surcharge   85.00
    Preprinted   —
b.   Message card normal, reply card
    double surcharge   85.00
    Preprinted   —
c.   Message card double surcharge,
    reply card normal   85.00
    Preprinted   —
d.   Message card no surcharge, re-
    ply card normal   85.00
    Preprinted   —
e.   Message card no surcharge, re-
    ply card double surcharge   85.00
    Preprinted   —
m.   PM5 Message card detached   5.00   4.00
    Preprinted   3.00
r.   PR5 Reply card detached   5.00   4.00
    Preprinted   3.00

One press printed type

UY10 PM5+PR5 1c on 2c+1c on 2c **red,**
buff, unsevered   375.00 200.00
    Preprinted   150.00
a.   Message card no surcharge, re-
    ply card normal   *1,100.*
    Preprinted   —
b.   Surcharge double on message
    card, reply card normal   *950.00*
m.   PM5 Message card detached   75.00 45.00
    Preprinted   40.00
r.   PR5 Reply card detached   75.00 45.00
    Preprinted   40.00

Designs same as PM2 and PR2

1924, Mar. 18   **For International Use**
     Size: 139x89mm
UY11 PM2+PR2 2c +2c **red,** *cream,* unsevered   2.50 *50.00*
    Preprinted   1.50
m.   PM2 Message card detached   .50 *14.00*
    Preprinted   .40
r.   PR2 Reply card detached   .50 *20.00*
    Preprinted   .40

PM6

PR6 inscribed "REPLY CARD."

For International Use

1926, Feb. 1
UY12 PM6+PR6 3c +3c **red,** *buff,* unsevered   12.00 *27.50*
    Preprinted   6.00
a.   3c +3c **red,** *yellow,* unsevered   12.00 *27.50*
    Preprinted   6.00
    First day cancel   —
m.   PM6 Message card detached   3.00   7.50
    Preprinted   1.50
r.   PR6 Reply card detached   3.00 10.00
    Preprinted   1.50

Type of 1910
Single frame line around instructions

1951, Dec. 29
UY13 PM4+PR4 2c +2c **carmine,** *buff,* unsevered   1.25 *2.00*
    Preprinted   .65
    First day cancel, Washington,
    D.C.   1.25
m.   PM4 Message card detached   .35 *1.00*
    Preprinted   .25
r.   PR4 Reply card detached   .35 *1.00*
    Preprinted   .25

No. UY7a Surcharged Below Stamp in Green by Canceling Machine

1952, Jan. 1
UY14 PM4+PR4 2c on 1c+2c on 1c **green,**
   buff, unsevered   1.25 2.00
    Preprinted   .50
a. Surcharge vertical at left of stamps 12.50 7.50
    Preprinted   7.50
b. Surcharge horizontal at left of
  stamps   15.00 12.50
    Preprinted   8.50
c. Inverted surcharge horizontal at
  left of stamps   140.00 90.00
    Preprinted   75.00
d. Message card normal, reply card
  no surcharge   40.00 40.00
    Preprinted   —
e. Message card normal, reply card
  double surcharge   40.00 40.00
    Preprinted   —
f. Message card no surcharge, reply
  card normal   40.00 40.00
    Preprinted   —
g. Message card double surcharge,
  reply card normal   40.00 40.00
    Preprinted   —
h. Both cards, dbl. surch.   50.00 50.00
    Preprinted   —
m. PM4 Message card detached .40 1.00
    Preprinted   .30
r. PR4 Reply card detached   .40 1.00
    Preprinted   .30

No. UY7a with Similar Surcharge (horizontal) Typographed at Left of Stamp in Dark Green

1952
UY15 PM4+PR4 2c on 1c+2c on 1c **green,**
   buff, unsevered   115.00 45.00
    Preprinted   35.00
a. Surcharge on message card only 175.00
m. PM4 Message card detached 17.50 10.00
    Preprinted   9.00
r. PR4 Reply card detached   17.50 10.00
    Preprinted   9.00

On No. UY15a, the surcharge also appears on blank side of card.

Liberty Type
For International Use

1956, Nov. 16
UY16 PC24 4c +4c **carmine & dark violet**
   blue, *buff,* unsevered 1.25 75.00
   First day cancel, New York,
   N. Y. *(127,874)*   1.00
a. Message card printed on both halves 125.00 —
b. Reply card printed on both halves 125.00 —
c. Double scarlet on reply side 200.00 —
   First day cancel   350.00
d. Double scarlet on message side 200.00
e. Double violet blue on message side —
f. Double violet blue on both sides —
g. Message side blank, reply side normal   —
m. Message card detached   .40 45.00
r. Reply card detached   .40 45.00

Liberty Type of 1956

1958, July 31
UY17 PC25 3c +3c **purple,** *buff,* unsevered 3.00 2.00
   First day cancel, Boise, Idaho
   (136,768)   1.00
a. One card blank   500.00
b. Double impression on one card,
  preprinted   *1,000.*

Both halves of No. UY17 are identical, inscribed as No. UX46, "This side of card is for address."

Lincoln Type

1962, Nov. 19
Precanceled with 3 printed red violet lines
UY18 PC26 4c +4c **red violet,** unsevered 3.00 *2.50*
   First day cancel, Springfield, Ill.
   (107,746)   1.00
a. Tagged, *Mar. 7, 1967* 6.50 3.00
   First day cancel, Dayton, OH 30.00

Both halves of No. UY18 are identical, inscribed as No. UX48, "This side of card is for address."
No. UY18a was printed with luminescent ink.

Map Type

1963, Aug. 30   **For International Use**
UY19 PC27 7c +7c **blue & red,** unsevered 2.50 60.00
   First day cancel, New York   1.00
a. Message card normal, reply card
  blank   400.00 100.00
b. Message card blank, reply card normal   400.00 —

---

c. Additional message card on back of
  reply card   550.00
d. Double red on message side   —
e. Double red & blue on message side —
m. Message card detached   .85 *40.00*
r. Reply card detached   .85 *40.00*
s. Double impression of blue on message side   —

Message card inscribed "Postal Card With Paid Reply" in English and French. Reply card inscribed "Reply Postal Card Carte Postale Réponse."

Map Type of 1963

1967, Dec. 4   **For International Use**
UY20 PC27 8c +8c **blue & red,** unsevered 2.50 60.00
   First day cancel, Washington,
   D.C.   1.00
m. Message card detached   .85 *40.00*
r. Reply card detached   .85 *40.00*
s. Message card normal, reply card blank

Message card inscribed "Postal Card With Paid Reply" in English and French. Reply card inscribed "Reply Postal Card Carte Postale Réponse."

Tagged
Paid Reply Postal cards from No. UY21 onward are either tagged or printed with luminescent ink unless otherwise noted.

Lincoln Type

1968, Jan. 4
UY21 PC33 5c +5c **emerald,** unsevered 1.25 2.00
   First day cancel, Hodgenville,
   Ky.   1.50
a. Printed on one side only   —

Paul Revere Type

1971, May 15
Precanceled with 3 printed brown lines.
UY22 PC36 6c +6c **brown,** unsevered .85 2.00
   First day cancel, Boston, Mass. 1.00

John Hanson Type

1972, Sept. 1
Precanceled with 3 printed blue lines.
UY23 PC41 6c +6c **blue,** unsevered 1.00 2.00
   First day cancel, Baltimore, Md. 1.00

Samuel Adams Type

1973, Dec. 16
Precanceled with 3 printed orange lines
UY24 PC42 8c +8c **orange,** unsevered .75 2.00
   First day cancel, Boston, Mass.
   (105,369)   1.00
a. Coarse paper   1.25 2.00
b. Printed on one side only, preprinted 750.00

Thomson, Witherspoon, Rodney, Hale & Hancock Types

1975-78
Precanceled with 3 printed emerald lines
UY25 PC44 7c +7c **emerald,** unsevered,
   Sept. 14, 1975   .75 8.00
   First day cancel, Bryn Mawr,
   Pa.   1.00

Precanceled with 3 printed yellow brown lines
UY26 PC45 9c +9c **yellow brown,** unsev-
   ered, *Nov. 10, 1975* .75 2.00
   First day cancel, Princeton,
   N.J.   1.00

Precanceled with 3 printed blue lines
UY27 PC46 9c +9c **blue,** unsevered, *July 1,
   1976*   1.00 2.00
   First day cancel, Dover, Del. 1.00

Precanceled with 3 printed green lines
UY28 PC48 9c +9c **green,** unsevered, *Oct.
   14, 1977*   1.00 2.00
   First day cancel, Coventry,
   Conn.   1.00

Inscribed "U.S. Domestic Rate"
Precanceled with 3 printed brown orange lines
UY29 PC50 (10c +10c) **brown orange,** un-
   severed, *May 19, 1978* 7.50 9.00
   First day cancel, Quincy,
   Mass.   1.75

Precanceled with 3 printed brown orange lines
UY30 PC50 10c +10c **brown orange,** unsev-
   ered, *June 20, 1978* 1.00 .25
   First day cancel, Quincy,
   Mass.   1.00
a. One card "Domestic Rate," other
  "Postage 10¢"   —
b. Printed on one side only 800.00
   Nos. UY25-UY30 (6) 12.00

Eagle Type
Inscribed "U. S. Domestic Rate"

1981, Mar. 15
Precanceled with 3 printed violet lines
UY31 PC63 (12c +12) **violet,** unsevered 1.00 2.00
   First day cancel, Memphis, TN 1.00

Isaiah Thomas Type

1981, May 5
Precanceled with 3 printed lines
UY32 PC64 12c +12c **light blue,** unsevered 5.00 2.00
   First day cancel, Worcester, MA 1.00
a. Small die on one side   3.00

Morris Type
Inscribed "U.S. Domestic Rate"

1981
Precanceled with 3 printed lines
UY33 PC67 (13c +13c) **buff,** *Oct. 11,* unsev-
   ered   1.50 2.00
   First day cancel, Memphis, TN 1.25

Inscribed "U.S. Postage 13¢"
UY34 PC67 13c +13c **buff,** *Nov. 10,* unsevered .85 .20
   First day cancel, Philadelphia,
   PA   1.25
a. Message card normal, reply card blank 200.00
b. Extra copyright symbol and "USPS
  1981" on back of reply card —

Charles Carroll Type
Inscribed: U.S. Domestic Rate

1985
Precanceled with 3 printed lines
UY35 PC79 (14c +14c) **pale green,** *Feb. 1,*
   unsevered   2.50 2.00
   First day cancel, New Car-
   rollton, MD   1.25

Inscribed: USA
UY36 PC79 14c +14c **pale green,** *Mar. 6,*
   unsevered   1.00 2.00
   First day cancel, Annapolis,
   MD   1.25
a. One card blank   425.00

George Wythe Type

1985, June 20
Precanceled with 3 printed lines
UY37 PC81 14c +14c **bright apple green,**
   unsevered   .75 2.00
   First day cancel, Williamsburg, VA   1.25
a. One card blank, preprinted 300.00

Flag Type

1987, Sept. 1
UY38 PC90 14c +14c **black, blue & red,** unsevered   .75 2.00
   First day cancel, Washington, DC
   (22,314)   1.25

America the Beautiful Type

1988, July 11
UY39 PC93 15c +15c **multicolored,** unsevered .75 1.50
   First day cancel, Buffalo, WY
   (24,338)   1.25

Flag Type

1991, Mar. 27
UY40 PC122 19c +19c **rose, ultramarine &
   black,** unsevered   .80 1.50
   First day cancel, Washington, DC *(25,562)*   1.25
a. Printed on one side only 750.00

Red Barn Type

1995, Feb. 1   Litho.
UY41 PC147 20c +20c **multi,** unsevered .80 1.50
   First day cancel, Williams-
   burg, PA   1.50
a. One card blank   —

Block Island Lighthouse Type

1999, Nov. 10   Litho.
UY42 PC165 20c +20c **multi,** unsevered .85 1.50
   First day cancel, Block Island,
   RI   1.75

White Barn Type

2001, Sept. 20   Litho.
UY43 PC173 21c +21c **multi,** unsevered .90 1.50
   First day cancel, Washington,
   DC   1.50

Carlsbad Caverns Type

2002, June 7   Litho.
UY44 PC174 23c+23c **multi,** unsevered 1.00 1.25
   First day cancel, Carlsbad,
   NM   1.50
   First day cancel, any other
   city   1.50

Pikes Peak Type of 2006

2006, Jan. 9   **Litho.**
UY45 PC178 24c+24c **multicolored,** unsevered   1.10   *1.25*
     First day cancel, Washington, DC   1.50
     First day cancel, any other city   1.50

Pineapple Type of 2007

2007, May 12   **Litho.**
UY46 PC179 26c+26c **multicolored,** unsevered   1.25   *1.40*
     First day cancel, Washington, DC   2.40

Corinthian Column Type of 2008

2008, May 12   **Litho.**
UY47 PC181 27c+27c **multicolored,** unsevered   1.25   *1.40*
     First day cancel, Washington, DC   2.40

AIR POST POSTAL CARDS

Eagle in Flight — APC1

1949, Jan.10   **Typo.**
UXC1 APC1 4c **red orange,** *buff*   .60   *.75*
     Preprinted   .35
     First day cancel, Washington, D.C. *(236,620)*   3.00
  a.   4c **deep red,** *buff*   600.00   *450.00*
     First day cancel, Washington, D.C.   *250.00*
     Expertization is recommended for No. UXC1a.

Type of Air Post Stamp, 1954

1958, July 31
UXC2 AP31 5c **red,** *buff*   2.00   *.75*
     First day cancel, Wichita, Kans. *(156,474)*   1.00

Type of 1958 Redrawn

1960, June 18   **Lithographed (Offset)**
UXC3 AP31 5c **red,** *buff,* bicolored border   6.50   *2.00*
     First day cancel, Minneapolis, Minn. *(228,500)*   1.50
  a.   Red omitted   —
  b.   Two lozenges at left double printed, red over blue   200.00

Size of stamp of No. UXC3: 18½x21mm; on No. UXC2: 19x22mm. White cloud around eagle enlarged and finer detail of design on No. UXC3. Inscription "AIR MAIL-POSTAL CARD" has been omitted and blue and red border added on No. UXC3.

Bald Eagle — APC2

1963, Feb. 15
     Precanceled with 3 printed red lines
UXC4 APC2 6c **red,** bicolored border   1.10   *2.50*
     First day cancel, Maitland, Fla. *(216,203)*   1.50

Emblem of Commerce Department's Travel Service — APC3

Issued at the Sixth International Philatelic Exhibition (SIPEX), Washington, D.C., May 21-30.

1966, May 27   **For International Use**
UXC5 APC3 11c **blue & red**   .65   *25.00*
     First day cancel, Washington, D.C. *(272,813)*   1.00

Four photographs at left on address side show: Mt. Rainier, New York skyline, Indian on horseback and Miami Beach. The card has blue and red border.
See Nos. UXC8, UXC11.

Virgin Islands and Territorial Flag — APC4

50th anniv. of the purchase of the Virgin Islands.

Designed by Burt Pringle

1967, Mar. 31   **Litho.**
UXC6 APC4 6c **multicolored**   .75   *10.00*
     First day cancel, Charlotte Amalie, V. I. *(346,906)*   1.00
  a.   Red & yellow omitted   *1,700.*
  b.   Orange red (instead of red)   6.00
     The orange red in No. UXC6b is most easily seen in the two lines at the bottom of the card.

Borah Peak, Lost River Range, Idaho, and Scout Emblem — APC5

12th Boy Scout World Jamboree, Farragut State Park, Idaho, Aug. 1-9.

Designed by Stevan Dohanos

1967, Aug. 4   **Litho.**
UXC7 APC5 6c **blue, yellow, black & red**   .75   *15.00*
     First day cancel, Farragut State Park, ID *(471,585)*   1.00
  a.   Blue omitted   —
  b.   Blue & black omitted   *11,000.*
  c.   Red & yellow omitted   *11,000.*

Travel Service Type of 1966

Issued in connection with the American Air Mail Society Convention, Detroit, Mich.

1967, Sept. 8   **For International Use**
UXC8 APC3 13c **blue & red**   1.50   *30.00*
     First day cancel, Detroit, Mich. *(178,189)*   1.00

Stylized Eagle APC6

Designed by Muriel R. Chamberlain

1968, Mar. 1
     Precanceled with 3 printed red lines
UXC9 APC6 8c **blue & red**   .75   *2.50*
     First day cancel, New York, N.Y. *(179,923)*   1.00
  a.   Tagged, *Mar. 19, 1969*   2.50   *3.00*
     Tagged, first day cancel   15.00
  b.   **Blue & pale pink,** tagged   *1,250.*
     No. UXC9a is known with tagging omitted. It can be distinguished from No. UXC9, as No. UXC9a was printed on fluorescent stock. Believed to be unique. Value $2,500.

Tagged

Air Post Postal Cards from No. UXC10 onward are either tagged or printed with luminescent ink unless otherwise noted.

1971, May 15
     Precanceled with 3 printed blue lines
UXC10 APC6 9c **red & blue**   .50   *1.25*
     First day cancel, Kitty Hawk, N.C.   1.00

Travel Service Type of 1966

1971, June 10
     For International Use
UXC11 APC3 15c **blue & red**   1.75   *45.00*
     First day cancel, New York, N.Y.   1.00

Grand Canyon APC7

Niagara Falls APC8

Tourism Year of the Americas 1972.

Designed by Melbourne Brindle

1972, June 29   **Litho.**
     Size: 152½x108½mm
UXC12 APC7 9c **black,** Grand Canyon, *buff* (Statue of Liberty, Hawaii, Alaska, San Francisco on back)   .75   *75.00*
     First day cancel, any city   1.50
  a.   Red and blue lozenges omitted   *2,250.*
  b.   Red lozenges omitted   —
  c.   Tagging omitted   —

     For International Use
UXC13 APC8 15c **black,** Niagara Falls, *buff* (Mt. Vernon, Washington, D.C., Lincoln, Liberty Bell on back)   .75   *75.00*
     First day cancel, any city   1.50
  a.   Address side blank   400.00
  b.   Double blue lozenges   *6,000.*
  c.   Tagging omitted   *2,500.*
  d.   Red and blue lozenges omitted   —

See note after No. UX63.

Mail early in the day

Stylized
Eagle — APC9

Eagle Weather
Vane — APC10

Designed by David G. Foote (11c) & Stevan Dohanos (18c)

1974, Jan. 4   **Litho.**
UXC14 APC9 11c **ultramarine & red**   1.10   *25.00*
      First day cancel, State
      College, Pa. *(160,500)*   1.00
  a.   Double tagging   *500.00*
  b.   Tagging omitted   *500.00*
        For International Use
UXC15 APC10 18c **multicolored**   1.10   *25.00*
      First day cancel, Miami,
      Fla. *(132,114)*   1.00
  a.   Tagging omitted   *350.00*
  b.   Black and yellow omitted   *7,500.*

All following issues are for international use.

Angel Gabriel
Weather
Vane — APC11

Designed by Stevan Dohanos

1975, Dec. 17   **Litho.**
UXC16 APC11 21c **multicolored**   .85   *40.00*
      First day cancel,
      Kitty Hawk, N.C.   1.00
  a.   Blue & red omitted   *7,500.*
  b.   Tagging omitted   275.00   —

Curtiss (JN4H) Jenny — APC12

Designed by Keith Ferris

1978, Sept. 16   **Litho.**
UXC17 APC12 21c **multicolored**   1.00   *40.00*
      First day cancel, San Die-
      go, Cal. *(174,886)*   1.25

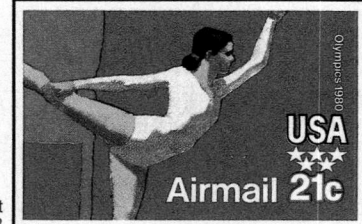

Gymnast
APC13

22nd Olympic Games, Moscow, July 19-Aug. 3, 1980.

Designed by Robert M. Cunningham

1979, Dec. 1   **Litho.**
UXC18 APC13 21c **multicolored**   1.25   *40.00*
      First day cancel, Fort
      Worth, Tex.   1.00

Pangborn, Herndon and Miss Veedol — APC14

First non-stop transpacific flight by Clyde Pangborn and Hugh
Herndon, Jr., 50th anniv.

Designed by Ken Dallison

1981, Jan. 2   **Litho.**
UXC19 APC14 28c **multicolored**   1.00   *22.50*
      First day cancel, Wenatch-
      ee, WA   1.25

Gliders — APC15

Designed by Robert E. Cunningham

1982, Mar. 5   **Litho.**
UXC20 APC15 28c **magenta, yellow, blue &**
            black   1.00   *30.00*
      First day cancel, Houston,
      TX *(106,932)*   1.25

Speedskater — APC16

Designed by Robert Peak

1983, Dec. 29   **Litho.**
UXC21 APC16 28c **multicolored**   1.00   *30.00*
      First day cancel, Milwaukee,
      WI *(108,397)*   1.25
  a.   Red, pink, yellow, double impression,
      one inverted   *4,000.*

No. UXC21a also exhibits a dramatic color shift.

Martin M-130 China Clipper Seaplane — APC17

Designed by Chuck Hodgson

1985, Feb. 15   **Litho.**
UXC22 APC17 33c **multicolored**   1.00   *30.00*
      First day cancel, San Fran-
      cisco, CA   1.50

First day cancellation was applied to 269,229 of Nos. UXC22
and C115.

Chicago Skyline — APC18

AMERIPEX '86, Chicago, May 22-June 1.

Designed by Ray Ameijide

1986, Feb. 1   **Litho.**
UXC23 APC18 33c **multicolored**   1.00   *30.00*
      First day cancel, Chicago,
      IL *(84,480)*   1.25

No. UXC23 was sold at Sudposta '87 by the U.S.P.S. with a
show cachet.

DC-3 — APC19

Designed by Chuck Hodgson

1988, May 14   **Litho.**
UXC24 APC19 36c **multicolored**   .85   *30.00*
      First day cancel, San Die-
      go, CA   1.25

No. UXC24 was sold at SYDPEX '88 by the USPS with a
cachet for Australia's bicentennial and SYDPEX '88.
  First day cancellations applied to 167,575 of Nos. UXC24 and
C118.

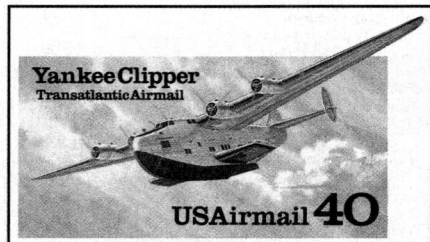

Yankee Clipper — APC20

Designed by Chuck Hodgson.

1991, June 28   **Litho.**
UXC25 APC20 40c **multicolored**   .90   *30.00*
      First day cancel, Flushing,
      NY *(24,865)*   1.50

Mt. Rainier — APC22

Designed by Ethel Kessler.

POSTAL CARDS

1999, May 15   **Litho.**
UXC27 APC22 55c **multicolored**   1.25 *30.00*
    First day cancel, Denver, CO   1.50
  First day cancellation was applied to 19,658 of Nos. UXC27 and UC65.
  See note before No. C133.

Badlands Natl. Park, South Dakota — APC23

Designed by Ethel Kessler.

2001, Feb. 22   **Litho.**
UXC28 APC23 70c **multicolored**   1.40 *20.00*
    First day cancel, Wall, SD   1.50

OFFICIAL POSTAL CARDS

PO1

1913, July
       Size: 126x76mm
UZ1 PO1 1c **black**   700.00 475.00
  All No. UZ1 cards have printed address and printed form on message side.

Used values are for contemporaneous usage without additional postage applied.

Great Seal — PO2

1983-85
UZ2 PO2 13c **blue,** *Jan. 12*   .75 *100.00*
    First day cancel, Washington, DC   1.00
UZ3 PO2 14c **blue,** *Feb. 26, 1985*   .80 *80.00*
    First day cancel, Washington, DC
    (62,396)   1.25

  Official postal cards from No. UZ4 onward are tagged unless otherwise noted.

PO3

Designed by Bradbury Thompson.

1988, June 10   **Litho.**
UZ4 PO3 15c **multicolored**   .80 *90.00*
    First day cancel, New York
    (133,498)   1.25

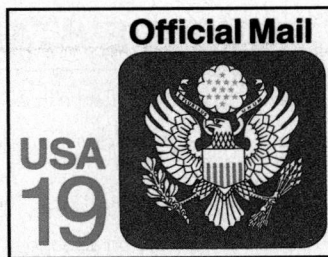

PO4

Designed by Bradbury Thompson

1991, May 24   **Litho.**
UZ5 PO4 19c **multicolored**   .80 *90.00*
    First day cancel, Seattle, WA
    (23,097)   1.25

PO5

1995, May 9   **Litho.**
UZ6 PO5 20c **multicolored**   .90 *90.00*
    First day cancel, Washington, DC   1.25

REVENUE STAMPS

The Commissioner of Internal Revenue advertised for bids for revenue stamps in August, 1862, and the contract was awarded to Butler & Carpenter of Philadelphia.

Nos. R1-R102 were used to pay taxes on documents and proprietary articles including playing cards. Until December 25, 1862, the law stated that a stamp could be used only for payment of the tax upon the particular instrument or article specified on its face. After that date, stamps, except the Proprietary, could be used indiscriminately.

Most stamps of the first issue appeared in the latter part of 1862 or early in 1863. The 5c and 10c Proprietary were issued in the fall of 1864, and the 6c Proprietary on April 13, 1871.

Plate numbers and imprints are usually found at the bottom of the plate on all denominations except 25c and $1 to $3.50. On these it is nearly always at the left of the plate. The imprint reads "Engraved by Butler & Carpenter, Philadelphia" or "Jos. R. Carpenter."

Plates were of various sizes: 1c and 2c, 210 subjects (14x15); 3c to 20c, 170 subjects (17x10); 25c to 30c, 102 subjects (17x6); 50c to 70c, 85 subjects (17x5); $1 to $1.90, 90 subjects (15x6); $2 to $10, 72 subjects (12x6); $15 to $50, 54 subjects (9x6); $200, 8 subjects (2x4). No. R132, one subject.

The paper varies, the first employed being thin, hard and brittle until September, 1869, from which time it acquired a softer texture and varied from medium to very thick. Early printings of some revenue stamps occur on paper which appears to have laid lines. Some are found on experimental silk paper, first employed about August, 1870.

Some of the stamps were in use eight years and were printed several times. Many color variations occurred, particularly if unstable pigments were used and the color was intended to be purple or violet, such as the 4c Proprietary, 30c and $2.50 stamps. Before 1868 dull colors predominate on these and the early red stamps. In later printings of the 4c Proprietary, 30c and $2.50 stamps, red predominates in the mixture and on the dollar values of red is brighter. The early $1.90 stamp is dull purple, imperforate or perforated. In a later printing, perforated only, the purple is darker.

In the first issue, canceling usually was done with pen and ink and all values quoted are for stamps canceled in that way. Handstamped cancellations as a rule sell for more than pen. Printed cancellations are scarce and command much higher prices. Herringbone, punched or other types of cancellation which break the surface of the paper adversely affect prices.

Many, but not all, of the pre-1898 revenue stamps exist unused with original gum. These are not valued in the listings, but they sell for more than used examples in the marketplace.

1862-72 revenue stamps from the first three issues were often used on large folded documents. As a result, multiples (blocks and strips of four or more) are not often found in sound condition. In addition, part perforate pairs of all but the most common varieties generally are off center. Catalogue values of the noted multiples are for items in fine condition or for very fine appearing examples with small faults. Examples of such multiples in a true very fine grade without any faults are scarce to rare and will sell for well above catalogue value.

Where a stamp is known in a given form or variety but insufficient information is available on which to base a value, its existence is indicated by a dash.

Part perforate stamps are understood to be imperforate horizontally unless otherwise stated.

Part perforate stamps with an asterisk (*) exist imperforate horizontally or vertically.

Part perforate PAIRS should be imperforate between the stamps as well as imperforate at opposite ends. See illustration **Type A** under "Information For Collectors-Perforations."

All imperforate or part perforate stamps listed are known in pairs or larger multiples. Certain unlisted varieties of this nature exist as singles and specialists believe them genuine. Exceptions are Nos. R13a, R22a and R60b, which have not been reported in multiples but are regarded as legitimate by most students.

Documentary revenue stamps were no longer required after December 31, 1967.

First Issue

George Washington
R1　　　　　　　R2

1862-71　　**Engr.**　　**Perf. 12**

		a. Imperf.	b. Part Perf.	Perforated c. Old Paper	d. Silk Paper
R1	R1 1c **Express, red**	70.00	40.00*	1.40	150.00
	Pair	160.00	180.00	3.25	
	Block of 4	650.00	600.00	12.50	
	Dble. transfer			45.00	
	Short transfer, No. 156	—	—	85.00	
	e. Vert. pair, imperf. btwn.			200.00	
R2	R1 1c **Playing Cards, red**	1,800.	1,500.	160.00	
	Pair	3,800.	3,600.	350.00	
	Block of 4			900.00	
	Cracked plate	—		225.00	
R3	R1 1c **Proprietary, red**	1,000.	250.00*	.50	57.50
	Pair	2,100.	700.00	1.25	140.00
	Block of 4		3,000.	3.25	350.00
R4	R1 1c **Telegraph, red**	600.00		17.50	
	Pair	1,700.		37.50	

		a. Imperf.	b. Part Perf.	Perforated c. Old Paper	d. Silk Paper
	Block of 4			110.00	

Double transfer (T5)

		a. Imperf.	b. Part Perf.	Perforated c. Old Paper	d. Silk Paper
R5	R2 2c **Bank Check, blue**	1.25	5.00*	.50	
	Pair	19.00	17.00	2.00	
	Block of 4	190.00	140.00	8.00	
	Double transfer (T5)	100.00	140.00	50.00	
	Cracked plate		22.50	10.00	
	e. Double impression			800.00	
	f. Vert. pair, imperf. btwn.			400.00	
R6	R2 2c **Bank Check, orange**		55.00*	.25	275.00
	Pair		—	.50	
	Block of 4			1.40	
	Double transfer (T5)			325.00	
	e. 2c orange, green			700.00	
	f. Vert. half used as 1c on document			—	

Double transfer (T7)

		a. Imperf.	b. Part Perf.	Perforated c. Old Paper	d. Silk Paper
R7	R2 2c **Certificate, blue**	14.00		30.00	
	Pair	45.00		75.00	
	Block of 4	200.00		300.00	
	Double transfer (T7)	400.00		350.00	
	Cracked plate			37.50	
R8	R2 2c **Certificate, orange**			40.00	
	Pair			190.00	
	Block of 4			850.00	
	Double transfer (T7)			450.00	
R9	R2 2c **Express, blue**	14.00	30.00*	.40	
	Pair	50.00	140.00	1.25	
	Block of 4	160.00	350.00	4.25	
	Dble. transfer	60.00		17.50	
	Cracked plate			20.00	
R10	R2 2c **Express, orange**		750.00	12.50	160.00
	Pair			29.00	
	Block of 4			60.00	
	Dble. transfer			22.50	
R11	R2 2c **Playing Cards, blue**	1,100.	250.00	4.00	
	Pair		600.00	13.00	
	Block of 4			50.00	
	Cracked plate			30.00	
R12	R2 2c **Playing Cards, orange**			50.00	
	Pair			450.00	

Double transfer (T13)

Double transfer (T13a)

	a. Imperf.	b. Part Perf.	c. Old Paper	d. Silk Paper
			Perforated	

R13	R2 2c	**Proprietary, blue**	700.	250.	.40 140.00
		Pair	700.		.90
		Block of 4	1,800.		5.00
		Double transfer (T13)			150.00
		Complete double transfer (T13a)			200.00
		Cracked plate			25.00
e.		2c ultra			300.00
		Pair			650.00
		Block of 4			—
		Dble. transfer (T13)			
		Complete dble. transfer (T13a)			850.00
f.		Horiz. half used as 1c on document			—
R14	R2 2c	**Proprietary, orange**			60.00
		Pair			350.00
		Block of 4			
		Double transfer (T13)			250.00
		Complete double transfer (T13a)			500.00

Double transfer (T15)

Double transfer (T15a)

R15	R2 2c	**U. S. Internal Revenue, or-ange** ('64)	—	—	.35 .40
		Pair			.80 1.00
		Block of 4			2.00
		Double transfer (T15)			65.00
		Double transfer (T15a)			50.00
		Dble. transfer			12.00
		Triple transfer			40.00
		Cracked plate			10.00
e.		2c orange, green			850.00
f.		Half used as 1c on document			—

R3

R16	R3 3c	**Foreign Exchange, green**	550.00		4.50 110.00
		Pair	1,500.		10.50
		Block of 4			75.00
		Dble. transfer			—
R17	R3 3c	**Playing Cards, green** ('63)	27,500.		150.00
		Pair	65,000.		350.00
		Block of 4			900.00
R18	R3 3c	**Proprietary, green**	575.00		7.50 85.00

	Pair	1,250.		17.00 200.00
	Block of 4			42.50
	Dble. transfer			11.50
	Cracked plate			
e.	Double impression			1,000.
f.	Printed on both sides			3,500.
R19	R3 3c	**Telegraph, green**	80.00	27.50	2.75
	Pair	500.00	82.50	8.75
	Block of 4	1,200.	300.00	80.00
	Sewing machine perf, unofficial	700.00		
R20	R3 4c	**Inland Exchange, brown** ('63)			2.00 140.00
	Pair			5.25
	Block of 4			22.50
	Double transfer at top			7.50
R21	R3 4c	**Playing Cards, slate** ('63)			600.00
	Pair			1,250.
	Block of 4			2,600.
R22	R3 4c	**Proprietary, purple**	—	475.00	7.50 160.00
	Pair	1,000.	17.50	350.00
	Block of 4	2,100.	55.00	—
	Double transfer at top			17.50
	Double transfer at bottom			12.50

There are shade and color variations of Nos. R21-R22. See foreword of Revenue Stamps section.

R23	R3 5c	**Agreement, red**		.50	2.25
		Pair		1.00	4.75
		Block of 4		2.10	20.00
		Dble. transfer in numerals		25.00	
e.		Diag. half used as 2c on document		2,500.	

R24	R3 5c	**Certificate, red**	3.50	13.00	.50 .55
		Pair	35.00	150.00	1.25 1.25
		Block of 4	250.00	400.00	3.00 6.00
		Double transfer in upper label			10.00
		Dble. transfer throughout			200.00
		Triple transfer (No. 121)			35.00
e.		Half used as 2c on document			—
f.		Impression of #R3 on back			2,750.
R25	R3 5c	**Express, red**	7.00	7.00*	.40
		Pair	22.50	100.00	.90
		Block of 4	210.00	300.00	2.25
		Double transfer			5.00
R26	R3 5c	**Foreign Exchange, red**		—	.50 475.00
		Pair			1.25
		Block of 4			15.00
		Double transfer at top			20.00
		Double transfer at bottom			10.00
R27	R3 5c	**Inland Exchange, red**	8.25	6.00	.50 17.50
		Pair	37.50	42.50	1.25 40.00
		Block of 4	120.00	110.00	3.00
		Double transfer at top	77.50	47.50	27.50
		Double transfer at bottom			—
		Cracked plate	95.00	90.00	32.50
e.		Double impression			—
R28	R3 5c	**Playing Cards, red** ('63)			35.00

No.	Die	Denom	Description			
			Pair	75.00		
			Block of 4	150.00		
e.			Double impression	1,000.		
R29	R3	5c	**Proprietary, red** ('64)	27.50	250.00	
			Pair	60.00		
			Block of 4	160.00		
R30	R3	6c	**Inland Exchange, orange** ('63)	2.00	160.00	
			Pair	18.50		
			Block of 4	100.00		
R31	R3	6c	**Proprietary, orange** ('71)	2,000.		

Nearly all examples of No. R31 are faulty and poorly centered. The Catalogue value is for a fine centered stamp with minor faults which do not detract from its appearance.

No.	Die	Denom	Description			
R32	R3	10c	**Bill of Lading, blue**	50.00	450.00	1.50
			Pair	300.00	950.00	4.00
			Block of 4	750.00		10.00
			Dble. transfer (#33 & 143)	—		
e.			Half used as 5c on document	200.00		
R33	R3	10c	**Certificate, blue**	250.00	750.00*	.35 / 6.00
			Pair	650.00	1,600.	.75 / 17.50
			Block of 4	1,800.	—	2.25 / 90.00
			Dble. transfer		7.50	
			Cracked plate		15.00	
e.			Half used as 5c on document	200.00		
R34	R3	10c	**Contract, blue**	475.00	.50	2.25
			Pair	1,250.	1.25	6.00
			Block of 4		4.75	60.00
			Complete double transfer	70.00		
e.			10c ultra	650.00	1.00	
			Pair	2.50		
			Block of 4	17.50		

No.	Die	Denom	Description			
f.			Vertical half used as 5c on document	200.00		
R35	R3	10c	**Foreign Exchange, blue**	12.50	—	
			Pair	27.50		
			Block of 4	92.50		
e.			10c **ultra**	18.00		
			Pair	55.00		
			Block of 4	125.00		
R36	R3	10c	**Inland Exchange, blue**	350.00	4.00*	.30 / 85.00
			Pair	900.00	15.00	.60 / 175.00
			Block of 4	3,250.	80.00	1.75 / —
e.			Half used as 5c on document	200.00		
R37	R3	10c	**Power of Attorney, blue**	850.00	27.50	1.00
			Pair	2,250.	100.00	2.25
			Block of 4	5,500.	300.00	8.00
e.			Half used as 5c on document	200.00		
R38	R3	10c	**Proprietary, blue** ('64)	17.50		
			Pair	40.00		
			Block of 4	110.00		
R39	R3	15c	**Foreign Exchange, brown** ('63)	15.00		
			Pair	50.00		
			Block of 4	250.00		
e.			Double impression	1,000.		
R40	R3	15c	**Inland Exchange, brown**	37.50	12.50	1.75
			Pair	250.00	50.00	3.50
			Block of 4	900.00	450.00	11.50
			Dble. transfer		6.25	
			Cracked plate	60.00	37.50	14.00
e.			Double impression		1,750.	550.00
R41	R3	20c	**Foreign Exchange, red**	75.00	60.00	
			Pair	350.00	150.00	
			Block of 4	1,000.	350.00	
R42	R3	20c	**Inland Exchange, red**	15.00	20.00	.45
			Pair	50.00	60.00	1.00
			Block of 4	300.00	300.00	14.00
e.			Half used as 10c on document	200.00		

R4   R5

No.	Die	Denom	Description	a. Imperf.	b. Part Perf.	Perforated c. Old Paper	Perforated d. Silk Paper
R43	R4	25c	**Bond, red**	250.00	6.00	3.50	
			Pair	675.00	60.00	8.00	
			Block of 4	5,000.	400.00	60.00	
R44	R4	25c	**Certificate, red**	10.00	6.00*	.50	2.75
			Pair	50.00	40.00	1.10	8.25
			Block of 4	500.00	250.00	8.00	27.50
			Double transfer, top or bottom			2.00	
			Triple transfer			—	
e.			Printed on both sides			3,500	
f.			Impression of No. R48 on back			6,500.	
R45	R4	25c	**Entry of Goods, red**	20.00	140.00*	1.25	80.00
			Pair	70.00	800.00	50.00	
			Block of 4	500.00		140.00	
			Top frame line double	72.50	300.00	11.00	
R46	R4	25c	**Insurance, red**	11.00	17.00	.30	5.50
			Pair	42.50	35.00	.75	13.00
			Block of 4	750.00	250.00	5.50	
			Cracked plate			17.50	
e.			Double impression			500.00	
R47	R4	25c	**Life Insurance, red**	45.00	525.00	9.50	
			Pair	150.00	1,300.	50.00	
			Block of 4	650.00		240.00	
R48	R4	25c	**Power of Attorney, red**	8.00	40.00	1.00	
			Pair	50.00	125.00	2.25	
			Block of 4	500.00	600.00	12.50	
			Dble. transfer			1.10	
			Bottom frame line double			5.50	
R49	R4	25c	**Protest, red**	30.00	800.00	7.50	
			Pair	200.00	1,600.	29.00	
			Block of 4	750.00		115.00	
R50	R4	25c	**Warehouse Receipt, red**	47.50	675.00	40.00	
			Pair	250.00	1,350.	95.00	
			Block of 4	1,200.		325.00	
R51	R4	30c	**Foreign Exchange, lilac**	120.00	2,250.	55.00	500.00
			Pair	600.00	5,000.	225.00	
			Block of 4	3,500.			
			Dble. transfer			100.00	

			a. Imperf.	b. Part Perf.	c. Old Paper	d. Silk Paper
		Top frame line double			—	
R52	R4 30c	**Inland Exchange, lilac**	65.00	80.00	8.00	—
		Pair	350.00	425.00	40.00	
		Block of 4	1,000.	—	140.00	
		Dble. transfer			30.00	

There are shade and color variations of Nos. R51-R52. See foreword of "Revenues" section.

			a. Imperf.	b. Part Perf.	c. Old Paper	d. Silk Paper
R53	R4 40c	**Inland Exchange, brown**	1,300.	8.00	7.50	—
		Pair	5,250.	50.00	16.00	
		Block of 4		210.00	275.00	
		Dble. transfer		50.00	30.00	
f.		Double impression			—	
R54	R5 50c	**Conveyance, blue**	17.00	3.00	.35	3.00
		Pair	100.00	45.00	.70	6.50
		Block of 4	600.00	160.00	2.50	
		Dble. transfer			6.00	
		Cracked plate			15.00	
		Scatched plate			—	
e.		50c **ultra**			.50	—
		Pair			1.25	
		Block of 4			10.00	
R55	R5 50c	**Entry of Goods, blue**		15.00	.45	90.00
		Pair		300.00	1.75	210.00
		Block of 4		650.00	25.00	
		Dble. transfer			5.00	
		Cracked plate			20.00	
R56	R5 50c	**Foreign Exchange, blue**	60.00	110.00	7.00	
		Pair	200.00	550.00	42.50	
		Block of 4			140.00	
		Double transfer at left			11.00	
e.		Double impression				500.00
f.		Half used as 25c on document				200.00
R57	R5 50c	**Lease, blue**	27.50	150.00	9.00	
		Pair	200.00	550.00	67.50	
		Block of 4	1,000.	1,300.	225.00	
R58	R5 50c	**Life Insurance, blue**	40.00	90.00	1.50	
		Pair	160.00		10.00	
		Block of 4	850.00		50.00	
		Dble. transfer	47.50		11.00	
e.		Double impression				800.00

Cracked Plate (C59)

			a. Imperf	b. Part Perf.	c. Old Paper	d. Silk Paper
R59	R5 50c	**Mortgage, blue**	20.00	4.50	.65	—

			a. Imperf.	b. Part Perf.	c. Old Paper	d. Silk Paper
		Pair	100.00	225.00	1.50	
		Block of 4	400.00	500.00	7.50	
		Cracked plate (C59)			37.50	12.50
		Scratched plate, diagonal	35.00	25.00	12.50	
		Dble. transfer			3.50	
e.		Double impression	—		—	

Scratch is across three stamps. Value is for a single.

			a. Imperf.	b. Part Perf.	c. Old Paper	d. Silk Paper
R60	R5 50c	**Original Process, blue**	5.00	600.00	1.00	4.00
		Pair	77.50		2.75	15.00
		Block of 4	1,000.		7.50	125.00
		Double transfer at top			5.00	
		Double transfer at bottom			8.00	
		Scratched plate			10.00	
e.		Half used as 25c on document			—	
R61	R5 50c	**Passage Ticket, blue**	100.00	325.00	2.00	
		Pair	300.00	1,400.	12.50	
		Block of 4	1,250.		225.00	
		Cracked plate			—	
R62	R5 50c	**Probate of Will, blue**	50.00	175.00	20.00	
		Pair	200.00	825.00	50.00	
		Block of 4	850.00	1,650.	350.00	
		Scratched plate			—	
R63	R5 50c	**Surety Bond, blue**	275.00	2.50	.30	
		Pair	1,200.	15.00	1.75	
		Block of 4		100.00	10.00	
e.		50c **ultra**			.75	
		Pair			5.50	
		Block of 4			55.00	
R64	R5 60c	**Inland Exchange, orange**	100.00	75.00	8.00	65.00
		Pair	300.00	225.00	17.50	150.00
		Block of 4	750.00	550.00	100.00	
R65	R5 70c	**Foreign Exchange, green**	600.00	175.00	12.00	110.00
		Pair	2,750.	950.00	40.00	225.00
		Block of 4		2,000.	250.00	
		Cracked plate			—	30.00

Pairs and blocks of No. R65b are valued in the grade of fine.

R6

R7

			a. Imperf.	b. Part Perf.	c. Old Paper	d. Silk Paper
R66	R6 $1	**Conveyance, red**	25.00	1,000.	25.00	140.00
		Pair	90.00	4,000.	65.00	

			a. Imperf.	b. Part Perf.	c. Old Paper	d. Silk Paper
		Block of 4	650.00		160.00	
		Dble. transfer	35.00		37.50	
		Right frame line double	90.00		77.50	
		Top frame line double	—		60.00	
R67	R6 $1	**Entry of Goods, red**	42.50		2.50	125.00
		Pair	150.00		6.50	
		Block of 4	700.00		55.00	
R68	R6 $1	**Foreign Exchange, red**	80.00		.75	110.00
		Pair	250.00		1.75	
		Block of 4	1,475.		11.00	
		Dble. transfer			5.50	
		Left frame line double	180.00		19.00	
e.		Diagonal half used as 50c on document				225.00
R69	R6 $1	**Inland Exchange, red**	15.00	650.00*	.70	3.75

	Pair	75.00	*4,000.*		2.00	9.00
	Block of 4	850.00	—		9.50	35.00
	Double transfer at bottom				4.25	
	Double transfer of top shields	110.00			21.00	
R70 R6 $1	**Lease, red**	42.50			4.00	
	Pair	110.00			12.00	
	Block of 4	500.00			80.00	
	Double transfer at bottom	50.00			11.00	
	Cracked plate				26.00	
e.	Half used as 50c on document				—	
R71 R6 $1	**Life Insurance, red**	200.00			9.00	—
	Pair	425.00			20.00	
	Block of 4	*1,000.*			60.00	
	Right frame line double	275.00			20.00	
e.	Half used as 50c on document				—	
R72 R6 $1	**Manifest, red**	42.50			35.00	
	Pair	120.00			85.00	
	Block of 4	600.00			210.00	
R73 R6 $1	**Mortgage, red**	25.00			200.00	
	Pair	85.00			400.00	
	Block of 4	600.00			825.00	
	Double transfer at left	—			230.00	
	Bottom frame line double	60.00			350.00	
R74 R6 $1	**Passage Ticket, red**	300.00			275.00	
	Pair	650.00			600.00	
	Block of 4	*1,325.*			1,550.	
R75 R6 $1	**Power of Attorney, red**	90.00			2.50	
	Pair	225.00			6.00	
	Block of 4	500.00			26.00	
	Dble. transfer				9.50	
	Recut				11.50	
R76 R6 $1	**Probate of Will, red**	90.00			50.00	
	Pair	275.00			125.00	
	Block of 4	*800.00*			325.00	
	Right frame line double	160.00			72.50	
R77 R7 $1.30	**Foreign Exchange, orange** ('63)	*6,500.*			75.00	
	Pair				190.00	
	Block of 4				—	

Double transfer (T78)

R78 R7 $1.50	**Inland Exchange, blue**	27.50		6.00	
	Pair	140.00		75.00	
	Block of 4	500.00		400.00	
	Double transfer (T78)			12.50	
R79 R7 $1.60	**Foreign Exchange, green** ('63)	1,300.		120.00	
	Pair	*5,500.*		375.00	
R80 R7 $1.90	**Foreign Exchange, purple** ('63)	10,000.		110.00	—
	Pair	300.00			
	Block of 4	700.00			

There are many shade and color variations of No. R80. See foreword of "Revenues" section.

R8

R81 R8 $2	**Conveyance, red**	180.00	2,500.		3.50	40.00
	Pair	400.00	*7,000.*		10.00	90.00
	Block of 4	1,000.			65.00	200.00
	Cracked plate				32.50	
e.	Half used as $1 on document				*600.00*	
R82 R8 $2	**Mortgage, red**	135.00			6.00	60.00
	Pair	300.00			14.00	125.00
	Block of 4	700.00			60.00	
	Dble. transfer				12.50	

e.	Half used as $1 on document			—	
R83 R8 $2	**Probate of Will, red** ('63)	5,500.		80.00	
	Pair	12,000.		200.00	
	Block of 4			425.00	
	Dble. transfer			90.00	
e.	Horiz. half used as $1 on document			*750.00*	
R84 R8 $2.50	**Inland Exchange, purple** ('63)	7,000.		20.00	30.00
	Pair	25,000.		40.00	75.00
	Block of 4			325.00	425.00
e.	Double impression			1,400.	

There are many shade and color variations of Nos. R84c and R84d. See foreword of "Revenues" section.

R85 R8 $3	**Charter Party, green**	175.00		10.00	150.00
	Pair	400.00		65.00	325.00
	Block of 4	2,750.		250.00	
	Double transfer at top			—	
	Double transfer at bottom			12.00	
e.	Printed on both sides			*4,500.*	
f.	Half used as $1.50 on document			—	
g.	Impression of No. RS208 on back			12,000.	
R86 R8 $3	**Manifest, green**	175.00		50.00	
	Pair	400.00		125.00	
	Block of 4	3,500.		300.00	
	Dble. transfer			210.00	
R87 R8 $3.50	**Inland Exchange, blue** ('63)	7,000.		65.00	
	Pair	27,500.		180.00	
	Block of 4			450.00	
e.	Printed on both sides			4,000.	

R9

R10

			a. Imperf	b. Part Perf.	Perforated c. Old Paper	d. Silk Paper
					Block of 4	400.00
					Double transfer at top	57.50
R97	R10	$15 Mortgage, blue			2,700.	225.00
		Pair			6,500.	500.00
		Block of 4			15,000.	2,750.
	e.	$15 ultra				250.00
		Pair				750.00
		Block of 4				4,000.
	f.	$15 milky blue				275.00
		Pair				1,500.
R98	R10	$20 Conveyance, orange			150.00	110.00 175.00
		Pair			400.00	250.00 350.00
		Block of 4			1,000.	800.00
R99	R10	$20 Probate of Will, orange			2,000.	2,000.
		Pair			4,250.	4,250.
		Block of 4			9,000.	9,000.
R100	R10	$25 Mortgage, red ('63)			1,500.	200.00 250.00
		Pair			3,250.	400.00
		Block of 4			9,000.	1,250.
	e.	Horiz. pair, imperf. between				2,500.
R101	R10	$50 U.S. Internal Revenue, green ('63)			250.00	150.00
		Pair			600.00	325.00
		Block of 4			2,300.	675.00
		Cracked plate				160.00

R11

R102	R11	$200 U.S. Internal Revenue, grn & red ('64)			2,500.	900.00
		Pair			5,500.	2,000.
		Block of 4			12,500.	6,750.

DOCUMENTARY STAMPS
Second Issue

After release of the First Issue revenue stamps, the Bureau of Internal Revenue received many reports of fraudulent cleaning and re-use. The Bureau ordered a Second Issue with new designs and colors, using a patented "chameleon" paper which is usually violet or pinkish, with silk fibers.

While designs are different from those of the first issue, stamp sizes and make up of the plates are the same as for corresponding denominations.

			a. Imperf	b. Part Perf.	Perforated c. Old Paper	d. Silk Paper
R88	R9	$5 Charter Party, red	300.00		9.00	90.00
		Pair	625.00		65.00	
		Block of 4	1,400.		200.00	
		Right frame line double	325.00		70.00	
		Top frame line double	325.00		60.00	
R89	R9	$5 Conveyance, red	40.00		10.00	140.00
		Pair	200.00		22.50	300.00
		Block of 4	900.00		110.00	
R90	R9	$5 Manifest, red	185.00		90.00	
		Pair	450.00		250.00	
		Block of 4	1,100.		550.00	
		Left frame line double	210.00		150.00	
R91	R9	$5 Mortgage, red	175.00		22.50	
		Pair	800.00		87.50	
		Block of 4	—		1,200.	
R92	R9	$5 Probate of Will, red	700.00		25.00	
		Pair	1,450.		100.00	
		Block of 4	3,000.		375.00	
R93	R9	$10 Charter Party, green	825.00		32.50	
		Pair	1,750.		95.00	
		Block of 4	—		450.00	
		Dble. transfer			85.00	
R94	R9	$10 Conveyance, green	125.00		70.00	
		Pair	350.00		175.00	
		Block of 4	900.00		700.00	
		Double transfer at top	150.00		125.00	
		Right frame line double			150.00	
R95	R9	$10 Mortgage, green	700.00		35.00	
		Pair	1,750.		120.00	
		Block of 4	5,500.		—	
		Top frame line double	725.00		52.50	
R96	R9	$10 Probate of Will, green	2,250.		40.00	
		Pair	6,750.		87.50	

George Washington — R12a
R12
Engraved and printed by Jos. R. Carpenter, Philadelphia.
Various Frames and Numeral Arrangements

1871 — *Perf. 12*

R103	R12	1c blue & black	70.00
		Cut cancel	24.00
		Pair	175.00
		Block of 4	400.00
	a.	Inverted center	1,750.
		Pair	3,750.
		Block of 4	—
R104	R12	2c blue & black	2.75
		Cut cancel	.20
		Pair	6.25
		Block of 4	40.00
	a.	Inverted center	6,000.
R105	R12a	3c blue & black	40.00
		Cut cancel	15.00
		Pair	90.00
		Block of 4	275.00
R106	R12a	4c blue & black	100.00
		Cut cancel	35.00
		Pair	225.00
		Block of 4	450.00
	a.	Horiz. half used as 2c on document	500.00
	b.	Vert. half used as 2c on document	1,000.
R107	R12a	5c blue & black	2.00
		Cut cancel	.50
		Pair	6.00
		Block of 4	22.50
	a.	Inverted center	4,500.
R108	R12a	6c blue & black	175.00
		Cut cancel	57.50
		Pair	350.00
		Block of 4	925.00
R109	R12a	10c blue & black	1.50
		Cut cancel	.20
		Pair	9.50
		Block of 4	25.00
	a.	Inverted center	2,500.
		Pair	5,750.
	b.	Double impression of center	—
	c.	Half used as 5c on document	250.00

No. R109a is valued in the grade of fine.

R110	R12a	15c blue & black	65.00
		Cut cancel	22.50
		Pair	130.00
		Block of 4	275.00
R111	R12a	20c blue & black	7.50
		Cut cancel	2.75
		Pair	22.50
		Block of 4	87.50
	a.	Inverted center	12,500.
		Pair	—

No. R111a is valued in the grade of fine.

R13   R13a

R112	R13	25c blue & black	1.50
		Cut cancel	.25
		Pair	3.25
		Block of 4	11.00
		Double transfer, position 57	25.00
	a.	Inverted center	11,000.
	b.	Sewing machine perf.	110.00
		Cut cancel	65.00
		Pair	300.00
		Block of 4	1,500.
	c.	Perf. 8	475.00

R113	R13	30c **blue & black**	125.00
		Cut cancel	45.00
		Pair	250.00
		Block of 4	625.00
R114	R13	40c **blue & black**	110.00
		Cut cancel	27.50
		Pair	240.00
R115	R13a	50c **blue & black**	1.00
		Cut cancel	.20
		Pair	2.25
		Block of 4	8.75
		Double transfer	25.00
a.		Sewing machine perf.	75.00
		Pair	200.00
		Block of 4	*900.00*
b.		Inverted center	1,500.
		Pair	*3,500.*
		Inverted center, punch cancellation	300.00
		Pair	700.00
R116	R13a	60c **blue & black**	160.00
		Cut cancel	52.50
		Pair	350.00
		Foreign entry, design of 70c	200.00
R117	R13a	70c **blue & black**	75.00
		Cut cancel	24.00
		Pair	160.00
a.		Inverted center	*4,000.*
		Cut cancel	*2,000.*

R13b

R13c

R118	R13b	$1 **blue & black**	8.00
		Cut cancel	1.75
		Pair	20.00
		Block of 4	50.00
a.		Inverted center	*5,000.*
		Punch cancel	*900.00*
R119	R13b	$1.30 **blue & black**	550.00
		Cut cancel	150.00
		Pair	1,150.
R120	R13b	$1.50 **blue & black**	19.00
		Cut cancel	8.00
		Pair	65.00
		Block of 4	
		Foreign entry, design of $1	450.00
a.		Sewing machine perf.	1,000.
		Pair	
R121	R13b	$1.60 **blue & black**	575.00
		Cut cancel	300.00
		Pair	1,200.
R122	R13b	$1.90 **blue & black**	400.00
		Cut cancel	120.00
		Pair	850.00
		Block of 4	
R123	R13c	$2 **blue & black**	20.00
		Cut cancel	7.50
		Pair	55.00
		Block of 4	350.00
		Double transfer	—
R124	R13c	$2.50 **blue & black**	35.00
		Cut cancel	16.00
		Pair	95.00
		Block of 4	750.00
R125	R13c	$3 **blue & black**	45.00
		Cut cancel	17.50
		Pair	110.00

		Block of 4	550.00
		Double transfer	—
R126	R13c	$3.50 **blue & black**	300.00
		Cut cancel	100.00
		Pair	900.00

R13d

R13e

R127	R13d	$5 **blue & black**	27.50
		Cut cancel	9.00
		Pair	100.00
		Block of 4	500.00
a.		Inverted center	*3,000.*
		Punch cancel	*1,100.*
R128	R13d	$10 **blue & black**	210.00
		Cut cancel	75.00
		Pair	475.00
		Block of 4	*1,000.*
R129	R13e	$20 **blue & black**	800.00
		Cut cancel	290.00
		Pair	1,750.
		Block of 4	*10,000.*
R130	R13e	$25 **blue & black**	900.00
		Cut cancel	325.00
		Pair	2,000.
R131	R13e	$50 **blue & black**	1,000.
		Cut cancel	375.00
		Pair	2,250.

R13f

R132	R13f	$200 **red, blue & black**	8,250.
		Cut cancel	3,500.

Printed in sheets of one.

R13g

R133	R13g	$500 **red orange, green & black**	16,000.

Printed in sheets of one.
Value for No. R133 is for a very fine appearing example with a light circular cut cancel or with minor flaws.
Inverted Centers: Fraudulently produced inverted centers exist, some excellently made.

Confusion resulting from the fact that all 1c through $50 denominations of the Second Issue were uniform in color, caused the ordering of a new printing with values in distinctive colors.
Plates used were those of the preceding issue.

Third Issue
Engraved and printed by Jos. R. Carpenter, Philadelphia.
Various Frames and Numeral Arrangements.
Violet "Chameleon" Paper with Silk Fibers.

1871-72				*Perf. 12*
R134	R12	1c **claret & black** ('72)		50.00
		Cut cancel		22.50
		Pair		125.00
		Block of 4		375.00

R135	R12	2c **orange & black**		.40
		Cut cancel		.20
		Pair		.80
		Block of 4		1.75
		Double transfer		1,500.
		Double impression of frame		1,600.
		Frame printed on both sides		150.00
		Double impression of center		700.00
a.		2c vermilion & black (error)		700.00
b.		Inverted center		2,100.
		Pair		—
		Block of 4		—
c.		Imperf., pair		—
		Block of 4		—
R136	R12a	4c **brown & black** ('72)		80.00
		Cut cancel		24.00
		Pair		190.00
R137	R12a	5c **orange & black**		.35
		Cut cancel		.20
		Pair		.75
		Block of 4		1.60
a.		Inverted center		5,000.
		"Block" of 3		

No. R137a is valued in the grade of fine.

R138	R12a	6c **orange & black** ('72)		90.00
		Cut cancel		27.50
		Pair		210.00
		Block of 4		950.00
R139	R12a	15c **brown & black** ('72)		25.00
		Cut cancel		6.00
		Pair		55.00
		Block of 4		175.00
a.		Inverted center		20,000.
		Pair		
R140	R13	30c **orange & black** ('72)		35.00
		Cut cancel		8.75
		Pair		80.00
		Block of 4		325.00
		Double transfer		
a.		Inverted center		3,250.
		Cut cancel		1,850.
R141	R13	40c **brown & black** ('72)		75.00
		Cut cancel		22.50
		Pair		175.00
		Block of 4		400.00
R142	R13a	60c **orange & black** ('72)		100.00
		Cut cancel		35.00
		Pair		300.00
		Block of 4		650.00
		Foreign entry, design of 70c		125.00
R143	R13a	70c **green & black** ('72)		85.00
		Cut cancel		27.50
		Pair		200.00
		Block of 4		500.00
R144	R13b	$1 **green & black** ('72)		2.00
		Cut cancel		.55
		Pair		8.50
		Block of 4		75.00
a.		Inverted center		11,500.
R145	R13c	$2 **vermilion & black** ('72)		37.50
		Cut cancel		16.00
		Pair		80.00
		Block of 4		300.00
		Double transfer		57.50
R146	R13c	$2.50 **claret & black** ('72)		70.00
		Cut cancel		26.00
		Pair		150.00
		Block of 4		325.00
a.		Inverted center		25,000.
R147	R13c	$3 **green & black** ('72)		70.00
		Cut cancel		24.00
		Pair		150.00
		Block of 4		325.00
		Double transfer		
R148	R13d	$5 **vermilion & black** ('72)		40.00
		Cut cancel		14.50
		Pair		85.00
		Block of 4		175.00
R149	R13d	$10 **green & black** ('72)		240.00
		Cut cancel		52.50
		Pair		500.00
		Block of 4		1,200.
R150	R13e	$20 **orange & black** ('72)		625.00
		Cut cancel		260.00
		Pair		1,300.
		Block of 4		3,000.
a.		$20 vermilion & black (error)		1,000.

(See note on Inverted Centers after No. R133.)

1874   **Perf. 12**

R151	R12	2c **orange & black,** *green*		.20
		Cut cancel		.20
		Pair		.40
		Block of 4		.90
a.		Inverted center		500.00

Liberty — R14

1875-78

			Silk Paper a. Perf.	Wmkd. 191R b. Perf.	c. Roul. 6
R152	R14	2c **blue,** *blue*	.45	.35	32.50
		Pair	.90	.70	125.00
		"L" shaped strip of 3			600.00
		Block of 4	1.90	2.10	
		Double transfer	5.50	5.50	
d.		Vert. pair, imperf. horiz.	525.00	350.00	
e.		Imperf., pair		*350.00*	

The watermarked paper came into use in 1878.

Nos. 279, 267a, 267, 279Bg, 279B, 272-274
Overprinted in Red or Blue:

a — Rectangular Periods

a — Square Periods

b — Small Period

I.R.

b

Overprint "a" exists in two (or possibly more) settings, with upright rectangular periods or with changed leg of "R" and square periods, both illustrated. Overprint "b" has 4 stamps with small period in each pane of 100 (pos. 41, 46, 91 & 96).

1898   **Wmk. 191**   **Perf. 12**

For Nos. R153-R160, values in the first column are for unused examples, values in the second column are for used.

R153	A87 (a)	1c **green,** red overprint	5.00	2.75
		Block of 4	29.00	12.00
		P# strip of 3, Impt.	35.00	
		P# block of 6, Impt.	95.00	
R154	A87 (b)	1c **green,** red overprint	.35	.35
		Block of 4	1.50	1.50
		P# strip of 3, Impt.	10.50	
		P# block of 6, Impt.	57.50	
a.		Overprint inverted	35.00	22.50
		Block of 4	175.00	
		P# strip of 3, Impt.	190.00	
		P# block of 6, Impt.	400.00	
b.		Overprint on back instead of face, inverted	—	
c.		Pair, one without overprint	10,000.	
R155	A88 (b)	2c **pink,** type III, blue overprint, *July 1, 1898*	.30	.25
		Block of 4	1.25	1.10
		P# strip of 3, Impt.	11.50	
		P# block of 6, Impt.	55.00	
		Dot in "S" of "CENTS"	1.10	
		P# strip of 3, Impt.	18.00	
b.		2c **carmine,** type III, blue overprint, *July 1, 1898*	.35	.25
		Block of 4	1.40	1.10
		P# strip of 3, Impt.	13.00	
		P# block of 6, Impt.	57.50	
		Dot in "S" of "CENTS"	1.40	
		P# strip of 3, Impt.	24.00	
c.		As No. R155, overprint inverted, *July 1898*	6.50	4.50
		Block of 4	27.50	20.00
		P# strip of 3, Impt.	65.00	
		P# block of 6, Impt.	160.00	
d.		Vertical pair, one without overprint	1,750.	
e.		Horiz. pair, one without overprint	—	
f.		As No. R155, overprint on back instead of face, inverted	250.00	

NOTE: Old No. R155 is now Nos. R155b, R155Ag; old No. R155a is Nos. R155c, R155Ah; old No. R155b is Nos. R155d, R155e; old No. R155c is No. R155f.

R155A	A88 (b)	2c **pink,** type IV, blue overprint *July 1, 1898*	.25	.25
		Block of 4	1.25	1.10
		P# strip of 3, Impt.	10.50	
		P# block of 6, Impt.	52.50	
g.		2c **carmine,** type IV, blue overprint, *July 1, 1898*	.25	.25
		Block of 4	1.40	1.10
		P# strip of 3, Impt.	11.50	

		P# block of 6, Impt.	55.00	
h.		As No. R155A, overprint inverted, *July 1898*	2.75	2.00
		Block of 4	13.00	9.25
		P# strip of 3, Impt.	32.50	
		P# block of 6, Impt.	77.50	

Handstamped Type "b" in Magenta

R156	A93	8c **violet brown**	5,750.	
R157	A94	10c **dark green**	4,000.	
		Block of 6	—	
R158	A95	15c **dark blue**	6,750.	

Nos. R156-R158 were emergency provisionals, privately prepared, not officially issued.

Privately Prepared Provisionals

No. 285
Overprinted in
Red

1898   **Wmk. 191**   **Perf. 12**

R158A	A100	1c **dark yellow green**	12,500.	10,000.

Same Overprinted "I.R./P.I.D. & Son" in Red

R158B	A100	1c **dark yellow green**	35,000.	32,500.

No. R158B is valued with small faults as each of the four recorded examples have faults.

Nos. R158A-R158B were overprinted with federal government permission by the Purvis Printing Co. upon order of Capt. L. H. Chapman of the Chapman Steamboat Line. Both the Chapman Line and P. I. Daprix & Son operated freight-carrying steamboats on the Erie Canal. The Chapman Line touched at Syracuse, Utica, Little Falls and Fort Plain; the Daprix boat ran between Utica and Rome. Overprintings of 250 of each stamp were made.

Dr. Kilmer & Co. provisional overprints and St. Louis provisional proprietary stamps are listed under "Private Die Medicine Stamps," Nos. RS307-RS315 and RS320-395.

Newspaper Stamp No.
PR121 Surcharged in Red

1898   **Perf. 12**

R159	N18	$5 **dark blue,** surcharge reading down	500.00	200.00
		Block of 4	2,100.	950.00
		P# strip of 3, Impt.	*2,250.*	
R160	N18	$5 **dark blue,** surcharge reading up	140.00	110.00
		Block of 4	550.00	*750.00*
		P# strip of 3, Impt.	2,000.	*750.00*

Battleship — R15

There are two styles of rouletting for the proprietary and documentary stamps of the 1898 issue, an ordinary rouletting 5½ and one by which small rectangles of the paper are cut out, usually called hyphen-hole perforation 7. Several stamps are known with an apparent roulette 14 caused by slippage of a hyphen-hole 7 rouletting wheel.

1898   **Wmk. 191R**

Rouletted 5½, Hyphen Hole Perf 7

			Roul. 5½		p. Hyphen Hole Perf. 7	
			Unused	Used	Unused	Used
R161	R15	½c **orange**	4.00	*17.50*		
		Block of 4	18.00	*140.00*		
		P# block of 6	350.00			
R162	R15	½c **dark gray**	.30	.25		
		Block of 4	1.60	1.10		

		Roul. 5½ Unused	Used	p. Hyphen Hole Perf. 7 Unused	Used
	P# block of 6	250.00			
	Double transfer		7.75		
a.	Vert. pair, imperf. horiz.	100.00			
R163 R15 1c	pale blue	.20	.20	.30	.25
	Block of 4	.40	.25	1.60	1.50
	P# block of 6	45.00		55.00	
	Double transfer	10.00			
a.	Vert. pair, imperf. horiz.	8.00			
b.	Imperf., pair	500.00			
R164 R15 2c	carmine rose	.30	.30	.35	.25
	Block of 4	1.50	1.50	2.75	1.10
	P# block of 6	55.00		65.00	
	Double transfer	1.10	.30		
a.	Vert. pair, imperf. horiz.	100.00			
b.	Imperf., pair	300.00			
c.	Horiz. pair, imperf. vert.	—			
R165 R15 3c	dark blue	4.00	.35	35.00	1.40
	Block of 4	15.00	1.40	150.00	6.25
	P# block of 6	450.00		750.00	
	Double transfer	—			
R166 R15 4c	pale rose	2.50	.35	13.00	1.60
	Block of 4	11.50	1.40	55.00	7.75
	P# block of 6	425.00		—	
a.	Vert. pair, imperf. horiz.	175.00			
R167 R15 5c	lilac	.65	.25	13.00	.35
	Block of 4	3.25	1.25	55.00	1.60
	P# block of 6	275.00		450.00	
a.	Pair, imperf. horiz. or vert.	275.00	175.00		
b.	Horiz. pair, imperf. between		650.00		
R168 R15 10c	dark brown	2.00	.25	7.50	.25
	Block of 4	12.00	1.25	32.50	1.25
	P# block of 6	350.00		475.00	
a.	Vert. pair, imperf. horiz.	40.00	35.00		
b.	Horiz. pair, imperf. vert.	—			
R169 R15 25c	purple brown	5.00	.50	15.00	.50
	Block of 4	21.00	2.25	65.00	1.75
	P# block of 6	750.00		—	
	Double transfer	—			
R170 R15 40c	blue lilac	125.00	1.25	175.00	30.00
	Block of 4	600.00	52.50	875.00	225.00
	P# block of 6	—		—	
	Cut cancel		.35		12.50
R171 R15 50c	slate violet	30.00	.25	60.00	1.00
	Block of 4	130.00	2.25	275.00	6.75

		Roul. 5½ Unused	Used	p. Hyphen Hole Perf. 7 Unused	Used
	P# block of 6	850.00		—	
a.	Imperf., pair	300.00			
b.	Horiz. pair, imperf. between			—	250.00
R172 R15 80c	bister	110.00	.50	210.00	50.00
	Block of 4	525.00	32.50	1,050.	240.00
	P# block of 6	—		—	
	Cut cancel		.20		20.00

Numerous double transfers exist on this issue.

Commerce — R16

		Roul. 5½ Unused	Used	p. Hyphen Hole Perf. 7 Unused	Used
R173 R16 $1	dark green	22.50	.25	32.50	2.00
	Block of 4	92.50	.60		10.00
	Cut cancel		.25		.75
a.	Vert. pair, imperf. horiz.	800.00			
b.	Horiz. pair, imperf. vert.		—	325.00	
R174 R16 $3	dark brown	42.50	1.25	72.50	3.50
	Block of 4	—	6.00		15.00
	Cut cancel		.30		.40
a.	Horiz. pair, imperf. vert.	500.00			
R175 R16 $5	orange red	75.00	2.00		
	Block of 4	—	10.00		
	Cut cancel		.30		
R176 R16 $10	black	160.00	3.50		
	Block of 4		17.00		
	Cut cancel		.65		
a.	Horiz. pair, imperf. vert.	—			
R177 R16 $30	red	500.00	160.00		
	Block of 4		700.00		
	Cut cancel		47.50		
R178 R16 $50	gray brown	250.00	5.75		
	Block of 4		29.00		
	Cut cancel		2.10		

John Marshall — R17

Alexander Hamilton — R18

James Madison — R19

Various Portraits in Various Frames, Each Inscribed "Series of 1898"

1899   *Imperf.*

Without Gum

				Unused	Used
R179 R17	$100	yellow brown & black		300.00	37.50
		Cut cancel			21.00
		Vertical strip of 4		—	175.00
		Vertical strip of 4, cut cancel			90.00
R180 R18	$500	carmine lake & black		1,600.	800.00
		Cut cancel			300.
		Vertical strip of 4		—	2,250.
		Vertical strip of 4, cut cancel			1,000.
R181 R19	$1000	green & black		1,400.	375.00
		Cut cancel			150.00
		Vertical strip of 4		—	1,750.
		Vertical strip of 4, cut cancel			600.00

1900   *Hyphen-hole perf. 7*

Allegorical Figure of Commerce

			Unused	Used
R182 R16	$1	carmine	40.00	.55
		Cut cancel		.30
		Block of 4	160.00	2.50
		Block of 4, cut cancel		1.25
R183 R16	$3	lake (fugitive ink)	275.00	52.50
		Cut cancel		9.00
		Block of 4	1,000.	275.00
		Block of 4, cut cancel		40.00

Warning: The ink on No. R183 will run in water.

Surcharged in Black with Open Numerals of Value

			Unused	Used
R184 R16	$1	gray	32.50	.40
		Cut cancel		.30
		Block of 4	—	1.75
		Block of 4, cut cancel		1.25
a.		Horiz. pair, imperf. vert	—	
b.		Surcharge omitted	140.00	
		Surcharge omitted, cut cancel		82.50
R185 R16	$2	gray	32.50	.35
		Cut cancel		.25
		Block of 4	140.00	1.60
		Block of 4, cut cancel		1.10
R186 R16	$3	gray	140.00	13.50
		Cut cancel		5.00
		Block of 4	—	60.00
		Block of 4, cut cancel		21.00
R187 R16	$5	gray	80.00	10.00
		Cut cancel		1.50
		Block of 4	—	42.50
		Block of 4, cut cancel		8.00

R188	R16	$10 **gray**	175.00 22.50
	Cut cancel		4.00
	Block of 4		— 100.00
	Block of 4, cut cancel		17.00
R189	R16	$50 **gray**	2,000. 550.00
	Cut cancel		140.00
	Block of 4		2,450.
	Block of 4, cut cancel		550.00

Surcharged in Black with Ornamental Numerals of Value

Warning: If Nos. R190-R194 are soaked, the center part of the surcharged numeral may wash off. Before the surcharging, a square of soluble varnish was applied to the middle of some stamps.

1902

R190	R16	$1 **green**	47.50 3.50
	Cut cancel		.30
	Block of 4		— 15.00
	Block of 4, cut cancel		1.25
a.	Inverted surcharge		190.00
R191	R16	$2 **green**	47.50 2.00
	Cut cancel		.40
	Block of 4		— 8.50
	Block of 4, cut cancel		1.60
a.	Surcharged as No. R185		125.00 75.00
b.	Surcharged as No. R185, in violet		2,000. —
c.	As "a," double surcharge		150.00
d.	As "a," triple surcharge		850.00
e.	Pair, Nos. R191c and R191d		1,650.
R192	R16	$5 **green**	225.00 37.50
	Cut cancel		4.50
	Block of 4		— 160.00
	Block of 4, cut cancel		22.50
a.	Surcharge omitted		250.00
b.	Pair, one without surcharge		500.00
R193	R16	$10 **green**	450.00 140.00
	Cut cancel		52.50
	Block of 4		— 600.00
	Block of 4, cut cancel		225.00
R194	R16	$50 **green**	2,000. 1,000.
	Cut cancel		250.00
	Block of 4		— —
	Block of 4, cut cancel		1,050.

R20   Wmk. 190

Inscribed "Series of 1914"

1914   Wmk. 190   Offset Printing   Perf. 10

R195	R20	½c **rose**	14.00 5.00
	Block of 4		57.50 21.00
R196	R20	1c **rose**	2.75 .30
	Block of 4		12.00 1.25
R197	R20	2c **rose**	4.00 .30
	Block of 4		17.00 1.25
	Double impression		—
R198	R20	3c **rose**	80.00 35.00
	Block of 4		350.00 150.00
R199	R20	4c **rose**	27.50 2.40
	Block of 4		110.00 10.50
	Recut U. L. corner		300.00
R200	R20	5c **rose**	10.00 .40
	Block of 4		42.50 1.75
R201	R20	10c **rose**	8.00 .25
	Block of 4		32.50 1.25
R202	R20	25c **rose**	50.00 .60
	Block of 4		225.00 2.50
R203	R20	40c **rose**	32.50 3.00
	Block of 4		140.00 13.00
R204	R20	50c **rose**	13.00 .35
	Block of 4		55.00 1.50
R205	R20	80c **rose**	210.00 17.00
	Block of 4		850.00 72.50

Wmk. 191R

R206	R20	½c **rose**	1.60 .50
	Block of 4		7.00 2.50
R207	R20	1c **rose**	.25 .20
	Block of 4		.70 .25
	Double impression		300.00 —
R208	R20	2c **rose**	.30 .25
	Block of 4		1.25 1.10

R209	R20	3c **rose**	1.50 .25
	Block of 4		6.50 1.10
R210	R20	4c **rose**	4.50 .50
	Block of 4		21.00 2.25
R211	R20	5c **rose**	2.00 .35
	Block of 4		9.00 1.50
R212	R20	10c **rose**	.80 .20
	Block of 4		3.75 .35
R213	R20	25c **rose**	8.00 1.50
	Block of 4		32.50 7.00
R214	R20	40c **rose**	110.00 14.00
	Cut cancel		.45
	Block of 4		525.00 57.50
R215	R20	50c **rose**	27.50 .40
	Cut cancel		.25
	Block of 4		125.00 1.75
R216	R20	80c **rose**	175.00 30.00
	Cut cancel		1.10
	Block of 4		750.00 225.00

Liberty — R21

Inscribed "Series 1914"

Engr.

R217	R21	$1 **green**	65.00 .55
	Cut cancel		.25
	Block of 4		— 3.00
	Block of 4, cut cancel		1.10
a.	$1 yellow green		45.00 .25
R218	R21	$2 **carmine**	90.00 .75
	Cut cancel		.20
	Block of 4		375.00 3.25
	Block of 4, cut cancel		.25
R219	R21	$3 **purple**	125.00 4.25
	Cut cancel		.75
	Block of 4		525.00 20.00
	Block of 4, cut cancel		3.25
R220	R21	$5 **blue**	95.00 4.50
	Cut cancel		.65
	Block of 4		400.00 19.00
	Block of 4, cut cancel		3.25
R221	R21	$10 **yellow orange**	225.00 6.50
	Cut cancel		1.00
	Block of 4		— 30.00
	Block of 4, cut cancel		4.50
R222	R21	$30 **vermilion**	775.00 21.00
	Cut cancel		2.25
	Block of 4		— 90.00
	Block of 4, cut cancel		11.50
R223	R21	$50 **violet**	2,000. 1,000.
	Cut cancel		350.00
	Block of 4		4,250.

Portrait Types of 1899 Inscribed "Series of 1915" (#R224), or "Series of 1914"

1914-15   Without Gum   Perf. 12

R224	R19	$60 **brown** (Lincoln)	250.00 150.00
	Vertical strip of 4		800.00
	Cut cancel		70.00
	Vertical strip of 4, cut cancel		325.00
R225	R17	$100 **green** (Washington)	77.50 45.00
	Vertical strip of 4		190.00
	Cut cancel		16.00
	Vertical strip of 4, cut cancel		70.00
R226	R18	$500 **blue** (Hamilton)	— 600.00
	Cut cancel		250.00
	Vertical strip of 4, cut cancel		1,000.
R227	R19	$1000 **orange** (Madison)	— 600.00
	Cut cancel		300.00
	Vert. strip of 4		1,300.

The stamps of types R17, R18 and R19 in this and subsequent issues were issued in vertical strips of 4 which are imperforate at the top, bottom and right side; therefore, single stamps are always imperforate on one or two sides.

R22

Two types of design R22 are known.
Type I — With dot in centers of periods before and after "CENTS."
Type II — Without such dots.
First printings were done by commercial companies, later printings by the Bureau of Engraving and Printing.

1917   Offset Printing   Wmk. 191R   Perf. 11

R228	R22	1c **carmine rose**	.35 .20
	Block of 4		1.50 .50
	Double impression		20.00 4.00

R229	R22	2c **carmine rose**	.25 .20
	Block of 4		1.10 .35
	Double impression		20.00 5.00
R230	R22	3c **carmine rose**	1.75 .40
	Block of 4		7.25 1.75
	Double impression		—
R231	R22	4c **carmine rose**	.75 .25
	Block of 4		3.50 1.10
	Double impression		—
R232	R22	5c **carmine rose**	.30 .20
	Block of 4		1.25 .35
R233	R22	8c **carmine rose**	3.00 .35
	Block of 4		13.50 1.60
R234	R22	10c **carmine rose**	.40 .20
	Block of 4		1.90 .35
	Double impression		5.25
R235	R22	20c **carmine rose**	.75 .25
	Block of 4		3.50 1.10
	Double impression		—
R236	R22	25c **carmine rose**	1.75 .25
	Block of 4		7.50 1.10
R237	R22	40c **carmine rose**	2.25 .50
	Block of 4		10.50 2.25
	Double impression		8.00 5.00
R238	R22	50c **carmine rose**	2.50 .20
	Block of 4		10.50 .35
	Double impression		—
R239	R22	80c **carmine rose**	7.50 .25
	Block of 4		32.50 1.10
	Double impression		40.00

No. R234 is known used provisionally as a playing card revenue stamp in August 1932. Value for this use, authenticated, $300.

Liberty Type of 1914 without "Series 1914"

1917-33   Engr.

R240	R21	$1 **yellow green**	10.00 .30
	Block of 4		45.00 1.25
a.	$1 green		7.25 .20
R241	R21	$2 **rose**	16.00 .25
	Block of 4		70.00 1.10
R242	R21	$3 **violet**	57.50 1.10
	Cut cancel		.25
	Block of 4		— 4.50
R243	R21	$4 **yellow brown**('33)	37.50 2.00
	Cut cancel		.30
	Block of 4		— 10.00
	Block of 4, cut cancel		1.40
R244	R21	$5 **dark blue**	27.50 .35
	Cut cancel		.25
	Block of 4		— 1.50
R245	R21	$10 **orange**	52.50 1.40
	Cut cancel		.30
	Block of 4		— 7.00
	Block of 4, cut cancel		1.25

Portrait Types of 1899 without "Series of" and Date

1917   Without Gum   Perf. 12

R246	R17	$30 **deep orange, green numerals** (Grant)	55.00 13.00
	Cut cancel		2.25
	Vertical strip of 4		3.50
a.	As "b," imperf. pair		750.00
b.	Numerals in blue		85.00 2.25
	Cut cancel		1.40
R247	R19	$60 **brown** (Lincoln)	65.00 8.00
	Cut cancel		.85
	Vertical strip of 4		5.00
R248	R17	$100 **green** (Washington)	42.50 1.25
	Cut cancel		.40
	Vertical strip of 4		2.50
R249	R18	$500 **blue, red numerals** (Hamilton)	325.00 40.00
	Cut cancel		12.50
	Vertical strip of 4		200.00
	Cut cancel		57.50
	Double transfer		52.50
a.	Numerals in orange		375.00 57.50
	Double transfer		—
R250	R19	$1000 **orange** (Madison)	150.00 12.50
	Cut cancel		4.25
	Vertical strip of 4		75.00
	Cut cancel		17.50
a.	Imperf., pair		2,000.

See note after No. R227.

1928-29   Offset Printing   Perf. 10

R251	R22	1c **carmine rose**	2.10 1.60
	Block of 4		9.50 7.50
R252	R22	2c **carmine rose**	.60 .30
	Block of 4		3.00 1.50
R253	R22	4c **carmine rose**	7.00 4.00
	Block of 4		32.50 19.00
R254	R22	5c **carmine rose**	1.75 .55
	Block of 4		8.50 2.50
R255	R22	10c **carmine rose**	2.75 1.25
	Block of 4		13.00 5.50
R256	R22	20c **carmine rose**	6.00 4.50
	Block of 4		27.50 20.00
	Double impression		—

Engr.

R257	R21	$1 **green**	190.00 45.00
	Block of 4		—
	Cut cancel		5.00
R258	R21	$2 **rose**	85.00 20.00
	Block of 4		—
	Cut cancel		20.00
R259	R21	$10 **orange**	275.00 65.00
	Block of 4		—
	Cut cancel		27.50

1929   Offset Printing   Perf. 11x10

R260	R22	2c **carmine rose**('30)	3.00	2.75
		Block of 4	13.00	12.00
		Double impression	—	—
R261	R22	5c **carmine rose**('30)	2.00	1.90
		Block of 4	10.00	8.75
R262	R22	10c **carmine rose**	9.25	6.75
		Block of 4	45.00	32.50
R263	R22	20c **carmine rose**	15.00	8.25
		Block of 4	70.00	42.50

Types of 1917-33 Overprinted in Black
SERIES 1940

1940   Wmk. 191R   Offset Printing   Perf. 11

R264	R22	1c **rose pink**	3.75	2.40
		Cut cancel		.35
		Perf. initial		.25
R265	R22	2c **rose pink**	5.00	2.25
		Cut cancel		.45
		Perf. initial		.35
R266	R22	3c **rose pink**	11.00	5.00
		Cut cancel		.90
		Perf. initial		.55
R267	R22	4c **rose pink**	5.00	.80
		Cut cancel		.30
		Perf. initial		.25
R268	R22	5c **rose pink**	5.00	1.25
		Cut cancel		.35
		Perf. initial		.25
R269	R22	8c **rose pink**	22.50	17.00
		Cut cancel		3.50
		Perf. initial		2.50
R270	R22	10c **rose pink**	2.50	.65
		Cut cancel		.25
		Perf. initial		.25
R271	R22	20c **rose pink**	3.25	.80
		Cut cancel		.30
		Perf. initial		.25
R272	R22	25c **rose pink**	8.00	1.50
		Cut cancel		.30
		Perf. initial		.25
R273	R22	40c **rose pink**	6.75	.90
		Cut cancel		.25
		Perf. initial		.25
R274	R22	50c **rose pink**	11.00	.55
		Cut cancel		.25
		Perf. initial		.25
R275	R22	80c **rose pink**	14.00	1.75
		Cut cancel		.35
		Perf. initial		.25

Engr.

R276	R21	$1 **green**	75.00	1.25
		Cut cancel		.35
		Perf. initial		.25
R277	R21	$2 **rose**	75.00	2.00
		Cut cancel		.35
		Perf. initial		.25
R278	R21	$3 **violet**	100.00	37.50
		Cut cancel		4.25
		Perf. initial		2.00
R279	R21	$4 **yellow brown**	175.00	35.00
		Cut cancel		5.50
		Perf. initial		2.10
R280	R21	$5 **dark blue**	85.00	20.00
		Cut cancel		1.60
		Perf. initial		.75
R281	R21	$10 **orange**	210.00	45.00
		Cut cancel		3.00
		Perf. initial		.60

Types of 1917 Handstamped "Series 1940" like R264-R281 in Blue (Nos. R282-R283), Green (Nos. R283-R284, R286) or Violet (No. R285)

1940   Wmk. 191R   Perf. 12
Without Gum

R282	R17	$30 **vermilion**		1,000.
		Cut cancel		425.
		Perf. initial		325.
a.		With black 2-line handstamp in larger type		12,500.
R283	R19	$60 **brown**		2,250.
		Cut cancel		775.
		Perf. initial		550.
a.		As #R282a, cut cancel		
R284	R17	$100 **green**		3,000.
		Cut cancel		1,250.
		Perf. initial		800.
R285	R18	$500 **blue**		2,750.
		Cut cancel		1,250.
		Perf. initial		1,000.
		Double transfer		
a.		As #R282a	3,250.	3,850.
		Cut cancel		2,750.
		Double transfer	—	—
b.		Blue handstamp; double transfer	—	
R286	R19	$1000 **orange**		825.
		Cut cancel		475.
		Perf. initial		325.
a.		Double overprint, cut cancel		—

Alexander Hamilton — R23

Levi Woodbury — R24

Overprinted in Black   **SERIES 1940**

Various Portraits: 2c, Oliver Wolcott, Jr. 3c, Samuel Dexter. 4c, Albert Gallatin. 5c. G. W. Campbell. 8c, Alexander Dallas. 10c, William H. Crawford. 20c, Richard Rush. 25c, S. D. Ingham. 40c, Louis McLane. 50c, William J. Duane. 80c, Roger B. Taney. $2, Thomas Ewing. $3, Walter Forward. $4, J. C. Spencer. $5, G. M. Bibb. $10, R. J. Walker. $20, William M. Meredith. The "sensitive ink" varieties are in a bluish-purple overprint showing minute flecks of gold.

1940   Engr.   Wmk. 191R   Perf. 11
Plates of 400 subjects, issued in panes of 100

R288	R23	1c **carmine**	5.75	4.50
		Cut cancel		1.75
		Perf. initial		.90
		Sensitive ink	9.00	4.25
a.		Imperf, pair, without gum	250.00	
		Block of 4	500.00	
R289	R23	2c **carmine**	8.50	4.00
		Cut cancel		1.75
		Perf. initial		1.00
		Sensitive ink	9.00	4.25
a.		Imperf, pair, without gum	250.00	
		Block of 4	500.00	
R290	R23	3c **carmine**	27.50	12.00
		Cut cancel		4.00
		Perf. initial		2.75
		Sensitive ink	29.00	9.25
a.		Imperf, pair, without gum	250.00	
		Block of 4	500.00	
R291	R23	4c **carmine**	62.50	27.50
		Cut cancel		5.25
		Perf. initial		4.25
a.		Imperf, pair, without gum	250.00	
		Block of 4	500.00	
R292	R23	5c **carmine**	4.75	.80
		Cut cancel		.35
		Perf. initial		.30
a.		Imperf, pair, without gum	250.00	
		Block of 4	500.00	
R293	R23	8c **carmine**	85.00	60.00
		Cut cancel		18.00
		Perf. initial		13.00
a.		Imperf, pair, without gum	250.00	
		Block of 4	500.00	
R294	R23	10c **carmine**	4.25	.60
		Cut cancel		.30
		Perf. initial		.25
a.		Imperf, pair, without gum	250.00	
		Block of 4	500.00	
R295	R23	20c **carmine**	5.50	4.25
		Cut cancel		1.25
		Perf. initial		.85
a.		Imperf, pair, without gum	250.00	
		Block of 4	500.00	
R296	R23	25c **carmine**	5.00	.75
		Cut cancel		.35
		Perf. initial		.25
a.		Imperf, pair, without gum	250.00	
		Block of 4	500.00	
R297	R23	40c **carmine**	70.00	30.00
		Cut cancel		6.50
		Perf. initial		2.75
a.		Imperf, pair, without gum	250.00	
		Block of 4	500.00	
R298	R23	50c **carmine**	8.00	.60
		Cut cancel		.30
		Perf. initial		.25
a.		Imperf, pair, without gum	250.00	
		Block of 4	500.00	
R299	R23	80c **carmine**	175.00	100.00
		Cut cancel		29.00
		Perf. initial		20.00
a.		Imperf, pair, without gum	475.00	
		Block of 4	1,400.	

Plates of 200 subjects, issued in panes of 50

R300	R24	$1 **carmine**	42.50	.60
		Cut cancel		.25
		Perf. initial		.25
		Sensitive ink	57.50	21.00
a.		Imperf, pair, without gum	250.00	
		Block of 4	550.00	
R301	R24	$2 **carmine**	80.00	.90
		Cut cancel		.25
		Perf. initial		.25
		Sensitive ink	65.00	10.50
R302	R24	$3 **carmine**	190.00	95.00
		Cut cancel		11.50
		Perf. initial		8.00
		Sensitive ink	175.00	87.50

a.		Imperf, pair, without gum	1,400.	
		Block of 4	3,000.	
R303	R24	$4 **carmine**	100.00	40.00
		Cut cancel		8.00
		Perf. initial		2.00
R304	R24	$5 **carmine**	70.00	3.00
		Cut cancel		.75
		Perf. initial		.35
R305	R24	$10 **carmine**	110.00	7.50
		Cut cancel		1.25
		Perf. initial		.50
R305A	R24	$20 **carmine**	2,500.	950.00
		Cut cancel		575.00
		Perf. initial		450.00
b.		Imperf, pair, without gum	700.00	
		Block of 4	1,500.	

Thomas Corwin — R25

Overprint: "SERIES 1940"

Various Frames and Portraits: $50, James Guthrie. $60, Howell Cobb. $100, P. F. Thomas. $500, J. A. Dix, $1,000, S. P. Chase.

Perf. 12
Plates of 16 subjects, issued in strips of 4
Without Gum

R306	R25	$30 **carmine**	190.00	65.00
		Cut cancel		18.00
		Perf. initial		13.50
R306A	R25	$50 **carmine**	—	10,000.
		Cut cancel		2,000.
		Perf. initial		800.00
R307	R25	$60 **carmine**	375.00	80.00
		Cut cancel		45.00
		Perf. initial		22.50
a.		Vert. pair, imperf. btwn.	2,750.	1,450.
R308	R25	$100 **carmine**	275.00	85.00
		Cut cancel		42.50
		Perf. initial		14.00
R309	R25	$500 **carmine**	—	5,000.
		Cut cancel		2,000.
		Perf. initial		800.00
R310	R25	$1000 **carmine**	—	550.00
		Cut cancel		260.00
		Perf. initial		190.00

The $30 to $1,000 denominations in this and following similar issues, and the $2,500, $5,000 and $10,000 stamps of 1952-58 have straight edges on one or two sides. They were issued without gum through No. R723.

Nos. R288-R310 Overprinted: **SERIES 1941**

1941   Wmk. 191R   Perf. 11

R311	R23	1c **carmine**	5.00	2.75
		Cut cancel		.85
		Perf. initial		.75
R312	R23	2c **carmine**	5.25	1.10
		Cut cancel		.55
		Perf. initial		.45
R313	R23	3c **carmine**	10.00	4.25
		Cut cancel		1.75
		Perf. initial		1.10
R314	R23	4c **carmine**	7.50	1.75
		Cut cancel		.40
		Perf. initial		.25
R315	R23	5c **carmine**	1.50	.40
		Cut cancel		.30
		Perf. initial		.30
R316	R23	8c **carmine**	21.00	8.50
		Cut cancel		3.75
		Perf. initial		2.75
R317	R23	10c **carmine**	2.00	.35
		Cut cancel		.30
		Perf. initial		.25
R318	R23	20c **carmine**	4.75	.65
		Cut cancel		.40
		Perf. initial		.30
R319	R23	25c **carmine**	2.40	.65
		Cut cancel		.30
		Perf. initial		.25
R320	R23	40c **carmine**	16.00	3.25
		Cut cancel		1.10
		Perf. initial		.65
R321	R23	50c **carmine**	3.50	.30
		Cut cancel		.25
		Perf. initial		.25
R322	R23	80c **carmine**	65.00	12.00
		Cut cancel		3.75
		Perf. initial		2.75
R323	R24	$1 **carmine**	15.00	.30
		Cut cancel		.25
		Perf. initial		.20

Scott	Type	Denom.	Unused	Used
R324	R24	$2 carmine	20.00	.50
		Cut cancel		.30
		Perf. initial		.25
R325	R24	$3 carmine	32.50	3.50
		Cut cancel		.40
		Perf. initial		.30
R326	R24	$4 carmine	47.50	27.50
		Cut cancel		1.10
		Perf. initial		.80
R327	R24	$5 carmine	60.00	1.10
		Cut cancel		.30
		Perf. initial		.20
R328	R24	$10 carmine	100.00	6.00
		Cut cancel		.30
		Perf. initial		.25
R329	R24	$20 carmine	850.00	350.00
		Cut cancel		75.00
		Perf. initial		50.00

Without Gum   **Perf. 12**

R330	R25	$30 carmine	200.00	55.00
		Cut cancel		17.50
		Perf. initial		11.50
R331	R25	$50 carmine	750.00	625.00
		Cut cancel		150.00
		Perf. initial		77.50
R332	R25	$60 carmine	225.00	87.50
		Cut cancel		27.50
		Perf. initial		13.50
R333	R25	$100 carmine	110.00	37.50
		Cut cancel		7.75
		Perf. initial		5.00
R334	R25	$500 carmine	—	325.00
		Cut cancel		160.00
		Perf. initial		55.00
R335	R25	$1000 carmine	—	200.00
		Cut cancel		55.00
		Perf. initial		29.00

Nos. R288-R310 Overprinted: **SERIES 1942**

1942   **Wmk. 191R**   **Perf. 11**

R336	R23	1c carmine	.65	.60
		Cut cancel		.30
		Perf. initial		.25
R337	R23	2c carmine	.60	.60
		Cut cancel		.30
		Perf. initial		.25
R338	R23	3c carmine	.90	.80
		Cut cancel		.35
		Perf. initial		.25
R339	R23	4c carmine	1.75	1.10
		Cut cancel		.30
		Perf. initial		.25
R340	R23	5c carmine	.60	.35
		Cut cancel		.25
		Perf. initial		.20
R341	R23	8c carmine	9.50	4.75
		Cut cancel		1.40
		Perf. initial		1.10
R342	R23	10c carmine	1.75	.35
		Cut cancel		.25
		Perf. initial		.25
R343	R23	20c carmine	1.75	.60
		Cut cancel		.30
		Perf. initial		.25
R344	R23	25c carmine	3.00	.55
		Cut cancel		.30
		Perf. initial		.20
R345	R23	40c carmine	6.50	1.75
		Cut cancel		.55
		Perf. initial		.35
R346	R23	50c carmine	4.00	.35
		Cut cancel		.25
		Perf. initial		.20
R347	R23	80c carmine	27.50	13.00
		Cut cancel		3.00
		Perf. initial		2.00
R348	R24	$1 carmine	12.50	.25
		Cut cancel		.20
		Perf. initial		.20
R349	R24	$2 carmine	15.00	.30
		Cut cancel		.25
		Perf. initial		.20
R350	R24	$3 carmine	27.50	3.25
		Cut cancel		.45
		Perf. initial		.25
R351	R24	$4 carmine	35.00	7.50
		Cut cancel		.55
		Perf. initial		.30
R352	R24	$5 carmine	37.50	1.50
		Cut cancel		.25
		Perf. initial		.20
R353	R24	$10 carmine	85.00	3.75
		Cut cancel		.40
		Perf. initial		.25
R354	R24	$20 carmine	160.00	45.00
		Cut cancel		20.00
		Perf. initial		11.50

Without Gum   **Perf. 12**

R355	R25	$30 carmine	100.00	42.50
		Cut cancel		15.00
		Perf. initial		7.00
R356	R25	$50 carmine	1,700.	1,100.
		Cut cancel		350.00
		Perf. initial		190.00
R357	R25	$60 carmine	2,500.	1,850.
		Cut cancel		450.00
		Perf. initial		150.00
R358	R25	$100 carmine	240.00	150.00
		Cut cancel		60.00
		Perf. initial		45.00
R359	R25	$500 carmine	1,600.	275.00
		Cut cancel		160.00
		Perf. initial		87.50
R360	R25	$1000 carmine	—	125.00
		Cut cancel		55.00
		Perf. initial		45.00

Nos. R288-R310 Overprinted: **SERIES 1943**

1943   **Wmk. 191R**   **Perf. 11**

R361	R23	1c carmine	.80	.65
		Cut cancel		.30
		Perf. initial		.25
R362	R23	2c carmine	.65	.55
		Cut cancel		.30
		Perf. initial		.25
R363	R23	3c carmine	3.75	3.50
		Cut cancel		.70
		Perf. initial		.40
R364	R23	4c carmine	1.60	1.50
		Cut cancel		.40
		Perf. initial		.35
R365	R23	5c carmine	.70	.45
		Cut cancel		.30
		Perf. initial		.25
R366	R23	8c carmine	6.00	4.00
		Cut cancel		1.90
		Perf. initial		1.25
R367	R23	10c carmine	.85	.30
		Cut cancel		.25
		Perf. initial		.20
R368	R23	20c carmine	2.50	.80
		Cut cancel		.40
		Perf. initial		.35
R369	R23	25c carmine	2.75	.50
		Cut cancel		.30
		Perf. initial		.30
R370	R23	40c carmine	7.50	4.00
		Cut cancel		1.75
		Perf. initial		.90
R371	R23	50c carmine	2.00	.30
		Cut cancel		.25
		Perf. initial		.25
R372	R23	80c carmine	27.50	8.00
		Cut cancel		3.00
		Perf. initial		1.50
R373	R24	$1 carmine	9.00	.35
		Cut cancel		.25
		Perf. initial		.25
R374	R24	$2 carmine	18.00	.35
		Cut cancel		.25
		Perf. initial		.20
R375	R24	$3 carmine	30.00	3.00
		Cut cancel		.45
		Perf. initial		.30
R376	R24	$4 carmine	45.00	7.50
		Cut cancel		.80
		Perf. initial		.50
R377	R24	$5 carmine	52.50	.75
		Cut cancel		.40
		Perf. initial		.25
R378	R24	$10 carmine	85.00	5.00
		Cut cancel		1.75
		Perf. initial		.70
R379	R24	$20 carmine	175.00	45.00
		Cut cancel		7.00
		Perf. initial		4.25

Without Gum   **Perf. 12**

R380	R25	$30 carmine	100.00	22.50
		Cut cancel		5.50
		Perf. initial		4.75
R381	R25	$50 carmine	200.00	45.00
		Cut cancel		15.00
		Perf. initial		6.00
R382	R25	$60 carmine	325.00	125.00
		Cut cancel		42.50
		Perf. initial		14.00
R383	R25	$100 carmine	35.00	22.50
		Cut cancel		6.75
		Perf. initial		4.25
R384	R25	$500 carmine	375.00	250.00
		Cut cancel		125.00
		Perf. initial		87.50
R385	R25	$1000 carmine	350.00	200.00
		Cut cancel		60.00
		Perf. initial		40.00

Nos. R288-R310 Overprinted: **Series 1944**

1944   **Wmk. 191R**   **Perf. 11**

R386	R23	1c carmine	.50	.45
		Cut cancel		.25
		Perf. initial		.25
R387	R23	2c carmine	.65	.55
		Cut cancel		.30
		Perf. initial		.25
R388	R23	3c carmine	.65	.40
		Cut cancel		.30
		Perf. initial		.25
R389	R23	4c carmine	.75	.65
		Cut cancel		.30
		Perf. initial		.25
R390	R23	5c carmine	.40	.25
		Cut cancel		.25
		Perf. initial		.25
R391	R23	8c carmine	2.25	1.75
		Cut cancel		.50
		Perf. initial		.45
R392	R23	10c carmine	.50	.25
		Cut cancel		.20
		Perf. initial		.25
R393	R23	20c carmine	1.10	.35
		Cut cancel		.25
		Perf. initial		.25
R394	R23	25c carmine	2.00	.30
		Cut cancel		.25
		Perf. initial		.25
R395	R23	40c carmine	3.75	.80
		Cut cancel		.40
		Perf. initial		.30
R396	R23	50c carmine	4.00	.35
		Cut cancel		.30
		Perf. initial		.30
R397	R23	80c carmine	21.00	5.50
		Cut cancel		1.75
		Perf. initial		.90
R398	R24	$1 carmine	10.00	.30
		Cut cancel		.25
		Perf. initial		.25
R399	R24	$2 carmine	15.00	.45
		Cut cancel		.35
		Perf. initial		.25
R400	R24	$3 carmine	25.00	2.40
		Cut cancel		.55
		Perf. initial		.25
R401	R24	$4 carmine	32.50	11.50
		Cut cancel		1.40
		Perf. initial		1.10
R402	R24	$5 carmine	32.50	.50
		Cut cancel		.35
		Perf. initial		.30
R403	R24	$10 carmine	65.00	1.60
		Cut cancel		.40
		Perf. initial		.30
R404	R24	$20 carmine	140.00	19.00
		Cut cancel		4.00
		Perf. initial		2.50

Without Gum   **Perf. 12**

R405	R25	$30 carmine	95.00	35.00
		Cut cancel		9.00
		Perf. initial		7.00
R406	R25	$50 carmine	42.50	22.50
		Cut cancel		7.00
		Perf. initial		4.75
R407	R25	$60 carmine	275.00	75.00
		Cut cancel		29.00
		Perf. initial		10.50
R408	R25	$100 carmine	52.50	12.50
		Cut cancel		5.25
		Perf. initial		3.25
R409	R25	$500 carmine	—	2,600.
		Cut cancel		1,200.
		Perf. initial		750.00
R410	R25	$1000 carmine	—	375.00
		Cut cancel		125.00
		Perf. initial		65.00

Nos. R288-R310 Overprinted: **Series 1945**

1945   **Wmk. 191R**   **Perf. 11**

R411	R23	1c carmine	.40	.30
		Cut cancel		.25
		Perf. initial		.25
R412	R23	2c carmine	.40	.30
		Cut cancel		.25
		Perf. initial		.25
R413	R23	3c carmine	.75	.50
		Cut cancel		.30
		Perf. initial		.25
R414	R23	4c carmine	.45	.35
		Cut cancel		.30
		Perf. initial		.25
R415	R23	5c carmine	.45	.30
		Cut cancel		.20
		Perf. initial		.25
R416	R23	8c carmine	6.25	2.75
		Cut cancel		.75
		Perf. initial		.40
R417	R23	10c carmine	1.25	.25
		Cut cancel		.25
		Perf. initial		.25
R418	R23	20c carmine	8.00	1.50
		Cut cancel		.60
		Perf. initial		.35
R419	R23	25c carmine	1.75	.30
		Cut cancel		.25
		Perf. initial		.20
R420	R23	40c carmine	9.00	1.25
		Cut cancel		.55
		Perf. initial		.40
R421	R23	50c carmine	4.00	.25
		Cut cancel		.20
		Perf. initial		.25
R422	R23	80c carmine	26.00	14.00
		Cut cancel		4.00
		Perf. initial		2.75
R423	R24	$1 carmine	13.50	.30
		Cut cancel		.25
		Perf. initial		.20
R424	R24	$2 carmine	13.50	.40
		Cut cancel		.25
		Perf. initial		.25
R425	R24	$3 carmine	27.50	3.00
		Cut cancel		1.00
		Perf. initial		.75
R426	R24	$4 carmine	35.00	4.25
		Cut cancel		.70
		Perf. initial		.45
R427	R24	$5 carmine	35.00	.50
		Cut cancel		.30
		Perf. initial		.25
R428	R24	$10 carmine	65.00	2.50
		Cut cancel		.40
		Perf. initial		.30
R429	R24	$20 carmine	140.00	16.00
		Cut cancel		3.75
		Perf. initial		3.00

Without Gum   **Perf. 12**

R430	R25	$30 carmine	175.00	40.00
		Cut cancel		10.00
		Perf. initial		5.75

R431	R25	$50 carmine	200.00	45.00
		Cut cancel		20.00
		Perf. initial		12.00
R432	R25	$60 carmine	375.00	80.00
		Cut cancel		32.50
		Perf. initial		14.00
R433	R25	$100 carmine	40.00	20.00
		Cut cancel		9.00
		Perf. initial		5.50
R434	R25	$500 carmine	425.00	225.00
		Cut cancel		80.00
		Perf. initial		52.50
R435	R25	$1000 carmine	300.00	110.00
		Cut cancel		32.50
		Perf. initial		17.50

Nos. R288-R310 Overprinted: **Series 1946**

1946   **Wmk. 191R**   *Perf. 11*

R436	R23	1c carmine	.30	.30
		Cut cancel		.25
		Perf. initial		.25
R437	R23	2c carmine	.45	.35
		Cut cancel		.25
		Perf. initial		.25
R438	R23	3c carmine	.55	.40
		Cut cancel		.30
		Perf. initial		.25
R439	R23	4c carmine	.80	.65
		Cut cancel		.30
		Perf. initial		.25
R440	R23	5c carmine	.45	.30
		Cut cancel		.25
		Perf. initial		.25
R441	R23	8c carmine	2.50	2.00
		Cut cancel		.40
		Perf. initial		.35
R442	R23	10c carmine	1.10	.30
		Cut cancel		.25
		Perf. initial		.25
R443	R23	20c carmine	1.75	.50
		Cut cancel		.30
		Perf. initial		.25
R444	R23	25c carmine	6.00	.35
		Cut cancel		.25
		Perf. initial		.20
R445	R23	40c carmine	4.50	.85
		Cut cancel		.40
		Perf. initial		.25
R446	R23	50c carmine	6.00	.30
		Cut cancel		.25
		Perf. initial		.20
R447	R23	80c carmine	17.50	5.00
		Cut cancel		.75
		Perf. initial		.50
R448	R24	$1 carmine	16.00	.30
		Cut cancel		.25
		Perf. initial		.20
R449	R24	$2 carmine	19.00	.30
		Cut cancel		.20
		Perf. initial		.20
R450	R24	$3 carmine	27.50	5.00
		Cut cancel		.90
		Perf. initial		.40
R451	R24	$4 carmine	40.00	11.50
		Cut cancel		2.25
		Perf. initial		1.10
R452	R24	$5 carmine	40.00	.50
		Cut cancel		.30
		Perf. initial		.25
R453	R24	$10 carmine	72.50	1.75
		Cut cancel		.40
		Perf. initial		.30
R454	R24	$20 carmine	140.00	16.00
		Cut cancel		3.50
		Perf. initial		1.60

Without Gum   *Perf. 12*

R455	R25	$30 carmine	60.00	17.50
		Cut cancel		5.25
		Perf. initial		3.25
R456	R25	$50 carmine	50.00	12.50
		Cut cancel		5.00
		Perf. initial		2.75
R457	R25	$60 carmine	95.00	22.50
		Cut cancel		14.00
		Perf. initial		7.75
R458	R25	$100 carmine	70.00	12.50
		Cut cancel		4.25
		Perf. initial		3.00
R459	R25	$500 carmine	*325.00*	150.00
		Cut cancel		47.50
		Perf. initial		26.00
R460	R25	$1000 carmine	*375.00*	160.00
		Cut cancel		37.50
		Perf. initial		18.00

Nos. R288-R310 Overprinted: **Series 1947**

1947   **Wmk. 191R**   *Perf. 11*

R461	R23	1c carmine	.85	.55
		Cut cancel		.30
		Perf. initial		.25
R462	R23	2c carmine	.75	.55
		Cut cancel		.30
		Perf. initial		.25
R463	R23	3c carmine	.85	.55
		Cut cancel		.30
		Perf. initial		.25
R464	R23	4c carmine	.90	.75
		Cut cancel		.30
		Perf. initial		.25
R465	R23	5c carmine	.55	.40
		Cut cancel		.30
		Perf. initial		.25

R466	R23	8c carmine	1.75	.80
		Cut cancel		.30
		Perf. initial		.25
R467	R23	10c carmine	1.40	.30
		Cut cancel		.25
		Perf. initial		.25
R468	R23	20c carmine	2.25	.55
		Cut cancel		.30
		Perf. initial		.25
R469	R23	25c carmine	3.00	.70
		Cut cancel		.30
		Perf. initial		.25
R470	R23	40c carmine	5.50	1.10
		Cut cancel		.35
		Perf. initial		.25
R471	R23	50c carmine	3.75	.30
		Cut cancel		.30
		Perf. initial		.25
R472	R23	80c carmine	12.00	8.00
		Cut cancel		.85
		Perf. initial		.35
R473	R24	$1 carmine	8.25	.35
		Cut cancel		.30
		Perf. initial		.25
R474	R24	$2 carmine	14.00	.65
		Cut cancel		.30
		Perf. initial		.20
R475	R24	$3 carmine	17.50	6.00
		Cut cancel		1.25
		Perf. initial		.90
R476	R24	$4 carmine	19.00	5.00
		Cut cancel		.55
		Perf. initial		.40
R477	R24	$5 carmine	27.50	.60
		Cut cancel		.30
		Perf. initial		.25
R478	R24	$10 carmine	67.50	3.00
		Cut cancel		.80
		Perf. initial		.30
R479	R24	$20 carmine	110.00	14.00
		Cut cancel		1.40
		Perf. initial		.90

Without Gum   *Perf. 12*

R480	R25	$30 carmine	140.00	27.50
		Cut cancel		6.00
		Perf. initial		2.75
R481	R25	$50 carmine	72.50	17.50
		Cut cancel		5.50
		Perf. initial		3.25
R482	R25	$60 carmine	175.00	60.00
		Cut cancel		25.00
		Perf. initial		9.25
R483	R25	$100 carmine	65.00	15.00
		Cut cancel		6.00
		Perf. initial		2.10
R484	R25	$500 carmine	*500.00*	175.00
		Cut cancel		67.50
		Perf. initial		37.50
R485	R25	$1000 carmine	*275.00*	100.00
		Cut cancel		40.00
		Perf. initial		24.00

Nos. R288-R310 Overprinted: **Series 1948**

1948   **Wmk. 191R**   *Perf. 11*

R486	R23	1c carmine	.35	.30
		Cut cancel		.25
		Perf. initial		.25
R487	R23	2c carmine	.50	.45
		Cut cancel		.30
		Perf. initial		.25
R488	R23	3c carmine	.60	.40
		Cut cancel		.30
		Perf. initial		.25
R489	R23	4c carmine	.55	.40
		Cut cancel		.30
		Perf. initial		.25
R490	R23	5c carmine	.50	.25
		Cut cancel		.25
		Perf. initial		.20
R491	R23	8c carmine	1.00	.50
		Cut cancel		.30
		Perf. initial		.30
R492	R23	10c carmine	1.00	.25
		Cut cancel		.25
		Perf. initial		.20
R493	R23	20c carmine	2.50	.40
		Cut cancel		.30
		Perf. initial		.25
R494	R23	25c carmine	2.25	.30
		Cut cancel		.25
		Perf. initial		.25
R495	R23	40c carmine	7.00	1.75
		Cut cancel		.35
		Perf. initial		.25
R496	R23	50c carmine	2.50	.30
		Cut cancel		.25
		Perf. initial		.25
R497	R23	80c carmine	12.00	8.00
		Cut cancel		3.25
		Perf. initial		.80
R498	R24	$1 carmine	10.50	.30
		Cut cancel		.25
		Perf. initial		.25
R499	R24	$2 carmine	18.00	.40
		Cut cancel		.30
		Perf. initial		.25
R500	R24	$3 carmine	24.00	3.50
		Cut cancel		.60
		Perf. initial		.40
R501	R24	$4 carmine	35.00	4.00
		Cut cancel		1.00
		Perf. initial		.70
R502	R24	$5 carmine	30.00	.50
		Cut cancel		.35
		Perf. initial		.25

R503	R24	$10 carmine	70.00	1.50
		Cut cancel		.40
		Perf. initial		.30
a.		Pair, one dated "1946"		—
R504	R24	$20 carmine	140.00	18.00
		Cut cancel		5.00
		Perf. initial		2.25

Without Gum   *Perf. 12*

R505	R25	$30 carmine	100.00	27.50
		Cut cancel		7.00
		Perf. initial		4.00
R506	R25	$50 carmine	125.00	27.50
		Cut cancel		12.00
		Perf. initial		3.75
a.		Vert. pair, imperf. btwn.	*2,750.*	
R507	R25	$60 carmine	200.00	50.00
		Cut cancel		22.50
		Perf. initial		8.00
a.		Vert. pair, imperf. btwn.	*2,750.*	
R508	R25	$100 carmine	80.00	12.00
		Cut cancel		5.50
		Perf. initial		3.50
a.		Vert. pair, imperf. btwn.	*2,000.*	
R509	R25	$500 carmine	500.00	160.00
		Cut cancel		60.00
		Perf. initial		32.50
R510	R25	$1000 carmine	275.00	90.00
		Cut cancel		40.00
		Perf. initial		22.50

Nos. R288-R310 Overprinted: **Series 1949**

1949   **Wmk. 191R**   *Perf. 11*

R511	R23	1c carmine	.40	.35
		Cut cancel		.30
		Perf. initial		.25
R512	R23	2c carmine	.75	.45
		Cut cancel		.30
		Perf. initial		.25
R513	R23	3c carmine	.60	.50
		Cut cancel		.30
		Perf. initial		.25
R514	R23	4c carmine	.80	.60
		Cut cancel		.30
		Perf. initial		.25
R515	R23	5c carmine	.55	.30
		Cut cancel		.25
		Perf. initial		.25
R516	R23	8c carmine	1.00	.70
		Cut cancel		.30
		Perf. initial		.25
R517	R23	10c carmine	.60	.35
		Cut cancel		.30
		Perf. initial		.25
R518	R23	20c carmine	1.75	.75
		Cut cancel		.40
		Perf. initial		.30
R519	R23	25c carmine	2.25	.85
		Cut cancel		.35
		Perf. initial		.25
R520	R23	40c carmine	6.50	2.75
		Cut cancel		.55
		Perf. initial		.40
R521	R23	50c carmine	5.00	.40
		Cut cancel		.30
		Perf. initial		.25
R522	R23	80c carmine	15.00	7.50
		Cut cancel		2.00
		Perf. initial		.90
R523	R24	$1 carmine	13.50	.85
		Cut cancel		.40
		Perf. initial		.30
R524	R24	$2 carmine	17.00	2.50
		Cut cancel		.50
		Perf. initial		.35
R525	R24	$3 carmine	27.50	8.00
		Cut cancel		3.00
		Perf. initial		1.10
R526	R24	$4 carmine	30.00	8.00
		Cut cancel		3.50
		Perf. initial		1.90
R527	R24	$5 carmine	32.50	4.25
		Cut cancel		.75
		Perf. initial		.50
R528	R24	$10 carmine	72.50	5.25
		Cut cancel		1.10
		Perf. initial		.90
R529	R24	$20 carmine	150.00	15.00
		Cut cancel		2.50
		Perf. initial		1.60

Without Gum   *Perf. 12*

R530	R25	$30 carmine	125.00	35.00
		Cut cancel		8.00
		Perf. initial		4.25
R531	R25	$50 carmine	160.00	60.00
		Cut cancel		16.00
		Perf. initial		7.50
R532	R25	$60 carmine	250.00	70.00
		Cut cancel		27.50
		Perf. initial		11.50
R533	R25	$100 carmine	80.00	21.00
		Cut cancel		4.50
		Perf. initial		2.75
R534	R25	$500 carmine	*500.00*	250.00
		Cut cancel		125.00
		Perf. initial		57.50
R535	R25	$1000 carmine	*375.00*	160.00
		Cut cancel		47.50
		Perf. initial		22.50

Nos. R288-R310 Overprinted: *Series 1950*

1950 — **Wmk. 191R** — *Perf. 11*

No.	Type	Denom.			
R536	R23	1c carmine		.40	.25
		Cut cancel			.25
		Perf. initial			.25
R537	R23	2c carmine		.40	.35
		Cut cancel			.30
		Perf. initial			.25
R538	R23	3c carmine		.50	.40
		Cut cancel			.30
		Perf. initial			.25
R539	R23	4c carmine		.70	.50
		Cut cancel			.30
		Perf. initial			.25
R540	R23	5c carmine		.45	.35
		Cut cancel			.30
		Perf. initial			.25
R541	R23	8c carmine		1.75	.80
		Cut cancel			.30
		Perf. initial			.25
R542	R23	10c carmine		.80	.30
		Cut cancel			.25
		Perf. initial			.25
R543	R23	20c carmine		1.40	.45
		Cut cancel			.35
		Perf. initial			.30
R544	R23	25c carmine		2.00	.45
		Cut cancel			.35
		Perf. initial			.30
R545	R23	40c carmine		6.00	2.10
		Cut cancel			.50
		Perf. initial			.30
R546	R23	50c carmine		8.00	.35
		Cut cancel			.30
		Perf. initial			.25
R547	R23	80c carmine		15.00	8.50
		Cut cancel			1.00
		Perf. initial			.60
R548	R24	$1 carmine		15.00	.40
		Cut cancel			.30
		Perf. initial			.25
R549	R24	$2 carmine		17.50	2.75
		Cut cancel			.45
		Perf. initial			.25
R550	R24	$3 carmine		20.00	6.00
		Cut cancel			1.40
		Perf. initial			.80
R551	R24	$4 carmine		27.50	7.50
		Cut cancel			2.75
		Perf. initial			1.40
R552	R24	$5 carmine		35.00	1.00
		Cut cancel			.35
		Perf. initial			.25
R553	R24	$10 carmine		70.00	10.00
		Cut cancel			1.00
		Perf. initial			.65
R554	R24	$20 carmine		150.00	15.00
		Cut cancel			3.50
		Perf. initial			2.10

Without Gum — *Perf. 12*

R555	R25	$30 carmine		125.00	70.00
		Cut cancel			17.50
		Perf. initial			10.50
R556	R25	$50 carmine		100.00	22.50
		Cut cancel			11.00
		Perf. initial			6.50
a.		Vert. pair, imperf. horiz.			—
R557	R25	$60 carmine		210.00	75.00
		Cut cancel			25.00
		Perf. initial			9.75
R558	R25	$100 carmine		85.00	22.50
		Cut cancel			6.00
		Perf. initial			3.25
R559	R25	$500 carmine		*300.00*	125.00
		Cut cancel			55.00
		Perf. initial			32.50
R560	R25	$1000 carmine		*300.00*	95.00
		Cut cancel			30.00
		Perf. initial			19.00

Nos. R288-R310 Overprinted: **Series 1951**

1951 — **Wmk. 191R** — *Perf. 11*

R561	R23	1c carmine		.30	.25
		Cut cancel			.20
		Perf. initial			.20
R562	R23	2c carmine		.30	.35
		Cut cancel			.25
		Perf. initial			.25
R563	R23	3c carmine		.30	.35
		Cut cancel			.25
		Perf. initial			.25
R564	R23	4c carmine		.30	.35
		Cut cancel			.25
		Perf. initial			.25
R565	R23	5c carmine		.30	.35
		Cut cancel			.25
		Perf. initial			.25
R566	R23	8c carmine		1.25	.45
		Cut cancel			.25
		Perf. initial			.25
R567	R23	10c carmine		.30	.35
		Cut cancel			.25
		Perf. initial			.25
R568	R23	20c carmine		.30	.55
		Cut cancel			.30
		Perf. initial			.25
R569	R23	25c carmine		.30	.50
		Cut cancel			.30
		Perf. initial			.25
R570	R23	40c carmine		3.75	1.60
		Cut cancel			.55
		Perf. initial			.35
R571	R23	50c carmine		3.00	.60
		Cut cancel			.30
		Perf. initial			.25

R572	R23	80c carmine		10.00	3.25
		Cut cancel			2.00
		Perf. initial			1.00
R573	R24	$1 carmine		16.00	.30
		Cut cancel			.20
		Perf. initial			.20
R574	R24	$2 carmine		21.00	.55
		Cut cancel			.35
		Perf. initial			.30
R575	R24	$3 carmine		16.00	4.00
		Cut cancel			2.10
		Perf. initial			1.25
R576	R24	$4 carmine		16.00	8.00
		Cut cancel			3.00
		Perf. initial			1.50
R577	R24	$5 carmine		10.00	.70
		Cut cancel			.35
		Perf. initial			.25
R578	R24	$10 carmine		18.00	2.50
		Cut cancel			1.25
		Perf. initial			.90
R579	R24	$20 carmine		55.00	16.00
		Cut cancel			5.00
		Perf. initial			3.25

Without Gum — *Perf. 12*

R580	R25	$30 carmine		100.00	17.50
		Cut cancel			6.00
		Perf. initial			3.75
a.		Imperf. pair		*2,000.*	775.00
R581	R25	$50 carmine		125.00	30.00
		Cut cancel			9.00
		Perf. initial			4.50
R582	R25	$60 carmine		175.00	62.50
		Cut cancel			24.00
		Perf. initial			16.00
R583	R25	$100 carmine		70.00	15.00
		Cut cancel			7.50
		Perf. initial			5.00
R584	R25	$500 carmine		*400.00*	140.00
		Cut cancel			60.00
		Perf. initial			26.00
R585	R25	$1000 carmine		*375.00*	125.00
		Cut cancel			45.00
		Perf. initial			29.00

No. R583 is known imperf horizontally. It exists as a reconstructed used vertical strip of 4 that was separated into single stamps.

Documentary Stamps and Types of 1940 Overprinted in Black

Series 1952

Designs: 55c, $1.10, $1.65, $2.20, $2.75, $3.30, L. J. Gage; $2500, William Windom; $5000, C. J. Folger; $10,000, W. Q. Gresham.

1952 — **Wmk. 191R** — *Perf. 11*

R586	R23	1c carmine		.35	.30
		Cut cancel			.25
		Perf. initial			.25
R587	R23	2c carmine		.50	.35
		Cut cancel			.25
		Perf. initial			.25
R588	R23	3c carmine		.40	.35
		Cut cancel			.30
		Perf. initial			.25
R589	R23	4c carmine		.45	.30
		Cut cancel			.25
		Perf. initial			.25
R590	R23	5c carmine		.35	.30
		Cut cancel			.25
		Perf. initial			.25
R591	R23	8c carmine		.90	.60
		Cut cancel			.30
		Perf. initial			.25
R592	R23	10c carmine		.50	.30
		Cut cancel			.25
		Perf. initial			.20
R593	R23	20c carmine		1.25	.40
		Cut cancel			.30
		Perf. initial			.25
R594	R23	25c carmine		2.50	.45
		Cut cancel			.30
		Perf. initial			.30
R595	R23	40c carmine		6.00	1.75
		Cut cancel			.55
		Perf. initial			.45
R596	R23	50c carmine		3.50	.30
		Cut cancel			.25
		Perf. initial			.25
R597	R23	55c carmine		.60	15.00
		Cut cancel			2.00
		Perf. initial			1.10
R598	R23	80c carmine		19.00	4.00
		Cut cancel			.80
		Perf. initial			.75
R599	R24	$1 carmine		7.00	1.50
		Cut cancel			.75
		Perf. initial			.40
R600	R24	$1.10 carmine		25.00	30.00
		Cut cancel			14.00
		Perf. initial			6.25
R601	R24	$1.65 carmine		175.00	62.50
		Cut cancel			37.50
		Perf. initial			21.00
R602	R24	$2 carmine		17.00	.90
		Cut cancel			.30
		Perf. initial			.25
R603	R24	$2.20 carmine		150.00	70.00
		Cut cancel			35.00
		Perf. initial			16.00

R604	R24	$2.75 carmine		190.00	70.00
		Cut cancel			35.00
		Perf. initial			16.00
R605	R24	$3 carmine		32.50	6.00
		Cut cancel			1.60
		Perf. initial			1.40
a.		Horiz. pair, imperf. btwn.			*1,300.*
R606	R24	$3.30 carmine		160.00	70.00
		Cut cancel			35.00
		Perf. initial			16.00
R607	R24	$4 carmine		37.50	6.00
		Cut cancel			2.10
		Perf. initial			1.60
R608	R24	$5 carmine		32.50	1.25
		Cut cancel			.50
		Perf. initial			.40
R609	R24	$10 carmine		60.00	1.25
		Cut cancel			.50
		Perf. initial			.35
R610	R24	$20 carmine		92.50	16.00
		Cut cancel			4.50
		Perf. initial			3.00

Without Gum — *Perf. 12*

R611	R25	$30 carmine		70.00	27.50
		Cut cancel			6.00
		Perf. initial			4.25
R612	R25	$50 carmine		60.00	25.00
		Cut cancel			7.00
		Perf. initial			5.25
R613	R25	$60 carmine		425.00	70.00
		Cut cancel			19.00
		Perf. initial			10.50
R614	R25	$100 carmine		55.00	10.00
		Cut cancel			4.00
		Perf. initial			2.10
R615	R25	$500 carmine		*750.00*	125.00
		Cut cancel			70.00
		Perf. initial			35.00
R616	R25	$1000 carmine		*250.00*	40.00
		Cut cancel			16.00
		Perf. initial			10.50
R617	R25	$2500 carmine		*375.00*	225.00
		Cut cancel			160.00
		Perf. initial			125.00
R618	R25	$5000 carmine		—	*5,500.*
		Cut cancel			1,900.
		Perf. initial			1,250.
R619	R25	$10,000 carmine		—	*1,400.*
		Cut cancel			900.00
		Perf. initial			750.00

Documentary Stamps and Types of 1940 Overprinted in Black

Series 1953

1953 — **Wmk. 191R** — *Perf. 11*

R620	R23	1c carmine		.40	.35
		Cut cancel			.25
		Perf. initial			.25
R621	R23	2c carmine		.40	.30
		Cut cancel			.25
		Perf. initial			.25
R622	R23	3c carmine		.45	.35
		Cut cancel			.25
		Perf. initial			.25
R623	R23	4c carmine		.60	.45
		Cut cancel			.30
		Perf. initial			.25
R624	R23	5c carmine		.50	.30
		Cut cancel			.25
		Perf. initial			.25
a.		Vert. pair, imperf. horiz.			*650.00*
R625	R23	8c carmine		1.10	.85
		Cut cancel			.30
		Perf. initial			.25
R626	R23	10c carmine		.65	.35
		Cut cancel			.25
		Perf. initial			.25
R627	R23	20c carmine		1.50	.50
		Cut cancel			.30
		Perf. initial			.25
R628	R23	25c carmine		1.75	.65
		Cut cancel			.35
		Perf. initial			.25
R629	R23	40c carmine		2.50	.90
		Cut cancel			.50
		Perf. initial			.35
R630	R23	50c carmine		3.00	.35
		Cut cancel			.25
		Perf. initial			.25
R631	R23	55c carmine		7.00	2.00
		Cut cancel			.80
		Perf. initial			.55
a.		Horiz. pair, imperf. vert.		375.00	
R632	R23	80c carmine		10.00	2.10
		Cut cancel			1.50
		Perf. initial			1.40
R633	R24	$1 carmine		5.25	.35
		Cut cancel			.25
		Perf. initial			.25
R634	R24	$1.10 carmine		12.00	2.50
		Cut cancel			2.10
		Perf. initial			1.60
a.		Horiz. pair, imperf. vert.		*700.00*	
b.		Imperf. pair		*600.00*	
R635	R24	$1.65 carmine		12.00	4.50
		Cut cancel			3.25
		Perf. initial			2.10
R636	R24	$2 carmine		9.00	.75
		Cut cancel			.35
		Perf. initial			.25
R637	R24	$2.20 carmine		20.00	6.00
		Cut cancel			2.75
		Perf. initial			2.10

No.	Type	Denom.	Color	Unused	Used
R638	R24	$2.75	carmine	1.75	7.00
		Cut cancel			3.75
		Perf. initial			2.75
R639	R24	$3	carmine	17.00	4.00
		Cut cancel			1.75
		Perf. initial			1.40
R640	R24	$3.30	carmine	35.00	8.00
		Cut cancel			5.25
		Perf. initial			3.50
R641	R24	$4	carmine	.32.50	10.00
		Cut cancel			2.75
		Perf. initial			2.10
R642	R24	$5	carmine	27.50	1.25
		Cut cancel			.55
		Perf. initial			.35
R643	R24	$10	carmine	60.00	2.25
		Cut cancel			1.10
		Perf. initial			.90
R644	R24	$20	carmine	125.00	22.50
		Cut cancel			4.50
		Perf. initial			2.40

Without Gum   *Perf. 12*

No.	Type	Denom.	Color	Unused	Used
R645	R25	$30	carmine	100.00	20.00
		Cut cancel			8.00
		Perf. initial			4.25
R646	R25	$50	carmine	160.00	42.50
		Cut cancel			15.00
		Perf. initial			6.25
R647	R25	$60	carmine	625.00	350.00
		Cut cancel			150.00
		Perf. initial			67.50
		With complete receipt tab		*2,000.*	
R648	R25	$100	carmine	55.00	15.00
		Cut cancel			5.75
		Perf. initial			3.75
R649	R25	$500	carmine	725.00	175.00
		Cut cancel			70.00
		Perf. initial			29.00
R650	R25	$1000	carmine	475.00	80.00
		Cut cancel			27.50
		Perf. initial			16.00
R651	R25	$2500	carmine	2,000.	1,250.
		Cut cancel			525.00
		Perf. initial			350.00
R652	R25	$5000	carmine	—	4,500.
		Cut cancel			2,750.
		Perf. initial			1,500.
R653	R25	$10,000	carmine	—	3,750.
		Cut cancel			1,750.
		Perf. initial			800.00

Types of 1940
Without Overprint

1954   **Wmk. 191R**   *Perf. 11*

No.	Type	Denom.	Color	Unused	Used
R654	R23	1c	carmine	.25	.25
		Cut cancel			.25
		Perf. initial			.20
a.		Horiz. pair, imperf. vert.		*1,500.*	
R655	R23	2c	carmine	.25	.30
		Cut cancel			.25
		Perf. initial			.20
R656	R23	3c	carmine	.25	.30
		Cut cancel			.25
		Perf. initial			.20
R657	R23	4c	carmine	.25	.30
		Cut cancel			.25
		Perf. initial			.20
R658	R23	5c	carmine	.25	.25
		Cut cancel			.20
		Perf. initial			.20
R659	R23	8c	carmine	.25	.25
		Cut cancel			.25
		Perf. initial			.20
R660	R23	10c	carmine	.25	.25
		Cut cancel			.25
		Perf. initial			.20
R661	R23	20c	carmine	.30	.40
		Cut cancel			.30
		Perf. initial			.25
R662	R23	25c	carmine	.35	.45
		Cut cancel			.30
		Perf. initial			.25
R663	R23	40c	carmine	.75	.60
		Cut cancel			.45
		Perf. initial			.35
R664	R23	50c	carmine	1.00	.25
		Cut cancel			.20
		Perf. initial			.20
a.		Horiz. pair, imperf. vert.		500.00	
R665	R23	55c	carmine	.90	1.25
		Cut cancel			.55
		Perf. initial			.45
R666	R23	80c	carmine	1.50	1.90
		Cut cancel			1.25
		Perf. initial			1.10
R667	R24	$1	carmine	.90	.35
		Cut cancel			.30
		Perf. initial			.25
R668	R24	$1.10	carmine	2.00	2.50
		Cut cancel			1.60
		Perf. initial			1.10
R669	R24	$1.65	carmine	25.00	10.00
		Cut cancel			5.00
		Perf. initial			1.00
R670	R24	$2	carmine	1.00	.45
		Cut cancel			.25
		Perf. initial			.25
R671	R24	$2.20	carmine	2.25	3.75
		Cut cancel			2.75
		Perf. initial			1.60
R672	R24	$2.75	carmine	25.00	65.00
		Cut cancel			37.50
		Perf. initial			21.00
R673	R24	$3	carmine	2.00	3.00
		Cut cancel			1.25
		Perf. initial			.80

No.	Type	Denom.	Color	Unused	Used
R674	R24	$3.30	carmine	3.50	5.00
		Cut cancel			3.25
		Perf. initial			2.10
R675	R24	$4	carmine	2.75	4.00
		Cut cancel			2.10
		Perf. initial			1.60
R676	R24	$5	carmine	3.25	.50
		Cut cancel			.35
		Perf. initial			.25
R677	R24	$10	carmine	5.00	1.50
		Cut cancel			.85
		Perf. initial			.70
R678	R24	$20	carmine	10.00	6.50
		Cut cancel			3.25
		Perf. initial			1.90

Documentary Stamps and Type of 1940 Overprinted in Black

1954   **Wmk. 191R**   *Perf. 12*
Without Gum

No.	Type	Denom.	Color	Unused	Used
R679	R25	$30	carmine	55.00	17.50
		Cut cancel			5.25
		Perf. initial			3.50
		With complete receipt tab		55.00	
a.		Booklet pane of 4		*225.00*	
		Complete booklet, 10 #R679a		*2,250.*	
R680	R25	$50	carmine	55.00	29.00
		Cut cancel			10.00
		Perf. initial			6.25
		With complete receipt tab		55.00	
a.		Booklet pane of 4		*225.00*	
		Complete booklet, 10 #R680a		*2,250.*	
R681	R25	$60	carmine	55.00	30.00
		Cut cancel			13.00
		Perf. initial			9.25
		With complete receipt tab		55.00	
a.		Booklet pane of 4		*225.00*	
		Complete booklet, 10 #R681a		*2,250.*	
R682	R25	$100	carmine	55.00	7.50
		Cut cancel			5.25
		Perf. initial			4.00
		With complete receipt tab		55.00	
a.		Booklet pane of 4		*225.00*	
		Complete booklet, 10 #R682a		*2,250.*	
R683	R25	$500	carmine	*150.00*	87.50
		Cut cancel			30.00
		Perf. initial			25.00
		With complete receipt tab		150.00	
a.		Booklet pane of 4		*600.00*	
		Complete booklet, 2 #R683a		*1,200.*	
R684	R25	$1000	carmine	300.00	90.00
		Cut cancel			21.00
		Perf. initial			17.00
		With complete receipt tab		*300.00*	
a.		Booklet pane of 4		*1,200.*	
		Complete booklet, 1 #R684a		*1,200.*	
R685	R25	$2500	carmine	*350.00*	300.00
		Cut cancel			100.00
		Perf. initial			65.00
		With complete receipt tab		*350.00*	
a.		Booklet pane of 4		*1,400.*	
		Complete booklet, 10 #R685a		*14,000.*	
R686	R25	$5000	carmine	*1,750.*	1,250.
		Cut cancel			550.00
		Perf. initial			500.00
		With complete receipt tab		*1,750.*	
a.		Booklet pane of 4		*7,000.*	
R687	R25	$10,000	carmine	*1,750.*	1,500.
		Cut cancel			700.00
		Perf. initial			275.00
		With complete receipt tab		*1,750.*	
a.		Booklet pane of 4		*7,000.*	

Documentary Stamps and Type of 1940 Overprinted in Black
Series 1955

1955   **Wmk. 191R**   *Perf. 12*
Without Gum

No.	Type	Denom.	Color	Unused	Used
R688	R25	$30	carmine	90.00	17.50
		Cut cancel			7.00
		Perf. initial			3.75
R689	R25	$50	carmine	100.00	30.00
		Cut cancel			11.00
		Perf. initial			7.00
R690	R25	$60	carmine	160.00	45.00
		Cut cancel			17.50
		Perf. initial			5.25

No.	Type	Denom.	Color	Unused	Used
R691	R25	$100	carmine	100.00	15.00
		Cut cancel			6.00
		Perf. initial			4.00
R692	R25	$500	carmine	750.00	160.00
		Cut cancel			45.00
		Perf. initial			21.00
R693	R25	$1000	carmine	*275.00*	65.00
		Cut cancel			21.00
		Perf. initial			14.00
R694	R25	$2500	carmine	*500.00*	225.00
		Cut cancel			95.00
		Perf. initial			55.00
R695	R25	$5000	carmine	*2,500.*	1,500.
		Cut cancel			600.00
		Perf. initial			400.00
R696	R25	$10,000	carmine	—	1,100.
		Cut cancel			550.00
		Perf. initial			190.00

Documentary Stamps and Type of 1940 Overprinted in Black "Series 1956"

1956   **Wmk. 191R**   **Without Gum**   *Perf. 12*

No.	Type	Denom.	Color	Unused	Used
R697	R25	$30	carmine	140.00	20.00
		Cut cancel			10.50
		Perf. initial			4.75
R698	R25	$50	carmine	150.00	27.50
		Cut cancel			15.00
		Perf. initial			6.50
R699	R25	$60	carmine	190.00	60.00
		Cut cancel			20.00
		Perf. initial			7.50
R700	R25	$100	carmine	110.00	15.00
		Cut cancel			6.00
		Perf. initial			5.00
R701	R25	$500	carmine	*450.00*	110.00
		Cut cancel			27.50
		Perf. initial			16.00
R702	R25	$1000	carmine	600.00	90.00
		Cut cancel			25.00
		Perf. initial			13.00
R703	R25	$2500	carmine	—	800.00
		Cut cancel			260.00
		Perf. initial			150.00
R704	R25	$5000	carmine	—	2,200.
		Cut cancel			1,300.
		Perf. initial			850.00
R705	R25	$10,000	carmine	—	750.00
		Cut cancel			250.00
		Perf. initial			150.00

Documentary Stamps and Type of 1940 Overprinted in Black "Series 1957"

1957   **Wmk. 191R**   *Perf. 12*
Without Gum

No.	Type	Denom.	Color	Unused	Used
R706	R25	$30	carmine	200.00	50.00
		Cut cancel			15.00
		Perf. initial			6.75
R707	R25	$50	carmine	125.00	47.50
		Cut cancel			14.00
		Perf. initial			5.75
R708	R25	$60	carmine	*800.00*	325.00
		Cut cancel			140.00
		Perf. initial			57.50
R709	R25	$100	carmine	110.00	20.00
		Cut cancel			9.00
		Perf. initial			4.50
R710	R25	$500	carmine	450.00	200.00
		Cut cancel			70.00
		Perf. initial			37.50
R711	R25	$1000	carmine	*300.00*	100.00
		Cut cancel			35.00
		Perf. initial			21.00
R712	R25	$2500	carmine	—	1,200.
		Cut cancel			450.00
		Perf. initial			300.00
R713	R25	$5000	carmine	*2,250.*	1,800.
		Cut cancel			800.00
		Perf. initial			250.00
R714	R25	$10,000	carmine	—	500.00
		Cut cancel			175.00
		Perf. initial			150.00

Documentary Stamps and Type of 1940 Overprinted in Black "Series 1958"

1958   **Wmk. 191R**   *Perf. 12*
Without Gum

No.	Type	Denom.	Color	Unused	Used
R715	R25	$30	carmine	110.00	27.50
		Cut cancel			17.50
		Perf. initial			8.25
R716	R25	$50	carmine	150.00	35.00
		Cut cancel			17.00
		Perf. initial			6.75
R717	R25	$60	carmine	160.00	42.50
		Cut cancel			20.00
		Perf. initial			10.50
R718	R25	$100	carmine	80.00	15.00
		Cut cancel			6.50
		Perf. initial			2.10
R719	R25	$500	carmine	350.00	95.00
		Cut cancel			42.50
		Perf. initial			21.00
R720	R25	$1000	carmine	*425.00*	90.00
		Cut cancel			35.00
		Perf. initial			25.00
R721	R25	$2500	carmine	—	1,100.
		Cut cancel			575.00
		Perf. initial			400.00
R722	R25	$5000	carmine	*4,000.*	2,750.
		Cut cancel			2,000.
		Perf. initial			2,000.
R723	R25	$10,000	carmine	—	2,000.
		Cut cancel			1,250.
		Perf. initial			700.00

Documentary Stamps and Type of 1940 Without Overprint

1958		Wmk. 191R With Gum		Perf. 12	
R724	R25	$30 **carmine**		11.00	7.00
		Cut cancel			6.00
		Perf. initial			4.25
		With complete receipt tab		14.00	
a.		Booklet pane of 4		57.50	
		Complete booklet, 10 #R724a		575.00	
b.		Vert. pair, imperf. horiz.		2,250.	
R725	R25	$50 **carmine**		12.00	7.00
		Cut cancel			4.00
		Perf. initial			3.25
		With complete receipt tab		15.00	
a.		Booklet pane of 4		60.00	
		Complete booklet, 10 #R725a		600.00	
b.		Vert. pair, imperf. horiz.			3,500.
R726	R25	$60 **carmine**		17.50	21.00
		Cut cancel			11.00
		Perf. initial			5.50
		With complete receipt tab		22.00	
a.		Booklet pane of 4		90.00	
		Complete booklet, 10 #R726a		900.00	
R727	R25	$100 **carmine**		13.00	4.75
		Cut cancel			3.25
		Perf. initial			2.00
		With complete receipt tab		16.00	
a.		Booklet pane of 4		65.00	
		Complete booklet, 10 #R727a		650.00	
R728	R25	$500 **carmine**		17.50	26.00
		Cut cancel			10.50
		Perf. initial			7.75
		With complete receipt tab		22.00	
a.		Booklet pane of 4		90.00	
		Complete booklet, 10 #R728a		900.00	
R729	R25	$1000 **carmine**		16.00	21.00
		Cut cancel			10.50
		Perf. initial			7.75

		With complete receipt tab		20.00	
a.		Booklet pane of 4		80.00	
		Complete booklet, 10 #R729a		800.00	
b.		Vert. pair, imperf. horiz.			1,750.
R730	R25	$2500 **carmine**		175.00	175.00
		Cut cancel			90.00
		Perf. initial			55.00
		With complete receipt tab		—	
a.		Booklet pane of 4		800.00	
		Complete booklet, 10 #R730a			
R731	R25	$5000 **carmine**		275.00	175.00
		Cut cancel			90.00
		Perf. initial			65.00
		With complete receipt tab		—	
a.		Booklet pane of 4		1,200.	
		Complete booklet, 10 #R731a		—	
R732	R25	$10,000 **carmine**		275.00	140.00
		Cut cancel			55.00
		Perf. initial			25.00
		With complete receipt tab		—	
a.		Booklet pane of 4		1,200.	
		Complete booklet, 10 #R732a		—	

Internal Revenue Building, Washington, D.C. — R26

Centenary of the Internal Revenue Service.

Giori Press Printing

1962, July 2		Unwmk.		Perf. 11	
R733	R26	10c **violet blue & bright green**		1.00	.40
		Never hinged		1.25	
		Cut cancel			.20
		Perf. initial			.25
		P# block of 4		15.00	
		Cross gutter block of 4		2,500.	
		Horiz. pair with vert. gutter		200.00	
		Vert. pair with horiz. gutter		400.00	

1963   "Established 1862" Removed

R734	R26	10c **violet blue & bright green**		3.00	.70
		Never hinged		5.00	
		Cut cancel			.25
		Perf. initial			.25
		P# block of 4		30.00	

Documentary revenue stamps were no longer required after Dec. 31, 1967.

PROPRIETARY STAMPS

Stamps for use on proprietary articles were included in the first general issue of 1862-71. They are R3, R13, R14, R18, R22, R29, R31 and R38.

Several varieties of "violet" paper were used in printing Nos. RB1-RB10. One is grayish with a slight greenish tinge, called "intermediate" paper by specialists. It should not be confused with the "green" paper, which is truly green.

All values prior to 1898 are for used examples. Printed cancellations on proprietary stamps command sizable premiums.

George Washington — RB1a
RB1
Engraved and printed by Jos. R. Carpenter, Philadelphia.

1871-74				Perf. 12	
				a. Violet Paper (1871)	b. Green Paper (1874)
RB1	RB1	1c	**green & black**	8.00	14.00
			Pair	17.00	35.00
			Block of 4	37.50	85.00
	c.		Imperf.	80.00	
			Imperf. pair	175.00	
			Imperf. block of 4	475.00	
	d.		Inverted center	4,500.	
RB2	RB1	2c	**green & black**	8.75	30.00
			Pair	19.00	67.50
			Block of 4	42.50	160.00
			Double transfer	20.00	
	c.		Inverted center	50,000.	9,000.
	d.		Vert. half used as 1c on document	—	—

No. RB2bc is valued with fine centering and small faults. Only two examples recorded of the inverted center on violet paper, No. RB2ac.

RB3	RB1a	3c	**green & black**	27.50	67.50
			Pair	65.00	150.00
			Block of 4	140.00	325.00
			Double transfer	—	

				a. Violet Paper (1871)	b. Green Paper (1874)
	c.		Sewing machine perf.	650.00	
	d.		Inverted center	16,000.	

No. RB3ad is valued with small faults as 6 of the 7 recorded examples have faults.

RB4	RB1a	4c	**green & black**	16.00	25.00
			Pair	37.50	60.00
			Block of 4	100.00	130.00
			Double transfer	—	
	c.		Inverted center	15,000.	
	d.		Vert. half used as 2c on document	—	—

No. RB4ac is valued with small faults as 6 of the 7 recorded examples have faults.

RB5	RB1a	5c	**green & black**	160.00	175.00
			Pair	350.00	400.00
			Block of 4	750.00	875.00
	c.		Inverted center	130,000.	

No. RB5ac is unique. Value represents price realized in 2000 auction sale.

RB6	RB1a	6c	**green & black**	57.50	140.00
			Pair	125.00	325.00
			Block of 4	350.00	725.00
			Double transfer	—	
RB7	RB1a	10c	**green & black** ('73)	250.00	65.00
			Pair	600.00	150.00
			Block of 4	—	350.00
			Double transfer	—	

(See note on Inverted Centers after No. R133.)

RB1b

				a. Violet Paper	b. Green Paper (1874)
RB8	RB1b	50c	**green & black** ('73)	1,000.	750.
			Pair	2,250.	
RB9	RB1b	$1	**green & black** ('73)	2,750.	12,000.
			Pair	—	

RB1c

	a. Violet Paper	b. Green Paper (1874)
RB10 RB1c $5 **green & black** ('73)	9,000.	85,000.
Pair	22,500.	

No. RB10b is valued with small faults.

When the Carpenter contract expired Aug. 31, 1875, the proprietary stamps remaining unissued were delivered to the Bureau of Internal Revenue. Until the taxes expired, June 30, 1883, the B.I.R. issued 34,315 of the 50c, 6,585 of the $1 and 2,109 of the $5, Nos. RB8-RB10. No. RB19, the 10c blue, replaced No. RB7b, the 10c on green paper, after 336,000 stamps were issued, exhausting the supply in 1881.

RB2

George Washington — RB2a

Plates prepared and printed by both the National Bank Note Co. and the Bureau of Engraving and Printing. No. RB11, and possibly others, also printed by the American Bank Note Co. All silk paper printings were by National, plus early printings of Nos. RB11b-RB14b, RB16b, RB17b. All rouletted stamps printed by the BEP plus Nos. RB15b, RB18b, RB19b. Otherwise, which company printed the stamps can be told only by guide lines (BEP) or full marginal inscriptions. ABN used National plates with A. B. Co. added on the second stamp to the left of the National inscription.

1875-81

				Silk Paper a. Perf.	Wmkd. 191R b. Perf.	c. Roul. 6
RB11	RB2	1c	**green**	2.25	.50	160.00
			Pair	5.00	1.25	375.00
			Block of 4	12.50	3.00	875.00
			Double transfer	—		
		d.	Vert. pair, imperf between		300.00	
RB12	RB2	2c	**brown**	3.25	2.00	175.00
			Pair	7.00	4.50	375.00
			Block of 4	65.00	11.00	900.00
RB13	RB2a	3c	**orange**	14.00	4.00	140.00
			Pair	30.00	9.00	325.00
			Block of 4	70.00	21.00	750.00
		d.	Horizontal pair, imperf. between			—

				Silk Paper a. Perf.	Wmkd. 191R b. Perf.	c. Roul. 6
		e.	Vertical pair, imperf. between			1,900
RB14	RB2a	4c	**red brown**	10.00	9.00	
			Pair	25.00	21.00	
			Block of 4	55.00	45.00	
RB15	RB2a	4c	**red**		6.00	300.00
			Pair		15.00	650.00
			Block of 4		35.00	
RB16	RB2a	5c	**black**	175.00	125.00	1,850.
			Pair	350.00	275.00	—
			Block of 4	—	—	
RB17	RB2a	6c	**violet blue**	35.00	25.00	450.00
			Pair	75.00	60.00	1,000.
			Block of 4	200.00	150.00	
RB18	RB2a	6c	**violet**		35.00	700.00
			Pair		85.00	
			Block of 4		225.00	
RB19	RB2a	10c	**blue** ('81)		350.00	
			Pair		750.00	
			Block of 4		—	

Many fraudulent roulettes exist.

Battleship — RB3

Inscribed "Series of 1898." and "Proprietary."
See note on rouletting preceding No. R161.

1898   Wmk. 191R   Engr.

				Roul. 5½ Unused	Used	p. Hyphen Hole Perf. 7 Unused	Used
RB20	⅛c	**yellow green**		.25	.25	.30	.25
		Block of 4		.50	.50	.75	.70
		P# block of 6		140.00		140.00	
		Double transfer		—			
a.		Vert. pair, imperf. horiz.		—			
RB21	¼c	**brown**		.25	.25	.25	.25
a.		¼c **red brown**		.20	.20		
b.		¼c **yellow brown**		.20	.20	.20	.20
c.		¼c **orange brown**		.20	.20	.20	.20
d.		¼c **bister**		.20	.20		
		Block of 4		.50	.25	.55	1.00
		P# block of 6		110.00		125.00	
		Double transfer		—	—		
e.		Vert. pair, imperf. horiz.		—			
f.		Printed on both sides		—			
RB22	⅜c	**deep orange**		.30	.30	.50	.35
		Block of 4		1.40	1.90	2.25	
		P# block of 6		200.00		200.00	
a.		Horiz. pair, imperf. vert.		12.50			
b.		Vert. pair, imperf. horiz.		—			
RB23	⅝c	**deep ultra**		.25	.25	.30	.25
		Block of 4		1.25	1.10	1.50	1.25
		P# block of 6		75.00		100.00	
		Double transfer		1.50			
a.		Vert. pair, imperf. horiz.		85.00	—		
b.		Horiz. pair, imperf. vert.		350.00			
RB24	1c	**dark green**		2.25	.40	30.00	15.00
		Block of 4		11.00	1.75	140.00	67.50
		P# block of 6		250.00		550.00	
a.		Vert. pair, imperf. horiz.		325.00			
RB25	1¼c	**violet**		.35	.25	.30	.30
		Block of 4		1.50	1.00	1.40	1.25
		P# block of 6		200.00		250.00	
a.		1¼c **brown violet**		.35	.20	.25	.30
b.		Vertical pair, imperf. between		—			
RB26	1⅞c	**dull blue**		15.00	2.00	35.00	9.00
		Block of 4		65.00	—	175.00	
		P# block of 6		800.00		1,250.	
		Double transfer		—			
RB27	2c	**violet brown**		1.40	.35	7.25	1.00
		Block of 4		6.75		27.50	
		P# block of 6		475.00			
		Double transfer		—			
a.		Horiz. pair, imperf. vert.		60.00			
RB28	2½c	**lake**		5.00	.35	6.00	.40
		Block of 4		25.00	1.50	32.50	—
		P# block of 6		250.00		375.00	
a.		Vert. pair, imperf. horiz.		225.00			
RB29	3¾c	**olive gray**		42.50	15.00	90.00	27.50
		Block of 4		210.00		425.00	140.00
		P# block of 6		—			
RB30	4c	**purple**		16.00	1.50	62.50	22.50
		Block of 4		75.00	7.50	325.00	100.00
		P# block of 6		—		—	

			Roul. 5½ Unused	Used	p. Hyphen Hole Perf. 7 Unused	Used
		Double transfer	—			
RB31	5c	**brown orange**	15.00	1.50	75.00	25.00
		Block of 4	70.00	7.00	375.00	190.00
		P# block of 6	—			
a.		Vert. pair, imperf. horiz.	—	325.00		
b.		Horiz. pair, imperf. vert.	—	425.00		

See note after No. RS315 regarding St. Louis Provisional Labels of 1898.

RB4

Inscribed "Series of 1914"

1914   Wmk. 190   Offset Printing   Perf. 10

				Unused	Used
RB32	RB4	⅛c	**black**	.25	.35
			Block of 4	1.25	1.60
RB33	RB4	¼c	**black**	4.00	1.50
			Block of 4	18.00	
RB34	RB4	⅜c	**black**	.35	.35
			Block of 4	1.50	1.50
RB35	RB4	⅝c	**black**	7.75	3.00
			Block of 4	35.00	
RB36	RB4	1¼c	**black**	5.50	1.75
			Block of 4	25.00	
RB37	RB4	1⅞c	**black**	67.50	22.50
			Block of 4	300.00	
RB38	RB4	2½c	**black**	16.00	3.50
			Block of 4	67.50	15.00
RB39	RB4	3⅛c	**black**	150.00	67.50
			Block of 4	650.00	
RB40	RB4	3¾c	**black**	65.00	27.50
			Block of 4	350.00	
RB41	RB4	4c	**black**	90.00	45.00
			Block of 4	450.00	
RB42	RB4	4⅝c	**black**	3,000.	—
			Block of 4	13,000.	
RB43	RB4	5c	**black**	175.00	110.00
			Block of 4	—	

Wmk. 191R

				Unused	Used
RB44	RB4	⅛c	**black**	.35	.30
			Block of 4	1.50	1.50
RB45	RB4	¼c	**black**	1.25	.25
			Block of 4	1.25	1.10
			Double impression	30.00	
RB46	RB4	⅜c	**black**	.75	.45
			Block of 4	3.50	2.00
RB47	RB4	½c	**black**	4.25	3.75
			Block of 4	17.50	
RB48	RB4	⅝c	**black**	.30	.25
			Block of 4	1.50	1.10
RB49	RB4	1c	**black**	5.50	5.50
			Block of 4	25.00	25.00
RB50	RB4	1¼c	**black**	.65	.40
			Block of 4	3.00	1.75
RB51	RB4	1½c	**black**	4.25	3.00
			Block of 4	17.50	14.00
RB52	RB4	1⅞c	**black**	1.35	.90
			Block of 4	6.00	4.00
RB53	RB4	2c	**black**	7.50	6.00
			Block of 4	32.50	
RB54	RB4	2½c	**black**	1.75	1.40
			Block of 4	8.00	7.50
RB55	RB4	3c	**black**	6.00	4.00
			Block of 4	27.50	
RB56	RB4	3⅛c	**black**	8.00	5.00
			Block of 4	35.00	
RB57	RB4	3¾c	**black**	17.50	11.00
			Block of 4	77.50	
RB58	RB4	4c	**black**	.50	.30
			Block of 4	2.25	1.50
			Double impression	—	
RB59	RB4	4⅝c	**black**	20.00	11.00
			Block of 4	85.00	
RB60	RB4	5c	**black**	4.50	3.75
			Block of 4	20.00	
RB61	RB4	6c	**black**	80.00	52.50
			Block of 4	375.00	
RB62	RB4	8c	**black**	25.00	16.00
			Block of 4	110.00	
RB63	RB4	10c	**black**	18.00	11.00
			Block of 4	87.50	
RB64	RB4	20c	**black**	35.00	24.00
			Block of 4	160.00	

RB5

1919		Offset Printing		Perf. 11	
RB65	RB5	1c	**dark blue**	.25	.25
			Block of 4	1.25	1.10
			Double impression	30.00	20.00
RB66	RB5	2c	**dark blue**	.35	.25
			Block of 4	1.50	1.10
			Double impression	70.00	

RB67	RB5	3c	**dark blue**	1.50	.75
			Block of 4	6.00	3.50
			Double impression	70.00	
RB68	RB5	4c	**dark blue**	2.25	.75
			Block of 4	10.00	
RB69	RB5	5c	**dark blue**	3.00	1.25
			Block of 4	13.50	5.75
RB70	RB5	8c	**dark blue**	22.50	16.00

			Block of 4	100.00	
RB71	RB5	10c	**dark blue**	11.00	4.25
			Block of 4	52.50	15.00
RB72	RB5	20c	**dark blue**	17.50	6.00
			Block of 4	87.50	
RB73	RB5	40c	**dark blue**	65.00	20.00
			Block of 4	300.00	

FUTURE DELIVERY STAMPS

Issued to facilitate the collection of a tax upon each sale, agreement of sale or agreement to sell any products or merchandise at any exchange or board of trade, or other similar place for future delivery.

Documentary Stamps of 1917 Overprinted in Black or Red

Type I

1918-34   Wmk. 191R   Offset Printing   Perf. 11
Overprint Horizontal (Lines 8mm apart)
Left Value — Unused
Right Value — Used

RC1	R22	2c **carmine rose**	8.75	.25
		Block of 4	37.50	1.10
RC2	R22	3c **carmine rose** ('34)	47.50	37.50
		Cut cancel		20.00
RC3	R22	4c **carmine rose**	15.00	.25
		Cut cancel		.20
		Block of 4	70.00	1.10
b.		Double impression of stamp		10.00
RC3A	R22	5c **carmine rose** ('33)	90.00	7.50
		Block of 4	—	37.50
RC4	R22	10c **carmine rose**	24.00	.35
		Block of 4	110.00	1.50
a.		Double overprint	—	5.25
b.		"FUTURE" omitted	—	325.00
c.		"DELIVERY FUTURE"		37.50
RC5	R22	20c **carmine rose**	35.00	.25
		Cut cancel		.20
		Block of 4	175.00	1.10
a.		Double overprint		21.00
RC6	R22	25c **carmine rose**	75.00	.60
		Cut cancel		.30
		Block of 4	350.00	3.00
		Block of 4, cut cancel		1.50
RC7	R22	40c **carmine rose**	85.00	1.25
		Cut cancel		.35
		Block of 4	375.00	5.75
		Block of 4, cut cancel		1.50
RC8	R22	50c **carmine rose**	22.50	.35
		Cut cancel		.20
		Block of 4	110.00	1.50
a.		"DELIVERY" omitted	—	110.00
RC9	R22	80c **carmine rose**	175.00	13.50
		Cut cancel		3.50
		Block of 4	825.00	67.50
		Block of 4, cut cancel		16.00
a.		Double overprint		37.50
		Double overprint, cut cancel		6.25

Engr.
Overprint Vertical, Reading Up (Lines 2mm apart)

RC10	R21	$1 **green** (R)	65.00	.35
		Cut cancel		.20
		Block of 4	275.00	1.60
a.		Overprint reading down		300.00
b.		Black overprint	—	
		Cut cancel		125.00
RC11	R21	$2 **rose**	75.00	.45
		Cut cancel		.25
		Block of 4	350.00	2.00
RC12	R21	$3 **violet** (R)	225.00	3.50
		Cut cancel		.30
		Block of 4	—	16.00
		Block of 4, cut cancel		1.50
a.		Overprint reading down	—	52.50
RC13	R21	$5 **dark blue** (R)	125.00	.60
		Cut cancel		.25
		Block of 4	—	2.75
		Block of 4, cut cancel		1.10
RC14	R21	$10 **orange**	150.00	1.35
		Cut cancel		.30
		Block of 4	675.00	5.00
		Block of 4, cut cancel		1.40
a.		"DELIVERY FUTURE"		110.00
RC15	R21	$20 **olive bister**	300.00	9.00
		Cut cancel		.80
		Perf initial		.35
		Block of 4		47.50
		Block of 4, cut cancel		3.50

Overprint Horizontal (Lines 11⅜mm apart)
Perf. 12
Without Gum

RC16	R17	$30 **vermilion**, green numerals	125.00	5.50
		Cut cancel		1.75
		Perf initial		1.25
		Vertical strip of 4		30.00
		Vertical strip of 4, cut cancel		8.25
a.		Numerals in blue	110.00	4.75
		Cut cancel		2.00
		Perf initial		1.50
b.		Imperf., blue numerals		110.00
RC17	R19	$50 **olive green** (Cleveland)	100.00	3.00
		Cut cancel		.90
		Vertical strip of 4		15.00
		Vertical strip of 4, cut cancel		3.50
a.		$50 olive bister	100.00	2.75
		Cut cancel		.25
		Perf initial		.50
RC18	R19	$60 **brown**	140.00	8.00
		Cut cancel		1.00
		Perf initial		.80
		Vertical strip of 4		35.00
		Vertical strip of 4, cut cancel		4.75
a.		Vert. pair, imperf. horiz.		425.00
RC19	R17	$100 **yellow green** ('34)	225.00	37.50
		Cut cancel		9.00
		Perf initial		7.00
		Vertical strip of 4	—	200.00
		Vertical strip of 4, cut cancel		37.50
RC20	R18	$500 **blue**, red numerals (R)	250.00	20.00
		Cut cancel		7.00
		Perf initial		5.50
		Vertical strip of 4		77.50
		Vertical strip of 4, cut cancel		30.00
		Double transfer		30.00
a.		Numerals in orange	—	60.00
		Cut cancel		12.50
		Perf initial		10.00
		Double transfer		90.00
RC21	R19	$1000 **orange**	200.00	7.50
		Cut cancel		2.00
		Perf initial		1.50
		Vertical strip of 4		32.50
		Vertical strip of 4, cut cancel		9.00
a.		Vert. pair, imperf. horiz.		1,350.

See note after No. R227.

1923-24   Offset Printing   Perf. 11
Overprint Horizontal (Lines 2mm apart)

RC22	R22	1c **carmine rose**	1.25	.25
		Block of 4	6.00	1.25
RC23	R22	80c **carmine rose**	175.00	3.50
		Cut cancel		.70
		Block of 4	—	18.00
		Block of 4, cut cancel		3.50

Type II

1925-34   **Engr.**

RC25	R21	$1 **green** (R)	85.00	2.00
		Cut cancel		.45
		Block of 4	—	8.00
		Block of 4, cut cancel		1.50
RC26	R21	$10 **orange** (Bk) ('34)	225.00	29.00
		Cut cancel		18.00
		Perf initial		11.50

Overprint Type I

1928-29		Offset Printing		Perf. 10
RC27	R22	10c **carmine rose**		5,000.
RC28	R22	20c **carmine rose**		5,000.

Some specialists have questioned the status of Nos. RC27-RC28, believing known examples to be either fraudulently reperforated examples of Nos. RC4 and RC5, or examples of Nos. R255 and R256 with fake overprints applied. The editors would like to see authenticated evidence of the existence of Nos. RC27 and RC28.

STOCK TRANSFER STAMPS

Issued to facilitate the collection of a tax on all sales or agreements to sell, or memoranda of sales or delivery of, or transfers of legal title to shares or certificates of stock.

Documentary Stamps of 1917 Overprinted in Black or Red

1918-22   Offset Printing   Wmk. 191R   Perf. 11
Overprint Horizontal (Lines 8mm apart)

RD1	R22	1c **carmine rose**	1.00	.25
		Block of 4	4.25	1.10
a.		Double overprint	—	
RD2	R22	2c **carmine rose**	.25	.25
		Block of 4	1.10	1.10
a.		Double overprint	—	5.00
		Double overprint, cut cancel		2.50
		Double impression of stamp	—	
RD3	R22	4c **carmine rose**	.25	.25
		Block of 4	1.25	1.10
a.		Double overprint	—	4.25
		Double overprint, cut cancel		2.10
b.		"STOCK" omitted		10.50
d.		Ovpt. lines 10mm apart	—	
		Double impression of stamp		6.00
RD4	R22	5c **carmine rose**	.30	.25
		Block of 4	1.40	1.10
RD5	R22	10c **carmine rose**	.30	.25
		Block of 4	1.40	1.10
a.		Double overprint	—	5.25
		Double overprint, cut cancel		2.75
b.		"STOCK" omitted		
		Double impression of stamp	—	
RD6	R22	20c **carmine rose**	.55	.25
		Perf initial		.20
		Block of 4	2.25	1.10
a.		Double overprint		6.25
b.		"STOCK" double		
		Double impression of stamp		6.00
RD7	R22	25c **carmine rose**	2.25	.25
		Cut cancel		.20
		Block of 4	10.50	1.10
RD8	R22	40c **carmine rose** ('22)	2.25	.25
		Block of 4	10.50	1.10
RD9	R22	50c **carmine rose**	.80	.25
		Block of 4	3.75	1.10
a.		Double overprint	—	
		Double impression of stamp	—	
RD10	R22	80c **carmine rose**	9.00	.45
		Cut cancel		.25
		Block of 4	42.50	2.00

Engr.
Overprint Vertical, Reading Up (Lines 2mm apart)

RD11	R21	$1 **green** (R)	175.00	32.50
		Cut cancel		7.00
		Block of 4	—	
		Block of 4, cut cancel		15.00
a.		Overprint reading down	225.00	35.00
		Overprint reading down, cut cancel		10.00
RD12	R21	$1 **green** (Bk)	3.00	.30
		Block of 4	13.00	1.40
a.		Pair, one without overprint	—	160.00
b.		Overprinted on back instead of face, inverted	—	110.00
c.		Overprint reading down	—	7.50
d.		$1 yellow green	3.00	.25
RD13	R21	$2 **rose**	3.00	.25
		Perf initial		.20
		Block of 4	13.00	.25
a.		Overprint reading down		11.50
		Overprint reading down, cut cancel		1.50
b.		Vert. pair, imperf. horiz.	500.00	
RD14	R21	$3 **violet** (R)	27.50	6.00
		Cut cancel		.30
		Perf initial		.20
		Block of 4	125.00	
		Block of 4, cut cancel		1.50
RD15	R21	$4 **yellow brown**	12.00	1.35
		Cut cancel		.25
		Block of 4	52.50	.20
RD16	R21	$5 **dark blue** (R)	8.00	1.10
		Cut cancel		.25
		Block of 4	40.00	.20
		Block of 4, cut cancel		1.10
a.		Overprint reading down	42.50	.20
		Overprint reading down, cut cancel		1.35
RD17	R21	$10 **orange**	30.00	.25
		Cut cancel		.45
		Block of 4	125.00	.20
		Block of 4, cut cancel		1.50
RD18	R21	$20 **olive bister** ('21)	125.00	.20
		Cut cancel		18.00
		Perf initial		5.00
		Block of 4	500.00	2.50
		Block of 4, cut cancel		82.50
				25.00

Shifted overprints on the $2, and $10 result in "TRANSFER STOCK," "TRANSFER" omitted, and possibly other varieties.

Overprint Horizontal (Lines 11½mm apart)
1918   Without Gum   Perf. 12

RD19	R17	$30 **vermilion**, green numerals	42.50	5.75
		Cut cancel		2.00
		Perf initial		1.25
		Vertical strip of 4		26.00
		Vertical strip of 4, cut cancel		7.75
a.		Numerals in blue	150.00	60.00
RD20	R19	$50 **olive green** (Cleveland)	140.00	62.50
		Cut cancel		26.00
		Perf initial		25.00
		Vertical strip of 4		300.00
		Vertical strip of 4, cut cancel		110.00
RD21	R19	$60 **brown**	250.00	25.00
		Cut cancel		10.50
		Perf initial		7.25
		Vertical strip of 4		100.00
		Vertical strip of 4, cut cancel		47.50
RD22	R17	$100 **green**	45.00	6.50
		Cut cancel		3.00
		Perf initial		2.25
		Vertical strip of 4		30.00
		Vertical strip of 4, cut cancel		13.00
RD23	R18	$500 **blue** (R)	425.00	150.00
		Cut cancel		75.00
		Perf initial		55.00
		Vertical strip of 4		
		Vertical strip of 4, cut cancel		325.00
		Double transfer	625.00	200.00
a.		Numerals in orange		150.00
		Numerals in orange, double transfer		250.00
RD24	R19	$1,000 **orange**	275.00	95.00
		Cut cancel		32.50
		Perf initial		22.50
		Vertical strip of 4		400.00
		Vertical strip of 4, cut cancel		150.00

See note after No. R227.

1928   Offset Printing   Perf. 10
Overprint Horizontal (Lines 8mm apart)

RD25	R22	2c **carmine rose**	5.50	.30
		Block of 4	24.00	1.40
RD26	R22	4c **carmine rose**	5.50	.30
		Block of 4	24.00	1.40
RD27	R22	10c **carmine rose**	5.50	.30
		Block of 4	24.00	1.40
a.		Inverted overprint		1,250.
RD28	R22	20c **carmine rose**	6.50	.35
		Perf initial		.20
		Block of 4	29.00	1.50
		Double impression of stamp		
RD29	R22	50c **carmine rose**	10.00	.50
		Block of 4	47.50	2.25

Engr.
Overprint Vertical, Reading Up (Lines 2mm apart)

RD30	R21	$1 **green**	47.50	.35
		Cut cancel		.25
		Block of 4	—	1.60
a.		$1 yellow green	47.50	.50
RD31	R21	$2 **carmine rose**	42.50	.35
		Perf initial		.20
		Block of 4	—	1.50
a.		Pair, one without overprint	225.00	190.00
RD32	R21	$10 **orange**	42.50	.50
		Cut cancel		.25
		Perf initial		.20
		Block of 4	—	2.25
		Perf. 11 at top or bottom	—	

Overprinted Horizontally in Black

1920   Offset Printing   Perf. 11

RD33	R22	2c **carmine rose**	12.50	1.00
		Block of 4	60.00	4.25

RD34	R22	10c **carmine rose**	3.00	.35
		Block of 4	14.00	1.50
b.		Inverted overprint	1,550.	1,000.
RD35	R22	20c **carmine rose**	5.75	.25
		Block of 4	26.00	1.10
a.		Horiz. pair, one without overprint	175.00	
d.		Inverted overprint (perf. initials)		—
RD36	R22	50c **carmine rose**	5.00	.30
		Block of 4	24.00	1.25

Shifted overprints on the 10c, 20c and 50c result in "TRANSFER STOCK," "TRANFSER" omitted, "STOCK" omitted, pairs, and other varieties.

Engr.

RD37	R21	$1 **green**	65.00	13.50
		Cut cancel		2.50
		Block of 4	300.00	62.50
		Block of 4, cut cancel		11.50
RD38	R21	$2 **rose**	70.00	13.50
		Cut cancel		2.50
		Block of 4	325.00	70.00
		Block of 4, cut cancel		11.50

Offset Printing
Perf. 10

RD39	R22	2c **carmine rose**	13.00	1.10
		Block of 4	67.50	5.00
		Double impression of stamp	—	
RD40	R22	10c **carmine rose**	5.25	.55
		Block of 4	26.00	2.50
RD41	R22	20c **carmine rose**	6.00	.25
		Cut cancel		.20
		Block of 4	30.00	1.10

Documentary Stamps of 1917-33 Overprinted in Black

1940   Offset Printing   Wmk. 191R   Perf. 11

RD42	R22	1c **rose pink**	4.50	.65
		Cut cancel		.25
		Perf. initial		.25
a.		"Series 1940" inverted	600.00	325.00
		Cut cancel		125.00

No. RD42a always comes with a natural straight edge at left.

RD43	R22	2c **rose pink**	4.75	.65
		Cut cancel		.25
		Perf. initial		.25
RD45	R22	4c **rose pink**	5.50	.35
		Cut cancel		.25
		Perf. initial		.25
RD46	R22	5c **rose pink**	6.00	.25
		Cut cancel		.20
		Perf. initial		.20
RD48	R22	10c **rose pink**	11.00	.35
		Cut cancel		.25
		Perf. initial		.20
RD49	R22	20c **rose pink**	12.50	.35
		Cut cancel		.25
		Perf. initial		.20
RD50	R22	25c **rose pink**	12.50	1.10
		Cut cancel		.35
		Perf. initial		.25
RD51	R22	40c **rose pink**	9.25	1.00
		Cut cancel		.35
		Perf. initial		.25
RD52	R22	50c **rose pink**	10.50	.35
		Cut cancel		.25
		Perf. initial		.25
RD53	R22	80c **rose pink**	175.00	100.00
		Cut cancel		50.00
		Perf. initial		27.50

Engr.

RD54	R21	$1 **green**	42.50	.60
		Cut cancel		.35
		Perf. initial		.25
RD55	R21	$2 **rose**	47.50	1.00
		Cut cancel		.40
		Perf. initial		.25
RD56	R21	$3 **violet**	275.00	18.00
		Cut cancel		.75
		Perf. initial		.50
RD57	R21	$4 **yellow brown**	110.00	1.60
		Cut cancel		.50
		Perf. initial		.30
RD58	R21	$5 **dark blue**	85.00	2.00
		Cut cancel		.55
		Perf. initial		.35
RD59	R21	$10 **orange**	250.00	10.00
		Cut cancel		1.10
		Perf. initial		.75
RD60	R21	$20 **olive bister**	400.00	150.00
		Cut cancel		25.00
		Perf. initial		11.50

Nos. RD19-RD24 Handstamped in Blue "Series 1940"

1940 **Wmk. 191R** *Perf. 12*
Without Gum

RD61	R17	$30 **vermilion**	1,000.	750.
	Cut cancel			375.
	Perf. initial			200.
RD62	R19	$50 **olive green**	1,750.	2,250.
	Cut cancel			1,000.
	Perf. initial			450.
a.	Double ovpt., perf. initial			1,000.
RD63	R19	$60 **brown**	2,400.	2,200.
	Cut cancel			675.
	Perf. initial			350.
RD64	R17	$100 **green**	1,500.	900.
	Cut cancel			300.
	Perf. initial			110.
RD65	R18	$500 **blue**	3,000.	
	Cut cancel			1,500.
	Perf. initial			800.
	Double transfer			3,250.
RD66	R19	$1,000 **orange**	3,750.	
	Cut cancel			2,750.
	Perf. initial			2,000.

Alexander Hamilton — ST1

Levi Woodbury — ST2

Overprinted in Black **SERIES 1940**

Same Portraits as Nos. R288-R310.

1940 **Engr.** **Wmk. 191R** *Perf. 11*

RD67	ST1	1c **bright green**	14.00	3.25
	Cut cancel			.65
	Perf. initial			.40
RD68	ST1	2c **bright green**	9.00	1.75
	Cut cancel			.30
	Perf. initial			.30
RD70	ST1	4c **bright green**	16.00	4.50
	Cut cancel			.65
	Perf. initial			.35
RD71	ST1	5c **bright green**	10.00	1.75
	Cut cancel			.25
	Perf. initial			.25
a.	Without overprint, cut cancel			400.00
RD73	ST1	10c **bright green**	14.00	2.10
	Cut cancel			.25
	Perf. initial			.25
RD74	ST1	20c **bright green**	16.00	2.40
	Cut cancel			.25
	Perf. initial			.25
RD75	ST1	25c **bright green**	55.00	10.50
	Cut cancel			.90
	Perf. initial			.45
RD76	ST1	40c **bright green**	110.00	40.00
	Cut cancel			3.00
	Perf. initial			1.00
RD77	ST1	50c **bright green**	14.00	2.10
	Cut cancel			.45
	Perf. initial			.30
RD78	ST1	80c **bright green**	160.00	65.00
	Cut cancel			27.50
	Perf. initial			3.50
RD79	ST2	$1 **bright green**	60.00	4.25
	Cut cancel			.55
	Perf. initial			.30
a.	Without overprint, perf. initial			400.00
RD80	ST2	$2 **bright green**	65.00	12.00
	Cut cancel			.75
	Perf. initial			.30
RD81	ST2	$3 **bright green**	90.00	15.00
	Cut cancel			.90
	Perf. initial			.25
RD82	ST2	$4 **bright green**	400.00	240.00
	Cut cancel			110.00
	Perf. initial			50.00
RD83	ST2	$5 **bright green**	90.00	16.00
	Cut cancel			2.00
	Perf. initial			.30
RD84	ST2	$10 **bright green**	225.00	50.00
	Cut cancel			6.00
	Perf. initial			3.00
RD85	ST2	$20 **bright green**	1,100.	95.00
	Cut cancel			15.00
	Perf. initial			5.75

Nos. RD67-RD85 exist imperforate, without overprint. Value, set of pairs, $1,100.

Thomas Corwin — ST3

Overprinted "SERIES 1940"
Various frames and portraits as Nos. R306-R310.

Without Gum *Perf. 12*

RD86	ST3	$30 **bright green**	750.00	175.00
	Cut cancel			82.50
	Perf. initial			37.50
RD87	ST3	$50 **bright green**	800.00	500.00
	Cut cancel			225.00
	Perf. initial			92.50
RD88	ST3	$60 **bright green**	3,000.	1,100.
	Cut cancel			450.00
	Perf. initial			120.00
RD89	ST3	$100 **bright green**	600.00	375.00
	Cut cancel			150.00
	Perf. initial			67.50
RD90	ST3	$500 **bright green**	—	2,000.
	Cut cancel			1,250.
	Perf. initial			700.
RD91	ST3	$1,000 **bright green**	—	2,500.
	Cut cancel			1,500.
	Perf. initial			650.00

Nos. RD86-RD91 exist as unfinished imperforates with complete receipt tabs, without overprints or serial numbers. Known in singles, pairs (Nos. RD86-RD88 and Nos. RD90-RD91, value $450 per pair; No. RD89, value $150 per pair), panes of four with plate number, uncut sheets of four panes (with two plate numbers), cross gutter blocks of eight, and blocks of four with vertical gutter between and plate number.

Nos. RD67-RD91 Overprint Instead: **SERIES 1941**

1941 **Wmk. 191R** *Perf. 11*

RD92	ST1	1c **bright green**	.80	.55
	Cut cancel			.25
	Perf. initial			.25
RD93	ST1	2c **bright green**	.60	.30
	Cut cancel			.25
	Perf. initial			.25
RD95	ST1	4c **bright green**	.65	.25
	Cut cancel			.20
	Perf. initial			.20
RD96	ST1	5c **bright green**	.60	.25
	Cut cancel			.20
	Perf. initial			.20
RD98	ST1	10c **bright green**	1.10	.25
	Cut cancel			.20
	Perf. initial			.20
RD99	ST1	20c **bright green**	2.40	.30
	Cut cancel			.25
	Perf. initial			.20
RD100	ST1	25c **bright green**	2.40	.45
	Cut cancel			.30
	Perf. initial			.30
RD101	ST1	40c **bright green**	3.75	.75
	Cut cancel			.30
	Perf. initial			.20
RD102	ST1	50c **bright green**	5.00	.35
	Cut cancel			.25
	Perf. initial			.25
RD103	ST1	80c **bright green**	30.00	8.50
	Cut cancel			.75
	Perf. initial			.50
RD104	ST2	$1 **bright green**	21.00	.20
	Cut cancel			.20
	Perf. initial			.20
RD105	ST2	$2 **bright green**	22.50	.30
	Cut cancel			.20
	Perf. initial			.20
RD106	ST2	$3 **bright green**	32.50	1.50
	Cut cancel			.35
	Perf. initial			.25
RD107	ST2	$4 **bright green**	57.50	8.50
	Cut cancel			.60
	Perf. initial			.30
RD108	ST2	$5 **bright green**	57.50	.65
	Cut cancel			.30
	Perf. initial			.25
RD109	ST2	$10 **bright green**	125.00	5.50
	Cut cancel			1.00
	Perf. initial			.25
RD110	ST2	$20 **bright green**	350.00	80.00
	Cut cancel			21.00
	Perf. initial			4.25

Perf. 12
Without Gum

RD111	ST3	$30 **bright green**	700.00	300.00
	Cut cancel			92.50
	Perf. initial			32.50

RD112	ST3	$50 **bright green**	1,000.	475.00
	Cut cancel			150.00
	Perf. initial			65.00
RD113	ST3	$60 **bright green**	1,350.	350.00
	Cut cancel			210.00
	Perf. initial			125.00
RD114	ST3	$100 **bright green**	300.00	190.00
	Cut cancel			65.00
	Perf. initial			45.00
RD115	ST3	$500 **bright green**	1,900.	1,650.
	Cut cancel			1,000.
	Perf. initial			750.00
RD116	ST3	$1,000 **bright green**	—	1,500.
	Cut cancel			850.00
	Perf. initial			750.00

Nos. RD67-RD91 Overprint Instead: **SERIES 1942**

1942 **Wmk. 191R** *Perf. 11*

RD117	ST1	1c **bright green**	.75	.30
	Cut cancel			.25
	Perf. initial			.25
RD118	ST1	2c **bright green**	.65	.35
	Cut cancel			.25
	Perf. initial			.25
RD119	ST1	4c **bright green**	3.50	1.10
	Cut cancel			.55
	Perf. initial			.45
RD120	ST1	5c **bright green**	.70	.20
	Cut cancel			.20
	Perf. initial			.20
a.	Overprint inverted			600.00
	Cut cancel			240.00
	Perf. initial			200.00
RD121	ST1	10c **bright green**	2.25	.20
	Cut cancel			.20
	Perf. initial			.20
RD122	ST1	20c **bright green**	2.75	.20
	Cut cancel			.20
	Perf. initial			.20
RD123	ST1	25c **bright green**	2.50	.20
	Cut cancel			.20
	Perf. initial			.20
RD124	ST1	40c **bright green**	5.75	.40
	Cut cancel			.25
	Perf. initial			.20
RD125	ST1	50c **bright green**	6.50	.20
	Cut cancel			.20
	Perf. initial			.20
RD126	ST1	80c **bright green**	27.50	6.00
	Cut cancel			1.50
	Perf. initial			.35
RD127	ST2	$1 **bright green**	24.00	.40
	Cut cancel			.25
	Perf. initial			.20
RD128	ST2	$2 **bright green**	37.50	.40
	Cut cancel			.25
	Perf. initial			.20
RD129	ST2	$3 **bright green**	42.50	1.10
	Cut cancel			.30
	Perf. initial			.20
RD130	ST2	$4 **bright green**	57.50	24.00
	Cut cancel			.65
	Perf. initial			.25
RD131	ST2	$5 **bright green**	50.00	.40
	Cut cancel			.25
	Perf. initial			.25
a.	Double overprint, perf. initial			1,250.
RD132	ST2	$10 **bright green**	110.00	9.50
	Cut cancel			2.00
	Perf. initial			1.10
RD133	ST2	$20 **bright green**	225.00	50.00
	Cut cancel			9.50
	Perf. initial			3.50

Perf. 12
Without Gum

RD134	ST3	$30 **bright green**	400.00	100.00
	Cut cancel			40.00
	Perf. initial			30.00
RD135	ST3	$50 **bright green**	425.00	175.00
	Cut cancel			55.00
	Perf. initial			27.50
RD136	ST3	$60 **bright green**	500.00	240.00
	Cut cancel			95.00
	Perf. initial			62.50
RD137	ST3	$100 **bright green**	625.00	100.00
	Cut cancel			35.00
	Perf. initial			21.00
RD138	ST3	$500 **bright green**	—	15,000.
	Cut cancel			10,000.
	Perf. initial			8,000.
RD139	ST3	$1,000 **bright green**	—	700.00
	Cut cancel			325.00
	Perf. initial			190.00

Nos. RD67-RD91 Overprint Instead: **SERIES 1943**

1943 **Wmk. 191R** *Perf. 11*

RD140	ST1	1c **bright green**	.55	.30
	Cut cancel			.25
	Perf. initial			.25
RD141	ST1	2c **bright green**	.60	.40
	Cut cancel			.20
	Perf. initial			.20
RD142	ST1	4c **bright green**	2.10	.20
	Cut cancel			.20
	Perf. initial			.20
RD143	ST1	5c **bright green**	.60	.20
	Cut cancel			.20
	Perf. initial			.20
RD144	ST1	10c **bright green**	1.40	.20
	Cut cancel			.20
	Perf. initial			.20

No.	Type	Denom.	Color	Unused	Used
RD145	ST1	20c	bright green	2.10	.20
		Cut cancel			.20
		Perf. initial			.20
RD146	ST1	25c	bright green	6.50	.35
		Cut cancel			.25
		Perf. initial			.25
RD147	ST1	40c	bright green	6.00	.30
		Cut cancel			.25
		Perf. initial			.20
RD148	ST1	50c	bright green	5.00	.30
		Cut cancel			.25
		Perf. initial			.20
RD149	ST1	80c	bright green	25.00	7.50
		Cut cancel			2.50
		Perf. initial			1.25
RD150	ST2	$1	bright green	22.50	.25
		Cut cancel			.20
		Perf. initial			.20
RD151	ST2	$2	bright green	25.00	.50
		Cut cancel			.25
		Perf. initial			.25
RD152	ST2	$3	bright green	30.00	2.00
		Cut cancel			.35
		Perf. initial			.30
RD153	ST2	$4	bright green	60.00	20.00
		Cut cancel			1.50
		Perf. initial			.90
RD154	ST2	$5	bright green	80.00	.60
		Cut cancel			.30
		Perf. initial			.25
RD155	ST2	$10	bright green	125.00	6.50
		Cut cancel			1.00
		Perf. initial			.35
RD156	ST2	$20	bright green	225.00	60.00
		Cut cancel			20.00
		Perf. initial			4.75

Perf. 12
Without Gum

No.	Type	Denom.	Color	Unused	Used
RD157	ST3	$30	bright green	500.00	225.00
		Cut cancel			70.00
		Perf. initial			32.50
RD158	ST3	$50	bright green	800.00	210.00
		Cut cancel			42.50
		Perf. initial			20.00
RD159	ST3	$60	bright green	—	1,500.
		Cut cancel			500.00
		Perf. initial			200.00
RD160	ST3	$100	bright green	225.00	80.00
		Cut cancel			22.50
		Perf. initial			20.00
RD161	ST3	$500	bright green	—	1,500.
		Cut cancel			575.00
		Perf. initial			225.00
RD162	ST3	$1,000	bright green	825.00	525.00
		Cut cancel			250.00
		Perf. initial			175.00

Nos. RD67-RD91 Overprint Instead: **Series 1944**

1944 — Wmk. 191R — Perf. 11

No.	Type	Denom.	Color	Unused	Used
RD163	ST1	1c	bright green	.90	.75
		Cut cancel			.35
		Perf. initial			.25
RD164	ST1	2c	bright green	.70	.25
		Cut cancel			.20
		Perf. initial			.20
RD165	ST1	4c	bright green	.70	.35
		Cut cancel			.25
		Perf. initial			.20
RD166	ST1	5c	bright green	.65	.25
		Cut cancel			.20
		Perf. initial			.20
RD167	ST1	10c	bright green	1.00	.30
		Cut cancel			.20
		Perf. initial			.20
RD168	ST1	20c	bright green	2.25	.25
		Cut cancel			.20
		Perf. initial			.20
RD169	ST1	25c	bright green	3.25	.90
		Cut cancel			.25
		Perf. initial			.25
RD170	ST1	40c	bright green	15.00	8.00
		Cut cancel			3.25
		Perf. initial			1.75
RD171	ST1	50c	bright green	5.50	.30
		Cut cancel			.25
		Perf. initial			.20
RD172	ST1	80c	bright green	14.50	6.25
		Cut cancel			2.75
		Perf. initial			1.75
RD173	ST2	$1	bright green	13.50	.50
		Cut cancel			.30
		Perf. initial			.25
RD174	ST2	$2	bright green	50.00	.75
		Cut cancel			.35
		Perf. initial			.25
RD175	ST2	$3	bright green	47.50	2.00
		Cut cancel			.35
		Perf. initial			.25
RD176	ST2	$4	bright green	65.00	9.00
		Cut cancel			.50
		Perf. initial			.30
RD177	ST2	$5	bright green	50.00	1.75
		Cut cancel			.40
		Perf. initial			.25
RD178	ST2	$10	bright green	125.00	7.25
		Cut cancel			1.00
		Perf. initial			.45
RD179	ST2	$20	bright green	210.00	12.00
		Cut cancel			5.25
		Perf. initial			3.75

Perf. 12
Without Gum

Designs: $2,500, William Windom. $5,000, C. J. Folger. $10,000, W. Q. Gresham.

No.	Type	Denom.	Color	Unused	Used
RD180	ST3	$30	bright green	350.00	110.00
		Cut cancel			42.50
		Perf. initial			16.00
RD181	ST3	$50	bright green	250.00	85.00
		Cut cancel			21.00
		Perf. initial			13.00
RD182	ST3	$60	bright green	350.00	225.00
		Cut cancel			80.00
		Perf. initial			60.00
RD183	ST3	$100	bright green	325.00	80.00
		Cut cancel			30.00
		Perf. initial			13.00
RD184	ST3	$500	bright green	1,000.	725.00
		Cut cancel			400.00
		Perf. initial			240.00
RD185	ST3	$1,000	bright green	2,500.	1,000.
		Cut cancel			400.00
		Perf. initial			190.00
RD185A	ST3	$2,500	bright green	—	
RD185B	ST3	$5,000	bright green	—	
RD185C	ST3	$10,000	bright green, cut cancel		27,500.

Nos. RD185A-R185C exist as unfinished imperforates with complete receipt tabs, without overprints or serial numbers. Known in singles, pairs, panes of four with plate number, uncut sheets of four panes (with two plate numbers), cross gutter blocks of eight, and blocks of four with vertical gutter between and plate number. Value, pairs $450 each.

Nos. RD67-RD91 Overprint Instead: **Series 1945**

1945 — Wmk. 191R — Perf. 11

No.	Type	Denom.	Color	Unused	Used
RD186	ST1	1c	bright green	.45	.20
		Cut cancel			.20
		Perf. initial			.20
RD187	ST1	2c	bright green	.45	.35
		Cut cancel			.20
		Perf. initial			.20
RD188	ST1	4c	bright green	.50	.35
		Cut cancel			.25
		Perf. initial			.20
RD189	ST1	5c	bright green	.45	.25
		Cut cancel			.20
		Perf. initial			.20
RD190	ST1	10c	bright green	1.25	.35
		Cut cancel			.25
		Perf. initial			.25
RD191	ST1	20c	bright green	2.10	.45
		Cut cancel			.25
		Perf. initial			.25
RD192	ST1	25c	bright green	3.00	.40
		Cut cancel			.30
		Perf. initial			.25
RD193	ST1	40c	bright green	4.50	.25
		Cut cancel			.20
		Perf. initial			.20
RD194	ST1	50c	bright green	9.50	.45
		Cut cancel			.30
		Perf. initial			.25
RD195	ST1	80c	bright green	12.50	4.75
		Cut cancel			1.00
		Perf. initial			.70
RD196	ST2	$1	bright green	17.50	.30
		Cut cancel			.25
		Perf. initial			.25
RD197	ST2	$2	bright green	30.00	.75
		Cut cancel			.30
		Perf. initial			.25
RD198	ST2	$3	bright green	55.00	1.75
		Cut cancel			.50
		Perf. initial			.25
RD199	ST2	$4	bright green	55.00	4.25
		Cut cancel			1.10
		Perf. initial			.65
RD200	ST2	$5	bright green	35.00	1.00
		Cut cancel			.30
		Perf. initial			.25
RD201	ST2	$10	bright green	85.00	10.50
		Cut cancel			1.25
		Perf. initial			.90
RD202	ST2	$20	bright green	210.00	20.00
		Cut cancel			3.00
		Perf. initial			1.40

Perf. 12
Without Gum

No.	Type	Denom.	Color	Unused	Used
RD203	ST3	$30	bright green	225.00	90.00
		Cut cancel			40.00
		Perf. initial			22.50
RD204	ST3	$50	bright green	125.00	40.00
		Cut cancel			9.50
		Perf. initial			6.00
RD205	ST3	$60	bright green	675.00	275.00
		Cut cancel			95.00
		Perf. initial			40.00
RD206	ST3	$100	bright green	150.00	65.00
		Cut cancel			20.00
		Perf. initial			10.50
RD207	ST3	$500	bright green	—	1,250.
		Cut cancel			475.00
		Perf. initial			300.00
RD208	ST3	$1,000	bright green	1,650.	1,400.
		Cut cancel			575.00
		Perf. initial			300.00
RD208A	ST3	$2,500	bright green		
		Cut cancel			30,000.
		Perf. initial			20,000.
RD208B	ST3	$5,000	bright green		22,250.
RD208C	ST3	$10,000	bright green		
		Cut cancel			22,250.

Stock Transfer Stamps and Type of 1940 Overprinted in Black
Series 1946

1946 — Wmk. 191R — Perf. 11

No.	Type	Denom.	Color	Unused	Used
RD209	ST1	1c	bright green	.50	.35
		Cut cancel			.25
		Perf. initial			.20
a.		Pair, one dated "1945"		550.00	
RD210	ST1	2c	bright green	.50	.25
		Cut cancel			.20
		Perf. initial			.20
RD211	ST1	4c	bright green	.50	.25
		Cut cancel			.20
		Perf. initial			.20
RD212	ST1	5c	bright green	.55	.25
		Cut cancel			.20
		Perf. initial			.20
RD213	ST1	10c	bright green	1.25	.25
		Cut cancel			.20
		Perf. initial			.20
RD214	ST1	20c	bright green	2.50	.30
		Cut cancel			.25
		Perf. initial			.20
RD215	ST1	25c	bright green	2.75	.40
		Cut cancel			.30
		Perf. initial			.25
RD216	ST1	40c	bright green	5.50	1.25
		Cut cancel			.40
		Perf. initial			.25
RD217	ST1	50c	bright green	6.75	.25
		Cut cancel			.20
		Perf. initial			.20
RD218	ST1	80c	bright green	17.50	9.50
		Cut cancel			3.25
		Perf. initial			1.60
RD219	ST2	$1	bright green	14.50	.75
		Cut cancel			.35
		Perf. initial			.25
RD220	ST2	$2	bright green	16.00	.80
		Cut cancel			.35
		Perf. initial			.25
RD221	ST2	$3	bright green	30.00	2.25
		Cut cancel			.45
		Perf. initial			.25
RD222	ST2	$4	bright green	30.00	9.00
		Cut cancel			3.50
		Perf. initial			1.25
RD223	ST2	$5	bright green	50.00	2.25
		Cut cancel			.35
		Perf. initial			.25
RD224	ST2	$10	bright green	87.50	3.75
		Cut cancel			1.00
		Perf. initial			.30
RD225	ST2	$20	bright green	225.00	62.50
		Cut cancel			16.00
		Perf. initial			8.75

Without Gum — Perf. 12

No.	Type	Denom.	Color	Unused	Used
RD226	ST3	$30	bright green	250.00	62.50
		Cut cancel			25.00
		Perf. initial			18.00
RD227	ST3	$50	bright green	190.00	75.00
		Cut cancel			27.50
		Perf. initial			15.00
RD228	ST3	$60	bright green	300.00	150.00
		Cut cancel			50.00
		Perf. initial			16.00
RD229	ST3	$100	bright green	225.00	90.00
		Cut cancel			27.50
		Perf. initial			17.00
RD230	ST3	$500	bright green	700.00	225.00
		Cut cancel			150.00
		Perf. initial			100.00
RD231	ST3	$1,000	bright green	425.00	250.00
		Cut cancel			175.00
		Perf. initial			95.00
RD232	ST3	$2,500	bright green		22,250.
		Cut cancel			15,000.
RD233	ST3	$5,000	bright green		20,000.
RD234	ST3	$10,000	bright green		
		Cut cancel			16,500.

Stock Transfer Stamps and Type of 1940 Overprinted in Black
Series 1947

1947 — Wmk. 191R — Perf. 11

No.	Type	Denom.	Color	Unused	Used
RD235	ST1	1c	bright green	2.25	.75
		Cut cancel			.35
		Perf. initial			.25
RD236	ST1	2c	bright green	2.25	.75
		Cut cancel			.35
		Perf. initial			.25
RD237	ST1	4c	bright green	1.60	.60
		Cut cancel			.35
		Perf. initial			.25
RD238	ST1	5c	bright green	1.60	.50
		Cut cancel			.35
		Perf. initial			.25
RD239	ST1	10c	bright green	1.75	.75
		Cut cancel			.35
		Perf. initial			.25
RD240	ST1	20c	bright green	3.25	.75
		Cut cancel			.30
		Perf. initial			.25
RD241	ST1	25c	bright green	4.00	.90
		Cut cancel			.35
		Perf. initial			.25

No.	Type	Denom.	Color	Unused	Used
RD242	ST1	40c	bright green	4.50	1.40
			Cut cancel		.35
			Perf. initial		.25
RD243	ST1	50c	bright green	5.00	.35
			Cut cancel		.25
			Perf. initial		.20
RD244	ST1	80c	bright green	25.00	14.00
			Cut cancel		5.50
			Perf. initial		3.75
RD245	ST2	$1	bright green	16.00	1.00
			Cut cancel		.35
			Perf. initial		.25
RD246	ST2	$2	bright green	27.50	1.25
			Cut cancel		.35
			Perf. initial		.25
RD247	ST2	$3	bright green	45.00	2.25
			Cut cancel		.50
			Perf. initial		.35
RD248	ST2	$4	bright green	62.50	9.50
			Cut cancel		1.60
			Perf. initial		.90
RD249	ST2	$5	bright green	45.00	2.50
			Cut cancel		.50
			Perf. initial		.25
RD250	ST2	$10	bright green	160.00	7.75
			Cut cancel		2.75
			Perf. initial		1.60
RD251	ST2	$20	bright green	160.00	42.50
			Cut cancel		9.75
			Perf. initial		6.75

Without Gum — Perf. 12

No.	Type	Denom.	Color	Unused	Used
RD252	ST3	$30	bright green	160.00	67.50
			Cut cancel		20.00
			Perf. initial		13.00
RD253	ST3	$50	bright green	350.00	190.00
			Cut cancel		57.50
			Perf. initial		22.50
RD254	ST3	$60	bright green	450.00	175.00
			Cut cancel		67.50
			Perf. initial		42.50
RD255	ST3	$100	bright green	175.00	62.50
			Cut cancel		22.50
			Perf. initial		17.00
RD256	ST3	$500	bright green	850.00	525.00
			Cut cancel		225.00
			Perf. initial		125.00
RD257	ST3	$1,000	bright green	550.00	140.00
			Cut cancel		67.50
			Perf. initial		37.50
RD258	ST3	$2,500	bright green	—	475.00
			Cut cancel		—
			Perf. initial		
RD259	ST3	$5,000	bright green	600.00	375.00
			Cut cancel		
			Perf. initial		
RD260	ST3	$10,000	bright green		55.00
			Cut cancel		
			Perf. initial		—
a.			Vert. pair, imperf. horiz., cut cancel		

Nos. RD67-RD91 Overprint Instead: **Series 1948**

1948 — Wmk. 191R — Perf. 11

No.	Type	Denom.	Color	Unused	Used
RD261	ST1	1c	bright green	.45	.35
			Cut cancel		.25
			Perf. initial		.20
RD262	ST1	2c	bright green	.45	.35
			Cut cancel		.25
			Perf. initial		.20
RD263	ST1	4c	bright green	.80	.45
			Cut cancel		.30
			Perf. initial		.25
RD264	ST1	5c	bright green	.45	.25
			Cut cancel		.20
			Perf. initial		.20
RD265	ST1	10c	bright green	.55	.35
			Cut cancel		.25
			Perf. initial		.20
RD266	ST1	20c	bright green	1.60	.40
			Cut cancel		.25
			Perf. initial		.20
RD267	ST1	25c	bright green	1.90	.55
			Cut cancel		.30
			Perf. initial		.25
RD268	ST1	40c	bright green	3.50	1.00
			Cut cancel		.35
			Perf. initial		.25
RD269	ST1	50c	bright green	5.75	.35
			Cut cancel		.25
			Perf. initial		.20
RD270	ST1	80c	bright green	26.00	9.50
			Cut cancel		3.50
			Perf. initial		2.25
RD271	ST2	$1	bright green	14.00	.45
			Cut cancel		.30
			Perf. initial		.20
RD272	ST2	$2	bright green	27.50	1.00
			Cut cancel		.30
			Perf. initial		.25
RD273	ST2	$3	bright green	40.00	6.00
			Cut cancel		3.00
			Perf. initial		1.60
RD274	ST2	$4	bright green	45.00	14.00
			Cut cancel		3.75
			Perf. initial		2.25
RD275	ST2	$5	bright green	47.50	3.75
			Cut cancel		.45
			Perf. initial		.25
RD276	ST2	$10	bright green	80.00	7.25
			Cut cancel		1.00
			Perf. initial		.75
RD277	ST2	$20	bright green	160.00	25.00
			Cut cancel		7.00
			Perf. initial		4.75

Perf. 12 — Without Gum

No.	Type	Denom.	Color	Unused	Used
RD278	ST3	$30	bright green	225.00	90.00
			Cut cancel		35.00
			Perf. initial		18.00
RD279	ST3	$50	bright green	175.00	85.00
			Cut cancel		32.50
			Perf. initial		16.00
RD280	ST3	$60	bright green	350.00	225.00
			Cut cancel		75.00
			Perf. initial		27.50
RD281	ST3	$100	bright green	140.00	30.00
			Cut cancel		10.00
			Perf. initial		7.00
RD282	ST3	$500	bright green	600.00	300.00
			Cut cancel		175.00
			Perf. initial		52.50
RD283	ST3	$1,000	bright green	325.00	175.00
			Cut cancel		62.50
			Perf. initial		32.50
RD284	ST3	$2,500	bright green	850.00	500.00
			Cut cancel		250.00
			Perf. initial		160.00
RD285	ST3	$5,000	bright green	650.00	425.00
			Cut cancel		225.00
			Perf. initial		150.00
RD286	ST3	$10,000	bright green		—
			Cut cancel		52.50
			Perf. initial		

Nos. RD67-RD91 Overprint Instead: **Series 1949**

1949 — Wmk. 191R — Perf. 11

No.	Type	Denom.	Color	Unused	Used
RD287	ST1	1c	bright green	2.25	.70
			Cut cancel		.35
			Perf. initial		.25
RD288	ST1	2c	bright green	2.25	.75
			Cut cancel		.35
			Perf. initial		.25
RD289	ST1	4c	bright green	2.50	.75
			Cut cancel		.35
			Perf. initial		.25
RD290	ST1	5c	bright green	2.50	.75
			Cut cancel		.35
			Perf. initial		.25
RD291	ST1	10c	bright green	5.00	1.00
			Cut cancel		.35
			Perf. initial		.25
RD292	ST1	20c	bright green	8.00	1.00
			Cut cancel		.35
			Perf. initial		.25
RD293	ST1	25c	bright green	9.50	1.25
			Cut cancel		.40
			Perf. initial		.25
RD294	ST1	40c	bright green	25.00	3.25
			Cut cancel		.50
			Perf. initial		.30
RD295	ST1	50c	bright green	27.50	.45
			Cut cancel		.35
			Perf. initial		.25
RD296	ST1	80c	bright green	32.50	10.00
			Cut cancel		4.25
			Perf. initial		3.00
RD297	ST2	$1	bright green	27.50	1.00
			Cut cancel		.35
			Perf. initial		.25
RD298	ST2	$2	bright green	50.00	1.40
			Cut cancel		.45
			Perf. initial		.30
RD299	ST2	$3	bright green	67.50	7.50
			Cut cancel		2.25
			Perf. initial		1.10
RD300	ST2	$4	bright green	65.00	12.00
			Cut cancel		3.00
			Perf. initial		1.75
RD301	ST2	$5	bright green	72.50	3.00
			Cut cancel		.30
			Perf. initial		.25
RD302	ST2	$10	bright green	110.00	8.00
			Cut cancel		2.50
			Perf. initial		1.25
RD303	ST2	$20	bright green	250.00	22.50
			Cut cancel		10.00
			Perf. initial		6.25

Perf. 12 — Without Gum

No.	Type	Denom.	Color	Unused	Used
RD304	ST3	$30	bright green	325.00	125.00
			Cut cancel		45.00
			Perf. initial		18.00
RD305	ST3	$50	bright green	375.00	225.00
			Cut cancel		62.50
			Perf. initial		27.50
RD306	ST3	$60	bright green	525.00	325.00
			Cut cancel		140.00
			Perf. initial		50.00
RD307	ST3	$100	bright green	225.00	80.00
			Cut cancel		35.00
			Perf. initial		18.00
RD308	ST3	$500	bright green	700.00	300.00
			Cut cancel		100.00
			Perf. initial		60.00
RD309	ST3	$1,000	bright green	450.00	125.00
			Cut cancel		52.50
			Perf. initial		32.50
RD310	ST3	$2,500	bright green		—
			Cut cancel		500.00
			Perf. initial		
RD311	ST3	$5,000	bright green		—
			Cut cancel		500.00
			Perf. initial		350.00

No.	Type	Denom.	Color	Unused	Used
RD312	ST3	$10,000	bright green	—	475.00
			Cut cancel		45.00
a.			Pair, one without ovpt., cut cancel		8,000.

No. RD312a is unique.

Nos. RD67-RD91 Overprint Instead: **Series 1950**

1950 — Wmk. 191R — Perf. 11

No.	Type	Denom.	Color	Unused	Used
RD313	ST1	1c	bright green	.80	.40
			Cut cancel		.30
			Perf. initial		.25
RD314	ST1	2c	bright green	.70	.35
			Cut cancel		.25
			Perf. initial		.20
RD315	ST1	4c	bright green	.65	.40
			Cut cancel		.25
			Perf. initial		.20
RD316	ST1	5c	bright green	.75	.25
			Cut cancel		.20
			Perf. initial		.20
RD317	ST1	10c	bright green	3.25	.30
			Cut cancel		.25
			Perf. initial		.25
RD318	ST1	20c	bright green	5.00	.80
			Cut cancel		.35
			Perf. initial		.20
RD319	ST1	25c	bright green	8.00	1.00
			Cut cancel		.25
			Perf. initial		.20
RD320	ST1	40c	bright green	11.00	1.50
			Cut cancel		.35
			Perf. initial		.25
RD321	ST1	50c	bright green	13.00	.50
			Cut cancel		.30
			Perf. initial		.25
RD322	ST1	80c	bright green	22.50	7.25
			Cut cancel		2.40
			Perf. initial		1.50
RD323	ST2	$1	bright green	22.50	.55
			Cut cancel		.25
			Perf. initial		.20
RD324	ST2	$2	bright green	35.00	1.25
			Cut cancel		.35
			Perf. initial		.25
RD325	ST2	$3	bright green	47.50	5.75
			Cut cancel		.90
			Perf. initial		.60
RD326	ST2	$4	bright green	60.00	12.50
			Cut cancel		5.00
			Perf. initial		2.75
RD327	ST2	$5	bright green	60.00	2.75
			Cut cancel		.35
			Perf. initial		.25
RD328	ST2	$10	bright green	175.00	7.50
			Cut cancel		2.25
			Perf. initial		1.00
RD329	ST2	$20	bright green	175.00	32.50
			Cut cancel		21.00
			Perf. initial		5.75

Perf. 12 — Without Gum

No.	Type	Denom.	Color	Unused	Used
RD330	ST3	$30	bright green	225.00	125.00
			Cut cancel		45.00
			Perf. initial		18.00
a.			Booklet pane of 4	3,300.	
RD331	ST3	$50	bright green	275.00	150.00
			Cut cancel		60.00
			Perf. initial		29.00
a.			Booklet pane of 4	3,300.	
RD332	ST3	$60	bright green	325.00	200.00
			Cut cancel		85.00
			Perf. initial		47.50
a.			Booklet pane of 4	4,750.	
RD333	ST3	$100	bright green	125.00	55.00
			Cut cancel		30.00
			Perf. initial		15.00
a.			Vert. pair, imperf. btwn.	2,500.	1,750.
RD334	ST3	$500	bright green	650.00	300.00
			Cut cancel		150.00
			Perf. initial		95.00
RD335	ST3	$1,000	bright green	225.00	85.00
			Cut cancel		35.00
			Perf. initial		22.50
RD336	ST3	$2,500	bright green	—	1,500.
			Cut cancel		1,000.
a.			Booklet pane of 4	10,000.	
RD337	ST3	$5,000	bright green	—	950.00
			Cut cancel		600.00
			Perf. initial		
a.			Booklet pane of 4	10,000.	
RD338	ST3	$10,000	bright green	—	1,100.
			Cut cancel		97.50
			Perf. initial		
a.			Booklet pane of 4	10,000.	

Nos. RD67-RD91 Overprint Instead: **Series 1951**

1951 — Wmk. 191R — Perf. 11

No.	Type	Denom.	Color	Unused	Used
RD339	ST1	1c	bright green	3.00	.75
			Cut cancel		.40
			Perf. initial		.25
RD340	ST1	2c	bright green	2.50	.50
			Cut cancel		.30
			Perf. initial		.25
RD341	ST1	4c	bright green	3.00	.75
			Cut cancel		.35
			Perf. initial		.25
RD342	ST1	5c	bright green	2.25	.55
			Cut cancel		.25
			Perf. initial		.20

RD343	ST1	10c **bright green**		3.00	.35
		Cut cancel			.25
		Perf. initial			.20
RD344	ST1	20c **bright green**		7.50	1.25
		Cut cancel			.35
		Perf. initial			.25
RD345	ST1	25c **bright green**		10.00	1.50
		Cut cancel			.35
		Perf. initial			.25
RD346	ST1	40c **bright green**		42.50	12.50
		Cut cancel			4.00
		Perf. initial			2.00
RD347	ST1	50c **bright green**		17.00	1.50
		Cut cancel			.30
		Perf. initial			.25
RD348	ST1	80c **bright green**		35.00	14.00
		Cut cancel			5.25
		Perf. initial			2.25
RD349	ST2	$1 **bright green**		32.50	1.25
		Cut cancel			.35
		Perf. initial			.25
RD350	ST2	$2 **bright green**		45.00	1.75
		Cut cancel			.35
		Perf. initial			.25
RD351	ST2	$3 **bright green**		60.00	14.00
		Cut cancel			4.50
		Perf. initial			2.00
RD352	ST2	$4 **bright green**		200.00	16.00
		Cut cancel			6.00
		Perf. initial			2.25
RD353	ST2	$5 **bright green**		75.00	4.00
		Cut cancel			.35
		Perf. initial			.25

RD354	ST2	$10 **bright green**		150.00	11.00
		Cut cancel			3.00
		Perf. initial			1.75
RD355	ST2	$20 **bright green**		250.00	30.00
		Cut cancel			10.00
		Perf. initial			5.75

Perf. 12
Without Gum

RD356	ST3	$30 **bright green**		325.00	150.00
		Cut cancel			45.00
		Perf. initial			20.00
RD357	ST3	$50 **bright green**		325.00	125.00
		Cut cancel			32.50
		Perf. initial			20.00
RD358	ST3	$60 **bright green**		—	1,600.
		Cut cancel			600.00
		Perf. initial			300.00
RD359	ST3	$100 **bright green**		210.00	90.00
		Cut cancel			30.00
		Perf. initial			13.00
RD360	ST3	$500 **bright green**		750.00	450.00
		Cut cancel			210.00
		Perf. initial			125.00
RD361	ST3	$1,000 **bright green**		225.00	125.00
		Cut cancel			85.00
		Perf. initial			57.50
RD362	ST3	$2,500 **bright green**		—	4,000.
		Cut cancel			1,750.
		Perf. initial			850.00
RD363	ST3	$5,000 **bright green**		—	1,600.
		Cut cancel			925.00
		Perf. initial			700.00

RD364	ST3	$10,000 **bright green**		1,650.	175.00
		Cut cancel			80.00
		Perf. initial			52.50

Nos. RD67-RD91 Overprint Instead: **Series 1952**

1952		Wmk. 191R			*Perf. 11*
RD365	ST1	1c **bright green**		42.50	27.50
		Cut cancel			7.00
		Perf. initial			3.00
RD366	ST1	10c **bright green**		45.00	27.50
		Cut cancel			7.00
		Perf. initial			3.00
RD367	ST1	20c **bright green**		500.00	—
		Cut cancel			—
		Perf. initial			—
RD368	ST1	25c **bright green**		650.00	—
		Cut cancel			—
		Perf. initial			—
RD369	ST1	40c **bright green**		140.00	55.00
		Cut cancel			18.00
		Perf. initial			12.00
RD370	ST2	$4 **bright green**		2,000.	800.00
		Perf. initial			—
RD371	ST2	$10 **bright green**		4,250.	—
		Cut cancel			—
		Perf. initial			—
RD372	ST2	$20 **bright green**		7,000.	—
		Cut cancel			—
		Perf. initial			—

Stock Transfer Stamps were discontinued in 1952.

CORDIALS, WINES, ETC. STAMPS

RE1

Inscribed "Series of 1914"

1914		Wmk. 190	Offset Printing		*Perf. 10*
RE1	RE1	¼c **green**		1.25	.60
RE2	RE1	½c **green**		.60	.55
RE3	RE1	1c **green**		.65	.35
RE4	RE1	1½c **green**		3.25	1.90
RE5	RE1	2c **green**		5.25	4.25
RE6	RE1	3c **green**		4.25	1.60
RE7	RE1	4c **green**		3.25	1.90
RE8	RE1	5c **green**		1.75	1.00
RE9	RE1	6c **green**		9.50	4.00
a.		Double impression		—	
RE10	RE1	8c **green**		7.25	1.90
RE11	RE1	10c **green**		4.50	3.75
RE12	RE1	20c **green**		6.00	2.40
RE13	RE1	24c **green**		19.00	10.00
RE14	RE1	40c **green**		4.50	.90

RE1a

		Without Gum			*Imperf.*
RE15	RE1a	$2 **green**		12.50	.25
a.		Double impression			125.00

1914		**Wmk. 191R**			*Perf. 10*
RE16	RE1	¼c **green**		8.50	6.50
RE17	RE1	½c **green**		7.50	4.00
RE18	RE1	1c **green**		.30	.25
RE19	RE1	1½c **green**		95.00	50.00
RE20	RE1	2c **green**		.30	.25
a.		Double impression			—
RE21	RE1	3c **green**		3.75	2.50
RE22	RE1	4c **green**		1.25	1.10
RE23	RE1	5c **green**		20.00	13.00
a.		Double impression			—
RE24	RE1	6c **green**		.90	.40
RE25	RE1	8c **green**		2.75	.65
RE26	RE1	10c **green**		.90	.35

RE27	RE1	20c **green**		1.10	.55
RE28	RE1	24c **green**		17.50	1.00
RE29	RE1	40c **green**		45.00	14.00

Imperf
Without Gum

RE30	RE1a	$2 **green**		55.00	3.75

Perf. 11

RE31	RE1	2c **green**		140.00	125.00

WINE STAMPS
Issued Without Gum

RE2

Inscribed: "Series of 1916"

1916	**Wmk. 191R**	Offset Printing	*Rouletted 3½*

Plates of 100 subjects

RE32	RE2	1c **green**		.50	.45
a.		Double impression		200.00	
RE33	RE2	3c **green**		6.50	5.25
RE34	RE2	4c **green**		.40	.50
a.		Double impression			—
RE35	RE2	6c **green**		2.75	1.10
RE36	RE2	7½c **green**		7.75	4.25
RE37	RE2	10c **green**		1.50	.45
RE38	RE2	12c **green**		5.25	4.75
RE39	RE2	15c **green**		1.75	1.90
RE40	RE2	18c **green**		30.00	32.50
RE41	RE2	20c **green**		.35	.30
RE42	RE2	24c **green**		6.00	4.00
a.		Double impression		200.00	
RE43	RE2	30c **green**		3.50	3.75
a.		Double impression			—
RE44	RE2	36c **green**		30.00	18.00
RE45	RE2	50c **green**		1.00	.50
RE46	RE2	60c **green**		7.00	3.00
RE47	RE2	72c **green**		40.00	37.50
RE48	RE2	80c **green**		1.50	.90
RE49	RE2	$1.20 **green**		9.00	7.25
RE50	RE2	$1.44 **green**		13.00	3.75
RE51	RE2	$1.60 **green**		35.00	30.00
RE52	RE2	$2 **green**		1.75	1.60

For rouletted 7 see Nos. RE60-RE80, RE102-RE105.

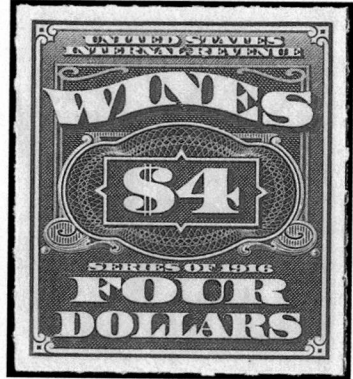

RE3

Engr.
Plates of 50 subjects

RE53	RE3	$4 **green**		1.10	.30
RE54	RE3	$4.80 **green**		4.50	4.00
RE55	RE3	$9.60 **green**		1.60	.45

Nos. RE32-RE55 exist in many shades. Size variations of 1c-$2 are believed due to offset printing. For rouletted 7 see Nos. RE81-RE83, RE106-RE107.

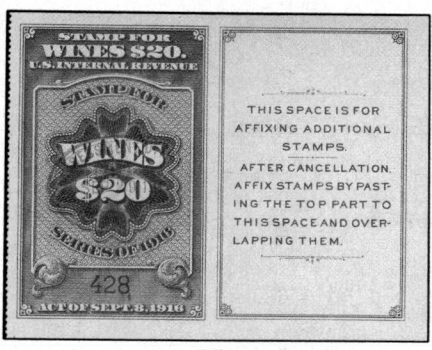

RE4

Illustration reduced.

Plates of 6 subjects
Perf. 12 at left

RE56	RE4	$20 **green**		110.00	60.00
RE57	RE4	$40 **green**		250.00	70.00
RE58	RE4	$50 **green**		80.00	57.50
RE59	RE4	$100 **green**		325.00	200.00

Stamps of design RE4 have an adjoining tablet at right for affixing additional stamps. Values are for examples with the tablets attached. Examples with the tablets removed sell for much less. Used stamps with additional stamps tied on the tablet with cancels sell for about ten times the values given. See Nos. RE107A-RE107D.

Same designs as Issue of 1916

1933   Wmk. 191R   Offset Printing   *Rouletted 7*

RE60	RE2	1c **light green**	3.25	.50
		a. Double impression		
RE61	RE2	3c **light green**	7.50	2.75
RE62	RE2	4c **light green**	2.25	.55
RE63	RE2	6c **light green**	13.00	7.50
RE64	RE2	7½c **light green**	6.75	1.40
RE65	RE2	10c **light green**	2.75	.25
		a. Double impression		
RE66	RE2	12c **light green**	13.00	6.00
RE67	RE2	15c **light green**	5.00	.40
RE69	RE2	20c **light green**	7.50	.25
		a. Double impression	—	—
RE70	RE2	24c **light green**	5.75	.25
		a. Double impression		160.00
RE71	RE2	30c **light green**	6.00	.25
		a. Double impression		—
RE72	RE2	36c **light green**	14.00	1.25
RE73	RE2	50c **light green**	4.75	.30
RE74	RE2	60c **light green**	10.00	.25
RE75	RE2	72c **light green**	17.50	.40
RE76	RE2	80c **light green**	17.50	.40
RE77	RE2	$1.20 **light green**	17.00	1.75
RE78	RE2	$1.44 **light green**	15.00	5.25
RE79	RE2	$1.60 **light green**	450.00	200.00
RE80	RE2	$2 **light green**	40.00	4.50

Engr.

RE81	RE3	$4 **light green**	42.50	8.75
RE82	RE3	$4.80 **light green**	47.50	17.50
RE83	RE3	$9.60 **light green**	190.00	100.00

RE5

Offset Printing

1934-40   Wmk. 191R   *Rouletted 7*
Inscribed: "Series of 1934"
Plates of 200 and 224 subjects
Issued With and Without Gum

RE83A	RE5	⅕c **green** ('40)	.75	.25
RE84	RE5	½c **green**	.55	.65
RE85	RE5	1c **green**	.70	.25
RE86	RE5	1¼c **green**	1.10	1.00
RE87	RE5	1½c **green**	7.50	8.75
RE88	RE5	2c **green**	2.25	1.00
RE89	RE5	2½c **green**	2.00	.70
RE90	RE5	3c **green**	5.25	4.25
RE91	RE5	4c **green**	3.00	.30
RE92	RE5	5c **green**	.70	.25
RE93	RE5	6c **green**	2.00	.60
RE94	RE5	7½c **green**	3.25	.25
RE95	RE5	10c **green**	.50	.70
RE96	RE5	12c **green**	2.10	.25
RE96A	RE5	14⅘c **green** ('40)	210.00	3.50
		b. Imperf, pair, without gum	5,000.	
RE97	RE5	15c **green**	.90	.25
RE98	RE5	18c **green**	1.75	.25
RE99	RE5	20c **green**	1.40	.25
RE100	RE5	24c **green**	2.75	.25
RE101	RE5	30c **green**	2.00	.25

Nos. RE83A-RE101 unused are valued without gum. Examples with gum sell for substantially more.
Nos. RE83A, RE86, RE96A were printed from plates of 200 only and all were issued without gum.

Plates of 100 subjects
Issued Without Gum

RE102	RE2	40c **green**	4.75	.25
RE102A	RE2	43⅕c **green** ('40)	21.00	2.75
RE103	RE2	48c **green**	35.00	4.00
RE104	RE2	$1 **green**	29.00	11.50
RE105	RE2	$1.50 **green**	45.00	17.00
		Perforated initials		5.75

Engr.
Plates of 50 subjects.

RE106	RE3	$2.50 **green**	52.50	18.00
		Perforated initials		9.00
RE107	RE3	$5 **green**	45.00	7.50
		Perforated initials		3.25

Stamps of types RE5 and RE2 overprinted "Rectified Spirits / Puerto Rico" are listed under Puerto Rico.

Nos. RE102-RE204 issued without gum.

Inscribed: "Series of 1916"
Plates of 6 subjects

1934   *Perf. 12 at left*

RE107A	RE4	$20 **yellow green**	1,800.	
RE107B	RE4	$40 **yellow green**	9,000.	

Perf. 12 or 12½ at left

RE107C	RE4	$50 **yellow green**	—	4,250.
RE107D	RE4	$100 **yellow green**	1,750.	500.00

The serial numbers of Nos. RE107A-RE107D are much thinner than on Nos. RE56-RE59. See valuing note after No. RE59.

RE6

Offset Printing
Inscribed "Series of 1941"

1942   Wmk. 191R   *Rouletted 7*

RE108	RE6	⅕c **green & black**	.80	.55
RE109	RE6	¼c **green & black**	2.50	2.50
RE110	RE6	½c **green & black**	3.25	2.10
		a. Horiz. pair, imperf. vertically	200.00	
RE111	RE6	1c **green & black**	1.25	1.25
RE112	RE6	2c **green & black**	6.00	5.25
RE113	RE6	3c **green & black**	6.00	4.50
RE114	RE6	3½c **green & black**	—	12,750.
RE115	RE6	3¾c **green & black**	11.50	7.25
RE116	RE6	4c **green & black**	4.25	3.25
RE117	RE6	5c **green & black**	3.00	2.40
RE118	RE6	6c **green & black**	3.75	2.75
RE119	RE6	7c **green & black**	7.50	5.50
RE120	RE6	7½c **green & black**	11.00	6.00
RE121	RE6	8c **green & black**	5.50	4.25
RE122	RE6	9c **green & black**	15.00	9.50
RE123	RE6	10c **green & black**	5.50	1.10
RE124	RE6	11¼c **green & black**	6.00	6.00
RE125	RE6	12c **green & black**	8.50	6.00
RE126	RE6	14c **green & black**	40.00	26.00
RE127	RE6	15c **green & black**	6.00	3.00
		a. Horiz. pair, imperf. vertically		925.00
RE128	RE6	16c **green & black**	14.00	9.00
RE129	RE6	19⅕c **green & black**	190.00	7.75
RE130	RE6	20c **green & black**	7.50	2.10
RE131	RE6	24c **green & black**	5.50	.25
RE132	RE6	28c **green & black**	2,750.	1,800.
RE133	RE6	30c **green & black**	1.50	.20
RE134	RE6	32c **green & black**	190.00	7.50
RE135	RE6	36c **green & black**	3.50	.25
RE136	RE6	40c **green & black**	3.00	.20
RE137	RE6	45c **green & black**	8.75	.25
RE138	RE6	48c **green & black**	21.00	9.25
RE139	RE6	50c **green & black**	12.00	7.50
RE140	RE6	60c **green & black**	4.25	.20
RE141	RE6	72c **green & black**	12.50	1.50
RE142	RE6	80c **green & black**	350.00	10.50
RE143	RE6	84c **green & black**	—	77.50
RE144	RE6	90c **green & black**	25.00	.20
RE145	RE6	96c **green & black**	15.00	.30

See Nos. RE182D-RE194.

Denomination Spelled Out in Two Lines — RE7

Engraved, Offset (denominations)

1942

RE146	RE7	$1.20 **yel grn & blk**	10.00	.25
RE147	RE7	$1.44 **yel grn & blk**	1.75	.30
		a. Denomination missing (FO)	—	—
		Pair, one with denomination missing (FO)	—	—
RE148	RE7	$1.50 **yel grn & blk**	150.00	67.50
RE149	RE7	$1.60 **yel grn & blk**	12.00	1.40
RE150	RE7	$1.68 **yel grn & blk**	120.00	50.00
		Perforated initials		35.00
RE151	RE7	$1.80 **yel grn & blk**	4.00	.20
		a. Pair, one with denomination missing (FO)		

No. RE151a may be collected as a vertical pair or a horizontal pair.

RE152	RE7	$1.92 **yel grn & blk**	80.00	72.50
RE153	RE7	$2.40 **yel grn & blk**	12.50	1.25
RE154	RE7	$3 **yel grn & blk**	100.00	42.50

RE155	RE7	$3.36 **yel grn & blk**	92.50	29.00
RE156	RE7	$3.60 **yel grn & blk**	200.00	10.00
RE157	RE7	$4 **yel grn & blk**	32.50	5.25
RE158	RE7	$4.80 **yel grn & blk**	175.00	3.75
RE159	RE7	$5 **yel grn & blk**	17.50	10.50
RE159A	RE7	$7.14 **yel grn & blk**	175.00	
RE160	RE7	$7.20 **yel grn & blk**	20.00	.50
RE161	RE7	$10 **yel grn & blk**	240.00	200.00
RE162	RE7	$20 **yel grn & blk**	130.00	77.50
RE163	RE7	$50 **yel grn & blk**	125.00	77.50
		Perforated initials		21.00
RE164	RE7	$100 **yel grn & blk**	375.00	30.00
		Perforated initials		21.00
RE165	RE7	$200 **yel grn & blk**	190.00	24.00
		Perforated initials		8.75
RE165A	RE7	$300 **yel grn & blk**	175.00	
RE165B	RE7	$400 **yel grn & blk**	8,000.	12,000.
RE166	RE7	$500 **yel grn & blk**	175.00	150.00
		Perforated initials		35.00
RE167	RE7	$600 **yel grn & blk**	200.00	125.00
RE167A	RE7	$700 **yel grn & blk**	175.00	
RE167B	RE7	$800 **yel grn & blk**	175.00	
RE168	RE7	$900 **yel grn & blk**	3,250.	4,000.
		Perforated initials		1,500.
RE169	RE7	$1,000 **yel grn & blk**	150.00	200.00
RE170	RE7	$2,000 **yel grn & blk**	4,000.	2,250.
RE171	RE7	$3,000 **yel grn & blk**	175.00	200.00
RE172	RE7	$4,000 **yel grn & blk**	1,600.	1,000.

Denomination Repeated, Spelled Out in One Line

1949

RE173	RE7	$1 **yellow green & black**	5.00	1.60
RE174	RE7	$2 **yellow green & black**	9.50	2.10
RE175	RE7	$4 **yellow green & black**	925.00	425.00
		Perforated initials		175.00
RE176	RE7	$5 **yellow green & black**	100.00	82.50
RE177	RE7	$6 **yellow green & black**	700.00	500.00
RE178	RE7	$7 **yellow green & black**	100.00	47.50
RE179	RE7	$8 **yellow green & black**	1,250.	450.00
		Perforated initials		85.00
RE179A	RE7	$9 **yel grn & blk**	175.00	
RE180	RE7	$10 **yellow green & black**	10.00	5.25
		Perforated initials		2.10
RE180A	RE7	$12 **yel grn & blk**	175.00	
RE181	RE7	$20 **yellow green & black**	25.00	5.25
		Perforated initials		1.90
RE182	RE7	$30 **yellow green & black**	2,000.	1,250.
RE182A	RE7	$40 **yel grn & blk**	175.00	
RE182B	RE7	$60 **yel grn & blk**	175.00	
RE182C	RE7	$70 **yel grn & blk**	175.00	
RE182D	RE7	$80 **yel grn & blk**	175.00	
RE182E	RE7	$90 **yel grn & blk**	175.00	

The $90 denomination, No. RE182E, was printed but was not delivered to the Internal Revenue Service for use.

Types of 1942-49

1951-54   Offset Printing

RE182F	RE6	1⁷⁄₁₀c **green & black**	22,500.	25,000.
RE183	RE6	3⅜c **green & black**	55.00	52.50
RE183A	RE6	6⁷⁄₁₀c **green & black**	—	
RE184	RE6	8½c **green & black**	30.00	20.00
RE184A	RE6	10⅕c **green & black**	—	
RE185	RE6	13⅖c **green & black**	100.00	82.50
RE186	RE6	17c **green & black**	16.00	15.00
RE187	RE6	20⅖c **green & black**	110.00	62.50
RE188	RE6	33½c **green & black**	90.00	92.50
RE189	RE6	38¼c **green & black**	150.00	90.00
RE190	RE6	40⅘c **green & black**	3.75	.80
RE191	RE6	51c **green & black**	4.00	1.40
RE192	RE6	67c **green & black**	12.50	4.25
RE193	RE6	68c **green & black**	3.75	.70
RE194	RE6	80⅘c **green & black**	175.00	110.00

The 6⁷⁄₁₀c and 10⅕c denominations, Nos. RE183A and RE184A, were printed but were not delivered to the Internal Revenue Service for use.

Engr.
Denomination Spelled Out in Two Lines in Small Letters

Two types of $1.60⅘:
I — The "4" slants sharply. Loop of "5" almost closes to form oval. Each numeral 2mm high.
II — The "4" is less slanted. Loop of "5" more open and nearly circular. Each numeral 2½mm high.

RE195	RE7	$1.50¾ **yel grn & blk**	50.00	47.50
RE196	RE7	$1.60⅘ **yel grn & blk** (I)	4.25	1.00
		a. "DOLLLAR"	52.50	15.00
		Perforated initials		10.00
		b. As "a," horiz. pair, one with denomination missing	5,000.	
		c. Type II	1,000.	250.00
RE197	RE7	$1.88³⁄₁₀ **yel grn & blk**	325.00	85.00
		Perforated initials		35.00

Denomination Spelled Out in Two Lines in Slightly Larger Letters Same as Nos. RE146-RE172

RE198	RE7	$1.60⅘ **yel grn & blk** (II)	35.00	6.25
		a. First line larger letters, second line small letters	14,000.	3,000.
		b. Type I ('53)	75.00	25.00
RE199	RE7	$2.01 **yel grn & blk**	3.50	1.00
RE200	RE7	$2.68 **yel grn & blk**	3.50	1.40
RE201	RE7	$4.08 **yel grn & blk**	95.00	35.00
RE202	RE7	$5.76 **yel grn & blk**	300.00	225.00
RE203	RE7	$8.16 **yel grn & blk**	17.50	7.00
RE204	RE7	$9.60 **yel grn & blk**	1,900.	5,000.

No. RE198a unused is unique.
Wine stamps were discontinued on Dec. 31, 1954.

BEER STAMPS

Basic stamps were printed by the Bureau of Engraving and Printing, unless otherwise noted.

All stamps are imperforate, unless otherwise noted.

Values for Nos. REA1-REA13 are for stamps with small faults, due to the fragile nature of the thin paper. Used values for Nos. REA14-REA199 are for canceled stamps with small faults.

All examples of Nos. REA1-REA13 contain a circular pattern of 31 perforations in the design, 27 or 28½mm in diameter, often poorly punched.

Values for cut squares of Nos. REA1-REA13 are for margins clear of the design. Die cut and cut to shape stamps are valued for margins clear to slightly cutting into the design.

Eric Jackson, Michael Aldrich, Henry Tolman II and Thomas W. Priester helped the editors extensively in compiling the listings.

An excellent study of beer stamps by Frank Applegate appeared in *Weekly Philatelic Gossip* from Oct. 1-Nov. 26, 1927.

A List of the Beer Stamps of the United States of America by Ernest R. Vanderhoof appeared in the *American Philatelist* in June 1934. This was reprinted in pamphlet form.

United States Beer Stamps by Thomas W. Priester, published in 1979, comprised an illustrated and priced catalogue, illustrations of all known provisional surcharges, background notes on the stamps and tax laws, and a census of over 27,500 stamps. The catalogue and census sections were updated in the 1990 edition.

Printed by the Treasury Department. Tax rate $1 per barrel (bbl.).

12½c = ⅛ barrel	$1 = 1 barrel
16⅔c = ⅙ barrel	$2 = 1 hogshead
25c = ¼ barrel	$5 = 5 barrels
33⅓c = ⅓ barrel	$10 = 10 barrels
50c = ½ barrel	$25 = 25 barrels

1866   **Engr.**

REA1	12½c **orange**	400.	600.
	Cut to shape		110.
a.	Die cut	450.	300.
b.	Silk paper		2,000.
REA2	16⅔c **dark green**	200.	250.
	Cut to shape		30.
a.	Die cut		85.
REA3	25c **blue**	75.	150.
	Cut to shape		25.
a.	Die cut		50.
b.	Silk paper		2,000.
	Double transfer		—
REA4	50c **orange brown**	35.	50.
	Printed cancellation, "A.S. 1869"		150.
	Cut to shape		10.
a.	Die cut		75.
REA5	$1 **black**	375.	275.
	Cut to shape		75.
a.	Die cut		225.
REA6	$2 **red**	1,200.	1,500.
	Cut to shape		190.
a.	Die cut		500.

Printed by the Treasury Department. See individual rates before No. REA1.

1867   **Engr.**

REA7	12½c **orange**	2,400.	1,850.
	Cut to shape		750.
a.	Die cut		1,250.
REA8	16⅔c **dark green**	2,600.	2,500.
	Cut to shape		525.
a.	Die cut		1,500.
REA9	25c **blue**	250.	300.
	Cut to shape		50.
a.	Die cut		250.
REA10	33⅓c **violet brown**		5,500.
	Cut to shape		2,500.
b.	Silk paper		3,500.
c.	33⅓c **ocher red**, cut to shape		3,500.
d.	33⅓c **ocher red**, die cut		14,500.
REA11	50c **orange brown**	75.	125.
	Printed cancellation, "A.S. 1869"		400.
	Cut to shape		35.
a.	Die cut		150.
REA12	$1 **black**	1,350.	
	Cut to shape		350.
a.	Die cut		750.
REA13	$2 **red**	2,000.	1,350.
	Cut to shape		500.
a.	Die cut		1,100.

See individual rates before No. REA1.

Silk Paper

1870   **Engr.**   **Lilac Security Lines**

REA14	12½c **brown**	350.00	250.
a.	Yellow security lines		1,750.
REA15	16⅔c **yellow orange**		300.
a.	Yellow security lines		1,100.
b.	Gray-green and yellow security lines		1,750.
c.	16⅔c **yellow ocher**, lilac security lines		1,000.
REA16	25c **green**		125.
a.	Yellow security lines		225.
b.	Gray-green & yellow security lines	1,000.	
REA17	50c **red**	300.	125.
a.	Yellow security lines		500.
b.	Gray-green and yellow security lines		1,400.
c.	50c **brick red**, lilac security lines		800.
d.	50c **brick red**, yellow security lines		2,500.
REA18	$1 **blue**	2,000.	850.
a.	Yellow security lines		350.
b.	Gray-green and yellow security lines		1,500.
REA19	$2 **black**	1,000.	875.
a.	Yellow security lines		2,500.
b.	Gray-green and yellow security lines		3,250.

The security lines were printed across the center of the stamp where the cancel was to be placed.

Andrew Jackson

Designs: 16⅔c, Abraham Lincoln. 25c, Daniel Webster. 33⅓c, David G. Farragut. 50c, William T. Sherman. $1, Hugh McCulloch. $2, Alexander Hamilton.

Centers printed by the Bureau of Engraving and Printing. Frames printed by the National Bank Co.

See individual rates before No. REA1.

1871   **Engr.**

Centers, Plate Letters and Position Numbers in Black

REA20	12½c **blue**, white silk paper	125.
a.	Pinkish gray silk paper	200.
b.	Gray silk paper	65.
c.	Green silk paper	150.
REA21	16⅔c **vermilion**, white silk paper	350.
a.	Pinkish gray silk paper	375.
b.	Gray silk paper	375.
c.	Green silk paper	375.
REA22	25c **green**, white silk paper	25.
a.	Pinkish gray silk paper	125.
b.	Gray silk paper	50.
c.	Green silk paper	30.
REA23	33⅓c **orange**, green silk paper	5,000.
b.	Gray silk paper	11,000.
REA24	33⅓c **violet brown**, white silk paper	6,250.
REA25	50c **brown**, gray silk paper	20.
a.	Pinkish gray silk paper	60.
c.	Green silk paper	75.
REA26	50c **red**, white silk paper	55.
REA27	$1 **yellow orange**, white silk paper	250.
a.	Pinkish gray silk paper	1,100.
b.	Gray silk paper	150.
REA28	$1 **scarlet**, gray silk paper	175.
a.	Pinkish gray silk paper	750.
c.	Green silk paper	350.
REA29	$2 **red brown**, white silk paper	200.
a.	Pinkish gray silk paper	1,450.
b.	Gray silk paper	350.
c.	Green silk paper	1,000.

Bacchus Serving the First Fermented Brew to Man

Printed by the National Bank Note Co. See individual rates before No. REA1.

1875   **Typo. & Engr.**

Center in Black

REA30	12½c blue	25.00
REA31	16⅔c red brown	150.00
REA32	25c green	40.00
a.	Inverted center	55,000.
REA33	33⅓c violet	100.00
REA34	50c orange	1,250.
REA35	$1 red	225.00
REA36	$2 brown	400.00
a.	Inverted center	—

Designs: 12½c, Washington. 16⅔c, Corwin. 25c, Benton. 33⅓c, Thomas. 50c, Jefferson. $1, Johnson. $2, Wright.
Stamps on pale green paper have short greenish blue fibers. Plate designations for center consist of plate letter or number at left and position number at right.
See individual rates before No. REA1.

1878   **Typo. & Engr.**   **Wmk. USIR**

Center, Plate Letters and Position Numbers in Black

REA37	12½c blue, green	7.50
b.	Green silk paper, unwmkd.	1,250.
c.	Pale green paper	200.00
	With plate number and position number	1,250.
d.	Light blue paper, with plate number (and position number)	35.00
e.	Blue paper, no plate letter or number or position number	30.00
f.	Dark blue paper, no plate letter or number or position number	50.00
REA38	16⅔c light brown, green	7.50
	One line under Cents	75.00
b.	Green silk paper, unwmkd., one line under Cents	140.00
c.	Pale green paper	75.00
	With plate number	500.00
d.	Light blue paper, with plate number (and position number)	40.00
e.	Blue paper, no plate letter or number or position number	150.00
	With plate number 1979	250.00
f.	Dark blue paper, no plate letter or number or position number	75.00
REA39	25c green, green	5.00
a.	Inverted center	55,000.
b.	Green silk paper, unwmkd.	200.00
c.	Pale green paper	100.00
	With plate number	35.00
d.	Light blue paper, with plate number (and position number)	7.50
e.	Blue paper, no plate letter or number or position number	30.00

f.	Dark blue paper, no plate letter or number or position number	32.50
REA40	33⅓c violet, green	85.00
b.	Green silk paper, unwmkd.	2,000.
c.	Pale green paper	1,250.
d.	Light blue paper, with plate number (and position number)	110.00
e.	Blue paper, no plate letter or number or position number	120.00
f.	Dark blue paper, no plate letter or number or position number	250.00
REA41	50c orange, green	11.00
	One line under Cents	100.00
b.	Green silk paper, unwmkd.	210.00
c.	Pale green paper	100.00
	With plate number	350.00
d.	Light blue paper, with plate number (and position number)	30.00
e.	Blue paper, no plate letter or number or position number	20.00
f.	Dark blue paper, no plate letter or number or position number	20.00
REA42	$1 red, green	27.50
	One line under Dollar	85.00
c.	Pale green paper	200.00
	One line under Dollar	400.00
d.	Light blue paper, with plate number (and position number)	175.00
e.	Blue paper, no plate letter or number or position number	125.00
	One line under Dollar	200.00
f.	Dark blue paper, no plate letter or number or position number	100.00
REA43	$2 brown, green	85.00
	One line under Dollars	100.00
b.	Green silk paper, unwmkd.	500.00
	One line under dollars	
c.	Pale green paper	900.00
	One line under dollars	1,000.
e.	Blue paper, no plate letter or number or position number	175.00
f.	Dark blue paper, no plate letter or number or position number	150.00

See Nos. REA58-REA64, REA65-REA71, REA75-REA81.

Stamps of 1878 Surcharged in Various Ways

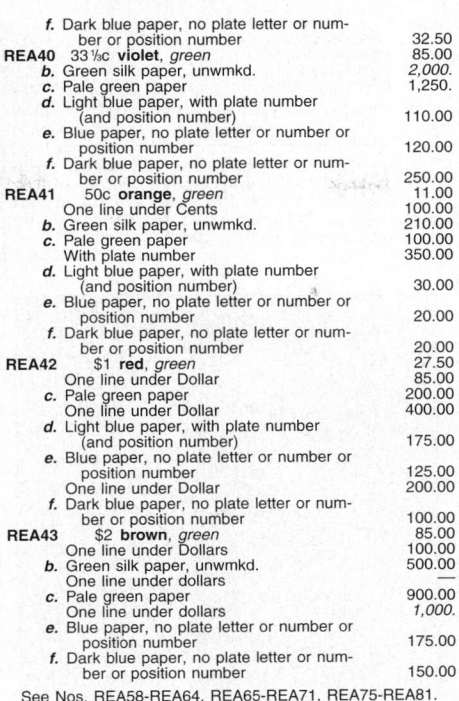

Type B

Four general surcharge types:
A — Bureau of Engraving and Printing surcharge "TAX $2 PER BBL./SERIES OF 1898" printed diagonally in red, letters 4¼mm high.
B — same, but letters 5½mm high.
C — handstamped provisional surcharge with similiar wording in 1-3 lines, more than 30 styles.
D — printed provisional 2-line surcharges, horizontal in various colors.
Tax rate $2 per bbl.

25c = ⅛ barrel	$1 = ½ barrel
33⅓c = ⅙ barrel	$2 = 1 barrel
50c = ¼ barrel	$4 = 1 hogshead
66⅔c = ⅓ barrel	

1898   **Type A**

REA44	(25c) on 12½c #REA37f	350.00
a.	Type C surcharge	250.00
b.	Type D surcharge	750.00
REA45	(33⅓c) on 16⅔c #REA38e	75.00
a.	on #REA38f	175.00
b.	As "a," type C surcharge	250.00
c.	As "a," type D surcharge	450.00
d.	on #REA38d	750.00
REA46	(50c) on 25c #REA39f	90.00
a.	Type C surcharge	150.00
b.	Type D surcharge	750.00
c.	on #REA39e	175.00
d.	on #REA39, type C surcharge	4,000.
REA47	(66⅔c) on 33⅓c #REA40	500.00
REA48	($1) on 50c #REA41f	35.00
a.	Type C surcharge	150.00
b.	Type D surcharge	450.00
REA49	($2) on $1 #REA42f	125.00
a.	Type C surcharge	175.00
b.	Type D surcharge	1,750.
c.	on #REA42e, type C surcharge	1,250.
REA50	($4) on $2 #REA43f	500.00
a.	Type C surcharge	500.00
b.	Type D surcharge	2,500.

c.	on #REA43e, type C surcharge	2,500.

Type B

REA51	(25c) on 12½c #REA37f	95.00
a.	on #REA37e	100.00
b.	As "a," type C surcharge	2,000.
REA52	(33⅓c) on 16⅔c #REA38d	700.00
a.	on #REA38f	700.00
b.	on #REA38e	700.00
REA53	(50c) on 25c #REA39f	25.00
a.	on #REA39e	25.00
REA54	(66⅔c) on 33⅓c #REA40f	9,000.
a.	Type D surcharge	7,500.
b.	On #REA40	6,000.
REA55	($1) on 50c #REA41f	12.50
REA56	($2) on $1 #REA42f	50.00
REA57	($4) on $2 #REA43f	275.00

Counterfeit type C and D overprints exist.

Designs: 25c, Washington. 33⅓c, Corwin. 50c, Benton. 66⅔c, Thomas. $1, Jefferson. $2, Johnson. $4, Wright.
See individual rates before No. REA44.

1898   **Typo. & Engr.**   **Wmk. USIR**

Center in Black, Dark Blue Paper

REA58	25c blue	110.
REA59	33⅓c brown	85.
REA60	50c green	25.
REA61	66⅔c violet	10,500.
REA62	$1 yellow	20.
REA63	$2 red	25.
REA64	$4 dark brown	225.

> **Used values for 1901-51 issues are for stamps canceled by perforated company name (or abbreviation) and date.**

Designs: 20c, Washington. 26⅔c, Corwin. 40c, Benton. 53⅓c, Thomas. 80c, Jefferson. $1.60, Johnson. $3.20, Wright.
Tax rate $1.60 per bbl.

20c = ⅛ barrel		80c = ½ barrel
26⅔c = ⅙ barrel		$1.60 = 1 barrel
40c = ¼ barrel		$3.20 = 1 hogshead
53⅓c = ⅓ barrel		

Engr. (center) & Typo. (frame)

1901   **Wmk. USIR**

Dark Blue Paper

REA65	20c blue	75.
REA66	26⅔c yellow orange	75.
REA67	40c green	17.50
REA68	53⅓c violet	7,000.
REA69	80c brown	17.50
REA70	$1.60 red	75.
REA71	$3.20 dark brown	275.

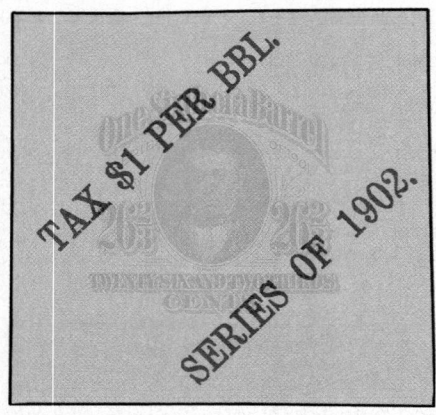

Stamps of 1901 Provisionally Surcharged by Bureau of
Engraving & Printing diagonally in red "TAX $1 PER
BBL./SERIES OF 1902."

1902

REA72	(16⅔c) on 26⅔c #REA66	150.
REA73	(33⅓c) on 53⅓c #REA68	*4,500.*
REA74	($2) on $3.20 #REA71	750.

Designs: 12½c, Washington. 16⅔c, Corwin. 25c, Benton.
33⅓c, Thomas. 50c, Jefferson. $1, Johnson. $2, Wright.
Stamps on pale green paper have short greenish blue fibers.
See individual rates before No. REA1.

1902	**Typo. & Engr.**	**Wmk. USIR**
	Center in Black	
REA75	12½c **blue**	
a.	Dark blue paper	75.00
b.	Pale green paper	350.00
c.	Light blue paper	110.00
d.	Bright blue paper	50.00
REA76	16⅔c **yellow orange**	
a.	Dark blue paper	250.00
b.	Pale green paper	350.00
c.	Light blue paper	225.00
d.	Bright blue paper	400.00
REA77	25c **green**	
a.	Dark blue paper	25.00
b.	Pale green paper	85.00
c.	Light blue paper	25.00
d.	Bright blue paper	30.00
REA78	33⅓c **violet**	
a.	Dark blue paper	225.00
c.	Light blue paper	450.00
d.	Bright blue paper	450.00
REA79	50c **brown**	
a.	Dark blue paper	20.00
b.	Pale green paper	30.00
c.	Light blue paper	25.00
d.	Bright blue paper	20.00
REA80	$1 **red**	
a.	Dark blue paper	125.00
b.	Pale green paper	300.00
c.	Light blue paper	75.00
d.	Bright blue paper	75.00

REA81	$2 **dark brown**	
a.	Dark blue paper	750.00
b.	Pale green paper	900.00
c.	Light blue paper	500.00
d.	Bright blue paper	600.00

For surcharges see Nos. REA99A, REA100A, REA100Ab,
REA141.

> In the 1911-33 issues, the 5-25 barrel sizes
> were generally available only as center cutouts
> of the stamp. Values for these are for cutout
> portions that show enough of the denomination
> (or surcharge) to identify the item.

See individual rates before No. REA1.

1909-11	**Engr.**		**Wmk. USIR**
	Paper of Various Shades of Blue		
REA82	12½c **black**		500.00
REA83	16⅔c **black**	200.00	90.00
REA84	25c **black**	550.00	450.00
REA85	33⅓c **black**		*20,000.*
REA86	50c **black**	55.00	6.00
REA87	$1 **black**	1,000.	750.00
REA88	$2 **black**		*4,500.*
	Center Cutout Only		
REA89	$5 **black**, *1911*		*150.00*
REA90	$10 **black**, *1911*		*125.00*
REA91	$25 **black**, *1911*		*100.00*

For surcharges see Nos. REA97, REA99-REA100, REA103-
REA105, REA128.

1910	**Engr.**	**Wmk. USIR**
	Paper of Various Shades of Blue	
REA92	12½c **red brown**	75.00
REA93	25c **green**	10.00
REA94	$1 **carmine**	110.00
REA95	$2 **orange**	125.00

For surcharges see Nos. REA96, REA98, REA101-REA102,
REA126.

1914 Provisional Issue

Stamps of 1902-11 with printed provisional BEP diagonal
surcharge "EMERGENCY/TAX/UNDER ACT OF 1914" in red,
black or yellow, or handstamped surcharge of value spelled out
in full and separate "Roscoe Irwin" handstamped facsimile
signature.
Tax rate $1.50 per bbl.

18¾c	= ⅛ barrel	$1.50	= 1 barrel
25c	= ⅙ barrel	$3	= 1 hogshead
37½c	= ¼ barrel	$7.5	= 5 barrels
50c	= ⅓ barrel	$15	= 10 barrels
75c	= ½ barrel	$37.50	= 25 barrels

1914		**Entire Stamps**
REA96	(18¾c) on 12½ #REA92	65.00
REA97	(25c) on 16⅔c #REA83	60.00
REA98	(37½c) on 25c #REA93	7.50
a.	37½c handstamped; 50mm signature	700.00
REA99	(50c) on 33⅓c #REA85	225.00
REA99A	(50c) on 33⅓c #REA78d	900.00
REA100	(75c) on 50c #REA86	7.50
c.	75c handstamped on #REA86; 50mm signature	175.00
d.	As "c," 65mm signature	325.00
REA100A	(75c) On 50c #REA79c	1,000.
b.	(75c) On 50c #REA79b	5,500.
REA101	($1.50) on $1 #REA94	50.00
a.	$1.50 handstamped; 50mm signature	700.00
b.	As "a," 65mm signature	9,000.

REA102	($3.00) on $2 #REA95	75.00
a.	$3 handstamped; 76mm signature	*2,750.*
	Center Cutout Only	
REA103	($7.50) on $5 #REA89	17.50
REA104	($15) on $10 #REA90	160.00
REA105	($37.50) on $25 #REA91	225.00

For surcharges see Nos. REA119, REA123, REA133,
REA140, REA140A.

See individual rates before No. REA96.

1914	**Engr.**	**Wmk. USIR**
	Paper of Various Shades of Blue	
	Entire Stamp	
REA106	18¾c **red brown**	85.00
REA107	25c **black**	175.00
a.	25c **violet blue**	*2,500.*
REA108	37½c **green**	17.50
a.	37½c **black**	*32,500.*
REA108B	50c **black**	—
REA109	75c **black**	6.00
REA110	$1.50 **red orange**	30.00
REA111	$3 **orange**	200.00
	Center Cutout Only	
REA112	$7.50 **black**	10.00
REA113	$15 **black**	15.00
REA114	$37.50 **black**	7.50

For surcharges see Nos. REA118, REA120, REA120a,
REA121, REA124-REA125, REA127, REA129-REA131,
REA134, REA134a, REA137, REA144, REA146-REA149.

See individual rates before No. REA96.

1916	**Engr.**	**Wmk. USIR**
	Paper of Various Shades of Greenish Blue	
	Entire Stamp	
REA115	37½c **green**	110.00
REA116	75c **black**	45.00

For surcharges see Nos. REA122, REA124, REA138.
Surcharge also exists in manuscript on No. REA115.

Stamps of 1914-16 Provisionally Surcharged Types A, B & C

Type C

Surcharge types:
A — "ACT OF 1917" handstamped in 1-3 lines in more than 30 styles.
B — "ACT OF 1917" locally printed horizontally in black or red.
C — "ACT OF 1917" printed in black or red by BEP, horizontally on ⅛ bbl-1 hhd and reading down on 5-25 bbl.
Surcharge also exists in manuscript on some values. Tax rate $3 per bbl.

37½c = ⅛ barrel	$3 = 1 barrel
50c = ⅙ barrel	$6 = 1 hogshead
75c = ¼ barrel	$15 = 5 barrels
$1 = ⅓ barrel	$30 = 10 barrels
$1.50 = ½ barrel	$75 = 25 barrels

1917   Type A Surcharge
Entire Stamp

REA117	(37½c) on #REA96		17,500.
REA118	(37½c) on #REA106		325.00
b.	Type B surcharge		
c.	Type C surcharge		500.00
REA119	(50c) on #REA97		150.00
REA120	(50c) on #REA107a		600.00
a.	On #REA107		500.00
REA121	(75c) on #REA108		140.00
REA122	(75c) on #REA115		60.00
b.	Type B surcharge		5,500.
c.	Type C surcharge		100.00
REA123	($1) on #REA99		175.00
REA124	($1.50) on #REA116		75.00
b.	Type B surcharge		6,000.
c.	Type C surcharge	45.00	7.50
d.	As "c," inverted surcharge		1,750.

$1.50 surcharge exists in manuscript on #REA109.

REA125	($3) on #REA110		100.00
c.	Type C surcharge		40.00
REA126	($6) on #REA102		2,750.
REA127	($6) on #REA111		500.00

Center Cutout Only

REA128	($15) on #REA103		500.00
REA129	($15) on #REA112, entire stamp, type C surcharge		6,000.
REA130	($30) on #REA113		100.00
c.	Type C surcharge		45.00
REA131	($75) on #REA114		225.00
c.	Type C surcharge		12.50

For surcharges see Nos. REA132, REA132a, REA135-REA136, REA139-REA139b, REA142-REA143, REA145, REA150-REA151.

Stamps of 1914-17 provisionally surcharged "ACT OF 1918" or "Revenue Act of 1918" with rubber stamp in various colors in more than 20 styles.

A subtype has the incorrect date of 1919 due to the effective date of the act (at least five styles).
Tax rate $6 per bbl.

75c = ⅛ barrel	$6 = 1 barrel	
$1 = ⅙ barrel	$12 = 1 hogshead	
$1.50 = ¼ barrel	$30 = 5 barrels	
$2 = ⅓ barrel	$60 = 10 barrels	
$3 = ½ barrel	$150 = 25 barrels	

1918   Entire Stamp

REA132	(75c) on #REA118		600.
a.	On #REA118c		1,200.
REA133	($1) on #REA97		3,000.
REA134	($1) on #REA107		3,000.
a.	On #REA107a		10,000.

Exists with additional overprint "Non-Intoxicating, containing not to/exceed 2¾% of Alcohol by weight." Value, $1,750.

REA135	($1) on #REA119		8,000.
REA136	($1) on #REA120		2,500.
REA137	($1.50) on #REA108		600.
a.	Surcharge dated "1919"		2,250.
REA138	($1.50) on #REA115		1,250.
REA139	($1.50) on #REA122c		75.
a.	Surcharge dated "1919"	350.	60.
b.	On #REA122		350.

REA140	($2) on #REA99		1,000.
REA140A	($2) on #REA99A		1,500.
REA141	($2) on #REA99A		3,500.

No. REA141 bears additional 1917 provisional surcharge, as well as the 1914 surcharge, but was not issued in that form without 1918 surcharge.

REA142	($2) on #REA123		10,000.
REA143	($3) on #REA124c	175.	75.
a.	Surcharge dated "1919"		600.
REA144	($6) on #REA110		1,000.
REA145	($6) on #REA125c		50.
a.	Surcharge dated "1919"		500.
REA146	($12) on #REA111		700.
REA147	($12) on #REA111		75.

No. REA147 bears additional 1917 Type C provisional surcharge but was not issued in that form without 1918 surcharge.

Center Cutout Only

REA148	($30) on #REA112		85.
REA149	($60) on #REA113		85.
REA150	($60) on #REA130c		300.
a.	Entire stamp		3,500.
REA151	($150) on #REA131c		45.
a.	Entire stamp		4,000.

REA152-REA158

REA159-REA161

Tax rate $5 per barrel through Jan. 11, 1934. $6 rate also effective Dec. 5, 1933. Provisional handstamp "Surcharged $6.00 Rate" in 1-3 lines (seven styles).

1933   Engr.   Wmk. USIR
Paper of Various Shades of Greenish Blue to Blue
Type A
Entire Stamp

REA152	⅛ bbl., violet red		17.50
a.	Provisional surcharge, $6 rate		1,500.
REA153	⅙ bbl., purple		450.00
REA154	¼ bbl., green		8.00
REA155	⅓ bbl., brown orange		2,750.
REA156	½ bbl., orange	70.00	5.00
a.	Provisional surcharge, $6 rate		1,750.
REA157	1 bbl., blue		25.00
a.	Provisional surcharge, $6 rate		3,000.
REA158	1 hhd., black		7,500.
REA159	5 bbl., black, center cutout only		250.00
REA160	10 bbl., black, with cut-out center, rouletted 7 at left		7,500.
a.	Center cutout only		250.00
REA161	25 bbl., black, with cut-out center, rouletted 7 at left		7,500.
a.	Center cutout only		250.00

Center cutout portions of Nos. REA159-REA161 are on greenish blue paper. See Nos. REA177-REA178A for examples on bright blue paper.

Nos. REA152-REA159, REA161 Surcharged in Black

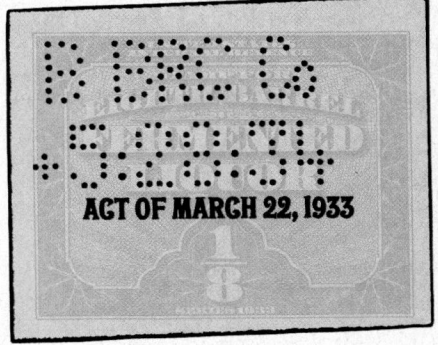

Type B

A — additional provisional handstamped surcharge.
B — additional manuscript and handstamped surcharges.
Tax rate same as Nos. REA152-REA161.

1933   Engr.   Wmk. USIR
Entire Stamp

REA162	⅛ bbl., violet red		10.00
REA163	⅙ bbl., purple		175.00
REA164	¼ bbl., green		15.00
a.	With 1918 provisional handstamped surcharge, $6 rate		2,250.
b.	Type A surcharge, $6 rate		2,750.
REA165	⅓ bbl., brown orange		6,000.
REA166	½ bbl., orange		15.00
a.	Type A surcharge, $6 rate		3,000.
b.	Type B surcharge, $6 rate		1,500.
REA167	1 bbl., blue		25.00
REA168	1 hhd., black		16,000.
REA169	5 bbl., black		6,500.
a.	Center cutout only		500.00
REA170	25 bbl., black, center cutout only		450.00

REA171-REA176

REA177-REA178A

Tax rate same as previous issue. Provisional handstamp reads "SOLD AT $5.00 RATE" or "$5.00 RATE."

1933   Engr.   Wmk. USIR
Entire Stamp

REA171	⅛ bbl., violet red		35.00
REA172	⅙ bbl., purple		500.00
REA173	¼ bbl., green	75.00	8.00
a.	Provisional surcharge, $5 rate		7,500.
REA174	½ bbl., brown orange	100.00	5.00
a.	Provisional surcharge, $5 rate		1,500.
REA175	1 bbl., blue		110.00
REA176	1 hhd., black		6,500.

Bright Blue Paper

REA177	5 bbl., black		1,000.
a.	Entire stamp with cut-out center		7.50
b.	Center cutout only		1.00
REA178	10 bbl., black	800.00	500.00
a.	Entire stamp with cut-out center		10.00
b.	Center cutout only		1.00

REA178A	25 bbl., black	500.00
b.	Entire stamp with cut-out center	4.50
c.	Center cutout only	1.00
d.	Rouletted 7 at left	—

For surcharge see No. REA199.

Nos. REA173-REA174 with BEP Printed Surcharge, "Act of March 22, 1933"

Additional provisional handstamped surcharge, $6 rate as previous issue.

1933-40
Entire Stamp

REA179	¼ bbl., green	27.50
a.	Handstamped "Surcharged $6 rate," 1940	2,750.
REA180	½ bbl., brown orange	12.50
a.	Handstamped "Surcharged $6 rate," 1940	2,500.

No. REA178 with handstamp surcharge, "Value increased under Revenue Act of 1940."

1940
Entire Stamp

REA180B	10 bbl., black	—

REA181-REA187

REA188-REA189

Tax rates $5 per bbl; $6 from July 1, 1940; $7 from Nov. 1, 1942; $8 from Apr. 1, 1944.

1934-45		Engr.	Wmk. USIR
With Black Control Numbers			
REA181	⅛ bbl., violet red	140.00	7.50
a.	With cutout center		2.00
b.	Ovptd. "NOT LESS THAN 3⅝ GALLONS," uncut		—
REA182	⅛ bbl., purple		150.00
a.	With cutout center		100.00
b.	Ovptd. "NOT LESS THAN 4⅝ GALLONS," uncut		—
REA183	¼ bbl., green		4.00
a.	With cutout center		2.50
b.	Ovptd. "NOT LESS THAN 7 ¼ GALLONS," uncut		—
REA184	⅓ bbl., brown orange		*20,000.*
REA185	½ bbl., orange		3.00
a.	With cutout center		2.00
REA186	1 bbl., blue		7.50
a.	With cutout center		7.50
REA187	1 hhd., black, with cutout center		500.00
REA188	100 bbl., carmine, *1942*		200.00
a.	With cutout center		10.00
REA189	500 bbl., dark brown, with cut-out center, *1945*		500.00

Most values also exist as center cutout portions only.

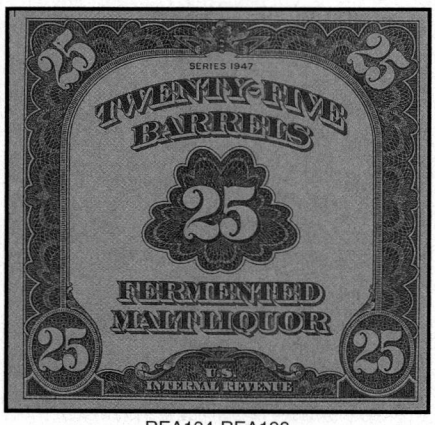

REA190-REA193

REA194-REA198

Tax rates $8 per bbl, $9 from Nov. 1, 1951.

1947			Litho.
Black Control Numbers			
REA190	⅛ bbl., carmine	125.00	60.00
a.	With cutout center		15.00
REA190B	⅛ bbl., purple	225.00	
REA191	¼ bbl., green	100.00	20.00
a.	With cutout center		22.50
REA192	½ bbl., orange	30.00	10.00
a.	With cutout center		12.50
REA193	1 bbl., blue	100.00	150.00
a.	With cutout center		15.00
Blue Paper			
REA194	5 bbl., black	100.00	200.00
a.	With cutout center		12.50
REA195	10 bbl., black	200.00	300.00
a.	With cutout center		27.50
REA196	25 bbl., black	*1,500.*	*3,200.*
a.	With cutout center		*3,000.*
White Paper			
REA197	100 bbl., carmine	175.00	250.00
a.	With cutout center		10.00
REA198	500 bbl., dark brown	550.00	600.00
a.	With cutout center		60.00

All values except No. REA190B also exist as center cutouts only.

No. REA190B was not officially issued.

No. REA178A Provisionally Handstamp Surcharged "Value increased under / Revenue Act of 1951" in black or purple.

Tax rate $9 per bbl.

1951

REA199	($225) on 25 bbl., #REA178A, un-cut	*20,000.*

Also exists as center cutout only, showing portion of hand-stamped surcharge. Value, $150.

FERMENTED FRUIT JUICE STAMPS

Fermented fruit juice stamps were issued pending the ratification of the Repeal Amendment (Dec. 5, 1933) that made full-strength beer and wine legal again.

Congress, as a temporary measure, redefined intoxicating beverages by changing the legal definition from .5% to 3.2%, thus permitting the sale of 3.2 beer and wine beginning April 7, 1933.

Regular wine stamps were available to pay the Internal Revenue taxes. However, these Fermented Fruit Juice stamps were authorized for placement on individual bottles or containers of fermented fruit juice. Use was discontinued at the end of 1933.

Stamps are valued in the grade of very fine. Most stamps are found in average to fine condition. Unused stamps are valued with original gum.

REF1

Plates of 220 subjects in two panes of 110.

1933		Wmk. USIR	Engr.	*Perf. 11*
REF1	REF1	4 oz gray		125.00
REF3	REF1	8 oz light green	125.00	100.00
REF4	REF1	12 oz light blue	22.50	8.00
REF5	REF1	13 oz olive green		70.00
REF6	REF1	16 oz lavender	550.00	175.00
REF7	REF1	24 oz orange		110.00
REF8	REF1	29 oz brown	225.00	175.00
REF9	REF1	32 oz red	95.00	75.00

A dark blue 7-ounce stamp was issued, but the only recorded examples currently are in the National Postal Museum collection.

No. REF4 stamps canceled "H. B. Co." (Hoffman Beverage Company) or "M. D. C." (Mission Dry Corporation) command a premium of 10-100 percent. Specialists collect them by date (H. B. Co. and M. D. C.) and control number (M. D. C.).

Earliest known use: May 28, 1933.

Beer Stamp No. REA154 Overprinted "WINE OR FERMENTED FRUIT JUICE" in Red

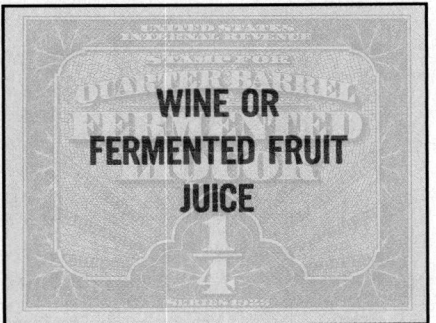

REF10ovpt

1933		Engr.		*Imperf.*
REF10		¼ bbl., **green**, *blue*		*30,000.*

The ½ barrel and 1 barrel stamps Beer Stamps, Nos. REA156-REA157, also were issued with this overprint, but no examples are currently recorded.

PLAYING CARDS

Stamps for use on packs of playing cards were included in the first general issue of 1862-71. They are Nos. R2, R11, R12, R17, R21 and R28. The tax on playing cards was repealed effective June 22, 1965.

"ON HAND . . ." — RF1

"ACT OF . . ." — RF2

1894		Engr.	Unwmk.		*Rouletted 5½*	
RF1	RF1	2c **lake**			.90	.60
a.		Horizontal pair, imperf. between			*600.00*	—
b.		Horiz. pair, imperf. vert.			—	
RF2	RF2	2c **ultramarine**			27.50	2.75
a.		2c **blue**			35.00	3.75
b.		Imperf., pair			600.00	
c.		Imperf. horizontally			160.00	160.00
d.		Rouletted 12½			100.00	100.00
e.		Imperf. horizontally, rouletted 12½ vertically, pair			225.00	225.00

No vertical pairs of No. RF2e are known. Pairs will be horizontal. Singles are valued at 50% of the pair value.

Rouletted 5½, 7; Hyphen Hole 7

1896-99				*Wmk. 191R*	
RF3	RF2	2c **blue**		10.00	.65
a.		2c **ultramarine** ('99)		10.00	2.00
b.		Imperf., pair		125.00	

No. RF3 surcharged " VIRGIN / ISLANDS / 4 CTS" are listed under Danish West Indies.

1902				*Perf. 12*
RF4	RF2	2c **deep blue**		65.00

No. RF4 is known with cancel date "1899" but that is due to the use of an old canceling plate. The stamp was first used in 1902.

Stamp of 1899 Surcharged in Rose

1917				*Wmk. 191R*		*Rouletted 7*	
RF5	RF2	7c on 2c **ultramarine**				*850.00*	700.00
a.		Inverted surcharge					

The surcharge on No. RF5 was handstamped at the Internal Revenue Office in New York City. Different handstamps were used at other Internal Revenue Offices as well, values $350 to $400.

Surcharged in Black

1917					
RF6	RF2	(7c) on 2c **blue**			62.50
a.		Inverted surcharge			62.50

The "17" indicated that the 7 cent tax had been paid according to the Act of 1917.
Used by N. Y. Consolidated Card Co.
Cancellations are in red.

Surcharged in Black

RF7	RF2	7c on 2c **blue**			1,100.
a.		Inverted surcharge			650.00

Used by Standard Playing Card Co.

The surcharges on Nos. RF7-RF10, RF13, RF15, RF18 were applied by the manufacturers, together with their initials, dates, etc., thus forming a combination of surcharge and precancellation. The surcharge on No. RF16 was made by the Bureau of Engraving and Printing. After it appeared the use of some combinations was continued but only as cancellations.

Surcharged Vertically Reading Up in Red or Violet

RF8	RF2	7c on 2c **blue**			1,350.
a.		Double surcharge			2,000.
b.		Reading down			2,250.

Used by Russell Playing Card Co.

Surcharged Vertically, Reading Up in Black, Violet or Red

RF9	RF2	7c on 2c **blue**			10.00
a.		Double surcharge (violet)			100.00
b.		Numeral omitted (black)			90.00
c.		Surcharge reading down			13.00
d.		As "c," numeral omitted (black)			77.50
e.		As "c," double surcharge (violet)			275.00
f.		Double surcharge, one down (red)			300.00
g.		Surcharge and "A.D." in violet			375.00
h.		Surcharge and "A.D." in red, "U.S.P.C. Co." in black			1,050.
i.		Surcharge and "A.D." in red reading up, "U.S.P.C. Co." in black reading down			775.00
j.		As "g," reading down			—
k.		Double surcharge (black)			1,000.
l.		Double surcharge (red)			400.00
m.		Double surcharge and "A.D.," both reading down (red)			—
n.		Double surcharge and "U.S. P.C. Co.," both reading down (black)			2,500.

"A.D." (Andrew Dougherty Co.) printed in red, "S. P. C. Co." (Standard Playing Card Co.) printed in violet, "U.S.P.C. Co." printed in black. The first two became divisions of United States Playing Card Co.
See No. RF13.

Surcharged in Carmine

RF10	RF2	7c on 2c **blue**		85.00	
a.		Inverted surcharge		50.00	
b.		Double surcharge		550.00	
c.		Double surcharge, inverted		550.00	
d.		Triple surcharge		—	

Used by Russell Playing Card Co.

RF3

1918 Size: 21x40mm *Imperf.*

RF11	RF3	**blue**	50.00	32.50
	Block of 4		190.00	150.00

Private Roulette 14

RF12	RF3	**blue**	300.
a.		Rouletted 13 in red	1,800.
b.		Rouletted 6½	500.
c.		Perf. 12 horiz., imperf. vert.	300.
d.		Perf. 12 on 4 sides	1,600.

Nos. RF11-RF12 served as 7c stamps when used before April 1, 1919, and as 8c stamps when used after that date.

No. RF11 is known handstamped "7" or "8," or both "7" and "8," as well as "Act of 1918" in black or magenta, either by the user to indicate the value when applied to the pack or by the IRS district offices at the time of sale.

No. RF12 was used by N. Y. Consolidated Card Co., Nos. RF12a, RF12b were used by Russell Playing Card Co., Nos. RF12, RF12d were used by Logan Printing House.

Surcharged like No. RF9 (but somewhat smaller) in Violet, Red or Black

Private Roulette 9½

RF13	RF3	7c **blue**	55.00
a.		Inverted surcharge	60.00
b.		Double surcharge	450.00
c.		Double surcharge, inverted	500.00
d.		Surcharge omitted	

Stamp of 1899 Surcharged in Magenta or Rose

1919 *Rouletted 7*

RF14	RF2	8c on 2c **ultramarine**	125.00
a.		Double surcharge	300.00
b.		Inverted surcharge	400.00

The surcharge on No. RF14 was handstamped at the Internal Revenue Office in New York City. A handstamp in black is known.

Exists in pair, one double surcharge, also in pair, one with inverted surcharge.

Inverted Surcharge in Carmine

RF15	RF2	8c on 2c **blue**	625.00	
a.		Double surcharge	1,500.	

No. RF15 is surcharged only with large "8c" inverted, and overprinted with date and initials (also inverted). No. RF16 is often found with additional impression of large "8c," as on No. RF15, but in this usage the large "8c" is a cancellation.

Used by Russell Playing Card Co.

Surcharged in Carmine or Vermilion

RF16	RF2	8c on 2c **blue**	225.00	.90
a.		Inverted surcharge		3,000.

See note after No. RF15.

RF4

1922 Size: 19x22mm *Rouletted 7*

RF17	RF4	(8c) **blue**	30.00	1.50
	Block of 4		140.00	—

No. RF17, rouletted 7 and perforated 11, surcharged " VIR-GIN / ISLANDS / 4 cts." are listed under Danish West Indies.

Surcharged in Carmine, Blue or Black

RF18	RF4	8c on (8c) **blue**	65.00
a.		Inverted surcharge	65.00

Used by Pyramid Playing Card Co.

RF5

1924 *Rouletted 7*

RF19	RF5	10c **blue**	22.50	.45
	Block of 4		100.00	

ROTARY PRESS COIL STAMP

1926 *Perf. 10 Vertically*

RF20	RF5	10c **blue**		.30
	Pair			3.25
	Joint line pair			6.50

No. RF20 exists only precanceled. **Bureau precancels: 11** different.

FLAT PLATE PRINTING

1927 *Perf. 11*

RF21	RF5	10c **blue**	37.50	5.25
	Block of 4		175.00	

1929 *Perf. 10*

RF22	RF5	10c **blue**	27.50	5.00
	Block of 4		110.00	

RF6

ROTARY PRESS COIL STAMP

1929 *Perf. 10 Horizontally*

RF23	RF6	10c **light blue**		.25
	Pair			2.50
	Joint line pair			5.00

No. RF23 exists only precanceled. **Bureau precancels: 16** different.

FLAT PLATE PRINTING

1930 *Perf. 10*

RF24	RF6	10c **blue**	25.00	1.40
	Block of 4		110.00	11.00
a.		Horiz. pair, imperf. vert.	175.00	

1931 *Perf. 11*

RF25	RF6	10c **blue**	22.50	1.40
	Block of 4		110.00	

No. R234 is known used provisionally as a playing card revenue stamp August 6 and 8, 1932. Value for this use, authenticated, $400.

RF7

ROTARY PRESS COIL STAMP

1940 Wmk. 191R *Perf. 10 Vertically*

RF26	RF7	**blue**, wet printing	—	.45
	Pair			2.25
	Joint line pair			4.50

Unwmk.

RF26A	RF7	**blue**, dry printing	27.50	.40

See note after No. 1029.

Bureau precancels: 11 different.

RF8

ROTARY PRESS COIL STAMP

1940 Wmk. 191R *Perf. 10 Horizontally*

RF27	RF8	**blue**, wet printing	3.00	.25
	Pair		7.50	
	Joint line pair		12.50	

Unwmk.

RF27A	RF8	**blue**, dry printing		3.25

Bureau precancels: 10 different.

FLAT PLATE PRINTING

Wmk. 191R *Perf. 11*

RF28	RF8	**blue**, wet printing	5.25	.80
	Block of 4		26.00	—
a.		Dry printing	5.25	4.25

Unwmk.

RF28B	RF8	**blue**, dry printing		5.25
	Block of 4			

ROTARY PRESS PRINTING

Wmk. 191R *Perf. 10x11*

RF29	RF8	**blue**	200.00	92.50
	Block of 4		850.00	
a.		Imperforate (P.C. Co.)		1,000.

SILVER TAX STAMPS

The Silver Purchase Act of 1934 imposed a 50 per cent tax on the net profit realized on a transfer of silver bullion occurring after May 15, 1934. The tax was paid by affixing stamps to the transfer memorandum. Congress authorized the Silver Tax stamps on June 19, 1934. They were discontinued after June 4, 1963.

Documentary Stamps of 1917 Overprinted

1934 Offset Printing Wmk. 191R Perf. 11

RG1	R22	1c **carmine rose**	2.00	.95
RG2	R22	2c **carmine rose**	2.10	.65
		Double impression of stamp		
RG3	R22	3c **carmine rose**	2.40	.80
RG4	R22	4c **carmine rose**	2.50	1.60
RG5	R22	5c **carmine rose**	4.00	1.40
RG6	R22	8c **carmine rose**	5.50	3.25
RG7	R22	10c **carmine rose**	5.75	3.00
RG8	R22	20c **carmine rose**	8.25	3.75
RG9	R22	25c **carmine rose**	7.50	4.25
RG10	R22	40c **carmine rose**	8.75	6.00
RG11	R22	50c **carmine rose**	12.00	7.50
RG12	R22	80c **carmine rose**	20.00	10.50

Engr.

RG13	R21	$1 **green**	45.00	16.00
RG14	R21	$2 **rose**	52.50	25.00
RG15	R21	$3 **violet**	95.00	35.00
RG16	R21	$4 **yellow brown**	77.50	24.00
RG17	R21	$5 **dark blue**	95.00	27.50
RG18	R21	$10 **orange**	140.00	22.50

Perf. 12
Without Gum

RG19	R17	$30 **vermilion**	300.00	75.00
		Cut cancel		20.00
RG20	R19	$60 **brown**	325.00	90.00
		Cut cancel		27.50
		Vertical strip of 4		400.00
RG21	R17	$100 **green**	350.00	50.00
		Vertical strip of 4		210.00
RG22	R18	$500 **blue**	700.00	325.00
		Cut cancel		110.00
		Vertical strip of 4		
RG23	R19	$1000 **orange**	—	125.00
		Cut cancel		60.00
		Vertical strip of 4		

See note after No. R227.

Same Overprint, spacing 11mm between words "SILVER TAX"
Without Gum

1936 Perf. 12

RG26	R17	$100 **green**	700.00	125.00
		Vertical strip of 4		
RG27	R19	$1000 **orange**	2,000.	

Documentary Stamps of 1917 Handstamped "SILVER TAX" in Violet, Large Block Letters, in Two Lines

1939 Wmk. 191R Offset Printing Perf. 10

RG28	R22	1c **rose pink**	30,000.

Perf. 11

RG29	R22	3c **rose pink**	30,000.
RG30	R22	5c **rose pink**	30,000.
RG31	R22	10c **rose pink**	30,000.
RG32	R22	80c **rose pink**	30,000.

Other handstamps exist on various values. One has letters 4mm high, 2mm wide with "SILVER" and "TAX" applied in separate operations. Another has "Silver Tax" in two lines in a box, but it is believed this handstamp was privately applied.

Overprint Typewritten in Black ($2, $3) or Red ($5)

1934-35 Engr. Perf. 11

RG34	R21	$2 **carmine**	
RG35	R21	$3 **violet**	25,000.
RG36	R21	$5 **dark blue**	

No. RG35 is unique.
Typewritten overprints also exist on 2c, 3c, 4c, 20c and 50c.

Type of Documentary Stamps 1917, Overprinted in Black

1940 Offset Printing Perf. 11

RG37	R22	1c **rose pink**	30.00	—
RG38	R22	2c **rose pink**	30.00	—
RG39	R22	3c **rose pink**	30.00	—
RG40	R22	4c **rose pink**	35.00	—
RG41	R22	5c **rose pink**	22.50	—
RG42	R22	8c **rose pink**	35.00	—
RG43	R22	10c **rose pink**	30.00	—
RG44	R22	20c **rose pink**	35.00	—
RG45	R22	25c **rose pink**	30.00	—
RG46	R22	40c **rose pink**	52.50	—
RG47	R22	50c **rose pink**	52.50	—
RG48	R22	80c **rose pink**	52.50	

Engr.

RG49	R21	$1 **green**	250.00	—
RG50	R21	$2 **rose**	375.00	—
RG51	R21	$3 **violet**	500.00	—
RG52	R21	$4 **yellow brown**	900.00	—
RG53	R21	$5 **dark blue**	1,000.	—
RG54	R21	$10 **orange**	1,500.	—

Nos. RG19-RG20, RG26 Handstamped in Blue "Series 1940"

1940 Without Gum Perf. 12

RG55	R17	$30 **vermilion**	—	7,000.
RG56	R19	$60 **brown**	—	23,000.
RG57	R17	$100 **green**	—	6,000.

Nos. R274, R278, R280, R281, R308 Handstamped in Black "Silver Tax"

1940 Perf. 11

RG57A	R22	50c **rose pink**	—	3,600.
RG57B	R21	$3 **violet**	—	3,600.
RG57C	R21	$5 **dark blue**	—	3,600.
RG57D	R21	$10 **orange**	—	2,450.
RG57E	R17	$100 **carmine**	—	3,600.

Additional denominations bearing the provisional "Silver Tax" handstamp might exist.

Alexander Hamilton — RG1

Levi Woodbury — RG2

Thomas Corwin — RG3

Overprinted in Black SERIES 1941

1941 Wmk. 191R Engr. Perf. 11

RG58	RG1	1c **gray**	10.00	2.40
a.		Imperf, pair, without gum	75.00	

RG59	RG1	2c **gray** (Oliver Wolcott, Jr.)	10.00	3.00
a.		Imperf, pair, without gum	75.00	
RG60	RG1	3c **gray** (Samuel Dexter)	10.00	3.00
a.		Imperf, pair, without gum	75.00	
RG61	RG1	4c **gray** (Albert Gallatin)	10.00	5.25
a.		Imperf, pair, without gum	75.00	
RG62	RG1	5c **gray** (G.W. Campbell)	15.00	9.25
a.		Imperf, pair, without gum	75.00	
RG63	RG1	8c **gray** (A.J. Dallas)	15.00	—
a.		Imperf, pair, without gum	75.00	
RG64	RG1	10c **gray** (Wm. H. Crawford)	17.50	8.50
a.		Imperf, pair, without gum	75.00	
RG65	RG1	20c **gray** (Richard Rush)	30.00	7.75
a.		Imperf, pair, without gum	75.00	
RG66	RG1	25c **gray** (S.D. Ingham)	35.00	—
a.		Imperf, pair, without gum	75.00	
RG67	RG1	40c **gray** (Louis McLane)	60.00	37.50
a.		Imperf, pair, without gum	75.00	
RG68	RG1	50c **gray** (Wm. J. Duane)	60.00	32.50
a.		Imperf, pair, without gum	75.00	
RG69	RG1	80c **gray** (Roger B. Taney)	100.00	32.50
a.		Imperf, pair, without gum	125.00	
RG70	RG2	$1 **gray**	150.00	50.00
a.		Imperf, pair, without gum	600.00	
RG71	RG2	$2 **gray** (Thomas Ewing)	350.00	75.00
a.		Imperf, pair, without gum	600.00	
RG72	RG2	$3 **gray** (Walter Forward)	375.00	100.00
a.		Imperf, pair, without gum	600.00	
RG73	RG2	$4 **gray** (J.C. Spencer)	425.00	95.00
a.		Imperf, pair, without gum	600.00	
RG74	RG2	$5 **gray** (G.M. Bibb)	325.00	100.00
a.		Imperf, pair, without gum	600.00	
RG75	RG2	$10 **gray** (R.J. Walker)	750.00	125.00
a.		Imperf, pair, without gum	650.00	
RG76	RG2	$20 **gray** (Wm. M. Meredith)	1,000.	300.00
a.		Imperf, pair, without gum	2,000.	

Perf. 12
Without Gum

RG77	RG3	$30 **gray**	3,500.	400.
		Cut cancel		125.
RG78	RG3	$50 **gray** (James Guthrie)	6,000.	4,250.
RG79	RG3	$60 **gray** (Howell Cobb)	4,500.	500.
		Cut cancel		150.
RG80	RG3	$100 **gray** (P.F. Thomas)	7,500.	700.
		Cut cancel		175.
		Vertical strip of 4		
RG81	RG3	$500 **gray** (J.A. Dix)	—	37,500.
RG82	RG3	$1000 **gray** (S.P. Chase)	5,000.	2,750.
		Cut cancel		1,000.

Nos. RG58-RG82 Overprinted Instead: **SERIES 1942**

1942 Wmk. 191R Perf. 11

RG83	RG1	1c **gray**	3.25	—
RG84	RG1	2c **gray**	3.25	—
RG85	RG1	3c **gray**	3.25	—
RG86	RG1	4c **gray**	3.25	—
RG87	RG1	5c **gray**	3.25	—
RG88	RG1	8c **gray**	8.00	—
RG89	RG1	10c **gray**	8.00	—
RG90	RG1	20c **gray**	15.00	—
RG91	RG1	25c **gray**	26.00	—
RG92	RG1	40c **gray**	35.00	—
RG93	RG1	50c **gray**	40.00	—
RG94	RG1	80c **gray**	100.00	—
RG95	RG2	$1 **gray**	150.00	72.50
a.		Overprint "SERIES 5942"	650.00	
RG96	RG2	$2 **gray**	160.00	72.50
a.		Overprint "SERIES 5942"	1,350.	
RG97	RG2	$3 **gray**	275.00	140.00
a.		Overprint "SERIES 5942"	1,450.	
RG98	RG2	$4 **gray**	325.00	140.00
a.		Overprint "SERIES 5942"	1,450.	
RG99	RG2	$5 **gray**	300.00	175.00
a.		Overprint "SERIES 5942"	1,350.	
RG100	RG2	$10 **gray**	725.00	425.00
RG101	RG2	$20 **gray**	1,250.	—
a.		Overprint "SERIES 5942"	10,000.	

Perf. 12
Without Gum

RG102	RG3	$30 **gray**	7,500.	—
		Cut cancel		2,750.
RG103	RG3	$50 **gray**	45,000.	—
RG104	RG3	$60 **gray**	7,500.	2,250.
		Cut cancel		750.
RG105	RG3	$100 **gray**	—	2,500.
		Cut cancel		900.
RG106	RG3	$500 **gray**	—	6,000.
		Cut cancel		4,000.
RG107	RG3	$1000 **gray**	—	7,500.
		Cut cancel		4,500.

Silver Purchase Stamps of 1941 without Overprint

1944 Wmk. 191R Perf. 11

RG108	RG1	1c **gray**	1.00	.30
RG109	RG1	2c **gray**	1.00	.65
RG110	RG1	3c **gray**	1.40	1.00
RG111	RG1	4c **gray**	1.60	1.25
RG112	RG1	5c **gray**	3.25	2.75
RG113	RG1	8c **gray**	5.00	2.75
RG114	RG1	10c **gray**	6.50	3.25
RG115	RG1	20c **gray**	10.00	5.50
RG116	RG1	25c **gray**	16.00	6.00

RG117	RG1	40c **gray**		24.00	11.50
RG118	RG1	50c **gray**		25.00	14.00
RG119	RG1	80c **gray**		32.50	20.00
RG120	RG2	$1 **gray**		67.50	21.00
RG121	RG2	$2 **gray**		95.00	47.50
RG122	RG2	$3 **gray**		125.00	37.50
RG123	RG2	$4 **gray**		150.00	85.00
RG124	RG2	$5 **gray**		150.00	47.50
RG125	RG2	$10 **gray**		225.00	35.00
		Cut cancel			19.00
RG126	RG2	$20 **gray**		800.00	500.00
		Cut cancel			250.00

Perf. 12
Without Gum

RG127	RG3	$30 **gray**		400.00	175.00
		Cut cancel			80.00
		Vertical strip of 4			—
a.		Booklet pane of 4		7,250.	
RG128	RG3	$50 **gray**		825.00	675.00
		Cut cancel			350.00
		Vertical strip of 4			—
a.		Booklet pane of 4		9,500.	
RG129	RG3	$60 **gray**		1,500.	575.00
		Cut cancel			250.00
a.		Booklet pane of 4		10,000.	
RG130	RG3	$100 **gray**		—	35.00
		Cut cancel			15.00
		Vertical strip of 4			—

RG131	RG3	$500 **gray**		—	500.00
		Cut cancel			250.00
		With complete receipt tab		1,050.	
a.		Booklet pane of 4		5,500.	
		Complete booklet, 2 #RG131a	11,500.		
RG132	RG3	$1000 **gray**		—	160.00
		Cut cancel			80.00
		Vertical strip of 4			—
		With complete receipt tab		800.00	
a.		Booklet pane of 4		—	
		Complete booklet, 1 #RG132a	5,000.		

CIGARETTE TUBES STAMPS

These stamps were for a tax on the hollow tubes of cigarette paper, with or without thin cardboard mouthpieces attached. They were sold in packages so buyers could add loose tobacco to make cigarettes.

Documentary Stamp of 1917
Overprinted

1919   Offset Printing   Wmk. 191R   Perf. 11

RH1	R22	1c **carmine rose**		1.10	.70
		Block of 4		5.50	3.00
		On package			22.50
		Pair on package			45.00
a.		Without period		22.50	10.00
		On package			—

1929   Perf. 10

RH2	R22	1c **carmine rose**		70.00	11.00
		On package			—

RH1

1933   Without Gum   Wmk. 191R   Perf. 11

RH3	RH1	1c **rose** (shades)		5.00	2.50
		Block of 4		22.50	12.00
		On package			22.50

RH4	RH1	2c **rose** (shades)		14.50	5.50
		Pair			13.50
		On package			110.00

Cigarette tube on-package values for Nos. RH1 and RH3 are for fine undamaged stamps affixed to an empty package of Himyar Tobacco cigarette tubes manufactured by the Axton-Fisher Tobacco Co. Unopened packages containing cigarette tubes command a 50 to 100 percent premium. No. RH1 pairs are unseparated stamps. The listing for No. RH1 pair on package is not on a Himyar package.

Specialists have questioned whether Nos. RH1a or RH2 are known on packages. The editors would like to see evidence of the existence of these listings.

POTATO TAX STAMPS

These stamps were required by the Potato Act of 1935, an amendment to the Agricultural Adjustment Act that became effective Dec. 1, 1935. Potato growers were given allotments for which they were provided Tax Exempt Potato stamps. Growers exceeding their allotments would have paid for the excess with Tax Paid Potato stamps at the rate of ¾ cent per pound.

On Jan. 6, 1936, the U. S. Supreme Court declared the Agricultural Adjustment Act unconstitutional. Officially the Potato Act was in effect until Feb. 10, 1936, when it was repealed by Congress but, in essence, the law was ignored once the Supreme Court ruling was issued. Because of the Act's short life, Tax Paid stamps were never used.

Young Woman from
The Bouquet — RI1

RI2

Tax Paid Potatoes

1935   Engr.   Unwmk.   Perf. 11

RI1	RI1	¾c **carmine rose**	.50
RI2	RI1	1½c **black brown**	.70
RI3	RI1	2¼c **yellow green**	.75
RI4	RI1	3c **light violet**	.80
RI5	RI1	3¾c **olive bister**	.95
RI6	RI1	7½c **orange brown**	2.75
RI7	RI1	11¼c **deep orange**	3.00
RI8	RI1	18¾c **violet brown**	7.50
RI9	RI1	37½c **red orange**	8.00
RI10	RI1	75c **blue**	8.50
RI11	RI1	93¾c **rose lake**	10.00
RI12	RI1	$1.12½ **green**	17.50
RI13	RI1	$1.50 **yellow brown**	20.00
		Nos. RI1-RI13 (13)	80.95

Tax Exempt Potatoes

1935   Engr.   Unwmk.   Perf. 11x10½

RI14	RI2	2 lb **black brown**	1.00	10.50
a.		Booklet pane of 12	14.00	250.00
		Provisional booklet of 24, purple on pink cover	35.00	
		Provisional booklet of 96, purple on buff cover	100.00	
		Provisional booklet of 192, purple on white cover	250.00	
		Definitive booklet of 96, black on buff cover	100.00	
		Definitive booklet of 192, black on white cover	200.00	
RI15	RI2	5 lb **black brown**	22.50	
a.		Booklet pane of 12	550.00	
		Provisional booklet of 192, purple on white cover	5,000.	
RI16	RI2	10 lb **black brown**	22.50	
a.		Booklet pane of 12	450.00	
		Provisional booklet of 192, purple on white cover	5,000.	
RI17	RI2	25 lb **black brown**	600.00	
a.		Booklet pane of 12	7,000.	
		Provisional booklet of 24, purple on pink cover	14,000.	
RI18	RI2	50 lb **black brown**	1.10	50.00
a.		Booklet pane of 12	25.00	
		Provisional booklet of 24, purple on pink cover	50.00	
		Provisional booklet of 96, purple on buff cover	125.00	
		Provisional booklet of 192, purple on white cover	300.00	
		Definitive booklet of 96, black on buff cover	100.00	

	Definitive booklet of 192, black on white cover	200.00
	Nos. RI14-RI16, RI18 (4)	47.10

The booklet panes are arranged 4x3 with a tab at top. Edges are imperforate at left, right and bottom, yielding four stamps fully perforated, six stamps imperf. on one side and two stamps imperf. on two sides per pane. Values for single stamps are for examples perforated on all four sides. Stamps with straight edges generally sell for less.

These stamps were printed from 360-subject rotary booklet plates and cut into 30 panes of 12. The panes were stapled into booklets of 24 (2 panes, pink covers), 96 (8 panes, buff covers) and 196 (16 panes, white covers), with handstamped covers (provisionals) and later with covers printed with the Dept. of Agriculture seal in the center (definitives). Both types of cover were prepared by the Bureau of Engraving and Printing.

Values for booklets are for examples containing panes that have very good to fine centering, because the overwhelming majority of booklets are in this grade. It should be noted that Scott values for individual panes (listed above) are for very fine panes. For this reason, individual panes are valued higher than the per-pane value of panes in booklets. For example, a pane of No. RI14a is valued at $14, but the No. RI14 definitive booklet of 96 (8 panes) is valued at $100, or $12.50 per pane, which is a little more than what a collector would pay for an individual very good to fine pane. Booklets containing very fine panes will command a premium over the values given.

All recorded examples of No. RI17 were in three unbroken panes of 12 and two intact booklets. One pane has been broken up and sold. A 100 lb Tax Exempt stamp was printed, but all are believed to have been destroyed.

TOBACCO SALE TAX STAMPS

These stamps were required to pay the tax on the sale of tobacco in excess of quotas set by the Secretary of Agriculture. The tax was 25 per cent of the price for which the excess tobacco was sold. It was intended to affect tobacco harvested after June 28, 1934 and sold before May 1, 1936. The tax was stopped when the Agricultural Adjustment Act was declared unconstitutional by the Supreme Court on Dec. 1, 1935.
Values for unused stamps are for examples with original gum.

Stamps and Types of 1917
Documentary Issue
Overprinted

1934		Offset Printing	Wmk. 191R	Perf. 11	
RJ1	R22	1c carmine rose		.30	.20
RJ2	R22	2c carmine rose		.40	.20
RJ3	R22	5c carmine rose		1.25	.45
RJ4	R22	10c carmine rose		1.60	.40
a.		Inverted overprint		15.00	22.50
RJ5	R22	25c carmine rose		4.25	1.60
RJ6	R22	50c carmine rose		4.25	1.60
		Engr.			
RJ7	R21	$1 green		10.00	1.75
RJ8	R21	$2 rose		19.00	1.90
RJ9	R21	$5 dark blue		24.00	4.25

RJ10	R21	$10 orange		37.50	10.00
RJ11	R21	$20 olive bister		90.00	12.50
		Nos. RJ1-RJ11 (11)		192.55	34.85

On No. RJ11 the overprint is vertical, reading up. The right serif on the "T" of "TOBACCO" exists both normal and split. Both varieties exist within the same sheet, and the quantities of each type are approximately equal.
No. RJ2 is known with a counterfeit inverted overprint.

NARCOTIC TAX STAMPS

The Revenue Act of 1918 imposed a tax of 1 cent per ounce or fraction thereof on opium, coca leaves and their derivatives. The tax was paid by affixing Narcotic stamps to the drug containers. The tax lasted from Feb. 25, 1919, through Apr. 30, 1971.
Members of the American Revenue Association helped compile the listings in this section.

Documentary Stamps of 1914 Handstamped "NARCOTIC" in Magenta or Black

1919	Wmk. 191R	Offset Printing	Perf. 10	
RJA1	R20	1c rose	95.00	80.00

The overprint was applied by District Collectors of Internal Revenue.
It is always in capital letters and exists in various type faces and sizes, including: 21½x2½mm, serif; 21x2¼mm, sans-serif boldface; 15½x 2½mm, sans-serif; 13x2mm, sans-serif.
The ½c, 2c, 3c, 4c, 5c, 10c, 25c and 50c with similar handstamp in serif capitals measuring about 20x2¼mm are bogus.

Documentary Stamps of 1917 Handstamped "NARCOTIC," "Narcotic," "NARCOTICS" or "ACT/NARCOTIC/1918" in Magenta, Black, Blue, Violet or Red

1919	Wmk. 191R	Offset Printing	Perf. 11	
RJA9	R22	1c carmine rose	3.00	1.90
RJA10	R22	2c carmine rose	6.00	4.00
RJA11	R22	3c carmine rose	35.00	37.50
RJA12	R22	4c carmine rose	13.00	10.00
RJA13	R22	5c carmine rose	20.00	16.00
RJA14	R22	8c carmine rose	16.00	12.50
RJA15	R22	10c carmine rose	52.50	20.00
RJA16	R22	20c carmine rose	77.50	60.00
RJA17	R22	25c carmine rose	47.50	32.50
RJA18	R22	40c carmine rose	150.00	110.00
RJA19	R22	50c carmine rose	20.00	22.50
RJA20	R22	80c carmine rose	125.00	110.00
		Engr.		
RJA21	R21	$1 green	150.00	90.00
RJA22	R21	$2 rose		1,000.
RJA23	R21	$3 violet		1,200.
RJA24	R21	$5 dark blue		1,000.
RJA25	R21	$10 orange		1,200.

Drug manufacturer cancels have enabled experts to identify conclusively the origin of only six of the handstamped overprints. Four of these read simply "Narcotic." A 3-line handstamp, "Act / Narcotic / 1918," was used in Seattle; "Narcotics" in Kansas City, Missouri. Perhaps as many as 20 other styles and sizes have been recorded, although these occur only on mint stamps.
Many fake overprints exist.

No. R228 Overprinted in Black: "NARCOTIC / E.L. CO. / 3-19-19"

1919	Wmk. 191R	Perf. 11	
		"NARCOTIC" 14½mm wide	
RJA26	R22	1c carmine rose	4,250.

Overprinted by Eli Lilly Co., Indianapolis, for that firm's use.

No. R228 Overprinted in Black: "J W & B / NARCOTIC"

1919	Wmk. 191R	Perf. 11	
		"NARCOTIC" 14½mm wide	
RJA27	R22	1c carmine rose	2,000.
RJA27A	R22	2c carmine rose	3,250.

Overprinted by John Wyeth & Brother, Philadelphia, for that firm's use.

Nos. R228, R231-R232 Handstamped in Blue: "P-W-R-Co. / NARCOTIC"

1919	Wmk. 191R	Perf. 11	
RJA28	R22	1c carmine rose	850.00
RJA28A	R22	4c carmine rose	1,200.
RJA29	R22	5c carmine rose	—
RJA29A	R22	25c carmine rose	—
RJA29B	R21	$1 green (violet handstamp)	—

The handstamp was applied by the Powers-Weightmann-Rosengarten Co., Philadelphia, for that firm's use.

Proprietary Stamps of 1919 Handstamped "NARCOTIC" in Blue

1919	Wmk. 191R	Offset Printing	Perf. 11	
RJA30	RB5	1c dark blue	—	
RJA31	RB5	2c dark blue	—	
RJA32	RB5	4c dark blue	—	

No. RB65 is known with "Narcotic" applied in red ms.

Documentary Stamps of 1917 Overprinted in Black, "Narcotic" 17½mm wide

1919	Wmk. 191R	Offset Printing	Perf. 11	
RJA33	R22	1c carmine rose *(6,900,000)*	1.25	.80
RJA34	R22	2c carmine rose *(3,650,000)*	2.50	1.10
RJA35	R22	3c carmine rose *(388,400)*	40.00	21.00
RJA36	R22	4c carmine rose *(2,400,000)*	6.00	4.75
RJA37	R22	5c carmine rose *(2,400,000)*	15.00	10.50
RJA38	R22	8c carmine rose *(1,200,000)*	25.00	18.00
RJA39	R22	10c carmine rose *(3,400,000)*	3.75	2.75
RJA40	R22	25c carmine rose *(700,000)*	25.00	16.00
		Overprint Reading Up		
		Engr.		
RJA41	R21	$1 green *(270,000)*	47.50	19.00

The overprint on Nos. RJA33-RJA41 was produced by the Bureau of Engraving & Printing. Fake overprints exist on Nos. RJA33-RJA41. In the genuine the C's are not slanted.

NT1

NT2

Imperf., Rouletted

1919-64	Offset Printing	Wmk. 191R
	Left Value — "a" Imperf.	
	Right Value — "b" Rouletted 7	

RJA42	NT1	1c violet	5.25	.30
d.		1c purple		7.50

RJA43	NT2	1c violet	.55	.30
d.		1c purple	5.00	5.25
RJA44	NT2	2c violet	1.40	.55
d.		2c purple		5.25
RJA45	NT2	3c violet ('64)		200.00

NT3

NT4

Left Value — "a" Imperf.
Right Value — "b" Rouletted 7

RJA46	NT3	1c violet	2.75	.75
d.		1c purple		9.00
RJA47	NT3	2c violet	1.60	.75
d.		2c purple		8.25
RJA48	NT3	3c violet	1,000.	
RJA49	NT3	4c violet ('42)	—	11.00
d.		4c purple		30.00
RJA50	NT3	5c violet	42.50	4.00
d.		5c purple		13.00
RJA51	NT3	6c violet		1.00
d.		6c purple		9.25
RJA52	NT3	8c violet	57.50	4.25
d.		8c purple		26.00
RJA53	NT3	9c violet ('53)	67.50	21.00
RJA54	NT3	10c violet	32.50	.55
d.		10c purple		7.00
RJA55	NT3	16c violet	52.50	4.00
d.		16c purple		14.50
RJA56	NT3	18c violet ('61)	110.00	10.50
RJA57	NT3	19c violet ('61)	125.00	26.00
RJA58	NT3	20c violet	375.00	275.00

Nos. RJA47-RJA58 have "CENTS" below the value.

Left Value — "a" Imperf.
Right Value — "b" Rouletted 7

RJA59	NT4	1c violet	47.50	10.50
c.		Rouletted 3½		4.25
RJA60	NT4	2c violet	50.00	20.00
RJA61	NT4	3c violet	52.50	350.00
RJA62	NT4	5c violet		26.00
RJA63	NT4	6c violet	62.50	25.00
RJA64	NT4	8c violet		47.50
RJA65	NT4	9c violet ('61)	26.00	21.00
RJA66	NT4	10c violet	17.50	17.50
RJA67	NT4	16c violet	16.00	18.00
RJA68	NT4	18c violet ('61)	250.00	425.00
RJA69	NT4	19c violet	16.00	190.00
RJA70	NT4	20c violet	275.00	240.00
RJA71	NT4	25c violet	—	21.00
c.		Rouletted 3½		4.25
RJA72	NT4	40c violet	800.00	2,750.
c.		Rouletted 3½		67.50
RJA73	NT4	$1 green		1.60
RJA74	NT4	$1.28 green	32.50	10.50
c.		As "a," measuring ¾ inch by 8 inches with wide side margins	200.00	
d.		As "b," measuring ¾ inch by 8 inches with wide side margins	100.00	

On Nos. RJA60-RJA74 the value tablet is solid.

1963(?)-70   Offset Printing   *Imperf., Rouletted*
Unwatermarked
Left Value — "a" Imperf.
Right Value — "b" Rouletted 7

RJA75	NT1	1c violet	7.75	2.10+
RJA76	NT2	1c violet	1.10	1.10
RJA77	NT2	2c violet	5.25	2.10+
RJA78	NT2	3c violet		125.00
RJA79	NT3	1c violet	5.25	2.10
RJA80	NT3	2c violet	375.00+	2.00
RJA81	NT3	4c violet		10.00
RJA82	NT3	5c violet	72.50	
RJA83	NT3	6c violet	—	22.50+
RJA84	NT3	8c violet		5.25
RJA85	NT3	9c violet	—	50.00

RJA86	NT3	10c violet	—	22.50+
RJA87	NT3	16c violet	150.00	4.25
RJA88	NT3	18c violet		52.50+
RJA89	NT3	20c violet		325.00+

Nos. RJA80-RJA89 have "CENTS" below the value.
+ Items so marked currently are only known unused with original gum and are valued thus.

Unwatermarked
Left Value — "a" Imperf.
Right Value — "b" Rouletted 7

RJA91	NT4	1c violet	67.50	15.00
RJA92	NT4	2c violet		90.00+
RJA93	NT4	3c violet	85.00	160.00+
RJA94	NT4	6c violet	100.00	90.00+
RJA94C	NT4	8c violet		225.00+
RJA95	NT4	9c violet		210.00+
RJA96	NT4	10c violet		110.00+
RJA97	NT4	16c violet	40.00	21.00
RJA98	NT4	19c violet	26.00	400.00
RJA99	NT4	20c violet	—	500.00+
RJA100	NT4	25c violet		250.00
RJA101	NT4	40c violet	1,000.	
RJA102	NT4	$1 green		37.50+
RJA103	NT4	$1.28 green		60.00+
d.		As "b," measuring ¾ inch by 8 inches with wide side margins		175.00+
RJA104	NT4	$4 green ('70)	1,250.	

On Nos. RJA92-RJA104 the value tablet is solid.
+ Items so marked currently are only known unused with original gum and are valued thus.

NT5

Denomination added in black by rubber plate in an operation similar to precanceling.

1963   Engr.   Unwmk.   *Imperf.*
Left Value — Unused
Right Value — Used

RJA105	NT5	1c violet, type 2	110.00	85.00
a.		Type 1	140.00	140.00

Type 1 was produced with four electric eye markings, one in each corner. Type 2 was produced later and has two electric eye markings, one in each corner on the left side of the stamp. Type 2 is the more common of the two varieties and, therefore, is listed as the major number.
Nos. RAJ105 and RAJ105a were issued in vertical coil strips.

Denomination on Stamp Plate
1964   Offset Printing   *Imperf.*

RJA106	NT5	1c violet	90.00	5.25

RJA106 was issued in sheet of 80 stamps.

MARIHUANA TAX STAMPS

Act of Congress, 1937, to enforce uniform regulation of cannabis.

Nos. R240, R244, R245 overprinted

1937   Engr.   *Perf. 10*

RJM1	R21	$1 yellow green	525.	15,000.
		On document		
		P# block of 6	3,000.	
a.		Imperf, pair	1,200.	
RJM2	R21	$5 blue	600.	
		P# block of 6	4,000.	
a.		Imperf, pair	1,200.	
RJM3	R21	$10 yellow orange	550.	
		P# block of 6	3,750.	
a.		Imperf, pair	1,200.	

Same overprint on No. R248

(Illustration reduced)

Without Gum   *Perf. 12*
Control Number in Red

RJM4	R17	$100 green, with complete receipt tab	1,000.	
a.		Booklet pane of 4	4,000.	
		Complete booklet, 4 #RJM4a	16,500.	

Nos. R300, R304, R305 without date inscription overprinted:

1962   *Perf. 11*

RJM5	R24	$1 carmine	550.00
RJM6	R24	$5 carmine	550.00
RJM7	R24	$10 carmine	550.00

No. R306A without date inscription overprinted:

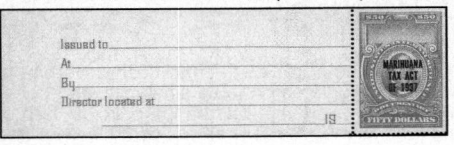

(Illustration reduced)

RJM8	R25	$50 **carmine**, with complete		
		receipt tab, no serial #	1,500.	
a.		Booklet pane of 4	6,000.	

CONSULAR SERVICE FEE STAMPS

Act of Congress, April 5, 1906, effective June 1, 1906, provided that every consular officer should be provided with special adhesive stamps printed in denominations determined by the Department of State.

Every document for which a fee was prescribed had to have attached a stamp or stamps representing the amount collected, and such stamps were used to show payment of these prescribed fees.

These stamps were usually affixed close to the signature, or at the lower left corner of the document. If no document was issued, the stamp or stamps were attached to a receipt for the amount of the fee and canceled either with pen and ink or rubber stamp showing the date of cancellation and bearing the initials of the canceling officer or name of the Consular Office. These stamps were not sold to the public uncanceled. Their use was discontinued Sept. 30, 1955.

CSF1

CSF2

1906   **Unwmk.**   **Engr.**   *Perf. 12*

RK1	CSF1	25c **dark green**	110.00
RK2	CSF1	50c **carmine**	140.00
RK3	CSF1	$1 **dark violet**	11.00
a.		Diagonal half used as 50c with 2 #RK3, paying $2.50 fee, on document	325.00
RK4	CSF1	$2 **brown**	6.00
RK5	CSF1	$2.50 **dark blue**	1.90
RK6	CSF1	$5 **brown red**	37.50
a.		Horizontal or diagonal half used as $2.50, on document	250.00
RK7	CSF1	$10 **orange**	125.00

Perf. 10

RK8	CSF1	25c **dark green**	110.00
RK9	CSF1	50c **carmine**	140.00
RK10	CSF1	$1 **dark violet**	700.00
RK11	CSF1	$2 **brown**	150.00
a.		Diagonal half used as $1, on document	
RK12	CSF1	$2.50 **dark blue**	32.50
RK13	CSF1	$5 **brown red**	250.00

Perf. 11

RK14	CSF1	25c **dark green**	125.00
RK15	CSF1	50c **carmine**	200.00
RK16	CSF1	$1 **dark violet**	2.00
a.		Diagonal half used as 50c, on document	425.00
RK17	CSF1	$2 **brown**	2.40
RK18	CSF1	$2.50 **dark blue**	1.10
RK19	CSF1	$5 **brown red**	5.00
a.		Diagonal half used as $2.50, on document	50.00
RK20	CSF1	$9 **gray**	30.00
RK21	CSF1	$10 **orange**	57.50
a.		Diagonal half used as $5, on document	90.00

1924   *Perf. 11*

RK22	CSF2	$1 **violet**	150.00
RK23	CSF2	$2 **brown**	190.00
RK24	CSF2	$2.50 **blue**	26.00
RK25	CSF2	$5 **brown red**	125.00
RK26	CSF2	$9 **gray**	475.00
		Nos. RK22-RK26 (5)	966.00

CSF3

1925-52   *Perf. 10*

RK27	CSF3	$1 **violet**	42.50
RK28	CSF3	$2 **brown**	110.00
RK29	CSF3	$2.50 **ultramarine**	2.75
RK30	CSF3	$5 **carmine**	24.00
RK31	CSF3	$9 **gray**	67.50

Perf. 11

RK32	CSF3	25c **green** ('37)	125.00
RK33	CSF3	50c **orange** ('34)	125.00
RK34	CSF3	$1 **violet**	3.75
a.		Diagonal half used as 50c, on document	—
RK35	CSF3	$2 **brown**	5.00
RK36	CSF3	$2.50 **blue**	.45
a.		$2.50 ultramarine	.40
RK37	CSF3	$5 **carmine**	3.25
RK38	CSF3	$9 **gray**	32.50
RK39	CSF3	$10 **blue gray** ('37)	160.00
RK40	CSF3	$20 **violet** ('52)	175.00
		Nos. RK27-RK40 (14)	876.70

Consular Fee

The "Consular Fee stamp" on revenue stamped paper (previously listed as No. RN-Y1 but since deleted) was found to be nothing more than an illustration. Two identical examples are known.

CUSTOMS FEE STAMPS

New York Custom House

Issued to indicate the collection of miscellaneous customs fees. Use was discontinued on February 28, 1918. The stamps were not utilized in the collection of customs duties.

Silas
Wright
CF1

Size: 48x34mm

1887   **Engr.**   *Rouletted 5½*

RL1	CF1	20c **dull rose**	125.00	1.00
a.		20c **red,** perf. 10		7,500.
b.		Vert. half used as 10c, on document		250.00
c.		20c **red,** rouletted 7		450.00
RL2	CF1	30c **orange**	175.00	2.50
RL3	CF1	40c **green**	200.00	4.25
RL4	CF1	50c **dark blue**	200.00	6.00
RL5	CF1	60c **red violet**	150.00	2.50
RL6	CF1	70c **brown violet**	160.00	35.00
RL7	CF1	80c **brown**	225.00	85.00
RL8	CF1	90c **black**	275.00	100.00
		Nos. RL1-RL8 (8)	1,510.	236.25

Each of these stamps has its own distinctive background.

EMBOSSED REVENUE STAMPED PAPER

Some of the American colonies of Great Britain used embossed stamps in raising revenue, as Britain had done from 1694. The British government also imposed stamp taxes on the colonies, and in the early 19th century the U.S. government and some of the states enacted similar taxes.

Under one statute or another, these stamps were required on such documents as promissory notes, bills of exchange, insurance policies, bills of lading, bonds, protests, powers of attorney, stock certificates, letters patent, writs, conveyances, leases, mortgages, charter parties, commissions and liquor licenses.

A few of these stamps were printed, but most were colorless impressions resembling a notary public's seal.

The scant literature of these stamps includes E.B. Sterling's revenue catalogue of 1888, *The Stamps that Caused the American Revolution: The Stamps of the British Stamp Act for America,* by Adolph Koeppel, published in 1976 by the Town of North Hempstead (New York) American Revolution Bicentennial Commission, *New Discovery from British Archives on the 1765 Tax Stamps for America,* edited by Adolph Koeppel and published in 1962 by the American Revenue Association, *First Federal Issue 1798-1801 U.S. Embossed Revenue Stamped Paper,* by W.V. Combs, published in 1979 by the American Philatelic Society, *Second Federal Issue, 1801-1802,* by W.V. Combs, published in 1988 by the American Revenue Association, and *Third Federal Issue, 1814-1817,* by W.V. Combs, published in 1993 by the American Revenue Association.

Values are for stamps of clear impression on entire documents of the most common usage in good condition. The document may be folded. Unusual or rare usages may sell for much more. Parts of documents, cut squares or poor impressions sell for much less.

Colin MacR. Makepeace originally compiled the listings in this section.

INCLUDING COLONIAL EMBOSSED REVENUES
I. COLONIAL ISSUES
A. MASSACHUSETTS
Act of January 8, 1755
In effect May 1, 1755-April 30, 1757

ERP1

ERP2

ERP3

ERP4

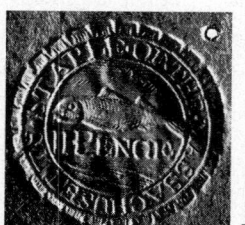

Die 2 — ERP2

Typo.

RM1	ERP1	½p **red**		2,500.

Embossed

RM2	ERP2	2p	400.
RM3	ERP3	3p	200.
RM4	ERP4	4p	800.

A second die of ERP2 with no fin on the under side of the codfish has been seen. There were at least two dies of the ½p.

B. NEW YORK
Act of December 1, 1756
In effect January 1, 1757-December 31, 1760

ERP9

Typo.

RM9	ERP9	½p **red**		2,000.

Embossed

RM10	ERP9	1p	650.
RM11	ERP9	2p	300.
RM12	ERP9	3p	500.
RM13	ERP9	4p	525.

II. BRITISH REVENUES FOR USE IN AMERICA
Act of March 22, 1765
In effect November 1, 1765-May 1, 1766.
A. ALMANAC STAMPS

ERP15

Engr.

RM15	ERP15	2p **red**	
RM16	ERP15	4p **red**	—
RM17	ERP15	8p **red**	

Proofs of all of these stamps printed in the issued color are known. Full size facsimile reproductions in the color of the originals were made about 1876 of the proof sheets of the 8p stamp, Plates 1 and 2, Dies 1 to 50 inclusive.

B. PAMPHLETS AND NEWSPAPER STAMPS

ERP18

Engr.

RM18	ERP18	½p **red**		2,000.
RM19	ERP18	1p **red**		
RM20	ERP18	2p **red**		

Proofs of all of these stamps printed in the issued color are known. Full size facsimile reproductions in the color of the originals were made about 1876 of the proof sheets of the 1p stamp, Plates 3 and 4, Dies 51 to 100 inclusive.

C. GENERAL ISSUE

ERP24

ERP25

ERP26

ERP27

ERP28

ERP29

ERP30

ERP31

ERP33

ERP34

ERP35

Embossed

RM24	ERP24	3p	3,000.
RM25	ERP25	4p	3,000.
RM26	ERP26	6p	3,000.
RM27	ERP27	1sh	1,750.
RM28	ERP28	1sh6p	1,250.
RM29	ERP29	2sh	3,000.
RM30	ERP30	2sh3p	2,250.
RM31	ERP31	2sh6p	2,750.
a.		Not on document	450.
RM33	ERP33	4sh	1,750.
RM34	ERP34	5sh	2,500.
RM35	ERP35	10sh	3,250.

Proofs exist of similar 1sh, 1sh6p and 2sh6p stamps inscribed "AMERICA CONT.& c."

Various Similar Designs

RM36	£1	—
RM37	£2	—
RM38	£3	—
RM39	£4	—
RM40	£6	—
RM41	£10	—

The £1 to £10 denominations probably exist only as proofs.

D. PLAYING CARDS STAMP
Type similar to EP29, with Arms of George III
Encircled by Garter.

RM42	1sh	—

All of these were embossed without color and most of them were embossed directly on the document except the 2sh 6p which was general embossed on a rectangular piece of bluish or brownish stiff paper or cardboard only slightly larger than the stamp which was attached to the document by a small piece of metal. Three dies exist of the 3p; two of the 4p, 6p, 1sh, 1sh 6p, 2sh and 2sh 3p.

All of these stamps have the word "America" somewhere in the design and this is the feature which distinguishes them from the other British revenues. The stamps of the general issue are occasionally found with a design of a British revenue stamp struck over the American design, as a number of them were afterwards re-struck and used elsewhere as British revenues.

These stamps are sometimes called the "Teaparty" or "Tax on Tea" stamps. This, however, is a misnomer, as the act under which these stamps were issued laid no tax on tea. The tax on tea was levied by an act passed two years later, and the duties imposed by that act were not collected by stamps.

It must be remembered that these stamps were issued under an act applicable to all of the British colonies in America which included many which are not now part of the United States. Examples have been seen which were used in Quebec, Nova Scotia and in the West Indies. So great was the popular clamor against taxation by a body in which the colonists had no representation that ships bringing the stamps from England were not allowed to land them in some of the colonies, the stamps were destroyed in others, and in practically all of those which were now a part of the United States the "Stamp Masters" who were to administer the act were forced to resign and to take oath that they would never carry out the duties of the offices. Notwithstanding the very general feeling about these stamps there is evidence that a very small number of them were actually used on ships' documents for one vessel clearing from New York and for a very small number of vessels clearing from the Savannah River. Florida was at this time under British authority and the only known examples of these stamps used in what is now the United States, a 4p (#RM25), a 1sh (#RM27), and two examples of the 5sh (#RM34) were used there.

III. ISSUES OF THE UNITED STATES
A. FIRST FEDERAL ISSUE
Act of July 6, 1797
In effect July 1, 1798-February 28, 1801

The distinguishing feature of the stamps of this issue is the name of a state in the design. These stamps were issued by the Federal Government, however, and not by the states. The design, with the exception of the name of the state, was the same for each denomination; but different denominations had the shield and the eagle in different positions. The design of only one denomination of these stamps is illustrated.

In addition to the eagle and shield design on the values from four cents to ten dollars there are two other stamps for each state, similar in design to one another, one of which is illustrated. All of these stamps are embossed without color. Values are for clearly impressed examples.

RM45	4c	Connecticut	45.00
RM46	10c	Connecticut	125.00
RM47	20c	Connecticut	300.00
RM48	25c	Connecticut	45.00
RM49	30c	Connecticut	2,750.
RM50	50c	Connecticut	135.00
RM51	75c	Connecticut	—
RM52	$1	Connecticut	1,750.
RM54	$4	Connecticut	1,250.
RM58	4c	Delaware	350.00
RM59	10c	Delaware	350.00
RM60	20c	Delaware	500.00
RM61	25c	Delaware	450.00
RM62	30c	Delaware	—
RM63	50c	Delaware	550.00
RM64	75c	Delaware	700.00
RM65	$1	Delaware	—
RM71	4c	Georgia	250.00
RM72	10c	Georgia	250.00
RM73	20c	Georgia	—
RM74	25c	Georgia	250.00
RM75	30c	Georgia	3,000.
RM76	50c	Georgia	400.00
RM77	75c	Georgia	1,750.
RM78	$1	Georgia	—
RM84	4c	Kentucky	20.00
RM85	10c	Kentucky	90.00
RM86	20c	Kentucky	250.00
RM87	25c	Kentucky	40.00
RM88	30c	Kentucky	275.00
RM89	50c	Kentucky	50.00
RM90	75c	Kentucky	125.00
RM91	$1	Kentucky	—
RM97	4c	Maryland	75.00
RM98	10c	Maryland	50.00
RM99	20c	Maryland	700.00
RM100	25c	Maryland	75.00
RM101	30c	Maryland	600.00
RM102	50c	Maryland	125.00
RM103	75c	Maryland	50.00
RM104	$1	Maryland	—
RM106	$4	Maryland	—
RM110	4c	Massachusetts	20.00
RM111	10c	Massachusetts	50.00
RM112	20c	Massachusetts	100.00
RM113	25c	Massachusetts	50.00
RM114	30c	Massachusetts	950.00
RM115	50c	Massachusetts	125.00
RM116	75c	Massachusetts	400.00
RM117	$1	Massachusetts	200.00
RM123	4c	New Hampshire	25.00
RM124	10c	New Hampshire	25.00
RM125	20c	New Hampshire	350.00
RM126	25c	New Hampshire	70.00
RM127	30c	New Hampshire	425.00
RM128	50c	New Hampshire	80.00
RM129	75c	New Hampshire	75.00
RM130	$1	New Hampshire	2,500.
RM136	4c	New Jersey	400.00
RM137	10c	New Jersey	175.00
RM138	20c	New Jersey	—
RM139	25c	New Jersey	110.00
RM140	30c	New Jersey	750.00
RM141	50c	New Jersey	200.00
RM142	75c	New Jersey	1,500.
RM143	$1	New Jersey	—
RM147	$10	New Jersey	4,750.
RM149	4c	New York	35.00
RM150	10c	New York	20.00
RM151	20c	New York	25.00
RM152	25c	New York	40.00
RM153	30c	New York	25.00
RM154	50c	New York	30.00
RM155	75c	New York	35.00
RM156	$1	New York	350.00
RM157	$2	New York	—
RM159	$5	New York	—
RM160	$10	New York	—
RM162	4c	North Carolina	45.00
RM163	10c	North Carolina	50.00
RM164	20c	North Carolina	950.00
RM165	25c	North Carolina	55.00
RM166	30c	North Carolina	2,500.
RM167	50c	North Carolina	175.00
RM168	75c	North Carolina	325.00
RM169	$1	North Carolina	3,750.
RM175	4c	Pennsylvania	30.00
RM176	10c	Pennsylvania	20.00
RM177	20c	Pennsylvania	27.50
RM178	25c	Pennsylvania	15.00
RM179	30c	Pennsylvania	30.00
RM180	50c	Pennsylvania	25.00
RM181	75c	Pennsylvania	75.00
RM182	$1	Pennsylvania	300.00
RM184	$4	Pennsylvania	13,000.
RM187		Pennsylvania, "Ten cents per centum"	—
RM188	4c	Rhode Island	35.00
RM189	10c	Rhode Island	50.00
RM190	20c	Rhode Island	200.00
RM191	25c	Rhode Island	65.00
RM192	30c	Rhode Island	1,500.
RM193	50c	Rhode Island	150.00
RM194	75c	Rhode Island	1,000.
RM195	$1	Rhode Island	1,750.
RM201	4c	South Carolina	90.00
RM202	10c	South Carolina	200.00
RM203	20c	South Carolina	350.00
RM204	25c	South Carolina	125.00
RM205	30c	South Carolina	—
RM206	50c	South Carolina	175.00
RM207	75c	South Carolina	4,000.
RM208	$1	South Carolina	6,000.

RM211	$5	South Carolina	—
RM214	4c	Tennessee	350.00
RM215	10c	Tennessee	200.00
RM216	20c	Tennessee	—
RM217	25c	Tennessee	275.00
RM218	30c	Tennessee	—
RM219	50c	Tennessee	900.00
RM220	75c	Tennessee	—
RM221	$1	Tennessee	—
RM227	4c	Vermont	75.00
RM228	10c	Vermont	35.00
RM229	20c	Vermont	350.00
RM230	25c	Vermont	100.00
RM231	30c	Vermont	1,350.
RM232	50c	Vermont	130.00
RM233	75c	Vermont	3,000.
RM234	$1	Vermont	—
RM238	$10	Vermont	—
RM240	4c	Virginia	15.00
RM241	10c	Virginia	20.00
RM242	20c	Virginia	125.00
RM243	25c	Virginia	20.00
RM244	30c	Virginia	500.00
RM245	50c	Virginia	25.00
RM246	75c	Virginia	50.00
RM247	$1	Virginia	1,000.

The Act called for a $2, $4, $5 and $10 stamp for each state; only the listed ones have been seen.

The Act also called for a "Ten cents per centum" and a "Six mills per dollar" stamp for each state, none of which has been seen except No. RM187.

A press and a set of dies, one die for each denomination, were prepared and sent to each state where it was the duty of the Supervisors of the Revenue to stamp all documents presented to them upon payment of the proper tax. The Supervisors were also to have on hand for sale blank paper stamped with the different rates of duty to be sold to the public upon which the purchaser would later write or print the proper type of instrument corresponding with the value of the stamp impressed thereon. So far as is now known there was no distinctive watermark for the paper sold by the government. The Vermont set of dies is in the Vermont Historical Society at Montpelier.

B. SECOND FEDERAL ISSUE
Act of April 23, 1800
In effect March 1, 1801-June 30, 1802

RM260   RM261

	(a)Government watermark in italics; laid paper	(b)Government watermark in Roman; wove paper	(c)No Government watermark
RM260 4c	15.00	15.00	50.00
RM261 10c	20.00	20.00	50.00
RM262 20c	65.00	75.00	85.00
RM263 25c	15.00	15.00	17.50
RM264 30c	75.00	75.00	400.00
RM265 50c	65.00	45.00	85.00
RM266 75c	30.00	50.00	100.00
RM267 $1	200.00	150.00	175.00
RM269 $4			500.00
RM271 $10	3,250.		

The distinguishing feature of the stamps of this issue is the counter stamp, the left stamp shown in the illustration which usually appears on a document below the other stamp. In the right stamp the design of the eagle and the shield are similar to their design in the same denomination of the First Federal Issue but the name of the state is omitted and the denomination appears below instead of above the eagle and the shield. All of these stamps were embossed without color.

All the paper which was furnished by the government contained the watermark vertically along the edge of the sheet, "GEN STAMP OFFICE," either in Roman capitals on wove paper or in italic capitals on laid paper. The wove paper also had in the center of each half sheet either the watermark "W. Y. & Co." or "Delaware." William Young & Co. who owned the Delaware Mills made the government paper. The laid paper omitted the watermark "Delaware." The two stamps were separately impressed. The design of the eagle and shield differed in each value.

All the stamping was done in Washington, the right stamp being put on in the General Stamp Office and the left one or counter stamp in the office of the Commissioner of the Revenue as a check on the stamping done in the General Stamp Office. The "Com. Rev. C. S." in the design of the counter stamp stands for "Commissioner of the Revenue, Counter Stamp."

The Second Federal issue was intended to include $2 and $5 stamps, but these denominations have not been seen.

C. THIRD FEDERAL ISSUE
Act of August 2, 1813
In effect January 1, 1814-December 31, 1817

RM276

		a. Watermark	b. Unwmkd.
RM275	5c	10.00	15.00
RM276	10c	10.00	10.00
RM277	25c	15.00	15.00
RM278	50c	10.00	10.00
RM279	75c	13.00	17.50
RM280	$1	14.50	30.00
RM281	$1.50	17.00	77.50
RM282	$2	35.00	62.50
RM283	$2.50	30.00	125.00
RM284	$3.50	200.00	110.00
RM285	$4		400.00
RM286	$5	110.00	140.00

The distinguishing features of the stamps of this issue are the absence of the name of a state in the design and the absence of the counter stamp. Different values show different positions of the eagle.

All stamps of this issue were embossed without color at Washington. The paper with the watermark "Stamp U. S." was sold by the government. Unwatermarked paper may be either wove or laid.

IV. ISSUES BY VARIOUS STATES
DELAWARE
Act of June 19, 1793
In effect October 1, 1793-February 7, 1794

ERP50　　　　　　ERP51

ERP53

RM291	EP50	5c	1,700.
RM292	EP51	20c	1,350.
RM294	EP53	50c	

In some cases a reddish ink was used in impressing the stamp and in other cases the impressions are colorless.

Besides the denominations listed, 3c, 33c, and $1 stamps were called for by the taxing act. Stamps of these denominations have not been seen.

VIRGINIA
Act of February 20, 1813
In effect May 1, 1813-April 30, 1815
Act of December 21, 1814
In effect May 1, 1815-February 27, 1816

ERP60

ERP61

			a. Die cut	b. On Document
RM305	EP61	4c	17.50	90.00
RM306	EP60	6c	17.50	200.00
RM307	EP61	10c		200.00
RM308	EP61	12c	25.00	200.00
RM309	EP61	20c	40.00	500.00
RM310	EP61	25c	17.50	225.00
RM311	EP61	37c	17.50	300.00
RM312	EP61	45c	40.00	200.00
RM313	EP61	50c	17.50	225.00
RM314	EP61	70c	40.00	
RM315	EP61	75c	22.50	90.00
RM316	EP61	95c	40.00	300.00
RM317	EP61	100c	40.00	300.00
RM318	EP61	120c		225.00
RM319	EP61	125c	17.50	
RM323	EP60	175c	17.50	
RM325	EP61	200c	17.50	475.00

All of these stamps are colorless impressions and with some exceptions as noted below those issued under the 1813 Act cannot be distinguished from those issued under the 1814 Act. The 10c, 20c, 45c, 70c, 95c, 120c, 145c, 150c, 170c and 190c were issued only under the 1813 Act, the 6c, 12c, and 37c only under the 1814 Act.

No. RM311 has the large lettering of EP60 but the 37 is to the left and the XXXVII to the right as in EP61. The design of the dogwood branch and berries is similar but not identical in all values.

When the tax on the document exceeded "two hundred cents," two or more stamps were impressed or attached to the document. For instance a document has been seen with 45c and 200c to make up the $2.45 rate, and another with 75c and 200c.

Since both the Virginia and the Third Federal Acts to some extent taxed the same kind of document, and since during the period from Jan. 1, 1814 to Feb. 27, 1816, both Acts were in effect in Virginia, some instruments have both stamps on them.

The circular die cut Virginia stamps about 29mm in diameter were cut out of previously stamped paper which after the Act was repealed, was presented for redemption at the office of the Auditor of Public Accounts. They were threaded on fine twine and until about 1940 preserved in his office as required by law. Watermarked die cut Virginia stamps are all cut out of Third Federal watermarked paper.

Not seen yet, the 145c, 150c, and 170c stamps were called for by the 1813 Act, and 195c by both the 1813 and 1814 Acts.

MARYLAND
1. Act of February 11, 1818
In effect May 1, 1818-March 7, 1819

ERP70

RM362	EP70	30c **red** (printed), unused	400.
		Sheet of 4, unused	2,500.

The Act called for six other denominations, none of which has been seen. The Act imposing this tax was held unconstitutional by the United States Supreme Court in the case of McCulloch vs. Maryland.

2. Act of March 10, 1845
In effect May 10, 1845-March 10, 1856

ERP71

RM370	EP71	10c	12.50
RM371	EP71	15c	10.00
RM372	EP71	25c	10.00
RM373	EP71	50c	12.50
RM374	EP71	75c	10.00
RM375	EP71	$1	10.00
RM376	EP71	$1.50	12.50
RM377	EP71	$2	45.00
RM378	EP71	$2.50	17.50
RM379	EP71	$3.50	55.00

RM380	EP71	$4	90.00
RM381	EP71	$5.50	50.00
RM382	EP71	$6	100.00

Nos. RM370-RM382 are embossed without color with a similar design for each value. They vary in size from 20mm in diameter for the 10c to 33mm for the $6.

V. FEDERAL LICENSES TO SELL LIQUOR, ETC.
1. Act of June 5, 1794
In effect September 30, 1794-June 30, 1802

ERP80

RM400	EP80	$5	550.00

Provisionals are in existence using the second issue Connecticut Supervisors' stamp with the words "Five Dollars" written or printed over it or the second issue of the New Hampshire Supervisors' stamp without the words "Five Dollars."

2. Act of August 2, 1813
In effect January 1, 1814-December 31, 1817

ERP81

RM451	EP81	$10	725.00
RM452	EP81	$12	750.00
RM453	EP81	$15	425.00
RM454	EP81	$18	900.00
RM455	EP81	$20	1,400.
RM456	EP81	$22.50	650.00
RM457	EP81	$25	550.00
RM458	EP81	$30	1,500.
RM459	EP81	$37.50	550.00

The Act of December 23, 1814, increased the basic rates of $10, $12, $15, $20 and $25 by 50 per cent, effective February 1, 1815. This increase applied to the unexpired portions of the year so far as licenses then in effect were concerned and these licenses were required to be brought in and to have the payment of the additional tax endorsed on them.

VI. FEDERAL LICENSES TO WORK A STILL
Act of July 24, 1813
In effect January 1, 1814-December 31, 1817

(Embossed)　　　　　(Printed)
ERP82　　　　　　　ERP83

			a. Embossed	b. Printed
RM466		4½c		2,000.
RM468		9c	1,250.	1,800.
RM471		18c	—	1,400.
RM477		36c		2,100.
RM478		42c		2,000.
RM480		52c	2,000.	
RM484		70c	2,100.	
RM488		$1.08	2,000.	

The statute under which these were issued provided for additional rates of 2½c, 5c, 10c, 16c, 21c, 25c, 26c, 32c, 35c, 42c, 50c, 54c, 60c, 64c, 84c, $1.04, $1.05, $1.20, $1.35, $1.40, $2.10, $2.16 and $2.70 per gallon of the capacity of the still. Stamps of these denominations have not been seen.

VII. SUPERVISORS' AND CUSTOM HOUSE SEALS

1. Seals came into use on required certificates, as follows: April 1, 1791, domestic and imported distilled spirits; July 1, 1792, imported wine.

ERP90

		Check Letter	State	
RM501	EP90	"B"	South Carolina	50.00
RM503	EP90	"D"	Virginia	1,350.
RM505	EP90	"F"	Delaware	—
RM506	EP90	"G"	Pennsylvania	75.00
RM508	EP90	"I"	New York	22.50
RM509	EP90	"K"	Connecticut	30.00
RM510	EP90	"L"	Rhode Island	90.00
RM511	EP90	"M"	Massachusetts	22.50
RM512	EP90	"N"	New Hampshire	700.00
RM514	EP90	"P"	Kentucky	—

Use of RM501-RM514 on certificates for domestic distilled spirits shows payment of the tax that was being resisted in the Whiskey Rebellion. All such reported uses are from the New

England states. Nos. RM501-RM514 were removed from service in late 1799. In Connecticut and Massachusetts, they were returned to service after July 1, 1802.

2. Use from October 2, 1799

ERP91

RM552	EP91	North Carolina	500.00	
RM553	EP91	Virginia	—	
RM554	EP91	Maryland	200.00	
RM556	EP91	Pennsylvania	250.00	
RM558	EP91	New York	20.00	
RM559	EP91	Connecticut	30.00	
RM560	EP91	Rhode Island	35.00	
RM561	EP91	Massachusetts	25.00	
RM562	EP91	New Hampshire	90.00	

Nos. RM552-RM562 were necessitated by excessive wear on Nos. RM501-RM514.

3. Custom House Seals

ERP92

RM575	EP92	Custom House, Philadelphia	50.00	
RM576	EP92	Custom House, Perth Amboy, N.J.	35.00	

Although no value is expressed in the Supervisors' and Custom House seals, and they do not evidence the payment of a tax in the same way that the other stamps do, some collectors of stamped paper include them in their collections if they are on instruments evidencing the payment of a tax.

They were all embossed without color and, as to Supervisors' seals issued under the Act of 1791, the only difference in design is that at the left of the eagle there was a different check letter for each state. Custom House seals used in the other cities are in existence, but, in view of the doubtful status of Custom House seals as revenue stamps, it is not proposed to list them.

REVENUE STAMPED PAPER

These stamps were printed in various denominations and designs on a variety of financial documents, including checks, drafts, receipts, specie clerk statements, insurance policies, bonds and stock certificates.

They were authorized by Act of Congress of July 1, 1862, effective October 1, 1862, although regular delivery of stamped paper did not begin until July 1, 1865. The 2-cent tax on receipts ended Oct. 1, 1870. The 2-cent tax on checks and sight drafts ended July 1, 1883. All other taxes ended Oct. 1, 1872. The use of stamped paper was revived by the War Revenue Act of 1898, approved June 13, 1898. Type X was used July 1, 1898 through June 30, 1902.

Most of these stamps were typographed; some, types H, I and J, were engraved. They were printed by private firms under supervision of government representatives from dies loaned by the Bureau of Internal Revenue. Types A-F, P-W were printed by the American Phototype Co., New York (1865-75); type G, Graphic Co., New York (1875-83); types H-L, Joseph R. Carpenter, Philadelphia (1866-75); types M-N, A. Trochsler, Boston (1873-75); type O, Morey and Sherwood, Chicago (1874). Type X was printed by numerous regional printers under contract with the government.

Samples of these stamps are known for types B-G, P and Q with a section of the design removed and replaced by the word "Sample." Types G, P-Q, U-W exist with a redemption clause added by typography or rubber stamp. Redeemed type X's have a 5mm punched hole.

Multiples or single impressions on various plain papers are usually considered proofs or printers' waste.

For further information see "Handbook for United States Revenue Stamped Paper," published (1979) by the American Revenue Association.

Illustration size varies, with actual size quoted for each type.

Values for types A-O are for clear impressions on plain entire checks and receipts. Attractive documents with vignettes sell for more. The value of individual examples is also affected by the place of use. For example, territorial usage generally sells for more than a similar item from New York City.

Values for types P-W are for stamps on documents with attractive engravings, usually stock certificates, bonds and insurance policies. Examples on plain documents and cut squares sell for less.

Type A

Size: 22x25mm

RN-A1	2c black	90.	75.
	a. Printed on both sides		30.
RN-A2	2c orange		160.
RN-A3	2c gray		2,000.
RN-A4	2c blue		8,000.
RN-A5	2c brown		5,000.
RN-A8	2c purple		2,000.
RN-A9	2c green		1,350.
	a. Inverted		

No. RN-A4 is unique. The unique example of No. RN-A9a is on a partial document. The catalogue value for RN-A8 is for an impression on William Moller & Son stationery; a second more violet shade is on Carter, Kirkland & Co. receipts. Value of latter is $3,250.

Same Type with 1 Entire and 53 or 56 Partial Impressions in Vertical Format
("Tapeworm")
Left Col. — Full Document
Right Col. — Strip with Bank Names

RN-A10	2c **orange**, 1 full plus 56 partial impressions	675.	100.
	Cut square (full strip without bank names)		45.
RN-A11	2c **orange**, 1 full plus 53 partial impressions	1,100.	250.

Nos. RN-A10 and RN-A11 were used by the Mechanics' National Bank of New York on a bank specie clerk's statement. It was designed so that the full stamp or one of the repeated bottom segments fell on each line opposite the name of a bank.

The three additional banks were added at the bottom of the form. No. RN-A11 must show white space below the "First National Bank" line.

Eagle Type B

Size: 31x48mm

RN-B1	2c **orange**	5.00	3.00
	yellow orange	5.00	3.00
	deep orange	5.00	3.00
	a. Printed on both sides	200.00	20.00
	b. Double impression	350.00	
	c. Printed on back		—

d.	With 10 centimes blue French handstamp, right	400.00	
e.	Inverted		600.00

The unique example of No. RN-B1e is on a partial document.

All examples of the previously-listed "yellow" have some red in them.

RN-B2	2c **black**		40.00
RN-B3	2c **blue**		40.00
	light blue		40.00
RN-B4	2c **brown**	125.00	40.00
RN-B5	2c **bronze**		40.00
RN-B6	2c **green** (shades)	110.00	15.00
RN-B10	2c **red** (shades)	200.00	22.50
RN-B11	2c **purple**		125.00
RN-B13	2c **violet** (shades)	125.00	40.00
a.	2c **violet brown**		45.00

"Good only for checks and drafts payable at sight." in Rectangular Tablet at Base

RN-B16	2c **orange**	45.00	12.50
a.	With 2c orange red Nevada	325.00	250.00

"Good only for checks and drafts payable at sight." in Octagonal Tablet at Base

RN-B17	2c **orange**	42.50	10.00
a.	Tablet inverted		1,750.
b.	With 2c orange red Nevada		35.00
c.	With 2c green Nevada		35.00
d.	With 2c dull violet Nevada		1,500.
e.	With 2c brownish violet Nevada		2,500.

"Good when issued for the payment of money." in Octagonal Tablet at Base

RN-B20	2c **orange**	70.00	15.00
a.	Printed on both sides	30.00	10.00
b.	As "a," one stamp inverted		1,500.
c.	Tablet inverted		3,750.

"Good when issued for the payment of money" in two lines at base in orange

RN-B23	2c **orange**		900.00

"Good when the amount does not exceed $100." in Octagonal Tablet at Base

RN-B24	2c **orange**	200.00	50.00

Washington Type C

Size: 108x49mm

RN-C1	2c **orange**	7.00	4.00
	red orange	7.00	4.00
	yellow orange	7.00	4.00
	salmon	8.00	4.00
	brown orange	8.00	4.00
a.	"Good when used..." vert. at left black		2,250.

All examples of the previously-listed "yellow" have some red in them.

RN-C2	2c **brown**	30.00	12.00
a.	2c **buff**	30.00	12.00
RN-C5	2c **pale red** (shades)	50.00	25.00
RN-C8	2c **green**		—

"Good only for Sight Draft" in two lines in color of stamp

RN-C9	2c **orange**, legend at lower right	85.00	50.00
RN-C11	2c **brown**, legend at lower right		110.00
RN-C13	2c **orange**, legend at lower left	45.00	20.00

"Good only for Receipt for Money Paid" in two lines in color of stamp

RN-C15	2c **orange**, legend at lower right	2,500.	—
RN-C16	2c **orange**, legend at lower left		350.00

"Good when issued for the payment of money" in one line at base in color of stamp

RN-C17	2c **orange** (shades)		575.00

"Good when issued for the/Payment of Money" in two tablets at lower left and right

RN-C19	2c **orange**		550.00
a.	Printed on both sides		35.00

"Good/only for Bank/Check" in 3-part Band

RN-C21	2c **orange**	60.00	12.50
	salmon		12.50
	yellow orange		20.00
a.	Inverted		750.00
b.	With 2c red orange Nevada	140.00	65.00
c.	Printed on back		2,900.
RN-C22	2c **brown**	300.00	25.00
a.	Printed on back		1,800.

"Good when the amount does not exceed $100" in tablet at lower right

RN-C26	2c **orange**		200.00

Franklin Type D

Size: 80x43mm

RN-D1	2c **orange** (shades)	10.00	4.00
a.	Double impression		—
b.	Printed on back	700.00	400.00
c.	Inverted		475.00

All examples of the previously-listed "yellow" have some red in them and are included in the "shades."

RN-D3	2c **brown**	3,000.	500.00
RN-D4	2c **buff** (shades)	9.00	5.00
RN-D5	2c **red**		2,000.

"Good only for/Bank Check" in panels within circles at left and right

RN-D7	2c **orange**	25.00	10.00
a.	Printed on back		2,100.

"Good only for/Bank Check" in two lines at lower right in color of stamp

RN-D8	2c **orange**		850.00

"Good only for Sight Draft" in two lines at lower left in color of stamp

RN-D9	2c **orange**	175.00	75.00

Franklin Type E

Size: 28x50mm

RN-E2	2c **brown**		1,200.
RN-E4	2c **orange**	12.50	5.00
	Broken die, lower right or left	40.00	20.00
a.	Double impression		925.00

"Good only for sight draft" in two lines at base in orange

RN-E5	2c **orange**	75.00	37.50

"Good only for Bank / Check" in two lines at base in orange

RN-E6	2c **orange**		—

"Good only for / Bank Check" in colorless letters in two lines above and below portrait

RN-E7	2c **orange**	75.00	17.50
a.	Double impression		—

Franklin Type F

Size: 56x34mm

RN-F1	2c **orange**	10.00	5.00
a.	Inverted		—

All examples of the previously-listed "yellow" have some red in them

Liberty Type G

Size: 80x48mm

RN-G1	2c **orange**	6.00	4.00
a.	Printed on back	65.00	40.00
b.	Printed on back, inverted	125.00	50.00

All examples of the previously-listed "yellow" have some red in them

Imprint: "Graphic Co., New York" at left and right in minute type

RN-G3	2c **orange**	100.00	100.00

Eagle Type H

Size: 32x50mm

RN-H3	2c **orange**	15.00	5.00
a.	Inverted		—
b.	Double impression		600.00
c.	"Good when used for payment of money," black		750.00
d.	"Good when used as a receipt for payment of money," black		750.00
e.	As "d," upward at left		1,600.
f.	As "d," legend in red		1,500.
g.	"Good when used as a receipt for the payment of money," black		400.00
h.	As "g," inverted legend		7,500.
i.	As "g," legend in two lines		700.00
j.	As "g," legend in violet		700.00
k.	As "g," legend in yellow		2,000.
l.	"Good only when used as a receipt for the payment of moneys," black		750.00

"Good for check or sight draft only" at left and right in color of stamp

RN-H5	2c **orange**		

Experts claim that No. RN-H5 exists only as a proof.

"Good for bank check or sight draft only" in black

RN-H6	2c **orange**		150.00

Type I
Design R2 of 1862-72 adhesive revenues
"BANK CHECK"
Size: 20x23mm

RN-I1	2c **orange**		225.00

"U.S. INTER. REV."

RN-I2	2c **orange**	650.00	350.00

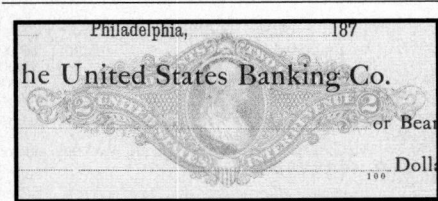

Washington Type J

Size: 105x40mm
Background of medallion crosshatched, filling oval except for bust

RN-J4	2c **orange**	20.00	10.00
	pale orange	20.00	10.00
	deep orange	50.00	12.50
a.	Double impression		500.00
b.	"Good only for . . ." added vertically at left in red orange		750.00
RN-J5	2c **red**	50.00	13.00
a.	Double impression		

"Good for check or sight draft only" curved, below

RN-J9	2c **red**	—	2,000.

Background shaded below bust and at left.

RN-J11	2c **orange**	60.00	15.00

Washington Type K

Size: 84x33mm

RN-K1	2c **blue**		—
RN-K4	2c **gray**	45.00	15.00
	pale gray	45.00	10.00
RN-K5	2c **brown**	160.00	125.00
RN-K6	2c **orange**	15.00	7.50
RN-K8	2c **red** (shades)	575.00	350.00
RN-K11	2c **olive**	175.00	175.00
	pale olive		110.00

Washington Type L

Size: 50x33mm

RN-L1	2c **blue** (shades)	175.00	—
RN-L2	2c **turquoise**	250.00	200.00
RN-L3	2c **gray**	35.00	20.00
	pale gray	35.00	20.00
RN-L4	2c **green**	900.00	600.00
	light green	600.00	400.00
RN-L5	2c **orange**	15.00	10.00
RN-L6	2c **olive**		55.00
	gray olive		30.00
RN-L10	2c **red**	15.00	10.00
a.	2c **violet red**	15.00	10.00
RN-L13	2c **brown**	—	275.00

Washington Type M

Size: 68x37mm

RN-M2	2c **orange**	50.00	10.00
a.	Printed on back, inverted		1,600.

All examples of the previously-listed "yellow" have some red in them.

RN-M3	2c **green**		475.00
RN-M4	2c **gray**		1,250.

Eagle, Numeral and Monitor Type N

Size: 107x48mm

RN-N3	2c **orange**	60.00	15.00
a.	Printed on back	300.00	225.00
b.	Inverted		900.00
RN-N4	2c **light brown**		150.00

Liberty Type O

Size: 75x35mm

RN-O2	2c **orange**	1,750.	600.

Values for types P-W
are for stamps on documents with attractive engravings, usually stock certificates, bonds and insurance policies. Examples on plain documents sell for less.

Lincoln Type P

Size: 32x49mm

RN-P2	5c **brown**		350.00
	Cut square		90.00
RN-P3	5c **green**		—
RN-P4	5c **pink**		—
RN-P5	5c **orange**	55.00	40.00
	Cut square		7.00

All examples of the previously listed "yellow" have some orange in them.

RN-P6	5c **red** (shades)	—	210.00
	Cut square		40.00

No. RN-P3 only exists in combination with a 25c green or 50c green. No. RN-P4 is unique and only exists in combination with a $1 pink. See Nos. RN-T2, RN-V1, RN-W6.

Madison Type Q (See note before No. RN-P2)

Size: 28x56mm

RN-Q1	5c **orange**	175.	150.
	Cut square		20.
	brownish orange	175.	150.
RN-Q2	5c **brown**		2,750.
	Cut square		500.

Type R
Frame as Type B, Lincoln in center
Size: 32x49mm

RN-R1	10c **brown**		2,500.
RN-R2	10c **pale red**	—	675.
	Cut square		100.
RN-R3	10c **orange**		500.
	Cut square		50.

"Good when the premium does not exceed $10" in tablet at base

RN-R6	10c **orange**	—	400.
	Cut square		50.

Motto Without Tablet

RN-R7	10c **orange**		500.
	Cut square		

Washington Type S (See note before No. RN-P2)

Size: 33x54mm

RN-S1	10c **orange**		3,750.

"Good when the premium does not exceed $10" in tablet at base

RN-S2	10c **orange**		4,750.
	Cut square		500.

Eagle Type T
(See note before
No. RN-P2)

For type T design with Lincoln in center see type V, Nos. RN-V1 to RN-V10.

Size: 33x40mm

RN-T1	25c **black**	—	—
	Cut square		
RN-T2	25c **green**		7,500.
RN-T3	25c **red**	175.00	100.00
	Cut square		9.00
RN-T4	25c **orange**	150.00	75.00
	Cut square		7.50
	light orange	150.00	75.00
	light orange, cut square		7.50
	brown orange		75.00
	brown orange, cut square		8.00

No. RN-T2 includes No. RN-P3, and a 25c green, type T, obliterating a No. RN-V4.

"Good when the premium does not exceed $50" in tablet at base

RN-T6	25c **orange**	450.	350.
	Cut square		50.
RN-T7	25c **orange,** motto without tablet		1,500.
	Cut square		400.

"Good when the amount insured shall not exceed $1000" in tablet at base

RN-T8	25c **deep orange**	800.	700.
	Cut square		75.
RN-T9	25c **orange,** motto without tablet		
	Cut square		600.

Franklin Type U (See note before No. RN-P2)

Size: 126x65mm

RN-U1	25c **orange**	35.00	35.00
	Cut square		5.00
RN-U2	25c **brown**	45.00	35.00
	Cut square		5.00

"Good when the premium does not exceed $50" in tablet at lower right

RN-U3	25c **orange**		2,500.
	Cut square		400.

Tablet at lower left

RN-U5	25c **red**	800.	
	Cut square		250.
RN-U6	25c **orange**	500.	450.
	Cut square		65.

All examples of the previously-listed "yellow" have some red in them.

Tablet at base

RN-U7	25c **brown**		1,750.
	Cut square		300.
RN-U9	25c **orange**		1,000.
	Cut square		400.

Lincoln Type V

Size: 32x41mm

RN-V1	50c **green**		175.00
	Cut square		52.50
RN-V2	50c **brown**	—	400.00
	Cut square		125.00
RN-V4	50c **orange**	175.00	90.00
	Cut square		17.50
	deep orange	175.00	90.00
	deep orange, cut square		17.50
RN-V5	50c **red**	700.00	
	Cut square		250.00

No. RN-V1 includes a 50c green, type V, and a No. RN-P3, obliterating a No. RN-W2.

"Good when the amount insured shall not exceed $5000" in tablet at base

RN-V6	50c **orange**	450.00	400.00
	Cut square		65.00
RN-V9	50c **red**	—	
	Cut square		550.00

Motto Without Tablet

RN-V10	50c **orange**		
	Cut square		550.00

Washington Type W
(See note before No. RN-P2)

Size: 34x73mm

RN-W2	$1 **orange**(shades)	150.00	85.00
	Cut square		15.00
RN-W5	$1 **brown**		4,500.
RN-W6	$1 **pink**		3,750.

The former light brown is now included with the orange shades.

No. RN-W6 used with No. RN-P4 is unique. Two examples of No. RN-W6 exist used alone.

SPANISH-AMERICAN WAR SERIES

Many of these stamps were used for parlor car tax and often were torn in two or more parts.

Liberty Type X

1898   **Size: 68x38mm**

RN-X1	1c **rose**	800.00	—
	Partial		65.00
	dark red, partial		65.00
RN-X4	1c **orange**	165.00	—
a.	On pullman ticket	600.00	
	Partial		25.00
b.	As "a," printed on back		—
	As "a," printed on back, partial		65.00
RN-X5	1c **green**	65.00	30.00
	Partial		25.00
a.	On parlor car ticket	65.00	15.00
b.	On pullman ticket	500.00	
	On pullman ticket, partial		15.00
RN-X6	2c **yellow**	2.00	1.00
	pale olive		900.00
RN-X7	2c **orange**	3.00	2.00
	pale orange	3.00	2.00
a.	Printed on back only	500.00	500.00
c.	Printed on front and back	—	
d.	Vertical		85.00
e.	Double impression		—
f.	On pullman ticket	1,000.	200.00
g.	Inverted		550.00

No. RN-X1 exists only as a four-part unused pullman ticket, used as an unsevered auditor's and passenger's parts of the four-part ticket, or partial as a used half of a two-part ticket. Nos. RN-X4a and RN-X5b exist as unused two-part tickets and as used half portions. No. RN-X7f exists as an unused four-part ticket and as a used two-piece portion with nearly complete stamp design.

PRIVATE DIE PROPRIETARY STAMPS

The extraordinary demands of the Civil War upon the Federal Treasury resulted in Congress devising and passing the Revenue Act of 1862. The Government provided revenue stamps to be affixed to boxes or packages of matches, and to proprietary medicines, perfumery, playing cards — as well as to documents, etc.

But manufacturers were permitted, at their expense, to have dies engraved and plates made for their exclusive use. Many were only too willing to do this because a discount or premium of from 5% to 10% was allowed on orders from the die which often made it possible for them to undersell their competitors. Also, the considerable advertising value of the stamps could not be overlooked. These are now known as Private Die Proprietary stamps.

The face value of the stamp used on matches was determined by the number, i.e., 1c for each 100 matches or fraction thereof. Medicines and perfumery were taxed at the rate of 1c for each 25 cents of the retail value or fraction thereof up to $1 and 2c for each 50 cents or fraction above that amount. Playing cards were first taxed at the same rate but subsequently the tax was 5c for a deck of 52 cards and 10c for a greater number of cards or double decks.

The stamp tax was repealed on March 3, 1883, effective July 1, 1883.

The various papers were:

a. Old paper, 1862-71. First Issue. Hard and brittle varying from thick to thin.

b. Silk paper, 1871-77. Second Issue. Soft and porous with threads of silk, mostly red, blue and black, up to ¼inch in length.

c. Pink paper, 1877-78. Third Issue. Soft paper colored pink ranging from pale to deep shades.

d. Watermarked paper, 1878-83. Fourth Issue. Soft porous paper showing part of "USIR." Roulettes on watermarked paper are rouletted 6.

e. Experimental silk paper. Medium smooth paper, containing minute fragments of silk threads either blue alone or blue and red (infrequent), widely scattered, sometimes but a single fiber on a stamp.

Early printings of some private die revenue stamps are on paper which appears to have laid lines.

These stamps were usually torn in opening the box or container. **Values quoted are for examples which are somewhat faulty but reasonably attractive, with the faults usually not readily apparent on the face.** Nos. RS278-RS306 are valued in the grade of very fine. Sound examples of these stamps (other than Nos. RS278-RS306) at a grade of fine-very fine can sell for 50% to 300% more than catalogue value. Outstanding examples of stamps in this section with a lower catalogue value can bring many multiples of catalogue value.

---

	a. Old Paper	b. Silk Paper	c. Pink Paper	d. Wmkd. USIR (191R)

PRIVATE DIE MATCH STAMPS

1864   **A**   *Perf. 12*

Akron Match Company — RO1

Akron Match Company

RO1	1c	blue	350.00

Alexander's Matches — RO2

J.J. Allen's Sons — RO4

Alexander's Matches

RO2	1c	orange	35.00	125.00
RO3	1c	blue		5,000.

J. J. Allen's Sons

RO4	1c	blue	16.00

Thos. Allen — RO5

Thos. Allen

RO5	1c	green	175.00

Allen & Powers — RO6

Allen & Powers

As No. RO141, inscribed "Allen & Powers" instead of "Orono Match Co."

RO6	1c	blue		7.75	35.00	11.00

Alligator Match Company

RO7	1c	blue	24.00
		Dbl. transfer	
RO8	1c	blue, roulette	140.00

American Fusee Company — RO9

American Fusee Company

RO9	1c	black	10.00	11.00	10.00
		Dbl. transfer	125.00		

American Match Company — RO10

American Match Co.

RO10	1c	black	130.00	35.00
	e.	Experimental silk paper	475.00	
RO11	3c	black	550.00	140.00
		Dbl. transfer		275.00
	e.	Experimental silk paper	1,500.	

American Match Co. — RO12

American Match Co. — RO13

RO12	1c	black	60.00	
RO13	3c	green, Rock Island	10,000.	

Arnold & Co. — RO14

Arnold & Co.

RO14	1c	black	60.00

B

Bagley & Dunham — RO15

Bagley & Dunham
RO15   1c   green   32.50

Geo. & O. C. Barber
As No. RO17, inscribed "Geo. & O. C. Barber" instead of "Barber Match Co."
RO16   1c   blue   72.50

Barber Match Co. — RO17

Barber Match Co.
RO17   1c   blue   25.00   1.25   20.00   1.75
       Dbl.   85.00   37.50 85.00   35.00
       transfer
    e. Experi-   140.00
       mental
       silk pa-
       per
    u. 1c ultra   475.00
RO18   1c   bl, rou-   5,000.
       lette
RO19   3c   black   200.00 140.00
    e. Experi-   550.00
       mental
       silk pa-
       per

Barber & Peckham — RO20

Barber & Peckham
RO20   1c   blue   67.50
RO21   3c   black   275.00

Bauer & Beudel
RO22   1c   blue   72.50   160.00
    u. 1c ultra   275.00

A.B. & S. (A. Beecher & Son) — RO23

A. B. & S. (A. Beecher & Son)
As No. RO175, inscribed "A. B. & S." instead of "C. B. C. S." in the four corners.
RO23   1c   orange   17.00   67.50
       Dbl.   —   —
       transfer
    e. Experi-   175.00
       mental
       silk pa-
       per
       As "e,"   225.00
       dbl.
       transfer

B. Bendel & Co. — RO25

Illustration reduced.

B. Bendel & Co.
RO24   1c   brown   2.75   725.00
       Dbl. transfer
RO25   12c brown   275.00

H. Bendel — RO26

H. Bendel
Nos. RO26-RO27 are RO24-RO25 altered to read "H. Bendel doing business as B. Bendel & Co."
RO26   1c   brown   5.00   2.50   2.00
RO27   12c brown   500.00

H. & M. Bentz — RO28

Bent & Lea — RO29

H. & M. Bentz
RO28   1c   blue   42.50

Bent & Lea
RO29   1c   black   40.00
       Double   125.00
       transfer
       at left
    e. Experi-   50.00
       mental
       silk pa-
       per
       As "e,"   600.00
       dbl.
       transfer

B. J. & Co. — RO30

Bock, Schneider & Co. — RO31

B. J. & Co. (Barber, Jones & Co.)
As No. RO100 with "B. J. & Co." added above eagle.
RO30   1c   green   140.00
       Dbl. transfer   175.00

Bock, Schneider & Co.
RO31   1c   black   20.00

Wm. Bond & Co. — RO32/RO33

Bousfield & Poole — RO34/RO35

Wm. Bond & Co.
RO32   4c   black   275.00
RO33   4c   green   175.00   200.00   18.00

Bousfield & Poole
RO34   1c   lilac   225.00
       Dbl.   250.00
       transfer
RO35   1c   black   18.00   15.00
       Dbl.   70.00   90.00
       transfer
    e. Experi-   90.00
       mental
       silk pa-
       per
RO36   3c   lilac   3,000.

For illustration of No. RO37, see large stamp illustration pages.
RO37   3c   black   200.00   150.00
       Dbl. trans-   175.00
       fer
    e. Experi-   500.00
       mental
       silk pa-
       per

Boutell & Maynard — RO38

Boutell & Maynard
RO38   1c   black   325.00

Bowers & Dunham
As No. RO15, inscribed "Bowers & Dunham" instead of "Bagley & Dunham."
RO39   1c   green   275.00
RO40   1c   blue   95.00

B. & N. (Brocket & Newton)
RO41   1c   lake, die I   45.00
RO42   1c   lake, die II   8.25
The initials "B. & N." measure 5¼mm across the top in Die I, and 4¾mm in Die II.

Brown & Durling

RO43

RO43   1c   black   2,500.
RO44   1c   green   82.50

L. W. Buck & Co. — RO45

L. W. Buck & Co.
RO45   1c   black   3,250.
    e. Experi-   2,250.
       mental
       silk pa-
       per

D. Burhans & Co. — RO46

D. Burhans & Co.

RO46	1c	black	160.00	*12,500.*
		Dbl. trans-fer	275.00	
	e.	Experimental silk paper	900.00	

Charles Busch — RO47

Charles Busch

| RO47 | 1c | black | | 35.00 |

Byam, Carlton & Co. — RO48

2 heads to left, 41x75mm.

Byam, Carlton & Co.

| RO48 | 1c | black, imperf | *5,750.* |

Byam, Carlton & Co. — RO49

RO49	1c	black, 19x23mm	27.50	7.75	2.00
		Dbl. transfer			140.00
	e.	Experimental silk paper	140.00		
	i.	Vert. pair, imperf horiz.			140.00
RO50	1c	black	2,750.		

2 heads to left, buff wrapper, 131x99mm.

For illustrations of Nos. RO51, RO52, RO54, RO55 and RO56, see large stamp illustration pages.

| RO51 | 1c | black | 250.00 |

As #RO50, 131x89mm.

| RO52 | 1c | black | 70.00 |

1 head to right, white wrapper, 94x54mm.

| RO53 | 1c | black | 175.00 |

As #RO52, buff wrapper.

| RO54 | 1c | black | 11.00 |
| | h. | Up | 60.00 |

2 heads to right, buff wrapper, 81x50mm. #RO54h has right block reading up.

| RO55 | 1c | black | 35.00 |

1 head to left, white wrapper, 94x56mm.

| RO56 | 1c | black | 9.00 |

As #RO50, 95x57mm.

--------- C ---------

Cannon Match Co. — RO57

Cannon Match Co.

As No. RO68, "Cannon Match Co." instead of "W. D. Curtis."

| RO57 | 1c | green | 55.00 |

Cardinal Match Co. — RO58

Cardinal Match Co.

| RO58 | 1c | lake | 32.50 |

F. E. C. (Frank E. Clark)

As No. RO41, "F.E.C." instead of "B. & N."

| RO59 | 1c | lake | 110.00 | 110.00 |
| | e. | Experimental silk paper | 150.00 | |

Chicago Match Co. — RO60

Henry A. Clark — RO61

Chicago Match Co.

| RO60 | 3c | black | 600.00 |

Henry A. Clark

| RO61 | 1c | green | 110.00 |

Jas. L. Clark — RO62/RO63

Clark Match Co. — RO64

Jas. L. Clark

RO62	1c	green	2.75	27.50	1.75
		Dbl. transfer			67.50
RO63	1c	green, rouletted			1,000.

The Clark Match Co.

| RO64 | 1c | lake | 10.00 |

Cramer & Kemp — RO65/RO66

Crown Match Co. — RO67

Cramer & Kemp

RO65	1c	black	72.50	
RO66	1c	blue,	125.00	7.75
	e.	Experimental silk paper	325.00	
	u.	1c ultra	500.00	

Crown Match Co.

| RO67 | 1c | black | 25.00 |

W. D. Curtis Matches — RO68

W. D. Curtis Matches

| RO68 | 1c | green | 160.00 | 140.00 |
| | e. | Experimental silk paper | 275.00 | |

--------- D ---------

G. W. H. Davis — RO69/RO70

G. W. H. Davis

| RO69 | 1c | black | 52.50 | |
| RO70 | 1c | carmine | | 90.00 |

W.E. Doolittle — RO71

W. E. Doolittle

| RO71 | 1c | blue | 450.00 |

E. P. Dunham

| RO72 | 1c | green | | 90.00 |

--------- E ---------

Jas. Eaton — RO73

Jas. Eaton — RO74

Jas. Eaton

| RO73 | 1c | black | 55.00 | 1.50 | 20.00 | 1.75 |
| | e. | Experimental silk paper | 225.00 | | | |

E.B. Eddy — RO75   E.B. Eddy — RO75A

E. B. Eddy

| RO75 | 1c | **car**, die I | 25.00 | |
| RO75A | 1c | **car**, die II | 40.00 | |

Die II shows eagle strongly recut; ribbon across bottom is narrower; color is deeper.

Aug. Eichele

Aug. Eichele — RO76

| RO76 | 1c | **black** | 160.00 | |

P. Eichele & Co. — RO77

P. Eichele & Co.

As No. RO78, "P. Eichele & Co." at top.

RO77	1c	**blue**	67.50	8.25
	e.	Experimental silk paper	225.00	
	u.	**1c ultra**	525.00	

Eichele & Co. —   J.W.
RO78/RO79   Eisenhart's — RO80

Eichele & Co.

| RO78 | 1c | **blue** | 5.00 | 20.00 | 4.50 |
| RO79 | 1c | **blue**, rouletted | | | 350.00 |

J. W. Eisenhart's Matches

| RO80 | 1c | **blue** | 55.00 | 125.00 | 42.50 |

Excelsior Match Co.
(Watertown) — RO81/RO82

Excelsior Match Co.

RO81	1c	**black**, Watertown, N.Y.	110.00		
RO82	1c	**black**, Syracuse, N.Y.	10.00	20.00	10.00
		Dbl. transfer			52.50

Excelsior Match,
Baltimore — RO83

Excelsior Match, Baltimore, Md.

| RO83 | 1c | **blue** | 95.00 | 125.00 |
| | u. | **1c ultra** | 900.00 | |

F

G. Farr &   L. Frank — RO85
Co. — RO84

G. Farr & Co.

| RO84 | 1c | **black** | 140.00 | |

L. Frank

| RO85 | 1c | **brown** | 110.00 | |

G

Gardner, Beer &   Wm. Gates — RO88
Co. — RO86

Gardner, Beer & Co.

| RO86 | 1c | **black** | 300.00 | |

Wm. Gates

RO87	1c	**black**, die I	9.00	6.00
RO88	1c	**black**, die II	50.00	5.50
		Dbl. transfer		35.00
	e.	Experimental silk paper	225.00	

The shirt collar is colorless in Die I and shaded in Die II. The colorless circle surrounding the portrait appears about twice as wide on Die I as it does on Die II.

For illustration of No. RO89, see large stamp illustration pages.

RO89	3c	**black**	60.00	52.50
		Dbl. transfer	92.50	90.00
	e.	Experimental silk paper	225.00	
RO90	6c	**black**	200.00	
RO91	3c	**black**, 3 1c stamps	160.00	

William Gates' Sons — RO92

William Gates' Sons

The 1c is as No. RO87, 3c as No. RO91, "William Gates' Sons" replaces "Wm. Gates."

For illustration of No. RO94, see large stamp illustration pages.

RO92	1c	**black**	35.00	11.00	2.25
RO93	1c	**black**, rouletted			_3,250._
RO94	3c	**black**, 3 1c stamps	140.00	200.00	95.00

A. Goldback & Co. — RO95

A. Goldback & Co.

| RO95 | 1c | **green** | 55.00 | |

A. Goldback

As No. RO95, "A. Goldback" instead of "A. Goldback & Co."

| RO96 | 1c | **green** | 200.00 | 13,000. |

T. Gorman & Bro.

As No. RO99, "T. Gorham & Bro." instead of "Thomas Gorham."

RO97	1c	**black**	900.00	
		Dbl. transfer	—	
RO98	1c	**green**	35.00	40.00
		Dbl. transfer	—	

Thomas Gorman

| RO99 | 1c | **green** | 4.50 | 40.00 | 82.50 |

Greenleaf & Co. —   Griggs & Goodwill
RO101/RO102   — RO103/RO104

Greenleaf & Co.

RO100	1c	**green**	100.00	125.00
	e.	Experimental silk paper	650.00	
RO101	3c	**carmine**	95.00	175.00
	e.	Experimental silk paper	1,100.	
RO102	5c	**orange**	175.00	4,500.
	e.	Experimental silk paper	475.00	

Griggs & Goodwill

RO103	1c	**black**	60.00	
RO104	1c	**green**	35.00	
		Dbl. transfer	160.00	

Griggs & Scott

As No. RO69, inscribed "Griggs & Scott" instead of "G. W. H. Davis."

| RO105 | 1c | **black** | 12.00 | 42.50 |
| | e. | Experimental silk paper | 80.00 | |

| RO74 | 1c | **black**, rouletted | 72.50 |

H

Charles S. Hale — RO106

Charles S. Hale
RO106 1c green   300.00

Henning & Bonhack
RO107 1c blue   350.00

W. E. Henry & Co. — RO108

W. E. Henry & Co.
RO108 1c red   35.00
RO109 1c black   17.00

J. G.
Hotchkiss — RO110

L. G.
Hunt — RO113

The J. G. Hotchkiss Match Co.
RO110 1c green   17.00 50.00 12.00

B. & H. D. Howard
RO111 1c lake   125.00
RO112 1c blue   12.00
       u. 1c ultra   375.00

L. G. Hunt
RO113 1c black   400.00 1,650.
       e. Experi-   450.00
           mental
           silk pa-
           per

D. F. Hutchinson Jr.
RO114 1c lake   22.50

I

Ives Matches
As No. RO116, "Ives Matches" instead of "P. T. Ives."
RO115 1c blue   7.75   —   6.75
       Dbl.
       transfer
       u. 1c ultra   425.00

P. T. Ives —
RO116/RO117

Ives &
Judd — RO119

P. T. Ives
For illustration of No. RO118, see large stamp illustration pages.

RO116 1c blue   7.75   45.00 5.00
RO117 1c blue, rouletted   550.00

RO118 8c blue   240.00
       e. Experi-   1,250.
           mental
           silk pa-
           per
       u. 8c ultra   3,250.

Ives & Judd
RO119 1c green   27.50 60.00 160.00

Ives & Judd Match
Co. — RO120

The Ives & Judd Match Co.
RO120 1c green   140.00
       Dbl. transfer   325.00

K

Kirby & Sons

Kirby & Sons — RO121

RO121 1c green   77.50

W. S. Kyle
RO122 1c black   22.50 17.00
       Dbl.   82.50
       transfer
       e. Experi-   —
           mental
           silk pa-
           per

L

Lacour's Matches
RO123 1c black   20.00 60.00
       Dbl.   110.00
       transfer
       e. Experi-   140.00
           mental
           silk pa-
           per

Leeds, Robinson &
Co. — RO124

Leeds, Robinson & Co.
RO124 1c green   82.50

H. Leigh
RO125 1c blue   11.00

Leigh & Palmer
As No. RO125, "Leigh & Palmer" replaces "H. Leigh."
RO126 1c black   25.00 77.50 47.50

John Loehr — RO127

John Loehr
RO127 1c blue   27.50

Joseph Loehr
As No. RO127, "Joseph" replaces "John."
RO128 1c blue   3.50   22.50 5.50

M

John J.
Macklin &
Co. — RO129

John J. Macklin & Co.
RO129 1c blk, rou-   10,000.
           lette

F. Mansfield &
Co. — RO130

Maryland Match
Co. — RO131

F. Mansfield & Co.
RO130 1c blue   7.25   15.00 14.00

Maryland Match Co.
RO131 1c blue   140.00 25,000.

"Matches" — RO132

A.
Messinger — RO133

"Matches"
RO132 1c blue   7.75   5.50
       Dbl.   110.00
       transfer
       e. Experi-   160.00
           mental
           silk pa-
           per
       u. 1c ultra   1,250.
       See Nos. RO168-RO169.

A. Messinger
RO133 1c black   4.50   20.00 4.00

Bousfield & Poole – RO37

Byam, Carlton & Co. – RO51

Byam, Carlton & Co. – RO52

Byam, Carlton & Co. – RO54

Byam, Carlton & Co. – RO55

Byam, Carlton & Co. – RO56

Wm. Gates – RO89

William Gates' Sons – RO94

P.T. Ives – RO118

—— **N** ——

National Match
Co. — RO134

F. P.
Newton — RO135

National Match Co.

RO134　1c　**blue**　　　　　　　　　77.50

Newbauer & Co. (N. & C.) follows No. RO139.

National Union Match Co. items are bogus.

F. P. Newton

RO135　1c　**lake**　　　3.50　13.50　4.50

See No. RO64 for another "The Clark Match Co." design.

New York Match Co. — RO136

New York Match Co.

No. RO136 is as No. RO22, "New York Match Co." instead of "Bauer & Beudel."

RO136　1c　**blue,**　　775.00　9.00
　　　　　shield

No. RO137 is as No. RO111, "New York Match Co." instead of "B. & H. D. Howard."

RO137　1c　**ver,** ea-　100.00　11,000.
　　　　　gle
　　e.　Experi-　　190.00
　　　　　mental
　　　　　silk pa-
　　　　　per
　　　　　As "e,"　　300.00
　　　　　dbl.
　　　　　transfer

RO139

RO138　1c　**green,**　　60.00　11.00
　　　　　22x60mm
　　e.　Experi-　　110.00
　　　　　mental
　　　　　silk pa-
　　　　　per
RO139　5c　**blue,**　　　　　3,000.
　　　　　22x60mm

N. & C. (Newbauer & Co.)

RO140　4c　**green**　　　5.50　140.00　6.75

—— **O** ——

Orono Match Co.

RO141　1c　**blue**　　40.00　40.00
　　e.　Experi-　　400.00
　　　　　mental
　　　　　silk pa-
　　　　　per
　　u.　1c **ultra**　725.00

—— **P** ——

Park City Match Co. — RO142

Park City Match Co.

RO142　1c　**green**　　55.00　52.50
　　e.　Experi-　　400.00
　　　　　mental
　　　　　silk pa-
　　　　　per
RO143　3c　**orange**　　60.00
　　e.　Experi-　　　—
　　　　　mental
　　　　　silk pa-
　　　　　per

Penn Match Co. Limited

RO144　1c　**blue**　　　　　　50.00

Pierce Match Co. — RO145

Pierce Match Co.

RO145　1c　**green**　4,000.

P. M. Co. (Portland M. Co.)

RO146　1c　**black**　　27.50

Portland Match Co.

RO147　1c　**black,**　　110.00
　　　　　wrap-
　　　　　per

The value of No. RO147 applies to commonest date (Dec. 1866); all others are much rarer.

RO148

V.R. Powell — RO149-
RO151

V. R. Powell

RO148　1c　**blue**　　10.00　12.00
　　　　Dbl.　　110.00
　　　　transfer

　　e.　Experi-　175.00
　　　　　mental
　　　　　silk pa-
　　　　　per
　　u.　1c **ultra**　975.00
RO149　1c　**black**　　7,000.
　　　　Buff wrapper, uncut.
RO150　1c　**black**　2,750.
　　　　Buff wrapper, cut to shape.
RO151　1c　**black**　4,500.
　　　　White wrapper, cut to shape.

—— **R** ——

Reading Match Company

RO152　1c　**black**　　　　　10.00

Reed & Thompson — RO153

Reed & Thompson

RO153　1c　**black**　　　　　22.50

D.M. Richardson
RO155　　　　　D.M. Richardson
　　　　　　　　　RO156

D. M. Richardson

RO154　1c　**red**　　175.00
RO155　1c　**black**　　4.00　3.25
　　　　Dbl.　　　　　80.00
　　　　transfer
　　e.　Experi-　　75.00
　　　　　mental
　　　　　silk pa-
　　　　　per
RO156　3c　**ver**　　190.00
RO157　3c　**blue**　　7.75　5.00
　　　　Dbl.　　　　　30.00
　　　　transfer
　　e.　Experi-　　92.50
　　　　　mental
　　　　　silk pa-
　　　　　per

The Richardson
Match Co. — RO158　　　H. & W.
　　　　　　　　　Roeber — RO160

The Richardson Match Co.

The 1c is as No. RO154, 3c as No. RO156, inscribed "The Richardson Match Co." instead of "D. M. Richardson."

RO158　1c　**black**　　2.25　6.75　9.00
RO159　3c　**blue**　　95.00

H. & W. Roeber

RO160　1c　**blue**　　8.00　3.00
　　　　Dbl.　　200.00
　　　　transfer
　　e.　Experi-　475.00
　　　　　mental
　　　　　silk pa-
　　　　　per
　　u.　1c **ultra**　300.00

William Roeber — RO161

William Roeber

As No. RO160, "William Roeber" instead of "H. & W. Roeber."

RO161	1c	blue	2.75	9.00	4.00
RO162	1c	bl, roulette			125.00

E. T. Russell — RO163

E. T. Russell

RO163	1c	black	10.00	20.00
	e.	Experimental silk paper	70.00	

R. C. & W. (Ryder, Crouse & Welch)

RO164	1c	lake	110.00

S

San Francisco Match Co. — RO165

Illustration reduced.

San Francisco Match Company

RO165	12c	blue	525.00

Schmitt & Schmittdiel — RO166/RO167

Schmitt & Schmittdiel

RO166	1c	ver	5.50	100.00	5.50
RO167	3c	blue		67.50	

E. K. Smith — RO168/RO169

Standard Match Co. — RO170

E. K. Smith

RO168	1c	blue	14.00	55.00	20.00
RO169	1c	blue, roulette			7,000.

See No. RO132.

The Standard Match Company

RO170	1c	black	35.00

H. Stanton — RO171

H. Stanton

RO171	1c	black	17.00	11.00	22.50	10.00
	e.	Experimental silk paper	125.00			

Star Match — RO172

Star Match

RO172	1c	black	5.50	1.10	2.00	1.25
		Dbl. transfer			—	20.00
	e.	Experimental silk paper	85.00			

Swift & Courtney — RO173

Swift & Courtney

As No. RO174, "Swift & Courtney" in one line.

RO173	1c	blue	3.50	3.50
		Dbl. transfer		
	e.	Experimental silk paper	47.50	
	u.	1c ultra	110.00	

RO174
Swift & Courtney & Beecher Co.

RO175
Swift & Courtney & Beecher

Swift & Courtney & Beecher Co.

RO174	1c	blue	3.50	5.50	2.25
		Dbl. transfer			—
RO175	1c	black			110.00

T

Trenton Match Co. — RO176

Trenton Match Co.

RO176	1c	blue	12.00

E. R. T. (E. R. Tyler)

As No. RO120, inscribed "E. R. T." instead of "The Ives & Judd Match Co."

RO177	1c	green	17.00	4.50
		Dbl. transfer		—
	e.	Experimental silk paper	125.00	

U

Alex Underwood & Co. — RO178

Alex. Underwood & Co.

RO178	1c	green	110.00	160.00
	e.	Experimental silk paper	500.00	

Union Match Co. — RO179

U.S.M. Co. — RO180

Union Match Co.

RO179	1c	black		55.00

U. S. M. Co. (Universal Safety Match Co.)

RO180	1c	black	4.50	30.00
	e.	Experimental silk paper	110.00	

W

Washington Match Co. — RO181

Wilmington Parlor Match Co. — RO182

Washington Match Co.

RO181	1c	black	50.00

Wilmington Parlor Match Co.

RO182	1c	black	175.00	*12,500.*
	e.	Experimental silk paper	500.00	

Wise & Co. — RO183

Wise & Co.

RO183	1c	black	2,000.

Z

F. Zaiss & Co. — RO184

F. Zaiss & Co.

RO184	1c	black	2.25	9.00	2.75

Zisemann, Griesheim & Co.

RO185	1c	green	2,500.	
RO186	1c	blue	160.00	25.00
u.	1c	ultra	1,750.	

PRIVATE DIE CANNED FRUIT STAMP

	a. Old Paper	b. Silk Paper	c. Pink Paper	d. Wmkd. USIR (191R)

T. Kensett & Co. — RP1

1867   *Perf. 12*

T. Kensett & Co.

RP1	1c	green	2,500.

	a. Old Paper	b. Silk Paper	c. Pink Paper	d. Wmkd. USIR (191R)

PRIVATE DIE MEDICINE STAMPS

1862   *Perf. 12*

A

Anglo American Drug Co. — RS1

Anglo American Drug Co.

RS1	1c	black	75.00

J. C. Ayer & Co.

For illustration of No. RS4, see large stamp illustration pages.

RS2	1c	brn car, imperf	10,000.			
RS3	1c	green, imperf	17,500.			
RS4	1c	black, imperf, type 1	160.00	140.00		82.50
		Type 2 Dbl. transfer	160.00	140.00	2,750.	77.50
e.		Experimental silk paper	—			

Type 1: long, full-pointed "y" in "Ayers;" Type 2: short, truncated "y" in "Ayers."

RS5	1c	blue, imperf	10,000.
RS6	1c	org, imperf	17,500.
RS6F	1c	red, imperf	—
RS7	1c	gray lilac, imperf	17,500.

	a. Old Paper	b. Silk Paper	c. Pink Paper	d. Wmkd. USIR (191R)

J.C. Ayer & Co. — RS8, RS9, RS11/RS13

J.C. Ayer & Co. RS10

			a. Old Paper	b. Silk Paper	d. Wmkd. USIR (191R)
RS8	4c	red, die cut	10,000.		
RS9	4c	blue, die cut	10.50	10.50	10.50
e.		Experimental silk paper	2,000.		
u.	4c	ultra (die cut)	775.00		
RS10	4c	blue, imperf	400.00	275.00	350.00
RS11	4c	purple, die cut	17,500.		
RS12	4c	green, die cut	15,000.		
RS13	4c	ver, die cut	10,000.		

The 4c in black was printed and sent to Ayer & Co. It may exist but has not been seen by collectors.

B

Barham Pile Cure Co.

For illustration of No. RS14, see large stamp illustration pages.

RS14	4c	green, wmkd. lozenges	90.00

D. S. Barnes

The 1c, 2c and 4c are about 184mm, 242mm and 304mm tall. The products mentioned differ. "D. S. Barnes" is in manscript.

For illustration of No. RS16 and RS17, see larger stamp illustration pages.

RS15	1c	ver	525.00
RS16	2c	ver	675.00
RS17	4c	ver	1,400.
RS18	1c	black	30.00
RS19	2c	black	60.00
RS20	4c	black	82.50

Demas Barnes

Same as above but with "Demas Barnes" in serifed letters.

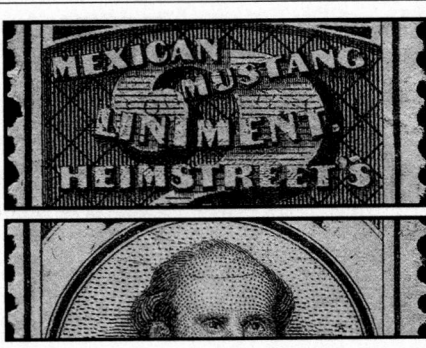

RS22 Foreign entry

For illustration of No. RS23, see large stamp illustration pages.

RS21	1c	black	27.50	
RS22	2c	black	75.00	
		Foreign entry of 1c (No. RS15 or RS21)	2,750.	
RS23	4c	black	35.00	

Demas Barnes & Co.

For illustration of No. RS24, see large stamp illustration pages.

RS24	1c	black	20.00	675.00
e.		Experimental silk paper	2,000.	
RS25	2c	black	20.00	500.00
e.		Experimental silk paper	325.00	
RS26	4c	black	20.00	

T. H. Barr & Co.

For illustration of No. RS27, see larger stamp illustration pages.

RS27	4c	black	30.00	
		Dbl. transfer	225.00	
e.		Experimental silk paper	450.00	

Barry's — RS28/RS29

Barry's

RS28	2c	green, Tricopherous	12.00	22.50	
RS29	2c	grn, Proprietary Dbl. transfer	6.75	275.00	6.00
			275.00		

D. M. Bennett — RS30

D. M. Bennett

RS30	1c	lake	20.00
e.		Experiment. silk paper	160.00

W. T. Blow — RS31

W. T. Blow

RS31	1c	green	325.00	77.50	450.00	95.00
e.		Experimental silk paper	1,900.		

B. Brandreth — RS33   R. Brandreth — RS35

B. Brandreth

RS32	1c	**black,** perf	725.00	775.00		
RS33	1c	**black,** imperf	2.75	1.75		
	e.	Experimental silk paper	42.50			

Nos. RS32-RS33 inscribed "United States Certificate of Genuineness" around vignette.

RS34	1c	**blk,** 41x50mm, imperf	275.00	
RS35	1c	**blk,** 24x30mm, imperf	2.00	11.00	2.25
	p.	Perf	550.00	

Dr. C.F. Brown — RS36

Dr. C. F. Brown

RS36	1c	**grnish blue**	500.00	87.50	100.00

Fred Brown Co.

For illustration of No. RS37, see larger stamp illustration pages.

RS37	2c	**black,** imperf, die I	140.00	47.50	3,750.	40.00
	e.	Experimental silk paper	575.00			
RS38	2c	**black,** imperf, die II		82.50		

Die I has "E" of "Fred" incomplete. Die II shows recutting in the "E" of "Fred" and "Genuine."

John I. Brown & Son.

For illustration of No. RS39, see larger stamp illustration pages.

RS39	1c	**black**	11.00	45.00		10.00
RS40	2c	**green** Dbl. transfer	11.00	20.00	400.00	400.00
	e.	Experimental silk paper	200.00			
RS41	4c	**brown**	550.00	140.00		2,250.

Dr. John Bull

For illustration of No. RS42, see larger stamp illustration pages.

RS42	1c	**black**	210.00	22.50	825.00	22.50
	e.	Experimental silk paper	450.00			
RS43	4c	**blue**	225.00	13.50	600.00	12.00
	e.	Experimental silk paper	775.00			
	u.	4c ultra	2,750.			

J. S. Burdsal & Co.

"J. S. Burdsal & Co./Sole Proprietors" added under United States Proprietary Medicine Co. design, as on Nos. RS245-RS247.

RS44	1c	**blk,** wrapper, white paper	60.00		40.00
RS45	1c	**blk,** wrapper, orange paper	4,250.		1,650.
RS45A	1c	**blk,** wrapper, yellow paper	4,000.		

Joseph Burnett & Co. — RS46

Joseph Burnett & Co.

RS46	4c	**black**	110.00	16.00	400.00	7.75

C

J. W. Campion & Co.

For illustration of No. RS47, see large stamp illustration pages.

RS47	4c	**black,** imperf	550.00		425.00
	p.	Pair, perf horiz.			2,750.
RS48	4c	**black,** die cut	160.00	550.00	125.00

Cannon & Co.

For illustration of No. RS49, see large stamp illustration pages.

RS49	4c	**green,** imperf	140.00	300.00	77.50

The Centaur Co. — RS50/RS52

The Centaur Co.

RS50	1c	**ver**		72.50	11.00
RS51	2c	**black**		16.00	4.00
RS52	4c	**black**			67.50

Dr. A. W. Chase, Son & Co.

For illustration of No. RS55, see large stamp illustration pages.

RS53	1c	**black**	160.00		5,500.
RS54	2c	**black**	160.00		
RS55	4c	**black**	225.00		

Wm. E. Clarke
RS56   RS57

Wm. E Clarke

RS56	3c	**blue**	225.00	
RS57	6c	**black**	100.00	

R. C. & C. S. Clark — RS58

R. C. & C. S. Clark

RS58	4c	**black**	20.00	27.50

Collins Bros. — RS59   W. H. Comstock — RS60

Collins Bros.

RS59	1c	**black**	29.00	550.00

W. H. Comstock

RS60	1c	**black**	5.50

Cook & Bernheimer

RS61	4c	**blue**	110.00

Charles N. Crittenton — RS62/RS64

Charles N. Crittenton

RS62	1c	**black**	11.00		
RS63	1c	**blue**		14.00	7.25
RS64	2c	**black**	95.00	55.00	5.50

Oliver Crook & Co.

For illustration of No. RS65, see larger stamp illustration pages.

RS65	4c	**black**	140.00	27.50
	e.	Experimental silk paper	150.00	

Jeremiah Curtis & Son

For illustration of No. RS67, see larger stamp illustration pages.

RS66	1c	**black**	140.00			
		Die I, small "1s."				
RS67	1c	**black**		125.00		
		Die II, large "1s."				
RS68	2c	**black** Dbl. transfer	11.00	11.00	175.00	400.00

Die II numerals nearly fill the circles.

Curtis & Brown RS69

Curtis & Brown

RS69	1c	**black**	6.25	4.50
	e.	Experimental silk paper	3,250.	
RS70	2c	**black**	200.00	

Curtis & Brown Mfg. Co. RS71

Curtis & Brown Mfg. Co.

These are identical to RS69-RS70 with "Mfg. Co. Limtd." instead of the right hand "TWO CENTS."

For illustration of No. RS72, see larger stamp illustration pages.

RS71	1c	**black**		275.00	10.00
RS72	2c	**black**		2,450.	1,100.

J.C. Ayer & Co. – RS4

Barham Pile Cure Co. – RS14

D.S. Barnes
RS16

D.S. Barnes
RS17

Demas
Barnes RS23

Demas Barnes & Co. – RS24

T.H. Barr & Co. – RS27

John I. Brown &
Son – RS39

Dr.
John Bull
RS42

J.W. Campion
& Co. – RS47

Cannon &
Co. – RS49

Dr. A.W.
Chase, Son &
Co. – RS55

Fred Brown Co. RS37

Oliver Crook & Co. – RS65

Jeremiah Curtis & Son – RS67

Curtis & Brown – RS72

Dalley's Galvanic Horse Salve – RS73

Dalley's Magical Pain Extractor – RS74

L. Pills – RS90

(Dr.) S.B. Hartman & Co. RS99

The Father Mathew Temperance & Manufacturing Company – RS85

(Dr.) S.B. Hartman & Co. – RS100

John F. Henry RS114

Hiscox & Co. RS123

Herrick's Pills RS117

D
Dalley's Galvanic Horse Salve

For illustration of No. RS73, see larger stamp illustration pages.

RS73	2c	green	125.00	225.00	300.00

Dalley's Magical Pain Extractor

For illustration of No. RS74, see larger stamp illustration pages.

RS74	1c	black	16.00	12.00	9.25
	h.	$100	500.00		20.00

#RS74h reads "$100" instead of "$1.00."

Perry Davis & Son — RS75/RS81

Perry Davis & Son

RS75	1c	blue	10.00	4.00	400.00	3.00
	e.	Experimental silk paper	210.00			
	u.	1c ultra	325.00			
RS76	2c	brown red	200.00			
RS77	2c	black	90.00			
RS78	2c	dull pur		11.00		
RS78A	2c	slate		14.00		7.25
RS79	2c	dull red	100.00			
RS80	2c	brown		6,000.		
RS81	4c	brown	14.50	4.50		3.25

P.H. Drake & Co. — RS82/RS83

P. H. Drake & Co.

RS82	2c	black	5,000.		
RS83	4c	black	67.50	77.50	
	e.	Experimental silk paper	275.00		

F

B. A. Fahnestock — RS84

B. A. Fahnestock

RS84	1c	lake, imperf	175.00	140.00	

The Father Mathew Temperance & Manufacturing Company

For illustration of No. RS85, see large stamp illustration pages.

RS85	4c	black			11.00

A. H. Flanders, M.D. — RS87

A. H. Flanders, M. D.

RS86	1c	green, perf			16.00	14.50
RS87	1c	green, part perf	27.50	2.25	45.00	3.25

Fleming Bros. — RS88/RS90

Fleming Bros.
Vermifuge

RS88	1c	black, imperf	16.00	25.00	70.00
	e.	Experimental silk paper	140.00		

L. Pills

For illustration of No. RS90, see large stamp illustration pages.

RS89	1c	black, imperf	8,000.		
RS90	1c	blue, imperf	7.75	9.00	11.00
		Dbl. transfer		77.50	77.50
	e.	Experimental silk paper	—		
	u.	1c ultra	2,400.		

Seth W. Fowle & Son — RS91

Seth W. Fowle & Son, J. P. Dinsmore

RS91	4c	black	22.50	3.25	3.25

G

G. G. Green — RS92/RS93

G. G. Green

RS92	3c	black		7.75
	h.	Tete beche pair		825.00
RS93	3c	blk, rouletted		250.00

H

Reuben P. Hall & Co.

RS94	4c	black	22.50	22.50	25.00
	e.	Experimental silk paper	550.		

Hall & Ruckel — RS95

Hall & Ruckel — RS96

Hall & Ruckel as agents for Xavier Bazin — RS95h/RS96h

Hall & Ruckel

RS95	1c	green	2.00	2.00	35.00	2.00
	e.	Experimental silk paper	35.00			
	h.	Hand-stamped "X.B." (Xavier Bazin) and obliteration				30.00
RS96	3c	black	3.50	3.25	67.50	3.25
	h.	Hand-stamped "X.B." (Xavier Bazin) and obliteration				60.00

Dr. Harter & Co.

RS97	1c	black	27.50	18.00
	e.	Experimental silk paper	275.00	

Dr. Harter — RS98

Dr. Harter

As No. RS97, inscribed "Dr. Harter" instead of "Dr. Harter & Co."

RS98	1c	black	4.50	17.50	5.50
		Dbl. impression	4,500.		

(Dr.) S. B. Hartman & Co.

For illustrations of Nos. RS99 and RS100, see large stamp illustration pages.

RS99	4c	black	2,250.	87.50	1,400.	1,900.
RS100	6c	black	775.00	400.00	

E. T. Hazeltine — RS101/RS103

E. T. Hazeltine

RS101	1c	black			21.00
RS102	2c	blue		42.50	
RS103	4c	black	900.00	27.50	20.00
	e.	Experimental silk paper	3,750.		
	i.	Imperf, pair	1,100.		

E. H. (Edward Heaton) — RS105

E. H. (Edward Heaton)

RS104	3c	black	55.00	
RS105	3c	brown	20.00	

Helmbold's — RS106/RS109

Helmbold's

RS106	2c	blue	2.00	400.00
		Dbl. transfer	—	
RS107	3c	green	55.00	40.00
RS108	4c	black	5.00	225.00
		Dbl. transfer	175.00	
RS109	6c	black	2.25	4.00
e.		Experimental silk paper	57.50	

A. L. Helmbold's

Same as "Helmbold's" but inscribed "A. L. Helmbold's."

RS110	2c	blue	140.00	200.00	110.00
RS111	4c	black	30.00	210.00	11.00

RS112

John F. Henry

RS112	2c	violet	900.00			
RS113	4c	bister	2,000.			

For illustration of No. RS114, see large stamp illustration pages.

RS114	1c	black	67.50	1.10	15.00	1.75
e.		Experimental silk paper	225.00			

Horiz. pairs imperf between were issued of No. RS114d. All known pairs were originally separated, and some have been matched and rejoined. Three rejoined pairs are reported.

RS115	2c	blue	40.00	7.25	160.00	6.75
u.		ultra	600.00			
RS116	4c	red	200.00	1.75	40.00	2.75
e.		Experimental silk paper	200.00			

Herrick's Pills

For illustration of No. RS117, see large stamp illustration pages.

RS117	1c	black	100.00	45.00	160.00	50.00
e.		Experimental silk paper	225.00			
i.		Imperf, pair	3,000.			

No. RS117i is valued in sound condition. Most pairs are faulty and sell for much less.

Herrick's Pills & Plasters — RS118

Herrick's Pills & Plasters

RS118	1c	red	2.75	5.50	82.50	2.75
e.		Experimental silk paper	—			

J.E. Hetherington — RS121

J. E. Hetherington

RS119	1c	black		20.00
RS120	2c	black		725.00
RS121	3c	black		25.00
i.		Imperf, pair		2,250.

Hiscox & Co.

For illustration of No. RS123, see large stamp illustration pages.

RS122	2c	black				17.00
RS123	4c	black	125.00	525.00	2,250.	

Holloway's Pills and Ointment — RS124/RS125

Holloway's Pills and Ointment

RS124	1c	blue, perf		11.00
RS125	1c	blue, imperf		450.00

Holman Liver Pad Co. — RS126/RS127

Holman Liver Pad Co.

RS126	1c	green		22.50
RS127	4c	green		11.00

The Home Bitters Co.

For illustration of No. RS128, see large stamp illustration pages.

RS128	2c	blue				250.00
		Dbl. transfer				—
RS129	3c	green	125.00	175.00	110.00	
RS130	4c	green	250.00		400.00	

Hop Bitters Co. — RS131

Hop Bitters Co.

RS131	4c	black	7.75

Hostetter & Smith

RS132	4c	blk, imperf	82.50	45.00	110.00	35.00
		Dbl. transfer	—	55.00	125.00	42.50
e.		Experimental silk paper	425.00			
RS133	6c	blk, imperf	100.00			
e.		Experimental silk paper	525.00			

S. D. Howe

For illustration of No. RS137, see large stamp illustration pages.

RS134	4c	black, Duponco's Pills	140.00	400.00
RS135	4c	red, Duponco's Pills	475.00	
RS136	4c	green, Duponco's Pills	475.00	

Nos. RS135 and RS136 were never used.

RS137	4c	blue, Arabian Milk	10.00		175.00

C.E. Hull & Co. — RS138

C. E. Hull & Co.

RS138	1c	black	200.00	6.25	60.00	6.25

T. J. Husband

For illustration of No. RS140, see large stamp illustration pages.

RS139	2c	vio, imperf	2,250.		
RS140	2c	ver, imperf	17.00	11.00	10.00

Hutchings & Hillyer

RS141	4c	grn, imperf	22.50	35.00	
e.		Experimental silk paper	240.00		

———— I ————

H. A. Ingham & Co.

RS142	1c	black	60.00

———— J ————

James A. Jackson & Co.

For illustration of No. RS143, see large stamp illustration pages.

RS143	4c	green	2,250.	400.00
		Dbl. transfer		—

Dr. D. Jayne & Son

For illustration of No. RS149, see large stamp illustration pages.

RS144	1c	blue, imperf	—	3,750.		600.00
p.		Perf	900.00			3,500.
RS145	2c	blk, imperf	8,750.	2,750.		1,500.
p.		Perf	3,750.			—
RS146	4c	grn, imperf	4,500.	2,400.	1,500.	650.00
p.		Perf	4,500.			
RS146F	4c	red, imperf				
RS146G	4c	org, imperf	—			
RS147	1c	bl, die cut	6.75	5.50	250.00	5.50

The Home Bitters Co. – RS128

S.D. Howe – RS137

T.J. Husband – RS140

James A. Jackson & Co. – RS143

Dr. D. Jayne & Son – RS149

Lyon Manufg. Co. – RS167

**J.B. Kelly & Co.
RS153**

Dr. Jas. C. Kerr – RS159

Jacob Lippman & Bro. – RS163

T.W. Marsden – RS175

T.W. Marsden – RS176

Mercado & Seully – RS177

Mette & Kanne – RS180

Mishler Herb Bitters Co. – RS181

Moody, Michel & Co. – RS182

Morehead's – RS186

New York Pharmacal Association
RS187

R. V.
Pierce
RS190

Dr. M. Perl & Co. – RS188

Bennett Pieters & Co. – RS191

Bennett Pieters & Co. – RS192

Radway & Co. – RS193

M., P.J. & H.M. Sands – RS209

	e.	Experimental silk paper	—			
	p.	Perf and die cut	160.00	275.00	275.00	550.00
		On horiz. laid paper	62.50			
RS148	2c	**blk,** die cut	11.00	9.00	110.00	5.50
		Dbl. transfer	60.00	60.00	125.00	100.00
	e.	Experimental silk paper	210.00			
	p.	Perf & die cut	45.00	250.00	400.00	
RS149	4c	**grn,** die cut	7.75	5.50	100.00	9.25
		Dbl. transfer	—			
	e.	Experimental silk paper	190.00			
	p.	Perf & die cut	50.00	240.00		300.00
		On vertically laid paper	40.00			

I. S. Johnson & Co. — RS150

Johnston Holloway & Co. — RS151/RS152

I. S. Johnson & Co.

RS150	1c	**ver**	1.50	16.00	1.00
		Dbl. transfer	22.50	60.00	27.50

Johnston Holloway & Co.

RS151	1c	**black**	4.00	3.00
RS152	2c	**green**	4.00	3.25

K

J. B. Kelly & Co.

For illustration of No. RS153, see large stamp illustration pages.

RS153	4c	**blk,** imperf	2,250.	
	e.	Experimental silk paper	2,500.	

B. J. Kendall & Co.

RS154	4c	**blue**	35.00

Dr. Kennedy — RS155

Dr. Kennedy — RS156

Dr. Kennedy

RS155	2c	**green**	60.00	9.00	40.00	6.75
		Dbl. transfer				

---

	e.	Experimental silk paper	1,650.		
RS156	6c	**black**	9.00	82.50	9.00

Kennedy & Co. RS157

Kennedy & Co.

RS157	2c	**black**	7.75	110.00	9.25

K & Co. (Kennedy & Co.)

RS158	1c	**green**	8.25

Dr. Jas. C. Kerr

For illustration of No. RS159, see large stamp illustration pages.

RS159	4c	**blue**	8,750.	350.00	200.00
RS160	6c	**black**	825.00		

L

Lawrence & Martin

RS161	4c	**black**	50.00

Lee & Osgood

RS162	1c	**blue**	16.00	22.50	17.00

Jacob Lippman & Bro.

For illustration of No. RS163, see large stamp illustration pages.

RS163	4c	**blue**	2,000.	2,500.
	e.	Experimental silk paper	3,750.	

Alvah Littlefield — RS165

Alvah Littlefield

RS164	1c	**black**	2.25	1.25	22.50
		Dbl. transfer	100.00	82.50	
	e.	Experimental silk paper	175.00		
		On horiz. laid paper	600.00		
RS165	4c	**green**	2,000.	250.00	

Prof. Low — RS166

Prof. Low

RS166	1c	**black**	3.50	20.00	3.50
		Dbl. transfer		60.00	45.00

Lyon Manufg. Co.

As No. RS24, inscribed "Lyon Manufg. Co." instead of "Demas Barnes & Co."

For illustration of No. RS167, see large stamp illustration pages.

RS167	1c	**black**	22.50	400.00	16.00
RS168	2c	**black**	10.00	200.00	10.00
	i.	Vert. pair, imperf btwn.			2,250.

M

J. McCullough

As No. RS137, inscribed "J. McCullough" instead of "S. D. Howe."

RS169	4c	**black**	140.00	125.00

J. H. McLean — RS170

Manhattan Medicine Co. — RS171/RS172

Dr. J. H. McLean

RS170	1c	**black**	2.75	1.75	17.00	1.75
		Dbl. transfer	55.00	72.50	—	40.00
	e.	Experimental silk paper	140.00			
	i.	Vert. pair, imperf horiz.	—			

Manhattan Medicine Co.

RS171	1c	**violet**			42.50
	u.	1c purple			67.50
RS172	2c	**black**	30.00	42.50	16.00

Mansfield & Higbee

As No. RS174, inscribed "Mansfield & Higbee Memphis, Tenn."

RS173	1c	**blue**	18.00
	i.	Pair, imperf btwn.	175.00
	j.	Block of 4, imperf btwn.	200.00

S. Mansfield & Co. — RS174

Merchant's Gargling Oil — RS178/RS179

S. Mansfield & Co.

RS174	1c	**blue**	30.00	210.00	17.00
	i.	Pair, imperf btwn.	300.00	750.00	375.00
	j.	Block of 4, imperf btwn.	500.00	1,000.	275.00

Nos. RS173-RS174 are perf on 4 sides. The i. and j. varieties served as 2c or 4c stamps. Straight-edged stamps from severed pairs or blocks are worth much less.

T. W. Marsden

For illustrations of Nos. RS175-RS176, see large stamp illustration pages.

RS175	2c	**blue**	10,000.
RS176	4c	**black**	525.00

Mercado & Seully

For illustration of No. RS177, see large stamp illustration pages.

RS177	2c	**blk,** imperf	8,000.

Merchant's Gargling Oil

RS178	1c	**black**	275.00	45.00	1,250.	35.00
	e.	Experimental silk paper	3,250.			
RS179	2c	**green**	275.00	35.00	1,500.	27.50
		Foreign entry	3,000.			3,750.
	e.	Experimental silk paper	3,250.			

Foreign entry is over design of #RO11.

Mette & Kanne

For illustration of No. RS180, see large stamp illustration pages.

RS180	3c	**black**	400.00

Mishler Herb Bitters Co.

For illustration of No. RS181, see large stamp illustration pages.

RS181	4c	black		150.00		
p.		Imperf at ends		225.00		

Moody, Michel & Co.

For illustration of No. RS182, see large stamp illustration pages.

RS182	4c	blk, imperf	200.00	

Dr. C. C. Moore — RS183

Dr. C. C. Moore

RS183	1c	ver, Pilules			6.75
RS184	2c	black, Sure Cure	82.50	15,000.	30.00

Morehead's

For illustration of No. RS186, see large stamp illustration pages.

RS185	1c	black, Magetic Plaster	30.00
RS186	4c	black, Neurodyne	3,250.

N

New York Pharmacal Association

For illustration of No. RS187, see larger stamp illustration pages.

RS187	4c	black	17.00	40.00	11.00

P

Dr. M. Perl & Co.

For illustration of No. RS188, see large stamp illustration pages.

RS188	6c	black, cut to shape	1,650.

R. V. Pierce — RS189/RS190

R. V. Pierce

For illustration of No. RS190, see large stamp illustration pages.

RS189	1c	green		25.00	200.00	27.50
RS190	2c	black	30.00	8.25	35.00	7.75
		Dbl. transfer				
e.		Experimental silk paper	160.00			

Bennett Pieters & Co.

For illustration of No. RS191, see large stamp illustration pages.

RS191	4c	black	600.00	6,000.
e.		Experimental silk paper	2,750.	
RS192	6c	black	1,750.	
i.		Imperf	1,600.	

R

Radway & Co.

For illustration of No. RS193, see large stamp illustration pages.

RS193	2c	black	5.00	3.25	12.00	5.50
		Dbl. transfer		72.50	110.00	82.50

e.		Experimental silk paper	90.00	

D. Ransom & Co.

RS194	1c	blue	5.00	3.00
		Dbl. transfer		
e.		Experimental silk paper	175.00	
RS195	2c	black	27.50	35.00
e.		Experimental silk paper	175.00	

D. Ransom, Son & Co. — RS197

D. Ransom, Son & Co.

As Nos. RS194-RS195 with "Son" added.

RS196	1c	blue	4.50	17.00	6.75
		Dbl. transfer			
RS197	2c	black	18.00	82.50	11.00

Redding's Russia Salve — RS198

Redding's Russia Salve

RS198	1c	black	9.00	9.00
		Dbl. transfer	150.00	

Ring's Vegetable Ambrosia — RS199/RS200

Ring's Vegetable Ambrosia

RS199	2c	blue, imperf	4,250.	
p.		Perf	3,500.	
RS200	4c	blk, imperf	5,000.	5,500.

Ring's Vegetable Ambrosia — RS201/RS202

RS203

RS201	2c	bl, die cut		25.00	
RS202	4c	black, die cut	17.00	17.00	25.00
e.		Experimental silk paper	175.00		
RS203	4c	black, perf		2,000.	3,250.
k.		Perf & die cut			1,100.
p.		Part perf		3,750.	

J. B. Rose & Co. — RS204/RS205

J. B. Rose & Co.

RS204	2c	black		6.75	35.00
		Dbl. transfer		160.00	225.00
RS205	4c	black	8,750.	160.00	
		Dbl. transfer			

Rumford Chemical Works

RS206	2c	green	5.00
RS207	2c	grn, imperf	27.50

S

A. B. & D. Sands

RS208	1c	green	11.00	22.50
e.		Experimental silk paper	110.00	

M., P. J. & H. M. Sands

The #RS208 die was altered to make #RS209.

For illustration of No. RS209, see large stamp illustration pages.

RS209	2c	green	20.00	125.00	17.00

Scheetz's Celebrated Bitter Cordial

For illustration of No. RS210, see large stamp illustration pages.

RS210	4c	black, perf	900.
RS211	4c	blk, imperf	8,000.

Schenck's Mandrake Pills

For illustration of No. RS212, see large stamp illustration pages.

RS212	1c	grn, imperf	5.50	11.00	125.00	5.50
		Dbl. transfer		50.00		—
e.		Experimental silk paper	400.00			
p.		Perf				2,500.

Schenck's Pulmonic Syrup

For illustration of No. RS213, see larger stamp illustration pages.

RS213	6c	blk, imperf	8.25	5.50	110.00	160.00
		Dbl. transfer		62.50		—

Scheetz's Celebrated Bitter Cordial – RS210

Schenck's Mandrake Pills – RS212

Schenck's Pulmonic Syrup – RS213

J.E. Schwartz & Co. – RS215

Dr. D.H. Seelye & Co. – RS222

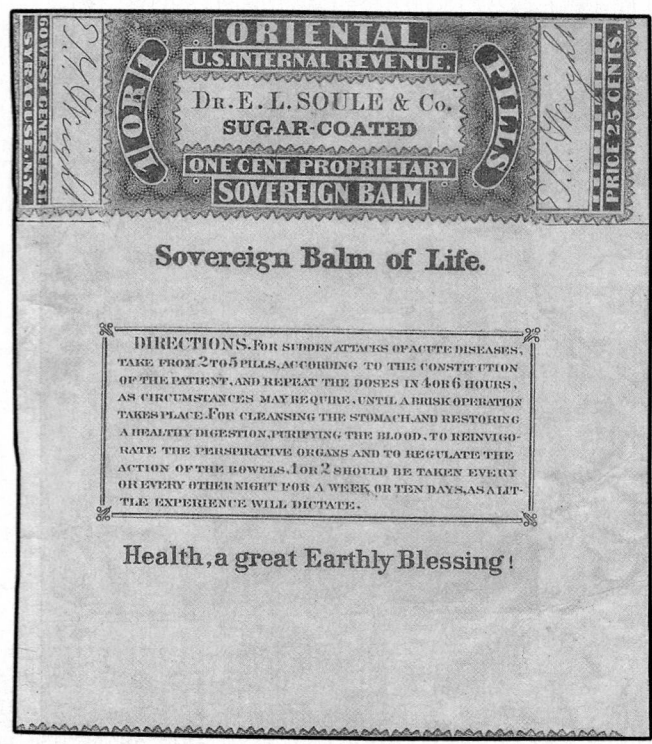

Dr. E.L. Soule & Co. – RS227

Jas. Swaim RS231

Wm. Swaim RS234

George Tallcot RS240

United States Proprietary
Medicine Co. – RS243

S.R. Van Duzer – RS249

United States Proprietary
Medicine Co. – RS247

World's Dispensary
Medical Association
RS272

World's
Dispensary
Medical
Association
RS273

West India Manufacturing Co. – RS264

Hostetter Co. – RS285

X. Bazin
RT1

E.W. Hoyt & Co.
RT7

E.W. Hoyt & Co.
RT8

E.W. Hoyt & Co. – RT11

e.	Experimental silk paper	210.00			
p.	Perf	240.00			

J. H. Schenck & Son — RS214

J. H. Schenck & Son

| RS214 | 4c | black | | 11.00 | |

J. E. Schwartz & Co.

As No. RS84, inscribed "J. E. Schwartz & Co." instead of "B. A. Fahnestock."

For illustration of No. RS215, see large stamp illustration pages.

| RS215 | 1c | lake, imperf | 160.00 | 1,100. | 125.00 |

"A. L. Scovill" follows No. RS219.

Seabury & Johnson — RS216

Seabury & Johnson — RS218

Seabury & Johnson

RS216	1c	black		82.50	
RS217	1c	black, printed obliteration over "porous"		5.50	
	h.	"Porous" obliterated by pen		5.50	
RS218	1c	lake		3,500.	

"Dr. D. H. Seelye & Co." follows No. RS221.

Dr. S. Brown Sigesmond

| RS219 | 4c | blue | | 125.00 | |

A. L. Scovill & Co. — RS220/RS221

A. L. Scovill & Co.

RS220	1c	black	2.00	2.75
		Dbl. transfer	—	—
	e.	Experimental silk paper	77.50	
	r.	Printed on both sides		2,500.
RS221	4c	green	2.25	5.50
	e.	Experimental silk paper	190.00	

Dr. D. H. Seelye & Co.

For illustration of No. RS222, see large stamp illustration pages.

| RS222 | 8c | blk, imperf | | 27.50 | |

Dr. M. A. Simmons

| RS223 | 1c | black, Iuka, Miss. | 125.00 | | 15,000. |
| RS224 | 1c | black, St. Louis, Mo. | 125.00 | | |

S. N. Smith & Co.

As No. RS65, inscribed "S. N. Smith & Co." instead of "Oliver Crook & Co."

For illustration of No. RS225, see large stamp illustration pages.

| RS225 | 4c | black | | 55.00 | 55.00 |

Dr. E. L. Soule & Co.

For illustration of No. RS227, see large stamp illustration pages.

N.Y. Wrapper

| RS226 | 1c | blue | | 82.50 | |
| | | For. entry | | | |

Syracuse Wrapper

RS227	1c	blue		82.50	40.00
		For. entry		400.00	1,250.
	u.	ultra		975.00	
		For. entry			

For Nos. RS226, RS227, the foreign entry is the design of No. RT1 (pos. 1).

H. R. Stevens — RS228/RS229

H. R. Stevens — RS230

H. R. Stevens

RS228	1c	brown		18.00	
RS229	2c	choc		6.75	
RS230	6c	black		125.00	6.75

Jas. Swaim

For illustration of No. RS231, see large stamp illustration pages.

RS231	6c	org		6,500.	
		Die cut, ms signature.			
RS232	8c	org, imperf		3,000.	
	h.	Ms.		10,000.	10,000.
RS233	8c	org, die cut		400.00	
	e.	Experimental silk paper		7,000.	
	h.	Ms.		4,500.	—

No. RS232h, RS233h have manuscript signature.

Wm. Swaim

For illustration of No. RS234, see large stamp illustration pages.

| RS234 | 8c | org, imperf | 9,000. | 6,000. | 2,650. |
| | k. | None | 10,000. | 10,000. | |

No. RS234k is without signature. No. RS234d is found with signature "Suaim" or "Swaim." Also, No. RS234b is found with a period under the raised "m" of "Wm" and the right leg of "w" of "Swaim" retouched, both by pen.

RS235	8c	org, die cut	1,650.	210.00	250.00
	h.	Ms.	25,000.		
	k.	Invt.	10,000.		

No. RS235h has manuscript signature and is unique. No. RS235k has signature inverted.

RS237

Dr. G. W. Swett

| RS236 | 4c | blk, die cut | | 18.00 | |
| RS237 | 4c | green, perf | | 250.00 | 3,250. |

| RS238 | 4c | green, perf and die cut | 450.00 | | 3,750. |

─────── T ───────

George Tallcot

For illustration of No. RS240, see large stamp illustration pages.

| RS239 | 2c | ver | | | 17.00 |
| RS240 | 4c | black | 95.00 | 12,000. | 22.50 |

Tarrant & Co. RS241

John L. Thompson RS242

Tarrant & Company

| RS241 | 4c | red | 3.25 | 100.00 | 2.25 |

John L. Thompson

RS242	1c	black	6.75	8.25	6.75
		Dbl. transfer	—		
	e.	Experimental silk paper	160.00		

─────── U ───────

United States Proprietary Medicine Co.

For illustration of No. RS243, see large stamp illustration pages.

RS243	4c	black	50.00	110.00	
	e.	Experimental silk paper	240.00		
RS244	6c	black	2,500.		

U. S. Proprietary Medicine Co.
Wrappers

For illustration of No. RS247, see larger stamp illustration pages.

RS245	1c	black, white	50.00	50.00	
	e.	Experimental silk paper	500.00		
RS246	1c	black, yel	140.00	250.00	
RS247	1c	black, org	275.00	7,000.	
RS248	1c	black, org red	3,750.	12,000.	

─────── V ───────

S. R. Van Duzer

For illustration of No. RS249, see large stamp illustration pages.

| RS249 | 4c | black | 45.00 | 40.00 | 210.00 |
| RS250 | 6c | black | | | 82.50 |

A. Vogeler & Co. — RS251

Vogeler, Meyer & Co. — RS252

A. Vogeler & Co.

| RS251 | 1c | black | 1.75 | 2.25 |

Vogeler, Meyer & Co.

| RS252 | 1c | ver | 4.50 | 1.50 |

─────── W ───────

Dr. J. Walker

RS253	4c	black	45.00	25.00	22.50
		Dbl. transfer	55.00		45.00
	e.	Experimental silk paper	325.00		

H. H. Warner & Co. —
RS254/RS255

H. H. W. & Co. (H. H. Warner & Co.)

RS254	1c	brown	6.75
RS255	6c	brown, 19x26mm	90.00
RS256	2c	brown, 88x11mm	35.00
RS257	4c	brown, 95x18mm	35.00
RS258	6c	brown	8.25
		Dbl. transfer	55.00

Weeks & Potter — RS259

RS261

RS262

Weeks & Potter

RS259	1c	black	7.75	6.00
RS260	2c	black	110.00	
RS261	4c	black	30.00	30.00 7.75
RS262	2c	red		40.00 7.75

Wells, Richardson
& Co. — RS263

Edward Wilder —
RS265/RS269

Wells, Richardson & Co.

RS263	4c	black	30.00

West India Manufacturing Co.

For illustration of No. RS264, see large stamp illustration pages.

RS264	4c	blk, die I	250.00	400.00 550.00
RS264A	4c	blk, die II		675.00

Die II shows evidence of retouching, particularly in the central disk.

Edward Wilder

RS265	1c	grn, imperf	2,250.	325.00	300.00
	e.	Experimental silk paper	7,500.		

RS266	1c	grn, die cut	55.00	50.00	25.00
	e.	Experimental silk paper	300.00		
RS266A	4c	ver, imperf			
	e.	Experimental silk paper	8,000.		
RS267	4c	ver, die	200.00	2,250.	
	e.	Experimental silk paper	300.00		
RS268	4c	lake, imperf		275.00	2,250.
RS269	4c	lake, die cut	2,000.	14.00	14.00

Rev. E. A. Wilson

RS270	12c	blue		80.00	550.00

Thos. E.
Wilson, M.D.
RS271

Thos. E. Wilson, M. D.

RS271	4c	black	25,000.

World's Dispensary Medical Assocn.

For illustration of No. RS273, see larger stamp illustration pages.

RS272	1c	green	27.50
RS273	2c	black, 56x256mm	9.00

Wright's Indian Vegetable
Pills — RS274

Wright's Indian Vegetable Pills

RS274	1c	green	2.25	1.75	40.00 3.50
		Dbl. transfer			
	e.	Experimental silk paper	150.		

--- Z ---

J.H. Zeilin & Co. —
RS275/RS277

J.H. Zeilin & Co.

RS275	2c	red	1,100.			
RS276	2c	green, perf	45.00		—	
RS277	2c	grn, imperf	200.00	8.25	140.00	5.50

	Roul. 5½		p. Hyphen Hole Perf. 7	
	Unused	Used	Unused	Used

1898-1900

See rouletting note preceding No. R161.

The Antikamnia
Chemical
Co. — RS278

	Roul. 5½		p. Hyphen Hole Perf. 7	
	Unused	Used	Unused	Used

The Antikamnia Chemical Co.

RS278	2½c	car	4.00	4.00

Fernet Branca (Branca Bros.) — RS279

Fernet Branca (Branca Bros.)

RS279	4c	black	9.50	9.50	9.50	9.50

Emerson Drug Co. — RS281

Emerson Drug Co.

RS280	¼c	car	7.00	3.00
RS281	⅝c	green	7.00	3.50
RS282	1¼c	vio brn	9.00	7.00
RS283	2½c	brn org	8.50	5.00

Chas. H. Fletcher — RS284

Chas. H. Fletcher

RS284	1¼c	black	.60	.60	.60	.60

Hostetter Co.

For illustration of No. RS285, see large stamp illustration pages.

RS285	2½c	black, imperf	.60	.60

Johnson &
Johnson — RS286

Johnson & Johnson

RS286	⅝c	car	.50	.50	.50	.50

Lanman &
Kemp — RS287

Lanman & Kemp

RS287	⅝c	green	8.50	6.00	11.00	4.50
RS288	1¼c	brown	11.00	6.50	16.00	12.00
RS289	1⅞c	blue	11.00	8.00	21.00	11.00

J. Ellwood Lee Co. — RS290

J. Ellwood Lee Co.

RS290	⅛c	dk bl		3.25	3.00
RS291	⅝c	car		2.75	2.00
RS292	1¼c	dk grn		2.25	2.00
RS293	2½c	org		2.75	2.50
RS294	5c	chocolate		3.00	2.75

Charles Marchand — RS295

Charles Marchand

RS295	⅝c	black	8.50	8.50	9.00	9.00
RS296	1¼c	black	1.75	1.75	1.75	1.75
RS297	1⅞c	black	2.50	2.50	3.00	3.00
RS298	2½c	black	3.00	3.00	3.00	3.00
RS299	3⅛c	black	8.50	8.50	8.50	8.50
RS300	4¾c	black	16.00	16.00	16.00	16.00
RS301	7½c	black	11.00	11.00	11.00	11.00

RS302

Od Chem. Co.

RS302	2½c	car		—	2.50

The Piso Company — RS303

The Piso Company (E. T. Hazeltine)

RS303	⅝c	blue	.50	.50	.50	.50

Radway & Co. — RS304

Radway & Co.

RS304	⅝c	blue	1.25	1.25	1.25	1.25

Warner's Safe Cure Co. — RS305

Warner's Safe Cure Co.

RS305	3⅛c	brown	1.25	1.25	1.25	1.25

Dr. Williams Medicine Co. — RS306

Dr. Williams Medicine Co.

RS306	1¼c	pink		3.50	3.50

DR. KILMER & CO., PROVISIONAL PROPRIETARY STAMPS

Postage Stamps of 1895, 1897-1903, Nos. 267a, 279, 279Bg and 268, Precancel Overprinted in Black:

Dr. K. & Co.
I. R.
7-5-'98.
a

b

c

1898		Wmk. 191		*Perf. 12*

Overprint "a," Large "I.R." Dated July 5, 1898.

RS307	A87	1c	deep green	175.00
a.			Red (trial) plus black ovpt.	—
RS308	A88	2c	pink, type III	160.00
RS308A	A88	2c	pink, type IV	175.00
b.			Dark blue (trial) ovpt.	—
RS309	A89	3c	purple	160.00
a.			Red (trial) ovpt.	—
b.			Inverted ovpt.	—

A trial overprint in dark blue on the 2c stamp is known used on July 5.

Overprint "b," Small "I.R.," "Dr. K. & Co." with Serifs Dated July 6, 7, 9, 11 to 14, 1898

RS310	A87	1c	deep green	140.00
RS311	A88	2c	pink, type III	150.00
RS311A	A88	2c	pink, type IV	77.50
RS312	A89	3c	purple	67.50
a.			Inverted ovpt.	—

Overprint "c," Small "I.R.," "Dr. K. & Co." without Serifs Dated July 7, 9, 11 to 14, 1898

RS313	A87	1c	deep green	150.00
RS314	A88	2c	pink, type III	150.00
RS314A	A88	2c	pink, type IV	100.00
RS315	A89	3c	purple	125.00
a.			Inverted ovpt.	—

Nos. RS307a, RS308Ab and RS309a were all overprinted on July 5, the first day of overprinting. Though called "trials," there is every reason to believe they were used in the regular course of business, as they represented money spent by Dr. Kilmer & Co. and there was no reason not to use them. Four examples are recorded of No. RS307a, three of No. RS308Ab and one of No. RS309a. For the inverted overprints, four examples are recorded of No. RS309b, 16 of No. RS312a and three of No. RS315a. Forgeries exist of No. RS312a, all dated July 6. The height of "I.R." is shorter on the forgeries, and the periods after these letters are circular rather than diamond shaped. Many varieties of the Kilmer overprints exist. For the complete listing see "The Case of Dr. Kilmer's," by Morton Dean Joyce, 1954 (also serialized in "The Bureau Specialist," Mar.-Nov. 1957).

ST. LOUIS PROVISIONAL PROPRIETARY STAMPS

U.S. "Battleship" revenue stamps (Nos. RB20-RB31) not being available to meet the July 1, 1898, effective date of new taxes on proprietary medicines, eleven proprietary drug companies (10 in St. Louis, Missouri, and one in Macon, Georgia) struck agreements with local collectors of internal revenue to print their own revenue stamps for temporary use and pay their taxes by sworn returns until the government-issued stamps were available. Even though one company that used such stamps was from Macon, Georgia, these stamps are commonly referred to as the St. Louis Provisionals.

The Antikamnia Chemical Co. — RS320/RS321

The Antikamnia Chemical Co. — RS323

Antikamnia Chemical Co., St. Louis

1898				*Imperf.*
RS320	⅛c	black, *yellow*		550.00
RS321	2½c	black		175.00
RS323	No value,	black, *yellow*		350.00

No. RS323 was for use on free samples not subject to tax.

Fairchild Chemical Laboratory Co. — RS325

Fairchild Chemical Laboratory Co., St. Louis
Imperf

RS325	⅝c	black		2,750.

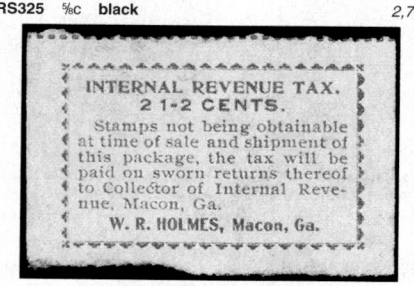

W.R. Holmes — RS330

W.R. Holmes, Macon, Georgia
Rouletted 9½ Horiz. in Green, Imperf Vert.

RS330	2½c	green		2,750.

INTERNAL REVENUE TAX 2 1-2 CENTS.
Stamps not being obtainable at time of
sale and shipment of this package, will be
paid on sworn returns thereof to Collector
of Internal Revenue, 1st Dist. Mo.
LAMBERT PHARMACAL Co., St. Louis, Mo.

Lambert Pharmacal Co. — RS335

Lambert Pharmacal Co., St. Louis
Imperf

RS335 2½c **red** 275.00

INTERNAL REVENUE TAX.
1-8 CENT.
Stamps not being obtainable
at time of sale and shipment of
this package, the tax will be
paid on sworn returns thereof
to Collector of Internal Revenue, 1st Dist. Mo.
Meyer Brothers Drug Co., St. Louis.

Meyer Brothers Drug Co. — RS340/RS350

INTERNAL REVENUE TAX.
1-8 CENT.
Stamps not being obtainable
at time of sale and shipment of
this package, the tax will be
paid on sworn returns thereof
to Collector of Internal Revenue, 1st Dist. Mo.
Meyer Brothers Drug Co., St. Louis.

Meyer Brothers Drug Co. — RS351/RS361

Meyer Brothers Drug Co., St. Louis

These stamps were printed on at least three distinct papers: white, buff and rough manila.

Rouletted 9½ Horiz. in Green, Perf 12 and/or Imperf Vert.

	a. White Paper	b. Buff Paper	c. Rough Manila Paper
RS340 ⅛c **green**	2,750.		
RS343 ⅝c **green**		2,250.	
RS345 1¼c **green**			2,750.
RS349 5c **green**	2,750.		
RS350 11¼c **green**			2,750.

Imperf

RS351 ⅛c **black**	110.00
RS352 ¼c **black**	110.00
RS353 ⅜c **black**	110.00
RS354 ⅝c **black**	110.00
RS355 1c **black**	110.00
RS357 2c **black**	110.00
RS358 3c **black**	110.00
RS359 4c **black**	110.00
RS360 5c **black**	110.00
RS361 11¼c **black**	110.00

Internal Revenue Tax 1-8 Cent.
Stamps not being obtainable at time
of sale and shipment of this
package, will be paid on sworn
returns thereof to Collector of
Internal Revenue, 1st Dist. Mo.
Jno. T. Milliken & Co.

John T. Milliken & Co. — RS365/RS366

John T. Milliken & Co., St. Louis
Imperf

RS365 ⅛c **black**	550.00
RS366 ⅝c **black**	675.00

Internal Revenue Tax, ¼c
Stamps not being obtainable at time
of sale and shipment of this pack-
age, will be paid on sworn returns
thereof to COLLECTOR of INTERNAL
REVENUE, 1st District of Mo.
Phénique Chemical Co.,
G. E. REMICK, Gen'l Mgr.,
ST. LOUIS, MO.

Phenique Chemical Co. — RS370/RS377

Phenique Chemical Co., St. Louis

These stamps were printed on two distinct papers: yellow and buff.

Imperf

	a. Yellow Paper	b. Buff Paper
RS370 ⅛c **black**		2,750.
RS371 ¼c **black**	2,750.	2,750.
RS372 ⅝c **black**	1,650.	2,750.
RS375 2½c **black**	2,750.	
RS376 3⅛c **black**		2,750.
RS377 3¾c **black**		2,750.

INTERNAL REVENUE TAX.
2 1-2 CENTS.
Stamps not being obtainable
at time of sale and shipment of
this package, the tax will be
paid on sworn returns thereof
to Collector of Internal Revenue, 1st Dist. Mo.
Prickly Ash Bitters Co., St. Louis.

Prickly Ash Bitters Co. — RS381

Prickly Ash Bitters Co., St. Louis
Rouletted 9½ Horiz. in Green, Imperf Vert.

RS381 2½c **green** 1,650.

Internal Revenue Tax ¼ cent
Stamps not being obtain-
able at time of sale and
shipment of this package,
Revenue will be paid on
sworn returns thereof to
Collector of Internal Revenue, 1st Dist. Mo.
T. M. SAYMAN.

T.M. Sayman — RS385/RS387

T.M. Sayman, St. Louis
Imperf

RS385 ¼c **dark blue**	2,750.
RS386 ⅝c **dark blue**	2,250.
RS387 1¼c **dark blue**	2,750.

INTERNAL REVENUE TAX, 2½c.
Stamps not being obtainable at time of
sale and shipment of this package, will
be paid on sworn returns thereof to
COLLECTOR OF INTERNAL REVE-
NUE, 1st District of Mo.
Van Dyke Bitters Co.,
ST. LOUIS, MO.

Van Dyke Bitters Co. — RS390

Van Dyke Bitters Co., St. Louis
Imperf

RS390 2½c **blue**, *bluish glazed* 1,100.

Internal Revenue Tax 2 1-2 Cents.
Stamps not being obtainable at
time of sale and shipment of this
package, will be paid on sworn
returns thereof to Collector of
Internal Revenue, 1st Dist. Mo.
Walker Phar. Co.

Walker Pharmacal Co. — RS395

Walker Pharmacal Co., St. Louis
Imperf

RS395 2½c **black** 2,750.

PRIVATE DIE PERFUMERY STAMPS
1864   **Perf. 12**

X. Bazin

For illustration of No. RT1, see large stamp illustration pages.

	a. Old Paper	b. Silk Paper	c. Pink Paper	d. Wmkd. USIR (191R)
RT1 2c **blue**, die cut	1,400.			

This stamp was never placed in use.

Corning & Tappan — RT2/RT4

Corning & Tappan

RT2 1c **black**, imperf	2,750.
h. Die cut, 19mm diameter	125.00
k. Die cut, 21mm diameter	175.00
RT3 1c **black**, perf	825.00
RT4 1c **blue**, perf	4.50

Fetridge & Co. — RT5

Fetridge & Co.

RT5 2c **ver**, cut to shape 125.00

E. W. Hoyt & Co. — RT6

E. W. Hoyt & Co.

For illustrations of Nos. RT7, RT8 and RT11, see large stamp illustration pages.

	a.	b.	c.
RT6 1c **black**, imperf	6,500.	5,000.	160.00
RT7 1c **black**, die cut	37.50	37.50	18.00
RT8 2c **black**, imperf			1,000.
RT9 2c **black**, die cut			100.00
RT10 4c **black**, imperf	2,750.	350.00	2,250.
RT11 4c **black**, die cut	125.00	80.00	80.00

The 2c is larger than the 1c, 4c larger than 2c.

Kidder & Laird

RT12 1c **vermilion**	17.00
RT13 2c **vermilion**	17.00

George W. Laird — RT14/RT15

George W. Laird

RT14	3c	blk, imperf	1,000.	1,250.	1,000.
		Double transfer	1,250.	2,250.	1,250.
	p.	Perf	3,250.	4,000.	
		As "p," double transfer	4,250.		
RT15	3c	black, die cut	3,000.	110.00	3,250.	110.00
		Double transfer	275.00	6,500.	325.00
	e.	Experimental silk paper, double transfer	—		
	p.	Perf and die cut	1,250.		

Lanman & Kemp — RT16/RT18

Tetlow's Perfumery — RT19

Lanman & Kemp

RT16	1c	black	8.25	450.00	8.25
		Dbl. transfer	—		
RT17	2c	brown	35.00		11.00
RT18	3c	green	9.00		9.00
		Dbl. transfer	175.00		77.50

Tetlow's Perfumery

RT19	1c	vermilion			3.75

C. B. Woodworth & Son — RT20/RT21

R. & G. A. Wright — RT22/RT25

C. B. Woodworth & Son

RT20	1c	green	6.00	20.00	7.75
		Dbl. transfer	67.50	82.50	67.50
RT21	2c	blue	180.00	3,750.	10.00

R. & G. A. Wright

RT22	1c	blue	6.75	9.00	67.50
	e.	Experimental silk paper	125.00		
RT23	2c	black	13.00	25.00	375.00
RT24	3c	lake	35.00	125.00	525.00
RT25	4c	green	100.00	140.00	400.00

Young, Ladd & Coffin — RT26/RT33

Young, Ladd & Coffin

RT26	1c	green, imperf	110.00	100.00	110.00
RT27	1c	green, perf	25.00	17.00	17.00
RT28	2c	blue, imperf	150.00	130.00	90.00
RT29	2c	blue, perf	60.00	95.00	17.00
RT30	3c	ver, imperf	130.00	150.00	95.00
RT31	3c	ver, perf	40.00	8.25	7.75
RT32	4c	brown, imperf	6,500.	160.00	110.00
RT33	4c	brown, perf	45.00	14.00	5.50

a. Old Paper	b. Silk Paper	c. Pink Paper	d. Wmkd. USIR (191R)

PRIVATE DIE PLAYING CARD STAMPS

1864

Caterson Brotz & Co.

RU1	5c	brown	10,000.

This stamp was never placed in use.

A. Dougherty — RU2/RU6

A. Dougherty — RU5

A. Dougherty

RU2	2c	orange	77.50		
RU3	4c	black	55.00		
RU4	5c	blue, 20x26mm	2.00	2.00	14.00
		Double transfer	—		
	e.	Experimental silk paper	325.00		
		As "e," inverted dbl. transfer	—		
	u.	5c ultra	200.00		

RU5	5c	blue, 18x23mm			1.75
RU6	10c	blue	45.00		

The 2c, 4c and 5c have numerals in all four corners.

Eagle Card Co. — RU7

Eagle Card Co.

RU7	5c	black	95.00

Goodall — RU8

Samuel Hart & Co. — RU9

Goodall (London, New York)

As No. RU13, "London Goodall New York" replaces both "American Playing Cards" and "Victor E. Mauger and Petrie New York."

RU8	5c	black	175.00	4.50
	e.	Experimental silk paper	2,750.	

Samuel Hart & Co.

RU9	5c	black	6.75	6.75
	e.	Experimental silk paper	2,750.	

Lawrence & Cohen — RU10/RU11

Lawrence & Cohen

RU10	2c	blue	90.00	
RU11	5c	green	6.00	7.75
	e.	Experimental silk paper	140.00	

Jn. J. Levy

RU12	5c	black	27.50	30.00
	e.	Experimental silk paper	140.00	

Victor E. Mauger & Petrie — RU13

New York Consolidated Card Co. — RU14

Victor E. Mauger and Petrie

RU13	5c	blue	2.25	2.25	1.25

New York Consolidated Card Co.

RU14	5c	black	5.50	17.00	5.00

Paper
Fabrique — RU15

Russell, Morgan &
Co. — RU16

Russell, Morgan & Co.

RU16	5c	black	22.50

Paper Fabrique Company

RU15	5c	black	10.00	22.50	10.00

MOTOR VEHICLE USE REVENUE STAMPS

When affixed to a motor vehicle, permitted use of that vehicle for a stated period.

RV1

1942   Wmk. 191R   OFFSET PRINTING   *Perf. 11*
With Gum on Back

RV1	RV1	$2.09	**light green** *(February)*	1.75	.50

With Gum on Face
Inscriptions on Back

RV2	RV1	$1.67	**light green** *(March)*	30.00	8.50
RV3	RV1	$1.25	**light green** *(April)*	22.50	7.50
RV4	RV1	84c	**light green** *(May)*	25.00	7.25
RV5	RV1	42c	**light green** *(June)*	25.00	7.25

With Gum and Control Number on Face
Inscriptions on Back

RV6	RV1	$5	**rose red** *(July)*	3.25	1.50
RV7	RV1	$4.59	**rose red** *(August)*	55.00	13.00
RV8	RV1	$4.17	**rose red** *(September)*	60.00	16.00
RV9	RV1	$3.75	**rose red** *(October)*	55.00	12.50
RV10	RV1	$3.34	**rose red** *(November)*	55.00	12.50
RV11	RV1	$2.92	**rose red** *(December)*	55.00	12.50
		Nos. RV1-RV11 (11)		387.50	99.00

1943

RV12	RV1	$2.50	**rose red** *(January)*	62.50	16.00
RV13	RV1	$2.09	**rose red** *(February)*	42.50	11.00
RV14	RV1	$1.67	**rose red** *(March)*	37.50	12.50
RV15	RV1	$1.25	**rose red** *(April)*	37.50	9.00
RV16	RV1	84c	**rose red** *(May)*	37.50	9.00
RV17	RV1	42c	**rose red** *(June)*	37.50	10.00
RV18	RV1	$5	**yellow** *(July)*	3.75	1.00
RV19	RV1	$4.59	**yellow** *(August)*	65.00	17.00
RV20	RV1	$4.17	**yellow** *(September)*	82.50	21.00
RV21	RV1	$3.75	**yellow** *(October)*	82.50	21.00
RV22	RV1	$3.34	**yellow** *(November)*	90.00	22.00
RV23	RV1	$2.92	**yellow** *(December)*	110.00	25.00
		Nos. RV12-RV23 (12)		688.75	174.50

1944

RV24	RV1	$2.50	**yellow** *(January)*	125.00	25.00
RV25	RV1	$2.09	**yellow** *(February)*	72.50	19.00
RV26	RV1	$1.67	**yellow** *(March)*	62.50	16.00
RV27	RV1	$1.25	**yellow** *(April)*	62.50	17.00
RV28	RV1	84c	**yellow** *(May)*	55.00	16.00
RV29	RV1	42c	**yellow** *(June)*	55.00	16.00

Gum on Face
Control Number and Inscriptions on Back

RV30	RV1	$5	**violet** *(July)*	2.40	1.75
RV31	RV1	$4.59	**violet** *(August)*	92.50	21.00
RV32	RV1	$4.17	**violet** *(September)*	67.50	19.00
RV33	RV1	$3.75	**violet** *(October)*	67.50	19.00
RV34	RV1	$3.34	**violet** *(November)*	62.50	12.50
RV35	RV1	$2.92	**violet** *(December)*	62.50	12.50
		Nos. RV24-RV35 (12)		787.40	194.75

1945

RV36	RV1	$2.50	**violet** *(January)*	55.00	12.00
RV37	RV1	$2.09	**violet** *(February)*	47.50	12.00
RV38	RV1	$1.67	**violet** *(March)*	47.50	10.50
RV39	RV1	$1.25	**violet** *(April)*	47.50	10.50
RV40	RV1	84c	**violet** *(May)*	37.50	9.00
RV41	RV1	42c	**violet** *(June)*	28.50	7.25

Daniel Manning — RV2

Gum on Face
Control Number and Inscriptions on Back
1945   Wmk. 191R   Offset Printing   *Perf. 11*
Bright Blue Green & Yellow Green

RV42	RV2	$5	*(July)*	3.25	1.00
RV43	RV2	$4.59	*(August)*	67.50	19.00
RV44	RV2	$4.17	*(Sept.)*	67.50	19.50
RV45	RV2	$3.75	*(October)*	62.50	12.50
RV46	RV2	$3.34	*(November)*	50.00	12.00
RV47	RV2	$2.92	*(December)*	45.00	9.00
		Nos. RV36-RV47 (12)		559.25	134.25

1946
Bright Blue Green & Yellow Green

RV48	RV2	$2.50	*(January)*	47.50	12.50
RV49	RV2	$2.09	*(February)*	47.50	12.00
RV50	RV2	$1.67	*(March)*	37.50	9.00
RV51	RV2	$1.25	*(April)*	30.00	9.00
RV52	RV2	84c	*(May)*	30.00	9.00
RV53	RV2	42c	*(June)*	22.50	1.20
		Nos. RV48-RV53 (6)		215.00	52.70

BOATING STAMPS

Required on applications for the certificate of number for motorboats of more than 10 horsepower, starting April 1, 1960. The pictorial upper part of the $3 stamp was attached to the temporary certificate and kept by the boat owner. The lower part (stub), showing number only, was affixed to the application and sent by the post office to the U.S. Coast Guard, which issued permanent certificates. The $3 fee was for three years. The $1 stamp covered charges for reissue of a lost or destroyed certificate of number. These stamps were used in the 12 states and the District of Columbia that had not passed laws in conformity with the Boating Act of 1958.

> Catalogue value for unused stamps in this section are for Never Hinged items.

Outboard and Inboard Motorboats — RVB1

Offset Printing, Number Typographed

1960, Apr. 1			Unwmk.		Rouletted
RVB1	RVB1	$1	**rose red,** black number	37.50	*750.00*
			P# block of 4	160.00	
			On license		—
RVB2	RVB1	$3	**blue,** red number	45.00	*30.00*
			P# block of 4	190.00	
			On license		50.00
			First day license		*700.00*

Nos. RVB1 and RVB2 unused stamp values are for MNH complete two-part stamps. Used values are for stamps, without the stubs, bearing a complete cancel dated between April 1, 1960, and January 31, 1964. On-license values are for clean licenses with undamaged stamps and a complete cancel. A license fold can be expected. Mute oval cancels are usually favor cancels.

CAMP STAMPS

The Camp Stamp program of the Department of Agriculture's National Forest Service was introduced in 1985. The public was offered the option of prepaying their recreation fees through the purchase of camp stamps. The fees varied but were typically $3 to $4.

The stamps were supplied in rolls with the backing rouletted 9 horizontally. The letter preceding the serial number indicated the face value and printer (A-D, Denver; E-J, Washington). The stamps were designed so that any attempt to remove them from the fee envelope would cause them to come apart.

The program ended in the summer of 1988. The envelopes containing the stamps were destroyed by the National Forerst Service after use. No used examples have been reported.

> Catalogue value for unused stamps in this section are for Never Hinged items.

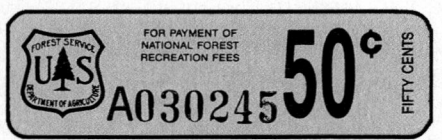

National Forest Service Logo — RVC1

Printed in Denver, CO.

1985   Typo.   Die Cut
Self-Adhesive, Coated Paper

RVC1	RVC1	50c	**black,** *pink,* "A"	70.00
RVC2	RVC1	$1	**black,** *red,* "B"	70.00
RVC3	RVC1	$2	**black,** *yellow,* "C"	70.00
RVC4	RVC1	$3	**black,** *green,* "D"	70.00

RVC2

Printed by the Government Printing Office, Washington, DC (?).

1986   Typo.   Die Cut
Self-Adhesive, Coated Paper

RVC5	RVC2	50c	**black,** *pink,* "E"	150.00
RVC6	RVC2	$1	**black,** *red,* "F"	160.00
RVC7	RVC2	$2	**black,** *yellow,* "G"	175.00
RVC8	RVC2	$3	**black,** *green,* "H"	175.00
RVC9	RVC2	$5	**black,** *silver,* "I"	350.00
RVC10	RVC2	$10	**black,** *bronze,* "J"	—

TRAILER PERMIT STAMPS

Issued by the National Park Service of the Department of the Interior. Required to be affixed to "License to Operate Motor Vehicle" starting July 1, 1939, when a house trailer was attached to a motor vehicle entering a national park or national monument.

Issued to rangers in booklets of 50 (five 2x5 panes).

Use was continued at least until 1952.

Unused stamps may have a ranger's handwritten control number.

Trailer and
Automobile
RVT1

1939		Unwmk.	Offset Printing	Perf. 11	
RVT1	RVT1	50c **bright blue**		2,750.	1,250.
		On license			2,750.
RVT2	RVT1	$1 **carmine**		500.00	250.00
		On license			750.00

Earliest known use: July 1939.

DISTILLED SPIRITS EXCISE TAX STAMPS

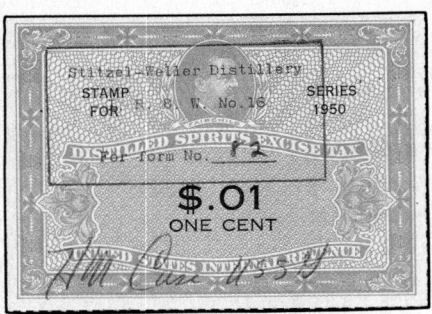

Charles S. Fairchild, Secretary of Treasury 1887-
89 — DS1

Actual size: 89½x63½mm

Inscribed "STAMP FOR SERIES 1950"

1950		Wmk. 191R	Offset Printing	Rouletted 7	
			Left Value — Unused		
			Right Value — Used		
RX1	DS1	1c **yellow green & black**		50.00	27.50
		Punched cancel			21.00
RX2	DS1	3c **yellow green & black**		140.00	100.00
		Punched cancel			92.50
RX3	DS1	5c **yellow green & black**		27.50	20.00
		Punched cancel			17.50
RX4	DS1	10c **yellow green & black**		25.00	17.50
		Punched cancel			15.00
RX5	DS1	25c **yellow green & black**		40.00	11.00
		Punched cancel			9.00
RX6	DS1	50c **yellow green & black**		25.00	11.00
		Punched cancel			8.00
RX7	DS1	$1 **yellow green & black**		30.00	3.00
		Punched cancel			1.75
RX8	DS1	$3 **yellow green & black**		40.00	20.00
		Punched cancel			15.00
RX9	DS1	$5 **yellow green & black**		30.00	6.50
		Punched cancel			4.50
RX10	DS1	$10 **yellow green & black**		15.00	3.00
		Punched cancel			1.75
RX11	DS1	$25 **yellow green & black**		25.00	12.50
		Punched cancel			9.25
RX12	DS1	$50 **yellow green & black**		25.00	8.75
		Punched cancel			5.00
RX13	DS1	$100 **yellow green & black**		15.00	4.00
		Punched cancel			3.00
RX14	DS1	$300 **yellow green & black**		45.00	25.00
		Punched cancel			21.00
RX15	DS1	$500 **yellow green & black**		30.00	15.00
		Punched cancel			10.00
RX16	DS1	$1,000 **yellow green & black**		25.00	11.00
		Punched cancel			8.00
RX17	DS1	$1,500 **yellow green & black**		70.00	50.00
		Punched cancel			40.00
RX18	DS1	$2,000 **yellow green & black**		12.50	5.00
		Punched cancel			4.00
RX19	DS1	$3,000 **yellow green & black**		35.00	25.00
		Punched cancel			15.00
RX20	DS1	$5,000 **yellow green & black**		35.00	25.00
		Punched cancel			17.50
RX21	DS1	$10,000 **yellow green & black**		45.00	27.50
		Punched cancel			22.50
RX22	DS1	$20,000 **yellow green & black**		55.00	35.00
		Punched cancel			30.00
RX23	DS1	$30,000 **yellow green & black**		90.00	70.00
		Punched cancel			50.00
RX24	DS1	$40,000 **yellow green & black**		1,200.	950.00
		Punched cancel			600.00
RX25	DS1	$50,000 **yellow green & black**		200.00	95.00
		Punched cancel			75.00

Inscription "STAMP FOR SERIES 1950" omitted

1952					
			Left Value — Unused		
			Right Value — Used		
RX27	DS1	3c **yellow green & black**		900.00	
RX28	DS1	5c **yellow green & black**		300.00	
		Punched cancel			40.00
RX29	DS1	10c **yellow green & black**		35.00	90.00
		Punched cancel			5.00
RX30	DS1	25c **yellow green & black**		45.00	90.00
		Punched cancel			15.00
RX31	DS1	50c **yellow green & black**		45.00	90.00
		Punched cancel			15.00
RX32	DS1	$1 **yellow green & black**		30.00	90.00
		Punched cancel			2.50
RX33	DS1	$3 **yellow green & black**		55.00	90.00
		Punched cancel			22.50
RX34	DS1	$5 **yellow green & black**		55.00	90.00
		Punched cancel			25.00
RX35	DS1	$10 **yellow green & black**		30.00	90.00
		Punched cancel			2.50
RX36	DS1	$25 **yellow green & black**		40.00	90.00
		Punched cancel			10.00
RX37	DS1	$50 **yellow green & black**		90.00	90.00
		Punched cancel			25.00
RX38	DS1	$100 **yellow green & black**		30.00	90.00
		Punched cancel			2.50
RX39	DS1	$300 **yellow green & black**		40.00	90.00
		Punched cancel			7.50
RX40	DS1	$500 **yellow green & black**		450.00	
		Punched cancel			30.00
RX41	DS1	$1,000 **yellow green & black**		140.00	75.00
		Punched cancel			6.00
RX42	DS1	$1,500 **yellow green & black**		900.00	
RX43	DS1	$2,000 **yellow green & black**		700.00	
		Punched cancel			75.00
RX44	DS1	$3,000 **yellow green & black**		1,200.	700.00
		Punched cancel			700.00
RX45	DS1	$5,000 **yellow green & black**		600.00	
		Punched cancel			50.00
RX46	DS1	$10,000 **yellow green & black**		700.00	
		Punched cancel			90.00

Five other denominations with "Stamp for Series 1950" omitted were prepared but are not known to have been put into use:
1c, $20,000, $30,000, $40,000 and $50,000.

Stamps listed as used have staple holes.

Distilled Spirits Excise Tax stamps were discontinued in 1959.

FIREARMS TRANSFER TAX STAMPS

Used on transfer tax documents for tax paid transfers of National Firearms Act weapons. Prior to 1968, transfers of NFA weapons were processed by the Alcohol, Tobacco and Firearms division of the Internal Revenue Service. Current examples of firearms transfer stamps are not available for sale to collectors because of the possibility of fraudulent misuse.

Documentary Stamp of 1917
Overprinted Vertically in Black.
Reading Up

1934   Engr.   Wmk. 191R   *Perf. 11*
Without Gum

RY1   R21 $1 **green**   450.00   —
          On license

RY1

Actual size: 89½x64mm

RY2

Eagle, Shield and Stars from U.S. Seal

Two types of $200:
I — Serial number with serifs, not preceded by zeros. Tips of 6 lines project into left margin.
II — Gothic serial number preceded by zeros. Five line tips in left margin.

1934   Wmk. 191R   *Perf. 12*
Size: 28x42mm
Without Gum

RY2   RY1 $200 **dark blue & red**, type I, #1-   1,750.   900.00
                1500
          On license   *1,000.*

Issued in vertical strips of 4 which are imperforate at top, bottom and right side.
See Nos. RY4, RY6-RY8.

1938   Size: 28x33½mm   *Perf. 11*
RY3   RY2 $1 **green**   85.00   35.00
          On license   —

          See No. RY5.

1950 (?)   Wmk. 191R   *Perf. 12*
Size: 29x43mm
RY4   RY1 $200 **dull blue & red**, type II,   750.00   450.00
                #1501-3000
          On license   500.00

No. RY4 has a clear impression and is printed on white paper. No. RY2 has a "muddy" impression in much darker blue ink and is printed on off-white paper.

1960, July 1   Size: 29x34mm   *Perf. 11*
RY5   RY2 $5 **red**   25.00   *40.00*
          On license   200.00

No. RY5 was issued in sheets of 50 (10x5) with straight edge on four sides of sheet.
The watermark is hard to see on many examples of #RY2-RY5.

1974   Unwmk.   *Perf. 12*
Size: 29x43mm
RY6   RY1 $200 **dull blue & red**, type II,   225.00   110.00
                #3001-up
          On license   125.00

Panes of 32
1990(?)   Litho.   Without Gum   *Imperf.*
RY7   RY1 $200 **dull blue**   *500.00*
          On license   *750.00*

1990   *Perf. 12½*
RY8   RY1 $200 **dull blue**   325.00   125.00
          On license   140.00
RY9   RY2 $5 **red**, *1994*   125.00
          On license   200.00

Nos. RY7 and RY8 do not have a printed serial number or the tabs at left. Because the stamps do not have a serial number mint stamps were not sold to the public.
WARNING: Nos. RY7-RY9 are usually taped or glued to the transfer of title documents. The glue used is NOT water soluble. Attempts to soak the stamps may result in damage.

2001(?)   Serpentine Die Cut 11.5
Self-Adhesive
RY10   RY2 $5 **dull red**   —
          On license   *250.00*

RECTIFICATION TAX STAMPS

Used to indicate payment of the tax on distilled spirits that were condensed and purified for additional blending through repeated distillations.

RZ9	RZ1	$5 **blue & black**	30.00	10.00
		Punched cancel		6.00
RZ10	RZ1	$10 **blue & black**	22.50	3.00
		Punched cancel		1.25
RZ11	RZ1	$25 **blue & black**	90.00	10.00
		Punched cancel		3.00
RZ12	RZ1	$50 **blue & black**	90.00	7.50
		Punched cancel		3.00
RZ13	RZ1	$100 **blue & black**	*175.00*	9.50
		Punched cancel		3.50
RZ14	RZ1	$300 **blue & black**	220.00	10.00
		Punched cancel		7.50
RZ15	RZ1	$500 **blue & black**	240.00	10.00
		Punched cancel		7.00
RZ16	RZ1	$1000 **blue & black**	240.00	18.00
		Punched cancel		15.00
RZ17	RZ1	$1500 **blue & black**	260.00	60.00
		Punched cancel		45.00
RZ18	RZ1	$2000 **blue & black**	260.00	80.00
		Punched cancel		60.00

Stamps listed as used have staple holes.

1946   Offset Printing   Wmk. 191R   *Rouletted 7*

RZ1	RZ1	1c **blue & black**	6.75	4.00
		Punched cancel		2.00
RZ2	RZ1	3c **blue & black**	22.50	8.00
		Punched cancel		7.50
RZ3	RZ1	5c **blue & black**	12.50	2.50
		Punched cancel		1.25
RZ4	RZ1	10c **blue & black**	12.50	3.00
		Punched cancel		1.25
RZ5	RZ1	25c **blue & black**	12.50	3.00
		Punched cancel		2.00
RZ6	RZ1	50c **blue & black**	17.50	5.00
		Punched cancel		3.50
RZ7	RZ1	$1 **blue & black**	17.50	4.00
		Punched cancel		2.50
RZ8	RZ1	$3 **blue & black**	90.00	18.00
		Punched cancel		9.00

HUNTING PERMIT STAMPS

Authorized by an Act of Congress, approved March 16, 1934, to license hunters. Receipts go to maintain waterfowl life in the United States. Sales to collectors were made legal June 15, 1935.

No. RW1 used is valued with handstamp or manuscript cancel, though technically it was against postal regulations to deface the stamp or to apply a postal cancellation. Beginning with No. RW2, the used values are for stamps with signatures.

Plate number blocks of six have selvage on two sides.

Hunting permit stamps are valid from July 1 - June 30. Stamps have been made available prior to the date of validity, and stamps are sold through the philatelic agency after the period of validity has passed.

All hunting permit stamps through No. RW68A were printed by the Bureau of Engraving & Printing.

> Catalogue values for all unused stamps in this section are for stamps with never-hinged original gum. Minor natural gum skips and bends are normal on Nos. RW1-RW20. No-gum stamps are without signature or other cancel.

Department of Agriculture

Mallards Alighting — HP1

Engraved: Flat Plate Printing
Issued in panes of 28 subjects.

1934	Unwmk.		Perf. 11	
RW1 HP1 $1 blue			800.	150.
	Hinged		400.	
	No gum		150.	
	P# block of 6		16,500.	
a.	Imperf., vertical pair		—	
b.	Vert. pair, imperf. horiz.		—	

Used value is for stamp with handstamp or manuscript cancel.

It is almost certain that No. RW1a is No. RW1b with vertical perfs trimmed off. No horizontal pairs of No. RW1a are known. All recorded pairs are vertical, with narrow side margins. Both varieties probably are printer's waste since copies exist with gum on front or without gum.

Canvasbacks Taking to Flight — HP2

1935	Inscribed "Void after June 30, 1936"		
RW2 HP2 $1 rose lake		800.	160.
	Hinged	400.	
	No gum	200.	
	P# block of 6	11,500.	

Canada Geese in Flight — HP3

1936	Inscribed "Void after June 30, 1937"		
RW3 HP3 $1 brown black		350.	75.00
	Hinged	175.	
	No gum	115.	
	P# block of 6	4,000.	

Scaup Ducks Taking to Flight — HP4

1937	Inscribed "Void after June 30, 1938"		
RW4 HP4 $1 light green		400.	60.00
	Hinged	170.	
	No gum	85.	
	P# block of 6	3,250.	

Pintail Drake and Hen Alighting — HP5

1938	Inscribed "Void after June 30, 1939"		
RW5 HP5 $1 light violet		475.	60.00
	Hinged	225.	
	No gum	80.	
	P# block of 6	4,500.	

Department of the Interior

Green-winged Teal — HP6

1939	Inscribed "Void after June 30, 1940"		
RW6 HP6 $1 chocolate		275.	45.00
	Hinged	125.	
	No gum	60.	
	P# block of 6	2,900.	

Black Mallards — HP7

1940	Inscribed "Void after June 30, 1941"		
RW7 HP7 $1 sepia		250.	45.00
	Hinged	120.	
	No gum	60.	
	P# block of 6	2,900.	

Family of Ruddy Ducks — HP8

1941   Inscribed "Void after June 30, 1942"
RW8   HP8 $1   **brown carmine**   250.   45.00
     Hinged   110.
     No gum   60.
     P# block of 6   2,900.

Baldpates — HP9

1942   Inscribed "Void after June 30, 1943"
RW9   HP9 $1   **violet brown**   250.   45.00
     Hinged   115.
     No gum   60.
     P# block of 6   2,900.

Wood Ducks — HP10

1943   Inscribed "Void After June 30, 1944"
RW10   HP10 $1   **deep rose**   125.00   35.00
     Hinged   50.00
     No gum   40.00
     P# block of 6   800.00

White-fronted Geese — HP11

1944   Inscribed "Void after June 30, 1945"
RW11   HP11 $1   **red orange**   135.00   45.00
     Hinged   60.00
     No gum   50.00
     P# block of 6   825.00

Shoveller Ducks in Flight — HP12

1945   Inscribed "Void after June 30, 1946"
RW12   HP12 $1   **black**   110.00   25.00
     Hinged   50.00
     No gum   30.00
     P# block of 6   675.00

> Beginning with No. RW13, there is a message printed on the back of the sheet stamps telling hunters to sign their names on the face of the stamp. On Nos. RW13-RW17, offset plate no. 47510 for the printing on the backs of the stamps appears on the back of the selvage opposite the stamp in position 24 on the upper right panes. These are collected as plate blocks of six with side and bottom selvage bearing the plate number on the back of the selvage opposite the center margin stamp. Value, mint never hinged $550 each for Nos. RW13-RW16, $1,500 for No. RW17.

Redhead Ducks — HP13

1946   Inscribed "Void after June 30, 1947"
RW13   HP13 $1   **red brown**   55.00   16.00
     No gum   18.00
     P# block of 6   350.00
   a. $1 **bright rose pink**   35,000.

Snow Geese — HP14

1947   Inscribed "Void after June 30, 1948"
RW14   HP14 $1   **black**   57.50   17.50
     No gum   20.00
     P# block of 6   350.00

Buffleheads in Flight — HP15

1948   Inscribed "Void after June 30, 1949"
RW15   HP15 $1   **bright blue**   60.00   16.00
     No gum   21.00
     P# block of 6   425.00

Goldeneye Ducks — HP16

1949   Inscribed "Void after June 30, 1950"
RW16   HP16 $2   **bright green**   70.00   15.00
     No gum   25.00
     P# block of 6   450.00

Trumpeter Swans in Flight — HP17

1950   Inscribed "Void after June 30, 1951"
RW17   HP17 $2   **violet**   95.00   12.00
     No gum   22.50
     P# block of 6   575.00

Gadwall Ducks — HP18

1951   Inscribed "Void after June 30, 1952"
RW18   HP18 $2   **gray black**   95.00   12.00
     No gum   22.50
     P# block of 6   575.00

Harlequin Ducks — HP19

1952   Inscribed "Void after June 30, 1953"
RW19   HP19 $2   **deep ultramarine**   95.00   12.00
     No gum   22.50
     P# block of 6   575.00

Blue-winged Teal — HP20

1953   **Inscribed "Void after June 30, 1954"**
RW20 HP20 $2 **deep brown rose**   95.00   12.00
          No gum   22.50
          P# block of 6   600.00

> No. RW21 and following issues are printed on dry, pregummed paper and the back inscription is printed on top of the gum, except for the self-adhesive stamp issues starting in 1998.

Ring-necked Ducks — HP21

1954   **Inscribed "Void after June 30, 1955"**
RW21 HP21 $2 **black**   85.00   10.50
          No gum   22.50
          P# block of 6   600.00

Blue Geese — HP22

1955   **Inscribed "Void after June 30, 1956"**
RW22 HP22 $2 **dark blue**   85.00   10.50
          No gum   22.50
          P# block of 6   600.00
  a.   Back inscription inverted   5,500.   4,500.

American Merganser — HP23

1956   **Inscribed "Void after June 30, 1957"**
RW23 HP23 $2 **black**   85.00   10.50
          No gum   22.50
          P# block of 6   625.00

American Eiders — HP24

1957   **Inscribed "Void after June 30, 1958"**
RW24 HP24 $2 **emerald**   85.00   10.50
          No gum   22.50
          P# block of 6   600.00
  a.   Back inscription inverted   5,000.

Canada Geese — HP25

1958   **Inscribed "Void after June 30, 1959"**
RW25 HP25 $2 **black**   85.00   10.50
          No gum   22.50
          P# block of 6   600.00
  a.   Back inscription inverted   —

Labrador Retriever Carrying Mallard Drake — HP26

Giori Press Printing
Issued in panes of 30 subjects

1959   **Inscribed "Void after June 30, 1960"**
RW26 HP26 $3 **blue, ocher & black**   125.00   11.00
          No gum   45.00
          P# block of 4   575.00
  a.   Back inscription inverted   27,500.   —

Redhead Ducks — HP27

1960   **Inscribed "Void after June 30, 1961"**
RW27 HP27 $3 **red brown, dark blue &**   95.00   10.50
             bister
          No gum   37.50
          P# block of 4   475.00

Mallard Hen and Ducklings — HP28

1961   **Inscribed "Void after June 30, 1962"**
RW28 HP28 $3 **multicolored**   110.00   10.50
          No gum   50.00
          P# block of 4   525.00

Pintail Drakes Coming in for Landing — HP29

1962   **Inscribed "Void after June 30, 1963"**
RW29 HP29 $3 dark blue, dark red brown
                  & black   125.00   12.50
                  No gum   60.00
                  P# block of 4   600.00
  a.   Back inscription omitted   —

Pair of Brant Landing — HP30

1963   **Inscribed "Void after June 30, 1964"**
RW30 HP30 $3 multicolored   120.00   12.50
                  No gum   57.50
                  P# block of 4   500.00

Hawaiian Nene Geese — HP31

1964   **Inscribed "Void after June 30, 1965"**
RW31 HP31 $3 multicolored   110.00   12.50
                  No gum   55.00
                  P# block of 6   2,300.

Three Canvasback Drakes — HP32

1965   **Inscribed "Void after June 30, 1966"**
RW32 HP32 $3 multicolored   110.00   12.50
                  No gum   55.00
                  P# block of 4   550.00

Whistling Swans — HP33

1966   **Inscribed "Void after June 30, 1967"**
RW33 HP33 $3 multicolored   110.00   12.50
                  No gum   55.00
                  P# block of 4   550.00

Old Squaw Ducks — HP34

1967   **Inscribed "Void after June 30, 1968"**
RW34 HP34 $3 multicolored   125.00   12.50
                  No gum   60.00
                  P# block of 4   600.00

Hooded Mergansers — HP35

1968   **Inscribed "Void after June 30, 1969"**
RW35 HP35 $3 multicolored   70.00   10.50
                  No gum   27.50
                  P# block of 4   325.00
  a.   Back inscription omitted   —

White-winged Scoters — HP36

1969   **Inscribed "Void after June 30, 1970"**
RW36 HP36 $3 multicolored   70.00   8.00
                  No gum   27.50
                  P# block of 4   300.00

Ross's Geese — HP37

1970   **Engraved & Lithographed**
                  Inscribed "Void after June 30, 1971"
RW37 HP37 $3 multicolored   70.00   8.00
                  No gum   27.50
                  P# block of 4   300.00

Three Cinnamon Teal — HP38

1971   **Inscribed "Void after June 30, 1972"**
RW38 HP38 $3 multicolored   45.00   7.75
                  No gum   22.00
                  P# block of 4   200.00

Emperor Geese — HP39

1972   **Inscribed "Void after June 30, 1973"**
RW39 HP39 $5 multicolored   25.00   7.00
                  No gum   12.50
                  P# block of 4   110.00

Steller's Eiders — HP40

1973   **Inscribed "Void after June 30, 1974"**
RW40 HP40 $5 multicolored   20.00   7.00
                  No gum   11.50
                  P# block of 4   95.00

Wood Ducks — HP41

RW41a

1974   **Inscribed "Void after June 30, 1975"**
RW41 HP41 $5 **multicolored**   18.00   6.00
                No gum   9.50
                P# block of 4   80.00
  a.   Back inscription missing, but printed
         vertically on face of stamp and
         selvage, from foldover   —

Canvasback Ducks and Decoy — HP42

1975   **Inscribed "Void after June 30, 1976"**
RW42 HP42 $5 **multicolored**   17.50   6.00
                No gum   9.00
                P# block of 4   65.00

Family of Canada Geese — HP43

1976   **Engr.**
            Inscribed "Void after June 30, 1977"
RW43 HP43 $5 **green & black**   17.50   6.00
                No gum   9.00
                P# block of 4   65.00

Pair of Ross's Geese — HP44

1977   **Litho. & Engr.**
            Inscribed "Void after June 30, 1978"
RW44 HP44 $5 **multicolored**   17.50   6.00
                No gum   9.00
                P# block of 4   65.00

Hooded Merganser Drake — HP45

1978   **Inscribed "Void after June 30, 1979"**
RW45 HP45 $5 **multicolored**   15.00   6.00
                No gum   7.50
                P# block of 4   57.50

Green-winged Teal — HP46

1979   **Inscribed "Void after June 30, 1980"**
RW46 HP46 $7.50 **multicolored**   17.50   7.00
                No gum   9.00
                P# block of 4   75.00

Mallards — HP47

1980   **Inscribed "Void after June 30, 1981"**
RW47 HP47 $7.50 **multicolored**   17.50   7.00
                No gum   9.00
                P# block of 4   75.00

Ruddy Ducks — HP48

1981   **Inscribed "Void after June 30, 1982"**
RW48 HP48 $7.50 **multicolored**   17.50   7.00
                No gum   9.00
                P# block of 4   75.00

Canvasbacks — HP49

1982   **Inscribed "Void after June 30, 1983"**
RW49 HP49 $7.50 **multicolored**   17.50   7.00
                No gum   9.00
                P# block of 4   75.00
  a.   Orange and violet omitted   10,000.

A certificate from a recognized expertization committee is
required for No. RW49a.

Pintails — HP50

1983   **Inscribed "Void after June 30, 1984"**
RW50 HP50 $7.50 **multicolored**   17.50   7.00
                No gum   9.00
                P# block of 4   75.00

Widgeons — HP51

1984   **Inscribed "Void after June 30, 1985"**
RW51 HP51 $7.50 **multicolored**   17.50   7.00
                No gum   9.00
                P# block of 4   75.00

See Special Printings section that follows.

Cinnamon Teal — HP52

1985   **Inscribed "Void after June 30, 1986"**
RW52 HP52 $7.50 **multicolored**   17.50   8.00
                No gum   9.00
                P# block of 4   75.00
  a.   Light blue (litho.) omitted   22,500.

The omitted color on No. RW52a coincides with a double
paper splice affecting the top row of five stamps from the sheet
and top ⅓ of stamps in the second row. There is also a color
changeling of the brownish red ducks and their reflections in the
water to yellow and yellow orange, respectively, on the error
stamps. This error currently exists as three vertical strips of 6
(top stamp the error) and a plate number block of 12 (2x6,
two stamps the error).

Fulvous Whistling Duck — HP53

1986   Inscribed "Void after June 30, 1987"
RW53 HP53 $7.50 **multicolored**   17.50   7.00
                   No gum   9.50
                   P# block of 4   75.00
a.   Black omitted   3,000.

Redheads — HP54

1987   **Perf. 11½x11**
        Inscribed "Void after June 30, 1988"
RW54 HP54 $10 **multicolored**   17.50   9.50
                   No gum   10.00
                   P# block of 4   75.00

Snow Goose — HP55

1988   Inscribed "Void after June 30, 1989"
RW55 HP55 $10 **multicolored**   17.50   10.00
                   No gum   11.00
                   P# block of 4   75.00

Lesser Scaup — HP56

1989   Inscribed "Void after June 30, 1990"
RW56 HP56 $12.50 **multicolored**   20.00   10.00
                   No gum   12.00
                   P# block of 4   85.00

Black Bellied Whistling Duck — HP57

1990   Inscribed "Void after June 30, 1991"
RW57 HP57 $12.50 **multicolored**   20.00   10.00
                   No gum   12.00
                   P# block of 4   85.00
a.   Back inscription omitted   375.00
b.   Black inscription printed on the
        stamp paper rather than the
        gum   3,500.
                   No gum   3,500.

The back inscription is normally on top of the gum so beware
of examples with gum removed offered as No. RW57a. Full
original gum must be intact on No. RW57a. Used examples of
No. RW57a cannot exist.
   All known examples of No. RW57b are used or have no gum.
Expertization is recommended.

King
Eiders
HP58

1991   Inscribed "Void after June 30, 1992"
RW58 HP58 $15 **multicolored**   30.00   11.00
                   No gum   16.00
                   P# block of 4   140.00
a.   Black (engr.) omitted   20,000.

Spectacled Eider — HP59

1992   Inscribed "Void after June 30, 1993"
RW59 HP59 $15 **multicolored**   30.00   11.00
                   No gum   16.00
                   P# block of 4   140.00

Canvasbacks — HP60

1993   Inscribed "Void after June 30, 1994"
RW60 HP60 $15 **multicolored**   27.50   11.00
                   No gum   16.00
                   P# block of 4   130.00
a.   Black (engr.) omitted   3,000.

Red-breasted Mergansers — HP61

1994   **Perf. 11¼x11**
        Inscribed "Void after June 30, 1995"
RW61 HP61 $15 **multicolored**   30.00   11.00
                   No gum   16.00
                   P# block of 4   140.00

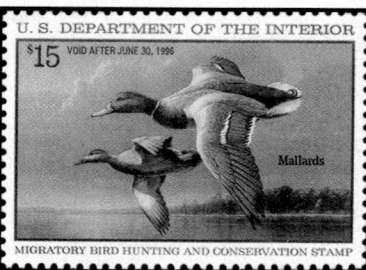

Mallards — HP62

1995   Inscribed "Void after June 30, 1996"
RW62 HP62 $15 **multicolored**   30.00   11.00
                   No gum   15.00
                   P# block of 4   140.00

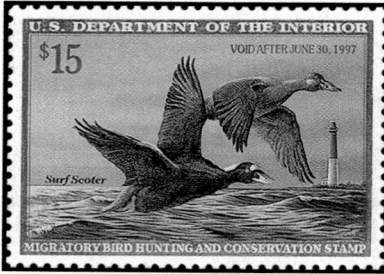

Surf Scoters — HP63

1996   Inscribed "Void after June 30, 1997"
RW63 HP63 $15 **multicolored**   30.00   11.00
                   No gum   15.00
                   P# block of 4   140.00

Canada Goose — HP64

"Long breast feather" plate flaw

"Short breast feather" plate flaw

1997   Inscribed "Void after June 30, 1998"
RW64   HP64 $15 **multicolored**   30.00   11.00
     No gum   16.00
     P# block of 4   125.00
     "Long breast feather" plate
      flaw, pos. 28   85.00   —
     In pair with normal stamp   125.00
     "Short breast feather" plate
      flaw, pos. 28   65.00   —
     In pair with normal stamp   100.00

Barrow's Goldeneye — HP65

1998   *Perf. 11¼*
     Inscribed "Void after June 30, 1999"
RW65   HP65 $15 **multicolored**   45.00   20.00
     No gum   25.00
     P# block of 4   190.00

Self-Adhesive
Die Cut Perf. 10

RW65A   HP65 $15 *Barrow's Goldeneye*   25.00   15.00
     No gum   15.00

> Nos. RW65 and later issues were sold in panes of 30 (RW65 and RW66) or 20 (RW67 and later issues), with four plate numbers per pane. The self-adhesives starting with No. RW65A were sold in panes of 1. The self-adhesives are valued unused as complete panes and used as single stamps.

Greater Scaup — HP66

1999   *Perf. 11¼*
     Inscribed "Void after June 30, 2000"
RW66   HP66 $15 **multicolored**   40.00   15.00
     No gum   22.50
     P# block of 4   170.00

Self-Adhesive
Die Cut Perf. 10

RW66A   HP66 $15 **multicolored**   25.00   12.00
     No gum   15.00

Mottled Duck — HP67

2000   *Perf. 11¼*
     Inscribed "Void after June 30, 2001"
RW67   HP67 $15 **multicolored**   30.00   14.00
     No gum   17.50
     P# block of 4   130.00

Self-Adhesive
Die Cut 10

RW67A   HP67 $15 **multicolored**   22.50   14.00
     No gum   17.50

Northern Pintail — HP68

2001   *Perf. 11¼*
     Inscribed "Void after June 30, 2002"
RW68   HP68 $15 **multicolored**   27.50   15.00
     No gum   16.00
     P# block of 4   110.00

Self-Adhesive
Die Cut Perf. 10

RW68A   HP68 $15 **multicolored**   25.00   10.00
     No gum   15.00

Black Scoters — HP69

Printed by Banknote Corporation of America.

2002   *Perf. 11¼*
     Inscribed "Void after June 30, 2003"
RW69   HP69 $15 **multicolored**   27.50   15.00
     No gum   16.00
     P# block of 4   110.00

Self-Adhesive
Serpentine Die Cut 11x10¾

RW69A   HP69 $15 **multicolored**   25.00   10.00
     No gum   15.00

Snow Geese — HP70

Printed by Ashton-Potter (USA) Ltd.

2003   *Perf. 11*
     Inscribed "Void after June 30, 2004"
RW70   HP70 $15 **multicolored**   27.50   15.00
     No gum   16.00
     P# block of 4   120.00
   b.   Imperf, pair   *7,500.*
   c.   Back inscription omitted   *4,500.*

Self-Adhesive
Serpentine Die Cut 11x10¾

RW70A   HP70 $15 **multicolored**   25.00   10.00
     No gum   15.00

Redheads — HP71

Printed by Banknote Corporation of America for Sennett Security Products.

2004   *Perf. 11*
     Inscribed "Void after June 30, 2005"
RW71 $15 **multicolored**   27.50   11.00
     No gum   16.00
     P# block of 4   100.00

Self-Adhesive
Serpentine Die Cut 11x10¾

RW71A   HP71 $15   25.00   10.00
     No gum   15.00

Hooded Mergansers — HP72

Printed by Banknote Corporation of America for Sennett Security Products

Two types of RW72: I, No framelines at top, right or bottom (from left two panes of the press sheet); II, Gray framelines at top, right and bottom (from right two panes of the press sheet).

2005   Litho. & Engr.   *Perf. 11*
     Inscribed "Void after June 30, 2006"
RW72   HP72 $15 **multicolored**, type I   22.50   11.00
     No gum   16.00
     P# block of 4   100.00
   b.   Souvenir sheet of 1   *2,000.*
   c.   Type II   22.50   11.00
     No gum   16.00
     P# block of 4   100.00

Self-Adhesive
Litho. & Debossed
Serpentine Die Cut 11x10¾

RW72A   HP72 $15 **multicolored**   22.50   11.00
     No gum   15.00

One hundred press sheets containing four panes of 20 of No. RW72 and one hundred press sheets containing 18 of No. RW72A were offered for sale by the U.S. Fish and Wildlife Service.

No. RW72b sold for $20. 1,000 No. RW72b were issued. Approximately 750 were signed by the artist in black, value $2,000 as shown. Approximately 150 were signed in blue ink, value $2,500. Approximately 100 were signed in gold ink, value $3,000. Most examples of No. RW72b are in the grade of F-VF. Catalogue values are for Very Fine examples.

The Duck Stamp Office never announced the existence of No. RW72b to the public through a press release or a website announcement during the time the sheet was on sale, apparently because it was not clear beforehand that the souvenir sheet could be produced successfully and on time. No. RW72b sold out before a public announcement of the item's existence could be made.

Ross's Goose — HP73

Printed by Banknote Corporation of America for Sennett Security Products

2006   Litho. & Engr.   Perf. 11
Inscribed "Void after June 30, 2007"

RW73	HP73 $15 **multicolored**		22.50	11.00
	No gum		15.00	
	P# block of 4		100.00	
b.	Souvenir sheet of 1		160.00	—
c.	As "b," without artist's signature			
	(error)		3,000.	

Self-Adhesive
Serpentine Die Cut 11x10¾

RW73A	HP73 $15 **multicolored**		22.50	11.00
	No gum		15.00	

Two hundred fifty press sheets containing four panes of 20 of No. RW73 and two hundred fifty press sheets containing 18 of No. RW73A were offered for sale by the U.S. Fish and Wildlife Service.

No. RW73b sold for $25. All examples of No. RW73b have a black signature of the artist on a designated line in the sheet margin. Ten thousand were issued.

The sheet margin has a line designated for the signature of the engraver, Piotr Naszarkowski, but no sheets were sold with his signature. Naszarkowski signed approximately 2,500 sheets during three days at the Washington 2006 World Philatelic Exhibition, and he signed another 2,500 or more after the conclusion of the exhibition. Value $225.

Ring-necked Ducks — HP74

Designed by Richard C. Clifton. Printed by Banknote Corporation of America for Sennett Security Products.

2007   Litho.   Perf. 11
Inscribed "Void after June 30, 2008"

RW74	HP74 $15 **multicolored**		22.50	11.00
	No gum		15.00	
	P# block of 4		100.00	
b.	Souvenir sheet of 1		140.00	
c.	As "b," without artist's signature			
	(error)		2,250.	

Self-Adhesive
Serpentine Die Cut 11x10¾

RW74A	HP74 $15 **multicolored**		22.50	11.00
	No gum		15.00	

No. RW74b sold for $25 plus a shipping fee. Ten thousand were issued. There is no back inscription on No. RW74b.

Five hundred press sheets containing four panes of 20 of No. RW74 and 500 press sheets containing 18 of No. RW74A were offered for sale by the Fish and Wildlife Service.

Northern Pintails — HP75

Designed by Joe Hautman. Printed by Ashton-Potter (USA) Ltd.

2008   Litho.   Perf. 13¼
Inscribed "Void after June 30, 2009"

RW75	HP75 $15 **multicolored**		22.50	11.00
	No gum		15.00	
	Inscription block of 4		100.00	
b.	Souvenir sheet of 1		75.00	—
c.	As "b," without artist's signature			
	(error)		750.00	

Self-Adhesive
Serpentine Die Cut 10¾

RW75A	HP75 $15 **multicolored**		22.50	11.00
	No gum		20.00	

No. RW75 was sold in panes of 20. No. RW75A was sold in panes of 1. No. RW75A is valued unused as a complete pane and used as a single stamp. A sheet commemorating the 75th anniversary of Hunting Permit stamps containing one example of No. RW75 and a label with the vignette of No. RW1 sold for $50. Value, $90.

No. RW75b sold for $30 plus a shipping fee. Ten thousand were prepared. There is no back inscription on No. RW75b.

Long-tailed Duck and Decoy — HP76

Designed by Joshua Spies. Printed by Ashton-Potter (USA) Ltd.

2009   Litho.   Perf. 13¼
Inscribed "Void after June 30, 2010"

RW76	HP76 $15 **multicolored**		22.50	11.00
	No gum		15.00	
	Inscription block of 4		100.00	

Self-Adhesive
Serpentine Die Cut 11x10¾

RW76A	HP76 $15 **multicolored**		22.50	11.00
	No gum		20.00	

No. RW76 was sold in panes of 20. No. RW76A was sold in panes of 1. No. RW76A is valued unused as a complete pane and used as a single stamp.

SPECIAL PRINTING

After No. RW51 became void, fifteen uncut sheets of 120 (4 panes of 30 separated by gutters) were over-printed "1934-84" and "50th ANNIVERSARY" in the margins and auctioned by the U.S. Fish and Wildlife Service.

Bids were accepted from September 1 through November 1, 1985. Minimum bid for each sheet was $2,000. The face value of each sheet, had they still been valid, was $900. Each sheet also had the sheet number and pane position printed in the corner of each pane ("01 of 15-1," "01 of 15-2," etc.). Fourteen of the sheets were sold at this and one subsequent auction and one was donated to the Smithsonian.

An individual sheet could be broken up to create these identifiable collectibles: 4 margin overprint blocks of 10; cross gutter block of 4; 6 horizontal pairs with gutter between; 8 vertical pairs with gutter between.

Single stamps from the sheet cannot be distinguished from No. RW51. No used examples can exist.

RW51x $7.50   *Widgeons*

DESIGNERS

1934 —	*RW1*	J.N. Darling
1935 —	*RW2*	Frank W. Benson
1936 —	*RW3*	Richard E. Bishop
1937 —	*RW4*	J.D. Knap
1938 —	*RW5*	Roland Clark
1939 —	*RW6*	Lynn Bogue Hunt
1940 —	*RW7*	Francis L. Jaques
1941 —	*RW8*	E.R. Kalmbach
1942 —	*RW9*	A. Lassell Ripley
1943 —	*RW10*	Walter E. Bohl
1944 —	*RW11*	Walter A. Weber
1945 —	*RW12*	Owen J. Bromme
1946 —	*RW13*	Robert W. Hines
1947 —	*RW14*	Jack Murray
1948 —	*RW15*	Maynard Reece
1949 —	*RW16*	"Roge" E. Preuss
1950 —	*RW17*	Walter A. Weber
1951 —	*RW18*	Maynard Reece
1952 —	*RW19*	John H. Dick
1953 —	*RW20*	Clayton B. Seagears
1954 —	*RW21*	Harvey D. Sandstrom
1955 —	*RW22*	Stanley Stearns
1956 —	*RW23*	Edward J. Bierly
1957 —	*RW24*	Jackson Miles Abbott,
1958 —	*RW25*	Leslie C. Kouba
1959 —	*RW26*	Maynard Reece
1960 —	*RW27*	John A. Ruthven,
1961 —	*RW28*	Edward A. Morris
1962 —	*RW29*	Edward A. Morris
1963 —	*RW30*	Edward J. Bierly
1964 —	*RW31*	Stanley Stearns
1965 —	*RW32*	Ron Jenkins
1966 —	*RW33*	Stanley Stearns
1967 —	*RW34*	Leslie C. Kouba
1968 —	*RW35*	C.G. Pritchard
1969 —	*RW36*	Maynard Reece
1970 —	*RW37*	Edward J. Bierly
1971 —	*RW38*	Maynard Reece
1972 —	*RW39*	Arthur M. Cook
1973 —	*RW40*	Lee LeBlanc
1974 —	*RW41*	David A. Maass
1975 —	*RW42*	James L. Fisher
1976 —	*RW43*	Alderson Magee
1977 —	*RW44*	Martin R. Murk
1978 —	*RW45*	Albert Earl Gilbert
1979 —	*RW46*	Kenneth L. Michaelsen
1980 —	*RW47*	Richard W. Plasschaert
1981 —	*RW48*	John S. Wilson
1982 —	*RW49*	David A. Maass
1983 —	*RW50*	Phil Scholer
1984 —	*RW51*	William C. Morris
1985 —	*RW52*	Gerald Mobley
1986 —	*RW53*	Burton E. Moore, Jr.
1987 —	*RW54*	Arthur G. Anderson
1988 —	*RW55*	Daniel Smith
1989 —	*RW56*	Neal R. Anderson
1990 —	*RW57*	Jim Hautman
1991 —	*RW58*	Nancy Howe
1992 —	*RW59*	Joe Hautman
1993 —	*RW60*	Bruce Miller
1994 —	*RW61*	Neal R. Anderson
1995 —	*RW62*	Jim Hautman
1996 —	*RW63*	Wilhelm Goebel
1997 —	*RW64*	Robert Hautman
1998 —	*RW65*	Robert Steiner
1999 —	*RW66*	Jim Hautman
2000 —	*RW67*	Adam Grimm
2001 —	*RW68*	Robert Hautman
2002 —	*RW69*	Joe Hautman
2003 —	*RW70*	Ron Louque
2004 —	*RW71*	Scot Storm
2005 —	*RW72*	Mark Anderson
2006 —	*RW73*	Sherrie Russell Meline
2007 —	*RW74*	Richard Clifton
2008 —	*RW75*	Joe Hautman
2009 —	*RW76*	Joshua Spies

QUANTITIES SOLD

(Quantities from No. RW65 on are quantities ordered. Quantities sold of these numbers were much less.)

RW1	635,001	RW43	2,170,194

RW2	448,204	RW44	2,196,774
RW3	603,623	RW45	2,216,621
RW4	783,039	RW46	2,090,155
RW5	1,002,715	RW47	2,045,114
RW6	1,111,561	RW48	1,907,120
RW7	1,260,810	RW49	1,926,253
RW8	1,439,967	RW50	1,867,998
RW9	1,383,629	RW51	1,913,861
RW10	1,169,352	RW52	1,780,636
RW11	1,487,029	RW53	1,794,484
RW12	1,725,505	RW54	1,663,270
RW13	2,016,841	RW55	1,402,096
RW14	1,722,677	RW56	1,415,882
RW15	2,127,603	RW57	1,408,373
RW16	1,954,734	RW58	1,423,374
RW17	1,903,644	RW59	1,347,393
RW18	2,167,767	RW60	1,402,569
RW19	2,296,628	RW61	1,471,751
RW20	2,268,446	RW62	1,539,622
RW21	2,184,550	RW63	1,560,123
RW22	2,369,940	RW64	1,697,590
RW23	2,332,014	RW65	1,195,000
RW24	2,355,190	RW65A	2,805,000
RW25	2,176,425	RW66	1,194,000
RW26	1,626,115	RW66A	2,799,600
RW27	1,725,634	RW67	1,200,000
RW28	1,344,236	RW67A	2,800,000
RW29	1,147,212	RW68	1,194,000
RW30	1,448,191	RW68A	2,806,000
RW31	1,573,155	RW69	1,194,000
RW32	1,558,197	RW69A	2,806,000
RW33	1,805,341	RW70	1,000,000
RW34	1,934,697	RW70A	3,000,000
RW35	1,837,139	RW71	1,000,000
RW36	2,072,108	RW71A	3,000,000
RW37	2,420,244		
RW38	2,445,977		
RW39	2,184,343		
RW40	2,094,414		
RW41	2,214,056		
RW42	2,237,126		

JUNIOR DUCK STAMPS

As a courtesy to Duck stamp collectors, we list here the Duck stamps issued under the Federal Junior Duck Stamp program, run by the U.S. Fish and Wildlife Service branch of the Department of the Interior and the Federal Duck Stamp Office. The purpose of this program is to teach youth through the medium of art the importance of conserving wetlands and migratory birds.

Students in kindergarden to 12th grade from all 50 states, the District of Columbia, American Samoa and the U.S. Virgin Islands are invited to participate in an annual art competition. The winning entry from each state, district or territory competes for the national championship. The national winner's art appears on that year's Junior Duck stamp, which is sold to raise funds to support the Junior Duck Stamp art and educational program. The United States Postal Service, through its Stamp Fulfillment Services unit, acts as a sales agent for these stamps.

These stamps are not valid for hunting, nor is it required that hunters buy the stamps in order to hunt.

A precursor sheet of nine stamps was released in 1992 as a part of a pilot program instituted before the formal, annual Junior Duck Stamp art competition was begun. The sheet shows stamps from Arkansas, California (2), Florida (2), Illinois (2), Kansas and Vermont. Value, $30.

All issues were printed in panes of 30 with four control/plate numbers. Imperforate examples of Nos. JDS1, JDS2 and JDS3 exist and are believed to be printer's waste.

> Catalogue values for all stamps in this section are for stamps with never-hinged original gum.

JD1

1993   **Artist: Jason Parsons (IL)**
JDS1   JD1 $5   *Redhead*   75.00

1994   **Artist: Clark Weaver (PA)**
JDS2   JD1 $5   *Hooded mergansers*   175.00

1995
JDS3   JD1 $5   *Pintail*   350.00
   a.   Imperf, pair   *3,000.*

1996   **Artist: Clark Weaver (PA)**
JDS4   JD1 $5   *Canvasbacks*   400.00

1997   **Artist: Scott Russell (CA)**
JDS5   JD1 $5   *Canada geese*   450.00

1998   **Artist: Eric Peterson (MI)**
JDS6   JD1 $5   *Black ducks*   425.00

1999   **Artist: Ryan Kirby (IL)**
JDS7   JD1 $5   *Wood ducks*   450.00

2000   **Artist: Bonnie Latham (MN)**
JDS8   JD1 $5   *Pintails*   425.00

2001   **Artist: Aremy McCann (MN)**
JDS9   JD1 $5   *Trumpeter swan*   85.00

2002   **Artist: Nathan Closson (MT)**
JDS10   JD1 $5   *Mallards*   50.00

2003   **Artist: Nathan Bauman (PA)**
JDS11   JD1 $5   *Green-winged teals*   30.00

2004   **Artist: Adam Nisbett (MO)**
JDS12   JD1 $5   *Fulvous whistling ducks*   25.00

2005   **Artist: Kerissa Nelson (WI)**
JDS13   JD1 $5   *Ring-necked ducks*   15.00

2006   **Artist: Rebekah Nastav (MO)**
JDS14   JD1 $5   *Redhead*   15.00

2007   **Artist: Paul Willey (AR)**
JDS15   JD1 $5   *Wigeons*   12.00

Type of 1993
2008   **Artist: Seokkyun Hong (TX)**
JDS16   JD1 $5   *Hawaiian Nene Geese*   10.00

Type of 1993
2009   **Artist: Lily Spang (OH)**
JDS17   JD1 $5   *Wood duck*   10.00

STATE HUNTING PERMIT STAMPS

These stamps are used on licenses for hunting waterfowl (ducks, geese, swans) by states and Indian reservations. Stamps which include waterfowl along with a variety of other animals are listed here. Stamps for hunting birds that exclude waterfowl are not listed.

A number of states print stamps in sheets as well as in booklets. The booklets are sent to agents for issuing to hunters. Both varieties are listed. The major listing is given to the sheet stamp since it generally is available in larger quantities and has been the more popularly collected item. In some cases the stamp removed from a booklet, with no tabs or selvage, is identical to a single sheet stamp (see Rhode Island). In these cases the identifiable booklet stamp with tabs and selvage receives an unlettered listing. If the single booklet stamp can be identified by type of perforation or the existence of one or more straight edges, the item receives a lettered listing (see Oregon).

Governor's editions are sold at a premium over the license fee with proceeds intended to help waterfowl habitats. Only those which differ from the regular stamp are listed.

After the period of validity, a number of these stamps were sold at less than face value. This explains the low values on stamps such as Montana Nos. 30, 33, and Flathead Indian Reservation Nos. 2-10.

When used, most stamps are affixed to licenses and signed by the hunter. Values for used stamps are for examples off licenses and without tabs. Although used examples may be extremely scarce, they will always sell for somewhat less than unused examples (two-thirds of the unused value would be the upper limit).

ALABAMA

Printed in sheets of 10.
Stamps are numbered serially.

Catalogue values for all unused stamps in this section are for Never Hinged items.

Artists: Barbara Keel, #1; Wayne Spradley, #2; Jack Deloney, #3; Joe Michelet, #4; John Lee, #5, 25; William Morris, #6, 14; Larry Martin, #7; Danny W. Dorning, #8; Robert C. Knutson, #9, 16, 20; John Warr, #10; Elaine Byrd, #11; Steven Garst, #12; Larry Chandler, #13, 24; James Brantley, #15; Neil Blackwell, #17; Judith Huey, #18; E. Hatcher, #19; Eddie LeRoy, #21; David Sellers, #22, 26, 27; H. Andrew McNeely, #23. Clarence Stewart, #28. David Nix, #29; Jim Denney, #30.

1979-2008

1	$5 Wood ducks, rouletted	12.00	3.00
2	$5 Mallards, 1980	12.00	3.00
3	$5 Canada geese, 1981	12.00	3.00
4	$5 Green-winged teal, 1982	12.00	3.00
5	$5 Widgeons, 1983	12.00	3.00
6	$5 Buffleheads, 1984	12.00	3.00
7	$5 Wood ducks, 1985	12.00	3.00
8	$5 Canada geese, 1986	12.00	3.00
9	$5 Pintails, 1987	12.00	3.00
10	$5 Canvasbacks, 1988	10.00	3.00
11	$5 Hooded mergansers, 1989	12.00	3.00
12	$5 Wood ducks, 1990	10.00	2.50
13	$5 Redheads, 1991	10.00	2.50
14	$5 Cinnamon teal, 1992	10.00	2.50
15	$5 Green-winged teal, 1993	10.00	2.50
16	$5 Canvasbacks, 1994	10.00	2.50
17	$5 Canada geese, 1995	10.00	2.50
18	$5 Wood ducks, 1996	12.00	2.50
19	$5 Snow goose, 1997	10.00	2.50
20	$5 Barrow's goldeneye, 1998	10.00	2.50
21	$5 Redheads, 1999	10.00	2.50
22	$5 Buffleheads, 2000	9.00	2.50
23	$5 Ruddy duck, 2001	9.00	2.50
24	$5 Pintail, 2002	9.00	2.50
25	$5 Wood ducks, 2003	9.00	2.50
26	$5 Ring-necked ducks, 2004	9.00	2.50
27	$5 Canada geese, 2005	9.00	2.50
28	$5 Canvasback, 2006	9.00	2.50
29	$5 Blue-winged teal, 2007	8.00	2.50
30	$5 Hooded mergansers, 2008	8.00	2.50

ALASKA

Printed in sheets of 30.
Stamps are numbered serially on reverse. Booklet pane stamps printed in panes of 5.

Catalogue values for all unused stamps in this section are for Never Hinged items.

1985 Alaska Waterfowl Stamp

Artist: Daniel Smith, #1; James Meger, #2; Carl Branson, #3; Jim Beaudoin, #4; Richard Timm, #5; Louis Frisino, #6; Ronald Louque, #7; Fred Thomas, #8; Ed Tussey, #9; George Lockwood, #10, 13, 23; Cynthia Fisher, #11, 20; Wilhelm Goebel, #12; Robert Steiner, #14, 18, 22; Sherrie Russell Meline, #15; Adam Grimm, #16, 19; Greg Alexander, #17; Don Moore, #21, 24.

1985-2008

1	$5 Emperor geese	10.00	3.00
2	$5 Steller's eiders, 1986	10.00	3.00
3	$5 Spectacled eiders, perforated, 1987	10.00	
a.	Bklt. single, rouletted, with tab	10.00	2.50
4	$5 Trumpeter swans, perforated, 1988	10.00	
a.	Bklt. single, rouletted, with tab	10.00	2.50
5	$5 Barrow's goldeneyes, perforated, 1989	10.00	
a.	Bklt. single, rouletted, with tab	10.00	2.50
b.	Governor's edition	140.00	

No. 5b was sold in full panes through a sealed bid auction.

6	$5 Old squaws, perforated, 1990	9.50	
a.	Bklt. single, rouletted, with tab	9.50	2.50
7	$5 Snow geese, perforated, 1991	9.50	
a.	Bklt. single, rouletted, with tab	9.50	2.50
8	$5 Canvasbacks, perforated, 1992	9.50	
a.	Bklt. single, rouletted, with tab	9.50	2.50
9	$5 Tule white front geese, perforated, 1993	14.00	
a.	Bklt. single, rouletted, with tab	14.00	2.50
10	$5 Harlequin ducks, perforated, 1994	20.00	
a.	Bklt. single, rouletted, with tab	15.00	2.50
b.	Governor's edition	90.00	
11	$5 Pacific brant, perforated, 1995	22.00	
a.	Bklt. single, rouletted, with tab	20.00	2.50
12	$5 Canada geese, 1996	25.00	
a.	Bklt. single, rouletted, with tab	20.00	2.50
13	$5 King eiders, 1997	20.00	
a.	Bklt. single, rouletted, with tab	16.00	2.50
14	$5 Barrow's goldeneye, 1998	12.00	
a.	Bklt. single, with tab	12.00	2.50
15	$5 Pintail, 1999	11.00	
a.	Bklt. single, with tab	11.00	2.50
16	$5 Common eider, 2000	10.00	
a.	Bklt. single, with tab	10.00	2.50
17	$5 American wigeon, 2001	10.00	
a.	Bklt. single, with tab	10.00	2.50
18	$5 Black scoters, 2002	10.00	
a.	Bklt. single, with tab	10.00	2.50
19	$5 Lesser Canada geese, 2003	12.00	
a.	Bklt. single, with tab	12.00	2.50
20	$5 Lesser scaup, 2004	10.00	
a.	Bklt. single, with tab	10.00	2.50
21	$5 Hooded merganser, 2005	8.50	
a.	Bklt. single, with tab	8.50	2.50
22	$5 Pintails, mallard, green-winged teal, 2006	8.50	
a.	Bklt. single, with tab	8.50	2.50
23	$5 Northern shovelers, 2007	8.50	
a.	Bklt. single, with tab	8.50	2.50
24	$5 Northern pintails, 2008	7.50	
a.	Bklt. single, with tab	8.50	2.50

ARIZONA

Printed in booklet panes of 5 with tab and in sheets of 30.
Stamps are numbered serially.

Catalogue values for all unused stamps in this section are for Never Hinged items.

Artists: Daniel Smith, #1; Sherrie Russell Meline, #2, 6-7, 9, 11-18, 21, 22; Robert Steiner, #3; Ted Blaylock, #4; Brian Jarvi, #5; Harry Adamson, #8, Larry Hayden, #10; Tom Finley, #19, 20.

1987-2008

1	$5.50 Pintails, perf. 4 sides	11.00	
a.	Bklt. single, perf. 3 sides, with tab	11.00	3.00
2	$5.50 Green-winged teal, perf. 4 sides, 1988	12.00	
a.	Bklt. single, perf. 3 sides, with tab	12.00	3.00
3	$5.50 Cinnamon teal, perf. 4 sides, 1989	11.00	
a.	Bklt. single, perf. 3 sides, with tab	11.00	2.50
b.	$5.50 +$50 Governor's edition	75.00	
4	$5.50 Canada geese, perf. 4 sides, 1990	12.00	
a.	Bklt. single, perf. 3 sides, with tab	12.00	2.50
b.	$5.50 +$50 Governor's edition	75.00	
5	$5.50 Blue-winged teal, perf. 4 sides, 1991	10.00	
a.	Bklt. single, perf. 3 sides, with tab	11.00	2.50
b.	$55.50 Governor's edition	75.00	
6	$5.50 Buffleheads, perf. 4 sides, 1992	10.00	
a.	Bklt. single, perf. 3 sides, with tab	11.00	2.50
b.	$55.50 Governor's edition	75.00	
7	$5.50 Mexican ducks, perf. 4 sides, 1993	12.00	
a.	Bklt. single, perf. 3 sides, with tab	12.00	2.50
b.	$55.50 Governor's edition	75.00	
8	$5.50 Mallards, perf. 4 sides, 1994	12.00	
a.	Bklt. single, perf. 3 sides, with tab	12.00	2.50
b.	$55.50 Governor's edition	75.00	
9	$5.50 Widgeon, perf. 4 sides, 1995	12.00	
a.	Bklt. single, perf. 3 sides, with tab	12.00	2.50
b.	$55.50 Governor's edition	75.00	
10	$5.50 Canvasbacks, perf. 4 sides, 1996	11.00	
a.	Bklt. single, perf 3 sides, with tab	11.00	2.50
b.	$55.50 Governor's edition	75.00	
11	$5.50 Gadwalls, 1997	12.00	
a.	Bklt. single, perf 3 sides, with tab	12.00	2.50
b.	$55.50 Governor's edition	75.00	
12	$5.50 Wood duck, 1998	12.00	
a.	Bklt. single, perf 3 sides, with tab	12.00	2.50
b.	$55.50 Governor's edition	—	
13	$5.50 Snow goose, 1999	12.00	
a.	Bklt. single, perf 3 sides, with tab	12.00	2.50
b.	$55.50 Governor's edition	75.00	
14	$7.50 Ruddy duck, 2000	14.00	
a.	Bklt. single, perf 3 sides, with tab	14.00	2.50
b.	$55.50 Governor's edition	75.00	
15	$7.50 Redheads, 2001	14.00	
a.	Bklt. single, perf 3 sides, with tab	14.00	2.50
b.	$55.50 Governor's edition	75.00	
16	$7.50 Ring-necked ducks, 2002	14.00	
a.	Bklt. single, perf. 2 sides, with tabs	14.00	2.50
b.	$55.50 Governor's edition	75.00	
17	$7.50 Northern shovelers, 2003	14.00	
a.	Bklt. single, perf. 2 sides, with tabs	14.00	2.50
b.	$55.50 Governor's edition	75.00	
18	$7.50 Lesser scaup, 2004	12.00	
a.	Bklt. single, perf. 2 sides, with tabs	12.00	2.50
b.	$55.50 Governor's edition	75.00	—

19	$7.50 Pintails, *2005*	9.50	
a.	Bklt. single, perf. 3 sides, with tabs	10.50	2.50
20	$7.50 Canada geese, *2006*	9.50	
a.	Bklt. single, perf. 3 sides, with tabs	10.50	2.50
b.	$55 Governor's edition	75.00	
21	$8.75 Wood ducks, *2007*	11.00	
a.	Bklt. single, perf. 2 or 3 sides, with tabs	12.00	2.50
b.	$55 Governor's edition	75.00	
22	$8.75 Canvasbacks, *2008*	11.00	
a.	Bklt. single, perf. 2 or 3 sides, with tabs	12.00	2.50

ARKANSAS

Imperforate varieties of these stamps exist in large quantities. Imperforate copies of Nos. 1 and 2 were sold by the state for $1 each.

No. 1 printed in sheets and booklet panes of 30, others in sheets and booklet panes of 10.

Stamps are numbered serially on reverse.

> **Catalogue values for all unused stamps in this section are for Never Hinged items.**

Artists: Lee LeBlanc, #1; Maynard Reece, #2, 8; David Maass, #3, 10, 21; Larry Hayden, #4, 15; Ken Carlson, #5, 13; John P. Cowan, #6; Robert Bateman. #7; Phillip Crowe, #9, 16, 22, 30, 31; Daniel Smith, #11, 14; Jim Hautman, #12, 19; L. Chandler, #17, 20, 26, 27; John Dearman, #18; Zettie Jones, #23; Ralph McDonald; #24-25. Scot Storm, #28-29; Cynthie Fisher, #32-33.

1981-2008

1	$5.50 Mallards	55.00	12.00
	Booklet single with top tab, Nos. 110,001-200,000 on back	60.00	
2	$5.50 Wood ducks, *1982*	45.00	9.00
3	$5.50 Green-winged teal, *1983*	65.00	12.00
4	$5.50 Pintails, *1984*	22.50	5.00
5	$5.50 Mallards, *1985*	13.00	2.50
6	$5.50 Black swamp mallards, *1986*	11.00	2.50
7	$7 Wood ducks, *1987*	11.00	2.50

Stamps like Nos. 7 and 8 with $5.50 face values were following an order of the state Supreme Court restoring the fee level of 1986. The stamps were sold after the 1988 season had ended. Value, $11 each.

8	$7 Pintails, *1988*	10.00	2.50

See footnote following No. 7.

9	$7 Mallards, *1989*	10.00	2.50
10	$7 Black ducks & mallards, *1990*	12.00	2.50
11	$7 Sulphur river widgeons, *1991*	10.00	2.50
12	$7 Shirey Bay shovelers, *1992*	12.00	2.50
13	$7 Grand prairie mallards, *1993*	12.00	2.50
14	$7 Canada goose, *1994*	14.00	2.50
15	$7 White River mallards, *1995*	14.00	2.50
16	$7 Mallards, black labrador, *1996*	14.00	2.00
17	$7 Labrador retriever, mallards, *1997*	15.00	2.00
18	$7 Labrador retriever, mallards, *1998*	12.00	2.00
19	$7 Wood duck, *1999*	12.00	2.00
20	$7 Mallards and golden retriever, *2000*	11.00	2.00
21	$7 Canvasbacks, *2001*	11.00	2.00
22	$7 Mallards, *2002*	11.00	2.00
23	$7 Mallards & Chesapeake retriever, *2003*	14.00	2.00
24	$7 Mallards, *2004*	11.00	2.00
25	$20 Mallards, *2004*	26.00	2.00
26	$7 Mallards, Labrador retriever *2005*	9.00	2.00
27	$20 Mallards, Labrador retriever *2005*	26.00	2.00
28	$7 Mallards, *2006*	9.00	2.00
29	$20 Mallards, *2006*	26.00	2.00
30	$7 Mallards, Labrador retriever *2007*	9.00	2.00
31	$20 Mallards, Labrador retriever *2007*	25.00	2.00
32	$7 Mallards, Labrador retriever, *2008*	9.00	2.00
33	$20 Mallards, Labrador retriever, *2008*	25.00	2.00

Resident and non-resident fees begin in 2004.

CALIFORNIA

Honey Lake Waterfowl Stamps

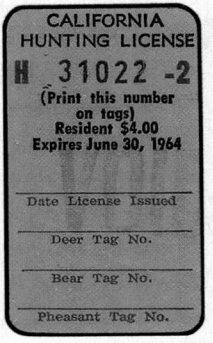

Required to hunt waterfowl at Honey Lake. Valid for a full season. Stamps are rouletted. Used values are for signed copies. Unsigned stamps without gum probably were used. Values for these stamps are higher than used values, but lower than values shown for gummed unused stamps.

1956-86

A1	$5 black, *1956-1957*		—
A2	$5 black, *blue green, 1957-1958*		—
A3	$5 black, *dark yellow, 1958-1959*		—
A4	$5 black, *dark yellow, 1959-1960*	1,000.	550.00
A5	$5 black, *1960-1961*		1,200.
A6	$5 black, *bluish green, 1961-1962*	—	1,200.
A7	$5 black, *dark yellow, 1962-1963*		700.00
A8	$5 black, *1963-1964*		400.00
A9	$6.50 black, *pink, 1964-1965*	1,200.	400.00
A10	$6.50 black, *1965-1966*		350.00
A11	$6.50 black, *yellow*, Nos. 1-700, printer's information at bottom right, *1966-1967*		375.00
a.	Serial Nos. 701-1050, no printer's information		9,500.
A12	$10 black, *pink, 1967-1968*	—	350.00
A13	$10 black, *blue, 1968-1969*		450.00
A14	$10 black, *green, 1969-1970*	—	500.00
A15	$15 black, *dark yellow, 1970-1971*	—	650.00
A16	$15 black, *pink, 1971-1972*		1,950.
A17	$15 black, *blue, 1972-1973*		2,950.
A18	$15 black, *blue, 1973-1974*		
A19	$15 black, *pink, 1974-1975*	40.00	25.00
A20	$15 black, *green, 1975-1976*	135.00	35.00
A21	$15 black, *light yellow, 1976-1977*	135.00	35.00
A22	$20 black, *blue, 1977-1978*	135.00	35.00
A23	$20 blk, *light yel brown, 1978-1979*	135.00	35.00
A24	$20 black, *light yellow, 1979-1980*	135.00	35.00
A25	$15 black, *light blue, 1980-1981*	100.00	30.00
A26	$20 black, *light yellow, 1981-1982*	—	
A27	$20 black, *pink, 1982-1983*	90.00	30.00
A28	$20 black, *light green, 1983-1984*	45.00	25.00
A29	$20 black, *dark yellow, 1984-1985*	42.50	25.00
A30	$20 black, *light blue, 1985-1986*	37.50	20.00

Eighteen $5 black on dark yellow permit stamps were sold for hunting at the state-owned and operated Madeline Plains waterfowl management area for the 1956-57 season. No examples have been recorded.

Statewide Hunting License Validation Stamps

Fees are for resident, junior and non-resident hunters. "No fee" stamps were for disabled veterans. Stamps with special serial numbers for state officials are known for some years. Nos. 2A1-2A3 imperf on 3 sides, rouletted at top. Others die cut.

Stamps are numbered serially.

Used values are for written-upon stamps. Starting with No. 2A4, unused values are for stamps on backing paper.

1962-1963

2A1	$4 black	450.00	7.00
a.	Ovptd. "NO FEE"	425.00	300.00
2A2	$1 black, *yellow*	1,500.	75.00
2A3	$25 black, *green*	3,500.	150.00

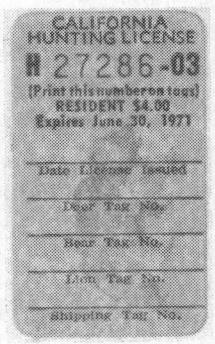

No. 2A25

1963-1964

2A4	$4 black, *green*	—	3.00
a.	Ovptd. "NO FEE"		
2A5	$1 black, *gray*	—	20.00
2A6	$25 black, *yellow orange*		450.00

1964-1965

2A7	$4 black, *pink*	30.00	1.00
a.	Ovptd. "NO FEE"	450.00	225.00
2A8	$1 black, *yellow brown*	225.00	25.00
2A9	$25 black, *dark gray*		70.00

1965-1966

2A10	$4 black, *gray*	25.00	1.00
a.	Ovptd. "NO FEE"		
2A11	$1 black, *yellow gray*		25.00
2A12	$25 black, *ivory*		75.00

1966-1967

2A13	$4 black, *salmon*	25.00	1.00
a.	Ovptd. "NO FEE"		550.00
2A14	$1 black, *lt blue*	75.00	10.00
2A15	$25 black, *burgundy*		65.00

1967-1968

2A16	$4 black, *yellow*	20.00	1.00
a.	Ovptd. "NO FEE"		500.00

2A17	$1 black, *green*	45.00	5.00
a.	black, *yellow gray*		—
2A18	$25 black, *brown*	75.00	25.00

1968-1969

2A19	$4 black, *pink*	55.00	1.00
a.	Ovptd. "NO FEE"		550.00
2A20	$1 black, *blue gray*	175.00	20.00
2A21	$25 black, *light orange*		85.00

1969-1970

2A22	$4 black	55.00	1.00
a.	Ovptd. "NO FEE"		500.00
2A23	$1 black, *dark pink*	175.00	20.00
2A24	$25 black, *light yellow*	70.00	25.00

1970-1971

2A25	$4 black, *manila*	70.00	2.00
a.	Ovptd. "NO FEE"	1,500.	1,000.
2A26	$1 black, *blue gray*	75.00	10.00
2A27	$25 black, *gray brown*	100.00	25.00

1971-1972

2A28	$4 black, *green*	45.00	1.00
a.	Ovptd. "NO FEE"		500.00
b.	Ovptd. "DISABLED VETERANS/NO FEE"		650.00
2A29	$1 black, *lavender*		20.00
2A30	$25 black, *peach*	275.00	35.00

1972-1973

2A31	$6 black, *pink*		1.00
a.	Ovptd. "DISABLED VETERANS/NO FEE"		650.00
2A32	$2 black, *light yellow*		30.00
2A33	$35 black, *lavender*	225.00	

1973-1974

2A34	$6 black, *blue*		1.00
a.	Ovptd. "DISABLED VETERANS/NO FEE"		650.00
2A35	$2 black, *lavender*	175.00	20.00
2A36	$35 black, *gray*	275.00	35.00

1974-1975

2A37	$6 black, *green*	35.00	1.00
a.	Ovptd. "DISABLED VETERANS/NO FEE"		700.00
2A38	$2 black, *orange*		20.00
2A39	$35 black, *reddish purple*	175.00	25.00

1975-1976

2A40	$10 red brown, *brown*	40.00	1.00
a.	Ovptd. "DISABLED VETERANS/NO FEE"	—	800.00
2A41	$2 black, *dark red*	80.00	20.00
2A42	$35 black, *yellow*	85.00	25.00

1976-1977

2A43	$10 black, *blue*	30.00	1.00
a.	Ovptd. "DISABLED VETERANS/NO FEE"		900.00
2A44	$2 black, *gray violet*	100.00	20.00
a.	Inscibed "Deer Tag No." instead of "Bear Tag No."	—	
2A45	$35 black, *lavender*	85.00	25.00

1977-1978

2A46	$10 black, *red orange*	30.00	1.00
a.	Ovptd. "DISABLED VETERANS/NO FEE"		750.00
2A47	$2 black, *yellow green*	95.00	25.00
2A48	$35 black, *pink*	95.00	

1978-1979

2A49	$10 black, *yellow*	40.00	1.50
a.	Ovptd. "DISABLED VETERANS/NO FEE"		700.00
2A50	$2 black, *red*	80.00	20.00
2A51	$35 black, *light brown*	85.00	

1979-1980

2A52	$10 black, *red*	30.00	1.00
a.	Ovptd. "DISABLED VETERANS/NO FEE"		800.00
2A53	$2 black, *yellow green*	80.00	20.00
2A54	$35 black, *dark blue*	85.00	

1980-1981

2A55	$10.25 black, *blue*	30.00	1.00
a.	Ovptd. "DISABLED VETERANS/NO FEE"		1,250.
2A56	$2 black, *light brown*	75.00	15.00
2A57	$36.25 black, *tan*	75.00	25.00

1981-1982

2A58	$11.50 black, *dark green*	30.00	1.00
2A59	$2.25 black, *blue*	75.00	20.00
2A60	$40 black, *gray*	200.00	

1982-1983

2A61	$12.50 black, *pink*	30.00	1.00
2A62	$2.50 black, *brown*	75.00	20.00
2A63	$43.50 black, *orange*	140.00	

1983-1984

2A64	$13.25 black, *blue*	50.00	1.00
2A65	$2.75 black, *purple*	150.00	20.00
2A66	$46.50 black, *green*	175.00	

1984-1985

2A67	$13.25 black, *yellow*	50.00	1.00
2A68	$2.75 black, *green*	150.00	20.00
2A69	$49.25 black, *brown*	175.00	

1985-1986

2A70	$14 black, *blue*	50.00	1.00
2A71	$3.50 black, *yellow*	150.00	20.00
2A72	$51.75 black, *purple*	175.00	

1986-1987

2A73	$18.50 black, *green*		1.00

2A74	$4.50 black, *dark blue*		15.00

1987-1988

2A76	$17.50 black, *dark blue*		1.00
2A77	$4.50 black, *purple*		15.00

1988-1989

2A79	$19.25 black, *tan*		1.00
2A80	$5 black, *yellow*		15.00

1989-1990

2A82	$19.75 black, *blue gray*		1.00
2A83	$5 black, *dark green*		15.00

1990-1991

2A85	$21.50 black, *reddish gray*		1.00
2A86	$5.50 black, *yellow*		15.00
2A87	$73 black, *pink*		25.00

1991-1992

2A88	$23.10 black, *lime green*		1.00
2A89	$5.50 black, *bluish purple*		15.00
2A90	$79.80 black, *brown*		25.00

1992-1993

2A91	$24.15 black, *yellow*	—	1.00
2A92	$5.80 black, *greenish gold*	—	15.00
2A93	$83.75 black, *mauve*	—	25.00

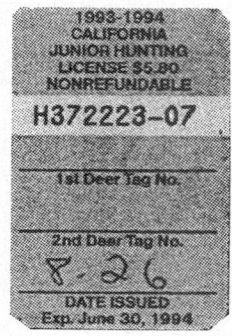

1993-1994

2A94	$24.40 black & white, *green*		1.00
2A95	$5.80 black & white, *light blue*		15.00

1994-1995

2A97	$24.95 black & white, *pale yellow*		1.00
2A98	$6.05 black & white, *lavender*		15.00
2A99	$86.90 black & white, *gray*		25.00

1996-1997

2A100	$25.45 black, *gray brown*		1.00
2A101	$6.30 black, *pink*		15.00
2A102	$88.70 black, *pale blue*		25.00

Statewide Waterfowl Issues

Nos. 1-24 printed in booklet panes of five, No. 25 in pane of 4.

Issues through 1978 are die cut and self-adhesive. Starting with the 1979 issue, stamps are rouletted. Stamps are numbered serially.

> **Catalogue values for all unused stamps in this section are for Never Hinged items.**

Artists: Paul Johnson, #1-8, 38; Ken Michaelson, #9; Walter Wolfe, #10-11; Robert Steiner, #12, 18-20, 26-35; Robert Richert, #13; Charles Allen, #14; Robert Montanucci, #15; Richard Wilson, #16; Sherrie Russell Meline, #17, 23, 37; Ronald Louque, #21; Larry Hayden, #22; Richard Clifton, #24-25; Richard Radigonda, #36; Harry Adamson, #39.

Stamps valued with original backing paper. Caution should be used when buying especially Nos. 1 and 2. Both these issues have wider rouletting on the backing paper than Nos. 3-9.

1971-2008

1	$1 Pintails	550.00	65.00
2	$1 Canvasbacks, *1972*	1,800.	150.00
3	$1 Mallards, *1973*	14.50	2.50
4	$1 White-fronted geese, *1974*	3.00	2.50

5	$1 Green-winged teal, backing paper with red wavy lines, *1975*	35.00	8.00
	Waxy backing paper without lines	150.00	

The gum bleeds through the stamp with red wavy lines resulting in a spotted or blotchy effect. Little or no gum bleeds through on stamps with waxy backing paper.

6	$1 Widgeons, *1976*	22.50	2.50
7	$1 Cinnamon teal, *1977*	45.00	9.00
8	$5 Cinnamon teal, *1978*	12.50	2.50
9	$5 Hooded mergansers, *1978*	110.00	15.00
10	$5 Wood ducks, *1979*	9.00	2.50
11	$5 Pintails, *1980*	9.00	2.50
12	$5 Canvasbacks, *1981*	9.00	2.50
13	$5 Widgeons, *1982*	9.00	2.50
14	$5 Green-winged teal, *1983*	12.00	2.50
15	$7.50 Mallard decoy, *1984*	11.00	2.50
16	$7.50 Ring-necked ducks, *1985*	11.00	2.50
17	$7.50 Canada goose, *1986*	11.00	3.00
18	$7.50 Redheads, *1987*	11.00	3.00
19	$7.50 Mallards, *1988*	11.00	3.00
20	$7.50 Cinnamon teal, *1989*	11.00	3.00
21	$7.50 Canada goose, *1990*	11.00	3.00
22	$7.50 Gadwalls, *1991*	11.00	3.00
23	$7.90 White-fronted goose, *1992*	13.00	3.00
24	$10.50 Pintails, *1993*	16.00	4.00

Rouletted Horiz.

25	$10.50 Wood duck, *1994*	15.00	4.00

Perf. Vertically

Birds in flight, denomination at: b, UL. c, UR. d, LL. e, LR.

26	$10.50 Snow geese, booklet pane of 4, #b.-e., *1995*	60.00	
a.	Souvenir sheet of 4, #b.-e. (decorative border)		150.00
b.-e.	Booklet single, each	15.00	4.00

Stamps in No. 26a are perfed on all four sides.

Perf. Horizontally

27	$10.50 Mallards, *1996*	16.00	2.50

Issued in panes of 4.

28	$10.50 Pintails, *1997*	16.00	2.50
29	$10.50 Green-winged teal, pair, *1998*	32.50	
a.-b.	a, Female, b, Male, each	15.00	2.50

No. 29 issued in strips of 4 stamps.

30	$10.50 Wood duck, pair, *1999*	32.50	
a.-b.	a, Male, b, Male and female, each	14.00	2.50

No. 30 issued in strips of 2 pairs.

31	$10.50 Canada geese, mallard, widgeon *2000*	16.00	2.50
32	$10.50 Canvasbacks, *2001*	16.00	2.50
33	$10.50 Pintails, *2002*	16.00	2.50
34	$10.50 Mallards, *2003*	16.00	2.50
35	$13.90 Cinnamon teal, *2004*	17.00	2.50

Perf. Vertically

36	$14.20 Pintails, *2005*	17.50	2.50
37	$14.95 White-fronted goose, *2006*	18.50	2.50
38	$16 Pintails, *2007*	20.00	2.50

Perf. Horizontally

39	$16.80 Mallards, *2008*	21.00	2.50

COLORADO

North Central Goose Stamp

Used in an area extending from Ft. Collins to approximately 50 miles east of the city.

Illustration reduced.

1973

A1	$2 black	—	—

No. A1 is die cut and self-adhesive. Unused stamps have glassine backing.

Statewide Issues

Printed in booklet panes of 5 and panes of 30. Stamps are numbered serially. Imperforate varieties of these stamps are printer's proofs.

> **Catalogue values for all unused stamps in this section are for Never Hinged items.**

Artists: Robert Steiner, #1-2; Charles Allen, #3; Dan Andrews, #4; Sarah Woods, #5; Cynthie Fisher, #6, 9-14; Bill Border, #7; Gerald G. Putt, #8; Jeffrey Klinefelter, #15-16, 18-19. Michael Ashman, #17.

1990-2008

1	$5 Canada geese		12.00	
	Bklt. single, with tab, Nos. 80,001-150,000		12.50	3.00
a.	$5 +$50 Governor's edition		60.00	
2	$5 Mallards, *1991*		17.50	
	Bklt. single, with tab, Nos. 80,001-150,000		16.00	3.00
a.	$5 +$50 Governor's edition		60.00	
3	$5 Pintails, *1992*		10.00	
	Bklt. single, with tab, Nos. 80,001-150,000		10.00	3.00
a.	$5 +$50 Governor's edition		60.00	
4	$5 Green-winged teal, *1993*		12.00	
	Bklt. single, with tab, Nos. 80,001-150,000		12.00	3.00
a.	$5 +$50 Governor's edition		60.00	
5	$5 Wood ducks, *1994*		12.00	
	Bklt. single, with tab		12.00	2.50
6	$5 Buffleheads, *1995*		12.00	
	Bklt. single, with tab		12.00	2.50
7	$5 Cinnamon teal, *1996*		12.00	
	Bklt. single, with tab and top selvage		12.00	2.50
8	$5 Widgeons, gold text, *1997*		10.00	
a.	Bklt. single, with tab and top selvage, text in black & white		12.00	2.50
9	$5 Redheads, *1998*		10.00	
	Bklt. single, with tab and top selvage		10.00	2.50
10	$5 Blue-winged teal, *1999*		10.00	
a.	Bklt. single, with tab and top selvage		10.00	2.50
11	$5 Gadwalls, *2000*		10.00	
a.	Bklt. single, with tab and top selvage		10.00	2.50
12	$5 Ruddy ducks, *2001*		10.00	2.50
13	$5 Common goldeneyes, *2002*		10.00	2.50
14	$5 Canvasbacks, *2003*		10.00	2.50
15	$5 Snow geese, *2004*		10.00	2.50
16	$5 Shovelers, *2005*		10.00	2.50
17	$5 Ring-necked ducks, *2006*		7.50	2.50
18	$5 Hooded mergansers, *2007*		7.50	2.50
19	$5 Lesser scaup, *2008*		7.50	2.50

CONNECTICUT

Printed in booklet panes of 10 and sheets of 30.
Stamps are numbered serially.
Imperforate varieties are proofs.

Artists: Thomas Hirata, #1; Robert Leslie, #2, 9; Phillip Crowe, #3; Keith Mueller, #4, 7, 15; Robert Steiner, #5; Joe Hautman, #6; George Lockwood, #8; Robert Richert, #10; Paul Fusco, #11-14; Burt Schuman, #16.

1993-2008

1	$5 Black ducks		12.00	3.00
	Booklet pane pair with L & R salvage, Nos. 51,001-81,000		24.00	
a.	Sheet of 4		80.00	
b.	$5 +$50 Governor's edition		75.00	
2	$5 Canvasbacks, *1994*		11.00	3.00
	Booklet pair with L & R salvage, Nos. 53,000-up		22.50	
a.	Sheet of 4		47.50	
3	$5 Mallards, *1995*		15.00	3.00
	Booklet pair with L & R selvage		30.00	
4	$5 Old squaw ducks, *1996*		16.00	3.00
	Booklet pair with L & R selvage		32.50	
5	$5 Green-winged teal, *1997*		11.00	3.00
a.	$5 +$50 Governor's edition		*150.00*	

6	$5 Mallards, *1998*		10.00	3.00
7	$5 Canada geese, *1999*		15.00	3.00
a.	$5 +$50 Governor's edition		*450.00*	
8	$5 Wood duck, *2000*		10.00	3.00
a.	$5 +$50 Governor's edition		*425.00*	
9	$5 Buffleheads, *2001*		9.00	3.00
a.	$5 +$50 Governor's edition		*425.00*	
10	$5 Greater scaups, *2002*		12.00	3.00
a.	$5 +$50 Governor's edition		*450.00*	
11	$5 Black Duck, *2003*		10.00	3.00
12	$5 Wood duck, *2004*		10.00	3.00
13	$10 Mallards, *2005*		14.00	3.00
14	$10 Buffleheads, *2006*		14.00	3.00
15	$10 Black duck decoy, *2007*		14.00	3.00
16	$10 Common goldeneyes, *2008*		14.00	3.00

DELAWARE

Printed in sheets of 10.
Starting in 1991, a portion of the printing is numbered serially on the reverse.

Artists: Ned Mayne, #1; Charles Rowe, #2; Lois Butler, #3; John Green, #4; Nolan Haan, #5; Don Breyfogle, #6; Robert Leslie, #7, 10; Bruce Langton, #8; Jim Hautman, #9; Francis Sweet, #11; Ronald Louque, #12; Richard Clifton, #13, 17, 19, 26; Robert Metropulos, #14; Louis Frisino, #15; Michael Ashman, #16, 21; Jeffrey Klinefelter, #18, 24; Russ Duerksen, #20; Brian Blight, #22; George Lockwood, #23, 28; Bonnie Field, #25; Joanna Rivera, #26; John Stewart, #29.

1980-2008

1	$5 Black ducks		90.00	20.00
2	$5 Snow geese, *1981*		70.00	20.00
3	$5 Canada geese, *1982*		70.00	20.00
4	$5 Canvasbacks, *1983*		40.00	10.00
5	$5 Mallards, *1984*		15.00	5.00
6	$5 Pintail, *1985*		12.00	3.00
7	$5 Widgeons, *1986*		11.00	3.00
8	$5 Redheads, *1987*		11.00	3.00
9	$5 Wood ducks, *1988*		9.00	3.00
10	$5 Buffleheads, *1989*		9.00	3.00
11	$5 Green-winged teal, *1990*		10.00	3.00
a.	$5 +$50 Governor's edition		85.00	
12	$5 Hooded merganser, no serial number on reverse, *1991*		10.00	
	With serial number on reverse		11.00	3.00
13	$5 Blue-winged teal, no serial number on reverse, *1992*		10.00	
	With serial number on reverse		10.00	2.50
14	$5 Goldeneye, no serial number on reverse, *1993*		10.00	
	With serial number on reverse		10.00	2.50
15	$5 Blue goose, no serial number on reverse, *1994*		12.00	
	With serial number on reverse		12.00	2.50
16	($6) Scaup, no serial number on reverse, *1995*		11.00	
	With serial number on reverse		11.00	2.50
17	$6 Gadwall, no serial number on reverse, *1996*		12.00	
	With serial number on reverse		12.00	2.50
18	$6 White-winged scoter, no serial number on reverse, *1997*		12.00	
	With serial number on reverse		12.00	2.50
19	$6 Blue-winged teal, *1998*		11.00	2.50
20	$6 Tundra swan, *1999*		11.00	
21	$6 American brant, *2000*		12.00	2.50
22	$6 Oldsquaw, *2001*		11.00	2.50
23	$6 Ruddy ducks, *2002*		11.00	2.50
24	$9 Ring-necked ducks, *2003*		12.00	3.00
25	$9 Black scoters and lighthouse, *2004*		12.00	3.00
a.	$9 +$50 Governor's edition		95.00	
26	$9 Common mergansers and lighthouse, *2005*		12.00	3.00
a.	$9 +$50 Governor's edition		75.00	
27	$9 Red-breasted mergansers, *2006*		12.00	3.00
28	$9 Surf scoters, lighthouse *2007*		12.00	3.00
29	$9 Greater scaup, lighthouse, *2008*		12.00	3.00

FLORIDA

#1-7 issued in booklet panes of 5. Nos. 8-19 in sheets of 10. No. 20 in sheet of 12.
Stamps are numbered serially and rouletted. Serial numbers for stamps with survey tabs attached end in -04.

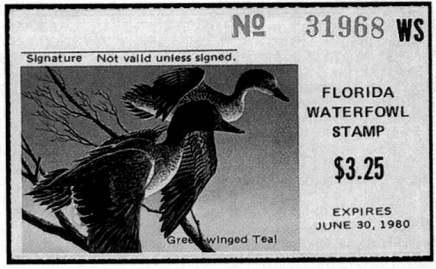

Illustration reduced.

Artists: Bob Binks, #1, 7; Ernest Simmons, #2; Clark Sullivan, #3; Lee Cable, #4; Heiner Hertling, #5; John Taylor, #6; Robert Steiner, #8; Ronald Louque, #9-10; J. Byron Test, #11; Ben Test, #12; Richard Hansen, #13; Richard Clifton, #14; John Mogus, #15; Antonie Rossini, #16; Kenneth Nanney, #17; Wally Makuchal, #18; M. Frase, #19; Brian Blight, #20; John Harris, #21, 23; Jeffrey Klinefelter, #22; John Nelson Harris, #24.

1979-2003

1	$3.25 Green-winged teal		175.00	20.00
	With tab		210.00	
2	$3.25 Pintails, *1980*		15.00	5.00
	With tab		20.00	

3	$3.25 Widgeon, *1981*	15.00	5.00
	With tab	40.00	
4	$3.25 Ring-necked ducks, *1982*	22.50	5.00
	With tab	30.00	
5	$3.25 Buffleheads, *1983*	45.00	5.00
	With tab	60.00	
6	$3.25 Hooded merganser, *1984*	11.00	3.50
	With tab	35.00	
7	$3.25 Wood ducks, *1985*	11.00	3.50
	With tab	30.00	
8	$3 Canvasbacks, *1986*	11.00	3.50
	With small tab at top	11.00	
	With larger survey tab at side and small tab at top	25.00	
9	$3.50 Mallards, *1987*	9.00	3.50
	With small tab at top	9.00	
	With larger survey tab at side and small tab at top	25.00	
10	$3.50 Redheads, *1988*	8.00	2.50
	With small tab at top	8.00	
	With larger survey tab at side and small tab at top	20.00	
11	$3.50 Blue-winged teal, *1989*	8.00	2.50
	With small tab at top	8.00	
	With larger survey tab at side and small tab at top	35.00	
12	$3.50 Wood ducks, *1990*	8.00	2.50
	With small tab at top	8.00	
	With larger survey tab at side and small tab at top	35.00	
13	$3.50 Northern Pintails, *1991*	9.00	2.50
	With small tab at top	9.00	
	With larger survey tab at side and small tab at top	30.00	
14	$3.50 Ruddy duck, *1992*	8.00	2.50
	With small tab at top	7.00	
	With larger survey tab at side and small tab at top	12.00	
15	$3.50 American widgeon, *1993*	8.00	2.50
	With small tab at top	8.00	
	With larger survey tab at side and small tab at top	27.50	
16	$3.50 Mottled duck, *1994*	9.00	2.50
	With small tab at top	9.00	
	With larger survey tab at side and small tab at top	27.50	
17	$3.50 Fulvous whistling duck, *1995*	9.00	2.50
	With small tab at top	9.00	
	With larger survey tab at side and small tab at top	27.50	
18	$3.50 Goldeneyes, *1996*	15.00	2.50
	With small tab at top	15.00	
	With larger survey tab at side and small tab at top	27.50	
19	($3.00) Hooded merganser, *1997*	11.00	2.50
	With small tab at top	11.00	
	With larger survey tab at side and small tab at top	27.50	

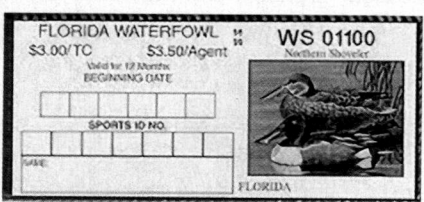

Self-Adhesive

20	$3 Shoveler, *1998*	20.00	2.50
	Sold for $3.50 through agents.		
21	$3 Pintail, *1999*	12.00	2.50
	Sold for $3.50 through agents.		
22	$3 Ring-necked duck, *2000*	9.00	2.50
	Sold for $3.50 through agents.		
23	$3 Canvasback, *2001*	9.00	2.50
	Sold for $3.50 through agents.		
24	$3 Mottled duck, *2002*	9.00	2.50

Sold for $3.50 through agents. No. 24 with rouletting and with duck facing right come from a special limited reprinting

demanded by the artist to correct the appearance of his work. Value, $50.

The 2003 stamp was sold by Florida officials only to the stamp's artist. Values: $110; with small tab at top, $150.

GEORGIA

Not required to hunt waterfowl until 1989.
Nos. 1-4 printed in sheets of 30, others in sheets of 20.
Starting with No 5, stamps are numbered serially.

> **Catalogue values for all unused stamps in this section are for Never Hinged items.**

Artists: Daniel Smith, #1; Jim Killen, #2, 14; James Partee, Jr., #3; Paul Bridgeford, #4; Ralph J. McDonald, #5; Guy Coheleach, #6; Phillip Crowe, #7-8, 11; Jerry Raedeke, #9, 13, 15; Herb Booth, #10; David Lanier, #12.

1985-99

1	$5.50 Wood ducks	15.00	
2	$5.50 Mallards, *1986*	9.00	
3	$5.50 Canada geese, *1987*	9.00	
4	$5.50 Ring-necked ducks, *1988*	9.00	
5	$5.50 Duckling & golden retriever puppy, *1989*	14.00	2.50
6	$5.50 Wood ducks, *1990*	9.00	2.50
7	$5.50 Green-winged teal, *1991*	9.50	2.50
8	$5.50 Buffleheads, *1992*	15.00	2.50
9	$5.50 Mallards, *1993*	15.00	2.50
10	$5.50 Ring-necked ducks, *1994*	15.00	2.50
11	$5.50 Widgeons, Labrador retriever, *1995*	32.50	2.50
12	$5.50 Black ducks, *1996*	25.00	2.50
13	$5.50 Lesser scaup, Cockspur Island lighthouse, *1997*	40.00	2.50
14	$5.50 Labrador retriever, ring-necked ducks, *1998*	27.50	2.50
15	$5.50 Pintails, *1999*	22.50	2.50

HAWAII

Required for the hunting of small game. Hunting birds was illegal in Hawaii until 2003. Game bird hunting was permitted beginning July 1, 2003. Game birds that can be hunted include pheasants, francolins, partridges, quail, sand grouses, doves and wild turkeys.

Artists: Patrick Ching, #1; D. Van Zyle, #2; Michael Furuya, #3; Norman Nagai, #4, 7, 10, 13; Marion Berger, #5; Daniel Wang, #6; Joy Keown, #8, 9. Shane Hamamoto, #11. Dan Hoyes, #12.

1996-2008

1	$5 Nene goose	5.00	
a.	$5 +$50 Governor's edition	75.00	
b.	As No. 1, sheet of 4	45.00	
	No. 1b exists imperf.		
2	$5 Hawaiian duck, *1997*	5.00	
	With tab	10.00	
a.	As No. 2, sheet of 4	45.00	
	No. 2a exists imperf.		
3	$5 Wild turkey, *1998*	5.00	
	With tab	10.00	
4	$5 Ring-necked pheasant, *1999*	5.00	
	With tab	14.00	
5	$5 Erckel's francolin, *2000*	5.00	
	With tab	12.00	
6	$5 Green pheasant, *2001*	5.00	
	With tab	12.00	5.00
7	$10 Chukar partridge, *2002*	5.00	
8	$10 Nene geese, *2003*	5.00	
9	$10 Nene geese, *2004*	5.00	
10	$10 California quail, *2005*	5.00	
11	$10 Black francolin, *2006*	5.00	
12	$10 Gray francolin, *2007*	15.00	
13	$10 Chukar partridge, *2008*	15.00	

IDAHO

Printed in booklet panes of 5 and sheets of 30, except No. 5, which was issued in booklets of 10. Numbered serially except for No. 11.

> **Catalogue values for all unused stamps in this section are for Never Hinged items.**

Artists: Robert Leslie, #1; Jim Killen, #2; Daniel Smith, #3; Francis E. Sweet, #4, Richard Clifton, #6, 11; Richard Plasschaert, #7; Sherrie Russell Meline, #8; Bill Moore, #9; David Gressard, #10; T. Smith, #12; Maynard Reece, #13.

1987-98

1	$5.50 Cinnamon teal, perforated	15.00	
a.	Bklt. single, rouletted, with 2-part tab	12.00	3.00
2	$5.50 Green-winged teal, perforated, *1988*	13.00	
a.	Bklt. single, rouletted, with 2-part tab	13.00	3.00
3	$6 Blue-winged teal, perforated, *1989*	10.00	
a.	Bklt. single, rouletted, with 2-part tab	11.00	3.00
4	$6 Trumpeter swans, perforated, *1990*	21.00	
a.	Bklt. single, rouletted, with 2-part tab	21.00	3.00

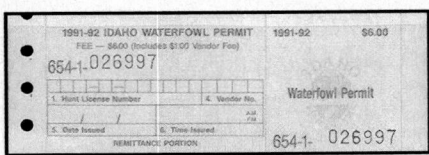

Die cut self-adhesive

5	$6 green, *1991*	175.00	*35.00*

No. 5 was used provisionally in 1991 when the regular stamps were delayed. Unused value is for stamp, remittance tab and selvage pieces on backing paper.

Designs like No. 1

6	$6 Widgeons, perforated, *1991*	10.00	
a.	Bklt. single, rouletted, with 2-part tab	10.00	2.50
7	$6 Canada geese, perforated, *1992*	10.00	
a.	Bklt. single, rouletted, with 2-part tab	10.00	2.50
8	$6.00 Common goldeneye, perforated, *1993*	12.00	
a.	Bklt. single, rouletted, with 2-part tab	12.00	2.50
9	$6 Harlequin ducks, perforated, *1994*	12.00	
a.	Bklt. single, rouletted, with 2-part tab	12.00	2.50
10	$6 Wood ducks, perforated, *1995*	12.00	
a.	Bklt. single, rouletted, with 2-part tab	12.00	2.50
11	$6.50 Mallard, *1996*	16.00	2.50
12	$6.50 Shovelers, *1997*	22.50	2.50
13	$6.50 Canada geese, *1998*	15.00	2.50

ILLINOIS

Daily Usage Stamps for State-operated Waterfowl Areas.

Date and fee overprinted in black. $2 and $3 stamps were for hunting ducks, $5 stamps for hunting geese and pheasants. 1953-58 had separate pheasant stamps. No duck stamp was printed in 1971.
Some unused stamps have dry gum.
Used stamps have no gum or have staple holes.
Black printing.
Stamps are numbered serially.

1953-1972

A1	$2 orange, *blue*	—	—
A4	$2 green, *manila, 1956*	—	—
A5	$2 orange, *light blue green, 1957*	950.	400.
A6	$2 green, *manila, 1958*	850.	400.
A7	$3 green, *manila, 1959*	675.	300.
A8	$5 red brown, *light blue green, 1959*	675.	300.
A9	$3 red brown, *light blue green, 1960*	675.	300.
A10	$3 green, *manila, 1960*	675.	300.
A11	$3 green, *manila, 1961*	675.	300.
A12	$5 red brown, *light blue green, 1961*	675.	300.
A15	$3 green, *manila, 1962*	675.	300.
A14	$5 red brown, *light blue green, 1962*	675.	300.
A15	$3 orange, *light blue green, 1963*	675.	300.
A16	$3 green, *manila, 1963*	675.	300.
A17	$3 green, *manila, 1964*	675.	300.
A18	$5 red, *light blue green, 1964*	675.	250.
A19	$3 orange, *light blue green, 1965*	675.	300.
A20	$5 orange, *manila, 1965*	675.	300.
A21	$3 green, *manila, 1966*	675.	300.
A22	$5 orange, *light blue green, 1966*	675.	300.
A23	$3 orange, *light blue green, 1967*	675.	300.
A24	$5 green, *yellow, 1967*	675.	300.
A25	$3 orange, *yellow, 1968*	675.	300.
A26	$5 orange, *light blue, 1968*	675.	300.
A27	$3 orange, *light blue, 1969*	675.	300.
A28	$5 green, *manila, 1969*	675.	300.
A29	$3 green, *manila, 1970*	1,500.	900.
A30	$5 orange, *light blue, 1970*	1,750.	900.
A31	$5 green, *manila, 1971*	1,950.	1,000.
A32	$3 orange, *light blue green, 1972*	5,500.	
A33	$5 orange, *light blue green, 1972*	5,500.	2,250.

> Catalogue values for unused stamps in this section, from this point to the end, are for Never Hinged items.

No. A34

No. A35

1977-91(?)

A34	black, *light blue,* duck, *1991*	—	—
A35	black, *manila,* goose	—	—

Nos. A34-A35 do not show year or denomination and were used until 1994. No. A34 used before 1991 should exist but has not been reported yet. Separate pheasant and controlled quail and pheasant stamps of a similar design have also been used.

No. A36

No. A37

1996

A36	black, *light blue,* duck	— —
A37	black, *manila,* goose	— —

Nos. A36-A37 do not show year or denomination.

Statewide Issues

Nos. 1-10 in sheets of 10. Starting with No. 11, in booklet panes of 5; starting with No. 22, in panes of 10.
Stamps are numbered serially and rouletted.

> Catalogue values for all unused stamps in this section are for Never Hinged items.

Artists: Robert Eschenfeldt, #1; Robert G. Larson, #2; Richard Lynch, #3; Everett Staffeldt, #4; John Eggert, #5; Bart Kassabaum, #6, 9, 11, 13; Jim Trindel, #7; Arthur Sinden, #8, 12, 14; George Kieffer, #10; Charles McKay Freeman, #15; John Henson, #16; Phillip Crowe, #17-21; Thomas Hirata, #22-24; Jim Killen, #25-29; Gerald Putt, #30-32. Christina Van Dellen, #33; Karen Latham, #34.

1975-2008

1	$5 Mallard	525.00	85.00
2	$5 Wood ducks, *1976*	225.00	50.00
3	$5 Canada goose, *1977*	150.00	35.00
4	$5 Canvasbacks, *1978*	125.00	22.50
5	$5 Pintail, *1979*	115.00	16.00
6	$5 Green-winged teal, *1980*	100.00	16.00
7	$5 Widgeons, *1981*	115.00	16.00
a.	"Green-winged teal"	450.00	
8	$5 Black ducks, *1982*	60.00	12.50
9	$5 Lesser scaup, *1983*	75.00	10.00
10	$5 Blue-winged teal, *1984*	60.00	10.00
11	$5 Redheads, *1985*	16.00	3.00
	With 2-part tab	22.50	
12	$5 Gadwalls, *1986*	12.00	3.00
	With 2-part tab	20.00	
13	$5 Buffleheads, *1987*	12.00	3.00
	With 2-part tab	15.00	
14	$5 Common goldeneyes, *1988*	12.00	2.50
	With 2-part tab	15.00	
15	$5 Ring-necked ducks, *1989*	10.00	2.50
	With 2-part tab	10.00	
16	$10 Lesser snow geese, *1990*	16.00	3.00
	With 2-part tab	17.00	
17	$10 Labrador retriever & Canada goose, *1991*	16.00	3.00
	With 2-part tab	16.00	
a.	Governor's edition with tab	85.00	
18	$10 Retriever & mallards, *1992*	25.00	3.00
	With 2-part tab	27.50	
19	$10 Pintail decoys and puppy, *1993*	32.50	3.00
	With 2-part tab	35.00	
20	$10 Canvasbacks & retrievers, *1994*	32.50	3.00
	With 2-part tab	35.00	
21	$10 Retriever, green-winged teal, decoys, *1995*	32.50	3.00
	With 2-part tab	35.00	
22	$10 Wood ducks, *1996*	20.00	2.50
23	$10 Canvasbacks, *1997*	17.50	2.50
24	$10 Canada geese, *1998*	17.50	2.50
25	$10 Canada geese, black Labrador retriever, *1999*	22.50	2.50
a.	Anniversary edition, perforated	92.50	
b.	Governor's edition, perforated	92.50	
c.	Silver edition, perforated	92.50	

Nos. 25a-25c were sold as a set of three.

26	$10 Mallards, golden retriever, *2000*	22.50	2.50
27	$10 Pintails, yellow Labrador retriever, *2001*	22.50	2.50
28	$10 Canvasbacks, Chesapeake retriever, *2002*	22.50	2.50
29	$10 Green-winged teal, Labrador retriever, *2003*	15.00	2.50
30	$10 Wood ducks, *2004*	15.00	2.50
31	$10 Green-winged teals, *2005*	15.00	2.50
32	$10 Northern pintails, *2006*	14.00	2.50
33	$10 Bufflehead, *2007*	14.00	2.50
34	$10 Greater scaup, *2008*	14.00	2.50

INDIANA

Issued in booklet panes of 4 (Nos. 1-10) and booklet panes of 2, starting with No. 11.
Stamps are numbered serially and rouletted.

> Catalogue values for all unused stamps in this section are for Never Hinged items.

IOWA DEPT. OF NATURAL RESOURCES

Artists: Justin H. (Sonny) Bashore, #1-2; Carl (Spike) Knuth, #3; Daniel Renn Pierce, #4; Dean Barrick, #5; Rodney Crossman, #6; George Metz, #7; Kieth Freeman, #8; Lyn Briggs, #9; Rick Pas, #10; Ronald Louque, #11; Susan Hastings Bates, #12.

Bruce Langton, #13, 17; Ann Dahoney, #14; Ken Bucklew, #15, 20, 22, 24, 29, 32; Richard Hansen, #16; Jeffrey Klinefelter, #18, 26, 28, 30, 33; Jeffrey Mobley. #19; Charles Riggles, #21, 23, 31; George Lockwood; #25; Biran Blight, 27.

1976-2008

1	$5 Green-winged teal		12.00	2.50
2	$5 Pintail, 1977		10.00	2.50
3	$5 Canada geese, 1978		8.00	2.50
4	$5 Canvasbacks, 1979		8.00	2.50
5	$5 Mallard ducklings, 1980		8.00	2.50
6	$5 Hooded mergansers, 1981		8.00	2.50
7	$5 Blue-winged teal, 1982		8.00	2.50
8	$5 Snow geese, 1983		8.00	2.50
9	$5 Redheads, 1984		8.00	2.50
10	$5 Pintail, 1985		10.00	2.50
	With tab		10.50	
11	$5 Wood duck, 1986		8.00	2.50
	With tab		10.00	
12	$5 Canvasbacks, 1987		8.00	2.50
	With tab		10.00	
13	$6.75 Redheads, 1988		10.00	2.50
	With tab		10.50	
14	$6.75 Canada goose, 1989		10.00	2.50
	With tab		10.50	
15	$6.75 Blue-winged teal, 1990		10.00	2.50
	With tab		10.50	
16	$6.75 Mallards, 1991		10.00	2.50
	With tab		10.50	
17	$6.75 Green-winged teal, 1992		10.00	2.50
	With tab		10.50	
18	$6.75 Wood ducks, 1993		10.00	2.50
	With tab		10.50	
19	$6.75 Pintail, 1994		10.00	2.50
	With tab		10.50	
20	$6.75 Goldeneyes, 1995		10.00	2.50
	With tab		10.50	
21	$6.75 Black ducks, 1996		10.00	2.50
	With tab		10.50	
22	$6.75 Canada geese, 1997		10.00	2.50
	With tab		10.50	
23	$6.75 Widgeon, 1998		10.00	2.50
	With tab		10.50	
24	$6.75 Bluebills, 1999		9.00	2.50
	With tab		10.00	
25	$6.75 Ring-necked duck, 2000		9.00	2.50
	With tab		10.00	
26	$6.75 Hooded mergansers, 2001		9.00	2.50
	With tab		10.00	
27	$6.75 Green-winged teal, 2002		9.00	2.50
	With tab		10.00	
28	$6.75 Northern shovelers, 2003		9.00	2.50
	With tab		10.00	
29	$6.75 Wood duck, 2004		9.00	2.50
	With tab		10.00	
30	$6.75 Buffleheads, 2005		9.00	2.50
	With tab		10.00	
31	$6.75 Gadwalls, 2006		9.00	2.50
	With tab		10.00	
32	$6.75 Pintails, 2007		9.00	2.50
	With tab		10.00	
33	$6.75 Shovelers, 2008		9.00	2.50
	With tab		10.00	

IOWA

Catalogue values for all unused stamps in this section are for Never Hinged items.

Issued in booklet pane of 5 (No. 1), 10 (others) and sheets of 10 (No. 19).

Artists: Maynard Reece, #1, 6, 22; Thomas Murphy, #2; James Landenberger, #3; Mark Reece, #4; Nick Klepinger, #5, 7; Andrew Peters, #8; Paul Brigford, #9, 12, 15; Brad Reece, #10; Tom Walker, #11; Larry Zach, #13.

Jack C. Hahn, #14, 18; John Heidersbach, #16; Mark Cary, #17; Patrick Murillo, #19; Jerry Raedeke, #20; Charlotte Edwards, #21, 26; Dietmar Krumrey, #23, 25, 33; Cynthia Fisher, #24; Sherrie Russell Meline, #27, 29, 35; Mark Anderson, #28; Darren Maurer, #30, 31, 36; Neal Anderson, #32, 34; Ronnie Hughes, #37.

1972-98

1	$1 Mallards		135.00	25.00
2	$1 Pintails, 1973		35.00	7.50
3	$1 Gadwalls, rouletted, 1974		85.00	7.00
4	$1 Canada geese, 1975		95.00	9.00
5	$1 Canvasbacks, 1976		25.00	2.50
6	$1 Lesser scaup, rouletted, 1977		21.00	2.50
7	$1 Wood ducks, rouletted, 1978		50.00	5.00
8	$5 Buffleheads, 1979		325.00	25.00
9	$5 Redheads, 1980		27.50	6.00
10	$5 Green-winged teal, rouletted, 1981		27.50	4.00
11	$5 Snow geese, rouletted, 1982		18.00	2.50
12	$5 Widgeons, 1983		18.00	2.75
13	$5 Wood ducks, 1984		35.00	3.00
14	$5 Mallard & mallard decoy, 1985		20.00	2.50
15	$5 Blue-winged teal, 1986		15.00	2.50
16	$5 Canada goose, 1987		15.00	2.50
17	$5 Pintails, 1988		15.00	2.50
18	$5 Blue-winged teal, 1989		15.00	2.50
19	$5 Canvasbacks, 1990		10.00	2.50
20	$5 Mallards, 1991		10.00	2.50
21	$5 Labrador retriever & ducks, 1992		10.00	2.50
22	$5 Mallards, 1993		10.00	2.50
23	$5 Green-winged teal, 1994		10.00	2.50
24	$5 Canada geese, 1995		10.00	2.50
25	$5 Canvasbacks, 1996		10.00	2.50
26	$5 Canada geese, 1997		10.00	2.50
27	$5 Pintails, 1998		12.00	2.50

DEPARTMENT OF NATURAL RESOURCES

1999
28   Trumpeter swan, 1999   12.00   2.50

No. 28 not required for hunting. The Department of Natural Resources sent customers No. 28 upon receipt of a postcard given to the customer after paying license fee of $5.

IOWA DEPT. OF NATURAL RESOURCES

2000
29   Hooded merganser, 2000   10.00   2.50

No. 29 not required for hunting. The Department of Natural Resources sent customers No. 29 upon receipt of a postcard given to the customer after paying license fee of $5.

2001
30   Snow goose, 2001   11.00   2.50

No. 30 not required for hunting. The Department of Natural Resources sent customers No. 30 upon receipt of a postcard given to the customer after paying license fee of $5.

WATERFOWL STAMP
IOWA DEPT. OF NATURAL RESOURCES

2002
31   Shovelers, 2002   17.50   4.00

No. 31 not required for hunting. The Department of Natural Resources sent customers No. 31 upon receipt of a postcard given to the customer after paying license fee of $8.50.

2003
32   Ruddy duck, 2003   15.00   4.00

No. 32 not required for hunting. The Department of Natural Resources sent customers No. 32 upon receipt of a postcard given to the customer after paying license fee of $8.50.

2004
33   Wood ducks, 2004   14.00   4.00

No. 33 not required for hunting. The Department of Natural Resources sent customers No. 33 upon receipt of a postcard given to the customer after paying license fee of $8.50.

2005
34   Green-winged teals, 2005   14.00   4.00

No. 34 not required for hunting. The Department of Natural Resources sent customers No. 34 upon receipt of a postcard given to the customer after paying license fee of $8.50.

2006
35   Ring-necked duck, 2006   13.00   4.00

No. 35 not required for hunting. The Department of Natural Resources sent customers No. 34 upon receipt of a postcard given to the customer after paying license fee of $8.50.

36   Wigeon, 2007   13.00   4.00

No. 36 not required for hunting. The Department of Natural Resources sent customers No. 36 upon receipt of a postcard given to the customer after paying license fee of $8.50.

37   Wood duck, 2008   13.00   4.00

No. 37 not required for hunting. The Department of Natural Resources sent customers No. 37 upon receipt of a postcard given to the customer after paying license fee of $8.50.

KANSAS

Marion County Resident Duck Stamps

Wording, type face, border and perforation/roulette differs.

Used values are for stamps without gum.

1941-42

A1	25c black	—
A2	25c black, *1942*	—

Remainders from 1941 were rubber stamped "1942" in purple and initialed "J.E.M." by the Park and Lake Supervisor.

1943-73

A3	25c black, *pink*	—
A4	25c black, *green, 1944*	—
A5	25c green, *1945*	—
A6	25c black, *yellow, 1946*	17,500.
A7	25c black, *pink, 1947*	8,500.
A8	50c black, *blue, 1948*	19,500.
A9	50c black, *1949*	—
A10	50c black, *blue, 1950*	—
A11	50c black, *1951*	—
A13	50c black, *blue, 1953*	—
A14	50c black, *pink, 1954*	100. 65.
A15	50c black, *green, 1955*	100. 65.
A16	50c black, *1956*	125. 100.
A17	50c black, *blue, 1957*	95. 65.
a.	"1" instead of "I" in "RESIDENT," pos. 3	1,950. 1,350.
b.	1st 2 lines reversed, pos. 6	2,750. 1,900.
A18	50c black, *light yellow, 1958*	450. 850.
A19	50c black, *1959*	75. 55.
A20	50c black, *1960*	100. 75.
a.	Missing ornamental ball, pos. 9	2,750.
A21	50c black, *1961*	150. 100.
A22	50c black, *1962*	225. 150.
A23	50c black, *pink, 1963*	700. 450.
A24	50c black, *pink, 1964*	700. 450.
a.	2nd & 3rd lines reversed, pos. 10	15,500.
A25	50c black, *green, 1965*	500. 400.
A26	50c black, *yellow, 1966*	— 12,500.
A27	50c black, *green, 1967*	4,750. 2,750.
A28	50c black, *pink, 1968*	300. 250.
A29	50c black, *yellow, 1969*	300. 200.
a.	"Dusk" instead of "Duck," pos. 8	17,500.
A30	50c black, *1970*	450. 350.
A31	50c black, *pink, 1971*	3,500. 2,500.
A32	50c black, *blue, 1972*	3,500. 2,500.
A33	50c black, *pink, 1973*	10,500. 6,500.

Statewide Issues

Issued in booklet panes of 10 (Nos. 1-5) and sheets of 30 (starting with No. 2). Starting with No. 11, issued in sheets of 10. No. 1 issued in booklets with one pane of 10 (serial number has prefix "DD") and booklets with two panes of 10 (serial number has prefix "SS").

Nos. 1-4 numbered serially.

> Catalogue values for all unused stamps in this section are for Never Hinged items.

Artists: Guy Coheleach, #1; Ann Dahoney, #2, 8; Leon Parson, #3; Wes Dewey, #4; J. Byron Test, #5; Jerry Thomas, #6, 10; Jerry Roedeke, #7; Neal Anderson, #9; Dustin Teasley, #14-18.

1987-96

1	$3 Green-winged teal	10.00	2.50
	Pair from booklet pane with L & R selvage	20.00	
2	$3 Canada geese, *1988*	8.00	2.50
	Pair from booklet pane with L & R selvage	16.00	
a.	Serial number missing	—	
3	$3 Mallards, *1989*	8.00	2.50
	Pair from booklet pane with L & R selvage	16.00	
4	$3 Wood ducks, *1990*	8.00	2.50
	Pair from booklet pane with L & R selvage	16.00	
5	$3 Pintail, rouletted, *1991*	8.00	2.50
	Pair from booklet pane with selvage at L & straight edge at R	16.00	
6	$3 Canvasbacks, *1992*	8.00	2.50
7	$3 Mallards, *1993*	9.00	2.50
8	$3 Blue-winged teal, *1994*	9.00	2.50
9	$3 Barrow's goldeneye, *1995*	9.00	2.50
10	$3 American widgeon, *1996*	10.00	2.50

No. 2a resulted from a drastic misregistration of the serial numbers during printing. Only one example is documented.

Artist: Dustin Teasley.

1997-2004	**Self-Adhesive**	**Die Cut**	
11	$3 blue	9.00	2.50
12	$3 green, *1998*	9.00	2.50
13	$3 red, *1999*	8.50	2.50
14	$3 red lilac, *2000*	8.50	2.50
15	$3 orange, *2001*	8.50	2.50
16	$5 blue, *2002*	8.75	2.50
17	$5 green, *2003*	9.50	2.50
18	$5 red, *2004*	9.50	2.50

KENTUCKY

Printed in booklet panes of 5, starting with No. 12 in panes of 30.

Stamps are numbered serially.

> Catalogue values for all unused stamps in this section are for Never Hinged items.

Artists: Ray Harm, #1, 7; David Chapple, #2; Ralph J. McDonald, #3, 10; Lynn Kaatz, #4, 15; Phillip Crowe, #5, 9; Jim Oliver, #6; Phillip Powell, #8, 13; Jim Killen, #11; Laurie Parsons Yarnes, #12; Harold Roe, #14, 17; Tim Donovan, #16; Larry Chandler, #18; Ben Burney, #19; Chris Walden, #20-24.

1985-2008

1	$5.25 Mallards, rouletted	15.00	3.00
	With tab	15.00	

2	$5.25 Wood ducks, rouletted, *1986*	10.00	2.50
	With tab	10.00	
3	$5.25 Black ducks, *1987*	9.00	2.50
	With tab	10.00	
4	$5.25 Canada geese, *1988*	9.00	2.50
	With tab	10.00	
5	$5.25 Retriever & canvasbacks, *1989*	15.00	2.50
	With tab	16.00	
6	$5.25 Widgeons, *1990*	9.00	2.50
	With tab	11.00	
7	$5.25 Pintails, *1991*	9.00	2.50
	With tab	11.00	
8	$5.25 Green-winged teal, *1992*	13.00	2.50
	With tab	15.00	
9	$5.25 Canvasback & decoy, *1993*	20.00	2.50
	With tab	22.50	
10	$5.25 Canada goose, *1994*	16.00	2.50
	With tab	19.00	
11	$7.50 Retriever, decoy, ringnecks, *1995*	25.00	3.00
	With tab	27.50	
12	$7.50 Blue-winged teal, *1996*	13.00	3.00
13	$7.50 Shovelers, *1997*	13.00	3.00
14	$7.50 Gadwalls, *1998*	15.00	3.00
15	$7.50 Common goldeneyes, *1999*	14.00	3.00
16	$7.50 Hooded mergansers, *2000*	16.00	3.00
17	$7.50 Mallards, *2001*	12.00	3.00
18	$7.50 Pintails, *2002*	12.00	3.00
19	$7.50 Snow geese, *2003*	12.00	3.00
20	$7.50 Black ducks, *2004*	12.00	3.00
21	$7.50 Canada geese, *2005*	12.00	3.00
22	$7.50 Mallards, *2006*	12.00	3.00
23	$7.50 Green-winged teal, *2007*	9.50	3.00
24	$7.50 Pintails, *2008*	9.50	3.00

Nos. 19-24 not required for hunting.

LOUISIANA

Printed in sheets of 30.

Stamps are numbered serially. Stamps without numbers are artist presentation copies.

Two fees: resident and non-resident.

> Catalogue values for all unused stamps in this section are for Never Hinged items.

Artists: David Noll, #1-2; Elton Louviere, #3-4; Brett J. Smith, #5-6; Bruce Heard, #7-8; Ronald Louque, #9-10, 15-16, 21-22; Don Edwards, #11-12; John Bertrand, #13-14; R. Hall, #17-18; R. C. Davis, #19-20; Jude Brunet, #23-24; Edward Butler, #25-26; Reggie McLeroy, #27-28; Dale Pousson, #29-30; Jeffrey Klinefelter, #31-32, 39-40; Ken Michaelsen, #33-34. Edward Suthoff, #35-36. Tony Bernard, #37-38.

1989-2008

1	$5 Blue-winged teal	12.00	2.50
a.	Governor's edition	100.00	
2	$7.50 Blue-winged teal	14.00	2.50
a.	Governor's edition	150.00	

Nos. 1a and 2a were available only through a sealed bid auction where sheets of 30 of each denomination with matching serial numbers were sold as a unit.

3	$5 Green-winged teal, *1990*	9.50	2.50
4	$7.50 Green-winged teal, *1990*	12.00	2.50
5	$5 Wood ducks, *1991*	9.00	2.50
6	$7.50 Wood ducks, *1991*	13.00	2.50
7	$5 Pintails, *1992*	9.00	2.50
8	$7.50 Pintails, *1992*	13.00	2.50
9	$5 American widgeon, *1993*	12.00	2.50
10	$7.50 American widgeon, *1993*	13.00	2.50
11	$5 Mottled duck, *1994*	12.00	2.50
12	$7.50 Mottled duck, *1994*	13.00	2.50
13	$5 Speckle bellied goose, *1995*	12.00	2.50
14	$7.50 Speckle bellied goose, *1995*	13.00	2.50
15	$5 Gadwall, *1996*	12.00	2.50
16	$7.50 Gadwall, *1996*	13.00	2.50
17	$5 Ring-necked ducks, *1997*	10.00	2.50
18	$13.50 Ring-necked ducks, *1997*	22.50	2.50
19	$5.50 Mallards, *1998*	11.00	2.50
a.	Governor's edition	150.00	
20	$13.50 Mallards, *1998*	22.50	2.50
a.	Governor's edition	200.00	
21	$5.50 Snow geese, *1999*	11.00	2.50
22	$13.50 Snow geese, *1999*	22.50	2.50
23	$5.50 Lesser scaup, *2000*	11.00	2.50
24	$13.50 Lesser scaup, *2000*	35.00	2.50

No. 24 sold for $25 as stamps were printed before fee increase was finalized.

25	$5.50 Shovelers, *2001*	11.00	2.50
26	$25 Shovelers, *2001*	35.00	2.50

27	$5.50 Canvasbacks, *2002*	11.00	2.50
28	$25 Canvasbacks, *2002*	35.00	2.50
29	$5.50 Redheads, *2003*	11.00	2.50
30	$25 Redheads, *2003*	35.00	2.50
31	$5.50 Hooded mergansers, *2004*	10.00	2.50
32	$25 Hooded mergansers, *2004*	35.00	2.50
33	$5.50 Pintails, Labrador retriever, *2005*	9.00	2.50
34	$25 Pintails, Labrador retriever, *2005*	32.50	2.50
35	$5.50 Mallards, Labrador retriever, *2006*	9.00	2.50
36	$25 Mallards, Labrador retriever, *2006*	32.50	2.50
37	$5.50 Mallards, Labrador retriever, *2007*	8.00	2.50
38	$25 Mallards, Labrador retriever, *2007*	30.00	2.50
39	$5.50 Wood ducks, Golden retriever, *2008*	8.00	2.50
40	$25 Wood ducks, Golden retriever, *2008*	30.00	2.50

Nos. 29-40 not required for hunting.

MAINE

Printed in sheets of 10. Nos. 1-10 are numbered serially.

Catalogue values for all unused stamps in this section are for Never Hinged items.

Artists: David Maass, #1-3; Ron Van Gilder, #4; Rick Allen, #5; Jeannine Staples, #6, 10, 15, 18, 20, 23, 25; Thea Flanagan, #7; Patricia D. Carter, #8; Persis Weirs, #9; Susan Jordan, #11; Richard Alley, #12, 19, 16, 21, 24; Paul Fillion, #13; T. Kemp, #14; Darby Mumford, #17; Daniel Cake, #22.

1984-2008

1	$2.50 Black ducks	22.50	5.00
2	$2.50 Common eiders, *1985*	40.00	5.00
3	$2.50 Wood ducks, *1986*	9.00	2.50
4	$2.50 Buffleheads, *1987*	8.00	2.50
5	$2.50 Green-winged teal, *1988*	8.00	2.50
6	$2.50 Common goldeneyes, *1989*	8.00	2.50
7	$2.50 Canada geese, *1990*	8.00	2.50
8	$2.50 Ring-necked duck, *1991*	8.00	2.50
9	$2.50 Old squaw, *1992*	8.00	2.50
10	$2.50 Hooded merganser, *1993*	8.00	2.50
11	$2.50 Mallards, *1994*	9.00	2.50
12	$2.50 White-winged scoters, *1995*	12.00	2.50
13	$2.50 Blue-winged teal, *1996*	12.00	2.50
14	$2.50 Greater scaup, *1997*	12.00	2.50
15	$2.50 Surf scoters, *1998*	8.00	2.50
16	$2.50 Black duck, *1999*	9.00	2.50
17	$2.50 Common eider, *2000*	8.00	2.50
18	$2.50 Wood duck, *2001*	8.00	2.50
19	$2.50 Buffleheads, *2002*	8.00	2.50
20	$5.50 Green-winged teal, *2003*	10.00	2.50
21	$8.50 Barrow's goldeneye, *2004*	12.50	2.50
22	$8.50 Canada goose, *2005*	12.50	2.50
23	$7.50 Ring-necked ducks, *2006*	11.50	2.50
24	$7.50 Long-tailed ducks, *2007*	11.50	2.50
25	$7.50 Hooded mergansers, *2008*	11.50	2.50

MARYLAND

Nos. 1-19 printed in sheets of 10. Starting with No. 20, printed in sheets of 5 with numbered tab at bottom and selvage at top.
Each stamp has tab. Unused value is for stamp with tab. Many used copies have tab attached.

Catalogue values for all unused stamps in this section are for Never Hinged items.

Artists: John Taylor, #1, 6, 24; Stanley Stearns, #2, 5; Louis Frisino, #3, 13, 20; Jack Schroeder, #4, 7; Arthur Eakin, #8; Roger Bucklin, #9; Roger Lent, #10, 16; Carla Huber, #11, 17; David Turnbaugh, #12, 18, 23, 27, 31; Francis Sweet, #14; Christopher White, #15; Will Wilson, #19; Robert Bealle, #21, 30, 35; Charles Schauck, #22; Paul Makuchal, #25, 33; Wally Makuchal, #26; Wilhelm Goebel, #28, 32; James Kinnett, #29. Jim Taylor, #34.

1974-2008

1	$1.10 Mallards	11.00	2.50
2	$1.10 Canada geese, rouletted, *1975*	10.00	2.50
3	$1.10 Canvasbacks, rouletted, *1976*	10.00	2.50
4	$1.10 Greater scaup, *1977*	10.00	2.50
5	$1.10 Redheads, *1978*	10.00	2.50
6	$1.10 Wood ducks, rouletted, *1979*	10.00	2.50
7	$1.10 Pintail decoy, rouletted, *1980*	10.00	2.50
8	$3 Widgeon, rouletted, *1981*	9.00	2.50
9	$3 Canvasback, *1982*	8.00	2.50
10	$3 Wood duck, *1983*	12.00	2.50
11	$6 Black ducks, *1984*	14.00	2.50
12	$6 Canada geese, *1985*	12.00	2.50
13	$6 Hooded mergansers, *1986*	12.00	2.50
14	$6 Redheads, *1987*	13.00	2.50
15	$6 Ruddy ducks, *1988*	12.00	2.50
16	$6 Blue-winged teal, *1989*	12.00	2.50
17	$6 Lesser scaup, *1990*	12.00	2.50
18	$6 Shovelers, *1991*	12.00	2.50
19	$6 Bufflehead, *1992*	12.00	2.50
20	$6 Canvasbacks, *1993*	12.00	2.50
21	$6 Redheads, *1994*	12.00	2.50
22	$6 Mallards, *1995*	22.50	2.50
23	$6 Canada geese, *1996*	27.50	2.50
24	$6 Canvasbacks, *1997*	12.00	2.50
25	$6 Pintails, *1998*	12.00	2.50
26	$6 Wood ducks, *1999*	12.00	2.50
27	$6 Old squaws, *2000*	20.00	2.50
28	$6 Wigeons, *2001*	11.00	2.50
29	$9 Black scoters, *2002*	13.00	2.50
30	$9 Lesser scaup, *2003*	13.00	2.50
31	$9 Pintails, *2004*	13.00	2.50
32	$9 Ruddy duck, *2005*	13.00	2.50
33	$9 Canada geese, *2006*	13.00	2.50
34	$9 Wood ducks, *2007*	12.00	2.50
35	$9 Canvasback, *2008*	12.00	2.50

Public Lands Hunting Stamps
Required to hunt waterfowl in state-managed wildlife areas.
Issued in booklet panes of 10.

1975-79

A1	$2 purple	1,950.	75.
A2	$2 black, *pink, 1976*	1,350.	45.
A3	$2 black, *yellow, 1977*	1,200.	45.
A4	$2 black, *1978*	3,250.	125.
A5	$2 black, *yellow, 1979*	1,000.	35.

MASSACHUSETTS

Printed in sheets of 12.

Catalogue values for all unused stamps in this section are for Never Hinged items.

Artists: Milton Weiler, #1; Tom Hennessey, #2; William Tyner, #3-5; Randy Julius, #6, 8, 10, 12, 19, 27; John Eggert, #7, 9, 24; Joseph Cibula, #11; Robert Piscatori, #13, 15, 25, 30; Peter Baedita, #14, 29; Lou Barnicle, #16; Warren Racket Shreve, #17; Benjamin Smith, #18; Donald Little, #20, 32; Sergio Roffo, #21; David Brega, #22; Christine Wilkinson, #23; Stephen Badlam; Barry Julius, #28; Larry Denton, #31. Randy Julius, #33. Matthew Schulz, #34; Gregg Coppolo, #35.

1974-2008

1	$1.25 Wood duck decoy, rouletted	15.00	3.00
2	$1.25 Pintail decoy, *1975*	13.00	3.00
3	$1.25 Canada goose decoy, *1976*	13.00	3.00
4	$1.25 Goldeneye decoy, *1977*	13.00	3.00
5	$1.25 Black duck decoy, *1978*	13.00	3.00
6	$1.25 Ruddy turnstone duck decoy, *1979*	15.00	3.00
a.	Imperf, pair	160.00	
7	$1.25 Old squaw decoy, *1980*	15.00	3.00
8	$1.25 Red-breasted merganser decoy, *1981*	15.00	3.00
9	$1.25 Greater yellowlegs decoy, *1982*	15.00	3.00
10	$1.25 Redhead decoy, *1983*	15.00	3.00
11	$1.25 White-winged scoter decoy, *1984*	15.00	3.00
12	$1.25 Ruddy duck decoy, *1985*	12.00	3.00
13	$1.25 Preening bluebill decoy, *1986*	12.00	2.50
14	$1.25 American widgeon decoy, *1987*	12.00	2.50
15	$1.25 Mallard decoy, *1988*	12.00	2.50
16	$1.25 Brant decoy, *1989*	10.00	2.50
17	$1.25 Whistler hen decoy, *1990*	10.00	2.50
18	$5 Canvasback decoy, *1991*	10.00	2.50
19	$5 Black-bellied plover decoy, *1992*	10.00	2.50
20	$5 Red-breasted merganser decoy, *1993*	10.00	2.50
21	$5 White-winged scoter decoy, *1994*	10.00	2.50
22	$5 Female hooded merganser decoy, *1995*	10.00	2.50
23	$5 Eider decoy, *1996*	10.00	2.50
24	$5 Curlew decoy, *1997*	10.00	2.50
25	$5 Canada goose decoy, *1998*	10.00	2.50
26	$5 Old squaw decoy, *1999*	10.00	2.50
27	$5 Merganser hen decoy, *2000*	10.00	2.50
28	$5 Black duck decoy, *2001*	10.00	2.50
29	$5 Bufflehead decoy, *2002*	10.00	2.50
30	$5 Greenwing teal decoy, *2003*	10.00	2.50
31	$5 Wood duck drake decoy, *2004*	8.00	2.50
32	$5 Old squaw drake decoy, *2005*	8.00	2.50
33	$5 Long-billed curlew decoy, *2006*	8.00	2.50
34	$5 Goldeneye decoy, *2007*	8.00	2.50
35	$5 Black duck decoy, *2008*	8.00	2.50

MICHIGAN

Nos. 1-5 printed in sheets of 10 with center gutter, rouletted. Printed in sheets of 10 die cut self-adhesives on backing paper (Nos. 6-19), or sheets of 15 (starting with No. 20).
Nos. 1, 3-19 are serially numbered.

Catalogue values for all unused stamps in this section are for Never Hinged items.

Artist: Oscar Warbach.

1976

1	$2.10 Wood duck	5.00	2.50

Artists: Larry Hayden, #2, 5, 12; Richard Timm, #3; Andrew Kurzmann, #4; Dietmar Krumrey, #6, 14, 23-24; Gjisbert van Frankenhuyzen, #7; Rod Lawrence, #8, 15, 20, 25, 27, 32; Larry Cory, #9, 16; Robert Steiner, #10; Russell Cobane, #11; John Martens, #13; Heiner Hertling, #17; Clark Sullivan, #18; David Bollman, #19; Rusty Fretner, #21; M. Monroe, #22; Kim Diment, #26; Dietmar Krumrey, #28, 33; Tim McDonald, #29; Christopher Smith, #30; Peter Mathios, #31.

1977-2008

2	$2.10 Canvasbacks	275.00	35.00
	With numbered tab	400.00	
3	$2.10 Mallards, *1978*	20.00	5.00
	With tab	47.50	
4	$2.10 Canada geese, *1979*	60.00	5.00
	With tab	75.00	
5	$3.75 Lesser scaup, *1980*	17.50	4.00
	With tab	25.00	
6	$3.75 Buffleheads, *1981*	25.00	4.00
7	$3.75 Redheads, *1982*	25.00	4.00

Unused value is for stamp with sufficient margin to show printed spaces for date and time the stamp was sold.

8	$3.75 Wood ducks, *1983*	25.00	4.00
9	$3.75 on $3.25 Pintails, *1984*	25.00	3.00

No. 9 not issued without surcharge.

10	$3.75 Ring-necked ducks, *1985*	25.00	3.00
11	$3.75 Common goldeneyes, *1986*	22.00	2.50
12	$3.85 Green-winged teal, *1987*	11.00	2.50
13	$3.85 Canada geese, *1988*	10.00	2.50
14	$3.85 Widgeons, *1989*	10.00	2.50
15	$3.85 Wood ducks, *1990*	10.00	2.50
16	$3.85 Blue-winged teal, *1991*	9.00	2.50
17	$3.85 Red-breasted merganser, *1992*	9.00	2.50
18	$3.85 Hooded merganser, *1993*	9.00	2.50
19	$3.85 Black duck, *1994*	9.00	2.50
20	$4.35 Blue winged teal, *1995*	9.00	3.00
21	$4.35 Canada geese, *1996*	9.00	3.00
22	$5 Canvasbacks, *1997*	20.00	3.00
23	$5 Pintail, *1998*	9.00	3.00
24	$5 Shoveler, *1999*	9.00	3.00
25	$5 Mallards, *2000*	30.00	3.00

Self-Adhesive Die Cut

26	$5 Ruddy ducks, *2001*	10.00	3.00
27	$5 Wigeons, *2002*	9.00	3.00
28	$5 Redheads, *2003*	9.00	3.00

Rouletted

29	$5 Wood duck, *2004*	9.00	3.00
30	$5 Blue-winged teals, *2005*	9.00	3.00
31	$5 Widgeon, *2006*	9.00	3.00
32	$5 Pintails, *2007*	8.00	3.00
33	$5 Wood ducks, *2008*	8.00	3.00

Nos. 24-33 not required for hunting.

MINNESOTA

License Surcharge Stamps

No. A1 printed in sheets of 10. These stamps served as a $1 surcharge to cover the cost of a license increase.

Nos. A1-A2 issued to raise funds for acquisition and development of wildlife lands.

1957

A1	$1 Mallards & Pheasant	Perf. 12½	100.00	6.00

> **1971 MINNESOTA $1.00**
> Department of Natural Resources
> Additional one dollar surcharge to be paid by sportsmen, pursuant to Laws 1971 Chapter 867, for the acquisition and development of wildlife lands.

1971

A2	$1 black, *dark yellow*	Rouletted 9½	4,500.	20.00

Cancellation of No. A2 was not required. Value for used stamp is for an example without gum.

Regular Issues
Printed in sheets of 10.

> **Catalogue values for all unused stamps in this section are for Never Hinged items.**

Artists: David Maass, #1, 3; Leslie Kouba, #2; James Meger, #4; Terry Redlin, #5, 9, Phil Scholer, #6, 17; Gary Moss, #7; Thomas Gross, #8; Brian Jarvi, #10; Ron Van Gilder, #11; Robert Hautman, #12, 16, 25; Jim Hautman, #13, 20; Kevin Daniel, #14, 21; Daniel Smith, #15; Edward DuRose, #18; Bruce Miller, #19; Thomas Moen, #22, 31; John House, #23; Kim Norlien, #24; John Freiberg, #26; Mark Kness, #27; Scot Storm, #28; David Chapman, #29; Joe Hautman, #30; Thomas Moen, #31; Sara Stack, #32.

1977-2008

1	$3 Mallards	15.00	2.50
2	$3 Lesser scaup, *1978*	12.00	2.50
3	$3 Pintails, *1979*	12.00	2.50
4	$3 Canvasbacks, *1980*	12.00	2.50
5	$3 Canada geese, *1981*	9.50	2.50
6	$3 Redheads, *1982*	12.00	2.50
7	$3 Blue geese & snow goose, *1983*	12.00	2.50
8	$3 Wood ducks, *1984*	12.00	2.50
9	$3 White-fronted geese, *1985*	9.00	2.50
10	$5 Lesser scaup, *1986*	10.00	2.50

Beginning with this issue, left side of sheet has an agent's tab, detachable from the numbered tab.

11	$5 Common goldeneyes, *1987*	11.00	2.50
	With numbered tab	11.00	
	With agent's and numbered tabs	16.00	
12	$5 Buffleheads, *1988*	11.00	2.50
	With numbered tab	11.00	
	With agent's and numbered tabs	17.50	
13	$5 Widgeons, *1989*	11.00	2.50
	With numbered tab	11.00	
	With agent's and numbered tabs	17.50	
14	$5 Hooded mergansers, *1990*	25.00	2.50
	With numbered tab	25.00	
	With agent's and numbered tabs	40.00	
15	$5 Ross's geese, *1991*	10.00	2.50
	With numbered tab	10.00	
	With agent's and numbered tabs	14.00	
16	$5 Barrow's goldeneyes, *1992*	10.00	2.50
	With numbered tab	10.00	
	With agent's and numbered tabs	14.00	
17	$5 Blue-winged teal, *1993*	10.00	2.50
	With numbered tab	10.00	
	With agent's and numbered tabs	14.00	
18	$5 Ringneck duck, *1994*	10.00	2.50
	With numbered tab	10.00	
	With agent's and numbered tabs	13.00	
19	$5 Gadwall, *1995*	10.00	2.50
	With numbered tab	10.00	
	With agent's and numbered tabs	13.00	
20	$5 Greater scaup, *1996*	12.00	2.50
	With numbered tab	12.00	
	With agent's and numbered tabs	18.00	
21	$5 Shovelers, *1997*	11.00	2.50
	With numbered tab	11.00	
	With agent's and numbered tabs	15.00	
22	$5 Harlequins, *1998*	13.00	2.50
	With numbered tab	13.00	
	With agent's and numbered tabs	19.00	
23	$5 Green-winged teal, *1999*	11.00	2.50
	With numbered tab	11.00	
	With agent's and numbered tabs	15.00	

Self-Adhesive Die Cut

24	$5 Red-breasted merganser, *2000*	10.00	2.50

No. 24 is on backing paper affixed to back of license form.

25	$5 Black duck, *2001*	12.50	2.50

No. 25 is on backing paper affixed to back of license form.

26	$5 Ruddy duck, *2002*	12.50	2.50
27	$5 Oldsquaws, *2003*	12.50	2.50
28	$7.50 Common mergansers, *2004*	11.50	2.50
29	$7.50 White-winged scoters, lighthouse, *2005*	11.50	2.50
30	$7.50 Mallard, *2006*	11.50	2.50
31	$7.50 Lesser scaups, *2007*	11.50	2.50
32	$7.50 Ross's geese, *2008*	11.50	2.50

Nos. 26-32 are on backing paper affixed to mailing envelopes.

MISSISSIPPI

Starting with No. 2, stamps are printed in sheets of 10. Nos. 2-14 are rouletted. All stamps are numbered serially.

> **Catalogue values for all unused stamps in this section are for Never Hinged items.**

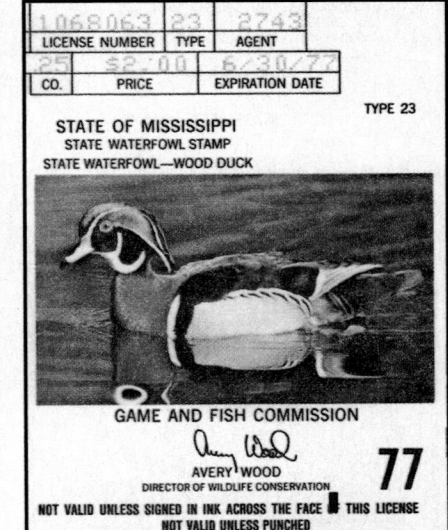

Illustration reduced.

Artists: Carroll & Gwen Perkins, #1; Allen Hughes, #2; John C. A. Reimers, #3, 6; Carole Pigott Hardy, #4; Bob Tompkins, #5, 13; Jerry Johnson, #7; Jerrie Glasper, #8; Tommy Goodman, #9; Lottie Fulton, #10; Joe Lattl, #11, 17, 22-23; Robert Garner, #12; Debra Aven Swartzendruber, #14; Kathy Dickson, #15; Phillip Crowe, #16; Eddie Suthoff, #18; Emitt Thames, #19-20; James Josey, #21; John Mac Hudspeth, #24, 25; Joe Mac Hudspeth, #26-38.

1976   Without Gum

1	$2 Wood duck	18.00	5.00
a.	Complete 2-part data processing card	25.00	

1977-2008

2	$2 Mallards	10.00	2.50
3	$2 Green-winged teal, *1978*	10.00	2.50
4	$2 Canvasbacks, *1979*	10.00	2.50
5	$2 Pintails, *1980*	10.00	2.50
6	$2 Redheads, *1981*	10.00	2.50
7	$2 Canada geese, *1982*	10.00	2.50
8	$2 Lesser scaup, *1983*	10.00	2.50
9	$2 Black ducks, *1984*	10.00	2.50
10	$2 Mallards, *1985*	10.00	2.50
a.	Vert. serial No., imperf btwn. serial No. and stamp	150.00	
b.	Horiz. serial No., no vert. silver bar	700.00	
11	$2 Widgeons, *1986*	10.00	2.50
12	$2 Ring-necked ducks, *1987*	10.00	2.50
13	$2 Snow geese, *1988*	10.00	2.50
14	$2 Wood ducks, *1989*	7.00	2.50
15	$2 Snow geese, *1990*	12.50	2.50
16	$2 Labrador retriever & canvasbacks, *1991*	7.50	2.50
17	$2 Green-winged teal, *1992*	7.50	2.50
18	$5 Mallards, *1993*	9.00	2.50
19	$5 Canvasbacks, *1994*	10.00	2.50
20	$5 Blue-winged teals, *1995*	15.00	2.50
21	$5 Hooded merganser, *1996*	17.00	2.50
22	$5 Pintail, *1997*	22.50	2.50
23	$5 Pintails, *1998*	13.00	2.50
24	$5 Ring-necked duck, *1999*	10.00	2.50
25	$5 Mallards, *2000*	10.00	2.50
26	$5 Gadwall, *2001*	15.00	2.50
27	$10 Wood duck, *2002*	15.00	2.50
28	$10 Pintail, *2003*	15.00	2.50
29	$10 Wood ducks, *2004*	15.00	2.50
30	$10 Blue-winged teal, *2005*	15.00	2.50
31	$10 Wood duck, *2006*	15.00	2.50
32	$15 Wood duck, self-adhesive, die cut, *2006*	15.00	2.50
33	$10 Wood ducks, perf., *2007*	14.00	2.50
34	$10 Wood ducks, self-adhesive, die cut, *2007*	14.00	2.50
35	$15 Wood ducks, self-adhesive, die cut, *2007*	21.00	2.50
36	$10 Green-winged teal, perf., *2008*	14.00	2.50

| 37 | $10 Green-winged teal, self-adhesive, die cut, *2008* | 14.00 | 2.50 |
| 38 | $15 Green-winged teal, self-adhesive, die cut, *2008* | 21.00 | 2.50 |

MISSOURI

Issued in booklet panes of five with tab. Nos. 1-8 are rouletted. No. 18 issued in pane of 30.

> Catalogue values for all unused stamps in this section are for Never Hinged items.

Artists: Charles Schwartz, #1; David Plank, #2; Tom Crain, #3, 8; Gary Lucy, #4; Doug Ross, #5; Glenn Chambers, #6; Ron Clayton, #7; Ron Ferkol, #9, 13, 18; Bruce Bollman, #10; Kathy Dickson, #11; Eileen Melton, #12; Kevin Guinn, #14; Thomas Bates, #15; Keith Alexander, #16; Ryan Peterson, #17.

1979-96

1	$3.40 Canada geese	*450.00*	75.00
	With tab	*550.00*	
2	$3.40 Wood ducks, *1980*	*100.00*	18.00
	With tab	*125.00*	
3	$3 Lesser scaup, *1981*	60.00	9.00
	With tab	75.00	
4	$3 Buffleheads, *1982*	60.00	8.00
	With tab	75.00	
5	$3 Blue-winged teal, *1983*	45.00	8.00
	With tab	55.00	
6	$3 Mallards, *1984*	40.00	7.00
	With tab	50.00	
7	$3 American widgeons, *1985*	22.50	3.00
	With tab	25.00	
8	$3 Hooded mergansers, *1986*	12.00	3.00
	With tab	15.00	
9	$3 Pintails, *1987*	9.00	3.00
	With tab	13.00	
10	$3 Canvasback, *1988*	8.00	2.50
	With tab	11.00	
11	$3 Ring-necked ducks, *1989*	8.00	2.50
	With tab	9.25	

All examples of Nos. 12b, 13b, 14b, 15b, 16b, 17b are signed by the governor.

12	$5 Redheads, *1990*	8.00	2.50
	With two part tab	10.00	
a.	$50 Governor's edition with tab	75.00	
b.	$100 Governor's edition with tab	—	
13	$5 Snow geese, *1991*	8.00	2.50
	With two part tab	9.00	
a.	$50 Governor's edition with tab	72.50	
b.	$100 Governor's edition with tab	—	
14	$5 Gadwalls, *1992*	8.00	2.50
	With tab	9.00	
a.	$50 Governor's edition with tab	75.00	
b.	$100 Governor's edition with tab	—	
15	$5 Green-winged teal, *1993*	8.00	2.50
	With tab	9.00	
a.	$50 Governor's edition with tab	75.00	
b.	$100 Governor's edition with tab	—	
16	$5 White-fronted goose, *1994*	8.00	2.50
	With 2-part tab	9.00	
a.	$50 Governor's edition with tab	75.00	
b.	$100 Governor's edition with tab	—	
17	$5 Goldeneyes, *1995*	8.00	2.50
	With 2-part tab	9.00	
a.	$50 Governor's edition with tab	75.00	
b.	$100 Governor's edition with tab	—	
18	$5 Black ducks, *1996*	8.00	2.50

MONTANA

Bird License Stamps

Required to hunt waterfowl.
Resident ($2, $4, $6), youth ($1, $2), and non-resident ($25, $30, $53) bird licenses. Licenses were no longer produced for youth, beginning in 1985, and non-resident, beginning in 1989.
Nos. 1-33 rouletted.

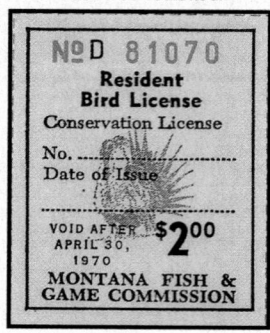

1969

A1	$2 Sage grouse	625.00	15.00
A2	$1 Sage grouse	625.00	50.00
A3	$25 Sage grouse	625.00	75.00

1970

A4	$2 Sage grouse	675.00	10.00
a.	Missing "1" in "1971," pos. 10		500.00
A5	$1 Sage grouse	*1,950.*	150.00
A6	$25 Sage grouse	—	275.00

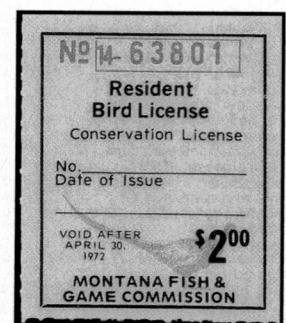

1971

A7	$2 Pheasant	675.00	10.00
A8	$1 Pheasant	675.00	35.00
A9	$25 Pheasant	675.00	50.00

1972

A10	$2 Pheasant	675.00	10.00
A11	$1 Pheasant	675.00	35.00
A12	$25 Pheasant	675.00	50.00

1973

A13	$2 Pheasant	675.00	10.00
A14	$1 Pheasant	675.00	35.00
A15	$25 Pheasant	675.00	50.00

1974

A16	$2 Pheasant	675.00	10.00
A17	$1 Pheasant	675.00	35.00
A18	$25 Pheasant	675.00	50.00

1975

A19	$2 Pheasant	675.00	10.00
A20	$1 Pheasant	675.00	35.00
A21	$25 Pheasant	675.00	50.00

1976

A22	$4 Pheasant	675.00	10.00
A23	$2 Pheasant	675.00	35.00
A24	$30 Pheasant	675.00	50.00

1977

A25	$4 Pheasant	675.00	10.00
A26	$2 Pheasant	675.00	35.00
A27	$30 Pheasant	675.00	50.00

1978

A28	$4 Sage grouse	8.00	2.00
A29	$2 Sage grouse	8.00	5.00
A30	$30 Sage grouse	8.00	5.50

1979

A31	$4 Snow geese	8.00	2.00
A32	$2 Snow geese	8.00	5.00
A33	$30 Snow geese	8.00	5.50

1980

| A36 | $30 black, *gray green* | | 50.00 |

1982

| A40 | $4 black, *yellow* | | 5.00 |

1983

A43	$4 black, *yellow gray*	750.00	5.00
A44	$2 black, *gray*	750.00	
A45	$30 black, *light blue*	750.00	

1984

A46	$4 black, *light blue green*	450.00	5.00
A47	$2 black, *light violet*	550.00	
A48	$30 black, *gray*	450.00	

1985

| A49 | $4 black, *light blue* | 550.00 | 5.00 |
| A50 | $30 black, *lavender* | 450.00 | |

1986

| A51 | $4 black, *orange* | 550.00 | 5.00 |
| A52 | $30 black, *light blue* | 550.00 | |

1987

| A53 | $4 black, *orange brown* | 300.00 | 3.00 |
| A54 | $30 black, *tan* | 450.00 | |

1988

| A55 | $6 black, *light blue* | 300.00 | 3.00 |
| A56 | $53 black, *purple* | 450.00 | |

1989-99

A57	$6 black, *rose*	175.00	2.00
A58	$6 black, *lavender, 1990*	150.00	2.00
A59	$6 black, *pale blue, 1991*	100.00	2.00
A60	$6 black, *brown, 1992*	70.00	2.00
A61	$6 black, *blue, 1993*	60.00	1.50
A62	$6 black, *red orange, 1994*	55.00	1.50
A63	$6 black, *blue, 1995*	42.50	1.50
A64	$6 black, *purple, 1996*	25.00	1.00
A65	$6 black, *mauve, 1997*	15.00	1.00
A66	$6 black, *gray, 1998*	13.00	1.00
A67	$6 black, *green, 1999*	13.00	1.00

Waterfowl Stamps

Issued in booklet panes of 10 and sheets of 30.
Stamps are numbered serially.
Stamps with serial numbers above 31,000 (1986)
and above 21,000 (other years) are from booklet
panes.

> Catalogue values for all unused stamps in this
> section are for Never Hinged items.

Artist: Joe Thornbrugh, #34, 38, 39, 45, 46, 48; Roger Cruwys, #35, 37, 42; Dave Samuelson, #36; Craig Philips, #40; Darrell Davis, #41; Wayne Dowdy, #43; Jim Borgreen, #44, 50, 51; Cliff Rossberg, #47, 49.

1986-2003

34	$5 Canada geese	12.00	3.00
	Pair from booklet pane with L & R selvage	1,850.	
	Top pair from booklet pane with agent tabs and L & R selvage	—	
35	$5 Redheads, 1987	15.00	3.00
	Pair from booklet pane with L & R selvage	30.00	
	Top pair from booklet pane with agent tabs and L & R selvage	55.00	
36	$5 Mallards, 1988	11.00	3.00
	Pair from booklet pane with L & R selvage	25.00	
	Top pair from booklet pane with agent tabs and L & R selvage	40.00	
37	$5 Black Labrador retriever & pintail, 1989	11.00	3.00
	Pair from booklet pane with L & R selvage	25.00	
	Top pair from booklet pane with agent tabs and L & R selvage	40.00	
a.	Governor's edition	140.00	

No. 37a was available only in full sheets only through a sealed bid auction.

38	$5 Blue-winged & cinnamon teal, 1990	10.00	2.50
	Pair from booklet pane with L & R selvage	20.00	
	Top pair from booklet pane with agent tabs and L & R selvage	25.00	
39	$5 Snow geese, 1991	10.00	2.50
	Pair from booklet pane with L & R selvage	20.00	
	Top pair from booklet pane with agent tabs and L & R selvage	25.00	
40	$5 Wood ducks, 1992	10.00	2.50
	Pair from booklet pane with L & R selvage	20.00	
	Top pair from booklet pane with agent tabs and L & R selvage	25.00	
41	$5 Harlequin ducks, 1993	10.00	2.50
	Pair from booklet pane with L & R selvage	22.00	
	Top pair from booklet pane with agent tabs and L & R selvage	25.00	
42	$5 Widgeons, 1994	11.00	2.50
	Pair from booklet pane with L & R selvage	25.00	
	Top pair from booklet pane with agent tabs and L & R selvage	25.00	
43	$5 Tundra swans, 1995	11.00	2.50
	Pair from booklet pane with L & R selvage	25.00	
	Top pair from booklet pane with agent tabs and L & R selvage	25.00	
44	$5 Canvasbacks, 1996	11.00	2.50
	Pair from booklet pane with L & R selvage	25.00	
	Top pair from booklet pane with agent tabs and L & R selvage	30.00	
45	$5 Golden retriever, mallard, 1997	11.00	2.50
	Pair from booklet pane with L & R selvage	25.00	
	Top pair from booklet pane with agent tabs and L & R selvage	30.00	
46	$5 Gadwalls, 1998	11.00	2.50
	Pair from booklet pane with L & R selvage	25.00	
	Top pair from booklet pane with agent tabs and L & R selvage	30.00	
47	$5 Barrow's goldeneye, 1999	11.00	2.50
	Pair from booklet pane with L & R selvage	25.00	
	Top pair from booklet pane with agent tabs and L & R selvage	30.00	
48	$5 Mallard decoy, Chesapeake retriever, 2000	12.00	2.50
	Pair from booklet pane with L & R selvage	25.00	
	Top pair from booklet pane with agent tabs and L & R selvage	30.00	
49	$5 Canada geese, 2001	11.00	2.50
	Pair from booklet pane with L & R selvage	25.00	
	Top pair from booklet pane with agent tabs and L & R selvage	30.00	
50	($5) Sandhill crane, 2002	11.00	2.50
51	$5 Mallards, 2003	11.00	2.50

No. 51 is not required for hunting.

NEBRASKA

Habitat Stamps

Required to hunt waterfowl.
Printed in sheets of 20.

> Catalogue values for all unused stamps in this
> section are for Never Hinged items.

1977-98

A1	$7.50	Ring-necked pheasant	12.00	1.50
A2	$7.50	White-tailed deer, 1978	12.00	1.50
A3	$7.50	Bobwhite quail, 1979	12.00	1.50
A4	$7.50	Pheasant, 1980	12.00	1.50
A5	$7.50	Cottontail rabbit, 1981	12.00	1.50
A6	$7.50	Coyote, 1982	12.00	1.50
A7	$7.50	Wild turkey, 1983	12.00	1.50
A8	$7.50	Canada goose, 1984	12.00	1.50
A9	$7.50	Cardinal, 1985	12.00	1.50
A10	$7.50	Sharp-tailed grouse, 1986	12.00	1.50
A11	$7.50	Sandhill crane, 1987	12.00	1.50
A12	$7.50	Snow geese, 1988	12.00	1.50
A13	$7.50	Mallards, 1989	12.00	1.50
A14	$7.50	Pheasants, 1990	12.00	1.50
A15	$7.50	Canada geese, 1991	12.00	1.50
A16	$10.00	Raccoon, 1992	15.00	1.50
A17	$10.00	Fox squirrel, 1993	15.00	1.50
A18	$10.00	Hungarian partridge, 1994	15.00	1.50
A19	$10.00	Prairie pronghorns, 1995	15.00	1.50
A20	$10.00	Ring-necked pheasant, 1996	15.00	1.50
A21	$10.00	White-tailed deer, 1997	15.00	1.50
A22	$10.00	Mourning doves, 1998	15.00	1.50

Pictorial Labels

These stamps are not valid for any hunting fees.
Printed in sheets of 10.
Stamps are numbered serially.

> Catalogue values for all unused stamps in this
> section are for Never Hinged items.

Artist: Neal Anderson.

1991-95

Artist: Neal Anderson

1	$6 Canada geese	11.00
2	$6 Pintails, 1992	11.00
3	$6 Canvasbacks, 1993	11.00
4	$6 Mallards, 1994	11.00
5	$6 Wood ducks, 1995	11.00

Waterfowl Stamp

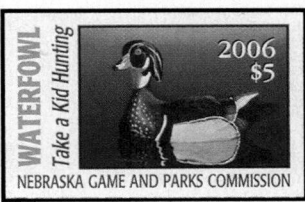

Artist: Brett Cooper

2006-08

			Rouletted	
6	$5 Wood duck		10.00	2.50
7	$5 Canvasbacks, 2007		10.00	2.50
8	$5 Trumpeter swans, 2008		10.00	2.50

Nos. 6-8 are required for hunting.

NEVADA

Printed in booklet panes of 4.
Stamps are rouletted and selvage is found above
and below stamps on the pane. The tab portion of
the panes in imperforate.
Starting with No. 4 stamps are numbered serially.

> Catalogue values for all unused stamps in this
> section are for Never Hinged items.

Artists: Larry Hayden, #1; Dick Mcrill, #2; Phil Scholer, #3; Richard Timm, #4; Charles Allen, #5; Robert Steiner, #6; Richard Wilson, #7; Nolan Haan. #8, 12; Sherrie Russell Meline, #9, 21; Jim Hautman, #10; Robert Hautman, #11; Tak Nakamura, #13, 17; Richard Clifton, #14, 22; Steve Hopkins, #15; Mark Mueller, #16; Jeffrey Klinefelter, #18, 23, 28; B. Blight, #19; Janie Kreutzjans, #20; Jeff Hoff, #24; David Brevick, #25; Louis Frisino, #26; Adam Oswald, #27. Ken Michaelsen, #29; James Edwards, #30.

1979-2008

1	$2 Canvasbacks and decoy	45.00	12.00
	With numbered tab	55.00	

Stamps with tabs without numbers are printer's waste.

2	$2 Cinnamon teal, 1980	8.00	3.00
	With tab	10.00	
3	$2 Whistling swans, 1981	10.00	3.00
	With tab	12.00	
4	$2 Shovelers, 1982	10.00	3.00
	With tab	12.00	
5	$2 Gadwalls, 1983	10.50	3.00
	With tab	11.00	
6	$2 Pintails, 1984	11.00	3.00
	With tab	12.00	
7	$2 Canada geese, 1985	20.00	3.00
	With tab	25.00	
8	$2 Redheads, 1986	17.50	2.50
	With tab	25.00	
9	$2 Buffleheads, 1987	15.00	2.50
	With tab	20.00	
10	$2 Canvasbacks, 1988	11.00	2.50
	With tab	13.00	
11	$2 Ross's geese, 1989	12.00	2.50
	With tab	15.00	
12	$5 Green-winged teal, 1990	11.00	2.50
	With tab	13.00	
13	$5 White-faced ibis, 1991	11.00	2.50
	With tab	13.00	
14	$5 American widgeon, 1992	10.00	2.50
	With tab	11.00	
15	$5 Common goldeneye, 1993	10.00	2.50
	With tab	11.00	
16	$5 Mallards, 1994	10.00	2.50
	With tab	11.00	
17	$5 Wood duck, 1995	10.00	2.50
	With tab	11.00	
18	$5 Ring-necked ducks, 1996	15.00	2.50
	With tab	20.00	
19	$5 Ruddy ducks, 1997	11.00	2.50
	With tab	13.00	
20	$5 Hooded merganser, 1998	12.00	2.50
	With tab	15.00	

21	$5 Canvasback decoy, *1999*	11.00	2.50
	With tab	13.00	
22	$5 Canvasbacks, *2000*	15.00	2.50
	With tab	18.00	
23	$5 Lesser Scaups, *2001*	12.00	2.50
	With tab	15.00	
24	$5 Cinnamon teal, *2002*	11.00	2.50
25	$5 Green-winged teal, *2003*	11.00	2.50
	With tab	11.00	
26	$10 Redheads, *2004*	14.00	2.50
	With tab	16.00	
27	$10 Gadwalls, *2005*	14.00	2.50
	With tab	16.00	
28	$10 Tundra swans, *2006*	14.00	2.50
	With tab	16.00	
29	$10 Wood ducks, *2007*	15.00	2.50
	With tab	16.00	
30	$10 Pintail, *2008*	15.00	2.50
	With tab	16.00	

NEW HAMPSHIRE

Printed in booklet panes of 1 with 2-part tab and in sheets of 30. Sheet stamps are perf on four sides.

Stamps are numbered serially.

> Catalogue values for all unused stamps in this section are for Never Hinged items.

Artists: Richard Plasschaert, #1; Phillip Crowe, #2; Thomas Hirata, #3; Durrant Bell, #4; Robert Steiner, #5-9; Richard Clifton, #10-11, 15; Louis Frisino, #12; Matthew Scharle, #13; Jeffrey Klinefelter, #14; Jim Collins, #16, 20, 23, 24; Bruce Holloway, #17, 21; Susan Knowles Jordan, #18; Charles Freeman, #19; Lindsey Rothe, #22. Kate Kotulak, #25.

1983-2007

1	$4 Wood ducks	135.00	
a.	Booklet single with 2-part tab	95.00	25.00
2	$4 Mallards, *1984*	90.00	
a.	Booklet single with 2-part tab	175.00	20.00
3	$4 Blue-winged teal, *1985*	80.00	
a.	Booklet single with 2-part tab	100.00	20.00
4	$4 Hooded mergansers, *1986*	20.00	
a.	Booklet single with 2-part tab	30.00	6.00
5	$4 Canada geese, *1987*	12.00	
a.	Booklet single with 2-part tab	14.00	4.00
b.	$50 Governor's edition	325.00	
6	$4 Buffleheads, *1988*	12.00	
a.	Booklet single with 2-part tab	14.00	3.00
b.	$4 +$46 Governor's edition	60.00	
7	$4 Black ducks, *1989*	11.00	
a.	Booklet single with 2-part tab	12.00	3.00
b.	$4 +$50 Governor's edition	67.50	
8	$4 Green-winged teal, *1990*	11.00	
a.	Booklet single with 2-part tab	12.00	3.00
b.	$4 +$50 Governor's edition	62.50	
9	$4 Golden retriever & mallards, *1991*	15.00	
a.	Booklet single with 2-part tab	17.00	3.00
b.	$4 +$50 Governor's edition	80.00	

Governor's Editions that follow are so inscribed.

10	$4 Ring-necked ducks, *1992*	10.00	
a.	Booklet single with 2-part tab	12.00	3.00
b.	Governor's edition	*500.00*	
11	$4 Hooded mergansers, *1993*	10.00	
a.	Booklet single with 2-part tab	12.00	3.00
b.	Governor's edition	*500.00*	
12	$4 Common goldeneyes, *1994*	10.00	
a.	Bklt. single with 2-part tab	12.00	2.50
b.	Governor's edition	*175.00*	
13	$4 Northern pintails, *1995*	10.00	
a.	Bklt. single with 2-part tab	12.00	2.50
b.	Governor's edition	*150.00*	
14	$4 Surf scooters, *1996*	10.00	
a.	Bklt. single with 2-part tab	12.00	2.50
b.	Governor's edition	*150.00*	
15	$4 Wood ducks, *1997*	10.00	
a.	Bklt. single with 2-part tab	12.00	2.50
b.	Governor's edition	*125.00*	
16	$4 Canada geese, *1998*	10.00	
a.	Bklt. single with 2-part tab	12.00	2.50
b.	Governor's edition	*130.00*	
17	$4 Mallards, *1999*	11.00	
a.	Bklt. single with 2-part tab	12.00	2.50
b.	Governor's edition	*130.00*	

18	$4 Black ducks, *2000*	11.00	
a.	Bklt. single with 2-part tab	12.00	2.50
b.	Governor's edition	—	
19	$4 Blue-winged teal, *2001*	11.00	
a.	Bklt. single with 2-part tab	12.00	2.50
b.	Governor's edition	—	
20	$4 Pintails, *2002*	8.00	
a.	Bklt. single with 2-part tab	10.00	2.50
b.	Governor's edition	*150.00*	
21	$4 Wood ducks, *2003*	8.00	
a.	Bklt. single with 2-part tab	10.00	2.50
b.	Governor's edition	*125.00*	
22	$4 Wood duck, *2004*	8.00	
a.	Bklt. single with 2-part tab	10.00	2.50
b.	Governor's edition	*125.00*	
23	$4 Old squaws, lighthouse, *2005*	8.00	
a.	Bklt. single with 2-part tab	10.00	
b.	Governor's edition	*125.00*	
24	$4 Common eiders, *2006*	8.00	
a.	Bklt. single with 2-part tab	10.00	2.50
b.	Governor's edition	*125.00*	
25	$4 Black ducks, *2007*	6.00	
a.	Bklt. single with 2-part tab	8.00	2.50
b.	Governor's edition	*125.00*	

NEW JERSEY

Resident and non-resident fees.

Printed in sheets of 30 (starting with No. 1) and booklet panes of 10 (all but Nos. 2, 4, 6, 17b, 18b). Sheet stamps are perf on 4 sides.

Stamps are numbered serially.

> Catalogue values for all unused stamps in this section are for Never Hinged items.

Artists: Thomas Hirata, #1-2, 17-18; David Maass, #3-4; Ronald Louque, #5-6; Louis Frisino, #7-8; Robert Leslie, #9-10, 19-20, 29-30, 51-52; Daniel Smith, #11-12; Richard Plasschaert, #13-14; Bruce Miller, #21-22; Wilhelm Goebel, #23-24, 27-28; Joe Hautman, #25-26, 35-36; Phillip Crowe, #31-32, 43-46; Richard Clifton, #33-34; Bob Hautman, #37-40; Jim Killen, #41-42; Roger Cruwys, #47-50.

1984-2008

1	$2.50 Canvasbacks	45.00	
a.	Booklet single, #51,000-102,000	70.00	10.00
2	$5 Canvasbacks	60.00	10.00
3	$2.50 Mallards, *1985*	15.00	
a.	Booklet single, #51,000-102,000	25.00	6.00
4	$5 Mallards, *1985*	18.00	5.00
5	$2.50 Pintails, *1986*	15.00	
a.	Booklet single, #51,000-102,000	15.00	3.00
6	$5 Pintails, *1986*	13.00	3.00
7	$2.50 Canada geese, *1987*	17.00	
a.	Booklet single, #51,000-102,000	17.00	3.00
8	$5 Canada geese, *1987*	17.00	
a.	Booklet single, #45,001-60,000	17.00	3.00
9	$2.50 Green-winged teal, *1988*	12.00	
a.	Booklet single, #51,000-102,000	12.00	3.00
10	$5 Green-winged teal, *1988*	12.00	
a.	Booklet single, #45,001-60,000	12.00	3.00
11	$2.50 Snow geese, *1989*	11.00	
a.	Booklet single, #45,001-60,000	11.00	3.00
b.	Governor's edition	*72.50*	
12	$5 Snow geese, *1989*	11.00	
a.	Booklet single, #45,001-60,000	11.00	3.00
b.	Governor's edition	*140.00*	

Nos. 11b and 12b were available only in sets of sheets of 30 stamps with matching serial numbers through a sealed bid auction.

13	$2.50 Wood ducks, *1990*	12.00	
a.	Booklet single, #45,001-60,000	12.00	3.00
14	$5 Wood ducks, *1990*	12.00	
a.	Booklet single, #45,001-60,000	12.00	3.00
17	$2.50 Atlantic brant, *1991*	9.00	
a.	Booklet single, #45,001-60,000	9.00	3.00
b.	Atlantic "brandt"	32.50	
18	$5 Atlantic brant, *1991*	12.00	
a.	Booklet single, #45,001-60,000	12.00	3.00
b.	Atlantic "brandt"	37.50	

Matching serial number sets of Nos. 17b and 18b were available for sale only with the purchase of matching serial number sets of Nos. 17 and 18.

19	$2.50 Bluebills, *1992*	10.00	
a.	Booklet single, #27,691-78,690	10.00	2.50
20	$5 Bluebills, *1992*	10.00	
a.	Booklet single, #27,691-57,690	10.00	2.50

21	$2.50 Buffleheads, *1993*	10.00	
a.	Booklet single, #27,691-78,690	10.00	2.50
b.	Sheet of 4	*75.00*	
c.	Governor's edition, signed by Florio or Whitman	42.50	
22	$5 Buffleheads, *1993*	10.00	
a.	Booklet single, #27,691-57,690	10.00	2.50
b.	Sheet of 4	*75.00*	
c.	Governor's edition, signed by Florio or Whitman	82.50	

Nos. 21b and 22b were available only in sets of sheets with matching serial numbers. The set of sheets sold for $35.

Nos. 21c and 22c were available only in sets with matching serial numbers.

23	$2.50 Black ducks, *1994*	12.00	
a.	Bklt. single, perf. 2 or 3 sides	12.00	2.50
24	$5 Black ducks, *1994*	14.00	
a.	Bklt. single, perf. 2 or 3 sides	14.00	2.50
25	$2.50 Widgeon, lighthouse, *1995*	12.00	
a.	Bklt. single, perf. 3 sides	12.00	2.50
26	$5 Widgeon, lighthouse, *1995*	14.00	
a.	Bklt. single, perf. 3 sides	14.00	2.50
27	$5 Goldeneyes, lighthouse, *1996*	14.00	
a.	Bklt. single, perf. 2 or 3 sides	14.00	2.50
28	$10 Goldeneyes, lighthouse, *1996*	16.00	
a.	Bklt. single, perf. 2 or 3 sides	16.00	2.50

The $2.50 was printed but not used as the rate no longer existed. Later they were sold to collectors. Value, unused $10.

29	$5 Old squaws, schooner, *1997*	12.00	
a.	Bklt. single, perf. 2 or 3 sides	12.00	2.50
30	$10 Old squaws, schooner, *1997*	16.00	
a.	Bklt. single, perf. 2 or 3 sides	16.00	2.50
31	$5 Mallards, *1998*	12.00	
a.	Bklt. single, perf. 2 or 3 sides	12.00	2.50
32	$10 Mallards, *1998*	15.00	
a.	Bklt. single, perf. 2 or 3 sides	15.00	2.50
33	$5 Redheads, perf. 4 sides, *1999*	12.00	
a.	Bklt. single, perf. 2 or 3 sides	12.00	2.50
34	$10 Redheads, perf. 4 sides, *1999*	15.00	
a.	Bklt. single, perf. 2 or 3 sides	15.00	2.50
35	$5 Canvasbacks, perf. 4 sides, *2000*	13.00	
a.	Bklt. single, perf. 2 or 3 sides	13.00	2.50
36	$10 Canvasbacks, perf. 4 sides, *2000*	15.00	
a.	Bklt. single, perf. 2 or 3 sides	15.00	2.50
37	$5 Tundra swans, perf. 4 sides, *2001*	11.00	
a.	Bklt. single, perf. 2 or 3 sides	11.00	2.50
38	$10 Tundra swans, perf. 4 sides, *2001*	14.00	
a.	Bklt. single, perf. 2 or 3 sides	14.00	2.50
39	$5 Wood ducks, perf. 4 sides, *2002*	11.00	
a.	Bklt. single, perf. 2 or 3 sides	11.00	2.50
40	$10 Wood ducks, perf. 4 sides, *2002*	14.00	
a.	Bklt. single, perf. 2 or 3 sides	14.00	2.50
41	$5 Pintails, Labrador retriever perf. 4 sides, *2003*	11.00	
a.	Bklt. single, perf. 2 or 3 sides	11.00	2.50
42	$10 Pintails, Labrador retriever, perf. 4 sides, *2003*	14.00	
a.	Bklt. single, perf. 2 or 3 sides	14.00	2.50
43	$5 Hooded merganser decoy, Labrador retriever, perf. 4 sides, *2004*	10.00	
a.	Bklt. single, perf. 2 or 3 sides	10.00	2.50
44	$10 Hooded merganser decoy, Labrador retriever, perf. 4 sides, *2004*	14.00	
a.	Bklt. single, perf. 2 or 3 sides	14.00	2.50
45	$5 Canvasback decoys, Chesapeake Bay retriever, perf. 4 sides, *2005*	10.00	
a.	Bklt. single, perf. 2 or 3 sides	10.00	2.50
46	$10 Canvasback decoys, Chesapeake Bay retriever, perf. 4 sides, *2005*	14.00	
a.	Bklt. single, perf. 2 or 3 sides	14.00	2.50
47	$5 Wood duck decoy, Golden retriever, perf. 4 sides, *2006*	10.00	
a.	Bklt. single, perf. 2 or 3 sides	10.00	2.50
48	$10 Wood duck decoy, Golden retriever, perf. 4 sides, *2006*	14.00	
a.	Bklt. single, perf. 2 or 3 sides	14.00	2.50
49	$5 Green-winged teal, Labrador retriever, perf. 4 sides, *2007*	7.50	
a.	Bklt. single, perf. 2 or 3 sides	7.50	2.50
50	$10 Green-winged teal, Labrador retriever, perf. 4 sides, *2007*	12.50	
a.	Bklt. single, perf. 2 or 3 sides	13.00	2.50
51	$5 Canvasbacks, perf. 4 sides, *2008*	7.50	
a.	Bklt. single, perf. 2 or 3 sides	7.50	2.50
52	$10 Canvasbacks, perf. 4 sides, *2008*	12.50	
a.	Bklt. single, perf. 2 or 3 sides	13.00	2.50

NEW MEXICO

Printed in booklet panes of 5 and sheets of 30.
Stamps are numbered serially.

> Catalogue values for all unused stamps in this section are for Never Hinged items.

Artist: Robert Steiner.

1991-94

1	$7.50 Pintails	14.00	
	Booklet single, with large tab and selvage	14.00	5.00
a.	$7.50 +$50 Governor's edition	72.50	
2	$7.50 American widgeon, *1992*	14.00	
	Booklet single, with large tab and selvage	14.00	4.00
a.	$7.50 +$50 Governor's edition	65.00	
3	$7.50 Mallard, *1993*	14.00	
	Booklet single, with large tab and selvage	14.00	4.00
a.	Sheet of 4	60.00	
b.	$7.50 +$50 Governor's edition	65.00	

No. 3a exists imperf. Value, $100.

No. 4: b, Three birds in flight. c, Two birds in flight. d, Two birds flying over land. e, Bird's head close-up.

4	$7.50 Green-winged teal, sheet of 4, #b.- e., *1994*	85.00	
a.	Souvenir sheet of 4, #b.-e. (decorative border)	85.00	
b.-	Bklt. single with large tab and selvage, each		
e.		15.00	4.00
f.	Bklt. pane of 4, #b.-e.	85.00	

Stamps in Nos. 4-4a are printed with continuous design and have serial numbers reading down. Stamps in No. 4f have framelines around each design, inscriptions at the top and serial numbers reading up.

NEW YORK

Not required to hunt. Printed in sheets of 30.

> **Catalogue values for all unused stamps in this section are for Never Hinged items.**

Artists: Larry Barton, #1; David Maass, #2; Lee LeBlanc, #3; Richard Plasschaert, #4; Robert Bateman, #5; John Seerey-Lester, #6; Terry Isaac, #7; Anton Ashak, #8; Ron Kleiber, #9; Jerome Hageman, #10; Frederick Szatkowski, #11; Len Rusin, #12; R. Easton, #13; Barbara Woods, #14; Richard Clifton, #15; Rob Leslie, #16; Bruce Miller, #17; Adam Grimm, #18.

1985-2002

1	$5.50 Canada geese	13.00	
2	$5.50 Mallards, *1986*	9.00	
3	$5.50 Wood ducks, *1987*	9.00	
4	$5.50 Pintails, *1988*	9.00	
5	$5.50 Greater scaup, *1989*	9.00	
6	$5.50 Canvasbacks, *1990*	9.00	
7	$5.50 Redheads, *1991*	11.00	
8	$5.50 Wood ducks, *1992*	11.00	
9	$5.50 Blue-winged teal, *1993*	10.00	
10	$5.50 Canada geese, *1994*	12.00	
11	$5.50 Common goldeneye, *1995*	12.00	
12	$5.50 Common loon, *1996*	11.00	
13	$5.50 Hooded merganser, *1997*	9.00	
14	$5.50 Osprey, *1998*	9.00	
15	$5.50 Buffleheads, *1999*	14.00	
16	$5.50 Wood ducks, *2000*	17.00	
17	$5.50 Pintails, *2001*	9.00	
18	$5.50 Canvasbacks, *2002*	9.00	3.00

NORTH CAROLINA

Not required to hunt until 1988. Printed in sheets of 30. Starting with No. 6, stamps are numbered serially.

> **Catalogue values for all unused stamps in this section are for Never Hinged items.**

Artists: Richard Plasschaert, #1, 10; Jim Killen, #2, 13; Thomas Hirata, #3-4, 17-18; Larry Barton, #5; Ronald Louque, #6, 21-22, 23-26; Louis Frisino, #7; Robert Leslie, #8, 14; Phillip Crowe, #9, 12; Bruce Miller, #11; Wilhelm Goebel, #15-16, 27-28; Robert Flowers, #19-20; Gerald Putt, #29-36; Scot Storm, #37-38.

1983-2008

1	$5.50 Mallards	65.00	
2	$5.50 Wood ducks, *1984*	45.00	
3	$5.50 Canvasbacks, *1985*	25.00	
4	$5.50 Canada geese, *1986*	20.00	
5	$5.50 Pintails, *1987*	15.00	
6	$5 Green-winged teal, *1988*	10.00	3.00
7	$5 Snow geese, *1989*	16.00	3.00
8	$5 Redheads, *1990*	16.00	3.00
9	$5 Blue-winged teals, *1991*	16.00	3.00
10	$5 American widgeons, *1992*	16.00	3.00
11	$5 Tundra swans, *1993*	16.00	3.00
12	$5 Buffleheads, *1994*	16.00	3.00
13	$5 Brant, lighthouse, *1995*	16.00	3.00
14	$5 Pintails, *1996*	16.00	3.00
15	$5 Wood ducks, perf., *1997*	12.00	3.00
16	$5 As #15,, self-adhesive, die cut, *1997*	35.00	
17	$5 Canada geese, perf., *1998*	12.00	3.00
18	$5 As #17, self-adhesive, die cut, *1998*	25.00	
19	$5 Green-winged teal, perf., *1999*	12.00	3.00
20	$5 As #19, self-adhesive, die cut, *1999*	20.00	
21	$10 Green-winged teals, perf., *2000*	25.00	3.00
22	$10 Green-winged teals, self-adhesive, die cut, *2000*	20.00	
23	$10 Black duck, perf., *2001*	17.00	3.00
24	$10 Black duck, self-adhesive, die cut, *2001*	20.00	
25	$10 Pintails, hunters, dog, perf., *2002*	17.00	3.00
26	$10 Pintails, hunters, dog, self-adhesive, die cut, *2002*	25.00	
27	$10 Ring-necked ducks, hunters, dog, perf., *2003*	17.00	3.00
28	$10 Ring-necked ducks, hunters, dog, self-adhesive, die cut, *2003*	20.00	
29	$10 Mallards, perf., *2004*	14.00	3.00
30	$10 Mallards, self-adhesive, die cut, *2004*	20.00	
31	$10 Green-winged teals, perf., *2005*	14.00	3.00
32	$10 Green-winged teals, self-adhesive, die cut, *2005*	14.00	
33	$10 Lesser scaups, perf., *2006*	14.00	3.00
34	$10 Lesser scaups, self-adhesive, die cut, *2006*	14.00	
35	$10 Wood ducks, perf., *2007*	14.00	3.00
36	$10 Wood ducks, self-adhesive, die cut, *2007*	14.00	
37	$10 Surf scoters, perf., *2008*	14.00	3.00
38	$10 Surf scoters, self-adhesive, die cut, *2008*	14.00	

Nos. 27-38 not required for hunting.

NORTH DAKOTA

Small Game Stamps

Required to hunt small game and waterfowl statewide. Resident and non-resident fees.

Values for 1967-70 non-resident stamps are for examples with staple holes.

Used values are for signed stamps. Unused values for Nos. 12, 16, 18, 20, 22, 24, 26 and 28 are for stamps on backing.

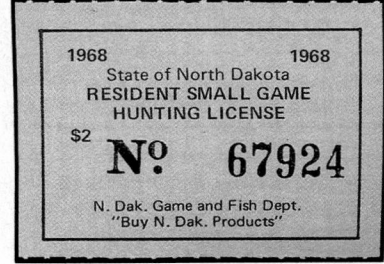

1967-80

1	$2 black, *green*	850.00	60.00
2	$25 black, *green*	3,750.	350.00
3	$2 black, *pink, 1968*	200.00	20.00
4	$25 black, *yellow, 1968*	450.00	
5	$2 black, *green, 1969*	190.00	20.00
6	$35 black, *1969*	400.00	
7	$2 blue, *1970*	160.00	15.00
8	$35 black, *pink, 1970*	250.00	50.00
9	$2 black, *yellow, 1971*	125.00	10.00
10	$35 black, *1971*		150.00
11	$3 black, *pink, 1972*	65.00	5.00
12	$35 red, *1972*	400.00	75.00
13	$3 black, *yellow, 1973*	65.00	5.00
14	$35 green, *1973*	2,250.	175.00
15	$3 black, *blue, 1974*	125.00	15.00
16	$35 red, *1974*	350.00	50.00
17	$3 black, *1975*	95.00	10.00
18	$35 green, *1975*	275.00	40.00
19	$3 black, *dark yellow, 1976*	55.00	5.00
20	$35 red, *1976*	125.00	25.00
21	$3 black, *1977*	90.00	10.00
22	$35 red, *1977*	100.00	25.00
23	$5 black, *1978*	45.00	5.00
24	$40 red, *1978*	85.00	20.00
25	$5 black, *1979*	35.00	5.00
26	$40 red, *1979*	45.00	15.00
27	$5 black, *1980*	35.00	5.00
28	$40 green, *1980*	45.00	15.00

Small Game and Habitat Stamps

Required to hunt small game and waterfowl statewide.

Resident ($9), youth ($6) and non-resident ($53) fees.

Resident stamps issued in booklet panes of 5 numbered 20,001-150,000 (1982-86 issues) or 20,001-140,000 (starting with 1987 issue) or sheets of 30 numbered 150,001 and up (1982-86 issues) or 140,001 and up (starting with 1987 issue).

Starting with 1984, resident booklet stamps have straight edges at sides.

Nos. 31, 34, 37, 40 are die cut self adhesives.

Unused values are for stamps on backing.

All youth stamps were issued in booklet panes of 5. Non-resident stamps for 1981, 1982, 1996 and following years were issued in booklet panes of 5.

The 1984-95 non-resident stamps were issued se-tenant with non-resident waterfowl and non-resident general game stamps (rouletted on three sides). The 1994 and 1995 non-resident stamps also were issued se-tenant with only the non-resident general game stamp (rouletted at sides), as well as in booklet panes of 5 (rouletted top and bottom).

> **Catalogue values for all unused stamps in this section, from this point to the end, are for Never Hinged items.**

1981
29 A1 $9 black   35.00   3.00
30 A1 $6 black, *blue green*   175.00 25.00
31 A1 $53 blue   110.00 20.00

A2

Artists: Richard Plaschaert, #32, 73; Terry Radlin, #35; David Maass, #38; Leslie Kouba, #41; Mario Fernandez, #44; Ronald Louque, #47, 75; Louis Frisino, #50; Robert Leslie, #53; Roger Cruwys, #56; Thomas Hirata, #59; Phillip Crowe, #62, 77, 81; Bruce Miller, #65; Darrell Davis, #67; Richard Clifton, #69; Wilhelm Goebel, #71; Jeffrey Klinefelter, #79.

1982
32 A2 $9 Canada geese   125.00
    Booklet single with L & R selvage *850.00* 25.00
  Serial numbers 1-20,000 are from sheets of 10. Stamps without selvage from booklets sell for considerably less.
33 A1 $6 black, *blue*   175.00 25.00
34 A1 $53 black   35.00 15.00

1983
35 A2 $9 Mallards   75.00
    Booklet single with L & R selvage *2,000.* 25.00
  Serial numbers 1-20,000 are from sheets. Stamps without selvage from booklets sell for considerably less.
36 A1 $6 black, *orange*   25.00
37 A1 $53 black   40.00

1984
38 A2 $9 Canvasbacks   40.00
  a. Booklet single, perforated horiz. on 1 or
      2 sides   *2,500.* 25.00
39 A1 $6 black, *light blue*   25.00
40 A1 $53 black   40.00

1985
41 A2 $9 Bluebills   20.00
  a. Booklet single, perforated horiz. on 1 or
      2 sides   *3,500.* 25.00
42 A1 $6 black, *light blue*   25.00
43 A1 $53 black   40.00

1986
44 A2 $9 Pintails   20.00
  a. Booklet single, perforated horiz. on 1 or
      2 sides   450.00 20.00
45 A1 $6 black, *light blue*   20.00
46 A1 $53 black   35.00

1987
47 A2 $9 Snow geese   18.00
  a. Booklet single, perforated horiz. on 1 or
      2 sides   60.00 18.00
48 A1 $6 black, *light blue*   25.00
49 A1 $53 black   30.00

1988
50 A2 $9 White-winged scoters 14.00
  a. Booklet single, perforated horiz. on 1 or
      2 sides   30.00 12.00
51 A1 $6 black, *light blue*   25.00
52 A1 $53 black   30.00

Stamps Inscribed "Small Game"

Resident ($6), youth ($3) and non-resident ($50, $75) fees.

1989
53 A2 $6 Redheads   12.00
  a. Booklet single, perforated horiz. on 1 or 2
      sides   15.00 8.00
54 A1 $3 black, *light blue*   25.00
55 A1 $50 black   30.00

1990
56 A2 $6 Labrador retriever & mallard 15.00
  a. Booklet single, perforated horiz. on 1 or 2
      sides   15.00 8.00
57 A1 $3 black, *light blue* 200.00 25.00
58 A1 $50 black   25.00

1991
59 A2 $6 Green-winged teal   12.50
  a. Booklet single, perforated horiz. on 1 or 2
      sides   13.00 6.00
60 A1 $3 black, *light blue* 200.00 25.00
61 A1 $50 black   350.00 25.00

1992
62 A2 $6 Blue-winged teal   12.50
  a. Booklet single, perforated horiz. on 1 or 2
      sides   13.00 6.00
63 A1 $3 black, *light blue* 325.00
64 A1 $50 black   25.00
  When supplies of No. 64 ran out, No. 58 was used with the date changed by hand. Unused examples exist. Value, $300.

1993
65 A2 $6 Wood ducks   12.50
  a. Booklet single, perforated horiz. on 1 or 2
      sides   13.00 6.00
66 A1 $50 black   *550.00* 25.00

1994
67 A2 $6 Canada geese   10.00
  a. Booklet single, perforated horiz. on 1 or 2
      sides   10.00 6.00
68 A1 $75 black, rouletted on 2 adjacent
      sides   400.00 20.00
  a. Booklet single, rouletted top and bottom —

1995
69 A2 $6 Widgeon   10.00
  a. Booklet single, perforated horiz. on 1 or 2
      sides   10.00 5.00
70 A1 $75 black, rouletted on 2 adjacent sides *350.00* 20.00
  a. Booklet single, rouletted top and bottom —

1996
71 A2 $6 Mallards   10.00
  a. Booklet single, perforated horiz. on 1 or 2
      sides   10.00 2.50
72 A1 $75 black, rouletted at top and bottom —

1997
73 A2 $6 White-fronted geese   10.00
  a. Booklet single, perforated horiz. on 1 or 2
      sides   10.00 2.50
74 A1 $75 black, rouletted at top and bottom —

1998
75 A2 $6 Blue-winged teal   10.00
  a. Bklt. single, perforated horiz. on 1 or 2
      sides   10.00 2.50
76 A1 $75 black, rouletted at top and bottom —

1999
77 A2 $6 Gadwalls   10.00
  a. Bklt. single, perforated horiz. on 1 or 2
      sides   10.00 2.50
78 A1 $75 black, rouletted at top and bottom —

2000-01
79 $6 Pintails, *2000*   10.00
  a. Bklt. single, perforated horiz. on 1 or 2
      sides   10.00 2.50
81 A2 $6 Canada geese, *2001*   10.00
  a. Bklt. single, perforated horiz. on 1 or 2
      sides   10.00 2.50

A3

2002-08
83 A3 $6 black, *green, 2002*   12.00
84 A3 $6 black, *green, 2003*   12.00
85 A3 $6 black, *green, 2004*   12.00
86 A3 $6 black, *green, 2005*   12.00
87 A3 $6 black, *green, 2006*   9.00
88 A3 $6 black, *green, 2007*   8.00
89 A3 $6 black, *green, 2008*   8.00

Non-Resident Waterfowl Stamps

Required by non-residents to hunt waterfowl only. Unused examples of Nos. A1a, A13a-A19a have no serial number. Used stamps have number written in. Nos. A1-A10 are self-adhesive, die cut. Others are rouletted.

> Catalogue values for all unused stamps in this section are for Never Hinged items.

17	18	19	20	21	22	23	24	25	26	27	28	29	30	31

☐ SEPT.   1975 - Zone_____$5   1975
☐ OCT.   State of N. Dak.
        NR. Waterfowl Stamp
☐ NOV.   NON-TRANSFERABLE
☐ DEC.   N. Dak. Game & Fish Dept.

1	2	3	4	5	6	7	8	9	10	11	12	13	14	15	16

Illustration reduced.

1975-99
A1 $5 green   *150.00*
  a. No serial number   160.00   —
A2 $5 red, *1976*   475.00 100.00
A3 $5 red, *1977*   275.00 75.00
A4 $5 red, *1978*   110.00 25.00
A5 $5 red, *1979*   85.00 20.00
A6 $5 green, *1980*   90.00 20.00
A7 $8 blue, *1981*   175.00 25.00
A8 $8 black, *1982*   27.50 15.00
A9 $8 black, *1983*   55.00
A10 $8 black, *1984*   50.00
A11 $8 black, *1985*   45.00
A12 $8 black, *1986*   45.00
A13 $8 black, *1987*   40.00
  a. No serial number   400.00 50.00
A14 $8 black, *1988*   35.00
  a. No serial number   350.00 50.00
A15 $8 black, *1989*   25.00
  a. No serial number, light green paper 350.00 50.00
A16 $8 black, *1990*   25.00
  a. No serial number   300.00 50.00
A17 $8 black, *1991*   400.00 25.00
  a. No serial number   250.00 35.00
A18 $8 black, *1992*   20.00
  a. No serial number   200.00 35.00
  When supplies of No. A18 ran out, No. A16 was used with the date changed by hand. Values, unused $200, used $50.
A19 $10 black, *1993*   275.00 20.00
  a. No serial number   175.00 30.00
A20 $10 black, rouletted on 2 adjacent
      sides, *1994*   250.00 20.00
  a. No serial number, rouletted top and bottom 175.00 30.00
A21 $10 black, rouletted on 2 adjacent
      sides, *1995*   225.00 20.00
  a. No serial number, rouletted top and bottom 100.00 25.00
A22 $10 black, rouletted top and bottom, *1996*   95.00 20.00
A23 $10 black, rouletted top and bottom, *1997*   85.00 14.00
A24 $10 black, rouletted top and bottom, *1998*   75.00 12.00
A25 $10 black, rouletted top and bottom, *1999*   65.00 12.00

Resident Sportsmen's Stamps

Required to hunt a variety of game, including waterfowl.

> Catalogue values for all unused stamps in this section are for Never Hinged items.

> **1992-93 Resident**
> **ND Sportsmens License**
> **$25.00**
> **Fishing - Small Game**
> **General Game & Habitat**
> **Furbearer**
> **№ 12968**
> NON-TRANSFERABLE

1992-98
2A1 $25 black & purple, *1992-1993* *3,250.* 75.00
2A2 $25 black & purple, *1993-1994* *1,650.* 35.00
2A3 $25 black & purple, *1994-1995* 375.00 25.00
2A4 $25 black & purple, *1995-1996* 250.00 20.00
2A5 $25 black & purple, *1996-1997* 200.00 15.00
2A6 $27 black & purple, *1997-1998* 125.00 12.00

Below the A3 illustration:

> Expires June 30, 2003
> State of North Dakota
> **Resident Small Game**
> **$6.00**
> **№ 105573**
> N.D. Game and Fish Dept.
> NON-TRANSFERABLE

OHIO

Pymatuning Lake Waterfowl Hunting Stamps

1938-45

A1	$1 black, *light yellow*	—
A2	$1 black, *gray, 1939*	—
A3	$1 black, *blue, 1940*	—
A4	$1 black, *pink, 1941*	—
A5	$1 black, *green, 1942*	—
A6	$1 black, *1943*	—
A7	$1 black, *manila, 1944*	—
A8	$1 black, *manila, 1945*	—

Statewide Issues

Nos. 1-18 printed in sheets of 16. Starting with No. 19, stamps are printed in souvenir sheets of 1.

Catalogue values for all unused stamps in this section are for Never Hinged items.

Artists: John Ruthven, #1; Harry Antis, #2; Harold Roe, #3, 6, 15, 17; Ronald Louque, #4; Lynn Kaatz, #5, 8; Cynthia Fisher, #7; Jon Henson, #9; Gregory Clair, #10, 25; Samuel Timm, #11; Kenneth Nanney, #12; Richard Clifton, #13, 26; Ron Kleiber, #14; D. J. Cleland-Hura, #16: Timothy Donovan, #18; Mark Anderson, #19; Brian Bright, #20, 22; Jeffrey Klinefelter, #21, 27; Robert Mertopulos, #23; Adam Grimm, #24.

1982-2008

1	$5.75 Wood ducks	80.00	10.00
2	$5.75 Mallards, *1983*	70.00	10.00
3	$5.75 Green-winged teal, *1984*	70.00	8.00
4	$5.75 Redheads, *1985*	35.00	6.00
5	$5.75 Canvasback, *1986*	35.00	5.00
6	$6 Blue-winged teal, *1987*	12.00	4.00
7	$6 Common goldeneyes, *1988*	12.00	4.00
8	$6 Canada geese, *1989*	12.00	3.00
9	$9 Black ducks, *1990*	16.00	3.00
10	$9 Lesser scaup, *1991*	16.00	3.00
11	$9 Wood ducks, *1992*	16.00	3.00
12	$9 Buffleheads, *1993*	16.00	3.00
13	$11 Mallards, *1994*	21.00	3.00
14	$11 Pintails, *1995*	22.50	2.50
15	$11 Hooded mergansers, *1996*	24.00	2.50
16	$11 Widgeons, *1997*	20.00	2.50
17	$11 Gadwall, *1998*	20.00	2.50
18	$11 Mallard, *1999*	18.00	2.50

Souvenir Sheet
Rouletted

19	$11 Buffleheads, *2000*	18.00	2.50
20	$11 Canvasback, *2001*	18.00	2.50
21	$11 Ring-necked ducks, *2002*	17.00	2.50
22	$11 Hooded mergansers, *2003*	17.00	2.50
23	$15 Tundra swans, *2004*	20.00	2.50
24	$15 Wood duck, *2005*	20.00	2.50
25	$15 Pintail, *2006*	20.00	2.50
26	$15 Canada goose, *2007*	19.00	2.50
27	$15 Green-winged teal, *2008*	19.00	2.50

Nos. 19-27 not required for hunting.

OKLAHOMA

Printed in booklet panes of 10 (Nos. 1-3) and booklet panes of 5 (Starting with No. 4). No. 10 was the first to be printed in a sheet of 30, No. 17 in a sheet of 24.

Catalogue values for all unused stamps in this section are for Never Hinged items.

Artists: Patrick Sawyer, #1; Hoyt Smith, #2, 5, 7, 20; Jeffrey Frey, #3; Gerald Mobley, #4, 6; Rayburn Foster, #8, 12; Jim Gaar, #9; Wanda Mumm, #10; Ronald Louque, #11; Jeffrey Mobley, #13; Jerome Hageman, #14; Richard Kirkman, #15; Richard Clifton, #16; Greg Everhart, #17; M. Anderson, #18, 24; Jeffrey Klinefelter, #19, 26; Paul Makuchal, #21; Daniel Brevick, #22; Brian Blight, #23; Scot Storm, #25; James Hublick, #27. Jeffrey Hoff, #28; Russell Duerksen, #29.

1980-2008

1	$4 Pintails	55.00	10.00
2	$4 Canada goose, *1981*	25.00	8.00
3	$4 Green-winged teal, *1982*	10.00	4.00
4	$4 Wood ducks, *1983*	10.00	10.00
5	$4 Ring-necked ducks, *1984*	10.00	3.00
	With tab	10.00	
6	$4 Mallards, *1985*	8.00	3.00
	With tab	10.00	
7	$4 Snow geese, *1986*	10.00	3.00
	With tab	10.00	
8	$4 Canvasbacks, *1987*	8.00	3.00
	With tab	9.00	
9	$4 Widgeons, *1988*	8.00	3.00
	With tab	9.00	
10	$4 Redheads, *1989*	8.00	3.00
	Booklet single, with tab & selvage at L, selvage at R	9.00	
a.	Governor's edition	125.00	

No. 10a was available only in sheets of 30 through a sealed bid auction.

11	$4 Hooded merganser, *1990*	7.50	3.00
	Booklet single, with tab & selvage at L, selvage at R	8.50	
12	$4 Gadwalls, *1991*	7.50	3.00
	Booklet single, with tab & selvage at L, selvage at R	8.50	
13	$4 Lesser scaup, *1992*	7.50	3.00
	Booklet single, with tab & selvage at L, selvage at R	8.50	
14	$4 White-fronted geese, *1993*	7.50	3.00
	Booklet single, with tab & selvage at L, selvage at R	8.50	
15	$4 Blue-winged teal, *1994*	7.50	3.00
	Booklet single, with tab & selvage at L, selvage at R	8.50	
16	$4 Ruddy ducks, *1995*	7.50	3.00
	Booklet single, with tab & selvage at L, selvage at R	8.50	
17	$4 Bufflehead, *1996*	7.50	3.00
	Booklet single, with selvage at L & R	8.50	
18	$4 Goldeneyes, *1997*	7.50	3.00
	Bklt. single, with selvage at L & R	8.50	
19	$4 Shovelers, *1998*	7.50	3.00
	Bklt. single, with selvage at L & R	8.50	
20	$4 Canvasbacks, *1999*	8.00	3.00
21	$4 Pintails, *2000*	8.00	3.00
22	$4 Canada goose, *2001*	8.00	3.00
23	$4 Green-winged teal, *2002*	8.00	3.00
24	$10 Wood duck, *2003*	15.00	3.00
25	$10 Mallard, *2004*	15.00	3.00
26	$10 Snow geese, *2005*	15.00	3.00
27	$10 Widgeons, *2006*	15.00	3.00
28	$10 Redheads, *2007*	14.00	3.00
29	$10 Mallards, Labrador retriever, *2008*	14.00	3.00

OREGON

Non-resident fees begin in 1994.
Issued in sheets of 30, except for No. 6. Nos. 2-4 also exist from booklet panes of 5.
Stamps are numbered serially. Nos. 11b, 11c have serial numbers on sheet selvage.
Nos. 10 and 11 were issued on computer form.
Unused values are for stamps on form.

Catalogue values for all unused stamps in this section are for Never Hinged items.

Artists: Michael Sieve, #1-3; Dorothy M. Smith, #4; Darrell Davis, #5; Phillip Crowe, #7; Roger Cruwys, #8; Louis Frisino, #9; Kip Richmond, #10; R. Bruce Horsfall, #11; Richard Plasschaert, #12-13; Robert Steiner, #14-32.

1984-88

1	$5 Canada geese	22.50	7.00
2	$5 Lesser snow goose, *1985*	35.00	10.00
	Booklet single, with 3 tabs (2 at left)	500.00	
3	$5 Pacific brant, perf. 4 sides, *1986*	15.00	
a.	Booklet single, with 2-part tab	15.00	4.00
4	$5 White-fronted geese, perf. 4 sides, *1987*	15.00	
a.	Booklet single, with 2-part tab	15.00	3.00
5	$5 Great Basin Canada geese, *1988*	15.00	3.00
a.	Booklet pane of 1	15.00	

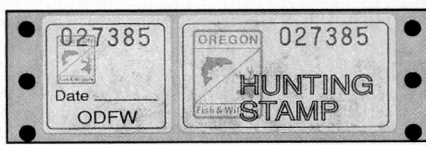

1989-2008   **Die cut self-adhesive**

6	($5) Red Nos., 16,001 and up	15.00	6.00
a.	Black Nos., 001-16,000	30.00	12.50

This provisional stamp was used in early 1989, when the regular stamps were delayed. Unused value is for stamp and adjacent label with serial number on backing paper.

Designs like No. 1

7	$5 Black Labrador retriever & pintails, *1989*	15.00	2.50
a.	Booklet pane of 1	15.00	
8	$5 Mallards & golden retriever, *1990*	15.00	2.50
a.	Booklet pane of 1	15.00	
9	$5 Buffleheads & Chesapeake Bay retriever, perf, *1991*	15.00	
a.	Rouletted at L	15.00	2.50

No. 9a is straight edged on 3 sides and stamp is attached to paper by selvage. Unused value is for stamp attached to paper.

10	$5 Green-winged teal, *1992*	15.00	
a.	Die cut, self-adhesive	15.00	2.50
11	$5 Mallards, vert., *1993*	15.00	
a.	Die cut self-adhesive	15.00	2.50
b.	Sheet of 2	22.50	
c.	$50 Governor's edition sheet of 1	75.00	

No. 11b contains No. 11 and the Oregon upland bird stamp. Nos. 11b, 11c exist imperf.

12	$5 Pintails, perf. 4 sides, *1994*	15.00	
a.	Die cut self-adhesive	15.00	2.50
13	$25 Pintails, diff., die cut self-adhesive, *1994*	40.00	—
14	$5 Wood ducks, *1995*	15.00	
a.	Booklet pane of 1	15.00	2.50
15	$25 Columbian sharp-tailed grouse, bklt. pane of 1, *1995*	160.00	—
16	$5 Mallards, *1996*	20.00	
a.	Booklet pane of 1	15.00	2.50
17	$25 Common snipe, booklet pane of 1, *1996*	140.00	—
18	$5 Canvasbacks, *1997*	20.00	
a.	Booklet pane of 1	15.00	2.50
19	$25 Canvasbacks, booklet pane of 1, *1997*	140.00	
20	$5 Pintails, *1998*	20.00	
a.	Booklet pane of 1	15.00	2.50
21	$25 Pintails, booklet pane of 1, *1998*	37.50	
22	$5 Canada geese, *1999*	17.50	
a.	Booklet pane of 1	15.00	2.50
23	$25 Canada geese, booklet pane of 1, *1999*	65.00	
24	$7.50 Canada geese, mallard, widgeon, *2000*	15.00	2.50
a.	Booklet pane of 1, no cover	—	
25	$7.50 Redheads, *2001*	15.00	2.50
a.	Booklet pane of 1, no cover	20.00	
26	$7.50 American wigeon, *2002*	14.00	2.50
a.	Booklet pane of 1, no cover	14.00	
27	$7.50 Wood duck, *2003*	14.00	2.50
a.	Booklet pane of 1, no cover	14.00	
28	$7.50 Ross's goose, *2004*	13.00	2.50
a.	Booklet pane of 1, no cover	13.00	
29	$7.50 Hooded merganser, *2005*	13.00	2.50
a.	Booklet pane of 1, no cover	13.00	
30	$7.50 Pintail, mallard, *2006*	12.00	2.50
a.	Booklet pane of 1, no cover	12.00	

31	$7.50 Wood ducks, *2007*	12.00	2.50
a.	Booklet pane of 1, no cover	12.00	
32	$7.50 Pintails, *2008*	12.00	2.50
a.	Booklet pane of 1, no cover	12.00	

Nos. 27-32 not required for hunting.

PENNSYLVANIA

Not required to hunt.
Printed in sheets of 10.

> Catalogue values for all unused stamps in this section are for Never Hinged items.

Artists: Ned Smith, #1, 3; Jim Killen, #2; Robert Knutson, #4; Robert Leslie, #5; John Heldersbach, #6; Ronald Louque, #7; Thomas Hirata, #8, 12; Gerald W. Putt, #9, 14, 16, 18, 20, 23, 25; Robert Sopchick, #10; Glen Reichard, #11; Mark Bray, #13; Clark Weaver, #15, 17, 19; Jocelyn Beatty, #21; Carl Clark, #22; Kerry Holzman, #24; Scott Calpino, #26.

1983-2008

1	$5.50 Wood ducks	15.00	
2	$5.50 Canada geese, *1984*	12.00	
3	$5.50 Mallards, *1985*	12.00	
4	$5.50 Blue-winged teal, *1986*	12.00	
5	$5.50 Pintails, *1987*	12.00	
6	$5.50 Wood ducks, *1988*	12.00	
7	$5.50 Hooded mergansers, *1989*	9.00	
8	$5.50 Canvasbacks, *1990*	9.00	
9	$5.50 Widgeons, *1991*	9.00	
10	$5.50 Canada geese, *1992*	9.00	
11	$5.50 Northern shovelers, *1993*	9.00	
12	$5.50 Pintails, *1994*	9.00	
13	$5.50 Buffleheads, *1995*	9.00	
14	$5.50 Black ducks, *1996*	9.00	
15	$5.50 Hooded merganser, *1997*	9.00	
16	$5.50 Wood ducks, *1998*	9.00	
17	$5.50 Ring-necked ducks, *1999*	9.00	
18	$5.50 Green-winged teal, *2000*	9.00	
19	($5.50) Pintails, *2001*	9.00	
20	$5.50 Snow geese, *2002*	9.00	2.50
21	$5.50 Canvasbacks, *2003*	9.00	2.50
22	$5.50 Hooded mergansers, *2004*	9.00	2.50
23	$5.50 Red-breasted mergansers, *2005*	8.00	2.50
24	$5.50 Pintails, *2006*	8.00	2.50
25	$5.50 Wood ducks, *2007*	7.50	2.50
26	$5.50 Redheads, *2008*	7.50	2.50

RHODE ISLAND

Issued in booklet panes of 5 and sheets of 30.
Starting with No. 8, the spacing of the reverse text of the booklet stamp differs from the sheet stamp.
Stamps are numbered serially.

> Catalogue values for all unused stamps in this section are for Never Hinged items.

Artists: Robert Steiner, #1-7, 9-10, 16; Charles Allen, #8; Keith Mueller, #11-15, 17-20.

1989-2008

1	$7.50 Canvasbacks	12.00	3.00
	Booklet single, with tab	16.00	
a.	$7.50 +$50 Governor's edition	92.50	

No. 1a exists without serial number.

2	$7.50 Canada geese, *1990*	12.00	3.00
	Booklet single, with tab	15.00	
a.	$7.50 +$50 Governor's edition	72.50	

No. 2a exists without serial number.

3	$7.50 Wood ducks & Labrador retriever, *1991*	20.00	3.00
	Booklet single, with tab	22.50	
a.	$7.50 +$50 Governor's edition	60.00	

No. 3a exists without serial number.

4	$7.50 Blue-winged teal, *1992*	15.00	3.00
	Booklet single, with tab	15.00	
a.	$7.50 +$50 Governor's edition	60.00	

No. 4a exists without serial number.

5	$7.50 Pintails, *1993*	13.00	3.00
	Booklet single, with tab	13.00	
a.	Sheet of 4	65.00	

No. 5a imperf. is printer's waste.

6	$7.50 Wood ducks, *1994*	17.00	2.50
	Booklet single, with tab and selvage	17.00	
7	$7.50 Hooded mergansers, *1995*	13.00	2.50
	Booklet single, with tab and selvage	13.00	
a.	Governor's edition	*110.00*	

No. 7a inscribed "Governor's edition."

8	$7.50 Harlequin, *1996*	22.50	2.50
	Booklet single, with tab and selvage	22.50	
a.	Governor's edition	*125.00*	

No. 8a inscribed "Governor's edition" and has serial number with "G" prefix.

9	$7.50 Greater scaup, *1997*	13.00	2.50
	Booklet single, with tab and selvage	14.00	
a.	Governor's edition	*110.00*	

No. 9a inscribed "Governor's edition" and has serial number with "G" prefix.

10	$7.50 Black ducks, *1998*	13.00	2.50
	Booklet single, with tab and selvage	14.00	
a.	Governor's edition	*125.00*	

No. 11-14 do not have a serial number.

Rouletted

11	$7.50 Common eiders, *1999*	17.00	2.50
	Horiz. pair from booklet pane	60.00	

Booklet pane contains 10 stamps.

12	$7.50 Canvasbacks, *2000*	16.00	2.50
a.	Inscribed "Hunter"	18.00	
a.	Governor's edition	—	
13	$7.50 Mallard, black duck, *2001*	15.00	2.50
a.	Inscribed "Hunter"	16.00	
a.	Governor's edition	*125.00*	
14	$7.50 White-winged scoter, lighthouse, *2002*	13.00	2.50
a.	Inscribed "Hunter"	13.00	
b.	Governor's edition	*130.00*	—
15	$7.50 Oldsquaws, *2003*	12.00	2.50
a.	Inscribed "Hunter"	13.00	
b.	Governor's edition	*130.00*	—
16	$7.50 Canvasbacks, *2004*	11.00	2.50
a.	Inscribed "Hunter"	12.00	
b.	Governor's edition	*130.00*	—
17	$7.50 Black ducks, lighthouse, *2005*	11.00	2.50
a.	Inscribed "Hunter"	11.00	
18	$7.50 Canvasbacks, lighthouse, *2006*	11.00	2.50
a.	Inscribed "Hunter"	11.00	
b.	Governor's edition	*130.00*	—
19	$7.50 Harlequin decoy, *2007*	9.50	2.50
a.	Inscribed "Hunter"	9.50	
b.	Governor's edition	*130.00*	—
20	$7.50 Mallard decoys, *2008*	9.50	2.50
a.	Inscribed "Hunter"	9.50	

Nos. 15-20 have no serial number.

SOUTH CAROLINA

Issued in sheets of 30. Stamps with serial numbers were to be issued to hunters.

> Catalogue values for all unused stamps in this section are for Never Hinged items.

Artists: Lee LeBlanc, #1; Bob Binks, #2; Jim Killen, #3, 8, 11, 27-28; Al Dornish, #4; Rosemary Millette, #5; Daniel Smith, #6; Steve Dillard, #7; Lee Cable, #9; John Wilson, #10; Russell Cobane, #12; Bob Bolin, #13; Joe Hautman, #14; Rodney Huckaby, #15, 17, 22, 25; D. J. Cleland-Hura, #16, 18; Denise Nelson, #19; Mark Constantine, #20; Jeffrey Klinefelter, #21; James Hublick, #23; Eddie LeRoy, #24; Richard D. Benson, #26.

1981-2008

1	$5.50 Wood ducks	60.00	15.00

No. 2-22 do not have a serial number.

2	$5.50 Mallards, *1982*	95.00	
a.	Serial number on reverse	495.00	25.00
3	$5.50 Pintails, *1983*	95.00	
a.	Serial number on reverse	450.00	25.00
4	$5.50 Canada geese, *1984*	65.00	
a.	Serial number on reverse	190.00	15.00
5	$5.50 Green-winged teal, *1985*	60.00	
a.	Serial number on reverse	100.00	15.00
6	$5.50 Canvasbacks, *1986*	25.00	
a.	Serial number on reverse	42.50	10.00
7	$5.50 Black ducks, *1987*	20.00	
a.	Serial number on reverse	22.50	5.00
8	$5.50 Widgeon & spaniel, *1988*	20.00	
a.	Serial number on reverse	30.00	5.00
9	$5.50 Blue-winged teal, *1989*	11.00	
a.	Serial number on reverse	14.00	4.00
10	$5.50 Wood ducks, *1990*	10.00	
a.	Serial number on reverse	10.00	4.00
b.	$5.50 +$44.50 Governor's edition	82.50	
c.	$5.50 +$94.50 Governor's edition	225.00	

All copies of No. 10c are signed by the governor.

11	$5.50 Labrador retriever, pintails & decoy, *1991*	11.00	
a.	Serial number on reverse	11.00	4.00
12	$5.50 Buffleheads, *1992*	14.00	
a.	Serial number on front	14.00	3.00
13	$5.50 Lesser scaups, *1993*	14.00	
a.	Serial number on front	14.00	3.00
14	$5.50 Canvasbacks, *1994*	14.00	
a.	Serial number on front	14.00	2.50
15	$5.50 Shovelers, lighthouse, *1995*	14.00	
a.	Serial number on front	14.00	2.50
16	$5.50 Redheads, lighthouse, *1996*	17.50	
a.	Serial number on front	17.50	2.50
17	$5.50 Old squaws, *1997*	17.50	
a.	Serial number on front	17.50	2.50
18	$5.50 Green-winged teals, *1998*	17.50	
a.	Serial number on front	17.50	2.50
19	$5.50 Barrow's goldeneyes, *1999*	11.00	2.50
20	$5.50 Wood ducks, boykin spaniel, *2000*	13.00	2.50
21	$5.50 Mallard, decoy, yellow Labrador retriever, *2001*	13.00	2.50
22	$5.50 Wigeons, chocolate Labrador retriever, *2002*	11.00	2.50
23	$5.50 Green-winged teal, *2003*	11.00	2.50
24	$5.50 Pintails, Labrador retriever, *2004*	11.00	2.50
25	$5.50 Canvasbacks, *2005*	9.00	2.50
26	$5.50 Black ducks, *2006*	9.00	2.50
27	$5.50 Redheads, Golden retriever, *2007*	8.00	2.50
28	$5.50 Blue-winged teal, Labrador retriever, *2008*	8.00	2.50

Nos. 23-28 have no serial number.

SOUTH DAKOTA

Resident Waterfowl Stamps

Vertical safety paper (words read up)

1949-50

1	$1 blk, *grn*, vert. safety paper	1,450.	85.00
a.	Horizontal safety paper	—	150.00
2	$1 blk, *lt brn*, vert. safety paper	1,200.	65.00
a.	Horizontal safety paper	—	175.00

Safety paper design of Nos. 1 and 2 washes out if stamp is soaked. Washed out examples sell for considerably less. Used values are for stamps showing safety paper design.

Printed in booklet panes of 5.
Stamps are numbered serially.

> Catalogue values for all unused stamps in this section, from this point to the end of the Resident Waterfowl stamps, are for Never Hinged items.

Artists: Robert Kusserow, #3; Don Steinbeck, #4; John Moisan, #5; John Wilson, #6, 12; Rosemary Millett, #7, 9; Marion Toillion, #8; John Green, #10, 17; Russell Duerksen, #11, 15-16, 19-20; Mark Anderson, #13, 18, 21, 22; Jeff Reuter, #14; Joshua Spies. #23.

1976-2003

3	$1 Mallards	35.00	3.00
a.	Serial number 4mm high	65.00	10.00
4	$1 Pintails, *1977*	27.50	2.50
5	$1 Canvasbacks, *1978*	13.00	2.50
6	$2 Canada geese, *1988*	8.50	2.50
7	$2 Blue geese, *1987*	7.00	2.50
8	$2 White-fronted geese, *1988*	6.00	2.50
9	$2 Mallards, *1989*	6.00	2.50
10	$2 Blue-winged teal, *1990*	6.00	2.50
11	$2 Pintails, *1991*	6.00	2.50
12	$2 Canvasbacks, *1992*	6.00	2.50
13	$2 Lesser scaup, *1993*	6.00	2.50
14	$2 Redheads, *1994*	6.00	2.50
15	$2 Wood ducks, *1995*	6.00	2.50
16	$2 Canada geese, *1996*	6.00	2.50
17	$2 Widgeons, *1997*	6.00	2.50
18	$2 Green-winged teal, *1998*	6.00	2.50

Migratory Bird Certification Stamps

19	$3 Tundra swan, *1999*	9.00	2.50
20	$3 Buffleheads, *2000*	9.00	2.50
21	$3 Mallards, *2001*	9.00	2.50
22	$3 Canvasbacks, *2002*	9.00	2.50
23	$3 Pintails, *2003*	9.00	2.50

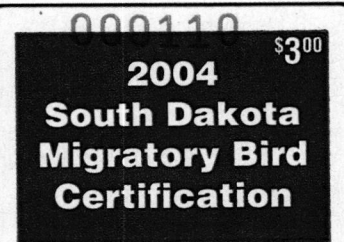

2004-07

24	$3 purple	9.00	2.50
25	$5 magenta, *2005*	9.00	2.50
26	$5 brown orange, *2006*	9.00	2.50
27	$5 brown, *2007*	9.00	2.50

Non-resident Waterfowl Stamps

Nos. A1-A7, A9 have serial No. in red. Nos. A1-A18 issued in booklet panes of 5. Type faces and designs of Nos. A1-A18 vary.

Unused values are for unpunched stamps. Used values are for signed and punched stamps.

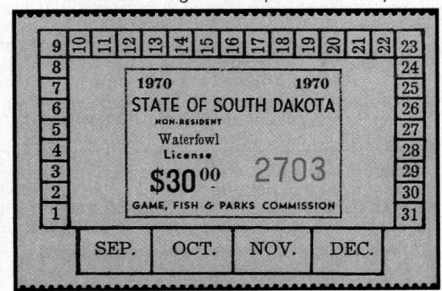

Illustration reduced.

1970-86

A1	$30 black, *pink*	20.00	
a.	Missing serial number	7,000.	
A2	$30 black, *pink, 1971*	9.00	
a.	Overprinted "3"		350.00
A3	$30 black, *1972*	3.75	
A4	$30 black, *blue, 1973*	8.00	
a.	Overprinted "2"	2,950.	
A5	$30 black, *green, 1974*	5.50	
a.	Overprinted "1"	25.00	
b.	Overprinted "2"	30.00	
c.	Overprinted "4"	30.00	
A6	$30 black, *yellow, 1975*	6.50	
a.	Overprinted "UNIT 1"	45.00	
b.	Overprinted "UNIT 4"	35.00	
c.	Overprinted "UNIT 3"	—	
A7	$30 black, *yellow, 1976*	5.00	
a.	Overprinted "1"	18.00	
b.	Overprinted "2"	30.00	20.00
c.	Serial No. 4mm high	18.00	
d.	As "c," overprinted "1"	35.00	
e.	As "c," overprinted "2"	85.00	
A8	$30 black, *red, 1977*	7.00	
a.	Overprinted "1"	20.00	
b.	Overprinted "2"	30.00	
c.	Overprinted "3"	35.00	
d.	Overprinted "4"	30.00	
e.	Overprinted "5"	200.00	
A9	$30 black, *yellow, 1978*	7.00	
a.	Overprinted "1" and 3 strikes of "UNIT 2"	150.00	
b.	Overprinted "1"	175.00	
A10	$30 black, *red, 1979*	2.50	
A11	$30 black, *light manila, 1980*	4.50	
a.	Overprinted "1"	6.00	
b.	Overprinted "2"	10.00	
A12	$30 black, *light yellow, 1981*	4.50	
a.	Overprinted "UNIT 1"	6.00	
b.	Overprinted "UNIT 2"	10.00	5.00
A13	$30 black, *blue, 1982*	6.50	
A14	$50 black, *dark yellow, 1982*	7.00	
a.	Overprinted "UNIT 2"	—	
A15	$50 black, *red, 1983*	8.00	
a.	Overprinted "AREA 1"	50.00	
b.	Overprinted "AREA 2"	65.00	
c.	Serial No. with serifs	650.00	
A16	$50 black, *light manila, 1984*	16.00	
a.	Overprinted "A"	325.00	
b.	Overprinted "B"	125.00	
A17	$50 black, *red, 1985*	3,500.	750.00
A18	$50 black, *1986*	9.00	5.00

Bennett County Canada Goose Stamps

Type faces and designs vary. Nos. 2A1-2A2 imperf. Nos. 2A3-2A12 printed in booklet panes of 5, perforated horizontally. Some show vertical perforations.

Nos. 2A1-2A4 were free. No. 2A5 cost $5. Stamps were issued to hunters by means of a drawing.

Used values are for signed stamps.

Illustration reduced.

1974-78

2A1	black	75.00	35.00
2A2	black, *pink, 1975*	250.00	

2A3	black, *blue, 1976*	47.50	25.00
2A4	black, *yellow, 1977*	42.50	25.00
2A5	black, *greenish blue, 1978*	800.00	

West River Unit Canada Goose

Counties handstamped.
Used values are for signed stamps.

1979

2A6	$2 black, *yellow*	500.00	
a.	Bennett County	750.00	275.00
b.	Haakon County	275.00	
c.	Jackson County	275.00	
d.	Pennington County	225.00	100.00

Stamps overprinted for Perkins County exist but may not have been regularly issued.

1980

2A7	$2 black, *blue*	75.00	
a.	Bennett County	225.00	75.00
b.	Haakon County	100.00	
c.	Jackson County	110.00	
d.	As "c," missing serial number	7,500.	
e.	Pennington County	90.00	45.00
f.	Perkins County	110.00	

Prairie Canada Geese

Counties or Units handstamped.
Used values are for signed stamps.

1981
Perf. 12

2A8	$2 black, *red*	8.00	
a.	Bennett County	80.00	35.00
b.	Haakon County	60.00	20.00
c.	Jackson County	60.00	20.00
d.	Pennington County	60.00	
e.	Perkins County	60.00	

1982

2A9	$2 black, *blue*	125.00	
a.	Bennett County	950.00	350.00
b.	Haakon County	650.00	
c.	Jackson County	650.00	
d.	Pennington County	650.00	
e.	Perkins County	650.00	

1983
Perf. 12

2A10	$2 black, *yellow*	60.00	
a.	UNIT 2A	70.00	
b.	UNIT 31	70.00	35.00
c.	UNIT 39	70.00	35.00
d.	UNIT 49	70.00	35.00
e.	UNIT 53	70.00	35.00
f.	UNIT 11, 3mm type	100.00	50.00
g.	UNIT 23	100.00	

Rouletted top and bottom

2A11	$2 black, *yellow*	11.00	
a.	UNIT 2A	65.00	
b.	UNIT 6	45.00	
c.	UNIT 11, 3mm type	60.00	
d.	UNIT 11, 4½mm type	45.00	
e.	UNIT 23	45.00	
f.	UNIT 31	65.00	
g.	UNIT 32	45.00	
h.	UNIT 39	65.00	
i.	UNIT 42	45.00	
j.	UNIT 49	65.00	
k.	UNIT 53, 3mm type	45.00	
l.	UNIT 53, 4½mm type	50.00	

1984
Perf. 12

2A12	$2 black, *green*	45.00	
a.	UNIT 6	75.00	
b.	UNIT 11, 3mm type	85.00	
c.	UNIT 11, 4½mm type	75.00	
d.	UNIT 23, 3mm type	85.00	
e.	UNIT 23, 4½mm type	75.00	30.00
f.	UNIT 32	85.00	
g.	UNIT 42	75.00	
h.	UNIT 47, 3mm type	85.00	
i.	UNIT 47, 3mm type	75.00	
j.	UNIT 47, 4½mm type		65.00
k.	UNIT 53, 4½mm type		65.00

1985
Rouletted two adjacent sides

2A13	$2 black, *red*		
a.	UNIT 47		100.00
b.	UNIT 53		100.00
c.	UNIT 23		125.00
d.	UNIT 32		175.00
e.	UNIT 42		125.00
f.	UNIT 11		175.00

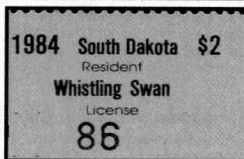

1986
No fee printed on stamp
Imperf. on 3 sides, rouletted at top

2A14	black		
a.	UNIT 11		110.00
b.	UNIT 47		110.00
c.	UNIT 53		110.00
d.	UNIT 23		150.00

---

105 stamps for hunting whistling swans during the 1984 season exist. The season was canceled. Value, unused $375.

Pheasant Restoration Stamps

Required to hunt all small game, including waterfowl. Printed in booklet panes of 5. No. 3A4 rouletted, others perforated. Stamps are numbered serially.

> **Catalogue values for all unused stamps in this section, from this point to the end of the Wildlife Habitat stamps, are for Never Hinged items.**

1977-88

3A1	$5 Pheasants	13.00	2.50
a.	Rubber-stamped serial number	—	
3A2	$5 Pheasants, *1978*	13.00	1.50
3A3	$5 Pheasants, *1979*	13.00	1.50
3A4	$5 Pheasants, *1980*	13.00	2.00
a.	Serial number omitted	—	
3A5	$5 Pheasants, *1981*	13.00	1.50
3A6	$5 Pheasants, *1982*	13.00	1.50
a.	Pair, imperf. between	—	
3A7	$5 Pheasant, *1983*	13.00	1.00
3A8	$5 Pheasant, *1984*	13.00	2.00
3A9	$5 Pheasant, *1985*	13.00	2.00
3A10	$5 Pheasants, *1986*	13.00	2.50
3A11	$5 Pheasants, *1987*	15.00	2.00
3A12	$5 Pheasants, *1988*	13.00	2.00

Wildlife Habitat Stamps

Required to hunt all small game, including waterfowl. Printed in booklet panes of 5. Starting with No. 3A18 stamps are rouletted, others are perforated. Stamps are numbered serially.

1989-99

3A13	$8 Pheasants	13.00	2.00
3A14	$8 White-tailed deer, *1990*	13.00	2.00
3A15	$8 Greater prairie chicken, *1991*	13.00	2.00
3A16	$8 Mule Deer, *1992*	13.00	2.50
3A17	$8 Sharp-tailed grouse, *1993*	13.00	2.00
a.	Pair, imperf. between	—	
3A18	$8 Turkey, *1994*	13.00	2.00
3A19	$8 Elk, *1995*	13.00	2.00
3A20	$8 Pheasants, *1996*	13.00	2.00
3A21	$8 Antelope, *1997*	13.00	2.00
3A22	$8 Buffalo, *1998*	13.00	2.00
3A23	$8 Buffalo, *1999*	13.00	2.00

Resident Small Game Stamps

Required by residents wishing to hunt small game, including waterfowl. Nos. 4A1, 4A2 issued panes of 10. Others issued in booklet panes of 5. Stamps are numbered serially in red from 1960 to 1967 and 1978. Non-resident small game stamps were not required for hunting.

> **Catalogue values for all unused stamps in this section are for Never Hinged items.**

1960-79

4A1	$2 black, *pink*	12.00	2.00
4A2	$2 black, *blue, 1961*	25.00	3.00
4A3	$2 black, *dark yellow, 1962*	35.00	3.00
4A4	$2 black, *light yellow, 1963*	25.00	3.00
4A5	$2 black, *green, 1964*	25.00	3.00
4A6	$2 black, *1965*	25.00	3.00
4A7	$2 black, *yellow, 1966*	10.00	2.00
4A8	$2 black, *light green, 1967*	25.00	2.00
4A9	$2 black, *light yellow, 1968*	10.00	2.00
4A10	$3 black, *blue, 1969*	25.00	2.00
4A11	$3 black, *light yellow, 1970*	10.00	2.00
4A12	$3 black, *green, 1971*		3.00
4A13	$3 black, *light yellow, 1972*	10.00	2.00
4A14	$3 black, *light yellow, 1973*	9.00	2.00
4A15	$3 black, *1974*	10.00	2.00
4A16	$3 black, *pink, 1975*	8.00	2.00
4A17	$3 black, *gray, 1976*	6.00	1.00
4A18	$3 black, *red, 1977*	5.00	1.00
4A19	$3 black, *1978*	6.00	1.00
4A20	$3 black, *red, 1979*	7.00	1.00

1980-98

4A21	$6 black	8.00	1.00
4A22	$6 black, *light yellow, 1981*	9.00	1.00
4A23	$6 black, *blue, 1982*	5.00	.50
4A24	$6 black, *green, 1983*	10.00	1.00
4A25	$6 black, *light blue, 1984*	20.00	1.00
4A26	$6 black, *light blue, 1985*	12.00	1.00
4A27	$6 black, *light blue green, 1986*		2.00
4A28	$6 black, *1987*		2.00
4A29	$6 black, *light green, 1988*	5.00	.50
4A30	$6 black, *1989*		1.00
4A31	$6 black, *light green, 1990*	8.00	.50
4A32	$6 black, *light blue green, 1991*	5.00	.50
4A33	$6 black, *light green, 1992*		1.00
4A34	$6 black, *light pink, 1993*	5.00	.50
4A35	$6 black, *light blue, 1994*	5.00	.50
4A36	$6 black, *yellow, 1995*		1.00
4A37	$6 black, *pink, 1996*	5.00	.50
4A38	$6 black, *light blue, 1997*		.50
4A39	$6 black, *pink, 1998*	8.00	.50

TENNESSEE

Stamps are die cut self-adhesives and are numbered serially.

Cards include both license cost and a fee of 30c (Nos. 1-5), 50c (Nos. 6-13) or $1 (starting with No. 14).

Nos. 3, 5, 7-15 come as 3-part card.

Starting with No. 12, cards come in four parts as well.

1979 and 1980 issues are for resident and non-resident fees.

Unused values are for stamps on original computer card stub.

> **Catalogue values for all unused stamps in this section are for Never Hinged items.**

Artists: Dick Elliott, #1-2; Phillip Crowe, #3-4, 7, 17; Bob Gillespie, #5; Ken Schulz, #6; Allen Hughes, #8; Jimmy Stewart, #9; Ralph J. McDonald, #10, 18; Thomas Hirata, #11, 16; Jim Lamb, #12; Roger Cruwys, #13; Tom Freeman, #14; Richard Clifton, #15, 19; Bob Leslie, #20; Bethany Carter, #21; Beth Ann McMurray, #22; Nick Williamson, #23, 24.; J. Mefford, #25; Joshua Lester, #26-27; Lauren Pollard, #28; Kaydee Hankes, #29-30.

1979-2008

1	$2 Mallards		125.00	25.00
2	$5 Mallards		650.00	150.00
3	$2 Canvasbacks, *1980*		60.00	15.00
	3-part card		600.00	
4	$5 Canvasbacks, *1980*		275.00	75.00
5	$2 Wood ducks, *1981*		45.00	10.00
	3-part card		—	
6	$6 Canada geese, *1982*		55.00	15.00
7	$6 Pintails, *1983*		50.00	15.00
	3-part card		75.00	
8	$6 Black ducks, *1984*		50.00	12.00
	3-part card		75.00	
9	$6 Blue-winged teal, *1985*		20.00	7.00
	3-part card		50.00	
10	$6 Mallard, *1986*		15.00	5.00
	3-part card		60.00	
11	$6 Canada geese, *1987*		12.00	5.00
	3-part card		25.00	

Card exists with 2/28/88 expiration date rather than correct 2/29 date.

12	$6 Canvasbacks, *1988*		12.00	4.00
	3-part card		20.00	
	4-part card		20.00	
13	$6 Green-winged teal, *1989*		12.00	4.00
	3-part card		20.00	
	4-part card		20.00	
14	$12 Redheads, *1990*		18.00	4.00
	3-part card		25.00	
	4-part card		25.00	
15	$12 Mergansers, *1991*		18.00	4.00
	3-part card		22.00	
	4-part card		22.00	
16	$13 Wood ducks, *1992*		18.00	4.00
	4-part card		22.00	
17	$13 Pintails & decoy, *1993*		20.00	4.00
	4-part card		25.00	
18	$15 Mallard, *1994*		25.00	5.00
	4-part card		30.00	
19	$16 Ring-necked duck, *1995*		25.00	5.00
	4-part card		30.00	
20	$17 Black ducks, *1996*		35.00	5.00
	4-part card		40.00	

Starting with No. 21 stamps are perforated. Not required for hunting.

21	$10 Mallard, *1999*		15.00	2.50
22	$10 Bufflehead, *2000*		15.00	2.50
23	$10 Wood ducks, *2001*		15.00	2.50
24	$10 Green-winged teal, *2002*		13.50	2.50
25	$10 Canada geese, *2003*		13.50	2.50
26	$10 Wood ducks, *2004*		13.50	2.50
27	$10 Mallards, *2005*		13.50	2.50
28	$10 Canada goose, *2006*		13.50	2.50
29	$10 Harlequin, *2007*		12.00	2.50
30	$10 Wood ducks, *2008*		12.00	2.50

TEXAS

Printed in sheets of 10.
Nos. 1-4 are rouletted.
Stamps are numbered serially.

> **Catalogue values for all unused stamps in this section are for Never Hinged items.**

Artists: Larry Hayden, #1, 12; Ken Carlson, #2, 14; Maynard Reece, #3; David Maass, #4, 9, 15, 26; John Cowan, #5, 8; Herb Booth, #6, 25; Gary Moss, #7; Robert Bateman, #10; Daniel Smith, #11, 16; Jim Hautman, #13, 17, 22, 28; Phillip Crowe, #18; Robert Hautman, #19; Sherrie Russell Meline, #20, 23; John Dearman, #21; Scott and Stuart Gentling, #24; Bruce Miller, #27.

1981-2008

1	$5 Mallards		40.00	8.00
2	$5 Pintails, *1982*		25.00	5.00
3	$5 Widgeons, *1983*		125.00	18.00
4	$5 Wood ducks, *1984*		25.00	5.00
5	$5 Snow geese, *1985*		10.00	3.00
6	$5 Green-winged teal, *1986*		10.00	2.50
7	$5 White-fronted geese, *1987*		10.00	2.50
8	$5 Pintails, *1988*		10.00	2.50
9	$5 Mallards, *1989*		10.00	2.50
10	$5 American widgeons, *1990*		10.00	2.50
11	$7 Wood duck, *1991*		11.00	2.50
12	$7 Canada geese, *1992*		11.00	2.50
13	$7 Blue-winged teal, *1993*		11.00	2.50
14	$7 Shovelers, *1994*		11.00	2.50
15	$7 Buffleheads, *1995*		11.00	2.50

Beginning with No. 16, these stamps were sold only in booklets with seven other wildlife stamps and were not valid for hunting.

16	$3 Gadwalls, *1996*		75.00	
17	$3 Cinnamon teal, *1997*		65.00	
18	$3 Pintail, labrador retreiver, *1998*		55.00	
19	$3 Canvasbacks, *1999*		40.00	
20	$3 Hooded merganser, *2000*		30.00	
21	$3 Snow geese, *2001*		20.00	
22	$3 Redheads, *2002*		20.00	
23	$3 Mottled duck, *2003*		20.00	
24	$3 American goldeneye, *2004*		15.00	
25	$7 Mallards, *2005*		15.00	
26	$7 Green-winged teals, *2006*		15.00	
27	$7 Wood duck, *2007*		13.00	
28	$7 Pintails, *2008*		13.00	

No. 23 was issued in booklets with seven other wildlife stamps and was not valid for hunting.
Nos. 25-28 were issued in booklets with five other wildlife stamps and were not valid for hunting.

UTAH

Game Bird Stamps

For hunting game birds, including waterfowl. In 1951 No. A1 or No. 2A1 were required, in 1952 No. A3 or 2A2. No. A1 printed in booklet panes of 25, others in booklet panes of 10. Perforated.

A1 A2

1951

A1	A1	$3 brown, resident	*35.00*	*7.00*
A2		$15 red, non-resident	*150.00*	*50.00*

1952

A3	A2	$3 red, resident	*110.00*	
A4	A2	$15 blue, non-resident	*300.00*	*50.00*

Resident Fishing and Hunting Stamps

For hunting game birds, including waterfowl. Printed in sheets of 40. No. 2A1 printed on linen. Unused values are for stamps with deer tags attached at left.

No. 2A1 — UT-2A1

No. 2A2 — UT-2A2

1951-52

2A1	$5 blue		4.50	1.50
2A2	$5 green, *1952*		4.50	1.50

Waterfowl Issues

Printed in sheets of 30 or in booklet panes of 5 (starting in 1990). No. 11 issued in sheets of 9. Stamps are numbered serially.

> **Catalogue values for all unused stamps in this section are for Never Hinged items.**

Artists: Leon Parsons, #1; Arthur Anderson, #2; David Chapple, #3; Jim Morgan, #4; Daniel Smith, #5; Robert Steiner, #6-12.

1986-97

1	$3.30 Whistling swans		10.00	3.00
2	$3.30 Pintails, *1987*		8.00	3.00
3	$3.30 Mallards, *1988*		8.00	2.50
4	$3.30 Canada geese, *1989*		8.00	2.50
5	$3.30 Canvasbacks, perf. 4 sides, *1990*		8.00	
a.	Booklet single, with 2-part tab		8.00	2.50
6	$3.30 Tundra swans, perf. 4 sides, *1991*		12.00	
a.	Booklet single, with 2-part tab		12.00	2.50
7	$3.30 Pintails, perf. 4 sides, *1992*		10.00	
a.	Booklet single, with 2-part tab		10.00	2.50
8	$3.30 Canvasbacks, perf. 4 sides, *1993*		10.00	
a.	Booklet single, with 2-part tab		10.00	2.50
9	$3.30 Chesapeake Retriever and ducks, perf. 4 sides, *1994*		85.00	
a.	Booklet single, with 2-part tab		85.00	2.50
10	$3.30 Green-winged teal, *1995*		12.00	
a.	Booklet single, with 2-part tab		12.00	2.50
b.	Governor's edition		130.00	
11	$7.50 White-fronted goose, *1996*		15.00	2.50
a.	$97.50 Governor's edition		125.00	

Redheads: a, Male, serial # at UL. b, Female, serial # at LL.

12	Pair, *1997*		40.00	
a.-b.	$7.50 Any single		14.00	2.50
c.	$97.50 Governor's Edition		110.00	

No. 12c is No. 12 without the central perforations. The denomination appears only in the upper right corner. The bottom inscription has Governor's Edition plus a serial number.

VERMONT

Printed in sheets of 30.

> **Catalogue values for all unused stamps in this section are for Never Hinged items.**

Artists: Jim Killen, #1-4; Richard Plasschaert, #5-8; Reed Prescott, #9, 11; Robert Mullen, #10; J. Collins, #12; George Lockwood; #13-17; Richard E. Bishop, #18-21; Heather Forcier, #22-23.

1986-2008

1	$5 Wood ducks	12.00	4.00
2	$5 Common goldeneyes, *1987*	12.00	3.00
3	$5 Black ducks, *1988*	12.00	2.50
4	$5 Canada geese, *1989*	12.00	2.50
5	$5 Green-winged teal, *1990*	12.00	2.50
6	$5 Hooded mergansers, *1991*	12.00	2.50
7	$5 Snow geese, *1992*	12.00	2.50
8	$5 Mallards, *1993*	12.00	2.50
9	$5 Ring-necked duck, *1994*	12.00	2.50
10	$5 Bufflehead, *1995*	12.00	2.50
11	$5 Lesser scaup, *1996*	12.00	2.50
12	$5 Pintails, *1997*	12.00	2.50
13	$5 Blue-winged teal, *1998*	12.00	2.50
14	$5 Canvasbacks, *1999*	12.00	2.50
15	$5 Widgeons, *2000*	10.00	2.50
16	$5 Oldsquaws, *2001*	10.00	2.50
17	$5 Greater scaups, *2002*	10.00	2.50
18	$5 Mallards, *2003*	10.00	2.50
19	$5 Pintails, *2004*	10.00	2.50
20	$5 Canvasbacks, *2005*	10.00	2.50
21	$5 Canada goose, *2006*	10.00	2.50
22	$5 Ring-necked duck, *2007*	7.00	2.50
23	$7.50 Harlequin, *2008*	12.00	2.50

VIRGINIA

Printed in booklet panes of 10 and/or sheets of 30.
Stamps are numbered serially.

Catalogue values for all unused stamps in this section are for Never Hinged items.

Artists: Ronald Louque, #1; Arthur LeMay, #2; Louis Frisino, #3; Robert Leslie, #4, 11; Carl Knuth, #5, 12, 17; Bruce Miller, #6; Francis Sweet, #7; Richard Clifton, #8; Wilhelm Goebel, #9; Roger Cruwys, #10; Tim Donovan, #13-14, 21-22; Jim Wilson, #15-16; Guy Crittenden, #18-20, 23-24; Spike Knuth, #25-26.

1988-2008

1	$5 Mallards, serial Nos. 1-40,000	13.00	2.50
	Booklet pair with L & R selvage, serial Nos. above 40,000	27.50	
2	$5 Canada geese, serial Nos. 1-40,000, *1989*	12.00	2.50
	Booklet pair with L & R selvage, serial Nos. above 40,000	25.00	
3	$5 Wood ducks, serial Nos. 1-20,000, *1990*	12.00	2.50
	Booklet pair with L & R selvage, serial Nos. above 20,000	24.00	
4	$5 Canvasbacks, serial Nos. 1-20,000, *1991*	12.00	2.50
	Booklet pair with L & R selvage, serial Nos. above 20,000	24.00	
5	$5 Buffleheads, serial Nos. 1-20,000, *1992*	12.00	2.50
	Booklet pair with L & R selvage, serial Nos. above 20,000	24.00	
6	$5 Black ducks, serial Nos. 1-20,000, *1993*	12.00	2.50
	Booklet pair with L & R selvage, serial Nos. above 20,000	24.00	
7	$5 Lesser scaup, *1994*	12.00	2.50
	Booklet pair with L & R selvage	24.00	
8	$5 Snow geese, *1995*	12.00	2.50
	Booklet pair with L & R selvage	24.00	

9	$5 Hooded mergansers, *1996*	12.00	2.50
10	($5) Pintail, Labrador retriever, *1997*	12.00	2.50
11	$5 Mallards, *1998*	12.00	2.50
12	$5 Green-winged teal, *1999*	12.00	2.50
13	$5 Mallards, *2000*	12.00	2.50
14	$5 Blue-winged teal, *2001*	10.00	2.50
15	$5 Canvasbacks, *2002*	10.00	2.50
16	$5 Tundra Swan, *2003*	10.00	2.50
17	$5 American goldeneye, *2004*	10.00	2.50
18	$9.75 Wood ducks, perf. *2005*	13.00	2.50
19	$9.75 Wood ducks, rouletted, with tab *2005*	13.00	2.50
20	$9.75 Wood ducks, self-adhesive, die cut 2005	14.00	2.50
21	$9.75 Black ducks, perf. *2006*	13.00	2.50
22	$9.75 Black ducks, self-adhesive, die cut 2006	14.00	2.50
23	$10 Canada geese, perf. *2007*	13.50	2.50
24	$10 Canada geese, self-adhesive, die cut 2007	13.50	2.50
25	$10 Wigeons, perf., *2008*	13.50	2.50
26	$10 Wigeons, self-adhesive, die cut, 2008	13.50	2.50

Starting with 2005, Virginia stamps are mandatory for hunting.

WASHINGTON

Printed in booklet panes of 1 and sheets of 30.
Stamps are numbered serially.
Booklet panes starting with No. 7 without staple holes were sold to collectors.

Catalogue values for all unused stamps in this section are for Never Hinged items.

Artists: Keith Warrick, #1; Ray Nichol, #2; Robert Bateman, #3; Maynard Reece, #4; Thomas Quinn, #5; Ronald Louque, #6-7; Phillip Crowe, #8; Fred Thomas, #9; David Hagenbaumer, #10; Cynthie Fisher, #11; Greg Beecham, #12; A. Young, #13; Robert Steiner, #14-16, 22-24; Adam Grimm, #17; Don Nicholson Miller, #18-19; Dan Smith, #20-21.

1986-2008

1	$5 Mallards, Nos. 1-60,000	9.00	
	Booklet pane of 1, Nos. 60,001-160,000	12.50	4.00
2	$5 Canvasbacks, Nos. 1-24,000, *1987*	12.00	
	Booklet pane of 1, Nos. 24,001-124,000	12.00	3.00
3	$5 Harlequin, Nos. 1-60,000, *1988*	9.00	
	Booklet pane of 1, Nos. 60,001-160,000	10.00	3.00
4	$5 American widgeons, Nos. 1-60,000, *1989*	9.00	
	Booklet pane of 1, Nos. 60,001-160,000	10.00	2.50
5	$5 Pintails & sour duck, Nos. 1-60,000, *1990*	9.00	
	Booklet pane of 1, Nos. 60,001-160,000	10.00	2.50
6	$5 Wood duck, Nos. 1-30,000, *1991*	12.00	
	Booklet pane of 1, Nos. above 30,000	12.00	4.00
7	$6 Wood duck, Nos. 100,000-130,000, *1991*	10.00	
	Booklet pane of 1, Nos. above 130,000	10.00	2.50
8	$6 Labrador puppy & Canada geese, Nos. 1-30,000, *1992*	14.00	
	Booklet pane of 1, Nos. above 30,000	14.00	2.50
9	$6 Snow geese, Nos. 1-30,000, *1993*	10.00	
	Booklet pane of 1, Nos. above 30,000	10.00	2.50
10	$6 Black brant, Nos. 1-30,000, *1994*	14.00	
	Booklet pane of 1, Nos. above 30,000	14.00	2.50
11	$6 Mallards, Nos. 1-30,000, *1995*	12.00	
	Booklet pane of 1, Nos. above 30,000	12.00	2.50
12	$6 Redheads, Nos. 1-25,050, *1996*	22.50	
	Booklet pane of 1, Nos. above 25,050	22.50	2.50
13	$6 Canada geese, Nos. 9600001-9625050, *1997*	12.00	
	Bklt. pane of 1, Nos. above 9625050	12.00	2.50
14	$6 Barrow's goldeneye Nos. 1-25,050, *1998*	15.00	
	Bklt. pane of 1, Nos. 25,051-27,050	15.00	2.50
15	$6 Bufflehead, *1999*	15.00	
a.	Bklt. pane of 1	15.00	2.50
16	$6 Canada geese, mallard, widgeon, *2000*	25.00	
a.	Bklt. pane of 1	25.00	2.50
17	$6 Mallards, *2001*	15.00	
a.	Bklt. pane of 1	15.00	2.50
18	$10 Green-winged teal, *2002*	17.50	
a.	Souvenir sheet of 1	17.50	2.50
19	$10 Pintails, *2003*	20.00	
a.	Souvenir sheet of 1	20.00	2.50
20	$10 Canada goose, *2004*	15.00	
a.	Souvenir sheet of 1	15.00	2.50
21	$10 Barrow's goldeneyes, *2005*	15.00	
a.	Souvenir sheet of 1	15.00	2.50

22	$10 Widgeons, mallard, *2006*	14.00	
a.	Souvenir sheet of 1	15.00	2.50
23	$10 Ross's goose, *2007*	13.50	
a.	Souvenir sheet of 1	15.00	2.50
24	$10 Wood ducks, *2008*	13.50	
a.	Souvenir sheet of 1	15.00	2.50

Nos. 19-24 not required for hunting.

WEST VIRGINIA

Printed in sheets of 30 and booklet panes of 5. All booklet stamps have straight edges at sides. Starting in 1990, booklet stamps are numbered serially. Some, but not all, of the 1988 booklet stamps are numbered serially. Stamps from sheets are not numbered serially.

Catalogue values for all unused stamps in this section are for Never Hinged items.

Artists: Daniel Smith, #1-2; Steven Dillard, #3-4; Ronald Louque, #5-6; Louis Frisino, #7-8; Robert Leslie, #9-10; Thomas Hirata, #11-12; Phillip Crowe, #13-14; Richard Clifton, #15-16; Fran Sweet, #17-18; Karl Badgley, #19-20.

1987-96

1	$5 Canada geese, resident	17.50	8.00
	Booklet single with tab at top	75.00	
2	$5 Canada geese, non-resident	16.00	8.00
	Booklet single with tab at top	75.00	
3	$5 Wood ducks, resident, *1988*	10.00	4.00
	Booklet single with tab at top, no serial number	40.00	
a.	Booklet single with serial number on reverse	60.00	4.00
4	$5 Wood ducks, non-resident, *1988*	12.00	4.00
	Booklet single with tab at top, no serial number	40.00	
a.	Booklet single with serial number on reverse	60.00	4.00
5	$5 Decoys, resident, *1989*	13.00	3.00
	Booklet single with tab at top	35.00	
a.	Governor's edition	80.00	
6	$5 Decoys, non-resident, *1989*	18.00	3.00
	Booklet single with tab at top	35.00	
a.	Governor's edition	80.00	

Nos. 5a and 6a were available only in sheets of 30 through a sealed bid auction.

7	$5 Labrador retriever & decoy, resident, *1990*	20.00	
a.	Booklet single	15.00	3.00
8	$5 Labrador retriever & decoy, non-resident, *1990*	22.00	
a.	Booklet single	15.00	3.00
9	$5 Mallards, resident, *1991*	12.00	
a.	Booklet single	12.00	2.50
10	$5 Mallards, non-resident, *1991*	12.00	
a.	Booklet single	12.00	2.50
b.	Sheet, 3 each #9-10	50.00	

No. 10b is numbered serially; exists imperf. without serial numbers.

11	$5 Canada geese, resident, *1992*	12.00	
a.	Booklet single	12.00	2.50
12	$5 Canada geese, non-resident, *1992*	12.00	
a.	Booklet single	12.00	2.50
13	$5 Pintails, resident, *1993*	12.00	
a.	Booklet single	12.00	2.50
14	$5 Pintails, non-resident, *1993*	12.00	
a.	Booklet single	12.00	2.50
15	$5 Green-winged teal, resident, *1994*	12.00	
a.	Booklet single	12.00	2.50
16	$5 Green-winged teal, non-resident, *1994*	12.00	
a.	Booklet single	12.00	2.50
17	$5 Mallards, resident, *1995*	12.00	
a.	Booklet single	12.00	2.50
18	$5 Mallards, non-resident, *1995*	12.00	
a.	Booklet single	12.00	2.50
19	$5 Widgeons, resident, *1996*	12.00	
a.	Booklet single	12.00	2.50
20	$5 Widgeons, non-resident, *1996*	12.00	
a.	Booklet single	12.00	2.50

WISCONSIN

Printed in sheets of 10. Starting in 1980 the left side of the sheet has an agent tab and a numbered tab, the right side a numbered tab.

> **Catalogue values for all unused stamps in this section are for Never Hinged items.**

Artists: Owen Gromme, #1; Rockne (Rocky) Knuth, #2, 6; Martin Murk, #3; Timothy Schultz, #4, 29; William Koelpin, #5; Michael James Riddet, #7, 15, 26; Greg Alexander, #8, 20; Don Moore, #9, 17, 23; Al Kraayvanger, #10; Richard Timm, #11; Rick Kelley, #12; Daniel Renn Pierce, #13; Terry Doughty, #14, 25, 28; Frank Middlestadt, #16, 22; Les Didler, #18, 21, 24; Sam Timm, #19; Arthur Anderson, #27, 30; Brian Kuether, #31.

1978-2008

1	$3.25 Wood ducks		100.00	9.00
2	$3.25 Buffleheads, rouletted, *1979*		20.00	6.00
3	$3.25 Widgeons, *1980*		12.00	2.50
	With tab		15.00	
4	$3.25 Lesser Scaup, *1981*		10.00	2.50
	With tab		13.00	
5	$3.25 Pintails, *1982*		9.00	2.50
	With numbered tab		9.00	
	With agent's and numbered tab		10.00	
6	$3.25 Blue-winged teal, *1983*		9.00	2.50
	With numbered tab		9.00	
	With agent's and numbered tab		10.00	
7	$3.25 Hooded merganser, *1984*		9.00	2.50
	With numbered tab		9.00	
	With agent's and numbered tab		10.00	
8	$3.25 Lesser scaup, *1985*		12.00	2.50
	With numbered tab		12.00	
	With agent's and numbered tab		15.00	
9	$3.25 Canvasbacks, *1986*		15.00	2.50
	With numbered tab		15.00	
	With agent's and numbered tab		21.00	
10	$3.25 Canada geese, *1987*		9.00	2.50
	With numbered tab		9.00	
	With agent's and numbered tab		10.00	
11	$3.25 Hooded merganser, *1988*		9.00	2.50
	With numbered tab		9.00	
	With agent's and numbered tab		10.00	
12	$3.25 Common goldeneye, *1989*		9.00	2.50
	With numbered tab		9.00	
	With agent's and numbered tab		10.00	
13	$3.25 Redheads, *1990*		9.00	2.50
	With numbered tab		9.00	
	With agent's and numbered tab		10.00	
14	$5.25 Green-winged teal, *1991*		9.00	2.50
	With numbered tab		9.00	
	With agent's and numbered tab		10.00	
15	$5.25 Tundra swans, *1992*		10.00	2.50
	With numbered tab		10.00	
	With agent's and numbered tab		12.00	
16	$5.25 Wood ducks, *1993*		10.00	2.50
	With numbered tab		10.00	
	With agent's and numbered tab		12.00	
17	$5.25 Pintails, *1994*		10.00	2.50
	With numbered tab		10.00	
	With agent's and numbered tab		12.00	
18	$5.25 Mallards, *1995*		10.00	2.50
	With numbered tab		10.00	
	With agent's and numbered tabs		12.00	
19	($5.25) Green-winged teal, *1996*		10.00	2.50
	With numbered tab		10.00	
	With agent's and numbered tabs		12.00	
20	($7) Canada geese, *1997*		15.00	2.50
	With numbered tab		15.00	
	With agent's and numbered tabs		17.00	
21	$7 Snow goose, *1998*		15.00	2.50
	With numbered tab		15.00	
	With agent's and numbered tabs		17.00	
22	$7 Greater scaups, *1999*		12.00	2.50
23	$7 Canvasbacks, *2000*		12.00	2.50
24	$7 Common goldeneyes, *2001*		14.00	2.50
25	$7 Shovelers, *2002*		11.00	2.50
26	$7 Ring-necked ducks, *2003*		11.00	2.50
27	$7 Pintail, *2004*		11.00	2.50
28	$7 Wood ducks, *2005*		11.00	2.50
29	$7 Green-winged teals, *2006*		9.00	2.50
30	$7 Redheads, *2007*		9.00	2.50
31	$7 Canvasbacks, *2008*		9.00	2.50

Nos. 26-31 not required for hunting.

WYOMING

Issued in panes of 5. Required to fish as well as to hunt all small and big game, including waterfowl. Stamps are numbered serially.

> **Catalogue values for all unused stamps in this section are for Never Hinged items.**

Artists: From photo by Luroy Parker, #1; Robert Kusserow, #2; Dan Andrews, #3; Ted Feeley, #4; Clark Ostergaard, #5; Dave Wade, #6, 8, 10, 13, 17; Connie J. Robinson, #7; Sarah Rogers, #9; James Brooks, #11; Peter Eades, #12; D. Enright, #14; Garth Hegeson, #15; Nick Reitzel, #16; Brent Todd, #18; Paul Kay, #19; R. Piskorski, #20; Dustin Van Wechel, #21; Ron Staker, #22; Scott Greenig, #23; Art Biro, #24; Jenny Forge, #25.

No. 1 is in vertical format. All others are horizontal.

1984-2008

1	$5 Meadowlark		60.00	6.00
2	$5 Canada geese, *1985*		50.00	5.00
3	$5 Antelope, *1986*		90.00	8.00
4	$5 Grouse, *1987*		85.00	8.00
5	$5 Trout, *1988*		100.00	12.00
6	$5 Mule deer, *1989*		175.00	15.00
7	$5 Bear, *1990*		50.00	5.00
8	$5 Rams, *1991*		45.00	3.50
9	$5 Bald eagle, *1992*		35.00	3.50
10	$5 Elk, *1993*		25.00	3.50
11	$5 Bobcat, *1994*		22.00	3.50
12	$5 Moose, *1995*		22.00	3.50
13	$5 Turkey, *1996*		22.00	3.00
14	$5 Mountain goats, *1997*		22.00	3.00
15	$5 Trumpeter swan, *1998*		20.00	3.00
16	$5 Brown trout, *1999*		20.00	3.00
17	$5 Buffalo, *2000*		20.00	3.00
18	$10 White-tailed deer, *2001*		20.00	5.00
19	$10 River otters, *2002*		20.00	5.00
20	$10 Mountain bluebirds, *2003*		17.50	5.00
21	$10 Mountain lion, *2004*		17.50	5.00
22	$10.50 Burrowing owls, *2005*		16.00	5.00
23	$10.50 Cut-throat trout, *2006*		16.00	5.00
24	$10.50 Blue grouses, *2007*		16.00	5.00
25	$12.50 Black-footed ferret, *2008*		21.00	5.00

INDIAN RESERVATIONS

Stamps for other reservations exist and will be listed after more information is received about them.

CHEYENNE RIVER INDIAN RESERVATION

South Dakota
Birds and Small Game Stamps

Nos. A1-A2 issued in booklet panes of 6, rouletted. Nos. A3-A4 issued in booklet panes of 5, perforated, self-adhesive. Nos. A5-A6 issued in booklet panes of 5, perforated.

A1

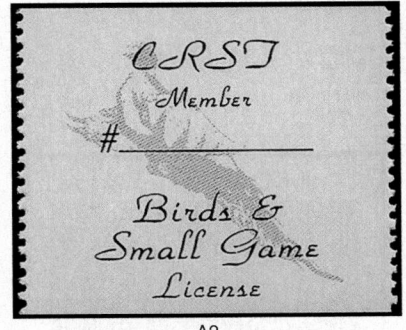

A2

A1	A1	black, *light yellow*, member		4,000.	350.
A2	A1	black, *yellow*, non-member		1,500.	150.

Nos. A1-A2 probably issued starting in 1984.

> **Catalogue values for all unused stamps in this section, from this point to the end, are for Never Hinged items.**

A3	A2	black, *yellow*, member		25.00	10.00
A4	A2	black, *yellow*, non-member		45.00	15.00
A5	A2	black, *light yellow*, member		13.00	5.00
A6	A2	black, *light yellow*, non-member		27.50	10.00

Nos. A3-A4 issued starting in 1989. Nos. A5-A6 issued starting in 1992.

Waterfowl Stamps

Issued starting in 1993 in panes of 5. Perforated.

> Catalogue values for all unused stamps in this section are for Never Hinged items.

1	black, *light yellow*, member	15.00	5.00
2	black *light yellow*, non-member	27.50	10.00

COLVILLE INDIAN RESERVATION

Washington
Bird Stamps

Required by non-tribal members to hunt birds, including waterfowl. Stamps are die cut, self-adhesive. No. 2 is numbered serially in red.

> Catalogue values for all unused stamps in this section are for Never Hinged items.

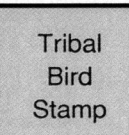

	Tribal Bird Stamp	1991 Tribal Bird Stamp No. 0011 $20.00
	A1	A2

1990-91

1	A1	black, *yellow*	—
2	A2 $20	black, *yellow*, 1992	—

CROW INDIAN RESERVATION

Montana
Waterfowl Stamps

Issued in panes of 5 stamps (4 each No. 1, 1 No. 1a). Die cut, self-adhesive. Numbered serially in red.

> Catalogue values for all unused stamps in this section are for Never Hinged items.

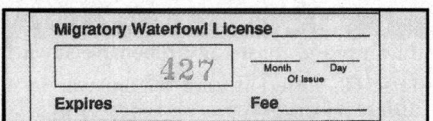

1992

1	blue	110.00	40.00
a.	Inscribed "Apr. 30, 199_"	300.00	75.00

Stamps without serial numbers exist. Some may have been issue to hunters during an abbreviated 1993 season.

CROW CREEK SIOUX INDIAN RESERVATION

South Dakota
Non-Indian Small Game Hunting Stamps

Issued 1961-64. The 1961 fee was $2.50. No example is recorded. The 1962 stamps were changed by hand for use in 1963 and 1964. No example of the 1964 stamp is recorded.

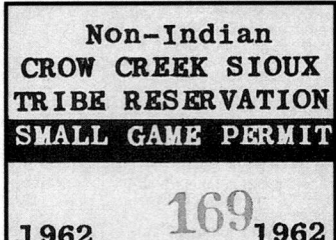

1962-63

2	$5 black		24,000.	—
3	$5 black, *1963*		—	—

Waterfowl Stamps

Fees: $10, reservation resident, non-tribal member; $30, South Dakota resident; $65, non-South Dakota resident.

> Catalogue values for all unused stamps in this section, from this point to the end, are for Never Hinged items.

1989

5	$10 black	400.	150.
6	$30 black	9,000.	1,000.
7	$65 black	1,250.	350.

1990

8	$10 black	250.	100.
9	$30 black	150.	
10	$65 black	850.	300.

Fees: $5, tribal member; $15, affiliate, reservation resident; $30 ($35), South Dakota resident/non-resident daily use; $75 ($100), South Dakota resident/non-resident season.

1994

11	$5 green	95.00	15.00
12	$15 blue	125.00	
13	$30 red	150.00	
a.	$25 red (error)	—	
14	$75 red	225.00	65.00

1995

15	$5 green	50.00	10.00
16	$15 blue	75.00	
17	$30 red	110.00	
18	$75 red	125.00	40.00

1996

19	$5 green	27.50	10.00
20	$15 blue	45.00	
21	$35 red	75.00	
22	$100 red	125.00	35.00

1997

23	$5 green	12.00
24	$15 blue	35.00
25	$35 red	85.00
26	$75 red	190.00

No. 25 is inscribed $75, but sold for $35.

1998

27	$5 green	12.00
28	$15 blue	35.00
29	$35 red	85.00
30	$75 red	190.00

1999

31	$5 green	12.00
32	$15 blue	35.00
33	$35 red	85.00
34	$75 red	190.00

Waterfowl Stamps

Fees: $5, tribal member; $15, $20, $30, affiliate; $35, $40, non-resident daily use; $75, $100, non-resident season.

2000

35	$5 green	75.00	—
36	$15 blue	75.00	—
37	$35 red	75.00	—
38	$75 red	75.00	—

2001

39	$5 green	100.00	—
40	$20 blue	100.00	—
41	$40 red	100.00	—
42	$100 red	100.00	—

2002

43	$5 green	125.00	—
44	$20 blue	125.00	—
45	$40 red	125.00	—
46	$100 red	125.00	—

2003

47	$5 green	—	—
48	$30 blue	—	—
49	$40 red	—	—
50	$100 red	—	—

2004

52	$30 blue	—	—
53	$40 red	—	—
54	$100 red	—	—

In 2001, $15 affiliate, $35 non-resident daily use and $75 non-resident season stamps were printed. It is not known whether these stamps with incorrect fees were sold. Value, set $200.

A $5 tribal stamp was printed in 2004 but no examples are known. Four stamps for 2005 were printed but no examples are known.

Fees: $10, tribal member; $25, affiliate; $40, non-resident daily use; $100, non-resident season.

2006

59	$10 blue	—	—
60	$25 green	—	—
61	$40 red	—	—
62	$100 red	—	—

Sportsmen's Stamps

For hunting game including waterfowl.

Fees: $10, tribal member; $25, reservation resident, non-tribal member; $100, South Dakota resident; $250, non-South Dakota resident.

Used values are for signed stamps.

Catalogue values for all unused stamps in this section are for Never Hinged items.

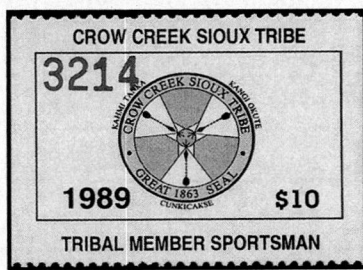

1989

A1	$10 black		450.	100.
A2	$25 black		1,150.	300.
A3	$100 black		450.	75.
A4	$250 black		450.	150.

1990

A5	$10 black		500.	100.
A6	$25 black		650.	150.
A7	$100 black		275.	125.
A8	$250 black		400.	150.

Goose Stamps

Fees: $5, tribal member; $10, $15, $20, affiliate; $50, non-resident.

1998

2A1	$5 green		—	—
2A2	$10 blue		—	—
2A3	$50 red		—	—

1999

2A4	$5 green		100.00	—
2A5	$10 blue		100.00	—
2A6	$50 red		100.00	—

2000

2A7	$5 green		60.00	—
2A8	$10 blue		60.00	—
2A9	$50 red		60.00	—

2001

2A10	$5 green		60.00	—
2A11	$10 blue		60.00	—
2A12	$50 red		60.00	—

2002

2A13	$5 green		150.00	—
2A14	$15 blue		150.00	—
2A15	$50 red		150.00	—

2003

2A16	$5 green		150.00	—
2A17	$20 blue		150.00	—
2A18	$50 red		150.00	—

2004

2A21	$50 red		—	—

In 1997, $5 tribal member, $10 affiliate, and $50 non-resident stamps were printed, but the season was canceled. Value, set $400.

Tribal member and affiliate stamps were printed for 2004 but no examples are known. In 2005, three stamps were printed but no examples are known.

Fees: $10, tribal member; $25, affiliate; $75, non-resident.

2006

2A25	$10 blue		—	—
2A26	$25 green		—	—
2A27	$75 red		—	—

FLATHEAD INDIAN RESERVATION

Montana
Bird or Fish Stamps

The 1988 stamp was printed in booklet panes of 10. Starting in 1989, printed in booklet panes of 5 stamps se-tenant with 5 stamps marked "Duplicate." Numbered serially in red. Rouletted.

Catalogue values for all unused stamps in this section are for Never Hinged items.

1987-90

1	$10 black		1,000.	350.00
1A	$10 black, *1988*		850.00	275.00
2	$10 blue, *1989*		16.00	5.00
3	$10 blue, *1990*		16.00	5.00

Joint Bird License Stamps

Printed in booklet panes of 10. Die cut, self-adhesive. Numbered serially.

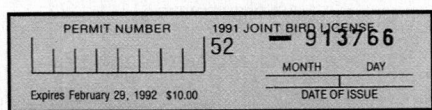

1991

4	$10 black, *green*		10.50	5.00

Bird License Stamps

Printed in booklet panes of 10. Die cut, self-adhesive. Numbered serially.

1992-2000

5	$12 black, *rose*, season		10.50	5.00
6	$12 black, *salmon*, 3-day		9.50	5.00
7	$12 black, *dark green*, season, *1993*		8.00	4.00
8	$12 black, *dark blue*, 3-day, *1993*		7.50	4.00
9	$12 black, *blue*, season, *1994*		8.00	4.00
10	$12 black, *orange*, 3-day, *1994*		7.00	3.00
11	$12 black, *yellow*, resident, *1995*		8.00	3.00
12	$55 black, *pale blue green*, non-resident, *1995*		17.50	9.00
13	$12 black, *turquoise*, resident, *1996*		11.00	3.00
14	$55 black, *pale orange*, non-resident, *1996*		18.00	15.00
15	$12 black, *pale yellow*, resident, *1997*		10.00	3.00
16	$55 black, *pale blue green*, non-resident, *1997*		11.00	
17	$13 black, *turquoise*, resident, *1998*		12.00	3.00
18	$56 black, *blue*, non-resident, *1998*		12.00	3.00
19	$13 black, *orange*, resident, *1999*		10.00	3.00
20	$56 black, *red*, non-resident, *1999*		10.00	3.00
21	$13 black, *yellow*, reservation, *2000*		12.00	3.00
22	$14 black, *green*, resident, *2000*		12.00	3.00
23	$110 black, *pink*, out-of-state, *2000*		12.00	3.00

FORT BERTHOLD INDIAN RESERVATION

North Dakota
Small Game Stamps

Stamps issued before 1990 may exist.
Issued in booklet panes of 6 stamps and 6 tabs. Required for hunting small game including waterfowl.
Values are for stamps with tabs. Fees varied, usually $6 for tribe members and $20-$30 for non-members.
Stamps are numbered serially.

Catalogue values for all unused stamps in this section are for Never Hinged items.

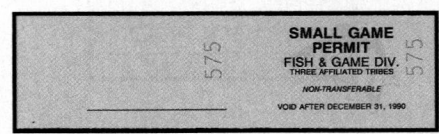

1990-98
Rouletted

A6	black, *pink*		85.00	25.00
A7	black, *green*, *1991*		80.00	
A8	black, *pink*, *1992*		80.00	
A9	black, *blue*, *1993*		175.00	
A10	black, *pink*, *1994*		70.00	
A11	black, *pink*, *1995*		100.00	25.00
A12	black, *green*, *1996*		57.50	
A13	black, *light green*, *1997*		50.00	12.00
A14	black, *green*, *1998*		30.00	

Waterfowl Stamps

Stamps issued before 1990 may exist.
Issued in booklet panes of 6 stamps and 6 tabs. Required for non-member waterfowl hunters only.
Values are for stamps with tabs.
Fees varied, usually $20-$30.
Stamps are numbered serially.

Catalogue values for all unused stamps in this section are for Never Hinged items.

1990-2000
Rouletted

2A6	black		2,500.	
2A7	black, *blue*, *1991*		850.00	
2A8	black, *yellow*, #1-60, *1992*		3,500.	
2A9	black, *yellow*, #61-120, *1993*		650.00	
2A10	black, *green*, #1-60, *1994*		625.00	
2A11	black, *green*, #61-120, *1995*		275.00	50.00
2A12	black, *green*, #121-198, *1996*		225.00	
2A13	black, *light green*, #199-276, *1997*		250.00	
2A14	black, *light green*, #277-, *1998*		300.00	
2A15	black, *light green*, #355-432, *1999*		300.00	
2A16	black, *light green*, #433-588, *2000*		250.00	

FORT PECK INDIAN RESERVATION

Montana
Stamps issued before 1975 may exist.

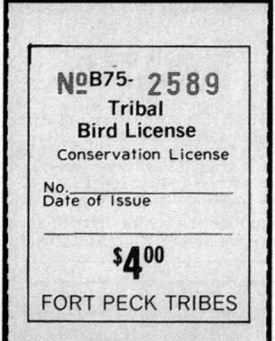

1975-78

		Rouletted	
2	$4 black		1,500.
3	$4 black, *1976*		100.
a.	Double impression		10,000.
4	$4 black, *1977*		18,000.
5	$5 black, *orange, 1978*		250.

JICARILLA APACHE INDIAN RESERVATION

New Mexico
Wildlife Stamp
Believed to have been issued starting in 1988. Issued in booklet panes of 4. Numbered serially. Rouletted.

> **Catalogue values for all unused stamps in this section are for Never Hinged items.**

1	$5 black & gold, *blue*	12.00

LAKE TRAVERSE (SISSETON-WAHPETON) INDIAN RESERVATION

South Dakota-North Dakota
Waterfowl Stamps
No examples are recorded of stamps from 1987-1990. No. 1 is die cut. Nos. 6, 8-9 are die cut, self-adhesive. No. 7 issued in booklet panes of 5, rouletted, numbered serially in red.

A1

A2

A3

A4

1986-2000

1	A1	green	250.00	75.00

> **Catalogue values for all unused stamps in this section, from this point to the end, are for Never Hinged items.**

6	A2	black, *bright green, 1991*	125.00	
7	A3	Wood duck, *1992*	15.00	
8	A2	black, *bright red, 1993*	25.00	
9	A4	black, *yellow orange, 1994*	7.50	4.00

Inscribed SWST

10	A4	black, *red orange, 1995*	12.00	4.00
11	A4	black, *blue, 1996*	10.00	4.00
12	A4	black, *bright green, 1997*	11.00	3.00
13	A4	black, *red, 1998*	40.00	
14	A4	black, *orange, 1999*	10.00	
15	A4	black, *orange, 2000*	35.00	

LOWER BRULE INDIAN RESERVATION

South Dakota
Waterfowl Stamps
Serial Nos. are in red. Year and fee are written by hand or typewritten on each stamp. The $5 fee was for for non-members and non-Indians. There was a $2.50 fee for tribal members but no examples of these stamps are recorded.
Numbers have been reserved for the $2.50 stamps.
Since no year is on an unused stamp, they are listed under the first year only.

1962-70

2	$5 black	—
4	$5 black, *1963*	—
6	$5 black, *1964*	3,500.
8	$5 black, *1965*	3,500.
10	$5 black, *1966*	3,250.
12	$5 black, *1967*	2,950.
14	$5 black, *1968*	2,850.
18	$5 black, *1969*	5,500.

1969-71

20	$5 black	6,500.
24	$5 black, *1971*	—
26	$5 black, *1972*	—

Migratory Bird Hunting and Conservation Stamps
Issued in panes of 20.
All stamps have serial number on reverse.

> **Catalogue values for all unused stamps in this section, from this point to the end, are for Never Hinged items.**

1995

27	$5 green, tribal member	7.00
28	$5 orange brown, resident deeded land owner / operator	7.00
29	$5 blue, resident government employee	7.00
30	$10 red, non-tribal S.D. resident	12.00
31	$10 purple, non-resident, out of state	12.00

1996

32	$5 multi, tribal / resident	7.00
33	$10 multi, non-tribal S.D. resident	12.00
34	$10 multi, non-resident, out of state	12.00

1997

35	$5 multi, tribal / resident	7.00
36	$10 multi, non-tribal S.D. resident	12.00
37	$10 multi, non-resident, out of state	12.00

Nos. 38-40 have been reserved for 1998 stamps which were printed, but use of which has not yet been verified.

1999

41	$5 multi, tribal / resident	7.00
42	$10 multi, non-tribal S. D. resident	14.00
43	$10 multi, non-resident, out of state	14.00

PINE RIDGE (OGLALA SIOUX) INDIAN RESERVATION

South Dakota
Waterfowl Stamps
Nos. 1-3 issued in booklet panes of 5, numbered serially in red.
No. 2 perforated, others rouletted.

A1

A2

MEMBER 1993-94

OGLALA SIOUX TRIBE   WATER FOWL STAMP

0777

A3

1	A1	$4 black		350.00

Earliest known use of No. 1 is 1988.

Catalogue values for all unused stamps in this section, from this point to the end, are for Never Hinged items.

2	A2	$4 black, perforated	15.00
3	A3	$4 Canada geese, *1992*	11.00

$6 stamps picturing Canada geese were produced and sold for the 1993 season. The same stamp was rubber hand-stamped for the 1994 season. However, there was no hunting season those years. Value, each $15.

ROSEBUD INDIAN RESERVATION

South Dakota
Tribal Game Bird Stamps

Nos. 1, 3-4 have red serial number. Stamps for 1960, 1963-69 may exist.

Since no year is on an unused stamp, they are listed under the first year only.

1959-62

1	$2 green		—
3	$2 green, *1961*		8,500.
4	$2 green, *1962*		9,500.

Small Game Stamps

Rosebud Reservation — **SMALL GAME** Nᵒ 2399

No. 12

Rosebud Reservation — **SMALL GAME**

No. 13

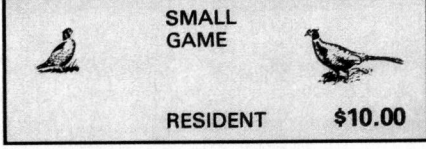

SMALL GAME   RESIDENT $10.00

Nos. 14, 15

Small Game Non-Resident $45.00

Nos. 16, 17

12		black	2,250.	
13		black	225.00	
14	$10	black	25.00	20.00
15	$45	black	150.00	

Die cut self-adhesive

16	$10 black (resident)	125.00	15.00
a.	Overprinted "RESIDENT" over "Non-resident"	6,500.	1,500.
17	$45 black	500.00	50.00

No. 12 was used in the 1970s, No. 13 in the early 1980s, Nos. 14 (resident) and 15 (non-resident) in the late 1980s, and Nos. 16 (resident) and 17 (non-resident) starting in 1990. Unused values for Nos. 16-17 are for never hinged stamps.

STANDING ROCK INDIAN RESERVATION

South Dakota-North Dakota
Waterfowl Stamps

Catalogue values for all unused stamps in this section are for Never Hinged items.

1992 WATER FOWL

Die cut, self-adhesive

1992-98

1	black	16.00	5.00
2	black, *1993*	10.00	4.00
3	black, inscribed "SRST," *1994*	8.50	3.00
4	black, *1995*	15.00	5.00
5	black, *1996*	13.00	4.00
6	black, *1997*	9.00	4.00
7	black, *1998*	15.00	4.00

SAVINGS STAMPS

"Savings Stamps" is a general philatelic category that includes four slightly different types of stamps issued at different times by either the U.S. Post Office Department or the U.S. Treasury Department. Their common feature was that they all effectively acted as a means for ordinary citizens to save and/or invest incrementally, a little bit at a time. At the same time, the investments effectively were loans to the federal government.

The four types of Savings Stamps are Postal Savings Stamps (issued from 1911-41) and Savings Stamps (1954-61), both issued by the Post Office Department; and War Savings Stamps (1917-45) and a Treasury Savings Stamp (1920), both issued by the Treasury Department.

Postal Savings Stamps were issued in 10c to $5.00 denominations and were redeemable in the form of credits to postal savings accounts. The 1911 10c stamps were available either as stamps or as a stamp imprint on a card to which other stamps could be added. The postal savings system was discontinued March 28, 1966.

Savings Stamps, also issued in 10c to $5.00 denominations, are the savings stamps most familiar to older philatelists. These collectors may remember buying these stamps at school and placing them in booklets. When full, the booklets were redeemable in the form of United States savings bonds. Sale of Savings Stamps was discontinued June 30, 1970.

War Savings Stamps were issued in 25c and $5 denominations (1917-20) and 10c to $5 denominations (1942-45). They were redeemable in the form of United States treasury war certificates, defense bonds or war bonds.

One Treasury Savings Stamp with a $1.00 denomination was issued in 1920. These stamps were redeemable in the form of either war savings stamps or treasury savings certificates.

POSTAL SAVINGS STAMPS

PS1

Plates of 400 subjects in four panes of 100 each
FLAT PLATE PRINTING

1911, Jan. 3   Wmk. 191   Engr.   *Perf. 12*
Size of design: 18x21½mm

PS1	PS1	10c **orange**	8.50	1.40
		Never hinged	17.50	
		Block of 4, 2mm spacing	37.50	
		Block of 4, 3mm spacing	40.00	
		P# strip of 3, Impt. open star	57.50	
		P# block of 6, Impt. open star	550.00	

Plate Nos. 5504-5507.

1911, Jan. 3   Unwmk.
Size of design: 137x79mm

PS2	PS1	10c **orange**	210.00	55.00

A 10c deep blue with head of Washington in circle imprinted on deposit card (design 136x79mm) exists, but there is no evidence that it was ever placed in use.

1911, Aug. 14   Wmk. 190   *Perf. 12*

PS4	PS1	10c **deep blue**	5.00	1.00
		Never hinged	8.50	
		Block of 4, 2mm spacing	22.50	
		Block of 4, 3mm spacing	25.00	
		P# strip of 3, Impt. open star	30.00	
		P# block of 6, Impt. open star	200.00	
		Never hinged	375.00	

Plate Nos. 5504-5507.

1911   Unwmk.
Imprinted on Deposit Card
Size of design: 133x78mm

PS5	PS1	10c **deep blue**	160.00	25.00

Catalogue values for unused stamps in this section, from this point to the end, are for Never Hinged items.

1936   Unwmk.   *Perf. 11*

PS6	PS1	10c **deep blue**	5.50	1.25
		violet blue	5.50	1.25
		Block of 4	25.00	
		P# block of 6, Impt. solid star	150.00	

Plate Nos. 21485, 21486.

PS2

Plates of 400 subjects in four panes of 100 each
FLAT PLATE PRINTING

1940   Unwmk.   Engr.   *Perf. 11*
Size of design: 19x22mm

PS7	PS2	10c **deep ultramarine**, *Apr. 3*	27.50	6.00
		Block of 4	115.00	
		P# block of 6	300.00	

Plate Nos. 22540, 22541.

PS8	PS2	25c **dark car rose**, *Apr. 1*	32.50	9.00
		Block of 4	135.00	
		P# block of 6	340.00	

Plate Nos. 22542, 22543.

PS9	PS2	50c **dark blue green**, *Apr.*	80.00	17.50
		Block of 4	340.00	
		P# block of 6	1,125.	

Plate No. 22544.

PS10	PS2	$1 **gray black**, *Apr. 1*	225.00	17.50
		Block of 4	950.00	
		P# block of 6	2,400.	

Plate No. 22545.
Nos. PS11-PS15 redeemable in the form of United States Treasury Defense, War or Savings Bonds.

Minute Man — PS3

E.E. Plates of 400 subjects in four panes of 100 each
ROTARY PRESS PRINTING

1941, May 1   Unwmk.   *Perf. 11x10½*
Size of design: 19x22½mm

PS11	PS3	10c **rose red**	.60	
a.		10c **carmine rose**	.60	
		Block of 4	2.40	
		P# block of 4	7.25	
b.		Bklt. pane of 10, *July 30*, trimmed horizontal edges	50.00	
		As "b," with Electric Eye marks at left	55.00	
c.		Booklet pane of 10, perf. horizontal edges	100.00	
		As "c," with Electric Eye marks at left	115.00	

Plate Nos., sheet stamps, 22714-22715, 22722-22723, 148245-148246.
Plate Nos., booklet panes, 147084, 147086, 148241-148242.

PS12	PS3	25c **blue green**	2.00	
		Block of 4	8.25	
		P# block of 4	22.50	
b.		Bklt. pane of 10, *July 30*	60.00	
		Booklet pane with Electric Eye marks at left	65.00	

Plate Nos., sheet stamps, 22716-22717, 22724-22725, 148247-148248.
Plate Nos., booklet panes, 147087-147088, 148243-148244.

PS13	PS3	50c **ultramarine**	7.50	
		Block of 4	32.50	
		P# block of 4	50.00	

Plate Nos. 22718-22719, 22726-22727.

PS14	PS3	$1 **gray black**	12.50	
		Block of 4	52.50	
		P# block of 4	75.00	

Plate Nos. 22720, 22728.

FLAT PLATE PRINTING
Plates of 100 subjects in four panes of 25 each
Size: 36x46mm   *Perf. 11*

PS15	PS3	$5 **sepia**	42.50	
		Block of 4	175.00	
		P# block of 6 at top or bottom	475.00	

Plate Nos. 22730-22737, 22740.

SAVINGS STAMPS

Catalogue values for unused stamps in this section are for Never Hinged items.

Minute Man — S1

E.E. Plates of 400 subjects in four panes of 100 each
ROTARY PRESS PRINTING

1954-57   Unwmk.   *Perf. 11x10½*
Size of design: 19x22½mm

S1	S1	10c **rose red**, wet printing, *Nov. 30, 1954*	.50	
		Block of 4	2.00	

		P# block of 4	3.50
a.		Booklet pane of 10, *Apr. 22, 1955*	150.00
		Booklet pane with Electric Eye marks at left	165.00
b.		Dry printing	.50
		Block of 4	2.00
		P# block of 4	3.50
c.		As "b," booklet pane of 10	150.00
		Booklet pane with Electric Eye marks at left	165.00

Plate Nos., sheet stamps, 164991-164992 (wet), 165917-165918, 166643-166644, 167089-167090, 168765-168766 (dry).
Plate Nos., booklet panes, 165218-165219 (wet), 165954-165955, 167001-167002 (dry).

S2	S1	25c **blue green**, wet printing, *Dec. 30, 1954*	7.50
		Block of 4	30.00
		P# block of 4	35.00
a.		Booklet pane of 10, *Apr. 15, 1955*	800.00
		Booklet pane with Electric Eye marks at left	825.00
b.		Dry printing	7.50
		Block of 4	30.00
		P# block of 4	35.00
c.		As "b," booklet pane of 10	800.00
		Booklet pane with Electric Eye marks at left	825.00

Plate Nos., sheet stamps, 165007-165008 (wet), 165919-165920 (dry), booklet panes, 165220-165221 (wet), 165956-165957 (dry).

S3	S1	50c **ultramarine**, wet printing, *Dec. 31, 1956*	9.00
		Block of 4	37.50
		P# block of 4	50.00
a.		Dry printing	9.00
		Block of 4	37.50
		P# block of 4	50.00

Plate Nos. 165050-165051 (wet), 166741-166742, 166941-166942 (dry).

S4	S1	$1 **gray black**, *Mar. 13, 1957*	25.00
		Block of 4	100.00
		P# block of 4	125.00

Plate Nos. 166097-166098, 166683-166684.

FLAT PLATE PRINTING
Plates of 100 subjects in four panes of 25 each
Size: 36x46mm   *Perf. 11*

S5	S1	$5 **sepia**, *Nov. 30, 1956*	95.00
		Block of 4	400.00
		P# block of 6 at top or bottom	725.00

Plate No. 166068.

Minute Man and 48-Star Flag — S2

GIORI PRESS PRINTING
Plates of 400 subjects in four panes of 100 each
1958, Nov. 18   Unwmk.   *Perf. 11*

S6	S2	25c **dark blue & carmine**	2.00
		Block of 4	8.00
		P# block of 4	10.00
a.		Booklet pane of 10	75.00

Plate Nos.: sheet stamps, 166921, 166925, 166946; booklet panes, 166913, 166916.

Minute Man and 50-Star Flag — S3

Plates of 400 subjects in four panes of 100 each.
1961   Unwmk.   *Perf. 11*

S7	S3	25c **dark blue & carmine**	1.50
		Block of 4	6.00
		P# block of 4	11.00
a.		Booklet pane of 10	300.00

Plate Nos.: sheet stamps, 167473, 167476, 167486, 167489, 169089; booklet panes, 167495, 167502, 167508, 167516.

WAR SAVINGS STAMPS

Unused values of War Savings stamps are for copies with full original gum. Used values are for stamps without gum that generally have been removed from savings certificates or booklets. **Caution:** beware of used stamps that have been regummed to appear unused.

 WS1

Plates of 300 subjects in six panes of 50 each
FLAT PLATE PRINTING

1917, Dec. 1   Unwmk.   Engr.   *Perf. 11*
Size of design: 28x18½mm

WS1	WS1	25c **deep green**	16.00	2.25
		Never hinged	30.00	
		Block of 4	70.00	
		Margin strip of 3, P#	80.00	
		P# block of 6	1,200.	

Plate Nos. 56800, 56810-56811, 56817, 57074-57077, 57149-57152, 57336, 57382, 57395-57396, 57399, 57443, 58801-58804, 59044-59045, 59156, 61207-61210.

George Washington — WS2

Plates of 80 subjects in four panes of 20 each
FLAT PLATE PRINTING

1917   Unwmk.   Engr.   *Perf. 11*
Size of design: 39x55mm

WS2	WS2	$5 **deep green**, *Nov. 17*	85.00	35.00
		Never hinged	175.00	
		No gum	30.00	
		Block of 4	325.00	
		Margin stamp with P#	90.00	
		P# block of 6	1,600.	
b.		Vert. pair, imperf. horiz.	—	

Plate Nos. 56914-56917, 57066-57073, 57145-57148, 57169-57176, 57333-57334, 57343-57348, 58431, 58433-58438, 58726-58729, 59071, 60257-60260, 60659-60662, 60665-60668, 60846-60852, 60899, 61203-61206, 61265-61268, 61360-61367, 61388, 61435, 61502.

Rouletted 7

WS3	WS2	$5 **deep green**	1,200.	650.
		Never hinged	2,500.	
		No gum	600.	
		Block of 4	5,000.	
		Margin copy with P#	1,500.	

Benjamin Franklin — WS3

Plates of 150 subjects in six panes of 25 each
FLAT PLATE PRINTING

1919, July 3   Unwmk.   Engr.   *Perf. 11*
Size of design: 27x36mm

WS4	WS3	$5 **deep blue**	325.	160.
		Never hinged	650.	
		No gum	150.	
		Block of 4	1,350.	
		Margin stamp with P#	350.	
		Margin stamp with inverted P#	375.	

Plate Nos. 61882-61885, 61910-61913, 61970-61972, 61997-61998, 62007-62013.

George Washington WS4

Plates of 100 subjects in four panes of 25 each
FLAT PLATE PRINTING

1919, Dec. 11   Unwmk.   Engr.   *Perf. 11*
Size of design: 36x41½mm

WS5	WS4	$5 **carmine**	800.	350.
		Never hinged	1,650.	
		No gum	500.	
		Block of 4	3,500.	
		Margin stamp with P#	850.	

Plate Nos. 67545-67552, 69349-69352, 69673-69675, 69677-69680, 69829.

Abraham Lincoln WS5

Plates of 100 subjects in four panes of 25 each
FLAT PLATE PRINTING

1920, Dec. 21   Unwmk.   Engr.   *Perf. 11*
Size of design: 39½x42mm

WS6	WS5	$5 **orange**, *green*	4,250.	1,500.
		Never hinged	8,500.	
		No gum	1,750.	
		Block of 4	18,000.	
		Margin stamp with P#	4,500.	

Plate Nos. 73129-73136.

> **Catalogue values for unused stamps in this section, from this point to the end, are for Never Hinged items.**

Minute Man — WS6

Plates of 400 subjects in four panes of 100 each
ROTARY PRESS PRINTING

1942   Unwmk.   *Perf. 11x10½*
Size of design: 19x22½mm

WS7	WS6	10c **rose red**, *Oct. 29*	.50	.20
a.		10c carmine rose	.50	
		Block of 4	2.00	
		P# block of 4	5.00	
b.		Booklet pane of 10, *Oct. 27*	50.00	
		Booklet pane with Electric Eye marks at left	55.00	

Plate Nos., sheet stamps, 149492-149495, 150206-150207, 150706-150707, 155311-155312.
Plate Nos., booklet panes, 149655-149657, 150664.

WS8	WS6	25c **dark blue green**, *Oct. 15*	1.10	.25
		Block of 4	5.00	
		P# block of 4	8.25	
b.		Booklet pane of 10, *Nov. 6*	50.00	
		Booklet pane with Electric Eye marks at left	55.00	

Plate Nos., sheet stamps, 149587-149590, 150320-150321, 150708-150709, 155313-155314, 155812-155813, 156517-156518, booklet panes, 149658-149660, 150666.

WS9	WS6	50c **deep ultra**, *Nov. 12*	4.00	1.25
		Block of 4	16.00	
		P# block of 4	22.50	

Plate Nos. 149591-149594.

WS10	WS6	$1 **gray black**, *Nov. 17*	12.50	3.50
		Block of 4	52.50	
		P# block of 4	70.00	

Plate Nos. 149595-149598.

Type of 1942
FLAT PLATE PRINTING
Plates of 100 subjects in four panes of 25 each

1945   Unwmk.   Size: 36x46mm   *Perf. 11*

WS11	WS6	$5 **violet brown**	55.00	17.50
		Block of 4	240.00	
		P# block of 6 at top or bottom	500.00	

Plate Nos. 150131-150134, 150291.

Type of 1942
Coil Stamps

1943, Aug. 5   Unwmk.   *Perf. 10 Vertically*

WS12	WS6	10c **rose red**	2.75	.90
		Pair	6.00	
		Line pair	10.50	

Plate Nos. 153286-153287.

WS13	WS6	25c **dark blue green**	5.00	1.75
		Pair	10.50	
		Line pair	22.50	

Plate Nos. 153289-153290.

TREASURY SAVINGS STAMP

Alexander
Hamilton — TS1

FLAT PLATE PRINTING

1920, Dec. 21	Unwmk.	Engr.	Perf. 11

Size of design: 33½x33½mm

TS1	TS1	$1 **red**, *green*	3,500.	1,250.
		Never hinged		
		No gum	*1,750.*	
		Block of 4	15,000.	
		Margin stamp with P#	3,750.	

Plate Nos. 73196-73203.

Values for No. TS1 are for very fine stamps. However, perhaps 95% of the issue exists with average centering. Unused stamps in average condition sell for $800-$1,000.

TELEGRAPH STAMPS

These stamps were issued by the individual companies for use on their own telegrams, and can usually be divided into three classes: Free franking privileges issued to various railroad, newspaper and express company officials, etc., whose companies were large users of the lines; those issued at part cost to the lesser officials of the same type companies; and those bearing values which were usually sold to the general public. Occasionally, some of the companies granted the franking privilege to stockholders and minor State (not Federal) officials. Most Telegraph Stamps were issued in booklet form and will be found with one or more straight edges.

Serial numbers may show evidence of doubling, often of a different number. Such doubling is not scarce.

American Rapid Telegraph Company

Organized Feb. 21, 1879, in New York State. Its wires extended as far north as Boston, Mass., and west to Cleveland, Ohio. It was amalgamated with the Bankers and Merchants Telegraph Co., but when that company was unable to pay the fixed charges, the properties of the American Rapid Telegraph Company were sold on Mar. 11, 1891, to a purchasing committee comprised of James W. Converse and others. This purchasing committee deeded the property and franchise of the American Rapid Telegraph Company to the Western Union Telegraph Company on June 25, 1894. Issued three types of stamps: Telegram, Collect and Duplicate. Telegram stamps were issued in sheets of 100 and were used to prepay messages which could be dropped in convenient boxes for collection. Collect and duplicate stamps were issued in alternate rows on the same sheet of 100 subjects. Collect stamps were attached to telegrams sent collect, the receiver of which paid the amount shown by the stamps, while the Duplicate stamps were retained by the Company as vouchers. **Remainders with punched cancellations were bought up by a New York dealer.**

T1   T2

"Prepaid Telegram" Stamps
Engraved and Printed by the American Bank Note Co.

1881				**Perf. 12**
1T1	T1	1c **black**	20.00	4.75
		Punched		.20
		Block of 4	87.50	
		Punched		1.00
1T2	T1	3c **orange**	50.00	32.50
		Punched		1.50
		Block of 4, punched		10.00
1T3	T1	5c **bister brown**	4.75	1.25
		Punched		.25
		Block of 4	21.00	
		Punched		1.10
a.		5c **brown**	4.75	1.40
		Punched		.20
		Block of 4	21.00	
		Punched		1.00
1T4	T1	10c **purple**	20.00	5.75
		Punched		.20
		Block of 4	85.00	
		Punched		1.00
1T5	T1	15c **green**	8.75	2.50
		Punched		.20
		Block of 4	40.00	
		Punched		1.00
1T6	T1	20c **red**	8.75	2.50
		Punched		.20
		Block of 4, punched		.80
1T7	T1	25c **rose**	12.00	1.75
		Punched		.20
		Block of 4	52.50	
		Punched		1.00
1T8	T1	50c **blue**	32.50	12.50
		Punched		1.50
		Block of 4, punched		8.00

"Collect" Stamps

1T9	T2	1c **brown**	8.00	5.50
		Punched		.20
1T10	T2	5c **blue**	6.50	4.00
		Punched		.20
1T11	T2	15c **red brown**	6.75	3.25
		Punched		.25
1T12	T2	20c **olive green**	6.50	4.00
		Punched		.20

T3

"Office Coupon" Stamps

1T13	T3	1c **brown**	14.50	4.40
		Punched		.20
a.		Pair, #1T9, 1T13, punched		2.00
		As "a," block of 4, punched		4.50
1T14	T3	5c **blue**	12.00	5.25
		Punched		.20
a.		Pair, #1T10, 1T14	60.00	
		Punched		3.00
		As "a," block of 4	125.00	
		Punched		7.00
1T15	T3	15c **red brown**	21.00	4.75
		Punched		.25
a.		Pair, #1T11, 1T15	50.00	
		Punched		2.50
		As "a," block of 4	110.00	
		Punched		5.50
1T16	T3	20c **olive green**	21.00	4.75
		Punched		.20
a.		Pair, #1T12, 1T16, punched		2.75
		As "a," block of 4, punched		6.00

Atlantic Telegraph Company

Organized 1884 at Portland, Maine. Its lines extended from Portland, Me., to Boston, Mass., and terminated in the office of the Baltimore and Ohio Telegraph Company at Boston. Later bought out by the Baltimore and Ohio Telegraph Co. Stamps issued by the Atlantic Telegraph Company could also be used for messages destined to any point on the Baltimore and Ohio system. Stamps were printed in panes of six and a full book sold for $10. **Remainders of these stamps, without control numbers, were purchased by a Boston dealer and put on the market about 1932.**

T4

1888				**Perf. 13**
2T1	T4	1c **green**	5.00	
		Remainders	—	2.25
		Pane of 6		14.00
		Remainders	—	
2T2	T4	5c **blue**	7.50	
		Remainders	—	2.25
		Pane of 6		

		Remainders	14.00	
a.		Horiz. pair, imperf. vert.	—	
b.		Vert. pair, imperf. horiz.	25.00	—
2T3	T4	10c **purple brown**	9.00	—
		Remainders		2.25
		Pane of 6	—	
		Remainders		14.00
a.		Horiz. pair, imperf. between	40.00	
2T4	T4	25c **carmine**	6.00	—
		Remainders		2.25
		Pane of 6, remainders		16.00
a.		Vert. pair, imperf. horiz., remainders	—	

Baltimore & Ohio Telegraph Companies

"The Baltimore & Ohio Telegraph Co. of the State of New York" was incorporated May 17, 1882. Organization took place under similar charter in 26 other states. It absorbed the National Telegraph Co. and several others. Extended generally along the lines of the Baltimore & Ohio Railroad, but acquired interests in other states. Company absorbed in 1887 by the Western Union Telegraph Co. Stamps were issued in booklet form and sold for $5 and $10, containing all denominations.

T5   T6

Engraved by the American Bank Note Co.

1885				**Perf. 12**
3T1	T5	1c **vermilion**	100.00	25.00
		Pane of 6	650.00	
3T2	T5	5c **blue**	100.00	35.00
3T3	T5	10c **red brown**	50.00	12.50
		Pane of 6	325.00	
3T4	T5	25c **orange**	85.00	25.00
3T5	T6	**brown**	1.75	
		Pane of 4	12.50	

1886				
3T6	T6	**black**	2.00	*25.00*
		Pane of 4	22.50	

Imprint of Kendall Bank Note Co.
Thin Paper

1886				**Perf. 14**
3T7	T5	1c **green**	7.00	3.00
a.		Thick paper	12.00	.85
b.		Imperf., pair	90.00	
3T8	T5	5c **blue**	5.00	1.25
a.		Thick paper	10.00	4.00
b.		Imperf., pair		55.00
3T9	T5	10c **brown**	7.00	.75
a.		Thick paper	11.50	1.50
3T10	T5	25c **deep orange**	47.50	.75
a.		Thick paper	50.00	1.50

Used examples of Nos. 3T7-3T20 normally have heavy grid cancellations. Lightly canceled stamps command a premium.

Litho. by A. Hoen & Co.

1886		**Imprint of firm**		**Perf. 12**
3T11	T5	1c **green**	3.00	.65
		Pane of 6	22.50	
3T12	T5	5c **blue**	7.50	.65
		Pane of 6	50.00	
a.		Imperf., pair	90.00	
3T13	T5	10c **dark brown**	7.50	.75
		Pane of 6	45.00	
a.		Vert. pair, imperf. between	60.00	

Wmk. "A HOEN AND CO. BALTIMORE" in double lined capitals in sheet
Perf. 12

3T14	T5	1c **green**	15.00	1.25
		Pane of 6	90.00	
3T15	T5	5c **blue**	25.00	1.50
		Pane of 6	160.00	—
a.		Imperf., pair	52.50	
3T16	T5	10c **dark brown**	17.50	1.25
		Pane of 6	115.00	

Lithographed by Forbes Co., Boston

1887		**Imprint of firm**		**Perf. 12½**
3T17	T5	1c **green**	50.00	2.75
3T18	T5	5c **blue**	80.00	6.00
3T19	T5	10c **brown**	80.00	5.50
3T20	T5	25c **yellow**	80.00	8.25
a.		25c **orange**	80.00	5.50

Baltimore & Ohio-Connecticut River Telegraph Companies

The Connecticut River Telegraph Co. ran from New Haven to Hartford. An agreement was entered wherein the Baltimore & Ohio System had mutual use of their lines. This agreement terminated when the Baltimore & Ohio System was absorbed by the Western Union. The Connecticut River Telegraph Company then joined the United Lines. In 1885 stamps (black on yellow) were issued and sold in booklets for $10. In 1887 the Connecticut River Telegraph Co. had extended its lines to New Boston, Mass., and new books of stamps (black on blue) were issued for use on this extension. **Remainders were canceled with bars and sold to a New York dealer.**

T7

1885-87				**Perf. 11**
4T1	T7	1c **black,** *yellow*	7.50	6.00
		Remainders		1.25
		Pane of 10	75.00	
		Remainders		6.00
a.		Imperf., pair	40.00	
b.		Vert. pair, imperf. horiz., remainders		—
4T2	T7	5c **black,** *yellow*	5.00	10.00
		Remainders		1.00
		Pane of 10	50.00	
		Remainders		6.00
a.		Horizontal pair, imperf. between, remainders		—
b.		Vert. pair, imperf. between, remainders		35.00
c.		Imperf., pair, remainders		35.00
4T3	T7	1c **black,** *blue* ('87)	12.50	
		Remainders		4.00
		Pane of 10	125.00	
		Remainders		35.00
4T4	T7	5c **black,** *blue* ('87)	15.00	9.00
		Remainders		4.00
		Pane of 10	160.00	
		Remainders		52.50

California State Telegraph Company

Incorporated June 17, 1854 as the California Telegraph Company and constructed a line from Nevada through Grass Valley to Auburn. Extended to run from San Francisco to Marysville via San Jose and Stockton. Later absorbed Northern Telegraph Co. and thus extended to Eureka. It was incorporated as the California State Telegraph Company on April 6, 1861. At the time of its lease to the Western Union on May 16, 1867 the California State consisted of the following companies which had been previously absorbed:

Alta California Telegraph Co., Atlantic and Pacific States Telegraph Co., National Telegraph Co., Northern California Telegraph Co., Overland Telegraph Co., Placerville and Humboldt Telegraph Co., Tuolumne Telegraph Co. Stamps were issued in booklets, six to a pane. **Remainders of Nos. 5T1 and 5T4 are without frank numbers.**

T8

1870				**Perf. 13½**
5T1	T8	**black & blue**	700.	
		Pane of 6	4,500.	
		Without number	275.	

T9   T10

1870				**Perf. 12, 13**
5T2	T9	**black & red,** without number	375.00	200.00
1871				**Dated "1871"**
5T3	T9	**black & red,** without number	850.00	
a.		Imperf., pair	—	
5T4	T10	**black & salmon,** blue number	900.00	300.00
		Pane of 6	6,000.	
		Without number	275.00	

1872				
5T5	T10	**green & red,** red number (no year date)	450.00	
		Pane of 6	—	

1873				**Dated "1873"**
5T6	T10	**red & salmon,** blue number	575.00	375.00

1874				**Dated "1874"**
5T7	T10	**blue & salmon,** black number	650.00	
		Pane of 6	—	

1875				**Dated "1875"**
5T8	T10	**brown & green,** black number	550.00	
		Pane of 6	—	

City & Suburban Telegraph Company
(New York City and Suburban Printing Telegraph Company)

Organized 1855. Extended only through New York City and Brooklyn. Sold out to the American Telegraph Co. Stamps were sold to the public for prepayment of messages, which could be dropped in convenient boxes for collection. Stamps were issued in sheets of 60 having a face value of $1. These were arranged in six vertical rows of ten, the horizontal rows having the following denominations: 2c, 1c, 1c, 1c, 2c, 3c.

Counterfeits are known both in black and blue, mostly on pelure or hard white paper. Originals are on soft wove paper, somewhat yellowish. Scalloped edge is more sharply etched on the counterfeits.

T11

		Typo.		**Imperf.**
6T1	T11	1c **black**	550.	300.
		Pair	—	
		Block of 4	—	
6T2	T11	2c **black**	700.	375.
		Pair	—	
		Pair, 2c + 1c	1,400.	
6T3	T11	3c **black**	900.	500.
		Pair	—	
		Strip of 3, 1c, 2c & 3c	*3,750.*	

Colusa, Lake & Mendocino Telegraph Company

Was organized in California early in 1873. First known as the Princeton, Colusa and Grand Island Telegraph Co. In May, 1873 they completed their line from Princeton through Colusa, at which point it was connected with the Western Union office, to Grand Island. On Feb. 10, 1875 it was incorporated as the Colusa, Lake & Mendocino Telegraph Co. Its lines were extended into the counties of Colusa, Lake, Mendocino and Napa. Eventually reached a length of 260 miles. Went out of business in 1892. Stamps were issued for prepayment of messages and were sold in books. When sold they were stamped "P.L.W." (the superintendent's initials) in blue. The 5c value was printed 10 to a pane, being two horizontal rows of five. Of the 10c and 25c nothing definite is known about the settings.

T11a

1876 Perf. 12

7T1	T11a	5c	**black**	900.
			Block of 4	4,000.
			Pane of 10	10,000.
			Without "P.L.W."	1,000.
7T2	T11a	10c	**black**	9,000. —
7T3	T11a	25c	**red**	9,000. —

Commercial Union Telegraph Company

Incorporated in New York State on March 31, 1886. Its lines ran from Albany through Troy to Berlin, N.Y., thence to North Adams, Mass. The lines of this Company, which was controlled by the Postal Telegraph Company, were later extended throughout Northern New York and the States of Massachusetts, Vermont, New Hampshire and Maine. Stamps issued in panes of four.

T12

T13

T14

1891 Lithographed by A. C. Goodwin Perf. 12

8T1	T12	25c	**yellow**	30.00 —
			Pane of 4	125.00
8T2	T13	25c	**green**	30.00 10.00
			Pane of 4	125.00
a.			Horiz. pair, imperf. vert.	90.00
8T3	T14		**lilac rose**	67.50 —

Mutual Union Telegraph Company

Incorporated October 4, 1880. Extended over 22 states. Absorbed about 1883 by the Western Union Telegraph Co. Franks issued for use of stockholders, in books, four to a pane.

T15

Engr. by Van Campen Engraving Co., New York

1882-83 Perf. 14

9T1	T15	**blue**	50.00 20.00
		Pane of 4	225.00
a.		Vert. pair, imperf. horizontal	140.00 —
b.		Imperf., pair	150.00 —
9T2	T15	**carmine**	50.00 —
		Pane of 4	225.00

North American Telegraph Company

Incorporated October 15, 1885 to run from Chicago to Minneapolis, later being extended into North and South Dakota. Absorbed in 1929 by the Postal System.

Apparently these stamps were not canceled when used. Issued in panes of four.

T15a

1899-1907 Perf. 12

10T1	T15a	**violet** (1899)	325.00
		Pane of 4	1,250.
10T2	T15a	**green** (1901)	325.00
10T3	T15a	**dark brown** (1902)	575.00
10T4	T15a	**blue** (1903)	575.00
10T5	T15a	**violet** (1904)	200.00
		Pane of 4	800.00
a.		Horiz. pair, imperf. vertically	500.00
10T6	T15a	**red brown** (1905)	375.00
10T7	T15a	**rose** (1906)	425.00
10T8	T15a	**green** (1907)	2,400.

Nos. 10T1 to 10T8 are known imperforate.

Northern Mutual Telegraph Company

Incorporated in New York State as the Northern Mutual Telegraph and Telephone Company on June 20, 1882. Its line, which consisted of a single wire, extended from Syracuse to Ogdensburg via Oswego, Watertown and Clayton, a distance of 170 miles. It was sold to the Bankers and Merchants Telegraph Company in 1883. Stamps were in use for a few days only in April, 1883. Issued in panes of 35 having a face value of $5. Seven horizontal rows of five covering all denominations as follows: 2 rows of 25c, 1 of 20c, 2 of 10c, 2 of 5c. **The remainders and plates were purchased by a New York dealer in 1887.**

T16

1883 Perf. 14

11T1	T16	5c	**yellow brown**	6.50 —
			Block of 4	30.00
11T2	T16	10c	**yellow brown**	8.50 —
			Block of 4	37.50
11T3	T16	20c	**yellow brown**	20.00 —
			Horizontal pair	45.00
11T4	T16	25c	**yellow brown**	5.50 —
			Block of 4	30.00
			Pane of 35	375.00

The first reprints are lighter in color than the originals, perf. 14 and the gum is yellowish instead of white. The pane makeup differs in the reprints. The second reprints are darker than the original, perf. 12. Value $1 each.

Northern New York Telegraph Company

Organized about 1892. Extended from Malone, N.Y. to Massena, N.Y. Re-incorporated as the New York Union Telegraph Co. on April 2, 1896.

T16a

Typo. by Charles H. Smith, Brushton, N.Y.

1894-95 Rouletted

12T1	T16a	**green** (overprinted in red "Frank 1894")	45.
		Pane of 6	290.
a.		Imperf., pair	50.
12T2	T16a	**red** (overprinted in black "Frank 1895")	160.
		Pane of 6	1,500.
a.		Imperf., pair	50.
12T3	T16a 1c	**yellow** (overprinted in black "One")	80.
		Pane of 6	525.
a.		Imperf., pair	50.
12T4	T16a 10c	**blue** (overprinted in red "10")	150.
		Pane of 6	950.
a.		Imperf., pair	50.

Some specialists believe that Nos. 12T1-12T4 were not issued and probably are essays. However, one Northern New York stamp is recorded tied to a piece of a telegraph form by a punch cancel.

Pacific Mutual Telegraph Company

Incorporated in Missouri on June 21, 1883. Operated between St. Louis and Kansas City, Mo., during the years 1884 and 1885. It had 15 offices, 425 miles of poles and 850 miles of wire. The controlling interests were held by the Bankers and Merchants Telegraph Company. The name was changed on Sept. 10, 1910 to Postal Telegraph-Cable Company of Missouri. Stamps were issued in booklets having a face value of $10 and containing 131 stamps as follows: 50-1c, 20-5c, 45-10c, 16-25c. They are not known used.

T17

1883 Perf. 12

13T1	T17	1c	**black**	30.00
13T2	T17	1c	**slate**	.35
			Block of 4	1.50
a.			1c gray	.35
			Block of 4	1.50
13T3	T17	5c	**black,** *buff*	1.00
			Block of 4	4.50
13T4	T17	10c	**black,** *green*	.35
			Block of 4	1.75
a.			Horiz. pair, imperf. between	
13T5	T17	25c	**black,** *salmon buff*	1.00
			Block of 4	4.50

Pacific Postal Telegraph-Cable Company

The Pacific Postal Telegraph-Cable Company was the Pacific Coast Department of the Postal Telegraph-Cable Company, and was organized in 1886. Its first wire ran from San Francisco to New Westminster, B.C., where it touched the lines of the Canadian Pacific Railway Company, then the only connection between the Eastern and Western Postal systems. Later the Postal's own wires spanned the continent and the two companies were united.

Stamps issued in booklet form in vertical panes of five.

T17a

Perf. 12 Horiz.

14T1	T17a	10c	**brown**	150.00 100.00
			Pane of 5	775.00
14T2	T17a	15c	**black**	150.00 100.00
			Pane of 5	775.00
14T3	T17a	25c	**rose red**	150.00 100.00
			Pane of 5	775.00
14T4	T17a	40c	**green**	150.00 100.00
			Pane of 5	775.00
14T5	T17a	50c	**blue**	175.00 100.00
			Pane of 5	900.00

These stamps were issued with three sizes of frank numbers; large closely spaced, small closely spaced and small widely spaced figures. They also exist without frank numbers.

Postal Telegraph Company

Organized in New York in 1881. Reorganized in 1891 as the Postal Telegraph-Cable Co. The Postal Telegraph Co stamps of 1885 were issued in sheets of 100. **Some years after the reorganization a New York dealer purchased the remainders which were canceled with a purple star.** The Postal

Telegraph-Cable Co. issued frank stamps in booklets, usually four stamps to a pane. This company was merged with the Western Union Telegraph Company in 1943.

T18

T19

T20

T21

Engraved by Hamilton Bank Note Co.

1885				Perf. 14	
15T1	T18	10c **green**		3.50	—
		Remainders			.25
		Block of 4		15.00	
		Remainders			1.25
a.		Horiz. pair, imperf. btwn., remainders		20.00	
b.		10c **deep green**		3.50	
		Remainders			.25
		Block of 4		15.00	
		Remainders			1.25
15T2	T19	15c **orange red**		3.50	
		Remainders			.60
		Block of 4		15.00	
		Remainders			3.00
a.		Horizontal pair, imperf. between		37.50	
15T3	T20	25c **blue**		2.00	5.00
		Remainders			.20
		Block of 4		9.00	
		Remainders			.75
a.		Horizontal pair, imperf. between		37.50	
15T4	T21	50c **brown**		1.75	—
		Remainders			.60
		Block of 4		8.00	
		Remainders			3.00

The 25c in ultramarine and the 50c in black were printed and perforated 16 but are not known to have been issued. Value about $7.50 each.

T22

T22a

Typographed by Moss Engraving Co.

1892-1920			Perf. 14	
Signature of A.B. Chandler				
15T5	T22	**blue gray** (1892)	50.00	
a.		Imperf., pair	120.00	

Perf. 13 to 14½ and Compound

15T6	T22	**gray lilac** (1892)	55.00	
15T7	T22	**red** (1893)	20.00	10.00
		Pane of 4	85.00	
15T8	T22	**red brown** (1893)	6.00	4.00

Perf. 12

15T9	T22	**violet brown** (1894)	6.75	
15T10	T22	**gray green** (1894)	4.50	
a.		Imperf., pair	10.00	
15T11	T22	**blue** (1895)	50.00	
15T12	T22	**rose** (1895)	375.00	

Nos. 15T11 and 15T12 are from a new die resembling T22 but without shading under "Postal Telegraph Co."

15T13	T22a	**slate green** (1896)	5.50	
		Pane of 4	25.00	
15T14	T22a	**brown** (1896)	325.00	

Signature of Albert B. Chandler

15T15	T22a	**lilac brown** (1897)	1.50	10.00
		Pane of 4	6.50	
15T16	T22a	**orange** (1897)	275.00	

Typographed by Knapp & Co.

15T17	T22a	**pale blue** (1898)	2.25	
		Pane of 4	10.00	
15T18	T22a	**rose** (1898)	325.00	

Typographed by Moss Engraving Co.

Perf. 12

15T19	T22a	**orange brown** (1899)	1.75	
		Pane of 4	8.25	

Perf. 11

15T20	T22a	**blue** (1900)	3.00	3.00
a.		"I" of "Complimentary" omitted	.75	1.00
		Pane of 4	3.25	

The variety 15T20a represents a different die with many variations in the design.

Perf. 14

15T21	T22a	**sea green** (1901)	.60	.60
		Pane of 4	2.50	
a.		Horiz. pair, imperf. between	—	

Signature of John W. Mackay

15T22	T22a	**chocolate** (1902)	1.25	.65
		Pane of 4	5.50	
a.		Horiz. pair, imperf. vert.	—	

Signature of Clarence H. Mackay

15T23	T22a	**blue** (1903)	2.75	2.50
		Pane of 4	12.50	

Perf. 12

15T24	T22a	**blue,** *blue* (1904)	4.00	3.00
		Pane of 4	17.50	
15T25	T22a	**blue,** *yellow* (1905)	5.00	
		Pane of 4	22.50	
15T26	T22a	**blue,** *light blue* (1906)	5.00	5.00
		Pane of 4	22.50	
a.		Horiz. pair, imperf. vert.	—	

T22b

Perf. 12

15T27	T22b	**black,** *yellow* (laid paper) (1907)	75.00	
		Pane of 4	290.00	
15T28	T22b	**blue,** *pink* (laid paper) (1907)	45.00	
		Pane of 4	190.00	

"One Telegram of 10 Words" — T22c

15T29	T22c	**blue** (1908)	65.00	
		Pane of 4	275.00	
15T30	T22c	**yellow** (1908)	300.00	
		Pane of 4	1,250.00	
15T31	T22c	**black** (1908)	55.00	
		Pane of 4	225.00	
15T32	T22c	**brown** (1909)	45.00	
		Pane of 4	190.00	
a.		Date reads "1908"	2,000.	
15T33	T22c	**olive green** (1909)	25.00	
		Pane of 4	105.00	
15T34	T22c	**dark blue** (1910)	40.00	
15T35	T22c	**dark brown** (1910)	40.00	
		Pane of 4	150.00	
15T36	T22c	**violet** (1911)	400.00	
15T37	T22c	**blue** (1912)	700.00	
15T38	T22c	**violet** (1913)	850.00	

Perf. 14

15T39	T22c	**violet** (not dated) (1914)	225.00	
a.		Red violet	200.00	
		Pane of 4	950.00	

"One Telegram"

Perf. 12

15T40	T22c	**blue** (1908)	60.00	
		Pane of 4	260.00	
a.		Horiz. pair, imperf. between	350.00	
15T41	T22c	**lilac** (1909)	25.00	
		Pane of 4	110.00	
15T42	T22c	**black,** *yellow* (laid paper) (1910)	700.00	
a.		Date reads "1909"	—	
15T43	T22c	**violet** (1910)	15.00	
a.		**Red violet**	15.00	
		Pane of 8	140.00	
15T44	T22c	**dark blue** (1911)	60.00	
		Pane of 4	260.00	
a.		Vert. pair, imperf between	400.00	
15T45	T22c	**light violet** (1912)	40.00	
		Pane of 4	180.00	

Perf. 14

15T46	T22c	**dark blue** (1913)	175.00	
		Pane of 8	1,500.	
a.		Imperf. vertically, pair	260.00	
b.		Perf. 12	100.00	
		Pane of 4	425.00	
15T47	T22c	**dark blue** (not dated) (1914)	.25	
		Pane of 4	2.50	
		Pane of 8	5.00	

In panes of four the stamps are 4½mm apart horizontally, panes of eight 5½mm. There are two types of design T22c, one with and one without spurs on colored curved lines above "O" of "Postal" and below "M" of "Company". No. 15T47 comes in both types.

Nos. 15T39 and 15T47 handstamped with date in double line numerals, all four numerals complete on each stamp.

15T47A	T22c	**violet**	(1916)	2,750.
15T48	T22c	**dark blue**	(1917)	1,500.
15T49	T22c	**dark blue**	(1918)	2,000.
15T49A	T22c	**dark blue**	(1919)	90.00
		Pane of 8		800.00
15T49B	T22c	**dark blue**	(1920)	70.00
		Pane of 8		650.00

No. 15T49B is handstamped "1920" in small single line numerals.

T22d

T22e

1907				Perf. 12	
15T50	T22d	1c **dark brown**		30.00	20.00
		Pane of 4		125.00	
15T51	T22d	2c **dull violet**		25.00	20.00
		Pane of 4		110.00	
15T52	T22d	5c **green**		30.00	22.50
		Pane of 4		125.00	
15T53	T22d	25c **light red**		32.50	20.00
		Pane of 4		140.00	

1931				Perf. 14	
15T54	T22e	25c **gray blue** (1931)		.25	
		Pane of 6		2.00	

1932

No. 15T54 overprinted "1932" and control number in red

15T55	T22e	25c	**gray blue**	100.00
			Pane of 6	650.00

Many varieties between Nos. 15T5 and 15T55 are known without frank numbers.

OFFICIAL

1900-14		**Inscribed "Supts."**		***Perf. 11, 12***
15TO1	T22c	**black**, *magenta*		2.00 2.00

For Use of Railroad Superintendents
Perf. 12
"C. G. W." (Chicago, Great Western Railroad) at top

15TO2	T22c	**carmine** (1908)		50.00
		Pane of 4		240.00
15TO3	T22c	**carmine** (1909)		200.00
15TO4	T22c	**carmine** (1910)		160.00
15TO5	T22c	**carmine** (1911)		125.00
15TO6	T22c	**carmine** (1912)		140.00

Perf. 14

15TO7	T22c	**carmine** (1913)		200.00
a.		Perf. 12		—
15TO8	T22c	**dull red** (not dated) (1914)		.50
		Pane of 8		5.00

Perf. 12
"E. P." (El Paso and Northeastern Railroad) at top

15TO9	T22c	**orange** (1908)		250.00

"I. C." (Illinois Central Railroad) at top

15TO10	T22c	**green** (1908)		60.00
		Pane of 4		270.00
15TO11	T22c	**yellow green** (1909)		15.00
		Pane of 4		—
		Pane of 8		130.00
15TO12	T22c	**dark green** (1910)		160.00
15TO13	T22c	**dark green** (1911)		95.00
		Pane of 4		410.00
		Pane of 8		825.00
15TO14	T22c	**dark green** (1912)		1,250.
15TO15	T22c	**dark green** (1913)		1,250.

Perf. 14

15TO16	T22c	**dark green** (not dated) (1914)		2.50
		Pane of 4		11.00
		Pane of 8		22.50
a.		Green (spurs)		1.25
		Pane of 4		7.50
b.		Line under "PRESIDENT" (no spurs)		1.00
		Pane of 8		12.50

(See note after No. 15T47.)
Both types of design T22c are known of 15TO16.

Perf. 12
"O. D." (Old Dominion Steamship Co.) at top

15TO17	T22c	**violet** (1908)		2,100.

"P. R." (Pennsylvania Railroad) at top

15TO18	T22c	**orange brown** (1908)		35.00
		Pane of 4		150.00
		Pane of 8		300.00
15TO19	T22c	**orange brown** (1909)		40.00
		Pane of 4		175.00
		Pane of 8		375.00
15TO20	T22c	**orange brown** (1910)		40.00
		Pane of 4		175.00
		Pane of 8		375.00
15TO21	T22c	**orange brown** (1911)		175.00
15TO22	T22c	**orange brown** (1912)		110.00
		Pane of 4		*700.00*

Perf. 14

15TO23	T22c	**orange brown** (1913)		40.00
		Pane of 8		350.00
a.		Perf. 12		150.00

"P. R. R." (Pennsylvania Rail Road) at top

15TO24	T22c	**orange** (not dated) (1914)		27.50
		Pane of 4		125.00
		Pane of 8		250.00

Perf. 12
"S. W." (El Paso Southwestern Railroad) at top

15TO25	T22c	**yellow** (1909)		375.00
15TO26	T22c	**yellow** (1910)		1,600.
15TO27	T22c	**yellow** (1911)		500.00
15TO28	T22c	**yellow** (1912)		500.00
		Pane of 4		1,500.

Nos. 15TO1-15TO17 and 15TO25-15TO28 are without frank numbers.

TO1

1942		**Litho.**		**Unwmk.**
15TO29	TO1	5c **pink**		6.50 3.00
		Pane of 8		55.00
15TO30	TO1	25c **pale blue**		7.75 4.00
		Pane of 8		65.00

The stamps were issued in booklets to all Postal Telegraph employees in the Armed Forces for use in the United States. They were discontinued Oct. 8, 1943. Used stamps normally bear manuscript cancellations.

Western Union Telegraph Company

Organized by consolidation in 1856. Now extends throughout the United States. Frank stamps have been issued regularly since 1871 in booklet form. The large size, early issues, were in panes of four, 1871-1913; the medium size, later issues, were in panes of six, 1914-32; and the recent small size issues are in panes of nine, 1933 to 1946.

T23   T24

Engraved by the National Bank Note Co.
1871-94				***Perf. 12***

Signature of William Orton

16T1	T23	**green** (not dated) (1871)	35.00	22.50
16T2	T23	**red** (not dated) (1872)	40.00	20.00
		Pane of 4	175.00	
16T3	T23	**blue** (not dated) (1873)	45.00	22.50
		Pane of 4	200.00	
16T4	T23	**brown** (not dated) (1874)	35.00	22.50
		Pane of 4	160.00	
16T5	T24	**deep green** (1875)	37.50	21.00
16T6	T24	**red** (1876)	40.00	
		Pane of 4	180.00	
16T7	T24	**violet** (1877)	42.50	28.00
16T8	T24	**gray brown** (1878)	40.00	

Signature of Norvin Green

16T9	T24	**blue** (1879)	40.00	28.00
		Pane of 4	180.00	

Engraved by the American Bank Note Co.

16T10	T24	**lilac rose** (1880)	27.50	
		Pane of 4	120.00	
16T11	T24	**green** (1881)	25.00	
		Pane of 4	110.00	
16T12	T24	**blue** (1882)	15.00	
		Pane of 4	70.00	
16T13	T24	**yellow brown** (1883)	27.50	
		Pane of 4	120.00	
16T14	T24	**gray violet** (1884)	.60	.30
		Pane of 4	3.00	
16T15	T24	**green** (1885)	3.25	1.75
		Pane of 4	15.00	
16T16	T24	**brown violet** (1886)	3.25	2.00
		Pane of 4	15.00	
a.		Imperf pair, without frank numbers	—	
16T17	T24	**red brown** (1887)	4.50	
		Pane of 4	22.50	
16T18	T24	**blue** (1888)	3.25	
		Pane of 4	15.00	
16T19	T24	**olive green** (1889)	1.75	.80
		Pane of 4	8.00	
16T20	T24	**purple** (1890)	.75	.40
		Pane of 4	3.25	
16T21	T24	**brown** (1891)	1.50	
		Pane of 4	6.50	
16T22	T24	**vermilion** (1892)	1.75	
		Pane of 4	8.00	
16T23	T24	**blue** (1893)	1.40	.40
		Pane of 4	6.25	

Signature of Thos. T. Eckert

16T24	T24	**green** (1894)	.60	.40
		Pane of 4	3.00	

T25

Engraved by the International Bank Note Co.
1895-1913				***Perf. 14***

Signature of Thos. T. Eckert

16T25	T25	**dark brown** (1895)	.50	.40
		Pane of 4	2.50	
16T26	T25	**violet** (1896)	.50	.40
		Pane of 4	2.50	
16T27	T25	**rose red** (1897)	.50	.40
		Pane of 4	2.50	
16T28	T25	**yellow green** (1898)	.50	.40
		Pane of 4	2.50	
a.		Vertical pair, imperf. between		
16T29	T25	**olive green** (1899)	.50	.40
		Pane of 4	2.25	
16T30	T25	**red violet**, perf. 13 (1900)	.50	.45
		Pane of 4	3.00	
16T31	T25	**brown**, perf. 13 (1901)	.50	.40
		Pane of 4	2.50	
16T32	T25	**blue** (1902)	8.00	
		Pane of 4	40.00	

Signature of R.C. Clowry

16T33	T25	**blue** (1902)	8.00	
		Pane of 4	40.00	
16T34	T25	**green** (1903)	.60	.40
		Pane of 4	4.00	
16T35	T25	**red violet** (1904)	.60	
		Pane of 4	2.75	
16T36	T25	**carmine rose** (1905)	.60	.50
		Pane of 4	2.75	
16T37	T25	**blue** (1906)	.80	.40
		Pane of 4	4.00	
a.		Vertical pair, imperf. between	*200.00*	
16T38	T25	**orange brown** (1907)	1.75	.90
		Pane of 4	10.00	
16T39	T25	**violet** (1908)	2.00	1.00
		Pane of 4	9.00	
16T40	T25	**olive green** (1909)	2.00	
		Pane of 4	10.00	

Perf. 12

16T41	T25	**buff** (1910)	.75	.50
		Pane of 4	3.25	

Engraved by the American Bank Note Co.
Signature of Theo. N. Vail

16T42	T24	**green** (1911)	14.00	
		Pane of 4	65.00	
16T43	T24	**violet** (1912)	9.00	
		Pane of 4	42.50	

Imprint of Kihn Brothers Bank Note Company
Perf. 14

16T44	T24	**brown** (1913)	10.00	
		Pane of 4	50.00	
a.		Vert. pair, imperf. between	35.00	
b.		Horiz. pair, imperf. between	40.00	

T26   T27

Engraved by the E.A. Wright Bank Note Co.
1914-15		**Signature of Theo. N. Vail**		***Perf. 12***
16T45	T26	5c **brown** (1914)	1.10	
		Pane of 6	8.00	
a.		Vert. pair, imperf. between	—	
b.		Horiz. pair, imperf. between		
16T46	T26	25c **slate** (1914)	7.00	5.00
		Pane of 6	45.00	

Signature of Newcomb Carlton

16T47	T26	5c **orange** (1915)	1.50	
		Pane of 6	10.00	
		orange yellow	5.00	
16T48	T26	25c **olive green** (1915)	4.00	
		Pane of 6	30.00	
a.		Vert. pair, imperf. horizontally	45.00	

Engraved by the American Bank Note Co.
1916-32
16T49	T27	5c light blue (1916)	1.50	
		Pane of 6	11.00	
16T50	T27	25c carmine lake (1916)	1.75	
		Pane of 6	11.00	

Engraved by the Security Bank Note Co.
Perf. 11
16T51	T27	5c yellow brown (1917)	1.00	
		Pane of 6	7.50	
16T52	T27	25c deep green (1917)	3.00	
		Pane of 6	20.00	
16T53	T27	5c olive green (1918)	.60	
		Pane of 6	4.50	
16T54	T27	25c dark violet (1918)	1.75	
		Pane of 6	14.00	
16T55	T27	5c brown (1919)	1.25	
		Pane of 6	9.00	
16T56	T27	25c blue (1919)	3.25	
		Pane of 6	22.50	

Engraved by the E.A. Wright Bank Note Co.
Perf. 12
16T57	T27	5c dark green (1920)	.65	
		Pane of 6	4.25	
a.		Vert. pair, imperf. between	300.00	
16T58	T27	25c olive green (1920)	.75	
		Pane of 6	5.00	

Engraved by the Security Bank Note Co.
16T59	T27	5c carmine rose (1921)	.55	
		Pane of 6	4.25	
16T60	T27	25c deep blue (1921)	1.30	
		Pane of 6	8.50	
16T61	T27	5c yellow brown (1922)	.55	
		Pane of 6	3.75	
a.		Horizontal pair, imperf. between	16.00	
16T62	T27	25c claret (1922)	1.65	
		Pane of 6	11.50	
16T63	T27	5c olive green (1923)	.65	
		Pane of 6	4.25	
16T64	T27	25c dull violet (1923)	1.35	
		Pane of 6	9.00	
16T65	T27	5c brown (1924)	1.75	
		Pane of 6	12.00	
16T66	T27	25c ultramarine (1924)	4.00	
		Pane of 6	30.00	
16T67	T27	5c olive green (1925)	.65	
		Pane of 6	4.25	
16T68	T27	25c carmine rose (1925)	1.10	
		Pane of 6	7.00	
16T69	T27	5c blue (1926)	1.00	
		Pane of 6	6.50	
16T70	T27	25c light brown (1926)	2.25	
		Pane of 6	14.00	
16T71	T27	5c carmine (1927)	.85	
		Pane of 6	5.75	
16T72	T27	25c green (1927)	7.25	
		Pane of 6	47.50	

Engraved by the E. A. Wright Bank Note Co.
Without Imprint
16T73	T27	5c yellow brown (1928)	.75	
		Pane of 6	4.50	
16T74	T27	25c dark blue (1928)	1.00	
		Pane of 6	6.25	

Engraved by the Security Bank Note Co.
Without Imprint
16T75	T27	5c dark green (1929)	.30	.25
		Pane of 6	2.00	
16T76	T27	25c red violet (1929)	.85	.50
		Pane of 6	5.50	
16T77	T27	5c olive green (1930)	.25	.20
		Pane of 6	1.75	
16T78	T27	25c carmine (1930)	.25	.25
		Pane of 6	2.00	
a.		Horiz. pair, imperf. vertically	35.00	
16T79	T27	5c brown (1931)	.20	.20
		Pane of 6	1.25	
16T80	T27	25c blue (1931)	.20	.20
		Pane of 6	1.50	
16T81	T27	5c green (1932)	.20	.20
		Pane of 6	1.50	
16T82	T27	25c rose carmine (1932)	.20	.20
		Pane of 6	1.50	

T28

1933-40
Lithographed by Oberly & Newell Co.
Without Imprint
Perf. 14x12½
16T83	T28	5c pale brown (1933)	.25	
		Pane of 9	3.25	
16T84	T28	25c green (1933)	.25	
		Pane of 9	3.25	

Lithographed by Security Bank Note Co.
Without Imprint
Perf. 12, 12½
Signature of R. B. White
16T85	T28	5c lake (1934)	.20	
		Pane of 9	2.00	
16T86	T28	25c dark blue (1934)	.20	
		Pane of 9	2.50	
16T87	T28	5c yellow brown (1935)	.20	
		Pane of 9	2.00	
16T88	T28	5c lake (1935)	.20	
		Pane of 9	2.00	
16T89	T28	5c blue (1936)	.25	.20
		Pane of 9	2.75	
16T90	T28	25c apple green (1936)	.20	.20
		Pane of 9	2.50	
16T91	T28	5c bister brown (1937)	.20	
		Pane of 9	2.50	
16T92	T28	25c carmine rose (1937)	.20	
		Pane of 9	2.00	
16T93	T28	5c green (1938)	.25	.20
		Pane of 9	3.00	
16T94	T28	25c blue (1938)	.30	.20
		Pane of 9	3.50	
16T95	T28	5c dull vermilion (1939)	1.00	
		Pane of 9	11.50	
a.		Horiz. pair, imperf. between	—	
16T96	T28	25c bright violet (1939)	.50	
		Pane of 9	6.00	
16T97	T28	5c light blue (1940)	.55	
		Pane of 9	5.75	
16T98	T28	25c bright green (1940)	.50	
		Pane of 9	5.50	

Samuel F. B. Morse
T29

Plates of 90 stamps.
Stamp designed by Nathaniel Yontiff.
Unlike the frank stamps, Nos. 16T99 to 16T103 were sold to the public in booklet form for use in prepayment of telegraph services.

Engraved by Security Bank Note Co. of Philadelphia
1940   Unwmk.   Perf. 12, 12½x12, 12x12½
16T99	T29	1c yellow green	1.25	
		Pane of 5	6.50	
a.		Imperf., pair	50.00	
16T100	T29	2c chestnut	1.75	1.00
		Pane of 5	15.00	
a.		Imperf., pair	50.00	
16T101	T29	5c deep blue	3.00	
		Pane of 5	18.00	
a.		Vert. pair, imperf. btwn.	65.00	
b.		Imperf., pair	50.00	
16T102	T29	10c orange	5.00	
		Pane of 5	27.50	
a.		Imperf., pair	50.00	
16T103	T29	25c bright carmine	4.00	
		Pane of 5	24.00	
a.		Imperf., pair	50.00	

Type of 1933-40
1941   Litho.   Perf. 12½
Without Imprint
Signature of R.B. White
16T104	T28	5c dull rose lilac	.25	
		Pane of 9	2.50	
16T105	T28	25c vermilion	.60	
		Pane of 9	6.00	

1942   Signature of A.N. Williams
16T106	T28	5c brown	.30	
		Pane of 9	3.50	
16T107	T28	25c ultramarine	.30	
		Pane of 9	3.50	

1943
16T108	T28	5c salmon	.30	
		Pane of 9	3.50	
16T109	T28	25c red violet	.30	
		Pane of 9	3.50	

1944
16T110	T28	5c light green	.65	
		Pane of 9	7.25	
16T111	T28	25c buff	.35	
		Pane of 9	3.75	

1945
16T112	T28	5c light blue	.40	
		Pane of 9	5.00	
a.		Pair, imperf. between	—	
16T113	T28	25c light green	.35	
		Pane of 9	3.75	

1946
16T114	T28	5c light bister brown	1.25	
		Pane of 9	15.00	
16T115	T28	25c rose pink	1.00	
		Pane of 9	12.00	

Many of the stamps between 16T1 and 16T98 and 16T104 to 16T115 are known without frank numbers. Several of them are also known with more than one color used in the frank number and with handstamped and manuscript numbers. The numbers are also found in combination with various letters: O, A, B, C, D, etc.

Western Union discontinued the use of Telegraph stamps with the 1946 issue.

United States
Telegraph-Cable-Radio Carriers

Booklets issued to accredited representatives to the World Telecommunications Conferences, Atlantic City, New Jersey, 1947. Valid for messages to points outside the United States. Issued by All America Cables & Radio, Inc., The Commercial Cable Company, Globe Wireless, Limited, Mackay Radio and Telegraph Company, Inc., R C A Communications, Inc., Tropical Radio Telegraph Company and The Western Union Telegraph Company.

TX1

1947   Litho.   Unwmk.   Perf. 12½
17T1	TX1	5c olive bister	7.00	
		Pane of 9	70.00	
		Pane of 9, 8 5c + 1 10c	700.00	
17T2	TX1	10c olive bister	750.00	
17T3	TX1	50c olive bister	9.00	
		Pane of 9	90.00	

UNLISTED ISSUES

Several telegraph or wireless companies other than those listed above have issued stamps or franks, but as evidence of actual use is lacking, they are not listed. Among these are:
American District Telegraph Co.
American Telegraph Typewriter Co.
Continental Telegraph Co.
Los Angeles and San Gabriel Valley Railroad
Marconi Wireless Telegraph Co.
Mercantile Telegraph Co.
Telepost Co.
Tropical Radio Telegraph Co.
United Fruit Co. Wireless Service.
United Wireless Telegraph Co.

ESSAYS

An essay is a proposed design that differs in some way from the issued stamp.

During approximately 1845-1890, when private banknote engravers competed for contracts to print U.S. postage stamps, essays were produced primarily as examples of the quality of the firms' work and as suggestions as to what their finished product would look like. In most cases, dies were prepared, often with stock vignettes used in making banknotes. These dies were used to print essays for the Post Office Department. Rarely did the competitors go so far as to have essay plates made.

From 1894 onward, virtually all stamps were engraved and printed by the Bureau of Engraving and Printing (BEP). This usually required two types of essays. The first was a model design which was approved — or disapproved — by the Postmaster General. Sometimes preliminary drawings were made by the BEP designers, often in an enlarged size, subsequently photographically reduced to stamp size. An accepted stamp design usually became the engraver's model.

Occasionally during the course of engraving the die, a "progressive proof" was pulled to check the progress of the engraver's work. Because these were produced from an incompletely engraved die, they differ from the final design and are listed here as essays.

During approximately 1867-1870, various experiments were conducted to prevent the reuse of postage stamps. These included experimental grill types, safety papers, water-sensitive papers and inks, coupon essays, and others. These also differed in some way from issued stamps, even if the design was identical. A preliminary listing has been made here.

Because the essays in all their various colors have not been examined by the editors, traditional color names have been retained. Some color names have been taken from *Color Standards and Color Nomenclature,* by Robert Ridgway.

Only essays in private hands have been listed. Others exist but are not available to collectors. Some essays were produced after the respective stamps were issued. Year dates are given where information is available.

Essay papers and cards are white, unless described otherwise.

Values are for full-size essays, where they are known. Measurements are given where such information is available. Essays are valued in the grade of very fine, where such exist. Cut-down or faulty examples sell for less, often much less. A number of essays are unique or are reported in very limited quantities. Such items are valued in the conditions in which they exist.

The listings are by manufacturer. Basic stamps may appear in two or more places.

This listing is not complete. Other designs, papers and colors exist. The editors would appreciate reports of unlisted items, as well as photos of items listed herein without illustrations.

POSTMASTERS' PROVISIONALS

NON-CONTIGUOUS LISTINGS
Because many listings are grouped by manufacturer, some catalogue numbers are separated.

No. 5-E1 to 5-E2	follow 11-E16
No. 11-E17 to 72-E5	follow 5-E2
No. 65-E5 to 72-E8	follow 72-E5
No. 63-E13 to 113-E2	follow 72-E8
No. 112-E2 to 129-E2	follow 113-E2
No. 120-E1 to 122-E5	follow 129-E2
No. 115-E3a to 129-E6	follow 122-E5
No. 115-E11 to 116-E8	follow 129-E6
No. 115-E17 to 148-E1	follow 116-E8
No. 145-E2 to 179-E3	follow 148-E1
No. 156-E2 to 191-E2	follow 179-E3
No. 184-E8	follows 191-E2
No. 182-E4 to 190-E3	follow 184-E8
No. 184-E17 to 293-E11	follow 190-E3
No. 285-E10 to 856-E2	follow 293-E11

Albany, N.Y.
Gavit & Co.

1Xa-E1

Design size: 23½x25½mm
Die size: 58x48mm

Benjamin Franklin. With crosshatching about 2mm outside border (usually cut off).

1847
1Xa-E1   5c
  a. Die on India die sunk on large card, printed through a mat to eliminate cross-hatching

brownish black	600.
scarlet	600.
red brown	600.
blue	600.
green	600.

  b. Die on India; some mounted on small card

bluish black	325.
scarlet	325.
brown	325.
yellow green	325.
gray blue	325.

  c. Die on India cut close

black	250.
blue	250.
red brown	250.
scarlet	250.
green	250.
yellow green	250.
brown violet	250.
rose red	250.

  d. Die on bond (1858)

bluish black	375.
scarlet	375.
brown	375.
blue	375.
blue green	375.
violet	375.

  e. Die on ivory glazed paper (1905)

black	900.
dark brown	900.
scarlet	900.
blue	900.

New York, N.Y.
Rawdon, Wright & Hatch

9X1-E1

Design 22mm wide
Die size: 50x102mm

Vignette of Washington. Two transfers laid down vertically on the die 22mm apart; top one retouched, with frame around it (this is a proof). Values are for combined transfers. Vignette essay exists cut apart from proof, value $200 each.

1845
9X1-E1   5c
  a. Die on India (1879)

black	450.
violet black	450.
gray black	450.
scarlet	450.
dull scarlet	450.
orange	450.
brown	450.
dull brown	450.
green	450.
dull green	450.
ultramarine	450.
dull blue	450.
red violet	450.

  b. Die on white bond (1879)

gray black	550.
dull scarlet	550.
dull brown	550.
dull green	550.
dull blue	550.

  c. Die on white glazed paper, die sunk (1879)

gray black	700.

POSTAGE STAMPS

1847 ISSUE
Rawdon, Wright, Hatch & Edson

The original model for No. 1 exists, engraved vignette of Franklin mounted on frame, part of frame engraved, rest in pencil, ink and a gray wash. Formerly

No. 1-E1, now in the National Postal Museum collection.

Engraved vignette only, matted.
1-E2   5c Die on India (1895), brown   2,500.

1-E3

Engraved frame only, matted from complete die.
1-E3   5c Die on India (1895), brown   2,500.
         The 1895 dates are suppositional.

The original model for No. 2 exists, engraved vignette of Washington mounted (replaced) on frame, "POST OFFICE" and "FIVE CENTS" engraved on former No. 1-E1, "U" and "S" at top and "X" in bottom corners in black ink, rest in pencil and a gray wash. Formerly No. 2-E1, now in the National Postal Museum collection.

Incomplete engraving of entire design, area around vignette incomplete, frame lines and "RWH&E" printer's initials not yet added.
2-E1   10c Die on proof paper, affixed to stiff
          blue laid paper backing, black   —

2-E2   2-E3

Engraved vignette only.
2-E2   10c Die on India (1895)
         black   2,500.
         brownish black   2,500.
         brown   2,500.

Engraved frame only.
2-E3   10c Die on India (1895)
         black   2,500.
         brown orange   2,500.
         The 1895 dates are suppositional.

1851 ISSUE
Attributed to
Rawdon, Wright, Hatch & Edson

11-E1   11-E2

Design size: 18½x23mm
Large 3 in vignette.
11-E1   3c Die on India
          black   3,000.
          blue   10,000.

Design size: 19x24mm
Vignette of Washington.
11-E2   3c
   a. Die on India
          black   4,500.
   b. Die on proof paper, die sunk on
          40x51mm card
          black   4,500.

Attributed to
Gavit & Co.

11-E3   11-E4

Design size: 19x23mm
Vignette of Franklin. Three states of die. Second state has double line dash above P of POSTAGE, third state has single dash above P and dot in O of POSTAGE.

11-E3   3c
   a. Die on India, die sunk on card
          warm black   750.
          scarlet   750.
          red brown   750.
          blue green   750.
   b. Die on India, 41x43mm or smaller
          black   300.
          greenish black   300.
          carmine   300.
          scarlet   300.
          yellow green   300.
          brown   300.
          blue green   300.
          dull blue   300.
          dark blue   300.
   c. Die on India, cut to shape
          warm black   250.
          cool black   250.
          black   250.
          carmine   250.
          orange   250.
          brown   250.
          dark green   250.
          yellow green   250.
          olive   250.
          light blue   250.
          dark blue   250.
          violet   250.
          scarlet   250.
   d. Die on bond
          cool black   250.
          scarlet   250.
          orange brown   250.
          brown   250.
          green   250.
          blue   250.

   e. Die on ivory glazed paper
          black   750.
          dark brown   750.
          scarlet   750.
          blue   750.
   f. Die on thin card, dusky blue, cut to shape 200.
   g. Die on Francis Patent experimental paper
          with trial cancel
          black   1,250.
          dark blue   1,250.
          brown   1,250.

Design size: 19x22mm
Die size: 47x75mm
Vignette of Washington. Two states of die. Second state has small diagonal dash in top of left vertical border below arch.

11-E4   3c
   a. Die on India, die sunk on card
          black   750.
          scarlet   750.
          brown red   750.
          blue green   750.
   b. Die on India, about 30x40mm or smaller
          orange   400.
          orange brown   400.
          brown   400.
          dusky yellow brown   400.
          yellow green   400.
          blue green   400.
          dull blue   400.
          red violet   400.
          deep red orange   400.
          black   400.
   c. Die on bond (1858)
          black   400.
          scarlet   400.
          brown   400.
          green   400.
          blue   400.
   d. Die on ivory glazed paper (1858)
          black   750.
          dark brown   750.
          scarlet   750.
          blue   750.
   e. Die on proof paper (1858)
          cool black   475.
          dull red   475.
          dull brown   475.
          dull blue green   475.
          dull blue   475.

Bradbury, Wilkinson & Co., England

11-E5

Design size: 20½x23½mm
Vignette of Washington.

11-E5 3c
  a. On stiff stamp paper about stamp size
black	1,250.
violet red	1,250.
deep carmine	1,250.
dusky carmine	1,250.
deep scarlet	1,250.
orange brown	1,250.
deep green	1,250.
blue	1,250.
ultramarine	1,250.
brown	1,250.
  b. On card
violet black	1,250.
dull scarlet	1,250.
blue	1,250.
green	1,250.
brown	1,250.
  c. On stiff bond
brown	1,250.
blue	1,250.
violet black	1,250.

Draper, Welsh & Co.

11-E6   11-E7

Design size: 18x23mm
Vignette of Washington.

11-E6 3c Surface printed on card, black   750.

Design size: 17½x24mm
Die size: 44x106mm
Engraved vignette of Washington.

11-E7 3c
  a. Die on India, about 44x105mm, die sunk
    on card, in vert. pair with No. 11-E8
black	1,500.
scarlet	1,500.
brown red	1,500.
green	1,500.
  b. Die on India, about 40x45mm or smaller
warm black	400.
cool black	400.
dark carmine	400.
scarlet	400.
brown red	400.
orange brown	400.
brown	400.
yellow green	400.
blue green	400.
blue	400.
dull blue	400.
brown violet	400.
  c. Die on India, stamp size
rose	350.
scarlet	350.
red brown	350.
brown	350.
green	350.
cool black	350.
warm black	350.
yellow green	350.
brown violet	350.
ultramarine blue	350.
  d. Die on bond
black	400.
scarlet	400.
brown	400.
blue green	400.
blue	400.
  e. Die on ivory glazed paper
black	750.
dark brown	750.
scarlet	750.
blue	750.

11-E8

Design size: 19½x24mm
Die size: 44x106mm
On same die 30mm below No. 11-E7
Vignette of Washington.

11-E8 3c
  a. Die on India, 28x32mm or smaller
black	300.
dark carmine	300.
scarlet	300.
brown red	300.
red brown	300.
orange brown	300.
brown	300.
yellow green	300.
green	300.
blue green	300.
blue	300.
  b. Die on bond, about 32x40mm
black	225.
scarlet	225.
brown	225.
green	225.
blue	225.
  c. Die on ivory glazed paper
black	750.
dark brown	750.
scarlet	750.
blue	750.

11-E8D   11-E9

Design size: 18x23mm
Vignette of Washington.
Washington vignette only. Same head as No. 11-E6 through
11-E8, but with more bust. No gridwork in background.

11-E8D 3c Die on proof paper, mounted on
          card, black   750.

Design size (No. 11-E9a): 18x33mm
Vignette design size (Nos. 11-E9b, 11-E9c): 18x22mm
As No. 11-E8D, gridwork added to background oval.

11-E9 3c
  a. Die on India
black	350.
scarlet	350.
  b. Die on India, single line frame
black	300.
blue	300.
dark carmine	300.
orange red	300.
lilac	300.
brown	300.
scarlet	300.
rose violet	300.
deep yellow green	300.
  c. Die on India, imprint of Jocelyn, Draper,
    Welsh & Co., New York
black	300.
blue	300.
dark carmine	300.
orange red	300.
lilac	300.
brown	300.
scarlet	300.
rose violet	300.
deep yellow green	300.

Danforth, Bald & Co.

11-E10   11-E11

Vignette size: 18x22mm
Design size: 20x26mm

Die size: 57x74mm
Vignette of Washington. Double line frame.

11-E10 3c
  a. Die on India, die sunk on card
black	750.
scarlet	750.
red brown	750.
green	750.
  b. Die on India, off card, about 33x38mm
black	175.
scarlet	175.
brown	175.
blue	175.
green	175.
dull violet	175.
dull blue	175.
red brown	175.
rose	175.
  c. Die on bond, black   350.
  d. Die on ivory glazed paper
black	750.
dark brown	750.
scarlet	750.
blue	750.

Washington vignette only.

11-E11 3c Die on India
black	325.
dull rose	325.
scarlet	325.
orange	325.
brown orange	325.
brown	325.
green	325.
dark blue	325.
dull violet	325.
rose violet	325.

11-E12

Design size: 20x26mm
Die size: 62x66mm
Vignette of Washington. Single line frame. Two states of die.
Second state shows scars in lathe lines in front of neck over T,
and small dot below design. A third printing has more scars in
front of neck.

11-E12 3c
  a. Die on India, die sunk on card
black	750.
scarlet	750.
brown red	750.
dusky brown yellow	750.
brown	750.
green	750.
blue	750.
dull blue	750.
  b. Die on India, about 43x45mm
black	300.
scarlet	300.
deep scarlet	300.
brown	300.
yellow brown	300.
green	300.
yellow green	300.
blue	300.
dull blue	300.
dark blue	300.
ultramarine blue	300.
orange	300.
red	300.
  c. Die on bond
dusky brown yellow	275.
blue	275.
  d. Die on ivory glazed paper
black	750.
dark brown	750.
scarlet	750.
blue	750.
  e. Plate on thick buff wove
rose	125.
violet brown	125.
orange	125.
dark orange	125.
pink orange	125.
  f. Plate on India, dark red orange   150.
  g. Plate on ivory wove (head more com-
    pletely engraved, ruled lines between
    designs)
black	125.
dark carmine	125.
yellow	125.
blue	125.

11-E13

Design size: 20x26mm
Die size: 62x66mm
Vignette of Washington. No. 11-E12 reengraved: more dark
dots in forehead next to hair, thus line between forehead and
hair more distinct.

11-E13 3c
  a. Die on India, die sunk on card
black	750.
scarlet	750.
brown red	750.
brown	750.
green	750.

  b. Die on ivory glazed paper
black	750.
dark brown	750.
scarlet	750.
blue	750.

Bald, Cousland & Co.

11-E14

11-E15

Design size: 22x28mm
Die size: 95x43mm
Vignette of Washington. On same die with Nos. 11-E16 and
incomplete 11-E14.

11-E14 3c
  a. Die on India
black	450.
scarlet	450.
red brown	450.
brown	450.
yellow green	450.
green	450.
blue green	450.
orange brown	450.
rose pink	450.
dull blue	450.
violet	450.

  b. Die on bond
black	250.
scarlet	250.
brown	250.
blue green	250.
blue	250.

Design size: 28x22½mm
POSTAGE / 3 / CENTS in scalloped frame.

11-E15 3c
  a. Die on India, die sunk on card
black	750.
scarlet	750.
red brown	750.
green	750.
slate	750.

  b. Die on bond, about 40x30mm
black	175.
scarlet	175.
brown	175.
green	175.
blue	175.
slate	275.

  c. Die on ivory glazed paper
black	750.
dark brown	750.
scarlet	750.
blue	750.

11-E16

Design size: 28x22½mm
U.S. at sides of 3.

11-E16 3c
  a. Die on India, cut small
black	275.
light red	275.

red brown	275.
brown	275.
yellow green	275.
blue green	275.
green	275.
blue	275.
red violet	275.

  b. Die on bond, about 40x30mm
black	175.
scarlet	175.
brown	175.
red brown	175.
green	175.
blue green	175.
blue	175.
violet	175.
slate	175.

  c. Die on India, Nos. 11-E14 and 11-E16
    with albino 11-E14
black	1,000.
scarlet	1,000.
brown	1,000.
green	1,000.
blue	1,000.
red violet	1,000.

  d. Die on bond
black	225.
scarlet	225.
brown	225.
green	225.
blue green	225.
gray blue	225.

  e. Die on ivory glazed paper, 64x78mm,
black	650.

  f. Die on India, die sunk on card
black	900.
scarlet	900.

Toppan, Carpenter, Casilear & Co.

5-E1

5-E1E

5-E1Ef

Design size: 20½x26mm
Franklin vignette.

5-E1 1c
  a. Die on old proof paper, master die short-
    ened to 18½x22½mm, black   1,500.
  b. Die on thick old proof paper, black   1,500.
  c. Pair, Nos. 5-E1b, 11-E23, black   2,000.

Design size: 20x24mm
Similar to No. 5-E1 but with no additional shaded oval border.

5-E1E 1c Die on thin card, black blue   —
  f. Block of 4 in combination with pair of No.
    11-E23, on old proof paper, black   3,500.

5-E2

Complete design, but with SIX CENTS in value tablet.
5-E2 1c Die on India, black, cut to shape   2,750.

11-E17

11-E18

Design size: 21½x25mm
Die size: 50½x60mm
Vignette of Washington.

11-E17 3c
  a. Die on India, 22x26mm, rose carmine   2,500.
  b. Die on old ivory paper, rose carmine   2,500.
  c. Die on proof paper, printed through a
    mat (1903)
black	175.
bright carmine	175.
dull carmine	175.
dark violet red	175.
dull scarlet	175.
dull violet	175.
dull red violet	175.
deep yellow	175.
deep orange	175.
orange brown	175.
dull brown olive	175.
deep green	175.
dark blue green	175.
ultramarine	175.
dark blue	175.
brown	175.

  d. Die on colored card (1903)
deep orange, *ivory*	300.
dark blue, *pale green*	300.
orange brown, *light blue*	300.

      See note above No. 63-E1.

Design size: 20½x22½mm
Washington. Vignette has solid color background. Crack
between N and T of CENTS.

11-E18 3c Die on India, card mounted,
    24½x25mm
black	2,000.
carmine	2,000.

Design size: 20½x22½mm
Washington. Like No. 11-E18 except background of vignette
is clearly engraved horizontal and vertical lines. Crack between
N and T of CENTS.

11-E18A 3c Die on India, die sunk on
    60x50mm card, carmine   7,000.
  b. As No. 11-E18A, cut down to stamp's
    size, black   2,000.
  c. As No. 11-E18A, on old ivory paper,
    cut down to stamp size, rose car-
    mine   2,000.

11-E19

11-E20

No. 11-E19
Design size: 20½x22½mm
Similar to No. 11-E18, with a slightly modified design,
vignette background engraved horiz. and vert. lines. In pair with
No. 11-E20.

No. 11-E20
Design size: 20x22½mm
Blank curved top and bottom labels. In pair with 11-E19. Also
found in pair with 11-E21.

11-E19 3c Die on India, Nos. 11-E19, 11-E20
    mounted on card, black   6,000.

11-E21

Straight labels. Similar to No. 11-E19 but labels erased and
vignette cut out. In pair with No. 11-E20.

11-E21 3c Die on India, Nos. 11-E20, 11-E21
    mounted on card, black   4,500.

11-E22

11-E23

Die size: 37½x46mm
Similar to issued stamp except lathework impinges on colorless oval.

11-E22 3c Die on India
dusky blue   *5,000.*
black   *5,000.*

Some students consider No. 11-E22 to be proof strikes of the die used to make the "Roosevelt" and Panama-Pacific small die proofs, as the lathework impinges on the colorless oval of Nos. 11P2 and 11P2a as well.

Design size: 18x22mm
Washington vignette only. From master die (21½mm high) with more robe and dark background.

11-E23 3c
  a. Master die impression, old proof paper,
    black   *900.*
  b. Block of 4, 2mm between ovals, thick old
    ivory paper, black   *3,000.*

13-E1   13-E2

Design as adopted but top label has pencil lettering only, also no lines in leaf ornaments around Xs in top corners.

13-E1 10c Die on India, black   *3,000.*

Similar to No. 13-E1 but vert. shading around Xs and lines added in leaf ornaments. No lettering in top label.

13-E2 10c Die on India, black   *3,000.*

17-E1   17-E2

Design size: 19x21½mm
Block sinkage size: 57x49mm
Engine engraved frame without labels or interior shadow lines from straight bands and left side rosettes. No small equilateral crosses in central row of diamonds. Original vignette cut out and replaced by engraved vignette of Washington as adopted.

17-E1 12c Die on India, cut close, mounted
    on block sunk card, 77x57mm,
    black   *10,000.*

Similar to adopted design but no small vertical equilateral crosses in center rows of diamond networks at top, sides and bottom.

17-E2 12c Die on India, brown violet, cut close   *900.*
17-E3 12c As No. 17-E2, die on wove, brown
    violet, cut close   *750.*

37-E1   37-E2

Design size: 19½x25½mm
Die size: 46x49mm or larger
Probably not the die used to make the plates. No exterior layout lines. Oval outline recut at bottom of jabot and vignette

background etched much darker. Light horizontal lines on stock below chin.

37-E1 24c Die on India, black   *2,500.*

Incomplete essay for frame only as adopted: no outer frame-line and lathework not retouched. Also known with 37TC1 struck above it on same piece.

37-E2 24c Die on India, black   —

38-E1

Design size: 19x24mm
Incomplete engraving of entire design. Scrolls at each side of 30 have only one outer shading line.

38-E1 30c Die on India, black, cut to stamp
    size, black   *2,500.*

1861 ISSUE
Toppan, Carpenter & Co.

Examples on 1861 paper and in 1861 colors are rare. Most of the following listed on proof paper, colored card and bond paper are 1903 reprints. Ten sets of reprints on proof paper (and fewer on colored card, bond and pelure papers) supposedly were made for Ernest Schernikow, who bought the original dies about 1903. Similar reprints in similar colors on the same papers also were made of Nos. LO1-E2, 11-E18 and the Philadelphia sanitary fair stamps, plus several master dies of vignettes.

63-E1b   63-E2b

Vignette size: 18½x21½mm
Die size: 49x51mm
Franklin vignette only.

63-E1 1c
  a. Die on proof paper (1903)
    black   *75.*
    carmine   *75.*
    dark carmine   *75.*
    scarlet   *75.*
    red brown   *75.*
    orange   *75.*
    yellow brown   *75.*
    dark brown   *75.*
    violet brown   *75.*
    light green   *75.*
    green   *75.*
    dark blue   *75.*
    ultramarine   *75.*
    red violet   *75.*
    dark violet   *75.*
    dusky olive green   *75.*
  b. Die on colored card (1903)
    orange red, *pale yellow*   *125.*
    orange, *pale pink*   *125.*
    yellow brown, *buff*   *125.*
    dark blue, *pink*   *125.*
    dark violet, *pale olive*   *125.*
    dull violet, *blue*   *125.*
    deep green, *pale blue*   *125.*
    violet, *light green*   *125.*
  c. Die on green bond (1903)
    black   *125.*
    dismal red   *125.*
    green   *125.*

Franklin vignette with U S POSTAGE at top and ONE CENT at bottom.

63-E2 1c
  a. Die on proof paper (1903)
    black   *100.*
    carmine   *100.*
    dark carmine   *100.*
    scarlet   *100.*
    red brown   *100.*
    orange   *100.*
    yellow brown   *100.*
    violet brown   *100.*
    gray brown   *100.*
    light green   *100.*
    green   *100.*
    blue   *100.*
    red violet   *100.*
    ultramarine   *100.*
    dusky olive   *100.*

  b. Die on old proof paper, outer line at sides
    of oval missing (1861), black   *1,000.*
  c. Die on green bond (1903)
    orange   *150.*
    orange brown   *150.*
    violet   *150.*
  d. Die on colored card (1903)
    deep green, *pale blue*   *150.*
    violet, *light green*   *150.*
    dark orange red, *pale dull green*   *150.*
    olive, *ivory*   *150.*
    brown, *pink*   *150.*
    scarlet, *yellow*   *150.*

63-E3

Side ornaments added.

63-E3 1c
  a. Die on old proof paper (1861)
    black   *1,250.*
    blue   *1,250.*
  b. Die on stiff old ivory paper (1861)
    black   *1,250.*
    blue   *1,750.*
  c. Die on colored card (1903)
    black, *ivory*   *150.*
    brown, *pale pink*   *150.*
    blue, *blue*   *150.*
    orange brown, *pale pink*   *150.*
    gray olive, *ivory*   *150.*
    gray olive, *buff*   *150.*
    scarlet, *pale yellow*   *150.*
  d. Die on proof paper (1903)
    black   *85.*
    carmine   *85.*
    dark carmine   *85.*
    scarlet   *85.*
    red brown   *85.*
    orange   *85.*
    yellow brown   *85.*
    violet brown   *85.*
    light green   *85.*
    green   *85.*
    blue   *85.*
    violet   *85.*
    red violet   *85.*
    orange brown   *85.*
    dusky olive   *85.*
    ultramarine   *85.*
  e. Die on green bond (1903)
    carmine   *150.*
    orange   *150.*
    violet   *150.*
  f. Die on glazed card, black   —

63-E4   63-E4E

With upper and lower right corners incomplete. Serifs of 1s point to right.

63-E4 1c Die on old proof paper (1861), black   *2,250.*

As No. 63-E4 but with pencil shading in upper right corner around the "1".

63-E4E 1c Die on old proof paper (1861),
    black   *3,500.*

63-E5   63-E6

With four corners and numerals in pencil (ornaments differ in each corner).

63-E5 1c Die on old proof paper (1861), blue — 2,750.

As No. 63-E5 but ornaments different.

63-E6 1c Die on old proof paper (1861), blue — 3,500.

63-E7

As Nos. 63-E5 and 63-E6 but ornaments different.

63-E7 1c Die on old proof paper (1861), blue — 3,250.

Die proof of No. 5 with lower corners cut out of India paper and resketched in pencil on card beneath.

63-E8 1c Die on India, on card (1861), black — 2,000.

63-E9

Completely engraved design.

63-E9 1c
  a. Die on India, cut to shape (1861)
    black, on brown toned paper — 1,000.
    blue — 600.
  b. Die on India, about 58x57mm, die sunk
    on card (1861)
    blue — 2,000.
  c. Die on old proof paper, about 48x55mm
    (1861)
    black — 2,000.
  d. Die on large old white ivory paper (1861)
    black — 2,000.
    blue — 2,000.
  e. Die on proof paper, printed through mat
    (1903)
    black — 100.
    carmine — 100.
    dark carmine — 100.
    scarlet — 100.
    orange — 100.
    orange brown — 100.
    yellow brown — 100.
    light green — 100.
    green — 100.
    black blue — 100.
    violet — 100.
    red violet — 100.
    violet brown — 100.
    gray — 100.
    blue — 100.
    ultramarine — 100.
  f. Die on bond (1903)
    orange — 125.
    dismal blue green — 125.
  g. Die on bond, Walls of Troy wmk. (1903)
    carmine — 200.
    orange red — 200.
    orange — 200.
    orange brown — 200.
    dark green — 200.
    light ultramarine — 200.
  h. Die on bond, double line of scallops wmk.
    (1903)
    orange red — 200.
    dark green — 200.
  i. Die on green bond (1903)
    dismal carmine — 125.
    dismal violet brown — 125.
    dull dark green — 125.
  j. Die on pinkish pelure (1903)
    orange red — 300.
    brown red — 300.
    brown orange — 300.
    dull blue green — 300.
    violet — 300.
  k. Die on colored card (1903)
    black, *pale blue* — 225.
    carmine, *pale yellow* — 225.
    carmine, *pale pink* — 225.
    brown red, *pale pink* — 225.
    chestnut, *pale olive* — 225.
    dismal olive, *buff* — 225.
    ultramarine, *ivory* — 225.
  l. Die on stiff card (1903), green — 250.

65-E1

65-E2

Vignette size: 16½x19mm
Die size: 49x50mm
1851 master die of Washington vignette only.

65-E1 3c
  a. Die on proof paper (1903)
    black — 75.
    carmine — 75.
    dark carmine — 75.
    scarlet — 75.
    red brown — 75.
    orange — 75.
    brown orange — 75.
    violet brown — 75.
    dusky olive — 75.
    light green — 75.
    green — 75.
    dark blue — 75.
    ultramarine — 75.
    lilac — 75.
    red violet — 75.
  b. Die on green bond (1903)
    red — 125.
    brown — 125.
    blue — 125.
    olive — 125.
  c. Die on colored card (1903)
    carmine, *pale green* — 125.
    scarlet, *yellow* — 125.
    orange, *ivory* — 125.
    olive brown, *blue* — 125.
    dark blue, *pink* — 125.
    violet, *buff* — 125.
    dark green, *pink* — 125.

With tessellated frame, bottom label and diamond blocks. Without rosettes, top label and diamond blocks.

65-E2 3c
  a. Die on old proof paper (1861)
    black — 1,000.
    red — 1,000.
  b. Die on proof paper, printed through a mat
    (1903)
    black — 85.
    carmine — 85.
    dark carmine — 85.
    scarlet — 85.
    orange — 85.
    yellow — 85.
    yellow brown — 85.
    dusky gray — 85.
    light green — 85.
    green — 85.
    black blue — 85.
    ultramarine — 85.
    lilac — 85.
    dark lilac — 85.
    red violet — 85.
  c. Die on green bond (1903)
    black — 150.
    dull orange red — 150.
    orange — 150.
    orange brown — 150.
    blue violet — 150.
    black blue — 150.
    dusky green — 150.
  d. Die on dull pale gray blue thin wove
    (1903)
    dull red — 300.
    orange — 300.
    yellow brown — 300.
    dusky green — 300.
    black blue — 300.
  e. Die on colored card (1903)
    black, *light blue* — 150.
    orange red, *yellow* — 150.
    red brown, *ivory* — 150.
    light green, *pink* — 150.
    green, *light green* — 150.
    blue, *buff* — 150.
  f. Die on India
    black — —
    rose — —

65-E3

65-E4

With top label and diamond blocks.

65-E3 3c
  a. Die on old proof paper (1861)
    brown red — 1,500.
    black — 1,500.

  b. Same as No. 65-E3 with numerals in pen-
    cil, Die on old proof paper (1861), black — 3,500.
  c. Die on proof paper, no numerals, printed
    through a mat (1903)
    black — 90.
    carmine — 90.
    dark carmine — 90.
    scarlet — 90.
    orange — 90.
    yellow — 90.
    yellow brown — 90.
    dusky olive — 90.
    light green — 90.
    green — 90.
    black blue — 90.
    violet blue — 90.
    violet brown — 90.
    lilac — 90.
    red violet — 90.
  d. Die on green bond (1903)
    dull scarlet — 150.
    dim red — 150.
    orange — 150.
    yellow brown — 150.
    green — 150.
    dusky blue — 150.
    violet — 150.
    black — 150.
  e. Die on colored card (1903)
    black, *buff* — 150.
    scarlet, *ivory* — 150.
    orange, *light yellow* — 150.
    brown, *light blue* — 150.
    violet blue, *light pink* — 150.
    violet, *light green* — 150.
  f. Die on pink thin wove (1903)
    dull yellow — 300.
    dismal red — 300.
    yellow brown — 300.
    dusky blue green — 300.
    dusky blue — 300.

Complete die, with numerals in rosette circles.

65-E4 3c
  a. Die on India, 75x76mm die sinkage
    (1861)
    black — 1,500.
    carmine — 1,500.
  b. Die on old proof paper (1861)
    black — 1,500.
    dark red — 1,500.
  c. Die on India, cut to shape (1861)
    black — 1,000.
    carmine — 1,000.

67-E1a, Die I   67-E1b, Die II

Vignette size: 13½x16mm
Jefferson vignette only. Two dies: die I incomplete, light background in vignette; die II background essentially complete.

67-E1 5c
  a. Die I on old proof paper, black (1861) — 750.
  b. Die II on proof paper (1903)
    black — 75.
    carmine — 75.
    dark carmine — 75.
    scarlet — 75.
    red brown — 75.
    orange brown — 75.
    brown — 75.
    dusky olive — 75.
    green — 75.
    dark green — 75.
    black blue — 75.
    ultramarine — 75.
    violet brown — 75.
    red violet — 75.
    lilac — 75.
  c. Die II on colored card (1903)
    olive, *buff* — 150.
    carmine, *pale yellow* — 150.
    scarlet, *green* — 150.
    brown, *pink* — 150.
    black, *ivory* — 150.
    ultramarine, *pale blue* — 150.
  d. Die II on green bond (1903)
    orange brown — 150.
    dismal red brown — 150.
    dark green — 150.
    violet — 150.
    black blue — 150.
  e. Die II on old thin ivory paper (1903)
    green — 175.
    dark carmine — 175.
  f. Die I on old thin ivory paper (1861), dark
    blue — 1,000.
  g. Die I on old proof paper (1861), dusky ul-
    tramarine — 1,500.
  h. Die II on old ivory paper (1861), navy
    blue — 750.

67-E2

Vignette die II framed, with spaces for numerals.

67-E2   5c
   a. Die II on proof paper (1903)

black	95.
carmine	95.
dark carmine	95.
scarlet	95.
red brown	95.
orange	95.
yellow brown	95.
dusky olive	95.
violet brown	95.
light green	95.
green	95.
blue	95.
ultramarine	95.
red violet	95.
lilac	95.

   b. Die II on colored card (1903)

orange brown, *light yellow*	175.
deep blue, *light pink*	175.
dusky olive, *light buff*	175.
dark green, *pale blue*	175.
red violet, *ivory*	175.

   c. Die II on green bond (1903)

orange brown	160.
olive green	160.
violet	160.
blue	160.
ultramarine	160.

   d. Die I on old proof paper (1861), black   2,000.

67-E3

67-E4

With numerals.

67-E3   5c
   a. Die I on proof paper, printed through a
      mat (1903)

black	125.
carmine	125.
dark carmine	125.
scarlet	125.
red brown	125.
yellow brown	125.
dark brown	125.
violet brown	125.
light green	125.
green	125.
dark blue	125.
lilac	125.
ultramarine	125.
red violet	125.
dusky olive	125.

   b. Die I on soft laid paper (1861)

black	750.
dark brown	750.
orange brown	750.

   c. Die II on old proof paper, pencil designs
      drawn in corners (1861), black   2,500.
   d. Die I on old proof paper, outer lines on
      corner curves missing (1861), black   500.
   e. Die I on colored card (1903)

orange red, *buff*	175.
orange red, *light yellow*	175.
olive green, *pale green*	175.
deep green, *ivory*	175.
dark blue, *light pink*	175.
violet brown, *light blue*	175.

   f. Die I on green bond (1903)

black	160.
scarlet	160.
brown	160.
green	160.

   g. Die I on yellow pelure (1903)

scarlet	350.
brown red	350.
brown	350.
dark green	350.
violet	350.
blue	350.

   h. Die I on bond, Walls of Troy wmk. (1903)

dark orange	250.
blue	250.
carmine	250.

   i. Die I on bond, two line scalloped border
      wmk. (1903)

dark blue green	250.
scarlet	250.

Complete die II design with corner ornaments.

67-E4   5c
   a. Die II on India, cut to shape (1861), black   500.
   b. Die II on brown toned paper (1861), cut
      to shape

black	1,000.
brown	1,000.

   c. Die II on old proof paper (1861)

orange brown	1,500.
black	1,500.

   d. Die II on old ivory paper (1861), black   1,500.
   e. Die II on old proof paper, additional
      frameline drawn on curved corners and
      small circle drawn in each corner
      (1861), black   2,500.
   f. Die II on proof paper, printed through a
      mat (1903)

black	125.
carmine	125.
dark carmine	125.
scarlet	125.
orange	125.
brown	125.
yellow brown	125.
dusky olive	125.
light green	125.
green	125.
blue	125.
black blue	125.
violet brown	125.
red violet	125.
lilac	125.
ultramarine	125.

   g. Die II on colored card (1903)

red, *light yellow*	150.
brown, *buff*	150.
olive green, *light pink*	150.
dark violet	150.
violet brown, *pale green*	150.
dusky yellow green, *dull pale*	150.
blue green	150.
brown, *ivory*	150.

   h. Die II on green bond (1903)

black	125.
dull dark orange	125.
violet	125.

   i. Die II on bond, Walls of Troy wmk. (1903)

scarlet	250.
deep red	250.
dark green	250.

   j. Die II on bond, two-line scalloped border
      wmk. (1903)

deep orange	250.
blue	250.

   k. Die II on greenish pelure (1903)

orange	350.
olive brown	350.
dark green	350.

   l. Die II on bluish pelure (1903), red brown   450.

69-E1

69-E2

Vignette size: 15x17mm
   Washington vignette only. Two dies: die I incomplete, horiz.
background lines irregularly spaced, space occurring about
every 2mm; die II more engraving on face, horiz. background
lines regularly spaced, outer oval border smudged. Die II known
only as 1851 master die.

69-E1   12c
   a. Die I on old proof paper (1851), black   650.
   b. Die I on proof paper (1903)

black	60.
carmine	60.
dark carmine	60.
scarlet	60.
red brown	60.
orange	60.
yellow brown	60.
violet brown	60.
gray brown	60.
light green	60.
green	60.
blue	60.
black blue	60.
red violet	60.
lilac	60.
ultramarine	60.

   c. Die I on green bond (1903)

black	150.
red brown	150.
brown	150.

   d. Die I on colored card (1903)

dark carmine, *ivory*	150.
dark carmine, *light blue*	150.
dark olive, *buff*	150.
dark green, *light yellow*	150.
dark blue, *pale green*	150.
violet brown, *light pink*	150.

Die II with curved labels at top and bottom.

69-E2   12c
   a. Die II on proof paper, some printed
      through a mat (1903)

black	75.
carmine	75.
dark carmine	75.
scarlet	75.
orange	75.
yellow	75.
yellow brown	75.
violet brown	75.
gray brown	75.
light green	75.
green	75.
light blue	75.
black blue	75.
red violet	75.
lilac	75.
ultramarine	75.

   b. Die I on old proof paper (1861)

dim red violet	500.
red violet	500.

   c. Die I on dull light green bond (1903)

black	150.
dull red	150.
dim orange	150.
yellow brown	150.
dusky green	150.
dusky blue	150.
red violet	150.

   d. Die I on pale yellow thin wove (1903)

dim red	200.
deep orange red	200.
yellow brown	200.
dusky blue	200.
red violet	200.

   e. Die I on colored card (1903)

dull red, *light pink*	150.
orange red, *buff*	150.
brown, *light blue*	150.
dark olive, *light yellow*	150.
dull dark blue, *ivory*	150.
violet, *pale green*	150.

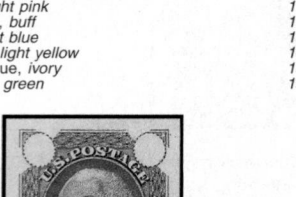
69-E3

Frame incomplete: all four rosettes blank.

69-E3   12c
   a. Die on proof paper (1903)

black	125.
carmine	125.
dark carmine	125.
scarlet	125.
red brown	125.
orange	125.
orange brown	125.
violet brown	125.
light green	125.
green	125.
light blue	125.
black blue	125.
red violet	125.
lilac	125.
ultramarine	125.

   b. Die on old proof paper (1861)

black	800.
olive gray	800.

   c. Die on old ivory, top border and half of
      rosettes missing (1861), black   800.
   d. Die on stiff old ivory, top border missing
      (1861), bluish black   800.
   e. Die on colored card, top border missing
      (1903)

orange brown, *light blue*	175.
deep green, *light yellow*	175.
deep blue, *light pink*	175.
violet, *ivory*	175.
deep yellow orange, *pale yellow green*	175.
brown, *buff*	175.

   f. Die on green bond, top border missing
      (1903)

orange	175.
green	175.
violet	175.

   g. Die on old proof paper, 1851 die with bor-
      der lines complete, upper right rosette
      blank (1861)

orange	800.
dark green	800.
ultramarine	800.
violet	800.

   h. Die I on old proof paper, vignette back-
      ground incomplete or worn, stock on
      neck unfinished (1861)
   i. Die I on old proof paper, as 69-E3h but
      both upper rosettes blank (1861), ul-
      tramarine   1,000.

69-E3j

69-E3k

j. Die I on old proof paper, as No. 69-E3h but both upper plus lower left rosettes blank (1861), ultramarine .... 1,000.
k. Die I on old proof paper, as No. 69-E3h but both lower plus upper left rosettes blank, corner borders removed around blank rosettes (1861), ultramarine .... 1,000.
l. Die I on old proof paper, as No. 69-E3h but all rosettes blank, border lines complete (1861)
  dim scarlet .... 750.
  orange .... 750.
  green .... 750.
  ultramarine .... 750.
  violet .... 750.
m. Die I on white wove, as No. 69-E3l (1861), scarlet .... 750.
n. Die I on old proof paper, complete design (1861)
  orange .... 750.
  dark red .... 750.
  orange red .... 750.
  ultramarine .... 750.
o. Die I on pale yellow thin wove (1903), dark red .... 750.
p. Die I on pink thin wove (1903), blue .... 750.
q. Die I on pale pink (1903), blue .... 750.

69-E4

Original complete design with numerals in corners.
69-E4 12c
a. Die on India, card mounted (1861)
  black .... 800.
  gray black .... 800.
b. Die on India, cut to shape (1861), black .... 500.
c. Die on old proof paper (1861), black .... 500.
d. Die on old proof paper, corners drawn in pencil (1861), black .... 1,500.
e. Die on old proof paper, as No. 69-E3a but numerals sketched in diagonally and vert. (1861), black .... 3,000.
f. Die on stiff old ivory paper, as No. 69-E4e but without top border (1861), bluish black .... 1,500.
g. Die on thin card, black .... —

70-E1

70-E2c

Vignette size: 7x16mm
Washington die II vignette only.
70-E1 24c
a. Die II on proof paper (1903)
  black .... 60.
  carmine .... 60.
  dark carmine .... 60.
  scarlet .... 60.
  orange .... 60.
  yellow .... 60.
  yellow brown .... 60.
  violet brown .... 60.
  gray olive .... 60.
  light green .... 60.
  green .... 60.
  light blue .... 60.
  black blue .... 60.
  red violet .... 60.
  lilac .... 60.
b. Die II on green bond (1903)
  black .... 150.
  red brown .... 150.
  violet .... 150.
  orange .... 150.
c. Die II on colored card (1903)
  dull red, *ivory* .... 150.
  brown red, *buff* .... 150.
  brown orange, *light pink* .... 150.

dark green, *light yellow* .... 150.
blue, *pale green* .... 150.
violet, *blue* .... 150.

Washington vignette with oval label. Background complete, eyes retouched.
70-E2 24c
a. Die II on proof paper (1903)
  black .... 60.
  carmine .... 60.
  dark carmine .... 60.
  scarlet .... 60.
  orange .... 60.
  yellow .... 60.
  yellow brown .... 60.
  violet brown .... 60.
  light green .... 60.
  green .... 60.
  light blue .... 60.
  black blue .... 60.
  red violet .... 60.
  lilac .... 60.
  gray olive .... 60.
  ultramarine .... 60.
b. Die I on old proof paper, background lines incomplete (1861)
  black .... 750.
  dim red violet .... 750.
c. Die I on colored card (1903)
  black, *light pink* .... 150.
  orange, *buff* .... 150.
  orange, *light blue* .... 150.
  dark green, *pale green* .... 150.
  violet blue, *light yellow* .... 150.
  violet, *ivory* .... 150.
d. Die I on green bond (1903), brown .... 150.
e. Die I on dull light blue green bond (1903)
  black .... 150.
  orange red .... 150.
  orange .... 150.
  yellow brown .... 150.
  dusky green .... 150.
  dull blue .... 150.
  red violet .... 150.
f. Die I on dull pale green blue thin wove (1903)
  orange red .... 300.
  orange .... 300.
  yellow brown .... 300.
  dusky green .... 300.
  dull blue .... 300.

70-E3

70-E4

With frame. Blank areas in corners for numerals.
70-E3 24c
a. Die on proof paper (1903)
  black .... 100.
  carmine .... 100.
  dark carmine .... 100.
  scarlet .... 100.
  orange .... 100.
  yellow brown .... 100.
  orange brown .... 100.
  violet brown .... 100.
  gray olive .... 100.
  light green .... 100.
  green .... 100.
  light blue .... 100.
  black blue .... 100.
  red violet .... 100.
  lilac .... 100.
  ultramarine .... 100.
b. Die on old proof paper (1861), dusky red violet .... 1,000.
c. Die on colored card (1903)
  carmine, *light blue* .... 175.
  blue, *pale green* .... 175.
  scarlet, *buff* .... 175.
  yellow brown, *cream* .... 175.
  dull violet, *pink* .... 175.
  dusky green, *light yellow* .... 175.
  gray olive, *ivory* .... 175.
d. Die on green bond (1903)
  black .... 175.
  orange brown .... 175.
  green .... 175.

Complete design with numerals in corners.
70-E4 24c
a. Die on old proof paper, cut to shape (1861)
  lilac .... 400.
  black .... 400.
  red violet .... 400.
b. Die on India, cut close (1861)
  black .... 400.
  lilac .... 400.

brown lilac .... 400.
c. Die on India (1861), dark blue .... 750.
d. Die on India, mounted on 80x115mm card (1861), lilac .... 750.
e. On stiff old ivory paper (1861)
  black .... 1,000.
  lilac .... 1,000.
f. Die on proof paper, printed through a mat (1903)
  black .... 125.
  carmine .... 125.
  dark carmine .... 125.
  scarlet .... 125.
  red borwn .... 125.
  yellow brown .... 125.
  brown .... 125.
  violet brown .... 125.
  gray olive .... 125.
  light green .... 125.
  green .... 125.
  light blue .... 125.
  black blue .... 125.
  red violet .... 125.
  lilac .... 125.
  ultramarine .... 125.
g. Die on blue pelure (1903)
  dark carmine .... 300.
  scarlet .... 300.
  orange .... 300.
  brown .... 300.
  dusky green .... 300.
h. Die on bond (1903)
  black .... 175.
  scarlet .... 175.
  orange .... 175.
  dark green .... 175.
  blue .... 175.
i. Die on green bond (1903)
  black .... 250.
  dark red .... 250.
  green .... 250.
j. Die on bond, Walls of Troy wmk. (1903), dark green .... 300.
k. Die on bond, double line of scallops wmk. (1903)
  deep orange red .... 300.
  scarlet .... 300.
  orange .... 300.
  light blue .... 300.
l. Die on colored card, printed through a mat
  dark orange, *ivory* .... 150.
  dark orange, *light pink* .... 150.
  brown, *light blue* .... 150.
  dull dark blue, *pale green* .... 150.
  violet, *light yellow* .... 150.
  violet brown, *buff* .... 150.

72-E1

72-E2

Vignette size: 16x17½mm
Washington vignette only.
72-E1 90c
a. Die on proof paper (1903)
  black .... 100.
  carmine .... 100.
  dark carmine .... 100.
  scarlet .... 100.
  red brown .... 100.
  orange .... 100.
  orange brown .... 100.
  violet brown .... 100.
  gray olive .... 100.
  light green .... 100.
  green .... 100.
  dark blue .... 100.
  lilac .... 100.
  red violet .... 100.
  yellow brown .... 100.
  ultramarine .... 100.
b. Die on colored card (1903)
  black, *light yellow* .... 165.
  red brown, *light pink* .... 165.
  carmine, *buff* .... 165.
  brown, *pale green* .... 165.
  dark brown, *light blue* .... 165.
  ultramarine, *ivory* .... 165.
c. Die on dull light blue green bond (1903)
  violet brown .... 165.
  dusky green .... 165.
  dusky blue .... 165.
  red violet .... 165.

Vignette with blank top and bottom labels.
72-E2 90c
a. Die on proof paper (1903)
  black .... 100.
  carmine .... 100.
  dark carmine .... 100.
  scarlet .... 100.
  orange .... 100.
  yellow brown .... 100.
  brown .... 100.

violet brown	100.
gray olive	100.
light green	100.
green	100.
dark blue	100.
red violet	100.
lilac	100.
ultramarine	100.

b. Die on green bond (1903)

dull orange	150.
dull orange brown	150.
red violet	150.

c. Die on colored card (1903)

black, *buff*	185.
orange red, *light yellow*	185.
brown, *ivory*	185.
olive green, *light pink*	185.
green, *light blue*	185.
violet brown, *pale green*	185.

72-E3   72-E5

U.S. POSTAGE in top label.

72-E3 90c

a. Die on proof paper (1903)

black	125.
carmine	125.
dark carmine	125.
scarlet	125.
yellow	125.
yellow brown	125.
brown	125.
violet brown	125.
gray olive	125.
light green	125.
green	125.
dark blue	125.
lilac	125.
red violet	125.
ultramarine	125.

b. Die on colored card (1903)

orange, *light blue*	185.
orange red, *light yellow*	185.
dark blue, *buff*	185.
violet, *pale green*	185.
violet brown, *ivory*	185.
orange brown, *pale pink*	185.

c. Die on green bond (1903)

black	175.
brown	175.
green	175.

Lower corners of vignette cut out, "NINETY 90 CENTS" in pencil in bottom label.

72-E4 90c Die on India (1861), black   2,000.

Complete design.

72-E5 90c

a. Die on India, cut to shape (1861)

black	350.
dark blue	350.

b. Die on India, die sunk on card (1861), blue   2,000.

c. Die on India, cut close (1861)

black	350.
blue	350.

d. Die on proof paper, printed through a mat (1903)

black	175.
carmine	175.
dark carmine	175.
scarlet	175.
orange	175.
yellow brown	175.
brown	175.
violet brown	175.
gray olive	175.
light green	175.
green	175.
dark blue	175.
lilac	175.
red violet	175.
ultramarine	175.

e. Die on colored card (1903)

carmine, *light blue*	250.
dismal brown, *light pink*	250.
orange brown, *buff*	250.
blue, *ivory*	250.
violet, *pale green*	250.
green, *pale yellow*	250.

f. Die on green bond (1903)

dark carmine	225.
red brown	225.
green	225.

g. Die on bond (1903), orange brown   250.

h. Die on bond, "Bond No. 1" wmk. (1903), orange brown   350.

i. Die on bond, "Bond No 2" wmk. (1903), orange brown   350.

j. Die on bond, Walls of Troy wmk. (1903)

carmine	*300.*
scarlet	*300.*
orange	*300.*
dark green	*300.*
ultramarine	*300.*

k. Die on pink pelure (1903)

brown red	*350.*
dull yellow	*350.*
very dark green	*350.*
dark blue	*350.*
dull violet	*350.*

American Bank Note Co.

65-E5   65-E6

Design size: 19x23½mm
Engraved frame with pencil border, center cut out, mounted over 22x27mm engraved vignette of Washington.

65-E5 3c Die on India, black   2,500.

Design size: 19x24½mm
Engraved frame with pencil border, center cut out, mounted over engraved ruled background with engraved Washington vignette mounted on it.

65-E6 Three Cents Die on India, on card about 23x27½mm, black   2,500.

65-E7   65-E8

Master die No. 80 of frame only.

65-E7 3c Die on India, card mounted

deep orange	2,000.
dark brown	2,000.
green	2,000.
dark blue	2,000.
black	2,000.

Design size: 19½x24½mm
Engraved lathework frame with Bald, Cousland & Co. engraved Washington vignette and engraved lettered labels and numerals mounted on it.

65-E8 3c Die on India, on 22x27mm card, black   11,000.

65-E9   65-E10

Master die No. 81 of frame only.

65-E9 3c Die on India

black	2,750.
brown yellow	2,750.
dark green	2,750.
orange red	2,750.

Engraved lathework frame with Bald, Cousland & Co. engraved Washington vignette and engraved lettered labels and numerals mounted on it.

65-E10 3c Die on India, on 28x35mm card, black   7,000.

67-E5

Design size: 21x25mm
Engraved frame used for the 1860 Nova Scotia 5c stamp cut to shape, with engraved lettered labels and Washington vignette No. 209-E7 mounted on it.

67-E5 Five Cents Die on India, on 23x27mm card, black   2,500.

67-E6   67-E7

Design size: 19x24
Engraved lathework background with Bald, Cousland & Co. engraved Washington vignette and engraved lettered labels and numerals mounted on it.

67-E6 5c Die on India, mounted on 22x26mm card, black   7,000.

Design size: 19x24mm
Engraved lathework background with Bald, Cousland & Co. engraved Washington vignette and engraved lettered labels and numerals mounted on it.

67-E7 5c Die on India, mounted on 21x26½mm card, black   7,000.

National Bank Note Co.

The following essays include those formerly listed as Nos. 55-57, 59 and 62 in the Postage section, and the corresponding die and plate essays formerly listed in the Proof section. Former No. 58 is now No. 62B. Former Nos. 60 and 61 are now Nos. 70eTC and 71bTC in the Trial Color Proofs section.

63-E10

Frame essay with blank areas for Franklin vignette, labels, numerals, U and S.

63-E10 1c Die on India, black   2,000.

63-E11   63-E12

Die size: 58x56mm
"Premiere Gravure" die No. 440.

63-E11 1c

a. "Premiere Gravure" die essay on India (formerly Nos. 55P1, 55TC1)

black	4,000.
indigo	1,500.
ultramarine	2,250.

b. "Premiere Gravure" small die essay on white wove, 28x31mm (**formerly No. 55P2**), indigo   325.

c. "Premiere Gravure" plate essay on India (**formerly Nos. 55P3, 55TC3**)

indigo	300.
blue	
ultramarine	300.
violet ultramarine	—

d. "Premiere Gravure" plate essay on semitransparent stamp paper (**formerly No. 55TC4**), ultramarine   400.

e. Finished "Premiere Gravure" plate essay on semitransparent stamp paper, perf. 12, gummed (**formerly No. 55**), indigo   50,000.

No. 63-E11e is valued with perfs cutting slightly into design at top.

Die size: 47x55mm
Apparently complete die except value numerals have been cut out.

63-E12   1c Die on India, die sunk on card, black   1,500.

65-E11   65-E12

Die size: 64x76½mm
Incomplete engraving of Washington head only.

65-E11   3c
  a. Die on India, on card, carmine   750.
  b. Die on white glazed paper
      black   750.
      scarlet   750.
      brown violet   750.

Die size: 78x55mm
Incomplete engraved design, no scrolls outside framelines, no silhouette under chin, no ornaments on 3s, U and S.

65-E12   3c Die on India, die sunk on card
      black   1,000.
      blue   1,000.

65-E13   65-E14

As No. 65-E12 but ornaments on 3s, U and S. Shows traces of first border design erased. With imprint and No. 441 below design.

65-E13   3c Die on India, card mounted
      scarlet   1,000.
      brown red   1,000.
      ultramarine   1,000.

Die size: 59x55mm
As No. 65-E13 but with ornaments outside frame.

65-E14   3c Die on India, die sunk on card
      black   750.
      scarlet   750.
      pink   1,250.
      brown orange   750.
      deep orange red   750.
      deep red   750.

As No. 65-E14 but top of head silhouetted, lines added or strengthened in hair at top of head, around eye, on chin, in hair behind ear. The three lines on bottom edge of bust extended to back. No imprint or die number.

65-E15

65-E15   3c
  a. Die on India, card mounted, deep orange red   1,000.
  b. "Premiere Gravure" die essay on semitransparent stamp paper, 20x25mm-30x37mm
      deep orange red   750.
      deep red orange   750.
      dim red   750.
      dim deep red   750.
      dim orange red   750.
      dull pink   750.

---

      dull violet red   750.
  c. "Premiere Gravure" die essay on India (**formerly Nos. 56P1, 56TC1**)
      red   1,350.
      black   2,000.
      scarlet   2,000.
      pink   2,850.
      orange red   2,000.
      dark orange red   2,000.
  d. Small die essay on white wove, 28x31mm altered laydown die of complete design but with outer scrolls removed and replaced by ones similar to "Premiere Gravure" design (1903) (**formerly No. 56P2**), dim deep red   325.
  e. As "c," small die essay on pale cream soft wove, 24x29mm (1915) (**formerly No. 56P2a**), deep red   1,250.
  f. "Premiere Gravure" plate No. 2 essay on India (**formerly Nos. 56P3, 56TC3**)
      red   250.
      scarlet   350.
  g. "Premiere Gravure" plate essay on semitransparent stamp paper (**formerly Nos. 56aP4, 56TC4**)
      red, pair with gum   1,750.
      black   400.
  h. Finished "Premiere Gravure" plate essay on semitransparent stamp paper, perf. 12, gummed (**formerly No. 56**)
      brown rose   550.
      P# block of 8, Impt.   20,000.
      orange red   475.
      bright orange red   475.
      dark orange red   475.
      dim deep red   475.
      pink   475.
      deep pink   475.

67-E8   67-E9

Incomplete impression from die No. 442, border lines and corner scrolls missing.

67-E8   5c Die on India, mounted on 34x50mm card, black   1,750.

Size of die: 58x59mm
"Premiere Gravure" design, with corner scrolls but without leaflets.

67-E9   5c
  a. "Premiere Gravure" die essay on India, card mounted (**formerly No. 57TC1**)
      black   2,500.
      scarlet   2,500.
  b. Small die essay on white wove, 28x31mm, altered laydown die of complete design but with scrolls removed from corners to resemble "Premiere Gravure" (1903) (**formerly No. 57P2**), **brown**   325.
  c. As "b," die essay on pale cream soft wove, 24x29mm (1915) (**formerly No. 57P2a**), brown   1,750.
  d. "Premiere Gravure" plate No. 3 essay on India (**formerly Nos. 57P3, 57TC3**)
      brown   250.
      light brown   300.
      dark brown   300.
      red brown   300.
  e. Finished "Premiere Gravure" plate essay on semitransparent stamp paper, perf. 12, gummed (**formerly No. 57**), brown   30,000.

68-E1   68-E2

Design size: 14x17½mm
Die size: 26x31mm
Washington vignette only.

68-E1   10c
  a. Die on ivory paper, black   1,000.
  b. Die on India   1,000.

Incomplete die No. 443.

68-E2   10c Die on India, 22x26mm, dark green   2,500.

Incomplete die of No. 68P1, thin lines missing on top of frame

68-E3

68-E3   10c Die on India
      yellowish green   1,000.
      dark green   1,000.

      (12c design)

69-E5   69-E6

Design size: 12½x16mm
Die size: about 62x65mm
Washington vignette only.

69-E5   12c
  a. Die on India, die sunk on card
      black   400.
      dark red   400.
      orange red   400.
  b. Die on ivory paper, about 24x28mm
      black   500.
      scarlet   500.
      black brown   500.
      blue   500.

Incomplete die No. 444, without corner ornaments.

69-E6   12c
  a. "Premiere Gravure" die essay on India, mounted on card (**formerly Nos. 59P1, 59TC1**)
      black   2,500.
      scarlet   2,500.
      dark green   2,500.
  b. "Premiere Gravure" small die essay on white wove, 28x31mm (1903) (**formerly No. 59P2**), black   450.
  c. "Premiere Gravure" small die essay on pale cream soft wove, 24x29mm (1915) (**formerly No. 59P2a**), black   1,750.
  d. "Premiere Gravure" plate No. 5 essay on India (**formerly No. 59P3**), black   350.
  e. Finished "Premiere Gravure" plate essay on semitransparent stamp paper, perf. 12, gummed (**formerly No. 59**), black   85,000.

70-E5   70-E6

Washington vignette in incomplete frame.

70-E5   24c Die on India, black   3,250.

Die size: 56½x56mm
Incomplete die (No. 445): silhouette unfinished, especially scrolls around numerals; shadows over numerals not acid etched.

70-E6   24c Die on India, die sunk on card
      black   900.
      violet   900.
      gray violet   900.
      dark violet   900.
      scarlet   900.
      green   900.
      orange   900.
      red brown   900.
      orange brown   900.
      orange yellow   900.
      rose red   900.
      gray   900.
      steel blue   900.
      blue   900.

For finished "Premiere Gravure" trial color plate proof on semitransparent stamp paper, perf 12, gummed (formerly No. 60), see 70eTC in the Trial Color Proof section.

71-E1   71-E2

Die size: 46x60mm
Incomplete die (No. 446): additional ornaments at top and bottom in pencil, as later engraved.

71-E1 30c Die on India, black   *1,750.*

"Premiere Gravure" die: left side of frame and silhouette at lower right unfinished.

71-E2 30c
- **a.** "Premiere Gravure" die essay on India, die sunk on card (**formerly No. 61TC1**)
  - black   *1,750.*
  - green   *1,750.*
  - dull gray blue   *1,750.*
  - violet brown   *1,750.*
  - scarlet   *1,750.*
  - dull rose   *1,750.*
- **b.** "Premiere Gravure" plate essay on India (**formerly No. 61P3**), deep red orange   *500.*
- **c.** "Premiere Gravure" plate essay on card
  - black (split thin)   *500.*
  - blue   *750.*
- **d.** "Premiere Gravure" plate essay on card, black 12x2mm SPECIMEN overprint, blue   *750.*
- **e.** "Premiere Gravure" plate essay on semi-transparent stamp paper
  - deep red orange   *1,250.*
  - yellow orange   *1,250.*
  - lemon yellow   *1,250.*
  - dark orange yellow   *1,250.*
  - dull orange yellow   *1,250.*

For finished "Premiere Gravure" trial color proof on semi-transparent stamp paper, perf 12, gummed (formerly No. 61), see No. 71bTC in the Trial Color Proof section.

72-E6   72-E7

Die size: 54x63mm
Incomplete die: without thin lines at bottom of frame and in upper left triangle between label and frame, and without leaves at left of U and right of S.

72-E6 90c Die on India, blue (shades)   *1,000.*

Similar to 72-E6 but lines added in upper left triangle, leaves added at left of U and at right of S. Exists with and without imprint and Die No. 447 added below design.

72-E7 90c
- **a.** Die on India, die sunk on card, black   *1,750.*
- **b.** "Premiere Gravure" die essay on India, thin line under bottom center frame (**formerly Nos. 62P1, 62TC1**)
  - blue   *1,350.*
  - black   *1,750.*
- **c.** "Premiere Gravure" small die essay on white wove, 28x31mm (1903) (**formerly No. 62P2**), blue   *500.*
- **d.** "Premiere Gravure" small die essay on pale cream soft wove, 24x29mm (1915) (**formerly No. 62P2a**), blue   *1,750.*
- **e.** "Premiere Gravure" plate essay on India, blue   *500.*
- **f.** "Premiere Gravure" plate essay on card, black (split thin)   *500.*
- **g.** "Premiere Gravure" plate essay on semi-transparent stamp paper (**formerly Nos. 62aP4, 62TC4**)
  - blue, pair, gummed   *5,500.*
  - blue green   *275.*
- **h.** Finished "Premiere Gravure" plate essay on semitransparent stamp paper, perf. 12, gummed (**formerly No. 62**), blue   *50,000.*

Die size: 54x63mm
Similar to Nos. 72-E6 and 72-E7 but leaf at left of "U" only, no shading around "U" and "S," leaf and some shading missing at bottom right above "S," shading missing in top label, etc., faint ms. "8" at bottom of backing card.

72-E8 90c Die on India, die sunk on 3¼x3½-inch card, dark blue   —

63-E13

Design size: 20x47mm
Die size: 57x95mm
Bowlsby patent coupon at top of 1c stamp design.

63-E13 1c
- **a.** Die on India, die sunk on card
  - black   *1,750.*
  - red   *1,750.*
  - scarlet   *1,750.*
  - orange   *1,750.*
  - orange brown   *1,750.*
  - brown   *1,750.*
  - yellow brown   *1,750.*
  - blue green   *1,750.*
  - olive green   *1,750.*
  - olive   *1,750.*
  - blue   *1,750.*
  - violet   *1,750.*
  - red violet   *1,750.*
  - gray   *1,750.*
  - gray brown   *1,750.*
  - dull orange yellow   *1,750.*
- **b.** Die on white glazed paper
  - black   *1,750.*
  - dark brown   *1,750.*
  - scarlet   *1,750.*
  - blue   *1,750.*
- **c.** Plate on pelure paper, gummed, red   *300.*
- **d.** Plate on white paper, red   *250.*
- **e.** Plate on white paper, with 13x16mm points-up grill, red   *350.*
  - Split grill   *600.*
- **f.** Plate on white paper, perf. all around and between stamp and coupon
  - red   *175.*
  - blue   *175.*
- **g.** Plate on white paper, perf. all around, imperf. between stamp and coupon
  - red   *175.*
  - blue   *175.*
- **h.** Plate on white paper, perf. all around, rouletted between stamp and coupon
  - red   *300.*
  - blue   *300.*

1861-66 Essays
Authors Unknown

73-E2   73-E3

Design size: 21x26mm
73-E2 2c Pencil and watercolor on thick card, bright green   *3,750.*

Design size: 21x26mm
Indian vignette. Typographed printings from woodcuts. Plates of three rows of three, one row each of Nos. 73-E3, 73-E4, 73-E5. Listings are of singles.

73-E3 2c
- **a.** Plate on white wove
  - red   *30.*
  - scarlet   *30.*
  - violet   *30.*
  - black   *30.*
  - blue   *30.*
  - green   *30.*
- **b.** Plate on mauve wove
  - red   *50.*
  - violet   *50.*
  - black   *50.*
  - blue   *50.*
  - green   *50.*
- **c.** Plate on yellow wove
  - red   *50.*
  - violet   *50.*
  - black   *50.*

- blue   *50.*
- green   *50.*
- **d.** Plate on yellow laid
  - red   *50.*
  - violet   *50.*
  - black   *50.*
  - blue   *50.*
  - green   *50.*
- **e.** Plate on pink laid
  - red   *50.*
  - violet   *50.*
  - black   *50.*
  - blue   *50.*
  - green   *50.*
- **f.** Plate on green laid
  - red   *50.*
  - violet   *50.*
  - black   *50.*
  - blue   *50.*
  - green   *50.*
- **g.** Plate on cream laid
  - red   *50.*
  - violet   *50.*
  - black   *50.*
  - blue   *50.*
  - green   *50.*
- **h.** Plate on pale yellow wove
  - red   *50.*
  - green   *50.*
  - blue   *50.*
- **i.** Plate on yellow-surfaced card, violet   *50.*

73-E4   73-E5

Design size: 23x26½mm
Small head of Liberty in shield. Typographed printings from woodcuts. On plate with Nos. 73-E3 and 73-E5. Listings are of singles.

73-E4 3c
- **a.** Plate on white wove
  - red   *30.*
  - scarlet   *30.*
  - violet   *30.*
  - black   *30.*
  - blue   *30.*
  - green   *30.*
- **b.** Plate on mauve wove, violet   *50.*
- **c.** Plate on yellow wove
  - red   *50.*
  - violet   *50.*
  - black   *50.*
  - blue   *50.*
  - green   *50.*
- **d.** Plate on yellow laid
  - red   *50.*
  - violet   *50.*
  - black   *50.*
  - blue   *50.*
  - green   *50.*
- **e.** Plate on pink laid
  - carmine   *50.*
  - violet   *50.*
  - black   *50.*
  - blue   *50.*
  - green   *50.*
- **f.** Plate on green laid
  - carmine   *50.*
  - green   *50.*
  - dull violet   *50.*
  - blue   *50.*
- **g.** Plate on cream laid
  - red   *50.*
  - violet   *50.*
  - black   *50.*
  - blue   *50.*
  - green   *50.*
- **h.** Plate on pale yellow wove
  - red   *50.*
  - green   *50.*
  - blue   *50.*
- **i.** Plate on yellow-surfaced card, violet   *50.*
- **j.** Plate on fawn wove, green   *50.*

Design size: 22½x25½mm
Large head of Liberty. Typographed impressions from woodcut. On plate with Nos. 73-E3 and 73-E4. Listings are of singles.

73-E5 5c
- **a.** Plate on white wove
  - red   *30.*
  - scarlet   *30.*
  - violet   *30.*
  - black   *30.*
  - blue   *30.*
  - green   *30.*
- **b.** Plate on mauve wove, violet   *50.*
- **c.** Plate on yellow wove
  - red   *50.*
  - violet   *50.*
  - black   *50.*
  - blue   *50.*
  - green   *50.*
- **d.** Plate on yellow laid
  - red   *50.*

violet 50.
black 50.
blue 50.
green 50.
e. Plate on pink laid
red 50.
black 50.
blue 50.
green 50.
f. Plate on green laid
red 50.
violet 50.
black 50.
blue 50.
green 50.
g. Plate on cream laid
red 50.
black 50.
blue 50.
green 50.
h. Plate on pale yellow wove
red 50.
blue 50.
green 50.
i. Plate on yellow-surfaced card, violet 50.

73-E6

Size of design: 21x27mm
Indian vignette. Typographed impressions from woodcut.

73-E6 10c
a. Die on proof paper
black 200.
gray black 200.
carmine 200.
dusky red 200.
brown 200.
green 200.
blue 200.
violet 200.
b. Plate on white paper (pane of 4)
red 600.
violet 600.
brown 600.
black 600.
blue 600.
green 600.
c. Plate on soft cream card (pane of 4)
black 600.
red 600.
blue 600.
green 600.
red violet 600.

1864 Decalcomania Essays
Re-use Prevention
Henry Lowenberg

79-E65P5

79-E66P5

79-E67P5   79-E71P5

79-E72P5   79-E73P5

The following Decalcomania essays, patented in 1864, are plate proofs of the 1861 issue printed on the back of goldbeaters' skin paper and gummed on the side of the impressions. Impressions can be seen on the non-gummed side and show in reverse. The concept was that any attempt to remove the stamp from an envelope would result in the image remaining on the envelope, and the goldbeaters' skin would come off the envelope without an image. All the essays listed below are printed on goldbeaters' skin except where noted, and all are imperforate except one version of the 3c denomination.
Values are for essentially sound examples with a very minimal amount of flaking or creasing.

79-E65P5 3c
a. Imperforate
rose 50.00
blue 150.00
b. Perforated, rose 75.00
79-E66P5 3c
a. Lake 100.00
b. Lake on pale green 150.00
79-E67P5 5c
brown 75.00
79-E68P5 10c
a. Green 150.00
b. Green on pale rose 250.00
79-E69P5 12c
black 150.00
79-E70P5 24c
a. Lilac 75.00
b. Lilac on pale green 250.00
79-E71P5 30c
a. Orange 100.00
b. Orange on blue-green 250.00
79-E72P5 90c
dark blue 75.00
79-E73P5 2c
a. Black 75.00
b. Black on pale rose 250.00

1867 Essays
Re-use Prevention
Authors Unknown

Unfolded — 79-E1   Folded — 79-E1

Design size (folded): 18x23mm
Design size (unfolded): 18x58mm
Folded and scored four times, horiz. crease at center. Bronze overprint U 2 S, (2 punched out). Lower ⅔ gummed below second fold so top ⅓ could be torn off for canceling.
79-E1 2c On white paper, dull red violet 5,000.

79-E2

Similar to No. 79-E1 but larger and not folded. Pierced with S-shaped cuts as well as punched out 2.
79-E2 2c
a. On white paper, US 7½mm high, bronze,
US in dull black 5,000.
b. On white paper, US 10mm high, bronze,
US in violet 5,000.

79-E3

Cuts as on back

U.S. No. 73 as issued but pierced with S-shaped cuts, ovptd. in metallic color.
79-E3 2c Essay on 2c stamp, gold overprint 7,500.

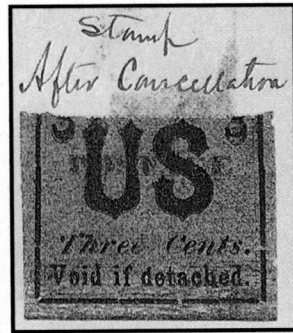

79-E4   79-E6

Similar to No. 79-E1 but with punched out 3.
79-E4 3c
a. On white paper, U 3 S black above,
bronze below and on face beneath
folds 5,000.
b. On green paper, 3 not punched out, 3
black, POSTAGE blue 5,000.

Similar to No. 79-E4, with "3 U.S. 3 / Three Cents / Void if detached."

79-E5

79-E5 3c On green paper, black 3,000.

Similar to No. 79-E2 but with punched out 3, gummed.
79-E6 3c
a. On white paper, bronze over violet 3,000.
b. On white paper, U S black, rest bronze 3,000.

79-E7

Vignette map of U.S.
79-E7 3c On thick white paper, rouletted,
green, gold 3 on map 2,500.

79-E7A

Similar to 79-E7, without "3" on map.

79-	3c On thick white paper, imperforate	
E7A	block of 9 (unique), black	—

1867 Essays
Henry Lowenberg

79-E8   79-E9

Washington vignette. Printed in reverse on back of transparent paper, reads correctly from front. Plate essays from sheets of 25.

79-E8 3c
- **a.** Plate on onionskin paper, imperf., gummed
  - brown — 10.
  - orange brown — 10.
  - deep orange brown — 10.
  - orange — 10.
  - green — 10.
  - light green — 10.
  - blue green — 10.
  - pale green — 10.
  - red — 10.
  - light red — 10.
  - dark red — 10.
  - violet red — 10.
  - violet — 10.
  - light violet — 10.
  - dull pale violet — 10.
  - blue — 10.
  - dark blue — 10.
  - deep blue — 10.
  - pale blue — 10.
  - dull blue — 10.
  - gold — 50.
  - gray — 7.
  - black — 7.
  - carmine — 7.
- **b.** Plate on onionskin paper, perf. 12, gummed
  - gray black — 25.
  - gray — 25.
  - gray violet — 25.
  - dull violet — 25.
  - brown red — 25.
- **c.** Plate on more opaque onionskin paper, imperf.
  - black — 25.
  - red violet — 25.
  - dull violet — 25.
- **d.** Plate on thick transparent paper
  - gray — 25.
  - black — 25.

Washington vignette. Printed with design reversed on front of various opaque papers. Plate essays are from sheets of 25.

79-E9 3c
- **a.** Plate on white wove, imperf., gummed
  - blue — 10.
  - red — 10.
  - gray — 10.
  - brown — 10.
  - orange — 10.
  - green — 10.
  - yellow green — 10.
- **b.** Plate on clear white paper, imperf.
  - orange — 10.
  - blue — 10.
  - gray — 10.
  - dark gray — 10.
- **c.** Plate on thick wove, fugitive ink, perf., gummed
  - carmine — 10.
  - violet carmine — 10.
  - pale dull red — 10.
  - gray — 10.
  - pale gray — 10.
  - pale dull tan — 10.
  - green — 10.
- **d.** As "c," strip of 3, signed Henry Lowenberg, pale tan — 400.
- **e.** Plate on white chemically treated paper (turns blue if wet), imperf.

- carmine — 10.
- Prussian blue — 10.
- orange — 10.
- green — 10.
- brown — 10.
- black — 10.
- **f.** As "e," perf.
  - carmine — 10.
  - scarlet — 10.
  - orange — 10.
  - blue — 10.
  - green — 10.
  - brown — 10.
- **g.** Plate on India
  - violet brown — 10.
  - green — 10.
  - blue — 10.
  - dark blue — 10.
- **h.** Plate on India, signed D.H. Craig, red — 350.
- **i.** On white card, 62x72mm, design deeply indented, green — 15.
- **j.** On blue wove, red — 15.
- **k.** On orange laid
  - black — 15.
  - gray — 15.
- **l.** On blue laid, scarlet — 15.
- **m.** On white laid, blue — 15.
- **n.** On pink laid, blue — 15.
- **o.** On linen cloth
  - green — 50.
  - red — 50.
  - blue — 50.
- **p.** On glazed white paper, blue — 20.

1867 Essays
John M. Sturgeon

79-E10

Liberty vignette. Curved labels top and bottom. Self-canceling: CANCELLED in colorless sensitive ink, becomes colored when wet. Patented 1867, 1868.

79-E10 10c
- **a.** Die on stiff card, cut close, clearly engraved, not canceled, both labels completely blank, dark carmine — 350.
- **b.** Die on wove, rough impression, CANCELLED diagonally each way, dark carmine — 450.
- **c.** Die on thick white or tinted paper, gummed, rough impression, about 21x26mm, two lines in upper label, one line in lower label
  - carmine — 200.
  - dark carmine — 200.
  - very dark carmine — 200.
  - green — 200.
  - dark green — 200.
  - dull red violet — 200.
- **d.** As "c," on thick pinkish paper, dark green — 250.
- **g.** Single centered in 6-inch wide strip of thick white paper, almost always cut in at top and bottom, dark carmine — 400.
- **h.** Horiz. row of five designs on thick white paper, 10mm apart
  - dark carmine — 1,200.
  - dark purple — 1,200.
  - black — 1,200.
- **i.** Single on blue card, ovptd. seal BRITISH CONSULATE, V.R. in center, black — 1,250.

American Bank Note Co.

79-E11

Design size: 18x21mm
Vignette of Columbia. Probably submitted by Charles F. Steel.

79-E11 2c and 3c
- **a.** Engraved plate on thick yellowish wove, imperf. (usually found in upper left margin blocks)
  - rose scarlet — 300.
  - Block of 4 — 1,250.
  - blue green — 300.
  - Block of 4 — 1,250.

- **b.** Engraved plate on stamp paper, perf. 12, gummed
  - black — 175.
  - rose scarlet — 175.
  - blue green — 175.
  - blue — 175.

Author Unknown

79-E12

Design size: 20x26mm
Vignette of Liberty in circle of stars. Vertical color lines outside design to 24x28mm. Curved labels blank. Lithographed.

79-E12 No denomination
- **a.** Die on white paper, dull violet — 2,750.
- **b.** Die on bluish paper, blue — 2,750.

1867 Grill Essays
National Bank Note Co.

79-E13a

Grill essays patented by Charles F. Steel.

79-E13
- **a.** Wove paper, 80x140mm, impressed with four diff. seals, crossed lines and square dots down, circles 11 or 12mm — 9,000.

79-E13b

- **b.** Grills in odd shapes on white wove, each about 20x25mm
  - cross — 1,500.
  - star in square — 1,500.

horizontal lined oval in square 1,500.
diagonal lined oval in square 1,500.
c. White wove, gummed, 15mm circle with
points down grill, surrounded by 24
perforated holes 1,000.
d. White wove, quadrille batonne watermark, 12mm colored circle with points
down grill around 3, roughly grilled
colorless 3 below, carmine 1,250.

79-E13e

e. Colorless 12mm grilled circle as on "d,"
on tan wove, perf. 12 200.
f. As "e," yellow wove 200.
g. As "e," white wove, block of 6 with ms.
"Subject to a half hour pressure after
embossing" 3,500.
h. Colorless 15mm points down grilled circle on white wove, perf. 12 200.

79-E14a

79-E14b

Allover grill.
79-E14
a. White wove, about 55x30mm, points
down grill, stamped with red 6-digit
number 450.
b. Wove paper in various colors, about
85x40mm, points up grill as adopted
white 200.
pale pink 200.
salmon 200.
light yellow 200.
light gray green 200.
light blue 200.
pale lilac 200.
light gray 200.

79-E15

Experimental grills on perf. or imperf. stamps or stamp-size
pieces of paper.
79-E15
a. Allover grill of small squares, points
down (points do not break paper as
on issued stamp, No. 79)
on 3c rose, gummed (No. 65) 250.
on 3c lake, imperf. pair, gummed (No.
66aP4) 250.
b. As "a" but points up, on 3c stamp, perf.
12, gummed
black 200.
rose 200.

c. As "a" but points up, imperf pair,
gummed
3c rose (**formerly No. 79P4**) 500.
3c lake (**formerly No. 66aP4**) 500.

79-E15d

d. Allover pinpoint grill (so-called "Music
Box" grill), points up, on No. 65 (plates
11, 34, 52) 75.
e. As "d" but points down, on 3c rose (plate
11) 125.
f. 15x16mm grill on stamp size white wove
paper, perf. 12, gummed 125.
g. C grill, 13x16mm, points down on stamp
size wove paper, perf. 12, gummed
white 100.
yellowish 100.
pinkish 100.
h. As "g" but points up, on white wove 100.
i. C grill on 1c stamp (No. 63), points
down 4,000.
j. C grill on 3c stamp (No. 65)
points up 4,000.
points down 4,000.

The 3c C grill essay is almost identical to the issued stamp.
There are slight differences in the essay grill which match those
on No. 79-E15i and Nos. 79-E15k through 79-E15n.

k. C grill on 5c stamp (No. 76)
points up 4,000.
points down 4,000.
l. C grill on 10c stamp (No. 68)
points up 4,000.
points down 4,000.
m. C grill on 12c stamp (No. 69)
points up 4,000.
points down 4,000.
n. C grill on 30c stamp (No. 71)
points up 4,000.
points down 4,000.
o. E grill, 11x13mm, points up, on stamp
size white wove paper, perf. 12,
gummed 100.
p. As "o," points down 100.

**1867 "Z" grill
Experimental Essays**

85C-E1

85C-E1 Sheet of white wove stamp paper,
imperf., gummed, with experimental
"Z" grill impressions, 11x14mm,
points down 175.

85C-E2

85C-E2 Z grill, 11x14mm, points down on
stamp size wove paper, perf. 12,
partly gummed
white 200.
salmon 200.
yellow 200.
greenish 200.
dull violet 200.
pale lilac 200.

These were made on fully perforated sheet selvage from the
3c and 12c essay panes.

85E-E1 12c Experimental "Z" grill essay,
11x14mm, on heavily horizontal-
ly laid paper, gummed, perforated 12
a. On thin transparent paper white paper
(not laid), blue 250.
b. On salmon paper
black 250.
brown 250.

green 250.
blue 250.
c. On deep orange paper
black 250.
scarlet 250.
brown 250.
green 250.
blue 250.
d. On yellow paper
black 250.
brown 250.
e. On straw paper
brown 250.
green 250.
f. On green paper
black 250.
scarlet 250.
brown 250.
green 250.
blue 250.
g. On lilac paper
black 250.
scarlet 250.
brown 250.
green 250.
blue 250.
h. On pale rose paper
black 250.
scarlet 250.
brown 250.
green 250.
blue 250.

Continental Bank Note Co.

White wove paper about 6x9 inches with 7x9½mm grills
spaced as they would fall on centers of stamps in a sheet.

79-E16

79-E16
a. End roller grill at left, ms. "Chas. F.
Steel-Sample of Grill used by Continental Bank Note Co. in 1874. Alexander Reid. J.K. Myers." 2,000.
b. Without end roller grill, ms. "Grill of Continental Bank Note Co. Chas. F.
Steel." 2,000.
c. End roller grill at right, same inscription
as "b" 2,000.
d. On soft card, six grills 600.

Wilbur I. Trafton

79-E17

Coarse grill in 15mm circle with 7 points up in 11mm, found
on 1873 1c, some with 18mm circular cancel, stuck down on
printed ad circular along with black, red and albino grill impressions (two each) on paper labeled "The Security Impression
from the plates."

79-E17 Entire ad circular with grill examples 750.

National Bank Note Co.

79-E18

Albino 3 in points down shield-shaped grill in lithographed frame of 3c 1861 stamp.

79-E18 3c
- *a.* Die on thick white paper, gummed
  - black — 1,000.
  - deep pink — 1,000.
- *b.* As "a," with Washington, D.C. Feb. 21 pmk.
  - black — 1,750.
  - deep pink — 1,750.

79-E18c

- *c.* As "a" but grill with points up, black — 1,000.
- *d.* As "a," perf. 12, gummed, black — 1,000.
- *e.* Die on yellow wove, gummed
  - black — 1,000.
  - red — 1,000.
- *f.* Die on orange wove
  - black — 1,000.
  - carmine — 1,000.
- *g.* Die on yellow laid, black — 1,000.
- *h.* Numeral handcolored, dull carmine — 1,500.
- *i.* Frame only, no grill, on grayish wove with pencil "McDonald P.O. Dept. Steel Nature(?)", pale orange brown — 1,500.

79-E18j   79-E18k

Albino 3 in 13x14mm shield made up of embossed narrow spaced horiz. lines.

- *j.* White wove stamp paper, 22x27mm, perf. 12, gummed — 450.

Albino 3 in 13x14mm shield slightly different from No. 79-E18j.

- *k.* As "j," different shield — 350.

79-E19a

Illustration reduced.

Typographed impression of frame, lettering and numerals of 3c 1861 stamp with 3 in double lined shield in center. In strip of three about 20mm apart, impression of 3 and shield progressively lighter on impressions two and three.

79-E19 3c
- *a.* Engraved (die No. 1570), green — 3,000.
- *b.* Typographed in color on white paper
  - blue green — 2,750.
  - dark red brown — 2,750.
- *c.* As "b," colored and colorless parts interchanged, on thick paper
  - blue green — 2,750.
  - dark red brown — 2,750.

79-E21

Lathework frame with shield shaped vignette cut out, albino 3 in circular grill in center.

79-E21 3c
- *a.* Thick paper, perf. 12
  - blue — 500.
  - carmine — 500.
- *b.* At left in strip of 3 with 2 No. 79-E13f, latter black cancels, blue — 3,500.
- *c.* Lathework frame on thin wove, allover diagonal grill, imperf., gummed, blue — 500.

Lathework frame similar to No. 79-E21 but vignette of 6 horiz. bars with 3 in center printed in glossy ink.

79-E22

79-E22 3c On pink lilac paper, blue — 3,000.

79-E23

Design of 3c 1861 stamp typographed in relief for surface printing. Single impression lightly block sunk 63x62mm in color. Design has 21x26½mm border inside 23x28½mm colorless rectangle.

79-E23 3c
- *a.* Die on 64x75mm ivory paper, black — 325.
- *b.* Die on India, dull violet-red red — 325.
- *c.* Die on 59x54mm stiff white card, color about 40mm wide (not extending to edges)
  - light red violet — 325.
  - carmine — 325.
  - blue — 325.
- *d.* Washington head only, lines on face around eye, on soft card
  - dim blue-green blue — 250.
  - dim orange-orange red — 250.

On 17x21mm plain colored rectangle printed through a mat, surrounded by 55x62mm colorless rectangle, vert. 4½mm wide color bands at sides inside 64x62mm die sinkage.

- *e.* Washington head with dots around eye, on 17x42mm solid color, on 77x45mm stiff white paper, dull violet-red — 250.
- *f.* India paper on soft white card block sunk 63x62mm, dull violet-red-red with solid color margins — 250.

Colored India generally cut away outside colorless rectangle 23x28½mm, design heavily embossed through to card beneath.

- *g.* As "f," trimmed to shape
  - dark carmine — 350.
  - orange — 350.
  - blue green — 350.
  - red violet — 350.
- *h.* Complete design on India, sunk on card, trimmed to shape
  - blue — 100.
  - dull green blue — 100.
- *i.* Plate typographed on white wove, imperf., gummed
  - dim red — 50.
  - dim light orange red — 50.
  - dim blue green — 50.
  - dim pale blue — 50.
  - dim dark blue — 50.
  - dusky violet red — 50.

Color outside design generally fills rectangle, design impression shows on back.

- *j.* Complete design on glossy sticky paper, deep violet red — 150.
- *k.* As "j," on pelure, perf. 12, gummed, rose — 175.
- *l.* As "k," allover grill, dim red — 150.
- *m.* As "k," 13x16mm grill, gray black — 150.

79-E24

79-E24c

Block sinkage: 65x76mm
Washington head only.

79-E24 3c
- *a.* Lithographed, face dotted, on 65x76mm solid color background
  - black — 750.
  - red violet — 750.
  - olive black — 750.
- *b.* Typographed, background irregular edge, on card, gray black — 1,500.
- *c.* Face lined, on 64x72mm solid color background
  - black — 750.
  - scarlet — 750.

79-E25

Plate essays of complete 1861 3c design.

79-E25 3c
- *a.* Plate on hard white transparent wove, dark red — 50.
- *b.* Plate on more opaque white wove, dim red — 50.
- *c.* Plate on Gibson patent starch coated opaque white paper, generally crinkled, lathework design usually poorly printed
  - orange red — 25.
  - deep orange red — 25.
  - pink — 25.
  - dull yellow — 25.
  - yellow orange — 25.
  - dull yellow orange — 25.
  - brown yellow — 25.
  - brown — 25.
  - green — 25.
  - blue green — 25.
  - blue — 25.
  - light blue — 25.
- *d.* Plate on semitransparent white wove
  - dull pale blue — 20.
  - green — 20.
  - dull yellow orange — 20.
- *e.* Plate on pale green paper, clearly printed, dark g-b green — 40.
- *f.* Plate on white wove, 13x16mm points down grill, gummed, dark blue — 40.
- *g.* Plate on lilac gray paper, 13x16mm grill, gummed
  - dark blue — 40.
  - dull red — 40.
  - black — 40.
- *h.* Plate on white paper (ungrilled), perf. 12, gummed
  - red — 25.
  - light red — 25.
  - pale red — 25.
  - light orange red — 25.
  - deep yellow orange — 25.
  - brown — 25.
  - dark green — 25.
  - deep blue — 25.
  - dull g-b blue — 25.
  - gray black — 25.
- *i.* As "h," ms. A or B in UL corner, red — 50.
- *j.* Plate on white paper, 13x16mm points down grill, perf. 12, gummed
  - black — 25.
  - gray black — 25.
  - pale red — 25.
  - light red — 25.
  - orange red — 25.
  - deep orange yellow — 25.
  - brown — 25.
  - dark brown — 25.
  - green — 25.
  - blue — 25.
  - dark blue — 25.
- *k.* As "j," ms. "s No. 6" on back
  - red — 50.
  - gray black — 50.
  - dark blue — 50.
- *l.* As "j," but grill points up
  - red — 40.
  - pink — 40.
  - pale rose — 40.
  - brown — 40.

orange yellow 40.
deep red orange 40.
green 40.
dull blue 40.
dull light blue 40.
m. As "l," pair with blue oval "American
 Bank Note Co. April 17, '79", pink 150.
n. Plate on greenish gray chemical paper,
 13x16mm grill, perf. 12
 black 50.
 green 50.
 dark blue 50.
 orange red 50.
 light yellow gray 50.
 light red gray 50.
o. As "n," without grill
 red 50.
 rose 50.
p. Plate on pelure, without grill, imperf.,
 gummed, dim red 50.
q. As "p," perf. 12, dim red 50.

79-E26

Plate impressions of 1861 3c stamp overprinted with various
safety network designs. Inks probably fugitive.

79-E26 3c
a. Vert. pair on 58x80mm India, overprint
 die 54x71mm or more, small ONE repeated in 41 vert. lines per 40mm,
 rose pink, overprint deep orange yellow 2,000.
b. As "a," block of 6 inscribed "J. Sangster
 Pat. 190376, Jan. 6, 1877" 3,500.
c. 65TC3, "VEINTE" overprint, in miniature
 sheet of 12, perf. 12, black, overprint
 orange 7,500.

3c 1861 printed in various colors in miniature sheets of 12
with safety ovpts. (Apparently only one sheet printed of each
color combination, except two Type D combinations known both
perf. and imperf.)

d. Type A
 perf. 12, dull violet, overprint gray 425.
 perf. 12, rose red, overprint gray blue 425.
 perf. 12, violet, overprint gray tan 425.
 imperf., pale olive, overprint pale tan 425.
 imperf., green, overprint gray tan 425.

e. Type B
 perf. 12, green, overprint pale tan 425.
 perf. 12, violet, overprint gray tan 425.
 perf. 12, dull red brown, ovpt. pale
 brown 425.
 perf. 12, dark dull red brown, overprint
 pale brown 425.

Type C

Type D

f. Type C
 perf. 12, dull violet, overprint gray tan 550.
 perf. 12, dull red, overprint gray blue 550.
 perf. 12, rose red, overprint gray blue 550.
 perf. 12, green, overprint gray tan 550.
 imperf., rose red, overprint pale tan 550.
 imperf., pale rose red, overprint pale tan 550.
 imperf., yellow brown, overprint tan 550.

g. Type D
 perf. 12, dull violet, overprint gray blue 550.
 perf. 12, rose red, overprint gray blue 550.

perf. 12, light red brown, overprint pale
 brown 550.
perf. 12, dark green, overprint dull blue 550.
imperf., pale olive, overprint tan 550.
imperf., ultramarine, overprint tan 550.
imperf., dull violet, overprint gray blue 550.
imperf., dull violet, overprint pale green 550.
imperf., dark green, overprint dull blue 550.

79-E27

Design size: 20½x26½mm
Engraved in relief for surface printing, large 2 vignette, on
same die with No. 79-E28, 20mm apart. Also essayed for envelopes on thick papers.

79-E27 2c
a. Untrimmed die, 30x42mm, on paper with
 "US" monogram, pale rose 850.
b. Die on stiff glazed paper, 63x50mm,
 black 600.
c. Trimmed die on India, on thick soft card,
 colorless parts in relief
 black 450.
 red 450.
 orange 450.
 violet red 450.
d. Die on 35x40mm white wove, imperf.,
 gummed
 blue 450.
 albino 450.
e. Die on white wove, perf. 12, gummed,
 smoky violet red 450.
f. Untrimmed die on white wove,
 61x42mm, black 550.

79-E28

79-E28g

Design size: 21x25½mm
Engraved in relief for surface printing, large 3 in shield
vignette, on same die with No. 79-E27, 20mm apart. Also
essayed for envelopes on thick papers.

79-E28 3c
a. Untrimmed die on stiff ivory paper,
 showing color 30x42mm
 black 700.
 rose 700.
 orange 700.
 blue 700.
b. Untrimmed die on India with No. 79-E27,
 both embossed, yellow orange 1,000.
c. Trimmed die heavily struck on India,
 card mounted, colorless parts in relief
 black 500.
 red 500.
 orange 500.
d. Die on wide laid paper, "US" monogram,
 perf. 12, gummed
 pale rose 250.
 dull brown yellow 250.
e. Die on greenish wove, 10x12mm points
 down grill, imperf., gummed, dull
 brown 250.
f. Die on white paper, perf. 12, gummed
 smoky violet red 250.
 green 250.
g. Underprinted design only on thin white
 wove
 light blue 350.
 albino 350.

79-E28H

Illustration reduced.
Design size: 68x38mm
Two compound surface-printed designs, "3" within ornate
frame.

79-E28H 3c Untrimmed die on wove paper,
 green 1,250.

79-E29

1861 1c frame only.
79-E29 1c
a. Die on thin crisp paper, safety design
 underprint, black on dull olive green 2,750.
b. Die on pink paper, 18x13mm points
 down grill, imperf., gummed, red
 brown 1,750.
c. Die on pink "laid" paper, red 1,750.
d. Die on pale pink paper, red brown 1,750.
e. Die on transparent white paper, red
 brown 1,750.
f. Die on thick yellow paper, red brown 1,750.
g. Die on thin transparent white paper,
 11x13mm points down grill, perf. 12,
 gummed, red brown 1,750.
h. As "g," imperf. 2,000.

79-E29i

As No. 79-E29 but with monogram in vignette.

i. Die on transparent white stamp paper, perf. 12, gummed, red brown 11,000.

79-E30

Design size: 20x26mm

Block size: 64x76 ½mm
Vignette of Liberty. Typographed.

79-E30 3c
  a. Head only on solid color (die size: 67x76mm), on 32x37mm stiff yellowish wove
    black ... 750.
    blue green ... 750.
  b. Vignette only, on 66x100mm card
    black ... 750.
    blue green ... 750.
    blue ... 750.
  c. Vignette only, on proof paper
    bright blue ... 600.
    black ... 600.
  d. Complete design, untrimmed block, colorless 22x27 rectangle around design, broad outer edge in color, on stiff yellowish wove
    black ... 750.
    blue green ... 750.
    violet brown ... 750.
    bright violet red ... 750.
    red violet ... 750.
    buff ... 750.
  e. As "d," on proof paper
    buff ... 750.
    deep blue green ... 750.
    red brown ... 750.
    carmine ... 750.
    black ... 750.
  f. Die on proof paper, perf. 12, vignette oval perf. 16, carmine ... 200.
  g. Die on stiff ivory paper about 28x32mm
    black ... 150.
    carmine ... 150.
    yellow ... 150.
    dark blue green ... 150.
    rose violet ... 150.
  h. Die on stiff ivory paper, no color outside design, block of 4, carmine ... 500.
    Block of 8 with vert. pairs in orange, dull yellow green, dark green and dark violet ... 900.
  i. Die on deep orange-surfaced white paper, carmine ... 150.
  j. As "i," perf. 12, gummed, carmine ... 150.
  k. Die on yellow-surfaced wove, carmine ... 150.

79-E30l

  l. Die with outer color removed, on 64x90mm white wove stamp paper with imprint below, imperf., gummed
    carmine ... 150.
    scarlet ... 150.
    dim orange red ... 150.
    orange ... 150.
    dull yellow orange ... 150.
    pale dull yellow ... 150.
    brown ... 150.
    lemon ... 150.
    yellow green ... 150.
    dull olive green ... 150.
    dull greenish gray ... 150.
    dim blue green ... 150.
    dull blue ... 150.
    dull red violet ... 150.
    pale red violet ... 150.
  m. As "l," tete-beche pairs, each with imprint
    carmine, orange ... 350.
    buff, pale lilac ... 350.
    dark orange brown, yellow ... 350.
    dull green gray ... 350.

79-E30n

  n. As "l," perf. 12, vignette oval perf. 16 (also found without paper outside perfs.)
    carmine ... 150.
    pale rose ... 150.
    dim scarlet ... 150.
    dull scarlet ... 150.
    dim orange red ... 150.
    light red brown ... 150.
    dark brown ... 150.
    orange ... 150.
    dull orange ... 150.
    dismal orange ... 150.
    dull brown orange ... 150.

---

    pale dull yellow ... 150.
    dull brown ... 150.
    yellow brown ... 150.
    dull olive green ... 150.
    dim dark yellow orange ... 150.
    light yellow green ... 150.
    green ... 150.
    dim blue green ... 150.
    dark blue green ... 150.
    dull greenish gray ... 150.
    dull yellowish gray ... 150.
    dull blue ... 150.
    dim red violet ... 150.
    dull red violet ... 150.
    pale red violet ... 150.
    red violet ... 150.

79-E30o

  o. Plate essay on wove, vertical pair of designs 7mm apart, in two colors shading into each other, imperf.
    red brown to dark orange ... 150.
    dark orange to brown red ... 150.
    brown olive to red brown ... 150.
    red brown to yellow green ... 150.
    yellow green to dull carmine ... 150.
    dull carmine to yellow green ... 150.
    blue green to dull carmine ... 150.
    brown olive to dull carmine ... 150.
    dull carmine to orange ... 150.
    orange to deep blue ... 150.
    deep blue to orange brown ... 150.
    orange brown to dull orange ... 150.
    dull carmine to deep blue ... 150.

79-E30p Block

Illustration reduced.

  p. As "o," on transparent wove, imperf.
    red violet to deep violet ... 150.
    deep violet to carmine ... 150.
    dull scarlet to gold ... 150.
    gold to carmine ... 150.
    dark violet to blue green ... 150.
    blue green to dark violet red ... 150.
    violet to yellow green ... 150.
    yellow green to red violet ... 150.
  q. As "o," plate on stiff yellowish wove, imperf.
    dull carmine to orange ... 150.
    orange to deep blue ... 150.
    brown olive to brown red ... 150.
    brown red to yellow green ... 150.
    blue green to dull carmine ... 150.
    dull carmine to deep blue ... 150.
    deep blue to dark brown ... 150.
    dark brown to orange ... 150.
  r. As "q," outside edge perf. 12
    blue green to dull carmine ... 150.
    dull carmine to deep blue ... 150.
    deep blue to dark brown ... 150.
    dark brown to dull orange ... 150.
    dull carmine to dull orange ... 150.
    dull orange to deep blue ... 150.
    yellow green to dull carmine ... 150.
    dull carmine to yellow green ... 150.
    brown olive to brown red ... 150.
    brown red to yellow green ... 150.
  s. As "r," plate in single color, outside edge perf. 12, gummed
    carmine ... 150.
    dull carmine ... 150.
    orange brown ... 150.

---

    dark brown ... 150.
    brown olive ... 150.
    dark blue green ... 150.
    violet ... 150.
  t. As "s," imperf., gummed
    brown ... 125.
    brown orange ... 125.
    dull blue green ... 125.
    deep blue ... 125.
    carmine ... 125.
  u. As "t," one color directly over another (gives effect of one color), black on scarlet ... 275.
  v. As "b," heavily stamped on white card, only faint traces of vignette, albino ... 125.
  w. As "v," printed design at right, very dark blue green ... 250.

79-E31a   79-E31b

79-E31d   79-E31e

79-E31f   79-E31g

Same design as No. 79-E30, black green on white wove safety paper, underprinted with different designs in various colors, imperf.

79-E31 3c
  a. Red horiz. diamonds ... 1,400.
  b. Dull yellow green with ONE repeated ... 1,400.
  c. Red with 2 in circles ... 1,400.
  d. Red with 2 in circular stars ... 1,400.
  e. Red with 2 in ovals ... 1,400.
  f. Red with 3 in diamonds ... 1,400.
  g. Black with 5 in hexagons ... 1,400.
  h. Red with X repeated ... 1,400.

79-E32

Similar to No. 79-E30f, but perf. vignette removed and frame mounted over 18x23mm Washington vignette.

79-E32 3c Die on 34x40mm white wove, black vignette, blue frame ... 8,000.

1868 Essays
Experiments for bicolor printing

1c 1861 design, color reversed as adopted. Typographed frame with 43x60mm solid color border.

79-E33 1c Die on thin white paper, frame pink, vignette dark blue over pink ... 750.

79-E35a

79-E35c

Frame lithographed, colored and colorless parts interchanged, vignette engraved and printed in another color.
Die I: colorless vignette oval (Nos. 79-E35a, 79-E35b)
Die II: vignette with horiz. lines (Nos. 79-E35d through 79-E35f)

79-E35 5c
  a. Untrimmed die on thin white paper, 40x60mm (values for cut to stamp size)
    frame buff, vignette black   2,000.
    frame buff, vignette blue   2,000.
    frame buff, vignette red brown   2,000.
    frame buff, vignette dark brown   2,000.
    frame buff, vignette orange   2,000.
    frame buff, vignette carmine   2,000.
    frame blue green, vignette dark brown   2,000.
    frame blue green, vignette red brown   2,000.
    frame blue green, vignette orange   2,000.
    frame carmine, vignette blue   2,000.
    frame carmine, vignette red brown   2,000.
    frame violet, vignette orange   2,000.
    frame light red, vignette deep orange red   2,000.
    frame light red, vignette yellow orange   2,000.
  b. Die on stiff wove, frame brown, vignette scarlet   2,000.
  c. 45x65mm die impression of lithographed frame only, on ivory paper
    black   2,000.
    blue green   2,000.
  d. Die on thin white paper
    frame violet, vignette carmine   2,000.
    frame violet, vignette brown   2,000.
    frame violet, vignette red brown   2,000.
    frame carmine, vignette black   2,000.
  e. Vignette only on white glazed paper
    black   2,000.
    blue   2,000.
    scarlet   2,000.
    dark brown   2,000.
  f. As "e," without thin outer frameline, on India
    lake   2,000.
    red   2,000.
    deep red orange   2,000.
    scarlet   2,000.
    deep green   2,000.
    ultramarine   2,000.

79-E36

Die II vignette as No. 79-E35e, with gothic "United States" above.

79-E36 5c
  a. Die on white glazed paper
    black   450.
    scarlet   450.
    dark brown   450.
    green   450.
    blue   450.

79-E37

Die size: 51x63½
5c 1861 design, color reversed as adopted, vignette mounted on typographed frame.

79-E37 5c
  a. Die on white card, frame light blue, vignette black   1,000.
  b. Vignette only, die on India, black   350.
  c. Vignette only, die on white glazed paper
    blue   350.
    black   350.
    green   350.

100-E1

Design size: 20½x24½mm
Engraved circular Franklin vignette mounted on 43x75mm white card, engraved Washington head mounted thereon; background, silhouette, etc., retouched in black ink. With engraved frame of No. 71-E1 (vignette cut out) mounted over the double vignette.

100-E1 30c Die on India, 30x34mm, black   6,000.

1869 ISSUE
George T. Jones

112-E1

113-E1

Design size: 24x30mm
U.S. Grant vignette in frame with blank labels, ovals, etc. Paper overprinted with network of fine colored wavy lines in fugitive inks as on beer stamps.

112-E1 No Denomination
  a. Die on India cut to stamp size, 1 color
    black   2,250.
    blue   2,250.
  b. Die on India cut to stamp size, 2 colors (head in black)
    blue, light gray overprint   3,250.
    red, light gray overprint   3,250.
    black, light violet overprint   3,250.
    black brown, pale red violet ovpt.   3,250.
    carmine, gray overprint   3,250.
    blue, yellow overprint   3,250.

Design size: 24x30mm
U.S. Treasury Dept. seal in vignette oval.

113-E1 2c
  a. Die on India cut to stamp size, 1 color
    carmine   2,500.
    blue   2,500.
  b. Die on India cut to stamp size, 3 colors, black on pale red violet wavy lines and blue green lined vignette   3,750.

Frame as 112-E1 but with Washington vignette and 2c denomination. Another Washington vignette below but in horiz. lined oval frame.

113-E2 2c Die on 1⅝x3½inch India, black   5,000.

National Bank Note Co.

All values originally essayed with numerals smaller than adopted. All designs are same size as issued stamps. Sheets of 150 of 1c-12c, sheets of 50 of 24c-90c. Many colors of plate essays exist from one sheet only, some colors from two sheets and a few from three. Some plate essays exist privately perforated.

112-E2

112-E3

Die size: 40x65mm
Vignette size: 17mm diameter
Vignette of Franklin.

112-E2 1c Die of vignette only on India
    orange   900.
    violet brown   900.
    black   900.

Circle of pearls added to vignette, suggestion for frame and 1 in circle at bottom penciled in.

112-E3 1c Die on India, black   1,500.

112-E4

112-E5

Complete design as issued but with small value numeral.

112-E4 1c
  a. Die on India, die sunk on card
    black   1,250.
    violet brown   1,250.
    dark brown   1,250.
    yellow brown   1,250.
    scarlet   1,250.
    carmine   1,250.
    deep violet   1,250.
    blue   1,250.
    green   1,250.
    yellow   1,250.
  b. Plate on stamp paper, imperf., gummed
    buff   100.
    deep orange brown   100.
    orange brown   100.
  c. Plate on stamp paper, perf. 12, gummed
    buff   100.
    orange brown   100.
    orange   125.
  d. As "c," with 9x9mm grill
    buff   110.
    orange brown   85.
    red brown   85.
    chocolate   85.
    black brown   85.
    dull red   85.
    violet   110.
    dark violet   110.
    blue   110.
    deep blue   110.
    green   110.
    yellow   110.
    orange   110.
    rose red   110.
  e. Horiz. pair, one #112-E4c, one #112-E4d   400.

Design size: 23x31mm
Die size: 51x55mm
Design as issued but surrounded by fancy frame with flags and shield. Also essayed for envelopes and wrappers on thick paper.

112-E5 1c
  a. Die on stamp paper, perf. 12, gummed, gray   3,000.
  b. Die on white ivory paper
    black   2,000.
    black brown   2,000.
    scarlet   2,000.
    blue   2,000.
  c. Die on India
    blue   2,000.
    blue green   2,000.
  d. Die on India, cut to shape
    carmine   750.
    yellow   750.

113-E3

Die size: 41x50mm
Design as issued but with small value numeral. Nos. 113-E3a and 113-Eb have incomplete shading around "UNITED STATES."

113-E3 2c
  a. Die on India, die sunk on card
    black   1,500.
    yellow   1,500.
    red orange   1,500.
    deep scarlet   1,500.
    brown   1,500.
    green   1,500.
    dusky blue   1,500.
    deep blue   1,500.
  b. Die on India, cut to stamp size
    deep orange red   400.
    deep orange yellow   400.
    blue green   400.
    gray black   400.
    light blue   400.
    rose   400.
  c. Complete die on India, die sunk on card
    brown   1,500.

rose	1,500.
mauve	1,500.
green	1,500.
dark chocolate	1,500.
red brown	1,500.

d. Plate on stamp paper, perf. 12, gummed

brown	425.
dark brown	425.
yellow	425.

e. As "d," with 9x9mm grill

brown	80.
dark brown	80.
orange brown	80.
dark orange brown	80.
rose	80.
brown rose	80.
copper red	80.
deep copper red	80.
green	80.
deep green	80.
blue green	80.
yellow	80.
orange	80.
dull yellow orange	80.
blue	80.
light violet	80.
violet	80.
dark violet	80.

f. As "e," double grill, orange   300.

g. Horiz. pair, one #113-E3d, one #113-E3e   1,000.

113-E4

Original sketch of postrider, printed "NATIONAL BANK NOTE COMPANY. BUSINESS DEPARTMENT. 1868" at top, pencil instructions at bottom, "Reduce to this length" and "2 copies on one plate. Daguerrotype."

113-E4   2c Drawing on paper, black   —

114-E3   114-E4

Die size: 53x47mm

Design nearly as issued: larger motive above and below "POSTAGE" erased, no shading on numeral shield, top leaves and corner leaves do not touch, no dots in lower corners or scrolls beside bottom of shield, no vert. shading lines in "POSTAGE" label. Small value numeral.

114-E3   3c Die on 30x30mm ivory paper, black   1,500.

Similar to 114-E3, but smaller motive around "POSTAGE," shield shaded.

114-E4   3c

a. Die on India, die sunk on card

black	1,500.
carmine	1,500.
scarlet	1,500.
orange red	1,500.
yellow orange	1,500.
dull yellow	1,500.
red sepia	1,500.
blue green	1,500.
blue	1,500.
dull red	1,500.
orange brown	1,500.

b. Die on India, cut to stamp size

black	500.
rose	500.
scarlet	500.
chocolate	500.
dull dusky orange	500.
red violet	500.
blackish slate	500.

114-E5

Similar to No. 114-E4 but vert. shading lines added to "POSTAGE" frame.

114-E5   3c Die on India, chocolate   1,500.

114-E6   114-E7

Completed small numeral die essay: leaves at top and sides touch, dots in lower corners added, vert. shading lines in frame around "POSTAGE," shield shaded darker at bottom, scrolls added to bottom of shield.

114-E6   3c

a. Die on India, card mounted

black	1,750.
blue	1,750.
deep orange red	1,750.

b. Plate on stamp paper, imperf., gummed

ultramarine	125.
dark ultramarine	125.
light brown	85.
red brown	85.
dark red brown	85.
pale rose	85.
rose	85.
brown rose	85.

c. Plate on stamp paper, perf. 12, gummed

ultramarine	500.
dark ultramarine	500.

d. As "c," with 9x9mm grill

blue	80.
deep blue	80.
orange brown	80.
black brown	80.
deep black brown	80.
rose red	80.
green	80.
yellow	80.
orange	80.
deep orange	80.
dull violet	80.
deep violet	80.
red violet	80.

Same design and color as issued stamp, but with allover essay grill of squares up.

114-E7   3c

a. Imperf., gummed, ultramarine   700.

b. As "a," 23mm "NATIONAL BANK NOTE CO. N.Y. SEP 27, 1869" circular pmk., ultramarine   1,100.

c. On thick paper, imperf., gummed, horiz. line defacement, ultramarine   700.

d. Perf. 12, horiz. line defacement, ultramarine   700.

115-E1   115-E2

Die size: 40x60mm

Vignette of Washington. Design as issued 6c stamp but with 5c denomination. Large lettering, large U and S in corners. Also essayed for envelopes on thick paper.

115-E1   6c

a. Die on India, no frameline, solid vignette background, corner spandrels short at centers

black	700.
carmine	700.
dismal red brown	700.
smoky dusky brown	700.
gray violet	700.

b. Completed die on India, die sunk on card

black	600.
carmine	600.
deep rose	600.
red violet	600.
red brown	600.
deep yellow brown	600.
black brown	600.
dull yellow	600.
orange	600.
dusky blue	600.
dusky slate blue	600.
green	600.
blue green	600.
scarlet	600.

c. Die on proof paper, about 40x65mm

black	600.
carmine	600.
scarlet	600.
red orange	600.
orange	600.

dull yellow	600.
orange brown	600.
olive brown	600.
dusky green	600.
dusky yellow green	600.
light blue	600.
deep blue	600.
red violet	600.

d. Die on pink bond

orange	600.
brown	600.
blue	600.

e. Die on light yellow green bond, black   600.

f. Die on pale olive buff bond

black	600.
carmine	600.
orange	600.
red orange	600.
brown	600.

g. Die on cream wove

black	600.
orange	600.
brown	600.
blue	600.

h. Die on clear white bond

black	600.
blue	600.
orange	600.
red orange brown	600.

i. Die on thick cloudy bond

black	600.
red	600.
orange	600.
orange brown	600.
blue	600.
reddish brown	600.

j. Die on pale lilac bond

dark red orange	700.
orange	700.
blue	700.

k. Die on glazed paper

black	550.
scarlet	550.
yellow	550.
dark brown	550.
blue	550.

l. Die on marbled white card

green on red violet veined	1,750.
black on green veined	1,750.
red violet on green veined	1,750.

m. Die on ivory card

black	1,500.
blue	1,500.

n. Die on white card, cut to stamp size, red orange   250.

Die size: 43x63mm
Similar to No. 115-E1 but lettering, U and S smaller.

115-E2   6c

a. Incomplete die on India (incomplete spandrel points, hair on top of head, etc.)

black	750.
dull red brown	750.

b. Complete die on India, die sunk on card

black	750.
blue	750.
dull dusky violet	750.
scarlet	750.
dark orange red	750.
dim dusky red orange	750.
dusky green	750.
dusky green blue green	750.
dusky blue green	750.

c. Plate essay on wove, imperf., gummed

deep ultramarine	150.
orange	150.
dull red violet	80.
deep red violet	80.
red brown	80.
dull red brown	80.
buff	80.
green	80.

d. Plate essay on wove, perf. 12, gummed

orange	200.
blue	200.

115-E3

Vignette of Washington as used on stamp but with longer shirt front.

115-E3E   6c Die on india, affixed to card, 35x37mm, black   —

116-E1

Vignette of Lincoln as on No. 77, but surrounded by double frame line.

116-E1 10c Die on India, 24x24mm, black   1,500.

116-E1D

Die size: 14x18mm

Vignette of Lincoln as on No. 77. As No. 116-E1, but double frame lines removed.

116-E1D 10c Die on India, on card, black   1,000.

116-E1a

Design size:14x14½mm
Vignette of Lincoln as on No. 77, reduced.

116-E1a   Die on India, on card, black   1,500.

116-E1b

Design size: about 19½x19½mm
Die size: 64x68½mm
Head as on No. 77 but less bust, large unshaded collar, no cross shading in triangles between labels and fasces, no shading on diamonds at end of value label.

116-E1b   Incomplete die on India, on card,
                 black   5,750.

116-E1c

Small collar, shading on diamonds at end of value label. Also essayed for envelopes on yellow laid paper.

116-E1c   Complete die on India, die sunk on
                 card
         black   1,000.
         brown black   1,000.
         gray black   1,000.
         carmine   1,000.
         scarlet   1,000.
         brown red   1,000.
         orange   1,000.
         deep orange   1,000.
         deep red   1,000.
         yellow brown   1,000.
         yellow   1,000.
         green   1,000.
         blue green   1,000.
         deep blue   1,000.
         red violet   1,000.
         brown   1,000.
   d. Die on proof paper

         black   1,000.
         carmine   1,000.
         bright red   1,000.
         orange red   1,000.
         orange   1,000.
         dark chocolate   1,000.
         dusky yellow brown   1,000.
         green   1,000.
         blue   1,000.
         red violet   1,000.
   e. Die on ivory paper
         black   1,000.
         scarlet   1,000.
         black brown   1,000.
         blue   1,000.
   f. Die on clear white thin bond, about
            30x35mm
         black   1,000.
         red orange   1,000.
         red brown   1,000.
         orange   1,000.
         yellow   1,000.
         blue   1,000.
   g. Die on cloudy cream bond, about
            30x35mm
         black   1,000.
         light red brown   1,000.
         red orange   1,000.
         blue   1,000.
   h. Die on pink bond, about 39x45mm
         red orange   1,000.
         red brown   1,000.
         yellow   1,000.
   i. Die on pale greenish gray bond,
            about 33x37mm
         black   1,000.
         deep carmine   1,000.
         dull scarlet   1,000.
         dark brown   1,000.
         blue   1,000.
   j. Die on marbled white ivory card,
            about 38x62mm
         black on green veined   1,900.
         orange red on green veined   1,900.
         red orange on green veined   1,900.
         dark orange brown on red violet
            veined   1,900.
   k. Plate on stamp paper, imperf.,
            gummed
         deep green   150.
         blue   125.
         ultramarine   125.
         dark ultramarine   125.
         light ultramarine   125.
   l. Plate on stamp paper, perf. 12,
            gummed, orange   200.

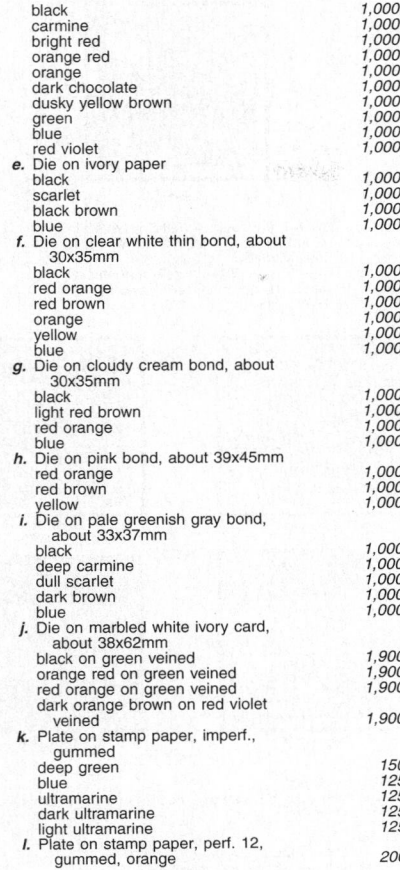

116-E2

Die size: 101x62mm
Vignette of signing the Declaration of Independence as adopted for 24c.

116-E2 10c
   a. Die on India, die sunk on card
         black   3,750.
         carmine   3,750.
         dim rose   3,750.
         dull scarlet   3,750.
         red orange   3,750.
         orange yellow   3,750.
         red brown   3,750.
         orange brown   3,750.
         green   3,750.
         blue   3,750.
         gray   3,750.
   b. Die on India, cut to stamp size
         black   1,500.
         red orange   1,500.
         blue green   1,500.
         dim rose   1,500.
         brown   1,500.
         buff   1,500.
         dull scarlet   1,500.

Other colors reported to exist.

116-E3

116-E4

Die size: 63x75mm

Design as adopted for issued stamp, but incomplete shading on bottom ribbon, thin shading lines behind "States," and center of "0" of "10" not filled in.

116-E3 10c Die on India on 61x53mm card,
                 black   2,500.

Similar to No. 116-E3 except shading lines added behind "Ten Cents" and center of "0" of "10" filled in.

116-E4 10c Die on India, die sunk on card
         black   2,500.
         orange   2,500.
         blue   2,500.

117-E1

117-E2

Die size: 47x51mm
Design as issued but with smaller value numerals.

117-E1 12c
   a. Die on card, black   1,600.
   b. Vignette die on India, pencil "Adriatic",
            black   1,600.
   c. Complete die on India, die sunk on card
         black   1,350.
         rose   1,350.
         yellow   1,350.
         scarlet   1,350.
         dark red brown   1,350.
         blue green   1,350.
         blue   1,350.
         dull violet   1,350.
         gray black   1,350.
         orange brown   1,350.
         yellow brown   1,350.
         dull orange red   1,350.
   d. Die on India, cut to stamp size
         black   600.
         dusky red orange   600.
         deep orange red   600.
         dim blue   600.
   e. Plate on stamp paper, 9x9mm grill, perf.
            12, gummed
         green   125.
         rose red   125.
         pale rose red   125.
         yellow brown   125.
         red brown   125.
         orange   125.
         blue   125.
         dull violet   125.
         dull red violet   125.
         yellow orange   125.

Similar to No. 117-E1, but small numeral not printed, large 12 drawn in pencil.

117-E2 12c Die on India, black   2,750.

117-E3

117-E4

Typographed small numeral design similar to No. 117-E1, relief engraved for surface printing. Heavier lines, upper label with solid background, letters of "UNITED STATES POSTAGE" colorless. Nos. 117-E3a through 117-E3c from untrimmed die, heavily struck with uncolored areas in relief, color covering borders beyond white line exterior of frame. Untrimmed die size: 58x45mm.

117-E3 12c
   a. Untrimmed die on card
         brown red   750.
         green   750.
         black   750.
         red brown   750.
   b. Untrimmed die on thin pinkish wove
         gray black   450.
         dull deep red orange   450.
         dark red orange   450.
   c. Untrimmed die on thick white wove
         carmine   600.
         green   600.
   d. Die on white paper, stamp size
         carmine   400.
         orange   400.
         brown   400.
         lilac   400.
         green   400.
   e. Die on thin white wove
         carmine   400.
         gray black   400.
         dull deep red orange   400.
         deep orange red   400.

g. Die on pinkish wove, perf. 12, gummed,
red brown   400.
h. Die on yellow wove, imperf.
gray black   400.
carmine   400.
red brown   400.
dark red violet   400.
i. Die on yellow wove, 11x13mm grill, imperf., red brown   400.
j. Die on white laid
gray   400.
gray black   400.
brown   400.
red brown   400.
k. Die on yellow laid
red brown   400.
brown   400.
dull red violet   400.
carmine   400.
l. Die on salmon laid, red brown   400.
m. Die on pinkish laid
red brown   400.
gray   400.
n. Die on pinkish laid, 11x13mm grill, gummed, red brown   400.
o. Die on dull red violet laid, gray   400.

Vignette size: 15x11mm
Untrimmed die size: 63x32mm
Vignette only, similar to No. 117-E3 but lithographed instead of typographed.

117-E4   12c
a. Die on white ivory paper, black   1,000.
b. Complete impression from untrimmed stone in solid color about 63x63mm, on white ivory paper, black   750.
c. Die on glossy-surfaced thin white wove, trimmed to stamp size
carmine   750.
rose pink   750.
yellow   750.
blue green   750.
dim red violet   750.
pale red violet   750.
deep red orange   750.
dull dark red orange   750.
dull dark yellow orange   750.
dark violet red   750.
pale gray   750.
d. Die on thick white wove
yellow   750.
violet red   750.
deep red violet   750.

118-E1a

Die size: 62x49mm
Type I design as issued but with smaller value numerals.

118-E1   15c
a. Die of vignette only on India, mounted on 62x62mm India, die sunk on card, dark blue   3,500.
b. Incomplete die (no outer frameline or shading outside frame scrolls) on India, black   4,500.

118-E1c

c. Complete die on India, die sunk on card
black   5,000.
scarlet   5,000.
orange brown   5,000.
green   5,000.
dull violet   5,000.
red brown   5,000.

119-E1a

Type II design with large value numerals as issued.

119-E1   15c
a. Type II frame only, die on India
black   3,000.
red brown   3,000.
b. Vignette only, die on India, blue   —

119-E1c

c. Type II frame with vignette mounted in place, die on India, red brown frame, blue vignette   7,500.
d. Type II frame with vignette mounted at right, die on India, red brown frame, blue vignette   —

129-E1   129-E2

129-E7   129-E8

Die size: 65x49
Type III design as adopted, except in various single colors, large "15" overprint in diff. color.

129-E1   15c
a. Die on India, die sunk on card
orange brown, red overprint   3,500.
blue green, red overprint   3,500.
ultramarine, red overprint   3,500.
violet, red overprint   3,500.
red brown, red overprint   3,500.
b. Die on India, die sunk on card
rose red, ultramarine overprint   3,500.
dull scarlet, ultramarine overprint   3,500.
dark red brown, ultramarine ovpt.   3,500.
c. Die on India, die sunk on card
scarlet, blue green overprint   3,500.
orange brown, blue green overprint   3,500.
dark red brown, blue green overprint   3,500.

Similar to No. 129-E1 but without the "15" overprint.

129-E2   Die on India, 34x30mm, dark blue   10,000.

Type III frame only.

129-E7   15c
a. Die on India, red brown   2,750.
b. Die on India, with vignette mounted in place, blue frame, yellow vignette   3,500.

Type III frame only.

129-E8   15c Die on pink-tinted paper, perforated   3,750.

120-E1

120-E2a

120-E2b

Die size: 102x63mm

Design nearly as issued, but shading under leaves at top of frame and ribbon over "TWENTY" are unfinished. Small value numerals. Single color.

120-E1   24c Die on India, black   4,000.

Completed small numeral design in single color. No. 120-E2a has 8mm-high bands of shaded colored lines 31mm long overprinted above and below vignette, printed in various single colors with bands in contrasting color.

120-E2   24c
a. Die on India
black with carmine bands   4,000.
black with violet brown bands   4,000.
black with brown orange bands   4,000.
orange brown with deep dull violet bands   4,000.
orange brown with blue green bands   4,000.
b. Die on India
black   2,250.
scarlet   2,250.
dark red brown   2,250.
blue   2,250.
violet   2,250.
c. Plate on red salmon tinted paper, black   200.
d. Plate on orange buff tinted paper, black   250.
e. Plate on dull yellowish tinted paper, black   250.
f. Plate on blue tinted paper, black   250.
g. Plate on gray tinted paper, black   500.
h. Plate on India, black   300.
j. Plate on card, imperf., black   250.

120-E3a   120-E3b

No. 120-E3a bicolor design as issued, except vignette printed separately and mounted in place; No. 120-E3b frame only with 3 border lines around vignette space; No. 120-E3c frame only with 2 border lines around vignette space as issued.

120-E3   24c
a. Die on India, card mounted
dull violet frame, green vignette   2,500.
violet frame, red vignette   2,500.
green frame, violet vignette   2,500.
rose frame, green vignette   2,500.
b. Frame die on India, card mounted
black   5,000.
light green   2,500.
dark green   2,500.
c. Frame die on India, block sunk on India, green   2,500.

121-E1

Design size: 21½x22mm
Die Size: 71x51mm
Vignette of Surrender of Gen. Burgoyne in ornate frame.

121-E1   30c
a. Die on India, die sunk on card
black   800.
carmine   800.
rose red   800.
light brown red   800.
red brown   800.
brown orange   800.
orange   800.
red orange   800.
yellow green   800.
blue   800.
dull dark violet   800.
yellow brown   800.
scarlet   800.
b. Die on stiff ivory paper
black   650.
c. Die on India, cut to stamp size
dim deep orange red   250.
deep yellow orange   250.
dim deep blue green   250.
dim dusky blue   250.
d. Die on India die sunk on 78x58mm white card
dusky blue   1,000.
e. Die on white card, cut to stamp size
dim orange   500.
f. Die on proof paper, about 70x50mm
black   500.
carmine   500.
scarlet   500.
red orange   500.
green   500.

violet ... 500.

g. Die on ivory paper, about 64x50mm
black ... 750.
dark brown ... 750.
scarlet ... 750.
blue ... 750.
h. Die on ivory card
black ... 1,000.
carmine ... 1,000.
i. Die on clear white bond, about
33x33mm
black ... 600.
blue ... 600.
light red brown ... 600.
orange ... 600.
j. Die on yellowish cloudy bond, about
34x34mm
black ... 600.
orange ... 600.
light red brown ... 600.
blue ... 600.
k. Die on smoky yellow greenish bond
black ... 600.
carmine ... 600.
orange ... 600.
l. Die on pink bond, about 40x40mm
blue ... 600.
dim orange red ... 600.
orange ... 600.
m. Die on pale olive buff paper
black ... 600.
dim orange red ... 600.
orange ... 600.
n. Die on thick yellowish wove, dim green
blue ... 600.
o. Die on marbled white ivory card, about
40x60mm
black on green veined ... 2,500.
black on red violet veined ... 2,500.
p. Plate essay in black on thin surface-
tinted paper
pale gray ... 275.
salmon red ... 175.
yellow ... 175.
orange ... 275.
orange buff ... 275.
pink ... 275.
pale pink ... 275.
blue ... 275.
light blue ... 275.
pale green ... 275.
brown violet ... 275.
q. Plate essay in black on India ... 300.
r. Plate on thick rough pitted card, black ... 300.

121-E1s

s. Plate on bond, red bands overprinted
top and bottom as on No. 120-E2a,
dull red violet ... 350.

121-E2

121-E3

Flags, stars and rays only as adopted for issued stamp. Black essay shows traces of vignette also.

121-E2 30c Die on India, mounted on India,
block sunk on card
black ... 7,500.
light ultramarine ... 6,000.
dark blue ... 6,000.

Eagle, shield and value only as adopted for issued stamp.

121-E3 30c Die on India, card mounted, black ... 8,500.

122-E1

Die size: 62x69mm

Vignette of Washington in frame similar to that of issued stamp but no shading over U and S in lower corners, small value numerals.

122-E1 90c Die on India, black ... 3,250.

Similar to No. 122-E1 but shading over U and S.

122-E2

122-E2 90c
a. Die on India, die sunk on card
black ... 2,500.
carmine ... 2,500.
scarlet ... 2,500.
red brown ... 2,500.
blue green ... 2,500.
violet ... 2,500.
b. Plate essay with black vignette on stamp
paper, imperf.
dull violet ... 275.
red brown ... 275.
orange red ... 275.
pale orange red ... 275.
blue ... 275.

122-E3

122-E4

Frame as No. 122-E2, vignette oval with narrow-spaced horiz. lines in same color as frame, but no head.

122-E3 90c Plate on medium India paper, imperf.
red brown ... 225.
blue ... 225.
dark blue ... 225.
red violet ... 225.
dull violet ... 225.
dark violet ... 225.
rose red ... 225.
deep rose red ... 225.
yellow ... 225.
orange brown ... 225.
dark navy blue ... 225.
blue green ... 225.
deep blue green ... 225.
dark blue green ... 225.
orange ... 225.

Small numeral frame but with black Lincoln vignette on India from No. 77 mounted in place.

122-E4 90c
a. Die on medium India
yellow ... 2,000.
red brown ... 2,000.
rose red ... 2,000.
deep blue green ... 2,000.
dark navy blue ... 2,000.
b. Plate of Lincoln vignette only, on rough
pitted thick gray paper, black ... 600.
Block of 4 ... 2,500.
c. Die on India, Lincoln vignette as used
on No. 77, black ... 2,500.

122-E5

Similar to No. 122-E1, with Washington vignette but with large numerals as on issued stamp.

122-E5 90c
a. Die on India, die sunk on card
black ... 5,000.
carmine ... 5,000.
b. Plate of frame only, 2 lines at top, 3 lines
at bottom, on India, mounted on block
sunk card, rose red ... 1,250.
c. As "b," 3 lines at top, 2 lines at bottom
rose red ... 4,500.
red brown ... 1,250.

Safety essays: die essays on thin wove, underprinted with various engraved safety paper designs in another color, probably with fugitive ink.
Found on 5c (No. 115-E1), 10c (No. 116-E1), 15c (No. 129-E1 without overprint) and 30c (No. 121-E1). Stamp color given first.

115-E3a

Design 1: wavy lines
115-E3
a. 5c
carmine on scarlet ... 3,250.
orange on scarlet ... 3,250.
b. 10c blue on scarlet ... 5,000.
c. 30c carmine on scarlet ... 3,500.

115-E4

Design 2: banknote type
115-E4
a. 5c
carmine on violet ... 3,250.
orange on violet ... 3,250.
b. 10c carmine on violet ... 5,000.
c. 30c
carmine on violet ... 3,500.
orange on violet ... 3,500.
orange on gray ... 3,500.

115-E5

Design 3: banknote type
115-E5
a. 5c
carmine on orange and red ... 3,250.
carmine on brown ... 3,250.
orange on brown ... 3,250.
b. 10c
carmine on orange and red ... 5,000.
blue on orange and red ... 5,000.
c. 30c
carmine on orange and red ... 3,500.
orange on brown ... 3,500.

115-E6

Design 4: continuous wavy lines
115-E6
a. 5c orange on scarlet ... 3,250.
b. 10c
blue on scarlet ... 5,000.
carmine on scarlet ... 5,000.
c. 30c black on scarlet ... 3,500.

115-E7

Design 5: wavy lines
115-E7
  a. 5c
    orange on scarlet   3,250.
    orange on black   3,250.
  b. 10c
    dark brown on black   5,000.
    orange red on black   5,000.
    carmine on scarlet   5,000.
  c. 30c
    carmine on black   3,500.
    carmine on scarlet   3,500.

115-E8

Design 6: wavy lines
115-E8
  a. 5c orange on black   3,250.
  b. 10c blue on black   5,000.
  c. 30c
    carmine on black   3,500.
    orange on black   3,500.

115-E9

Design 7: crossed wavy lines
115-E9
  a. 5c
    carmine on black   3,250.
    orange on black   3,250.
  b. 10c blue on black   5,000.
  c. 30c orange on black   3,500.

115-E10

Design 8: wavy lines
115-E10
  a. 5c carmine on scarlet   3,250.
  b. 10c
    blue on scarlet   5,000.
    carmine on scarlet   5,000.
    orange red on scarlet   5,000.

129-E3

Design 9: wavy lines
129-E3   15c
    orange brown on orange, vert.   3,500.
    blue green on orange, horiz.   3,500.
    dark blue on orange, horiz.   3,500.

129-E4

Design 10: banknote type
129-E4   15c
    orange brown on scarlet   3,500.
    blue green on scarlet   3,500.
    dark blue on scarlet   3,500.

129-E5

Design 11: banknote type
129-E5   15c
    orange brown on light scarlet   3,500.
    blue green on light scarlet, vert.   3,500.
    dark blue on light scarlet   3,500.

129-E6

Design 12: banknote type
129-E6   15c
    orange brown on deep scarlet   3,500.
    blue green on deep scarlet   3,500.
    dark blue on deep scarlet   3,500.

115-E11

Design 13: banknote type
115-E11
  a. 5c orange on brown   3,250.
  b. 10c
    carmine on brown   5,500.
    orange red on brown   5,500.
    blue on brown (horiz. underprinting)   5,500.
    blue on brown (vert. underprinting)   5,500.
  c. 30c carmine on brown   3,500.

115-E12

Design 14: banknote type
115-E12
  a. 5c
    carmine on scarlet (horiz.)   4,000.
    black on scarlet (vert.)   4,000.
  b. 10c
    carmine on scarlet   5,500.
    orange on scarlet   5,500.
    sepia on scarlet   5,500.
    blue on scarlet   5,500.
  c. 30c black on scarlet   3,500.

115-E13

Design 15: banknote type
115-E13
  a. 5c carmine on orange brown   3,250.
  b. 30c carmine on deep orange   3,500.

115-E14

Design 16: multiple rosettes
115-E14
  a. 5c orange on scarlet   3,250.
  b. 10c
    carmine on scarlet   5,500.
    orange red on scarlet   5,500.
    sepia on scarlet   5,500.
    blue on scarlet   5,500.

115-E15

Design 17: multiple oval rosettes
115-E15
  a. 5c carmine on scarlet   3,250.
  b. 30c
    carmine on scarlet   3,500.
    orange on scarlet   3,500.

115-E16

Design 18: negative stars in diagonal lines
115-E16
  a. 5c
    black on scarlet   3,250.
    carmine on scarlet   3,250.
  b. 10c
    carmine on scarlet   5,500.
    sepia on scarlet   5,500.
  c. 30c carmine on scarlet   3,500.

116-E6a

Design 19: multiple 6-point stars in lathework
116-E6
  a. 10c blue on blue green   5,500.
  b. 30c carmine on blue green   3,500.

116-E7

Design 20: banknote type
116-E7
a. 10c
    brown on orange   5,500.
    blue on orange   5,500.
b. 30c carmine on orange   3,500.

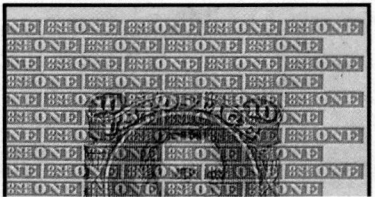

116-E8

Design 21: multiple "ONE"
116-E8 10c blue on scarlet   5,500.

115-E17

Design 22: multiple "TWO"
115-E17
a. 5c orange on scarlet   3,250.
b. 10c carmine on scarlet   5,500.

115-E18

Design 23: multiple "5"s in oval rosettes
115-E18 5c black on carmine   3,250.

115-E19

Design 24: multiple "TEN 10"
115-E19
a. 5c
    orange on scarlet   3,250.
    carmine on scarlet   3,250.
b. 10c
    carmine on scarlet   5,500.
    orange red on scarlet   5,500.
    brown on scarlet   5,500.
    blue on scarlet   5,500.
c. 30c
    carmine on scarlet   3,500.
    orange red on scarlet   3,500.
    brown on scarlet   3,500.
    blue on scarlet   3,500.

115-E20

Design 25: multiple "50"
115-E20 5c
    black on black   3,250.
    orange on black   3,250.

1870 ISSUE
Continental Banknote Co.

145-E1

Vignette of Washington in large ornate "1." Labels and side ornaments not yet engraved.
145-E1   1c engraved die on India, black   —

145-E1C

Vignette of Washington in large ornate "1."
145-E1C   One Cent
a. Die on India, die sunk on card
    black   1,500.
    scarlet   1,500.
    green   1,500.
    ultramarine   1,500.
    blue   1,500.
b. On proof paper, about 25x30mm
    black   1,000.
    green   1,000.

146-E1   147-E1

Blank vignette in large ornate "2."
146-E1   2c Engraved die on India, die sunk on card
    black   1,500.
    scarlet   1,500.
    ultramarine   1,500.
    blue   1,500.
    green   1,500.

Design size: 20x25mm
Die size: 43x48mm
Vignette of Lincoln in large ornate "3" with rounded top.
147-E1   3c Engraved die on proof paper
    black   2,250.
    scarlet   1,750.
    ultramarine   1,750.
    green   1,750.

147-E1A   147-E1B

Design size: 11½x15½mm
Die size: 25x32mm
Vignette only of Columbia. Imprint and die number below design.
147-E1A 3c Engraved die on India, black   —

Design size: 21x25mm

Blank vignette in frame of large ornate "3" with upper and lower labels not yet engraved.
147-E1B 3c Engraved die on India, die sunk on card
    black   2,250.
    green   2,000.

147-E1C

Design size: 21x25mm
No. 147-E1A cut to shape and mounted in frame of large ornate "3" with upper and lower labels not yet engraved.
147-E1C 3c Engraved die on India, die sunk on card
    black   2,250.
    green   2,000.

147-E2

Design size: 21x25mm
Blank vignette in frame only as No. 147-E1B but with upper and lower labels engraved.
147-E2 3c Engraved die on India, die sunk on card
    black   2,250.
    green   2,000.

Vignette of Columbia mounted in place on No. 147-E2.
147-E3 3c Engraved die on India, die sunk on card
    black   2,250.
    green   2,000.

147-E4

Complete design with Columbia vignette in large ornate "3" surrounded by foliate ornamentation.
147-E4 3c Engraved die on India, die sunk on card
    black   2,250.
    green   2,000.

147-E5

Design size: 22x27mm
Blank vignette in large ornate "3" surrounded by scrolled ornamentation.
147-E5 3c Engraved die on India, die sunk on card
    black   2,250.
    green   2,000.

147-E6

Vignette of Columbia mounted in place on No. 147-E5B.

147-E6   3c Engraved die on India, die sunk on
card
black   2,250.
green   2,000.

148-E1

Blank vignette in large ornate "6."

148-E1   6c
a. Engraved die on India, die sunk on card
black   2,000.
scarlet   2,000.
green   2,000.
dark green   2,000.
ultramarine   2,000.
b. Engraved die on India, cut close
black   1,750.
scarlet   1,750.
blue   1,750.
green   1,750.

National Banknote Co.

145-E2   145-E3

Die size: 64x74mm
Engraved vignette of Franklin facing right.

145-E2   1c Die on India, die sunk on card
black (with pencil lines on bust   700.
dull dark orange   700.

Engraved incomplete Franklin vignette facing right mounted
over pencil sketch of frame.

145-E3   1c Die on thin white card, 55x66mm,
black   2,850.

145-E4   145-E5

Incomplete Franklin vignette mounted on more complete pencil sketch of frame.

145-E4   1c Die on thin white card, orange
brown   2,000.

Design size: 20x26mm
Engraved vignette mounted on pencil and watercolor frame
design.

145-E5   1c Die on thin white card, 45x51mm,
dull dark orange   2,000.

145-E6

Incomplete engraving of entire design; lower edge of bust
vert. shading only.

145-E6   1c
a. Die on 64x71mm India, die sunk on card
ultramarine   475.
red   475.
orange brown   475.
red brown   475.
blue green   475.
mauve   475.
dull lilac   475.
black   475.
gray   475.
carmine   475.
carmine rose   475.
dull rose   475.
dull yellow brown   475.
brown violet   475.
light green   475.
green   475.
gray olive   475.
yellow   475.
b. Die on bond, die sunk on card, dark yellow   750.

145-E8

Completed die: additional shading lines in background, four
horiz. shading lines at top of lower edge of bust.

145-E8   1c
a. Die on India, die sunk on card
black   475.
blue green   475.
carmine   475.
yellow   475.
orange brown   475.
orange   475.
gray green   475.
dull red violet   475.
dark blue   475.
b. Die on ivory glazed paper, 65x72mm
black   425.
black brown   425.
scarlet   425.
blue   425.
c. Completed die on thick wove, dismal
dusky yellow   425.

145-E9

Die size: 50½x64mm
Engraved vignette of Franklin facing left, no shading lines at
top of bust, etc.

145-E9   1c
a. Die on white glazed paper, black   475.
b. Die on India, mounted on card stamped
"J.I. PEASE.", black   450.

146-E2   146-E3

Die size: 62x76mm

Vignette only of Jackson in high stiff collar.

146-E2   2c Die on India, die sunk on card
black   900.
orange brown   900.
dull violet   900.

Engraved Jackson vignette mounted on watercolor frame.

146-E3   2c Die on thin white card, 46x89mm,
black vignette, dark gray frame   5,000.

146-E4   146-E5

Engraved Jackson vignette, mounted on watercolor frame
(diff. from No. 146-E3).

146-E4   2c Die on thin white card, 46x89mm,
black vignette, gray frame   5,000.

Similar to No. 146-E4 but with pencil border around frame.

146-E5   2c Die on thin white card, 45x50mm,
dark orange   5,000.

Incomplete die: without shading lines under value ribbon,
vert. lines in colorless strips, and broken horiz. lines at top and
bottom of frame.

146-E6

146-E6   2c Die on thin white card, dark orange   1,250.

146-E7

Die size: 64½x73mm
Completed die of unadopted design.

146-E7   2c
a. Die on India
carmine   1,000.
deep rose   1,000.
scarlet   1,000.
dim dusky orange orange red   1,000.
deep yellow orange   1,000.
bone brown   1,000.
orange brown   1,000.
brown   1,000.
canary yellow   1,000.
yellow brown   1,000.
dark olive green   1,000.
green   1,000.
dim dusky blue green   1,000.
dark blue   1,000.
deep ultramarine   1,000.
bright blue   1,000.
dull violet   1,000.
smoky deep red violet red   1,000.
gray   1,000.
black   1,000.
b. Die on ivory glazed paper, about
64x77mm
black   1,000.
brown black   1,000.
scarlet   1,000.
blue   1,000.
c. Die on thin wove, dark yellow   1,000.

146-E8

Die size: 62x76mm
Incomplete vignette of Jackson as on issued stamp: incomplete shading in eye and hair in front of ear, right neck tendon on chest not shaded.
146-E8 2c
a. Die on India, on 55x66mm card
black 750.
orange 750.
deep yellow orange 750.
red brown 750.
orange brown 750.
dark blue green 750.
red violet 750.

Also known on 87x143mm card showing full die sinkage, pencil inscribed "2c" above and "Jackson" below sinkage area. Value, $750.
b. Die on glazed paper, die sinkage 50x63mm, black 1,000.

Completed Jackson vignette.

146-E9

146-E9 2c Die on glazed paper, black 750.

146-E11

Engraved vignette with pencil and watercolor frame design, labels blank.
146-E11 2c Die on thin white card, 50x60mm, dim dusky bright blue green vignette, dark green frame 6,250.

146-E12

Die size: 62x75mm
Incomplete engraving of entire design: no leaves on wide bands at sides below vignette, neck tendon and hair in front of ear changed, top of head incomplete, ear hole too dark. This design essayed for envelopes on thick papers.
146-E12 2c Die on India, die sunk on card
carmine 1,250.
orange 1,250.
brown orange 1,250.
brown 1,250.
blue 1,250.
violet 1,250.
green 1,250.

147-E7

Incomplete engraved vignette of Lincoln (horiz. line background), mounted on pencil and watercolor frame design.
147-E7 3c Die on thin white card, black vignette, gray black frame 3,500.

147-E8

147-E9

Design size: 20x25mm
Die Size: 62x72½mm
Incomplete engraving of head only of Washington.
147-E8 3c Die on white glazed paper, black 550.

Engraved Washington vignette only as adopted.
147-E9 3c Die on white glazed paper, black 650.
Nos. 147-E8 and 147-E9 may have been made from completed dies of No. 147 to produce Nos. 184-E9 and 184-E10.

147-E11

Design size: 20x25½mm
Incomplete engraved vignette (horiz. lined background), mounted on pencil and watercolor frame design.
147-E11 3c Die on thin white card, 45x54mm, carmine vignette, dim light red violet red frame 5,000.

Incomplete engraving of entire design: no horizontal lines on nose, parts of hair, chin, collar, forehead unfinished.

147-E12

147-E12 3c Die on India, die sunk on card
black 575.
deep red 575.
carmine 575.
yellow orange 575.
brown 575.
red brown 575.
dark red brown 575.
yellow brown 575.
ultramarine 575.
dark blue 575.
dark violet blue 575.
blue green 575.
dark red violet 575.

147-E12A

Similar to No. 147-E12 but two sets of horizontal lines in collar area have been lengthened and strengthened; also 11 scored lines cut across thick ink lines of the shoulder cut of vignette.
147-E12A Die on India, dull grayish red —

Issued stamp, No. 147, in trial colors, underprinted network in fugitive ink.
147-E13 3c
a. On thick paper, perf. 12, gummed
gray blue, underprinting gray brown 150.
gray blue, underprinting olive gray 150.
green, underprinting olive gray 150.
dim red, underprinting olive gray 150.
dull orange, underprinting olive gray 150.
brown, underprinting olive gray 150.
b. As "a," faint 6mm-high horiz. bar trial cancel
dim red 450.
dull orange 450.
c. As "a," underprinting omitted
gray blue —
dim red —
dull orange —
brown —
d. As "a," imperf, green, underprinting olive gray 325.
Pair 700.
e. As "d," underprinting omitted 325.
Pair 700.
P# block of 10 —

Multiples of the No. 147-E13 varieties can be found with fully or partially underprinted stamps in conjunction with underprinting-omitted stamps.

148-E2   148-E3

Design size: 19½x25½mm
Die size: 63x76mm
Engraved Lincoln vignette only, hair brushed back, horiz. line background.
148-E2 6c Die on India, die sunk on card
black 700.
blue 700.

Incomplete engraved Lincoln vignette (horiz. lined background) mounted on pencil and watercolor frame with blank labels.
148-E3 6c Die on thin white card, 45x52mm, dim blue vignette, dim dark blue frame 4,000.

148-E4

Incomplete engraving of entire design: horiz. line background in vignette, lines on cheek and hair unfinished.
148-E4 6c Die on India, on card, about 50x52mm
carmine 600.
rose 600.
dull rose 600.
red violet 600.
dull violet 600.
deep ultramarine 600.
dark black blue 600.
yellow 600.
green 600.
dark green 600.
dark red brown 600.
deep yellow brown 600.
yellow brown 600.
orange brown 600.

Incomplete engraving of entire design: horiz. line background in vignette, no shading directly under value label, shadows on "SIX CENTS" and shading on ornaments in upper corners unfinished.
148-E5 6c Die on India, on card, ultramarine 900.

148-E6

Similar to No. 148-E5 but with diagonal lines added to vignette background. (Essay in orange brown has pencil notations for changes.)

148-E6 6c Die on India, die sunk on card
black	1,000.
dull carmine	1,000.
dark rose	1,000.
yellowish black	1,000.
brown	1,000.
gray brown	1,000.
black brown	1,000.
yellow	1,000.
gray olive green	1,000.
dark green	1,000.
ultramarine	1,000.
deep ultramarine	1,000.
dull ultramarine	1,000.
violet	1,000.
dark violet	1,000.
red violet	1,000.
orange brown	1,000.

148-E7

Similar to No. 148-E6 but with dots added to top of hair.

148-E7 6c Die on India, on card
dark carmine	1,000.
dull rose	1,000.
orange	1,000.
yellow brown	1,000.
dark brown	1,000.
black brown	1,000.
yellow green	1,000.
blue green	1,000.
ultramarine	1,000.
dark red violet	1,000.

Completed die with lines on cheek softened to dots only.

148-E8

148-E8 6c Die on India
yellow green	250.
brown	250.
rose	250.

All known examples are much reduced.

Incomplete engraving of entire design, similar to No. 148-E10 but with hair brushed forward as on adopted design but shadow under hair in front of ear is round at bottom, not pointed as on approved design. Shading on cheek behind nostril is dotted instead of lined on completed design.

148-E9

148-E9 6c Die on India, on card, red violet   750.

148-E10

Die size: 64x75mm
Frame as adopted, vignette similar to No. 148-E6 but with hair brushed back; lines on cheek.

148-E10 6c
   a. Die on India, die sunk on card, deep
      blue   850.
   b. Die on India, about 30x35mm, carmine   600.
   c. As "a," but no panels above top label,
      carmine   850.

Similar to No. 148-E10a but dots (not lines) on cheek and on lower lip. Shadow under hair in front of ear is rounded at bottom, not pointed as on approved design.

148-E11

148-E11 6c Die on India, on card
rose pink	700.
deep rose	700.
pale rose	700.
brown rose	700.
rose carmine	700.
deep carmine	700.
brown	700.
yellow brown	700.
blue	700.
red violet	700.

Die of completed vignette only with hair brushed forward.
148-E12 6c Die on white glazed paper, black   1,500.

149-E4   149-E4a

Die size: 62x75mm
Vignette of Stanton.

149-E4 7c Die on India, on card, black   1,000.

Engraved frame of adopted 30c design but with vignette cut out and mounted over Stanton vignette on India No. 149-E4.

149-E4a Stanton vignette with 30c frame
    on thin, stiff paper mounted on
    top, black   500.

The status of No. 149-E4a has been questioned.

149-E6

Design as issued but shading under ear incomplete.

149-E6 7c Die on India, die sunk on card
black	500.
dark red	500.
light red	500.
gray green	500.
gray black	500.
yellow brown	500.
dark brown	500.

dull yellow brown	500.
dull red brown	500.
blue green	500.
ultramarine	500.
dim blue	500.
lilac	500.
red orange	500.
yellow orange	500.

Similar to No. 149-E6 but with dots added on forehead.
149-E7 7c Die on India, brown   1,250.

150-E1   150-E2

Design size: 20x25½mm
Incomplete engraved vignette of Jefferson (horiz. line background) mounted on pencil and watercolor frame design with blank labels.

150-E1 10c Die on thin white card, 45x51mm,
    black vignette, gray frame   3,000.

Design size: 19½x25½mm
Die size: 62x75mm
Jefferson vignette with incomplete engraving of frame: unfinished shading under "TEN" ribbon, under oval at ends of "U.S. POSTAGE," and under shield over ends of value label ribbons.

150-E2 10c Die on India, on card, deep blue
    green   2,500.

Similar to No. 150-E2 but showing horizontal shading lines only.
150-E2A 10c Die on India, die sunk on
     152x225mm card
     blue green   750.
     red violet   750.

150-E3

Completed engraving of unadopted design.

150-E3 10c
   a. Die on India, die sunk on card
carmine	750.
rose	750.
gray brown rose	750.
yellow	750.
yellow brown	750.
orange	750.
orange brown	750.
brown	750.
chocolate	750.
green	750.
blue green	750.
greenish gray	750.
blue	750.
dull violet	750.
dull red violet	750.
dark navy blue	750.
ultramarine	750.
deep ultramarine	750.
dull dusky blue	750.
navy blue	750.
slate	750.

   b. Die on bond
dull dusky brown	500.
brown gray	500.

All known examples of No. 153-E3b are reduced.

150-E4   150-E5

Three separate designs. Left one dark blue green, similar to No. 150-E3 but shows engraved attempt to remove coat collar to obtain nude neck (some coat still shows under chin). Middle one brown orange (No. 150-E2) with coat collar and top of hair cut out, neck and bust drawn in. Right one black vignette of head finally adopted (No. 150-E7).

150-E4 10c Dies on India, on card   2,500.

Design size: 19½x25½mm
Same frame as No. 150-E2, but Jefferson vignette has hair arranged differently and bust has no clothing.

150-E5 10c
   a. Die on India, die sunk on card
      black   600.
      scarlet   600.
      brown   600.
      blue   600.
      green   600.
   b. Die on ivory glazed paper, 66x75mm
      black   500.
      black brown   500.
      scarlet   500.
      blue   500.
   c. Die on thin wove, dark yellow   500.

150-E6   150-E7

Frame of No. 150-E5 with vignette cut out and replaced by black vignette as adopted.

150-E6 10c Die on India
      deep orange brown   1,500.
      black   1,500.

Die size: 62x76mm
Vignette of Jefferson as adopted.

150-E7 10c Die on India, die sunk on card
      dark ultramarine   700.
      yellow   700.
      brown   700.

151-E1   151-E2

Design size: 20x25½mm
Engraved vignette of Washington (No. 79-E37b) mounted on incomplete pencil drawing of frame design.

151-E1 12c Die on India, on 38x47½mm card, black vignette, pencil frame   2,500.

Design size: 20x25½mm
Engraved vignette of Washington (No. 79-E37b) mounted on pencil and watercolor frame design with blank labels.

151-E2 12c Die on card, 46x89mm, black vignette, gray frame   3,000.

151-E3   151-E4

Design size: 20x25½mm
Engraved vignette of Washington (No. 79-E37b) mounted on pencil and watercolor frame design with ribbons and blank labels.

151-E3 12c Die on card, 46x89mm, black vignette, gray frame   3,000.

Design size: 20x25½mm
Engraved vignette of Washington (No. 79-E37b) mounted on pencil and watercolor frame design with "U, S, 12" and blank labels.

151-E4 12c Die on card, 46x89mm, black vignette, gray frame   3,000.

151-E5   151-E6

Design size: 19½x25½mm
Die size: 62x74mm
Vignette of Henry Clay only.

151-E5 12c Die on India, die sunk on card
      black   600.
      deep carmine   600.
      yellow   600.
      yellow brown   600.
      brown orange   600.
      dark orange brown   600.
      black brown   600.
      ultramarine   600.
      dark blue green   600.
      red violet   600.

Incomplete Clay vignette mounted on watercolor shield-like frame design on gray background, pencil notation "background of stars to be gray."

151-E6 12c Die on card, 53x75mm, blue black vignette, blue frame   3,250.

151-E7

Die sinkage size: 63x77mm
Completed die of unadopted design similar to No. 151-E6. This design essayed for envelopes on thick paper.

151-E7 12c
   a. Die on India, on card
      deep orange brown   900.
      green   900.
      deep ultramarine   900.
      violet   900.
      deep red   900.
      deep orange red   900.
      orange   900.
      dusky red   900.
   b. Die on wove
      carmine   700.
      orange   700.
      brown   700.
      orange brown   700.
      ultramarine   700.
   c. Die on card colored yellow, black   700.

Engraved vignette of Washington mounted on partly complete pencil drawing of frame, pencil notation "new border for clay 12c."

151-E8

151-E8 12c Die on card, black, pencil frame   2,750.

151-E9

Die size: 55x63mm

Incomplete engraving of entire adopted design, without 3 vert. shading lines at left side of lower triangle.

151-E9 12c
   a. Die on India, die sunk on card
      black   650.
      carmine   650.
      blue green   650.
      blue   650.
      light blue   650.
      orange   650.
      orange brown   650.
      dull red   650.
      brown red   650.
   b. Die on proof paper, about 38x45mm
      carmine   650.
      dull carmine   650.
      orange brown   650.
      dull red   650.
      ultramarine   650.
   c. Die on India, on card, about 30x35mm, dark blue   650.

152-E1   152-E2

Design size: 19½x25mm
Incomplete vignette of Webster with side whiskers bolder than as adopted, mounted on watercolor frame design with 15 and blank labels.

152-E1 15c Die on white card, 40x61mm, dim red vignette, light red violet frame   2,250.

Design size: 19½x25mm
Die size: 63x76mm
Incomplete engraving of vignette only: missing shading under ear and at back of neck.

152-E2 15c Die on India, die sunk on card, black   750.

152-E3

Vignette similar to No. 152-E2 but with shading under ear, more shading at back of neck.

152-E3 15c Die on India, die sunk on card
      black   700.
      dark orange   700.
      orange   700.
      yellow   700.
      red violet   700.
      ultramarine   700.
      brown   700.

152-E5

Incomplete engraved design: shading on corner panel bevels incomplete, side whiskers bolder than as adopted. Also essayed for envelopes on thick paper.

152-E5 15c Die on India, die sunk on card, orange brown   750.

Similar to No. 152-E5 but with pencil marks suggesting shading on corner panels.

152-E6 15c Die on India, orange brown   750.

Similar to No. 152-E5 with engraved shading added to corner panels but white areas incomplete.

152-E7

152-E7 15c Die on India
  orange   650.
  orange yellow   650.
  orange brown   650.
  green   650.
  red violet   650.
  rose carmine   650.

Similar to No. 152-E7 but shading on corner panels complete.

152-E8

152-E8 15c Die on India, on card, black   1,000.

153-E1   153-E2

Design size: 18x23mm
Incomplete engraved vignette of Scott mounted on pencil
sketch of partial frame design.
153-E1 24c Die on white card, 33x39mm, dull
            red violet vignette, pencil frame   1,750.

Design size: 19½x25mm
Complete engraved vignette mounted on pencil and watercolor frame design with "U.S. POSTAGE" in ink.
153-E2 24c Die on white card, 73x110mm, dim
            blue green   3,250.

153-E3   153-E4

Die size: 62x76mm
Incomplete engraved vignette only.
153-E3 24c Die on India, die sunk on card
  black   600.
  yellow   600.
  yellow brown   600.
  dark orange brown   600.
  ultramarine   600.
  dark ultramarine   600.
  red violet   600.

Die size: 62x77mm
Incomplete design as adopted: upper corners not squared
outside scrolls, no periods after U and S in stars.
153-E4 24c Die on India, die sunk on card
  carmine   650.
  orange   650.
  brown orange   650.
  yellow brown   650.
  deep brown   650.
  ultramarine   650.
  dark red violet   650.
  green   650.

Value off card, cut down, $275.

Previous No. 154-E1 is now No. 149-E4a.

154-E2

Pencil drawing of entire design, labeled "Scott."
154-E2 30c Pencil drawing on white card,
            53x92mm   2,400.

Engraved vignette of Hamilton mounted on pencil drawing of
frame.
154-E3 30c Die on card, yellow brown vignette,
            pencil frame   1,500.

154-E4

Incomplete engraved vignette of Hamilton.
154-E4 30c Die on India, die sunk on card
  yellow brown   700.
  dark ultramarine blue   700.
  orange   700.

Vignette of Hamilton with more engraving on forehead, nose,
neck, etc.

154-E5

154-E5 30c Die on India, die sunk on card
  dark red brown   700.
  dull carmine   700.
  ultramarine   700.

155-E1   155-E2

Pencil drawing of entire design, labeled "Perry."
155-E1 90c Pencil drawing on white card,
            53x92mm   2,000.

Design size: 19½x25mm
Engraved vignette of Perry mounted on pencil and watercolor
frame design.
155-E2 90c Die on white card, 73x110mm, dull
            dark violet vignette, dull red violet
            frame   3,250.

155-E3

Die size: 58x79mm

Incomplete engraving of Perry vignette as adopted.
155-E3 90c
  a. Die on India, die sunk on card
       deep yellow orange   600.
       orange brown   600.
       dark brown   600.
       dull carmine   600.
       ultramarine blue   600.
       dark blue green   600.
       dark red violet   600.
  b. Die on white ivory paper, black   600.

Similar to No. 155-E3 but more lines in hair above forehead.

155-E4

155-E4 90c Die on India, on card, black   600.

155-E5

Incomplete engraving of design as adopted: rope above
vignette unfinished. Also essayed for envelopes on thick paper.
155-E5 90c Die on India, die sunk on card
  black   750.
  carmine, off card   325.
  orange   750.
  dark orange   750.
  yellow brown   750.
  brown   750.
  deep orange brown   750.
  deep ultramarine   750.
  blue green   750.
  red violet   750.

Value off card, cut down, $250.

1873 ISSUE
Continental Bank Note Co.

179-E1   179-E2

Die size: 20x25mm
Vignette of Taylor by Bureau of Engraving and Printing, in
engraved frame.
179-E1   Five Cents, Die on India
  black   4,500.
  blue   4,500.

Design size: 24x29mm
Vignette of Taylor by Bureau of Engraving and Printing, in
ornate wash drawing of frame ("FIVE CENTS" black, on shaded
ribbon).
179-E2 5c Die on card, black   4,000.

Incomplete vignette: hair, coat, background, etc., unfinished.

179-E3

179-E3 5c Die on India, violet   2,000.

George W. Bowlsby 1873 essay similar in concept to his No. 63-E13 but without coupon attached. It consisted of an unused 1c stamp (No. 156) with horiz. sewing machine perfs. through center, gummed on upper half only, as described in his Dec. 26, 1865 patent. Stamp was meant to be torn in half by postal clerk as cancellation, to prevent reuse.

156-E1	1c blue	250.

1876 Experimental Ink and Paper Essays

Plate designs of 1873-75 issues in normal colors, printed on paper tinted with sensitive inks and on heavily laid (horiz.) colored papers (unless otherwise noted).

156-E2	1c Blue on:	
	carmine	150.
	pale rose	150.
	deep yellow	150.
	pale violet	150.
158-E1	3c Green on:	
	pale rose	150.
	deep yellow	150.
	pale violet	150.
158-E2	3c Green on paper covered with pink varnish which vanishes with the color	100.
158-E3	3c Green on thick white blotting paper which absorbs canceling ink	100.
161-E1	10c Brown on:	
	pale rose	150.
	deep yellow	150.
	pale violet	150.
163-E1	15c Yellow orange on:	
	pale rose	200.
	deep yellow	200.
	pale violet	200.
165-E1	30c Gray black on:	
	pale rose	200.
	deep yellow	200.
	pale violet	200.
166-E1	90c Rose carmine on:	
	pale rose	200.
	deep yellow	200.
	pale violet	200.
178-E1	2c Vermilion on:	
	pale rose	150.
	deep yellow	150.
	pale violet	150.

179-E4

179-E4	5c Blue on:	
	pale rose	300.
	deep yellow	300.
	pale violet	300.

See No. 147-E13.

1877 Essays
Philadelphia Bank Note Co.

Die essays for this section were all engraved. The frame-only dies for all values of this series were engraved with two values appearing per die, except the 3c (No. 184-E1) which was engraved alone. In each case the listing is under the lower denomination. The Washington vignette associated with each value of the frames is from engraved master die No. 14. (No. 182-E1).

Except as noted, plate essays in this section are all lithographed from a composite stone plate of two panes. The left pane ("plate 1") consists of horiz. rows of four of the 1c, 3c, 7c, 24c and 90c. The right pane ("plate 2") consists of horiz. rows of four 2c, 6c, 12c and 30c. "Printed by Philadelphia Bank Note Co. Patented June 16, 1876" imprint below 2nd and 3rd designs on each row.

See note above No. 63-E1.

182-E1

Vignette master die "No. 14": two slightly diff. vignettes of Washington, one above the other, bottom one with truncated queue, bust and shading in front of neck.

182-E1		
a.	Die on old white glazed paper, black	500.
b.	Die on proof paper (1903)	
	black	100.
	carmine	100.
	dull carmine	100.
	dusky carmine	100.
	yellow	100.
	dull scarlet	100.
	dull orange	100.
	brown orange	100.
	brown	100.
	gray olive	100.
	blue green	100.
	dark green	100.
	black blue	100.
	ultramarine	100.
	violet	100.
	red violet	100.

182-E2b

Design size: 20x25mm
Die size: 98x53mm
Frames of 1c and 2c side by side.

182-E2	1c + 2c	
a.	Die on white pelure	
	dark carmine	250.
	orange	250.
	brown	250.
	blue green	250.
	blue	250.
b.	Die with vertical line between designs (die size 85x54mm), on India, die sunk on card	
	dusky red	400.
	deep orange	400.
	orange brown	400.
	dark green	400.
	dark blue	400.
c.	Die on stiff glazed paper, black	400.
d.	Die on proof paper, printed through a mat (1903)	
	black	100.
	bright carmine	100.
	dull carmine	100.
	dim scarlet	100.
	dark orange	100.
	dull yellow	100.
	dark orange brown	100.
	black olive	100.
	dark blue green	100.
	dark blue	100.
	ultramarine	100.
	dark navy blue	100.
	blue violet	100.
	dull violet	100.
	red violet	100.
e.	Plate sheet of 1c, 2c, 3c, 12c, 24c, 30c, 90c frames only, on card, pale green blue	1,500.

182-E3b

Complete 1c design, lithographed.

182-E3	1c	
a.	Plate on stamp paper, imperf., gummed	
	black	75.
	blue green	75.
	bright ultramarine	75.
	yellow	75.
b.	Plate on stamp paper, perf. 12, gummed	
	dark red orange	50.
	orange brown	50.
	red brown	50.
	red violet	50.
	violet blue	50.
	ultramarine	50.
c.	Plate 1 "sheet" of 20, complete designs, without imprint, on old glazed paper, imperf., deep brown orange	800.
d.	As "c," with imprint, on old glazed paper, imperf., gummed	
	dull deep violet red	800.
	ultramarine	800.
	scarlet	800.
	orange	800.
	carmine	800.
	dark carmine	800.
	green	800.
	bluish green	800.
e.	As "d," perf. 12, gummed	
	dull deep violet red	700.
	ultramarine	700.
	red brown	700.
	violet blue	700.

Concerning plate 1 sheets of 20, note that composite stone plates also contained the plate 2 sheets of 16 listed as Nos. 183-E2c to 183-E2e. Many such composite sheets remain intact. All separated plate 1 or plate 2 sheets originally were part of a composite sheet.

183-E2b

Complete 2c design, lithographed.

183-E2	2c	
a.	Plate on stamp paper, imperf.	
	blue green	60.
	bright ultramarine	60.
	brown	60.
b.	Plate on stamp paper, perf. 12, gummed	
	bright red orange	35.
	dull red orange	35.
	dark red orange	35.
	red brown	35.
	dark red brown	35.
	dark orange brown	35.
	yellow brown	35.
	dull yellow green	35.
	green	35.
	dull ultramarine	35.
	bright ultramarine	35.
	blue violet	35.
	red violet	35.
	light red violet	35.
	violet red	35.
c.	Plate 2 "sheet" of 16, complete designs, without imprint, on old glazed paper, imperf., deep brown orange	600.
d.	As "c," with imprint, on old glazed paper, imperf., gummed, dull deep violet red	600.
e.	As "d," perf. 12, gummed, dull deep violet red	500.

See note following No. 182-E3e.

Design size: 20x25mm
Die size: 54x55mm
Engraved frame of 3c alone on die.

184-E1	3c	
a.	Die on pelure paper	
	dark carmine	250.
	dark orange	250.
	orange brown	250.
	bright blue	250.

green	250.
dark green	250.
b. Die on proof paper (1903)	
black	100.
bright carmine	100.
dull carmine	100.
dim scarlet	100.
dark orange	100.
dull yellow	100.
dark orange brown	100.
black olive	100.
dark rose	100.
green	100.
yellow green	100.
dark blue green	100.
dark blue	100.
deep ultramarine	100.
dark navy blue	100.
blue violet	100.
dull violet	100.
red violet	100.

Built-up model of engraved frame cut to shape inside and out, mounted atop engraved vignette of the same color. Warning: fraudulent models combining engraved and lithographed materials exist.

184-E2   3c
a. Die on proof paper, cut close
dark scarlet	250.
blue green	250.
deep blue	250.
b. Four examples mounted 2½mm apart on stiff white card, 80x87mm	
red	1,000.
orange brown	1,000.
green	1,000.
blue	1,000.
violet	1,000.
green frame, light blue vignette	1,000.

Built-up model as No. 184-E2, vignette as No. 184-E5 with dark background.

184-E3   3c Die on proof paper, scarlet   250.

184-E4d

Complete 3c design, vignette with light background.

184-E4   3c
c. Plate lithographed on stamp paper, imperf.
black	75.
green	75.
dark green	75.
bright ultramarine	75.
orange	75.

No. 184-E4c exists in two plates of 9 tete-beche, in diff. colors, on same piece of paper. Value, $800 sheet of 18.

d. Plate lithographed on stamp paper, perf. 12, gummed
dark red orange	50.
red brown	50.
red voilet	50.
brown orange	50.
ultramarine	50.
violet blue	50.
e. Plate sheet of 9 (3x3), imprint below, on stiff white wove	
carmine	300.
blue green	300.
f. Plate sheet of 9 (3x3), on glazed thin wove	
carmine	300.
blue green	300.
blue	300.
orange	300.
g. Plate sheet of 9 (3x3), on yellowish wove	
carmine	300.
blue green	300.
blue	300.
h. Die of complete design on old stiff glazed paper (die size: 55x66mm), black	350.
i. Complete die on glazed wove	
deep carmine	200.
scarlet	200.
ultramarine	200.
j. Complete die on India, light orange red	200.
k. Complete die on proof paper (1903)	
black	75.
bright carmine	75.
dull carmine	75.
dim scarlet	75.
dark orange	75.
dull yellow	75.
dark orange brown	75.
black olive	75.
green	75.
dark blue green	75.

deep ultramarine	75.
dark navy blue	75.
blue violet	75.
dull violet	75.
red violet	75.
l. Complete die on large colored card (1903)	
black, *light green*	150.
deep scarlet, *ivory*	150.
red violet, *light blue*	150.
carmine, *pink*	150.

184-E5

Design size: 19x24½mm
Die No. 1 size: about 63x94mm Vignette of Washington slightly diff. from rest of series but with quite diff. frame design.

184-E5   3c
a. Die on glazed paper, about 50x75mm, black	350.
b. Die on proof paper (with and without printing through mats) (1903)	
black	100.
dark carmine	100.
carmine	100.
bright carmine	100.
brown	100.
red brown	100.
yellow	100.
orange	100.
violet	100.
red violet	100.
violet brown	100.
blue	100.
steel blue	100.
light green	100.
dark green	100.
dull olive	100.
c. Die on colored card, 61x93mm (1903)	
scarlet, *yellow*	150.
olive gray, *pale pink*	150.
dull violet, *buff*	75.

Plate proofs printed in sheets of 25 (plate size: 140x164mm). A horiz. crack extends through upper 3s from 2mm back of head on position 11 to vignette on position 12.
All plate essay items valued as singles except No. 184-E5d.

d. Engraved plate of 25 on India, mounted on large card, red brown	750.
e. Plate on proof paper (1903)	
black	15.
blue black	15.
greenish black	15.
dull red violet	15.
dark red violet	15.
dull violet	15.
violet brown	15.
light red brown	15.
orange brown	15.
brown carmine	15.
brown	15.
dim orange	15.
yellow	15.
dull yellow	15.
carmine	15.
light carmine	15.
dark carmine	15.
dull carmine	15.
dull scarlet	15.
dark green	15.
light green	15.
dull olive green	15.
deep ultramarine	15.
f. Plate on proof paper, perf. 12, lithographed	
carmine	100.
rose lilac	100.
red orange	100.
g. Plate on green bond, "Crane & Co. 1887" wmk. (1903)	
black	25.
carmine	25.
dull carmine	25.
scarlet	25.
brown	25.
brown red	25.
orange brown	25.
red violet	25.
yellow	25.
orange	25.
dark green	25.
light green	25.
yellow green	25.
deep ultramarine	25.
dark navy blue	25.
h. Plate (printed before plate crack developed) on semiglazed yellowish wove, laid watermark	
carmine	30.
dull red	30.
bright orange red	30.
deep orange red	30.
scarlet	30.
deep orange	30.

yellow orange	30.
orange brown	30.
orange yellow	30.
dark yellow green	30.
dusky blue green	30.
dull green blue	30.
violet blue	30.
red violet	30.
black	30.
i. Plate single from sheets of 100 with imprint on yellowish glazed chemically prepared wove, lithographed	
black	20.
brown	20.
scarlet	20.
light red	20.
rose pink	20.
carmine	20.
deep carmine	20.
violet rose	20.
deep violet rose	20.
violet red	20.
red violet	20.
violet	20.
blue	20.
pale blue	20.
pale dull blue	20.
yellow	20.
dull brown yellow	20.
orange	20.
red orange	20.

184-E6

Illustration with card margins reduced.
Similar to No. 184-E1 but engraved vignette of Lincoln on India facing ¾ to right. Each design has vignette attached to frame from behind.

184-E6   3c Four examples mounted on 80x89mm card to resemble block of 4
blue	3,500.
green	3,500.

Frame of No. 184-E5 with engraved vignette of Lincoln mounted in place.

184-E7   3c Die on card, brown   —

There is some doubt whether No. 184-E7 exists as a genuine essay. The editors would like to see authenticated evidence of its existence.

186-E1a

Design size: 20x25mm
Die size: 92x50mm
Frames of 6c and 7c side by side (6c at right).

186-E1   6c + 7c
a. Die on white pelure, orange	375.
b. Die on proof paper, printed through a mat (1903)	
black	100.
bright carmine	100.
dull carmine	100.
dim scarlet	100.
dark orange	100.
dull yellow	100.
dark orange brown	100.
black olive	100.
green	100.
dark blue green	100.
dark blue	100.
deep ultramarine	100.
dark navy blue	100.
blue violet	100.
dull violet	100.

red violet	100.
c. Die on white pelure, both 7s reversed on 7c frame, orange	750.
d. Die on old stiff glazed, black	400.

dull violet	100.
red violet	100.
c. Die on old stiff glazed, black	400.

blue violet	100.
dull violet	100.
red violet	100.

186-E2a

188a-E2a

190-E2a

191-E2

Complete 6c design, lithographed.

186-E2   6c
a. Plate on stamp paper, perf. 12, gummed

bright red orange	35.
dull red orange	35.
dark red orange	35.
red brown	35.
dark red brown	35.
dark orange brown	35.
yellow brown	35.
dull yellow green	35.
green	35.
dull ultramarine	35.
bright ultramarine	35.
blue violet	35.
red violet	35.
light violet red	35.
violet red	35.

b. Plate on stamp paper, gummed

ultramarine	60.
lilac	60.
scarlet	60.
orange	60.
carmine	60.
dark carmine	60.
blue green	60.

Complete 12c design, lithographed.

188a-E2   12c
a. Plate on stamp paper, perf. 12, gummed

bright red orange	35.
dull red orange	35.
dark red orange	35.
red brown	35.
dark red brown	35.
dark orange brown	35.
yellow brown	35.
dull yellow green	35.
green	35.
dull ultramarine	35.
bright ultramarine	35.
blue violet	35.
red violet	35.
light red violet	35.
violet red	35.

b. Plate on stamp paper, gummed

ultramarine	60.
lilac	60.
scarlet	60.
orange	60.
carmine	60.
dark carmine	60.
blue green	60.

Complete 30c design, lithographed.

190-E2   30c
a. Plate on stamp paper, perf. 12, gummed

bright red orange	35.
dull red orange	35.
dark red orange	35.
red brown	35.
dark red brown	35.
dark orange brown	35.
yellow brown	35.
dull yellow green	35.
green	35.
dull ultramarine	35.
bright ultramarine	35.
blue violet	35.
red violet	35.
light red violet	35.
violet red	35.

b. Plate on stamp paper, gummed

ultramarine	60.
lilac	60.
scarlet	60.
orange	60.
carmine	60.
dark carmine	60.
blue green	60.

Complete 90c design, lithographed.

191-E2   90c
a. Plate on stamp paper, perf. 12, gummed

black	50.
red brown	50.
dark red orange	50.
brown orange	50.
ultramarine	50.
violet blue	50.
red violet	50.
violet red	50.
dark blue green	50.
orange brown	50.

b. Plate on stamp paper, gummed

ultramarine	75.
lilac	75.
scarlet	75.
orange	75.
carmine	75.
dark carmine	75.
green	75.

186a-E2b

Complete 7c design, lithographed.

186a-E2   7c
a. Plate on stamp paper, imperf.

black	75.
carmine	75.
red orange	75.
yellow orange	75.
green	75.
dark green	75.
dark blue	75.

b. Plate on stamp paper, perf. 12, gummed

red brown	50.
dark red orange	50.
brown orange	50.
red violet	50.
ultramarine	50.
violet blue	50.

Design size: 20x25mm
Die size: 78½x64mm
Frames of 12c and 24c side by side (12c on right).

188a-E1   12c + 24c
a. Die on white pelure

deep carmine	300.
brown orange	300.
orange brown	300.
blue green	300.
blue	300.

b. Die on proof paper, printed through a mat (1903)

black	100.
bright carmine	100.
dull carmine	100.
dim scarlet	100.
dark orange	100.
dull yellow	100.
dark orange brown	100.
black olive	100.
green	100.
dark blue green	100.
dark blue	100.
deep ultramarine	100.
dark navy blue	100.
blue violet	100.

189a-E2a

Complete 24c design, lithographed.

189a-E2   24c
a. Plate on stamp paper, perf. 12, gummed

red brown	50.
dark red orange	50.
brown orange	50.
ultramarine	50.
violet blue	50.
red violet	50.

b. Plate on stamp paper, gummed

ultramarine	75.
lilac	75.
scarlet	75.
orange	75.
carmine	75.
dark carmine	75.
green	75.

Design size: 20x25mm
Die size: 79x64mm
Frames of 30c and 90c side by side.

190-E1   30c + 90c
a. Die on white pelure

dark carmine	300.
dark red orange	300.
dark orange brown	300.
brown	300.
blue green	300.
bright blue	300.

b. Die on stiff glazed paper, blue black | 500.
c. Die on proof paper, printed through a mat (1903)

black	100.
bright carmine	100.
dull carmine	100.
dim scarlet	100.
dark orange	100.
dull yellow	100.
dark orange brown	100.
black olive	100.
green	100.
dark blue green	100.
dark blue	100.
deep ultramarine	100.
dark navy blue	100.

1879 Coupon Essay
Azariah B. Harris

184-E8a

Size of coupon design: 25x7½mm
A proposed $300 30-year Postal Revenue Bond with 3.65% interest. Daily coupons 3c each, "Receivable for Postage in all parts of the U.S." after date thereon. Entire bond contained six pages of coupons with 16 rows of four (one for each day of two months); 20% bear month and day, others blank.

184-E8   3c
a. Coupon on bond (dated Jan. or Feb.), imperf., black | 350.
b. Engraved die on old ivory paper (undated), black | 900.
c. Single coupon on bond (dated), perf. 12, gummed, blue green | 125.
d. Single coupon on bond (undated), perf. 12, gummed, blue green | 50.

Continental Bank Note Co.

182-E4

Design size: 18x22mm
Die size: 59x67mm
Engraved vignette of Franklin on white background in unadopted frame.

182-E4 1c
a. Die on India, blue 575.
b. Die on proof paper
black 500.
dull scarlet 500.
dull brown 500.
dull green 500.
dull blue 500.
c. Die on ivory glazed paper
black 750.
black brown 750.
scarlet 750.
blue 750.

All known examples of "b" have reduced margins.

184-E9   184-E10

Die size: 61½x76½mm
Vignette of Washington on white background in incomplete frame as adopted: no veins in trifoliate ornaments in upper corners.

184-E9 3c Die on India, on card
black 750.
green 750.

Similar to No. 184-E9 but completed frame with veins in trifoliate ornaments.

184-E10 3c
a. Die on India, die sunk on card, green 750.
b. Die on proof paper, about 35x40mm
gray black 350.
dull red 350.
dull blue 350.
dull green 350.
dull brown 350.
c. Die on ivory glazed paper
black 600.
black brown 600.
scarlet 600.
blue 600.

Nos. 147-E8 and 147-E9 may have been made from completed dies of No. 147 to produce Nos. 184-E9 and 184-E10.

184-E11

Design size: 17½x21½mm
Die size: 60x75mm
Complete unadopted design with vignette of Liberty on white background.

184-E11 3c
a. Die on India
black 350.
brown red 350.
orange 350.
green 350.
blue 350.
scarlet 350.
b. Die on proof paper
brown 350.
green 350.
gray black 350.
dull red 350.
dull blue 350.
c. Die on ivory glazed paper
black 750.
black brown 750.
scarlet 750.
blue 750.

All known examples of Nos. 184-E11a, 184-E11b have reduced margins.

184-E12

Design size: 19½x24½mm
Die size: 61x71mm
Complete unadopted design with vignette of Washington on white background in frame similar to No. 184-E11 but with numerals of value.

184-E12 3c
a. Die on India, die sunk on card
black 650.
dull scarlet 650.
brown 650.
green 650.
b. Die on white glazed paper
black 500.
black brown 500.
scarlet 500.
blue 500.
c. Plate on India (some adhering to original card backing), imperf.
black 100.
scarlet 100.
orange red 100.
green 100.
d. Plate on white paper, perf. 12, gummed
black 75.
green 75.
blue 75.
brown 75.
red brown 75.
orange 75.
dull scarlet 75.
orange brown 75.
e. Plate on Francis Patent bluish chemical paper, perf. 12, gummed
black 150.
scarlet 150.
red brown 150.
brown 150.
yellow 150.
green 150.
gray 150.
f. Plate on brown chemical paper, perf. 12, gummed
blue 150.
ultramarine 150.
g. Hybrid die on India, mounted on India, block sunk on card, green 400.

184-E13   184-E14

Design size: 18x22mm
Die size: about 61x62mm
Similar to No. 184-E12 but slightly different frame.

184-E13 3c
a. Die on India, die sunk on card
black 650.
scarlet 650.
green 650.
blue 650.
black brown 650.
blue green 650.
b. Die on ivory glazed paper
black 750.
black brown 750.
scarlet 750.
blue 750.
c. Plate on India, imperf.
black 100.
deep scarlet 100.
green 100.
dark green 100.
dark yellow brown 100.
olive brown 100.
violet brown 100.
orange 100.
d. Plate on stamp paper, perf. 12, gummed
black 75.
dull scarlet 75.
blue green 75.
brown 75.
red brown 75.
dull blue 75.
dark blue 75.
orange 75.
yellow 75.
yellow brown 75.
gray 75.

Design size: 19x24½mm
Die size: about 67x71mm
Similar to No. 184-E13 but value label with "THREE" above "CENTS."

184-E14 3c
a. Hybrid die on India mounted on India, block sunk on card
brown red 400.
green 400.
b. Die on ivory glazed paper
black 500.
black brown 500.
scarlet 500.
blue 500.
c. Die on proof paper, about 35x35mm
black 300.
dull scarlet 300.
dull brown 300.
dull green 300.
dull blue 300.
brown red 300.
red brown 300.

184-E15   184-E16

Design size: 20x25½mm
Die size: 60x73mm
Vignette of Indian maiden in headdress, "PORTAGE" error in top label.

184-E15 3c
a. Hybrid die on India, cut close, mounted on India, block sunk on card
black 900.
dark green 900.
b. Die on proof paper, about 28x35mm
black 600.
dull scarlet 500.
dull brown 500.
dull blue 500.
dull green 500.
c. Die on ivory glazed paper
black 750.
black brown 750.
scarlet 750.
blue 750.
d. Die on India, scarlet —

Similar to No. 184-E15 but with spelling corrected to "POSTAGE."

184-E16 3c Die on India, cut close, mounted on India, block sunk on card
black 1,250.
blue 1,250.
steel blue 1,250.
carmine 1,250.
scarlet 1,250.
brown 1,250.
dark green 1,250.

190-E3

Die size: 44½x71½mm
Vignette of Hamilton on white background in frame as adopted.

190-E3 30c
a. Die on proof paper, about 35x48mm
gray black 500.
dull red 500.
dull green 500.
dull brown 500.
dull blue 500.
b. Die on ivory glazed paper
black 750.
black brown 750.
scarlet 750.
blue 750.

American Bank Note Co.

184-E17

Design size: 22x30mm
Silver photo print of engraved vignette of Washington mounted on pencil and ink frame design.

184-E17 3c
a. Die on white card, 38x49mm
light brown vignette, black frame .... 1,250.
b. Die on white card, 38x50mm
light brown vignette, black frame .... 1,250.

Frame ornaments extend beyond framelines, lettering less complete than on No. 184-E17a.

1881-82 ISSUE
American Bank Note Co.

205-E1

Die size: 59x74mm
Vignette of Garfield in lined oval.

205-E1 5c Die on India, die sunk on card,
black .... 500.

205-E2   205-E3

Die No. C-47 size: 70x83mm
Vignette of Garfield in beaded oval, in plain border of horiz. lines. Found with and without imprint and die number.

205-E2 5c Die on India, die sunk on card
gray brown .... 250.
gray black .... 250.

No. 205-E2 may not be a stamp essay.

Die size: 78x78mm
Vignette of Garfield in beaded oval with cutout at bottom for top of star.

205-E3 5c
a. Die on India, die sunk on card
black .... 750.
deep red orange .... 750.
red brown .... 750.
blue .... 750.
green .... 750.
b. Die on ivory glazed paper
black .... 750.
green .... 750.
blue .... 750.
scarlet .... 750.
red brown .... 750.
c. Negative impression, solid color outside design, die on India, bright red orange .... 1,000.

205-E4

Vignette of Garfield as No. 205-E1 in lined oval and finished frame as adopted.

205-E4 5c Die on India, 24x30mm, black .... 900.

E206-E1

Image of unadopted frame, printed on 40x60mm India paper with text and right "1" cut out.

206-E1 1c Black on India .... 2,500.

206-E1B

Image of frame with "DOS CENTAVOS" in upper label and "ONE CENT" pasted on bottom label, affixed to 57x71mm card with additional pencil sketch at right.

206-E1B 1c Black image affixed to card .... 2,500.

206-E1C   206-E2

Design size: 21x26mm
Engraved frame of unadopted design.

206-E1C 1c
a. Die on white glazed paper, 42x74mm, black .... 1,000.
b. Die on surface-tinted glazed paper, cut close
green, *buff* .... 600.
black, *orange* .... 600.
brown orange, *blue* .... 600.

Engraved frame almost identical to No. 206-E1C with small typographed vignette of Peace.

206-E2 1c Die on blue surface-tinted ivory paper, cut close, buff vignette, carmine frame .... 800.

206-E3

Vignette of Peace only.
206-E3 1c
a. Engraved vignette
black .... 350.
dull red violet .... 350.
b. Typographed vignette .... 350.

206-E4

Engraved frame (No. 206-E1) with typographed vignette of Lincoln mounted on it. Four diff. colors (dull carmine, dull scarlet, dark brown, green) on cream white ivory paper, 22x27mm each, mounted together on 92x114mm thick white card, ms. "American Bank Note Co. N.Y." at lower right.

206-E4 1c Four designs on cream white ivory on card .... 2,500.

Design size: 18x23½mm
Typographed vignette of Lincoln only.

206-E5

206-E5 1c Die on white ivory paper
dull carmine .... 400.
dark yellowish brown .... 400.
dull purple .... 400.
dull dark blue .... 400.
orange .... 400.

206-E6

Incomplete engraving of complete design as issued: no shading in upper arabesques.
206-E6 1c
a. Die on India
gray blue .... 750.
green blue .... 750.
b. Die on India, cut close, on India block sunk on card, deep gray blue .... 350.

207-E1   207-E2

207-E3

Design size: 20½x25½mm

Die size: 49x54½mm
Engraved unadopted frame design with 3's at sides and large 3 at top.

207-E1   3c
  a. Die on India
yellow brown	750.
dull brown	750.
dull blue	750.
green	750.

  b. Die on white glazed paper, 32x38mm
black	650.
dull dark yellow	650.

  c. Die on surface-tinted ivory paper, cut
     close
black, *orange*	500.
green, *buff*	500.
violet blue, *orange*	500.

Engraved frame as No. 207-E1, with typographed vignette of Peace.

207-E2   3c   Die on blue surface-tinted ivory pa-
       per, cut close, buff vignette, car-
       mine frame   850.

Engraved frame (No. 207-E1) with typographed vignette of Peace mounted on it. Four diff. color combinations (orange red vignette, dull carmine frame; dull carmine vignette, dull red brown frame; yellow brown vignette and frame; blue green vignette and frame) on cream white ivory paper, 22x27mm each, mounted together on 92x114mm thick white card, ms. "American Bank Note Co. N.Y." at lower right.

207-E3   3c   4 designs on cream white ivory on
          card   2,500.

208-E1

Incomplete engraving of design as adopted: unfinished shading on top label and bottom ribbon, four lines between frame sinkage at right and left edges, horiz. line at bottom.

208-E1   6c   Die on India, on card, black   1,500.

This is a new die engraved by the Bureau of Engraving & Printing for "Roosevelt" proof albums.

209-E1

Design size: 20x25mm
Die size: 58x76mm
Engraving of unadopted frame only, no horiz. lines in background.

209-E1   10c   Die on thick white card, about
             25x33mm
blue	800.
green	800.

Similar to No. 209-E1 but with horiz. lines added to background.

209-E2

209-E2   10c
  a. Die on thick white card
black	700.
red	700.
green	700.
blue	700.

  b. Die on India, on 50x70mm card, black   800.
  c. Die on white glazed paper, black   800.

209-E3

Engraved frame similar to No. 209-E2 with typographed vignette of Peace.

209-E3   10c
  a. Die on blue surface-tinted glazed paper,
     cut close, buff vignette, carmine frame   650.
  b. Die on orange surface-tinted glazed pa-
     per
dull carmine vignette, violet frame	650.
dull yellow vignette, violet frame	650.
yellow vignette, green frame	650.

209-E4

Vignette diameter: 17mm
Engraved Franklin vignette.

209-E4   10c
  a. Die on India
black	575.
dusky carmine	575.
dull scarlet	575.
dim orange	575.
orange brown	575.
yellow green	575.
dim blue green	575.
deep blue	575.
red brown on blue ground	575.
dark red violet	575.

  b. Die sunk on glazed paper, approx.
     51x69mm
dusky carmine	775.
dim scarlet	775.
dim orange	775.
deep blue	775.
dim blue green	775.

209-E5

Design size: 21x26mm
Engraved frame with typographed vignette mounted on it. Four diff. color combinations (dull scarlet vignette, dull carmine frame; dull orange vignette, brown orange frame; yellow brown vignette, dark brown frame; blue green vignette and frame) on cream white ivory paper, 22x27mm each, mounted together on 92x114mm thick white card, ms. "American Bank Note Co. N.Y." at lower right.

209-E5   10c   Four designs on cream white ivory
          on card   2,500.

209-E6

209-E7a

Vignette diameter: 18mm
Engraved Washington vignette.

209-E6   10c
  a. Die on India
black	600.
dim deep carmine	600.
dim deep scarlet	600.
dull orange	600.
dull brown	600.
dim blue green	600.
blue	600.
dusky red violet	600.

  b. Die sunk on white ivory paper, 55x67mm
dusky carmine	800.
dull orange	800.
dull blue green	800.
scarlet	800.
dull brown	800.
red violet	800.

Design size: 21x26mm
Engraved frame with typographed vignette mounted on it. Four diff. color combinations (dull carmine vignette and frame; dull orange vignette, brown orange frame; yellow brown vignette, dark brown frame; blue green vignette and frame) on cream white ivory paper, 22x27mm each, mounted together on 92x114mm thick white card, ms. "American Bank Note Co. N.Y." at lower right.

209-E7   10c
  a. Four designs on cream white ivory on
     card   2,500.
  b. Single composite off card, dull carmine
     vignette, blue green frame   400.

Issued stamp, No. 209, in trial color, overprinted network in fugitive ink.

209-E8   10c   On thick paper, perf. 12, gummed,
          sepia, overprint olive gray   150.

1883 ISSUE
American Bank Note Co.

210-E1   210-E2

Design size: 20x25½mm
Engraved vignette of Washington (from proof on India of No. 207) with watercolor frame design nearly as adopted but with "TWO" and "CENTS" at an angle, rubber stamp "Feb. 17, 1883" on back.

210-E1   2c   Die on white card, 80x90mm, black
          vignette, gray and white frame   3,000.

Design size: 20x25mm
Engraved vignette of Washington (from proof on India of No. 207) mounted on unadopted watercolor and ink frame design. backstamped "American Bank Note Co. Feb. 27, 1883."

210-E2   2c   Die on thick white card,
          87x100mm, black and white   3,000.

210-E3   210-E4

Design size: 20x25½mm

Engraved vignette of Washington (from proof on India of No. 207) mounted on watercolor frame design as adopted, ms. "2 March 1883 No. 1."

210-E3   2c Die on white card, 80x90mm, black vignette, gray & white frame   3,000.

Design size: 20x25mm
Engraved vignette of Washington on white background mounted on a brush and pen watercolor drawing of unadopted fancy frame design, backstamped "American Bank Note Co. Mar. 2, 1883" and pencil "No. 2."

210-E4   2c Die on white card, 88x101mm, dusky blue green   3,000.

210-E5

Design size: 20x25mm
Engraved vignette of Washington (from revenue stamp No. RB17) mounted on wash drawing of unadopted ornate frame design, backstamped "American Bank Note Co. Mar. 2, 1883" and pencil "No. 3."

210-E5   2c Die on white card, 88x101mm, blue violet vignette, black frame   2,500.

211-E1

Design size: 20x25½mm
Engraved vignette of Jackson mounted on unadopted watercolor frame design.

211-E1   4c Die on white card, 70x70mm, blue green vignette and frame   3,500.

211-E2

Engraved head of Jackson only.

211-E2   4c Die on India, die sunk on card, black   2,500.

211-E3

Incomplete engraved vignette of Jackson: lower edge of bust incomplete.

211-E3   4c Die on India, die sunk on card
    black   2,500.
    green   2,500.
    red brown   2,500.

Complete engraved vignette of Jackson.

211-E4   4c Die on India, die sunk on card, blue green   2,500.

211-E6

Die size: 60x62mm
Complete design as adopted but with pencil sketch of pedestal top under bust.

211-E5   4c Die on India, die sunk on card, gray black   5,750.

Similar to No. 211-E5 but with incomplete shading engraved on pedestal.

211-E6   4c Die on India, die sunk on card, blue green   2,500.

1887 ISSUE
American Bank Note Co.

212-E1

Die size: 55x63mm
Incomplete engraved vignette of Franklin facing right: horiz. background lines only.

212-E1   1c Die on 32½x35mm card, India mounted, die sunk on card
    black   600.
    ultramarine   600.

Die size: 62x62mm
Franklin vignette similar to No. 212-E1 but diagonal lines (in one direction only) added to background.

212-E2

212-E2   1c Die on India, die sunk on card
    black   600.
    ultramarine   600.

Die size: 55x64mm
Similar to No. 212-E2 but diagonal lines in both directions.

212-E3   1c Die on India, die sunk on card, black   500.

212-E4

Complete design as issued except Franklin facing right.

212-E4   1c
  a. Die on India, die sunk on card
    black   600.
    ultramarine   600.
  b. Die on ivory glazed paper, about 64x76mm
    black   750.
    black brown   750.
    scarlet   750.
    blue   750.

Die size: 62x62mm
Incomplete vignette of Franklin facing left as adopted.

212-E5   1c Die on India, die sunk on card, ultramarine   450.

212-E6

212-E7

Die size: 56x64½mm
Incomplete design as adopted except three lines below value label and taller numeral, shadow on edge of bust and in background below chin too dark.

212-E6   1c Die on India, die sunk on card
    ultramarine   750.
    green   750.

Similar to No. 212-E6 but with shadows lightened.

212-E7   1c Die on India, die sunk on card, ultramarine   750.

1890 ISSUE
American Bank Note Co.

219-E1

Design size: 19x22½mm
Die size: 58x64mm
Engraved die of frame only with blank labels quite similar to adopted design.

219-E1   1c Die on ivory paper, 64x72mm, black   700.

219-E2

219-E3

219-E4

Design size: 19x22mm
Engraved Franklin vignette cut down from 1887 1c stamp (No. 212) mounted on watercolor frame design.

219-E2   1c Die on thick light buff card, ultramarine frame   3,500.

Die size: 62x62mm
Engraved Franklin vignette with lettered label above.

219-E3   1c Die on India, die sunk on card, blue   800.

Engraved die of vignette only with outer line around the oval.

219-E4   1c Die on India, die sunk on card, 71x70mm, ultramarine   800.

220-E1

220-E2

Design size: 19x22mm

Engraved Washington vignette from 3c stamp (from proof on India of No. 184) mounted on watercolor frame design.

220-E1 2c Die on thick white card, 62x66mm, light carmine frame   3,750.

Design size: 19x23mm
Engraved Washington vignette cut from 1887 2c stamp (No. 213) mounted on shield-like watercolor frame design.

220-E2 2c Die on thick light buff card, gray frame   3,000.

220-E3   220-E4

Design size: 19x23mm
Engraved Washington vignette cut from 1887 2c stamp (No. 213) mounted on watercolor frame design.

220-E3 2c Die on white card, 105x135mm, gray black frame   3,000.

Design size: 19x22mm
Die size: 56x63mm
Engraved unadopted frame only.

220-E4 2c Die on white ivory paper, black   1,250.

220-E5   220-E6

Die size: 62x62mm
Engraved vignette of Washington in oval line frame.

220-E5 2c Die on India, die sunk on card, dark carmine   800.

Engraved Washington vignette with lettered label above.

220-E6 2c Die on India, dusky carmine   1,250.

220-E7   220-E8

Design size: 19x22½mm
Engraved Washington vignette and lettered top label mounted on pencil drawing of frame design adopted, ms. "J.J.M. — engraved background only without figures or words;" backstamped "Nov. 15, 1889 American Bank Note Co."

220-E7 2c Die on 50x55mm white card, mounted on thick white card, 119x122mm, black vignette, pencil frame   3,000.

Design size: 19x22mm
Die size: 56x63mm
Engraved frame only as adopted with numerals, blank curved top label.

220-E8 2c
  a. Die on ivory paper, 64x71mm, black   900.
  b. Die on India, 51x62mm
     black   700.
     brown black   700.
     dark brown   700.
     dull scarlet   700.
     dark blue green   700.
     dark blue   700.
     red violet   700.
     red orange   700.

220-E9

Incomplete engraving of entire design as adopted: no dots in rectangular spaces between shading lines on cheek under hair in front of ear and on back of neck.

220-E9 2c Die on India, die sunk on card, lake   1,250.

(Probably by) The Times, Philadelphia

220-E11

Surface-printed essay for proposed business advertising on stamps.

220-E11 2c Die on India, on card, bright green blue   —

American Bank Note Co.

221-E1   221-E2

Engraved 3c frame as adopted with vignette cut out, mounted over photo of James Madison.

221-E1 3c Die on India, cut close, dark green   2,500.

Engraved vignette of Jackson with lettered label above.

221-E2 3c Die on India, die sunk on card, purple   750.

Design size: 19x22mm
Incomplete engraved design as adopted except Lincoln facing ¾ left: unfinished shading under collar.

222-E1 4c Die on India, die sunk on card, black brown   1,250.

222-E2   222-E3

Die No. C-226 size: 62½x62½mm
Completed design with die no. and impt., Lincoln facing ¾ left.

222-E2 4c Die on India, on 25x32mm card, black brown   1,000.

Incomplete engraving as adopted: no wart on face, no lines on shirt.

222-E3 4c Die on India, die sunk on card, black brown   1,000.

223-E1

Design size: 19x21½mm

Photo of Seward vignette mounted on watercolor frame design.

223-E1 5c Gray and white on light buff paper in upper right corner of short envelope   1,750.

223-E2   223-E3

Design size: 19x26½mm
Die size: 63x62mm
Incomplete engraved design as adopted except Grant facing ¾ left: hair neatly combed.

223-E2 5c Die on India, die sunk on card
     black   700.
     orange brown   700.

Design size: 19x26½mm
Die size: 63x62mm
Incomplete engraving of complete bearded left-facing design: eye pupils not solid color, light shading on right side of face, only one diagonal shading line on left coat shoulder.

223-E3 5c Die on India, die sunk on card, chocolate   700.

Similar to No. 223-E3 but more complete. Left beard has no diagonal lines and is light at top center.

223-E4 5c Die on India, die sunk on card, chocolate   700.

Third state of die: no horiz. lines on left moustache or under lower lip.

223-E5 5c Die on India, die sunk on card, chocolate   700.

223-E6   223-E7

Completed left-facing design: shows lines omitted from No. 223-E5, several diagonal shading lines on left shoulder of coat.

223-E6 5c Die on India, die sunk on card
     black   700.
     chocolate   700.

Design size: 19x26½mm
Die size: 62x62mm
Left-facing design with slightly diff. portrait, hair neatly combed. Horiz. shading lines on left coat shoulder, no wash-etched shadows on coat, beard and tie.

223-E7 5c
  a. Die on India, die sunk on card
     black   700.
     dark brown   700.
  b. Die on glazed paper, impt. and "ESSAY MARCH 1890"
     black   750.
     black brown   750.
     scarlet   750.
     blue   750.

Design size: 19x26½mm
Die similar to No. 223-E7 but diagonal shading lines on left coat shoulder, wash-etched shadows on coat, beard and tie.

223-E8 5c Die on India, on card, brown   700.

223-E9   223-E10

Die size: 62x63mm
Engraving of right-facing Grant design diff. than adopted: light oval line around vignette, three diagonal lines on shirtfront under tie. Incomplete engraving: right collar unshaded.

223-E9 5c Die on India, dark orange brown   700.

Similar to No. 223-E9 but engraving completed: right collar shaded.

223-E10 5c
  a. Die on India, die sunk on card, dark
        orange brown   700.
  b. Die on ivory paper, impt. and "ESSAY
        MARCH 1890"
        black   750.
        black brown   750.
        scarlet   750.
        blue   750.

Ferrotype plate 39x51mm of Grant facing ¾ right, outlines engraved, filled with red.

223-E11 5c Metal plate   650.

223-E12

Printing from ferrotype plate, No. 223-E11.

223-E12 5c Die on card, 43x56mm, red   650.

226-E1   226-E2

Design size: 19x22½mm
Incomplete engraved vignette of Webster with curved label above, mounted on pencil drawing of frame design (includes additional pencil drawings of lower part of frame, value lettering), backstamped "D.S. Ronaldson," frame engraver.

226-E1 10c Die on white card, 51x55mm,
            black   13,500.

Design size: 19x22½mm
Engraving of unadopted frame design.

226-E2 10c Die on white glazed paper, black   1,000.

226-E3   226-E4

Design size: 19x22mm
Engraved 10c frame as adopted, vignette cut out and mounted over photo of John Adams.

226-E3 10c Die on India, cut close, dark green   2,500.

Design size: 19x22mm
Engraved 10c frame as adopted, vignette cut out and mounted over photo of William T. Sherman.

226-E4 10c Die on India, cut close, dark green   2,500.

227-E1

Design size: 19x22½mm
Engraved vignette of Henry Clay with curved label above, mounted on wash drawing of frame design (includes additional enlarged pencil and wash drawing of frame).

227-E1 15c Die on white card, mounted at left
             on light buff card, 110x123mm
             (frame drawing at right), black   1,750.

228-E1

Design size: 19x22½mm
Die size: 62x61mm
Incomplete engraved vignette of Jefferson with curved lettered label at top: hair shading incomplete.

228-E1 30c Die on India, die sunk on card,
             black   750.

Similar to No. 228-E1 but more shading on hair, vert. shading lines on chin.

228-E2 30c Die on India, die sunk on card,
             black   750.

229-E1

Design size: 19x22½mm
Die size: 62x62mm
Engraved vignette of Perry with curved lettered label at top.

229-E1 90c Die on India, die sunk on card, red
             orange   750.

COLUMBIAN ISSUE
Lyman H. Bagg

230-E1   237-E1

Design sizes: 22x22mm
  Left: No. 230-E1 — pencil drawing of Columbus in armor, on paper. "I do not know whether these designs will be of any use to you or not — they are so rough. L.H.B." written at top, "My idea illustrated" at bottom.
  Right: No. 237-E1 — pencil drawing of North American continent, on paper.

230-E1 One Cent, Ten Cents, Drawings on
            114x72mm white wove, Nos. 230-E1,
            237-E1   6,000.

American Bank Note Co.

230-E2

230-E3

230-E4

Design size: 33x22mm
Silver print photo vignette of Columbus head mounted on watercolor drawing of unadopted frame design.

230-E2 1c Red violet on stiff white drawing pa-
            per   4,500.
230-E3 1c Blue green on stiff white drawing
            paper   4,500.
230-E4 1c Light red on stiff white drawing pa-
            per   4,500.

230-E5

Ferrotype metal plate with outline of adopted vignette (reversed) and drawings of Indian man and woman at sides in single line frame 39mm long.

230-E5 1c Metal plate, 57x38mm   1,250.

230-E6

Vignette size: 16x15mm
Engraved vignette only as adopted.

230-E6 1c Die on 53x39mm India, on card
            yellow brown   2,000.
            black   2,000.

230-E7

Incomplete engraving of vignette, lettering, value numerals and tablet as issued: without palm tree, incomplete shading on and behind Indian and maiden, on Columbus' head, no shading on scrollwork, etc.

230-E7 1c Die on 39x28mm stiff wove, deep
            blue   2,000.

230-E8

Incomplete engraving of entire design as issued: maiden's skirt only lightly engraved, chief's torso and shoulder incompletely engraved, incomplete shading in frame design at top, etc.

230-E8 1c Die on India, die sunk on
            99x84mm card, deep blue   1,500.

231-E1

Design size: 34x22mm
Silver print photo of vignette as adopted, mounted on watercolor drawing of unadopted frame design.

231-E1   2c Die on stiff white drawing paper, red violet   *8,500.*

Die size: 74x61½mm
Incomplete engraving of adopted vignette only.

231-E2   2c Die on India, die sunk on card
   black   *1,500.*
   sepia   *1,500.*

231-E3

Design size: 35½x22mm
Engraved vignette of Columbus asking aid of Isabella as adopted for 5c, mounted on watercolor drawing of frame design similar to that adopted for 2c.

231-E3   2c Die on stiff white drawing paper, dark brown   *4,000.*

231-E4

Vignette size: 29x15mm
Die size: 74x61½mm
Incomplete engraving of vignette as adopted (probably first state of die): cape on back of central figure incomplete, etc.

231-E4   2c Die on India, die sunk on card, black   *2,500.*

231-E5

Incomplete engraving of vignette as adopted (probably second state of die): more shading on top right face, etc.; also pencil sketches for lengthening vignette.

231-E5   2c Die on India, die sunk on card, black   *3,250.*

231-E6

Vignette size: 31½x15mm
Die size: 74x61½mm
Incomplete engraving of vignette, longer than Nos. 231-E4 and 231-E5, later shortened as adopted: Columbus' legs, central figure's cape, etc., are incomplete.

231-E6   2c Die on India, die sunk on card, black   *2,500.*

231-E7

Design size: 33x22mm
Die size: 74x61½mm
Incomplete engraving of entire design almost as adopted: figures of value narrower, unfinished crosset shadows in lower corners.

Ridgway numbers used for colors of No. 231-E7.

231-E7   2c
   a. Die on India, die sunk on card
     13m/4 smoky dusky o-yellow-orange   *1,250.*
   b. Die on thin white wove card
     69o/5 black   *800.*
     1m/0 dusky red   *800.*
     3k/2 dull dark orange-red   *800.*
     5i/0 deep o-orange-red   *800.*
     5i/1 deep v-deep o-orange-red   *800.*
     6i/0 deep m. red-orange   *800.*
     9i/0 deep o-yellow-orange   *800.*
     9m/0 dusky o-red-orange   *800.*
     9m/3 dismal dusky o-red-orange   *800.*
     9m/4 smoky dusky o-red-orange   *800.*
     9n/2 dull v. dusky o-red-orange   *800.*
     10k/0 m. dark orange   *800.*
     11i/0 deep orange   *800.*
     11k/1 dim dark orange   *800.*
     13m/1 dim dusky o-yellow-orange   *800.*
     13m/4 smoky dusky o-yellow-orange   *800.*
     33m/2 dull dusky g-yellow-green   *800.*
     37m/1 dim dusky g-blue-green   *800.*
     43m/2 dull dusky green-blue   *800.*
     49m/0 dusky blue   *800.*
     49m/1 dim dusky blue   *800.*
     55m/2 dull dusky blue-violet   *800.*
     59m/2 dull dusky violet   *800.*
     65m/2 dull dusky r-red-violet   *800.*
     70i/0 deep violet-red-red   *800.*

231-E8

Design size: 33x22mm
Incomplete engraving of entire design as adopted: value numerals same as on issued stamp but without thick shading bars at ends of outer frame rectangles, etc.

231-E8   2c Die on India, card mounted, sepia   *1,500.*

232-E1

Design size: 33½x22mm
Silver print photo of vignette unadopted for any value (Columbus embarking on voyage of discovery), mounted on watercolor drawing of unadopted frame design.

232-E1   3c Die on stiff white drawing paper, 41x29mm, orange brown   *4,000.*

Ferrotype metal plate showing 19x15mm outline of *Santa Maria* (reversed) in 33x15mm vignette frame, outline engraved and filled with red ink.

232-E2   3c Metal plate, 51x30mm   *1,250.*

232-E3

Printing from ferrotype plate No. 232-E3.

232-E3   3c Die on stiff white card with rounded corners, 55x42mm, red   *1,250.*

232-E4

Vignette size: 30x15mm
Die size: 74x61mm

Incomplete engraving of vignette as adopted: sky composed of horiz. ruled lines, no clouds.

232-E4   3c Die on India, die sunk on card
   black   *1,250.*
   dark yellow-orange   *1,250.*
   sepia   *1,750.*

232-E5

Engraved vignette similar to No. 232-E4 but with "1492 UNITED STATES OF AMERICA 1892" and scrolls around numerals engraved in outline only, pencil outline of frame.

232-E5   3c Die on thick artist's card with beveled edges, 50x38mm, dark yellow orange   *3,000.*

233-E1

Design size: 33½x22mm
Silver print photo of wash drawing of vignette as adopted, mounted on watercolor drawing of frame design as adopted but titled "COLUMBUS ON VOYAGE OF DISCOVERY. SHIPS AT SEA."

233-E1   4c Die on stiff white drawing paper, 41x29mm, brown red   *4,750.*

233-E2

Design size: 33x22mm
Die size: 74x61½mm
Incomplete engraving of complete design as adopted: unfinished crosset shadows in lower corners.

Ridgway numbers used for some colors of No. 233-E2.

233-E2   4c
   a. Die on India, die sunk on card
     black   *1,250.*
     dark yellow orange   *1,250.*
   b. Die on thin white wove card, die sunk on card
     1m/0 dusky red   *800.*
     3i/1 dim deep orange-red   *800.*
     3k/2 dull dark orange-red   *800.*
     5i/0 deep o-orange-red   *800.*
     9i/0 deep o-red-orange   *800.*
     9m/1 dim dusky o-red-orange   *800.*
     11i/0 deep orange   *800.*
     11k/1 dim dark orange   *800.*
     11m/2 dull dusky orange   *800.*
     13k/1 dim dark o-yellow-orange   *800.*
     13m/2 dull dusky o-yellow-orange   *800.*
     13k/3 dismal dark o-yellow-orange   *800.*
     13k/4 smoky dark o-yellow-orange   *800.*
     13m/4 smoky dusky o-yellow-orange   *800.*
     15m/2 dull dusky yellow-orange   *800.*
     33m/2 dull dusky g-yellow-green   *800.*
     35m/5 gloomy dusky green   *800.*
     37m/1 dim dusky g-blue-green   *800.*
     39m/1 dim dusky blue-green   *800.*
     41m/1 dim dusky b-blue-green   *800.*
     47m/0 dusky green-blue-blue   *800.*
     55m/2 dull dusky blue-violet   *800.*
     63m/2 dull dusky red-violet   *800.*
     69m/1 dull dusky red-violet-red   *800.*
     69k/3 dismal dark red-violet-red   *800.*
     71i/0 deep violet-red-red   *800.*
     71m/0 dusky violet-red-red   *800.*
     71o/5 black   *800.*
     ultramarine   *800.*
     violet   *800.*
     red violet   *800.*
     brown violet   *800.*
     orange brown   *800.*
     dark brown   *800.*

234-E1

Design size: 38½x22mm
Engraved vignette as adopted, mounted on watercolor drawing of frame design similar to but longer than adopted. Vignette also used on No. 231-E3.

234-E1   5c Die on thick artist's card, block
        sunk as die essay, black brown   *4,000.*

234-E2

Design size: 34x22½mm
Die size: 67x63mm
Engraved vignette as adopted, mounted on watercolor drawing of frame design as adopted, pencil "Oct. 5/92," approval monogram of J.D. Macdonough and ⅞x1¹⁄₃₂ inches. Vignette also used on No. 231-E3.

234-E2   5c Die on thick artist's card, die sunk,
        black brown & white   *4,000.*

234-E3

Vignette size: 29½x15mm
Die size: 74x61½mm
Engraved vignette only as adopted.

234-E3   5c Die on India, die sunk on card, se-
        pia   *1,250.*

234-E4

Incomplete engraving of entire design: bench at left has horiz. shading only, incomplete shading in Columbus' face, etc.

234-E4   5c Die on 74x60mm India, on card
        sepia   *1,000.*
        blue   *1,000.*

Ferrotype metal plate with engraved outline design (reversed) of vignette as used on 6c, engraved lines filled with red ink.

235-E1   6c Metal plate, 38x38mm   *1,100.*

235-E2

Printing from ferrotype plate No. 235-E1.

235-E2   6c Die on stiff white card with round-
        ed corners, 55x42mm, red   *1,250.*

235-E3

Incomplete engraving of frame as adopted: unfinished crosset shadows in lower corners.

235-E3   6c Die on India, black   *2,000.*

235-E4

Design size: 34x22mm
Die size: 73x60mm
Incomplete engraving of entire design as adopted: neck and shoulder of horse, side figures in niches, crosset shadows in lower corners all unfinished.

235-E4   6c Die on India, die sunk on card,
        blue violet   *1,500.*

236-E1

Design size: 33½x22mm
Die size: 73x62mm
Design as adopted but frame incompletely engraved: unfinished crosset shadows in lower corners.

236-E1   8c Die on India, on card, black   *2,500.*

236-E2

Design as adopted but frame incompletely engraved: unfinished crosset shadows in lower corners, incomplete gown at left and faces at right.

236-E2   8c Die on India, on card, black   *1,000.*

237-E2

Ferrotype metal plate with engraved outline design (reversed) of vignette as used on 10c, engraved lines filled with red ink.

237-E2   10c Metal plate, 43x28mm   *1,000.*

237-E3

Printing from ferrotype plate No. 237-E2.

237-E3   10c Die on stiff white card with round-
        ed corners, 55x42mm, red   *1,000.*

237-E4

Design size: 33x22mm
Die size: 74x62mm
Incomplete engraving of entire design as adopted: surroundings of Columbus, floor, etc., three figures behind King Ferdinand, crosset shadows in lower corners all unfinished.

237-E4   10c Die on India, card mounted
        black brown   *1,000.*
        rose carmine   *1,000.*

Similar to No. 237-E4 but more completely engraved: missing lines on ankle bracelet of Indian, many details in vignette and crosset shadows in lower corners.

237-E5   10c Die on India, die sunk on card
        black brown   *1,500.*
        carmine   *1,500.*

238-E1

Design size: 33½x22mm
Silver print photo of vignette unadopted for any value (Columbus relating incidents of voyage to Ferdinand and Isabella), mounted on watercolor drawing of frame design similar to that adopted.

238-E1   15c Die on stiff white drawing paper,
        42x30mm, bright ultramarine   *5,000.*

238-E2

Vignette size: 30x15mm
Die size: 71x59mm
Incomplete engraving of vignette only as adopted: shading on Columbus' tunic and arms, Isabella's sholder, Ferdinand's robe, seated Indian's robe, robe of kneeling figure in lower left corner, etc., all unfinished.

238-E2   15c Die on India, die sunk on card,
        black brown   *1,500.*

Complete engraving of vignette adopted.

238-E3   15c Die on India, black brown   *1,500.*

238-E4

Design size: 33½x22mm
Die size: 73½x62mm
Incomplete engraving of complete design as adopted: shading on Isabella's shoulder, Ferdinand's robe, seated Indian's blanket and crosset shadows in lower corners all unfinished.

238-E4   15c Die on India, on card
        black brown   *1,500.*
        blue green   *1,500.*

239-E1

Design size: 34½x22½mm

Silver print photo of vignette adopted for 15c, mounted on watercolor and ink drawing of unadopted frame design, titled "COLUMBUS PRESENTING NATIVES TO FERDINAND AND ISABELLA."

239-E1 30c Bluish gray on stiff white drawing
paper, 42x30mm   5,000.

239-E2

Ferrotype metal plate with engraved outline design (reversed) of vignette as used on 30c, engraved lines filled with red ink.

239-E2 30c Metal plate, 39x29mm   1,000.

239-E3

Printing from ferrotype plate No. 239-E2.

239-E3 30c Die on stiff white card with rounded corners, 55x43mm, red   1,000.

239-E4

Vignette size: 30x15mm
Die size: 74x62mm
Incomplete engraving of adopted vignette only: table cloth dark at top; horiz. lines on front edge of octagonal footstool, horiz. dots in shadow below windowsill at left, dots on top of head of man standing next to Columbus, etc., all missing.

239-E4 30c Die on India, die sunk on card,
black   1,750.

Similar to No. 239-E4 but further engraved: has horiz. lines on front of footstool, etc. Eight pencil instructions for finishing vignette engraving written on large card backing, e.g., "Too much color on table cloth near top."

239-E5 30c Die on India, die sunk on
177x117mm card
black   2,000.
black brown   2,000.

239-E6

Design size: 33½x22mm
Die size: 74x63mm
Incomplete engraving of entire design as adopted: table cloth dark at top, diagonal dashes in one direction only between horiz. lines at lower left of vignette, etc.

239-E6 30c Die on India, die sunk on card
black   2,000.
black brown   2,000.

Similar to No. 239-E6 but diagonal dashes in two directions, more dots on head and hand of man seated at near end of table.

239-E7 30c Die on India, die sunk on card
black brown   1,750.
orange   1,750.

Incomplete engraving of entire design: window frame, horiz. shading lines on shoulder of man at right, vert. lines on front of

---

table cloth below Columbus all missing. Lighter shading at top of table cloth as on issued stamp.

239-E8 30c Die on India, on card, orange   2,500.

240-E1

Design size: 34x22mm
Die size: Incomplete engraving of entire design as adopted: unfinished shadows between right arm and body of man on donkey, distant object in front of bowing man's head darker than on issued stamp.

240-E1 50c Die on India, on card, slate blue   1,500.

240-E2

Incomplete engraving of entire design: missing dots on don-key's flank and long lines on wrist of bowing man, no etching on two riders or their mounts.

240-E2 50c Die on India, on card, slate blue   1,500.

240-E3

Incomplete engraving of entire design: additional engraving on donkey's hindquarters and face of figure to left of Columbus.

240-E3 50c Die on India, on card, slate blue   1,500.

241-E1

Ferrotype metal plate with engraved outline design (reversed) of vignette as used on $1, engraved lines filled with red ink.

241-E1 $1 Metal plate, 45x29mm   1,000.

241-E2

Printing from ferrotype plate No. 241-E1.

241-E2 $1 Die on stiff white card with round-
ed corners, 55½x43mm, red   1,000.

241-E3

Vignette size: 31x15mm
Die size: 72x59mm

Incomplete engraving of vignette only as adopted (very early state of die): very little shading on Isabella, floor, walls, etc.

241-E3 $1 Die on India, die sunk on card,
black brown   2,000.

241-E4

Incomplete engraving of entire design as adopted: shadow on table cloth, woman in front of table, crosslet shadows at lower corners all unfinished.

241-E4 $1 Die on India, on card, black brown   2,000.

241-E5

Later state of complete design: horiz. lines in rectangle above Isabella missing.

241-E5 $1 Die on India, die sunk on
86x69mm card, black brown   2,000.

242-E1

Design size: 33½x22mm
Die size: 75x62mm
Incomplete engraving of entire design as adopted: about 12 horiz. lines missing on back of cape of tall man at right, some vert. dashes missing on corselet of soldier at right, incomplete foliage over "C" of "COLUMBUS," etc.

242-E1 $2 Die on India, die sunk on card
dull yellow orange   2,000.
olive brown   2,000.

243-E1

Ferrotype metal plate with engraved outline design (reversed) of vignette as used on $3, engraved lines filled with red wax.

243-E1 $3 Metal plate, 45x29mm   1,250.

243-E2

Printing from ferrotype plate No. 243-E1.

243-E2 $3 Die on stiff white card with round-
ed corners, 55x43mm, red   1,250.

243-E3

Design size: 33½x22mm
Incomplete engraving of entire design as adopted: unshaded crossets in lower corners, shading lines on crossets and frame above title label too light. Pencil marks correct these.

243-E3 $3 Die on India, die sunk on card,
          dark yellow green   *1,500.*

243-E4

Incomplete engraving of entire design as adopted, before etching of shadows on Columbus, Ferdinand, backs of chairs, etc.

243-E4 $3 Die on India, on card, dark red   *2,000.*

Ferrotype metal plate with engraved outline design (reversed) of Queen Isabella vignette as used on $4, engraved lines filled with red wax.

244-E1 $4 Metal plate, 33x44mm   *1,500.*

244-E2

Printing from ferrotype plate No. 244-E1.

244-E2 $4 Die on stiff white card with round-
          ed corners, 43x55mm, red   *1,500.*

244-E3

Vignette diameter: 14mm
Incomplete engraving of Isabella head with background of uniform ruled horiz. lines only, blank circle for Columbus vignette at right adjoining.

244-E3 $4 Die on India, on card, black   *3,000.*

Similar to No. 244-E3 but background has diagonal shading also.

244-E4 $4 Die on India, on card, black   *3,000.*

244-E5

Design size: about 34x21½mm
Die size: 74½x61½mm
Incomplete engraving of vignettes and lettering only: no diagonal shading lines in background of Columbus vignette.

244-E5 $4 Die on India, die sunk on card
          black   *3,500.*
          dark red   *4,000.*

244-E6

Design size: 34x22mm
Same engraving as No. 244-E5 but with wash drawing of frame design as adopted.

244-E6 $4 Die on thick artist's card with bev-
          eled edges, 50x39mm, gray black   *3,000.*

244-E7

Incomplete engraving of entire design as adopted: shadow at top of vert. bar and lines on leaves at bottom between vignettes unfinished; no circular line bordering vignette at Isabella's right shoulder.

244-E7 $4 Die on India, on card, black brown   *2,000.*

244-E8

More complete engraving than No. 244-E7 but still missing circular line at Isabella's shoulder; only light shading on Columbus' collar.

244-E8 $4 Die on India, on card
          black brown
          dark red   *2,000.* —

245-E1

Design size: 34½x22½mm
Incomplete engraved vignette as adopted for 1c: missing sky, etc., with pencil drawing of part of frame design.

245-E1 $5 Die on 50x38mm artist's card-
          board, on thicker card, 55x43mm,
          black   *4,000.*

Design size: 34x22½mm
Die size: 74½x61½mm
Incomplete engraving of vignette, lettering and frame as adopted (side panels blank): shading unfinished on Columbus' neck, hair and background, and with white and black wash touches.

245-E2 $5 Die on India, die sunk on card,
          black   *3,000.*

245-E3

Similar to No. 245-E2 but further engraved: shading lines on neck, diagonal lines in background, etc.

245-E3 $5 Die on India, on card, 49x38mm,
          black   *3,000.*

Model with photos of female figures mounted each side of vignette, pencil "Design approved subject to inspection of engraved proof, color to be black. A.D.H. Dec. 6 '92" (A.D. Hazen, 3rd asst. PMG).

245-E4 $5 Die on thick white card, on
          117x116mm card, black   *3,000.*

245-E5

Engraving of No. 245-E3 with retouched photos of side subjects mounted in place.

245-E5 $5 Die on white artist's cardboard,
          56½x46mm, die sunk on card,
          black   *2,000.*

Design size: 33½x22mm
Incomplete engraving of entire design: one line under "POSTAGE FIVE DOLLARS", no lines outside and no diagonal lines in sky to upper right and upper left of vignette, etc.

245-E6 $5 Die on India, on card, black   *2,000.*

245-E7

Similar to No. 245-E2 but with pencil marks to show engraver where to place diagonal shading lines behind head and in front of bust.

245-E7 $5 Die on 65x55mm India, card
          mounted, black   *3,000.*

245-E8

Similar to No. 245-E6 but with pencil marks and white ink suggestions for further engraving.

245-E8 $5 Die on India, die sunk on
          83x68mm card, black   *2,000.*

245-E9

Similar to No. 245-E6 but further engraved: with diagonal shading above side figures, below numerals and around vignette circle, but still incomplete in arched band above vignette.

245-E9 $5 Die on India, die sunk on
          110x83mm card, black   *2,000.*

245-E10

Similar to No. 245-E9 but further engraved: with shading lines in arched band above vignette but no shading on pole of liberty cap, object below shield has dotted shading only, spear tip shading incomplete.

245-E10 $5 Die on India, die sunk on 85x70mm card, black — 2,000.

1894 ISSUE
Bureau of Engraving and Printing

The 1c-15c designs of the 1890 issue engraved by the American Bank Note Co. were worked over by the BEP, including the addition of triangles in the upper corners. The 1890 30c was changed to a 50c and the 90c to a $1. Some 1894 essays have American Bank Note Co. imprints below the design.

247-E1

Design size: 18½x22mm
Die size: 61x62mm
Large die engraving of 1890 1c with pencil drawing of UL triangle 3½mm high with straight side next to curved upper label, freehand horiz. ink line at UR.

247-E1 1c Die on India, die sunk on card, black — 2,000.

247-E2

Experimental laydown die with 1890 1c proof 4mm to left of similar design with 15-line high type I triangle in UR corner. Same laydown die also contains two 2c designs 18mm below, 5½mm apart, either uninked or lightly inked in color of 1c (sometimes found separated from 1c designs). No. 247-E2b nearly always found cracked horiz. through designs.

247-E2 1c
a. Die on semiglazed white wove with pencil notations
  blue — 1,850.
  ultramarine — 1,850.
b. Die on white card with pencil notations re color
  "1-1 Antwerp, 4 Ultra." — 1,500.
  "2--little lighter--" — 1,500.
  "1 Antwerp blue, 1 Ultra." (not cracked) — 1,750.
  "4 Cobalt and Indigo" — 1,500.
  "No 5" — 1,500.
  "No. 6--Antwerp blue" — 1,500.
  "No. 6--with little Antwerp blue" — 1,500.

Die impression of 1890 1c with 15-line high type I triangle in UR corner.

247-E3 1c Die on India, 50x52mm, dusky green — 2,000.

Experimental die impression of single 1890 1c with 2c 18mm below, triangles added in ink to upper corners of both designs, ms. "Approved" notations.

247-E4 1c +2c, Die on India, mounted on 57x102mm card, mounted on another card, 144x195mm
  green — 2,500.
  dull violet (without added triangles) — 2,400.

247-E5   247-E6

Large die engraving of 1890 1c with 18-line high triangle in UL corner (inner lines very thick).

247-E5 1c Die on India, die sunk on card, dusky blue green — 1,250.

Similar to No. 247-E5 but inner line of triangle almost as thin as outer line.

247-E6 1c Die on India, die sunk on card, dusky blue green — 1,250.

247-E7

Similar to No. 247-E6 but inner line of triangle same thickness as adopted.

247-E7 1c Die on India, die sunk on card, dusky blue green — 1,250.

Incomplete engraving of entire design as adopted including triangles: coat collar, scroll under "U," horiz. lines on frame, oval line of vignette, etc., all unfinished; vignette background not re-etched.

247-E8 1c Die on India, die sunk on card
  ultramarine — 1,000.
  blue ("Cobalt 2--Indigo 4") — 1,250.

Design size: 18½x22mm
Die size: 61x62½mm
Large die engraving of 1890 2c with pencil drawing of UL triangle 2½mm high.

250-E1 2c Die on India, die sunk on card, black — 2,250.

Die width: 92mm
Experimental laydown die with 1890 2c proof 5½mm to left of similar design with 14-line high type I triangles in upper corners (found cut apart from No. 247-E2 and used for trial colors as noted thereon in pencil).

250-E2 2c Die on white card
  "1 R&D Lake, 1½P. white" — 2,000.
  "M3 1 white, 7 Gem Lake, ¼ Car. Lake" — 2,000.
  "2 White, 4 Ger. Lake No. 1, ½ R&D Lake" — 2,000.
  "Opal Red" — 2,000.
  "Opal Orange" — 2,000.
  "Opal Maroon" — 2,000.

250-E3

Die size: 61½x62½mm
American Banknote Co. die No. C-224 annealed, with 18-line high type I triangles engraved in upper corners, ms "No. 1" at lower left of card backing.

250-E3 2c Die on India, die sunk on card
  medium deep red — 1,000.
  deep red — 1,000.
  dusky red — 1,000.
  dim red — 1,000.
  medium deep orange-red — 1,000.
  deep o-orange-red — 1,000.
  dusky g-blue-green — 1,000.
  dark medium violet-red-red — 1,000.

Incomplete engraving of entire design: shadows on frame not etched; lines on foliage, front collar and oval line at vignette bottom not recut; dots instead of lines over corner of eye; only one line on truncated scroll at left of right 2 and no line on similar scroll at right of left 2; shadows of TWO CENTS not etched.

250-E4 2c Die on India, die sunk on card
  bright red — 1,000.
  light red — 1,000.
  dark red — 1,000.
  deep orange red — 1,000.

Similar to No. 250-E4 but line added to scroll at right of left 2, ms. "A.B.N.Co. Die worked over and ornaments put in" at top, ms. "No. 1" at lower left.

250-E5 2c medium deep red — 1,250.

Incomplete engraving of entire design: two lines on truncated scroll at left of right 2 (one later removed), scroll at left of right 2 unfinished, profile of nose and forehead darker than on issued stamp, shadows of "TWO CENTS" not etched, short dashes on inside of outer edge of white oval at lower right, veins on scrolls around 2s not recut. Pencil notations incl. "Old A.B.N.Co. annealed & triangles engraved and rehardened to take up roll for plate."

250-E6 2c Die on India, die sunk on card, medium deep red — 1,250.

Incomplete engraving of entire design: bottom of ear still angular and not yet rounded, dots on lobe not yet gathered into

two lines, dot shading under corner of eye not yet gathered into four lines, shadows of "TWO CENTS" have been etched.

250-E7 2c Die on India, die sunk on card, medium deep red — 1,000.

Die size: 57x76mm
Incomplete engraving of entire design with type II triangles: top of head not silhouetted. Pencil notation "2/ Transfer from roll taken from No. 1 so as to change portrait and make cameo effect. Unfinished."

251-E1 2c Die on India, die sunk on card, dark violet red — 1,250.

Similar to No. 251-E1 but hair in front of ear unfinished, forehead and hair lightened.

251-E2 2c Die on India, die sunk on card, dusky gray — 1,500.

252-E1

Die size: 57x81mm
Incomplete engraving of entire design with type III triangles: top of head not silhouetted, unfinished shadow over eye, etc.

252-E1 2c Die on India, die sunk on card, medium deep red — 1,000.

Incomplete engraving of entire design with type III triangles: unfinished shadow over eye, etc.

252-E2 2c Die on India, die sunk on card
  dusky blue green — 1,500.
  dark violet red — 1,000.

252-E3

Design size: 19x22mm
Die size: 56x80½mm
Discarded die, vignette overengraved: too much shading on front hair, cheek, nose, below eye; background too dark; hair in front of ear very prominent.

252-E3 2c Die on India, die sunk on card
  light carmine — 2,000.
  green — 2,250.

253-E1

Die size: 60x63mm
Complete engraved design as adopted but with type II triangles.

253-E1 3c
a. Die on India, die sunk on card
  dusky blue green — 1,500.
  dark red violet — 1,000.
  dusky red violet — 1,000.
b. Die printed directly on card, die sunk on card, violet — 1,250.

254-E1

Design size: about 19x22mm
Die size: 61x63mm

Incomplete engraving of entire design: line under collar wings missing, oval line around vignette not recut; hair, beard, forehead, neck, collar, shirt, etc., all incomplete.

254-E1 4c Die on India, die sunk on card,
dark yellow brown   1,500.

Entire design engraved further than No. 254-E1 but still incomplete: shadows in lettering, etc., not etched, faint lines under collar incomplete, oval around vignette not recut.

254-E2 4c Die on India, die sunk on card,
dark yellow brown   1,500.

Entire design engraved further than No. 254-E2 but still incomplete: beard, collar and necktie, etc., unfinished. Some veins recut on foliage under oval label.

254-E3 4c Die on India, die sunk on card,
dark brown   1,250.

255-E1

Design size: 19x22mm
Engraved frame of American Bank Note Co. die No. C-227 with triangles, vignette cut out, mounted over engraved vignette of Washington.

255-E1 5c Die on 41x53mm India, on white
wove, 48x75mm, black   3,500.

Washington vignette only as on No. 255-E1.

255-E2 5c Die on India, green   2,000.

255-E3   255-E4

Design size: 19x22mm
Engraved frame as adopted with William H. Seward photo mounted on it.

255-E3 5c Die on India, cut close, mounted
on 74x84mm white card, black   3,500.

Design size: about 19x22mm
Die size: 62½x75mm
Incomplete engraving of entire design as adopted: no oval border line around vignette.

255-E4 5c Die on India, die sunk on card, orange brown   1,250.

256-E1

Design size: about 19x22mm
Die size: 62x61½mm
Incomplete engraving of entire design as adopted: white spot on eye and shadows not darkened, diagonal lines missing on beard under mouth, lines on coat unfinished.

256-E1 6c Die on India, die sunk on card,
dark red   1,250.

256-E2

Entire design engraved further than No. 256-E1 but still incomplete: diagonal lines on beard under mouth incomplete, lines on coat not as dark as on issued stamp.

256-E2 6c Die on India, die sunk on card,
dim dusky red   1,000.

257-E1

Design size: about 19x22mm
Die size: 58½x60mm
Incomplete engraving of entire design as adopted: lines on coat not recut darker, vignette background not etched darker.

257-E1 8c Die on India, die sunk on card,
dusky red violet   1,000.

258-E1

Design size: about 19x22mm
Die size: 61½x61½mm
Incomplete engraving of entire design as adopted: shading unfinished on cheek, in ear, etc.

258-E1 10c Die on India, die sunk on card,
dark brown   1,500.

Entire design engraved further than No. 258-E1 but still incomplete: unfinished shading on cheek under eye.

258-E2 10c Die on India, die sunk on card, red
brown   1,500.

261-E1

Design size: 19x22mm
Die size: 50x101mm
Large die engraving of 1890 90c with value label and figure circles blank, no triangles.

261-E1 $1 Die on India, die sunk on card,
black   3,500.

Similar to No. 261-E1 but head further re-engraved and background shadows etched deeper.

261-E2 $1 Die on India, die sunk on card,
blue green   3,750.

261-E3   261-E4

Design size: 19x22mm
Model of engraved Perry vignette mounted on 1890 engraved frame with penciled in triangles, values painted in white and black. Ms. "O.K. July 14/94 TFM" below.

261-E3 $1 Die on India, cut close, mounted
on 63x101mm white card, green
vignette, black frame   4,000.

Similar to No. 261-E3 but with value lettering and circles added, background of circles unfinished, no triangles.

261-E4 $1 Die on India, die sunk on card,
dark indigo blue   3,500.

Incomplete engraving of entire design: hair on top and back of head, whiskers and back of neck, and shading in value circles all unfinished. Triangles are engraved.

261-E5 $1 Die on India, die sunk on card,
black   1,750.

261-E6

Similar to No. 261-E5 but hair at back of head and whiskers darker, face in front of whiskers darker as on issued stamp. Circular lines extend into colorless vignette oval.

261-E6 $1 Die on India, die sunk on card
black   1,500.
blue green   2,000.

261-E7

Design size: 19x21½mm
Die size: 49x100mm
Incomplete engraving of unadopted dollar value design with portrait of Sen. James B. Beck: value label and numerals blank.

261-E7 $1 Die on India, die sunk on card,
black   4,000.

262-E1   262-E2

Design size: 19x22mm
Die size: 50x101mm
Incomplete engraving of frame only nearly as adopted: smaller $2's.

262-E1 $2 Die on India, die sunk on card,
blue green   3,500.

Design size: 19x22mm
Die size: 51x112mm
Incomplete engraving of entire design: left value circle blank, right circle engraved $2 outline only.

262-E2 $2 Die on India, die sunk on card,
black   3,250.

Die size: 51x112mm
Incomplete engraving of entire design: vignette shading unfinished, no veins in leaves around value circles.

262-E3 $2 Die on India, die sunk on card,
black   2,850.

262-E4

Incomplete engraving of entire design: inside of right border line above $2 unfinished.

262-E4 $2 Die on India, die sunk on card,
black   2,750.

Similar to No. 262-E4 but border line complete.

262-E5 $2 Die on India, die sunk on card,
black   2,500.

263-E1

Die size: 50x112½mm
Incomplete engraving of entire design: only one line in each scroll at right and left of $5, inner line of right border above $5 unfinished, etc., veins on leaves around right value circle unfinished.

263-E1 $5 Die on India, die sunk on card,
black 2,750.

Similar to No. 263-E1 but horiz. lines cut into oval line at top and inner oval line above L and R of DOLLARS required retouching as indicated by pencil instructions. Two lines in scrolls around value circles as adopted.

263-E2 $5 Die on India, die sunk on card,
black 3,250.

The bicolored essays commonly offered as No. 285-293 bicolored proofs can be found under the following listings: Nos. 285-E8, 286-E8, 287-E9, 288-E5, 289-E4, 290-E4, 291-E8, 292-E6, 293-E7. Values are for full-size cards (approximately 8x6 inches).

TRANS-MISSISSIPPI ISSUE

Die size: 79x68mm
Incomplete engraving of vignette only: initial state of die, no lines in sky or water.

285-E1 1c Die on India, die sunk on card,
black 2,500.

Vignette further engraved: lines in sky and water.

285-E2 1c Die on India, die sunk on card,
black 2,500.

Vignette further engraved: more background lines added.

285-E3 1c Die on India, die sunk on card,
black 2,500.

285-E4

Vignette further engraved: Indian at right darker, robe shadow etched.

285-E4 1c Die on India, die sunk on card,
black 2,500.

Vignette further engraved: rock in water more complete.

285-E5 1c Die on India, die sunk on card,
black 2,500.

Design size: 34x22mm
Die size: 73x62mm
Incomplete bicolor engraving of entire design: no second inner line in numerals.

285-E6 1c Die on India, die sunk on card, orange red & black 2,500.

Die size: 83x68mm
Incomplete engraving of entire design: vignette unfinished and unetched, frame has second inner line in numerals.

285-E7 1c Die on India, die sunk on card,
black 3,500.

285-E8

Die size: 63x51mm
Complete bicolor engraving of entire design.

285-E8 1c Die with black vignette on India,
die sunk on card
dark yellow green ("normal" bicolor) 300.
dusky green 2,000.
dusky blue green 2,000.
brown 2,000.

Incomplete engraving of entire design: corn husks and panels in ends of cartouche unfinished, lines under MARQUETTE and MISSISSIPPI not as thick as on completed die.

285-E9 1c Die on India, die sunk on card,
dusky green 2,500.

285-E10

Unfinished frame in red brown missing second inner line in numerals, with black unfinished "Cattle in the Storm" vignette as used on the $1 value, foreground snow at left incomplete.

285-E10 1c Die on India, red brown & black 3,500.

Die size: 78x68mm
Incomplete engraving of Mississippi River Bridge vignette (originally intended for 2c but eventually used on $2): initial state of die, very lightly engraved.

286-E1 2c Die on India, die sunk on card,
black 3,750.

Vignette further engraved but no lines on bridge beside two trolley cars.

286-E2 2c Die on India, die sunk on card,
black 5,000.

286-E3

Vignette further engraved but foreground between bridge and boat and foretopdeck incomplete, horse truck visible (later removed).

286-E3 2c Die on India, die sunk on card,
black 3,000.

Complete engraving of vignette only.

286-E4 2c Die on India, die sunk on card,
black 3,000.

286-E5

Design size: 137x88½mm
Pencil sketch by R. Ostrander Smith of 2c frame design as adopted except titled "ST. LOUIS BRIDGE."

286-E5 2c Sketch on tracing paper,
120x178mm 1,500.

286-E6

Complete pencil drawing by R.O. Smith of frame design ("P" of "POSTAGE" in ink), titled "ST. LOUIS BRIDGE."

286-E6 2c Drawing on Whatman drawing
board, 1889 wmk., 237x184mm 1,500.

286-E7

Pencil drawing by R.O. Smith, no title.

286-E7 2c Drawing on 72x61mm tracing paper 1,500.

286-7EA

Ink and wash drawing of frame, stamp size, similar to adopted design.

286-E7A 2c Drawing on hard, thick paper,
black 11,000.

286-E8

Die size: 63x51mm
Complete bicolor engraving of 2c design but with Mississippi River Bridge vignette as used on $2.

Ridgway numbers used for colors of No. 286-E8.

286-E8 2c Die with black vignette on India,
die sunk on card
dark red ("normal" bicolor) 300.
3k/0 dark orange red 2,000.
5k/0 dark o-orange-red 2,000.
5m/1 dim dusky o-orange-red 2,000.
7i/0 deep red orange 2,000.
7m/0 dusky red orange 2,000.
9m/0 dusky o-red-orange 2,000.
9k/2 dull dark o-red-orange 2,000.
13m/3 dismal dusky o-yellow-orange 2,000.
35m/1 dim dusky green 2,000.
49m/1 dim v. dusky blue 2,000.
63m/1 dim dusky red violet 2,000.
71-/0 deep violet-red-red 2,000.

286-E10

Die size: 82x68mm
Complete engraving with "FARMING IN THE WEST" vignette as adopted but from a die not used for the stamp: horses at left vignette border engraved dark up to border line which is solid complete line at both left and right.

286-E10 2c Die on India, die sunk on card
(marked "Proof from 1st die.")
black 2,500.
dark orange red 2,500.

Design size: 34x22mm
Die No. 259 size: 63x51mm
Initial state of die, very lightly engraved.

287-E1 4c Die on India, die sunk on card,
black 3,000.

Vignette further engraved: sky lines ruled in.

287-E2 4c Die on India, die sunk on card,
black 3,000.

287-E3

Vignette further engraved: more lines added, no right forefoot on bison.

287-E3 4c Die on India, die sunk on card,
black 4,500.

Shadow under bison incomplete.

287-E4 4c Die on India, die sunk on card,
black 3,750.

Shadow under bison and foreground penciled in.

287-E5 4c Die on India, die sunk on card,
black 3,750.

Vignette further engraved: right forefoot added, shadow under bison engraved but not etched.

287-E6 4c Die on India, die sunk on card,
black 3,750.

287-E7

Die size: 83x67mm
Incomplete engraving of entire design: no lines in sky, frame shadow etching unfinished.

287-E7 4c Die on India, die sunk on card
black 3,500.
deep orange 3,500.

287-E8

Die size: 63x51mm
Incomplete engraving of entire design: corn husks at lower sides of frame unfinished.

Ridgway numbers used for colors of No. 287-E8.

287-E8 4c Die with black vignette on India,
die sunk on card
5k/0 dark o-orange-red 2,000.
5m/0 dusky o-orange-red 2,000.
7m/0 dusky red orange 2,000.
11o/2 dull v. dusky orange 2,000.
13m/3 dismal dusky o-yellow-orange 2,000.

35m/1 dim dusky green 2,000.
39m/1 dim dusky blue green 2,000.
49o/1 dim v. dusky blue 2,000.
61k/1 dim dark violet-red violet 2,000.
63k/1 dim dusky red violet 2,000.
71m/0 dusky violet-red-red 2,000.

Complete bicolor engraving.

287-E9 4c Die with black vignette on India,
die sunk on card
red orange ("normal" bicolor) 300.
deep red orange ("normal" bicolor) 300.

Die size: 77x69mm
Initial state of die, very lightly engraved.

288-E1 5c Die on India, die sunk on card,
black 3,500.

Vignette further engraved: lower clouds at right darkened.

288-E2

288-E2 5c Die on India, die sunk on card,
black 5,500.

Vignette further engraved: shading penciled in on figures at right, etc.

288-E3 5c Die on India, die sunk on card,
black 3,750.

288-E4

Vignette further engraved but dots in sky at left of flag unfinished.

288-E4 5c Die on India, die sunk on card,
black 3,750.

288-E5

Design size: 34x22mm
Die size: 63x51mm
Incomplete bicolor engraving of entire design: unfinished crosshatching at left of "FREMONT," lines against bottom label and frame unfinished, no etching on flag.

Ridgway numbers used for colors of No. 288-E5.

288-E5 5c Die with black vignette on India,
die sunk on card
49m/1 dim dusky blue ("normal" bicolor) 300.
49k/1 dim dark blue ("normal" bicol-
or) 300.
3k/0 dark orange red 2,000.
3m/0 dusky orange red 2,000.
7m/0 dusky red orange 2,000.
7m/1 dim dusky red orange 2,000.
9m/0 dusky o-red-orange 2,000.
11o/2 dull v. dusky orange 2,000.
37m/1 dim dusky g-blue-green 2,000.
39m/1 dim dusky blue green 2,000.
49o/1 dim v. dusky blue 2,000.
63m/1 dim dusky red violet 2,000.
71n/0 medium deep violet-red-red 2,000.
35m/1 dim dusky green 2,000.

Die size: 82x68 ½mm
Incomplete engraving of entire design: cornhusks, panels at ends of cartouche, mountains, foreground at sides of title label, sky, etc., all unfinished, figures and mountains not etched dark.

288-E7 5c Die on India, die sunk on card,
black 3,250.

Incomplete engraving of vignette: no dots on mountain tops next to right border, unfinished crosshatching at left end of title label.

288-E8 5c Die on India, die sunk on card,
black 3,750.

289-E1

Engraved vignette only of mounted Indian, not used for any value.

289-E1 8c Die on India, on card, black 7,500.

Incomplete engraving of vignette only as adopted: blank area for label wider than completed bicolor vignette, knee of kneeling soldier unfinished, etc.

289-E2 8c Die on India, die sunk on card,
black 3,000.

289-E3

Design size: about 33 ½x21 ½mm
Incomplete engraving of frame only: shading of sunken center of cartouche at right of vignette unfinished.

289-E3 8c Die on India, 26x37mm, black 3,000.

289-E4

Incomplete engraving of entire design: top row of distant shrubbery under "ERICA" missing, crosshatching on distant mountains at left, blades of grass at left end of label, some dots against top label all unfinished.

Ridgway numbers used for colors of No. 289-E4.

289-E4 8c Die with black vignette on India,
die sunk on card
dark red ("normal" bicolor) 375.
dusky red ("normal" bicolor) 375.
3m/0 dusky orange red 2,750.
5m/0 dusky o-orange-red 2,750.
7i/0 deep red orange 2,750.
7m/0 dusky red orange 2,750.
9m/0 dusky o-red-orange 2,750.
11o/2 dull v. dusky orange 2,750.
35m/1 dim dusky green 2,750.
39m/1 dim dusky blue-green 2,750.
49o/1 dim v. dusky blue 2,750.
63m/1 dim dusky red violet 2,750.
71-/0 deep violet-red-red 2,750.

290-E1

Die size: 77x64mm
Incomplete engraving of vignette only: two rows of dots in sky over wagon.

290-E1 10c Die on India, die sunk on card,
black 8,500.

290-E2

Vignette further engraved: three rows of dots in sky over wagon.

290-E2 10c Die on India, die sunk on card,
black 3,750.

Vignette further engraved: front of wagon canvas crosshatched.

290-E3 10c Die on India, die sunk on card,
black   3,750.

290-E4

Incomplete bicolor engraving of entire design: cornhusks unfinished, blades of grass to right of girl's feet and some to right of dark horse's feet are missing. Five lines of dots in sky over wagon.

Ridgway numbers used for colors of No. 290-E4.

290-E4 10c Die with black vignette on India,
die sunk on card
dull dusky violet blue ("normal" bicolor)   350.
dusky blue violet ("normal" bicolor)   350.
1i/0 deep red   2,500.
3k/0 dark orange red   2,500.
5k/0 dark o-orange-red   2,500.
5m/0 dusky o-orange-red   2,500.
7i/0 deep red orange   2,500.
9m/0 dusky o-red-orange   2,500.
11o/2 dull v. dusky orange   2,500.
35m/1 dim dusky green   2,500.
39m/1 dim dusky blue green   2,500.
49o/1 dim v. dusky blue   2,500.
55m/2 smoky dark v.-blue violet   2,500.
63m/1 dim dusky red violet   2,500.
71-/0 deep violet-red-red   2,500.

Incomplete engraving of entire design: cornhusks unfinished, vignette from No. 290-E4 trimmed by engraving to fit frame.

290-E6 10c Die on India, die sunk on card,
dark red orange   3,000.

Incomplete engraving of entire design: cornhusks and panels at ends of cartouche and both sides and bottom of vignette next to border unfinished.

290-E7 10c Die on India, die sunk on card, dull
red violet   3,000.

Incomplete engraving of entire design: cornhusks and both sides and bottom of vignette next to border are unfinished, vert. lines on cartouche frame at right of vignette missing.

290-E8 10c Die on India, die sunk on card, dull red violet   3,000.

291-E1

Die size: 62x52mm
Incomplete engraving of vignette only: without sky or mountains.

291-E1 50c Die on India, die sunk on card,
black   3,750.

Vignette further engraved: sky ruled in.

291-E2 50c Die on India, die sunk on card,
black   3,750.

291-E3

Vignette further engraved but no shading on distant mountains.

291-E3 50c Die on India, die sunk on card,
black   3,750.

Vignette further engraved: light shading on distant mountains.

291-E4 50c Die on India, die sunk on card,
black   3,750.

Vignette further engraved: more shading on distant mountains.

291-E5 50c Die on India, die sunk on card,
black   3,750.

291-E6

Vignette further engraved: shadows on miner's hat darker (etched).

291-E6 50c Die on India, die sunk on card,
black   3,750.

291-E7

Vignette further engraved: girth under donkey darkened.

291-E7 50c Die on India, die sunk on card,
black   9,000.

291-E8

Design size: 34x22mm
Die size: 89x71mm
Incomplete bicolor engraving of entire design: shading lines on scroll in LR corner of frame and shrubbery in UL corner of vignette unfinished, sky incomplete.

Ridgway numbers used for colors of No. 291-E8.

291-E8 50c Die with black vignette on India,
die sunk on card
**dull dusky b-blue-green ("normal"
bicolor; die size: 63x51mm)**   300.
**dull dusky g-blue-green ("normal"
bicolor; die size: 63x51mm)**   300.
1i/0 deep red   2,500.
3k/0 dark orange red   2,500.
5m/0 dusky o-orange-red   2,500.
7m/0 dusky red orange   2,500.
9i/0 deep o-yellow-orange   2,500.
9m/0 dusky o-red-orange   2,500.
11m/2 dull dusky orange   2,500.
13m/3 dismal dusky o-yellow-orange   2,500.
35m/1 dim dusky green   2,500.
39m/1 dim dusky blue green   2,500.
47n/2 dull v. dusky green-blue blue   2,500.
49o/1 dim v. dusky blue   2,500.
61k/1 dim dark violet-red-violet   2,500.
71m/0 dusky violet-red-red   2,500.

Incomplete engraving of entire design: vignette against top frame unfinished.

291-E9 50c Die on India, die sunk on card
black   3,000.
deep red orange   3,000.

Incomplete engraving of entire design: engraving on bottom of miner's pan dots only, not lines as on issued stamp.

291-E10 50c Die on wove, sage green   3,000.

292-E1

Incomplete engraving of vignette only: initial state of die, lightly engraved.

292-E1 $1 Die on India, die sunk on card,
black   4,500.

292-E2

Vignette further engraved: light shield-shaped vignette outline (later removed.)

292-E2 $1 Die on India, die sunk on card,
black   4,500.

Vignette further engraved: left front hoof of lead bull darker.

292-E3 $1 Die on India, die sunk on card,
black   3,750.

Vignette similar to No. 292-E3 but with penciled modeling in snow and among cattle.

292-E4 $1 Die on India, die sunk on card,
black   3,750.

292-E5

Vignette further engraved: foreground snow at left darkened, shield outline removed.

292-E5 $1 Die on India, die sunk on card,
black   10,000.

292-E6

Incomplete engraving of entire bicolored design: right cornhusk and sky against top of frame unfinished, bull's right forefoot does not touch frame, foreground at right end of label unfinished.

Ridgway numbers used for colors of No. 292-E6, where available.

292-E6 $1 Die with black vignette on India,
die sunk on card
dull violet blue ("normal" bicolor)   450.
dull blue ("normal" bicolor)   450.
dull violet ("normal" bicolor)   3,000.
3k/0 dark orange red   3,000.
5m/0 dusky-o-orange-red   3,000.
7m/0 dusky red orange   3,000.
9m/0 dusky o-red-orange   3,000.
9n/3 dismal v. dusky o-red-orange   3,000.
13n/3 dismal v. dusky o-yellow-orange   3,000.
35m/1 dim dusky green   3,000.
43m/1 dim dusky green blue   3,000.
49m/1 dim dusky blue   3,000.
57k/4 smoky dark violet-blue violet   3,000.
63m/1 dim dusky red violet   3,000.
71-/0 violet-red-red   3,000.
47n/2 dull dusky green blue   3,000.
dark brown   3,000.

Incomplete engraving of entire design: left frameline, cornhusks and shading in frame over cornhusks all unfinished.

292-E7 $1 Die on India, die sunk on card,
dusky red orange   3,000.

293-E1

Design size: 34x22mm
Die size: 73x63mm
Vignette of Western mining prospector as used on 50c, but labeled HARVESTING IN THE WEST, frame shows $ same size as numeral 2.

293-E1 $2 Die on India, on card, dusky violet & black   3,500.

293-E2

Die size: 77x66mm

Incomplete engraving of Farming in the West vignette (origi- nally intended for $2 but eventually used on 2c): initial state of die, very lightly engraved.

293-E2 $2 Die on India, die sunk on card,
            black   *3,000.*

Vignette further engraved: four horses shaded.

293-E3 $2 Die on India, die sunk on card,
            black   *3,000.*

Vignette further engraved: shading added to background figures and horses, pencil shading above and below half horse at left.

293-E4 $2 Die on India, die sunk on card,
            black   *3,000.*

Vignette further engraved: foreground and shadows under horse teams darkened, no shading dots above half horse at left, etc.

293-E5 $2 Die on India, die sunk on card,
            black   *3,000.*

293-E6

Vignette further engraved but foreground in front of plow wheel still unfinished.

293-E6 $2 Die on India, die sunk on card,
            black   *3,000.*

293-E7

Die size: 62x51mm

Incomplete engraving of entire bicolor design: only one plow- share shown, label longer, less foreground than on issued stamp.

Ridgway numbers used for colors of No. 293-E7.

293-E7 $2 Die with black vignette on India,
            die sunk on card
            dusky orange red ("normal" bicolor;
            die size: 63x61mm)   *450.*
            dark red orange ("normal" bicolor;
            die size: 63x61mm)   *450.*
            1-/0 red   *3,000.*
            3k/0 dark orange red   *3,000.*
            7m/0 dusky red orange   *3,000.*
            35m/1 dim dusky green   *3,000.*
            39m/1 dim dusky blue green   *3,000.*
            45o/1 dim v. dusky blue-green blue   *3,000.*
            45m/2 dull dusky blue-green blue   *3,000.*
            63m/1 dim dusky red violet   *3,000.*
            71i/0 deep violet-red-red   *3,000.*
            47n/2 dull dusky green blue   *3,000.*

Incomplete engraving of entire design as adopted: black wash over engraving on side of bridge and foreground (engrav- ing under wash unfinished).

293-E9 $2 Die on India, die sunk on card,
            black   *3,500.*

Complete design, vignette further engraved: engraving com- pleted between title label and steamboat and city next to right frame, near side of bridge and smoke shadow on water lighter than on issued stamp.

293-E10 $2 Die on India, die sunk on card,
            black   *3,500.*

Incomplete engraving of entire design: circles in upper cor- ners of vignette next to value ovals, water next to right end of value label, panels at ends of cartouche all unfinished.

293-E11 $2 Die on India, die sunk on card,
            black   *3,500.*

Edward Rosewater

Rosewater, of St. Louis, was asked by the Post Office Dept. in 1897 to submit proposed designs for the Trans-Mississippi Exposition issue. For that reason, they are listed here.

All are drawings on tracing paper, on 91x142mm buff card.

285-E11

Design size: 62x97mm
Wash drawing of cattle.

285-E11   1c dull orange   *12,500.*

286-E11

Design size: 57x98mm
Wash drawing of mounted Indian saluting wagon train.

286-E11   2c deep orange red   *12,500.*

288-E9

Design size: 61x100mm
Wash drawing of man plowing field.

288-E9   5c dark yellow   *12,500.*

290-E9

Design size: 62x99mm
Wash drawing of train coming around mountain.

290-E9   Ten Cents, dusky blue   *12,500.*

292-E9

Design size: 60x98mm
Wash drawing of woman holding light, standing on globe.
292-E9 $1 deep orange yellow   *12,500.*

PAN-AMERICAN ISSUE
Bureau of Engraving and Printing

294-E1

Design size: 108x82mm
Preliminary pencil drawing for frame design as adopted.
294-E1 1c Drawing on tracing paper, black   *1,500.*

294-E2

Design size: 114x82 ½mm
Final ink drawing for frame design as adopted.
294-E2 1c Drawing on white card, about
    6 ½x5 inches, black   *1,500.*

294-E3

Die size: 87x68 ½mm
Incomplete engraving of vignette only.
294-E3 1c Die on India, die sunk on card,
    black   *1,500.*

295-E1

Design size: 108x82mm
Preliminary pencil drawing of frame similar to that adopted
(side ornaments, etc., different); UR corner, etc., unfinished.
295-E1 2c Drawing on tracing paper, black   *1,500.*

295-E2

Design size: 114x83mm
Preliminary pencil drawing of frame similar to No. 295-E1
(minor differences) but with UR corner complete.
295-E2 2c Drawing on tracing paper, black   *1,500.*

295-E3

Design size: 108x82mm
Preliminary pencil drawing of frame design similar to No. 295-
E2 but with minor differences at top, in lettering, etc.
295-E3 2c Drawing on tracing paper, black   *1,500.*

295-E4

Design size: 95x70mm
Ink and wash drawing model of frame design as adopted,
side torchbearers engraved on India as on U.S. Series of 1901
$10 note.
295-E4 2c Die on white card, about
    108x82mm, black   *1,500.*

295-E4A

Design size: 88x69mm
Incomplete engraving of vignette only.
295-E4A 2c Die on India, die sunk on card,
    black   *3,500.*

295-E5   295-E6

Design size: 27x19 ½mm
Die size: 88x68mm
Complete engraving of frame only as adopted.
295-E5 2c Die on India, die sunk on card,
    carmine   *3,750.*

Die size: 88 ½x69mm
Engraving of entire design with vignette incomplete near
frame and on cars.
295-E6 2c Die on India, die sunk on card,
    carmine & black   *4,750.*

296-E1

Preliminary pencil drawing of unadopted frame design.
296-E1 4c Drawing on tracing paper, black   *1,500.*

296-E2

Design size: 114x82 ½mm
Final ink drawing for frame design as adopted.
296-E2 4c Drawing on white card, about
    6 ½x5 inches, black   *1,500.*

296-E3

Design size: 27x19mm
Die size: 88x67mm
Incomplete engraving of entire design as adopted: lines missing at base of capitol dome, above driver's head.
296-E3 4c Die on India, die sunk on card,
    deep red brown & black   *1,750.*

297-E1

Photo reproduction of pencil sketch of unadopted frame design on photosensitive tan paper, reduced to stamp size. Incomplete preliminary pencil drawing of frame design as adopted.

297-E1   5c Photo reproduction on tan paper   *1,500.*

297-E2

Design size: 114x83mm
Incomplete preliminary pencil drawing of frame design as adopted.

297-E2   5c Drawing on tracing paper, black   *1,500.*

297-E3

Design size: 114x82½mm
Final ink drawing for frame design as adopted.

297-E3   5c Drawing on white card, about 6½x5 inches, black   *1,500.*

297-E4

Photo reproduction of sketch of adopted frame design on photosensitive paper, reduced to stamp size.

297-E4   5c Photo reproduction on tan paper   *750.*

297-E5   297-E6

Die size: 87x68mm
Incomplete engraving of vignette only.

297-E5   5c Die on India, die sunk on card, black   *1,500.*

Die size: 87x68mm
As No. 297-E5, but more completely engraved.

297-E6   5c Die on India, die sunk on card, black   *1,500.*

297-E7

Design size: 27x19½mm
Die size: 87x68mm
Incomplete engraving of entire design as adopted: shading at bottom of battleaxes and scrolls at ends of title frame unfinished.

297-E7   5c Die on India, die sunk on card, blue & black   *1,750.*

298-E1

Design size:108x82mm
Preliminary pencil drawing of unadopted frame design.

298-E1   8c Drawing on tracing paper, black   *1,500.*

298-E2

Design size: 114x83mm
Incomplete preliminary pencil drawing of unadopted frame design.

298-E2   8c Drawing on tracing paper, black   *1,500.*

298-E3

Design size: 114x83mm
Preliminary pencil drawing of unadopted frame design.

298-E3   8c Drawing on tracing paper, black   *1,500.*

298-E4

Design size: 114x83mm
Preliminary pencil drawing of frame design as adopted.

298-E4   8c Drawing on tracing paper, black   *1,500.*

298-E5

Design size: 114x82½mm
Final ink drawing for frame design as adopted. No. 298-E5 has an example of No. 298 mounted in the vignette area.

298-E5   8c Drawing on white card, about 6½x5 inches, black   *1,500.*

   298-E6

Photo reproduction of sketch of adopted frame design on photosensitive paper, reduced to stamp size.

298-E6   8c Photo reproduction on tan paper   *1,500.*

298-E7

Design size: 27x20mm
Die size: 87x69mm
Incomplete engraving of entire design: shading lines of ornaments, scrolls and ribbons at top unfinished, vignette incomplete at right, no etching on building in left foreground.

298-E7   8c Die on India, die sunk on card, bi-colored   *1,750.*

299-E1

Design size: 114x83mm
Preliminary pencil drawing of unadopted frame design (small blank oval at center).

299-E1 10c Drawing on tracing paper, black   *1,500.*

299-E2

Design size: 114x82 ½mm
Similar to No. 299-E1 but with outline of eagle and shield in center oval.

299-E2 10c Drawing on tracing paper, black   *1,500.*

299-E3

Design size: 114x83mm
Preliminary pencil drawing for frame design as adopted.

299-E3 10c Drawing on tracing paper, black   *1,500.*

299-E4

Design size: 114x82 ½mm
Final ink drawing for frame design as adopted.

299-E4 10c Drawing on white card, about 6 ½x9 inches, black   *1,500.*

299-E5

Photo reproduction of sketch of adopted frame design on photosensitive paper, reduced to stamp size.

299-E5 10c Photo reproduction on tan paper   *750.*

299-E6

Die size: 87x68mm
Incomplete engraving of entire design: frame complete but lines later engraved in the mast, smokestack and sky.

299-E6 10c Die on India, die sunk on card, bi-colored   *1,750.*

1902 ISSUE

300-E1   300-E2

Incomplete engraving of vignette and lower part of frame.

300-E1 1c Die on India, die sunk on card, black   *4,000.*

Design size: 19x22mm
Die size: 74 ½x88 ½mm
Incomplete engraving of entire design: vignette background has horiz. lines only, neckpiece, men at sides, etc., all unfinished.

300-E2 1c Die on India, die sunk on card, black   *3,500.*

300-E3

Design size: 136x190mm

Preliminary ink drawing for 5c frame design but later adopted for 1c.

300-E3 1c Drawing on manila paper, black & blue green   *2,000.*

No. 300-E3 is on the opposite side of the same piece of paper bearing No. 307-E1. Value is for both essays.

300-E4

Design size: 116x135mm
Preliminary pencil and ink drawing for frame design as adopted.

300-E4 1c Drawing on white card, black   *3,000.*

301-E1

Design size: 164x181mm
Paper size: 169x214mm
Preliminary pencil drawing of frame design (Raymond Ostrander Smith). Not adopted.

301-E1 2c Drawing on yellowed transparent tracing paper, black   *1,500.*

301-E1A

Preliminary pencil and ink drawing of unadopted frame design, on 77x82mm yellowish wove paper, folded vertically and with ink tracing of frame on reverse.

301-E1A   2c Drawing on woven paper, black   2,000.

301-E1B

Design size: 145x168mm
Preliminary pencil drawing of frame design as adopted.

301-E1B   2c Drawing on tracing paper, black   3,500.

301-E2

301-E3

Model with vignette of Houdon bust of Washington, on wash drawing over photo reduced to stamp size for approval by PMG.

301-E2   2c Model mounted on card, black   750.

Design size: 19x22mm
Die size: 75x87½mm
Incomplete engraving of entire design: head unfinished, horiz. background lines only, frame unfinished, lettering either blank or unfinished.

301-E3   2c Die on India, die sunk on card, black   4,000.

301-E4

Design size: 60x88mm
Preliminary pencil drawing of right numeral 2 design as adopted.

301-E4   2c Drawing on tracing paper, black   500.

301-E5

Design size: 176x120mm
Preliminary pencil drawing of lower left and upper right design.

301-E5   2c Drawing on tracing paper, black   700.

301-E6

Design size: 19x22mm
Die size: 74x89mm
Incomplete engraving of entire design: head unfinished, horiz. background lines only, frame almost finished, lettering complete. No. 62057 on back.

301-E6   2c Die on India, die sunk on
153x202mm card, black   3,000.

302-E1

303-E1

Design size: 19x22mm
Die size: 74½x88mm
Incomplete engraving of entire design: vignette unfinished, horiz. background lines only, atlantes at sides unfinished. No. 66218 on back.

302-E1   3c Die on India, die sunk on card, black   3,250.

Design size: 19x22mm
Die size: 75x88mm
Incomplete engraving of entire design: vignette unfinished on eyes, hair, beard, etc. No. 58920 on back.

303-E1   4c Die on India, die sunk on card, black   3,250.

Design size: 19x22mm
Incomplete engraving of entire design, shading lines in top of frame unfinished. No. 60085 on back.

303-E2   4c Die on India, die sunk on card, black   2,000.

Photograph of unaccepted design, stamp size, with white wash inside vignette and eagles in corners drawn in pen over protions of photo.

303-E3   4c Retouched photo-sensitive paper, black   900.

Photograph of unaccepted design with additional overlay photo of top portion of frame with eagles similar to those on No. 303-E3.

303-E4   4c Photo-sensitive paper mounted on paper, black   1,100.

304-E1

Design size: 19x22mm

Die size: 74x87½mm
Rejected die: figure at right poorly draped, blank triangles below "UNITED STATES," no shading in frame around "POSTAGE/FIVE CENTS" except at extreme ends.

304-E1   5c Die on India, die sunk on card, blue   2,300.

Incomplete engraving of entire design: shading on side figures unfinished.

304-E2   5c Die on India, die sunk on card, blue   1,250.

304-E3

Design size: 107x110mm
Paper size: 141x128mm
Preliminary pencil and ink drawing of unadopted frame design.

304-E3   5c Drawing on onion skin paper, black   —

Incomplete engraving of entire design as adopted.

305-E1   6c Die on India, lake   1,250.

305-E2

Design size: 123x210mm
Preliminary ink drawing for unadopted frame design.

305-E2   6c Drawing on kraft paper, black & blue green   4,500.

Nos. 305-E2, 306-E3 and 308-E2, are all on same piece of kraft paper, with No. 306-E3 on one side and the other two on the other side. Value is for the entire unit of three essays.

306-E1

Design size: 7x3½ inches
Preliminary pencil drawing of left side of frame design as adopted.
306-E1   8c Drawing on tracing paper, black   *2,200.*

306-E2

Die size: 76x89mm
Incomplete engraving of vignette and numerals only: head drapery unfinished, horiz. background lines only.
306-E2   8c Die on India, die sunk on card,
                   black   *5,000.*

306-E3

Design size: 165x175mm
Preliminary ink drawing for unadopted frame design.
306-E3   8c Drawing on kraft paper, black,
                   blue & green   *4,500.*
          See note after No. 305-E2.

307-E1

Design size: 135x174mm
Preliminary ink drawing for unadopted frame design.
307-E1   10c Drawing on kraft paper, black, blue
                   & green   *2,000.*
          No. 307-E1 is on the opposite side of the same piece of paper bearing No. 300-E3. Value is for both essays.

308-E1

Design size: 19x22mm
Die size: 69x85½mm
Incomplete engraving of entire design: hair, beard, right cheek, eyes and right shoulder all unfinished, horiz. background lines only, name panel blank, ribbon shading unfinished, etc. No. 57796 on back.
308-E1   13c Die on India, die sunk on card,
                   black   *3,750.*

308-E2

Design size: 177x220mm
Preliminary ink drawing of 3c frame design but later adopted for 13c.
308-E2   13c Drawing on kraft paper, black &
                   blue green   *4,500.*
          See note after No. 305-E2.

310-E1

Design size: 19x22mm
Die size: 74x87½mm
Incomplete engraving of entire design: hair and right cheek unfinished, horiz. background lines only, top of frame and eagles unfinished.
310-E1   50c Die on India, die sunk on card,
                   black   *4,000.*

310-E2

Incomplete engraving of entire design, further engraved than No. 310-E1: oval line outside top label thinner at bottom ends than on issued stamp.
310-E2   50c Die on India, die sunk on card,
                   black   *4,000.*

312-E1   313-E1

Design size: 19x22mm
Die size: 76x88mm
Incomplete engraving of entire design: hair, neckpiece, etc., unfinished, horiz. background lines only; top of frame, leaves and numeral surrounds all unfinished.
312-E1 $2 Die on India, die sunk on card,
                   black   *4,500.*

Design size: 19x22mm
Die size: 75½x87½mm
Incomplete engraving of entire design: eyes, cheeks, hair, neckpiece all unfinished, horiz. background lines only, frame engraved in outlines only.
313-E1 $5 Die on India, die sunk on card,
                   dark green   *8,000.*

319-E1

Design size: 19½x22mm
Die size: 75x87½mm
Incomplete engraving of entire design from rejected die (central star between UNITED and STATES, four lines above small lettering, bottom of shield curved): name and date ribbon blank.
319-E1   2c Die on India, die sunk on card,
                   carmine   *5,250.*

319-E2   319-E3

Incomplete engraving of entire design from rejected die: shading on leaves and vignette completed, lettering added to bottom ribbon and started on label above vignette. Blue pencil note on card backing, "May 1903. This die was abandoned at this stage because of crowded condition of lettering above portrait. G.F.C.S." No. 83909 on back.

319-E2 2c Die on India, die sunk on card, carmine   5,250.

Design size: 19½x22mm
Die I size: 75½x88mm
Incomplete engraving of entire design as adopted (no star between UNITED and STATES, bottom of shield straight): small label above vignette is blank.

319-E3 2c Die on India, die sunk on card, black   5,250.

LOUISIANA PURCHASE ISSUE

324-E1

Incomplete engraving of entire design: head, hair, eyes, chin, coat all unfinished, horiz. background lines only, bottom label and upper corner labels blank, frame shading unfinished.

324-E1 2c Die on India, die sunk on card, black   2,500.

325-E1

Incomplete engraving of entire design: head only lightly engraved, horiz. background lines only, laurel leaves unshaded, leaves' background and numeral shields blank.

325-E1 3c Die on India, die sunk on card, black   2,500.

326-E1

Incomplete engraving of entire design: vignette unfinished, horiz. background lines only, much of frame blank or incomplete.

326-E1 5c Die on India, die sunk on card, black blue   2,500.

JAMESTOWN ISSUE

328-E1

Incomplete engraving of entire design: vignette, shading on heads in upper corners, numerals and numeral shields all unfinished.

328-E1 1c Die on pale cream soft wove, 30x24mm, dusky green   1,250.

Incomplete engraving of entire design: vignette, shading on heads in upper corners, and value tablets unfinished, pencil note "unfinished" at bottom of card.

328-E2 1c Die on India, die sunk on card, 109x94mm, green   2,500.

330-E1

330-E2

Incomplete engraving of vignette only: collar, hat, corselet, etc., unfinished. No. 245910 on back.

330-E1 5c Die on India, die sunk on card, 123x132mm, black   2,250.

Incomplete engraving of entire design: no shading in frame background.

330-E2 5c Die on India, die sunk on card, 109x95mm, blue   6,000.

330-E3

Incomplete engraving of entire design: shading on corselet and arm of Pocahontas unfinished, horiz. background lines only, shading around date and name ribbon unfinished. No. 247606 on back.

330-E3 5c Die on card, 123x175mm, die sunk, blue   4,250.

Incomplete engraving of entire design: shading on ribbons unfinished.

330-E4 5c Die on India, die sunk on card, 108x98mm, black   5,000.

1908 ISSUE

331-E1

Photograph of wash drawing of entire design, head and vignette background retouched with black wash. Ms. "GVLM-Sept. 26th-1908" (PMG) in LR corner of backing card.

331-E1 1c Retouched photo on thick gray cardboard, 83x100mm, black   5,000.

332-E1

332-E2

Design size: 6⅛x7¼ inches
Wash drawing of frame design with vignette cut out, mounted over retouched glossy black photo of Houdon bust of Washington.

332-E1 Two Cents, Design on drawing paper, black   1,250.

Design size: 19x22mm
Photograph of wash drawing of entire design, almost completely retouched with black ink and wash. Pencil "GVLM" (PMG) at top of backing card.

332-E2 Two Cents, Retouched photo on thick gray cardboard, 81x100mm, black   2,000.

332-E3

Design size: 19x22mm
Incomplete engraving of entire design: shading on leaves at right unfinished. Pencil "Oct 15 - 1908" at LR of backing card.

332-E3 Two Cents, Die on India, die sunk on card, carmine   1,250.

333-E1

333-E2

Design size: 18½x22mm
Engraving of design as adopted except "THREE CENTS" at bottom.

333-E1 Three Cents, Die printed directly on card, deep violet   1,250.

Design size: 19x22mm
Photograph of wash drawing of entire design with "3 CENTS 3" drawn in black and white wash. Ms. "Nov. 24/08. J.E.R." (BEP director) in LR corner of backing card.

333-E2 3c Retouched photo on thick gray cardboard, 80x100mm, black   2,000.

334-E1

334-E2

Design size: 18½x22mm
Engraving of design as adopted except "FOUR CENTS" at bottom.

334-E1 Four Cents, Die printed directly on card, orange brown   1,250.

Design size: 19x22mm
Photograph of wash drawing of entire design with "4 CENTS 4" drawn in black and white wash. Ms. "Nov. 24/08. J.E.R." (BEP director) in LR corner of backing card.

334-E2 4c Retouched photo on thick gray cardboard, 80x100mm, black   2,000.

335-E1

335-E2

Design size: 18½x22mm
Engraving of design as adopted except "FIVE CENTS" at bottom.

335-E1 Five Cents, Die printed directly on card, blue   1,500.

Design size: 19x22mm
Photograph of wash drawing of entire design with "5 CENTS 5" drawn in black and white wash. Ms. "Nov. 24/08. J.E.R." (BEP director) in LR corner of backing card.

335-E2 5c Retouched photo on thick gray cardboard, 80x100mm, black   2,000.

Design size: 18½x22mm
Incomplete engraving of design with "SIX CENTS" at bottom.

336-E1 Six Cents, Die on India, on card, red orange   1,250.

336-E2

Design size: 19x22mm
Photograph of wash drawing of entire design with "6 CENTS 6" drawn in black and white wash. Ms. "Nov. 24/08. J.E.R." (BEP director) in LR corner of backing card.

336-E2   6c   Retouched photo on thick gray cardboard, 80x100mm, black   *2,000.*

337-E1   338-E1

Design size: 19x22mm
Photograph of wash drawing of entire design with "8 CENTS 8" drawn in black and white wash. Ms. "Nov. 24/08. J.E.R." (BEP director) in LR corner of backing card.

337-E1   8c   Retouched photo on thick gray cardboard, 80x100mm, black   *2,000.*

Design size: 19x22mm
Photograph of wash drawing of entire design with "10 CENTS 10" drawn in black and white wash. Ms. "Nov. 24/08. J.E.R." (BEP director) in LR corner of backing card.

338-E1   10c   Retouched photo on thick gray cardboard, 80x100mm, black   *2,000.*

338a-E1

Design size: 18½x22mm
Complete engraving of entire adopted design but a value not issued: "12 CENTS 12" at bottom. Virtually all are stamp size, imperf.

Ridgway numbers used for colors of No. 338a-E1.

338a-E1   12c
   a. Die on bluish white wove
     41n/1 dim v. dusky b-blue-green   *900.*
   b. Die on 1f/1 dim pale red wove
   c. Die on 7d/1 dim light red orange wove
     47m/1 dim dusky g-b. blue   *900.*
   d. Die on 17b/1 dim bright o-y. yellow wove
     1i/0 deep red   *900.*
     5i/0 deep o-orange-red   *900.*
     27m/0 dusky green yellow   *900.*
     37m/0 dusky g-blue-green   *900.*
     41m/0 dusky b-blue-green   *900.*
     55m/1 dim dusky blue violet   *900.*
     59m/1 dim dusky violet   *900.*
     69m/3 dismal dusky r-violet-red   *900.*
   e. Die on 19f/0 pale y-orange yellow wove
     1i/0 deep red   *900.*
     15i/1 dim deep yellow orange   *900.*
     35m/0 dusky green   *900.*
     43d/1 dim light green blue   *900.*
     61m/3 dismal dusky v-red-violet   *900.*
     690/5 black   *900.*
   f. Die on 31f/2 dull pale yellow green wove
     69o/5 black   *900.*
   g. Die on 42d/1 dim bright green blue wove
     41m/1 dim dusky b-blue-green   *900.*
   h. Die on 44-/1 dim medium green blue wove
     9k/2 dull dark o-r-orange   *900.*
   i. Die on 45l/1 dim v. dark b-green-blue wove
     5i/0 deep o-orange-red   *900.*
     27m/2 dull dusky green yellow   *900.*
   j. Die on 69g/0 pale r-v. red wove   *900.*
   k. Die on dark blue bond, 69o/5 black   *900.*

339-E1   340-E1

Design size: 19x22mm
Photograph of wash drawing of entire design with "13 CENTS 13" drawn in black and white wash. Ms. "Oct. 7-08. J.E.R.-GVLM" (BEP director, PMG) in LL corner of backing card.

339-E1   13c   Retouched photo on thick gray cardboard, 80x100mm, black   *2,000.*

Design size: 19x22mm
Photograph of wash drawing of entire design with "15 CENTS 15" drawn in black and white wash. Ms. "Oct. 7-08. J.E.R.-GVLM" (BEP director, PMG) at bottom of backing card.

340-E1   15c   Retouched photo on thick gray cardboard, 80x100mm, black   *2,000.*

341-E1   342-E1

Design size: 19x22mm
Photograph of wash drawing of entire design with "50 CENTS 50" drawn in black and white wash. Ms. "Oct. 7-08. J.E.R.-GVLM" (BEP director, PMG) at bottom of backing card.

341-E1   50c   Retouched photo on thick gray cardboard, 80x100mm, black   *2,000.*

Design size: 19x22mm
Photograph of wash drawing of entire design with "1 DOLLAR 1" drawn in black and white wash. Ms. "Oct. 7-08. J.E.R.-GVLM" (BEP director, PMG) at bottom of backing card.

342-E1 $1   Retouched photo on thick gray cardboard, 80x100mm, black   *2,000.*

LINCOLN MEMORIAL ISSUE

Design size: 7x8 inches
Photostat of 1980 2c frame design with wash drawing of ribbons and vignette photo of Lincoln's head.

367-E1   Two Cents, Model of Lincoln design, black   *1,500.*

Photo of No. 367-E1 reduced to stamp size, retouched to highlight hair and beard.

367-E2   Two Cents, Retouched photo, black   *1,500.*

367-E3

Design size: 19x22mm
Incomplete engraving of entire design: head, background, name/date ribbon all unfinished.

367-E3   Two Cents, Die on India, die sunk on card, 148x201mm, carmine   *3,500.*

ALASKA-YUKON-PACIFIC EXPOSITION ISSUE

Design size: 18½x22mm
Wash drawing of frame similar to 1908 2c design with photo of wash drawing of seal on ice cake as vignette. Ms. "#1" at UL corner of backing card.

370-E1   2c   Model on card, about 3x4 inches, black   *1,500.*

370-E2

Design size: 18½x22mm
Engraved frame similar to 1908 2c but with wash drawing of "1870 1909" in ribbons and "2 CENTS 2" at bottom, vignette cut out, mounted over engraved vignette of Wm. H. Seward from snuff stamp. Ms. "#2" at UL corner of backing card.

370-E2   2c   Model on card, about 3x4 inches, black   *1,500.*

370-E3

Design size: 27½x20½mm
Photo of seal on ice cake vignette as originally approved, mounted on ink and wash drawing of frame design as approved. Ms. "#3" at UL corner of backing card, engraved Seward vignette pasted on at bottom, "Approved April 3, 1909 FH Hitchcock Postmaster-General" at right.

370-E3   2c   Model on glazed card, 93x70mm, black, white and gray   *2,250.*

370-E4

Design size: 27½x20mm
Photo of wash drawing of frame and arched ribbon as adopted, vignette cut out, mounted over photo of engraved Seward vignette, background retouched with black wash. Ms. "Approved subject to addition of the name Seward, as indicated in letter of Director, Bureau of Engraving and Printing, dated April 24, 1909. F.H. Hitchcock Postmaster General."

370-E4   2c   Model on 93x75mm thick gray card, black   *2,250.*

370-E5

Design size: 27x20mm
Retouched photo of wash drawing of adopted frame with seal on ice cake vignette but pencil "WILLIAM H. SEWARD" on white wash ribbon below. Ms. "April 26/09 Approved J.E.R." (BEP director) at LR corner of backing card.

370-E5   2c   Retouched photo and pencil on 94x66mm thick gray card, black   *2,000.*

Incomplete engraving of entire design: no shading on head or vignette background, no shading lines on ribbons.

370-E6   2c   Die on India, die sunk on 8x6 inch card, carmine   *2,000.*

370-E7

Design size: 26½x19½mm
Similar to No. 370-E6 but further engraved: face and collar lightly engraved, horiz. background lines only, no shading lines on ribbons.

370-E7   2c   Die on wove, 32x26½mm, carmine   *2,000.*

372-E1

Wash drawing of adopted vignette design.

372-E1 2c Drawing on artist's cardboard, 11¼x6¾ inches, black *2,000.*

372-E2

Wash drawing of frame design as adopted except "HUDSON-FULTON CENTENARY" at top.

372-E2 2c Drawing on artist's cardboard, 7¾x6¾ inches, black *2,000.*

Design size: 33x21½mm
Wash drawing of frame design as adopted with dates "1609-1807" and photo of No. 372-E1 reduced to fit and worked over with wash.

372-E3 2c Model on card, 4x3 inches, black *2,000.*

Design size: 33x21½mm
Wash drawing of frame with vignette cut out, mounted over photo of No. 372-E1. Typed/ms. "Approved August 17, 1909 F.H. Hitchcock Postmaster General" and "August 19, 1909 Amend by substituting word 'Celebration' for 'Centenary.' F.H. Hitchcock Postmaster General." Pencil "P.O. 488" in LR corner.

372-E4 2c Model on white card, 129x103mm, black *2,000.*

372-E5

Incomplete engraving of entire design: lettering on flag at masthead of *Clermont* has "N" reversed and no "T."

372-E5 2c Die on wove, 38x27mm, carmine *2,000.*

PANAMA-PACIFIC ISSUE

397-E1

Design size: 27x20mm
Photo of incomplete frame with overlay of circular photo vignette as adopted, with wash drawing of palm trees on each side and "1 CENT 1" in wash. Ms. "Approved July 16, 1912 Frank H. Hitchcock Postmaster General" on backing card.

397-E1 1c Model on card, about 89x77mm, black *1,500.*

Design size: 27x20mm
Photo of incomplete frame with overlay circular photo vignette as adopted, with wash drawing of palm trees on each side and "1 CENT 1" in wash, with "Approved" and signed by the BEP Director J.E. Ralph, but "Opening of Panama Canal 1913" later changed for stamp to "San Francisco 1913."

397-E2 1c Model on thick gray card, 106x86mm, black *1,500.*

398-E1

Design size: about 29½x20mm
Ink and wash drawing of frame design longer than adopted with photo of wash drawing of Golden Gate as eventually used (reduced) on 5c. Backstamp "STAMP DIVISION FEB. 12, 1912 P.O. DEPT" on backing card.

398-E1 2c Model on card, about 4x3 inches, black *1,500.*

398-E2

Design size: 27x20mm
Photo of incomplete frame with photo of wash drawing of vignette as adopted with title "GATUN LOCKS," wash drawing of value numerals. Ms. "Approved Aug. 27, 1912 Frank H. Hitchcock Postmaster General" on backing card.

398-E2 2c Model on thick gray card, 99x72mm, black *1,500.*

Very similar to No. 398-E2 with slightly different wash touch-up and "2"s, with "Approved" and signed by BEP Director J.E. Ralph.

398-E2A 2c Model on thick gray card, 107x86mm, black *1,500.*

398-E3

Completely engraved design as adopted except titled "GATUN LOCKS" in error (design pictures Pedro Miguel locks).

398-E3 2c
 a. Large die on India, die sunk on card, 202x152mm, carmine *10,000.*
 b. Small die on India (formerly #398AP2), carmine *6,000.*

398-E4

Design size: 27x20mm
Photo of incomplete engraving (no sky in vignette) with "GATUN LOCKS" in error, ms. "Approved Dec. 17, 1912 Frank Hitchcock Postmaster General" on backing card.

398-E4 2c Model on thick gray card, 97x74mm, black *1,500.*

399-E1

Design size: 27x20mm
Photo of wash drawing of frame design as adopted with photo of wash drawing of adopted vignette mounted in place, with additional hand touch-up done in wash on vignette, ms. "Approved July 16, 1912 Frank H., Hitchcock Postmaster General" on backing card.

399-E1 5c Model on 30x22mm white paper, mounted on card, 97x73mm, black *1,500.*

Very similar to No. 399-E1 with slightly different wash touch-up and no steamship below sun, with "Approved" and signed by BEP Director J.E. Ralph.

399-E2 5c Model on thick gray card, 106x86mm, black *1,500.*

400-E1

Design size: 27x20mm
Photo of wash drawing of frame design as adopted with photo of painting adopted for vignette mounted in place, ms. printed "Approved" and dated and signed " Aug. 22, 1912, Frank H. Hitchcock Postmaster General" on backing card.

400-E1 10c Model on 31x34mm white paper, on thick gray card, 98x73mm, black *1,500.*

Very similar to No. 400-E1 with more extensive touching-up of the vignette and frame, with "Approved" and signed by BEP Director J.E. Ralph.

400-E1A 10c Model on thick gray card, 107x86mm, black *1,500.*

Design size: 27x20mm
Photo of wash drawing of frame design as adopted with photo of wash drawing of two galleons at anchor in bay, titled "CABRILLO 1542" mounted in place. Backing card marked "II."

400-E2 10c Model on white paper, on 91x85mm thick gray card, black *1,500.*

400-E3

Design size: 27x20mm
Photo of wash drawing of frame design as adopted with photo of wash drawing of Liberty standing among palm fronds, wash touch-up on vignette and "10" denominations drawn in black and white wash, two battleships in bay. Backing card marked "III."

400-E3 10c Model on white paper, on thick gray card, 90x84mm, black *1,500.*

400-E4

Design size: 27x20mm
Similar to No. 400-E3 but steamships replace battleships. Backing card marked "IV."

400-E4 10c Model on white paper, on thick gray card, 90x83mm, black *1,500.*

400-E5

Design size: 27x20mm
Similar to No. 400-E2 but different hand drawn vignette picturing two galleons under full sail in front of snowclad mountains. Backing card marked "V."

400-E5 10c Model on white paper, on thick gray card, 89x83mm, black *1,500.*

1912 ISSUE

Incomplete engraving of entire design: wash drawing of "1 CENT 1" at bottom. Ms. "Approved. July 17, 1911 Frank H. Hitchcock. P.M. Gen." on backing card.

405-E1 1c Model on 3½x3¾-inch card, black *5,750.*

406-E1

Incomplete engraving of, except value tablet area which is "2 CENTS 2" at bottom drawn in wash. Ms. "Approved. July 17, 1911 Frank H. Hitchcock P. M. Gen" on backing card.

406-E1   2c Model on 3⅜x3¹¹⁄₁₆-inch card,
black   —

Wash drawing of design as adopted, worked over partial photo with 8 in lower corners drawn in wash. Ms. "Approved. July 17, 1911 Frank H. Hitchcock Postmaster General" on backing card.

414-E1   8c Model on 3½x3¾-inch card, black   —

414-E2

Vignette of head only without background gridwork, control #490311 on back of card.

414-E2   8c Die on India, die sunk on
152x202mm, olive green   *2,250.*

416-E1

418-E1

Design size: 19x22mm
Photo of wash drawing of generic design with 10 in lower corners drawn in black ink. Ms. "July 17, 1911. (May, 1911 erased) Approved: Frank H. Hitchcock PM Gen" on backing card, backstamped "STAMP DIVISION P.O. DEPT. MAY 15, 1911."

416-E1   10c Model on 87x113mm thick gray
card, black   *1,000.*

Design size: 19x22mm
Photo of wash drawing of generic design with background of frame between oval and outer colorless line in dark gray wash and some colorless retouching, 15 in lower corners drawn in black ink. Ms. "July 17, 1911. (May, 1911 erased) Approved: Frank H. Hitchcock PM Gen" on backing card, backstamped "STAMP DIVISION P.O. DEPT. MAY 15, 1911."

418-E1   15c Model on 87x113mm thick gray
card, black   *1,000.*

421-E1

423-E1

Design size: 19x22mm
Photo of wash drawing of generic design with 50 in lower corners drawn in black ink. Ms. "July 17, 1911. (May, 1911 erased) Approved: Frank H. Hitchcock PM Gen" on backing card, backstamped "STAMP DIVISION P.O. DEPT. MAY 15, 1911."

421-E1   50c Model on 77x112mm thick gray
card, black   *1,000.*

Design size: 19x22mm
Photo of wash drawing of generic design with entire value label drawn in black ink. Ms. "July 17, 1911. (May, 1911 erased) Approved: Frank H. Hitchcock PM Gen" on backing card, backstamped "STAMP DIVISION P.O. DEPT. MAY 15, 1911."

423-E1 $1 Model on 87x113mm thick gray
card, black   *1,000.*

1916 PRECANCEL ESSAYS

499-E1

Design size: 19x22mm
Die size: 90x88mm
"NEW YORK/N.Y." precancel engraved directly onto type I die, printed in one color. Ms. "8/16/22 J.S." in LR corner of backing card on No. 499-E1a. Although dated 1922, records indicate an original proof was pulled in 1916.

499-E1   2c
  a. Die on India, die sunk on card, lake   —
  b. Die on bond paper, 33x36mm, dark
carmine   —

1918 ISSUE

Complete engraving of Franklin head only as on $2 and $5 values, no shading around head, control #834424 on back of card.

523-E2 $2 Die on India, die sunk on
151x103mm card, black   *1,750.*

523-E3

Design size: 16x18¾mm
Complete engraving of vignette only including shading. Pencil control # "837660 May 1917" on back of India paper, pencil "Schofield" at bottom of backing card (#523-E3a), or control #837662 (1917) on back of card (No. 523-E3b).

523-E3 $2
  a. Die on 32x33mm India, card mounted,
black   *1,000.*
  b. Die on wove, die sunk on card,
203x151mm, black   *1,000.*

PEACE ISSUE

537-E1

537-E2

Design size: 21½x18½mm
Stamp never issued due to World War I.

537-E1   2c
  a. Die on India, die sunk on card, deep
red   *1,500.*
  b. Die on wove, die sunk on card,
201x138mm, signed on card by Harry S. New   *4,000.*

Die size: 22x19mm
Stamp never issued due to World War I.

537-E2   5c
  a. Die on India, die sunk on card, dim
dusky g-b-blue   *1,500.*
  b. Die on wove, die sunk on card,
201x138mm, signed on card by Harry S. New   *4,000.*

SAMUEL F.B. MORSE ISSUE

537-E3

Design size: 21½x18½mm
Incomplete engraving of entire design: vignette and lettering finished but blank spaces beside vignette. Backstamped "932944" and "Jan. 1, 1919" or "932945" and "Jan. 7, 1919". Frame design subsequently used for 3c Victory issue, No. 537, though lettering and value numerals made slightly smaller.

537-E3   3c Die on India, die sunk on card,
141x173mm (#932944) or
151x202mm (#932945), black   *3,000.*

VICTORY ISSUE

537-E4

Design size: 21½x18½mm
Die size: 85½x75½mm
Incomplete engraving of entire design: no shading in border and some flags unfinished. Backstamped "936356 Jan. 25, 1919."

537-E4   3c Die on India, die sunk on card,
black   *1,500.*

PILGRIM ISSUE

548-E1

Design size: 26x19mm
Incomplete engraving of entire design: sky blank, sails unshaded.

548-E1   1c Die on India, die sunk on card,
201x151mm, green   *1,600.*

PILGRIM ISSUE

Almost complete engraving of entire design as adopted, but no crosshatching behind the "1" denominations.

548-E2   1c Die on India, die sunk on card,
203x151mm, green   *1,600.*

549-E1

Incomplete engraving of frame only: "CENTS" engraved but numeral circles blank (probably an essay for the 2c and 5c).

549-E1   Die on India, die sunk on card
black   *1,600.*
green   *1,600.*

549-E2

Design size: 26x19mm
Incomplete engraving of entire design: vignette unfinished, control #1063097 on back of card.

549-E2   2c Die on India, die sunk on card,
202x151mm, black   *1,600.*

Incomplete engraving of entire design, virtually complete but no crosshatching behind the numeral "2" denominations.

549-E3   2c
  a. Die on India, die sunk on card,
202x151mm, control #1063875 on
back, black   *1,600.*
  b. Die on India, die sunk on card,
202x151mm, control #1064174 or
#1064271 on back, carmine rose   *1,600.*

1922 ISSUE

551-E1

Design size: 19x22mm
Incomplete engraving of entire design as adopted: name label blank, vignette unfinished. Ms. "Approved--Harry S. New" on backing card on olive brown essay; others not signed but with notation of denomination of stamp for color used ("1c" for green, etc.)

551-E1	½c Die on India, die sunk on	
	151x202mm card	
	olive brown	3,000.
	green	2,500.
	carmine	2,500.
	orange	2,500.
	rose	2,500.
	yellow	2,500.
	blue green	2,500.
	yellow green	2,500.
	carmine rose	2,500.

Incomplete engraving of entire design but further engraved than No. 551-E1: no lines in white oval over ends of title ribbon and ribbon foldunders not etched as darkly as on issued stamp.

551-E2	½c Die on India, die sunk on	
	149x201mm card, olive brown	1,500.

555-E2

Complete engraving with horizontal lines surrounding bust of Lincoln.

555-E2	3c Die on India, affixed to card,	
	26x30mm, violet	2,750.

560-E1

Complete engraving with background of cross-hatched lines surrounding slightly larger bust of Grant.

560-E1	8c Die on India, die sunk on	
	97x111mm card, dark olive	
	green	2,000.

567-E2   568-E2

Design size: 19x22mm
Engraving of unadopted vignette with unadopted engraved frame cut away.

567-E2	20c Die on India, die sunk on	
	151x201mm card, cobalt blue	1,750.

Design size: 19x15mm
Die size: 88x75mm
Engraving of adopted vignette with engraved frame cut away.

568-E2	25c Die on India, die sunk on	
	202x151mm card, green	1,750.

Pencil drawings for unadopted frame design.

555-E1	3c black	1,150.
557-E1	5c black	1,150.
557-E2	5c black	1,150.
566-E1	15c black	1,150.
571-E1	$1 black	1,150.

573-E1

Engraving of accepted vignette.

573-E1	$5 Die on India, affixed to card,	
	73x87mm, blue	3,750.

HUGUENOT-WALLOON TERCENTENARY ISSUE

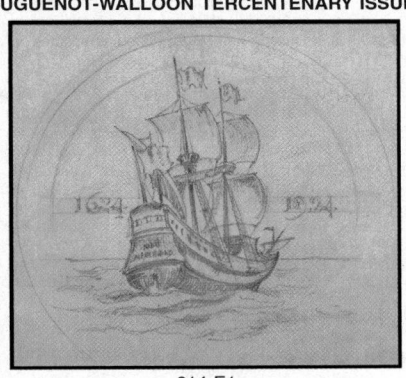

614-E1

Design size: 8½x7¼ inches
Preliminary pencil drawing of *Nieu Nederland* in circular frame. Pencil note: "Reverse--Sailing to America, not away from America--J. B. Stoudt" originally on drawing has been removed.

614-E1	1c black	1,000.

Incomplete engraving of entire design, background of vignette incomplete and central figures only roughed in.

615-E1	2c Die on India, 82x69mm, black	4,500.

616-E1

Design size: 5½x3⅛ inches
Wash drawing of design adopted for vignette.

616-E1	5c black	1,500.

Almost complete engraving of entire design, lacking strong shading in the foreground of the vignette.

617-E1	5c Die on India, die sunk on card,	
	126x115mm, green	1,500.

618-E1

Design size: 36x21mm
Incomplete engraving of entire design as adopted: spaces between letters of "BIRTH OF LIBERTY" not solid color.

618-E1	2c Die on India, die sunk on card,	
	carmine	1,250.

Design size: 36x21mm
Incomplete engraving of entire design as adopted: numeral circles blank, many shading lines missing in vignette, no shading around "TWO CENTS," etc.

618-E2	2c Die on India, die sunk on	
	91x71mm card, black	1,500.

Design size: 36x21mm
Engraving of frame only, without vignette or value tablets, control #1317765 on back of card.

618-E3	2c Die on India, die sunk on card,	
	202x118mm, carmine	1,500.

ERICSSON MEMORIAL ISSUE

Wash drawing of design as adopted, stamp size.

628-E1	5c black	750.

BATTLE OF WHITE PLAINS ISSUE

629-E1

Design size: 8⅜x9 inches
Preliminary ink and watercolor drawing of entire design quite similar to that adopted.

629-E1	2c black & red	750.

BURGOYNE CAMPAIGN ISSUE

644-E1

Design size: 22x19mm
Essay size: 25x22mm
Card size: 78x98mm
Photo of wash drawing of unadopted design, on white paper mounted on thick gray card with "Approved" in ink and "May 7, 1927" in pencil subsequently crossed out with "X's."

644-E1	2c black	1,500.

683-E1

Design size: 13x17 inches
Preliminary ink drawing of design nearly as adopted.

683-E1	2c Drawing on artist's cardboard,	
	black	500.

American flag and pencil touch-up of outer frame on photo of artist's model with vignette as adopted but entirely different frame.

690-E1	2c black	400.

702-E1

Engraving of entire design without red cross, engraved cross shows faintly, control #70015 on back of card.

702-E1 2c Die on India, die sunk on
120x142mm card, black   *5,000.*

704-E1

Design size: 119x150mm
Preliminary pencil sketch of unadopted ½c design.

704-E1 ½c Drawing on tracing paper, mounted on 195x192mm manila pa-
per, black   *1,250.*

718-E1

Design size: 6x7 inches
Watercolor drawing of unadopted design with 2c denomination.

718-E1 2c Drawing on thick artist's card, red   *1,250.*

719-E1

Design size: 6x7 inches
Watercolor drawing of entire design similar to that eventually adopted for 5c but with 2c denomination.

719-E1 2c Drawing on thick artist's card,
150x175mm, blue   *1,250.*

Engraving of vignette as adopted, within frame, but reversed from final design, without denomination or inscriptions.

742-E1 3c Die on white card, 88x69mm,
black   *1,750.*

Unadopted engraving of entire design without denomination, portraits as adopted but rest of design different from accepted design, control #70027 on back of card.

786-E1 2c Die on wove, die sunk on card,
202x153mm, carmine   *1,500.*

Engravings of Decatur and MacDonough as adopted, widely spaced.

791-E1 2c Die on wove, die sunk on card,
202x153mm, carmine   *1,500.*

Engraving of incomplete design without central vignette, control #491747 (1936) on back of card.

791-E2 2c Die on wove, die sunk on card,
198x136mm, carmine   *1,500.*

Unfinished engravings of three portraits only, control #70031 on back.

793-E1 4c Die on wove, die sunk on card,
202x153mm, red brown   *1,500.*

Engraving of entire design, lacks crosshatching in the shading of background.

899-E1 1c Die on wove, die sunk on card,
140x162mm, green   *1,000.*

Engraving of frame as adopted, with "84075" at top and "United States of America" at bottom of die impression, stamped "For Approval" at top of card, signed and dated by four individuals on card.

909-921-E1 5c Die on India, die sunk on
card, 227x151mm, violet   *4,000.*

Unadopted design showing steamship under sail, without denomination or background shading, handstamp "Engraver's Stock Proof/Authorized by," initials, "Brooks" (the engraver) in pencil and control #818347A all on back of stamp.

923-E1 3c Die on wove, die sunk on card,
201x152mm, violet   *1,500.*

Unfinished engraving of adopted design, lacking smoke from the smokestack and background shading. "Modeling" handstamp and control #818995A on back of card.

923-E2 3c Die on wove, die sunk on card,
201x150mm, violet   *1,500.*

Engraved vignette as adopted, "Engraver's Stock Proof/Authorized by," initials, "Brooks" (the engraver) in pencil and control #867263A all on back of stamp.

930-933-E2 Die on wove, die sunk on card,
202x151mm, black   *1,500.*

PANAMA CANAL ISSUE

856-E1

Design size: 37x21 ½mm
Essay size: 99x81mm
Card size: 141x117mm
Engraving of unadopted design: "3 CENTS 3" and "25th ANNIVERSARY PANAMA CANAL" changed for final design. "W. O. Marks" at lower right corner, "Engraver's Stock Proof 594256 / Authorized by 'OML'" on reverse.

856-E1 3c Die on India, die sunk on card,
deep violet   —

922-E1

Incomplete engraving of entire design, sky unshaded, no smoke from engine, additional background shading missing, blue control number and "MODELING" on reverse of card.

922-E1 3c Die on India, die sunk on card,
200x148mm, violet   *1,000.*

As No. 922-E1, with additional background shading added.

922-E2 3c Die on India, die sunk on card,
200x148mm, violet   *1,000.*

As No. 922-E2, with shading of sky added.

922-E3 3c Die on India, die sunk on card,
200x148mm, violet   *1,000.*

As No. 922-E3, with additional background and figure shading added.

922-E4 3c Die on India, die sunk on card,
200x148mm, violet   *1,000.*

1016-E1

Engraving of adopted design, except "c" cut in design at right where cross should be printed (held in place by tape on back); "Engraver's Stock Proof, Authorized by," initials and blue "103120B" control number on back.

1016-E1 3c Die on wove, die sunk on card,
202x152mm, deep blue   *2,500.*

1140-E1

Drawing, similar to issued design but with different symbol at left and different signature of Benjamin Franklin, signed by Frank V. Conley (designer of Credo issue).

1140-E1 4c Drawing on tracing paper,
129x81mm, red, blue and white
ink   *1,000.*

AIR POST STAMPS

1918 ISSUE

Complete engraving of frame only as adopted. Backstamped "626646A ENGRAVER'S STOCK PROOF AUTHORIZED BY" (signature), plus pencil "663" and "Weeks" (?).

C3-E1 24c Die on India, die sunk on card,
deep carmine   *5,000.*

Incomplete engraving of entire design as adopted: unfinished plumes above value numerals and no serial number on biplane.

C3-E2 24c Die on wove, 40x37mm, black
vignette, blue frame   —

Engraving of adopted design except without denomination, "C" punch where denominations go, control #722657A (1942) on back of card.

C25-C31-E1 Die on wove, die sunk on card,
201x150mm, black   *5,500.*

SPECIAL DELIVERY STAMPS

1885 ISSUE
American Bank Note Co.

E1-E1

Incomplete engraving of entire design as adopted: ornaments missing at each side of "SPECIAL," line under messenger is in pencil, shading on left side of messenger tablet missing, leaves and vert. background lines unfinished (latter shaded over with pencil).

E1-E1 10c Die on India, dim dusky g-b. green   *2,500.*

1888 ISSUE

No. E1P1 with "AT ANY OFFICE" drawn in wash on small piece of thin paper and mounted over "AT A SPECIAL / DELIVERY / OFFICE." Pencil "any post office" and ms. "At once O.K. / J.C.M. 14 Aug. 86" (?) on backing card.

E2-E1 10c Die on India, on card, black   *2,500.*

1908 ISSUE
Bureau of Engraving and Printing

E7-E1

Design size: about 8 ½ x 7 ⅛ inches
Preliminary ink and pencil drawing of entire design somewhat
similar to that adopted: ("V.S." for U.S. and other minor
changes).

E7-E1 10c Drawing on vellum, black —

E7-E2

Design size: about 8 ½ x 7 ⅛ inches
Preliminary ink and pencil drawing of entire design nearly as
adopted: ("V.S." for U.S.)

E7-E2 10c Drawing on white drawing paper,
black —

E7-E3

Design size: 213 ½ x 179mm
Similar to No. E7-E2 but with "U.S."

E7-E3 10c Drawing on white drawing paper,
black _750._

E7-E4   E7-E5

Design size: 26x21 ½mm
Woodblock size: 45x42mm
Woodblock of entire design as adopted with about 5mm colorless border outside design, solid color beyond, engraved on
wood by Giraldon of Paris. (One exists with ms. "Wood cut
made in Paris by Mr. Whitney Warren — The cuts and the
impression therefrom were turned over to the Director of the
Bureau of Engraving & Printing, and by him turned over to the
Custodian of Dies, Rolls and Plates and given No. 446. They
are now held by the Custodian." Another has typewritten "Prints
made in Paris, France, from a wood-cut engraving by an
unknown engraver from a design made by Mr. Whitney Warren,

architect, of New York City." with ms. "Compliments J.E. Ralph"
director of B.E.P. and pencil date "9/7/1917.")

Ridgeway numbers used for colors of Nos. E7-E4 and E7-E5.

E7-E4 10c
  a. Woodcut on 19g/2 yellowish wove
    43k/1 dim dark green blue _450._
    44m/2 dull dusky m. g-blue _450._
    45j/1 dim v. dark b-g-blue _450._
    45m/1 dim dusky b-g-blue _450._
  b. Woodcut on 19f/2 dull faint y-o-yellow
    wove
    43k/1 dim dark g-blue _450._
    43m/1 dim dusky g-blue _450._
    44k/1 dim dark m. g-blue _450._
    44k/2 dull dark m. g-blue _450._
    45m/1 dim dusky b-g-blue _450._
    45m/2 dull dusky b-g-blue _450._
  c. Woodcut on 19g/2 dull v. faint y-o-yellow
    wove
    43k/1 dim dark g-blue _450._
    43m/1 dim dusky g-blue _450._

Design size: 26x21 ½mm
Complete engraving of entire design fairly similar to that
adopted but with minor differences.

E7-E5 10c
  a. Die on India, die sunk on card, 37m/0
    dusky g-b. green blue _750._
  b. Die on soft white wove, 30x35mm, 37m/0
    dusky g-blue-green _750._

REGISTRATION STAMP

F1-E1

Design size: 19x22 ½mm
Retouched circular photo of vignette mounted on wash draw-
ing of frame design as adopted. Ms. "Approved July 8/11 —
Frank H. Hitchcock — Postmaster General" on backing card.

F1-E1 10c Model on white paper, mounted on
thick gray cardboard, 81x92mm,
black _1,250._

POSTAGE DUE STAMPS

1879 ISSUE
American Bank Note Co.

J1-E1

Design size: 19 ½ x25 ½mm
Die size: 54x66 ½mm
Complete engraving of entire design as adopted except
"UNPAID POSTAGE" instead of "POSTAGE DUE" above
vignette oval.

J1-E1 1c
  a. Die on India, die sunk on card
    orange brown _850._
    slate gray _850._
    dark red violet _850._
    dull yellow _850._
    light orange _850._
    red brown _850._
  b. Die on India, cut small (1-4mm)
    gray black _400._
    dull red _400._
    dull brown _400._
    dull green _400._
    dull blue _400._
  c. Die on India, cut close (0-1mm)
    orange brown _400._
    slate gray _400._
    dark red violet _400._
    dull yellow _400._
  d. Die on ivory glazed paper, die sunk
    black _700._
    black brown _700._
    scarlet _700._
    blue _700._

Design size: 19 ½ x25 ½mm

Die size: 53 ½ x53 ½mm
Complete engraving of entire design as adopted except
"UNPAID POSTAGE" instead of "POSTAGE DUE" above
vignette oval.

J2-E1 2c
  a. Die on India, die sunk on card
    dark red violet _850._
    black _850._
  b. Die on India, cut small
    gray black _400._
    dull red _400._
    dull brown _400._
    dull green _400._
    dull blue _400._
  c. Die on India, cut close
    orange brown _400._
    dark red violet _400._
    slate gray _400._
  d. Die on ivory glazed paper, die sunk
    black _700._
    black brown _700._
    scarlet _700._
    blue _700._

Design size: 19 ½ x25 ½mm
Die size: 53x53mm
Complete engraving of entire design as adopted except
"UNPAID POSTAGE" instead of "POSTAGE DUE" above
vignette oval.

J3-E1 3c
  a. Die on India, die sunk on card, dull yel-
    low _850._
  b. Die on India, cut small
    gray black _400._
    dull red _400._
    dull brown _400._
    dull green _400._
    dull blue _400._
  c. Die on India, cut close, dull yellow _400._
  d. Die on ivory glazed paper, die sunk
    black _700._
    black brown _700._
    scarlet _700._
    blue _700._

Design size: 19 ½ x25 ½mm
Complete engraving of entire design as adopted except
"UNPAID POSTAGE" instead of "POSTAGE DUE" above
vignette oval.

J4-E1 5c
  a. Die on India, die sunk on card, slate
    gray _850._
  b. Die on India, cut small
    gray black _400._
    dull red _400._
    dull brown _400._
    dull green _400._
    dull blue _400._
  c. Die on India, cut close
    orange brown _400._
    slate gray _400._
    dark red violet _400._
    dull yellow _400._
  d. Die on ivory glazed paper, die sunk
    black _700._
    black brown _700._
    scarlet _700._
    blue _700._

As No. J4-E1 except frame a pencil and wash drawing,
vignette engraved numeral and oval lathework numeral cut to
shape and pasted over lathework, with design notations.

J4-E2 5c Engraved vignette, frame pencil
and wash, on thick card,
70x88mm, brown —

1894 ISSUE
Bureau of Engraving and Printing

J31-E1   J31-E2

Design size: 18 ½ x22 ½mm
Die size: 50x99mm
Incomplete engraving of entire design: no engraved lines on
numeral, lathework unfinished on two inclined spots at each
side of numeral.

J31-E1 1c Die on India, die sunk on card,
deep claret _1,000._

Design size: 18 ½ x22 ½mm
Die size: 50x99mm
Incomplete engraving of entire design: engraved lines on
numeral but lathework still unfinished on two inclined spots at
each side of numeral.

J31-E2 1c Die on India, die sunk on card,
claret _1,000._

J33-E1

J33-E2

Incomplete engraving of entire design: blank space for numeral with "3" drawn in pencil.

J33-E1 3c Die on India, die sunk on card, black   1,000.

Incomplete engraving of entire design: no engraved lines on numeral, bottom lettering in pencil only, no hand retouching of lathework around numeral.

J33-E2 3c Die on India, die sunk on card, black   1,000.

J33-E3

Incomplete engraving of entire design: no engraved lines on numeral.

J33-E3 3c Die on India, die sunk on card, claret   1,000.

J35-E1

J36-E1

Incomplete engraving of entire design: no engraved lines on numerals.

J35-E1 10c Die on India, die sunk on card, black   1,000.

Incomplete engraving of entire design: no engraved lines on numerals.

J36-E1 30c Die on India, die sunk on card, claret   1,000.

J37-E1   J37-E2

Incomplete engraving of entire design: 9x9mm blank space for numerals.

J37-E1 50c Die on India, die sunk on card
   black   1,000.
   claret   1,000.

Incomplete engraving of entire design: numerals engraved but hand engraving to retouch lathework around numerals missing.

J37-E2 50c Die on India, die sunk on card, black   1,000.

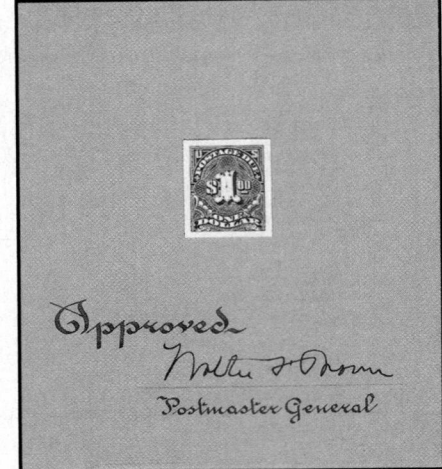

J67-E1

Complete engraving of unissued 1917 denomination, "Approved / Walter F. Brown (signature) / Postmaster General" below design.

J67-E1 $1 Die on white card, mounted on gray card, black   4,500.

OFFICIAL STAMPS

Continental Bank Note Co.
AGRICULTURE

O1-E1

Engraved Franklin vignette with 1 and value label.

O1-E1 1c Die on India, on card (1873), black   2,000.

O2-E1

Engraved Jackson vignette with 2 and value label.

O2-E1 2c Die on glazed paper (1873), black   1,750.

O2-E2

Design size: 20x25mm
Engraved vignette, numeral and value label from 1873 2c (No. O2-E1) mounted on pencil and wash drawing for frame design as adopted for Agriculture set. Pencil signature "J. Claxton" on backing card. Frame differs for each dept.

O2-E2 2c Model on yellowish card, 23x30mm, on 90x118mm white card, black vignette, gray black frame   6,500.

O3-E1

Washington vignette, 3 and value label.

O3-E1 3c Die on India, card mounted (1873), black   1,600.

O4-E1

Completed vignette with 6 and value label.

O4-E1 6c Die on India, on card (1873), black   1,500.

O6-E1

Completed Clay vignette with 12 and value label.

O6-E1 12c Die on white glazed paper (1873), black   1,250.

O7-E1

Vignette of Webster with 15 below.

O7-E1 15c Die on white glazed paper (1873), black   1,000.

O9-E1

Completed vignette with 30 below.

O9-E1 30c Die on white glazed paper (1873), black   1,750.

EXECUTIVE

O12-E1

O12-E2

Design size: 20x25mm

See design note for No. O2-E1.

O12-E1   3c   Model on yellowish card,
23x30mm, on 90x118mm white
card, black   *6,000.*

Design size: 19½x25mm
Die size: 64x76mm
Engraving of complete design of No. O12-E1 with "DEP'T" in top label.

O12-E2   3c
   a. Die on India, die sunk on card, green   *2,750.*
   b. Die on India, cut close
     black   *2,250.*
     green   *2,250.*

INTERIOR

O17-E1

Design size: 20x25mm
See design note for No. O2-E1.

O17-E1   3c   Model on yellowish card,
23x30mm, on 90x118mm white
card, black   *9,000.*

JUSTICE

O27-E1

Design size: 20x25mm
See design note for No. O2-E1.

O27-E1   3c   Model on yellowish card,
23x30mm, on 90x118mm
white card, black   *10,000.*

NAVY

O37-E1

Design size: 20x25mm
See design note for No. O2-E1.

O37-E1   3c   Model on yellowish card,
23x30mm, on 90x118mm white
card, black   *4,750.*

O39-E1

Die size: 62x76mm
Completed vignette with 7 and value label.

O39-E1   7c
   a. Die on India, on card (1873), black   *1,000.*
   b. Die on white glazed paper, black   *1,000.*

POST OFFICE

O47-E1

Design size: 19½x25mm
Complete engraving of entire design as adopted except with Franklin vignette instead of large numeral.

O47-E1   1c
   a. Die on India, mounted on white ivory
     card
     blue   *1,750.*
   b. Die on proof paper
     gray black   *1,250.*
     dull scarlet   *1,250.*
     dull brown   *1,250.*
     dull green   *1,250.*
     dull blue   *1,250.*
   c. Die on ivory glazed paper
     brown black   *1,750.*
     orange red   *1,750.*
     blue   *1,750.*

O48-E1

Design size: 19½x25mm
Complete engraving of entire design as adopted except with Jackson vignette instead of large numeral.

O48-E1   2c
   a. Die on India, mounted on white ivory
     card
     orange brown   *1,500.*
   b. Die on proof paper
     gray black   *1,250.*
     dull scarlet   *1,250.*
     dull brown   *1,250.*
     dull green   *1,250.*
     dull blue   *1,250.*
   c. Die on ivory glazed paper
     brown black   *1,750.*
     orange red   *1,750.*
     blue   *1,750.*

O49-E1   O49-E2

Design size: 20x25mm
Engraved vignette, numeral and value label from 1873 3c (No. 147-E10) mounted on pencil and wash drawing for frame design not adopted for Post Office set.

O49-E1   3c   Model on yellowish card,
23x30mm, on 90x118mm white
card, black   *5,750.*
O49-E2   3c   Model on yellowish card,
23x30mm, on 90x118mm white
card, black   *5,750.*

O49-E3

Design size: 20x25mm

See design note for No. O2-E1.

O49-E3   3c   Model on yellowish card,
23x30mm, on 90x118mm white
card, black   *5,750.*

O49-E4

Design size: 19½x25mm
Complete engraving of entire design as adopted except with Washington vignette instead of large numeral.

O49-E4   3c
   a. Die on India, mounted on white ivory
     card
     green   *1,500.*
   b. Die on proof paper
     gray black   *1,250.*
     dull scarlet   *1,250.*
     dull brown   *1,250.*
     dull green   *1,250.*
     dull blue   *1,250.*
   c. Die on ivory glazed paper
     brown black   *1,750.*
     orange red   *1,750.*
     blue   *1,750.*

O49-E5

1870 1c stamp (No. 145) with vignette cut out, "OFFICIAL 3 STAMP" drawn in pencil on envelope on which stamp is mounted. Blue pencil notations on backing envelope "1st design of official stamp for POD" and "Design by Mr. J. Barber for P O Official."

O49-E5   1c   Stamp frame mounted on envelope, ultramarine frame, black
vignette   *7,500.*

O49-E6   O49-E8

Model of engraved frame from No. O49-E4 with hollow oval engraved lathework band with "OFFICIAL / STAMP" drawn in wash mounted in place, numeral drawn in pencil and wash. Ms. "No. 1" on backing card.

O49-E6   3c   Model on stiff white card,
50x75mm, green   *7,500.*

Like No. O49-E6, Ms. "No. 3" on backing card.

O49-E8   3c   Model on stiff white card,
50x75mm, black   *7,500.*

O50-E1

Incomplete engraving of design with Lincoln vignette, without rectangular frame design.

O50-E1   6c   Die on white ivory paper, black   *4,250.*

O56-E1

Design size: 19½x25mm
Complete engraving of entire design as adopted except with Perry vignette instead of large numeral.

O56-E1 90c
    a. Die on India, mounted on white ivory card
        brown   1,500.
        blue   1,500.
        orange red   1,500.
    b. Die on proof paper
        gray black   1,500.
        dull scarlet   1,500.
        dull brown   1,500.
        dull green   1,500.
        dull blue   1,500.
    c. Die on ivory glazed paper
        brown black   1,750.
        orange red   1,750.
        blue   1,750.

STATE

O59-E1

O68-E1

Design size: 20x25mm
Engraved vignette, numeral and value label from 1873 3c (No. 147-E10) mounted on pencil and wash drawing for frame design as adopted for State set. Pencil signature "J. Claxton" on backing card.

O59-E1   3c Model on yellowish card, 23x30mm, on 90x118mm white backing card.   4,750.

Design size: 25½x40mm
Engraved vignette of Seward mounted in watercolor drawing of adopted frame design. Ms. signatures of J. Claxton and Chas. Skinner on backing card.

O68-E1   Two Dollars, Model on 29x43mm grayish white card, mounted on 96x120mm white card, black   7,500.

O68-E2

Complete engraving of adopted frame only with "TWO DOLLARS." in value label at bottom. With "FIVE DOLLARS." and "TEN DOLLARS." value labels outside design at left and "TWENTY DOLLs." value tablet at right.

O68-E2   Two Dollars, Die on India, black   8,750.

O68-E3

Plate engraved frame only (three examples in a block of four with complete bicolor plate proof of $2 at upper left in block).

O68-E3   Two Dollars, Plate essay on India, green   10,000.

O71-E1

Plate engraving of top half of frame only, paired with $20 plate proof.

O71-E1   Die on India, mounted on card, green   9,000.

WAR

O85-E1

Design size: 20x25mm
Engraved vignette, numeral and value label from 1873 3c (No. 147-E10) mounted on pencil and wash drawing for frame design as adopted for War set. Pencil signature "J. Claxton" on backing card.

O85-E1   3c Model on yellowish card, 23x30mm, on 90x118mm white card, black   2,500.

NEWSPAPER AND PERIODICALS

1865 ISSUE
National Bank Note Co.

PR1-E1

Design size: 51x89mm
Typographed design somewhat similar to that adopted but with large Franklin vignette facing left, "PACKAGE" at bottom, other minor differences.

PR1-E1   5c Die on stiff white ivory paper
        deep orange red   2,000.
        dusky g-b. blue   2,000.
        bright blue   2,000.
    a. Die on paper with blue ruled lines
        deep orange red   2,000.
        carmine   2,000.

1875 ISSUE
National Bank Note Co.

PR5-E1

Design size: 52x96½mm

Typographed design as issued but lacking "National Bank Note Company, New York" imprint at bottom.

PR5-E1   5c Die on wove paper, blue   —

1875 ISSUE
Continental Bank Note Co.

PR9-E1   PR9-E2

Design size: 19½x25mm
Engraved vignette and numerals (25's) with pencil sketch of unadopted frame design.

PR9-E1   25c Die on India, on card, black   2,750.

Design size: 19½x25mm
Complete engraving of unadopted design with "U S" at top and "25 CENTS 25" at bottom.

PR9-E2   25c
   a. Die on India, on card
     black   1,350.
     scarlet   1,350.
     blue   1,350.
     green   1,350.
   b. Die on white ivory paper
     black   1,350.
     black brown   1,350.
     scarlet   1,350.
     blue   1,350.

PR14-E1   PR23-E1

Design size: 25x35mm
Wash drawing of complete design as adopted. Backing card signed by both designers, Chas. Skinner and Jos. Claxton.

PR14-E1   9c Drawing on 26x36mm card, on
     56x74mm card, black   900.

Design size: 24x35½mm
Wash drawing similar to that adopted, backing card signed by designers Skinner and Claxton, also has pencil "$12" and ms. "Continental Bank Note Co."

PR23-E1   96c Drawing on 88x121mm card,
     black   900.

PR27-E1   PR28-E1

Design size: 24½x35mm
Incomplete engraving of entire design: unshaded (shading pencilled in) inside left, right and bottom framelines, value label, top of "9." Upper corners unfinished.

PR27-E1 $9 Die on India, die sunk on
     76x82mm card, black   1,350.

Design size: 24½x35mm
Incomplete engraving of entire design: no shading on dollar signs and numerals. No shading on frame around numerals and around value tablet.

PR28-E1 $12 Die on India, die sunk on
     66x80mm card, black   1,350.

Incomplete engraving of entire design, shading pencilled in around bottom value tablet and top right and left dollar signs and numerals.

PR28-E2 $12 Die on India, die sunk on card,
     75x90mm, black   —

PR29-E1

Design size: 24x35½mm
Wash drawing similar to that adopted but with "U S" in six-pointed stars instead of at top. Backing card signed by designers Skinner and Claxton, also pencil "31/32" and "8 13/32," pencil "Alter" with lines to stars.

PR29-E1 $24 Drawing on 88x121mm card,
     black   750.

PR31-E1   PR31-E2

Vignette size: 13½x26mm
Engraved vignette only as adopted.

PR31-E1 $48 Die on India, die sunk on card,
     black   750.

Design size: 24x36mm
Wash drawing similar to that adopted, backing card signed by designers Skinner and Claxton, also has pencil "$48" above each value numeral.

PR31-E2 $48 Drawing on 88x121mm card,
     black   1,350.

PR32-E1

Design size: 24½x35½mm
Wash drawing similar to that adopted, backing card signed by designers Skinner and Claxton.

PR32-E1 $60 Drawing on 88x121mm card,
     black   750.

1885 ISSUE
American Bank Note Co.

PR81-E1

Design size: 23x25mm
Complete engraving of entire design as adopted for 12c-96c.

PR81-E1   1c
   a. Die on India, die sunk on card
     black   1,350.
   b. Die on white ivory paper
     black   600.
     black brown   600.
     scarlet   600.
     blue   600.

1895 ISSUE
Bureau of Engraving and Printing

Incomplete engraving of entire design: background at upper ends of value label, shading on side lettering and numerals missing.

PR102-E2   1c Die on India, die sunk on card
     black   900.
     green   1,250.

Incomplete engraving of entire design but further engraved than No. PR102-E2: shading on PA is light, no shading on PE of NEWSPAPERS or IO of PERIODICALS and shading on OD is light.

PR102-E3   1c Die on India, die sunk on card,
     black   900.

Incomplete engraving of entire design but further engraved than No. PR102-E3: shading on PERIODICALS is finished but not on PAPE.

PR102-E4   1c Die on India, die sunk on card,
     black   900.

PR103-E1   PR103-E2

Design size: 21½x34½mm
Die size: 56x75½mm
Incomplete engraving of entire design: spaces for numerals and value label blank but with pencil outline of lettering.

PR103-E1   2c Die on India, die sunk on card,
     black   1,750.

Incomplete engraving of entire design but further engraved than No. PR103-E1: shading on leaves at ends of value label unfinished, numerals unshaded, unfinished shading on APE of NEWSPAPERS and RIO of PERIODICALS.

PR103-E2   2c Die on India, black   1,250.

Incomplete engraving of entire design but further engraved than No. PR103-E2: no shading on PE of NEWSPAPERS, unfinished shading on PA of NEWSPAPERS and RIO of PERIODICALS.

PR103-E3   2c Die on India, die sunk on card,
     black   1,250.

PR104-E1

Design size: 21½x34½mm
Die size: 57x73mm
Incomplete engraving of entire design: spaces for numerals and value label blank but with pencil outline of lettering.

PR104-E1 5c Die on India, die sunk on card, black 1,500.

PR105-E1

PR105-E2

Design size: 21½x34½mm
Die size: 56x75mm
Incomplete engraving of entire design: spaces for numerals and value label blank but with pencil outline of lettering.

PR105-E1 10c Die on India, die sunk on card, black 1,500.

Incomplete engraving of entire design but further engraved than No. PR105-E1: numerals unfinished, lower corners blank.

PR105-E2 10c Die on India, die sunk on card, black 1,500.

Incomplete engraving of entire design but further engraved than No. PR105-E2: lower right corner blank.

PR105-E3 10c Die on India, die sunk on card, black 1,250.

Incomplete engraving of entire design but further engraved than No. PR105-E3: numerals blank, no inner lines.

PR105-E4 10c Die on India, die sunk on card, black 1,250.

PR105-E5

Design size: 21½x34½mm
Die size: 56x75mm
Incomplete engraving of entire design (early state of die similar to No. PR105-E1) with "10" pencilled in upper right corner and "TEN CENTS" pencilled in at bottom. Pencil notes on India include "Make top of 1 a little larger and put on spur," "Work up Vignette" and "Use same scrolls as marked on 5c-."

PR105-E5 10c Die on India, die sunk on card, black 2,750.

PR106-E1

PR106-E2

Vignette size: 13x25½mm
Die size: 56x72mm
Incomplete engraving of vignette only (transfer of Continental Banknote Co. die for 72c with left side cut off): eagle crest faces front and its right wing is not pointed, shading on left thigh near sword hilt incomplete, bottom of vignette straight instead of curved.

PR106-E1 25c Die on India, die sunk on card
black 2,250.
deep red 2,250.

Design size: about 21x34½mm
Die size: 57½x75mm
Entire design with frame incompletely engraved: vert. lines around CENTS label missing, no shading on TWENTY FIVE, colorless beads under E and FI of same.

PR106-E2 25c Die on India, die sunk on card
black 2,250.
deep red 2,250.

An impression from No. PR106-E2 with pencil shading on TWENTY FIVE and vert. ink lines in spaces around CENTS label, colorless beads also blacked out in ink. Below engraving are three diff. pencil sketches for shape and shading to be engraved.

PR106-E3 25c Die on India, die sunk on card, black 2,250.

An impression from No. PR106-E2 but with shading suggestions from No. PR106-E3 partly engraved except colorless beads have pencil shading only. Below engraving is pencil sketch for corner of CENTS label.

PR106-E4 25c Die on India, die sunk on card
black 2,250.
deep red 2,000.

PR106-E5

Design size: 21½x34½mm
Die size: 55x72mm
Large die proof of PR107 with bottom value label cut out and "TWENTY-FIVE CENTS" pencilled in on backing card.

PR106-E5 25c Die on India, die sunk on card, black 1,500.

PR107-E1

PR107-E3

Incomplete engraving of entire design: eagle's head and much of bottom of stamp's design unfinished, top of frame unfinished, value lettering sketched in pencil.

PR107-E1 50c Die on India, die sunk on card, black 1,750.

Incomplete engraving of entire design: top of frame and scrolls below FIFTY CENTS unfinished.

PR107-E3 50c Die on India, die sunk on card, black 1,500.

PR108-E1

PR108-E2

Design size: 24½x37mm
Die size: 75x76mm
Incomplete engraving of entire design: vignette and spaces around numerals incomplete, pencil sketch instructions for engraver at top and side for these spaces.

PR108-E1 $2 Die on India, die sunk on card, black 1,650.

Design size: 24½x37mm
Die size: 75x76mm
Incomplete engraving of entire design but further engraved than No. PR108-E1: space for ornaments under POSTAGE blank, numerals unshaded.

PR108-E2 $2 Die on India, die sunk on card, scarlet 1,500.

Further engraved than No. PR108-E2: scrolls under POSTAGE engraved but unfinished.

PR108-E3 $2 Die on India, die sunk on card, black 1,500.

Incomplete engraving of design, no frame line under "Postage" and other small differences from final design.

PR110-E1 $10 Die on India, green 1,500.

PR111-E1

PR112-E1

Design size (incomplete): 24½x30mm
Die size: 75x84mm
Incomplete engraving of partial design: spaces for stars and 0s of numerals blank, design missing below bottom of vignette.

PR111-E1 $20 Die on India, die sunk on card, black 1,850.

Design size: 24½x35½mm
Die size: 72½x76mm
Incomplete engraving of entire design: upper corners around value numerals unfinished, etc.

PR112-E1 $50 Die on India, on card, black 1,850.

PR113-E1

Design size: 24½x35½mm
Die size: 75x74mm
Incomplete engraving of entire design: spaces at lower inner corners of value shields blank, shading on numerals and letters at top unfinished.

PR113-E1 $100 Die on India, on card, black 1,350.

Further engraved than No. PR113-E1: vignette completed but numerals not shaded, shadows on frame not etched dark.

PR113-E2 $100 Die on India
black 1,350.
red-violet 1,350.

Further engraved than No. PR113-E2: numerals shaded, shadows on frame not finally etched, especially above POSTAGE.

PR113-E3 $100 Die on India, black   *1,350.*

PARCEL POST STAMPS

Q1-E1

Design size: 35½x23mm
Photo of wash drawing of frame design with numerals, CENT and POST OFFICE CLERK in black ink, vignette in black wash. Ms. "Changed from 15c" and "Approved Nov. 15, 1912 — Frank H. Hitchcock — Postmaster General" on backing card.

Q1-E1   1c Model on thick gray card,
                  106x91mm, black   *3,000.*

Q2-E1

Design size: 35x23½mm
Photo of wash drawing of frame only as adopted. Ms. "Approved Oct. 10, 1912, for border and size of stamps. Engraving to be ⅞ by 1⅜ inches. Frank H. Hitchcock. Postmaster General" on backing card.

Q2-E1   2c Model on thick gray cardboard,
                  122x110mm, black   *1,500.*

Q2-E2

Design size: 35x23mm
Photo of wash drawing of frame design and retouched photo of ship vignette as eventually used for 10c, numerals and STEAMSHIP AND MAIL TENDER in black ink. Ms. "Changed to 10c" and "Approved Oct. 11, 1912. Frank H. Hitchcock. Postmaster General" on backing card.

Q2-E2   2c Model on thick gray cardboard,
                  110x83mm, black   *2,500.*

Q2-E3

Design size: 34x22mm
Photo of wash drawing of entire design with adopted vignette, numerals in white wash and CITY CARRIER in black ink. Ms. "Changed from 5c" and "Approved Nov. 14, 1912. Frank H. Hitchcock. Postmaster General" on backing card.

Q2-E3   2c Model on thick gray cardboard,
                  111x92mm, black   *2,500.*

Design size: 34½x22mm
Engraving of adopted design with blank value tablets and "CITY CARRIER" inscription, mail carrier unfinished.

Q2-E4   2c Die on India, sunk on 118x89mm
                  card, black   —

Q3-E1

Design size: 35x23mm
Complete engraving of unadopted design: vignette shows mail truck backing up to railroad mail train with clerk about to handle pouches.

Q3-E1   3c Die on white wove, about
                  43x31mm, carmine   *2,000.*

Q3-E2

Design size: 35x22mm
Photo of wash drawing of entire design with adopted vignette (retouched around door to mail car). Ms. "Approved Feb. 22, 1913. Frank H. Hitchcock. Postmaster General" on backing card.

Q3-E2   3c Model on thick gray cardboard,
                  black   *2,500.*

Q3-E3

Design size: 35x22mm
Almost complete engraving of adopted design with subtle differences (most evident in shading on windows), on 100x76mm card, affixed with tape to 125x98mm card, small cutout in design, blue control No. 578444 on back.

Q3-E3   3c Die sunk on card, affixed to card,
                  carmine   *2,500.*

Q4-E1

Design size: 33½x22mm
Photo of wash drawing of entire design with adopted vignette, numerals drawn in white and RURAL CARRIER in black ink. Ms. "Changed from 10c" and "Approved Nov. 14, 1912. Frank H. Hitchcock. Postmaster General" on backing card.

Q4-E1   4c Model on thick gray cardboard,
                  116x92mm, black   *2,500.*

Q5-E1

Design size: 35x23mm
Photo of wash drawing of entire design with vignette (retouched) eventually used for 2c, numerals and CITY LETTER CARRIER in black ink and white wash. Ms. "Changed to 2c.--City Carrier" and "Approved Oct. 10, 1912. Frank H. Hitchcock. Postmaster General" on backing card.

Q5-E1   5c Model on thick gray cardboard,
                  110x84mm, black   *2,500.*

Q5-E2

Design size: 33½x21½mm
Photo of wash drawing of entire design with numerals in gray, unadopted vignette with MAIL TRAIN in black ink, first car retouched with wash. Ms. "Approved . . . 1912 / . . . Postmaster General" on backing card.

Q5-E2   5c Model on thick gray cardboard,
                  104½x92mm, black   *2,500.*

Q5-E3

Design size: 33½x22mm
Photo of wash drawing of entire design with numerals in gray, MAIL TRAIN in black ink, first car retouched with wash. Ms. "Approved . . . 1912 / . . . Postmaster General" on backing card.

Q5-E3   5c Model on thick gray cardboard,
                  104½x92mm, black   *2,500.*

Q5-E4

Design size: 33½x22mm
Photo of wash drawing of entire design with numerals in white with black background, MAIL TRAIN and pouch catcher in black ink. Ms. "Approved Nov. 19, 1912 Frank H. Hitchcock Postmaster General" on backing card.

Q5-E4   5c Model on thick gray cardboard,
                  94x90mm, black   *2,500.*

Q6-E1

Design size: 35½x23mm
Photo of wash drawing of entire design with vignette (retouched) eventually used for 4c, numerals and RURAL DELIVERY in black ink and white wash. Ms. "Changed to 4c." and "Approved Oct. 10, 1912. Frank H. Hitchcock. Postmaster General" on backing card.

Q6-E1   10c Model on thick gray cardboard,
                  111x83mm, black   *2,500.*

Q6-E2

Design size: 35x23mm
Photo of wash drawing of entire design with adopted vignette, numerals and STEAMSHIP AND MAIL TENDER in black ink and white wash. Ms. "Changed from 2c." and "Approved Nov. 8, 1912. Frank H. Hitchcock. Postmaster General" on backing card.

Q6-E2   10c Model on thick gray cardboard,
                  116x92mm, black   *2,500.*

Q7-E1

Design size: 33½x22mm
Photo of wash drawing of entire design (redrawn in front of autocar and U S MAIL and STATION A) with AUTOMOBILE SERVICE in black ink. Ms. "Approved . . . 1912 / . . . Postmaster General" on backing card.

Q7-E1 15c Model on thick gray cardboard,
115x93mm, black   1,500.

Design size:
Complete engraving of entire design with unadopted title label "COLLECTION SERVICE" instead of the adopted "AUTO-MOBILE SERVICE."

Q7-E2 15c Die on white wove, card mounted,
carmine   1,500.

Q8-E1

Design size: 35x22mm
Incomplete engraved design nearly as adopted: aviator wears football helmet, head tilted far forward and one leg dangling over edge of plane, mail bag "No. 1" at his right while another sack hangs loosely out of plane.

Q8-E1 20c Die on white wove, about
37x24mm, carmine   1,500.

Q8-E2

Design size: 35x22mm
Photo of incomplete engraved design as adopted. Ms. "Approved Nov. 19, 1912. Frank H. Hitchcock. Postmaster General" on backing card.

Q8-E2 20c Model on thick gray cardboard,
98x95mm, black   2,500.

Q9-E1

Design size: 34½x22½mm
Photo of wash drawing of entire design with numerals and smoke at right painted in. Ms. "Changed from $1.00." and "Approved Nov. 14, 1912. Frank H. Hitchcock. Postmaster General" on backing card.

Q9-E1 25c Model on thick gray cardboard,
112x92mm, black   2,500.

Q10-E1

Design size: 35x23mm
Photo of drawing of entire design with vignette eventually used for 25c with roof, smokestacks and smoke drawn in. Typed

label "Stamp Division / Feb / 21 / 1912 / P.O. Dept" on back of backing paper.

Q10-E1 50c Model on thick white paper, black   1,500.

Q10-E2

Design size: 33x21½mm
Photo of wash drawing of frame design with vignette cut out, mounted over photo of wash drawing of unadopted vignette design, retouched with wash on cows, etc., with DAIRYING in black ink. Pencil "Original" and ms. "Approved . . . 1912 / . . . Postmaster General" on backing card.

Q10-E2 50c Model on thick gray cardboard,
98x93mm, black   1,500.

Q10-E3

Design size: 35x23mm
Complete engraving of entire design with unadopted vignette: silo and barns placed closer to front of design.

Q10-E3 50c Die on white wove, about
43x31mm, carmine   1,750.

Q10-E4

Design size: 35x22mm
Photo of incomplete engraved design: no vert. lines on frame around corner foliate spandrels or in numeral circles. Ms. "Approved Jan. 8, 1913. Frank H. Hitchcock. Postmaster General" on backing card.

Q10-E4 50c Model on thick gray cardboard,
99x94mm, black   2,500.

Q11-E1

Design size: 33½x21½mm
Photo of wash drawing of entire design with central horses and thresher retouched. Ms. "Approved Dec. 12, 1912. Frank H. Hitchcock. Postmaster General" on backing card.

Q11-E1 75c Model on thick gray cardboard,
108x89mm, black   2,500.

Q12-E1

Photo of wash drawing of entire design with vignette much retouched in black ink, numerals, MANUFACTURING and DOL-LAR drawn in black ink and white wash. Ms. "Changed to 25c" and "Approved Oct. 22, 1912. Frank H. Hitchcock. Postmaster General" on backing card.

Q12-E1 $1 Model on thick gray cardboard,
114x86mm, black   2,500.

Q12-E2

Design size: 35x22mm
Photo of wash drawing of complete design with DOLLAR painted in white and black and FRUIT GROWING in black ink, vignette retouched with wash on fruit pickers. Ms. "Approved . . . 1912 . . . Postmaster General" on backing card.

Q12-E2 $1 Model on thick gray cardboard,
105x94mm, black   1,500.

Q12-E3

Design size: 36x23½mm
Incomplete engraving of entire design: no shading lines in sky. This may be from a rejected die.

Q12-E3 $1 Die on white wove, about
43x31mm, carmine   1,500.

Q12a-E1

Engraving of entire design as adopted for 1917 offset Documentary Revenues, etc., but with "U.S. PARCEL POST" around value oval.

Q12a-E1	1c	Die on card, green	1,000.
Q12b-E1	2c	Die on card, carmine	1,000.
Q12c-E1	3c	Die on card, deep violet	1,000.
Q12d-E1	4c	Die on card, brown	1,000.
Q12e-E1	5c	Die on card, blue	1,000.
Q12f-E1	10c	Die on card, orange yellow	1,000.
Q12g-E1	15c	Die on card, gray	1,000.
Q12h-E1	20c	Die on wove, carmine rose, affixed to card	1,500.

PARCEL POST POSTAGE DUE

Retouched photo of design as adopted, officially dated and approved.

QJQ5-E1a 25c Model, black   1,500.

CARRIER'S STAMPS

Essays by Toppan, Carpenter, Casilear & Co. in 1851

LO1-E1

Unfinished die with lathework impinging on white oval and framelines complete at top and bottom, plus uncleaned horizontal and vertical layout lines.

1851
LO1-E1 (1c) Die on 34x42mm,
white bond, black 10,000.

LO1-E1A

Die size: 57x50mm
Unfinished die distinguished by having top and bottom frame
lines, lathework impinging on white oval, and rosettes in lower
right corner.

LO1- (1c) Die on 62x54mm, pale
E1A green bond, red 4,000.

**Essays by Schernikow in 1903 from a new soft
steel die made from the original 1851 transfer
roll.
See note above No. 63-E1.**

LO1-E2

LO1-E3

Die size: 50x50mm
Engraving of Franklin vignette only.

1903
LO1-E2 (1c)
a. Die on proof paper
black 75.
carmine 75.
red 75.
light red 75.
orange 75.
orange brown 75.
yellow 75.
olive 75.
green 75.
dark green 75.
dark blue 75.
violet 75.
violet brown 75.
b. Die on colored card, about
75x75mm
deep red, *pinkish white* 175.
yellow brown, *pale blue* 175.
violet brown, *pale green* 175.
dark green, *pale pink* 175.
dark blue, *pale pink* 175.
violet, *pale yellow* 175.
c. Die on green bond (die size:
49x50mm)
dull scarlet 175.
dull olive 175.
dark ultramarine 175.

Design size: 19½x25mm
Die size: 50x50mm
Design as No. LO1-E1, but distinguished by addition of left
and right inner frame lines.

1903
LO1- (1c)
E3
a. Die on proof paper
black 100.
carmine 100.
dark carmine 100.
scarlet 100.
orange 100.
yellow 100.
yellow brown 100.
olive 100.
light green 100.
green 100.
steel blue 100.
violet 100.
red violet 100.
violet brown 100.
ultramarine 100.
b. Die on colored card
dull carmine, *pale olive* 175.
brown orange, *pink* 175.
brown, *pale buff* 175.
brown, *pale blue* 175.
gray green, *buff* 175.
gray green, *yellow* 175.
violet, *ivory* 175.
dull carmine, *pale blue* 175.
c. Die on blue pelure

carmine 200.
scarlet 200.
orange 200.
brown 200.
dark green 200.
d. Die on green bond
scarlet 250.
orange 250.
green 250.
dull violet 250.
e. Die on gummed thick rose paper, cut to
stamp size 6,500.

**Essays by Clarence Brazer in 1952 using the
Schernikow complete die with addition of two
diagonal lines in upper right corner.**

Die size: 50x50mm

1952
LO1-E4 (1c) Die on glazed card
scarlet 500.
brown 500.
green 500.
red 500.

POST OFFICE SEALS

**Registry Seals
1872 ISSUE
National Bank Note Co.**

Design size: 72x40mm
Block size: 100x56½mm
Typographed design similar to that adopted but inscription
STAMP HERE DATE AND PLACE OF MAILING around central
circular disk is in colorless capitals, remainder of lettering in
solid colors without shading lines. The word REGISTERED
obliterates other words where it touches them.

OXF1-E1
a. Block impression on white card,
brown 2,000.
b. Die on India, dark brown —

Similar to No. OXF1-E1 except REGISTERED appears to be
under other words it touches and does not obliterate them, as in
design adopted.

OXF1-E2
a. Block impression on white paper,
card mounted, brown 2,000.
b. Block impression on large card
brown 2,000.
red 2,000.
yellow 2,000.

Similar to adopted type but circular disk in center has a
ground of concentric circles, REGISTERED without colorless
shading and obliterates other words where it touches them.

OXF1-E3 Block impression on white card,
red violet —

LO1-E4 — OXF1-E4

Similar to adopted design except REGISTERED obliterates
other words where it touches them; colored shading as
adopted.

OXF1-E4
a. Block on India, on card
carmine 1,000.
yellow 1,000.
blue 1,000.
green 1,000.
red brown 1,000.
rose 1,000.
brown orange 1,000.
b. Block on India, printed in two colors
top dark green, bottom light green 1,000.
left half blue, right half green 1,000.
c. Block sunk on white card, colored
border around stamp (full size
57x100mm)
deep carmine 1,000.
brown orange 1,000.
brown 1,000.
light green 1,000.
blue 1,000.
d. Block sunk on white wove, colorless
border, stamp size, imperf., dim
dusky blue 1,000.
e. As "d," perf. 12, gummed, dim dusky
blue 1,000.

OXF1-E5

Block size: 80x128mm
Engraving of entire design as adopted but in reverse for making typographed block.

OXF1-E5 Die on white wove, chocolate 1,000.

**Post Office Seals
1877 ISSUE**

OX1-E3

Design size: 45x27½mm
Incomplete engraving of entire design: no shading lines on
2mm-wide border frame, no cap or background in vignette.

OX1-E3 Die on India, on card, orange brown 1,000.

1861 FIRST DESIGN ESSAYS AND TRIAL COLOR PROOFS

For the convenience of collectors and dealers, the Scott editors present here in one location the important 1861 First Design Essays and Trial Color Proofs that were at one time listed in the Postage section as Nos. 55-57 and 59-62. These so-called "August" issues or "Premiere Gravure" issues, printed on thin and semitransparent stamp paper, gummed and perforated, were not issued as prepared, but were either engraved further to complete the issued designs (1c, 3c, 5c, 12c and 90c) or issued in slightly revised colors (24c and 30c), and they were therefore appropriately moved to the Essay and Trial Color Proof sections of the U.S. Specialized catalogue in 1991.

The 10c denomination of this First Design series, previously No. 58, was pressed into service as an issued stamp, No. 62B, presumably because the demand for this denomination was greater than could be supplied by the plate or plates in use. Former No. 58 and current No. 62B are the same stamp, and it is listed in the Postage section as No. 62B.

The listings here duplicate the listings in the Essay and Trial Color Proof sections rather than replace them. Their listing here is for the convenience of catalogue users only.

63-E11e

"Premiere Gravure" die No. 440.

63-E11e   1c **indigo,** finished "Premiere Gravure" plate essay on semitransparent stamp paper, gummed, perf. 12 (formerly No. 55)   50,000.

No. 63-E11e is valued with perfs cutting slightly into design at top.

65-E15h

65-E15h   3c **brown rose,** finished "Premiere Gravure" plate essay on semitransparent stamp paper, gummed, perf. 12 (formerly No. 56)   550.
     orange red   475.
     bright orange red   475.
     dark orange red   475.
     dim deep red   475.
     pink   475.
     deep pink   475.
     P# block of 8, Impt. (any shade)   20,000.

67-E9e

67-E9e   5c **brown,** finished "Premiere Gravure" plate essay on semitransparent stamp paper, gummed, perf. 12 (formerly No. 57)   30,000.

No. 67-E9e is valued with small faults, as all recorded original-gum examples come thus.

69-E6e

69-E6e   12c **black,** finished "Premiere Gravure" plate essay on semitransparent stamp paper, gummed, perf. 12 (formerly No. 59)   85,000.

70eTC

70eTC   24c **dark violet,** trial color plate proof on semitransparent stamp paper, gummed, perf. 12 (formerly No. 60)   15,000.

71bTC

71bTC   30c **red orange,** trial color plate proof on semitransparent stamp paper, gummed, perf. 12 (formerly No. 61)   45,000.

No. 71bTC is valued in the grade of fine.

72-E7h

72-E7h   90c **blue,** finished "Premiere Gravure" plate essay on semitransparent stamp paper, gummed, perf. 12 (formerly No. 62)   50,000.

DIE AND PLATE PROOFS

PROOFS are known in many styles other than those noted in this section. For the present, however, listings are restricted to die proofs, large and small, and plate proofs on India paper and card, and occasionally on stamp paper. The listing of normal color proofs includes several that differ somewhat from the types and colors of the issued stamps.

Large Die Proofs are so termed because of the relatively large piece of paper on which they are printed which is about the size of the die block, 40mm by 50mm or larger. The margins of this group of proofs usually are from 15mm to 20mm in width though abnormal examples prevent the acceptance of these measurements as a complete means of identification.

These proofs were prepared in most cases by the original contracting companies and 19th century issues often show the imprint thereof and letters and numbers of identification. They are listed under "DIE-Large (1)." The India paper on which these proofs are printed is of an uneven texture and in some respects resembles hand-made paper. These large die proofs were usually mounted on cards though many are found removed from the card. Large Die Proofs autographed by the engraver or officially approved are worth much more, except for those of the 1922-29 period, which are generally approved and signed proofs.

Values for Large Die Proofs are for the full die proofs mounted on cards unless noted otherwise. Full large die proofs measure 5-6" x 7-8". Cut-down Large Die Proofs sell for less. Values for die proofs of the bicolored 1869 issue are for examples which are completely printed. Occasionally the vignette has been cut out and affixed to an impression of the border.

Die Proofs of all United States stamps of later issues exist. Only those known outside of government ownership are listed.

Small Die Proofs are so called because of the small piece of paper on which they are printed. Proofs of stamps issued prior to 1904, are reprints, and not in all cases from the same dies as the large die proofs.

Small Die Proofs (Roosevelt Album, "DIE-Small (2)") — These 302 small die proofs are from sets prepared for 85 ("Roosevelt presentation") albums in 1903 by the Bureau of Engraving and Printing but bear no imprint to this effect. The white wove paper on which they are printed is of a fibrous nature. The margins are small, seldom being more than from 3-5mm in width. Values are for proofs affixed to the original gray card backing from the Roosevelt album. Proofs without the card backing sell for less.

Small Die Proofs (Panama-Pacific Issue, "DIE-Small (2a)") — A special printing of 413 different small die proofs was made in 1915 for the Panama-Pacific Exposition. These have small margins (2 ½-3mm) and are on soft yellowish wove paper. They are extremely scarce as only 3-5 of each are known and a few exist only in this special printing. 6-10 exist of No. E6 in two slightly different colors.

Plate Proofs are, quite obviously, impressions taken from finished plates and differ from the stamps themselves chiefly in their excellence of impression and the paper on which they are printed. Some of the colors vary.

Hybrids are plate proofs of all issues before 1894 which have been cut to shape, mounted and pressed on large cards to resemble large die proofs. These sell for somewhat less than the corresponding large die proofs.

India Paper is a thin, soft, opaque paper which wrinkles when wet. It varies in thickness and shows particles of bamboo.

Card is a plain, clear white card of good quality, which is found in varying thicknesses for different printings. Plate proofs on card were made in five printings in 1879-94. Quantities range from 500 to 3,200 of the card proofs listed between Scott 3P and 245P.

Margin blocks with full imprint and plate number are indicated by the abbreviation "P# blk. of -."

Numbers have been assigned to all proofs consisting of the number of the regular stamp with the suffix letter "P" to denote Proof.

Proofs in other than accepted or approved colors exist in a large variety of shades, colors and papers produced at various times by various people for many different reasons. The field is large. The task of listing has been begun under "Trial Colors" following the regular proofs.

Some proofs are not identical to the issued stamps. Some of these are now listed in the Essay section. Others have been left in the proof section to keep sets together at this time.

Values are for items in very fine condition. Most "Panama-Pacific" small die proofs are toned. Values are for moderately toned examples. **Plate proof pairs on stamp paper are valued with original gum unless otherwise noted.**

NORMAL COLORS

1845   **New York**

		DIE		PLATE	
	(1) Large	(2) Small	(2a)	(3) India	(4) Card
9X1P 5c black on India paper	750.	350.		—	
a. With scar on neck		300.			
b. Dot in "P" of "POST" and scar on neck	525.	300.			
c. As "b," on Bond	525.	300.		—	
d. As "b," on glazed paper	525.				
e. As "a," on Bond	525.				

The above listed Large Die varieties have an additional impression of the portrait medallion. Some experts question the existence of plate proofs from the sheets of 40. Plate proofs from the sheet of 9 exist on white and bluish bond paper. Value $125.

Providence, R.I.

10X1P 5c black				300.
10X2P 10c black				500.
Sheet of 12				3,250.

General Issues

1847

		(1)	(3)
1P 5c red brown on India paper	800.	600.	
a. White bond paper	800.		
b. Colored bond paper	1,250.		
c. White laid paper	800.		
d. Bluish laid paper	800.		
e. Yellowish wove paper	800.		
f. Bluish wove paper	800.		
g. White wove paper	800.		
h. Card	1,000.		
i. Glazed paper	1,000.		
2P 10c black on India paper Double transfer (31R1)	800.	900.	
a. White bond paper	800.		
b. Colored bond paper	1,250.		
c. White laid paper	800.		
d. Bluish laid paper	800.		
e. Yellowish wove paper	800.		
g. White wove paper	800.		
h. Card	1,000.		
i. Glazed paper	1,000.		

Original die proofs are generally found cut to stamp size; full size die proofs sell at higher prices. Reprint proofs with cross-hatching are valued as full size; cut down examples sell for less.

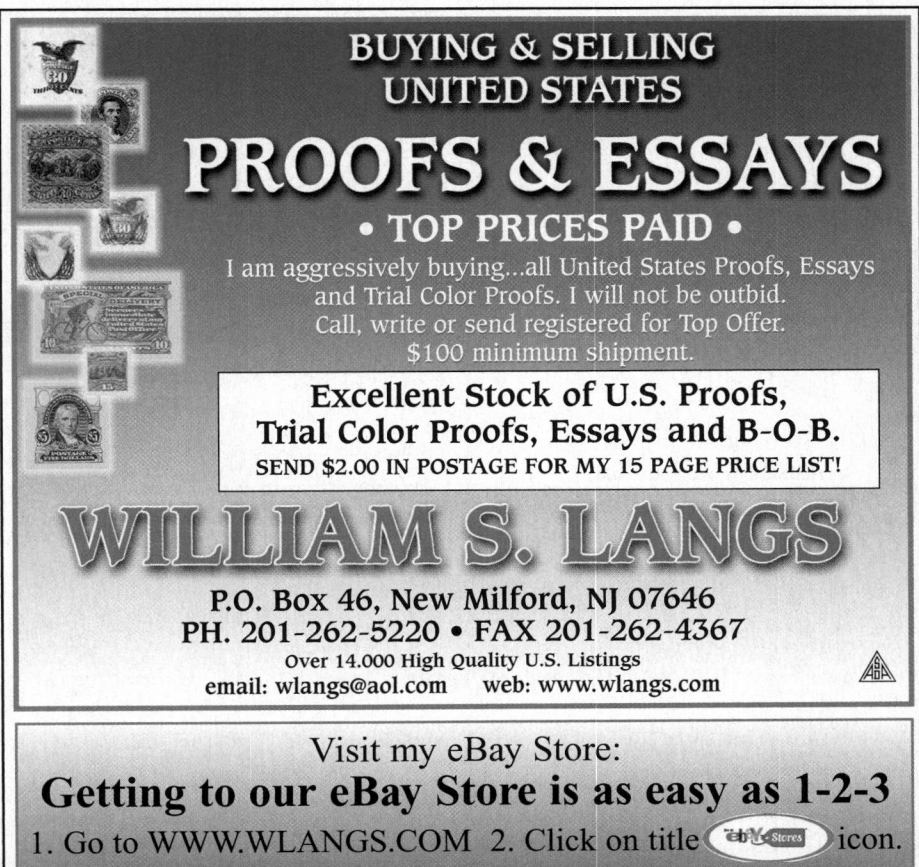

Plate proofs overprinted "Specimen" sell for about half the above figures.

Reproductions of 1847 Issue

Actually, official imitations made about 1875 from new dies and plates by order of the Post Office Department.

No	Description	Large	Small	(2a)	India	Card
3P	5c red brown	900.	425.	2,750.	250.	200.
	Block of 4				1,300.	900.
a.	On bond paper		650.			
4P	10c black	900.	425.	2,750.	250.	200.
	Block of 4				1,300.	900.
a.	On bond paper		650.			

1851-60

No	Description	Large	Small	(2a)	India	Card
5P	1c blue, type I	5,000.				
11P	3c red, type I	5,000.				
	brush obliteration				1,000.	
	Block of 4				5,000.	
	P# block of 8				20,000.	
12P	5c brn, type I	7,000.	5,000.			
13P	10c grn, type I	5,000.				
17P	12c black	12,500.				
24P	1c blue, type V (pl. 9)				1,250.	
	Pair				3,000.	
26P	3c red, type II (pl. 20)				1,250.	
	Pair				3,000.	
30P	5c brn, type II				1,250.	
35P	10c grn, type V				1,250.	
36BP	12c black, plate III (broken frame lines)				1,250.	
	Block of 4				5,500.	
d.	On stamp paper Pair				—	
	Block of 4				—	
37P	24c lilac			—	1,250.	
	Pair				3,000.	
c.	On stamp paper					1,500.
	Pair					10,000.
38P	30c orange	—	—		1,250.	
	Pair				3,000.	
a.	On stamp paper					1,500.
	Pair					7,750.
39P	90c blue	—	—		1,250.	
	Pair				3,000.	
a.	On stamp paper					4,500.
	Pair					37,500.

Plate proofs of 24P to 39P are from the original plates. They may be distinguished from the 40P to 47P by the type in the case of the 1c, 3c, 10c and 12c, and by the color in the case of the 5c, 24c, 30c and 90c.

The 3c plate proofs (No. 11) are on proof paper and all known examples have a vertical brush stroke obliteration.

Die proofs of the 30c show full spear point in corners of design.

Reprints of 1857-60 Issue

No	Description	DIE Large (1)	DIE Small (2)	(2a)	PLATE India (3)	PLATE Card (4)
40P	1c bright blue, type I (new plate)	325.	350.	2,500.	90.	75.
	Block of 4				550.	300.
a.	On stamp paper, blue					750.
41P	3c scarlet, type I (new plate)	325.	350.	2,500.	90.	50.
	Block of 4				550.	250.
	Orange brown			2,500.		
a.	On stamp paper, scarlet				—	
42P	5c orange brown type II (plate II)	325.	350.		90.	50.
	Block of 4				550.	250.
	P# blk. of 8				1,450.	—
43P	10c blue green, type I (new plate)	325.	350.	2,500.	90.	50.
	Block of 4				550.	250.
a.	On stamp paper, green				—	
44P	12c greenish black (new plate, frame line complete)	325.	350.	3,500.	125.	50.
	Block of 4				625.	250.
a.	On stamp paper, greenish black				—	
45P	24c blksh vio (pl. I)	325.	350.	2,500.	90.	50.
	Block of 4				400.	250.
	P# blk. of 8				1,050.	
46P	30c yel org (pl. I)	325.	350.	2,500.	90.	50.
	Block of 4				550.	250.
	P# blk. of 8				1,450.	
47P	90c deep blue (pl. I)	325.	350.	2,500.	125.	75.
	Block of 4				625.	375.
	P# blk. of 8				2,000.	1,050.

Nos. 42P2-44P2 were printed from original dies, and the 5c shows type I projections at top and bottom.

Nos. 40P-47P, large die, exist only as hybrids.

SECOND DESIGNS (Regular Issue)

For "First Designs" see Essay section (former Nos. 55-57, 59, 62), Proofs and Trial Color Proofs (former No. 58) and Trial Color Proofs (former Nos. 60-61).

1861

No	Description	Large	Small	(2a)	India	Card
62BP	10c dark green		325.		375.	
63P	1c blue	700.	225.	2,750.	55.	40.
	Block of 4				225.	250.
	P# blk. of 8				1,500.	
	Indigo			2,750.		
64P	3c pink	3,500.	—			
65P	3c rose	1,000.	—	2,750.	100.	150.
	Block of 4				550.	
	P# blk. of 8				1,500.	
a.	3c dull red				100.	
c.	On stamp paper, pair					1,000.
	P# blk. of 8					—
67P	5c buff	5,000.		2,750.		
76P	5c brown	700.	225.	2,750.	45.	30.
	Block of 4				225.	140.
	P# blk. of 8				1,500.	—
68P	10c green	650.	225.	2,750.	65.	30.
	Block of 4				300.	140.
	P# blk. of 8				1,500.	—
69P	12c black	700.	225.	2,750.	65.	30.
	Block of 4				300.	140.
	P# blk. of 8				1,500.	—
70P	24c red lilac	—		2,750.		500.
78P	24c lilac		225.	2,750.	80.	75.
	Block of 4				400.	375.
	P# blk. of 8				1,750.	—
71P	30c orange	500.	225.	2,750.	50.	30.
	Block of 4				250.	140.
	P# blk. of 8				1,500.	—
72P	90c blue	500.	225.	2,750.	50.	30.
	Block of 4				225.	140.
	P# blk. of 8				1,500.	—

1861-67

No	Description	Large	Small	(2a)	India	Card
73P	2c black, die I	10,000.			150.	
	Block of 4				750.	
	P# blk. of 8				2,000.	—
a.	Die II	2,500.	1,350.	8,750.	110.	75.
	Block of 4				550.	400.
	P# blk. of 8				1,500.	—
77P	15c black	1,250.	500.	2,750.	55.	45.
	Block of 4				250.	200.
	P# blk. of 8				3,000.	—
79P	3c rose, A grill, on stamp paper, pair					1,500.
	Block of 4					4,000.
	P# blk. of 8					10,000.
83P	3c rose, C grill, on stamp paper, pair					1,750.
94P	3c red, F grill, on stamp paper, pair					1,500.

The listed plate proofs of the 1c (63P), 5c (76P), 10c (68P) and 12c (69P) are from the 100 subject re-issue plates of 1875. Single proofs of these denominations from the regular issue plates cannot be told apart from the reprints. As the reprint plates had wider spacing between the subjects, multiples can be differentiated. Values are for proofs from the reprint plates. The 2c Die II has a small dot on the left cheek.

1869

No	Description	Large	Small	(2a)	India	Card
112P	1c buff	750.	350.	2,000.	55.	65.
	Block of 4				250.	300.
	P# blk. of 10				950.	
113P	2c brown	750.	350.	2,000.	40.	50.
	Block of 4				175.	225.
	P# blk. of 10				800.	
114P	3c ultra.	900.	575.	2,000.	45.	85.
	Block of 4				190.	375.
	P# blk. of 10				1,000.	
115P	6c ultra.	900.	350.	2,000.	45.	85.
	Block of 4				190.	375.
	P# blk. of 10				1,000.	
116P	10c yellow	900.	350.	2,000.	45.	55.
	Block of 4				190.	250.
	P# blk. of 10				2,000.	
117P	12c green	900.	350.	2,000.	45.	55.
	Block of 4				190.	265.
	P# blk. of 10				2,250.	
119P	15c brown & blue (type II)	550.	450.	2,000.	120.	
	Block of 4				600.	
	P# blk. of 8				3,500.	
129P	15c Reissue (type III)	550.	450.	2,000.	350.	140.
	Block of 4				1,600.	725.
	P# blk. of 8				3,500.	—
a.	Center inverted (100)					8,000.
	Block of 4					15,000.
	P# blk. of 8					65,000.
120P	24c green & violet	550.	450.	2,000.	140.	140.
	Block of 4				625.	650.
	P# blk. of 8				6,000.	—
a.	Center inverted (100)					2,750.
	Block of 4					15,000.
	P# blk. of 8					65,000.
121P	30c ultra & carmine	1,250.	450.	2,000.	140.	170.
	Block of 4				625.	875.
	P# blk. of 8				6,000.	—
a.	Flags inverted (100)					2,750.
	Block of 4					15,000.
	P# blk. of 8					65,000.
122P	90c carmine & black	550.	450.	2,000.	180.	170.
	Block of 4				825.	875.
	P# blk. of 8				6,500.	—
a.	Center inverted (100)					2,750.
	Block of 4					15,000.
	P# blk. of 8					75,000.

Large die proofs of Nos. 119, 129, 120 and 122 exist only as hybrids.

1880

No	Description	Large	India	Card
133P	1c dark buff	1,000.		100.
	Block of 4			450.
	P# blk. of 10			1,250.

1870-71   National Bank Note Co.

No	Description	Large	Small	(2a)	India	Card
136P	3c green, grill, on stamp paper, pair					1,200.
	P# blk. of 12					—
145P	1c ultra	250.	175.	1,200.	20.	
	Block of 4				90.	
	P# blk. of 12				750.	
146P	2c red brown	250.			20.	
	Block of 4				90.	
	P# blk. of 12				750.	
147P	3c green	300.			20.	
	Block of 4				90.	
	P# blk. of 12				750.	

The former No. 147Pc4 is now listed in the Essay section as No. 147-E13e.

No	Description	Large	India
148P	6c carmine	450.	35.
	Block of 4		150.
	P# blk. of 12		1,250.
149P	7c vermilion	250.	15.
	Block of 4		70.
	P# blk. of 12		750.
150P	10c brown	300.	40.
	Block of 4		165.
	P# blk. of 12		2,000.
151P	12c violet	250.	16.
	Block of 4		70.
	P# blk. of 12		750.
152P	15c orange	300.	30.
	Block of 4		70.
	P# blk. of 12		750.
153P	24c purple	300.	30.
	Block of 4		135.
	P# blk. of 12		750.
154P	30c black	300.	40.
	Block of 4		170.
	P# blk. of 12		2,250.
155P	90c carmine	300.	45.
	Block of 4		195.
	P# blk. of 12		2,500.

Secret Marks on 24, 30 and 90c Dies of the Bank Note Issues

National 24c — Rays of lower star normal.

Continental 24c — Rays of lower star strengthened.

National 30c — Lower line does not join point of shield.

Continental and American 30c — Lower line joins point of shield and bottom line of shield thicker.

National 90c — Rays of star in upper right normal.

Continental and American 90c — Rays of star in upper right strengthened.

1873 — Continental Bank Note Co.

			DIE		PLATE	
		(1) Large	(2) Small	(2a)	(3) India	(4) Card
156P	1c ultra	450.			55.	300.
	Block of 4				250.	
	P# blk. of 14				1,150.	
157P	2c brown	350.	175.	1,200.	35.	20.
	Block of 4				165.	100.
	P# blk. of 12				1,150.	—
a.	On stamp paper					
158P	3c green	350.	175.	1,200.	55.	150.
	Block of 4				250.	
	P# blk. of 14				1,150.	
f.	On stamp paper, pair					750.
g.	On stamp paper, grill, pair					650.
159P	6c pink	750.	250.	1,400.	110.	300.
	Block of 4				525.	
	P# blk. of 12				2,000.	
160P	7c orange vermilion	250.	175.	1,200.	35.	20.
	Block of 4				165.	100.
	P# blk. of 14				1,150.	—
161P	10c brown	450.	200.	1,200.	60.	300.
	Block of 4				300.	
	P# blk. of 14				1,300.	
162P	12c blackish violet	200.	175.	1,200.	38.	20.
	Block of 4				190.	100.
	P# blk. of 14				1,150.	—
a.	On stamp paper					
163P	15c yellow orange	400.	175.	1,200.	65.	20.
	Block of 4				250.	100.
	P# blk. of 12				1,000.	—
a.	On stamp paper					
164P	24c violet	400.	175.	1,200.	50.	30.
	Block of 4				225.	140.
	P# blk. of 12				1,150.	
165P	30c gray black	400.	175.	1,200.	40.	20.
	Block of 4				200.	90.
	P# blk. of 12				1,150.	
166P	90c rose carmine	400.	175.	1,200.	55.	40.
	Block of 4				250.	190.
	P# blk. of 12				1,500.	

Die proofs of the 24c, 30c and 90c show secret marks, as illustrated, but as plates of these denominations were not made from these dies, plate proofs can be identified only by color.

178P	2c vermilion					
a.	On stamp paper, pair					600.
	P# blk. of 12					6,000.
179P	5c blue					

1879 — American Bank Note Co.

182P	1c gray blue	525.			60.	
	Block of 4				275.	
					1,000.	
183P	2c vermilion	300.	190.	1,200.	35.	25.
	Block of 4				160.	120.
	P# blk. of 12				600.	

184P	3c green on stamp paper, pair					500.
	P# blk. of 12					—
185P	5c blue	450.	225.	1,200.	70.	25.
	Block of 4				325.	110.
	P# blk. of 12				1,300.	
190P	30c full black				—	150.
	Block of 4				—	600.
	P# blk. of 12					2,500.
191P	90c carmine on stamp paper, pair					2,500.
	P# strip of 5					—
193P	2c black brown					400.
	Block of 4					600.
	P# blk. of 12					2,500.

1881-82 — American Bank Note Co.

205P	5c yellow brown	250.	200.	1,200.	40.	15.
	Block of 4				175.	75.
	P# blk. of 12				1,000.	
206P	1c blue	375.	200.	1,200.	40.	20.
	Block of 4				175.	90.
	P# blk. of 12				1,000.	
207P	3c blue green	375.	200.	1,200.	40.	20.
	Block of 4				175.	90.
	P# blk. of 12				1,000.	
208P	6c rose	800.	200.	1,200.	90.	60.
	Block of 4				425.	210.
a.	6c brown red			1,200.	100.	50.
209P	10c brown	800.	200.	1,200.	40.	25.
	Block of 4				170.	110.
	P# blk. of 12				1,000.	

1883

210P	2c red brown	400.	200.	1,200.	40.	20.
	Block of 4				180.	85.
	P# blk. of 12				1,000.	
a.	On stamp paper, pair					—
211P	4c green	500.	200.	1,200.	40.	25.
	Block of 4				165.	110.
	P# blk. of 12				1,000.	
a.	On stamp paper, pair					—

1887-88

212P	1c ultra	650.	200.	1,200.	125.	2,000.
	Block of 4				600.	—
	P# blk. of 12				2,250.	—
a.	On stamp paper, pair					—

Examples of No. 212P3 mounted on card are frequently offered as No. 212P4.

213P	2c green	500.	190.	1,200.	75.	50.
	Block of 4				325.	225.
	P# blk. of 12				1,150.	—
a.	On stamp paper, pair					2,000.
214P	3c vermilion	500.	190.	1,200.	75.	50.
	Block of 4				325.	225.
	P# blk. of 12					—

Nos. 207P1 & 214P1 inscribed: "Worked over by new company, June 29th, 1881."

215P	4c carmine	650.	190.	1,200.	95.	50.
	Block of 4				475.	225.
	P# blk. of 12					—
216P	5c indigo	650.	190.	1,200.	75.	50.
	Block of 4				325.	225.
	P# blk. of 12					—
b.	On stamp paper, pair					1,400.
217P	30c orange brown	750.	190.	1,200.	75.	50.
	Block of 4				325.	225.
	P# blk. of 10					—
a.	On stamp paper, pair					1,750.
218P	90c purple	1,100.	190.	1,200.	90.	50.
	Block of 4				400.	225.
	P# blk. of 10					—
a.	On stamp paper, pair					—

1890-93

219P	1c ultra	225.	190.	1,100.	25.	40.
	Block of 4				110.	180.
	P# blk. of 12				500.	650.
c.	On stamp paper, pair					190.
219DP	2c lake	550.	190.	1,100.	80.	165.
	Block of 4				385.	700.
	P# blk. of 12				1,650.	3,250.
e.	On stamp paper, pair					80.
220P	2c carmine	450.	190.		300.	200.
	Block of 4				1,250.	825.
	P# blk. of 12				3,850.	2,500.
d.	On stamp paper, pair					125.
	As "d," without gum					60.
	P# blk. of 12					—
221P	3c purple	225.	190.	1,100.	35.	25.
	Block of 4				160.	110.
	P# blk. of 12				650.	600.
a.	On stamp paper, pair					225.
222P	4c dark brown	225.	190.	1,100.	35.	25.
	Block of 4				160.	110.
	P# blk. of 12				650.	600.
a.	On stamp paper, pair					210.

223P	5c chocolate	225.	190.	1,100.	32.	25.
	Block of 4				135.	110.
	P# blk. of 12				600.	625.
b.	Yellow brown, on stamp paper, pair					225.
224P	6c brown red	225.	190.	1,100.	32.	20.
	Block of 4				135.	85.
	P# blk. of 12				600.	775.
a.	On stamp paper, pair					225.
225P	8c lilac	600.	190.	1,100.	55.	110.
	Block of 4				250.	500.
	P# blk. of 12				1,100.	2,000.
a.	On stamp paper, pair					1,000.
226P	10c green	225.	190.	1,100.	45.	40.
	Block of 4				200.	180.
	P# blk. of 12				700.	750.
a.	On stamp paper, pair					325.
227P	15c indigo	300.	190.	1,100.	45.	40.
	Block of 4				190.	180.
	P# blk. of 12				825.	875.
a.	On stamp paper, pair					625.
228P	30c black	300.	190.	1,100.	45.	45.
	Block of 4				190.	190.
	P# blk. of 12				825.	875.
a.	On stamp paper, pair					1,000.
229P	90c orange	300.	190.	1,100.	60.	50.
	Block of 4				275.	225.
	P# blk. of 12				1,100.	1,150.
a.	On stamp paper, pair					1,450.

COLUMBIAN ISSUE

1893

230P	1c blue	700.	325.	1,400.	40.	25.
	Block of 4				175.	125.
	P# blk. of 8				400.	350.
231P	2c violet	800.	350.	1,750.	225.	65.
	Block of 4				1,000.	280.
	P# blk. of 8				2,250.	825.
b.	On stamp paper, pair					2,000.
c.	"Broken hat" variety					130.

Almost all examples of No. 231Pb are faulty. Value is for pair with minimal faults.

232P	3c green	700.	325.	2,000.	60.	50.
	Block of 4				260.	225.
	P# blk. of 8				675.	600.
233P	4c ultra.	700.	325.	2,000.	60.	50.
	Block of 4				260.	225.
	P# blk. of 8				675.	600.

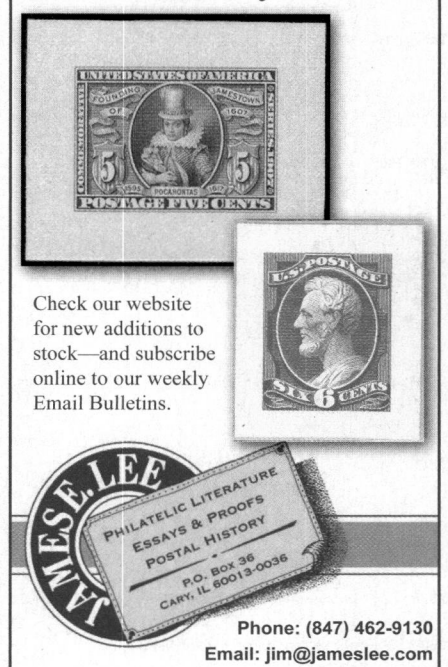

No.		Description					
233aP	4c	blue (error) on thin card			2,750.		
234P	5c	chocolate	700.	325.	2,000.	60.	45.
		Block of 4				260.	200.
		P# blk. of 8				675.	550.
235P	6c	purple	700.	325.	2,000.	60.	50.
		Block of 4				260.	225.
		P# blk. of 8				675.	600.
236P	8c	magenta	700.	325.	2,000.	60.	100.
		Block of 4				260.	450.
		P# blk. of 8				675.	1,250.
237P	10c	black brown	700.	325.	2,000.	60.	50.
		Block of 4				260.	225.
		P# blk. of 8				675.	600.
238P	15c	dark green	700.	325.	2,000.	60.	55.
		Block of 4				260.	250.
		P# blk. of 8				675.	1,400.
239P	30c	orange brown	700.	325.	2,000.	90.	65.
		Block of 4				400.	300.
		P# blk. of 8				1,250.	1,100.
240P	50c	slate blue	700.	325.	2,000.	135.	75.
		Block of 4				575.	350.
		P# blk. of 8				1,500.	1,100.
241P	$1	salmon	900.	450.	2,000.	160.	130.
		Block of 4				775.	575.
		P# blk. of 8				1,900.	
242P	$2	brown red	900.	450.	2,000.	180.	125.
		Block of 4				750.	550.
		P# blk. of 8				2,050.	1,500.
243P	$3	yellow green	900.	450.	2,000.	225.	150.
		Block of 4				1,000.	675.
		P# blk. of 8				2,700.	1,900.
244P	$4	crimson lake	900.	450.	2,000.	275.	175.
		Block of 4				1,200.	775.
		P# blk. of 8				3,000.	2,500.
245P	$5	black	900.	450.	2,000.	325.	225.
		Block of 4				1,425.	1,000.
		P# blk. of 8				3,500.	3,000.

This set also exists as Large Die proofs, not die sunk, but printed directly on thin card. Set value $4,725. 1c through 50c, $225 each; $1 through $5, $450 each.

Nos. 234P1, 234P2 differ from issued stamp.

Bureau of Engraving and Printing

1894

No.		Description					
246P	1c	ultra	450.				
247P	1c	blue	250.	250.	1,100.		100.
		Block of 4					450.
		P# blk. of 6					950.
248P	2c	pink, type I					100.
		Block of 4					475.
		P# blk. of 6					950.
250P	2c	car, type I	250.	250.			
251P	2c	car, type II	250.	—			

The existence of No. 251P2 has been questioned by specialists. The editors would like to see evidence that the item exists.

No.		Description				
252P	2c	car, type III	350.			
		Block of 4	1,500.			
253P	3c	purple (triangle I)	750.			
	a.	On stamp paper, pair				300.
		Block of 4				625.
		P# blk. of 6				3,500.
253AP	3c	purple (triangle II)	325.	250.	1,100.	
254P	4c	dark brown	250.	250.	1,100.	
	a.	On stamp paper, pair				300.
		Block of 4				625.
		P# blk. of 6				4,000.
255P	5c	chocolate	250.	250.	1,100.	
	b.	On stamp paper, pair				300.
		Block of 4				625.
		P# blk. of 6				4,500.
256P	6c	brown	250.	250.	1,100.	450.
		Block of 4				1,900.
		P# blk. of 6				3,750.
257P	8c	violet brown	275.	250.	1,100.	
258P	10c	green	275.	250.	1,100.	
	a.	On stamp paper, pair				500.
		Block of 4				1,100.
		P# blk. of 6				5,000.
259P	15c	dark blue	300.	250.	1,100.	
260P	50c	orange	450.	210.	1,100.	
261AP	$1	black	475.	350.	1,100.	
262P	$2	dark blue	475.	350.	1,100.	450.
		Block of 4				2,250.
		Margin block of 4, arrow				2,750.
		P# blk. of 6				6,250.
263P	$5	dark green	650.	375.	1,100.	450.
		Block of 4				2,250.
		Margin block of 4, arrow				2,750.
		P# blk. of 6				6,250.

1895

Imperf, with gum

No.		Description	
264P	1c	blue, on stamp paper, pair	275.
		Block of 4	750.
		P# blk. of 6	—
	b.	Horiz. P# strip of 3, perf horiz., imperf. vert.	7,500.
267P	2c	carmine, type III, on stamp paper, pair	225.
		Block of 4	600.
		P# blk. of 6	—
268P	2c	purple, on stamp paper, pair	275.
		Block of 4	750.
		P# blk. of 6	—
269P	4c	dark brown, on stamp paper, pair	275.
270P	5c	chocolate, on stamp paper, pair	275.
		Block of 4	750.
271P	6c	dull brown, on stamp paper, pair	300.
		Block of 4	800.
272P	8c	violet brown, on stamp paper, pair	450.
		Block of 4	1,250.
		P# blk. of 6	—
273P	10c	dark green, on stamp paper, pair	350.
		Block of 4	1,000.
274P	15c	dark blue, on stamp paper, pair	1,100.
		Block of 4	3,000.
275P	50c	orange, on stamp paper, pair	1,250.
		Block of 4	3,500.
276P	$1	black, type I, on stamp paper, pair	1,600.
		Block of 4	4,000.
277P	$2	bright blue, on stamp paper, pair	3,500.
		Block of 4	8,250.
278P	$5	dark green, on stamp paper, pair	3,500.
		Block of 4	8,250.

No. 264Pb exists only as a bottom margin P#24 and imprint strip of 3.

1897-1903

No.		Description				
279P	1c	green	700.	375.	1,100.	
279BdP	2c	orange red, type IV			1,100.	
279BfP	2c	car, type IV	400.		1,100.	
280P	4c	rose brown	700.		1,100.	
281P	5c	blue	700.	375.	1,100.	
282P	6c	lake	700.		1,100.	
283P	10c	orange brown, type II	800.	375.	1,100.	
283aP	10c	brown, type II	800.			
284P	15c	olive green, type II	800.	375.	1,100.	

TRANS-MISSISSIPPI ISSUE

1898

No.		Description				
285P	1c	green	650.	650.	1,250.	
286P	2c	copper red	650.	650.	1,250.	4,500.
287P	4c	orange	650.	650.	1,250.	
288P	5c	dull blue	650.	650.	1,250.	
289P	8c	violet brown	650.	650.	1,250.	
290P	10c	gray violet	650.	650.	1,250.	
291P	50c	sage green	650.	650.	1,250.	
292P	$1	black	750.	650.	1,250.	
293P	$2	orange brown	750.	650.	1,250.	6,000.
		Block of 4				30,000.
		P# block of 4				35,000.

The bicolored items commonly offered as No. 285-293 bicolored proofs can be found under the following essay listings: No. 285-E8a, 286-E8a, 287-E9a, 288-E5a, 289-E4a, 290-E4a, 291-E8a, 292-E6a, 293-E7a.

PAN-AMERICAN ISSUE

1901

No.		Description			
294P	1c	green & black	575.	575.	2,000.
295P	2c	carmine & black	575.	575.	2,000.
	b.	Small die proof on yellowish bond		1,250.	
296P	4c	chocolate & black	575.	575.	2,000.
297P	5c	ultra & black	575.	575.	2,000.
298P	8c	brown violet & black	575.	575.	2,000.
299P	10c	yel brn & blk	575.	575.	2,000.

1902-03

No.		Description			
300P	1c	green	1,500.	300.	2,500.
301P	2c	carmine	1,500.	300.	2,500.
302P	3c	purple	1,500.	300.	2,500.
303P	4c	orange brown	1,500.	300.	2,500.
304P	5c	blue	1,500.	300.	2,500.
305P	6c	lake	1,500.	300.	2,500.
306P	8c	violet black	1,500.	300.	2,500.
307P	10c	orange brown	1,500.	300.	2,500.
308P	13c	deep vio brn	1,500.	300.	2,500.
309P	15c	olive green	1,500.	300.	2,500.
310P	50c	orange	1,500.	300.	2,500.
311P	$1	black	1,500.	300.	2,500.
312P	$2	blue	2,000.	300.	2,500.
313P	$5	green	2,500.	375.	2,500.

1903

No.		Description			
319P	2c	carmine, Type I	1,500.		
319aP	2c	lake, Type I	—		
319iP	2c	carmine, Type II	2,000.	1,000.	3,500.
	b.	Small die proof on yellowish wove	1,000.		

LOUISIANA PURCHASE ISSUE

1904

No.		Description			
323P	1c	green	1,400.	750.	1,250.
324P	2c	carmine	1,400.	750.	1,250.
325P	3c	violet	1,400.	750.	1,250.
326P	5c	dark blue	1,400.	750.	1,250.
327P	10c	brown	1,400.	750.	1,250.

JAMESTOWN EXPOSITION ISSUE

1907

No.		Description			
328P	1c	green	1,000.	900.	1,250.
329P	2c	carmine	1,000.	900.	1,250.
330P	5c	blue	1,000.	900.	1,250.

1908-09

No.		Description			
331P	1c	green	1,250.	725.	1,200.
332P	2c	carmine	1,250.	725.	1,200.
		carmine, amber			
		carmine, lt blue			
333P	3c	deep violet	1,250.	725.	1,200.
334P	4c	brown	1,250.	725.	1,200.
335P	5c	blue	1,250.	725.	1,200.
		blue, salmon			
336P	6c	red orange	1,250.	725.	1,200.
337P	8c	olive green	1,250.	725.	1,200.
		olive green, yellow			
338P	10c	yellow	1,250.	725.	1,200.
339P	13c	blue green	1,250.	725.	1,200.
340P	15c	pale ultramarine	1,250.	725.	1,200.
341P	50c	violet	1,250.	725.	1,200.
		violet, pale lilac	—		
		violet, yellow	—		
		violet, greenish	—		
342P	$1	violet black	1,500.	725.	1,200.

LINCOLN MEMORIAL ISSUE

1909

No.		Description			
367P	2c	carmine	1,100.	1,000.	1,750.

ALASKA-YUKON ISSUE

1909

No.		Description			
370P	2c	carmine	1,100.	1,000.	1,750.

HUDSON-FULTON ISSUE

1909

No.		Description			
372P	2c	carmine	1,250.	1,000.	1,750.

PANAMA-PACIFIC ISSUE

1912-13

No.		Description			
397P	1c	green	1,750.	1,500.	1,250.
398P	2c	carmine	1,750.	1,500.	1,250.
399P	5c	blue	1,750.	1,500.	1,250.
400P	10c	org. yellow	1,750.	1,500.	1,250.
400AP	10c	orange	1,750.	1,500.	1,250.

No. 398P inscribed "Gatun Locks" is listed in the Essay section as No. 398-E3.

1912-19

No.		Description	DIE (1) Large	(2) Small	(2a)
405P	1c	green	1,400.	650.	1,200.
406P	2c	carmine	1,400.	650.	1,200.
407P	7c	black	1,400.	650.	1,200.
414P	8c	olive green	1,400.	650.	1,200.
415P	9c	salmon red	1,400.	650.	1,200.
416P	10c	orange yellow	1,400.	650.	1,200.
434P	11c	dark green	1,500.		
417P	12c	claret brown	1,400.	650.	1,200.
513P	13c	apple green	1,500.		
418P	15c	gray	1,400.	650.	1,200.
419P	20c	ultramarine	1,400.	650.	1,200.
420P	30c	orange red	1,400.	650.	1,200.
421P	50c	violet	1,400.	650.	1,200.
423P	$1	violet black	1,400.	650.	1,200.

1918-20

No.		Description	
524P	$5	deep green & black	1,500.
547P	$2	carmine & black	1,500.

VICTORY ISSUE

1919

No.		Description		
537P	3c	violet	1,100.	850.

PILGRIM ISSUE

1920

No.		Description		
548P	1c	green	1,250.	1,200.
549P	2c	carmine rose	1,250.	1,200.
550P	5c	deep blue	1,250.	1,200.

1922-26

No.		Description	LARGE DIE (1) India	(1a) White Wove	PLATE (3) White Wove	(4) Card
551P	½c	olive brown	1,500.			
552P	1c	deep green	1,000.	700.	—	
553P	1½c	yel brn	1,500.			
554P	2c	carmine	1,000.	700.	—	
555P	3c	violet	1,250.	1,000.		
556P	4c	yel brn	1,200.	700.	—	
557P	5c	dark blue	1,000.	700.	—	
558P	6c	red orange	1,000.	700.	—	
559P	7c	black	1,000.	700.	—	
560P	8c	olive green	1,000.	700.	—	
561P	9c	rose	1,000.	700.	—	
562P	10c	orange	1,000.	700.	—	
563P	11c	light blue	1,500.	700.	—	
564P	12c	brn vio	1,000.	700.	—	
622P	13c	green	1,000.	700.	—	
565P	14c	dark blue	1,250.	700.	—	
566P	15c	gray	1,250.	700.	—	
623P	17c	black	1,000.			
567P	20c	car rose	1,000.	700.	—	
568P	25c	deep green	1,000.	700.	—	
569P	30c	olive brown	1,000.	700.	—	
570P	50c	lilac	1,250.	700.	—	
571P	$1	vio brn	1,500.	700.	—	
572P	$2	deep blue	2,500.	700.	—	

No.	Description	LARGE DIE (1) India	(1a) White Wove	PLATE (3) White Wove	(4) Card
572P	$2 deep blue, small die on India	—			
573P	$5 carmine & dark blue	5,000.			

1923-26

No.	Description	LARGE DIE (1) India	(1a) White Wove	SMALL DIE (2) White or Yellowish Wove
610P	Harding, 2c black	1,400.	1,400.	1,000.
614P	Huguenot Walloon, 1c	750.	700.	700.
615P	Huguenot Walloon, 2c	750.	700.	700.
616P	Huguenot Walloon, 5c	750.	700.	700.
617P	Lexington Concord, 1c	750.	700.	700.
618P	Lexington Concord, 2c	750.	700.	700.
619P	Lexington Concord, 5c	750.	700.	700.
620P	Norse American, 2c	850.	850.	850.
621P	Norse American, 5c	850.	850.	850.
627P	Sesquicentennial, 2c	800.	750.	850.
628P	Ericsson, 5c	800.	750.	850.
629P	White Plains, 2c	800.	750.	850.

1927-29

No.	Description	India	White Wove	Small Die
643P	Vermont, 2c	800.	750.	850.
644P	Burgoyne, 2c	800.	750.	850.
645P	Valley Forge, 2c	800.	750.	850.
649P	Aeronautics, 2c	1,250.	900.	900.
650P	Aeronautics, 5c	1,250.	900.	900.
651P	Clark, 2c	900.	800.	850.
654P	Edison, 2c	900.	800.	850.
657P	Sullivan, 2c	850.	800.	850.
680P	Fallen Timbers, 2c	850.	800.	850.
681P	Ohio River Canalization, 2c	850.	800.	850.

1930-31

No.	Description	India	White Wove	Small Die
682P	Massachusetts Bay, 2c	850.	800.	750.
683P	Carolina Charleston, 2c	850.	800.	750.
684P	1½c brown	650.		
685P	4c brown	650.		
688P	Braddock's Field, 2c	850.	800.	750.
689P	von Steuben, 2c	850.	800.	750.
690P	Pulaski, 2c	850.	800.	750.
702P	Red Cross, 2c black & red		900.	900.
703P	Yorktown, 2c	1,250.	800.	750.

1932

Washington Bicentennial

No.	Description	India	White Wove	Small Die
704P	½c olive brown	1,000.	800.	750.
705P	1c green	1,000.	800.	750.
706P	1½c brown	1,000.	800.	750.
707P	2c carmine rose	1,000.	800.	750.
708P	3c deep violet	1,000.	800.	750.
709P	4c light brown	1,000.	800.	750.
710P	5c blue	1,000.	800.	750.
711P	6c red orange	1,000.	800.	750.
712P	7c black	1,000.	800.	750.
713P	8c olive bister	1,000.	800.	750.
714P	9c pale red	1,000.	800.	750.
715P	10c orange yellow	1,000.	800.	750.
716P	Winter Games, 2c	1,100.	950.	900.
717P	Arbor Day, 2c	900.	900.	800.
718P	Olympic Games, 3c violet	10,000.	950.	900.
719P	Olympic Games, 5c blue	15,000.	950.	900.
720P	3c deep violet	1,000.		
724P	Penn, 3c violet	800.	850.	750.
725P	Webster, 3c violet	800.	850.	750.

1933-34

No.	Description	India	White Wove	Small Die
726P	Georgia, 3c violet	700.	800.	650.
727P	Peace, 3c violet	700.	800.	650.
728P	Century of Progress, 1c	700.	800.	650.
729P	Century of Progress, 3c	700.	800.	650.
732P	N.R.A., 3c violet		900.	650.
733P	Byrd Antarctic, 3c	1,250.	900.	650.
734P	Kosciuszko, 5c blue	1,250.	800.	650.
736P	Maryland, 3c carmine rose	1,250.	800.	650.
737P	Mothers Day, 3c	800.		650.
739P	Wisconsin, 3c deep violet		800.	650.
740P	Parks, 1c green		800.	650.
741P	Parks, 2c red			650.
742P	Parks, 3c violet		800.	650.
743P	Parks, 4c brown			650.
744P	Parks, 5c blue			650.
745P	Parks, 6c dark blue			650.
746P	Parks, 7c black		800.	650.
747P	Parks, 8c sage green			650.
748P	Parks, 9c red orange	800.		650.
749P	Parks, 10c gray black			650.

1935-37

No.	Description	India	White Wove	Small Die
772P	Conn., 3c violet	1,150.		650.
773P	San Diego, 3c purple			650.
774P	Boulder Dam, 3c purple			650.
775P	Michigan, 3c purple			650.
776P	Texas, 3c purple			650.
777P	Rhode Is., 3c purple			650.
782P	Arkansas, 3c pur.	800.	800.	650.
783P	Oregon, 3c purple	—	800.	650.
784P	Anthony, 3c violet			650.
785P	Army, 1c green			800.
786P	Army, 2c carmine			800.
787P	Army, 3c purple	800.	800.	800.
788P	Army, 4c gray			800.
789P	Army, 5c ultramarine	1,350.	800.	800.
790P	Navy, 1c green			800.
791P	Navy, 2c car.	800.		800.
792P	Navy, 3c purple			800.
793P	Navy, 4c gray			800.
794P	Navy, 5c ultramarine			800.
795P	Ordinance, 3c red violet			650.
796P	Virginia Dare, 5c	800.		650.
797P	S.P.A. Sheet, 10c			650.
798P	Constitution, 3c red violet			650.
799P	Hawaii, 3c violet	800.		650.
800P	Alaska, 3c violet			750.
801P	Puerto Rico, 3c	800.		650.
802P	Virgin Is., 3c light violet	—		650.

PRESIDENTIAL ISSUE

1938

No.	Description	India	White Wove	Small Die
803P	½c deep orange	2,000.		650.
804P	1c green			650.
805P	1½c bister brown			650.
806P	2c rose carmine		1,800.	650.
807P	3c deep violet			650.
a.	On glazed card			
808P	4c red violet			650.
809P	4½c dark gray	1,500.		650.
810P	5c bright blue	1,500.		650.
811P	6c red orange			650.
812P	7c sepia	1,500.		650.
813P	8c olive green		1,800.	650.
814P	9c olive rose	1,800.	1,800.	650.
815P	10c brown red	2,500.		650.
816P	11c ultramarine			650.
817P	12c bright violet	1,500.		650.
818P	13c blue green			650.
819P	14c blue			650.
820P	15c blue gray	1,800.	1,800.	650.
821P	16c black	1,500.		650.
822P	17c rose red			650.
823P	18c brown carmine			650.
824P	19c bright violet	1,800.	1,800.	650.
825P	20c bright blue green	1,800.	1,800.	650.
826P	21c dull blue			650.
827P	22c vermilion			650.
828P	24c gray black	1,800.		650.
829P	25c deep red lilac			650.
830P	30c deep ultramarine			650.
831P	50c light red violet	1,250.		650.
832P	$1 purple & black			650.
833P	$2 yellow green & black			800.
834P	$5 carmine & black			800.

1938

No.	Description	India	White Wove	Small Die
835P	Constitution, 3c	—		600.
836P	Swedes & Finns, 3c			600.
837P	N.W. Territory, 3c			600.
838P	Iowa, 3c violet	1,250.		600.

1939

No.	Description	India	White Wove	Small Die
852P	Golden Gate, 3c	1,800.		600.
853P	World's Fair, 3c	1,250.		700.
854P	Inauguration, 3c	1,250.		650.
855P	Baseball, 3c violet	1,500.	2,000.	600.
856P	Panama Canal, 3c			600.
857P	Printing, 3c violet			600.
858P	Statehood, 3c rose violet			600.

FAMOUS AMERICANS ISSUE

1940

No.	Description	India	White Wove	Small Die
859P	Authors, 1c bright blue green			800.
860P	Authors, 2c rose carmine			800.
861P	Authors, 3c bright red violet			800.
862P	Authors, 5c ultramarine	800.		800.
863P	Authors, 10c dark brown	2,500.		800.
864P	Poets, 1c bright blue green	1,300.		800.
865P	Poets, 2c rose carmine			800.
866P	Poets, 3c bright red violet			800.
867P	Poets, 5c ultramarine	—		800.
868P	Poets, 10c dark brown	1,450.		800.
869P	Educators, 1c bright blue green			800.
870P	Educators, 2c rose carmine			800.
871P	Educators, 3c bright red violet			800.
872P	Educators, 5c ultramarine	800.		800.
873P	Educators, 10c dark brown	900.		800.
874P	Scientists, 1c bright blue green	1,450.		800.
875P	Scientists, 2c rose carmine	800.		800.
876P	Scientists, 3c bright red violet	800.		800.
877P	Scientists, 5c ultramarine			800.
878P	Scientists, 10c dark brown	1,300.		800.
879P	Composers, 1c bright blue green			800.
880P	Composers, 2c rose carmine	900.		800.
881P	Composers, 3c bright red violet			800.
882P	Composers, 5c ultramarine	800.		800.
883P	Composers, 10c dark brown			800.
884P	Artists, 1c bright blue green			800.
885P	Artists, 2c rose carmine	800.		800.
886P	Artists, 3c bright red violet			800.
887P	Artists, 5c ultramarine	800.		800.
888P	Artists, 10c dark brown			800.
889P	Inventors, 1c bright blue green			800.
890P	Inventors, 2c rose carmine	1,275.		800.
891P	Inventors, 3c bright red violet	800.		800.
892P	Inventors, 5c ultramarine			800.
893P	Inventors, 10c dark brown			800.

1940

No.	Description	India	White Wove	Small Die
894P	Pony Express, 3c henna brown	1,100.		600.
895P	Pan American, 3c light violet			600.
896P	Idaho, 3c bright violet	800.		600.
897P	Wyoming, 3c brown violet			600.
898P	Coronado, 3c violet	1,100.		600.
899P	Defense, 1c bright blue green	800.		600.
900P	Defense, 2c rose carmine	800.		600.
901P	Defense, 3c bright violet	800.		600.
902P	Emancipation, 3c deep violet	800.		750.

1941-44

No.	Description	India	White Wove	Small Die
903P	Vermont, 3c light violet			600.
904P	Kentucky, 3c violet	750.		600.
905P	Win the War, 3c violet			600.
906P	China, 5c bright blue			1,700.
907P	Allied Nations, 2c rose carmine			600.
908P	Four Freedoms, 1c br blue green	800.		600.
922P	Railroad, 3c violet	800.		600.
923P	Steamship, 3c violet	1,500.		600.
924P	Telegraph, 3c br red violet	800.		600.
925P	Corregidor, 3c deep violet	1,275.		600.
926P	Motion Picture, 3c deep violet	800.		600.

1945-46

No.	Description	India	White Wove	Small Die
927P	Florida, 3c br red violet	1,100.		600.
928P	United Nations, 5c ultramarine			600.
929P	Iwo Jima, 3c yellow green			600.
930P	Roosevelt, 1c br blue green			600.
931P	Roosevelt, 2c carmine rose	800.		600.
932P	Roosevelt, 3c purple	1,400.		600.
933P	Roosevelt, 5c bright blue			600.
934P	Army, 3c olive	1,250.		600.
935P	Navy, 3c blue	800.		600.
939P	Merchant Marine, 3c blue green			600.
941P	Tennessee, 3c dark violet	800.		
942P	Iowa, 3c deep blue	800.	800.	
944P	Kearny, 3c brown violet	800.		

1947-50

No.	Description	India	White Wove	Small Die
945P	Edison, 3c br red violet	700.		
946P	Pulitzer, 3c purple	1,100.	—	
947P	Stamp Centenary, 3c deep blue	—		
949P	Doctors, 3c brown violet	1,325.		
951P	Constitution, 3c blue green	700.	—	
955P	Mississippi, 3c brown violet	—		
956P	Four Chaplains, 3c gray black	—		
958P	Wisconsin, 5c deep blue	700.		
959P	Women, 3c dark violet	700.		
960P	White, 3c br red violet	900.		
962P	Key, 3c rose pink	700.		
965P	Stone, 3c bright violet	700.		
967P	Barton, 3c rose pink	1,900.		
971P	Volunteer Firemen, bright rose carmine	—		
972P	Indian Centennial, 3c dark brown	900.		
973P	Rough Riders, 3c violet brown	700.		
975P	Rogers, 3c br red violet	—		
976P	Fort Bliss, 3c henna brown	—		
977P	Michael, 3c rose pink	1,150.	—	
981P	Minnesota Terr., 3c blue green	1,500.	—	
983P	Puerto Rico, 3c green	1,000.		
985P	G.A.R., 3c br rose carmine	1,500.		
988P	Gompers, 3c br red violet	1,500.		
989P	Statue of Freedom, 3c br blue	1,500.	—	
991P	Supreme Court, 3c light violet	700.		
992P	Capitol, 3c br red violet	700.		

1951-53

No.	Description	India	White Wove	Small Die
999P	Nevada, 3c lt olive green	1,000.		
1000P	Cadillac, 3c blue	800.		
1001P	Colorado, 3c blue violet	1,250.		
1002P	Chemical, 3c violet brown	700.		
1003P	Brooklyn, 3c violet	1,325.	—	
1004P	Betsy Ross, 3c carmine rose	800.		
1005P	4H Clubs, 3c blue green	1,250.		
1006P	B. & O. Railroad, 3c br blue	1,750.		
1007P	A.A.A., 3c deep blue	700.	—	
1009P	Grand Coulee Dam, 3c blue green	700.		
1010P	Lafayette, 3c br blue	800.	800.	
1011P	Mt. Rushmore, 3c blue green	700.	—	
1012P	Engineering, 3c violet blue	—		
1013P	Service Women, 3c deep blue	800.		
1016P	Red Cross, 3c dp blue * carmine	—		
1017P	National Guard, 3c br blue	700.		
1018P	Ohio Statehood, 3c chocolate			
1019P	Washington, 3c green	700.		

1020P Louisiana, 3c violet brown   *800.*
1021P Japan, 5c green   *1,650.*
1022P American Bar, 3c rose   *700.*
     violet
1025P Trucking, 3c violet   *1,100.*
1026P Gen. Patton, 3c blue violet   *700.* —

1954

1029P Columbia, 3c blue   *700.*

LIBERTY ISSUE

1030P Franklin, ½c red orange   *1,250.*
1031P Washington, 1c dark green   *700.*
1032P Mount Vernon, 1½c brown   *900.*
     carmine
1033P Jefferson, 2c carmine rose   — —
1036P Lincoln, 4c red violet   *700.*
1038P Monroe, 5c dp blue   *700.*
1039P Roosevelt, 6c carmine   — —
1044P Independence Hall, 10c   —
     rose lake
1047P Monticello, 20c ultramarine   *1,100.*
1049P Lee, 30c black   *700.*
1050P Marshall, 40c brown red   *700.*
1051P Anthony, 50c br purple   *1,000.*
1052P Henry, $1 purple   *700.*
1053P Hamilton, $5 black   *1,200.*

1954-61

1060P Nebraska, 3c violet   *950.*
1062P Eastman, 3c brown orange   *900.*
1063P Lewis & Clark, 3c violet   *825.*   *825.*
     brown
1064P Academy of Fine Arts, 3c   *800.*
     rose brown
1067P Armed Forces Reserve, 3c   *1,275.*
     purple
1068P New Hampshire, 3c green   *700.*
1069P Soo Locks, 3c blue   *825.*
1071P Fort Ticonderoga, 3c lt   *825.*
     brown
1073P Franklin, 3c br carmine   *700.*   *700.*
1074P Washington, 3c dp blue   *700.*
1076P FIPEX, 3c & 8c S/S   *700.*
1077P Turkey, 3c rose lake   *800.*
1078P Antelope, 3c brown   *700.*
1079P Salmon, 3c bl green   *700.*
1080P Pure Food & Drug Act, 3c   *800.*
     dk bl green
1081P Wheatland, 3c black brown   *700.*
1082P Labor Day, 3c dp blue   *700.*
1083P Nassau Hall, 3c black,   *700.*
     orange
1085P Children, 3c dk blue   *800.*
1086P Hamilton, 3c rose red   *700.*
1087P Polio, 3c red lilac   *800.*
1088P Coast & Geodetic Survey,   — —
     3c dk blue
1090P Steel, 3c br ultramarine   *700.*
1092P Oklahoma, 3c dk blue   —
1178P Ft. Sumter, lt green   *1,500.*
1193P Project Mercury, dark blue   —
     & yellow

Nos. 1789P through 2788aP are all from the proof files of the American Bank Note Co. archives that were sold and that are available to collectors. Nos. 3261P-3262P were printed by the Banknote Corporation of America. All items listed are on gummed stamp paper and are imperf unless otherwise noted, and they therefore have the appearance of imperf or part-perf stamps, though their source makes clear that they are, in fact, proofs. This group includes progressive proofs in the different colors, plus one variety of No. 2624P and three varieties of No. 2770aP that differ slightly from the issued designs and, therefore, are actually essays. Where single proofs are listed, pairs are worth double the values shown.

1979-93

1789Pg finished design as issued, pair

1789Pd blue color only, pair

1789P   15c John Paul Jones
   a. Single, red color ("John Paul Jones") only   —
     pair with vert. gutter between   —
     pair with horiz. gutter between   —
     cross gutter block of four   —
   b. Single, yellow color only   —
     pair with vert. gutter between   —
     pair with horiz. gutter between   —
     cross gutter block of four   —
   c. Single, magenta color only   —
     pair with vert. gutter between   —
     pair with horiz. gutter between   —
     cross gutter block of four   —
   d. Single, blue color only   —
     pair with vert. gutter between   —
     pair with horiz. gutter between   —
     cross gutter block of four   —
   e. Single, black color only   —
     pair with vert. gutter between   —
     pair with horiz. gutter between   —
     cross gutter block of four   —
   f. Single, tagging blocks only   —
     pair with vert. gutter between   —
     pair with horiz. gutter between   —
     cross gutter block of four   —
   g. Single, finished design as issued   —
     pair   *50.*
     pair with vert. gutter between   *700.*
     pair with horiz. gutter between   *600.*
     cross gutter block of four   *3,000.*

2418P

2418P   25c Ernest Hemingway, pair   —
     Pair with vert. gutter between   —
     Pair with horiz. gutter between   —
     Cross gutter block of four   —

2478Pa cross gutter block

Illustration reduced.

2476P   1c Kestrel, pair   *300.*
     pair with vert. gutter between   *450.*
     pair with horiz. gutter between   *450.*
     cross gutter block of four   —
   a. Perforated
     Pair with vert. gutter between   *500.*
     Pair with horiz. gutter between   *500.*
     Cross gutter block of four   —
2478P   3c Bluebird, pair   *300.*
     pair with vert. gutter between   *450.*
     pair with horiz. gutter between   *450.*

---

     cross gutter block of four   —
   a. Se-tenants, Nos. 2476P and 2478P
     pair, one No. 2476P and one No.
     2478P, with vert. gutter between   —
     cross gutter block of four, two No.
     2476P at left and two No. 2478P
     at right   —
   b. Perforated
     pair with vert. gutter between   —
     pair with horiz. gutter between   —
     cross gutter block of four   —
   c. Perforated se-tenants
     pair, one No. 2476Pa and one No.
     2478Pb, with vert. gutter be-
     tween   —
     cross gutter block of four, two No.
     2476Pa at left and two No.
     2478Pb at right (unique)   —
2500aP   25c Olympics, horiz. strip of five   —
     two strips of five with vert. gutter
     between   —
     two strips of five with horiz. gutter
     between   —
     cross gutter block of four strips of
     five   —
2513P   25c Dwight D. Eisenhower, pair   —
2517P   (29c) "F" stamp, perforated
     pair with vert. gutter between   —
     pair with horiz. gutter between   —
     cross gutter block of four (unique)   —

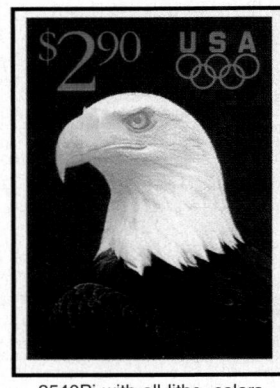

2540Pi with all litho. colors

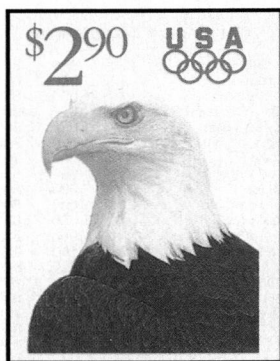

2540Pf magenta, yellow and blue colors only

2540P $2.90 Eagle
   a. Single, magenta color only   —
     pair with vert. gutter between   —
     pair with horiz. gutter between   —
     cross gutter block of four   —
   b. Single, yellow color only   —
     pair with vert. gutter between   —
     pair with horiz. gutter between   —
     cross gutter block of four   —
   c. Single, blue color only   —
     pair with vert. gutter between   —
     pair with horiz. gutter between   —
     cross gutter block of four   —
   d. Single, magenta and yellow colors only   —
     pair with vert. gutter between   —
     pair with horiz. gutter between   —
     cross gutter block of four   —
   e. Single, yellow and blue colors only   —
     pair with vert. gutter between   —
     pair with horiz. gutter between   —
     cross gutter block of four   —
   f. Single, magenta, yellow and blue colors only   —
     pair with vert. gutter between   —
     pair with horiz. gutter between   —
     cross gutter block of four   —
   g. Single, black (litho.) color only   —
     pair with vert. gutter between   —
     pair with horiz. gutter between   —
     cross gutter block of four   —
   h. Single, black (litho.) and yellow colors only   —
     pair with vert. gutter between   —
     pair with horiz. gutter between   —
     cross gutter block of four   —
   i. Single, all litho. colors but without black
     engr.   —

pair with vert. gutter between —
pair with horiz. gutter between —
cross gutter block of four —
j. Single, finished design as issued —
   pair —
   pair with vert. gutter between —
   pair with horiz. gutter between —
   cross gutter block of four —
k. Perforated, all litho. colors but without black
   engr. —
   pair with vert. gutter between —
   pair with horiz. gutter between —
   cross gutter block of four —
l. Perforated, finished design as issued —
   pair with vert. gutter between —
   pair with horiz. gutter between —
   cross gutter block of four —

2605P, with plate numbers

2605P	23c Flag Presorted First Class Coil,	
	vert. pair, uncut between	*400.*
	vert. pair, uncut between, with	
	P#A111	—
2624P	1c, 4c and $1 Columbian souvenir sheet	—
	pair of sheets	—
a.	As No. 2624P, but with background of No. 2627P (essay)	—
2625P	2c, 3c and $4 Columbian souvenir sheet	—
	pair of sheets	—
2626P	5c, 30c and 50c Columbian souvenir sheet	—
	pair of sheets	—
2627P	6c, 8c and $3 Columbian souvenir sheet	—
	pair of sheets	—
2628P	10c, 15c and $2 Columbian souvenir sheet	—
	pair of sheets	—
2629P	$4 Columbian souvenir sheet	—
	pair of sheets	—

2646aPi finished design as issued

2646aPe brown color only

Illustrations reduced.

2646aP	29c Hummingbirds booklet pane	
b.	Pane of five, yellow color only	—
	two panes of five with vert. gutter between	—
	two panes of five with horiz. gutter between	—
	cross gutter block of four panes of five	—
c.	Pane of five, magenta color only	—
	two panes of five with vert. gutter between	—
	two panes of five with horiz. gutter between	—
	cross gutter block of four panes of five	—
d.	Pane of five, blue color only	—
	two panes of five with vert. gutter between	—
	two panes of five with horiz. gutter between	—
	cross gutter block of four panes of five	—
e.	Pane of five, brown color (birds) only	—
	two panes of five with vert. gutter between	—
	two panes of five with horiz. gutter between	—
	cross gutter block of four panes of five	—
f.	Pane of five, brown color ("USA/29") only	—

two panes of five with vert. gutter
  between —
two panes of five with horiz. gutter
  between —
cross gutter block of four panes of
  five —
g. Pane of five, green color (frames) only —
  two panes of five with vert. gutter
    between —
  two panes of five with horiz. gutter
    between —
  cross gutter block of four panes of
    five —
h. Pane of five, orange color (frames) only —
  two panes of five with vert. gutter
    between —
  two panes of five with horiz. gutter
    between —
  cross gutter block of four panes of
    five —
i. Pane of five, finished design as issued —
  two panes of five with vert. gutter
    between —
  two panes of five with horiz. gutter
    between —
  cross gutter block of four panes of
    five —

2718aPd

2718aPe

Illustrations reduced.

2718aP	29c Christmas Toys booklet pane	*800.*
	horiz. pair of panes of four	*1,800.*
	vert. pair of panes of four	*1,800.*
b.	As No. 2718aP, pane of four with two stamps at top from bottom row of normal pane and two stamps at bottom from top row of normal pane	*1,200.*
c.	As No. 2718aP, perforated, pair of panes, uncut horiz.	*2,000.*
d.	Pane of four with two stamps at top from bottom row of normal pane and two stamps at bottom from top row of normal pane, perforated	*1,200.*
e.	Pane of four without red "Greetings" or green denominations	*1,200.*
f.	As No. 2718aPe, two stamps at top from bottom row of "normal" pane and two stamps at bottom from top row of "normal" pane	*1,500.*
g.	Pane of four without green denominations	*1,200.*
h.	As No. 2718aPg, two stamps at top from bottom row of "normal" pane and two stamps at bottom from top row of "normal" pane	*1,500.*
2737aP	29c American Music booklet pane of eight	—
	pair of panes of eight	—
c.	As No. 2737aP, perforated horiz., uncut vert., pair of panes of eight	—
2737bP	29c American Music booklet pane of four	—
d.	As No. 2737bP, perforated horiz., uncut vert., pair of panes of four	—
e.	Pair of panes, one No. 2737aP + one 2737bP	—
f.	Pair of panes, one No. 2737aPc + one 2737bPd	—

2754Pa

2754Pb

Illustration of No. 2754Pa reduced.

2754P	29c Cherokee Strip Land Run, pair	—
	pair with vert. gutter between	—
	pair with horiz. gutter between	—
	cross gutter block of four	—
a.	Perforated	—
	pair with vert. gutter between	—
	pair with horiz. gutter between	—
	cross gutter block of four	—
b.	As No. 2754P, without purple inscriptions and black denominations, pair	—
	pair with vert. gutter between	—
	pair with horiz. gutter between	—
	cross gutter block of four	—
c.	Die proof, signed 11/25/92 for color and/or engraving	—
2770aP	29c American Musicals booklet pane of four	—
	pair of panes	—
a.	Perforated horiz., uncut vert., pair of panes of four	—
b.	Pane of four, blue color only, with designs slightly different from issued designs (essay)	—
c.	Pane of four, blue and magenta colors only, with designs slightly different from issued designs (essay)	—
d.	Pane of four, blue, magenta and yellow colors only, with designs slightly different from issued designs (essay)	—
2778aP	29c American Music booklet pane of four	
a.	Pane of four, yellow color only	—
	on approval card (unique)	—
b.	Pane of four, pink color only	—
	on approval card (unique)	—
c.	Pane of four, red color only	—
	on approval card (unique)	—
d.	Pane of four, blue color only	—
	on approval card (unique)	—
e.	Pane of four, black color (frames and wording) only	—
	on approval card (unique)	—
f.	Pane of four, black color (Musicians) only	—
	on approval card (unique)	—
g.	Pane of four, finished design as issued	—
	on approval card (unique)	—
h.	Pane of four, finished design as issued, on cromalin paper, taped to approval card (unique)	—
i.	Booklet cover, finished design as issued, on card stock, pair of covers	—
j.	Booklet cover, finished design as issued, on cromalin paper, taped to approval card (unique)	—
k.	Perforated horiz., uncut vert., pair of panes of four	—

Some of the sets of progressive proofs are in panes that are 2 ½ to 3 ½ stamps tall. These sell for somewhat less than the full panes.

About 20 percent of the examples of No. 2778aPk are split into two pieces. From these pieces come horizontal pairs or blocks of booklet stamps imperf vertically.

2788aP	29c Classic Books, block of four	—
	pair of blocks with vert. gutter between	—
	pair of blocks with horiz. gutter between	—
	cross gutter block of four blocks	—

3261P

3262P

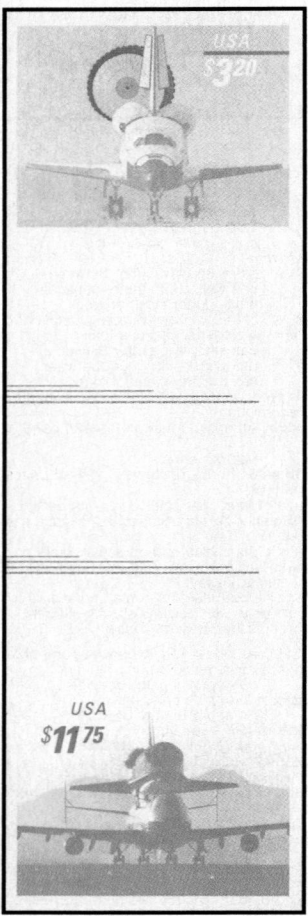

3262Pc

3261P $3.20 Space Shuttle, magenta color only
  a.   On coated paper   —
  b.   On uncoated paper   —
3262P $11.75 Piggyback Space Shuttle, cyan color only
  a.   On coated paper   —
  b.   On uncoated paper   —
  c.   As "a," vertical pair, #3261P and 3262P, with full horiz. gutter between   —
  d.   As "b," vertical pair, #3261P and 3262P, with full horiz. gutter between   —

AIR POST

1918

			DIE (1) Large (2) Small	
C1P	6c	orange	8,500.	
C2P	16c	green	7,000.	
C3P	24c	carmine rose & blue	8,500.	

1923

C4P	8c	dark green	4,750.	6,500.
C5P	16c	dark blue	4,750.	6,500.
C6P	24c	carmine	4,750.	6,500.

1926-27

C7P	10c	dark blue	3,000.	
C8P	15c	olive brown	3,000.	—
C9P	20c	yellow green	3,000.	

LINDBERGH ISSUE

1927

C10P	10c	dark blue	6,000.	6,000.

1928

C11P	5c	carmine & blue	6,000.	

1930

C12P	5c	violet	3,000.	

ZEPPELIN ISSUE

1930

C13P	65c	green	15,000.	8,250.
a.		on wove	15,000.	
b.		on stamp paper, imperf corner margin plate single		—
C14P	$1.30	brown	15,000.	8,500.
a.		on wove	15,000.	
b.		on stamp paper, imperf corner margin plate single		—
C15P	$2.60	blue	15,000.	8,500.
a.		on wove	15,000.	
b.		on stamp paper, imperf corner margin plate single		—

1932

C17P	8c	olive bister	4,000.	

CENTURY OF PROGRESS ISSUE

1933

C18P	50c	green	12,500.	8,250.

1935-39

C20P	25c	blue on wove		2,750.
C21P	20c	green on wove		2,750.
C22P	50c	carmine on wove		2,750.
C23P	6c	dark blue & carm. on wove		2,750.
C24P	30c	dull blue	3,500.	2,750.

1941-53

C25P	6c	carmine on wove		3,000.
C26P	8c	olive green on wove		3,000.
C27P	10c	violet on wove	5,000.	3,000.
C28P	15c	brown carmine on wove		3,000.
C29P	20c	bright green on wove		3,000.
C30P	30c	blue on wove		3,000.
C31P	50c	orange on wove		3,000.
C33P	5c	carmine	5,500.	
C40P	6c	carmine	5,000.	
C44P	25c	rose carmine	5,000.	3,500.
C45P	6c	magenta	6,000.	5,000.
C46P	80c	bright red violet	5,000.	
C47P	6c	carmine	6,000.	
C48P	4c	bright blue		—

AIR POST SPECIAL DELIVERY

1934

CE1P	16c	dark blue on wove	3,000.	

1936

CE2P	16c	red & blue on wove	3,000.	

SPECIAL DELIVERY

1885

			(1) Large	DIE (2) Small	(2a)	PLATE (3) India	(4) Card
E1P	10c	blue	600.	250.	2,250.	35.	30.
		Block of 4				175.	150.
		P# blk. of 8					—

1888

E2P	10c	blue	750.	250.	2,250.	35.	30.
		Block of 4				200.	150.
		P# blk. of 8				525.	—

1893

E3P	10c	orange	1,100.	300.	2,250.	65.	70.
		Block of 4				280.	310.
		P# blk. of 8					875.

1894-95

E4P	10c	blue	500.	250.	2,250.		
a.		On stamp paper, pair					5,500.
E5P	10c	blue, on stamp paper, pair					4,500.

1902

E6P	10c	ultra	900.	250.	1,250.		

1908

E7P	10c	green	2,250.	1,500.	2,250.		

1922

			LARGE DIE (1) India	(1a) White Wove	DIE (2) Small

1922

E12P	10c	deep ultra	1,850.	1,100.	

1925-54

E13P	15c	deep orange	1,750.		
E14P	20c	black	1,750.		
E17P	13c	blue			—
E20P	20c	deep blue	1,500.		

REGISTRATION

1911

			(1) Large	DIE (2) Small	(2a)	PLATE (3) India	(4) Card
F1P	10c	ultra	8,500.	1,000.	1,100.		

POSTAGE DUE

1879

J1P	1c	brown	250.	100.	500.	22.	10.
		Block of 4				105.	65.
		P# blk. of 12				450.	
J2P	2c	brown	250.	100.	500.	20.	10.
		Block of 4				90.	65.
		P# blk. of 12				425.	
		2c dark brown	—				
J3P	3c	brown	250.	100.	500.	20.	10.
		Block of 4				90.	65.
		P# blk. of 12				425.	
		3c dark brown	—	—			
J4P	5c	brown	250.	100.	500.	20.	10.
		Block of 4				90.	65.
		P# blk. of 12				425.	
		5c dark brown	—				
J5P	10c	brown	250.	—	500.		10.
		10c dark brown				32.	
		Block of 4				145.	65.
		P# blk. of 12				675.	
J6P	30c	brown	250.	100.	500.		10.
		30c dark brown	—			32.	
		Block of 4				145.	65.
		P# blk. of 12				675.	
J7P	50c	brown	250.	100.	500.		10.
		50c dark brown	—			32.	
		Block of 4				145.	65.
		P# blk. of 12				675.	

1887

J15P	1c	red brown	500.		15.
		Block of 4			
		P# blk. of 12			
J16P	2c	red brown	500.		15.
		Block of 4			
		P# blk. of 12			
J17P	3c	red brown	500.		20.
		Block of 4			
		P# blk. of 12			
J18P	5c	red brown	500.		15.
		Block of 4			
		P# blk. of 12			
J19P	10c	red brown	500.	19.	25.
		Block of 4		90.	
		P# blk. of 12		360.	
J20P	30c	red brown	500.	19.	18.
		Block of 4		90.	
		P# blk. of 12		360.	
J21P	50c	red brown	500.	45.	25.
		Block of 4		210.	
		P# blk. of 12		900.	

1891-93

J22P	1c	bright claret	140.	125.	500.	12.	17.
		Block of 4				65.	80.
		P# blk. of 12					—
a.		On stamp paper, pair					425.
J23P	2c	bright claret	140.	125.	500.	12.	17.
		Block of 4				65.	80.
		P# blk. of 12					—
a.		On stamp paper, pair					425.
J24P	3c	bright claret	140.	125.	500.	12.	17.
		Block of 4				65.	80.
		P# blk. of 12					—
a.		On stamp paper, pair					425.
J25P	5c	bright claret	140.	125.	500.	12.	17.
		Block of 4				65.	80.
		P# blk. of 12					—
a.		On stamp paper, pair					425.
J26P	10c	bright claret	140.	125.	500.	12.	17.

	Block of 4				65.	80.	
	P# blk. of 12					—	
a.	On stamp paper, pair					425.	
J27P	30c	bright claret	140.	125.	500.	28.	17.
	Block of 4				140.	80.	
	P# blk. of 12					—	
a.	On stamp paper, pair					500.	
J28P	50c	bright claret	140.	125.	500.	19.	17.
	Block of 4				90.	80.	
	P# blk. of 12					—	
a.	On stamp paper, pair					500.	

Values for J22Pa-J28Pa are for pairs with original gum and minor faults.

1894

J31P	1c	claret	165.	120.	500.	
a.	On stamp paper, pair					225.
	Block of 4					500.
J32P	2c	claret	165.	120.	500.	100.
	Block of 4					475.
	P# blk. of 6					3,000.
J33P	3c	claret	165.	120.	500.	
J34P	5c	claret	165.	120.	500.	
J35P	10c	claret	165.	120.	500.	
J36P	30c	claret	165.	120.	500.	
J37P	50c	claret	165.	120.	500.	

1925

J68P	½c	dull red	5,750.

1930-31

J69P	½c	deep car	450.
J70P	1c	deep car	450.
J71P	2c	deep car	450.
J72P	3c	deep car	450.
J73P	5c	deep car	450.
J74P	10c	deep car	450.
J75P	30c	deep car	450.
J76P	50c	deep car	450.
J77P	$1	deep car	1,400.
J78P	$5	deep car	1,400.

PARCEL POST POSTAGE DUE

1912

			DIE		PLATE	
			(1)	(2)	(3)	(4)
			Large	Small	(2a) India	Card
JQ1P	1c	dark green	600.	500.	700.	
JQ2P	2c	dark green	600.	500.	700.	
JQ3P	5c	dark green	600.	500.	700.	
JQ4P	10c	dark green	600.	500.	700.	
JQ5P	25c	dark green	600.	500.	700.	

CARRIERS

1851

LO1P	1c	blue (Franklin)	800.	300.	1,500.	50.	30.
	Block of 4					210.	125.
	Cracked plate					—	
LO2P	1c	blue (Eagle)	800.	300.	1,500.	50.	30.
	Block of 4					210.	125.
	P # blk. of 8					675.	

Nos. LO1P (1) and LO2P (1) exist only as hybrids.

OFFICIAL

AGRICULTURE

1873

O1P	1c	yellow	80.	100.	500.	15.	8.
	Block of 4					65.	50.
	P# blk. of 12						225.
O2P	2c	yellow	80.	100.	500.	15.	8.
	Block of 4					65.	50.
	P# blk. of 10						225.
O3P	3c	yellow	80.	100.	500.	15.	8.
	Block of 4					65.	50.
	P# blk. of 12						225.
O4P	6c	yellow	80.	100.	500.	15.	8.
	Block of 4					65.	50.
	P# blk. of 12						225.
O5P	10c	yellow	80.	100.	500.	15.	8.
	Block of 4					65.	50.
	P# blk. of 12						225.
O6P	12c	yellow	80.	100.	500.	15.	8.
	Block of 4					65.	50.
	P# blk. of 12						225.
O7P	15c	yellow	80.	100.	500.	15.	8.
	Block of 4					65.	50.
	P# blk. of 12						225.
O8P	24c	yellow	80.	100.	500.	15.	8.
	Block of 4					65.	50.
	P# blk. of 12						225.
O9P	30c	yellow	80.	100.	500.	15.	8.
	Block of 4					65.	50.
	P# blk. of 12						225.

EXECUTIVE

O10P	1c	carmine	100.	100.	500.	15.	10.
	Block of 4					65.	50.
	P# blk. of 14						225.
O11P	2c	carmine	100.	100.	500.	15.	10.
	Block of 4					65.	50.
	P# blk. of 12						225.
	Foreign entry of 6c Agriculture (pos. 40)					—	
O12P	3c	carmine	100.	100.	500.	15.	10.
	Block of 4					65.	50.
	P# blk. of 12						225.
O13P	6c	carmine	100.	100.	500.	25.	15.
	Block of 4					125.	85.
	P# blk. of 10						350.
O14P	10c	carmine	100.	100.	500.	15.	10.
	Block of 4					65.	50.
	P# blk. of 12						225.

INTERIOR

O15P	1c	vermilion	80.	100.	500.	15.	8.
	Block of 4					65.	50.
	P# blk. of 12						225.
O16P	2c	vermilion	80.	100.	500.	15.	8.
	Block of 4					65.	50.
	P# blk. of 10						200.
O17P	3c	vermilion	80.	100.	500.	15.	8.
	Block of 4					65.	50.
	P# blk. of 10						225.
O18P	6c	vermilion	80.	100.	500.	20.	10.
	Block of 4					90.	50.
	P# blk. of 12						250.
O19P	10c	vermilion	80.	100.	500.	15.	8.
	Block of 4					65.	45.
	P# blk. of 12						225.
O20P	12c	vermilion	80.	100.	500.	15.	8.
	Block of 4					65.	45.
	P# blk. of 10						225.
O21P	15c	vermilion	80.	100.	500.	15.	8.
	Block of 4					65.	45.
	P# blk. of 12						225.
O22P	24c	vermilion	80.	100.	500.	15.	8.
	Block of 4					65.	45.
	P# blk. of 12						225.
O23P	30c	vermilion	80.	100.	500.	15.	8.
	Block of 4					65.	45.
	P# blk. of 12						225.
O24P	90c	vermilion	80.	100.	500.	15.	8.
	Block of 4					65.	45.
	P# blk. of 12						225.

JUSTICE

O25P	1c	purple	80.	100.	500.	15.	8.
	Block of 4					65.	50.
	P# blk. of 12						225.
O26P	2c	purple	80.	100.	500.	15.	8.
	Block of 4					65.	50.
	P# blk. of 12						225.
O27P	3c	purple	80.	100.	500.	15.	8.
	Block of 4					65.	50.
	P# blk. of 12						225.
	Plate Scratches						—
O28P	6c	purple	80.	100.	500.	15.	8.
	Block of 4					65.	50.
	P# blk. of 12						225.
O29P	10c	purple	80.	100.	500.	15.	8.
	Block of 4					65.	50.
	P# blk. of 10						225.
O30P	12c	purple	80.	100.	500.	15.	8.
	Block of 4					65.	50.
	P# blk. of 12						225.
O31P	15c	purple	80.	100.	500.	15.	8.
	Block of 4					65.	50.
	P# blk. of 10						225.
O32P	24c	purple	80.	100.	500.	15.	8.
	Block of 4					65.	50.
	P# blk. of 12						225.
	Short transfer (pos. 98)						—
O33P	30c	purple	80.	100.	500.	15.	8.
	Block of 4					65.	50.
	P# blk. of 12						225.
O34P	90c	purple	80.	100.	500.	15.	8.
	Block of 4					65.	50.
	P# blk. of 10						225.

NAVY

O35P	1c	ultramarine	80.	100.	500.	15.	8.
	Block of 4					65.	50.
	P# blk. of 12						225.
O36P	2c	ultramarine	80.	100.	500.	15.	8.
	Block of 4					65.	50.
	P# blk. of 12						225.
O37P	3c	ultramarine	80.	100.	500.	15.	8.
	Block of 4					65.	50.
	P# blk. of 10						225.
O38P	6c	ultramarine	80.	100.	500.	20.	15.
	Block of 4					90.	75.
	P# blk. of 10						350.
O39P	7c	ultramarine	80.	100.	500.	15.	8.
	Block of 4					65.	50.
	P# blk. of 10						225.
O40P	10c	ultramarine	80.	100.	500.	15.	8.
	Block of 4					65.	50.
	P# blk. of 12						225.
O41P	12c	ultramarine	80.	100.	500.	15.	8.
	Block of 4					65.	50.
	P# blk. of 12						225.
O42P	15c	ultramarine	80.	100.	500.	15.	8.
	Block of 4					65.	50.
	P# blk. of 12						225.
O43P	24c	ultramarine	80.	100.	500.	15.	8.
	Block of 4					65.	50.
	P# blk. of 12						225.
O44P	30c	ultramarine	80.	100.	500.	15.	8.
	Block of 4					65.	50.
	P# blk. of 12						225.

O45P	90c	ultramarine	80.	100.	500.	15.	8.
	Block of 4					65.	50.
	P# blk. of 12						225.
	Short transfer at upper left (106, pos. 1, 5)						

POST OFFICE

O47P	1c	black	80.	100.	500.	15.	8.
	Block of 4					65.	50.
	P# blk. of 10						225.
O48P	2c	black	80.	100.	500.	15.	8.
	Block of 4					65.	50.
	P# blk. of 14						225.
O49P	3c	black	80.	100.	500.	15.	8.
	Block of 4					65.	50.
	P# blk. of 12						225.
O50P	6c	black	80.	100.	500.	15.	8.
	Block of 4					65.	50.
	P# blk. of 12						225.
O51P	10c	black	80.	100.	500.	15.	8.
	Block of 4					65.	50.
	P# blk. of 12						225.
O52P	12c	black	80.	100.	500.	15.	8.
	Block of 4					65.	50.
	P# blk. of 12						225.
O53P	15c	black	80.	100.	500.	15.	8.
	Block of 4					65.	50.
	P# blk. of 12						225.
O54P	24c	black	80.	100.	500.	15.	8.
	Block of 4					65.	50.
	P# blk. of 12						225.
O55P	30c	black	80.	100.	500.	15.	8.
	Block of 4					65.	50.
	P# blk. of 12						225.
O56P	90c	black	80.	100.	500.	15.	8.
	Block of 4					65.	50.
	P# blk. of 12						225.

STATE

O57P	1c	green	80.	100.	600.	15.	8.
	Block of 4					65.	50.
	P# blk. of 12						225.
O58P	2c	green	80.	100.	600.	15.	8.
	Block of 4					65.	50.
	P# blk. of 10						225.
O59P	3c	green	80.	100.	600.	15.	8.
	Block of 4					65.	50.
	P# blk. of 10						225.
O60P	6c	green	80.	100.	600.	25.	16.
	Block of 4					120.	85.
	P# blk. of 12						375.
O61P	7c	green	80.	100.	600.	15.	8.
	Block of 4					65.	50.
	P# blk. of 12						225.
O62P	10c	green	80.	100.	600.	15.	8.
	Block of 4					65.	50.
	P# blk. of 12						225.
O63P	12c	green	80.	100.	600.	15.	8.
	Block of 4					65.	50.
	P# blk. of 10						225.
O64P	15c	green	80.	100.	600.	15.	8.
	Block of 4					65.	50.
	P# blk. of 12						225.
O65P	24c	green	80.	100.	600.	15.	8.
	Block of 4					65.	50.
	P# blk. of 12						225.
O66P	30c	green	80.	100.	600.	15.	8.
	Block of 4					65.	50.
	P# blk. of 12						225.
O67P	90c	green	80.	100.	600.	15.	8.
	Block of 4					65.	50.
	P# blk. of 12						225.
O68P	$2	green & black	150.	125.	750.	85.	35.
	Block of 4					375.	175.
	Sheet of 10					—	5,000.
a.	Invtd. center						8,500.
	Half sheet of 5						42,500.
O69P	$5	green & black	150.	125.	750.	85.	35.
	Block of 4					375.	175.
	Sheet of 10						5,000.
a.	Invtd. center						8,500.
	Half sheet of 5						42,500.
	Sheet of 10						100,000.
O70P	$10	green & black	150.	125.	800.	85.	35.
	Block of 4					375.	
	Sheet of 10						5,000.
O71P	$20	green & black	150.	125.	800.	85.	35.
	Block of 4					375.	175.
	Sheet of 10						5,000.
a.	Invtd. center						7,500.
	Block of 4						40,000.
	Half sheet of 5						47,500.

O68P to O71P Large Dies exist as hybrids only.

TREASURY

O72P	1c	brown	80.	100.	500.	15.	8.
	Block of 4					65.	50.
	P# blk. of 12						225.
O73P	2c	brown	80.	100.	500.	15.	8.
	Block of 4					65.	50.
	P# blk. of 12						225.
O74P	3c	brown	80.	100.	500.	15.	8.
	Block of 4					65.	50.
	P# blk. of 14						225.
O75P	6c	brown	80.	100.	500.	20.	15.
	Block of 4					100.	75.
	P# blk. of 12						375.
O76P	7c	brown	80.	100.	500.	15.	8.
	Block of 4					65.	50.
	P# blk. of 12						225.
O77P	10c	brown	80.	100.	500.	15.	8.
	Block of 4					65.	50.
	P# blk. of 12						225.
O78P	12c	brown	80.	100.	500.	15.	8.
	Block of 4					65.	50.
	P# blk. of 12						225.

O79P	15c	brown	80.	100.	500.	15.	8.
		Block of 4				65.	50.
		P# blk. of 12					275.
O80P	24c	brown	80.	100.	500.	15.	8.
		Block of 4				65.	50.
		P# blk. of 12					225.
O81P	30c	brown	80.	100.	500.	15.	8.
		Block of 4				65.	45.
		P# blk. of 12					225.
O82P	90c	brown	80.	100.	500.	15.	8.
		Block of 4				65.	50.
		P# blk. of 12					225.

WAR

O83P	1c	rose	80.	100.	500.	15.	8.
		Block of 4				65.	50.
		P# blk. of 12					225.
O84P	2c	rose	80.	100.	500.	15.	8.
		Block of 4				65.	50.
O85P	3c	rose	80.	100.	500.	15.	8.
		Block of 4				65.	50.
		Plate flaw at upper left (32R20)					—
O86P	6c	rose	80.	100.	500.	15.	8.
		Block of 4				65.	50.
		P# blk. of 12					225.
O87P	7c	rose	80.	100.	500.	15.	8.
		Block of 4				65.	50.
		P# blk. of 10					225.
O88P	10c	rose	80.	100.	500.	15.	8.
		Block of 4				65.	50.
		P# blk. of 10					225.
O89P	12c	rose	80.	100.	500.	15.	8.
		Block of 4				65.	50.
		P# blk. of 12					225.
O90P	15c	rose	80.	100.	500.	15.	8.
		Block of 4				65.	50.
		P# blk. of 12					225.
O91P	24c	rose	80.	100.	500.	15.	8.
		Block of 4				65.	50.
		P# blk. of 10					225.
O92P	30c	rose	80.	100.	500.	15.	8.
		Block of 4				65.	50.
		P# blk. of 10					225.
O93P	90c	rose	80.	100.	500.	15.	8.
		Block of 4				65.	50.
		P# blk. of 12					225.

O83-O93 exist in a plum shade.

POSTAL SAVINGS MAIL

1911

O124P	1c	dark violet	450.	275.	1,000.
O121P	2c	black	450.	275.	1,000.
O126P	10c	carmine	450.	275.	1,000.
O122P	50c	dark green	450.	275.	1,000.
O123P	$1	ultramarine	450.	275.	1,000.

NEWSPAPERS

1865

			DIE			PLATE	
			(1) Large	(2) Small	(2a)	(3) Wove Paper	(4) Card
PR1P	5c	blue			3,500.		
PR2P	10c	green	575.	225	3,500.	40.	75.
		Block of 4				200.	375.
		P# blk. of 6					—
PR3P	25c	orange red	575.	225.	3,500.	45.	75.
		Block of 4				225.	375.
		P# blk. of 6					—
PR4P	5c	blue	575.	225.		40.	75.
		Block of 4				200.	375.
		P# blk. of 6					—

1875

PR5P	5c	dark blue					65.
PR6P	10c	deep green					65.
PR7P	25c	dark car red					65.
PR9P	2c	black	100.	50.	250.	15.	12.
		Block of 4				65.	55.
		P# blk. of 8					—
PR10P	3c	black	100.	50.	250.	15.	12.
		Block of 4				65.	55.
		P# blk. of 8					—
PR11P	4c	black	100.	50.	250.	15.	12.
		Block of 4				65.	55.
		P# blk. of 8					—
PR12P	6c	black	100.	50.	250.	15.	12.
		Block of 4				65.	55.
		P# blk. of 8					—
PR13P	8c	black	100.	50.	250.	15.	12.
		Block of 4				65.	55.
		P# blk. of 8					—
PR14P	9c	black	100.	50.	250.	15.	12.
		Block of 4				65.	55.
		P# blk. of 8					—
PR15P	10c	black	100.	50.	250.	15.	12.
		Block of 4				65.	55.
		P# blk. of 8					—
PR16P	12c	rose	100.	50.	250.	15.	12.
		Block of 4				65.	55.
		P# blk. of 8					—
PR17P	24c	rose	100.	50.	250.	15.	12.
		Block of 4				65.	55.
		P# blk. of 8					—
PR18P	36c	rose	100.	50.	250.	15.	12.
		Block of 4				65.	55.
		P# blk. of 8					—
PR19P	48c	rose	100.	50.	250.	15.	12.
		Block of 4				65.	55.

		P# blk. of 8					—
PR20P	60c	rose	100.	50.	250.	15.	12.
		Block of 4				65.	55.
		P# blk. of 8					—
PR21P	72c	rose	100.	50.	250.	15.	12.
		Block of 4				65.	55.
		P# blk. of 8					—
PR22P	84c	rose	100.	50.	250.	15.	12.
		Block of 4				65.	55.
		P# blk. of 8					—
PR23P	96c	rose	100.	50.	250.	15.	12.
		Block of 4				65.	55.
		P# blk. of 8					—
PR24P	$1.92	dark brown	100.	50.	250.	18.	15.
		Block of 4				80.	70.
PR25P	$3	vermilion	100.	50.	250.	18.	15.
		Block of 4				80.	70.
		P# blk. of 8					—
PR26P	$6	ultra	100.	50.	250.	18.	15.
		Block of 4				80.	70.
		P# blk. of 8					—
PR27P	$9	yellow	100.	50.	250.	18.	15.
		Block of 4				80.	70.
PR28P	$12	blue green	100.	50.	250.	18.	15.
		Block of 4				80.	70.
		P# blk. of 8					—
PR29P	$24	dark gray violet	100.	50.	250.	18.	15.
		Block of 4				80.	70.
		P# blk. of 8					—
PR30P	$36	brown rose	100.	50.	250.	21.	15.
		Block of 4				90.	70.
PR31P	$48	red brown	100.	50.	250.	23.	15.
		Block of 4				100.	70.
		P# blk. of 8					—
PR32P	$60	violet	100.	50.	250.	25.	18.
		Block of 4				110.	85.
		P# blk. of 8					—

1879

PR57P	2c	deep black	100.			25.	15.
		Block of 4				125.	90.
a.		On stamp paper, pair					—
PR58P	3c	deep black	100.			25.	15.
		Block of 4				125.	90.
a.		On stamp paper, pair					—
PR59P	4c	deep black	100.			25.	15.
		Block of 4				125.	90.
a.		On stamp paper, pair					—
PR60P	6c	deep black	100.			25.	15.
		Block of 4				125.	90.
a.		On stamp paper, pair					—
PR61P	8c	deep black	100.			25.	15.
		Block of 4				125.	90.
a.		On stamp paper, pair					—
PR62P	10c	deep black	100.			25.	15.
		Block of 4				125.	90.
a.		On stamp paper, pair					—
PR63P	12c	red	100.			25.	15.
		Block of 4				125.	90.
PR64P	24c	red	100.			25.	15.
		Block of 4				125.	90.
PR65P	36c	red	100.			25.	15.
		Block of 4				125.	90.
PR66P	48c	red	100.			25.	15.
		Block of 4				125.	90.
PR67P	60c	red	100.			25.	15.
		Block of 4				125.	90.
PR68P	72c	red	100.			25.	15.
		Block of 4				125.	90.
PR69P	84c	red	100.			25.	15.
		Block of 4				125.	90.
PR70P	96c	red	100.			25.	15.
		Block of 4				125.	90.
PR71P	$1.92	pale brown	100.			25.	15.
		Block of 4				125.	90.
a.		On stamp paper, pair					—
PR72P	$3	red verm.	100.			25.	15.
		Block of 4				125.	90.
a.		On stamp paper, pair					—
PR73P	$6	blue	100.			25.	15.
		Block of 4				125.	90.
a.		On stamp paper, pair					—
PR74P	$9	orange	100.			25.	15.
		Block of 4				125.	90.
a.		On stamp paper, pair					—
PR75P	$12	yel. green	100.			25.	15.
		Block of 4				125.	90.
a.		On stamp paper, pair					—
PR76P	$24	dark violet	100.			25.	15.
		Block of 4				125.	90.
a.		On stamp paper, pair					—
PR77P	$36	Indian red	100.			25.	15.
		Block of 4				125.	90.
a.		On stamp paper, pair					—
PR78P	$48	yellow brown	100.			25.	15.
		Block of 4				125.	90.
a.		On stamp paper, pair					—
PR79P	$60	purple	100.			25.	15.
		Block of 4				125.	90.
a.		On stamp paper, pair					

1885

PR81P	1c	black	100.	60.	250.	25.	15.
		Block of 4				125.	90.
		P# blk. of 8					425.
a.		On stamp paper, pair					—
PR82P	12c	carmine			80.	250.	25.	15.
		Block of 4				125.	
a.		On stamp paper, pair					—
PR83P	24c	carmine			80.	250.	25.	15.
		Block of 4				125.	
a.		On stamp paper, pair					—
PR84P	36c	carmine			80.	250.	25.	15.
		Block of 4				125.	
a.		On stamp paper, pair					—
PR85P	48c	carmine			80.	250.	25.	15.
		Block of 4				125.	
a.		On stamp paper, pair					—
PR86P	60c	carmine			80.	250.	25.	15.
		Block of 4				125.	
a.		On stamp paper, pair					—
PR87P	72c	carmine			80.	250.	25.	15.
		Block of 4				125.	
a.		On stamp paper, pair					—
PR88P	84c	carmine			80.	250.	25.	15.
		Block of 4				125.	
a.		On stamp paper, pair					—
PR89P	96c	carmine			80.	250.	25.	15.
		Block of 4				125.	
a.		On stamp paper, pair					—

1895

PR102P	1c	black	125.	100.	275.
PR103P	2c	black	125.	100.	275.
PR104P	5c	black	125.	100.	275.
PR105P	10c	black	125.	100.	275.
PR106P	25c	carmine	125.	100.	275.
PR107P	50c	carmine	125.	100.	275.
PR108P	$2	scarlet	125.	100.	275.
PR109P	$5	blue	125.	100.	275.
PR110P	$10	green	125.	100.	275.
PR111P	$20	slate	125.	100.	275.
PR112P	$50	carmine	125.	100.	275.
PR113P	$100	purple	125.	100.	275.

PARCEL POST

1912-13

			DIE ON INDIA			PLATE	
			(1) Large	(2) Small	(2a)	(3) India	(4) Card
Q1P	1c	car rose	1,400.	1,200.	1,200.		
Q2P	2c	car rose	1,400.	1,200.	1,200.		
Q3P	3c	car rose	1,400.	1,200.	1,200.		
Q4P	4c	car rose	1,400.	1,200.	1,200.		
Q5P	5c	car rose	1,400.	1,200.	1,200.		
Q6P	10c	car rose	1,400.	1,200.	1,200.		
Q7P	15c	car rose	1,400.	1,200.	1,200.		
Q8P	20c	car rose	1,400.	1,200.	1,200.		
Q9P	25c	car rose	1,400.	1,200.	1,200.		
Q10P	50c	car rose	1,400.	1,200.	1,200.		
Q11P	75c	car rose	1,400.	1,200.	1,200.		
Q12P	$1	car rose	1,400.	1,200.	1,200.		

SPECIAL HANDLING

1925-28

QE1P	10c	yel grn	1,500.
QE2P	15c	yel grn	1,500.
QE3P	20c	yel grn	1,500.
QE4P	25c	deep grn	1,500.
QE4aP	25c	yel grn	1,500.

LOCAL

1844

5L1P	5c	black	3,500.

TELEGRAPH

AMERICAN RAPID TELEGRAPH CO.

1881

			DIE (2) Small	PLATE (3) India
1T1P	1c	black	80.	32.
		Pair		68.
1T2P	3c	orange		32.
		Pair		68.
1T3P	5c	bister brown	80.	32.

No.	Denom.	Description	DIE (2) Small	PLATE (3) India
		Pair		68.
1T4P	10c purple			32.
		Pair		68.
1T5P	15c green		80.	32.
		Pair		68.
1T6P	20c red		80.	32.
		Pair		68.
1T7P	25c rose		80.	32.
		Pair		68.
1T8P	50c blue			32.
		Pair		68.

"Collect"

No.	Denom.	Description	Small	India
1T9P	1c brown			32.
		Pair, Nos. 1T9P, 1T13P		68.
		Same, block of 4		145.
1T10P	5c blue			32.
		Pair, Nos. 1T10P, 1T14P		68.
		Same, block of 4		145.
1T11P	15c red brown			32.
		Pair, Nos. 1T11P, 1T15P		68.
		Same, block of 4		145.
1T12P	20c olive green			32.
		Pair, Nos. 1T12P, 1T16P		68.
		Same, block of 4		145.

Office Coupon

No.	Denom.	Description	Small	India
1T13P	1c brown			32.
1T14P	5c blue			32.
1T15P	15c red brown			32.
1T16P	20c olive green			32.

BALTIMORE & OHIO TELEGRAPH CO.

1885

No.	Denom.	Description	Small	India
3T1P	1c vermilion			32.
		Pair		68.
3T2P	5c blue			32.
		Pair		68.
3T3P	10c red brown			32.
		Pair		68.
3T4P	25c orange			32.
		Pair		68.

1886

No.	Denom.	Description	Small	India
3T6P		black		32.
		Pair		68.
3T7P	1c green			32.
3T8P	5c blue			32.
3T9P	10c brown			32.
3T10P	25c orange			32.

POSTAL TELEGRAPH CO.

1885

No.	Denom.	Description	DIE (1) Large	(2) Small	PLATE (3) India
15T1P	10c green			55.	32.
15T2P	15c orange red				32.
15T3P	25c blue		65.		32.
15T4P	50c brown			65.	32.

WESTERN UNION TELEGRAPH CO.

No.	Year	Color	India
16T1P	(1871)	green	17.
		Pair	35.
16T2P	(1872)	red	17.
		Pair	35.
16T3P	(1873)	blue	17.
		Pair	35.
16T4P	(1874)	brown	17.
		Pair	35.
16T5P	(1875)	deep green	17.
16T6P	(1876)	red	—
16T7P	(1877)	violet	
16T8P	(1878)	gray brown	20.
16T9P	(1879)	blue	14.
16T10P	(1880)	lilac rose	16.
16T11P	(1881)	green	16.
16T12P	(1882)	blue	20.
16T13P	(1883)	yellow brown	16.
16T14P	(1884)	gray violet	20.
16T15P	(1885)	green	20.
16T16P	(1886)	brown violet	13.
		Pair	28.
16T17P	(1887)	red brown	13.
		Pair	28.
16T18P	(1888)	blue	13.
		Pair	28.
16T19P	(1889)	olive green	16.
16T22P	(1892)	vermilion	16.
16T30P	(1900)	red violet	28.
16T44P	(1913)	brown	— — —

REVENUE

NORMAL COLORS

1862-68 by Butler & Carpenter, Philadelphia.
1868-75 by Joseph R. Carpenter, Philadelphia.

In the following listing the so-called small die proofs on India paper may be, in fact probably are, plate proofs. The editors shall consider them die proofs, however, until they see them in pairs or blocks. Many revenue proofs on India are mounted on card.

FIRST ISSUE

1862-71

No.	Denom.	Description	DIE ON INDIA (1) Large	(2) Small	PLATE (3) India	(4) Card
R1P	1c	Express, red			70.	65.
		Block of 4				275.
R2P	1c	Playing Cards, red	600.		60.	65.
		Block of 4			250.	275.
R3P	1c	Proprietary, red			140.	45.
		Block of 4				200.
R4P	1c	Telegraph, red				28.
		Block of 4				125.
R5P	2c	Bank Check, blue		525.		33.
		Block of 4				140.
R6P	2c	Bank Check, orange			60.	
		Block of 4				250.
R7P	2c	Certificate, blue				28.
		Block of 4				125.
R8P	2c	Certificate, orange			82.	
		Block of 4				350.
R9P	2c	Express, blue				28.
		Block of 4				125.
R10P	2c	Express, orange	600.		60.	
		Pair			250.	
R11P	2c	Playing Cards, blue				38.
		Block of 4				160.
R13P	2c	Proprietary, blue		400.		28.
		Block of 4				125.
R15P	2c	U.S.I.R., orange			1,250.	
R16P	3c	Foreign Exchange, green	600.	225.		38.
		Block of 4				160.
		R16P1 + R19P1 composite	—			
R17P	3c	Playing Cards, green	700.	400.		100.
		Block of 4				425.
R18P	3c	Proprietary, green			60.	28.
		Block of 4			250.	125.
R19P	3c	Telegraph, green	600.	225.		28.
		Block of 4				125.
R20P	4c	Inland Exchange, brown			225.	28.
		Block of 4				125.
R21P	4c	Playing Cards, violet		400.		95.
		Block of 4				400.
R22P	4c	Proprietary, violet	600.		110.	60.
		Block of 4			475.	250.
R23P	5c	Agreement, red				33.
		Block of 4				140.
R24P	5c	Certificate, red			95.	110.
		Block of 4			400.	
		R24P1 + R25P1 composite	—			
R25P	5c	Express, red		250.		33.
		Block of 4				145.
R26P	5c	Foreign Exchange, red				300.
R27P	5c	Inland Exchange, red		250.		28.
		Block of 4				125.
R28P	5c	Playing Cards, red		—	105.	325.
		Block of 4			440.	
R29P	5c	Proprietary, red on blue wove, gummed				—
R30P	6c	Inland Exchange, orange			60.	33.
		Block of 4			250.	140.
R32P	10c	Bill of Lading, blue				33.
		Block of 4				140.
R33P	10c	Certificate, blue			140.	33.
		Block of 4				140.
R34P	10c	Contract, blue				33.
		Block of 4				140.
R35P	10c	Foreign Exchange, blue				33.
		Block of 4				140.
R36P	10c	Inland Exchange, blue				33.
		Block of 4				140.
R37P	10c	Power of Attorney, blue				33.
		Block of 4				140.
R38P	10c	Proprietary, blue		700.	70.	
		Block of 4			300.	

No.	Denom.	Description	DIE ON INDIA (1) Large	(2) Small	PLATE (3) India	(4) Card
R39P	15c	Foreign Exchange, brown			90.	325.
		Block of 4			375.	1,600.
R40P	15c	Inland Exchange, brown			120.	33.
		Block of 4				140.
R41P	20c	Foreign Exchange, red	600.		90.	100.
		Block of 4			375.	425.
		R41P1 + R42P1 composite	—			
R42P	20c	Inland Exchange, red	600.	250.	260.	33.
		Block of 4				140.
R43P	25c	Bond, red				500.
		Block of 4				2,500.
R44P	25c	Certificate, red				33.
		Block of 4				140.
R45P	25c	Entry of Goods, red				550.
R46P	25c	Insurance, red			60.	33.
		Block of 4			250.	140.
R47P	25c	Life Insurance, red				33.
		Block of 4				140.
R48P	25c	Power of Attorney, red				33.
		Block of 4				140.
R49P	25c	Protest, red				33.
		Block of 4				140.
R50P	25c	Warehouse Receipt, red				33.
		Block of 4				140.
R51P	30c	Foreign Exchange, lilac			110.	100.
		Block of 4			475.	425.
R52P	30c	Inland Exchange, lilac			65.	55.
		Block of 4			275.	230.
R53P	40c	Inland Exchange, brown			150.	75.
		Block of 4				325.
R54P	50c	Conveyance, blue		250.		33.
		Block of 4				140.
R55P	50c	Entry of Goods, blue			65.	45.
		Block of 4			275.	190.
R56P	50c	Foreign Exchange, blue			65.	45.
		Block of 4			275.	190.
R57P	50c	Lease, blue			65.	38.
		Block of 4			275.	160.
R58P	50c	Life Insurance, blue			65.	38.
		Block of 4			275.	160.
R59P	50c	Mortgage, blue				110.
		Block of 4			65.	475.
R60P	50c	Original Process, blue				38.
		Block of 4			275.	160.
R61P	50c	Passage Ticket, blue				55.
		Block of 4				230.
R62P	50c	Probate of Will, blue			65.	55.
		Block of 4			275.	230.
R63P	50c	Surety Bond, blue				55.
		Block of 4				230.
R64P	60c	Inland Exchange, orange			55.	38.
		Block of 4				160.
R65P	70c	Foreign Exchange, green			120.	55.
		Block of 4				230.
R66P	$1	Conveyance, red				45.
		Block of 4				190.
R67P	$1	Entry of Goods, red		525.		45.
		Block of 4				190.
R68P	$1	Foreign Exchange red				33.
		Block of 4				140.
R69P	$1	Inland Exchange, red				55.
		Block of 4				230.
R70P	$1	Lease, red				*425.*
R71P	$1	Life Insurance, red				33.
		Block of 4				140.
R72P	$1	Manifest, red			55.	33.
		Block of 4			—	140.
R73P	$1	Mortgage, red			55.	
		Block of 4				230.

FIRST ISSUE (continued)

			DIE ON INDIA (1) Large	(2) Small	PLATE (3) India	(4) Card
R74P	$1	Passage Ticket, red				425.
		Block of 4				1,850.
R75P	$1	Power of Attorney, red				100.
		Block of 4				425.
R76P	$1	Probate of Will, red				33.
		Block of 4				140.
R77P	$1.30	Foreign Exchange, orange	700.		140.	100.
		Block of 4			575.	425.
R78P	$1.50	Inland Exchange, blue			110.	45.
		Block of 4			475.	190.
R79P	$1.60	Foreign Exchange green			140.	100.
		Block of 4				425.
R80P	$1.90	Foreign Exchange, violet			140.	100.
		Block of 4			575.	425.
R81P	$2	Conveyance, red			120.	33.
		Block of 4				140.
R82P	$2	Mortgage, red			120.	33.
		Block of 4			—	140.
R83P	$2	Probate of Will, red				110.
		Block of 4				—
R84P	$2.50	Inland Exchange, violet			250.	225.
		Block of 4				—
R85P	$3	Charter Party, green			120.	65.
		Block of 4			500.	275.
R86P	$3	Manifest, green	—	350.	180.	65.
		Block of 4				275.
R87P	$3.50	Inland Exchange, blue			180.	140.
		Block of 4				575.
R88P	$5	Charter Party, red			70.	55.
		Block of 4			300.	230.
R89P	$5	Conveyance, red			450.	55.
		Block of 4				230.
R90P	$5	Manifest, red		300.		55.
		Block of 4				230.
R91P	$5	Mortgage, red			650.	55.
		Block of 4				230.
R92P	$5	Probate of Will, red		300.		55.
		Block of 4				230.
R93P	$10	Charter Party, green			120.	55.
		Block of 4				230.
R94P	$10	Conveyance, green				55.
		Block of 4				230.
R95P	$10	Mortgage, green				55.
		Block of 4				230.
R96P	$10	Probate of Will, green	700.	300.		75.
		Block of 4				325.
R97P	$15	Mortgage, dark blue		—		180.
		Block of 4				800.
R97eP	$15	Mortgage, ultramarine		—		350.
		Block of 4				—
R97fP	$15	Mortgage, milky blue			290.	
R98P	$20	Conveyance, orange			220.	100.
		Block of 4			900.	425.
R99P	$20	Probate of Will, orange			220.	
		Block of 4				—
R100P	$25	Mortgage, red			220.	160.
		Block of 4				675.
R101P	$50	U.S.I.R., green			220.	230.
		Block of 4				950.
R102P	$200	U.S.I.R., green & orange red			1,400.	

SECOND ISSUE
1871-72

			DIE ON INDIA (1) Large	(2) Small	PLATE (3) India	(4) Card
R105P	3c	blue & black			20.	15.
		Block of 4			90.	65.
R109P	10c	blue & black			20.	15.
		Block of 4			90.	65.
R111P	20c	blue & black			20.	15.
		Block of 4			90.	65.
R112P	25c	blue & black			20.	15.
		Block of 4			90.	65.
R115P	50c	blue & black			50.	15.
		Block of 4			225.	65.
R119P	$1.30	blue & black			50.	38.
		Block of 4			225.	160.
R120P	$1.50	blue & black			28.	22.

(continued)

			DIE ON INDIA (1) Large	(2) Small	PLATE (3) India	(4) Card
		Block of 4			120.	100.
		Double transfer, design of $1				—
R121P	$1.60	blue & black			60.	60.
		Block of 4			260.	260.
R122P	$1.90	blue & black			50.	38.
		Block of 4			225.	170.
R126P	$3.50	blue & black			90.	100.
		Block of 4			400.	425.
R130P	$25	blue & black			150.	110.
		Block of 4			650.	500.
R131P	$50	blue & black			160.	140.
		Block of 4			700.	625.

The "small die proofs" formerly listed under Nos. R103P-R131P are plate proofs from the sheets listed under "Trial Color Proofs."

			DIE ON INDIA (1) Large	(2) Small	PLATE (3) India	(4) Card
R132P	$200	red, blue & black	3,500.	2,750.	2,500.	
		Red (frame) inverted				—
R133P	$500	red orange, green & black	3,750.			
R133AP	$5000	red orange, dark green & black	7,500.			

No. R133AP was approved in these colors but never issued. Shade differences of the red orange and dark green colors will be found. It comes both with and without manufacturer's imprints to the left and right of the design. One example exists on bond paper mounted on card with "853½" printed on the lower right card margin.

Due to the unusual manufacturing process of printing these tri-color stamps from single impression plates, proofs with imprints could also be considered to be plate proofs. All are extremely scarce or unique, and are valued in the grade, condition and scarcity in which they exist. For other colors see the trial color proofs listings under No. R133ATC.

THIRD ISSUE
1871-72

			PLATE (3) India	(4) Card
R134P	1c	claret & black		15.
		Block of 4		70.
R135P	2c	orange & black	16.	15.
		Block of 4	70.	70.
R136P	4c	brown & black	20.	15.
		Block of 4	85.	70.
R137P	5c	orange & black	20.	15.
		Block of 4	85.	70.
R138P	6c	orange & black	20.	15.
		Block of 4	85.	70.
R139P	15c	brown & black	20.	15.
		Block of 4	85.	70.
R140P	30c	orange & black	25.	18.
		Block of 4	105.	80.
R141P	40c	brown & black	25.	18.
		Block of 4	105.	80.
R142P	60c	orange & black	65.	50.
		Block of 4	270.	225.
a.		Foreign entry, design of 70c	200.	150.
		Center inverted		2,250.
		Block of 4		10,000.
		Foreign entry, design of 70c		
R143P	70c	green & black	45.	38.
		Block of 4	190.	170.
R144P	$1	green & black	40.	38.
		Block of 4	170.	170.
R145P	$2	vermilion & black	80.	105.
		Block of 4	335.	450.
R146P	$2.50	claret & black	50.	40.
		Block of 4	210.	170.
R147P	$3	green & black	65.	70.
		Block of 4	270.	300.
R148P	$5	vermilion & black	65.	55.
		Block of 4	270.	240.
R149P	$10	green & black	80.	55.
		Block of 4	335.	240.
R150P	$20	orange & black	115.	150.
		Block of 4	500.	635.

The "small die proofs" formerly listed under Nos. R134P-R150P are plate proofs from the sheets listed under "Trial Color Proofs."

1875   National Bank Note Co., New York City

			DIE ON INDIA (1) Large	(2) Small	PLATE (3) India
R152P	2c	blue (Liberty)	450.		110.
		Block of 4			475.

DOCUMENTARY
1898

R173P	$1	dark green	600.
R174P	$3	dark brown	600.
R175P	$5	orange red	600.
R176P	$10	black	600.
R177P	$30	red	600.
R178P	$50	gray brown	600.

1899

R180P	$500	car lake & blk	1,650.

1914

R197P	2c	rose	—

1914-15

R226P	$500	blue	675.

1917

R246P	$30	deep orange (without serial No.)	650.

1940

R298P	50c	car (without ovpt.)	700.
R305P	$10	carmine	825.
		Without overprint	
R306AP	$50	carmine	825.
		Without overprint	—

1952

R597P	55c	carmine	675.

PROPRIETARY
1871-75   Joseph R. Carpenter, Philadelphia

			DIE ON INDIA (2) Small	(3) India	PLATE (4) Card	(5) Bond
RB1P	1c	grn & blk	—		12.	12.
		Block of 4			52.	52.
		P# block of 10				175.
RB2P	2c	grn & blk	175.		12.	
		Block of 4			52.	
		P# block of 10				175.
RB3P	3c	grn & blk		22.	12.	
		Block of 4		100.	52.	
		P# block of 10				175.
RB4P	4c	grn & blk		22.	12.	
		Block of 4		100.	52.	
		P# block of 10				175.
RB5P	5c	grn & blk		22.	12.	
		Block of 4		100.	52.	
		P# block of 10				175.
RB6P	6c	grn & blk		22.	12.	
		Block of 4		100.	52.	
		P# block of 10				175.
RB7P	10c	grn & blk		22.	12.	
		Block of 4		100.	52.	
		P# block of 10				175.
RB8P	50c	grn & blk	1,400.		1,000.	
RB9P	$1	grn & blk	1,600.		1,250.	
RB10P	$5	grn & blk	6,000.	4,500.	2,750.	

The "small die proofs" formerly listed under Nos. RB1P-RB7P are from the composite plate proofs listed under "Trial Color Proofs."

National Bank Note Co., New York City
1875-83

			DIE ON INDIA (1) Large	(2) Small	PLATE (3) India	(4) Card
RB11P	1c	green	500.		65.	—
		Block of 4			325.	
RB12P	2c	brown	500.		65.	—
		Pair			160.	
RB13P	3c	orange	500.		65.	—
		Pair			160.	
		Block of 4				—
RB14P	4c	red brown	500.		65.	—
		Pair			160.	
		Block of 4				—
RB15P	4c	red	500.			—
RB16P	5c	black	500.		65.	—
		Pair			160.	
		Block of 4				—
RB17P	6c	violet blue	500.		65.	—
		Pair			160.	
RB18P	6c	blue	500.		175.	—
		Pair			400.	
RB19P	10c	blue	500.			

No. RB19P was produced by the Bureau of Engraving and Printing.

Battleship Type
1898

			DIE ON INDIA (1) Large
RB20P	⅛c	yellow green	2,000.
RB21P	¼c	brown	2,000.
RB22P	⅜c	deep orange	2,000.
RB23P	⅝c	deep ultramarine	2,000.
RB24P	1c	dark green	2,000.
RB25P	1¼c	violet	2,000.
RB26P	1⅞c	dull blue	2,000.
RB27P	2c	violet brown	2,000.
RB28P	2½c	lake	2,000.
RB29P	3¾c	olive gray	2,000.
RB30P	4c	purple	2,000.
RB31P	5c	brown orange	2,000.

Wines

1916

RE56P	$20	green	5,000.

PLAYING CARDS

1896 **Bureau of Engraving & Printing**

RF2P	2c	ultramarine	550.
	a.	2c blue	1,100.

PRIVATE DIE PROPRIETARY

The editors are indebted to Eric Jackson and Philip T. Bansner for the compilation of the following listing of Private Die Proprietary die and plate proofs as well as the corrresponding trial color proofs. The large die proofs range in size and format from die impressions on India die sunk on cards generally up to 6x9 inches, through die impressions on India on or off card in medium to stamp size. Many individual listings are known in more than one size and format. Values reflect the size and format most commonly seen.

PRIVATE DIE MATCH STAMPS

1864

			DIE ON INDIA (1) Large	(3) India	PLATE (4) Card
RO1P	1c	blue	225.		
RO2P	1c	orange	500.	90.	
RO3P	1c	blue	225.		
RO4P	1c	blue	500.		
RO5P	1c	green	500.		
RO6P	1c	Blue	175.		
RO7P	1c	blue	175.		
RO9P	1c	black	175.		
RO10P	1c	black	175.		
RO11P	3c	Black	250.		
RO12P	1c	black	225.		
RO12/185P	1c	black	750.		
RO13P	3c	green	1000.		
RO14P	1c	black	175.		
RO15P	1c	green	300.		
RO16P	1c	blue	225.	60.	
RO17P	1c	blue	175.		
RO17/19P	1c/3c	blue	1000.		
RO17/19P	1c/3c	black	750.		
RO19P	3c	black	375.		
RO20P	1c	blue	175.		
RO21P	3c	black	250.		
RO23P	1c	orange	225.		
RO24P	1c	brown	225.		
RO28P	1c	blue	300.	90.	
RO29P	1c	black	175.		
RO30P	1c	green	175.		
RO31P	1c	black	175.		
RO32P	4c	black	300.		
RO33P	4c	green	225.		
RO35P	1c	black	175.		
RO37P	3c	black	225.		
RO38P	1c	black	350.		
RO39P	1c	green	500.		
RO40P	1c	blue	175.		
RO41P	1c	lake	225.		
RO42P	1c	lake	225.		
RO43P	1c	black	225.		
RO44P	1c	green	225.		
RO45P	1c	black	225.		
RO46P	1c	black	300.		
RO47P	1c	black	225.	90.	75.
RO48P	1c	black	500.		
RO49P	1c	black	175.		
RO50P	1c	black	375.		
RO55P	1c	black	250.		
RO56P	1c	black	250.		
RO57P	1c	green	300.		
RO58P	1c	lake	225.	75.	
RO60P	3c	black	300.		
RO61P	1c	green	300.		
RO62P	1c	green	175.		
RO64P	1c	lake	225.		
RO65P	1c	black	225.		
RO66P	1c	blue	175.		
RO67P	1c	black	175.		
RO68P	1c	green	225.		
RO69P	1c	black	175.		
RO72P	1c	green	500.		
RO73P	1c	black	175.		
RO75P	1c	carmine	450.		
RO76P	1c	black	175.		
RO77P	1c	blue	225.		
RO78P	1c	blue	225.		
RO80P	1c	blue	300.		
RO81P	1c	black	175.		
RO82P	1c	black	175.		
RO83P	1c	blue	175.		
RO84P	1c	black	175.		
RO85P	1c	brown	300.	100.	
RO86P	1c	black	250.	125.	
RO87P	1c	black	500.	50.	
RO88P	1c	black	175.		
RO89P	3c	black	175.		
RO90P	6c	black	175.	125.	
RO91P	3c	black	225.	125.	
RO92P	1c	black	175.		
RO94P	3c	black	175.	175.	

			DIE ON INDIA (1) Large	(3) India	PLATE (4) Card
RO95P	1c	green	225.		
RO96P	1c	green	300.		
RO97P	1c	black	175.		
RO98P	1c	green	225.		
RO99P	1c	green	300.		
RO100P	1c	green	225.	65.	
RO101P	3c	carmine		75.	
RO102P	5c	orange		75.	
RO103P	1c	black	175.		
RO104P	1c	green	175.		
RO105P	1c	black	175.	100.	
RO106P	1c	green	300.		
RO107P	1c	blue	225.		
RO108P	1c	red	750.		
RO109P	1c	black	300.		
RO110P	1c	green	175.		
RO112P	1c	blue	225.	100.	
RO113P	1c	black	175.		
RO114P	1c	lake	750.		
RO115P	1c	blue	175.		
RO116P	1c	blue	175.		
RO118P	8c	blue	500.		
RO119P	1c	green	300.		
RO121P	1c	green	500.		
RO122P	1c	black	175.		
RO123P	1c	black	175.		
RO124P	1c	green	750.		
RO125P	1c	blue	300.		
RO126P	1c	black	175.		
RO127P	1c	blue	175.		
RO128P	1c	blue	225.		
RO130P	1c	blue	500.		
a. On thin card			—		
RO131P	1c	blue	300.		
RO132P	1c	blue	225.	125.	
RO133P	1c	black	225.		
RO134P	1c	blue	175.	75.	
RO135P	1c	lake	500.		
RO136P	1c	blue	175.		
RO138P	1c	green	175.		
RO139P	5c	blue	225.		
RO140P	4c	green	225.		
RO141P	1c	blue	175.		
RO142P	1c	green	225.		
RO143P	3c	orange	225.		
RO144P	1c	blue	400.		
RO146P	1c	black	175.		
RO148P	1c	blue	225.	100.	
RO152P	1c	black	175.	75.	
RO153P	1c	black	175.	75.	
RO155P	1c	black	175.	65.	
RO157P	3c	blue	225.	80.	
RO158P	1c	black	175.		
RO159P	3c	blue	175.		
RO160P	1c	blue	175.		
RO161P	1c	blue	500.		
RO163P	1c	black	175.		
RO164P	1c	lake	500.		
RO165P	12c	blue	750.		
RO166P	1c	vermilion	225.		
RO167P	3c	blue	175.		
RO168P	1c	blue	175.		
RO170P	1c	black	450.		
RO171P	1c	black	175.		
RO172P	1c	black	175.		
RO173P	1c	blue	225.	75.	
RO174P	1c	blue	175.		
RO175P	1c	black	225.		
RO176P	1c	blue	500.		
RO177P	1c	green	175.		
RO178P	1c	green	500.		
RO179P	1c	black	175.	75.	75.
RO180P	1c	black	175.	80.	
RO181P	1c	black	175.		
RO182P	1c	black	175.		
RO183P	1c	black	500.		
RO184P	1c	black	175.	75.	
RO186P	1c	blue	225.		

PRIVATE DIE CANNED FRUIT STAMP

RP1P	1c	green	375.

PRIVATE DIE MEDICINE STAMPS

			DIE ON INDIA (1) Large	(3) India	PLATE (4) Card
RS1P	1c	black	175.	—	
RS4P	1c	black	225.	125.	150.
RS5P	1c	blue	500.		
RS10P	4c	blue	225.	125.	150.
RS14P	4c	green	500.	10.	
RS16P	2c	vermilion	500.		
RS18P	1c	black	500.		125.
RS19P	2c	black			125.
RS20P	4c	black			125.
RS21P	1c	black	175.	125.	
RS22P	2c	black	225.	125.	
RS23P	4c	black	225.	125.	
RS24P	1c	black	175.		
RS25P	2c	black	175.		
RS26P	4c	black	175.		
RS27P	4c	black	175.		
RS28P	2c	green	175.		
RS29P	2c	green	225.		
RS29/RO120P	2c/1c	green	1250.		
RS30P	1c	lake	300.		
RS31P	1c	green	175.	100.	100.
RS33P	1c	black	175.	50.	50.
RS34P	1c	black	225.		
RS35P	1c	black	175.		
RS36P	1c	blue	175.		
RS37P	2c	black	450.		

			DIE ON INDIA (1) Large	(3) India	PLATE (4) Card
RS38P	2c	black	300.		
RS39P	1c	black	175.	100.	100.
RS40P	2c	green	500.	100.	100.
RS41P	4c	brown		125.	125.
RS42P	1c	black	175.		
RS43P	4c	blue	225.		
RS44P	1c	black	600.		
RS46P	4c	black	175.		
RS47P	4c	black	175.	125.	
RS49P	4c	green	175.		
RS50P	1c	vermilion	225.		
RS51P	2c	black	175.		
RS52P	4c	black	175.		
RS53P	1c	black	175.	125.	
RS54P	2c	black	175.	125.	
RS55P	4c	black	175.	125.	
RS56P	3c	blue	350.	125.	
RS57P	6c	black	175.	100.	
RS58P	4c	black	175.		
RS59P	1c	black	175.		
RS60P	1c	black	175.	65.	
RS61P	4c	blue	500.		
RS62P	1c	black	225.	125.	
RS63P	1c	blue	175.		
RS64P	2c	black	175.	125.	
RS65P	4c	black	175.		
RS66P	1c	black	500.		85.
RS67P	1c	black	175.		
RS68P	2c	black	175.	90.	
RS69P	1c	black	175.		
RS70P	2c	black	225.		
RS71P	1c	black	175.		
RS72P	2c	black	175.		
RS73P	2c	green	500.		
RS74P	1c	black	225.		
RS74hP	1c	black	175.		
RS75P	1c	blue	175.		
RS77P	2c	black	225.		
RS78P	2c	dull pur	750.		
RS81P	4c	brown	225.		
RS82P	2c	black	175.		
RS83P	4c	black	225.		
RS84P	1c	lake	500.	—	110.
RS85P	4c	black	250.		
RS86P	1c	green	175.		
RS88P	1c	black	225.	100.	100.
RS89P	1c	black	500.		
RS90P	1c	blue	225.	125.	125.
RS91P	4c	black	175.		
RS92P	3c	black	175.	—	
RS94P	4c	black	175.		
RS95P	1c	green	225.	90.	
RS96P	3c	black	175.	50.	
RS97P	1c	black	175.		
RS98P	1c	black	175.		
RS99P	4c	black	175.		
RS100P	6c	black	175.		
RS101P	1c	black	175.		
RS102P	2c	blue	175.		
RS103P	4c	black	175.		
RS104P	3c	black	750.		
RS105P	3c	brown	600.		
RS106P	2c	blue	225.	60.	
RS107P	3c	black	225.		
RS107/109P	3c/6c	black	1000.		
RS108P	4c	black	175.	45.	
RS109P	6c	black	225.		
RS110P	2c	blue	175.		
RS111P	4c	black	175.		
RS114P	1c	black	225.		
RS114/115P	1c/2c	black	1000.		
RS115P	2c	blue	225.		
RS116P	4c	red	225.		
RS117P	1c	black	250.		
RS118P	1c	red	300.	55.	50.
RS119P	1c	black	225.		
RS120P	2c	black	175.		
RS121P	3c	black	225.	75.	
RS122P	2c	black	175.	100.	
RS123P	4c	black	175.	125.	
RS124P	1c	blue	300.	90.	65.
RS126P	1c	green	175.		
RS127P	4c	green	175.	65.	
RS128P	2c	blue	275.	150.	
RS130P	4c	green	275.		
RS131P	4c	black	175.	75.	
RS132P	4c	black			75.
RS133P	6c	black	175.	125.	
RS134P	4c	blue	225.		
RS137P	4c	blue	500.		
RS138P	1c	black	175.		
RS141P	4c	green	300.	125.	
RS142P	1c	black	175.		
RS143P	4c	green	225.		
RS144P	1c	blue	175.	100.	100.
RS145P	2c	black	175.	100.	100.
RS146P	4c	green	225.	100.	100.
RS150P	1c	vermilion	225.	100.	
RS151P	1c	black	175.		
RS152P	2c	green	175.		
RS153P	4c	black	450.	175.	150.
RS154P	4c	blue	500.		
RS155P	2c	green	175.		
RS156P	6c	black	175.		
RS157P	2c	black	175.		
RS158P	1c	green	500.		
RS159P	4c	blue	225.		
RS160P	6c	black	225.		
RS161P	4c	black	300.	150.	
RS162P	1c	blue	300.		
RS163P	4c	blue	600.		
RS164P	1c	black	175.		
RS165P	4c	green	500.		
RS166P	1c	black	175.		
RS169P	4c	black	175.		

			DIE ON INDIA (1) Large	PLATE (3) India	(4) Card
RS170P	1c	black	175.		
RS171P	1c	violet	175.		
RS171uP	1c	purple	500.		
RS172P	2c	black	175.	100.	
RS173P	1c	blue	175.		
RS174P	1c	blue	175.		
RS176P	4c	black	250.		
RS177P	2c	black	350.		
RS178P	1c	black	225.		
RS179P	2c	green	225.		
RS180P	3c	black	275.	125.	
RS181P	4c	black	225.	—	
RS182P	4c	black	175.		
RS183P	1c	vermilion	225.	85.	
RS184P	2c	black	175.	100.	
RS185P	1c	black	175.	100.	
RS186P	4c	black	175.		
RS187P	4c	black	175.	100.	
RS188P	6c	black	300.		
RS189P	1c	green	225.		
RS190P	2c	black	175.		
RS191P	4c	black	250.		
RS192P	6c	black	250.	125.	
RS193P	2	black	175.		
RS194P	1c	blue	175.		
RS195P	2c	black	175.		
RS196P	1c	blue	175.		
RS197P	2c	black	175.		
RS198P	1c	black	225.		
RS199P	2c	black	175.		
RS204P	2c	black	175.		
RS205P	4c	black	175.		
RS208P	1c	green	175.	100.	95.
RS209P	2c	green	225.		
RS210P	4c	black	225.		
RS212P	1c	green	225.	100.	
RS213P	6c	black	175.	100.	150.
RS214P	4c	black	175.	65.	
RS215P	1c	lake	300.		
RS216P	1c	black	175.	75.	
RS219P	4c	blue	300.		
RS220P	1c	black	175.	50.	
RS221P	4c	green	225.	50.	
RS222P	8c	black	175.		
RS223P	1c	black	175.	—	
RS224P	1c	black	175.		
RS225P	4c	black	175.		
RS226P	1c	blue		350.	
RS228P	1c	brown	225.	—	
RS229P	2c	chocolate	175.	75.	
RS230P	6c	black	175.		
RS231P	6c	orange	750.		750.
RS232P	8c	orange	750.		
RS236P	4c	black	175.		
RS239P	2c	vermilion	225.	100.	
RS240P	4c	black	175.	125.	50.

"USIR" & "4 cents" obliterated on #RS240P4.

RS241P	4	red	225.		
RS242P	1c	black	175.	80.	75.
RS243P	4c	black	175.		
RS244P	6c	black	175.		
RS245P	1c	black	250.		
RS250P	6c	black	175.	100.	
RS251P	1c	black	175.		
RS252P	1c	ver	175.	100.	
RS253P	4c	black	175.		
RS258P	6c	brown	175.		
RS259P	1c	black	175.	90.	
RS260P	2c	black	225.	90.	
RS261P	4c	black	175.	100.	
RS262P	2c	black	175.		
RS263P	4c	black	225.	90.	
RS264P	4c	black	225.		
RS264AP	4c	black	300.		
RS265P	1c	green	225.		
RS267P	4c	lake	225.		
RS270P	12c	blue	175.		
RS271P	4c	black	2500.		
RS272P	1c	green	225.		
RS273P	2c	black	175.		
RS274P	1c	green	225.	65.	60.
RS276P	2c	green	175.		
RS300P	4⅜c	black	1,000.		
RS306P	1¼c	pink	1,000.		

PRIVATE DIE PERFUMERY STAMPS

			DIE ON INDIA (1) Large	PLATE (3) India	(4) Card
RT1P	2c	blue		125.	125.
RT2P	1c	black	250.	95.	
RT4P	1c	blue	225.		
RT5P	2c	ver		100.	
RT6P	1c	black	250.	150.	
RT8P	2c	black	500.		
RT10P	4c	black	250.	150.	
RT12P	1c	ver	225.	—	
RT14P	3c	black	500.		
RT16P	1c	black	175.		
RT17P	2c	brown	175.		
RT18P	3c	green	175.		
RT19P	1c	ver	225.		
RT20P	1c	green	225.		
RT21P	2c	blue	175.		
RT22P	1c	blue	225.		
RT23P	2c	black	175.		
RT25P	4c	green	175.		
RT26P	1c	green	175.		
RT27P	1c	green		100.	
RT28P	2c	black	175.		
RT30P	3c	ver	225.		
RT32P	4c	brown	175.		

PRIVATE DIE PLAYING CARD STAMPS

			DIE ON INDIA (1) Large	PLATE (3) India	(4) Card
RU1P	5c	black	2500.		
RU3P	4c	black	175.	100.	
RU4P	5c	blue	175.		
RU5P	5c	blue	175.		
RU6P	10c	blue	500.	100.	
RU7P	5c	black	250.	100.	
RU8P	5c	black	175.		
RU9P	5c	black	175.		
RU10P	2c	blue	175.		
RU11P	5c	green	225.		
RU12P	5c	black	175.		
RU13P	5c	blue	300.		
RU14P	5c	black	175.	—	
RU15P	5c	black	175.		
RU16P	5c	black	500.		

HUNTING PERMIT

				DIE (Wove) (1) Large	(2) Small	PLATE (3) Stamp Paper
RW1P	1934	$1	blue	—	22,500.	
RW2P	1935	$1	rose lake	—	12,500.	
RW3P	1936	$1	brown black	8,500.	8,500.	
RW4P	1937	$1	light green	—	8,500.	
RW5P	1938	$1	light violet	—	8,500.	
RW6P	1939	$1	chocolate		7,500.	
RW7P	1940	$1	sepia		7,500.	
RW8P	1941	$1	brown car-mine	7,500.	7,500.	
RW9P	1942	$1	violet brown		7,500.	
RW10P	1943	$1	deep rose	7,500.	7,500.	
RW11P	1944	$1	red orange		7,500.	
RW12P	1945	$1	black	7,500.	7,500.	
RW13P	1946	$1	red brown	7,500.	7,500.	
RW14P	1947	$1	black	7,500.	7,500.	
RW15P	1948	$1	bright blue	9,500.	7,500.	
RW16P	1949	$2	bright green		7,500.	
RW17P	1950	$2	violet		7,500.	
RW18P	1951	$2	gray black		7,500.	
RW19P	1952	$2	deep ultra.	7,500.	7,500.	
RW20P	1953	$2	deep brown rose		7,500.	
RW21P	1954	$2	black		7,500.	
RW22P	1949	$2	dark blue		7,500.	
RW23P	1956	$2	black	12,500.	7,500.	
RW24P	1957	$2	emerald		7,500.	
RW25P	1958	$2	black		7,500.	
RW26P	1959	$3	bl., ocher & blk.			3,000.
RW27P	1960	$3	red brn., dk. bl. & bis.			3,000.
RW28P	1961	$3	multicolored			3,000.
RW29P	1962	$3	dk. bl., dk. red brn. & blk.			3,000.
RW30P	1963	$3	multicolored			3,000.
RW32P	1965	$3	multicolored			3,000.
RW33P	1966	$3	multicolored			3,000.
RW34P	1967	$3	multicolored			3,000.
RW35P	1968	$3	multicolored			3,000.
RW36P	1969	$3	multicolored			3,000.
RW37P	1970	$3	multicolored			3,000.
RW38P	1971	$3	multicolored			3,000.
RW39P	1972	$5	multicolored			3,000.
RW40P	1973	$5	multicolored			3,000.
RW41P	1974	$5	multicolored			3,000.
RW42P	1975	$5	multicolored			3,000.
RW43P	1976	$5	grn. & blk.			3,000.
RW44P	1977	$5	multicolored			3,000.
RW45P	1978	$5	multicolored			3,000.
RW46P	1979	$7.50	multicolored			3,000.
RW47P	1980	$7.50	multicolored			3,000.
RW48P	1981	$7.50	multicolored			3,000.
RW49P	1982	$7.50	multicolored			3,000.
RW50P	1983	$7.50	multicolored			3,000.

POSTAL SAVINGS

1911

			DIE (1) Large	(2) Small	(2a)
PS1P	10c	orange	1,000.	750.	
PS4P	10c	deep blue		750.	

1940

PS7P	10c	deep ultra. on wove		1,200.	
PS8P	25c	dk. car. rose on wove		1,200.	
PS9P	50c	dk. bl. green on wove		1,200.	
PS10P	$1	gray black on wove		1,200.	

1941

PS11P	10c	rose red on wove		1,000.	
PS12P	25c	blue green on wove		1,000.	
PS13P	50c	ultramarine on wove		1,000.	
PS14P	$1	gray black on wove		1,000.	
PS15P	$5	sepia on wove	4,000.	1,000.	

WAR SAVINGS STAMP

1942

WS7P	10c	rose red	1,400.

POST OFFICE SEALS

1872

			DIE (1) Large	PLATE (3) India	(4) Card
OXF1P		green	275.		—
	a.	Wove paper	950.		750.
	b.	Glazed paper	190.		

1877

OX1P		brown	1,750.	125.	
		Block of 4		650.	

1879

OX2aP		brown	2,500.	125.	
		Block of 4		650.	

1888-94

OX5P		chocolate	750.		

1901-03

OX11P		red brown	750.		

No. OX11P is a hybrid proof sunk on card.

1972

OX41P		Pane of 5, blue line proof	—

TRIAL COLOR PROOFS

Values are for items in very fine condition. The listings of trial color proofs include several that are similar to the colors of the issued stamps.

New York
All on India paper unless otherwise stated.
Original Die

1845

			DIE (1) Lg.	(2) Sm.	PLATE (5) Bond
9X1TC	5c	dull dark violet		300.	
9X1TC	5c	brown violet		300.	
9X1TC	5c	deep rose violet		300.	
9X1TC	5c	deep blue		300.	200.
9X1TC	5c	dark green		300.	200.
9X1TC	5c	orange yellow		300.	
9X1TC	5c	brown		300.	200.
9X1TC	5c	scarlet			200.

With "Scar" on Neck

9X1TC	5c	dull blue		175.	
9X1TC	5c	vermilion		175.	

With "Scar" and dot in "P" of "POST"

9X1TC	5c	dull gray blue		300.	
9X1TC	5c	deep blue on Bond		250.	
9X1TC	5c	deep ultramarine on thin glazed card		450.	
9X1TC	5c	deep green		300.	
9X1TC	5c	deep green on Bond		250.	
9X1TC	5c	dull dark green		300.	
9X1TC	5c	orange vermilion on thin glazed card		450.	
9X1TC	5c	dull brown red on Bond		250.	
9X1TC	5c	dark brown red		300.	
9X1TC	5c	dull dark brown		300.	
9X1TC	5c	dull dark brown on Bond		250.	
9X1TC	5c	brown black on thin glazed card		450.	

Large die trial color proofs with additional impression of the portrait medallion are listed in the Essay section as Nos. 9X1-E1.

Plate proofs are from the small sheet of 9.

Providence, R. I.

1846

			Plate on Card
10X1TC	5c	gray blue	250.
10X1TC	5c	green	250.
10X1TC	5c	brown carmine	250.
10X1TC	5c	brown	250.
10X2TC	10c	gray blue	450.
10X2TC	10c	green	450.
10X2TC	10c	brown carmine	450.
10X2TC	10c	brown	450.
		Sheet of 12, any color	3,750.

General Issues

1847

			LARGE DIE India	Bond	Wove	Thin Glazed Card
1TC	5c	violet	1,000.			
1TC	5c	dull blue	1,000.			
1TC	5c	deep blue		800.	800.	
		Small, India				625.
1TC	5c	deep ultra				850.
1TC	5c	blue green	1,000.			
		Small, India				625.
1TC	5c	dull blue green		800.		
1TC	5c	dull green	1,000.			
		Small, bond				600.
1TC	5c	dark green	1,000.			
1TC	5c	yellow green, small India				625.
1TC	5c	orange yellow	1,000.	800.	800.	
		Small, India				625.
1TC	5c	deep yellow			800.	
1TC	5c	orange vermilion	1,000.	800.	800.	
1TC	5c	scarlet vermilion	1,000.	800.		850.
1TC	5c	rose lake	1,000.			
		Small, bond				625.
1TC	5c	black brown		800.		850.
1TC	5c	dull rose lake, small bond				625.
1TC	5c	brown red	1,000.			
1TC	5c	black	1,000.	800.		850.
		Small, India				675.
2TC	10c	violet	1,000.			
2TC	10c	dull blue				
2TC	10c	deep blue	1,000.	800.	800.	850.
		Small, India				675.
2TC	10c	dull gray blue, small bond				625.
2TC	10c	blue green		800.		
2TC	10c	dull blue green		800.		
2TC	10c	dull green		800.		
2TC	10c	dark green	1,000.			
2TC	10c	yel green, small India				675.
2TC	10c	dull yellow			800.	
2TC	10c	orange yellow	1,000.		800.	
2TC	10c	orange vermilion	1,000.	800.	800.	
		Small, India				625.

			LARGE DIE India	Bond	Wove	Thin Glazed Card
2TC	10c	scarlet vermilion				850.
2TC	10c	golden brown	1,000.	800.		850.
2TC	10c	light brown	1,000.			
2TC	10c	dark brown	1,000.	800.		
2TC	10c	red brown				675.
2TC	10c	dull red				675.
2TC	10c	rose lake	1,000.			
2TC	10c	dull rose lake, small India				625.
2TC	10c	black brown				850.
2TC	10c	yellow green on blue pelure paper	1,000.			

Original die proofs are often cut down and reduced in size; full-size die proofs sell at higher prices. Reprint proofs with cross-hatching are valued as full-size; cut down examples sell for less.

			DIE (1) Lg.	(2) Sm.	PLATE (3) India	(4) Card
1TC	5c	orange				600.
1TC	5c	black				600.
		Double transfer (80R1)				—
		Double transfer (90R1)				—
2TC	10c	orange				600.
2TC	10c	deep brown				600.

Nos. 1TC3-2TC3 exist with and without "specimen" overprint. Values are for examples without the overprint. Examples with the overprint are equally as scarce but sell for slightly less.

1875

3TC	5c	dull rose lake				600.
3TC	5c	black	900.			
3TC	5c	green	900.			
4TC	10c	green	900.		750.	

1851-60

			DIE (1) Lg.	(2) Sm.	PLATE (3) India	(5) Wove Paper
5TC	1c	black	—			
7TC	1c	black on stamp paper				3,750.
11TC	3c	black on stamp paper				3,000.
12TC	5c	pale brown				300.
12TC	5c	rose brown				300.
12TC	5c	deep red brown				1,500.
12TC	5c	dark olive bister				300.
12TC	5c	olive brown				300.
12TC	5c	olive green				300.
12TC	5c	deep orange				300.
12TC	5c	black	8,500.			5,000.
13TC	10c	black	5,000.			1,500.
15TC	10c	black				5,000.
37TC	24c	claret brown				600.
37TC	24c	red brown				600.
37TC	24c	orange				600.
37TC	24c	deep yellow				600.
37TC	24c	yellow				600.
37TC	24c	deep blue				600.
37TC	24c	black	7,000.			600.
37TC	24c	violet black				600.
37TC	24c	red lilac on stamp paper, perf. 15½, gummed (formerly No. 37b)				1,000.
		Block of 4				6,000.
38TC	30c	black	5,000.	1,250.	1,400.	1,000.
		Block of 4				9,000.
39TC	90c	rose lake				625.
39TC	90c	henna brown				625.
39TC	90c	orange red				625.
39TC	90c	brown orange	5,000.			625.
39TC	90c	sepia				625.
39TC	90c	dark green				625.
39TC	90c	dark violet brown				625.
39TC	90c	black	5,000.	1,250.		675.

Former Nos. 55-57, 59, 62 are now in the Essay section. Former Nos. 60-61 will be found below as Nos. 70TCe and 71TCb, respectively.

1875

40TC	1c	orange vermilion				275.
40TC	1c	orange				275.
40TC	1c	yellow orange				275.
40TC	1c	orange brown				275.
40TC	1c	dark brown				275.
40TC	1c	dull violet				275.
40TC	1c	violet				275.
40TC	1c	red violet				275.
40TC	1c	gray				275.
41TC	3c	red				—

1861

			PLATE (5) Wove Paper, Imperf.	(6) Wove Paper, Perf.
63TC	1c	rose	40.	50.
63TC	1c	deep orange red	40.	50.
63TC	1c	deep red orange	40.	50.
63TC	1c	dark orange	40.	50.
63TC	1c	yellow orange	40.	50.
63TC	1c	orange brown	40.	50.
63TC	1c	dark brown	40.	50.
63TC	1c	yellow green	40.	50.
63TC	1c	green	40.	50.
63TC	1c	blue green	40.	50.
63TC	1c	gray lilac	40.	50.
63TC	1c	gray black	40.	50.
63TC	1c	slate black	40.	50.
63TC	1c	blue	40.	50.
63TC	1c	light blue	40.	50.
63TC	1c	deep blue	100.	50.

The perforated 1861 1c trial colors are valued with perfs cutting the design on two sides. Well centered examples are extremely scarce and sell for more.

There are many trial color impressions of the issues of 1861 to 1883 made for experimentation with various patent papers, grills, etc. Some are fully perforated, gummed and with grill.

1861-62

			DIE (1) Lg.	(2) Sm.	(2a)	PLATE India (3)
62BTC	10c	black	2,500.			
62BTC	10c	green				300.
62BTC	10c	light green				300.
63TC	1c	black	2,500.	750.		
63TC	1c	red		750.		
63TC	1c	brown		750.		
63TC	1c	green				—
63TC	1c	orange				—
64TC	3c	carmine pink on thin stamp paper, perf 12, gummed				—
65TC	3c	dark carmine on thin stamp paper, perf 12, gummed				—
65TC	3c	black	2,500.			
65TC	3c	black on glazed	2,500.			
65TC	3c	blue green	2,500.			
65TC	3c	orange	2,500.			
65TC	3c	brown	2,500.			
65TC	3c	dark blue	2,500.			
65TC	3c	ocher	2,500.			
65TC	3c	green	2,500.			
65TC	3c	dull red	2,500.			
65TC	3c	slate	2,500.			
65TC	3c	red brown	2,500.			
65TC	3c	deep pink	2,500.			
65TC	3c	rose pink	2,500.			
65TC	3c	dark rose	2,500.			
67TC	5c	black	2,500.			
67TC	5c	dark orange	2,500.			
67TC	5c	green	2,500.			
67TC	5c	ultramarine	2,500.			
67TC	5c	gray	2,500.			
67TC	5c	rose brown				—
68TC	10c	orange	2,500.			
68TC	10c	red brown	2,500.			

		DIE (1) Lg.	(2) Sm.	(2a)	PLATE India (3)
68TC	10c dull pink	2,500.			
68TC	10c scarlet	2,500.			
68TC	10c black	2,500.	550.		
69TC	12c scarlet verm.	2,500.			
69TC	12c brown	2,500.			
69TC	12c red brown	2,500.			
69TC	12c green	2,500.			
69TC	12c orange yellow	2,500.			
69TC	12c black				550.
70TC	24c scarlet	2,500.			
70TC	24c green	2,500.			
70TC	24c orange	2,500.			
70TC	24c red brown	2,500.			
70TC	24c orange brown	2,500.			
70TC	24c orange yellow	2,500.			
70TC	24c rose red	2,500.			
70TC	24c gray	2,500.			
70TC	24c gray on bluish gray stamp paper				—
70TC	24c steel blue	2,500.			
70TC	24c blue	2,500.			
70TC	24c black	2,500.	500.		
70TC	24c violet	2,500.	375.	2,250.	500.
	Block of 4				2,250.
	e. dark violet, semitransparent stamp paper, perf. 12, gummed (formerly #60)				15,000.
71TC	30c rose	2,500.			
71TC	30c black		600.		
71TC	30c red orange	2,500.	375.	1,250.	
	Block of 4				
	b. red orange, semitransparent stamp paper, perf. 12, gummed (formerly #61)			45,000.	
72TC	90c black	2,500.	600.		
72TC	90c ultramarine	2,500.			
72TC	90c bluish gray	2,500.			
72TC	90c violet gray	2,500.			
72TC	90c red brown	2,500.			
72TC	90c orange	2,500.			
72TC	90c yellow orange	2,500.			
72TC	90c scarlet	2,500.			
72TC	90c green	2,500.			

1861

		STAMP PAPER Unused	Used
66TC	3c lake, perf. 12, gummed	2,000.	
	Pair	4,500.	
	Block of 4	9,250.	
	P# strip of 4	10,000.	
	Double transfer	2,250.	
	a. Imperf, pair, gummed		1,850.
	P# blk. of 8		

John N. Luff recorded the plate number for No. 66TC as 34.

74TC	3c scarlet, perf. 12, gummed	7,000.	
	Block of 4	29,000.	
	With 4 horiz. black pen strokes		5,500.
	a. Imperf, pair, gummed	4,000.	

John N. Luff recorded the plate number for No. 74TC as 19.

1861

		DIE (1) Large	(2) Small	(2a)	PLATE (3) India	(4) Card
66TC	3c lake	250.	1,100.		150.	
	Block of 4				850.	
	P# blk. of 8				2,250.	
74TC	3c scarlet	2,250.	375.	1,100.	100.	150.
	Block of 4				500.	725.
	P# blk. of 8				—	

1863

		DIE (1) Lg.	(2) Sm.	PLATE (3) India	(4) Card
73TC	2c light blue			250.	
73TC	2c dull chalky blue	8,000.		500.	
73TC	2c green	8,000.		250.	
73TC	2c olive green			250.	
73TC	2c blue green				400.
73TC	2c dull yellow	8,000.			
73TC	2c dark orange	8,000.			
73TC	2c vermilion			250.	
73TC	2c scarlet	8,000.		250.	
73TC	2c dull red			250.	
73TC	2c dull rose	8,000.		250.	
73TC	2c brown	8,000.			
73TC	2c gray black			250.	
73TC	2c ultramarine	8,000.			

1866

		DIE Lg.	PLATE India
77TC	15c deep blue	2,500.	335.
	Block of 4		1,650.
77TC	15c dark red	2,500.	
77TC	15c orange red	2,500.	
77TC	15c dark orange	2,500.	
77TC	15c yellow orange	2,500.	
77TC	15c yellow		

77TC	15c sepia	2,500.	
77TC	15c orange brown	2,500.	
77TC	15c red brown	2,500.	
77TC	15c blue green	2,500.	
77TC	15c dusky blue	2,500.	
77TC	15c gray black	2,500.	

1869

112TC	1c black	2,500.	
113TC	2c black	2,500.	
114TC	3c black	2,500.	
115TC	6c deep dull blue	2,500.	
115TC	6c black	2,500.	
116TC	10c black	2,500.	
116TC	10c dull dark violet	2,500.	
116TC	10c deep green	2,500.	
116TC	10c dull dark orange	2,500.	
116TC	10c dull rose	2,500.	
116TC	10c copper red	2,500.	
116TC	10c chocolate	2,500.	
116TC	10c dk Prussian bl	2,500.	
117TC	12c black	2,500.	
118TC	15c dull dark violet	2,500.	
118TC	15c deep blue	2,500.	
118TC	15c dull red brown	2,500.	
118TC	15c black	2,500.	
118TC	15c dark blue gray	2,500.	
120TC	24c black	3,500.	
121TC	30c deep blue & deep green	3,500.	
121TC	30c deep brown & blue	3,500.	
121TC	30c golden brown & carmine lake	3,500.	
121TC	30c carmine lake & dull violet	3,500.	
121TC	30c car lake & green	3,500.	
121TC	30c car lake & brown	3,500.	
121TC	30c car lake & black	3,500.	
121TC	30c dull orange red & deep green	3,500.	
121TC	30c deep ocher & golden brown	3,500.	
121TC	30c dull violet & golden brown	3,500.	
121TC	30c black & deep green	3,500.	
122TC	90c brown & deep green	3,500.	
122TC	90c green & black		1,500.

1870-71

		DIE (1) Lg.	(2) Sm.	PLATE India (3)	Card (4)
145TC	1c yellow orange	600.			
145TC	1c red brown	600.			
145TC	1c red violet	600.			
145TC	1c black	—		—	
145TC	1c green	600.			
146TC	2c black	600.			
147TC	3c brown	—		125.	
147TC	3c dark brown			125.	
147TC	3c red brown	—		125.	
147TC	3c orange brown			125.	
147TC	3c dark red			125.	
147TC	3c deep red brown, wove paper			125.	
147TC	3c light ultramarine	—		125.	
147TC	3c yellow brown	—		125.	
147TC	3c dull red violet	—		125.	
147TC	3c dull grayish red			125.	
147TC	3c yellow orange	—		125.	
147TC	3c red violet	—		125.	
147TC	3c black	600.			

Former Nos. 147aTC and 147bTC are now listed in the Essay section as No. 147-E13c.

148TC	6c deep magenta	600.	
148TC	6c ultramarine	600.	
148TC	6c carmine	600.	
148TC	6c maroon	600.	
149TC	7c black	550.	
150TC	10c blue	550.	
150TC	10c dull pale blue	550.	
150TC	10c ultramarine	550.	
150TC	10c blue green	550.	
150TC	10c carmine	550.	
150TC	10c bister	550.	
150TC	10c dull red	550.	
150TC	10c red orange	550.	
150TC	10c yellow brown	550.	
150TC	10c brown orange	550.	
151TC	12c orange	550.	
151TC	12c orange brown	550.	
151TC	12c brown red	550.	
151TC	12c dull red	550.	
151TC	12c carmine	550.	
151TC	12c blue	550.	
151TC	12c light blue	550.	
151TC	12c ultramarine	550.	
151TC	12c green	550.	
153TC	24c dark brown	550.	
155TC	90c carmine	550.	
155TC	90c ultramarine	550.	
155TC	90c black	550.	

1873

		DIE Lg.	PLATE India	Card
156TC	1c black		15.	30.
	Block of 4		65.	140.
156TC	1c scarlet	1,500.		
157TC	2c black	850.	15.	
	Block of 4		65.	
157TC	2c dull blue	850.		
157TC	2c rose	850.		
157TC	2c deep rose	850.		
158TC	3c black	750.	12.	
	Block of 4		55.	
158TC	3c orange red	—		

159TC	6c black		400.	30.	
	Block of 4			150.	
159TC	6c deep green		400.		
159TC	6c deep brown		400.		
159TC	6c dull red		400.		
159TC	6c dull gray blue		400.		
160TC	7c black		400.	75.	
	Block of 4			325.	
160TC	7c deep green		400.		
160TC	7c deep brown		400.		
160TC	7c dull gray blue		400.		
160TC	7c dull red		400.		
161TC	10c black		400.		
161TC	10c deep brown		400.		
161TC	10c dull gray blue		400.		
161TC	10c dull red		400.		
162TC	12c black		400.		
162TC	12c deep green		400.		
162TC	12c dull gray blue		400.		
162TC	12c deep brown		400.		
162TC	12c dull red		400.		
163TC	15c black		400.		
163TC	15c deep green		400.		
163TC	15c dull gray blue		400.		
163TC	15c deep brown		400.		
163TC	15c dull red		400.		
164TC	24c black		400.		
164TC	24c deep green		400.		
164TC	24c dull gray blue		400.		
164TC	24c deep green		400.		
164TC	24c dull red		400.		
165TC	30c black		400.		
165TC	30c deep green		400.		
165TC	30c dull gray blue		400.		
165TC	30c deep green		400.		
165TC	30c dull red		400.		
166TC	90c black		400.		
166TC	90c deep green		400.		
166TC	90c dull gray blue		400.		
166TC	90c deep brown		400.		
166TC	90c dull red		400.		

1875

		DIE Lg.	Sm.	PLATE India	Card
179TC	5c black	650.	400.	25.	45.
	Block of 4			125.	200.
179TC	5c deep green		400.		
179TC	5c dull gray blue		400.		
179TC	5c deep brown		400.		
179TC	5c dull red		400.		
179TC	5c scarlet		1,000.		

Small die proofs of 1873-75 issues are "Goodall" prints.

1879   **On stamp paper, gummed**   *Perf. 12*

182TC	1c ultramarine	300.
182TC	1c green	300.
182TC	1c deep green	300.
182TC	1c vermilion	300.
182TC	1c brown	300.
183TC	2c ultramarine	300.
183TC	2c blue	300.
183TC	2c green	300.
184TC	3c ultramarine	300.
184TC	3c blue	300.
184TC	3c vermilion	300.
	Block of 4	1,100.
184TC	3c brown	300.
185TC	5c ultramarine	300.
185TC	5c green	300.
185TC	5c vermilion	300.
186TC	6c ultramarine	300.
186TC	6c blue	300.
186TC	6c vermilion	300.
187TC	10c ultramarine	300.
187TC	10c blue	300.
187TC	10c vermilion	300.
187TC	10c green	300.
189TC	15c ultramarine	300.
189TC	15c green	300.
189TC	15c vermilion	300.
189TC	15c brown	300.
189TC	15c dull red	300.
190TC	30c ultramarine	300.
190TC	30c blue	300.
190TC	30c green	300.

See Specimens for No. 189 in deep blue (No. 189S L), No. 209 in green (No. 209S L), No. 210 in pale rose lake (No. 210S L).

1881-82

206TC	1c deep green	600.	125.
206TC	1c black	600.	125.
206TC	1c ultramarine	600.	
206TC	1c dark yellow green	600.	

1882-87

		LARGE DIE (1) India	(2) Card	PLATE (3) India	(4) Card
212TC	1c indigo	1,000.			
212TC	1c carmine	1,000.			
212TC	1c green	1,000.		450.	
212TC	1c deep green	1,000.		450.	
212TC	1c copper brown	1,000.		450.	
212TC	1c chestnut brown	1,000.			
210TC	2c brown red	1,000.		450.	
210TC	2c deep dull orange	1,000.			
210TC	2c chestnut brown	1,000.		450.	
210TC	2c violet rose	1,000.		450.	
210TC	2c indigo	1,000.		450.	
210TC	2c black	1,000.			
210TC	2c pale ultramarine	1,000.			

			LARGE DIE		PLATE	
			(1) India	(2) Card	(3) India	(4) Card
210TC	2c	olive green	1,000.	450.		
210TC	2c	olive brown		450.		
210TC	2c	lake				140.
210TC	2c	rose lake				140.
210TC	2c	dark carmine				140.
210TC	2c	deep red				140.
214TC	3c	green	1,000.	450.		
214TC	3c	dark green	—			—
214TC	3c	dark brown	1,000.	450.		
214TC	3c	chestnut brown	1,000.	450.		
214TC	3c	dull red brown	1,000.	450.		
214TC	3c	deep dull orange	—			—

All of 214TC above bear inscription "Worked over by new company, June 29th, 1881."

211TC	4c	green	1,000.	450.
211TC	4c	chestnut brown	1,000.	450.
211TC	4c	orange brown	1,000.	450.
211TC	4c	pale ultra.	1,000.	450.
211TC	4c	dark ultra	1,000.	
211TC	4c	black	1,000.	450.
205TC	5c	chestnut brown	1,000.	—
205TC	5c	deep dull orange	1,000.	
205TC	5c	pale ultra	1,000.	—
205TC	5c	deep green	1,000.	
205TC	5c	green	1,000.	200.
205TC	5c	carmine	1,000.	450.
205TC	5c	carmine lake		225.
205TC	5c	blue black	1,000.	
205TC	5c	black on glazed	1,000.	
208TC	6c	deep dull orange	1,000.	450.
208TC	6c	indigo	1,000.	
208TC	6c	orange vermilion	1,000.	450.
208TC	6c	dark violet	1,000.	450.
208TC	6c	chestnut brown	1,000.	450.
208TC	6c	carmine	1,000.	
209TC	10c	carmine	1,000.	450.	
209TC	10c	orange brown	1,000.	450.	125.
209TC	10c	orange	1,000.		
209TC	10c	deep dull orange	1,000.	450.	
209TC	10c	chestnut brown	1,000.	450.	
209TC	10c	indigo	1,000.	450.	
209TC	10c	pale ultra	1,000.	450.	
209TC	10c	green			125.
209TC	10c	black (glazed)	1,000.		
189TC	15c	orange vermilion	1,000.	450.
189TC	15c	orange brown	1,000.	450.
189TC	15c	chestnut brown	1,000.	450.
189TC	15c	dark brown	1,000.	450.
189TC	15c	deep green	1,000.	450.
189TC	15c	deep green	1,000.	450.
190TC	30c	black	1,000.	
190TC	30c	orange vermilion	1,000.	450.
190TC	30c	dark brown	1,000.	450.
190TC	30c	deep green	1,000.	450.
190TC	30c	dull red brown	1,000.	450.
190TC	30c	green	1,000.	450.
191TC	90c	carmine	1,000.	450.
191TC	90c	dark brown	1,000.	450.
191TC	90c	deep dull orange	1,000.	450.
191TC	90c	indigo	1,000.	450.
191TC	90c	dull red brown	1,000.	450.
191TC	90c	black	1,000.	450.

1890-93

			DIE		PLATE	
			(1) India	(2) Card	(3) India	(4) Card
219TC	1c	green	400.			
219TC	1c	dull violet	400.			
220TC	2c	dull violet	400.			
220TC	2c	blue green	400.			
220TC	2c	slate black	400.			
222TC	4c	orange brown on wove				—
222TC	4c	yellow brown on wove				—
222TC	4c	green	400.			
223TC	5c	blue on glossy wove	400.			
223TC	5c	dark brown on glossy wove	400.			
223TC	5c	bister on wove				—
223TC	5c	sepia on wove				—
223TC	5c	blk brown on wove				—
224TC	6c	deep orange red	400.			
224TC	6c	orange red on wove				120.
224TC	6c	vio. blk. on wove				120.
224TC	6c	yellow on wove				120.
224TC	6c	olive grn. on wove				120.
224TC	6c	purple on wove				120.
224TC	6c	red org. on wove				120.
224TC	6c	brown on wove				120.
224TC	6c	red brn. on wove				120.
224TC	6c	org. brn. on wove				120.
224TC	6c	blk. brn. on wove				120.
224TC	6c	slate grn. on wove				120.
224TC	6c	brn. olive on wove				120.
225TC	8c	dark violet red			400.	
225TC	8c	metallic green			400.	
225TC	8c	salmon			400.	
225TC	8c	yellow orange			—	
225TC	8c	orange brown			400.	
225TC	8c	green			—	
225TC	8c	light green			400.	
225TC	8c	blue			400.	
225TC	8c	steel blue			400.	

1893

231TC	2c	sepia	850.	850.
231TC	2c	orange brown		850.
231TC	2c	deep orange		850.
231TC	2c	light brown		850.
231TC	2c	blue green		850.
231TC	2c	bright rose red		850.
231TC	2c	rose violet		850.
232TC	3c	sepia		850.	
232TC	3c	blackish green		850.	800.
232TC	3c	black		850.	
233TC	4c	sepia		850.
233TC	4c	deep orange		850.
233TC	4c	light brown		850.
233TC	4c	blue green		850.
233TC	4c	rose red		850.
233TC	4c	rose violet		850.
234TC	5c	black	850.	
234TC	5c	dark violet	850.	850.
234TC	5c	rose violet	850.	850.
234TC	5c	red violet	850.	
234TC	5c	brown violet	850.	
234TC	5c	deep blue	850.	
234TC	5c	deep ultra	850.	
234TC	5c	green	850.	
234TC	5c	deep green	850.	
234TC	5c	blue green	—	850.
234TC	5c	dark olive green	850.	—
234TC	5c	deep orange	850.	
234TC	5c	orange red	850.	
234TC	5c	orange brown	850.	850.
234TC	5c	bright rose red	850.	
234TC	5c	claret	850.	
234TC	5c	brown rose	850.	
234TC	5c	dull rose brown		850.
234TC	5c	sepia	850.	850.
234TC	5c	black brown		850.

The 5c trial color proofs differ from the issued stamp.

237TC	10c	bright rose red	1,250.	
237TC	10c	claret	1,250.	
239TC	30c	sepia		1,000.	
239TC	30c	black			350.
240TC	50c	sepia		1,000.	
242TC	$2	blackish brown		1,000.	
242TC	$2	sepia	—	
242TC	$2	red brown	—	

1894

			DIE		PLATE	
			(1) Lg.	(2) Sm.	(3) India	(4) Card
246TC	1c	dusky blue green	—			
246TC	1c	dark blue	—			
253TC	3c	light red violet	—			
253TC	3c	dark red violet	—			
255TC	5c	black	1,250.			
256TC	6c	dark brown	1,000.			
257TC	8c	black	1,250.			
258TC	10c	olive	1,250.			
259TC	15c	red violet	1,250.			
259TC	15c	dark red orange	1,250.			
260TC	50c	black	1,500.			
261ATC	$1	lake	1,500.			
261ATC	$1	orange	1,500.			
262TC	$2	black	1,500.			
262TC	$2	dull violet	1,500.			
262TC	$2	violet	1,500.			
262TC	$2	turquoise blue	1,500.			
262TC	$2	orange brown	1,500.			
262TC	$2	olive green	1,500.			
262TC	$2	sepia	1,500.			
262TC	$2	greenish black	1,500.			
263TC	$5	black	1,500.			
263TC	$5	dark yellow	1,500.			
263TC	$5	orange brown	1,500.			
263TC	$5	olive green	1,500.			
263TC	$5	dull violet	1,500.			
263TC	$5	sepia	1,500.			
263TC	$5	brown red	1,500.			

1898

283TC	10c	orange	1,250.
283TC	10c	sepia	1,250.
284TC	15c	yellowish olive	
284TC	15c	red violet	*2,000.*

1898

285TC	1c	black		—
286TC	2c	purple		2,000.
286TC	2c	black		2,000.
286TC	2c	blue		2,000.
286TC	2c	brown		2,000.
286TC	2c	deep carmine rose		2,000.
287TC	4c	black		—
288TC	5c	black		—
288TC	5c	orange brown	*2,500.*	
289TC	8c	black		—
290TC	10c	black	1,500.	1,250.
291TC	50c	black	1,500.	1,250.
292TC	$1	black		—
293TC	$2	black	5,000.	

1901

| 298TC | 8c | violet & black on wove paper | *2,500.* |

1902-03

| 308TC | 13c | gray violet, type I | 1,000. |
| 319TC | 2c | black, type I | 3,250. |

1904

| 326TC | 5c | black on glazed card | — |

1907

| 330TC | 5c | ultramarine | 1,600. |
| 330TC | 5c | black | 1,700. |

1908

332TC	2c	dull violet	750.
332TC	2c	light ultra.	750.
332TC	2c	bright ultra.	750.
332TC	2c	light green	750.
332TC	2c	dark olive green	750.
332TC	2c	golden yellow	750.
332TC	2c	dull orange	750.
332TC	2c	rose carmine	750.
332TC	2c	ultramarine	750.
332TC	2c	black	—
332TC	2c	dark blue	—
332TC	2c	blue	850.
332TC	2c	lilac brown	850.
332TC	2c	lilac	850.
332TC	2c	blue black	850.
332TC	2c	sage green	850.
332TC	2c	lilac black	850.
332TC	2c	brown	850.
332TC	2c	brown black	850.
332TC	2c	purple	—
332TC	2c	orange brown	850.
332TC	2c	ultra. on orange brown	750.
332TC	2c	ultra. on green	750.
332TC	2c	green on pink	750.
332TC	2c	green on rose	750.
332TC	2c	dark green on grn	750.
332TC	2c	green on orange brown	750.
332TC	2c	purple on orange brown	750.
332TC	2c	blue on yellow	750.
332TC	2c	green on yellow	750.
332TC	2c	brown on orange brown	750.
332TC	2c	brown on yellow	750.
332TC	2c	green on amber yel	—
335TC	5c	green on pink	—
336TC	6c	brown	—
337TC	8c	green (shades) on yellow	—
337TC	8c	orange (shades) on yellow	—
337TC	8c	blue on buff	—
337TC	8c	blue on yellow	—
338TC	10c	carmine on pale yellow green	—
338TC	10c	brown on yellow	—
338TC	10c	green on pink	—
338TC	10c	orange on greenish blue	—
338TC	10c	brown on gray lavender	—
338TC	10c	orange on orange	—
338TC	10c	black on pink	—
338TC	10c	orange on yellow	—
338TC	10c	brown	—
338TC	10c	carmine	—
338TC	10c	blue on pink	—
338TC	10c	brown on pink	—
338TC	10c	black	—
339TC	13c	blue on yellow	—
339TC	13c	sea green on deep yellow	—
339TC	13c	sea green on pale blue	—
339TC	13c	deep violet on yellow	—
340TC	15c	blue on pale lilac	—
340TC	15c	blue on greenish blue	—
340TC	15c	blue on pink	—
340TC	15c	blue on yellow	—
340TC	15c	dark blue on buff	—
340TC	15c	orange brown on yellow	—
340TC	15c	dark purple on yel	—
340TC	15c	orange on yellow	—
340TC	15c	violet on yellow	—
340TC	15c	black on orange	—
341TC	50c	lilac on light blue	—
341TC	50c	dark violet on yellow	—
341TC	50c	violet on yellow	—
341TC	50c	orange on yellow	—
341TC	50c	orange brown on yellow	—
342TC	$1	brown on blue	—

1909

342TC	$1	carmine lake	1,200.	1,100.
342TC	$1	pink	1,200.	1,100.
342TC	$1	brown on blue green	—	
342TC	$1	violet brown on pink	—	
342TC	$1	violet brown on gray	—	

1912-13

| 400TC | 10c | brown red | 1,750. | 1,100. |
| 414TC | 8c | black | 1,750. | |

1918

| 524TC | $5 | carmine & black | 1,350. |

1919

513TC	13c	violet	650.
513TC	13c	lilac	650.
513TC	13c	violet brown	650.
513TC	13c	light ultra	650.
513TC	13c	ultramarine	650.
513TC	13c	deep ultra	650.
513TC	13c	green	650.
513TC	13c	dark green	650.
513TC	13c	olive green	650.
513TC	13c	orange yellow	650.
513TC	13c	orange	650.

513TC	13c	red orange	650.
513TC	13c	ocher	650.
513TC	13c	salmon red	650.
513TC	13c	brown carmine	650.
513TC	13c	claret brown	650.
513TC	13c	brown	650.
513TC	13c	black brown	650.
513TC	13c	gray	650.
513TC	13c	black	650.

1920

547TC	$2	green & black	1,500.

1922-25

552TC	1c	black (thin glazed card)	—
554TC	2c	black (bond paper)	1,250.
561TC	9c	red orange	2,250.
563TC	11c	deep green	2,250.
565TC	14c	dark brown	2,250.
566TC	15c	black	2,250.

1923

610TC	2c	Harding, green	4,000.

1925

618TC	2c	Lexington Concord, black	1,650.

1926

622TC	13c	black	2,250.
628TC	5c	Ericsson, dull dusky blue	1,000.
628TC		gray blue	1,000.

1932

718TC	3c	Olympic, carmine	10,000.
720TC	3c	black (bond paper)	750.

1935

772TC	3c	Connecticut Tercentenary, black (thin glazed card)	1,500.
773TC	3c	San Diego, org. red (yel. glazed card)	1,500.

1936-43

785TC	1c	Army, black (bond paper)	750.
788TC	4c	Army, dark brown	1,000.
789TC	5c	Army, blue	1,000.
793TC	4c	Navy, dark brown	1,000.
798TC	3c	Constitution, black (bond paper)	750.
799TC	3c	Hawaii, black (bond paper)	750.
800TC	3c	Alaska, black (bond paper)	750.
800TC		(India paper)	750.
801TC	3c	Puerto Rico, black (bond paper)	900. 750.
801TC		(India paper)	900.
802TC	3c	Virgin Islands, black (bond paper)	750.
803TC	½c	black	3,000.
815TC	10c	sepia	900.
826TC	21c	black	2,000.
829TC	25c	green	2,000.
836TC	3c	Swedes & Finns, purple	900.
837TC	3c	Northwest Terr., dark purple	900.
854TC	3c	Inauguration, purple	900.
855TC	3c	Baseball, red violet	2,250.
862TC	5c	Authors, dull blue	900.
866TC	3c	Poets, dark blue violet	900.
897TC	3c	Wyoming, red violet	—
929TC	3c	Iwo Jima, bright purple	2,300.
959TC	3c	Progress of Women, brt. violet	1,500.
963TC	3c	Youth, violet	900.
964TC	3c	Oregon, dull violet	900.
968TC	3c	Poultry, red brown	900.

1923-47

AIR POST

			DIE		PLATE	
			(1)	(2)	(3)	(4)
			Lg.	Sm.	India	Card
C5TC	16c	dark green	5,000.			
C8TC	15c	orange	4,750.			
C32TC	5c	blue	4,750.			
C35TC	15c	brown violet	4,750.			

1934

AIR POST SPECIAL DELIVERY

CE1TC	16c	black	3,500.

1885-1902

SPECIAL DELIVERY

E1TC	10c	black	2,500.	
E1TC	10c	dark brown	2,500.	
E1TC	10c	org. yellow (wove paper)		2,000.
E2TC	10c	black	2,500.	
E2TC	10c	green	2,500.	
E2TC	10c	olive yellow		800.

E6TC	10c	orange	2,500.
E6TC	10c	black	2,500.
E6TC	10c	rose red	4,000.

1922-25

E12TC	10c	black	1,500.

1911

REGISTRATION

F1TC	10c	black (glazed card)	1,500.

1851

CARRIERS

LO1TC		deep green	250.	
		Block of 4	1,250.	
a.		orange (wove paper)		350.
LO2TC		deep green	250.	
		Block of 4	1,250.	
a.		orange (wove paper)		350.

LOCALS

15L18TC	(1c)	brown	—
15L18TC	(1c)	blue	—
15L18TC	(1c)	green	—
15L18TC	(1c)	reddish brown	—

1879

POSTAGE DUE

			DIE		PLATE	
			(1)	(2)	(3)	(4)
			Lg.	Sm.	India	Card
J1TC	1c	black	500.			50.
J1TC	1c	gray black	500.			
J1TC	1c	ultramarine	500.			
J1TC	1c	blue	500.			
J1TC	1c	blue green	500.			
J1TC	1c	orange	500.	100.		
J1TC	1c	red orange	500.			
J1TC	1c	olive bister	500.			
J2TC	2c	black	500.			
J2TC	2c	gray black	500.			
J2TC	2c	ultramarine	500.			
J2TC	2c	blue	500.			
J2TC	2c	blue green	500.			
J2TC	2c	orange	500.	100.		
J2TC	2c	red orange	500.			
J2TC	2c	sepia	500.			
J3TC	3c	black	500.			
J3TC	3c	gray black		100.		
J3TC	3c	ultramarine	500.			
J3TC	3c	blue	500.			
J3TC	3c	blue green	500.			
J3TC	3c	orange	500.	100.		
J3TC	3c	red orange	500.			
J3TC	3c	light brown	500.			
J4TC	5c	black	500.			
J4TC	5c	gray black	500.			
J4TC	5c	ultramarine	500.			
J4TC	5c	blue	500.			
J4TC	5c	blue green	500.			
J4TC	5c	orange	500.	100.		
J4TC	5c	red orange	500.			
J5TC	10c	black	500.			
J5TC	10c	gray black	500.			
J5TC	10c	blue	500.			
J5TC	10c	olive yellow	500.			
J5TC	10c	blue green	500.			
J5TC	10c	orange	500.	100.		
J5TC	10c	red orange	500.			
J5TC	10c	olive bister	500.			
J5TC	10c	sepia	500.			
J5TC	10c	gray	500.			
J6TC	30c	black	500.			
J6TC	30c	gray black	500.			
J6TC	30c	blue	500.			
J6TC	30c	olive yellow		100.		
J6TC	30c	blue green	500.			
J6TC	30c	orange	500.	100.		
J6TC	30c	red orange	500.			
J6TC	30c	olive bister	500.			
J6TC	30c	sepia		100.		
J7TC	50c	black	500.			
J7TC	50c	gray black	500.			
J7TC	50c	blue	500.	100.		
J7TC	50c	olive yellow		100.		
J7TC	50c	blue green	500.			
J7TC	50c	orange	500.	100.		
J7TC	50c	red orange	500.			
J7TC	50c	olive bister	500.			
J7TC	50c	sepia	500.			
J7TC	50c	gray	500.			

OFFICIAL

Agriculture

O1TC	1c	black	500.	75.
O2TC	2c	black	500.	75.
O3TC	3c	black	500.	
O3TC	3c	deep green	500.	
O4TC	6c	black	500.	150.
O5TC	10c	black	500.	
O6TC	12c	black	500.	75.
O9TC	30c	black	500.	

Executive

O11TC	2c	black	500.	75.
O11TC	2c	deep brown	500.	
O11TC	2c	brown carmine		75.
O12TC	3c	black	500.	75.
O12TC	3c	deep green	500.	
O13TC	6c	black		90.
O14TC	10c	black		90.

Interior

O16TC	2c	black	500.	
O16TC	2c	deep brown	500.	
O17TC	3c	black	500.	90.
O17TC	3c	deep green	500.	

Justice

O27TC	3c	black	500.	90.
O27TC	3c	deep green	500.	
O27TC	3c	bister yellow		90.
O27TC	3c	dull orange		90.
O27TC	3c	black violet		90.

Navy

O35TC	1c	black		90.
O36TC	2c	black	500.	
O36TC	2c	deep brown	500.	
O36TC	2c	black on wove paper, perf.		250.
O36TC	2c	deep green on wove paper, perf.		250.
O36TC	2c	deep green on wove paper, imperf.		250.
O37TC	3c	black	500.	90.
O37TC	3c	deep green	500.	

Post Office

O48TC	2c	deep brown	500.	
O49TC	3c	deep green	500.	
O50TC	6c	deep brown	500.	
O50TC	6c	brown carmine	500.	

State

O57TC	1c	black	500.	
O57TC	1c	light ultramarine	500.	
O58TC	2c	black	500.	
O58TC	2c	deep brown	500.	
O59TC	3c	black	500.	
O67TC	90c	black	500.	
O68TC	$2	violet & black	2,500.	
O68TC	$2	brown red & black	2,500.	
O68TC	$2	orange red & slate blue	2,500.	

Treasury

O72TC	1c	black	500.
O72TC	1c	light ultramarine	500.
O73TC	2c	black	500.
O74TC	3c	black	500.
O74TC	3c	deep green	500.
O75TC	6c	black	500.
O77TC	10c	black	500.
O78TC	12c	black	500.
O79TC	15c	black	500.
O80TC	24c	black	500.
O81TC	30c	black	500.
O82TC	90c	black	500.

War

O83TC	1c	black	500.	80.	
O83TC	1c	light ultramarine	500.		
O84TC	2c	black	500.	80.	75.
O84TC	2c	deep brown	500.		
O85TC	3c	black	500.		
O85TC	3c	deep green	500.		
O85TC	3c	chocolate	675.		
O86TC	6c	black		80.	
O89TC	12c	black		80.	

1910

POSTAL SAVINGS MAIL

O121TC	2c	lake	500.
O126TC	10c	black (on wove)	1,250.

The so-called "Goodall" set of Small Die proofs on India Paper of Official Stamps in five colors

Agriculture

		(a) Black	(b) Deep green	(c) Dull gray blue	(d) Deep brown	(e) Dull red
O1TC	1c	150.	140.	140.	140.	140.
O2TC	2c	150.	140.	140.	140.	140.
O3TC	3c	150.	140.	140.	140.	140.
O4TC	6c	150.	140.	140.	140.	140.
O5TC	10c	150.	140.	140.	140.	140.
O6TC	12c	150.	140.	140.	140.	140.
O7TC	15c	150.	140.	140.	140.	140.
O8TC	24c	150.	140.	140.	140.	140.
O9TC	30c	150.	140.	140.	140.	

Executive

O10TC	1c	150.	140.	140.	140.	140.
O11TC	2c	150.	140.	140.	140.	140.
O12TC	3c	150.	140.	140.	140.	140.
O13TC	6c	150.	140.	140.	140.	140.
O14TC	10c	150.	140.	140.	140.	140.

Interior

O15TC	1c	150.	140.	140.	140.	140.
O16TC	2c	150.	140.	140.	140.	140.
O17TC	3c	150.	140.	140.	140.	140.
O18TC	6c	150.	140.	140.	140.	140.
O19TC	10c	150.	140.	140.	140.	140.
O20TC	12c	150.	140.	140.	140.	140.
O21TC	15c	150.	140.	140.	140.	140.
O22TC	24c	150.	140.	140.	140.	140.
O23TC	30c	150.	140.	140.	140.	140.
O24TC	90c	150.	140.	140.	140.	140.

Justice

O25TC	1c	150.	140.	140.	140.	140.
O26TC	2c	150.	140.	140.	140.	140.
O27TC	3c	150.	140.	140.	140.	140.
O28TC	6c	150.	140.	140.	140.	140.
O29TC	10c	150.	140.	140.	140.	140.
O30TC	12c	150.	140.	140.	140.	140.
O31TC	15c	150.	140.	140.	140.	140.

		(a) Black	(b) Deep green	(c) Dull gray blue	(d) Deep brown	(e) Dull red
O32TC	24c	150.	140.	140.	140.	140.
O33TC	30c	150.	140.	140.	140.	140.
O34TC	90c	150.	140.	140.	140.	140.

Navy

O35TC	1c	150.	140.	140.	140.	140.
O36TC	2c	150.	140.	140.	140.	140.
O37TC	3c	150.	140.	140.	140.	140.
O38TC	6c	150.	140.	140.	140.	140.
O39TC	7c	150.	140.	140.	140.	140.
O40TC	10c	150.	140.	140.	140.	140.
O41TC	12c	150.	140.	140.	140.	140.
O42TC	15c	150.	140.	140.	140.	140.
O43TC	24c	150.	140.	140.	140.	140.
O44TC	30c	150.	140.	140.	140.	140.
O45TC	90c	150.	140.	140.	140.	140.

Post Office

O47TC	1c	150.	140.	140.	140.	140.
O48TC	2c	150.	140.	140.	140.	140.
O49TC	3c	150.	140.	140.	140.	140.
O50TC	6c	150.	140.	140.	140.	140.
O51TC	10c	150.	140.	140.	140.	140.
O52TC	12c	150.	140.	140.	140.	140.
O53TC	15c	150.	140.	140.	140.	140.
O54TC	24c	150.	140.	140.	140.	140.
O55TC	30c	150.	140.	140.	140.	140.
O56TC	90c	150.	140.	140.	140.	140.

State

O57TC	1c	150.	140.	140.	140.	140.
O58TC	2c	150.	140.	140.	140.	140.
O59TC	3c	150.	140.	140.	140.	140.
O60TC	6c	150.	140.	140.	140.	140.
O61TC	7c	150.	140.	140.	140.	140.
O62TC	10c	150.	140.	140.	140.	140.
O63TC	12c	150.	140.	140.	140.	140.
O64TC	15c	150.	140.	140.	140.	140.
O65TC	24c	150.	140.	140.	140.	140.
O66TC	30c	150.	140.	140.	140.	140.
O67TC	90c	150.	140.	140.	140.	140.

O68TC	$2 scarlet frame, green center	3,250.
O68TC	$2 scarlet frame, black center	3,250.
O68TC	$2 scarlet frame, blue center	3,250.
O68TC	$2 scarlet frame, brown center	3,250.
O68TC	$2 violet frame, black center	3,250.
O68TC	$2 green frame, black center	3,250.
O68TC	$2 brown frame, green center	3,250.
O68TC	$2 brown frame, black center	3,250.
O68TC	$2 red brown frame, green center	3,250.

Treasury

		(a) Black	(b) Deep green	(c) Dull gray blue	(d) Deep brown	(e) Dull red
O72TC	1c	150.	140.	140.	140.	140.
O73TC	2c	150.	140.	140.	140.	140.
O74TC	3c	150.	140.	140.	140.	140.
O75TC	6c	150.	140.	140.	140.	140.
O76TC	7c	150.	140.	140.	140.	140.
O77TC	10c	150.	140.	140.	140.	140.
O78TC	12c	150.	140.	140.	140.	140.
O79TC	15c	150.	140.	140.	140.	140.
O80TC	24c	150.	140.	140.	140.	140.
O81TC	30c	150.	140.	140.	140.	140.
O82TC	90c	150.	140.	140.	140.	140.

War

O83TC	1c	150.	140.	140.	140.	140.
O84TC	2c	150.	140.	140.	140.	140.
O85TC	3c	150.	140.	140.	140.	140.
O86TC	6c	150.	140.	140.	140.	140.
O87TC	7c	150.	140.	140.	140.	140.
O88TC	10c	150.	140.	140.	140.	140.
O89TC	12c	150.	140.	140.	140.	140.
O90TC	15c	150.	140.	140.	140.	140.
O91TC	24c	150.	140.	140.	140.	140.
O92TC	30c	150.	140.	140.	140.	140.
O93TC	90c	150.	140.	140.	140.	140.

OFFICIAL SEALS

1872

OXF1TC	ultra	Die on India	1,000.
OXF1TC	blue	Die on card, colored border	1,000.
OXF1TC	dp bl	Die on card, colored border	1,000.
OXF1TC	green	Die on card, colored border	1,000.
OXF1TC	choc	Die on glossy bond	1,000.
OXF1TC	choc	Die on card, colored border	1,000.
OXF1TC	car	Die on India	1,000.
OXF1TC	brown	Die on India	1,000.
OXF1TC	red vio	Die on India	1,000.

1877

OX1TC	blue	Die on India	500.
OX1TC	green	Die on India	500.
OX1TC	green	Plate on bond	500.
OX1TC	green	Plate on bond, perforated and gummed	—
OX1TC	orange	Die on India	500.
OX1TC	red orange	Die on India	500.
OX1TC	black	Die on India	500.

1879

OX2TC	black	Die on India	—

POSTAL NOTE STAMPS

PN1TC	1c bister	imperf, on white wove	—

NEWSPAPERS

1865

			(1) Die on India	(5) Thick cream wove paper
PR1TC	5c	bright red	500.	
PR1TC	5c	deep reddish brown	2,000.	
PR1TC	5c	dark orange	2,000.	
PR1TC	5c	green	2,000.	
PR2TC	10c	brown	500.	
PR2TC	10c	dull red	500.	
PR2TC	10c	blue	500.	
PR2TC	10c	black		70.
PR2TC	10c	lake		70.
PR2TC	10c	blue green		70.
PR2TC	10c	blue		70.
PR3TC	25c	black		70.
PR3TC	25c	lake		70.
PR3TC	25c	blue green		70.
PR3TC	25c	blue		70.
PR3TC	25c	ocher	500.	
PR3TC	25c	brown	500.	
PR3TC	25c	brick red	500.	
PR4TC	5c	black		70.
PR4TC	5c	lake		70.
PR4TC	5c	blue green		70.
PR4TC	5c	blue		70.

1875

			(1) Die on India	(3) Plate on India
PR9TC	2c	dark carmine		35.
PR9TC	2c	brown rose		35.
PR9TC	2c	scarlet		35.
PR9TC	2c	orange brown	500.	35.
PR9TC	2c	black brown	500.	
PR9TC	2c	sepia		35.
PR9TC	2c	orange yellow		35.
PR9TC	2c	dull orange		35.
PR9TC	2c	green		35.
PR9TC	2c	blue green	500.	
PR9TC	2c	light ultramarine		35.
PR9TC	2c	light blue		35.
PR9TC	2c	dark violet		35.
PR9TC	2c	violet black		35.
PR10TC	3c	rose lake	500.	
PR16TC	12c	dark carmine		35.
PR16TC	12c	brown rose	500.	35.
PR16TC	12c	scarlet	500.	35.
PR16TC	12c	orange brown		35.
PR16TC	12c	sepia	500.	35.
PR16TC	12c	orange yellow		35.
PR16TC	12c	dull orange		35.
PR16TC	12c	green	500.	35.
PR16TC	12c	light ultramarine	500.	35.
PR16TC	12c	light blue		35.
PR16TC	12c	dark violet	500.	35.
PR16TC	12c	violet black	500.	35.
PR16TC	12c	black	500.	35.
PR17TC	24c	sepia	500.	
PR17TC	24c	green	500.	
PR17TC	24c	black	500.	35.
PR18TC	36c	black	500.	
PR18TC	36c	sepia	500.	
PR18TC	36c	green	500.	
PR19TC	48c	black	500.	35.
PR19TC	48c	sepia	500.	
PR19TC	48c	green	500.	
PR20TC	60c	black	500.	35.
PR21TC	72c	black	500.	35.
PR22TC	84c	black	500.	35.
PR23TC	96c	black		35.
PR24TC	$1.92	dark carmine		35.
PR24TC	$1.92	brown rose		35.
PR24TC	$1.92	scarlet		35.
PR24TC	$1.92	orange brown	500.	35.
PR24TC	$1.92	sepia		35.
PR24TC	$1.92	orange yellow		35.
PR24TC	$1.92	dull orange		35.
PR24TC	$1.92	green	500.	35.
PR24TC	$1.92	light ultramarine		35.
PR24TC	$1.92	dark violet		35.
PR24TC	$1.92	violet black		35.
PR24TC	$1.92	black		35.
PR25TC	$3	dark carmine	500.	35.
PR25TC	$3	brown rose		35.
PR25TC	$3	scarlet		35.
PR25TC	$3	orange brown		35.
PR25TC	$3	sepia		35.
PR25TC	$3	orange yellow	500.	35.
PR25TC	$3	dull orange	500.	35.
PR25TC	$3	green	500.	35.
PR25TC	$3	light ultramarine	500.	35.
PR25TC	$3	light blue		35.
PR25TC	$3	dark violet	500.	35.
PR25TC	$3	violet black	500.	35.
PR25TC	$3	black	500.	35.
PR26TC	$6	dark carmine	500.	35.
PR26TC	$6	brown rose	500.	35.
PR26TC	$6	scarlet	500.	35.
PR26TC	$6	orange brown		35.
PR26TC	$6	dark brown		35.
PR26TC	$6	sepia	500.	35.
PR26TC	$6	orange yellow	500.	35.
PR26TC	$6	dull orange	500.	35.
PR26TC	$6	green	500.	35.
PR26TC	$6	light ultramarine		35.
PR26TC	$6	light blue	500.	35.
PR26TC	$6	dark violet	500.	35.
PR26TC	$6	violet black	500.	35.
PR26TC	$6	black	500.	35.
PR27TC	$9	dark carmine	500.	35.

			(1) Die on India	(3) Plate on India
PR27TC	$9	brown rose	500.	35.
PR27TC	$9	scarlet	500.	35.
PR27TC	$9	orange brown		35.
PR27TC	$9	sepia	500.	35.
PR27TC	$9	orange yellow	500.	35.
PR27TC	$9	dull orange	500.	35.
PR27TC	$9	green	500.	35.
PR27TC	$9	light ultramarine	500.	35.
PR27TC	$9	light blue		35.
PR27TC	$9	dark violet	500.	35.
PR27TC	$9	violet black	500.	35.
PR27TC	$9	black	500.	35.
PR28TC	$12	black	500.	
PR28TC	$12	sepia	500.	
PR28TC	$12	orange brown	500.	
PR29TC	$24	black	500.	35.
PR29TC	$24	black brown	500.	
PR29TC	$24	orange brown	500.	
PR29TC	$24	green	500.	
PR30TC	$36	dark carmine	500.	
PR30TC	$36	black	500.	35.
PR30TC	$36	black brown	500.	
PR30TC	$36	orange brown	500.	
PR30TC	$36	sepia	500.	
PR30TC	$36	violet	500.	
PR30TC	$36	green	500.	
PR31TC	$48	violet brown	500.	35.
PR31TC	$48	black	500.	35.
PR31TC	$48	sepia	500.	
PR31TC	$48	green	500.	
PR32TC	$60	dark carmine	500.	40.
PR32TC	$60	scarlet	500.	40.
PR32TC	$60	sepia	500.	40.
PR32TC	$60	green	500.	40.
PR32TC	$60	light ultramarine	500.	40.
PR32TC	$60	black	500.	40.
PR32TC	$60	violet black	500.	
PR32TC	$60	orange brown	500.	
PR32TC	$60	orange yellow	500.	
PR32TC	$60	dull orange	500.	
PR32TC	$60	brown rose	500.	

1885

PR81TC	1c	salmon	500.	
PR81TC	1c	scarlet		120.
PR81TC	1c	dark brown		120.
PR81TC	1c	violet brown		120.
PR81TC	1c	dull orange		120.
PR81TC	1c	green		120.
PR81TC	1c	light blue		120.

1894

PR106TC	25c	deep carmine	500.
PR106TC	25c	dark carmine	500.
PR107TC	50c	black	500.
PR108TC	$2	deep scarlet	500.
PR108TC	$2	dark scarlet	500.
PR109TC	$5	light ultramarine	500.
PR109TC	$5	dark ultramarine	500.
PR110TC	$10	black	500.
PR112TC	$50	black	500.
PR112TC	$50	deep rose	500.
PR112TC	$50	dark rose	500.
PR113TC	$100	black	500.

The so-called "Goodall" set of Small Die proofs on India Paper of Newspaper Stamps in five colors

		(a) Black	(b) Deep green	(c) Dull gray blue	(d) Deep brown	(e) Dull red
PR9TC	2c	150.	125.	125.	125.	125.
PR10TC	3c	150.	125.	125.	125.	125.
PR11TC	4c	150.	125.	125.	125.	125.
PR12TC	6c	150.	125.	125.	125.	125.
PR13TC	8c	150.	125.	125.	125.	125.
PR14TC	9c	150.	125.	125.	125.	125.
PR15TC	10c	150.	125.	125.	125.	125.
PR16TC	12c	150.	125.	125.	125.	125.
PR17TC	24c	150.	125.	125.	125.	125.
PR18TC	36c	150.	125.	125.	125.	125.
PR19TC	48c	150.	125.	125.	125.	125.
PR20TC	60c	150.	125.	125.	125.	125.
PR21TC	72c	150.	125.	125.	125.	125.
PR22TC	84c	150.	125.	125.	125.	125.
PR23TC	96c	150.	125.	125.	125.	125.
PR24TC	$1.92	150.	125.	125.	125.	125.
PR25TC	$3	150.	125.	125.	125.	125.
PR26TC	$6	150.	125.	125.	125.	125.
PR27TC	$9	150.	125.	125.	125.	125.
PR28TC	$12	150.	125.	125.	125.	125.
PR29TC	$24	150.	125.	125.	125.	125.
PR30TC	$36	150.	125.	125.	125.	125.
PR31TC	$48	150.	125.	125.	125.	125.
PR32TC	$60	150.	125.	125.	125.	125.

1925

SPECIAL HANDLING

QE4TC	25c	apple green	1,500.
QE4TC	25c	olive green	1,500.
QE4TC	25c	light blue green	1,500.
QE4TC	25c	dark blue	1,500.
QE4TC	25c	orange yellow	1,500.
QE4TC	25c	orange	1,500.
QE4TC	25c	dull rose	1,500.
QE4TC	25c	carmine lake	1,500.
QE4TC	25c	brown	1,500.
QE4TC	25c	gray brown	1,500.

QE4TC	25c dark violet brown	1,500.
QE4TC	25c gray black	1,500.
QE4TC	25c black	1,500.

THE "ATLANTA" SET OF PLATE PROOFS

A set in five colors on thin card reprinted in 1881 for display at the International Cotton Exhibition in Atlanta, Ga.

1847 Designs (Reproductions)

		Black	Scarlet	Brown	Green	Blue
3TC	5c	300.	300.	300.	300.	300.
4TC	10c	300.	300.	300.	300.	300.

1851-60 Designs

		Black	Scarlet	Brown	Green	Blue
40TC	1c	120.	100.	100.	100.	100.
41TC	3c	120.	100.	100.	100.	100.
42TC	5c	120.	100.	100.	100.	100.
43TC	10c	120.	100.	100.	100.	100.
44TC	12c	120.	100.	100.	100.	100.
45TC	24c	120.	100.	100.	100.	100.
46TC	30c	120.	100.	100.	100.	100.
47TC	90c	120.	100.	100.	100.	100.

1861-66 Designs

		Black	Scarlet	Brown	Green	Blue
102TC	1c	100.	90.	90.	90.	90.
103TC	2c	175.	175.	175.	175.	175.
104TC	3c	100.	90.	90.	90.	90.
105TC	5c	100.	90.	90.	90.	90.
106TC	10c	100.	90.	90.	90.	90.
107TC	12c	100.	90.	90.	90.	90.
108TC	15c	100.	90.	90.	90.	90.
109TC	24c	100.	90.	90.	90.	90.
110TC	30c	100.	90.	90.	90.	90.
111TC	90c	100.	90.	90.	90.	90.

1869 Designs

		Black	Scarlet	Brown	Green	Blue
123TC	1c	175.	150.	150.	150.	150.
124TC	2c	175.	150.	150.	150.	150.
125TC	3c	175.	150.	150.	150.	150.
126TC	6c	175.	150.	150.	150.	150.
127TC	10c	175.	150.	150.	150.	150.
128TC	12c	175.	150.	150.	150.	150.

129TC	15c black frame, scarlet center	375.
129TC	15c black frame, green center	375.
129TC	15c scarlet frame, black center	375.
129TC	15c scarlet frame, blue center	375.
129TC	15c brown frame, black center	375.
129TC	15c brown frame, green center	375.
129TC	15c brown frame, blue center	375.
129TC	15c green frame, black center	375.
129TC	15c green frame, blue center	375.
129TC	15c blue frame, black center	375.
129TC	15c blue frame, brown center	375.
129TC	15c blue frame, green center	375.
130TC	24c black frame, scarlet center	375.
130TC	24c black frame, green center	375.
130TC	24c black frame, blue center	375.
130TC	24c scarlet frame, black center	375.
130TC	24c scarlet frame, blue center	375.
130TC	24c brown frame, black center	375.
130TC	24c brown frame, blue center	375.
130TC	24c green frame, black center	375.
130TC	24c green frame, brown center	375.
130TC	24c green frame, blue center	375.
130TC	24c blue frame, brown center	375.
130TC	24c blue frame, green center	375.
131TC	30c black frame, scarlet center	375.
131TC	30c black frame, green center	375.
131TC	30c black frame, blue center	375.
131TC	30c scarlet frame, black center	375.
131TC	30c scarlet frame, green center	375.
131TC	30c scarlet frame, blue center	375.
131TC	30c brown frame, black center	375.
131TC	30c brown frame, green center	375.
131TC	30c brown frame, blue center	375.
131TC	30c green frame, black center	375.
131TC	30c green frame, brown center	375.
131TC	30c green frame, scarlet center	375.
131TC	30c blue frame, brown center	375.
131TC	30c blue frame, green center	375.
132TC	90c black frame, scarlet center	550.
132TC	90c black frame, brown center	550.
132TC	90c black frame, green center	550.
132TC	90c scarlet frame, blue center	550.
132TC	90c brown frame, black center	550.
132TC	90c brown frame, blue center	550.
132TC	90c green frame, black center	—
132TC	90c green frame, brown center	550.
132TC	90c green frame, blue center	550.
132TC	90c blue frame, brown center	550.
132TC	90c blue frame, green center	550.

1873-75 Designs

		Black	Scarlet	Brown	Green	Blue
156TC	1c	55.	50.	50.	50.	50.
157TC	2c	55.	50.	50.	50.	50.
158TC	3c	60.	55.	55.	55.	55.
159TC	6c	65.	60.	60.	60.	60.
160TC	7c	55.	50.	50.	50.	50.
161TC	10c	55.	50.	50.	50.	50.
162TC	12c	55.	50.	50.	50.	50.
163TC	15c	55.	50.	50.	50.	50.
164TC	24c	55.	50.	50.	50.	50.
165TC	30c	60.	55.	55.	55.	55.
166TC	90c	55.	50.	50.	50.	50.
179TC	5c	80.	75.	75.	75.	75.

POSTAGE DUE

		Black	Scarlet	Brown	Green	Blue
J1TC	1c	55.	50.	50.	50.	50.
J2TC	2c	55.	50.	50.	50.	50.
J3TC	3c	55.	50.	50.	50.	50.
J4TC	5c	55.	50.	50.	50.	50.
J5TC	10c	55.	50.	50.	50.	50.
J6TC	30c	55.	50.	50.	50.	50.
J7TC	50c	55.	50.	50.	50.	50.

OFFICIALS

		Black	Scarlet	Brown	Green	Blue
Agriculture						
O1TC	1c	43.	37.	37.	37.	37.
O2TC	2c	43.	37.	37.	37.	37.
O3TC	3c	43.	37.	37.	37.	37.
O4TC	6c	55.	50.	50.	50.	50.
O5TC	10c	43.	37.	37.	37.	37.
O6TC	12c	43.	37.	37.	37.	37.
O7TC	15c	43.	37.	37.	37.	37.
O8TC	24c	43.	37.	37.	37.	37.
O9TC	30c	43.	37.	37.	37.	37.
Executive						
O10TC	1c	43.	37.	37.	37.	37.
O11TC	2c	43.	37.	37.	37.	37.
O12TC	3c	43.	37.	37.	37.	37.
O13TC	6c	55.	50.	50.	50.	50.
O14TC	10c	43.	37.	37.	37.	37.
Interior						
O15TC	1c	43.	37.	37.	37.	37.
O16TC	2c	43.	37.	37.	37.	37.
O17TC	3c	43.	37.	37.	37.	37.
O18TC	6c	55.	50.	50.	50.	50.
O19TC	10c	43.	37.	37.	37.	37.
O20TC	12c	43.	37.	37.	37.	37.
O21TC	15c	43.	37.	37.	37.	37.
O22TC	24c	43.	37.	37.	37.	37.
O23TC	30c	60.	55.	55.	55.	55.
O24TC	90c	43.	37.	37.	37.	37.
Justice						
O25TC	1c	43.	37.	37.	37.	37.
O26TC	2c	43.	37.	37.	37.	37.
O27TC	3c	43.	37.	37.	37.	37.
O28TC	6c	55.	50.	50.	50.	50.
O29TC	10c	43.	37.	37.	37.	37.
O30TC	12c	43.	37.	37.	37.	37.
O31TC	15c	43.	37.	37.	37.	37.
O32TC	24c	43.	37.	37.	37.	37.
O33TC	30c	60.	55.	55.	55.	55.
O34TC	90c	43.	37.	37.	37.	37.
Navy						
O35TC	1c	43.	37.	37.	37.	37.
O36TC	2c	43.	37.	37.	37.	37.
O37TC	3c	43.	37.	37.	37.	37.
O38TC	6c	55.	50.	50.	50.	50.
O39TC	7c	43.	37.	37.	37.	37.
O40TC	10c	43.	37.	37.	37.	37.
O41TC	12c	43.	37.	37.	37.	37.
O42TC	15c	43.	37.	37.	37.	37.
O43TC	24c	43.	37.	37.	37.	37.
O44TC	30c	60.	55.	55.	55.	55.
O45TC	90c	43.	37.	37.	37.	37.
Post Office						
O48TC	2c	43.	37.	37.	37.	37.
O49TC	3c	43.	37.	37.	37.	37.
O50TC	6c	43.	37.	37.	37.	37.
O51TC	10c	43.	37.	37.	37.	37.
O52TC	12c	43.	37.	37.	37.	37.
O53TC	15c	43.	37.	37.	37.	37.
O54TC	24c	43.	37.	37.	37.	37.
O55TC	30c	43.	37.	37.	37.	37.
O56TC	90c	43.	37.	37.	37.	37.
State						
O57TC	1c	43.	37.	37.	37.	37.
O58TC	2c	43.	37.	37.	37.	37.
O59TC	3c	43.	37.	37.	37.	37.
O60TC	6c	55.	50.	50.	50.	50.
O61TC	7c	43.	37.	37.	37.	37.
O62TC	10c	43.	37.	37.	37.	37.
O63TC	12c	43.	37.	37.	37.	37.
O64TC	15c	43.	37.	37.	37.	37.
O65TC	24c	43.	37.	37.	37.	37.
O66TC	30c	60.	55.	55.	55.	55.
O67TC	90c	43.	37.	37.	37.	37.

O68TC	$2 scarlet frame, black center	1,000.
O68TC	$2 scarlet frame, blue center	1,000.
O68TC	$2 brown frame, black center	1,000.
O68TC	$2 brown frame, blue center	1,000.
O68TC	$2 green frame, brown center	1,000.
O68TC	$2 blue frame, brown center	1,000.
O68TC	$2 blue frame, green center	1,000.
O69TC	$5 scarlet frame, black center	1,000.
O69TC	$5 scarlet frame, blue center	1,000.
O69TC	$5 brown frame, black center	1,000.
O69TC	$5 brown frame, blue center	1,000.
O69TC	$5 green frame, brown center	1,000.
O69TC	$5 blue frame, brown center	1,000.
O69TC	$5 blue frame, green center	1,000.
O70TC	$10 scarlet frame, black center	1,000.
O70TC	$10 scarlet frame, blue center	1,000.
O70TC	$10 brown frame, black center	1,000.
O70TC	$10 brown frame, blue center	1,000.
O70TC	$10 green frame, brown center	1,000.
O70TC	$10 blue frame, brown center	1,000.
O70TC	$10 blue frame, green center	1,000.
O71TC	$20 scarlet frame, black center	1,000.
O71TC	$20 scarlet frame, blue center	1,000.
O71TC	$20 brown frame, black center	1,000.
O71TC	$20 brown frame, blue center	1,000.
O71TC	$20 green frame, brown center	1,000.
O71TC	$20 blue frame, brown center	1,000.
O71TC	$20 blue frame, green center	1,000.

Treasury

		Black	Scarlet	Brown	Green	Blue
O72TC	1c	43.	37.	37.	37.	37.
O73TC	2c	43.	37.	37.	37.	37.
O74TC	3c	43.	37.	37.	37.	37.
O75TC	6c	55.	50.	50.	50.	50.
O76TC	7c	43.	37.	37.	37.	37.
O77TC	10c	43.	37.	37.	37.	37.
O78TC	12c	43.	37.	37.	37.	37.
O79TC	15c	43.	37.	37.	37.	37.
O80TC	24c	43.	37.	37.	37.	37.
O81TC	30c	60.	55.	55.	55.	55.
O82TC	90c	43.	37.	37.	37.	37.
War						
O83TC	1c	43.	37.	37.	37.	37.
O84TC	2c	43.	37.	37.	37.	37.
O85TC	3c	43.	37.	37.	37.	37.
	— Plate flaw at upper left (32R20)					
O86TC	6c	55.	50.	50.	50.	50.
O87TC	7c	43.	37.	37.	37.	37.
O88TC	10c	43.	37.	37.	37.	37.
O89TC	12c	43.	37.	37.	37.	37.
O90TC	15c	43.	37.	37.	37.	37.
O91TC	24c	43.	37.	37.	37.	37.
O92TC	30c	60.	55.	55.	55.	55.
O93TC	90c	43.	37.	37.	37.	37.

NEWSPAPERS

		Black	Scarlet	Brown	Green	Blue
PR9TC	2c	55.	40.	40.	40.	40.
PR10TC	3c	55.	40.	40.	40.	40.
PR11TC	4c	55.	40.	40.	40.	40.
PR12TC	6c	55.	40.	40.	40.	40.
PR13TC	8c	55.	40.	40.	40.	40.
PR14TC	9c	55.	40.	40.	40.	40.
PR15TC	10c	55.	40.	40.	40.	40.
PR16TC	12c	55.	40.	40.	40.	40.
PR17TC	24c	55.	40.	40.	40.	40.
PR18TC	36c	55.	40.	40.	40.	40.
PR19TC	48c	55.	40.	40.	40.	40.
PR20TC	60c	55.	40.	40.	40.	40.
PR21TC	72c	55.	40.	40.	40.	40.
PR22TC	84c	55.	40.	40.	40.	40.
PR23TC	96c	55.	40.	40.	40.	40.
PR24TC	$1.92	55.	40.	40.	40.	40.
PR25TC	$3	55.	40.	40.	40.	40.
PR26TC	$6	55.	40.	40.	40.	40.
PR27TC	$9	55.	40.	40.	40.	40.
PR28TC	$12	55.	40.	40.	40.	40.
PR29TC	$24	55.	40.	40.	40.	40.
PR30TC	$36	55.	40.	40.	40.	40.
PR31TC	$48	55.	40.	40.	40.	40.
PR32TC	$60	55.	40.	40.	40.	40.

CARRIERS

		Black	Scarlet	Brown	Green	Blue
LO1TC	1c Franklin	120.	110.	110.	110.	110.
LO2TC	1c Eagle	120.	110.	110.	110.	110.

TELEGRAPH

American Rapid Telegraph Co.

			DIE (2) Small	PLATE (3) India	(4) Card
1T1TC	1c	green	55.		
1T1TC	1c	brown	55.		
1T1TC	1c	red	55.		
1T1TC	1c	blue	55.		
1T1TC	1c	bluish green	55.		
1T3TC	5c	green	55.		
1T3TC	5c	black	55.		
1T3TC	5c	red	55.		
1T3TC	5c	blue	55.		
1T3TC	5c	bluish green	55.		
1T5TC	15c	red	55.		
1T5TC	15c	black	55.		
1T5TC	15c	brown	55.		
1T5TC	15c	bluish green	55.		
1T6TC	20c	green	55.		
1T6TC	20c	black	55.		
1T6TC	20c	brown	55.		
1T6TC	20c	blue	55.		
1T6TC	20c	bluish green	55.		

Collect

			DIE (1) Large	(2) Small	PLATE (3) India	(4) Card
1T10TC	5c	red		55.		
1T10TC	5c	black		55.		
1T10TC	5c	brown		55.		
1T10TC	5c	green		55.		
1T10TC	5c	bluish green		55.		
1T11TC	15c	red		55.		
1T11TC	15c	black		55.		
1T11TC	15c	brown		55.		
1T11TC	15c	green		55.		
1T11TC	15c	blue		55.		
1T11TC	15c	bluish green		55.		

Office Coupon

			(1) Large	(2) Small	(3) India	(4) Card
1T14TC	5c	red		55.		
1T14TC	5c	black		55.		
1T14TC	5c	brown		55.		
1T14TC	5c	green		55.		
1T14TC	5c	bluish green		55.		
1T15TC	15c	red		55.		
1T15TC	15c	black		55.		
1T15TC	15c	brown		55.		
1T15TC	15c	green		55.		
1T15TC	15c	blue		55.		
1T15TC	15c	bluish green		55.		

Baltimore & Ohio Telegraph Co.

			India	Card
3T2TC	5c	dark olive	65.	
3T4TC	25c	dark olive	65.	

Postal Telegraph Co.

			Small	India	Card
15T1TC	10c	brown red		65.	
15T1TC	10c	red	65.		
15T1TC	10c	blue	65.		
15T1TC	10c	black	65.		

Cat.	Denom.	Color	Large (1)	Small (2)	India (3)	Card (4)
15T1TC	10c	orange			65.	
15T2TC	15c	black	65.		55.	
15T2TC	15c	red	65.	55.		
15T2TC	15c	blue	65.	55.		
15T2TC	25c	brown red	65.		65.	
15T3TC	25c	black	65.			
15T3TC	25c	red	65.			
15T3TC	25c	ultramarine				40.
15T3TC	25c	brown		65.		40.
15T4TC	50c	dull blue		65.		
15T4TC	50c	black	65.			40.
15T4TC	50c	red	65.			
15T4TC	50c	blue	65.			
15T6TC		red brown				40.

Western Union Telegraph Co.

Cat.	Color	India	Card
16T1TC	lilac (1871)	20.	20.
	Pair	45.	45.
16T1TC	orange	20.	20.
	Pair	45.	45.
16T1TC	black	20.	20.
	Pair	45.	45.
16T1TC	violet brown	20.	
	Pair	45.	
16T1TC	light olive	20.	
	Pair	45.	
16T1TC	brown	20.	
	Pair	45.	
16T1TC	orange brown	20.	
	Pair	45.	
16T1TC	blue green	20.	
	Pair	45.	
16T6TC	violet blue (1876)	20.	20.
16T7TC	orange yellow (1877)		20.
	Pair		45.
16T7TC	dark brown		20.
	Pair		45.
16T7TC	black		20.
	Pane of 4		—
16T8TC	dark brown (1878)		—
16T9TC	blue (1879)		—
16T10TC	violet brown (1880)		—
16T10TC	rose		—
16T22TC	black (1892)		—

Die Proof Printed Directly on Card

Cat.	Color	
16T44TC	dull red	—
16T44TC	orange	—
16T44TC	rose red	—
16T44TC	orange brown	—
16T44TC	ocher	—
16T44TC	dark blue	—
16T44TC	dark ultramarine	—
16T44TC	green	—
16T44TC	brown lake	—
16T44TC	reddish brown	—
16T44TC	sepia	—
16T44TC	sepia, unsurfaced card	—
16T44TC	dull violet	—
16T44TC	slate green	—
16T44TC	slate blue	—
16T44TC	black	—
16T44TC	black, unsurfaced card	—

On India

Cat.	Color	
16T44TC	deep rose	—
16T44TC	carmine lake	—
16T44TC	rose lake	—
16T44TC	deep ultramarine	—

Plate Proofs, Sheets of 16 on India or Bond

Cat.	Color	
16T44TC	deep rose, on India	—
16T44TC	deep rose, on Bond	—
16T44TC	orange, on India	—
16T44TC	orange, on Bond	—
16T44TC	dark blue, on India	—
16T44TC	dark blue, on Bond	—
16T44TC	slate green, on India	—
16T44TC	slate green, on Bond	—
16T44TC	rose lake, on India	—
16T44TC	rose lake, on Bond	—
16T44TC	sepia, on Bond	—

REVENUES

Several lists of revenue proofs in trial colors have been published, but the accuracy of some of them is questionable. The following listings are limited to items seen by the editors. The list is not complete.

1862-71   **FIRST ISSUE**

Cat.	Denom.	Description	Color	Proof	Value
R3TC	1c	Proprietary, black		Plate on India	80.
R3TC			carmine	Plate on Card	125.
R3TC			dull red	Plate on Bond	125.
R3TC			orange red	Plate on Bond	125.
R3TC			dull yel.	Plate on Bond	125.
R3TC			violet rose	Plate on Bond	125.
R3TC			deep blue	Plate on Bond	125.
R3TC			red on blue	Plate on Bond	125.
R3TC			blue, perf. & gum	Plate on Bond	125.
R3TC			green	Plate on buff wove	—
R3TC			black	Die on India	950.
R7TC	2c	Certificate, ultra.		Plate on Card	65.
R11TC	2c	Playing Cards, black		Die on India	500.
R13TC	2c	Proprietary, black		Plate on India	75.
R13TC			black	Die on India	650.
R13TC			carmine	Die on India	650.
R15TC	2c	U.S.I.R., violet rose		Plate on Bond	110.
R15TC			light green	Plate on Bond	110.
R15TC			pale blue	Plate on Bond	110.
R15TC			pale rose	Plate on Bond	200.
R15TC			orange	Plate on blue Bond	—
R15TC			black	Plate on India	110.
R15TC			pale orange, perf. & gum	Plate on Bond	110.
R16TC	3c	Foreign Exchange, green on blue		Plate on Bond	140.
R16TC			blue	Plate on Goldbeater's Skin	110.
R18TC	3c	Proprietary, black		Die on India	300.
R21TC	4c	Playing Cards, black		Die (?) on India	300.
R22TC	4c	Proprietary, black		Plate on India	110.
R22TC			black	Die on India	350.
R22TC			deep red lilac	Die on India	400.
R22TC			red lilac	Plate on Card	110.
R24TC	5c	Certificate, carmine		Plate on India	110.
R25TC	5c	Express, pale olive		Plate on Wove	—
R26TC	5c	Foreign Exchange, orange		Plate on India	110.
R28TC	5c	Playing Cards, black		Die (?) on India	300.
R29TC	5c	Proprietary, red		Plate on blue Bond	—
R30TC	6c	Inland Exchange, black		Die on India	350.
R31TC	6c	Proprietary, black		Die on India	—
R32TC	10c	Bill of Lading, greenish blue		Die on India	350.
R32TC+R37TC		composite, dark green		Large Die on India	—
R35TC	10c	Foreign Exchange, black		Die (?) on India	350.
R37TC	10c	Power of Attorney, greenish blue		Die on India	350.
R38TC	10c	Proprietary, black		Die on India	350.
R43TC	25c	Bond, carmine		Plate on Card	90.
R44TC	25c	Certificate, blue		Plate on Bond	300.
R44TC			green	Plate on Bond	300.
R44TC			orange	Plate on Bond	300.
R45TC	25c	Entry of Goods, black		Hybrid Die on India	—
R46TC	25c	Insurance, dull red		Plate on Bond	150.
R46TC			dull red	Plate on Goldbeater's Skin	210.
R46TC			vermilion	Plate on Goldbeater's Skin	210.
R46TC			vermilion	Plate on Bond	170.
R46TC			blue	Plate on Bond	170.
R46TC			blue	Plate on Goldbeater's Skin	215.
R46TC			dark blue	Plate on Bond	155.
R46TC			dark blue	Plate on Goldbeater's Skin	215.
R46TC			green	Plate on Goldbeater's Skin	215.
R51TC	30c	Foreign Exchange, violet		Plate on India	130.
R51TC			violet gray	Plate on India	130.
R51TC			deep red lilac	Plate on India	155.
R51TC			slate blue	Plate on India	155.
R51TC			black	Plate on India	155.
R51TC			red	Plate on India	155.
R52TC		Inland Exchange, deep red lilac		Plate on India	155.
R53TC	40c	Inland Exchange, black		Hybrid Die on India	—
R55TC	50c	Entry of Goods, orange		Plate on Bond	275.
R55TC			green	Plate on Bond	275.
R55TC			red	Plate on Bond	340.
R55TC			deep blue	Plate on Bond	275.
R58TC	50c	Life Insurance, ultramarine		Plate on India	85.
R60TC	50c	Original Process, black		Die (?) on India	280.
R64TC	60c	Inland Exchange, green		Die (?) on India	—
R65TC	70c	Foreign Exchange, orange		Die (?) on India	—
R65TC			black	Die (?) on India	285.
R66TC	$1	Conveyance, carmine		Plate on India	85.
R67TC	$1	Entry of Goods, carmine		Plate on India	60.
R68TC	$1	Foreign Exchange, carmine		Plate on India	60.
R69TC	$1	Inland Exchange, carmine		Plate on India	60.
R70TC	$1	Lease, carmine		Plate on India	130.
R71TC	$1	Life Insurance, carmine		Plate on India	75.
R72TC	$1	Manifest, carmine		Plate on India	80.
R73TC	$1	Mortgage, carmine		Plate on India	85.
R73TC			black	Hybrid Die on India	—
R74TC	$1	Passage Ticket, carmine		Plate on India	120.
R75TC	$1	Power of Attorney, carmine		Plate on India	120.
R76TC	$1	Probate of Will, carmine		Plate on India	60.
R78TC	$1.50	Inland Exchange, black		Die on India	475.
R80TC	$1.90	Foreign Exchange, black		Plate on India	155.
R81TC	$2	Conveyance, carmine		Plate on Card	85.
R82TC	$2	Mortgage, carmine		Plate on Card	85.
R83TC	$2	Probate of Will, black		Hybrid Die on India	—
R84TC	$2.50	Inland Exchange, black		Die (?) on India	120.
R85TC	$3	Charter Party, dark green		Plate on Thin Card	—
R87TC	$3.50	Inland Exchange, black		Die on India	400.
R88TC	$5	Charter Party, carmine		Plate on India	85.
R88TC			black	Hybrid Die on India	—
R89TC	$5	Conveyance, carmine		Plate on India	90.
R91TC	$5	Mortgage, carmine		Plate on India	90.
R95TC	$10	Mortgage, yellow green		Plate on Thin Card	—
R98TC	$20	Conveyance, red orange		Plate on Card	120.
R98TC			red orange	Plate on India	220.
R99TC	$20	Probate of Will, red orange		Plate on Card	275.
R99TC			black	Plate on Card	275.
R101TC	$50	U.S.I.R., orange		Plate on Bond	275.
R101TC			deep blue	Plate on Bond	275.
R101TC			black	Hybrid Die on India	—
R102TC	$200	black & red		Plate on Card	1,600.
R102TC			gray brown & red	Plate on Bond	1,600.
R102TC			green & brown red	Plate on India	1,600.
R102TC			black	Plate on India	—

SECOND ISSUE

Cat.	Denom.	Description	Proof	Value
R104TC	2c	pale blue & black	Plate on Bond	60.
R132TC	$200	red, green & black	India	2,500.
R132TC		orange (master die)	India	2,500.
R132TC		blue (master die)	India	2,500.
R132TC		green (master die)	India	2,500.
R133TC	$500	black (master die)	India	10,000.
R133TC		yellow, green & black	India	5,000.
R133TC		bright green, orange brown & black	India	5,000.
R133TC		red, green & black	Bond	5,000.
R133TC		light green, light brown & black	Bond	5,000.
R133TC		blue, scarlet & black	Bond	5,000.
R133ATC	$5000	yel org, green & black	India	7,500.
R133ATC		olive brown, green & black	India	8,000.

R133ATC		org red, dark green & black	India	8,000.
R133ATC		org red, dark blue & black	India	20,000.

The master die is the completed stamp design prior to its division into separate color dies.
See note after No. R133AP in Die and Plate Proofs section.

THIRD ISSUE

R134TC	1c	brown & black	Plate on Card	60.

1875   National Bank Note Co., New York City

R152TC	2c	(Liberty), green	Die on India	600.
R152TC		(Liberty), brown	Die on India	600.
R152TC		(Liberty), black	Die on India	600.

1898

R161TC	½c	green	Lg. die on India	750.
R163TC	1c	green	Lg. die on India	750.
R163TC		black	Lg. die on India	750.
R165TC	3c	green	Sm. die on India	650.
R169TC	25c	green	Lg. die on India	650.
R170TC	40c	black	Lg. die on India	650.
R172TC	80c	green	Lg. die on India	650.

1898

R174TC	$3	black	Die on India	650.
R176TC	$10	green	Die on India	650.

1899

R179TC	$100	dark green & black	Die on India	1,250.
R181TC	$1000	dark blue & black	Die on India	1,250.

1914

R195TC	½c	black	Small die on Wove	—
R196TC	1c	blue green	Small die on Wove	—
R198TC	3c	ultramarine	Small die on Wove	—
R199TC	4c	brown	Small die on Wove	—
R200TC	5c	blue	Small die on Wove	—
R201TC	10c	yellow	Small die on Wove	—
R202TC	25c	dull violet	Small die on Wove	—
R203TC	40c	blue green	Small die on Wove	—
R204TC	50c	red brown	Small die on Wove	—
R205TC	80c	orange	Small die on Wove	—

PROPRIETARY

1871-75

RB1TC	1c	blue & black	Plate on Bond	70.
RB1TC		scarlet & black	Plate on Bond	70.
RB1TC		orange & black	Plate on Bond	70.
RB1TC		orange & ultramarine	Plate on Granite Bond	60.
RB3TC	3c	blue & black, with gum	Plate on Bond	60.
RB3TC		blue & black	Plate on Gray Bond	60.
RB3TC		blue & black	Plate on wove	—
RB8TC	50c	green & brown	Die on India	675.
RB8TC		green & purple	Die on India	675.
RB8TC		green & brown red	Die on India	675.
RB8TC		green & violet	Die on India	675.
RB8TC		green & dark carmine	Die on India	675.
RB8TC		ultramarine & red	Die on India	675.
RB9TC	$1	green & brown	Die on India	675.
RB9TC		green & purple	Die on India	675.
RB9TC		green & violet brown	Die on India	675.
RB9TC		green & brown red	Die on India	675.
RB9TC		green & violet	Die on India	675.
RB9TC		green & dark carmine	Die on India	675.

1875-83

RB11TC	1c	brown	Die on India	500.
RB11TC		red brown	Die on India	500.
RB11TC		blue	Die on India	500.
RB11TC		black	Die on India	500.
RB12TC	2c	green	Die on India	500.
RB12TC		black	Die on India	500.
RB12TC		brown	Die on India	500.

RB12TC		orange brown	Die on India	500.
RB12TC		blue	Die on India	500.
RB13TC	3c	brown	Die on India	500.
RB13TC		green	Die on India	500.
RB13TC		blue	Die on India	500.
RB13TC		black	Plate on India	150.
RB14TC	4c	dark brown	Die on India	450.
RB14TC		green	Die on India	450.
RB14TC		black	Die on India	450.
RB14TC		blue	Die on India	450.
RB14TC		black	Plate on India	150.
RB16TC	5c	green	Die on India	450.
RB16TC		dark slate	Die on India	450.
RB16TC		blue	Die on India	450.
RB17TC	6c	green	Plate on India	150.
RB17TC		black	Plate on India	150.
RB17TC		black	Die on India	500.
RB17TC		blue	Die on India	500.
RB17TC		purple	Die on India	500.
RB17TC		dull violet	Die on India	500.
RB17TC		violet	Die on India	500.
RB17TC		violet brown	Die on India	500.
RB17TC		dark brown	Die on India	500.
RB19TC	10c	black	Die on India	550.

SECOND, THIRD AND PROPRIETARY ISSUES
Stamps Nos. R103 to R131, R134 to R150 and RB1 to RB7.

A special composite plate was made and impressions taken in various colors and shades. Although all varieties in all colors must have been made, only those seen by the editors are listed.

PLATE PROOFS ON INDIA PAPER
CENTERS IN BLACK

1871-75

R103TC   1c

a.	dark purple	60.
b.	dull purple	60.
d.	brown	60.
e.	black brown	60.
g.	light blue	60.
h.	dark blue	70.
i.	ultramarine	70.
k.	yellow green	70.
n.	green	65.
o.	dark green	65.
p.	blue green	65.
q.	light orange	65.
r.	dark orange	65.
s.	deep orange	65.
t.	scarlet	65.
u.	carmine	65.
x.	dark brown red	65.
y.	dark brown orange, goldbeater's skin	90.

R104TC   2c

a.	dark purple	60.
b.	dull purple	60.
d.	brown	60.
e.	black brown	60.
g.	light blue	60.
h.	dark blue	70.
i.	ultramarine	70.
k.	yellow green	70.
l.	dark yellow green	70.
n.	green	65.
o.	dark green	65.
p.	blue green	65.
q.	light orange	65.
r.	dark orange	65.
s.	deep orange	65.
t.	scarlet	65.
u.	carmine	65.
x.	dark brown red	65.
y.	dark brown orange, goldbeater's skin	90.

R105TC   3c

a.	dark purple	60.
b.	dull purple	60.
d.	brown	60.
e.	black brown	60.
g.	light blue	60.
h.	dark blue	70.
i.	ultramarine	70.
k.	yellow green	70.
n.	green	65.
o.	dark green	65.
p.	blue green	65.
q.	light orange	65.
r.	dark orange	65.
s.	deep orange	65.
t.	scarlet	65.
u.	carmine	65.
x.	dark brown red	65.
y.	dark brown orange, goldbeater's skin	90.

R106TC   4c

a.	dark purple	60.
b.	dull purple	60.
d.	brown	60.
e.	black brown	60.
f.	orange brown	65.
g.	light blue	60.
h.	dark blue	70.
i.	ultramarine	70.
k.	yellow green	70.
n.	green	65.
o.	dark green	65.
p.	blue green	65.
q.	light orange	65.
r.	dark orange	65.
s.	deep orange	65.
t.	scarlet	65.
u.	carmine	65.

x.	dark brown red	65.
y.	dark brown orange, goldbeater's skin	90.

R107TC   5c

a.	dark purple	60.
b.	dull purple	60.
d.	brown	60.
e.	black brown	60.
f.	orange brown	65.
g.	light blue	60.
h.	dark blue	70.
i.	ultramarine	70.
k.	yellow green	70.
n.	green	65.
o.	dark green	65.
p.	blue green	65.
q.	light orange	65.
r.	dark orange	65.
s.	deep orange	65.
t.	scarlet	65.
u.	carmine	65.
v.	dark carmine	65.
w.	purplish carmine	65.
x.	dark brown red	65.
y.	dark brown orange, goldbeater's skin	90.

R108TC   6c

a.	dark purple	60.
b.	dull purple	60.
d.	brown	60.
e.	black brown	60.
f.	orange brown	65.
g.	light blue	60.
h.	dark blue	70.
i.	ultramarine	70.
k.	yellow green	70.
n.	green	65.
o.	dark green	65.
p.	blue green	65.
q.	light orange	65.
r.	dark orange	65.
s.	deep orange	65.
t.	scarlet	65.
u.	carmine	65.
v.	dark carmine	65.
w.	purplish carmine	65.
x.	dark brown red	65.
y.	dark brown orange, goldbeater's skin	90.

R109TC   10c

a.	dark purple	60.
b.	dull purple	60.
d.	brown	60.
e.	black brown	60.
g.	light blue	60.
h.	dark blue	70.
i.	ultramarine	70.
k.	yellow green	70.
n.	green	65.
o.	dark green	65.
p.	blue green	65.
q.	light orange	65.
r.	dark orange	65.
s.	deep orange	65.
t.	scarlet	65.
u.	carmine	65.
x.	dark brown red	65.

R110TC   15c

a.	dark purple	60.
b.	dull purple	60.
d.	brown	60.
e.	black brown	60.
f.	orange brown	65.
g.	light blue	60.
h.	dark blue	70.
i.	ultramarine	70.
k.	yellow green	70.
n.	green	65.
o.	dark green	65.
p.	blue green	65.
q.	light orange	65.
r.	dark orange	65.
s.	deep orange	65.
t.	scarlet	65.
u.	carmine	65.
x.	dark brown red	65.

R111TC   20c

a.	dark purple	60.
b.	dull purple	60.
d.	brown	60.
e.	black brown	60.
g.	light blue	60.
h.	dark blue	70.
i.	ultramarine	70.
k.	yellow green	70.
n.	green	65.
o.	dark green	65.
p.	blue green	65.
q.	light orange	65.
r.	dark orange	65.
s.	deep orange	65.
t.	scarlet	65.
u.	carmine	65.
w.	purplish carmine	65.
x.	dark brown red	65.
y.	dark brown orange, goldbeater's skin	90.

R112TC   25c

a.	dark purple	60.
b.	dull purple	60.
d.	brown	60.
e.	black brown	60.
g.	light blue	60.
h.	dark blue	70.
i.	ultramarine	70.
k.	yellow green	70.
l.	dark yellow green	70.
n.	green	65.

- o. dark green — 65.
- p. blue green — 65.
- q. light orange — 65.
- r. dark orange — 65.
- s. deep orange — 65.
- t. scarlet — 65.
- u. carmine — 65.
- x. dark brown red — 65.
- y. dark brown orange, goldbeater's skin — 90.

R113TC 30c
- a. dark purple — 60.
- b. dull purple — 60.
- d. brown — 60.
- e. black brown — 60.
- g. light blue — 60.
- h. dark blue — 70.
- i. ultramarine — 70.
- k. yellow green — 70.
- n. green — 65.
- o. dark green — 65.
- p. blue green — 65.
- q. light orange — 65.
- r. dark orange — 65.
- s. deep orange — 65.
- t. scarlet — 65.
- u. carmine — 65.
- v. dark carmine — 65.
- w. purplish carmine — 65.
- x. dark brown red — 65.
- y. dark brown orange, goldbeater's skin — 90.

R114TC 40c
- a. dark purple — 60.
- b. dull purple — 60.
- d. brown — 60.
- e. black brown — 60.
- f. orange brown — 65.
- g. light blue — 60.
- h. dark blue — 70.
- i. ultramarine — 70.
- k. yellow green — 70.
- n. green — 65.
- o. dark green — 65.
- p. blue green — 65.
- q. light orange — 65.
- r. dark orange — 65.
- s. deep orange — 65.
- t. scarlet — 65.
- u. carmine — 65.
- x. dark brown red — 65.

R115TC 50c
- a. dark purple — 60.
- b. dull purple — 60.
- d. brown — 60.
- e. black brown — 60.
- g. light blue — 60.
- h. dark blue — 70.
- i. ultramarine — 70.
- k. yellow green — 70.
- n. green — 65.
- o. dark green — 65.
- p. blue green — 65.
- q. light orange — 65.
- r. dark orange — 65.
- s. deep orange — 65.
- t. scarlet — 65.
- u. carmine — 65.
- x. dark brown red — 65.

R116TC 60c
- a. dark purple — 60.
- b. dull purple — 60.
- d. brown — 60.
- e. black brown — 60.
- g. light blue — 60.
- h. dark blue — 70.
- i. ultramarine — 70.
- k. yellow green — 70.
- n. green — 65.
- o. dark green — 65.
- p. blue green — 65.
- q. light orange — 65.
- r. dark orange — 65.
- s. deep orange — 65.
- t. scarlet — 65.
- u. carmine — 65.
- v. dark carmine — 65.
- x. dark brown red — 65.
- y. dark brown orange, goldbeater's skin — 90.

R117TC 70c
- a. dark purple — 60.
- b. dull purple — 60.
- d. brown — 60.
- e. black brown — 60.
- g. light blue — 60.
- h. dark blue — 70.
- i. ultramarine — 70.
- k. yellow green — 70.
- n. green — 65.
- o. dark green — 65.
- p. blue green — 65.
- q. light orange — 65.
- r. dark orange — 65.
- s. deep orange — 65.
- t. scarlet — 65.
- u. carmine — 65.
- x. dark brown red — 65.

R118TC $1
- a. dark purple — 70.
- b. dull purple — 70.
- d. brown — 70.
- e. black brown — 70.
- g. light blue — 80.
- h. dark blue — 85.
- i. ultramarine — 85.
- k. yellow green — 80.
- n. green — 75.

- o. dark green — 75.
- p. blue green — 75.
- q. light orange — 75.
- r. dark orange — 75.
- s. deep orange — 75.
- t. scarlet — 80.
- u. carmine — 80.
- w. purplish carmine — 80.
- x. dark brown red — 80.
- y. dark brown orange, goldbeater's skin — 90.

R119TC $1.30
- a. dark purple — 70.
- b. dull purple — 70.
- d. brown — 70.
- e. black brown — 70.
- g. light blue — 80.
- h. dark blue — 85.
- i. ultramarine — 85.
- k. yellow green — 80.
- n. green — 75.
- o. dark green — 75.
- p. blue green — 75.
- q. light orange — 75.
- r. dark orange — 75.
- s. deep orange — 75.
- t. scarlet — 80.
- u. carmine — 80.
- x. dark brown red — 80.

R120TC $1.50
- a. dark purple — 70.
- b. dull purple — 70.
- d. brown — 70.
- e. black brown — 70.
- g. light blue — 80.
- h. dark blue — 85.
- i. ultramarine — 85.
- j. bright yellow green, on card — 75.
- k. yellow green — 80.
- n. green — 75.
- o. dark green — 75.
- p. blue green — 75.
- q. light orange — 75.
- r. dark orange — 75.
- s. deep orange — 75.
- t. scarlet — 80.
- u. carmine — 80.
- x. dark brown red — 80.

R121TC $1.60
- a. dark purple — 70.
- b. dull purple — 70.
- d. brown — 70.
- e. black brown — 70.
- g. light blue — 80.
- h. dark blue — 85.
- i. ultramarine — 85.
- k. yellow green — 80.
- n. green — 75.
- o. dark green — 75.
- p. blue green — 75.
- q. light orange — 75.
- r. dark orange — 75.
- s. deep orange — 75.
- t. scarlet — 80.
- u. carmine — 80.
- x. dark brown red — 80.

R122TC $1.90
- a. dark purple — 70.
- b. dull purple — 70.
- d. brown — 70.
- e. black brown — 70.
- g. light blue — 80.
- h. dark blue — 85.
- i. ultramarine — 85.
- j. bright yellow green, on card — 75.
- k. yellow green — 80.
- n. green — 75.
- o. dark green — 75.
- p. blue green — 75.
- q. light orange — 75.
- r. dark orange — 75.
- s. deep orange — 75.
- t. scarlet — 80.
- u. carmine — 80.
- x. dark brown red — 80.

R123TC $2
- a. dark purple — 70.
- b. dull purple — 70.
- d. brown — 70.
- e. black brown — 70.
- g. light blue — 80.
- h. dark blue — 85.
- i. ultramarine — 85.
- j. bright yellow green, on card — 75.
- k. yellow green — 80.
- n. green — 75.
- o. dark green — 75.
- p. blue green — 75.
- q. light orange — 75.
- r. dark orange — 75.
- s. deep orange — 75.
- t. scarlet — 80.
- u. carmine — 80.
- w. purplish carmine — 80.
- x. dark brown red — 80.
- y. dark brown orange, goldbeater's skin — 90.

R124TC $2.50
- a. dark purple — 70.
- b. dull purple — 70.
- d. brown — 70.
- e. black brown — 70.
- g. light blue — 80.
- h. dark blue — 85.
- i. ultramarine — 85.
- k. yellow green — 80.
- n. green — 75.

- o. dark green — 75.
- p. blue green — 75.
- q. light orange — 75.
- r. dark orange — 75.
- s. deep orange — 75.
- t. scarlet — 80.
- u. carmine — 80.
- v. dark carmine — 80.
- x. dark brown red — 80.

R125TC $3
- a. dark purple — 70.
- b. dull purple — 70.
- d. brown — 70.
- e. black brown — 70.
- g. light blue — 80.
- h. dark blue — 85.
- i. ultramarine — 85.
- j. bright yellow green, on card — 75.
- k. yellow green — 80.
- n. green — 75.
- o. dark green — 75.
- p. blue green — 75.
- q. light orange — 75.
- r. dark orange — 75.
- s. deep orange — 75.
- t. scarlet — 80.
- u. carmine — 80.
- x. dark brown red — 80.

R126TC $3.50
- a. dark purple — 70.
- b. dull purple — 70.
- c. red purple — 75.
- d. brown — 70.
- e. black brown — 80.
- g. light blue — 80.
- h. dark blue — 85.
- i. ultramarine — 85.
- k. yellow green — 80.
- n. green — 75.
- o. dark green — 75.
- p. blue green — 75.
- q. light orange — 75.
- r. dark orange — 75.
- s. deep orange — 75.
- t. scarlet — 90.
- u. carmine — 80.
- x. dark brown red — 80.

R127TC $5
- a. dark purple — 70.
- b. dull purple — 70.
- d. brown — 70.
- e. black brown — 70.
- g. light blue — 80.
- h. dark blue — 85.
- i. ultramarine — 85.
- k. yellow green — 80.
- n. green — 75.
- o. dark green — 75.
- p. blue green — 75.
- q. light orange — 75.
- r. dark orange — 75.
- s. deep orange — 75.
- t. scarlet — 75.
- u. carmine — 75.
- w. purplish carmine — 75.
- x. dark brown red — 80.
- y. dark brown orange, goldbeater's skin — 100.

R128TC $10
- a. dark purple — 70.
- b. dull purple — 70.
- d. brown — 70.
- e. black brown — 70.
- g. light blue — 80.
- h. dark blue — 85.
- i. ultramarine — 85.
- j. bright yellow green, on card — 75.
- k. yellow green — 75.
- n. green — 75.
- o. dark green — 75.
- p. blue green — 75.
- q. light orange — 75.
- r. dark orange — 75.
- s. deep orange — 75.
- t. scarlet — 75.
- u. carmine — 80.
- x. dark brown red — 80.

R129TC $20
- a. dark purple — 95.
- b. dull purple — 95.
- d. brown — 95.
- e. black brown — 95.
- g. light blue — 90.
- h. dark blue — 90.
- i. ultramarine — 90.
- k. yellow green — 85.
- m. emerald green — 85.
- n. green — 75.
- o. dark green — 75.
- p. blue green — 75.
- q. light orange — 85.
- r. dark orange — 85.
- s. deep orange — 90.
- t. scarlet — 80.
- u. carmine — 90.
- v. dark carmine — 90.
- x. dark brown red — 80.

R130TC $25
- a. dark purple — 100.
- b. dull purple — 100.
- d. brown — 100.
- e. black brown — 100.
- g. light blue — 90.
- h. dark blue — 90.
- i. ultramarine — 90.
- k. yellow green — 85.

m.	emerald green	85.
n.	green	75.
o.	dark green	75.
p.	blue green	75.
q.	light orange	75.
r.	dark orange	85.
s.	deep orange	85.
t.	scarlet	90.
u.	carmine	80.
w.	purplish carmine	90.
x.	dark brown red	300.
y.	dark brown orange, goldbeater's skin	100.

R131TC $50

a.	dark purple	95.
b.	dull purple	95.
d.	brown	95.
e.	black brown	95.
g.	light blue	90.
h.	dark blue	90.
i.	ultramarine	90.
j.	bright yellow green, on card	85.
k.	yellow green	85.
m.	emerald green	85.
n.	green	75.
o.	dark green	75.
p.	blue green	75.
q.	light orange	75.
r.	dark orange	85.
s.	deep orange	85.
t.	scarlet	90.
u.	carmine	80.
x.	dark brown red	80.

RB1TC   1c

a.	dark purple	70.
b.	dull purple	70.
d.	brown	65.
e.	black brown	65.
g.	light blue	75.
h.	dark blue	75.
i.	ultramarine	70.
k.	yellow green	70.
l.	dark yellow green	70.
n.	green	65.
o.	dark green	65.
p.	blue green	65.
q.	light orange	65.
r.	dark orange	65.
s.	deep orange	65.
t.	scarlet	65.
u.	carmine	65.
x.	dark brown red	65.

RB2TC   2c

a.	dark purple	70.
b.	dull purple	70.
d.	brown	65.
e.	black brown	65.
g.	light blue	70.
h.	dark blue	70.
i.	ultramarine	70.
j.	bright yellow green, on card	70.
k.	yellow green	70.
n.	green	65.
o.	dark green	65.
p.	blue green	65.
q.	light orange	65.
r.	dark orange	65.
s.	deep orange	65.
t.	scarlet	65.
u.	carmine	65.
x.	dark brown red	65.

RB3TC   3c

a.	dark purple	70.
b.	dull purple	70.
d.	brown	65.
e.	black brown	65.
g.	light blue	70.
h.	dark blue	70.
i.	ultramarine	70.
k.	yellow green	70.
l.	dark yellow green	70.
n.	green	65.
o.	dark green	65.
p.	blue green	65.
q.	light orange	65.
r.	dark orange	65.
s.	deep orange	65.
t.	scarlet	65.
u.	carmine	65.
x.	dark brown red	65.

RB4TC   4c

a.	dark purple	70.
b.	dull purple	70.
d.	brown	65.
e.	black brown	65.
g.	light blue	70.
h.	dark blue	70.
i.	ultramarine	70.
k.	yellow green	70.
n.	green	65.
o.	dark green	65.
p.	blue green	65.
q.	light orange	65.
r.	dark orange	65.
s.	deep orange	65.
t.	scarlet	65.
u.	carmine	65.
x.	dark brown red	65.

RB5TC   5c

a.	dark purple	70.
b.	dull purple	70.
d.	brown	65.
e.	black brown	65.
g.	light blue	70.
h.	dark blue	70.
i.	ultramarine	70.

j.	bright yellow green, on card	70.
k.	yellow green	70.
l.	dark yellow green	70.
n.	green	65.
o.	dark green	65.
p.	blue green	65.
q.	light orange	65.
r.	dark orange	65.
s.	deep orange	65.
t.	scarlet	65.
u.	carmine	65.
x.	dark brown red	65.

RB6TC   6c

a.	dark purple	70.
b.	dull purple	70.
d.	brown	65.
e.	black brown	65.
g.	light blue	70.
h.	dark blue	70.
i.	ultramarine	70.
k.	yellow green	70.
l.	dark yellow green	70.
n.	green	65.
o.	dark green	65.
p.	blue green	65.
q.	light orange	65.
r.	dark orange	65.
s.	deep orange	65.
t.	scarlet	65.
u.	carmine	65.
x.	dark brown red	65.

RB7TC   10c

a.	dark purple	70.
b.	dull purple	70.
d.	brown	65.
e.	black brown	65.
g.	light blue	70.
h.	dark blue	70.
i.	ultramarine	70.
k.	yellow green	70.
l.	dark yellow green	70.
n.	green	65.
o.	dark green	65.
p.	blue green	65.
q.	light orange	65.
r.	dark orange	65.
s.	deep orange	65.
t.	scarlet	65.
u.	carmine	65.
x.	dark brown red	65.

1898

RB20TC	⅛c	light blue	Large die on card	1,000.
RB21TC	¼c	dull green	Large die on India	1,300.
RB22TC	⅜c	dull green	Large die on India	750.
RB24TC	1c	dull green	Large die on India	750.
RB26TC	1⅞c	dull green	Large die on India	750.
RB26TC	1⅞c	black	Large die on India	750.
RB27TC	2c	dull green	Large die on India	500.
RB31TC	5c	dull green	Large die on India	500.

1918-29

Stock Transfer

RD20TC	$50	black	Die on India	2,250.
RD20TC	$50	blue	Die on India	2,250.

1894

Playing Cards

RF1TC	2c	black (On hand)	Die on India	1,500.
RF2TC	2c	lake (Act of)	Die on India	1,000.

PRIVATE DIE MATCH STAMPS

For important valuing information see the note before Private Die Proprietary die and plate proofs.

1864

			DIE ON INDIA (1) Large	PLATE (3) India (4) Card
RO1TC	1c	black	175.	
RO1TC	1c	green	300.	
RO2TC	1c	black	225.	
RO2TC	1c	green	300.	
RO5TC	1c	black	275.	
RO5TC	1c	blue	500.	
RO6TC	1c	black	300.	
RO6TC	1c	green	500.	
RO7TC	1c	black	300.	
RO7TC	1c	dull green	300.	
RO7TC	1c	green	500.	
RO9TC	1c	blue	225.	
RO9TC	1c	brown	275.	
RO9TC	1c	dark green	500.	
RO9TC	1c	green	300.	
RO10TC	1c	blue	300.	
RO10TC	1c	green	500.	
RO11TC	3c	blue	500.	
RO11TC	3c	green	500.	
RO12TC	1c	blue	225.	
RO12TC	1c	green	500.	
RO13TC	3c	black	500.	
RO13TC	3c	blue	1,000.	
RO14TC	1c	blue	225.	
RO14TC	1c	green	500.	
RO15TC	1c	black	225.	
RO15TC	1c	blue	225.	
RO16TC	1c	black	225.	
RO16TC	1c	blue	225.	
RO17/19TC	1c/3c	green	1,250.	
RO17TC	1c	black	225.	
RO17TC	1c	green	500.	

			DIE ON INDIA (1) Large	PLATE (3) India (4) Card
RO19TC	3c	blue	250.	
RO19TC	3c	green	600.	
RO20TC	1c	black	175.	
RO20TC	1c	green	500.	
RO21TC	3c	blue	375.	
RO21TC	3c	green	375.	
RO22TC	1c	black	300.	
RO23TC	1c	black	225.	
RO23TC	1c	blue	225.	
RO23TC	1c	green	500.	
RO24TC	1c	black	225.	
RO24TC	1c	blue	225.	
RO24TC	1c	green	500.	
RO25TC	12c	black	400.	
RO25TC	12c	blue	750.	
RO25TC	12c	green	750.	
RO26TC	1c	black	225.	
RO26TC	1c	blue	225.	
RO26TC	1c	dark brn	225.	
RO26TC	1c	green	300.	
RO26TC	1c	light brn	300.	
RO27TC	12c	black	400.	
RO27TC	12c	blue	500.	
RO27TC	12c	green	750.	
RO28TC	1c	black	175.	
RO28TC	1c	brown	300.	
RO28TC	1c	green	300.	
RO29TC	1c	blue	300.	
RO29TC	1c	green	300.	
RO30TC	1c	black	175.	
RO30TC	1c	blue	225.	
RO30TC	1c	green	300.	
RO30TC	1c	red	500.	
RO31TC	1c	blue	300.	
RO31TC	1c	green	225.	
RO31TC	1c	red	500.	
RO32TC	4c	blue	500.	
RO32TC	4c	brown	500.	
RO32TC	4c	orange	500.	
RO32TC	4c	vermilion	500.	
RO35TC	1c	blue	300.	
RO35TC	1c	green	500.	
RO37TC	3c	blue	400.	
RO37TC	3c	green	400.	
RO38TC	1c	blue	350.	
RO38TC	1c	dk bl	500.	
RO38TC	1c	green	375.	
RO38TC	1c	red	600.	
RO39TC	1c	black	300.	
RO41TC	1c	black	225.	
RO41TC	1c	green	300.	
RO42TC	1c	black	300.	
RO42TC	1c	blue	300.	
RO42TC	1c	green	500.	
RO43TC	1c	blue	500.	
RO45TC	1c	blue	350.	
RO45TC	1c	green	750.	
RO46TC	1c	blue	350.	
RO46TC	1c	dk bl	500.	
RO46TC	1c	green	500.	
RO46TC	1c	orange	300.	
RO47TC	1c	blue	300.	
RO47TC	1c	green	500.	
RO49TC	1c	blue	225.	
RO49TC	1c	brown	500.	
RO49TC	1c	brn red	300.	
RO49TC	1c	dk bl	500.	
RO49TC	1c	green	500.	
RO49TC	1c	red brn	500.	
RO55TC	1c	blue	375.	
RO56TC	1c	blue	750.	
RO56TC	1c	green	300.	
RO57TC	1c	black	175.	
RO57TC	1c	blue	225.	
RO58TC	1c	black	300.	
RO58TC	1c	blue	225.	
RO58TC	1c	dark rose	500.	
RO58TC	1c	green	500.	
RO58TC	1c	rose	300.	
RO59TC	1c	black	225.	
RO60TC	3c	blue	500.	
RO60TC	3c	green	500.	
RO61TC	1c	black	175.	
RO61TC	1c	blue	300.	
RO62TC	1c	black	175.	
RO62TC	1c	blue	175.	
RO64TC	1c	black	225.	
RO64TC	1c	blue	300.	
RO64TC	1c	green	300.	
RO65TC	1c	green	300.	
RO67TC	1c	blue	225.	
RO67TC	1c	green	300.	
RO67TC	1c	red	500.	
RO67TC	1c	rose	500.	
RO68TC	1c	black	225.	
RO68TC	1c	blue	225.	
RO69TC	1c	blue	300.	
RO69TC	1c	green	500.	
RO71TC	1c	black	250.	
RO71TC	1c	green	400.	
RO72TC	1c	black	500.	
RO73TC	1c	blue	225.	
RO73TC	1c	green	300.	
RO73TC	1c	red	500.	
RO73TC	1c	red brn	225.	
RO76TC	1c	blue	500.	
RO76TC	1c	green	300.	
RO77TC	1c	black	225.	
RO77TC	1c	green	300.	
RO78TC	1c	black	225.	
RO78TC	1c	dk bl	500.	
RO78TC	1c	green	500.	

			DIE ON INDIA (1) Large	(3) India	PLATE (4) Card
RO80TC	1c	black	225.		
RO80TC	1c	green	500.		
RO81TC	1c	blue	175.		
RO81TC	1c	dark green	500.		
RO81TC	1c	green	225.		
RO81TC	1c	lake	500.		
RO81TC	1c	red	300.		
RO82TC	1c	blue	175.		
RO82TC	1c	green	500.		
RO83TC	1c	black	175.		
RO83TC	1c	green	300.		
RO83TC	1c	red	500.		
RO84TC	1c	blue	300.		
RO84TC	1c	green	500.		
RO85TC	1c	black	250.		
RO85TC	1c	blue	300.		
RO85TC	1c	green	350.		
RO85TC	1c	orange	500.		
RO85TC	1c	vermilion	500.		
RO86TC	1c	blue	500.		
RO86TC	1c	brown	500.		
RO86TC	1c	green	400.		
RO86TC	1c	orange	500.		
RO86TC	1c	red	500.		
RO87TC	1c	dull rose	500.		
RO87TC	1c	orange	500.		
RO88TC	1c	blue	300.		
RO88TC	1c	green	500.		
RO89TC	3c	blue	300.		
RO89TC	3c	green	300.		
RO90TC	6c	blue	225.		
RO90TC	6c	brown	500.		
RO90TC	6c	green	500.		
RO90TC	6c	orange	500.		
RO91TC	3c	blue	225.		
RO91TC	3c	brown	500.		
RO91TC	3c	green	500.		
RO91TC	3c	orange	500.		
RO91TC	3c	red	500.		
RO92TC	1c	blue	300.		
RO92TC	1c	green	500.		
RO94TC	3c	blue	225.		
RO94TC	3c	brown	300.		
RO94TC	3c	green	225.		
RO94TC	3c	orange	300.		
RO94TC	3c	red	500.		
RO94TC	3c	vermilion	500.		
RO95TC	1c	black	175.		
RO95TC	1c	blue	175.		
RO95TC	1c	brown	225.		
RO95TC	1c	dk bl	500.		
RO96TC	1c	black	175.		
RO96TC	1c	blue	225.		
RO97TC	1c	blue	300.		
RO99TC	1c	black	175.		
RO99TC	1c	blue	500.		
RO100TC	1c	blue	500.		
RO101TC	3c	black	175.		
RO101TC	3c	green	300.		
RO101TC	3c	orange			75.
RO102TC	5c	black	175.		
RO102TC	5c	blue	500.		
RO102TC	5c	green	500.		
RO103TC	1c	blue	225.		
RO103TC	1c	rose	300.		
RO105TC	1c	blue	300.		
RO105TC	1c	green	500.		
RO106TC	1c	black	175.		
RO106TC	1c	blue	225.		
RO107TC	1c	black	175.		
RO107TC	1c	green	300.		
RO110TC	1c	black	175.		
RO110TC	1c	blue	175.		
RO110TC	1c	orange	500.		
RO110TC	1c	red	225.		
RO112TC	1c	black	175.		
RO112TC	1c	green	500.		
RO113TC	1c	blue	300.		
RO113TC	1c	green	500.		
RO113TC	1c	orange	500.		
RO114TC	1c	black	750.		
RO115TC	1c	black	175.		
RO115TC	1c	green	500.		
RO116TC	1c	black	225.		
RO116TC	1c	green	300.		
RO118TC	8c	black	225.		
RO118TC	8c	dk bl	500.		
RO118TC	8c	green	500.		
RO119TC	1c	black	225.		
RO119TC	1c	blue	225.		
RO120TC	1c	black	500.		
RO121TC	1c	black	175.		
RO121TC	1c	blue	300.		
RO122TC	1c	blue	300.		
RO122TC	1c	green	500.		
RO123TC	1c	blue	500.		
RO125TC	1c	black	225.		
RO126TC	1c	blue	300.		
RO126TC	1c	green	500.		
RO127TC	1c	black	300.		
RO127TC	1c	green	225.		
RO128TC	1c	black	225.		
RO128TC	1c	green	500.		
RO130TC	1c	black	225.		
RO130TC	1c	green	300.		
RO131TC	1c	black	175.		
RO131TC	1c	green	225.		
RO131TC	1c	red	225.		
RO132TC	1c	black	225.		
RO132TC	1c	green	500.		
RO133TC	1c	blue	500.		
RO133TC	1c	green	300.		
RO134TC	1c	black	300.		150.
RO134TC	1c	green	300.		
RO135TC	1c	black	500.		
RO135TC	1c	blue	300.		
RO135TC	1c	green	300.		
RO135TC	1c	rose	225.		
RO136TC	1c	black	225.		
RO136TC	1c	green	300.		
RO137TC	1c	black	175.		
RO137TC	1c	blue	175.		
RO137TC	1c	green	500.		
RO138TC	1c	black	175.		
RO138TC	1c	blue	500.		
RO139TC	5c	black	175.		
RO139TC	5c	green	500.		
RO140TC	4c	black	225.		
RO140TC	4c	blue	300.		
RO141TC	1c	black	175.		
RO141TC	1c	dk bl	300.		
RO141TC	1c	green	500.		
RO141TC	1c	yellow green	300.		
RO141TC	1c	green	500.		
RO142TC	1c	black	175.		
RO142TC	1c	blue	225.		
RO143TC	3c	black	175.		
RO143TC	3c	blue	225.		
RO143TC	3c	green	300.		
RO144TC	1c	black	500.		
RO145TC	1c	black	500.		
RO145TC	1c	blue	500.		
RO146TC	1c	blue	500.		
RO146TC	1c	green	300.		
RO148TC	1c	black	175.		
RO148TC	1c	green	300.		
RO148TC	1c	red	300.		
RO152TC	1c	blue	300.		
RO152TC	1c	green	300.		
RO153TC	1c	blue	225.		
RO153TC	1c	brown	300.		
RO153TC	1c	green	225.		
RO153TC	1c	orange	300.		
RO153TC	1c	red	300.		
RO155TC	1c	blue	225.		
RO155TC	1c	green	500.		
RO157TC	3c	black	175.		
RO157TC	3c	green	300.		
RO158TC	1c	blue	300.		
RO158TC	1c	green	500.		
RO159TC	3c	black	225.		
RO159TC	3c	green	500.		
RO160TC	1c	black	225.		
RO160TC	1c	brown	500.		
RO160TC	1c	green	300.		
RO161TC	1c	black	225.		
RO161TC	1c	green	300.		
RO163TC	1c	blue	300.		
RO163TC	1c	green	500.		
RO164TC	1c	black	500.		
RO165TC	12c	black	750.		
RO165TC	12c	blue	1,000.		
RO165TC	12c	red	1,000.		
RO166TC	1c	black	300.		
RO166TC	1c	blue	225.		
RO166TC	1c	green	500.		
RO166TC	1c	red	175.		
RO167TC	3c	black	175.		
RO167TC	3c	green	300.		
RO167TC	3c	red	300.		
RO167TC	3c	ultramarine	300.		
RO168TC	1c	black	500.		
RO168TC	1c	green	300.		
RO171TC	1c	blue	300.		
RO171TC	1c	green	300.		
RO172TC	1c	blue	225.		
RO172TC	1c	green	500.		
RO173TC	1c	black	225.		
RO173TC	1c	green	300.		
RO174TC	1c	black	300.		
RO174TC	1c	green	300.		
RO175TC	1c	blue	275.		
RO175TC	1c	green	350.		
RO175TC	1c	red	500.		
RO177TC	1c	black	175.		
RO177TC	1c	blue	225.		
RO177TC	1c	green	500.		
RO178TC	1c	black	175.		
RO178TC	1c	blue	300.		
RO179TC	1c	blue	500.		
RO179TC	1c	green	500.		
RO180TC	1c	blue	225.		
RO180TC	1c	green	500.		
RO181TC	1c	blue	500.		
RO181TC	1c	green	300.		
RO182TC	1c	blue	300.		
RO182TC	1c	green	300.		
RO183TC	1c	blue	650.		
RO183TC	1c	green	650.		
RO184TC	1c	blue	225.		
RO184TC	1c	brown	300.		
RO184TC	1c	green	225.		
RO184TC	1c	orange	300.		
RO184TC	1c	red	300.		
RO186TC	1c	black	175.		

PRIVATE DIE CANNED FRUIT STAMP

			DIE ON INDIA (1) Large	(3) India	PLATE (4) Card
RP1TC	1c	black	375.		

PRIVATE DIE MEDICINE STAMPS

			DIE ON INDIA (1) Large	(3) India	PLATE (4) Card
RS1TC	1c	blue	300.		
RS4TC	1c	green	500.		
RS10TC	4c	black	300.		
RS14TC	4c	black	300.		
RS14TC	4c	blue	300.		
RS16TC	2c	green	500.		
RS21TC	1c	blue	500.		
RS21TC	1c	green	500.		
RS22TC	2c	blue	500.		
RS22TC	2c	green	500.		
RS23TC	4c	green	500.		
RS24TC	1c	blue	500.		
RS24TC	1c	green	500.		
RS25TC	2c	blue	500.		
RS25TC	2c	green	500.		
RS26TC	4c	blue	500.		
RS26TC	4c	green	500.		
RS27TC	4c	blue	225.		
RS27TC	4c	green	500.		
RS28TC	2c	black	225.		
RS28TC	2c	black	225.		
RS29TC	1c	black	175.		
RS29/RO120TC	2c/1c	black	750.		
RS29TC	2c	blue	175.		
RS29TC	2c	dk bl	500.		
RS29TC	2c	green	500.		
RS29TC	2c	red	300.		
RS30TC	1c	black	175.		
RS30TC	1c	blue	500.		
RS30TC	1c	green	500.		
RS30TC	1c	red	500.		
RS31TC	1c	black	500.		
RS31TC	1c	blue	225.		
RS31TC	1c	red	500.		
RS33TC	1c	blue	175.		
RS33TC	1c	green	225.		
RS33TC	1c	red	500.		
RS34TC	1c	blue	500.		
RS34TC	1c	green	500.		
RS35TC	1c	blue	300.		
RS35TC	1c	green	500.		
RS36TC	1c	black	500.		
RS36TC	1c	dk bl	500.		
RS36TC	1c	green	500.		
RS36TC	1c	ultramarine	500.		
RS36TC	1c	yellow green	225.		
RS38TC	2c	blue	750.		
RS38TC	2c	green	750.		
RS39TC	1c	blue	300.		
RS39TC	1c	green	300.		
RS39TC	1c	orange	500.		
RS40TC	2c	black	225.		
RS40TC	2c	blue	300.		
RS41TC	4c	black	225.		
RS41TC	4c	blue	500.		
RS41TC	4c	green	500.		
RS42TC	1c	green	500.		
RS43TC	4c	black	225.		
RS43TC	4c	green	500.		
RS44TC	1c	green	750.		
RS46TC	4c	blue	225.		
RS46TC	4c	green	300.		
RS47TC	4c	blue	300.		
RS47TC	4c	brown	500.		
RS47TC	4c	green	300.		
RS47TC	4c	orange	500.		
RS47TC	4c	red	500.		
RS49TC	4c	black	225.		
RS49TC	4c	blue	300.		
RS50TC	1c	black	300.		
RS50TC	1c	blue	500.		
RS50TC	1c	green	500.		
RS51TC	2c	blue	500.		
RS51TC	2c	green	500.		
RS52TC	4c	blue	500.		
RS52TC	4c	green	500.		
RS53TC	1c	blue	225.		
RS53TC	1c	brown	300.		
RS53TC	1c	green	225.		
RS53TC	1c	orange	300.		
RS53TC	1c	red	300.		
RS54TC	2c	blue	225.		
RS54TC	2c	brown	300.		
RS54TC	2c	green	225.		
RS54TC	2c	orange	300.		
RS54TC	2c	red	500.		
RS55TC	4c	blue	225.		
RS55TC	4c	green	225.		
RS55TC	4c	orange	225.		
RS55TC	4c	red	500.		
RS56TC	3c	black	350.		
RS56TC	1c	green	500.		
RS57TC	6c	blue	225.		
RS57TC	6c	brown	300.		
RS57TC	6c	green	225.		
RS57TC	6c	orange	300.		
RS57TC	6c	red	300.		
RS58TC	4c	blue	225.		
RS58TC	4c	blue green	500.		
RS58TC	4c	dk bl	500.		
RS58TC	4c	green	225.		
RS58TC	4c	light blue	500.		
RS58TC	4c	red	225.		
RS59TC	1c	blue	300.		
RS59TC	1c	green	500.		
RS60TC	1c	blue	500.		
RS62TC	1c	brown	300.		
RS62TC	1c	green	225.		
RS62TC	1c	orange	300.		
RS62TC	1c	red	500.		
RS62TC	1c	vermilion	500.		
RS64TC	2c	blue	225.		

			DIE ON INDIA (1) Large	(3) India	(4) Card	PLATE
RS64TC	2c	brown	300.			
RS64TC	2c	green	225.			
RS64TC	2c	orange	300.			
RS64TC	2c	red	500.			
RS64TC	1c	vermilion	500.			
RS65TC	4c	blue	500.			
RS65TC	4c	green	500.			
RS66TC	1c	blue	300.			
RS66TC	1c	green	500.			
RS66TC	1c	light green	500.			
RS66TC	1c	orange	500.			
RS66TC	1c	rose red	500.			
RS67TC	1c	green	500.			
RS69TC	1c	blue	500.			
RS69TC	1c	green	500.			
RS70TC	2c	blue	500.			
RS70TC	2c	green	500.			
RS71TC	1c	blue	500.			
RS71TC	1c	green	500.			
RS72TC	2c	blue	500.			
RS72TC	2c	green	500.			
RS73TC	2c	black	500.			
RS73TC	2c	blue	500.			
RS73TC	2c	red	1,000.			
RS74TC	1c	blue	500.			
RS74TC	1c	green	500.			
RS74hTC	1c	blue	500.			
RS74hTC	1c	green	500.			
RS75TC	1c	black	300.			
RS75TC	1c	green	500.			
RS76TC	2c	blue	300.			
RS76TC	2c	green	300.			
RS81TC	4c	black	225.			
RS81TC	4c	blue	500.			
RS81TC	4c	green	500.			
RS83TC	4c	blue	500.			
RS83TC	4c	green	500.			
RS84TC	1c	black	250.			
RS84TC	1c	blue	350.			
RS84TC	1c	green	250.			
RS84TC	1c	orange	650.			
RS84TC	1c	red	650.			
RS84TC	1c	slate	650.			
RS85TC	4c	blue	275.			
RS85TC	4c	brown	275.			
RS85TC	4c	green	300.			
RS85TC	4c	orange	375.			
RS86TC	1c	black	225.			
RS86TC	1c	blue	225.			
RS88TC	1c	blue	500.			
RS88TC	1c	green	500.			
RS89TC	1c	green	300.			
RS91TC	4c	blue	225.			
RS91TC	4c	green	500.			
RS92TC	3c	blue	225.			
RS92TC	3c	brown	300.			
RS92TC	3c	green	225.			
RS92TC	3c	orange	300.			
RS92TC	3c	red	500.			
RS92TC	3c	vermilion	500.			
RS94TC	4c	blue	500.			
RS94TC	4c	green	500.			
RS95TC	1c	black	300.			
RS95TC	1c	blue	225.			
RS95TC	1c	dk bl	90.			
RS96TC	3c	blue	225.			
RS96TC	3c	green	500.			
RS97TC	1c	blue	300.			
RS97TC	1c	green	500.			
RS98TC	1c	blue	225.			
RS98TC	1c	green	175.			
RS98TC	1c	red	500.			
RS99TC	4c	blue	500.			
RS100TC	6c	green	500.			
RS101TC	1c	blue	500.			
RS101TC	1c	green	500.			
RS102TC	2c	black	175.			
RS102TC	2c	green	225.			
RS102TC	2c	rose	225.			
RS103TC	4c	blue	500.			
RS103TC	4c	green	500.			
RS106TC	2c	black	500.			
RS106TC	2c	green	300.			
RS107/109TC	3c/6c	green	1,250.			
RS107TC	3c	blue	300.			
RS108TC	4c	blue	300.			
RS108TC	4c	green	500.			
RS109TC	6c	blue	300.			
RS110TC	2c	black	300.			
RS110TC	2c	green	300.			
RS111TC	4c	blue	300.			
RS111TC	4c	green	500.			
RS114TC	1c	green	300.			
RS116TC	4c	black	225.			
RS116TC	4c	blue	300.			
RS116TC	4c	brown	500.			
RS116TC	4c	green	500.			
RS116TC	4c	vermilion	500.			
RS117TC	1c	blue	350.			
RS117TC	1c	green	750.			
RS118TC	1c	black	175.			
RS118TC	1c	blue	225.			
RS118TC	1c	brn red	300.			
RS118TC	1c	green	300.			
RS120TC	2c	blue	225.			
RS120TC	2c	brown	300.			
RS120TC	2c	green	225.			
RS120TC	2c	orange	300.			
RS120TC	2c	red	500.			
RS120TC	2c	vermilion	500.			
RS121TC	3c	blue	500.			
RS121TC	3c	green	500.			
RS122TC	2c	blue	500.			
RS122TC	2c	green	500.			
RS123TC	4c	blue	225.			
RS123TC	4c	brown	300.			
RS123TC	4c	green	225.			
RS123TC	4c	orange	300.			
RS123TC	4c	red	500.			
RS123TC	4c	vermilion	500.			
RS124TC	1c	black	175.			
RS124TC	1c	blue green	300.			
RS124TC	1c	green	500.			
RS124TC	1c	orange	500.			
RS124TC	1c	red	225.			
RS126TC	1c	black	225.			
RS126TC	1c	blue	225.			
RS126TC	1c	brown	300.			
RS126TC	1c	orange	300.			
RS126TC	1c	red	500.			
RS126TC	1c	vermilion	500.			
RS127TC	4c	black	225.			
RS127TC	4c	blue	225.			
RS127TC	4c	brown	225.			
RS127TC	4c	orange	300.			
RS127TC	4c	red	500.			
RS127TC	4c	vermilion	500.			
RS128TC	2c	black	600.			
RS128TC	2c	green	400.			
RS128TC	2c	pale blue	500.			
RS130TC	4c	black	275.			
RS130TC	4c	blue	350.			
RS131TC	4c	blue	225.			
RS131TC	4c	brown	500.			
RS131TC	4c	green	300.			
RS131TC	4c	orange	300.			
RS131TC	4c	red	500.			
RS131TC	4c	vermilion	500.			
RS132TC	4c	blue	500.			
RS132TC	4c	orange	500.			
RS133TC	6c	blue	500.			
RS133TC	6c	green	500.			
RS134TC	4c	black	300.			
RS134TC	4c	green	300.			
RS134TC	4c	red	500.			
RS138TC	1c	blue	300.			
RS138TC	1c	green	500.			
RS138TC	1c	red	500.			
RS138TC	1c	yel grn	500.			
RS139TC	2c	black	225.			
RS139TC	2c	blackish violet				90.
RS139TC	2c	blue	500.			
RS139TC	2c	green	500.			
RS139TC	2c	red	225.			
RS139TC	2c	rose	500.			
RS141TC	4c	black	225.			
RS141TC	4c	blue	300.			
RS142TC	1c	blue	225.			
RS142TC	1c	brown	300.			
RS142TC	1c	green	225.			
RS142TC	1c	orange	300.			
RS142TC	1c	red	500.			
RS142TC	1c	vermilion	500.			
RS143TC	4c	black	225.			
RS143TC	4c	blue	225.			
RS144TC	1c	black	500.			
RS144TC	1c	green	500.			
RS145TC	2c	blue	500.			
RS146TC	4c	black	300.			
RS146TC	4c	blue	300.			
RS150TC	1c	black	300.			
RS150TC	1c	blue	175.			
RS150TC	1c	carmine	500.			
RS150TC	1c	green	225.			
RS151TC	1c	blue	500.			
RS151TC	1c	green	500.			
RS152TC	2c	black	175.			
RS152TC	2c	blue	300.			
RS153TC	4c	blue	750.			
RS153TC	4c	green	750.			
RS154TC	4c	black	500.			
RS155TC	2c	black	300.			
RS155TC	2c	black	300.			
RS155TC	2c	blue	225.			
RS155TC	2c	red	500.			
RS156TC	6c	blue	225.			
RS156TC	6c	green	225.			
RS156TC	6c	red	225.			
RS157TC	2c	blue	225.			
RS157TC	2c	green	225.			
RS157TC	2c	red	500.			
RS157TC	2c	vermilion	300.			
RS158TC	1c	black	500.			
RS159TC	4c	black	375.			
RS160TC	6c	blue	300.			
RS160TC	6c	green	500.			
RS161TC	4c	blue	500.			
RS161TC	4c	green	750.			
RS162TC	1c	black	175.			
RS162TC	1c	green	300.			
RS162TC	1c	red	500.			
RS163TC	4c	black	300.			
RS163TC	4c	green	600.			
RS163TC	4c	yellow green	600.			
RS164TC	1c	blue	225.			
RS164TC	1c	green	500.			
RS165TC	4c	black	175.			
RS165TC	4c	blue	225.			
RS166TC	1c	blue	300.			
RS166TC	1c	green	500.			
RS169TC	4c	blue	225.			
RS169TC	4c	green	500.			
RS169TC	4c	red	225.			
RS170TC	1c	blue	300.			
RS170TC	1c	green	500.			
RS171TC	1c	black	225.			
RS171TC	1c	blue	225.			
RS171TC	1c	brown	300.			
RS171TC	1c	dull blue	500.			
RS171TC	1c	green	225.			
RS171TC	1c	orange	300.			
RS171TC	1c	red	500.			
RS171TC	1c	vermilion	500.			
RS172TC	2c	blue	225.			
RS172TC	2c	brown	300.			
RS172TC	2c	green	225.			
RS172TC	2c	orange	225.			
RS172TC	2c	red	500.			
RS172TC	2c	vermilion	500.			
RS173TC	1c	black	225.			
RS173TC	1c	green	225.			
RS173TC	1c	red	300.			
RS174TC	1c	black	500.			
RS174TC	1c	dk bl	500.			
RS174TC	1c	green	300.			
RS175TC	2c	black	250.			
RS175TC	2c	blue	500.			
RS175TC	2c	green	500.			
RS176TC	4c	blue	375.			
RS176TC	4c	green	500.			
RS177TC	2c	blue	750.			
RS177TC	2c	green	1,000.			
RS178TC	6c	blue	300.			
RS178TC	6c	green	500.			
RS179TC	2c	black	300.			
RS179TC	2c	green	375.			
RS180TC	3c	blue	300.			
RS180TC	3c	green	300.			
RS181TC	4c	blue	225.			
RS181TC	4c	green	500.			
RS182TC	4c	blue	225.			
RS182TC	4c	green	225.			
RS182TC	4c	rose	300.			
RS183TC	1c	black	500.			
RS183TC	1c	blue	300.			
RS183TC	1c	green	500.			
RS183TC	1c	red	225.			
RS184TC	2c	blue	300.			
RS184TC	2c	brown	225.			
RS184TC	2c	green	225.			
RS184TC	2c	orange	300.			
RS184TC	2c	vermilion	300.			
RS185TC	1c	blue	300.			
RS186TC	4c	blue	225.			
RS186TC	4c	green	500.			
RS187TC	4c	blue	225.			
RS187TC	4c	brown	300.			
RS187TC	4c	green	300.			
RS187TC	4c	orange	500.			
RS187TC	4c	red	500.			
RS187TC	4c	vermilion	500.			
RS188TC	1c	blue	500.			
RS188TC	1c	green	500.			
RS189TC	1c	black	175.			
RS189TC	1c	blue	225.			
RS189TC	1c	red	225.			
RS190TC	2c	blue	500.			
RS190TC	2c	green	500.			
RS191TC	4c	blue	400.			
RS191TC	4c	green	400.			
RS192TC	6c	blue	400.			
RS192TC	6c	green	400.			
RS192TC	6c	rose	500.			
RS193TC	2c	blue	500.			
RS193TC	2c	green	500.			
RS194TC	1c	green	175.			
RS195TC	2c	blue	500.			
RS195TC	2c	green	500.			
RS196TC	1c	black	500.			
RS196TC	1c	green	225.			
RS197TC	2c	blue	300.			
RS198TC	1c	green	300.			
RS198TC	1c	red	500.			
RS199TC	2c	blue	225.			
RS199TC	2c	green	500.			
RS204TC	2c	blue	500.			
RS204TC	2c	green	500.			
RS205TC	4c	blue	225.			
RS205TC	4c	green	500.			
RS208TC	1c	black	225.			
RS208TC	1c	blue	225.			
RS208TC	1c	orange	300.			
RS209TC	2c	black	500.			
RS209TC	2c	blue	500.			
RS210TC	4c	blue	225.			
RS210TC	4c	green	225.			
RS210TC	4c	red	225.			
RS212TC	1c	black	225.			
RS212TC	1c	blue	300.			
RS212TC	1c	green	500.			
RS213TC	6c	blue	500.			
RS213TC	6c	green	500.			
RS214TC	4c	blue	300.			
RS214TC	4c	brown	300.			
RS214TC	4c	green	225.			
RS214TC	4c	orange	300.			
RS214TC	4c	red	500.			
RS214TC	4c	vermilion	500.			
RS215TC	1c	black	300.			
RS215TC	1c	blue	450.			
RS215TC	1c	dark red	500.			
RS215TC	1c	green	500.			
RS216TC	1c	blue	500.			
RS216TC	1c	green	500.			
RS220TC	1c	blue	300.			
RS221TC	4c	black	175.			

Number	Denom.	Color	Die on India (1) Large	Plate (3) India	Plate (4) Card
RS221TC	4c	blue	225.		
RS222TC	8c	green	500.		
RS223TC	1c	blue	300.		
RS223TC	1c	brown	300.		
RS223TC	1c	green	225.		
RS223TC	1c	orange	300.		
RS223TC	1c	vermilion	300.		
RS224TC	1c	blue	500.		
RS224TC	1c	brown	300.		
RS224TC	1c	green	225.		
RS224TC	1c	orange	300.		
RS224TC	1c	red	500.		
RS225TC	4c	blue	500.		
RS225TC	4c	green	500.		
RS226TC	1c	black	350.		
RS228TC	1c	black	175.		
RS228TC	1c	blue	225.		
RS228TC	1c	brown	500.		
RS228TC	1c	green	225.		
RS228TC	1c	orange	500.		
RS228TC	1c	red	500.		
RS228TC	1c	vermilion	500.		
RS229TC	2c	black	225.		
RS229TC	2c	blue	225.		
RS229TC	2c	brown	300.		
RS229TC	2c	green	225.		
RS229TC	2c	orange	225.		
RS229TC	2c	red	300.		
RS229TC	2c	vermilion	500.		
RS230TC	6c	blue	225.		
RS230TC	6c	brown	300.		
RS230TC	6c	green	225.		
RS230TC	6c	orange	300.		
RS230TC	6c	vermilion	225.		
RS231TC	6c	black	1,000.		
RS231TC	6c	blue	1,000.		
RS231TC	6c	green	1,000.		
RS231TC	6c	red	750.		
RS236TC	4c	blue	500.		
RS239TC	2c	black	225.		
RS239TC	2c	blue	300.		
RS239TC	2c	brown	500.		
RS239TC	2c	green	225.		
RS239TC	2c	orange	300.		
RS239TC	2c	vermilion	500.		
RS240TC	4c	red	500.		
RS240TC	4c	blue	175.		
RS240TC	4c	blue green	500.		
RS240TC	4c	brown	500.		
RS240TC	4c	green	225.		
RS240TC	4c	orange	225.		
RS240TC	4c	vermilion	225.		
RS241TC	4c	green	500.		
RS242TC	1c	blue	225.		
RS242TC	1c	green	500.		
RS243TC	4c	blue	500.		
RS243TC	4c	green	500.		
RS244TC	6c	blue	500.		
RS244TC	6c	green	500.		
RS245TC	1c	blue	500.		
RS250TC	6c	blue	500.		
RS250TC	6c	green	500.		
RS251TC	1c	blue	225.		
RS251TC	1c	brown	225.		
RS251TC	1c	green	225.		
RS252TC	1c	black	225.		
RS252TC	1c	blue	225.		
RS252TC	1c	brown	300.		
RS252TC	1c	green	225.		
RS252TC	1c	orange	500.		
RS252TC	1c	red	500.		
RS252TC	1c	rose	225.		
RS253TC	4c	blue	500.		
RS253TC	4c	green	500.		
RS258TC	6c	black	500.		
RS259TC	1c	blue	225.		
RS259TC	1c	brown	300.		
RS259TC	1c	green	225.		
RS259TC	1c	orange	300.		
RS259TC	1c	red	500.		
RS259TC	1c	vermilion	500.		
RS260TC	2c	blue	175.		
RS260TC	2c	brown	300.		
RS260TC	2c	green	225.		
RS260TC	2c	orange	300.		
RS260TC	2c	red	500.		
RS260TC	2c	rose	500.		
RS260TC	2c	vermilion	225.		
RS261TC	4c	blue	225.		
RS261TC	4c	brown	300.		
RS261TC	4c	green	225.		
RS261TC	4c	orange	300.		
RS261TC	4c	red	500.		
RS261TC	4c	vermilion	500.		
RS262TC	2c	blue	500.		
RS262TC	2c	green	500.		
RS264TC	4c	blue	300.		
RS264TC	4c	green	300.		
RS265TC	1c	black	225.		
RS265TC	1c	blue	500.		
RS267TC	4c	black	225.		
RS267TC	4c	blue	500.		
RS267TC	4c	green	300.		
RS270TC	12c	black	300.		
RS270TC	12c	blue	500.		
RS270TC	12c	blue green	300.		
RS270TC	12c	red	225.		
RS271TC	4c	blue	2,500.		
RS272TC	1c	black	300.		
RS272TC	1c	blue	300.		
RS273TC	2c	blue	500.		
RS274TC	1c	black	225.		
RS274TC	2c	blue	300.		

Number	Denom.	Color	Die on India (1) Large	Plate (3) India	Plate (4) Card
RS276TC	2c	black	225.		
RS276TC	2c	blue	300.		
RS278TC	2½c	black	1,000.		
RS280TC	¼c	black	1,000.		
RS302TC	2½c	black	1,000.		
RS303TC	⅝c	black	1,000.		

PRIVATE DIE PERFUMERY STAMPS

Number	Denom.	Color	Die on India (1) Large	Plate (3) India	Plate (4) Card
RT2TC	1c	brown	500.		
RT2TC	1c	green	400.		
RT2TC	1c	orange	300.		
RT2TC	1c	red	500.		
RT5TC	2c	black	175.		
RT5TC	2c	blue	225.		
RT5TC	2c	green	500.		
RT5TC	2c	orange	500.	125.	
RT6TC	1c	blue	375.		
RT6TC	1c	brown	500.		
RT6TC	1c	green	375.		
RT6TC	1c	orange	500.		
RT6TC	1c	red	500.		
RT10TC	4c	blue	375.		
RT10TC	4c	brown	500.		
RT10TC	4c	green	400.		
RT10TC	4c	orange	500.		
RT10TC	4c	red	500.		
RT12TC	1c	black	225.	90.	
RT12TC	1c	blue	225.		
RT12TC	1c	green	500.		
RT13TC	2c	black	225.	75.	
RT13TC	2c	blue	300.		
RT13TC	2c	green	300.		
RT13TC	2c	red	225.		
RT14TC	3c	blue	1,000.		
RT16TC	1c	blue	175.		
RT16TC	1c	green	225.		
RT17TC	2c	black	300.		
RT17TC	2c	blue	300.		
RT17TC	2c	green	300.		
RT17TC	2c	orange	500.		
RT18TC	3c	black	175.		
RT18TC	3c	blue	175.		
RT18TC	3c	green	500.		
RT18TC	3c	orange	500.		
RT18TC	3c	red	300.		
RT19TC	1c	black	500.		
RT20TC	1c	black	225.		
RT20TC	1c	blue	300.		
RT20TC	1c	green	175.		
RT21TC	2c	black	500.		
RT21TC	2c	green	500.		
RT22TC	1c	black	175.		
RT22TC	1c	blue	300.		
RT22TC	1c	green	300.		
RT22TC	1c	red brn	500.		
RT22TC	1c	ultramarine	500.		
RT23TC	2c	blue	225.		
RT23TC	2c	green	500.		
RT24TC	3c	black	175.		
RT24TC	3c	blue	225.		
RT24TC	3c	green	300.		
RT24TC	3c	red	225.		
RT25TC	4c	black	175.		
RT25TC	4c	blue	225.		
RT26TC	1c	black	175.		
RT26TC	1c	blue	225.		
RT26TC	1c	brown	300.		
RT26TC	1c	green	500.		
RT26TC	1c	orange	300.		
RT26TC	1c	red	500.		
RT28TC	2c	black	225.		
RT28TC	2c	brown	300.		
RT28TC	2c	green	225.		
RT28TC	2c	orange	300.		
RT28TC	2c	red	300.		
RT30TC	3c	black	225.		
RT30TC	3c	blue	225.		
RT30TC	3c	brown	300.		
RT30TC	3c	green	225.		
RT30TC	3c	orange	300.		
RT30TC	3c	red	175.		
RT32TC	4c	black	225.		
RT32TC	4c	blue	225.		
RT32TC	4c	brown	500.		
RT32TC	4c	green	225.		
RT32TC	4c	orange	225.		
RT32TC	4c	red	300.		

PRIVATE DIE PLAYING CARD STAMPS

Number	Denom.	Color	Die on India (1) Large	Plate (3) India	Plate (4) Card
RU2TC	2c	black	175.		
RU2TC	2c	blue	225.		
RU2TC	2c	green	300.		
RU3TC	4c	blue	225.		
RU3TC	4c	green	225.		
RU4TC	5c	black	225.		
RU4TC	5c	green	300.		
RU5TC	5c	black	225.		
RU5TC	5c	brown	300.		
RU5TC	5c	green	300.		
RU5TC	5c	light brn	500.		
RU5TC	5c	orange	500.		
RU5TC	5c	red	500.		
RU6TC	10c	black	175.		
RU6TC	10c	green	300.		
RU7TC	5c	blue	375.		

Number	Denom.	Color	Die on India (1) Large	Plate (3) India	Plate (4) Card
RU7TC	5c	green	375.		
RU8TC	5c	blue	225.		
RU8TC	5c	green	225.		
RU8TC	5c	orange	300.		
RU9TC	5c	blue	225.		
RU9TC	5c	green	500.		
RU10TC	2c	black	175.		
RU10TC	2c	brown	500.		
RU10TC	2c	green	500.		
RU11TC	5c	black	225.		
RU11TC	5c	blue	225.		
RU11TC	5c	brown	300.		
RU12TC	5c	blue	300.		
RU12TC	5c	green	300.		
RU13TC	5c	green	175.		
RU14TC	5c	blue	225.		
RU14TC	5c	brown	300.		
RU14TC	5c	green	300.		
RU14TC	5c	light brn	500.		
RU14TC	5c	orange	500.		
RU14TC	5c	red	300.		
RU15TC	5c	blue	300.		
RU15TC	5c	green	300.		

HUNTING PERMIT

Number	Denom.	Color	Die on India (1) Large
RW4TC	$1	light violet	5,500.

SPECIMEN STAMPS

These are regular stamps overprinted "Specimen." Each number has a suffix letter "S" to denote "specimen." The Scott number is that of the stamp as shown in the regular listings and the second letter "A," etc., indicates the type of overprint. Values are for items of a grade of fine-very fine, with at least part original gum.

𝕾pecimen
Type A;
12mm long

Specimen.
Type B; 15mm long

𝕾pecimen.
Type C; 30mm long

SPECIMEN
Type D;
Capital Letters

Specimen.
Type E;
Initial Capital

𝕾pecimen.
Type F; 22mm long

SPECIMEN
Type G;
14mm long

SPECIMEN
Type H;
16mm long

Type I; 20mm long

Overprinted in Black

1851-56			
7S	A	1c **blue**, type II	2,500.
11S	A	3c **dull red**, type I	6,500.
1857-60			
21S	A	1c **blue**, type III	1,500.
24S	A	1c **blue**, type V	1,000.
26S	A	3c **dull red**, type II	1,000.
30S	A	5c **orange brown**, type II	1,000.
35S	A	10c **green**, type V	1,250.
36BS	A	12c **black**	3,500.
37S	A	24c **lilac**	1,000.
38S	A	30c **orange**	1,000.
26S	F	3c **dull red**, type II	2,000.
26S	I	3c **dull red**, type II	4,000.
1861			
63S	A	1c **blue**	750.
65S	A	3c **rose**	750.
68S	A	10c **dark green**	750.
70S	A	24c **red lilac**	750.
72S	A	90c **blue**	750.
73S	A	2c **black**	1,750.
76S	A	5c **brown**	750.

𝕾pecimen.

Overprint Black, Except As Noted

1861-66			
63S	B	1c **blue** *(1300)*	120.
		P# block of 8, Impt.	1,750.
		Without period	—
65S	B	3c **rose** *(1500)*	120.
68S	B	10c **dark green** *(1600)*	120.
		P# block of 8, Impt.	—
69S	B	12c **black** (orange) *(1300)*	120.
71S	B	30c **orange** *(1400)*	120.
		P# block of 8, Impt.	15,000.
72S	B	90c **blue** *(1394)*	120.
		P# block of 8, Impt.	—
73S	B	2c **black** (vermilion) *(1306)*	250.
		Block of 4	1,100.
		Without period	500.
		Block of 4, one stamp without period	1,500.
76S	B	5c **brown** *(1306)*	120.
		P# block of 8, Impt.	—
77S	B	15c **black** (vermilion) *(1208)*	200.
		Block of 4	900.
78S	B	24c **lilac** *(1300)*	200.
1867-68			
86S	A	1c **blue**	1,000.
85ES	A	12c **black**	1,000.
93S	A	2c **black**	1,100.
94S	A	3c **rose**	1,000.
95S	A	5c **brown**	1,100.
97S	A	12c **black**	—
98S	A	15c **black**	1,000.
99S	A	24c **gray lilac**	1,250.
		Split grill	—
100S	A	30c **orange**	1,250.

1869			
112S	A	1c **buff**	1,750.
113S	A	2c **brown**	1,750.
115S	A	6c **ultramarine**	1,750.
116S	A	10c **yellow**	1,750.
117S	A	12c **green**	1,750.
119S	A	15c **brown & blue**	1,750.
120S	A	24c **green & violet**	1,750.
a.		Without grill	—
121S	A	30c **blue & carmine**	2,750.
a.		Without grill	—
122S	A	90c **carmine & black**	2,000.
a.		Without grill	—
123S	B	1c **buff**	3,500.
124S	B	2c **brown**	3,500.
125S	B	3c **blue** (blue)	3,500.
126S	B	6c **blue** (blue)	3,500.
127S	B	10c **yellow** (blue)	3,500.
129S	B	15c **brown & blue** (blue)	5,250.
1870-71			
145S	A	1c **ultramarine**	600.
146S	A	2c **red brown**	600.
146S	B	2c **red brown**	600.
147S	A	3c **green**	600.
148S	A	6c **carmine**	600.
149S	A	7c **vermilion**	600.
150S	A	10c **brown**	600.
151S	A	12c **dull violet**	600.
152S	A	15c **bright orange**	600.
155S	A	90c **carmine**	600.
155S	B	90c **carmine** (blue)	600.
1873			
158S	B	3c **green** (blue)	750.
159S	B	6c **dull pink**	700.
160S	B	7c **orange vermilion** (blue)	700.
162S	B	12c **blackish violet** (blue)	—
165S	B	30c **greenish black** (blue)	700.
166S	B	90c **carmine** (blue)	750.

Overprinted in Red   **SPECIMEN**

1879		**Type D**	
189S	D	15c **red orange**	80.
190S	D	30c **full black**	80.
191S	D	90c **carmine**	80.
a.		Overprint in black brown	80.
1881-82			
205S	D	5c **yellow brown**	80.
206S	D	1c **gray blue**	80.
207S	D	3c **blue green**	80.
208S	D	6c **brown red**	80.
209S	D	10c **brown**	80.
1883			
210S	D	2c **red brown**	100.
211S	D	4c **blue green**	100.

Handstamped in Dull Purple   **Specimen.**

1890-93		**Type E**	
219S	E	1c **dull blue**	150.
220S	E	2c **carmine**	150.
221S	E	3c **purple**	150.
222S	E	4c **dark brown**	150.
223S	E	5c **chocolate**	150.
224S	E	6c **dull red**	150.
225S	E	8c **lilac**	150.
226S	E	10c **green**	150.
227S	E	15c **blue**	150.
228S	E	30c **black**	150.
229S	E	90c **orange**	175.

COLUMBIAN ISSUE

1893			
230S	E	1c **deep blue**	400.
		Double overprint	—
231S	E	2c **violet**	400.
232S	E	3c **green**	400.
233S	E	4c **ultramarine**	400.
234S	E	5c **chocolate**	400.
235S	E	6c **purple**	400.
236S	E	8c **magenta**	400.
237S	E	10c **black brown**	400.
238S	E	15c **dark green**	400.
239S	E	30c **orange brown**	400.
240S	E	50c **slate blue**	400.
241S	E	$1 **salmon**	500.
242S	E	$2 **brown red**	500.
243S	E	$3 **yellow green**	550.
244S	E	$4 **crimson lake**	575.
245S	E	$5 **black**	675.

Overprinted in Magenta		**𝕾pecimen.**	
		Type F	
230S	F	1c **deep blue**	550.
232S	F	3c **green**	550.
233S	F	4c **ultramarine**	550.
234S	F	5c **chocolate**	550.
235S	F	6c **purple**	550.
237S	F	10c **black brown**	550.
243S	F	$3 **yellow green**	700.

Overprinted Type H in Black or Red

231S	H	2c **violet** (Bk)	625.
233S	H	4c **ultramarine** (R)	625.
234S	H	5c **chocolate** (R)	625.

Overprinted Type I in Black or Red

231S	I	2c **violet** (R)	625.
232S	I	3c **green** (R)	625.
233S	I	4c **ultramarine** (R)	625.
234S	I	5c **chocolate** (Bk)	625.
235S	I	6c **purple** (R)	625.
236S	I	8c **magenta** (Bk)	625.
237S	I	10c **black brown** (R)	625.
238S	I	15c **dark green** (R)	625.
239S	I	30c **orange brown** (Bk)	625.
240S	I	50c **slate blue** (R)	625.

1895
Handstamped Type E in Purple

264S	E	1c **blue**	90.
267S	E	2c **carmine**, type III	90.
267aS	E	2c **pink**, type III	90.
268S	E	3c **purple**	90.
269S	E	4c **dark brown**	100.
270S	E	5c **chocolate**	90.
271S	E	6c **dull brown**	90.
272S	E	8c **violet brown**	90.
273S	E	10c **dark green**	90.
274S	E	15c **dark blue**	90.
275S	E	50c **orange**	90.
276S	E	$1 **black**, type I	325.
276AS	E	$1 **black**, type II	2,000.
277S	E	$2 **dark blue**	300.
278S	E	$5 **dark green**	400.
1897-1903			
279S	E	1c **deep green**	90.
279BS	E	2c **light red**, type IV	90.
279BjS	E	2c Booklet pane of 6, **light red**, type IV (Bk)	525.
		Never hinged	750.
		With plate number	1,100.
		Never hinged	1,500.
a.		As No. 279BjS, inverted overprint	—
b.		As No. 279BjS, double impression of overprint on bottom two stamps	—
280S	E	4c **rose brown**	160.
281S	E	5c **dark blue**	80.
282S	E	6c **lake**	80.
282CS	E	10c **brown**, type I	80.
283S	E	10c **brown**, type II	—
284S	E	15c **olive green**	80.

Special Printing

In March 1900 one pane of 100 stamps of each of Nos. 279, 279B, 268, 280-282, 272, 282C, 284 and 275-278 were specially handstamped type E "Specimen" in black for displays at the Paris Exposition (1900) and Pan American Exposition (1901). The 2c pane was light red, type IV.

These examples were handstamped by H. G. Mandel and mounted by him in separate displays for the two Expositions. Examples from the panes in addition to those displayed were handstamped "Specimen," but most were destroyed after the Expositions. Examples of all issues that were handstamped are known.

Additional stamps, not from the mounted display panes, do exist with a black "Specimen" handstamp, but it is believed Mandel applied such handstamps to regularly issued stamps from his personal collection. These include Nos. 267, 267a and 279B in pale red.

TRANS-MISSISSIPPI ISSUE

1898			
		Type F	
285S	F	1c **dark yellow green**	250.
		Type E	
285S	E	1c **dark yellow green**	250.
286S	E	2c **copper red**	250.
287S	E	4c **orange**	250.
288S	E	5c **dull blue**	250.
289S	E	8c **violet brown**	250.
290S	E	10c **gray violet**	250.

291S	E	50c **sage green**	300.
292S	E	$1 **black**	600.
293S	E	$2 **orange brown**	750.

PAN-AMERICAN ISSUE

1901

294S	E	1c **green & black**	235.
295S	E	2c **carmine**	235.
296S	E	4c **chocolate & black**	235.
a.		Center inverted	*10,000.*
297S	E	5c **ultramarine & black**	235.
298S	E	8c **brown violet & black**	235.
299S	E	10c **yellow brown & black**	235.

1902

300S	E	1c **blue green**	125.
301S	E	2c **carmine**	125.
302S	E	3c **bright violet**	125.
303S	E	4c **brown**	125.
304S	E	5c **blue**	125.
305S	E	6c **claret**	125.
306S	E	8c **violet black**	125.
307S	E	10c **pale red brown**	125.
308S	E	13c **purple black**	125.
309S	E	15c **olive green**	125.
310S	E	50c **orange**	125.
311S	E	$1 **black**	250.
312S	E	$2 **dark blue**	375.
313S	E	$5 **dark green**	500.

1903

319S	E	2c **carmine**	110.

LOUISIANA PURCHASE ISSUE

1904

323S	E	1c **green**	350.
324S	E	2c **carmine**	350.
325S	E	3c **violet**	350.
326S	E	5c **dark blue**	350.
327S	E	10c **red brown**	350.

SPECIAL DELIVERY STAMPS

Overprinted in Red   **SPECIMEN**

1885

Type D

E1S	D	10c **blue**	140.

Handstamped in Dull Purple   *Specimen.*

1888

Type E

E2S	E	10c **blue**	150.

1893

E3S	E	10c **orange**	200.

1894

E4S	E	10c **blue**	300.

1895

E5S	E	10c **blue**	175.

1902

E6S	E	10c **ultramarine**	175.

POSTAGE DUE STAMPS

Overprinted in Red   **SPECIMEN**

1879

Type D

J1S	D	1c **brown**	250.00
J2S	D	2c **brown**	250.00
J3S	D	3c **brown**	250.00
J4S	D	5c **brown**	250.00

1884

J15S	D	1c **red brown**	45.00
J16S	D	2c **red brown**	45.00
J17S	D	3c **red brown**	45.00
J18S	D	5c **red brown**	45.00
J19S	D	10c **red brown**	45.00
J20S	D	30c **red brown**	45.00
J21S	D	50c **red brown**	45.00

Handstamped in Dull Purple   *Specimen.*

1895

Type E

J38S	E	1c **deep claret**	85.00
J39S	E	2c **deep claret**	85.00
J40S	E	3c **deep claret**	85.00
J41S	E	5c **deep claret**	85.00

J42S	E	10c **deep claret**	85.00
J43S	E	30c **deep claret**	85.00
J44S	E	50c **deep claret**	85.00

OFFICIAL STAMPS

Special printings of Official stamps were made in 1875 at the time the other Reprints, Re-issues and Special Printings were printed. The Official stamps reprints received specimen overprints, but philatelists believe they most properly should be considered to be part of the special printings. See Official section after No. O120.

NEWSPAPER STAMPS

Overprinted in Red   *Specimen.*

1865-75

Type C — Overprint 30mm Long

PR5S	C	5c **dark blue**	400.00
a.		Triple overprint	900.00
PR2S	C	10c **blue green**	400.00
PR3S	C	25c **carmine red**	400.00

Handstamped in Black   *Specimen*

1875

Type A

PR9S	A	2c **black**	500.00
PR11S	A	4c **black**	500.00
PR12S	A	6c **black**	500.00
PR16S	A	12c **rose**	500.00

Overprinted in Black, except as noted   *Specimen.*

1875

Type B
Overprint 15mm Long

PR9S	B	2c **black**	45.00
PR10S	B	3c **black**	45.00
PR11S	B	4c **black**	45.00
PR12S	B	6c **black**	45.00
PR13S	B	8c **black**	45.00
PR14S	B	9c **black**	45.00
a.		Overprint in blue	—
PR15S	B	10c **black**	45.00
PR16S	B	12c **rose**	45.00
PR17S	B	24c **rose**	45.00
PR18S	B	36c **rose**	45.00
PR19S	B	48c **rose**	45.00
a.		Overprint in blue	65.00
PR20S	B	60c **rose**	45.00
PR21S	B	72c **rose**	45.00
a.		Overprint in blue	65.00
PR22S	B	84c **rose**	45.00
a.		Overprint in blue	—
PR23S	B	96c **rose**	45.00
a.		Overprint in blue	—
PR24S	B	$1.92 **dark brown**	45.00
PR25S	B	$3 **vermilion**	45.00
a.		Overprint in blue	65.00
PR26S	B	$6 **ultramarine**	45.00
a.		Overprint in blue	250.00
PR27S	B	$9 **yellow**	45.00
a.		Overprint in blue	250.00
PR28S	B	$12 **dark green**	45.00
a.		Overprint in blue	250.00
PR29S	B	$24 **dark gray violet**	45.00
a.		Overprint in blue	65.00
PR30S	B	$36 **brown rose**	62.00
PR31S	B	$48 **red brown**	62.00
PR32S	B	$60 **violet**	62.00

Overprinted in Red   **SPECIMEN**

1875

Type D

PR14S	D	9c **black**	30.00

1879

PR57S	D	2c **black**	75.00
PR58S	D	3c **black**	75.00
PR59S	D	4c **black**	75.00
PR60S	D	6c **black**	75.00
PR61S	D	8c **black**	75.00
PR62S	D	10c **black**	75.00
a.		Double overprint	2,000.
PR63S	D	12c **red**	75.00
PR64S	D	24c **red**	75.00
PR65S	D	36c **red**	75.00
PR66S	D	48c **red**	75.00
PR67S	D	60c **red**	75.00
PR68S	D	72c **red**	75.00
PR69S	D	84c **red**	75.00
PR70S	D	96c **red**	75.00
PR71S	D	$1.92 **pale brown**	75.00
PR72S	D	$3 **red vermilion**	75.00
PR73S	D	$6 **blue**	75.00

PR74S	D	$9 **orange**	75.00
PR75S	D	$12 **yellow green**	75.00
PR76S	D	$24 **dark violet**	75.00
PR77S	D	$36 **Indian red**	75.00
PR78S	D	$48 **yellow brown**	75.00
PR79S	D	$60 **purple**	75.00

1885

PR81S	D	1c **black**	25.00

Handstamped in Dull Purple   *Specimen.*

1879

Type E

PR57S	E	2c **black**	125.00
PR58S	E	3c **black**	125.00
PR59S	E	4c **black**	125.00
PR60S	E	6c **black**	125.00
PR61S	E	8c **black**	125.00
PR62S	E	10c **black**	125.00
PR63S	E	12c **red**	125.00
PR64S	E	24c **red**	125.00
PR65S	E	36c **red**	125.00
PR66S	E	48c **red**	125.00
PR67S	E	60c **red**	125.00
PR68S	E	72c **red**	125.00
PR69S	E	84c **red**	125.00
PR70S	E	96c **red**	125.00
PR71S	E	$1.92 **pale brown**	125.00
PR72S	E	$3 **red vermilion**	125.00
PR73S	E	$6 **blue**	125.00
PR74S	E	$9 **orange**	125.00
PR75S	E	$12 **yellow green**	125.00
PR76S	E	$24 **dark violet**	125.00
PR77S	E	$36 **Indian red**	125.00
PR78S	E	$48 **yellow brown**	125.00
PR79S	E	$60 **purple**	125.00

1885

PR81S	E	1c **black**	125.00

1895   **Wmk. 191**

PR114S	E	1c **black**	125.00
PR115S	E	2c **black**	125.00
PR116S	E	5c **black**	125.00
PR117S	E	10c **black**	125.00
PR118S	E	25c **carmine**	125.00
PR119S	E	50c **carmine**	125.00
PR120S	E	$2 **scarlet**	125.00
PR121S	E	$5 **dark blue**	125.00
PR122S	E	$10 **green**	125.00
PR123S	E	$20 **slate**	125.00
PR124S	E	$50 **dull rose**	125.00
PR125S	E	$100 **purple**	125.00

REVENUE STAMPS

SPECIMEN

1862

Overprint 14mm Long

R5S	G	2c **Bank Check, blue** (red)	375.00
R15S	A	2c **U. S. I. R., orange**	

SPECIMEN

Overprint 16mm Long

R23S	H	5c **Agreement, red**	375.00
R34S	H	10c **Contract, blue** (red)	375.00
R35eS	H	10c **Foreign Exchange, ultra** (red)	375.00
R36S	H	10c **Inland Exchange, blue** (red)	375.00
R46S	H	25c **Insurance, red**	375.00
R52S	H	30c **Inland Exchange, lilac** (red)	375.00
R53S	H	40c **Inland Exchange, brown** (red)	375.00
R68S	H	$1 **Foreign Exchange, red**	375.00

Type I   *Specimen*

1898   **Overprint 20mm Long**

R153S	I	1c **green** (red)	475.00

1875

RB11S	H	1c **green** (red)	300.00

PRIVATE DIE MATCH STAMP

Overprinted with Type G in Red   **SPECIMEN**

RO133dS G	1c **black**, A. Messinger		*500.00*

SAVINGS STAMPS

Overprinted Vertically Reading Down in Red   **SPECIMEN**

1911
PS4S	10c **deep blue**	—

1917-18   Handstamped "SPECIMEN" in Violet
WS1S	25c **deep green**	—
WS2S	$5 **deep green**	—

VARIOUS OVERPRINTS

Overprinted with control numbers in carmine   **7890**

1861
Type J
63S	J A24	1c **pale blue** (overprint 9012)	200.00
65S	J A25	3c **brown red** (overprint 7890)	200.00
		Block of 4	*900.*
68S	J A27	10c **green** (overprint 5678)	200.00
69S	J A28	12c **gray black** (overprint 4567)	200.00
71S	J A30	30c **orange** (overprint 2345)	200.00
		Block of 4	*900.*
72S	J A31	90c **pale blue** (overprint 1234)	200.00
a.		Pair, one without overprint	

1863-66
73S	J A32	2c **black** (overprint 8901)	300.00
		Block of 4	*1,400.*
76S	J A26	5c **brown** (overprint 6789)	200.00
77S	J A33	15c **black** (overprint 235)	250.00
		Block of 4	*1,150.*
78S	J A29	24c **gray lilac** (overprint 3456)	200.00

Special Printings Overprinted in Red or Blue   **SAMPLE.**

1889
Type K
212S	K A59	1c **ultramarine** (red)	75.00
210S	K A57	2c **red brown** (blue)	75.00
210S	K A57	2c **lake** (blue)	75.00
210S	K A57	2c **rose lake** (blue)	75.00
210S	K A57	2c **scarlet** (blue)	75.00
214S	K A46b	3c **vermilion** (red)	75.00
211S	K A58	4c **blue green** (red)	75.00
205S	K A56	5c **gray brown** (red)	75.00
208S	K A47b	6c **brown red** (blue)	75.00
209S	K A49b	10c **brown** (red)	75.00
		Without overprint	80.00
189S	K A51a	15c **orange** (blue)	75.00
190S	K A53	30c **full black** (red)	75.00
191S	K A54	90c **carmine** (blue)	75.00

Special Printings Overprinted in Red or Blue   **SAMPLE A.**

Type L
212S	L A59	1c **ultramarine** (red)	75.00
210S	L A57	2c **rose lake** (blue)	75.00
		Without overprint	—
214S	L A46b	3c **purple** (red)	75.00
211S	L A58	4c **dark brown** (red)	75.00
205S	L A56	5c **yellow brown** (blue)	75.00
		Without overprint	—
208S	L A47b	6c **vermilion** (blue)	75.00
209S	L A49b	10c **green** (red)	75.00
		Without overprint	100.00
189S	L A51a	15c **blue** (red)	75.00
		Without overprint	100.00
190S	L A53	30c **full black** (red)	75.00
191S	L A54	90c **orange** (blue)	75.00

Overprinted with Type K Together with "A" in Black Manuscript
191S	M A54	90c **carmine** (blue)	140.00
209S	M A49b	10c **brown** (red)	140.00
211S	M A58	4c **blue green** (red)	140.00

"SAMPLE A" in Manuscript (red or black)
216S	N A56	5c **indigo**	160.00

Regular Issues Overprinted in Blue or Red   **UNIVERSAL POSTAL (CONGRESS**

125 sets were distributed to delegates to the Universal Postal Congress held in Washington, D. C., May 5 to June 15, 1897.

1897   **Type O**
264S	O A87	1c **blue**	110.00
267S	O A88	2c **carmine**, type III	110.00
268S	O A89	3c **purple**	110.00
269S	O A90	4c **dark brown**	110.00
270S	O A91	5c **chestnut**	110.00
271S	O A92	6c **claret brown**	110.00
272S	O A93	8c **violet brown**	110.00
273S	O A94	10c **dark green**	110.00
274S	O A95	15c **dark blue**	110.00
275S	O A96	50c **red orange**	110.00
276S	O A97	$1 **black**, type I	350.00
276AS	O A97	$1 **black**, type II	300.00
277S	O A98	$2 **dark blue**	250.00
278S	O A99	$5 **dark green**	350.00

SPECIAL DELIVERY
E5S	O SD3	10c **blue** (R)	250.00

POSTAGE DUE
J38S	O D2	1c **deep claret**	125.00
J39S	O D2	2c **deep claret**	125.00
J40S	O D2	3c **deep claret**	125.00
J41S	O D2	5c **deep claret**	125.00
J42S	O D2	10c **deep claret**	125.00
J43S	O D2	30c **deep claret**	125.00
J44S	O D2	50c **deep claret**	125.00

NEWSPAPERS
PR114S	O N15	1c **black**	150.00
PR115S	O N15	2c **black**	150.00
PR116S	O N15	5c **black**	150.00
PR117S	O N15	10c **black**	150.00
PR118S	O N16	25c **carmine**	150.00
PR119S	O N16	50c **carmine**	150.00
PR120S	O N17	$2 **scarlet**	150.00
PR121S	O N18	$5 **dark blue**	150.00
PR122S	O N19	$10 **green**	150.00
PR123S	O N20	$20 **slate**	150.00
PR124S	O N21	$50 **dull rose**	150.00
PR125S	O N22	$100 **purple**	150.00

ENVELOPES

Overprinted   **UNIVERSAL POSTAL CONGRESS**

Type P
U294S	P	1c **blue**	100.00
U296S	P	1c **blue**, *amber*	100.00
U300S	P	1c **blue**, *manila*	100.00
W301S	P	1c **blue**, *manila*	100.00
U304S	P	1c **blue**, *amber manila*	100.00
U311S	P	2c **green**, Die 2	100.00
U312S	P	2c **green**, Die 2, *amber*	100.00
U313S	P	2c **green**, Die 2, *oriental buff*	100.00
U314S	P	2c **green**, Die 2, *blue*	100.00
a.		Double impression of overprint	—
U315S	P	2c **green**, Die 2, *manila*	100.00
W316S	P	2c **green**, Die 2, *manila*	100.00
U317S	P	2c **green**, Die 2, *amber manila*	100.00
U324S	P	4c **carmine**	100.00
U325S	P	4c **carmine**, *amber*	120.00
U330S	P	5c **blue**, Die 1	110.00
U331S	P	5c **blue**, Die 1, *amber*	110.00

Two settings of type P overprint are found. See the July\August 1949 issue of the Scott Monthly Stamp Journal for others.

POSTAL CARDS

Overprinted   **UNIVERSAL POSTAL CONGRESS.**

Type Q
UX12S	Q	1c **black**, *buff*	750.00
UX13S	Q	2c **blue**, *cream*	750.00

PAID REPLY POSTAL CARDS
Overprinted with Type Q
UY1S	Q	1c **black**, *buff*	750.00
UY2S	Q	2c **blue**, *grayish white*	750.00

As Nos. UY1S-UY2S were made by overprinting unsevered reply cards, values are for unsevered cards.

SOUVENIR CARDS

These cards were issued as souvenirs of the philatelic and numismatic gatherings at which they were distributed by the United States Postal Service (USPS), its predecessor the United States Post Office Department (POD), or the Bureau of Engraving and Printing (BEP). They were not valid for postage.

Listed cards will have a philatelic theme, and most of the cards bear reproductions of United States stamps with the design enlarged, altered by removal of denomination, country name and "Postage" or "Air Mail" or defaced by diagonal bars. The cards are not perforated.

Numismatic cards are listed following the philatelic cards. Cards issued for numismatic shows but showing stamps are listed in the philatelic section. BEP cards having no obvious philatelic or numismatic theme are not listed.

A forerunner of the souvenir cards is the 1939 Philatelic Truck souvenir sheet which the Post Office Department issued and distributed in various cities visited by the Philatelic Truck. It shows the White House, printed in blue on white paper. A total of 730,040 were printed, 173,220 with gum (first printing, many destroyed) and the rest without gum. Value, with gum, $50; without gum, $8. Some of the first printing was made into coil rolls of 500. A joint line pair and a strip of three (both damaged) are known.

Standard abbreviations:
APS — American Philatelic Society
ASDA — American Stamp Dealers Association

No. SC28

1954
SC1 Postage Stamp Design Exhibition, Natl. Philatelic Museum, Mar. 13, 1954, Philadelphia. Card of 4 monochrome views of Washington. Inscribed: "Souvenir sheet designed, engraved and printed by members, Bureau, Engraving and Printing. Reissued by popular request." — 1,500.

1960
SC2 Barcelona, 1st Intl. Philatelic Congress, Mar. 26-Apr. 5, 1960. Vignette, Landing of Columbus from #231. (POD) — 350.00

1966
SC3 SIPEX, 6th Intl. Philatelic Exhibition, May 21-30, 1966, Washington. Card of 3 multicolored views of Washington. — 95.00
   a. Views inverted — 725.00

1968
SC4 EFIMEX, Intl. Philatelic Exhibition, Nov. 1-9, 1968, Mexico City. #292. Spanish text. (POD) — 2.00

1969
SC5 SANDIPEX, San Diego Philatelic Exhibition, July 16-20, 1969, San Diego, Cal. Card of 3 multicolored views of Washington. (BEP) — 40.00
SC6 ASDA Natl. Postage Stamp Show, Nov. 21-23, 1969, New York. Card of 4 #E4. (BEP) — 18.50

1970
SC7 INTERPEX, Mar. 13-15, 1970, New York. Card of 4, #1027, 1035, C35, C38. (BEP) — 42.50
SC8 COMPEX, Combined Philatelic Exhibition of Chicagoland, May 29-31, 1970. Card of 4 #C18. (BEP) — 9.00
SC9 PHILYMPIA, London Intl. Stamp Exhibition, Sept. 18-26 1970. Card of 3, #548-550. (POD) — 1.25
SC10 HAPEX, APS Convention, Nov. 5-8, 1970, Honolulu. Card of 3, #799, C46, C55. (BEP) — 8.00

1971
SC11 INTERPEX, Mar. 12-14, 1971, New York. Card of 4 #1193. Background includes #1331-1332, 1371, C76. (BEP) — 1.50
SC12 WESTPEX, Western Philatelic Exhibition, Apr. 23-25, 1971, San Francisco. Card of 4, #740, 852, 966, 997. (BEP) — 1.50
SC13 NAPEX 71, Natl. Philatelic Exhibition, May 21-23, 1971, Washington. Card of 3, #990, 991, 992. (BEP) — 2.00
SC14 TEXANEX 71, Texas Philatelic Association and APS conventions, Aug. 26-29, 1971, San Antonio, Tex. Card of 3, #938, 1043, 1242. (BEP) — 2.00
SC15 EXFILIMA 71, 3rd Inter-American Philatelic Exhibition, Nov. 6-14, 1971, Lima, Peru. Card of 3, #1111, 1126, Peru #360. Spanish text. (USPS) — 1.00

SC16 ASDA Natl. Postage Stamp Show, Nov. 19-21, 1971, New York. Card of 3, #C13-C15. (BEP) — 2.50
SC17 ANPHILEX '71, Anniv. Philatelic Exhibition, Nov. 26-Dec. 1, 1971, New York. Card of 2, #1-2. (BEP) — 1.00

1972
SC18 INTERPEX, Mar. 17-19, 1972, New York. Card of 4 #1173. Background includes #976, 1434-1435, C69. (BEP) — 1.25
SC19 NOPEX, Apr. 6-9, 1972, New Orleans. Card of 4 #1020. Background includes #323-327. (BEP) — 1.25
SC20 BELGICA 72, Brussels Intl. Philatelic Exhibition, June 24-July 9, 1972, Brussels, Belgium. Card of 3, #914, 1026, 1104. Flemish and French text. (USPS) — 1.00
SC21 Olympia Philatelie Munchen 72, Aug. 18-Sept. 10, 1972, Munich, Germany. Card of 4 #1460-1462, C85. German text. (USPS) — 1.00
SC22 EXFILBRA 72, 4th Inter-American Philatelic Exhibition, Aug. 26-Sept. 2, 1972, Rio de Janeiro, Brazil. Card of 3 #C14, Brazil #C18-C19. Portuguese text. (USPS) — 1.00
SC23 Natl. Postal Forum VI, Aug. 28-30, 1972, Washington. Card of 4 #1396. (USPS) — 1.25
SC24 SEPAD '72, Oct. 20-22, 1972, Philadelphia. Card of 4 #1044. (BEP) — 1.25
SC25 ASDA Natl. Postage Stamp Show, Nov. 17-19, 1972, New York. Card of 4, #883, 863, 868, 888. (BEP) — 1.25
SC26 STAMP EXPO, Nov. 24-26, 1972, San Francisco. Card of 4 #C36. (BEP) — 1.50

1973
SC27 INTERPEX, Mar. 9-11, 1973, New York. Card of 4 #976. (BEP) — 1.25
SC28 IBRA 73 Intl. Philatelic Exhibition, Munich, May 11-20, 1973. #C13. (USPS) — 1.25
SC29 COMPEX 73, May 25-27, 1973, Chicago. Card of 4 #245. (BEP) — 2.75
SC30 APEX 73, Intl. Airmail Exhibition, Manchester, England, July 4-7, 1973. Card of 3, #C3a, Newfoundland #C4, Honduras #C12. (USPS) — 1.25
SC31 POLSKA 73, World Philatelic Exhibition, Poznan, Poland, Aug. 19-Sept. 2, 1973. Card of 3, #1488, Poland #1944-1945. Polish text. (USPS) — 1.25
SC32 NAPEX 73, Sept. 14-16, 1973, Washington. Card of 4 #C3. Background includes montage of #C3a. (BEP) — 1.75
SC33 ASDA Natl. Postage Stamp Show, Nov. 16-18, 1973, New York. Card of 4 #908. Foreground includes #1139-1144. (BEP) — 1.00
SC34 STAMP EXPO NORTH, Dec. 7-9, 1973, San Francisco. Card of 4 #C20. (BEP) — 2.00

A card of 10, Nos. 1489-1498, was distributed to postal employees. Not available to public. Size: about 14x11 inches.

1974
SC35 Natl. Hobby Industry Trade Show, Feb. 3-6, 1974, Chicago. Card of 4, #1456-1459. Reproductions of silversmith (#1457) and glassmaker (#1456). (USPS) — 1.50
SC36 MILCOPEX 1974, Mar. 8-10, 1974, Milwaukee. Card of 4 #C43. (BEP) — 1.25
SC37 INTERNABA 1974, June 6, 1974, Basel, Switzerland. Card of 8, #1530-1537. German, French, and Italian text. (USPS) — 2.25
SC38 STOCKHOLMIA 74, Intl. Philatelic Exhibition, Sept. 21-29, 1974, Stockholm. Card of 3, #836, Sweden #300, 767. Swedish text. (USPS) — 2.25
SC39 EXFILMEX 74, Interamerican Philatelic Exposition, Oct. 26-Nov. 3, 1974, Mexico City. Card of 2, #1157, Mexico #910. Spanish text. (USPS) — 2.25

1975
SC40 ESPANA 75, World Stamp Exhibition, Apr. 4-13, 1975, Madrid. Card of 3, #233, #1271, Spain #1312. Spanish text. (USPS) — 1.25

SC41 NAPEX 75, May 9-11, 1975, Washington. Card of 4 #708. (BEP) — 4.00
SC42 ARPHILA 75, June 6-16, 1975, Paris. Card of 3. Designs of #1187, #1207, France #1117. French text. (BEP) — 2.00
SC43 Intl. Women's Year, 1975. Card of 3 #872, 878, 959. Reproduction of 1886 dollar bill. (BEP) — 15.00
SC44 ASDA Natl. Postage Stamp Show, Nov. 21-23, 1975. Bicentennial series. Card of 4 #1003. (BEP) — 18.00

1976
SC45 WERABA 76, 3rd Intl. Space Stamp Exhibition, Apr. 1-4, 1976, Zurich, Switzerland. Card of 2, #1434-1435. (USPS) — 2.25
SC46 INTERPHIL 76, 7th Intl. Philatelic Exhibition, May 29-June 6, 1976. Philadelphia. Bicentennial series. Card of 4 #120. (BEP) — 4.00

An Interphil '76 card issued by the American Revolution Bicentennial Administration was bound into the Interphil program. It shows an altered #1044 in black brown, the Bicentennial emblem and a view of Independence Hall. Printed by BEP.

SC48 Bicentennial Exposition on Science and Technology, May 30-Sept. 6, 1976, Kennedy Space Center, Fla. #C76. (USPS) — 2.50
SC49 STAMP EXPO 76, June 11-13, 1976, Los Angeles. Bicentennial series. Card of 4, #1351, 1352, 1345, 1348. (BEP) — 5.00
SC50 Colorado Statehood Centennial, Aug. 1, 1976. Card of 3, #743, 288, 1670. (USPS) — 2.25
SC51 HAFNIA 76, Intl. Stamp Exhibition, Copenhagen. Aug. 20-29, 1976. Card of 2, #5, Denmark #2. Danish and English text. (USPS) — 2.25
SC52 ITALIA 76, Intl. Philatelic Exhibition, Oct. 14-24, Milan. Card of 3, #1168, Italy #578, 601. Italian text. (USPS) — 2.25
SC53 NORDPOSTA 76, North German Stamp Exhibition, Oct. 30-31, Hamburg. Card of 3, #689, Germany #B366, B417. German text. (USPS) — 2.25

1977
SC54 MILCOPEX, Milwaukee Philatelic Society, Mar. 4-6, Milwaukee. Card of 2, #733, 1128. (BEP) — 1.75
SC55 ROMPEX 77, Rocky Mountain Philatelic Exhibition, May 20-22, Denver. Card of 4 #1001. (BEP) — 1.75
SC56 AMPHILEX 77, Intl. Philatelic Exhibition, May 26-June 5, Amsterdam. Card of 3, #1027, Netherlands #41, 294. Dutch text. (USPS) — 2.25
SC57 SAN MARINO 77, Intl. PhilatelicExhibition, San Marino, Aug. 28-Sept. 4. Card of 3, #1-2, San Marino #1. Italian text. (USPS) — 2.25
SC58 PURIPEX 77, Silver Anniv. Philatelic Exhibit, Sept. 2-5, San Juan, P. R. Card of 4 #801. (BEP) — 2.00
SC59 ASDA Natl. Postage Stamp Show, Nov. 15-20, New York. Card of 4 #C45. (BEP) — 2.25

1978
SC60 ROCPEX 78, Intl. Philatelic Exhibition, Mar. 20-29, Taipei. Card of 6, #1706-1709, China #1812, 1816. Chinese text. (USPS) — 2.50
SC61 NAPOSTA '78 Philatelic Exhibition, May 20-25, Frankfurt. Card of 3, #555, 563, Germany #1216. German text. (USPS) — 2.25
SC62 CENJEX 78, Federated Stamp Clubs of New Jersey, 30th annual exhibition, June 23-25, Freehold, NJ. Card of 9, #646, 680, 689, 1086, 1716, 4 #785. (BEP) — 2.00

1979
SC63 BRASILIANA 79, Intl. Philatelic Exhibition, Sept. 15-23, Rio de Janeiro. Card of 3, #C91-C92, Brazil #1295. Portuguese text. (USPS) — 3.00
SC64 JAPEX 79, Intl. Philatelic Exhibition, Nov. 2-4, Tokyo. Card of 2, #1158, Japan #1024. Japanese text. (USPS) — 3.00

1980

SC65 LONDON 1980, Intl. Philatelic Exhibition, May 6-14, London. #329. (USPS) — 3.00

SC66 NORWEX 80, Intl. Stamp Exhibition, June 13-22, Oslo. Card of 3, #620-621, Norway #658. Norwegian text. (USPS) — 3.00

SC67 NAPEX 80, July 4-6, Washington. Card of 4 #573. (BEP) — 8.50

SC68 ASDA Stamp Festival, Sept. 25-28, 1980, New York. Card of 4 #962. (BEP) — 9.50

SC69 ESSEN 80, 3rd Intl. Stamp Fair, Nov. 15-19, Essen. Card of 2, #1014, Germany #723. German text. (USPS) — 3.00

1981

SC70 STAMP EXPO '81 SOUTH, Mar. 20-22, Anaheim, Calif. Card of 6, #1331-1332, 4 #1287. (BEP) — 11.00

SC71 WIPA 1981, Intl. Stamp Exhibition, May 22-31, Vienna. Card of 2, #1252, Austria #789. German text. (USPS) — 3.00

SC72 Natl. Stamp Collecting Month, Oct., 1981. Card of 2, #245, 1918. (USPS) — 3.00

SC73 PHILATOKYO '81, Intl. Stamp Exhibition, Oct. 9-18. Tokyo. Card of 2, #1531, Japan #800. Japanese text. (USPS) — 3.00

SC74 NORDPOSTA 81, North German Stamp Exhibition, Nov. 7-8. Hamburg. Card of 2, #923, Germany #B538. German text. (USPS) — 3.00

1982

SC75 MILCOPEX '82, Milwaukee Philatelic Association Exhibition, Mar. 5-7. Card of 4 #1137. (BEP) — 11.00

SC76 CANADA 82, Intl. Philatelic Youth Exhibition, May 20-24, Toronto. Card of 2, #116, Canada #15. French and English text. (USPS) — 3.00

SC77 PHILEXFRANCE '82, Intl. Philatelic Exhibition, June 11-21, Paris. Card of 2, #1753, France #1480. French text. (USPS) — 3.00

SC78 Natl. Stamp Collecting Month, Oct. #C3a. (USPS) — 3.00

SC79 ESPAMER '82, Intl. Philatelic Exhibition, Oct. 12-17, San Juan, P.R. Card of 4 #244. English and Spanish text. (BEP) — 22.00

SC80 ESPAMER '82, Intl. Philatelic Exhibition, Oct. 12-17, San Juan, P.R. Card of 3, #801, 1437, 2024. Spanish and English text. (USPS) — 3.00

1983

SC81 Joint stamp issues, Sweden and US. Mar. 24. Card of 3, #958, 2036, Sweden #1453. Swedish and English text. (USPS) — 3.00

SC82 Joint stamp issues, Germany and US. Apr. 29. Card of 2, #2040, Germany #1397. German and English text. (USPS) — 3.00

SC83 TEMBAL 83, Intl. Philatelic Exhibition, Mar. 21-29, Basel. Card of 2, #C71, Basel #3L1. German text. (USPS) — 3.00

SC84 TEXANEX-TOPEX '83 Exhibition, June 17-19, San Antonio. Card of 5, #1660, 4 #776. (BEP) — 16.00

SC85 BRASILIANA 83, Intl. Philatelic Exhibition, July 29-Aug. 7, Rio de Janeiro. Card of 2, #2, Brazil #1. Portuguese text. (USPS) — 3.00

SC86 BANGKOK 83, Intl. Philatelic Exhibition, Aug. 4-13, Bangkok. Card of 2, #210, Thailand #1. Thai text. (USPS) — 3.00

SC87 Intl. Philatelic Memento, 1983-84. #1387. (USPS) — 3.00

SC88 Natl. Stamp Collecting Month, Oct. #293 bicolored. (USPS) — 4.00

SC89 Philatelic Show '83, Boston, Oct. 21-23. Card of 2, #718-719. (BEP) — 9.00

SC90 ASDA 1983, Natl. Postage Stamp Show, New York, Nov. 17-20. Card of 4 #881. (BEP) — 9.00

1984

SC91 ESPANA 84, World Exhibition of Philately. Madrid, Apr. 27-May 6. Card of 4 #241. Enlarged vignette, Landing of Columbus, from #231. English and Spanish text. (BEP) — 15.00

SC92 ESPANA 84, Intl. Philatelic Exhibition, Madrid, Apr. 27-May 6. Card of 2, #233, Spain #428. Spanish text. (USPS) — 3.00

SC93 Stamp Expo '84 South, Anaheim, CA, Apr. 27-29. Card of 4, #1791-1794. (BEP) — 12.00

SC94 COMPEX '84, Rosemont, IL, May 25-27. Card of 4 #728. (BEP) — 15.00

SC95 HAMBURG '84, Intl. Exhibition for 19th UPU Congress, Hamburg, June 19-26. Card of 2, #C66, Germany #669. English, French and German text. (USPS) — 3.00

SC96 St. Lawrence Seaway, 25th anniv., June 26. Card of 2, #1131, Canada #387. English and French text. (USPS) — 3.25

SC97 AUSIPEX '84, Australia's 1st intl. exhibition, Melbourne, Sept. 21-30. Card of 2, #290, Western Australia #1. (USPS) — 3.00

SC98 Natl. Stamp Collecting Month, Oct. #2104, tricolored. (USPS) — 3.00

SC99 PHILAKOREA '84, Seoul, Oct. 22-31. Card of 2, #741, Korea #994. Korean and English text. (USPS) — 3.00

SC100 ASDA 1984, Natl. Postage Stamp Show, New York, Nov. 15-18. Card of 4 #1470. (BEP) — 12.00

1985

SC101 Intl. Philatelic Memento, 1985. #2. (USPS) — 3.00

SC102 OLYMPHILEX '85. Intl. Philatelic Exhibition, Lausanne. Mar. 18-24. Card of 2, #C106, Switzerland #746. French and English text. (USPS) — 3.00

SC103 ISRAPHIL '85. Intl. Philatelic Exhibition, Tel Aviv, May 14-22. Card of 2, #566, Israel #33. Hebrew and English text. (USPS) — 3.00

SC104 LONG BEACH '85, Numismatic and Philatelic Exposition, Long Beach, CA, Jan. 31-Feb. 3. Card of 4 #954, plus a Series 1865 $20 Gold Certificate. (BEP) — 10.00

SC105 MILCOPEX '85, Milwaukee Philatelic Society annual stamp show, Mar. 1-3. Card of 4 #880. (BEP) — 10.50

SC106 NAPEX '85, Natl. Philatelic Exhibition, Arlington, VA, June 7-9. Card of 4 #2014. (BEP) — 9.50

SC107 ARGENTINA '85, Intl. Philatelic Exhibition, Buenos Aires, July 5-14. Card of 2, #1737, Argentina #B27. Spanish text. (USPS) — 3.00

SC108 MOPHILA '85, Intl. Philatelic Exhibition, Hamburg, Sept. 11-15. Card of 2, #296, Germany #B595. German text. (USPS) — 3.00

SC109 ITALIA '85, Intl. Philatelic Exhibition, Rome, Oct. 25-Nov. 3. Card of 2, #1107, Italy #830. Italian text. (USPS) — 3.00

1986

SC110 Statue of Liberty Centennial, Natl. Philatelic Memento, 1986. #C87. (USPS) — 5.00

SC111 Garfield Perry Stamp Club, Natl. Stamp Show, Cleveland, Mar. 21-23. Card of 4 #306. (USPS) — 9.50

SC112 AMERIPEX '86, Intl. Philatelic Exhibition, Chicago, May 22-June 1. Card of 3, #134, 2052, 1474. (BEP) — 9.50

SC113 STOCKHOLMIA '86, Intl. Philatelic Exhibition, Stockholm, Aug. 28-Sept. 7. Card of 2, #113, Sweden #253. Swedish text. (USPS) — 4.50

SC114 HOUPEX '86, Natl. Stamp Show, Houston. Sept. 5-7. Card of 3, #1035, 1042, 1044A. (BEP) — 11.50

SC115 LOBEX '86, Numismatic and Philatelic Exhibition, Long Beach, CA, Oct. 2-5. Long Beach Stamp Club 60th anniv. Card of 4, #291, plus a series 1907 $10 Gold Certificate. (BEP) — 15.00

SC116 DCSE '86, Dallas Coin and Stamp Exhibition, Dallas, Dec. 11-14. Card of 4 #550, plus $10,000 Federal Reserve Note. (BEP) — 15.00

1987

SC117 CAPEX '87, Intl. Philatelic Exhibition, Toronto, June 13-21. Card of 2, #569, Canada #883. English and French text. (USPS) — 4.50

SC118 HAFNIA '87, Intl. Philatelic Exhibition, Copenhagen, Oct. 16-25. Card of 2, #299, Denmark #B52. English and Danish text. (USPS) — 4.50

SC119 SESCAL '87, Stamp Exhibition of Southern California, Los Angeles, Oct. 16-18. #798. (BEP) — 11.00

SC120 HSNA '87, Hawaii State Numismatic Association Exhibition, Honolulu, Nov. 12-15. #799 and a Series 1923 $5 Silver Certificate. (BEP) — 20.00

SC121 MONTE CARLO, Intl. Philatelic Exhibition, Monte Carlo, Nov. 13-17. Card of 3, #2287, 2300, Monaco #1589. French and English text. (USPS) — 4.00

1988

SC122 FINLANDIA '88, Intl. Philatelic Exhibition, Helsinki, June 1-12. Card of 2, #836, Finland #768. English and Finnish text. (USPS) — 4.00

SC123 STAMPSHOW '88, APS natl. stamp show, Detroit, Aug. 25-28. #835. (BEP) — 9.50

SC124 MIDAPHIL '88, Kansas City, Nov. 18-20. #627. (BEP) — 9.50

1989

SC125 PHILEXFRANCE '89 intl. philatelic exhibition, Paris, July 7-17. Card of 2, #C120, France #2144. English and French text. (USPS) — 7.75

SC126 STAMPSHOW '89, APS natl. stamp show, Anaheim, CA, Aug. 24-27. #565. Various reproductions of the portrait of Chief Hollow Horn Bear from which the stamp was designed. (BEP) — 9.50

SC127 WORLD STAMP EXPO '89, Washington, Nov. 17-Dec. 3. Card of 4, #2433a-2433d. Embossed reproductions of Supreme Court, Washington Monument, Capitol and Jefferson Memorial. (USPS) — 8.00

1990

SC128 ARIPEX 90, Arizona Philatelic Exhibition, Phoenix, Apr. 20-22. Card of 2, #285 and #285 with black vignette. (BEP) — 9.50

SC129 STAMPSHOW '90, APS natl. stamp show, Cincinnati, Aug. 23-26. Card of 2, #286 and essay with frame of #286 in red with vignette of #293 in black. (BEP) — 9.50

SC130 STAMP WORLD LONDON 90, London, England, May 3-13. Card of 2, #1, Great Britain #1. (USPS) — 7.00

1991

SC131 STAMPSHOW '91, APS natl. stamp show, Philadelphia, Aug. 22-25. Card of 3, #537, Essays #537a-E1, 537b-E1. Embossed figure of "Freedom." (BEP) (card has no year date) — 11.00

1992

SC132 World Columbian Stamp Expo, Chicago, May 22-31. Card of 2, #118, 119b. (BEP) — 10.00

SC132A OLYMPHILEX '92, Barcelona, Spain, July 30-Aug. 7. Card of 6, #2619, #2637-2641. (USPS) — *70.00*

SC133 Savings Bond, produced as gift to BEP employees, available to public. 1954 Savings stamp, Series E War Savings bond. (BEP) — 14.00

SC134 STAMPSHOW '92. Oakland, CA (BEP) — 9.50

1993

SC135 Combined Federal Campaign, produced as gift to BEP employees, available to public. #1016. Photos of 6 other stamps. (BEP) — 11.00

SC136 ASDA stamp show, New York, May 1993. Card of 7, #859, 864, 869, 874, 879, 884, 889 (BEP) — 11.00

SC137 Savings Bonds, produced as gift to BEP employees, available to the public Aug. 1993. $200 War Savings Bond, #WS8 (BEP) — 13.00

SC138 Omaha Stamp Show, Sept. 1993. Card of 4, #E7, PR2, JQ5, QE4 (BEP) — 13.00

SC139 ASDA New York Show, Oct. 1993. Card of 2, #499-E1a and similar with negative New York precancel (BEP) — 11.00

1994

SC140 Sandical, San Diego, CA, Feb. 1994. Card of 4 #E4 (BEP) — 10.00

SC140A Centennial of U.S. Stamp Production, July 1994, BEP Intaglio Print. Card of 13 Types A87-A99 in black — 125.00

SC141 Savings Bonds, produced as gift to BEP employees, available to the public Aug. 1, 1994. #WS7-WS11. — 16.00

SC142 STAMPSHOW '94, APS National Stamp Show Pittsburgh, PA. Card of 3, 1c, 2c and 10c Type D2 — 10.00

SC143 American Stamp Dealers Association, Nov. 1994, New York, NY. Card of 4, 2c, 12c, $3, $6 Types N4-N5, N7-N8 — 11.00

1995

SC144 Natl. Exhibition of the Columbus Philatelic Club, Apr. 1995, Columbus, OH. Block of 4 of #261. — 9.00

No. 144 was issued folded in half.

SC145 Centennial of U.S. Stamp Production, June 1995, BEP Intaglio Print. Card of 13 of Types A87-A99 in blue — 85.00

SC146 Savings Bonds, produced as a gift to BEP employees, available to the public Aug. 1, 1995. Card of 3 #905, 907, 940 — 9.50

SC147 American Stamp Dealers Association, Nov. 1995, New York, NY. Block of 4, #292 — 11.00

No. SC147 issued folded in half.

1996

SC148 CAPEX '96, Toronto, Canada, June 1996. Block of 4 #291 — 11.00

SC149 Olymphilex '96, Atlanta, GA, July-August, 1996, Block of 4, #718 — 11.00

SC150 Billings Stamp Club, Billings, MT, Oct. 1996, Block of 4, #1130 — 11.00

1997

SC151 Long Beach Coin & Collectibles Expo, Feb. 1997, Lock Seal revenue stamp — 11.00

SC152 PACIFIC 97, May 1997, Process or renovated butter revenue stamp — 10.00

SC153 Milcopex, Milwaukee, WI, Sept. 1997, Newspaper Types N15, N16 and N19 — 11.00

1998

SC154 OKPEX 98, Oklahoma City, OK, May 1998, Block of 4, #922 — 11.00

SC155 Centennial of Trans-Mississippi Exposition Issue, Sept. 1998, BEP Engraved Print. Card of 9 die impressions in green of designs A100-A108 — 72.50

1999

SC156 Philadelphia National Stamp Exhibition, Oct. 1999, Card of 4, #RS281, RS284, RS290, RS306 — 12.00

2003

SC157   Georgia Numismatic Association, Dalton, GA (card of one #C45 in blue gray, without denomination and some inscriptions)   45.00

2005

SC158   ANA Coin, Stamp and Collectibles Show, Las Vegas, Oct. 2005, Card of 7, #999, 1248, RF1, RF11, RF26, 7c essay of #RF11, 5c essay of #RF26   40.00

2006

SC159   ANA World's Fair of Money, Denver, CO, card of #1001 without denomination and some inscriptions, 1908 $10 silver certificate   40.00

SC160   Long Beach Coin, Stamp & Collectible Expo, Long Beach, CA, Sept. 2006, Card of #997 in blue, California state shield, Reverse of Series 1923 $10 United States Note   40.00

SC160A   ANA Coin, Stamp and Collectibles Show, Las Vegas, Oct. 2006, Card of 5, #RF17, RF24, RF27, essay type of RF19, USPO vignette (BEP)   40.00

2007

SC161   Whitman Baltimore Coin and Collectibles Convention, Baltimore, MD, Nov. 2007, Card of #962, 1142 in black   35.00

2008

SC162   Florida United Numismatists, Orlando, FL, Jan. 2008, Card of #Q12, 952   35.00

SC163   ANA World's Fair of Money, Baltimore, MD, Aug. 2008, Card of 1% ounce snuff, $19.20 tobacco, 5 Class A cigars stamps   35.00

2009

SC164   ANA National Money Show, Portland, OR, Mar. 2009, Card of #222   35.00

SC165   Whitman Baltimore Coin and Collectibles Convention, Baltimore, MD, Mar. 2009, Card of #77   35.00

SC166   Texas Numismatic Association 51st Texas State Coin and Currency Show, Fort Worth, TX, May 2009, Card of #821   35.00

NUMISMATIC SOUVENIR CARDS

Included in this section are cards issued by the Bureau of Engraving and Printing showing fractional currency, paper money or parts thereof, for numismatic shows. Not included are press samples sold or given away only at the shows and other special printings. Cards showing both money and stamps are listed in the preceeding section.

Standard abbreviations:
ANA- American Numismatic Association
IPMS- International Paper Money Show
FUN- Florida United Numismatists

No. NSC8

1969-84

NSC1	ANA	60.00
NSC2	Fresno Numismatic Fair	*275.00*
NSC3	ANA ('70)	75.00
NSC4	ANA ('71)	8.00
NSC5	ANA ('72)	8.00
NSC6	ANA ('73)	10.00
NSC7	ANA ('74)	9.00
NSC8	ANA ('75)	9.50
NSC9	ANA ('76)	8.00
NSC10	ANA ('77)	12.00
NSC11	IPMS ('78)	4.00
NSC12	ANA ('80)	16.00
NSC13	IPMS ('80)	22.00
NSC14	IPMS ('81)	16.00
NSC15	ANA ('81)	12.00
NSC16	IPMS ('82)	13.00

NSC17	ANA ('82)	10.50
NSC18	FUN ('83)	20.00
NSC19	ANA ('83)	16.00
NSC20	FUN ('84)	19.00
NSC21	IPMS ('84)	22.00
NSC22	ANA ('84)	15.00

1985

NSC23	International Coin Club of El Paso	18.00
NSC24	Pacific Northwest Numismatic Assoc.	15.00
NSC25	IPMS	18.00
NSC26	ANA	16.00
NSC27	International Paper Money Convention (IPMC)	16.00

1986

NSC28	FUN	15.00
NSC29	ANA Midwinter	15.00
NSC30	IPMS	13.00
NSC31	ANA	12.00
NSC32	National World Paper Money Convention (NWPMC)	12.00

1987

NSC33	FUN	15.00
NSC34	ANA Midwinter	14.00
NSC35	BEP Fort Worth	20.00
NSC36	IPMS	14.00
NSC37	ANA	12.00
NSC38	Great Eastern Numismatic Association	15.00

1988

NSC39	FUN	12.00
NSC40	ANA Midwinter	16.00
NSC41	IPMS	14.00
NSC42	ANA	22.00
NSC43	Illinois Numismatic Association	13.00

1989

NSC44	FUN	13.50
NSC45	ANA Midwinter	17.50
NSC46	TNA	18.00
NSC47	IPMS	13.00
NSC48	ANA	15.00

1990

NSC49	FUN	14.00
NSC50	ANA Midwinter	12.00
NSC51	Central States Numismatic Society	13.00
NSC52	Dallas Coin and Stamp Exposition	15.00
NSC53	ANA, Seattle, WA	22.00
NSC54	Westex	14.50
NSC55	Hawaii State Numismatic Association (card has no year date)	15.00

1991

NSC56	FUN (card has no year date)	14.00
NSC57	ANA Midwinter, Dallas, Texas (card has no year date)	16.00
NSC58	IPMS (card has no year date)	14.00
NSC59	ANA Convention, Chicago, IL (card has no year date)	20.00

1992

NSC60	FUN	10.00
NSC61	Central States Numismatics Society	20.00
NSC62	IPMS, Memphis, TN	12.00
NSC63	ANA Convention, Orlando, FL	17.00

1993

NSC64	FUN	17.00
NSC65	ANA Convention, Colorado Springs, CO	18.00
NSC66	Texas Numismatic Association Show	13.00
NSC67	Georgia Numismatic Association Show	15.00
NSC68	ANA Convention, Baltimore, MD	18.00
NSC69	IPMS, Memphis, TN	18.00

1994

NSC70	FUN	12.00
NSC71	ANA Convention, New Orleans, LA	20.00
NSC72	European Paper Money Bourse, Netherlands	16.00
NSC73	IPMS, Memphis, TN	14.00
NSC74	ANA Convention, Detroit, MI	14.00

Nos. NSC75-NSC79 were issued folded in half.

1995

NSC75	FUN	20.00
NSC76	New York Intl. Numismatic Convention	18.00
NSC77	IPMS, Memphis, TN	15.00
NSC78	ANA Convention, Anaheim, CA	17.50
NSC79	Long Beach Numismatic/Philatelic Exposition, Long Beach, CA	14.00

1996

NSC80	FUN	16.00
NSC81	Suburban Washington/Baltimore Coin Show	16.00
NSC82	Central States Numismatic Association	18.00
NSC83	ANA Convention, Denver, CO	18.00

1997

NSC84	FUN	20.00
NSC85	Bay State Coin Show	18.00
NSC86	IPMS, Memphis, TN	18.00
NSC87	ANA Convention, New York, NY	17.00

1998

NSC88	FUN	15.00
NSC89	IPMS, Memphis, TN	16.00
NSC90	ANA Convention, Portland, OR	16.00
NSC91	Long Beach Coin & Collectibles Expo, Long Beach, CA	16.00

1999

NSC92	FUN	20.00
NSC93	Bay State Coin Club	16.00
NSC94	IPMS, Memphis, TN	18.00
NSC95	ANA Convention, Rosemont, IL	17.50

2001

NSC96	FUN	20.00
NSC97	Intl. Paper Money Show, Memphis, TN	18.00
NSC98	ANA Convention, Atlanta, GA	16.00
NSC99	Long Beach Coin & Collectibles Expo, Long Beach, CA	17.50

2002

NSC100	FUN	18.00
NSC101	Texas Numismatic Association, Fort Worth	20.00
NSC102	ANA Convention, New York, NY	18.00
NSC103	Long Beach Coin & Collectibles Expo, Long Beach, CA	20.00

2003

NSC104	FUN	45.00

2002

NSC106	ANA Convention, Baltimore, MD	45.00

2003

NSC107	Natl. & World Paper Money Convention, St. Louis, MO	45.00

2004

NSC108	ANA Convention, Portland, OR	70.00
NSC109	ANA Convention, Pittsburgh, PA	45.00

2005

NSC110	FUN	40.00
NSC111	Money Show of the Southwest, Houston, TX	40.00
NSC112	Long Beach Coin & Stamp Expo, Long Beach, CA	40.00
NSC113	ANA National Money Show, Kansas City, MO	40.00
NSC114	ANA World's Fair of Money, San Francisco, CA	40.00

2006

NSC115	ANA National Money Show, Atlanta, GA	35.00

2007

NSC116	ANA National Money Show, Charlotte, NC	35.00
NSC117	ANA World's Fair of Money, Milwaukee, WI	35.00

2008

NSC118	ANA National Money Show, Phoenix, AZ	35.00

2009

NSC119	Central States Numismatic Society, Cincinnati, OH	35.00

COMMEMORATIVE PANELS

The U.S. Postal Service began issuing commemorative panels September 20, 1972, with the Wildlife Conservation issue (Scott Nos. 1464-1467). Each panel is devoted to a separate issue. It includes unused examples of the stamp or stamps (usually a block of four), reproduction of steel engravings, and background information on the subject of the issue. Values are for panels without protective sleeves. Values for panels with protective sleeves are 10% to 25% higher.

No. CP53

1972
CP1	Wildlife Conservation, #1467a	7.00
CP2	Mail Order, #1468	7.00
CP3	Osteopathic Medicine, #1469	14.00
CP4	Tom Sawyer, #1470	13.00
CP5	Pharmacy, #1473	9.50
CP6	Christmas (angel), #1471	9.50
CP7	Santa Claus, #1472	9.50
CP8	Stamp Collecting, #1474	7.00

1973
CP9	Love, #1475	9.00
CP10	Pamphleteers, #1476	7.00
CP11	George Gershwin, #1484	9.00
CP12	Posting a Broadside, #1477	6.50
CP13	Copernicus, #1488	6.50
CP14	Postal Service Employees, #1489-1498	6.50
CP15	Harry S Truman, #1499	11.00
CP16	Postrider, #1478	9.00
CP17	Boston Tea Party, #1483a	25.00
CP18	Electronics Progress, #1500-1502, C86	11.00
CP19	Robinson Jeffers, #1485	6.50
CP20	Lyndon B. Johnson, #1503	9.00
CP21	Henry O. Tanner, #1486	6.50
CP22	Willa Cather, #1487	6.50
CP23	Drummer, #1479	12.00
CP24	Angus and Longhorn Cattle, #1504	9.00
CP25	Christmas (Madonna), #1507	13.50
CP26	Christmas Tree, needlepoint, #1508	11.50

1974
CP27	Veterans of Foreign Wars, #1525	6.50
CP28	Robert Frost, #1526	7.50
CP29	EXPO '74, #1527	9.50
CP30	Horse Racing, #1528	12.00
CP31	Skylab, #1529	14.00
CP32	Universal Postal Union, #1537a	9.00
CP33	Mineral Heritage, #1541a	12.00
CP34	Kentucky Settlement (Ft. Harrod), #1542	7.50
CP35	First Continental Congress, #1546a	9.00
CP36	Chautauqua, #1505	9.00
CP37	Kansas Wheat, #1506	9.00
CP38	Energy Conservation, #1547	7.50
CP39	Sleepy Hollow Legend, #1548	9.00
CP40	Retarded Children, #1549	6.50
CP41	Christmas (Currier-Ives), #1551	9.50
CP42	Christmas (angel), #1550	9.50

1975
CP43	Benjamin West, #1553	9.00
CP44	Pioneer 10, #1556	15.00
CP45	Collective Bargaining, #1558	7.50
CP46	Contributors to the Cause, #1559-1562	16.00
CP47	Mariner 10, #1557	17.50
CP48	Lexington-Concord Battle, #1563	7.50
CP49	Paul Laurence Dunbar, #1554	9.00
CP50	D. W. Griffith, #1555	12.00
CP51	Battle of Bunker Hill, #1564	9.00
CP52	Military Services (uniforms), #1568a	9.50
CP53	Apollo Soyuz, #1569a	16.00
CP54	World Peace through Law, #1576	7.50
CP55	International Women's Year, #1571	7.50
CP56	Postal Service 200 Years, #1575a	7.50
CP57	Banking and Commerce, #1577a	9.00
CP58	Early Christmas Card, #1580	9.00

CP59	Christmas (Madonna), #1579	9.00

1976
CP60	Spirit of '76, #1631a	12.50
CP61	Interphil '76, #1632	11.50
CP62	State Flags, block of 4 from #1633-1682	25.00
CP63	Telephone Centenary, #1683	9.50
CP64	Commercial Aviation, #1684	11.00
CP65	Chemistry, #1685	9.50
CP66	Benjamin Franklin, #1690	9.50
CP67	Declaration of Independence, #1694a	9.50
CP68	12th Winter Olympics, #1698a	11.50
CP69	Clara Maass, #1699	16.50
CP70	Adolph S. Ochs, #1700	11.00
CP71	Christmas (Currier print), #1702	11.50
CP72	Christmas (Copley Nativity), #1701	13.00

1977
CP73	Washington at Princeton, #1704	14.00
CP74	Sound Recording, #1705	40.00
CP75	Pueblo Art, #1709a	90.00
CP76	Lindbergh Flight, #1710	95.00
CP77	Colorado Statehood, #1711	16.50
CP78	Butterflies, #1715a	19.00
CP79	Lafayette, #1716	16.00
CP80	Skilled Hands for Independence, #1720a	16.00
CP81	Peace Bridge, #1721	16.00
CP82	Battle of Oriskany, #1722	16.00
CP83	Energy Conservation-Development, #1723a	16.00
CP84	Alta California, #1725	16.00
CP85	Articles of Confederation, #1726	24.00
CP86	Talking Pictures, #1727	19.00
CP87	Surrender at Saratoga, #1728	22.00
CP88	Christmas (Washington at Valley Forge), #1729	18.50
CP89	Christmas (rural mailbox), #1730	35.00

1978
CP90	Carl Sandburg, #1731	9.50
CP91	Captain Cook, #1732a	15.50
CP92	Harriet Tubman, #1744	12.00
CP93	American Quilts, #1748a	19.00
CP94	American Dance, #1752a	14.00
CP95	French Alliance, #1753	11.50
CP96	Pap Test, #1754	12.00
CP97	Jimmie Rodgers, #1755	14.50
CP98	Photography, #1758	14.50
CP99	George M. Cohan, #1756	19.00
CP100	Viking Missions, #1759	42.50
CP101	American Owls, #1763a	42.50
CP102	American Trees, #1767a	34.00
CP103	Christmas (Madonna), #1768	16.00
CP104	Christmas (hobby-horse), #1769	16.50

1979
CP105	Robert F. Kennedy, #1770	14.50
CP106	Martin Luther King, Jr., #1771	11.00
CP107	Year of the Child, #1772	9.50
CP108	John Steinbeck, #1773	8.50
CP109	Albert Einstein, #1774	11.50
CP110	Pennsylvania Toleware, #1778a	14.00
CP111	American Architecture, #1782a	11.00
CP112	Endangered Flora, #1786a	11.50
CP113	Seeing Eye Dogs, #1787	9.50
CP114	Special Olympics, #1788	9.00
CP115	John Paul Jones, #1789	11.00
CP116	Olympic Games, #1794a	11.50
CP117	Christmas (Madonna), #1799	12.00
CP118	Christmas (Santa Claus), #1800	12.00
CP119	Will Rogers, #1801	13.00
CP120	Viet Nam Veterans, #1802	11.50
CP121	10c, 31c Olympics, #1790, C97	12.00

1980
CP122	Winter Olympics, #1798a	9.00
CP123	W.C Fields, #1803	16.00
CP124	Benjamin Banneker, #1804	9.50
CP125	Frances Perkins, #1821	7.50
CP126	Emily Bissell, #1823	12.00
CP127	Helen Keller, #1824	7.50
CP128	Veterans Administration, #1825	7.50
CP129	Galvez, #1826	7.50
CP130	Coral Reefs, #1830a	10.50
CP131	Organized Labor, #1831	7.50
CP132	Edith Wharton, #1832	7.50
CP133	Education, #1833	7.50
CP134	Indian Masks, #1837a	17.00
CP135	Architecture, #1841a	9.00
CP136	Christmas Window, #1842	11.50
CP137	Christmas Toys, #1843	12.00

1981
CP138	Dirksen, #1874	8.50
CP139	Young, #1875	12.00
CP140	Flowers, #1879a	12.00
CP141	Red Cross, #1910	9.50
CP142	Savings and Loan, #1911	9.50
CP143	Space Achievements, #1919a	16.50
CP144	Management, #1920	7.50
CP145	Wildlife, #1924a	11.50
CP146	Disabled, #1925	7.50
CP147	Millay, #1926	7.50
CP148	Architecture, #1931a	9.00
CP149	Zaharias, Jones, #1932, 1933	42.50
CP150	Remington, #1934	12.00

CP151	18c, 20c Hoban, #1935, 1936	7.50
CP152	Yorktown, Va. Capes, #1938a	7.50
CP153	Madonna and Child, #1939	10.00
CP154	Teddy Bear, #1940	11.00
CP155	John Hanson, #1941	7.50
CP156	Desert Plants, #1945a	11.50

1982
CP157	FDR, #1950	12.00
CP158	Love, #1951	14.00
CP159	Washington, #1952	15.00
CP160	Birds and Flowers, block of 4 from #1953-2002	42.50
CP161	US-Netherlands, #2003	16.50
CP162	Library of Congress, #2004	14.00
CP163	Knoxville World's Fair, #2009a	12.00
CP164	Horatio Alger, #2010	13.00
CP165	Aging, #2011	13.00
CP166	Barrymores, #2012	16.00
CP167	Dr. Mary Walker, #2013	12.00
CP168	Peace Garden, #2014	13.00
CP169	Libraries, #2015	12.00
CP170	Jackie Robinson, #2016	40.00
CP171	Touro Synagogue, #2017	12.00
CP172	Wolf Trap Farm, #2018	14.00
CP173	Architecture, #2022a	15.00
CP174	Francis of Assisi, #2023	14.00
CP175	Ponce de Leon, #2024	14.00
CP176	Puppy, Kitten, #2025	22.50
CP177	Madonna and Child, #2026	19.00
CP178	Children Playing, #2030a	19.00

1983
CP179	Science, #2031	7.50
CP180	Ballooning, #2035a	9.00
CP181	US-Sweden, #2036	7.50
CP182	CCC, #2037	7.50
CP183	Priestley, #2038	7.50
CP184	Voluntarism, #2039	19.00
CP185	German Immigration, #2040	7.50
CP186	Brooklyn Bridge, #2041	9.50
CP187	TVA, #2042	7.50
CP188	Fitness, #2043	7.50
CP189	Scott Joplin, #2044	9.50
CP190	Medal of Honor, #2045	11.50
CP191	Babe Ruth, #2046	32.50
CP192	Hawthorne, #2047	7.50
CP193	13c Olympics, #2051a	9.00
CP194	28c Olympics, #C104a	9.00
CP195	40c Olympics, #C108a	9.50
CP196	35c Olympics, #C112a	11.50
CP197	Treaty of Paris, #2052	8.00
CP198	Civil Service, #2053	8.00
CP199	Metropolitan Opera, #2054	12.00
CP200	Inventors, #2058a	10.00
CP201	Streetcars, #2062a	12.00
CP202	Madonna and Child, #2063	11.50
CP203	Santa Claus, #2064	11.50
CP204	Martin Luther, #2065	10.00

1984
CP205	Alaska, #2066	7.00
CP206	Winter Olympics, #2070a	9.00
CP207	FDIC, #2071	7.00
CP208	Love, #2072	7.00
CP209	Woodson, #2073	9.00
CP210	Conservation, #2074	7.00
CP211	Credit Union, #2075	7.00
CP212	Orchids, #2079a	9.50
CP213	Hawaii, #2080	9.50
CP214	National Archives, #2081	7.00
CP215	Olympics, #2085a	9.00
CP216	World Expo, #2086	7.00
CP217	Health Research, #2087	7.00
CP218	Fairbanks, #2088	10.00
CP219	Thorpe, #2089	10.00
CP220	McCormack, #2090	10.00
CP221	St. Lawrence Seaway, #2091	10.00
CP222	Waterfowl, #2092	13.50
CP223	Roanoke Voyages, #2093	7.00
CP224	Melville, #2094	9.00
CP225	Horace Moses, #2095	7.00
CP226	Smokey Bear, #2096	32.50
CP227	Roberto Clemente, #2097	42.50
CP228	Dogs, #2101a	12.00
CP229	Crime Prevention, #2102	7.00
CP230	Hispanic Americans, #2103	7.00
CP231	Family Unity, #2104	7.00
CP232	Eleanor Roosevelt, #2105	16.00
CP233	Readers, #2106	7.00
CP234	Madonna and Child, #2107	9.00
CP235	Child's Santa, #2108	9.00
CP236	Vietnam Memorial, #2109	14.50

1985
CP237	Jerome Kern, #2110	9.50
CP238	Bethune, #2137	9.50
CP239	Duck Decoys, #2141a	22.50
CP240	Winter Special Olympics, #2142	7.00
CP241	Love, #2143	7.00
CP242	REA, #2144	7.00
CP243	AMERIPEX '86, #2145	7.50
CP244	Abigail Adams, #2146	7.00
CP245	Bartholdi, #2147	12.00
CP246	Korean Veterans, #2152	12.50
CP247	Social Security, #2153	3.00
CP248	World War I Veterans, #2154	8.00
CP249	Horses, #2158a	17.00

CP250	Education, #2159	7.00
CP251	Youth Year, #2163a	16.00
CP252	Hunger, #2164	7.00
CP253	Madonna and Child, #2165	10.00
CP254	Poinsettias, #2166	10.50

1986

CP255	Arkansas, #2167	7.50
CP256	Stamp Collecting booklet pane, #2201a	9.00
CP257	Love, #2202	11.50
CP258	Sojourner Truth, #2203	11.50
CP259	Texas Republic, #2204	9.50
CP260	Fish booklet pane, #2209a	11.50
CP261	Hospitals, #2210	7.00
CP262	Duke Ellington, #2211	11.50
CP263	Presidents Souvenir Sheet No. 1, #2216	10.00
CP264	Presidents Souvenir Sheet No. 2, #2217	10.00
CP265	Presidents Souvenir Sheet No. 3, #2218	10.00
CP266	Presidents Souvenir Sheet No. 4, #2219	10.00
CP267	Arctic Explorers, #2223a	11.50
CP268	Statue of Liberty, #2224	12.00
CP269	Navajo Art, #2238a	15.00
CP270	T.S. Eliot, #2239	9.50
CP271	Woodcarved Figurines, #2243a	12.00
CP272	Madonna and Child, #2244	8.00
CP273	Village Scene, #2245	8.00

1987

CP274	Michigan, #2246	9.50
CP275	Pan American Games, #2247	7.00
CP276	Love, #2248	9.50
CP277	du Sable, #2249	9.50
CP278	Caruso, #2250	11.50
CP279	Girl Scouts, #2251	14.50
CP280	Special Occasions booklet pane, #2274a	8.50
CP281	United Way, #2275	7.00
CP282	Wildlife, #2286, 2287, 2296, 2297, 2306, 2307, 2316, 2317, 2326, 2327	11.00
CP283	Wildlife, #2288, 2289, 2298, 2299, 2308, 2309, 2318, 2319, 2328, 2329	11.00
CP284	Wildlife, #2290, 2291, 2300, 2301, 2310, 2311, 2320, 2321, 2330, 2331	11.00
CP285	Wildlife, #2292, 2293, 2302, 2303, 2312, 2313, 2322, 2323, 2332, 2333	11.00
CP286	Wildlife, #2294, 2295, 2304, 2305, 2314, 2315, 2324, 2325, 2334, 2335	11.00

1987-90

CP287	Delaware, #2336	12.00
CP288	Pennsylvania, #2337	9.00
CP289	New Jersey, #2338	9.00
CP290	Georgia, #2339	9.00
CP291	Connecticut, #2340	9.00
CP292	Massachusetts, #2341	9.00
CP293	Maryland, #2342	9.00
CP294	South Carolina, #2343	9.00
CP295	New Hampshire, #2344	9.00
CP296	Virginia, #2345	9.00
CP297	New York, #2346	9.00
CP298	North Carolina, #2347	9.00
CP299	Rhode Island, #2348	9.00

1987

CP300	U.S.-Morocco, #2349	7.50
CP301	William Faulkner, #2350	7.50
CP302	Lacemaking, #2354a	12.00
CP303	Drafting of the Constitution booklet pane, #2359a	9.00
CP304	Signing of the Constitution, #2360	9.00
CP305	Certified Public Accounting, #2361	52.50
CP306	Locomotives booklet pane, #2366a	12.00
CP307	Madonna and Child, #2367	8.00
CP308	Christmas Ornaments, #2368	7.50

1988

CP309	Winter Olympics, #2369	9.00
CP310	Australia Bicentennial, #2370	11.50
CP311	James Weldon Johnson, #2371	12.00
CP312	Cats, #2375a	18.50
CP313	Knute Rockne, #2376	9.00
CP314	New Sweden, #C117	27.50
CP315	Francis Ouimet, #2377	9.00
CP316	25c, 45c Love, #2378 and #2379	9.00
CP317	Summer Olympics, #2380	9.00
CP318	Classic Automobiles booklet pane, #2385a	12.00
CP319	Antarctic Explorers, #2389a	9.00
CP320	Carousel Animals, #2393a	12.00
CP321	Special Occasions booklet singles, #2395-2398	9.00
CP322	Madonna and Child, Sleigh, #2399, 2400	9.00

1989

CP323	Montana, #2401	9.00
CP324	A. Philip Randolph, #2402	11.00
CP325	North Dakota, #2403	9.00
CP326	Washington Statehood, #2404	9.00
CP327	Steamboats booklet pane, #2409a	11.50
CP328	World Stamp Expo, #2410	7.50
CP329	Arturo Toscanini, #2411	11.50

1989-90

CP330	House of Representatives, #2412	11.50
CP331	Senate, #2413	11.50
CP332	Executive Branch, #2414	11.50
CP333	Supreme Court, #2415	11.50

1989

CP334	South Dakota, #2416	9.00
CP335	Lou Gehrig, #2417	40.00
CP336	French Revolution, #C120	9.00
CP337	Ernest Hemingway, #2418	16.00
CP338	Letter Carriers, #2420	9.00
CP339	Bill of Rights, #2421	9.00

CP340	Dinosaurs, #2425a	21.00
CP341	Pre-Columbian Artifacts, #2426, C121	9.25
CP342	Madonna, Sleigh with Presents, #2427, 2428	11.00
CP343	Traditional Mail Delivery, #2437a	9.00
CP344	Futuristic Mail Delivery, #C125a	11.50

1990

CP345	Idaho, #2439	9.00
CP346	Love, #2440	9.00
CP347	Ida B. Wells, #2442	15.00
CP348	Wyoming, #2444	9.00
CP349	Classic Films, #2448a	22.00
CP350	Marianne Moore, #2449	7.00
CP351	Lighthouses booklet pane, #2474a	22.00
CP352	Olympians, #2500a	15.00
CP353	Indian Headdresses booklet pane, #2505c	14.00
CP354	Micronesia, Marshall Islands, #2507a	9.00
CP355	Sea Creatures, #2511a	19.00
CP356	Grand Canyon & Tropical Coastline, #2512, C127	11.00
CP357	Eisenhower, #2513	11.50
CP358	Madonna and Child, Christmas Tree, #2514-2515	11.50

1991

CP359	Switzerland, #2532	12.00
CP360	Vermont Statehood, #2533	9.00
CP361	Savings Bonds, #2534	8.00
CP362	Love, #2535-2536	11.00
CP363	William Saroyan, #2538	21.00
CP364	Fishing Flies, #2549a	19.00
CP365	Cole Porter, #2550	9.00
CP366	Antarctic Treaty, C130	9.00
CP367	Operations Desert Shield & Desert Storm, #2551	40.00
CP368	Summer Olympics, #2557a	11.50
CP369	Numismatics, #2558	9.00
CP370	World War II, #2559	17.00
CP371	Basketball, #2560	21.00
CP372	District of Columbia, #2561	9.50
CP373	Comedians, #2566c	17.00
CP374	Jan E. Matzeliger, #2567	11.00
CP375	Space Exploration, #2577a	16.50
CP376	Bering Land Bridge, #C131	9.50
CP377	Madonna and Child, Santa in Chimney, #2578-2579	14.00

1992

CP378	Winter Olympics, #2615a	10.00
CP379	World Columbian Stamp Expo '92, #2616	11.00
CP380	W.E.B. DuBois, #2617	17.00
CP381	Love, #2618	10.00
CP382	Olympic Baseball, #2619	42.50
CP383	Voyages of Columbus, #2623a	13.00
CP384	Columbus, #2624-2625	70.00
CP385	Columbus, #2626, 2629	70.00
CP386	Columbus, #2627-2628	70.00
CP387	New York Stock Exchange, #2630	22.50
CP388	Space Accomplishments, #2634a	17.00
CP389	Alaska Highway, #2635	9.00
CP390	Kentucky Statehood, #2636	9.00
CP391	Summer Olympics, #2641a	11.00
CP392	Hummingbirds, #2646a	17.00
CP393	World War II, #2697	17.00
CP394	Wildflowers, #2647, 2648, 2657, 2658, 2667, 2668, 2677, 2678, 2687, 2688	40.00
CP395	Wildflowers, #2649, 2650, 2659, 2660, 2669, 2670, 2679, 2680, 2689, 2690	40.00
CP396	Wildflowers, #2651, 2652, 2661, 2662, 2671, 2672, 2681, 2682, 2691, 2692	40.00
CP397	Wildflowers, #2653, 2654, 2663, 2664, 2673, 2674, 2683, 2684, 2693, 2694	40.00
CP398	Wildflowers, #2655, 2656, 2665, 2666, 2675, 2676, 2685, 2686, 2695, 2696	40.00
CP399	Dorothy Parker, #2698	9.00
CP400	Dr. Theodore von Karman, #2699	15.00
CP401	Minerals, #2703a	17.00
CP402	Juan Rodriguez Cabrillo, #2704	11.00
CP403	Wild Animals, #2709a	15.00
CP404	Madonna and Child, wheeled toys, #2710, 2714a	15.00
CP405	Chinese New Year, #2720	30.00

1993

CP406	Elvis Presley, #2721	32.50
CP407	Space Fantasy, #2745a	19.00
CP408	Percy Lavon Julian, #2746	16.00
CP409	Oregon Trail, #2747	11.00
CP410	World University Games, #2748	11.00
CP411	Grace Kelly, #2749	28.00
CP412	Oklahoma!, #2722	11.00
CP413	Circus, #2753a	14.50
CP414	Cherokee Strip, #2754	11.00
CP415	Dean Acheson, #2755	16.00
CP416	Sports horses, #2759a	16.00
CP417	Garden flowers, #2764a	11.00
CP418	World War II, #2765	16.00
CP419	Hank Williams, #2723	29.00
CP420	Rock & Roll/Rhythm & Blues, #2737b	32.50
CP421	Joe Louis, #2766	39.00
CP422	Broadway Musicals, #2770a	16.00
CP423	National Postal Museum, #2782a	14.00
CP424	American Sign Language, #2784a	13.00
CP425	Country & Western Music, #2778a	28.50
CP426	Christmas, #2789, 2794a	16.50
CP427	Youth Classics, #2788a	16.50
CP428	Mariana Islands, #2804	13.00
CP429	Columbus' Landing in Puerto Rico, #2805	14.00
CP430	AIDS Awareness, #2806	14.00

Starting with No. CP431, panels are shrink wrapped in plastic with cardboard backing. Values are for items with plastic intact.

1994

CP431	Winter Olympics, #2807-2811	22.50
CP432	Edward R. Murrow, #2812	14.00
CP434	Love, #2814	16.00
CP436	Dr. Allison Davis, #2816	17.50
CP437	Chinese New Year, #2817	20.00
CP438	Buffalo Soldiers, #2818	17.50
CP439	Silent Screen Stars, #2828a	20.00
CP440	Garden Flowers, #2829-2833	16.00
CP441	World Cup Soccer, #2837	17.50
CP442	World War II, #2838	17.50
CP443	Norman Rockwell, #2839	29.50
CP444	Moon Landing, #2841	27.50
CP445	Locomotives, #2843-2847	17.50
CP446	George Meany, #2848	11.00
CP447	Popular Singers, #2853a	17.50
CP448	Jazz/Blues Singers, block of 10, 2854-2861	22.50

Block of 10 on No. CP448 may contain different combination of stamps.

CP449	James Thurber, #2862	11.00
CP450	Wonders of the Sea, #2866a	17.50
CP451	Cranes, block of 2 #2868a	17.50
CP453	Christmas Madonna and Child, #2871	11.00
CP454	Christmas stocking, #2872	11.00
CP455	Chinese New Year, #2876	17.50

1995

CP456	Florida Statehood, #2950	13.00
CP457	Earth Day, #2954a	13.00
CP458	Richard M. Nixon, #2955	22.50
CP459	Bessie Coleman, #2956	18.00
CP460	Love, #2957-2958	18.00
CP461	Recreational Sports, #2965a	18.00
CP462	Prisoners of War/Missing in Action, #2966	16.00
CP463	Marilyn Monroe, #2967	37.50
CP464	Texas Statehood, #2968	16.00
CP465	Great Lakes Lighthouses, #2973a	18.00
CP466	United Nations, #2974	13.00
CP467	Carousel Horses, #2979a	21.00
CP468	Woman Suffrage, #2980	13.00
CP469	World War II, #2981	20.00
CP470	Louis Armstrong, #2982	22.50
CP471	Jazz Musicians, #2992a	22.50
CP472	Garden Flowers, #2993-2997	13.00
CP473	Republic of Palau, #2999	13.00
CP474	Naval Academy, #3001	18.00
CP475	Tennessee Williams, #3002	16.00
CP476	Christmas, Madonna and Child, #3003	18.00
CP477	Santa Claus, Children with toys, #3007a	18.00
CP478	James K. Polk, #2587	13.00
CP479	Antique Automobiles, 3023a	22.50

1996

CP480	Utah Statehood, #3024	13.00
CP481	Garden Flowers, #3029a	13.00
CP482	Ernest E. Just, #3058	18.00
CP483	Smithsonian Institution, #3059	13.00
CP484	Chinese New Year, #3060	22.50
CP485	Pioneers of Communication, #3064a	18.00
CP486	Fulbright Scholarships, #3065	13.00
CP487	Summer Olympic Games, #3068, 2 pages	50.00

Beginning with No. CP487, some items contain two pages. One has text and engraved illustrations, the second has the stamp(s).

CP488	Marathon, #3067	18.00
CP489	Georgia O'Keeffe, #3069	13.00
CP490	Tennessee Statehood, #3070	13.00
CP491	Indian Dances, #3076a	22.50
CP492	Prehistoric Animals, #3080a	22.50
CP493	Breast Cancer Awareness, #3081	13.00
CP494	James Dean, #3082	22.50
CP495	Folk Heroes, #3086a	22.50
CP496	Olympic Games, Cent., #3087	16.00
CP497	Iowa Statehood, #3088	13.00
CP498	Rural Free Delivery, #3090	13.00
CP499	Riverboats, #3095a	22.50
CP500	Big Band Leaders, #3099a	21.00
CP501	Songwriters, #3103a	21.00
CP502	F. Scott Fitzgerald, #3104	22.50
CP503	Endangered Species, #3105, 2 pages	37.50
CP504	Computer Technology, #3106	22.50
CP505	Madonna & Child, #3107	18.00
CP506	Family Scenes, #3111a	18.00
CP507	Hanukkah, #3118	16.00
CP507A	Cycling, #3119	45.00

1997

CP508	Chinese New Year, #3120	24.00
CP509	Benjamin O. Davis, Sr., #3121	21.00
CP510	Love Swans, #3123-3124	16.00
CP511	Helping Children Learn, #3125	13.00
CP512	PACIFIC 97 Stagecoach & Ship, #3131a	20.00
CP513	Thornton Wilder, #3134	18.00
CP514	Raoul Wallenberg, #3135	16.00
CP515	Dinosaurs, #3136	30.00
CP516	Bugs Bunny, #3137c	24.00
CP517	PACIFIC 97 Franklin, #3139	55.00
CP518	PACIFIC 97 Washington, #3140	55.00
CP519	Marshall Plan, #3141	16.00
CP520	Classic American Aircraft, #3142, 2 pages	36.00
CP521	Football Coaches, #3146a	30.00

CP522	American Dolls, #3151	55.00
CP523	Humphrey Bogart, #3152	20.00
CP524	"The Stars & Stripes Forever!," #3153	16.00
CP525	Opera Singers, #3157a	19.00
CP526	Composers & Conductors, #3165a	20.00
CP527	Padre Felix Varela, #3166	16.00
CP528	Department of the Air Force, #3167	20.00
CP529	Movie Monsters, #3172a	22.50
CP530	Supersonic Flight, #3173	22.50
CP531	Women in Military Service, #3174	18.00
CP532	Kwanzaa, #3175	16.00
CP533	Madonna & Child, #3176a	21.00
CP534	Holly, #3177a	21.00

1998

CP535	Chinese New Year, #3179	17.50
CP536	Alpine Skiing, #3180	15.50
CP537	Madam C.J. Walker, #3181	18.00

1998-2000

Celebrate the Century

CP537A	1900s, #3182, 2 pages	27.00
CP537B	1910s, #3183, 2 pages	27.00
CP537C	1920s, #3184, 2 pages	27.00
CP537D	1930s, #3185, 2 pages	30.00
CP537E	1940s, #3186, 2 pages	35.00
CP537F	1950s, #3187, 2 pages	29.00
CP537G	1960s, #3188, 2 pages	32.50
CP537H	1970s, #3189, 2 pages	30.00
CP537I	1980s, #3190, 2 pages	29.00
CP537J	1990s, #3191, 2 pages	29.00

1998

CP538	Remember the Maine,inscribed "Key West, Florida" #3192	16.00
	a. Inscribed "Scottsdale, Arizona."	22.50
CP539	Flowering Trees, #3197a	18.00
CP540	Alexander Calder, #3202a	18.00
CP541	Cinco de Mayo, #3203	16.00
CP542	Sylvester & Tweety, #3204c	22.50
CP543	Wisconsin Statehood, #3206	17.50
CP544	Trans-Mississippi, #3209-3210, 2 pages	27.50
CP545	Berlin Airlift, #3211	15.00
CP546	Folk Musicians, #3215a	20.00
CP547	Gospel Singers, #3219a	20.00
CP548	Spanish Settlement, #3220	16.00
CP549	Stephen Vincent Benét, #3221	15.00
CP550	Tropical Birds, #3225a	17.00
CP551	Alfred Hitchcock, #3226	19.00
CP552	Organ & Tissue Donation, #3227	17.00
CP553	Bright Eyes, #3234a	17.00
CP554	Klondike Gold Rush, #3235	15.00
CP555	American Art, #3236	30.00
CP556	American Ballet, #3237	16.00
CP557	Space Discovery, #3242a	20.00
CP558	Giving & Sharing, #3243	15.00
CP559	Madonna & Child, #3244a	20.00
CP560	Wreaths, #3252a	16.00
CP561	Breast Cancer Awareness, #B1	25.00

1999

CP562	Chinese New Year, #3272	17.50
CP563	Malcolm X, #3273	16.00
CP564	Love, #3274a	22.50
CP565	Love, #3275	17.00
CP566	Hospice Care, #3276	16.00
CP567	Irish Immigration, #3286	21.00
CP568	Lunt & Fontanne, #3287	16.00
CP569	Arctic Animals, #3292a	18.00
CP570	Sonoran Desert, #3293, 2 pages	25.00
CP571	Daffy Duck, #3306c	25.00
CP572	Ayn Rand, #3308	32.50
CP573	Cinco de Mayo, #3309	17.00
CP574	John & William Bartram, #3314	18.00
CP575	Prostate Cancer, #3315	18.00
CP576	California Gold Rush, #3316	18.00
CP577	Aquarium Fish, #3320a	18.00
CP578	Extreme Sports, #3324a	18.00
CP579	American Glass, #3328a	18.00
CP580	James Cagney, #3329	18.00
CP581	Honoring Those who Served, #3331	16.00
CP582	Famous Trains, #3337a	22.50
CP583	Frederick Law Olmsted, #3338	18.00
CP584	Hollywood Composers, #3344a	20.00
CP585	Broadway Songwriters, #3350a	20.00
CP586	Insects & Spiders, #3351, 2 pages	30.00
CP587	Hanukkah, #3352	18.00
CP588	NATO, #3354	18.00
CP589	Madonna & Child, #3355	18.00
CP590	Deer, #3359a	18.00
CP591	Kwanzaa, #3368	18.00
CP592	Year 2000, #3369	22.50

2000

CP593	Chinese New Year, #3370	16.00
CP594	Patricia Roberts Harris, #3371	22.50
CP595	Los Angeles Class Submarine, #3372	25.00
CP596	Pacific Coast Rain Forest, #3378, 2 pages	29.00
CP597	Louise Nevelson, #3383a	20.00
CP598	Hubble Space Telescope Images, #3388a	23.00
CP599	American Samoa, #3389	18.00
CP600	Library of Congress, #3390	18.00
CP601	Road Runner & Wile E. Coyote, #3391c	20.00
CP602	Distinguished Soldiers, #3396a	22.00
CP603	Summer Sports, #3397	18.00
CP604	Adoption, #3398	22.00
CP605	Youth Team Sports, #3402a	22.00
CP606	The Stars and Stripes, #3403, 2 pages	34.50
CP607	Legends of Baseball, #3408, 2 pages	40.00
CP608	Stampin' the Future, #3417a	20.00
CP609	California Statehood, #3438	18.00
CP610	Deep Sea Creatures, #3443a	21.00

CP611	Thomas Wolfe, #3444	17.50
CP612	White House, #3445	21.50
CP613	Edward G. Robinson, #3446	10.00

2001

CP614	Non-denominated Love Letters, #3496	19.00
CP615	34c Love, #3497	19.00
CP615A	55c Love, #3499	21.00
CP616	Chinese New Year, #3500	25.00
CP617	Roy Wilkins, #3501	29.00
CP618	Nine-Mile Prairie, #C136	19.00
CP618A	American Illustrators, #3502, 2 pages	37.50
CP619	Diabetes Awareness, #3503	19.00
CP620	Nobel Prize, #3504	22.50
CP621	Pan-American Inverts, #3505, 2 pages	40.00
CP622	Mt. McKinley, #C137	20.00
CP623	Great Plains Prairie, #3506, 2 pages	37.50
CP624	Peanuts Comic Strip, #3507	27.50
CP625	Honoring Veterans, #3508	20.00
CP626	Frida Kahlo, #3509	26.00
CP627	Legendary Playing Fields, #3510-3519	45.00

No. CP627 consists of 2 pages. One has text and engraved illustrations. The other consists of the pane of stamps.

CP628	Leonard Bernstein, #3521	22.50
CP629	Lucille Ball, #3523	22.50
CP630	Amish Quilts, #3527a	22.50
CP631	Carnivorous Plants, #3531a	20.00
CP632	Eid, #3532	16.00
CP633	Enrico Fermi, #3533	20.00
CP634	That's All Folks!, #3535c	22.50
CP635	Madonna & Child, #3536	16.50
CP636	Santas, #3540b	19.00
CP637	James Madison, #3545	20.00
CP638	Thanksgiving, #3546	20.00
CP639	Hanukkah, #3547	19.00
CP640	Kwanzaa, #3548	21.00
CP641	57c Love, #3551	19.00
CP648	Greetings from America, #3610a	50.00
CP649	Longleaf Pine Forest, #3611	40.00

Nos. CP648 and CP649 each consist of 2 pages. One has text and engraved illustrations. The other contains the pane of stamps.

2002

CP642	Winter Olympics, #3555a	19.00
CP643	Mentoring a Child, #3556	19.00
CP644	Langston Hughes, #3557	19.00
CP645	Happy Birthday, #3558	19.00
CP646	Chinese New Year, #3559	25.00
CP647	U.S. Military Academy Bicentennial, #3560	21.00
CP650	Heroes of 2001, #B2	25.00
CP651	Masters of American Photography, #3649	45.00

No. CP651 consists of 2 pages. One has text and engraved illustrations. The other consists of the pane of stamps.

CP652	John James Audubon, #3650	21.00
CP653	Harry Houdini, #3651	21.00
CP654	Andy Warhol, #3652	21.00
CP655	Teddy Bears, #3653-3656	16.50
CP656	37c Love, #3657	19.00
CP657	60c Love, #3658	19.00
CP658	Ogden Nash, #3659	20.00
CP659	Duke Kahanamoku, #3660	27.50
CP660	American Bats, #3664a	27.50
CP661	Women in Journalism, #3668a	24.00
CP662	Irving Berlin, #3669	19.00
CP663	Neuter or Spay, #3671a	22.50
CP664	Hanukkah, #3672	20.00
CP665	Kwanzaa, #3673	20.00
CP666	Eid, #3674	16.00
CP667	Madonna & Child, #3675	19.00
CP668	Christmas Snowmen, #3679a	16.50
CP669	Cary Grant, #3692	22.50
CP670	Hawaiian Missionary Stamps, #3694	40.00

No. CP670 consists of 2 pages. One has text and engraved illustrations. The other contains the pane of stamps.

CP671	Happy Birthday, #3695	17.50
CP672	Greetings from America, #3745a	52.50

No. CP672 consists of 2 pages. One has text and engraved illustrations. The other contains the pane of stamps.

2003

CP673	Thurgood Marshall, #3746	19.00
CP674	Chinese New Year, #3747	21.00
CP675	Zora Neale Hurston, #3748	24.00
CP676	Special Olympics, #3771	21.00
CP677	American Filmmaking: Behind the Scenes, #3772	42.50

No. CP677 consists of 2 pages. One has text and engraved illustrations. The other contains the pane of stamps.

CP678	Ohio Statehood, Bicent., #3773	21.00
CP679	Pelican Island National Wildlife Refuge, #3774	21.00
CP680	Old Glory, #3780b	24.00
CP681	Cesar E. Chavez, #3781	21.00
CP682	Louisiana Purchase, #3782	21.00
CP683	First Flight of Wright Brothers, #3783b	21.00
CP684	Audrey Hepburn, #3786	25.00
CP685	Southeastern Lighthouses, #3791a	21.00
CP686	Arctic Tundra, #3802	40.00
CP687	Korean War Veterans Memorial, #3803	21.00
CP688	Mary Cassatt Paintings, #3807a	21.00
CP689	Early Football Heroes, #3811a	27.50

CP690	Roy Acuff, #3812	21.00
CP691	District of Columbia, #3813	21.00
CP692	Reptiles and Amphibians, #3818a	27.50
CP693	Stop Family Violence, #B3	21.00
CP694	Madonna and Child, #3820	21.00
CP695	Christmas Holiday Music Makers, #3824a	21.00

2004

CP696	Pacific Coral Reef, #3831	40.00

No. CP696 consists of 2 pages. One has text and engraved illustrations. The other contains the pane of stamps.

CP697	Chinese New Year, #3832	21.00
CP698	Love, #3833	21.00
CP699	Paul Robeson, #3834	22.50
CP700	Theodor Seuss Geisel (Dr. Seuss), #3835	27.50
CP701	Love (White Lilacs and Pink Roses), #3836	19.00
CP702	Love (Five Varieties of Pink Roses), #3837	19.00
CP703	U.S. Air Force Academy, #3838	21.00
CP704	Henry Mancini, #3839	21.00
CP705	American Choreographers, #3843a	22.50
CP706	Lewis and Clark, #3854	25.00
CP707	Lewis and Clark booklet pane, #3856b	25.00
CP708	Isamu Noguchi, #3861a	19.00
CP709	National World War II Memorial, #3862	22.50
CP710	Summer Olympics, Athens, Greece, #3863	24.00
CP711	Art of Disney, #3868a	24.00
CP712	USS Constellation, #3869	22.50
CP713	R. Buckminster Fuller, #3870	19.00
CP714	James Baldwin, #3871	18.00
CP715	Martin Johnson Heade, #3872	18.00
CP716	Art of the American Indian, #3873	42.50

No. CP716 consists of 2 pages. One has text and engraved illustrations. The other contains the pane of stamps.

CP717	John Wayne, #3876	26.00
CP718	Sickle Cell Disease, #3877	19.00
CP719	Cloudscapes, #3878	40.00

No. CP719 consists of 2 pages. One has text and engraved illustrations. The other contains the pane of stamps.

CP720	Christmas Madonna, #3879	19.00
CP721	Hanukkah, #3880	16.50
CP722	Kwanzaa, #3881	16.50
CP723	Moss Hart, #3882	19.00
CP724	Christmas Ornaments, #3886a	19.00

2005

CP725	Chinese New Year, #3895	35.00

No. CP725 consists of two pages. The other contains the pane of stamps.

CP726	Marian Anderson, #3896	25.00
CP727	Ronald Reagan, #3897	27.50
CP728	Love, #3898	21.00
CP729	Northeast Deciduous Forest, #3899	37.50

No. CP729 consists of two pages. One has text and engraved illustrations. The other contains the pane of stamps.

CP730	Spring Flowers, #3903a	19.00
CP731	Robert Penn Warren, #3904	16.00
CP732	Yip Harburg, #3905	16.00
CP733	American Scientists, #3909a	16.00
CP734	Modern American Architecture, #3910	42.50

No. CP734 consists of two pages. One has text and engraved illustrations. The other contains the pane of stamps.

CP735	Henry Fonda, #3911	17.50
CP736	Disney Characters, #3915a	30.00
CP737	Advances in Aviation, #3916-3925	42.50

No. CP737 consists of two pages. One has text and illustrations. The other contains the pane of stamps.

CP738	Rio Grande Blankets, #3929a	16.00
CP739	Presidential Libraries, #3930	16.00
CP740	Sporty Cars of the 1950s, #3935b	30.00
CP741	Arthur Ashe, #3936	20.00
CP742	To Form a More Perfect Union, #3937	32.50

No. CP742 consists of two pages. One has text and illustrations. The other contains the pane of stamps.

CP743	Child Health, #3938	16.00
CP744	Let's Dance, #3942a	16.00
CP745	Greta Garbo, #3943	25.00
CP746	Jim Henson and the Muppets, #3944	42.50

No. CP746 consists of two pages. One has text and engraved illustrations. The other contains the pane of stamps.

CP747	Constellations, #3948a	29.00
CP748	Christmas, #3952a	15.00
CP749	Distinguished Marines, #3964a	29.00

2006

CP750	Love, #3976	14.00
CP751	Children's Book Animals, #3994a	32.50

No. CP751 consists of two pages. One has text and illustrations. The other contains the pane of stamps.

CP752	2006 Winter Olympics, #3995	15.00
CP753	Hattie McDaniel, #3996	17.50
CP754	Chinese New Year, #3997	30.00

No. CP754 consists of two pages. One has text and illustrations. The other contains the pane of stamps.

CP755	39c Wedding, #3998	14.00
CP756	63c Wedding, #3999	14.00
CP757	Sugar Ray Robinson, #4020	14.00
CP758	Benjamin Franklin, #4024a	14.00
CP759	Disney Characters, #4028a	14.00
CP760	Love Birds, #4029	14.00

CP761	Katherine Anne Porter, #4030	14.00
CP762	Amber Alert, #4031	14.00
CP763	Wonders of America, #4033-4072	37.50

No. CP763 consists of two pages. One has text and illustrations. The other contains the pane of stamps.

CP764	Samuel de Champlain, #4073	14.00
CP765	Washington 2006 World Philatelic Exhibition, #4075	17.50
CP766	Distinguished American Diplomats, #4076	14.00

No. CP766 consists of two pages. One has text and illustrations. The other contains the pane of stamps.

CP767	Judy Garland, #4077	14.00
CP768	Ronald Reagan, #4078	15.00
CP769	Happy Birthday, #4079	14.00
CP770	Baseball Sluggers, #4083a	14.00
CP771	DC Comics Superheroes, #4084	32.50

No. CP771 consists of two pages. One has text and engraved illustrations. The other contains the pane of stamps.

CP772	Motorcycles, #4088a	15.00
CP773	Quilts of Gee's Bend, Alabama, #4098b	16.00
CP774	Southern Florida Wetland, #4099	35.00

No. CP774 consists of two pages. One has text and engraved illustrations. The other contains the pane of stamps.

CP775	Christmas Madonna, #4100	12.00
CP776	Christmas Snowflakes, #4104a	12.00
CP777	Eid, #4117	12.00
CP778	Hanukkah, #4118	12.00
CP779	Kwanzaa, #4119	12.00
CP780	39c Ella Fitzgerald, #4120	12.00
CP781	39c Oklahoma Statehood, #4121	12.00
CP782	39c Love, #4122	12.00
CP783	84c International Polar Year, #4123	12.00

CP784	39c Henry Wadsworth Longfellow, #4124	12.00
CP785	41c Settlement of Jamestown, #4136	30.00

No. CP785 consists of two pages. One has text and illustrations. The other contains the pane of stamps.

CP786	Star Wars, #4143	30.00

No. CP786 consists of two pages. One has text and engraved illustrations. The other contains the pane of stamps.

CP787	Pacific Lighthouses, #4150a	12.00
CP788	41c Wedding Hearts, #4151	12.00
CP789	58c Wedding Hearts, #4152	12.00
CP790	Pollination, #4156d	16.50
CP791	Marvel Comics Super Heroes, #4159	30.00

No. CP791 consists of two pages. One has text and engraved illustrations. The other contains the pane of stamps.

CP792	Vintage Mahogany Speedboats, #4163a	12.00
CP793	Louis Comfort Tiffany, #4165	12.00
CP794	Disney Characters, #4195a	12.00
CP795	Celebrate, #4196	12.00
CP796	James Stewart, #4197	12.00
CP797	Alpine Tundra, #4198	30.00

No. CP796 consists of two pages. One has text and engraved illustrations. The other contains the pane of stamps.

CP798	Gerald R. Ford, #4199	12.00
CP799	Jury Duty, #4200	12.00
CP800	Mendez v. Westminster School District, #4201	12.00
CP801	Eid, #4202	12.00
CP802	Polar Lights, #4204a	12.00
CP803	Yoda, #4205	12.00
CP804	Christmas Madonna, #4206	12.00
CP805	Christmas Holiday Knits #4210a	12.00
CP806	Hanukkah, #4219	12.00
CP807	Kwanzaa, #4220	12.00

2008

CP808	Chinese New Year, #4221	12.00
CP809	Charles W. Chesnutt, #4222	12.00
CP810	Marjorie Kinnan Rawlings, #4223	12.00
a.	With corrected date on panel	12.00
CP811	41c American Scientists, #4227a	12.00
CP812	42c American Journalists, #4252a	12.00
CP813	42c Frank Sinatra, #4265	12.00
CP814	42c Minnesota Statehood, #4266	12.00
CP815	42c Love, #4270	12.00
CP816	42c Wedding Hearts, #4271-4272	12.00
CP817	Charles and Ray Eames, #4333	30.00

No. CP817 consists of two pages. One has text and engraved illustrations. The other contains the pane of stamps.

CP818	Olympic Games, #4334	12.00
CP819	Vintage Black Cinema, #4340a	12.00
CP820	Take Me Out to the Ball Game, #4341	12.00
CP821	Disney Characters - Imagination, #4345a	12.00
CP822	Albert Bierstadt, #4346	12.00
CP823	Latin Jazz, #4349	12.00
CP824	Bette Davis, #4350	12.00
CP825	Great Lakes Dunes, #4352	30.00

No. CP825 consists of two pages. One has text and engraved illustrations. The other contains the pane of stamps.

CP826	Automobiles of the 1950s, #4357a	12.00
CP827	Alzheimer's Disease Awareness, #4358	12.00
CP828	Christmas Madonna, #4359	12.00
CP829	Christmas Nutcrackers, #4363a	12.00

2009

CP830	Alaska Statehood, #4374	12.00
CP831	Chinese New Year, #4375	12.00
CP832	Oregon Statehood, #4376	12.00
CP833	Edgar Allan Poe, #4377	12.00

SOUVENIR PAGES

These are post office new-issue announcement bulletins, including an illustration of the stamp's design and informative text. They bear a copy of the stamp, tied by a first day of issue cancellation. Varieties of bulletin watermarks and text changes, etc., are beyond the scope of this catalogue.

Values for Scott Nos. SP1-SP295 are for folded examples. Values for Official Souvenir Pages (Nos. SP296 on) are for examples that never have been folded.

No. SP674a

UNOFFICIAL SOUVENIR PAGES
Liberty Issue

1960-65

SP1	1¼c Palace of Governors, sheet, coil, #1031A, 1054A	50.00
SP2	8c Pershing, #1042A	30.00
SP3	11c Statue of Liberty, #1044A	27.50
SP4	25c Revere coil, #1059A	10.00

1959

SP5	4c 49 Star Flag, #1132	—
SP6	7c Hawaii Statehood, #C55	—
SP7	4c Soil Conservation, #1133	—
SP8	10c Pan American Games, #C56	—
SP9	4c Petroleum, #1134	—
SP10	4c Dental Health, #1135	—
SP11	4c, 8c Reuter, #1136, 1137	—
SP12	4c McDowell, #1138	—

1960-61

SP13	4c Washington Credo, #1139	75.00
SP14	4c Franklin Credo, #1140	75.00
SP15	4c Jefferson Credo, #1141	75.00

SP16	4c F.S. Key Credo, #1142	75.00
SP17	4c Lincoln Credo, #1143	65.00
SP18	4c P. Henry Credo, #1144	45.00

1961

SP19	4c Boy Scout, #1145	75.00
SP20	4c Winter Olympics, #1146	75.00
SP21	4c, 8c Masaryk, #1147, 1148	75.00
SP22	4c Refugee Year, #1149	45.00
SP23	4c Water Consevation, #1150	30.00
SP24	4c SEATO, #1151	30.00
SP25	4c American Women, #1152	30.00
SP26	10c Liberty Bell, #C57	—
SP27	15c Statue of Liberty, #C58	—
SP28	25c Lincoln, #C59	—
SP29	4c 50 Star Flag, #1153	50.00
SP30	4c Pony Express, #1154	50.00
SP31	7c Jet, carmine, #C60	25.00
SP32	7c Booklet pane of 6, #C60a	37.50
SP33	7c Jet coil, #C61	17.50
SP34	4c Handicapped, #1155	50.00
SP35	4c Forestry Congress, #1156	50.00
SP36	4c Mexican Independence, #1157	35.00
SP37	4c U.S., Japan Treaty, #1158	25.00
SP38	4c, 8c Paderewski, #1159-1160	40.00
SP39	4c Sen. Taft, #1161	45.00
SP40	4c Wheels of Freedom, #1162	45.00
SP41	4c Boys' Clubs, #1163	45.00
SP42	4c Automated Post Office, #1164	45.00
SP43	4c, 8c Mannerheim, #1165-1166	45.00
SP44	4c Camp Fire Girls, #1167	45.00
SP45	4c, 8c Garibaldi, #1168-1169	45.00
SP46	4c Sen. George, #1170	45.00
SP47	4c Carnegie, #1171	45.00
SP48	4c Dulles, #1172	45.00
SP49	4c Echo I, #1173	25.00

1961

SP50	4c, 8c Gandhi, #1174-1175	20.00
SP51	4c Range Conservation, #1176	20.00
SP52	4c Greeley, #1177	20.00

1961-65

SP53	4c Ft. Sumter, #1178	20.00
SP54	4c Shiloh, #1179	27.50
SP55	5c Gettysburg, #1180	9.00
SP56	5c Wilderness, #1181	9.50
SP57	5c Appomattox, #1182	9.50

1961

SP58	4c Kansas, #1183	15.00
SP59	13c Liberty Bell, #C62	20.00
SP60	4c Sen. Norris, #1184	14.00
SP61	4c Naval Aviation, #1185	20.00
SP62	4c Workmen's Compensation, #1186	20.00
SP63	4c Remington, #1187	12.00
SP64	4c Sun Yat sen, #1188	20.00
SP65	4c Basketball, #1189	20.00
SP66	4c Nursing, #1190	25.00

1962

SP67	4c New Mexico, #1191	12.50
SP68	4c Arizona, #1192	12.50
SP69	4c Project Mercury, #1193	10.00
SP70	4c Malaria, #1194	15.00
SP71	4c Hughes, #1195	21.00
SP72	4c Seattle World's Fair, #1196	17.50
SP73	4c Louisiana, #1197	17.50
SP74	4c Homestead Act, #1198	17.50
SP75	4c Girl Scouts, #1199	20.00
SP76	4c McMahon, #1200	17.50
SP77	4c Apprenticeship, #1201	17.50
SP78	4c Rayburn, #1202	17.50
SP79	4c Hammarskjold, #1203	17.50
SP80	4c Hammarskjold, yellow inverted, #1204	40.00
SP81	4c Christmas, #1205	50.00
SP82	4c Higher Education, #1206	12.00
SP83	8c Capitol, #C64	15.00
SP83a	8c Capitol sheet, booklet, coil, #C64, C64b, C65	20.00
SP84	8c Capitol, tagged, #C64a	37.50
SP85	8c Capitol booklet single, #C64b	25.00
SP86	8c Capitol coil, #C65	15.00
SP87	4c Winslow Homer, #1207	15.00
SP88	5c Flag, #1208	12.50
SP89	1c Jackson, #1209	12.50
SP90	5c Washington, #1213	17.50
SP91	5c Washington booklet pane of 5 + label, #1213a	30.00
SP92	1c Jackson coil, #1225	17.50
SP93	5c Washington coil, #1229	17.50
SP94	15c Montgomery Blair, #C66	

1963

SP96	5c Food for Peace, #1231	7.00
SP97	5c West Virginia, #1232	10.00
SP97A	6c Eagle, #C67	8.50
SP97B	8c Amelia Earhart, #C68	20.00
SP98	5c Emancipation Proclamation, #1233	12.50
SP99	5c Alliance for Progress, #1234	8.00
SP100	5c Cordell Hull, #1235	8.00
SP101	5c Eleanor Roosevelt, #1236	8.00
SP102	5c Science, #1237	7.50
SP103	5c City Mail Delivery, #1238	10.00
SP104	5c Red Cross, #1239	7.00
SP105	5c Christmas, #1240	9.00
SP106	5c Audubon, #1241	8.00

1964

SP107	5c Sam Houston, #1242	12.00
SP108	5c C.M. Russell, #1243	10.00
SP109	5c N.Y. World's Fair, #1244	9.00
SP110	5c John Muir, #1245	12.00
SP111	5c Kennedy (Boston, Mass.) (At least 4 other cities known), #1246	15.00
SP112	5c New Jersey, #1247	9.00
SP113	5c Nevada, #1248	9.00

SP114	5c Register and Vote, #1249	7.50
SP115	5c Shakespeare, #1250	9.00
SP116	5c Mayo Brothers, #1251	10.00
SP117	8c Goddard, #C69	9.00
SP118	5c Music, #1252	9.00
SP119	5c Homemakers, #1253	9.00
SP120	5c Christmas Plants, #1257b	20.00
SP121	5c Christmas, tagged, #1257c	90.00
SP122	5c Verrazano Narrows Bridge, #1258	9.00
SP123	5c Fine Arts, #1259	9.00
SP124	5c Amateur Radio, #1260	8.00

1965

SP125	5c New Orleans, #1261	8.00
SP126	5c Sokols, #1262	8.00
SP127	5c Cancer, #1263	8.00
SP128	5c Churchill, #1264	8.50
SP129	5c Magna Carta, #1265	8.00
SP130	5c I.C.Y., #1266	8.00
SP131	5c Salvation Army, #1267	8.00
SP132	5c Dante, #1268	8.00
SP133	5c Hoover, #1269	8.25
SP134	5c Fulton, #1270	8.00
SP135	5c Florida, #1271	8.50
SP136	5c Traffic Safety, #1272	8.00
SP137	5c Copley, #1273	8.50
SP138	11c I.T.U., #1274	8.50
SP139	5c Stevenson, #1275	8.00
SP140	5c Christmas, #1276	7.50

Prominent Americans

1965-73

SP141	1c Jefferson, #1278	7.50
SP141a	1c Jefferson sheet, booklet, coil, #1278, 1299	7.00
SP142	1c Jefferson booklet pane of 8, #1278a	8.25
SP143	1¼c Gallatin, #1279	7.50
SP144	2c Wright, #1280	6.50
SP145	2c Wright booklet pane of 5 + label, #1280a	9.50
SP146	3c Parkman, #1281	7.50
SP147	4c Lincoln, #1282	6.00
SP148	5c Washington, #1283	6.00
SP149	5c Washington, redrawn, #1283B	6.50
SP150	6c Roosevelt, #1284	6.00
SP151	6c Roosevelt booklet pane of 8, #1284b	13.00
SP151a	6c Roosevelt booklet, vert. coil, #1284b, 1298	6.00
SP151b	6c Roosevelt booklet, horiz. coil, #1284b, 1305	6.00
SP152	8c Einstein, #1285	10.00
SP153	10c Jackson, #1286	7.50
SP154	12c Ford, #1286A	11.00
SP155	13c Kennedy, #1287	20.00
SP156	15c Holmes, #1288	10.00
SP157	20c Marshall, #1289	9.00
SP158	25c Douglass, #1290	12.00
SP159	30c Dewey, #1291	30.00
SP160	40c Paine, #1292	40.00
SP161	50c Stone, #1293	35.00
SP162	$1 O'Neill, #1294	65.00
SP163	$5 Moore, #1295	150.00
SP164	6c Roosevelt, vert. coil, #1298	6.00
SP165	1c Jefferson, coil, #1299	6.50
SP166	4c Lincoln, coil, #1303	7.50
SP167	5c Washington, coil, #1304	7.00
SP168	6c Roosevelt, horiz. coil, #1305	6.50

Nos. 1297, 1305C and 1305E are known on unofficial pages. They are not listed here. For official pages of these issues, see Nos. SP296-SP298.

1966

SP169	5c Migratory Bird Treaty, #1306	10.00
SP170	5c ASPCA, #1307	8.00
SP171	5c Indiana, #1308	7.50
SP172	5c Circus, #1309	9.00
SP173	5c SIPEX, #1310	7.00
SP174	5c SIPEX Souvenir Sheet, #1311	7.25
SP175	5c Bill of Rights, #1312	8.00
SP176	5c Poland, #1313	8.00
SP177	5c National Park Service, #1314	7.50
SP178	5c Marine Corps Reserve, #1315	8.50
SP179	5c Women's Clubs, #1316	8.00
SP180	5c Johnny Appleseed, #1317	8.00
SP181	5c Beautifcation of America, #1318	8.50
SP182	5c Great River Road, #1319	7.50
SP183	5c Savings Bonds Servicemen, #1320	8.00
SP184	5c Christmas, #1321	7.00
SP185	5c Mary Cassatt, #1322	7.50

1967

SP186	8c Alaska, #C70	10.00
SP187	5c Grange, #1323	7.00
SP188	20c Audubon, #C71	10.00
SP189	5c Canada, #1324	7.00
SP190	5c Erie Canal, #1325	7.00
SP191	5c Search for Peace, #1326	7.50
SP192	5c Thoreau, #1327	7.00
SP193	5c Nebraska, #1328	7.00
SP194	5c VOA, #1329	7.00
SP195	5c Crockett, #1330	8.00
SP196	5c Space, #1332b	25.00
SP197	5c Urban Planning, #1333	7.00
SP198	5c Finland, #1334	7.50
SP199	5c Eakins, #1335	7.25
SP200	5c Christmas, #1336	7.00
SP201	5c Mississippi, #1337	7.00

1968-71

SP202	6c Flags, Giori Press, #1338	6.50
SP203	6c Flag, Huck Press, #1338D	6.00
SP204	8c Flag, #1338F	6.50
SP205	6c Flag coil, #1338A	6.25

1968

SP206	10c 50 star Runway, #C72	9.00
SP207	10c sheet, coil, booklet pane of 8, #C72, C72b, C73	25.00
SP207a	10c sheet, booklet single, coil, #C72, C72b, C73	9.00
SP208	10c 50 star Runway coil, #C73	9.00
SP209	6c Illinois, #1339	6.00
SP210	6c HemisFair, #1340	7.50
SP211	$1 Airlift, #1341	65.00
SP212	6c Youth, #1342	6.00
SP213	10c Air Mail Service, #C74	8.50
SP214	6c Law and Order, #1343	6.00
SP215	6c Register and Vote, #1344	6.00
SP216	6c Historic Flags, #1345-1354	90.00
SP217	6c Disney, #1355	20.00
SP218	6c Marquette, #1356	8.00
SP219	6c Daniel Boone, #1357	8.00
SP220	6c Arkansas River Navigation, #1358	7.50
SP221	6c Leif Erikson, #1359	15.00
SP222	6c Cherokee Strip, #1360	9.00
SP223	6c John Trumbull, #1361	7.50
SP224	6c Waterfowl, #1362	9.00
SP225	6c Christmas, #1363	7.50
SP226	6c Chief Joseph, #1364	9.00
SP227	20c USA, #C75	12.00

1969

SP228	6c Beautification, #1368a	20.00
SP229	6c American Legion, #1369	7.50
SP230	6c Grandma Moses, #1370	7.00
SP231	6c Apollo 8, #1371	15.00
SP232	6c W.C. Handy, #1372	10.00
SP233	6c California, #1373	7.00
SP234	6c Powell, #1374	7.50
SP235	6c Alabama, #1375	7.50
SP236	6c Botanical Congress, #1379a	20.00
SP237	10c Man on the Moon, #C76	14.00
SP238	6c Dartmouth, #1380	7.50
SP239	6c Baseball, #1381	40.00
SP240	6c Football, #1382	15.00
SP241	6c Eisenhower, #1383	7.50
SP242	6c Christmas, #1384	7.50
SP243	6c Hope, #1385	7.00
SP244	45c Special Delivery, #E22	35.00
SP245	6c Harnett, #1386	7.00

1970

SP246	6c Natural History, #1390a	40.00
SP247	6c Maine, #1391	9.00
SP248	6c Wildlife Conservation, #1392	12.00

Regular Issue

1970-71

SP249	6c Eisenhower, #1393	6.00
SP249a	6c sheet, booklet, coil stamps, #1393, 1393a, 1401	8.50
SP249b	6c sheet, coil stamps, #1393, 1401	8.00
SP250	6c Eisenhower booklet pane of 8, #1393a	12.50
SP250a	6c booklet, coil, #1393a, 1401	6.00
SP251	6c Eisenhower booklet pane of 5 + label, #1393b	6.00
SP252	8c Eisenhower, #1394	6.00
SP252a	8c sheet, booklet, coil, #1394-1395, 1402	6.00
SP253	8c Eisenhower booklet pane of 8, #1395a	15.00
SP254	8c Eisenhower booklet pane of 8, #1395b	15.00
SP255	8c U.S.P.S., #1396	10.00
SP256	16c Pyle, #1398	9.00
SP257	6c Eisenhower coil, #1401	7.00
SP258	8c Eisenhower coil, #1402	6.00

1970

SP259	6c Masters, #1405	7.50
SP260	6c Suffrage, #1406	7.00
SP261	6c So. Carolina, #1407	7.00
SP262	6c Stone Mountain, #1408	9.00
SP263	6c Ft. Snelling, #1409	7.50
SP264	6c Anti pollution, #1413a	22.50
SP265	6c Christmas Nativity, #1414	13.00
SP266	6c Christmas Toys, #1418b	10.00
SP267	6c Toys, precanceled, #1418c	45.00
SP268	6c U.N., #1419	9.00
SP269	6c Mayflower, #1420	7.50
SP270	6c DAV, Servicemen, #1422a	27.50

1971

SP271	6c Wool, #1423	9.00
SP272	6c MacArthur, #1424	10.00
SP273	6c Blood Donors, #1425	7.00
SP274	8c Missouri, #1426	8.00
SP275	9c Delta Wing, #C77	9.00
SP276	11c Jet, #C78	9.00
SP276a	11c sheet, booklet, coil, #C78, C78a, C82	12.50
SP277	11c Jet booklet pane, #C78a	17.50
SP278	60c Special Delivery, #E23	25.00
SP279	8c Wildlife, #1430a	15.00
SP280	8c Antarctic Treaty, #1431	12.00
SP281	8c Bicentennial Emblem, #1432	15.00
SP282	17c Statue of Liberty, #C80	15.00
SP283	21c USA, #C81	20.00
SP284	11c Jet coil, #C82	10.00
SP285	8c Sloan, #1433	11.00
SP286	8c Space, #1435b	20.00
SP287	8c Dickenson, #1436	12.50
SP288	8c San Juan, #1437	17.50
SP289	8c Drug Abuse, #1438	10.00
SP290	8c CARE, #1439	10.00

SP291	8c Historic Preservation, #1443a	12.50
SP292	8c Adoration, #1444	10.00
SP293	8c Patridge, #1445	10.00

1972

SP294	8c Lanier, #1446	10.00
SP295	8c Peace Corps, #1447	10.00

OFFICIAL SOUVENIR PAGES

In 1972 the USPS began issuing "official" Souvenir pages by subscription. A few more "unofficials" were produced.

Prominent Americans

1970-78

SP296	3c Parkman, coil, #1297	4.00
SP297	$1 O'Neill, #1305C	15.00
SP298	15c Holmes, coil, #1305E	4.00
SP299	7c Franklin, #1393D	5.00
SP300	14c LaGuardia, #1397	100.00
SP301	18c Blackwell, #1399	3.50
SP302	21c Giannini, #1400	4.50

1972

SP303	2c Cape Hatteras, #1451a	80.00
SP304	6c Wolf Trap Farm, #1452	32.50
SP305	8c Yellowstone, #1453	110.00
SP306	11c City of Refuge, #C84	95.00
SP307	15c Mt. McKinley, #1454	20.00
SP308	8c Family Planning, #1455	675.00

Unofficials exist, value $150.

SP309	8c Colonial Craftsmen, #1459a	13.00
SP310	Olympics, #1460-1462, C85	10.00
SP311	8c PTA, #1463	6.00
SP312	8c Wildlife, #1467a	7.00
SP313	8c Mail Order, #1468	4.50
SP314	8c Osteopathic, #1469	5.50
SP315	8c Tom Sawyer, #1470	8.00
SP316	8c Christmas, #1471-1472	6.00
SP317	8c Pharmacy, #1473	7.00
SP318	8c Stamp Collecting, #1474	5.00

1973

SP319	8c Love, #1475	7.00
SP320	8c Printing, #1476	5.00
SP321	8c Broadside, #1477	5.00
SP322	8c Postrider, #1478	5.00
SP323	8c Drummer, #1479	3.25
SP324	8c Tea Party, #1483a	6.00
SP325	8c Gershwin, #1484	6.00
SP326	8c Jeffers, #1485	5.25
SP327	8c Tanner, #1486	6.00
SP328	8c Cather, #1487	7.00
SP329	8c Copernicus, #1488	5.75
SP330	8c Postal People, #1489-1498	5.75
SP331	8c Truman, #1499	5.00
SP332	Electronics, #1500-1502, C86	9.00
SP333	8c L.B. Johnson, #1503	4.75

1973-74

SP334	8c Cattle, #1504	3.75
SP335	10c Chautauqua, #1505	3.25
SP336	10c Kansas Winter Wheat, #1506	3.00

1973

SP337	8c Christmas, #1507	6.25

Regular Issues

1973-74

SP338	10c Crossed Flags, #1509	3.50
SP339	10c Jefferson Memorial, #1510	3.50
SP340	10c ZIP, #1511	5.00
SP341	6.3c Liberty Bell coil, #1518	4.00
SP341A	13c Winged Envelope, #C79	4.00
SP341B	13c Airmail, coil, #C83	4.00

1974

SP342	18c Statue of Liberty, #C87	7.50
SP343	26c Mt. Rushmore, #C88	5.25
SP344	10c VFW, #1525	3.25
SP345	10c Robert Frost, #1526	5.25
SP346	10c EXPO '74, #1527	6.00
SP347	10c Horse Racing, #1528	6.00
SP348	10c Skylab, #1529	5.75
SP349	10c UPU, #1537a	6.00
SP350	10c Minerals, #1541a	6.00
SP351	10c Ft. Harrod, #1542	3.25
SP352	10c Continental Congress, #1546a	5.25
SP353	10c Energy, #1547	3.25
SP354	10c Sleepy Hollow, #1548	5.25
SP355	10c Retarded Children, #1549	3.25
SP356	10c Christmas, #1550-1552	5.25

1975

SP357	10c Benjamin West, #1553	3.75
SP358	10c Dunbar, #1554	5.00
SP359	10c D.W. Griffith, #1555	5.25
SP360	10c Pioneer, #1556	6.00
SP361	10c Mariner, #1557	6.00
SP362	10c Collective Bargaining, #1558	3.25
SP363	8c Sybil Ludington, #1559	3.25
SP364	10c Salem Poor, #1560	4.00
SP365	10c Haym Salomon, #1561	3.75
SP366	15c Peter Francisco, #1562	3.75
SP367	10c Lexington & Concord, #1563	3.75
SP368	10c Bunker Hill, #1564	3.75
SP369	10c Military Uniforms, #1568a	6.00
SP370	10c Apollo Soyuz, #1570a	7.50
SP371	10c Women's Year, #1571	3.25
SP372	10c Postal Service, #1575	4.00
SP373	10c Peace through Law, #1576	3.25
SP374	10c Banking and Commerce, #1578a	3.75

SP375	10c Christmas, #1579-1580	4.25

Americana Issue

1975-81

SP376	1c, 2c, Americana, #1581-1585	
	3c, 4c	4.00
SP377	9c Capitol Dome, #1591	3.25
SP378	10c Justice, #1592	3.25
SP379	11c Printing Press, #1593	3.50
SP380	12c Torch sheet, coil, #1594, 1816	3.50
SP381	13c Eagle and Shield, #1596	5.00
SP382	15c Flag sheet, coil, #1597, 1618C	3.25
SP383	16c Statue of Liberty sheet, coil, #1599, 1619	3.50
SP384	24c Old North Church, #1603	3.50
SP385	28c Ft. Nisqually, #1604	4.00
SP386	29c Lighthouse, #1605	5.00
SP387	30c Schoolhouse, #1606	4.75
SP388	50c "Betty" Lamp, #1608	4.25
SP389	$1 Candle Holder, #1610	4.75
SP390	$2 Kerosene Lamp, #1611	6.00
SP391	$5 R. R. Lantern, #1612	11.00
SP392	1c Inkwell, coil, #1811	3.50
SP393	3.1c Guitar, coil, #1613	6.50
SP394	3.5c Violin, coil, #1813	3.25
SP395	7.7c Saxhorns, coil, #1614	3.25
SP396	7.9c Drum, coil, #1615	3.25
SP397	8.4c Piano, coil, #1615C	4.25
SP398	9c Capitol Dome, coil, #1616	3.25
SP398A	10c Justice, coil, #1617	3.25
SP399	13c Liberty Bell, coil, #1618	3.25
SP400	13c 13 star Flag sheet, coil, #1622, 1625	3.25
SP401	9c, 13c Booklet pane, perf. 10, #1623Bc	17.50

1976

SP402	13c Spririt of '76, #1631a	5.00
SP403	25c, 31c Plane and Globes, #C89-C90	3.50
SP404	13c Interphil 76, #1632	3.75
SP405	13c State Flags, #1633-1642	9.00
SP406	13c State Flags, #1643-1652	9.00
SP407	13c State Flags, #1653-1662	9.00
SP408	13c State Flags, #1663-1672	9.00
SP409	13c State Flags, #1673-1682	9.00
SP410	13c Telephone, #1683	3.50
SP411	13c Aviation, #1684	3.50
SP412	13c Chemistry, #1685	3.50
SP413	13c Bicentennial Souvenir Sheet, #1686	10.00
SP414	18c Bicentennial Souvenir Sheet, #1687	10.00
SP415	24c Bicentennial Souvenir Sheet, #1688	10.00
SP416	31c Bicentennial Souvenir Sheet, #1689	10.00
SP417	13c Franklin, #1690	3.00
SP418	13c Declaration of Independence, #1694a	4.75
SP419	13c Olympics, #1698a	4.75
SP420	13c Clara Maass, #1699	6.50
SP421	13c Adolph Ochs, #1700	3.50
SP422	13c Christmas, #1701-1703	3.75

1977

SP423	13c Washington at Princeton, #1704	3.25
SP424	13c Sound Recording, #1705	4.00
SP425	13c Pueblo Indians, #1709a	7.00
SP426	13c Lindbergh Flight, #1710	4.00
SP427	13c Colorado, #1711	3.00
SP428	13c Butterflies, #1715a	5.00
SP429	13c Lafayette, #1716	3.00
SP430	13c Skilled Hands, #1720a	4.00
SP431	13c Peace Bridge, #1721	3.50
SP432	13c Oriskany, #1722	3.50
SP433	13c Energy, #1724a	3.50
SP434	13c Alta California, #1725	3.50
SP435	13c Articles of Confederation, #1726	4.50
SP436	13c Talking Pictures, #1727	4.50
SP437	13c Saratoga, #1728	3.25
SP438	13c Christmas, #1729-1730	3.25

1978

SP439	13c Sandburg, #1731	4.00
SP440	13c Capt. Cook, #1732, 1733	4.50
SP441	13c Indian Head Penny, #1734	3.25
SP442	15c A Sheet, coil, #1735, 1743	5.50
SP443	15c Roses booklet single, #1737	4.25
SP444	15c Windmills booklet pane of 10, #1742a	9.50
SP445	13c Tubman, #1744	4.00
SP446	13c Quilts, #1748a	5.00
SP447	13c American Dance, #1752a	6.00
SP448	13c French Alliance, #1753	3.50
SP449	13c Cancer Detection, #1754	4.50
SP450	13c Jimmie Rodgers, #1755	4.50
SP451	15c George M. Cohan, #1756	4.50
SP452	13c CAPEX '78 Souvenir Sheet, #1757	7.75
SP453	15c Photography, #1758	5.00
SP454	15c Viking Missions, #1759	6.25
SP455	15c Owls, #1763a	5.50
SP456	31c Wright Brothers, #C92a	4.00
SP457	15c Trees, #1767a	4.00
SP458	15c Madonna and Child, #1768	3.50
SP459	15c Hobby Horse, #1769	3.50

1979

SP460	15c Robert F. Kennedy, #1770	4.25
SP461	15c Martin Luther King Jr., #1771	5.00
SP462	15c Year of the Child, #1772	3.25
SP463	15c John Steinbeck, #1773	6.50
SP464	15c Einstein, #1774	6.50

SP465	21c Chanute, #C94a	4.00
SP466	15c Toleware, #1778a	5.50
SP467	15c Architecture, #1782a	4.00
SP468	15c Endangered Flora, #1786a	4.00
SP469	15c Seeing Eye Dogs, #1787	3.25
SP470	15c Special Olympics, #1788	3.25
SP471	15c John Paul Jones, #1789	3.25
SP472	10c Olympics, #1790	3.50
SP473	15c Olympics, #1794a	5.00
SP474	31c Olympics, #C97	4.50

1980

SP475	15c Winter Olympics, #1798a	5.25

1979

SP476	15c Madonna and Child, #1799	3.25
SP477	15c Santa Claus, #1800	3.25
SP478	15c Will Rogers, #1801	4.00
SP479	15c Vietnam Veterans, #1802	5.50
SP480	25c Wiley Post, #C96a	4.50

1980

SP481	15c W.C. Fields, #1803	5.00
SP482	15c Benjamin Banneker, #1804	4.25
SP483	15c Letter Writing Week, #1805-1810	4.00
SP484	18c B sheet, coil, #1818, 1820	3.25
SP485	18c B booklet pane of 8, #1819a	3.25
SP486	15c Frances Perkins, #1821	3.25
SP487	15c Dolley Madison, #1822	4.50
SP488	15c Emily Bissell, #1823	4.50
SP489	15c Helen Keller, #1824	3.25
SP490	15c Veterans Administration, #1825	3.25
SP491	15c Galvez, #1826	3.25
SP492	15c Coral Reefs, #1830a	5.50
SP493	15c Organized Labor, #1831	4.00
SP494	15c Edith Wharton, #1832	4.00
SP495	15c Education, #1833	3.50
SP496	15c Indian Masks, #1837a	5.00
SP497	15c Architecture, #1841a	4.00
SP498	40c Mazzei, #C98	3.75
SP499	15c Christmas Window, #1842	3.25
SP500	15c Christmas Toys, #1843	4.00
SP501	28c Blanche Stuart Scott, #C99	3.75
SP502	35c Curtiss, #C100	3.75

Great Americans

1980-85

SP503	1c Dix, #1844	3.50
SP504	2c Stravinsky, #1845	3.75
SP505	3c Clay, #1846	3.50
SP506	4c Schurz, #1847	4.25
SP507	5c Buck, #1848	4.00
SP508	6c Lippmann, #1849	4.25
SP509	7c Baldwin, #1850	3.25
SP510	8c Knox, #1851	3.25
SP511	9c Thayer, #1852	3.25
SP512	10c Russell, #1853	3.25
SP513	11c Partridge, #1854	3.25
SP514	13c Crazy Horse, #1855	4.00
SP515	14c Lewis, #1856	5.50
SP516	17c Carson, #1857	3.25
SP517	18c Mason, #1858	3.25
SP518	19c Sequoyah, #1859	3.25
SP519	20c Bunche, #1860	5.25
SP520	20c Gallaudet, #1861	3.25
SP521	20c Truman, #1862	3.25
SP522	22c Audubon, #1863	4.25
SP523	30c Laubach, #1864	3.25
SP524	35c Drew, #1865	3.25
SP525	37c Millikan, #1866	3.25
SP526	39c Clark, #1867	3.25
SP527	40c Gilbreth, #1868	3.25
SP528	50c Nimitz, #1869	4.00

1981

SP529	15c Dirksen, #1874	3.25
SP530	15c Young, #1875	5.50
SP531	18c Flowers, #1879a	4.00
SP532	18c Animals, #1889a	6.50
SP533	18c Flag sheet, coil, #1890-1891	3.25
SP534	6c, 18c Booklet pane, #1893a	3.25
SP535	20c Flag sheet, coil, #1894-1895	3.25
SP536	20c Flag booklet pane of 6, #1896a	3.25

1982

SP537	20c Flag booklet pane of 10, #1896b	4.50

Transportation Coils

1981-84

SP538	1c Omnibus, #1897	3.25
SP539	2c Locomotive, #1897A	4.50
SP540	3c Handcar, #1898	4.00
SP541	4c Stagecoach, #1898A	4.25
SP542	5c Motorcycle, #1899	5.75
SP543	5.2c Sleigh, #1900	4.75
SP544	5.9c Bicycle, #1901	6.50
SP545	7.4c Baby Buggy, #1902	4.00
SP546	9.3c Mail Wagon, #1903	4.25
SP547	10.9c Hansom Cab, #1904	4.50
SP548	11c Caboose, #1905	4.25
SP549	17c Electric Auto, #1906	3.25
SP550	18c Surrey, #1907	4.75
SP551	20c Fire Pumper, #1908	5.25

1983

SP552	$9.35 Express Mail single, #1909	80.00
SP552a	$9.35 Express Mail booklet pane of 3, #1909a	195.00

1981

SP553	18c Red Cross, #1910	3.25
SP554	18c Savings and Loan, #1911	3.25
SP555	18c Space Achievements, #1919a	8.00

SP556	18c Management, #1920	3.25
SP557	18c Wildlife, #1924a	4.00
SP558	18c Disabled, #1925	3.25
SP559	18c Millay, #1926	3.25
SP560	18c Alcoholism, #1927	3.25
SP561	18c Architecture, #1931a	4.50
SP562	18c Zaharias, #1932	17.50
SP563	18c Jones, #1933	20.00
SP564	18c Remington, #1934	5.00
SP565	18c, 20c Hoban, #1935-1936	3.25
SP566	18c Yorktown, Va. Capes, #1938a	4.00
SP567	20c Madonna and Child, #1939	3.25
SP568	20c Teddy Bear, #1940	4.75
SP569	20c John Hanson, #1941	3.25
SP570	20c Desert Plants, #1945a	4.50
SP571	20c C sheet, coil, #1946	4.00
SP572	20c C Booklet pane of 10, #1948a	3.75

1982

SP573	20c Bighorn Sheep, #1949a	4.00
SP574	20c FDR, #1950	3.25
SP575	20c Love, #1951	3.25
SP576	20c Washington, #1952	4.00
SP577	20c Birds and Flowers, #1953-1962	12.00
SP578	20c Birds and Flowers, #1963-1972	12.00
SP579	20c Birds and Flowers, #1973-1982	12.00
SP580	20c Birds and Flowers, #1983-1992	12.00
SP581	20c Birds and Flowers, #1993-2002	12.00
SP582	20c US Netherlands, #2003	3.25
SP583	20c Library of Congress, #2004	3.25
SP584	20c Consumer Education, #2005	4.25
SP585	20c Knoxville World's Fair, #2009a	3.25
SP586	20c Horatio Alger, #2010	3.25
SP587	20c Aging, #2011	3.25
SP588	20c Barrymores, #2012	4.25
SP589	20c Dr. Mary Walker, #2013	3.25
SP590	20c Peace Garden, #2014	3.25
SP591	20c Libraries, #2015	3.25
SP592	20c Jackie Robinson, #2016	14.00
SP593	20c Touro Synagogue, #2017	3.25
SP594	20c Wolf Trap Farm, #2018	3.25
SP595	20c Architecture, #2022a	4.50
SP596	20c Francis of Assisi, #2023	3.25
SP597	20c Ponce de Leon, #2024	3.25
SP598	13c Puppy, Kitten, #2025	4.25
SP599	20c Madonna and Child, #2026	4.00
SP600	20c Children Playing, #2030a	4.50

1983

SP601	1c, 4c, Official Mail, #O127-O129 13c	4.00
SP602	17c Official Mail, #O130	4.00
SP603	$1 Official Mail, #O132	5.50
SP604	$5 Official Mail, #O133	10.00
SP605	20c Official Mail coil, #O135	4.00
SP606	20c Science, #2031	3.25
SP607	20c Ballooning, #2035a	3.25
SP608	20c US Sweden, #2036	3.25
SP609	20c CCC, #2037	3.25
SP610	20c Priestley, #2038	3.25
SP611	20c Voluntarism, #2039	3.25
SP612	20c German Immigration, #2040	3.25
SP613	20c Brooklyn Bridge, #2041	3.25
SP614	20c TVA, #2042	3.25
SP615	20c Fitness, #2043	3.25
SP616	20c Scott Joplin, #2044	3.25
SP617	20c Medal of Honor, #2045	6.50
SP618	20c Babe Ruth, #2046	12.00
SP619	20c Hawthorne, #2047	3.25
SP620	13c Olympics, #2051a	4.00
SP621	28c Olympics, #C104a	4.00
SP622	40c Olympics, #C108a	4.00
SP623	35c Olympics, #C112a	4.00
SP624	20c Treaty of Paris, #2052	3.25
SP625	20c Civil Service, #2053	3.25
SP626	20c Metropolitan Opera, #2054	3.75
SP627	20c Inventors, #2058a	3.75
SP628	20c Streetcars, #2062a	4.75
SP629	20c Madonna and Child, #2063	3.25
SP630	20c Santa Claus, #2064	3.25
SP631	20c Martin Luther, #2065	5.25

1984-85

SP632	20c Alaska, #2066	3.25
SP633	20c Winter Olympics, #2070a	4.00
SP634	20c FDIC, #2071	3.25
SP635	20c Love, #2072	3.25
SP636	20c Woodson, #2073	4.00
SP637	14c, 22c D sheet, coil, #O138-O139	3.25
SP638	20c Conservation, #2074	3.25
SP639	20c Credit Union, #2075	3.25
SP640	20c Orchids, #2079a	5.25
SP641	20c Hawaii, #2080	3.75
SP642	20c National Archives, #2081	3.25
SP643	20c Olympics, #2085a	4.00
SP644	20c World Olympics, #2086	3.25
SP645	20c Health Research, #2087	3.25
SP646	20c Fairbanks, #2088	3.25
SP647	20c Thorpe, #2089	10.00
SP648	20c McCormack, #2090	5.25
SP649	20c St. Lawrence Seaway, #2091	3.25
SP650	20c Waterfowl, #2092	5.25
SP651	20c Roanoke Voyages, #2093	3.25
SP652	20c Melville, #2094	3.50
SP653	20c Horace Moses, #2095	3.25
SP654	20c Smokey Bear, #2096	10.00
SP655	20c Clemente, #2097	13.00
SP656	20c Dogs, #2101a	5.25
SP657	20c Crime Prevention, #2102	3.75
SP658	20c Hispanic Americans, #2103	3.25

SP659	20c Family Unity, #2104	3.25
SP660	20c Eleanor Roosevelt, #2105	4.75
SP661	20c Readers, #2106	3.25
SP662	20c Madonna and Child, #2107	3.25
SP663	20c Child's Santa, #2108	3.25
SP664	20c Vietnam Memorial, #2109	5.25

1985-87

SP665	20c Jerome Kern, #2110	3.25
SP666	22c D sheet, coil, #2111-2112	3.25
SP667	22c D booklet pane of 10, #2113a	4.25
SP668	33c Verville, #C113	4.25
SP669	39c Sperry, #C114	3.75
SP670	44c Transpacific, #C115	3.25
SP671	22c Flags sheet, coil, #2114-2115	3.25
SP671a	22c Flag "T" coil, #2115b	3.75
SP672	22c Flag booklet pane of 5, #2116a	3.25
SP673	22c Seashells, #2121a	5.50
SP674	$10.75 Express Mail single, #2122	47.50
SP674a	$10.75 Express Mail booklet pane of 3, #2122a	100.00

Transportation Coils

1985-89

SP675	3.4c School Bus, #2123	4.00
SP676	4.9c Buckboard, #2124	3.75
SP677	5.5c Star Route Truck, #2125	4.00
SP678	6c Tricycle, #2126	3.75
SP679	7.1c Tractor, #2127	3.25
SP679a	7.1c Tractor, Zip+4 precancel, #2127b	3.25
SP680	8.3c Ambulance, #2128	3.25
SP681	8.5c Tow Truck, #2129	3.25
SP682	10.1c Oil Wagon, #2130	3.25
SP682a	10.1c Red precancel, #2130a	3.25
SP683	11c Stutz Bearcat, #2131	3.75
SP684	12c Stanley Steamer, #2132	4.00
SP685	12.5c Pushcart, #2133	3.75
SP686	14c Iceboat, #2134	4.00
SP687	17c Dog Sled, #2135	3.25
SP688	25c Bread Wagon, #2136	4.00

1985

SP689	22c Bethune, #2137	5.25
SP690	22c Duck Decoys, #2141a	6.00
SP691	22c Winter Special Olympics, #2142	3.25
SP692	22c Love, #2143	3.50
SP693	22c REA, #2144	3.25
SP694	14c, 22c Official Mail, #O129A, O136	3.25
SP695	22c AMERIPEX '86, #2145	3.25
SP696	22c Abigail Adams, #2146	3.25
SP697	22c Bartholdi, #2147	3.75
SP698	18c Washington coil, #2149	3.25
SP699	21.1c Letters coil, #2150	3.75
SP700	22c Korean Veterans, #2152	4.00
SP701	22c Social Security, #2153	3.25
SP702	44c Serra, #C116	3.25
SP703	22c World War I Veterans, #2154	5.25
SP704	22c Horses, #2158a	5.75
SP705	22c Education, #2159	3.25
SP706	22c Youth Year, #2163a	5.75
SP707	22c Hunger, #2164	3.25
SP708	22c Madonna and Child, #2165	3.25
SP709	22c Poinsettias, #2166	3.25

1986

SP710	22c Arkansas, #2167	3.25

Great Americans

1986-94

SP711	1c Mitchell, #2168	5.50
SP712	2c Lyon, #2169	3.25
SP713	3c White, #2170	3.25
SP714	4c Flanagan, #2171	3.25
SP715	5c Black, #2172	4.00
SP716	5c Munoz Marin, #2173	5.50
SP717	10c Red Cloud, #2175	5.50
SP718	14c Howe, #2176	3.25
SP719	15c Cody, #2177	3.25
SP720	17c Lockwood, #2178	4.00
SP721	20c Apgar, #2179	4.75
SP722	21c Carlson, #2180	3.25
SP723	23c Cassatt, #2181	3.25
SP724	25c London, #2182	3.25
SP724a	25c London, pane of 10, #2182a	5.75
SP725	28c Sitting Bull, #2183	4.75
SP726	29c Warren, #2184	3.75
SP727	29c Jefferson, #2185	3.25
SP728	35c Chavez, #2186	4.00
SP729	40c Chennault, #2187	4.25
SP730	45c Cushing, #2188	3.25
SP731	52c Humphrey, #2189	3.50
SP732	56c Harvard, #2190	3.25
SP733	65c Arnold, #2191	4.50
SP734	75c Willkie, #2192	4.50
SP735	$1 Revel, #2193	3.75
SP736	$1 Hopkins, #2194	3.75
SP737	$2 Bryan, #2195	5.00
SP739	$5 Harte, #2196	10.00
SP740	25c London, #2197a	3.25

1986

SP741	22c Stamp Collecting, #2201a	4.50
SP742	22c Love, #2202	4.00
SP743	22c Sojourner Truth, #2203	5.50
SP744	22c Texas Republic, #2204	3.25
SP745	22c Fish booklet pane of 5, #2209a	6.00
SP746	22c Hospitals, #2210	2.75
SP747	22c Duke Ellington, #2211	6.00
SP748	22c Presidents Sheet #1, #2216	5.75
SP749	22c Presidents Sheet #2, #2217	5.75
SP750	22c Presidents Sheet #3, #2218	5.75
SP751	22c Presidents Sheet #4, #2219	5.75

SP752	22c Arctic Explorers, #2223a	5.25
SP753	22c Statue of Liberty, #2224	3.75

1987

SP754	2c Locomotive, reengraved, #2226	3.25

1986

SP755	22c Navajo Art, #2238a	5.25
SP756	22c T.S. Eliot, #2239	5.25
SP757	22c Woodcarved Figurines, #2243a	5.50
SP758	22c Madonna and Child, #2244	3.25
SP759	22c Village Scene, #2245	3.25

1987

SP760	22c Michigan, #2246	3.75
SP761	22c Pan American Games, #2247	3.25
SP762	22c Love, #2248	3.25
SP763	22c du Sable, #2249	6.50
SP764	22c Caruso, #2250	3.75
SP765	22c Girl Scouts, #2251	6.00

Transportation Coils

1987-88

SP766	3c Conestoga Wagon, #2252	3.25
SP767	5c, Milk Wagon, Racing Car, 17.5c #2253, 2262	3.25
SP768	5.3c Elevator, #2254	3.50
SP769	7.6c Carreta, #2255	3.50
SP770	8.4c Wheelchair, #2256	3.50
SP771	10c Canal Boat, #2257	3.75
SP772	13c Patrol Wagon, #2258	5.25
SP773	13.2c Coal Car, #2259	5.25
SP774	15c Tugboat, #2260	3.75
SP775	16.7c Popcorn Wagon, #2261	3.75
SP776	20c Cable Car, #2263	3.75
SP777	20.5c Fire Engine, #2264	4.75
SP778	21c Mail Car, #2265	4.75
SP779	24.1c Tandem Bicycle, #2266	3.50

1987

SP780	22c Special Occasions, #2274a	4.50
SP781	22c United Way, #2275	3.25

1987-89

SP782	22c Flag and Fireworks, #2276	3.25
SP783	22c Flag, pair from booklet, #2276a	3.25
SP784	(25c) "E" sheet, coil, #2277, 2279	3.50
SP785	(25c) "E" booklet pane of 10, #2282a	4.00
SP786	25c Flag with Clouds, #2278	3.25
SP787	25c Flag with Clouds booklet pane of 6, #2285c	3.75
SP788	25c Flag over Yosemite coil, block tagging, #2280	3.25
SP788a	25c Flag over Yosemite, prephosphored uncoated paper (mottled tagging), #2280a	3.25
SP789	25c Honeybee coil, #2281	4.75
SP790	25c Pheasant, #2283a	5.25
SP791	25c Owl and Grosbeak, #2285b	4.00
SP792	(25c) "E" Official coil, #O140	3.25
SP793	20c Official coil, #O138B	3.25
SP794	15c, 25c Official coils, #O138A, O141	3.25

1987

SP795	22c Wildlife, #2286-2295	6.50
SP796	22c Wildlife, #2296-2305	6.50
SP797	22c Wildlife, #2306-2315	6.50
SP798	22c Wildlife, #2316-2325	6.50
SP799	22c Wildlife, #2326-2335	6.50

Ratification of the Constitution

1987-90

SP800	22c Delaware, #2336	3.75
SP801	22c Pennsylvania, #2337	3.25
SP802	22c New Jersey, #2338	3.75
SP803	22c Georgia, #2339	3.75
SP804	22c Connecticut, #2340	3.75
SP805	22c Massachusetts, #2341	3.75
SP806	22c Maryland, #2342	3.75
SP807	25c South Carolina, #2343	3.25
SP808	25c New Hampshire, #2344	3.25
SP809	25c Virginia, #2345	3.75
SP810	25c New York, #2346	3.25
SP811	25c North Carolina, #2347	3.75
SP812	25c Rhode Island, #2348	3.25

1987

SP813	22c U.S./Morocco, #2349	3.25
SP814	22c William Faulkner, #2350	6.25
SP815	22c Lacemaking, #2354a	6.75
SP816	22c Constitution, #2359a	4.00
SP817	22c Signing of Constitution, #2360	3.25
SP818	22c Certified Public Accounting, #2361	6.00
SP819	22c Locomotives, #2366a	9.00
SP820	22c Madonna and Child, #2367	3.25
SP821	22c Christmas Ornament, #2368	3.25

1988

SP822	22c Winter Olympics, #2369	3.25
SP823	22c Australia Bicentennial, #2370	4.00
SP824	22c James Weldon Johnson, #2371	3.75
SP825	22c Cats, #2375a	6.50
SP826	22c Knute Rockne, #2376	10.00
SP827	44c New Sweden, #C117	3.25
SP828	45c Samuel P. Langley, #C118	3.25
SP829	25c Francis Ouimet, #2377	12.00
SP830	36c Igor Sikorsky, #C119	3.25
SP831	25c Love, #2378	3.25
SP832	45c Love, #2379	3.25

SP833	25c Summer Olympics, #2380	3.25
SP834	25c Classic Automobiles, #2385a	6.00
SP835	25c Antarctic Explorers, #2389a	3.75
SP836	25c Carousel Animals, #2393a	5.25
SP837	$8.75 Express Mail, #2394	23.50
SP838	25c Special Occasions, #2396a	20.00
SP839	25c Special Occasions, #2398a	20.00
SP840	25c Madonna and Child, #2399	3.25
SP841	25c Village Scene, #2400	3.25

1989

SP842	25c Montana, #2401	3.25
SP843	25c A. Philip Randolph, #2402	4.25
SP844	25c North Dakota, #2403	3.25
SP845	25c Washington Statehood, #2404	3.25
SP846	25c Steamboats, #2409a	6.50
SP847	25c World Stamp Expo, #2410	3.25
SP848	25c Toscanini, #2411	5.25

Branches of Government

1989-90

SP849	25c House of Representatives, #2412	3.25
SP850	25c Senate, #2413	3.25
SP851	25c Executive, #2414	3.25
SP852	25c Supreme Court, #2415	3.25

1989

SP853	25c South Dakota, #2416	3.25
SP854	25c Lou Gehrig, #2417	13.00
SP855	1c Official, litho., #O143	3.25
SP856	45c French Revolution, #C120	5.25
SP857	25c Ernest Hemingway, #2418	6.00
SP858	$2.40 Moon Landing, #2419	20.00
SP859	25c Letter Carriers, #2420	3.25
SP860	25c Bill of Rights, #2421	3.25
SP861	25c Dinosaurs, #2425a	8.00
SP862	25c, 45c Pre-Columbian Artifacts, #2426, C121	3.25
SP863	25c Madonna sheet single, booklet pane of 10, #2427, 2427a	7.25
SP864	25c Sleigh single, booklet pane of 10, #2428, 2429a	7.25
SP865	25c Eagle & Shield, #2431	3.25
SP866	90c World Stamp Expo '89, #2433	13.00
SP867	25c Traditional Mail Delivery, #2437a	5.00
SP868	45c Futuristic Mail Delivery, #C126	6.00
SP869	45c Futuristic Mail Delivery, #C125a	6.00
SP870	25c Traditional Mail Delivery, #2438	6.50

1990

SP871	25c Idaho, #2439	3.25
SP872	25c Love single, booklet pane of 10, #2440, 2441a	5.25
SP873	25c Ida B. Wells, #2442	5.25
SP874	15c Beach Umbrella, #2443a	5.25
SP875	25c Wyoming, #2444	4.00
SP876	25c Classic Films, #2448a	9.00
SP877	25c Marianne Moore, #2449	4.00

Transportation Coils

1990-92

SP879	4c Steam Carriage, #2451	3.50
SP880	5c Circus Wagon, #2452	3.75
SP880A	5c Circus Wagon, #2452B	5.25
SP880B	5c Circus Wagon with cent sign, #2452D	5.00
SP881	5c, 10c Canoe, engr., Tractor Trailer, #2453, 2457	3.50
SP882	5c Canoe, photo., #2454	3.75
SP883	10c Tractor trailer, photo., #2458	5.00
SP891	20c Cog Railway, #2463	4.00
SP892	23c Lunch Wagon, #2464	3.75
SP893	32c Ferry Boat, #2466	4.00
SP895	$1 Seaplane, #2468	6.50

1990-94

SP897	25c Lighthouses, booklet pane of 5, #2474a	9.00
SP898	29c Flag, #2475	3.75

Flora and Fauna Series

SP899	1c, 3c, Kestrel, Bluebird, Cardinal, 30c 2476, 2478, 2480	3.50
SP900	1c Kestrel with cent sign, #2477	3.50
SP901	19c Fawn, #2479	3.50
SP902	45c Pumpkinseed Sunfish, #2481	3.75
SP903	$2 Bobcat, #2482	5.25
SP904	20c Blue jay, #2483	3.50
SP905	29c Wood Ducks booklet panes of 10, #2484a, 2485a	13.00
SP906	29c African Violets bklt. pane of 10, #2486a	5.00
SP907	32c Peach & Pear, #2488b, 2493-2494	5.25
SP908	29c Red Squirrel, #2489	3.75
SP909	29c Red Rose, #2490	3.25
SP910	29c Pine Cone, #2491	3.75
SP911	32c Pink rose, #2492	5.25
SP919	25c Olympians, #2496-2500	5.75
SP920	25c Indian Headdresses, #2505a	6.75
SP921	25c Micronesia, Marshall Islands, #2507a	3.25
SP922	25c Sea Creatures, #2511a	7.00
SP923	25c, 45c Grand Canyon, Tropical Coastline, #2512, C127	3.25
SP924	25c Eisenhower, #2513	3.75
SP925	25c Madonna sheet single, booklet pane of 10, #2514, 2514a	6.00

SP926	25c Christmas Tree sheet single, booklet pane of 10, #2515, 2516a	6.00

1991-95

SP927	(29c) "F" Flower single, coil pair, #2517, 2518	3.25
SP928	(29c) "F" Flower booklet panes of 10, #2519a, 2520a	11.00
SP929	(4c) Make-up Rate, #2521	3.25
SP930	(29c) "F" Flag, #2522	3.75
SP931	(29c) "F" Official coil, #O144	3.25
SP932	29c Mt. Rushmore, #2523	3.75
SP933	29c Mt. Rushmore, photo., #2523A	3.25
SP934	29c Flower single, booklet pane of 10, #2524, 2527a	6.25
SP935	29c Flower coil, #2525	3.25
SP936	29c Flower coil, #2526	3.25
SP937	4c Official, #O146	3.50
SP938	29c Flag, Olympic Rings, #2528a	6.50
SP939	19c Fishing Boat coil, #2529	5.25
SP939A	19c Fishing Boat coil reissue, #2529C	4.00
SP940	19c Ballooning, #2530a	5.25
SP941	29c Flags on Parade, #2531	3.50
SP942	29c Liberty Torch, #2531A	3.50
SP943	50c Switzerland, #2532	3.25
SP944	20c Vermont Statehood, #2533	3.50
SP945	50c Harriet Quimby, #C128	3.75
SP946	29c Savings Bonds, #2534	3.25
SP947	29c, 52c Love, #2535, 2536a, 2537	13.00
SP948	40c William T. Piper, #C129	3.25
SP949	29c William Saroyan, #2538	6.00
SP950	Official 19c, 23c, 29c, #O145, O147-O148	3.50
SP951	$1.00 USPS/Olympic Rings, #2539	4.50
SP952	$2.90 Eagle, #2540	14.00
SP953	$9.95 Eagle, #2541	35.00
SP954	$14 Eagle, #2542	45.00
SP955	$2.90 Futuristic Space Shuttle, #2543	13.00
SP956	$3 Challenger Shuttle, #2544	15.00
SP956A	$10.75 Endeavour Shuttle, #2544A	27.50
SP957	29c Fishing Flies, #2549a	20.00
SP958	29c Cole Porter, #2550	3.75
SP959	50c Antarctic Treaty, #C130	3.75
SP960	29c Desert Shield, Desert Storm, #2551	12.00
SP961	29c 1992 Summer Olympics, #2553-2557	7.00
SP962	29c Numismatics, #2558	5.20
SP963	29c World War II, #2559	11.00
SP964	29c Basketball, #2560	8.00
SP965	29c District of Columbia, #2561	3.25
SP966	29c Comedians, #2566a	8.75
SP967	29c Jan E. Matzeliger, #2567	6.00
SP968	29c Space Exploration, #2577a	11.00
SP969	50c Bering Land Bridge, #C131	3.25
SP970	29c Madonna and Child sheet single, booklet pane of 10, #2578, 2578a	11.00
SP971	29c Santa Claus sheet and booklet singles, #2579, 2580 or 2581, 2582-2585	18.00
SP973	32c James K. Polk, #2587	7.00
SP976	$1 Surrender of Gen. Burgoyne, #2590	5.00
SP978	$5 Washington and Jackson, #2592	15.00
SP980	29c Pledge of Allegiance, #2593a	5.00
SP982	29c Eagle & Shield self-adhesives, #2595-2597	4.50
SP983	29c Eagle self-adhesive, #2598	3.50
SP984	29c Statue of Liberty, #2599	3.50
SP990	(10c) Eagle and Shield coil, #2602	5.25
SP991	(10c) Eagle and Shield coils, #2603-2604	5.25
SP993	23c Stars and Stripes coil, #2605	3.25
SP994	23c USA coil, #2606	4.00
SP994A	23c USA coil, #2607	3.25
SP994B	23c USA coil, #2608	3.50
SP995	29c Flag over White House, #2609	3.50

1992

SP997	29c Winter Olympics, #2611-2615	5.25
SP998	29c World Columbian Stamp Expo '92, #2616	4.50
SP999	29c W.E.B. DuBois, #2617	6.00
SP1000	29c Love, #2618	3.25
SP1001	29c Olympic Baseball, #2619	14.00
SP1002	29c First Voyage of Columbus, #2623a	4.50
SP1003	1c, 4c, First Sighting of Land souvenir sheet, #2624	10.00
SP1004	2c, 3c, Claiming a New World souvenir sheet, #2625	12.00
SP1005	5c, 30c, Seeking Royal Support souvenir sheet, #2626	9.00
SP1006	6c, 8c, Royal Favor Restored souvenir sheet, #2627	12.00
SP1007	10c, Reporting Discoveries souvenir sheet, #2628	11.50
SP1008	$5 Columbus souvenir sheet, #2629	15.00
SP1009	29c New York Stock Exchange, #2630	3.50
SP1010	29c Space Accomplishments, #2634a	7.50
SP1011	29c Alaska Highway, #2635	3.75
SP1012	29c Kentucky Statehood, #2636	3.50
SP1013	29c Summer Olympics, #2637-2641	5.25
SP1014	29c Hummingbirds, #2646a	8.00
SP1015	29c Wildflowers, #2647-2656	8.00
SP1016	29c Wildflowers, #2657-2666	8.00

SP1017	29c Wildflowers, #2667-2676	8.00
SP1018	29c Wildflowers, #2677-2686	8.00
SP1019	29c Wildflowers, #2687-2696	8.00
SP1020	29c World War II, #2697	7.75
SP1021	29c Dorothy Parker, #2698	3.75
SP1022	29c Dr. Theodore von Karman, #2699	6.00
SP1023	29c Minerals strip of 4, #2703a	5.75
SP1024	29c Juan Rodriguez Cabrillo, #2704	3.75
SP1025	29c Wild Animals, #2709a	7.25
SP1026	29c Madonna and Child sheet single, booklet pane of 10, #2710, 2710a	10.00
SP1027	29c Christmas Toys block of 4, booklet pane of 4 and booklet single, #2714a, 2718a, 2719	6.00
SP1028	29c Chinese New Year, #2720	11.00

1993

SP1029	29c Elvis Presley, #2721	14.00
SP1030	29c Oklahoma!, #2722	3.25
SP1030A	29c Hank Williams sheet stamp, #2723A	6.00
SP1030B	29c Rock & Roll/Rhythm & Blues sheet single, booklet pane of 8, #2737b	24.00

No. SP1030B exists with any one of #2724-2730 affixed along with #2737b.

SP1034	29c Space Fantasy, #2745a	10.00
SP1035	29c Percy Lavon Julian, #2746	5.25
SP1036	29c Oregon Trail, #2747	3.25
SP1037	29c World University Games, #2748	3.25
SP1038	29c Grace Kelly, #2749	9.00
SP1039	29c Circus, #2753a	6.00
SP1040	29c Cherokee Strip, #2754	5.00
SP1041	29c Dean Acheson, #2755	3.25
SP1042	29c Sporting Horses, #2759a	7.00
SP1043	29c Garden Flowers, #2764a	5.25
SP1044	29c World War II, #2765	9.00
SP1045	29c Joe Louis, #2766	12.00
SP1046	29c Broadway Musicals, #2770a	6.75
SP1047	29c National Postal Museum strip of 4, #2782a	4.50
SP1048	29c American Sign Language, #2784a	3.25
SP1049	29c Country & Western Music sheet stamp and booklet pane of 4, #2778a	15.00

No. SP1049 exists with any one of #2771-2774 affixed along with #2778a.

SP1050	10c Official Mail, #O146A	3.50
SP1052	29c Classic Books strip of 4, #2788a	4.25
SP1053	29c Traditional Christmas sheet stamp, booklet pane of 4, #2789, 2790a	6.75
SP1054	29c Contemporary Christmas booklet pane of 10, sheet and self-adhesive single stamps, #2803	18.00

No. SP1054 exists with any one of #2791-2794, 2798a, 2798b, 2799-2802 affixed along with #2803.

SP1055	29c Mariana Islands, #2804	3.25
SP1056	29c Columbus' Landing in Puerto Rico, #2805	4.00
SP1057	29c AIDS Awareness, #2806, 2806b	6.50

1994

SP1058	29c Winter Olympics, #2811a	6.75
SP1059	29c Edward R. Murrow, #2812	4.25
SP1060	29c Love self-adhesive, #2813	4.25
SP1061	29c, 52c Love booklet pane of 10, single sheet stamp, #2814a, 2815	9.00
SP1062	29c Love sheet stamp, #2814C	4.00
SP1063	29c Dr. Allison Davis, #2816	6.50
SP1064	29c Chinese New Year, #2817	4.75
SP1065	29c Buffalo Soldiers, #2818	7.00
SP1066	29c Silent Screen Stars, #2819-2828	8.00
SP1067	29c Garden Flowers, #2833a	8.00
SP1068	29c, World Cup Soccer, #2834-40c, 50c 2836	8.00
SP1069	World Cup Soccer, #2837	8.00
SP1070	29c World War II, #2838	7.25
SP1071	29c, 50c Norman Rockwell stamp, souvenir sheet, #2839-2840	14.00
SP1072	29c, Moon Landing, #2841-2842 $9.95	25.00
SP1073	29c Locomotives, #2847a	9.50
SP1074	29c George Meany, #2848	4.00
SP1075	29c Popular Singers, #2853a	8.00
SP1076	29c Jazz and Blues Singers block of 10, #2854-2861	11.00

Block of 10 on No. SP1076 may contain different combinations of stamps.

SP1077	29c James Thurber, #2862	5.25
SP1078	29c Wonders of the Sea, #2866a	6.50
SP1079	29c Cranes, #2868a	4.00
SP1079A	Legends of the West, #2869	24.00
SP1080	29c Traditional Christmas sheet stamp, booklet pane of 10, #2871, 2871b	9.75
SP1081	29c Contemporary Christmas sheet stamp, block of 4 from booklet pane, #2872	6.75
SP1082	29c Contemporary Christmas self-adhesive stamps, #2873-2874	8.00

SP1083	$2 Bureau of Engraving and Printing Souvenir Sheet, #2875	20.00

1995-96

SP1084	29c Chinese New Year, #2876	6.75
SP1085	G make-up rate, G stamps, #2877, 2884, 2890, 2893	5.25
SP1086	G make-up rate, G stamps, #2878, 2880, 2882, 2885, 2888, 2892	5.25
SP1087	G stamps, official G stamp, #2879, 2881, 2883, 2889, O152	5.25
SP1088	G self-adhesive stamps, #2886-2887	10.00
SP1091	32c Flag Over Porch, #2897, 2913, 2915-2916	6.50
SP1096	(5c) Butte coil, #2902	5.75
SP1097	(5c) Mountain coil, #2903, 2904	6.50
SP1099	Butte, Mountain, Juke Box, Auto Tail Fin, Auto, Flag over porch, #2902B, 2904A, 2906, 2910, 2912A, 2915B	5.50
SP1099A	Mountain, Juke Box, Flag Over Porch coil and booklet stamps, #2904B, 2912B, 2915D, 2921b	5.50
SP1100	(10c) Auto coil, #2905	5.25
SP1102	Eagle & shield, Flag over porch, #2907, 2920D, 2921	5.50
SP1103	(15c) Auto Tail Fin, #2908-2909	5.25
SP1105	(25c) Juke Box, #2911-2912	4.25
SP1110	32c Flag over Field self-adhesive, #2919	6.00
SP1114	(32c) Non-denominated Love, #2948-2949	3.25
SP1115	32c Florida Statehood, #2950	3.25

Great Americans Series

SP1126	32c Milton Hershey, #2933	3.25
SP1127	32c Cal Farley, #2934	4.00
SP1128	32c Henry R. Luce, #2935	7.25
SP1129	32c Lila & DeWitt Wallace, #2936	5.75
SP1131	46c Ruth Benedict, #2938	4.00
SP1133	55c Alice Hamilton, #2940	3.25
SP1134	55c Justin S. Morrill, #2941	7.25
SP1135	77c Mary Breckinridge, #2942	6.50
SP1136	78c Alice Paul, #2943	3.25

1995

SP1141	32c Kids Care, #2954a	4.00
SP1142	32c Richard Nixon, #2955	4.00
SP1143	32c Bessie Coleman, #2956	5.25
SP1144	1-32c Official, #O156	3.50
SP1145	32c, 55c Love (with denominations), #2957-2960	4.00
SP1146	32c Recreational Sports, #2965a	10.00
SP1147	32c Prisoners of War/Missing in Action, #2966	4.50
SP1148	32c Marilyn Monroe, #2967	16.00
SP1149	32c Texas Statehood, #2968	5.00
SP1150	32c Great Lakes Lighthouses, #2973a	10.00
SP1151	32c United Nations, #2974	3.25
SP1152	32c Civil War, #2975	17.50
SP1153	32c Carousel Horses, #2979a	7.00
SP1154	32c Woman Suffrage, #2980	3.25
SP1155	32c World War II, #2981	8.00
SP1156	32c Louis Armstrong, #2982	5.00
SP1157	32c Jazz Musicians, #2992a	9.00
SP1158	32c Garden Flowers, #2997a	8.00
SP1159	60c Eddie Rickenbacker, #2998	5.00
SP1160	32c Republic of Palau, #2999	4.00
SP1161	32c Comic Strip Classics, #3000	17.50
SP1162	32c Naval Academy, #3001	5.00
SP1163	32c Tennessee Williams, #3002	5.00
SP1164	32c Traditional Christmas sheet stamp, booklet pane of 10, #3003, 3003b	7.25
SP1165	32c Contemporary Christmas block of 4, self-adhesive stamps, #3007a, 3010-3011	6.00

No. SP1165 may include different combinations of Nos. 3008-3011.

SP1166	32c Midnight Angel, #3012	5.25
SP1167	32c Children Sledding, #3013	5.25
SP1168	32c Antique Automobiles, #3023a	7.50

1996

SP1169	32c Utah Statehood, #3024	4.00
SP1170	32c Garden Flowers, #3029a	7.25
SP1171	1, 32c Flag Over Porch, Love self-adhesives, Kestrel coil, #2920e, 3030, 3044	16.00

1996-99

Flora and Fauna Series

SP1171A	1c Kestrel, self-adhesive, #3031	7.25
SP1172	2c Woodpecker, #3032	4.00
SP1173	3c Bluebird, #3033	4.00
SP1184	$1 Red Fox, #3036	9.00
SP1185	2c Woodpecker coil, #3045	7.25
SP1187	20c Bluejay self-adhesive coil, booklet stamps, #3048, 3053	5.75
SP1188	32c Yellow Rose, #3049	6.00
SP1189	20c Ring-necked Pheasant, #3050, 3055	7.25
SP1191A	33c Coral Pink Rose, serpentine die cut 10¾x10½, #3052E	7.25
SP1191	33c Coral Pink Rose, #3052	7.25
SP1192	32c Yellow Rose coil, #3054	7.25

1996

SP1197	32c Ernest E. Just, #3058	6.00
SP1198	32c Smithsonian Institution, #3059	4.00
SP1199	32c Chinese New Year, #3060	7.25
SP1200	32c Pioneers of Communication, #3064a	5.50
SP1201	32c Fulbright Scholarships, #3065	4.00
SP1202	50c Jacqueline Cochran, #3066	4.00
SP1203	32c Marathon, #3067	4.00
SP1204	32c Olympic Games, #3068	17.50
SP1205	32c Georgia O'Keeffe, #3069	5.25
SP1206	32c Tennessee Statehood, #3070	4.00
SP1207	32c American Indian Dances, #3076a	5.25
SP1208	32c Prehistoric Animals, #3080a	5.25
SP1209	32c Breast Cancer Awareness, #3081	5.75
SP1210	32c James Dean, #3082	7.25
SP1211	32c Folk Heroes, #3086a	6.25
SP1212	32c Centennial Olympic Games, #3087	5.75
SP1213	32c Iowa Statehood, #3088-3089	5.75
SP1214	32c Rural Free Delivery, #3090	4.50
SP1215	32c Riverboats, #3095b	75.00
SP1216	32c Big Band Leaders, #3099a	7.25
SP1217	32c Songwriters, #3103a	7.25
SP1218	23c F. Scott Fitzgerald, #3104	4.50
SP1219	32c Endangered Species, #3105	19.50
SP1220	32c Computer Technology, #3106	4.50
SP1221	32c Madonna & Child sheet & booklet stamps, #3107, 3112	7.25
SP1222	32c Contemporary Christmas block of 4, self-adhesive stamp, #3111a, 3113	7.25

#SP1222 may contain #3114-3116 instead of #3113.

SP1223	32c Skaters, #3117	7.25
SP1224	32c Hanukkah, #3118	5.75
SP1225	32c Cycling souvenir sheet, #3119	7.25

1997

SP1226	32c Chinese New Year, #3120	8.75
SP1227	32c Benjamin O. Davis, Sr., #3121	7.25
SP1228	32c Statue of Liberty, #3122	6.50
SP1229	32, 55c Love Swans, #3123-3124	6.50
SP1230	32c Helping Children Learn, #3125	5.75
SP1231	32c Merian Botanical Prints, #3126-3129	6.50
SP1232	32c PACIFIC 97 Triangles, #3131a	7.25
SP1233	(25c), Flag Over Porch, Juke Box 32c linerless coils, #3132-3133	6.50
SP1234	32c Thornton Wilder, #3134	5.75
SP1235	32c Raoul Wallenberg, #3135	5.75
SP1236	32c Dinosaurs, #3136	19.50
SP1237	32c Bugs Bunny, #3137	19.50
SP1238	50c PACIFIC 97 Franklin, #3139	16.00
SP1239	60c PACIFIC 97 Washington, #3140	16.00
SP1240	32c Marshall Plan, #3141	6.50
SP1241	32c Classic American Aircraft, #3142	19.50
SP1242	32c Football Coaches, #3146a	16.00
SP1242A	32c Vince Lombardi, #3147	11.00
SP1242B	32c Bear Bryant, #3148	11.00
SP1242C	32c Pop Warner, #3149	11.00
SP1242D	32c George Halas, #3150	11.00
SP1243	32c Classic American Dolls, #3151	15.00
SP1244	32c Humphrey Bogart, #3152	7.25
SP1245	32c The Stars and Stripes Forever!, #3153	7.25
SP1246	32c Opera Singers, #3157a	11.00
SP1247	32c Composers & Conductors, #3165a	13.00
SP1248	32c Padre Felix Varela, #3155	7.20
SP1249	32c Department of the Air Force, #3167	11.00
SP1250	32c Movie Monsters, #3172a	14.00
SP1251	32c Supersonic Flight, #3173	11.00
SP1252	32c Women in Military Service, #3174	7.25
SP1253	32c Kwanzaa, #3175	8.00
SP1254	32c Madonna and Child, #3176	9.00
SP1255	32c Holly, #3177	9.00
SP1256	$3 Mars Pathfinder, #3178	19.50

1998

SP1257	32c Chinese New Year, #3179	8.00
SP1258	32c Alpine Skiing, #3180	8.00
SP1259	32c Madam C.J. Walker, #3181	8.00

1998-2000

Celebrate the Century

SP1259A	32c 1900s, #3182	17.50
SP1259B	32c 1910s, #3183	17.50
SP1259C	32c 1920s, #3184	17.50
SP1259D	32c 1930s, #3185	17.50
SP1259E	33c 1940s, #3186	17.50
SP1259F	33c 1950s, #3187	17.50
SP1259G	33c 1960s, #3188	17.50
SP1259H	33c 1970s, #3189	17.50
SP1259I	33c 1980s, #3190	17.50
SP1259J	33c 1990s, #3191	17.50

1998

SP1260	32c "Remember the Maine," #3192	8.00
SP1261	32c Flowering Trees, #3197a	9.75
SP1262	32c Alexander Calder, #3202a	9.75
SP1263	32c Cinco de Mayo, #3203	7.25
SP1264	32c Sylvester & Tweety, #3204a	9.75

SP1265	32c Wisconsin Statehood, #3206	8.00
SP1266	(5c), Wetlands, Diner Coils, (25c) #3207-3208	7.25
SP1266A	(25c) Diner coil, #3208A	7.25
SP1267	1c-$2 Trans-Mississippi, #3209	20.00
SP1268	$1 Trans-Mississippi, #3209h	15.00
SP1269	32c Berlin Airlift, #3211	9.00
SP1270	32c Folk Musicians, #3215a	10.00
SP1271	32c Gospel Singers, #3219a	9.00
SP1272	32c Spanish Settlement, #3220	7.25
SP1273	32c Stephen Vincent Benét, #3221	7.25
SP1274	32c Tropical Birds, #3225a	11.00
SP1275	32c Alfred Hitchcock, #3226	8.00
SP1276	32c Organ & Tissue Donation, #3227	7.25
SP1277	(10c) Modern Bicycle, #3229	7.25
SP1278	32c Bright Eyes, #3234a	10.00
SP1279	32c Klondike Gold Rush, #3235	8.00
SP1280	32c American Art, #3236	16.00
SP1281	32c Ballet, #3237	8.00
SP1282	32c Space Discovery, #3242a	9.75
SP1283	32c Giving & Sharing, #3243	7.25
SP1284	32c Madonna & Child, #3244	7.25
SP1285	32c Wreaths, #3248a, 3252a	9.75
SP1286	(32+8c) Breast Cancer Awareness, #B1	8.00
SP1287	(1c), Weather Vane, Uncle Sam's (33c) Hat, #3257-3258, 3260	8.00
SP1288	22c Uncle Sam, #3259, 3263	7.25
SP1289	$3.20 Space Shuttle Landing, #3261	17.50
SP1290	$11.75 Piggyback Space Shuttle, #3262	27.50
SP1291	(33c) Uncle Sam's Hat, #3267-3269	8.50
SP1292	(33c) Uncle Sam's Hat, #3264, 3266	9.00
SP1293	(5c), Wetlands, Eagle & Shield, (10c) #3207A, 3270-3271	8.00

1999

SP1294	33c Chinese New Year, #3272	9.75
SP1295	33c Malcolm X, #3273	13.00
SP1296	33c Love, #3274	8.00
SP1297	55c Love, #3275	8.00
SP1298	33c Hospice Care, #3276	7.25
SP1299	33c Flag and City, #3279-3280, 3282	8.00
SP1300	33c Flag Over Chalkboard, #3283	7.25
SP1301	33c Irish Immigration, #3286	7.25
SP1302	33c Lunt & Fontanne, #3287	7.25
SP1303	33c Arctic Animals, #3292a	9.75
SP1304	33c Sonoran Desert, #3293	16.00
SP1305	33c Berries, #3294-3297	9.00
SP1306	33c Daffy Duck, #3306a	9.75
SP1307	33c Ayn Rand, #3308	8.00
SP1308	33c Cinco de Mayo, #3309	7.25
SP1309	33c Tropical Flowers, #3310-3313	9.00
SP1310	48c Niagara Falls, #C133	8.50
SP1311	33c John & William Bartram, #3314	7.25
SP1312	33c Prostate Cancer, #3315	7.25
SP1313	33c California Gold Rush, #3316	7.25
SP1314	33c Aquarium Fish, #3317-3320	9.00
SP1315	33c Extreme Sports, #3321-3324	8.75
SP1316	33c American Glass, #3328a	9.00
SP1317	33c James Cagney, #3329	9.00
SP1318	55c Billy Mitchell, #3330	8.75
SP1319	40c Rio Grande, #C134	7.25
SP1320	33c Honoring Those Who Served, #3331	7.25
SP1321	45c Universal Postal Union, #3332	7.25
SP1322	33c Famous Trains, #3337a	10.00
SP1323	33c Frederick Law Olmsted, #3338	7.25
SP1324	33c Hollywood Composers, #3344a	15.00
SP1325	33c Broadway Songwriters, #3350a	14.50
SP1326	33c Insects & Spiders, #3351	18.00
SP1327	33c Hanukkah, #3352	7.25
SP1328	22c Uncle Sam, #3353	7.25
SP1329	33c Official coil, #O157	7.25
SP1330	33c NATO, #3354	7.25
SP1331	33c Madonna & Child, #3355	7.25
SP1332	33c Christmas Deer, #3359a	8.75
SP1333	33c Kwanzaa, #3368	7.25
SP1334	33c Year 2000, #3369	7.25

2000

SP1335	33c Chinese New Year, #3370	9.75
SP1336	60c Grand Canyon, #C135	7.25
SP1337	33c Patricia Roberts Harris, #3371	8.00
SP1338	33c Berries, dated 2000, #3294a-3296a, 3297c	8.00
SP1339	33c Los Angeles Class Submarine (sheet stamp), #3372	17.50
SP1340	33c Pacific Coast Rain Forest, #3378	18.50
SP1341	33c Louise Nevelson, #3383a	9.25
SP1342	33c Hubble Space Telescope Images, #3388a	9.25
SP1343	33c American Samoa, #3389	7.25
SP1344	33c Library of Congress, #3390	7.25
SP1345	33c Road Runner & Wile E. Coyote, #3391a	10.00
SP1346	33c Distinguished Soldiers, 3396a	9.75
SP1347	33c Summer Sports, #3397	7.25
SP1348	33c Adoption, #3398	11.00
SP1349	33c Youth Team Sports, #3402a	8.00
SP1350	33c The Stars and Stripes, #3403	17.50
SP1351	33c Legends of Baseball, #3408	22.50

SP1352	33c Stampin' the Future, #3417a	8.00

Distinguished Americans Series

2000-08

SP1355	10c Gen. Joseph W. Stilwell, #3420	7.25
SP1357	23c Wilma Rudolph, #3422, 3436	7.25
SP1361	33c Claude Pepper, #3426	7.25
SP1362	58c Margaret Chase Smith, #3427	7.50
SP1362A	59c James A. Michener, #3427A	7.50
SP1363	63c Dr. Jonas Salk, #3428	7.50
SP1365	75c Harriet Beecher Stowe, #3430	7.50
SP1366	76c Hattie Caraway, #3431	7.25
SP1366A	76c Edward Trudeau, #3432A	7.50
SP1367	83c Edna Ferber, #3432	7.25
SP1368	87c Dr. Albert Sabin, #3435	7.50

2000

SP1373	33c California Statehood, #3438	7.25
SP1374	33c Deep Sea Creatures, #3443a	9.25
SP1375	33c Thomas Wolfe, #3444	8.00
SP1376	33c White House, #3445	7.25
SP1377	33c Edward G. Robinson, #3446	8.00
SP1378	(10c) New York Public Library Lion, #3447	7.25
SP1379	(34c) Flag Over Farm, #3448-3450	7.25
SP1380	(34c) Statue of Liberty, #3451-3453	7.25
SP1381	(34c) Flowers, #3454-3457	7.25

2001

SP1382	34c Statue of Liberty self-adhesive coil, #3466	6.50
SP1382A	21c American Buffalo, #3467, 3484	6.50
SP1383	21c American Buffalo, #3468, 3475	6.50
SP1383A	23c George Washington, #3468A, 3475A	7.25
SP1384	34c Flag over Farm, #3469	6.50
SP1385	34c Flag over Farm self-adhesive, #3470	6.50
SP1386	55c Eagle, #3471	7.25
SP1386A	57c Eagle, #3471A	7.50
SP1387	$3.50 US Capitol, #3472	13.50
SP1388	$12.25 Washington Monument, #3473	27.50
SP1389	34c Statue of Liberty, #3476, 3477, 3485	7.50
SP1390	34c Flowers, #3478-3481	7.50
SP1391	20c George Washington, #3482	6.50
SP1392	34c Apple and Orange, #3491, 3492	7.25
SP1393	34c Flag over Farm self-adhesive booklet, #3495	8.00
SP1394	(34c) Love, #3496	6.50
SP1395	34c, 55c Love, #3497, 3499	9.00
SP1396	34c Chinese New Year, #3500	8.75
SP1397	34c Roy Wilkins, #3501	10.00
SP1398	34c American Illustrators, #3502	26.00
SP1399	34c Official, #O158	6.50
SP1400	70c Nine-Mile Prairie, #C136	7.25
SP1401	34c Diabetes Awareness, #3503	8.00
SP1402	34c Nobel Prize, #3504	8.00
SP1403	1c-80c Pan-American Inverts, #3505	18.00
SP1404	80c Mt. McKinley, #C137	9.00
SP1405	34c Great Plains Prairie, #3506	17.50
SP1406	34c Peanuts Comic Strip, #3507	12.00
SP1407	34c Honoring Veterans, #3508	9.00
SP1408	60c Acadia National Park, #C138	8.00
SP1409	34c Frida Kahlo, #3509	13.00
SP1410	34c Legendary Playing Fields, #3510-3519	27.50
SP1411	(10c) Atlas Statue, #3520	6.50
SP1412	34c Leonard Bernstein, #3521	8.00
SP1413	(15c) Woody Wagon, #3522	6.50
SP1414	34c Lucille Ball, #3523	11.50
SP1415	34c Amish Quilts, #3524-3527	8.75
SP1416	34c Carnivorous Plants, #3528-3531	8.75
SP1417	34c Eid, #3532	6.50
SP1418	34c Enrico Fermi, #3533	8.00
SP1419	34c That's All Folks!, #3534a	11.50
SP1420	34c Christmas Madonna, #3536	6.50
SP1421	34c Christmas Santas, #3537-3540	8.00
SP1422	34c James Madison, #3545	6.50
SP1423	34c Thanksgiving, #3546	6.50
SP1424	34c Hanukkah, #3547	6.50
SP1425	34c Kwanzaa, #3548	6.50
SP1426	34c United We Stand booklet and coil, #3549, 3550	13.50
SP1427	57c Love, #3551	7.50

2002

SP1428	34c Winter Olympics, #3552-3555	9.75
SP1429	34c Mentoring a Child, #3556	6.50
SP1430	34c Langston Hughes, #3557	6.50
SP1431	34c Happy Birthday, #3558	6.50
SP1432	34c Chinese New Year, #3559	8.00
SP1433	34c US Military Academy, Bicent., #3560	8.00
SP1434	34c Greetings from America, #3561-3610	37.50
SP1435	34c Longleaf Pine Forest, #3611	17.50
SP1436	5c Toleware Coffeepot, #3612	6.50
SP1437	3c Star, #3613-3615	6.50
SP1438	23c George Washington, #3616-3618	7.50
SP1439	(37c) Flag, #3620-3623	8.75
SP1440	(37c) Toy coils, #3626-3629	8.00

2003
SP1440A	37c Flag, perf. 11¼, #3629F	6.50

2002
| SP1441 | 37c Flag, #3630-3631, 3633, 3635 | 6.50 |

2003
| SP1441A | 37c Flag, self-adhesive booklet stamp, #3637 | 8.00 |

2002
| SP1442 | 37c Toy coils, #3638-3641 | 8.00 |

2003
| SP1442A | 37c Antique Toys booklet stamps, #3642a, 3643a, 3644a, 3644ff | 8.75 |

2002
SP1443	60c Coverlet Eagle, #3646	6.50
SP1444	$3.85 Jefferson Memorial, #3647	12.00
SP1445	$13.65 Capitol Dome, #3648	27.50
SP1446	(34c+11c) Heroes of 2001, #B2	16.00
SP1447	37c Masters of American Photography, #3649	25.00
SP1448	37c John James Audubon, #3650	7.25
SP1449	37c Harry Houdini, #3651	7.25
SP1450	37c Official coil, #O159	7.00
SP1451	37c Andy Warhol, #3652	7.25
SP1452	37c Teddy Bears, #3653-3656	8.00
SP1453	37c,60c Love, #3657-3658	8.00
SP1454	37c Ogden Nash, #3659	7.25
SP1455	37c Duke Kahanamoku, #3660	7.50
SP1456	37c American Bats, #3661-3664	8.00
SP1457	37c Women in Journalism, #3665-3668	9.75
SP1458	37c Irving Berlin, #3669	7.25
SP1459	37c Neuter and Spay, #3670-3671	7.75
SP1460	37c Hanukkah, #3672	7.00
SP1461	37c Kwanzaa, #3673	7.00
SP1462	37c Eid #3674	7.00
SP1463	37c Christmas Madonna, #3675	7.25
SP1464	37c Christmas Snowmen, #3676-3679	8.00
SP1465	37c Cary Grant, #3692	9.25
SP1466	(5c) Sea Coast, #3693	7.25
SP1467	37c Hawaiian Missionary Stamps, #3694	13.00
SP1468	37c Happy Birthday, #3695	7.25
SP1469	37c Greetings from America, #3696-3745	37.50

2003
SP1470	37c Thurgood Marshall, #3746	7.50
SP1471	37c Chinese New Year, #3747	7.50
SP1472	37c Zora Neale Hurston, #3748	7.50

2003-08
SP1473	1c Tiffany Lamp, #3749	7.00
SP1473A	1c Tiffany Lamp, litho., #3749A	6.00
SP1475	10c American Clock, #3757	7.00
SP1476	2c Navajo Necklace, #3751-3752, 2005	7.00
SP1477	2c Navajo Necklace, #3753	7.00
SP1478	3c Silver Coffeepot, #3754	7.00
SP1479	4c Chippendale Chair, #3755	7.00
SP1480	5c Toleware, #3756	7.00
SP1481	2c Navajo Necklace, #3750	7.00
SP1482	1c Tiffany Lamp coil, #3758	7.00
SP1482	1c Tiffany Lamp coil, litho., #3758A	6.00
SP1483	3c Silver Coffeepot coil, #3759	7.00
SP1484	4c Chippendale Chair coil, #3761	7.00
SP1486	10c American Clock coil, #3762	7.00
SP1487	10c American Clock litho. coil, #3763	6.00
SP1490	$1 Wisdom, #3766	9.00
SP1493	(10c) New York Public Library Lion, perf. 10 vert, #3769	7.50

2004
| SP1494 | (10c) Atlas Statue, #3770 | 7.00 |

2003
SP1495	80c Special Olympics, #3771	8.50
SP1496	37c American Filmmaking: Behind the Scenes, #3772	13.50
SP1497	37c Ohio Statehood, Bicent., #3773	7.50
SP1498	37c Pelican Island National Wildlife Refuge, #3774	7.50
SP1499	(5c) Sea Coast perforated coil, #3775	7.50
SP1500	37c Old Glory, #3776-3780	8.00
SP1501	37c Cesar E. Chavez, #3781	7.50
SP1502	37c Louisiana Purchase, #3782	7.50
SP1503	37c First Flight of Wright Brothers, #3783	7.50
SP1504	37c Purple Heart, #3784	7.50
SP1505	37c Purple Heart, #3784A	7.50
SP1506	37c Audrey Hepburn, #3786	8.50
SP1507	37c Southeastern Lighthouses, #3787-3791	9.00
SP1508	(25c) Eagles, two different stamps from #3792-3801	6.50
SP1508A	(25c) Eagles, #3792-3801	10.00
SP1508Ab	(25c) Eagles, dated 2005, #3792a-3801b	10.00
SP1509	37c Arctic Tundra, #3802	12.50
SP1510	37c Korean War Veterans Memorial, #3803	7.00

SP1511	37c Mary Cassatt Paintings, #3804-3807	8.00
SP1512	37c Early Football Heroes, #3808-3811	10.00
SP1513	37c Roy Acuff, #3812	7.00
SP1514	37c District of Columbia, #3813	6.50
SP1515	37c Reptiles And Amphibians, #3814-3818	9.00
SP1516	(37c+8c) Stop Family Violence, #B3	7.25
SP1517	37c Christmas Madonna, #3820	6.50
SP1518	37c Christmas Holiday Music Makers, 2 sets of #3821-3824	7.50
SP1519	37c Snowy Egret coil, #3829	6.50

2004
SP1520	37c Snowy Egret booklet stamp, #3830	6.50
SP1521	37c Pacific Coral Reef, #3831	17.50
SP1522	37c Chinese New Year, #3832	7.25
SP1523	37c Love, #3833	6.50
SP1524	37c Paul Robeson, #3834	6.00
SP1525	37c Theodor Seuss Geisel (Dr. Seuss), #3835	8.00
SP1526	37c Love (White Lilacs and Pink Roses), #3836	6.00
SP1527	60c Love (Five Varieties of Pink Roses), #3837	6.00
SP1528	37c US Air Force Academy, #3838	6.50
SP1529	(5c) Sea Coast coil reprint, serpentine die cut 9½x10, #3785	6.00

A souvenir page containing the original printing of No. 3785 was not prepared as there was no first day cancel applied to that stamp.

SP1530	37c Henry Mancini, #3839	6.50
SP1531	37c American Choreographers, #3840-3843	8.00
SP1532	(25c) Eagles, perforated, #3844-3853	10.00
SP1533	37c Lewis and Clark sheet stamp, #3854 (11 cancels)	12.00
SP1534	37c Lewis and Clark booklet stamps, #3855-3856 (11 cancels)	12.00
SP1535	37c Isamu Noguchi, #3857-3861	7.50
SP1536	37c National World War II Memorial, #3862	6.00
SP1537	37c Summer Olympic Games, Athens, #3863	6.00
SP1538	(5c) Sea Coast coil, perf. 9¾ vert., #3864	6.00
SP1539	37c Disney Characters, #3865-3868	9.00
SP1540	37c USS Constellation, #3869	6.00
SP1541	37c R. Buckminster Fuller, #3870	6.00
SP1542	37c James Baldwin, #3871	6.00
SP1543	37c Martin Johnson Heade, #3872	6.00
SP1544	37c Art of the American Indian, #3873	11.00
SP1547	37c John Wayne, #3876	9.00
SP1548	37c Sickle Cell Disease Awareness, #3877	6.00
SP1549	37c Cloudscapes, #3878	11.00
SP1550	37c Christmas Madonna, #3879	6.50
SP1551	37c Hanukkah, #3880	6.00
SP1552	37c Kwanzaa, #3881	6.00
SP1553	37c Moss Hart, #3882	6.00
SP1554	37c Christmas Santa Claus Ornaments, #3883-3894	10.00

2005
| SP1555 | 37c Chinese New Year double-sided sheet, #3895 | 20.00 |

No. SP1555 was sold in a shrink-wrapped package containing the announcement page, a stamp mount, a cardboard backing and one pane of No. 3895 canceled on both sides.

SP1556	37c Marian Anderson, #3896	6.00
SP1557	37c Ronald Reagan, #3897	11.00
SP1558	37c Love, #3898	6.00
SP1559	37c Northeast Deciduous Forest, #3899	13.50
SP1560	37c Spring Flowers, #3900-3903	7.50
SP1561	37c Robert Penn Warren, #3904	6.00
SP1562	37c Yip Harburg, #3905	6.00
SP1563	37c American Scientists, #3906-3909	7.50
SP1564	37c Modern American Architecture, #3910	12.00
SP1565	37c Henry Fonda, #3911	6.00
SP1566	37c Disney Characters, #3912-3915	9.00
SP1567	37c Advances in Aviation, pane of #3916-3925	15.00
SP1568	37c Rio Grande Blankets, #3926-3929	7.50
SP1568A	37c Presidential Libraries, #3930	10.00
SP1569	37c Sporty Cars, #3931-3935	8.75
SP1570	37c Arthur Ashe, #3936	6.50
SP1571	37c To Form a More Perfect Union, #3937	10.00
SP1572	37c Child Health, #3938	6.00
SP1573	37c Let's Dance, #3939-3942	8.00
SP1574	37c Greta Garbo, #3943	7.75
SP1575	37c Jim Henson and the Muppets, #3944	11.00
SP1576	37c Constellations, #3945-3948	7.50
SP1577	37c Christmas, #3949-3960	10.00
SP1578	37c Distinguished Marines, #3961-3964	8.00
SP1579	(37c) Flag and Statue of Liberty, #3965-3967, 3970, 3972, 3974, 3975	10.00

No. SP1579 consists of two sheets.

2006
| SP1580 | (39c) Love, #3976 | 6.00 |
| SP1582 | 39c Flag and Statue of Liberty, #3978, 3981, 3982, 3983, 3985 | 7.50 |

SP1583	39c Flag and Statue of Liberty Coil, perf. 10 vert, #3979	7.50
SP1584	39c Flag and Statue of Liberty Coil serpentine die cut 11 vert., #3980	6.00
a.	Like #1584, but dated and canceled 2/8/06, "S" plate number text	6.00
b.	Like #1584a, but with "V" in plate number text	6.00

No. SP1584 is dated and canceled 1/9/06.

SP1585	39c Flag and Statue of Liberty, #3985b	6.00
SP1591	39c Children's Book Animals, #3987-3994	10.00
SP1592	39c Turin Winter Olympics, #3995	6.00
SP1593	39c Hattie McDaniel, #3996	6.00
SP1594	39c Chinese New Year, #3997	10.00
SP1595	63c Bryce Canyon, #C139	6.00
SP1596	75c Great Smoky Mountains National Park, #C140	6.00
SP1597	84c Yosemite National Park, #C141	6.00
SP1598	39c Official, #O160	6.00
SP1599	Weddings, #3998-3999	7.50
SP1600	24c Common Buckeye Butterfly, #4000-4002	7.50
SP1601	39c Crops, #4003-4017	12.00
SP1602	$4.05 X-Plane, #4018	10.00
SP1603	$14.40 X-Plane, #4019	22.50
SP1604	39c Sugar Ray Robinson, #4020	6.00
SP1605	39c Benjamin Franklin, #4021-4024	7.50
SP1606	39c Disney Characters, #4025-4028	7.50
SP1607	39c Love, #4029	6.00
SP1608	39c Katherine Anne Porter, #4030	6.00
SP1609	39c Amber Alert, #4031	6.00
SP1610	39c Purple Heart, #4032	6.00
SP1611	39c Wonders of America, #4033-4072	40.00
SP1612	39c Samuel de Champlain, #4073	7.50
SP1613	Samuel de Champlain souvenir sheet, #4074	7.50
SP1614	Washington 2006 World Philatelic Exhibition souvenir sheet, #4075	16.00
SP1615	39c Distinguished American Diplomats souvenir sheet, #4076	7.50
SP1616	39c Judy Garland, #4077	6.00
SP1617	39c Ronald Reagan, #4078	6.00
SP1618	39c Happy Birthday, #4079	6.00
SP1619	39c Baseball Sluggers, #4080-4083	7.50
SP1620	39c DC Comics Superheroes, #4084	15.00
SP1621	39c Motorcycles, #4085-4088	7.50
SP1622	39c Quilts of Gee's Bend, Alabama, #4089-4098	10.00
SP1623	39c Southern Florida Wetland, #4099	10.00
SP1624	$1 Official with solid blue background, #O161	7.50
SP1625	39c Christmas Madonna, #4100	6.00
SP1626	39c Christmas Snowflakes, #4101-4116	10.00
SP1627	39c Eid, #4117	6.00
SP1628	39c Hanukkah, #4118	6.00
SP1629	39c Kwanzaa, #4119	6.00

2007-2008
SP1630	39c Ella Fitzgerald, #4120	6.00
SP1631	39c Oklahoma Statehood, #4121	6.00
SP1632	39c Love, #4122	6.00
SP1633	84c International Polar Year souvenir sheet, #4123	7.50
SP1634	39c Henry Wadsworth Longfellow, #4124	6.00
SP1635	(41c) "Forever" stamps, #4125-4128	7.50
SP1635a	(42c) Forever stamp dated 2008, #4127f	6.00
SP1635b	(42c) Forever stamps dated 2008, #4125b, 4126b	6.00
SP1635c	(42c) Forever stamp dated 2008, #4127j	6.00
SP1636	(41c) Non-denominated Flag, #4129-4135	10.00
SP1637	41c Settlement of Jamestown, #4136	6.00
SP1638	26c Florida Panther, #4137, 4139, 4141, 4142	7.50
SP1639	17c Bighorn Sheep, #4138	6.00
SP1640	17c Bighorn Sheep coil, #4140	6.00
SP1641	41c Star Wars, #4143	10.00
SP1642	69c Okefenokee Swamp, #C142	6.00
SP1643	90c Hagatna Bay, Guam, #C143	6.00
SP1644	$4.60 Air Force One, #4144	12.00
SP1645	$16.25 Marine One, #4145	27.50
SP1646	41c Pacific Lighthouses, #4146-4150	7.50
SP1647	41c Official coil, #O162	6.00
SP1648	Love Hearts, #4151-4152	7.50
SP1649	41c Pollination, #4156b, 4156c	6.00
SP1650	(10c) Patriotic Banner, #4157-4158	6.00
SP1651	41c Marvel Comics Superheroes, #4159	15.00
SP1652	41c Vintage Mahogany Speedboats, #4160-4163	7.50
SP1653	41c Purple Heart, #4164	6.00
SP1654	41c Louis Comfort Tiffany, #4165	6.00
SP1655	41c Flowers, #4166-4185	15.00
SP1656	41c Flag, #4186-4191	10.00
SP1657	41c Disney Characters, #4192-4195	7.50
SP1658	41c Celebrate, #4196	6.00
SP1659	41c James Stewart, #4197	6.00
SP1660	41c Alpine Tundra, #4198	10.00
SP1661	41c Gerald R. Ford, #4199	6.00
SP1662	41c Jury Duty, #4200	6.00
SP1663	41c Mendez v. Westminster, #4201	6.00
SP1664	41c Eid, #4202	6.00
SP1665	41c Auroras, #4203-4204	6.00
SP1666	41c Yoda, #4205	6.00
SP1667	41c Christmas Madonna, #4206	6.00
SP1668	41c Christmas Knits, #4209, 4210, 4212, 4215	7.50

No. SP1668 appears to have a representative sampling of Nos. 4207-4218, and other examples may show different stamps from the set.

SP1669	41c Hanukkah, #4219	6.00
SP1670	41c Kwanzaa, #4220	6.00
SP1671	41c Chinese New Year, #4221	6.00
SP1672	41c Charles W. Chesnutt, #4222	6.00
SP1673	41c Marjorie Kinnan Rawlings, #4223	6.00

2008

SP1674	41c American Scientists, #4224-4227	7.50
SP1675	41c Flags, #4230, 4244, 4245, 4247 (lilac sheet)	7.50

No. SP1675 appears to have a representative sampling of Nos. 4228-4231 and Nos. 4244-4247.

SP1676	41c Flags, #4234, 4236, 4237, 4243 (gray sheet)	7.50

No. SP1676 appears to have a representative sampling of Nos. 4232-4243.

SP1677	42c American Journalists, #4248-4252	7.50
SP1678	27c Tropical Fruit, #4253-4262	10.00
SP1679	42c Purple Heart, #4263-4264	6.00
SP1680	42c Frank Sinatra, #4265	6.00
SP1681	72c 13-Mile Woods, New Hampshire, #C144	6.00
SP1682	94c Trunk Bay, St. John, Virgin Islands, #C145	7.50
SP1683	42c Minnesota Statehood, #4266	6.00
SP1684	62c Dragonfly, #4267	7.50
SP1685	$4.80 Mount Rushmore, #4268	12.00

SP1686	$16.50 Hoover Dam, #4269	25.00
SP1687	42c Love, #4270	6.00
SP1688	42c, Wedding Hearts, #4271-4272 59c	7.50
SP1689	42c Flags of Our Nation, #4273-4282	10.00
SP1690	42c Flags of Our Nation, #4283-4292	10.00
SP1695	42c Charles and Ray Eames, #4333	15.00
SP1696	42c Summer Olympics, #4334	6.00
SP1697	42c Celebrate, #4335	6.00
SP1698	42c Vintage Black Cinema, #4336-4340	7.50
SP1699	42c Take Me Out to the Ball Game, #4341	6.00
SP1700	42c Disney Characters - Imagination, #4342-4345	7.50
SP1701	42c Albert Bierstadt, #4346	6.00
SP1702	42c Sunflower, #4347	6.00
SP1703	(5c) Sea Coast coil, litho. #4348	6.00
SP1704	42c Latin Jazz, #4349	6.00
SP1705	42c Bette Davis, #4350	6.00
SP1706	42c Eid, #4351	6.00
SP1707	42c Great Lakes Dunes, #4352	10.00
SP1708	42c Automobiles of the 1950s, #4353-4357	7.50
SP1709	42c Alzheimer's Disease Awareness #4358	6.00

SP1710	42c Christmas Madonna, #4359	6.00
SP1711	42c Christmas Nutcrackers, #4362, 4363, 4365, 4368	7.50

No. SP1711 appears to have a representative sampling of Nos. 4360-4371.

SP1712	42c Hanukkah, #4372	6.00
SP1713	42c Kwanzaa, #4373	6.00
SP1714	42c Alaska Statehood, #4374	6.00
SP1716	42c Oregon Statehood, #4376	6.00
SP1717	42c Edgar Allan Poe, #4377	6.00
SP1718	$4.95 Redwood Forest, #4378	12.00
SP1719	$17.50 Old Faithful, #4379	27.50
SP1720	42c Abraham Lincoln, #4380-4383	7.50

COMPUTER VENDED POSTAGE

1992

SPCVP1	29c Postage and Mailing Center (PMC) coil strip of 3, #31	4.75

1994

SPCVP2	29c Postage and Mailing Center (PMC) horiz. coil strip of 3, #32	5.00

1996

SPCVP3	32c Postage and Mailing Center (PMC) horiz. strip of 3, #33	6.00

INTERNATIONAL REPLY COUPONS

Coupons produced by the Universal Postal Union for member countries to provide for payment of postage on a return letter from a foreign country. Exchangeable for a stamp representing single-rate ordinary postage (and starting with the use of Type D3, airmail postage) to a foreign country under the terms of contract as printed on the face of the coupon in French and the language of the issuing country and on the reverse in four, five or six other languages.

Postmasters are instructed to apply a postmark indicating date of sale to the left circle on the coupon. When offered for exchange for stamps, the receiving postmaster is instructed to cancel the right circle.

Coupons with no postmark are not valid for exchange. Coupons with two postmarks have been redeemed and normally are kept by the post office making the exchange. **Coupons with one postmark are valued here.** Some coupons with a stamp added to pay an increased rate are listed in footnotes.

The following is a list of all varieties issued by the Universal Postal Union for any or all member countries.
Dates are those when the rate went into effect. The date that any item was put on sale in the United States can be very different.

Type A — Face

Wmk. "25c Union Postale Universelle 25c"
1907-20

| A1 | Face | Name of country in letters 1½mm high. |
| | Reverse | Printed rules between paragraphs German text contains four lines. |

1907-20

| A2 | Face | Same as A1. |
| | Reverse | Same as A1 but without rules between paragraphs. |

1910-20

| A3 | Face | Same as A1 and A2. |
| | Reverse | Same as A2 except German text has but three lines. |

1912-20

| A4 | Face | Name of country in bold face type; letters 2mm to 2½mm high. |
| | Reverse | Same as A3. |

1922-25

| A5 | Face | French words "le mois d'émission écoulé, deux mois encore." |
| | Reverse | As A3 and A4 but overprinted with new contract in red; last line of red German text has five words. |

Wmk. "50c Union Postale Universelle 50c"
1925-26

| A6 | Face | Same as A5. |
| | Reverse | Four paragraphs of five lines each. |

1926-29

| A7 | Face | French words "il est valable pendant un délai de six mois." |

| Reverse | As A6 but overprinted with new contract in red; last line of red German text has two words. |

Wmk. "40c Union Postale Universelle 40c"
1926-29

| A8 | Face | Design redrawn. Without lines in hemispheres. |
| | Reverse | Four paragraphs of four lines each. |

Type B — Face

1931-35 **Wmk. Double-lined "UPU"**

| B1 | Face | French words "d'une lettre simple." |
| | Reverse | Four paragraphs of three lines each. |

1935-36

| B2 | Face | French words "d'une lettre ordinaire de port simple." |
| | Reverse | Last line of German text contains two words. |

1936-37

| B3 | Face | Same as B2. |
| | Reverse | Last line of German text contains one word. |

1937-40

| B4 | Face | Same as B2 and B3. "Any Country of the Union." |
| | Reverse | German text is in German Gothic type. |

1945

| B5 | Face | "Any Country of the Universal Postal Union." |
| | Reverse | Each paragraph reads "Universal Postal Union." |

Type B5 exists without central printing on face.

1950

| B6 | Face | Same as B5. |
| | Reverse | Five paragraphs (English, Arabic, Chinese, Spanish, Russian). |

1954

| B7 | Face | Same as B5. |
| | Reverse | Six paragraphs (German, English, Arabic, Chinese, Spanish, Russian.) |

Type C — Face

1968 **Wmk. Single-lined "UPU" Multiple**

| C1 | Face | French words "d'une lettre ordinaire de port simple." |
| | Reverse | Six paragraphs (German, English, Arabic, Chinese, Spanish, Russian). |

Foreign coupons, but not U.S., of type C1 are known with large double-lined "UPU" watermark, as on type B coupons.

1971

| C2 | Face | French words "d'une lettre ordinaire du premier échelon de poids." |
| | Reverse | Six paragraphs (German, English, Arabic, Chinese, Spanish, Russian). |

Type D — Face

1975   Wmk. Single-lined "UPU" Multiple

D1	Face	French words "d'une lettre ordinaire, expédiée à l'étranger par voie de surface."
	Reverse	Six paragraphs (German, English, Arabic, Chinese, Russian).
D2	Face	Left box does not have third line of French and dotted circle.
	Reverse	Same as D1.

On D1 and D2 the watermark runs horizontally or vertically.

D3	Face	....aerienne. Left box as D2 with (facultative) added.
	Reverse	As D1, all references are to air service.
D4	Face	As D3, "CN 01 / (ancien C22)" replaces "C22."

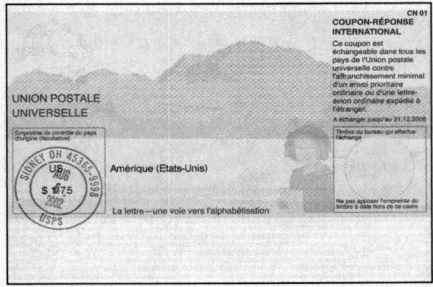

Type E — Face

Wmk. "UPU" in cross & 8-pointed star horiz. across sheet

2002

E1	Face	Shown
	Reverse	Six paragraphs (German, English, Arabic, Chinese, Spanish, Russian), repeating expiration date paragraph in same languages, bar code.

Coupons exist without the validating origination markings. Type E coupons have a bar code on the reverse that identifies the originating country and the date of printing.

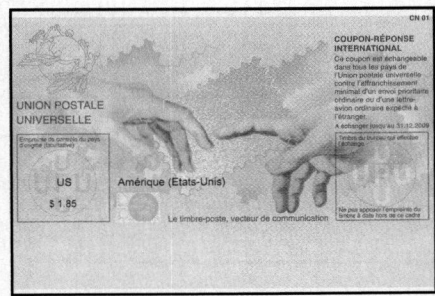

Type F — Face

Wmk. "UPU" in cross & 8-pointed star horiz. across sheet

2006

F1	Face	Shown
	Reverse	Six paragraphs (German, English, Arabic, Chinese, Spanish, Russian), repeating expiration date paragraph in same languages, bar code.

UNITED NATIONS (6/07)

REPLY COUPONS ISSUED FOR THE UNITED STATES

1907, Oct. 1
IRC2 A2 6c **slate green & gray green** 27.50
Rules omitted on reverse.
Earliest documented use: Oct. 10, 1907.

1912
IRC3 A4 6c **slate green & gray green** 32.50
Three line English paragraph on face.

1922, Jan. 1
IRC4 A5 11c **slate green & gray green,** name 81 ½mm long 25.00
    a. Name 88 ½mm long 25.00
Five line English paragraph on face. Red overprint on reverse.

1925-26
IRC5 A6 11c **slate green & gray green** 22.50
Five line English paragraph on face. No overprint on reverse.
IRC6 A6 9c **slate green & gray green,** *Oct. 1, 1925* 22.50

1926
IRC7 A7 9c **slate green & gray green** 32.50
Four line English paragraph on face. Red overprint on reverse.
IRC8 A8 9c **slate green & gray green** 25.00
Without lines in hemispheres.

1935
IRC9 B2 9c **blue & yellow** 11.00
On reverse, last line of German text contains two words.

1936
IRC10 B3 9c **blue and yellow** 11.00
On reverse, last line of German text contains one word.

1937
IRC11 B4 9c **blue & yellow** 8.00
On reverse, German text in German Gothic type.

1945
IRC12 B5 9c **blue & yellow,** Italian text on reverse in 4 lines 6.00
    a. Italian text on reverse in 3 lines 7.50

1948, Oct. 15
IRC13 B5 11c **blue & yellow** 5.00
On face, "Universal Postal Union" replaces "Union."

1950
IRC14 B6 11c **blue & yellow** 6.00
On reverse, text in English, Arabic, Chinese, Spanish, Russian.

1954, July 1
IRC15 B7 13c **blue & yellow** 6.00
On reverse, text in German, English, Arabic, Chinese, Spanish, Russian.
Varieties: period under "u" of "amount" in English text on reverse, and period under "n" of "amount." Also, country name either 47mm or 50mm long.

No. IRC15 Surcharged in Various Manners

1959, May 2
IRC16 B7 15c on 13c **blue & yellow** 6.00
Individual post offices were instructed to surcharge the 13c coupon, resulting in many types of surcharge in various inks. For example, "REVALUED 15 CENTS," reading vertically; "15," etc.

1959, May 2
IRC17 B7 15c **blue & yellow** 5.00

1964
IRC18 B7 15c **blue & yellow** 5.00
    a. Reverse printing 60mm deep instead of 65mm (smaller Arabic characters) 5.00
On face, box at lower left: "Empreinte de contrôle / du Pays d'origine / (date facultative)" replaces "Timbre du / Bureau / d'Emission."

1969
IRC19 C1 15c **blue & yellow** 4.50

1971, July 1
IRC20 C2 22c **blue & yellow** 4.50

No. IRC20 Surcharged in Various Manners

1974, Jan. 5
IRC21 C2 26c on 22c **blue & yellow** 6.50
See note after No. IRC16.

1975, Jan. 2
IRC22 D1 26c **blue & yellow** 4.00

No. IRC22 Surcharged in Various Manners

1976, Jan. 3
IRC23 D1 42c on 26c **blue & yellow** 6.50
See note after No. IRC16. Several post offices are known to have surcharged No. IRC21 (42c on 26c on 22c).

Provisional surcharges on Nos. IRC24-IRC27 were not permitted.

1976, Jan. 3
IRC24 D1 42c **blue & yellow** 4.50

Many foreign countries use non-denominated IRCs. The U.S. has never ordered or used these "generic" items.

1981, July 1
IRC26 D1 65c **blue & yellow** 5.50

1986, Jan. 1
IRC27 D2 80c **blue & yellow** 5.50

1988, Apr. 3
IRC28 D2 95c **blue & yellow** 5.00
IRC29 D3 95c **blue & yellow** 5.00
    a. "9.1992" in lower left corner 5.00
Post offices were authorized on July 11, 1995 to revalue remaining stock of 95c IRCs to $1.05 by applying 10c in stamps until new stock (No. 30) arrived. All 95c varieties are known revalued thus.
The date of issue of No. 29 is not known. Earliest documented use: Jan. 2, 1992.
No. 28 exists with inverted watermark (tops of letters facing right).

1995
IRC30 D4 $1.05 **blue & yellow,** "4.95" in lower left corner 3.75
    a. "10.98" in lower left corner 3.75
    b. As "a," with "United States of America" in left box 8.00
"1.05" comes 1 ½mm or 3mm high. 3mm height has numerals more widely spaced.
Earliest documented use: July 12, 1995.
Post offices were authorized on Jan. 7, 2001, to revalue remaining stock of $1.05 IRCs to $1.75 by applying 70c in stamps until new stock arrived. All $1.05 varieties are known revalued thus. Value $7.

2002, Jan. 1
IRC31 E1 $1.75 **multicolored** 3.50
Effective Jan. 8, 2006, the rate increased to $1.85. Post offices were authorized to revalue remaining stock of $1.75 IRCs to $1.85 by applying 10c in stamps.

2006, Aug. 17
IRC32 F1 $1.85 **multicolored** 3.75
Effective May 14, 2007, the rate increased to $2. Post offices were authorized to revalue remaining stock of $1.85 IRCs to $2 by applying 15c in stamps or postal validation imprinter labels.

POST OFFICE SEALS

Official Seals began to appear in 1872. They do not express any value, having no franking power.
   The first seal issued was designed to prevent tampering with registered letters while in transit. It was intended to be affixed over the juncture of the flaps of the large official envelopes in which registered mail letters were enclosed or stamp requisitions were shipped to postmasters and was so used exclusively. Beginning in 1877 (No. OX1 and later), Post Office Seals were used to repair damaged letters, reseal those opened by mistake or by customs inspectors, and to seal letters received by the Post Office unsealed.
   Values for unused Post Office Seals are for those without creases. Uncanceled seals without gum will sell for less.
   Used Post Office Seals will usually have creases from being applied over the edges of damaged or accidentally opened covers but will have either cancels, precancels or a signature or notation indicating use on the seal. Creased, uncanceled seals without gum are considered used and will sell for less than either an unused or a canceled used seal.
   Covers with Post Office Seals are almost always damaged except in cases when the seal was applied to a cover marked "Received Unsealed." The values shown are for covers where the damage is consistent with the application of the seal.
   Post Office Seals must be tied or exhibit some auxiliary marking or docketing to qualify for "on cover" values. No. OXF1 must bear a circular date stamp cancel and the cover to which it is affixed must bear the identical cancel to qualify for the "on cover" value.

REGISTRY SEALS

RGS1

National Bank Note Co.
Typographed from a copper plate of 30 subjects
(3x10) in two panes of 15 (3x5)

1872	Unwmk.	White Wove Paper	Perf. 12	
OXF1	RGS1	green	30.00	7.50
		On cover, Barber signature		40.00
		On cover, Terrell signature		60.00
		Block of 4	500.00	
		Pane of 15	2,500.	
a.		Yellow green, pelure paper	75.00	40.00
b.		Imperf., pair	1,250.	
c.		Horizontally laid paper	500.00	
d.		Printed on both sides	500.00	
e.		Printed on both sides, back inverted	800.00	
f.		Double impression	750.00	—
g.		Double impression, one inverted	—	750.00

The second impression of Nos. OXF1d-OXF1g, is very faint.
   Also issued as a pane of 9 (3x3) (attributed to Continental Bank Note Co.).

Cancellations

Black		7.50
Blue		+5.00
Red		+15.00
Green		+50.00
Magenta		+50.00
Carrier		+25.00
Panama		—
Shanghai		—

Special Printings
Continental Bank Note Co.
Plate of 30 subjects (5x6)

1875(?)		Hard White Wove Paper	Perf. 12
		Without Gum	
OXF2	RGS1	bluish green	1,000.

American Bank Note Co.
Plate of 15 subjects (5x3)

1880 (?)		Soft Porous Paper	Perf. 12
		Without Gum	
OXF3	RGS1	bluish green	1,000.

POSTAGE STAMP AGENCY SEALS

Used to seal registered pouches containing stamps for distribution to Post Offices.

PSA1

Background size: 102x52mm.

1875-93		Litho.	Unwmk.	*Die Cut*
		Barber Signature		
OXF4	PSA1	brown & black		25.00
		On cover		60.00

PSA2

Hazen Signature, Text 86mm Wide

OXF5	PSA2	brown & black, *1877*	25.00
		On cover	60.00

PSA3

Hazen Signature, Text 87mm Wide

OXF6	PSA3	pink & red, *1886*	50.00
		On cover	350.00
a.		Salmon & red	60.00
		On cover	400.00

PSA4

Harris Signature

OXF7	PSA4	pink & red, *1887*	45.00
		On cover	150.00
a.		Salmon & red,	55.00
		On cover	175.00

PSA5

Hazen Signature, Text 90½mm Wide

OXF8	PSA5	pink & red, *1889*	40.00
		On cover	140.00

PSA6

Craige Signature

OXF9	PSA6	pink & red, *1893*	45.00
		On cover	200.00

PSA7

Background size: 120½x67mm.

1894		Litho.	Unwmk.	*Die Cut*
		Craige Signature, "3rd Asst. P.M.G."		
OXF10	PSA7	pink & black		55.00
		On cover		200.00

PSA8

Craige Signature, "Third Assistant Postmaster General"

OXF11	PSA8	pink & black	35.00
		On cover	150.00
a.		Deep pink & black	35.00
		On cover	150.00

PSA9

**"John A. Merritt" in Sans-Serif Capitals at Left.
Two Horizontal Lines Obliterating "Kerr Craige."**

1897

OXF12	PSA9	pale pink & black	100.00
		On cover	500.00

OPEN AT END.

THE POSTMASTER TO WHOM THIS PACKAGE IS SENT MUST NOTE
ITS CONDITION AND CAREFULLY COUNT ITS CONTENTS.

If it shows signs of having been tampered
with, the fact should be reported to the THIRD
ASSISTANT POSTMASTER-GENERAL.

If the count shows a deficiency in the contents of the package, or an excess,
the case must be treated as indicated in Sec. 120 P. L. & R. The Postmaster
should not correspond with the Stamp Agent, but with the Third Assistant
Postmaster-General. See also Sec. 1088 as to misdirected packages.

JOHN A. MERRITT,
Third Assistant Postmaster-General.

PSA10

1897-1914

Merritt Signature

OXF13	PSA10	rose & black	35.00
		On cover	130.00

OPEN AT END.

THE POSTMASTER TO WHOM THIS PACKAGE IS SENT MUST NOTE
ITS CONDITION AND CAREFULLY COUNT ITS CONTENTS.

If it shows signs of having been tampered
with, the fact should be reported to the THIRD
ASSISTANT POSTMASTER-GENERAL.

If the count shows a deficiency in the contents of the package, or an excess,
the case must be treated as indicated in Sec. 120, P. L. & R. The Postmaster should
not correspond with the Stamp Agent, but with the Third Assistant Postmaster-
General. See also Sec. 1088 as to misdirected packages.

EDWIN C. MADDEN,
Third Assistant Postmaster-General.

PSA11

Madden Signature

OXF14	PSA11	rose & black, *1899*	40.00
		On cover	145.00

The first paragraph of text reads: "...MUST NOTE ITS CON-
DITION AND CAREFULLY COUNT..."

OPEN AT END.

THE POSTMASTER TO WHOM THIS PACKAGE IS SENT MUST NOTE ITS
CONDITION AND CAREFULLY COUNT ITS CONTENTS.

If it shows signs of having been tampered
with, the fact should be reported to the THIRD
ASSISTANT POSTMASTER-GENERAL.

INVOICE FOR THIS PACKAGE OF STAMPS WILL BE FOUND WITHIN.
Count the stamps carefully, IN THE PRESENCE OF A DISINTERESTED WITNESS, as indicated
on stub of invoice, and if an excess or shortage is found, treat the case as directed
in Section 333, P. L. & R., notifying the Third Assistant Postmaster-General, Division
of Stamps. See Section 878, P. L. & R., as to misdirected packages.

PSA13

"Section 878"

OXF15	PSA13	rose & black, *1907*	30.00
		On cover	140.00

OPEN AT END.

THE POSTMASTER TO WHOM THIS PACKAGE IS SENT MUST NOTE ITS CONDITION
AND IMMEDIATELY UPON ITS RECEIPT CAREFULLY COUNT ITS CONTENTS.

If it shows signs of having been tampered
with, the fact should be reported to the Third
Assistant Postmaster General.

INVOICE FOR THIS PACKAGE OF STAMPS WILL BE FOUND WITHIN. Count the
stamps carefully, IN THE PRESENCE OF A DISINTERESTED WITNESS, as indicated
on invoice, and if an excess or shortage is found, treat the case as directed in
Section 333, P. L. & R., as amended (1912 Postal Guide, page 43), notifying the
Third Assistant Postmaster-General, Division of Stamps. See Section 878, P. L. & R.,
as to misdirected packages.

PSA14

OXF15A	PSA14	rose & black, *1912*	—
		On cover	

OPEN AT END

THE POSTMASTER TO WHOM THIS PACKAGE IS SENT MUST NOTE ITS CONDITION
AND IMMEDIATELY UPON ITS RECEIPT CAREFULLY COUNT ITS CONTENTS.

If it shows signs of having been tampered with, the
fact should be reported to the Third Assistant Postmaster
General, Division of Stamps.

INVOICE FOR THIS PACKAGE OF STAMPS WILL BE FOUND WITHIN. Count
the stamps carefully, IN THE PRESENCE OF A DISINTERESTED WITNESS, as indicated on invoice, and if an excess or shortage is found, treat the case as directed
in Section 159, P. L. & R., notifying the Third Assistant Postmaster-General, Division
of Stamps. See Section 970, P. L. & R., as to misdirected packages.

PSA15

"Section 970"

OXF16	PSA15	rose & black, *1912*	35.00
		On cover	175.00

OPEN AT END

THE POSTMASTER TO WHOM THIS PACKAGE IS SENT MUST NOTE ITS CONDITION
AND IMMEDIATELY UPON ITS RECEIPT CAREFULLY COUNT ITS CONTENTS.

If it shows signs of having been tampered with, the fact should
be reported to the Third Assistant Postmaster General, Division
of Stamps.

INVOICE FOR THIS PACKAGE OF STAMPS WILL BE FOUND WITHIN. Count
the stamps carefully, IN THE PRESENCE OF A DISINTERESTED WITNESS, as indicated on invoice, and if an excess or shortage is found, treat the case as directed
in Section 159, P. L. & R., notifying the Third Assistant Postmaster-General, Division
of Stamps. See Section 970, P. L. & R., as to misdirected packages.

PSA16

OXF17	PSA16	rose & black, *1914*	40.00
		On cover	175.00

DEAD LETTER OFFICE SEALS

Nos. OXA1-OXA9 were used only on mail that could
be forwarded to the intended recipient, after examination in the Dead Letter Office. Nos. OXB1-OXB5 were
used only on mail returned to the originating post
office.

Post Office Department,
Office of Third Assistant Postmaster General,
DIVISION OF DEAD LETTERS,
TO THE PERSON ADDRESSED:
Inform your correspondent of the correct name of your
post office.
TO THE POSTMASTER:
If this letter cannot be delivered you will, at the expira-
tion of SEVEN days, stamp the letter with your postmarking
stamp, and send it to the Dead Letter Office as "Unmail-
able," as required by Sec. 443, Postal Regulations.
A. D. HAZEN,
Third Assistant P. M. Gen'l.

"Hazen" — DLO1

1884   Litho.   *Perf. 10½*

OXA1	DLO1	black	45.00
		On cover	175.00

Perf. 12

OXA1A	DLO1	black	25.00
		On cover	125.00

POST OFFICE DEPARTMENT,
DEAD-LETTER OFFICE.
TO THE PERSON ADDRESSED:
Inform your correspondent of the correct name of your
post office.
TO THE POSTMASTER:
If this letter cannot be delivered you will, at the expira-
tion of SEVEN days, stamp the letter with your postmarking
stamp, and send it to the Dead-Letter Office as "Unmail-
able," duly entered on bill (Form 1522½), as required by
Sec. 609 of the Postal Regulations.
JNO. B. BAIRD,
Superintendent.

"Baird" — DLO2

1889

OXA2	DLO2	black	45.00
		On cover	300.00

POST OFFICE DEPARTMENT,
DEAD-LETTER OFFICE.
TO THE PERSON ADDRESSED:
Inform your correspondent of the correct name of your
post office.
TO THE POSTMASTER:
If this letter cannot be delivered you will, at the expira-
tion of SEVEN days, stamp the letter with your postmarking
stamp, and send it to the Dead-Letter Office as "Unmail-
able," duly entered on bill (Form 1522½), as required by
Paragraph 6 of Sec. 609 of the Postal Regulations.
SUPERINTENDENT.

"Superintendent" — DLO3

1891   *Perf. 10½*

OXA3	DLO3	black	35.00
		On cover	175.00

Perf. 12

OXA3A	DLO3	black	25.00
		On cover	125.00

POST OFFICE DEPARTMENT,
Office of First Ass't P. M. General,
DEAD-LETTER OFFICE.
TO THE PERSON ADDRESSED:
Inform your correspondent of the correct name of your
post office.
TO THE POSTMASTER:
If this letter cannot be delivered you will, at the expira-
tion of SEVEN days, stamp the letter with your postmarking
stamp, and send it to the Dead-Letter Office as "Unmail-
able," duly entered on bill (Form 1522½), as required by
Paragraph 6 of Sec. 566 of the Postal Regulations.
5—2807

"5-2807" — DLO4

1892   *Perf. 12*

OXA4	DLO4	black	25.00
		On cover	125.00

POST OFFICE DEPARTMENT,
Office of First Ass't P. M. General,
DEAD-LETTER OFFICE.
TO THE PERSON ADDRESSED:
Inform your correspondent of the correct name of your
post office.
TO THE POSTMASTER:
If this letter can not be delivered you will, at the expira-
tion of SEVEN days, stamp the letter with your postmarking
stamp, and send it to the Dead-Letter Office as "Unmail-
able," duly entered on bill (Form 1522½), as required by
Paragraph 6 of Sec. 566 of the Postal Regulations.
5—3282

"5-3282" — DLO5

1895   *Perf. 12*

OXA5	DLO5	black	22.50
		On cover	110.00

1898(?)   *Hyphen hole perf. 7*

OXA6	DLO5	black	40.00
		On cover	175.00

The first paragraph of text reads: "...MUST NOTE ITS CON-
DITION AND IMMEDIATELY UPON.."

PSA12

OXF14A	PSA12	rose & black, *1899*	—
		On cover	

DLO6

Similar to DLO5 but smaller type used for instructions to the postmasters.

1900			**Perf. 12**
OXA7	DLO6	**black**	20.00
		On cover	100.00

"5-3282" at Right — DLO7

1902(?) 12			**Perf. 12**
OXA8	DLO7	**black**	25.00
		On cover	125.00

"5-3282" at Center — DLO8

1902(?)			**Perf. 12**
OXA9	DLO8	**black**	25.00
		On cover	125.00

DLO9

1881-91			**Die Cut**

Incomplete Year Date ("188")

OXB1	DLO9	**black**	—
		On cover	1,000.

"1883" — DLO10

Complete Year Date

OXB2	DLO10	**black** (1882)	75.00
		On cover	400.00
OXB3	DLO10	**black** (1883)	75.00
		On cover	400.00
OXB4	DLO10	**black** (1886)	75.00
		On cover	400.00

DLO11

Incomplete Year Date ("189")

OXB5	DLO11	**black** (1891?)	75.00
		On cover	500.00

POST OFFICE SEALS

No. OX1 supposedly was issued as a Dead Letter Office Seal. It was prepared for use in the Dead Letter Office but was distributed to other offices and used in the same way as later seals. Most on-cover examples are normal Post Office usages from larger East Coast cities. New York and Philadelphia predominate. Very few examples with Dead Letter Office markings are recorded. For that reason, No. OX1 is listed with the other Post Office Seals.

POS1

("Post Obitum" in background.)
National Bank Note Co.
Plate of 100 subjects (10x10)
Silk Paper

1877		**Engr.**		**Perf. 12**
OX1	POS1	**brown**	45.00	25.00
		On cover		1,200.
		Block of 4	500.00	

Earliest documented use: April 17, 1879.

POS2

American Bank Note Co.
Plate of 100 subjects (10x10) in two panes of 50 bearing imprint of American Bank Note Co. in the selvage.
(Also plates of 50 (10x5) subjects)

1879		**Engr.**		**Perf. 12**

Thin, crisp, semi-translucent paper, yellowish gum

OX2	POS2	**red brown**	3.00	1.00
		On cover		85.00
		Block of 4	15.00	
		Margin block with imprint	25.00	
a.		**Brown**	10.00	5.00
		On cover		200.00
		Block of 4	60.00	
		Margin block with imprint	85.00	

Seal impression can be clearly seen when viewed from the back.

Plate of 50 subjects (5x10). Four imprints of the American Bank Note Co. centered on each side of the pane in the selvage, with a reversed "2" to the right of the top imprint.

1879(?)
Thick, opaque paper, clear transparent gum

OX3	POS2	**yellow brown**	150.00	150.00

1881(?)
Thin, hard porous paper, clear transparent gum

OX4	POS2	**deep brown**	75.00	
		Block of 4	350.00	
		Margin block of 4 with imprint (side)	400.00	
		Margin block of 6 with imprint (bottom)	550.00	
		Margin block of 4 with imprint & reversed "2" (top)	575.00	

No. OX4 is the so-called "Special Printing." It was produced from a new plate prepared from the original die. It received little usage, but at least two full panes are known to have existed.

Colors
Beginning with OX5, many Official Seals exhibit a wide variety of shades. Minimal care was exercised in their printing. It is not uncommon for seals within a single pane to vary in shade from dark to very light. No attempt is being made here to list all of the various shades separately.

POS3

Typographed
Without words in lower label.
Outer frame line at top and left is thick and heavy (compare with POS4).
Plate of 72 subjects (8x9)

1888				**Rough perf. 12**

Medium thick, crisp paper

OX5	POS3	**chocolate** (shades)	.75	.75
		On cover		50.00
		On cover with typeset seal No. LOX8		—
		Block of 4	5.00	
a.		**Imperf, pair**	50.00	
		Sheet of 72, imperf	—	

Imperforates
Imperforates of Nos. OX6, OX7, OX10 and OX13 are believed to be printer's waste. No seals were issued imperforate, though some may have been sent to post offices.

Plate of 42 subjects (7x6)

1889				**Rough perf. 12**

Thick to extremely thick paper

OX6	POS3	**chocolate** (shades)	.75	.50
		On cover		40.00
		Block of 4	5.00	

1889(?)				**Perf. 12**
OX7	POS3	**bister brown** (shades)	.75	.50
		On cover		40.00
		Block of 4	5.00	
a.		**Rose brown**	4.00	2.50
		On cover		65.00
		Block of 4	22.50	
b.		**Yellow brown**	2.00	2.00

	On cover		50.00	
	Block of 4		10.00	
c.	Imperf. vertically, pair		25.00	—
d.	Imperf. horizontally, pair		25.00	—
e.	Vertical pair, imperf. between		20.00	
f.	Horizontal pair, imperf. between		75.00	
g.	Double impression			—

Cancellation

Puerto Rico		+75.00

Examples of No. OX7 with multiple impressions widely spaced or at angles to each other, are found on normal paper and various documents. These are printer's waste.

1892			**Rouletted 5½**	
OX8	POS3	light brown (shades)	20.00	15.00
		On cover		*1,250.*
		Block of 4	300.00	

1895 (?)			**Hyphen Hole Perf. 7**	
OX9	POS3	gray brown	7.50	5.00
		On cover		700.00
		Block of 4	200.00	

Earliest documented use: Feb. 3, 1897.

1898(?)			**Perf. 12**	

Thin soft paper

OX10	POS3	brown (shades)	1.50	1.50
		On cover		250.00
		Block of 4	8.00	

POS4

Plate of 143 (11x13)

Outer frame line at top and left is thin.
Otherwise similar to POS3.

1900		**Litho.**	**Perf. 12**	
OX11	POS4	red brown	.50	.25
		On cover		30.00
		Block of 4	2.50	
a.	Gray brown		2.00	1.25
		On cover		45.00
		Block of 4	15.00	
b.	Dark brown		2.50	*4.50*
		On cover		85.00
		Block of 4	15.00	
c.	Orange brown		.75	*2.00*
		On cover		75.00
		Block of 4	4.00	

Most imperfs and part perfs are printers waste. Some genuine perforation errors may have been issued to post offices.

Watermarks

Watermarks cover only a portion of the panes. Many stamps in each pane did not receive any of the watermark. Values for watermarked panes are for examples with at least 50% of the watermark present.

Similar to POS4 but smaller.
Design: 38x23mm
Issued in panes of 20 (5x4)

1907		**Typo.**	**Perf. 12**	
OX12	POS4	bright royal blue	2.00	2.00
		On cover		45.00
		Pane of 20	60.00	

Earliest documented use: June 1, 1907.

OX13	POS4	blue (shades)	.20	.20
		On cover		25.00
		Pane of 20	20.00	
a.	Wmkd. Seal of U.S. in sheet (2 types)		1.50	1.50
		Pane of 20	50.00	
b.	Wmkd. "Rolleston Mills" in sheet		1.00	1.00
		Pane of 20	40.00	
c.	Wmkd. "Birchwood Superfine" in sheet		—	—
		Pane of 20	—	
d.	Pelure paper		20.00	20.00
e.	Toned paper		25.00	25.00
f.	Printed on both sides		—	—

Numerous varieties such as imperf., part perf., tete beche, and double impressions exist. These seem to be from printer's waste. Some genuine perforation errors may have been issued to post offices.
All recorded examples of No. OX13f show the reverse-side impression inverted in relation to the impression on the face.

1912			**Hyphen Hole 6½**	
OX14	POS4	blue	1.75	1.50
		On cover		75.00
		Pane of 20	45.00	
a.	Wmkd. Seal of U.S. in sheet		10.00	10.00

		Pane of 20	300.00	
b.	Wmkd. "Rolleston Mills" in sheet		2.50	2.50
		Pane of 20	80.00	

Panes of 10 were made from panes of 20 for use in smaller post offices. Complete booklets with covers exist.

1913			**Perf. 12 x Hyphen Hole 6½**	
OX15	POS4	blue	3.50	3.00
		On cover		100.00
		Pane of 20	110.00	
a.	Hyphen-hole perf 6½ (right) x Perf. 12 (left, top, bottom)		15.00	—
		Pane of 20	150.00	
b.	Wmkd. Seal of U.S. in sheet		4.50	4.00
		Pane of 20	125.00	
c.	As "a" and "b"		20.00	—

No. OX15a comes from panes that are perfed between the left selvage and the seals.

1913			**Hyphen Hole 6½ x Perf. 12**	
OX16	POS4	blue	5.25	5.25
		On cover		400.00
		Pane of 20	250.00	
a.	Wmkd. Seal of U.S. in sheet		15.00	15.00
		Pane of 20	300.00	
b.	Wmkd. "Rolleston Mills" in sheet		—	—
		Pane of 20	—	—

1916			**Perf. 12**	
OX17	POS4	black, *pink*	1.25	1.25
		On cover		150.00
		Pane of 20	75.00	
a.	Vert. pair, imperf. horizontally			—

Three complete panes of No. OX17a have been reported.

1917			**Perf. 12**	
OX18	POS4	gray black	.40	.40
		On cover		27.50
		Pane of 20	40.00	
a.	Black		.50	.50
		On cover		30.00
		Pane of 20	45.00	
b.	Vert. pair, imperf horizontally		25.00	
c.	Horiz. pair, imperf vertically		20.00	
d.	Vertical pair, imperf between		60.00	
e.	Horizontal pair, imperf between		35.00	
f.	Imperf, pair		50.00	

POS5

Quartermaster General's Office
Issued in panes of 10 (2x5) without selvage.

1919			**Perf. 12**	
OX19	POS5	indigo	300.	
		Block of 4	*1,500.*	
		Pane of 10	*3,600.*	

Rouletted 7

OX20	POS5	indigo	—	*3,250.*

The pane format of No. OX20 is not known. One of the few reported examples is rouletted on four sides.
Nos. OX19-OX20 were used on mail to and from the Procurement Division of the Quartermaster General's Office. After five weeks of use the seals were withdrawn when the Mail and Records Section became a full branch of the Quartermaster General's Office.

POS6

Issued in panes of 20 (5x4) and 16 (4x4).
Panes of 10 were made from panes of 20 for use in smaller post offices.

1919			**Perf. 12 (sometimes rough)**	

Thin, white, crisp paper

OX21	POS6	black (shades)	.20	.20
		On cover		10.00
		Pane of 20	10.00	
a.	Imperf, pair		15.00	
		On cover		—
b.	Vert. pair, imperf horiz.		10.00	
c.	Horiz. pair, imperf vert.		10.00	
d.	Vert. pair, imperf btwn.		25.00	
e.	Horiz. pair, imperf btwn.		25.00	

f.	Wmkd. eagle and star in sheet (1936?)		2.00	2.00
		Pane of 20	70.00	
g.	As "f," imperf, pair		35.00	
h.	As "f," vert. pair, imperf horiz.		27.50	
i.	As "f," vert. pair, imperf btwn.		27.50	
j.	Wmkd. "Certificate Bond" in sheet (1936?)		10.00	10.00
		Pane of 20	300.00	

The paper used for Nos. OX21-OX27 is thin enough to allow reading text on the envelope.

Earliest documented use: 1920.

1936(?)			**Perf. 12x9**	
OX22	POS6	black (shades)	7.50	7.50
		On cover		85.00
		Pane of 20	200.00	
a.	Vert. pair, imperf horiz.		50.00	
b.	Horiz. pair, imperf vert.		50.00	
c.	Wmkd. eagle and star in sheet		7.50	7.50
		Pane of 20	200.00	
d.	As "c," vert. pair, imperf horiz.		50.00	
e.	As "c," horiz. pair, imperf vert.		50.00	

Earliest documented use: Oct. 1936 (No. OX22 or OX23.)

1936(?)			**Perf. 12x8½**	
OX23	POS6	black (shades)	2.50	2.50
		On cover		40.00
		Pane of 20	75.00	
a.	Wmkd. eagle and star in sheet		4.00	4.00
		Pane of 20	110.00	

1936(?)			**Perf. 12½**	
OX24	POS6	gray black, pane of 20		—

1936(?)			**Perf. 8½**	
OX25	POS6	gray black		—
a.	Wmkd. eagle and star in sheet			—

1936(?)			**Perf. 12x9½**	
OX26	POS6	gray black, pane of 20		—

1936(?)			**Perf. 11½**	
OX27	POS6	gray black		—
		On cover		—

Medium to thick, opaque, egg or cream colored paper

1946(?)			**Perf. 12**	
OX28	POS6	gray black	.40	.40
		On cover		25.00
		Pane of 20	22.50	
a.	Vert. pair, imperf btwn.		15.00	

1946(?)			**Perf. 12½**	
OX29	POS6	gray black	.50	.50
		On cover		25.00
		Pane of 20	25.00	

1947(?)			**Perf. 12½x8½**	
OX30	POS6	gray black	1.50	1.50
		On cover		45.00
		Pane of 20	50.00	

1947(?)			**Perf. 8½**	
OX31	POS6	gray black	1.50	1.50
		On cover		45.00
		Pane of 20	50.00	

1947(?)			**Perf. 8½x12**	
OX32	POS6	gray black		—

1947(?)			**Perf. 8½x8**	
OX33	POS6	gray black, on cover		—

1947(?)			**Perf. 8x8½**	
OX33A	POS6	gray black, on cover		—

Thick, gray, very soft paper

1948			**Perf. 12½ (sometimes rough)**	
OX34	POS6	gray black	1.00	1.00
		On cover		35.00
		Pane of 16	45.00	

1948(?)			**Perf. 8½**	
OX35	POS6	gray black	5.00	5.00
		On cover		60.00
		Pane of 16	—	

1948(?)			**Perf. 12½x8½**	
OX36	POS6	gray black		—
		Pane of 10		—
		Pane of 20		—

1948(?)			**Perf. 8½x12½**	
OX37	POS6	gray black		—

1948			**Hyphen Hole Perf. 9½**	
OX38	POS6	gray black	15.00	15.00
		On cover		100.00
		Pane of 5, imperf at sides	200.00	
		Pane of 16	350.00	

Pane of 5, tab inscribed "16-56146-1 GPO."

1950(?)   *Hyphen Hole Perf. 9½ x Imperf*
Medium thick, cream paper
Design width: 37½mm

OX39	POS6	**gray black,** imperf at		
		sides	.25	.20
		On cover		12.50
		Pane of 5, imperf at sides	1.25	
a.		Vert. pair, imperf between	10.00	
b.		Pane of 5, imperf	15.00	
c.		Pane of 5, imperf at top & btwn.		
		rows 2 & 3, 4 & 5	20.00	

Pane of 5 tab inscribed, "16-56164-1 GPO."
Earliest documented use: Jan. 23, 1950.

1969(?)   *Hyphen Hole Perf. 9½ x Imperf*
Medium thick, white paper
Design width: 38½mm

OX40	POS6	**gray black**	.25	.20
		On cover		30.00
		Pane of 5, imperf at sides	2.25	
a.		Vert. pair, imperf. btwn.	10.00	
b.		Pane of 5, Imperf	20.00	
c.		Double impression	—	

Tab inscribed, "c43-16-56164-1 GPO"

Earliest documented use: Feb. 11, 1969.

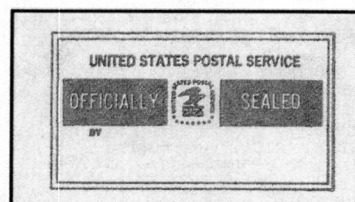

POS7

On Nos. OX41-OX50, tab is inscribed, "LABEL 21, JULY 1971."

1972   **Litho.**   *Rouletted 9½ x Imperf*

OX41	POS7	**black**	.20	.20
		On cover		12.50
		Pane of 5	2.00	
a.		Imperf, pair	10.00	

1972(?)   *Rouletted 6½ x Imperf*

OX42	POS7	**black**	.20	.20
		On cover		5.00
		Pane of 5	2.75	

1973(?)   **Litho.**   *Hyphen Hole 7 x Imperf*

OX43	POS7	**black**	.30	.20
		On cover		7.50
		Pane of 5	9.00	

1976(?)   **Litho.**   *Rouletted 8½ x Imperf*

OX44	POS7	**black**	.20	.20
		On cover		7.50
		Pane of 5	2.00	

1979(?)   **Litho.**   *Perf. 12½ x Imperf*

OX45	POS7	**black**	.20	.20
		On cover		7.50
		Pane of 5	2.25	
		Small holes	.20	.20
		On cover		7.50
		Pane of 5	2.25	

1988(?)   **Litho.**   *Die Cut*
Self-Adhesive

OX46	POS7	**black,** 38x21mm, tagged,		
		fluorescent paper	.25	.25
		On cover		7.50
		Pane of 5	3.50	
OX47	POS7	**bluish black,** 38x21mm,		
		untagged, non-fluores-		
		cent paper	.25	.25
		On cover		7.50
		Pane of 5	3.50	
OX48	POS7	**gray** (shades), 37x21mm	.25	.25
		On cover		7.50
		Pane of 5	3.50	
OX49	POS7	**black,** 40x21mm	.50	.50
		On cover		15.00

Imperf

OX50	POS7	**purple,** 37x21mm	—	—
		On cover		—

No. OX47 is on a creamier, thicker paper than No. OX46.
On No. OX49, BY is 2x1mm, P of POSTAL is left of P in POSTAL of Emblem. Tab inscribed as No. OX41, but 1's have no bottom serif.
Earliest documented use: No. OX50, Dec. 12, 1995.

POS8

Tab inscribed "LABEL 21, JAN. 1992."

1992   **Size: 44x22mm**   *Die Cut*
Self-adhesive

OX51	POS8	**black**	1.00	1.00
		On cover		25.00
		Pane of 5	10.00	

Earliest documented use: Mar. 1992.

1992?   *Die Cut*
Self-Adhesive
Size: 41x21mm

OX52	POS8	**black**	.25	.25
		On cover		7.50
		Pane of 5	3.50	

No. OX52 exists on both white and brown backing paper. Those on brown backing paper are worth more.

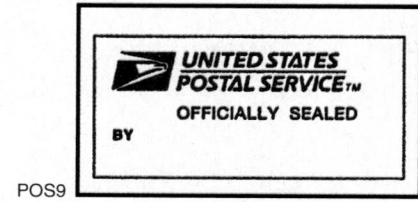

POS9

Tab inscribed "LABEL 21, April 1994."

1994   *Die Cut*
Self-Adhesive

OX53	POS9	**black**	.25	.25
		On cover		7.50
		Pane of 5	3.50	

POS10

Tab inscribed "LABEL 21, August 1996."

1996   *Die Cut*
Self-Adhesive

OX54	POS10	**black**	.25	.25
		On cover		7.50
		Pane of 5	2.00	
a.		"OFFICALLY"	1.00	—
		On cover		20.00
		Pane of 5	8.00	

POS11

Tab inscribed "LABEL 21, August 1996."

1996   *Die Cut*
Self-Adhesive

OX55	POS11	**black**	.25	.25
		On cover		7.50
		Pane of 5	3.00	

POS12

Seal inscribed "LABEL 21, August 1996."

2006 (?)   *Die Cut*
Self-Adhesive

OX56	POS12	**black**	.25	.25
		On cover		7.50
		Pane of 5	3.00	

Although No. OX56 is inscribed "August 1996," it likely was issued in 2006.

SEA POST SEAL

This seal was used by clerks on North German Lloyd ships on the New York - Bremen route.

SPS1

1895 (?)   *Perf. 12*

OXSP1	SPS1	**black**	400.00	400.00
		On cover		3,750.

TYPESET SEALS

These seals were privately printed for sale mostly to Fourth Class Post Offices. Many are extremely rare. Unquestioned varieties are listed. Many others exist.
All are imperf or die cut except Nos. LOX7-LOX11 and LOX36.

TSS1

LOX1	TSS1	**black**	500.00	500.00
		On cover		

TSS2

LOX2	TSS2	**black,** 15 diamonds vertically		
		in frame	1,500.	1,500.
a.		14 diamonds vertically		750.
b.		14 diamonds vertically, no period af-		
		ter "DEPARTMENT"		750.
c.		"OFFICALLY" misspelling, 14		
		diamonds vertically	1,500.	
		On cover		

TSS3

| LOX3 | TSS3 | black | — | — |
| | | On cover | | |

TSS4

| LOX4 | TSS4 | black, *pink* | 1,250. | |

No. LOX4 used is valued with minor flaws.

TSS5

| LOX5 | TSS5 | black | 500.00 | — |
| LOX5A | TSS5 | black, *pink* | | |

TSS6

| LOX6 | TSS6 | black | — | — |

TSS7

Rouletted 9½ horizontally

| LOX7 | TSS7 | black | 1,000. | — |

TSS8

Printed and distributed by Morrill Bros., P.O. Supply Printers, Fulton, N.Y., in panes of 4, two tete beche pairs.

Rouletted 11½, 12½, 16½ in black at top & side

LOX8	TSS8	black, rouletted 11½	100.00	100.00
		On cover		1,250.
a.		black, rouletted 12½	100.00	100.00
		On cover		1,250.
b.		black, rouletted 11½ by 12½	100.00	100.00
		On cover		1,250.
c.		black, rouletted 12½ by 11½	100.00	100.00
		On cover		1,250.
		Sheet of 4, 1 each Nos. LOX8, LOX8a-LOX8c	1,250.	
d.		black, rouletted 11½ and 12½ compound by 11½	250.00	150.00
e.		black, rouletted 11½ and 12½ compound by 12½	250.00	150.00
		Sheet of 4, 1 each Nos. LOX8a, LOX8c, LOX8d-LOX8e	1,500.	
f.		black, rouletted 16½	300.00	300.00
		On cover		1,750.
g.		black, rouletted 16½ on 3 sides	—	

Gauge of rouletting on Nos. LOX8d and LOX8e transitions about one-quarter of way across top edge of seal. A sheet of 4 of No. LOX8f exists and is in the Luff reference collection of the Philatelic Foundation. No. LOX8g is unique.

TSS9

Solid lines above and below "OFFICIALLY SEALED."

Rouletted 12½, 16½ in black between

| LOX9 | TSS9 | black | 500.00 | 500.00 |
| | | On cover | | |

TSS10

Dotted lines above and below "OFFICIALLY SEALED."

Rouletted 12½ in black

| LOX10 | TSS10 | black, *pink* | 500.00 | 750.00 |
| a. | | Dot after "OFFICIALLY" | | 1,500. |

Rouletted 11½, 12½ or 16½ in black

LOX11	TSS10	black, rouletted 12½ at top and side	2.00	75.00
		On cover		1,000.
		Sheet of 4	15.00	
a.		Double impression	400.00	
		Sheet of 4	2,000.	
b.		Double impression, one inverted	400.00	
c.		Dot after "OFFICIALLY"	4.00	150.00
		On cover		1,500.
		Sheet of 4, one seal with dot	12.50	
d.		black, rouletted 11½ at top or bottom	200.00	
e.		blue, rouletted 11½ at top or bottom		2,500.
f.		black, rouletted 11½ at top and side	100.00	
		Sheet of 4	1,500.	
g.		black, rouletted 12½ by 11½		
h.		black, rouletted 16½ at top or bottom	250.00	
		Sheet of 2, both seals with dot	1,750.	
		Sheet of 2, tete beche	—	
i.		black, rouletted 16½ at top and side	250.00	

Dyed examples of No. LOX11 are frequently misrepresented as No. LOX10.

TSS11

Printed and distributed by The Lemoyne Supply Co., Lemoyne, Pa.

| LOX12 | TSS11 | black | 250.00 | — |
| | | On cover | | |

Outer and inner framelines on No. LOX12 have wide spacing and are closed at the corners. Thick lines above and below "OFFICIALLY SEALED".

TSS11A

| LOX13 | TSS11A | blue | 750.00 | — |
| LOX13A | TSS11A | black | | |

Outer and inner framelines on Nos. LOX13 and LOX13A have narrow spacing at left and right and are open at the corners. Thin lines above and below "OFFICIALLY SEALED". No. LOX13A is unique.

TSS12

| LOX14 | TSS12 | blue | 1,750. | 1,750. |

Outer and inner framelines on No. LOX14 have wide spacing and are closed at the corners. Spacing between letters of "OFFICIALLY SEALED" compressed, and letters are flatter and wider.

TSS13

LOX15 TSS13   **black**   1,250.   —
         On cover   2,000.
No. LOX15 unused is valued with small faults and crease.
See No. LOX29 for a similar design in blue.

TSS14

LOX16 TSS14   **blue**   1,500.   1,000.
No. LOX16 used is valued with usual crease, thin spots and
small tear.

TSS15

Period after "Sealed"; 6mm between "Officially" and "Sealed".
LOX17 TSS15   **dark blue**   100.00   200.00
         On cover   1,000.
   a. Printed on both sides   1,750.
LOX18 TSS15   **black**   300.00   —
         On cover   1,250.
Two types of No. LOX18: Type I (shown) has vertical misalignment of "U. S. Po" in first line of text; Type II corrects the
misalignment. Both types found with approx. equal frequency.

TSS15A

No period after "Sealed"; 2mm between "Officially" and
"Sealed".
LOX18A TSS15A   **dark blue**   250.00   400.00

TSS16

LOX19 TSS16   **black**   600.00   —

TSS16A

LOX19A TSS16a   **black**   2,750.
No. LOX19A is unique. Valued based on 2000 auction sale.

Type I
TSS17

Type II — Bottom line in heavy type face. Period after "Office."
LOX20   TSS17   **black,** *light green* (Type I)   —   —
At least two different types or settings are known. The illus-
trated type has a dotted line above "BY" that does not show in
the illustration.
LOX20A TSS17   **black,** *light green* (Type II) 2,000.
No. LOX20A is valued with major thin at top center.

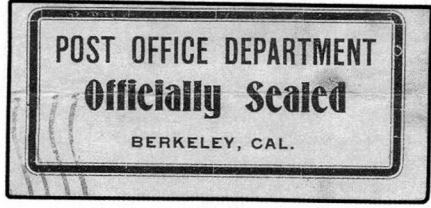

TSS18

LOX21   TSS18   **black**   750.00   —

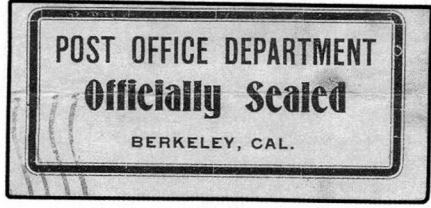

TSS18a

LOX21A TSS18a   **black**   —   1,500.
         On cover   1,500.
No. LOX21A unused is valued with crease and small faults.

TSS19

LOX22   TSS19   **black,** *blue*   2,000.
No. LOX22 is unique. It is creased and is valued as such.

TSS20

LOX23   TSS20   **black**   —

TSS21

LOX24   TSS21   **black, on cover**   3,000.

TSS22

LOX25   TSS22   **black**   1,350.
At least three examples of No. LOX25 exist. All have faults.
Value is for the finest example.

TSS23

LOX26   TSS23   **black**   1,100.
No. LOX26 used is valued with small fault.

TSS24

LOX27 TSS24 **black,** *dark brown red* 1,250.
No. LOX27 is valued with crease and small flaws.

TSS25

LOX28 TSS25 **black** —
On cover 2,700.
The on-cover seal shown was torn in half when the envelope was opened. Value is based on 2007 auction sale.

TSS26

LOX29 TSS26 **blue,** on cover 3,750.
No. LOX29 is unique.

TSS27

LOX30 TSS27 **black,** pair on cover 5,000.
No. LOX30 is unique. The seals were torn in half when the envelope was opened. Value is based on 2006 auction sale.

TSS28

LOX31 TSS28 **red,** *cream* 1,000.
No. LOX31 is unique. It has a thin spot and crease and is valued as such.

TSS29

LOX32 TSS29 **black** 1,250.

TSS30

LOX33 TSS30 **black** —

TSS31

LOX34 TSS31 **red,** *rose* 1,250.
On cover 1,500.

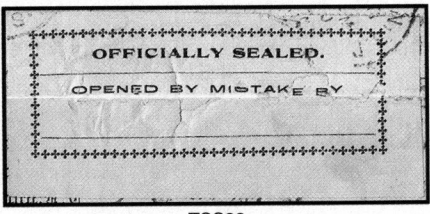

TSS32

LOX35 TSS32 **black,** on cover —

TSS33

Rouletted (at least one side)
LOX36 TSS33 **black**

TSS34

LOX37 TSS34 **green** —

TSS35

LOX38 TSS35 **black,** *tan* 1,250.

TSS36

LOX39 TSS36 **black,** *tan* 1,750.

TSS37

LOX40 TSS37 **black,** *tan* 1,750.

TSS38

LOX41 TSS38 **black**

Akron, N. Y. Post Office.

Officially Sealed.

Opened through mistake by

TSS39

LOX42   TSS39   **black,** on cover   —

OFFICIALLY SEALED.

OPENED BY MISTAKE.

By

TSS40

LOX43   TSS40   **black**   1,250.

U. S. Postoffice
OFFICIALLY SEALED

Opened by Mistake by

TSS41

LOX44   TSS41   **blue,** *yellow*   1,250.

TSS42

LOX45   TSS42   **dark blue**   1,250.

TEST STAMPS

Test stamps, also called "dummy stamps," came into being in the late 19th century, and their production continues to the present. These stamps have been printed by both the Bureau of Engraving and Printing and by private companies for use when the Post Office Department, United States Postal Service and other companies wanted to use test stamps rather than accountable paper (i.e., actual stamps that would have to be accounted for).

With the growth of automation and the development of vending equipment in the 20th century, the production and use of test stamps proliferated. A majority are very scarce, as these items generally were not made available to the general public or philatelists.

The test stamps listed here were produced for several purposes:
1. To develop and test production equipment, including printing presses and stamp and booklet manufacturing equipment.
2. To design stamp vending equipment by private companies.
3. To test, adjust and promote stamp affixing equipment by commercial vendors.
4. To test and adjust stamp vending equipment at dispensing sites by the Postal Service and private companies.

The test stamp listings are arranged into two sections, the first being sheet and coil stamps, and the second being booklets. These listings were formed by Steven R. Unkrich, in consultation with other leading collectors of test stamps. Thanks to Dan Undersander for supplying much of the information in this section's introduction. Those interested in learning more about test (dummy) stamps are invited to join the Dummy Stamps Study Group. Contact Terry Scott at trs@napanet.net.

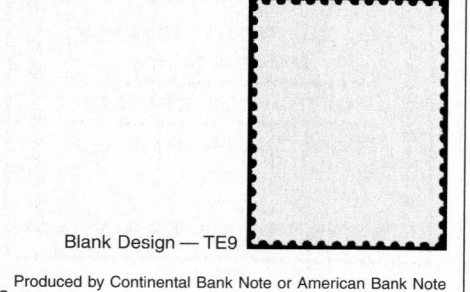

Blank Design — TE9

Produced by Continental Bank Note or American Bank Note Company.

1878-79   **Soft Paper**   **Unwmk.**   *Perf. 12*
TD9   TE9   blank   —
     Block of 4   —

See Nos. TD30, TD44-TD50A, TD75-TD76, TD79-TD82, TD83-TD86, TD106, TD113-TD114, TD122 for other blank design stamps.

Burt and Toby's Stamp Battery — TE9a

1890   *Perf. 12*
TD9A   TE9a   light green   —
        Perf. 12¼x12
TD9B   TE9a   lavender   —

Blank Design Type of 1878-79
Produced by Bureau of Engraving and Printing.

1907   **Wmk. 191**   *Perf. 12*
       Brownish Gum
TD10   TE9   blank   —

  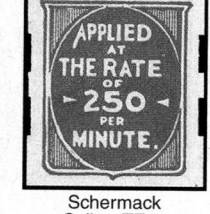

TE10   Schermack Coil — TE11

Mailometer Coil — TE12

1906-09   **Unwmk.**   *Perf. 12*
TD12   TE10   **rose red,** on cover   —
   Schermack Type III Perforations
TD13   TE11   **magenta**   —
         Pair   —
         Pasteup pair   —
TD14   TE12   **brown**   —
         On cover   —
         Pair   —
         Guide line pair   —
         Pasteup pair   —
  a.   Imperf.   100.00
         Pair   200.00
  b.   Pair, No. TD14 + No. TD14a   —
   Mailometer Type I Perforations
TD14C   TE11   **rose red**   —
         Pair   —
TD15   TE12   **brown**   —
         Pair   —
         Pasteup pair   —
   Mailometer Type II Perforations
TD15A   TE11   **brown**   —
         Pair   —
TD16   TE12   **red**   —
         Pair   —
         Guide line pair   —
         Pasteup pair   —
   Mailometer Type III Perforations
TD17   TE12   **brown**   —
         Pair   —

See Vending and Affixing Machines Perforations section for illustrations of perforation types.

Bureau of Engraving and Printing Test Stamps for Rotary Press Development

Numerals and Oval — TE13

Numerals and Alexander Hamilton — TE14

Nos. TD18-TD23 were the first test stamps used by the BEP during efforts to develop rotary press printing as a less costly method of stamp production than flat plate printing. Experiments were conducted with intaglio (engraving), letterpress (typography) and offset lithography printing. Engraving was the selected technique. The rotary press was developed under the direction of BEP Director Joseph E. Ralph, but is generally named the Stickney Press after its inventor and patent holder, Benjamin F. Stickney.

		1909-10	Engr.	Imperf.

Design: 19x22mm
Ungummed Soft Wove Paper

TD18	TE13	deep red	2,000.
		Block of 4	—
		Block of 12 with pencil inscription on back	14,000.

Inscription on block of 12 reads "first impression printed from an experimental press designed by J. E. Ralph & B. F. Stickney from intaglio roll JER."

Design: 19½x22½mm

TD19	TE14	red	125.00
		Block of 4	600.00

No. TD19 portrait has facial shading composed of fine lines and dots. Subjects spaced 3½mm horizontally and 2mm vertically. Large die proofs exist with "400894" on back. Value, $2,000.

Coil Stamps (Nos. TD20-TD21, TD23)
Typo.
Design: 19x22½mm
Perf. 12 Vert.
Ungummed Soft Wove Paper

TD20	TE14	deep red, 1910	1,000.

Three different die proofs are known for No. TD20. The first is black on thick glazed card, measuring 73x83mm, with inscription "first die proof impression of experimental surface die from surface print. JER April 25/10," with "420279" on back. Value, $2,000.

The second is deep red on thick glazed card, measuring 73x83mm, with inscription "Sample of surface printing from die: done by Bureau E&P 5/20/1910," with "420270" on back. Value, $1,500.

The third is deep red cut to design size on thick card with number stamps on back. Value, $1,000.

Perf. 12 Horiz.
Soft Wove Paper

TD21	TE14	deep red, 1910	3,100.

Perf. 12

TD22	TE14	deep red, 1910	—

The portrait on Nos. TD21-TD22 has facial shading composed of fine lines and small squares, open-centered when large.

Offset (Litho.)
Design: 19x21½mm
Perf. 10½ Horiz.

TD23	TE14	deep red, 1910	100.00
		Pair	200.00
		Pair, on cover	1,000.

The portrait of No. TD23 has facial shading composed of dots and short lines providing a coarse appearance.

Automatic Vending Co. Coil — TE15

		1909		Imperf.
TD24	TE15	dark red	—
		Horiz. pair	—
a.		Vert. pair, U.S. Automatic Vending Co. Type I separations	—

			On cover	—
b.		Vert. pair, imperf. horiz.	—

Rosback perf 11.75 Vert.

TD24C	TE15	red	—
		Horiz. pair	—
d.		Vert. pair, imperf. horiz.	—

Imperf

TD24E	TE15	green	—
		Vert. pair	—

No. TD24 exists as an imperf. block of 4. No. TD24C exists as a block of 4 imperf. horiz.

Simplex Mfg. Co. — TE16

		1909-10	Imperf.

Solid Background

TD25	TE16	red	75.00

Horizontal Lines in Background

TD26	TE16	green	60.00

Simplex Stamp Affixer — TE17

		1909-10	Imperf.
TD27	TE17	red	—

BEP Test Stamps for Offset Printing

Minerva Facing Right — TE18

Minerva Facing Left (Text Reversed) — TE19

Nos. TD28-TD29 were made to test the Harris offset press at the Bureau of Engraving and Printing. The offset method was not adopted in 1910 but several Harris presses were used to print revenue stamps and the offset postage issues of 1918-20.

		1910	Litho.	Imperf.

Design: 30½x34mm
Ungummed White Wove Paper

TD28	TE18	red	650.00
		Pair	1,300.
		Block of 4	—

Design: 30x33½mm

TD29	TE19	red	650.00
		Pair	1,300.
		Block of 4	—

Blank Design — TE20

		1910 ?	Rouletted 13¼ Vert.

Stamp Size: 25.5x25.75mm
Shiny Gum

TD30	TE20	blank, tan	20.00
		Pair	40.00

Standard Stamp Affixer Coils

Inscribed "Boston, Mass." — TE21

Inscribed "Everett, Mass." — TE22

Inscribed "Somerville, Mass." — TE23

		1910s		Perf. 10½ Vert.
TD31	TE21	green	—
		Pair	—
TD32	TE21	red	—
		Pair	—
TD33	TE22	green	20.00
		Pair	50.00
TD33A	TE22	red	20.00
		Pair	50.00

Alternating Perf. 8¼ and 8½ Vert.

TD34	TE23	green	20.00
		Pair	50.00

Perf. 8½ Vert.

TD35	TE23	light green	20.00
		Pair	50.00

Perf. 10½ Vert.

TD36	TE23	green	20.00
		Pair	50.00

Alternating Perf. 10.9 and 10.2 Vert.

TD36A	TE23	red	20.00
		Pair	50.00

Multipost Co. Coil — TE24a

TE24 Detail

TE24a Detail

Midland Supply Co. Coil — TE24b

1910-20   *Perf. 9¾ Vert.*
TD37	TE24	**red**	20.00
		Pair	50.00

Perf. 10¼ Vert.
TD38	TE24a	**carmine**	20.00
		Pair	50.00

Perf. 10½ Vert.
TD38A	TE24b	**red**	—
		Pair	—

No. TD37 has full shading lines, and No. TD38 has shorter shading lines.
No. TD38 exists precanceled Cleveland/Ohio between lines, in violet.

Extensive Manufacturing Co.
Coils — TE25

1911-13   *Perf. 8½ Horiz.*
TD39	TE25	**red & blue**	—
		Pair	—

Perf. 10¼ Vert.
TD40	TE25	**carmine & black**	35.00
		Pair	75.00

Perf. 10¾ Vert.
TD41	TE25	**carmine & black**	35.00
		Pair	75.00

Standard Mailing Machine Co.
Coils — TE26

1913   *Perf. 10½ Vert.*
TD42	TE26	**red**	40.00
		Pair	80.00
TD43	TE26	**light purple**	40.00
		Pair	80.00

Blank Designs Type of 1878-79

1910-27   *Imperf.*

Smooth Gum
TD44	TE9	**blank**	—
		Pair	—

Perf. 10½ Vert.
TD45	TE9	**blank**	—
		Pair	—

Schermack Type III Perforations
TD46	TE9	**blank**	—
		Pair	—
		Paste up pair	—

Mailometer Type I Perforations
TD47	TE9	**blank**	200.00
		Pair	—
		Paste up pair	—

Mailometer Type II Perforations
TD48	TE9	**blank**	—
		Pair	—
		Paste up pair	—

Mailometer Type III Perforations
TD49	TE9	**blank**	—
		Pair	—
		Paste up pair	—

Perf. 11 Vert. Schermack Type I 7-hole Perforations
TD50	TE9	**blank**	—
		Pair	—

Perf. 10 Vert. Schermack Type I 7-hole Perforations
TD50A	TE9	**blank**	—
		Pair	—

Expertization is recommended for No. TD44.

George Washington — TE27

1912   *Imperf.*

Without Gum
TD51	TE27	**brown**	100.00
		Pair	200.00
		Block of 4	450.00

No. TD51 tested a photo-etching process by Bruckmann A. G. of Munich, Germany.

Pence Mailing Machine —
TE27a

1914   *Perf 8½ Horiz.*
TD51A	TE27a	**red**	100.00
		Pair	—

New Jersey Vending Machine
Co. Coil — TE28

1914-16   *Perf. 10½ Vert.*
TD52	TE28	**red**	—
		Pair	—

National Envelope
Sealing and Stamp
Manufacturing
Coils — TE29

U.S. Stamp
Distributing and
Sales Corporation
Coil — TE29a

1915   *Perf. 8½ Horiz.*
TD53	TE29	**red & blue**	—
		Pair	—
TD54	TE29	**red**	—
		Pair	—

1919   *Perf. Alternating 8.5 and 8.35 Vert.*
TD54A	TE29a	**red**	—
		Pair	—

Mailometer Coils — TE30

1922   *Nine small perforation holes*
TD55	TE30	**red**	—
		Pair	—

Perf. 10¼ Vert. (10 small holes)
TD56	TE30	**deep purple**	—
		Pair	—

Perf. 12 Vert. (8 small holes)
TD57	TE30	**deep purple**	—
		Pair	—

Perf. 12 Vert. (9 small holes)
TD57A	TE30	**deep purple**	—
		Pair	—

Perf. 10¼ Vert.
TD58	TE30	**red**	—
		Pair	—
		On cover	—

Inscribed "10,000 Envelopes Per Hour"
Perf. 10½ Vert.
TD59	TE30	**red**	—
		Pair	—

TE30a

Perf. 10½ Vert.
TD60	TE30a	**red**	—
		Pair	—

TE30b

Perf. 10½ Vert.
TD60A	TE30b	**red**	—
		Pair	—

Wizard Label Affixer
Coil — TE31

1912-14   *Perf. 10¼ Vert.*
TD61	TE31	**red**	—
		Pair	—

Wizard Label Affixer
Coil — TE32

1920s   *Schermack Type III Perforations*
TD62 TE32   **red & blue**   —

Wizard Stamp Affixer Coil —
TE32a

1920s   *Perf. 10 Vert.*
TD62A TE32a   **red & blue**
                   Pair   —

Postage Stamp Machine Co.
Coil — TE33

1920s   *Perf. 8½ Vert.*
TD63 TE33   *red*
                 Pair   —

Natural Method Stamp Affixer
— TE33a

1910-30   *Perf. 11¾ Vert.*
TD63A TE33a   **red,** *tan*   —
                   Pair

Security Coil — TE33b

1910-30   *Perf. 8½ Horiz.*
TD63B TE33b   **red**   —
                   Pair

Licensed Sanitary
Postage Coil — TE34

1920s   *Perf. 10½ Horiz.*
TD64 TE34   **red**

TE34a

                   Pair   —
                              Perf. 10¾ Vert.
TD65 TE34a   **red**   20.00
                  Pair   50.00

Postcraft Stamp Affixer
Coil — TE35

1920s   *Perf. 10 Vert.*
TD66 TE35   color unknown   —
                 Pair

Vidaver Mailing Machine
Co. Inc. Coil — TE36

1920s   *Perf. 10½ Vert.*
TD67 TE36   **red**   90.00
                 Pair   180.00

Agnew Auto Mailing — TE37

1920s   *Perf.*
TD68 TE37   **red brown**   45.00

Royalty Stamp — TE38

1925 ?   *Perf.*
TD69 TE38   **red**   —

Molyneaux Automatic Mailing
Machine Coil — TE38a

1920s   *Perf. 11¾x12*
TD69A TE38a   **light blue green**   —
TD69B TE38a   **orange**   —

Stearns-Daniels Co.
Coil — TE39

1920s-30s   *Perf. 10 Vert.*
TD70 TE39   **green**   —
                 Pair

RO-TA-RE Stamp Affixer
Service Machines Company
— TE39a

1910-30   *Perf. Vert.*
TD70A TE39a   **blue**   —
                   Pair

Edison Dictating Machine
Coil — TE40

1920s-30s   *Perf. 10¼ Vert.*
TD71 TE40   **red**   60.00
                 Pair   125.00

Schermack Dummy
Coil — TE41

1920s-30s   *Perf. 10½ Horiz.*
TD72 TE41   **red**   —
                 Pair

National Postal Meter Co.,
Inc. Coil — TE42

1920s-30s   *Perf. 9¾ Vert.*
TD73 TE42   **red**   —
                 Pair

Stampmasters Inc.
Coil — TE43

1920s-30s   *Perf. 9¾ Vert.*
TD74 TE43   **violet**   15.00
                 Pair   30.00

Blank Design Types of 1878-79
Produced by Bureau of Engraving & Printing.

1927-30   *Perf. 9¾ Vert.*
                   Horiz. Ribbed Gum
TD75 TE9   blank, *cream*   .60
                Pair   1.25
        With Red Horizontal Lines 13½ mm Apart
TD76 TE9   blank, *1930-40*   .60
                Pair   1.25
                Pair with gap in lines   4.00
                Strip of 10 with wide and narrow line
                gaps   15.00
                Gaps appear every six stamps.

Central Machine & Supply Co.
Coil — TE44

1930s   *Perf. Vert.*

TD77	TE44	red	—
		Pair	—

Puritan Mailing Machine Co.
Coil — TE45

1930s   *Perf. 8½ Vert.*

TD78	TE45	red & black	—
		Pair	—

The Postamper Co. Coil —
TE45a

1930s   *Perf. 10½ Vert.*

TD78A	TE45a	red	—
		Pair	—

Peerless Stamp Affixer Coil —
TE45b

1930s   *Perf. 10½ Vert.*

TD78B	TE45b	red	—
		Pair	—

Blank Design Types of 1878-79
Produced by Electric Vendors (Zeigle), Inc.

1930s   *Perf. 10½ Vert.*
Shiny Smooth Gum

TD79	TE9	blank	15.00
		Pair	40.00
TD80	TE9	*blue*	15.00
		Pair	40.00
TD81	TE9	*green*	15.00
		Pair	40.00
TD82	TE9	*yellow*	15.00
		Pair	40.00

Blank Design Types of 1878-79
Produced by Bureau of Engraving & Printing.

1920s-1950s   *Perf. 10*
With Gum Breaker Ridges 5½mm Apart

TD83	TE9	blank, *1920s*	25.00
		Block of 4	100.00
		Vert. pair with horiz. gutter be-tween	—

With Gum Breaker Ridges 11mm Apart
Perf. 11x10½

TD84	TE9	blank, *1936*	25.00
		Block of 4	100.00
		Vert. pair with horiz. gutter be-tween	80.00

With Gum Breaker Ridges
Perf. 11x10½

TD84A	TE9	blank, *1956*	12.50
		Block of 4	50.00

Genuine examples of No. TD84A are known with blue, green or red defacement markings.

Stamp Size:40x25mm
With Gum Breaker Ridges
Brownish Gum
Perf. 11¼x10½

TD85	TE9	blank	50.00
		Block of 4	200.00

Produced by American Bank Note Co.
Perf. 12

TD86	TE9	blank pane of 50 with manuscript marginal markings, *1943*	—

No. TD86 was produced as a test for the Overrun Countries stamps.

Multipost Mailing System &
Equipment Coil — TE46

1930s-40s   *Perf. 9½ Vert.*

TD87	TE46	red	—
		Pair	—

Multipost Co. Walter I. Plant
Agent Coil — TE46a

1930s   *Perf. 11¾ Vert.*

TD87A	TE46a	red	—
		On cover	—
		Pair	—

Multipost Agents The Office
Appliance Co. Coil — TE46b

1930s   *Perf. 11¾ Vert.*

TD87B	TE46b	red	—
		Pair	—

Multipost Commercial
Controls Coil — TE47

1944-49   *Perf. 9¾ Vert.*

TD88	TE47	blue	20.00
		Pair	50.00
TD89	TE47	black	20.00
		Pair	50.00
		On cover	75.00
TD90	TE47	blue black	20.00
		Pair	50.00

Multipost Commercial
Controls Multipost
Mailmaster
Coil — TE48

Multipost Friden
Multipost Mailmaster
Coil — TE49

1944-49   *Perf. 9¾ Vert.*

TD91	TE48	purple	20.00
		Pair	50.00
TD92	TE48	carmine	30.00
		Pair	80.00
TD93	TE49	carmine	20.00
		Pair	50.00

Framed Rectangle — TE50

Printed by Bureau of Engraving & Printing.

1954   *Perf. 11.2x10.5*

TD94	TE50	carmine	75.00
		Block of 4	300.00
		P# block of 4, P#141730 or 141731	800.00

Imperf

TD94A	TE50	carmine	100.00
		Pair	200.00
		Block of 4	400.00
		P# block of 4, P#141730 or 141731	800.00
		Horiz. pair with vert. gutter	300.00

Coil Stamps
Perf. 9¾ Vert.

TD95	TE50	purple, large holes	3.00
		Pair	8.00
		Joint line pair	20.00
		On cover with "Parade of Postal Progress" cancel	85.00
		Small holes, *1959*	6.00
		Pair	15.00
		Joint line pair	35.00
a.		Imperf., pair	50.00
		Joint line pair	200.00

Examples of No. TD95 with poor centering are common and sell for less.

TD96	TE50	red violet, small holes	2.00
		Pair	5.00
		Joint line pair	15.00
		Large holes	5.00
		Pair	12.50
		Joint line pair	125.00
		On cover with "Parade of Postal Progress" cancel	85.00
a.		Imperf., pair	80.00
		Joint line pair	—
b.		Block of 8 with joint line, sheet margin and P#165939 and 165940, unslit horiz.	—

See "large hole" and "small hole" illustrations after No. 1053 in Postage section.

TD97	TE50	carmine	200.00
		Pair	400.00
		Joint line pair	600.00
a.		Imperf., horiz. pair	300.00
b.		Vert. pair, unslit horiz.	—

Expertization is recommended for Nos. TD97, TD97a and TD97b.

Nos. TD97a and TD97b exist as top or bottom P# blocks of 10, unslit horiz. Value, each $1,250. P# blocks of No. TD97b have selvage trimmed so EE marks do not show.

No. TD97a exists as a joint line pair, and No. TD97b also exists as a block of 4 with joint line, unslit horiz.

Kansas
Territorial
Centennial
Experimental
TE51

Printed by Bureau of Engraving and Printing.

1954   *Perf. 12x11¾*

TD98	TE51	*brown, red & yellow*	*30.00*
		Block of 4	*120.00*

Nebraska Territorial Centennial Experimental — TE52

1954   *Imperf.*

Size: 25x40mm

TD99	TE52	**brown**	30.00
		Block of 4	120.00
a.	**brown,** *tan*		
TD100	TE52	**black**	30.00
		Block of 4	120.00
TD101	TE52	**blue**	30.00
		Block of 4	120.00
a.	**blue,** *tan*		

Pitney Bowes Co. — TE53

1958-59   *Imperf.*

Helecon Paper

TD102	TE53	**rose carmine**	—
a.		Lumogen paper	—
TD103	TE53	**black**	—

Helecon paper glows reddish orange under shortwave UV light. Lumogen paper glows bright yellow-green under shortwave UV light.

Stamp-E-Z Postage Stamp Affixer Coil — TE54

1960s   *Imperf.*

TD104	TE54	**light purple**	—
		Pair	—

Perf. 9¾ Vert.

TD105	TE54	**red**	—
		Pair	—

Blank Design Type of 1878-79

Produced by Bureau of Engraving and Printing

1960-70s   **Overall Tagging**   **Perf. 9¾ Vert.**
         Dull Gum

TD106	TE9	blank	12.50
		Pair	25.00
		Joint line pair	100.00

No. TD106 was printed on an inked press. The ink was wiped, but some stamps have wiping marks and black joint lines.

For Testing Purposes Only Coil — TE55

Produced by Bureau of Engraving and Printing.

1962-88   **Engr.**   **Perf. 9¾ Vert.**
Design Size: Approximately 19½mm Wide

TD107	TE55	**black,** untagged, shiny gum	.50
		Pair	1.00
		Joint line pair	5.00
a.		Tagged, shiny gum	.50
		Pair	1.00
		Joint line pair	5.00
b.		Tagged, pebble-surfaced gum	1.50

		Pair	3.00
		Joint line pair	15.00
c.	As "b," imperf. pair		50.00
		Joint line pair	200.00
d.	Tagged, dull gum		2.00
		Pair	4.00
		Joint line pair	20.00
e.	Untagged, dull gum		1.00
		Pair	2.00
		Joint line pair	10.00

No. TD107 is known on hi-brite fluorescent paper.

No. TD107b has been found with red, dark red, rose red, blue, blue green, green, orange, violet, brown, black violet, black, gray black, gray and silver defacement lines, which vary in number and thickness and which have been known to have been forged. Some defacement line colors may all be forgeries.

No. TD107e is known on fluorescent and non-fluorescent papers, as well as on papers with diagonal gum striations or wavy, intermittent gum striations.

TD108	TE55	**carmine,** tagged, *1970*	875.00
		Pair	1,750.
		Joint line pair	—

The tagging on Nos. TD108 and TD114 is orange red. All other stamps glow yellow green.

TD109	TE55	**green,** untagged, dull gum, *1970*	90.00
		Pair	180.00
		Joint line pair	450.00
		Block of 12 with joint line, imperf or unslit horiz., P# 36111 and 36112	1,500.
a.		Imperf., pair	400.00
		Joint line pair	550.00
b.		Vert. pair, imperf. horiz.	200.00
c.		Tagged, gray paper, shiny gum	160.00
		Pair	325.00
		Joint line pair	—
d.		As "c," imperf, pair	150.00
		Joint line pair	500.00
e.		As "c," vert. pair, imperf. horiz.	175.00

No. TD109 was sent to Germany in large imperf. and part perforate sheets to test coil production equipment.

TD110	TE55	**orange,** *gray,* tagged, *1975*	1,000.
		Pair	2,000.
		Joint line pair	—
TD111	TE55	**brown,** untagged, *1978*	3.00
		Pair	10.00
		Joint line pair	30.00

Design Size: Approximately 19mm Wide

TD112	TE55	**black,** untagged, dull gum *1978*	.50
		Pair	1.00

No. TD107 was printed on the Cottrell press. No. TD112 was printed on the B press.

See Nos. TD121, TD126-TD127, TD133, TD136-TD137.

Blank Design Type of 1878-79

Produced by Bureau of Engraving and Printing, with tagging added by Pitney Bowes.

1964   **Perf. 11**

TD113	TE9	blank, yellow green tagging	75.00
		Block of 4	300.00
TD114	TE9	blank, orange red tagging	75.00
		Block of 4	300.00

Nos. TD113-TD114 was produced as a test for Nos. 1254-1257.

Flag — TE56

Produced by Avery Products Corp.

1970s   *Die Cut*

TD115	TE56	**blue,** on rouletted backing paper	200.00
a.		On imperforate backing paper	—

Proclaim Liberty TE57

1970s   *Perf. 12x11½*

TD116	TE57	**blue, red & green**	75.00

Christmas Test Stamp TE58

Printed by Bureau of Engraving and Printing for Avery Products Corp. to add die cutting.

1973   *Die Cut*

Self-Adhesive

TD117	TE58	**black,** rouletted backing paper	2.50
		Block of 4 with intact matrix	10.00
		Pane of 50	150.00
		Press sheet of 200	750.00
a.		With imperforate backing paper	—

No. TD117 was produced as a test for No. 1552.

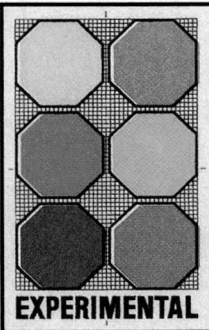

Octagons — TE59

Printed by Bureau of Engraving and Printing.

1980s   *Imperf.*

TD118	TE59	**multicolored**	140.00
		Block of 4	600.00
		P# block of 4, P#173404	1,200.

Flag and Eagle Over Trees Coil — TE60

Printed by Stamp Venturers.

1989   *Perf. 10 Vert.*

TD119	TE60	**gray**	.25
		Pair	.50

Rouletted

TD120	TE60	**gray**	.25
		Pair	.50

A similar design, in multicolor, with "Sennett Security Products" at lower left was a souvenir distributed at World Stamp Expo 2000.

For Testing Purposes Only Type of 1962-88

Printed by Martin Marietta Corp.

1990s		**Photo.**	**Untagged**		*Imperf.*
TD121	TE55	**black**			75.00
		Pair			150.00
		Block of 4			400.00

Blank Design Type of 1878-79

Produced by Bureau of Engraving and Printing.

1990s		**Untagged**	*Perf. 9¾ Vert.*
TD122	TE9	blank, shiny gum	10.00
		Pair	30.00
		Dull gum	10.00
		Pair	30.00

No. TD122 with shiny gum is known on hi-brite fluorescent paper.

Stylized Eagle Coil — TE61

Printed by 3M Corp.

Linerless Self-Adhesive

1992			Imperf.
TD123	TE61	multicolored	15.00
		Pair	30.00
		P# strip of 5, #1111	350.00

Stamps have simulated perforations.

Rectangle With Thick Lines
Coil — TE62

Printed by Bureau of Engraving and Printing.

1996			Perf. 9¾ Vert.
TD124	TE62	blue, shiny gum	50.00
		Pair	100.00
		Strip of 5 with one stamp with crudely etched reversed "2"	1,500.
		Strip of 5 with one stamp with crudely etched reversed "12"	1,500.

Reversed numbers appear in the center of every 24th stamp.

TD125	TE62	gray black, dull gum	125.00
		Pair	250.00

For Testing Purposes Only Type of 1962-88
Printed by Bureau of Engraving and Printing (#TD126), Avery-Dennison (#TD127).

1996			Die Cut
		Self-Adhesive	
TD126	TE55	black, blue	.25
		Pair	.50
		P# strip of 5, #1111	5.00

TE55a

Serpentine Die Cut 11.2 Vert.

TD127	TE55a	black	.25
		Pair	.50
		P# strip of 5, #V1	15.00

Design TE55a has printed perforation "holes" in addition to serpentine die cutting.

Polar Bear Ice Skating —
TE62a

Printed by Ashton-Potter (USA) Ltd.

1995		Serpentine Die Cut 11x10.9
		Design Size: 21x35mm
		Self-Adhesive
TD127A	TE62a	multicolored	750.00
		Block of 4	—
		Sheetlet of 20	—

The sheetlet of 20 has vertical and horizontal gutters between the stamps with the matrix removed.

Serpentine Die Cut 11x11.5

TD127B	TE62a	multicolored	750.00
		Block of 4	—
		Sheetlet of 20	—

The sheetlet of 20 has no vertical or horizontal gutters between the stamps.

Avery
Dennison —
TE62b

Printed by Avery Dennison.

1996		Serpentine Die Cut 11x11.2
		Design size: 36x21mm
		Self-Adhesive
TD127C	TE62b	red	—
		Block of 4	—
		Sheetlet of 20	—

Parrot — TE63

TE63a

Printed by Banknote Corporation of America.

1996		Serpentine Die Cut 11¾x11½
		Design Size: 22x31mm
		Self-Adhesive (#TD128)
TD128	TE63	multicolored	300.00
		Design Size: 25x40mm
		Perf. 11½
TD129	TE63a	multicolored	—

No. TD129 was used to test luminescent inks.

Printed by Dittler Brothers Inc. and American Bank Note Co.

Flower — TE63b

1997			Imperf.
		Self-Adhesive	
		Design Size: 18x18mm	
TD129A	TE63b	multicolored	375.00
		Design Size: 18x21mm	
TD129B	TE63b	multicolored	250.00
		Design Size: 22x31mm	
TD129C	TE63b	multicolored	375.00
TD129D	TE63b	multicolored	375.00

Nos. TD129A and TD129C-TD129D were printed by photogravure and intaglio. No. TD129B was printed by photogravure only. No. TD129D has engraved black lines in the flower. No. TD129C does not have these engraved lines.

Rectangle With Thin Lines
Coil — TE64

Printed by Bureau of Engraving and Printing.

1998		Serpentine Die Cut 9¾ Vert.
		Self-Adhesive
TD130	TE64	blue	125.00
		Pair	250.00
		Strip of 3 with one stamp with "3" printed horizontally	—

Star Spangled Banner/Not for
Postage Coil — TE64a

1998		Serpentine Die Cut 11¼ Vert.
		Self-Adhesive
TD130A	TE64a	multicolored	35.00
		On cover	—

All known examples of No. TD130A were affixed to envelope backs for use in testing.
Mis-cut examples of No. TD130A, showing parts of either two or four stamps, are known. These were intentionally produced from rolls of printed stamp paper for testing purposes. Value, single $35.

Octagons — TE64b

1998		Serpentine Die Cut 12.6
		Self-Adhesive
TD130B	TE64b	multicolored	45.00
		On cover	—

All known examples of No. TD130B were affixed to envelope backs for use in testing.
Examples of No. TD130B are known intentionally printed with medium or very light coloring in the octagons. Value, single $45.

RENA Test Stamp
Coil — TE65

1999   *Die Cut*

Self-Adhesive

TD131	TE65	blue	10.00
		Pair	25.00

Mailbox Coil — TE66

Printed by Avery Dennison.

2000   *Imperf.*

Linerless Self-Adhesive

TD132	TE66	red	100.00
		Pair	200.00
a.		Pair with "xxxx" on one stamp	1,500.

Pairs have 1-2mm slit marks between stamps in right margin.

For Testing Purposes Only Type of 1962-88

Printed by Bureau of Engraving and Printing.

2000   *Serpentine Die Cut 9¾ Vert.*

Self-Adhesive

TD133	TE55	black	.50
		Pair	1.00
		P# strip of 5, #1111	7.50

No. TD133 is printed on white backing paper with 2mm gap between perforation tips. A four digit counting number is on the back of the backing paper on every 20th stamp. Stamps appear to be printed on light blue paper. The blue color is caused by the buildup of white ink with a blue tint, which was applied to white paper.

TD133A	TE55	black	15.00
		Pair	30.00
		P# strip of 5, #1111	300.00

No. TD133A is printing on white backing paper with no gap between perforation tips.

South Carolina Flag
Coil — TE67

Printed by Avery Dennison.

2000   *Serpentine Die Cut 8½ Vert.*

Self-Adhesive

TD134	TE67	dark blue	—
		Pair	—
		P# strip of 5, #V1	—
TD135	TE67	light blue	15.00
		Pair	30.00
		P# strip of 5, #V1	225.00

Plate-number examples of Nos. TD134 and TD135 bear a "2000" year date at lower left.

For Testing Purposes Only Type of 1962-88

Printed by Bureau of Engraving and Printing (#TD136), Sennett Security Products (#TD137).

For Testing Purposes Only
Coil with Vertical Line
Between "N" and "L" of "Only"
— TE55b

1997   *Serpentine Die Cut 9¾ Vert.*

Self-Adhesive

TD136	TE55b	black	.65
		Pair	1.25
		Strip of 5 with white line on left or right margin of center stamp	7.50

Stamps with white lines appear every 21st stamp. Stamps appear to be printed on light blue paper. The blue color is caused by the buildup of white ink with a blue tint, which was applied to white paper.

Serpentine Die Cut 11¼ Vert.

TD137	TE55	black	.50
		Pair	1.00
		P# strip of 5, #S1	7.00

SSP Test Void Coil — TE69

Printed by Sennett Security Products.

2005   *Serpentine Die Cut 10½ Vert.*

Self-Adhesive

TD138	TE69	black	2.00
		Pair	4.00

2000   *Serpentine Die Cut 11.6 Vert.*

Self-Adhesive

TD138A	TE69	black	10.00
		Pair	20.00

RENA No Postage Test Stamp
Coil — TE70

2006   *Die Cut*

Self-Adhesive

TD139	TE70	blue	2.00
		Pair	4.00

TEST STAMP PROOFS

Bureau of Engraving and Printing

1910

TD28TC	**black,** large die proof, die sunk on card	1,000.
TD28TC	**blue,** large die proof on India, die sunk on card	1,000.
TD28TC	**carmine,** large die proof on India, die sunk on card	1,000.
TD28TC	**dark brown,** large die proof on India, die sunk on card	1,000.
TD28TC	**dark green,** large die proof on India, die sunk on card	1,000.
TD28TC	**dark violet brown,** large die proof on India, die sunk on card	1,000.

TEST BOOKLETS: PANES & COVERS

Test booklets normally are collected as complete booklets, and the major listings are for complete booklets. Very often the booklet panes in different booklets are the same or similar. Booklet panes are presented as lettered minor listings. Where similar booklet panes can be differentiated by gum breaker measurements, size measurements, or other factors, they are given separate minor listings. Single stamps from these booklets are not given minor listings.

This test booklet section is divided into four categories: stapled booklets, folded and glued booklets with water-activated gum, folded and glued booklets with self-adhesive gum, and ATM sheetlets.

STAPLED BOOKLETS

Small Postrider — BC5A

Blank Stamps — TDP1

1927-30   *Perf. 11¼x10½*

TDB1	BC5A	25c **green,** *green,* 4 #TDB1a		—
a.		TDP1 Pane of 6		—

Horiz. gum breakers are 22mm apart on No. TDB1a. No. TDB1 has 5 waxed glassine interleaves, 1 in front of the first pane and 1 behind each pane.

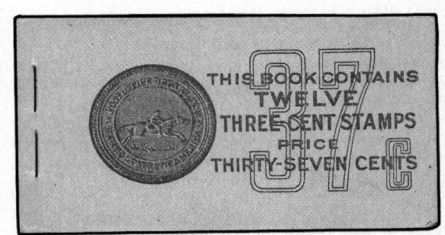

Post Office Seal — BC9A

Blank Stamps — TDP2

1930s
TDB2 BC9A 37c **violet,** *buff,* 2 #TDB2a   —
  a.   TDP2 Pane of 9, 6 definitive and 3 com-
        memorative sized stamps   —

No. TDB2 has a cover composed of two BC9A items unseparated horizontally. No. TDB2 has 2 waxed glassine interleaves, 1 behind each pane.

Framed Rectangles — TDP3

1940
TDB3 BC9A 37c **violet,** *buff,* 2 #TDB3a   600.00
  a.   TDP3 **purple,** pane of 6   250.00

Horiz. gum breakers are 11mm apart on No. TDB3a. No. TDB3 has 2 waxed glassine interleaves, 1 behind each pane. Earliest documented use: Jan. 13, 1941 (single stamp)

Type of 1940

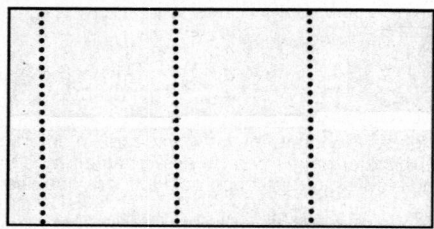

Blank Stamps — TDP4

1940s
TDB4 BC9A 37c **violet,** *buff,* #TDB4a, TDB4b   450.00
  a.   TDP1 Pane of 6   —
  b.   TDP4 Pane of 3, perf. 10 vert.

Horiz. gum breakers are 6mm apart on Nos. TDB4a and TDB4b. No. TDB4 has 2 waxed glassine interleaves, 1 behind each pane.

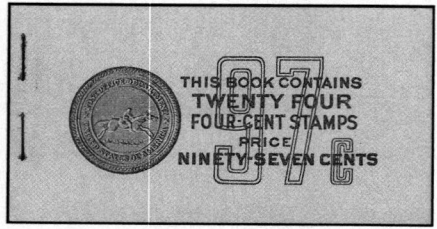

Post Office Seal — BC9H

1959
TDB5 BC9H 97c **blue,** *pink,* 4 #TDB5a   175.00
  a.   TDP1 Pane of 6   —
  b.   As #TDB5, with silicone interleaves   325.00

Horiz. gum breakers are 5 ½mm apart, and vert. gum breakers are 21mm apart on No. TDB5a. No. TDB5 has 4 waxed

glassine interleaves, and No. TDB5a has 4 silicone interleaves, 1 behind each pane. Some panes may show a joint line and/or EE markings.

U.S. Airmail Wings — BC11C

1959
TDB6 BC11C 97c **blue,** 2 #TDB6a   175.00
  a.   TDP1 Pane of 6   —

Horiz. gum breakers are 5 ½mm apart on No. TDB6a. Some panes may exhibit faint vertical gum breakers. Nos. TDB6 has 2 waxed glassine interleaves, 1 behind each pane.

Post Office Seal Type of 1959

Misperforated and Miscut Framed
Rectangles — TDP5

1960-62
TDB7 BC9H 97c **blue,** *pink,* 4 #TDB7a   *900.00*
  a.   TDP5 **red violet,** pane of 6   *200.00*

Horiz. gum breakers are 4 ½-6 ½mm apart and vert. gum breakers are 22 ½mm apart on No. TDB7a. Panes were made from coil sheet stock and therefore are always miscut and misperforated. No. TDB7 has 4 glassine interleaves, 1 behind each pane.

Small Postrider With "DUMMY"
Handstamp — TBC12A

For Testing Purposes Only — TDP6

No. TDP6 panes were made from coil stock and therefore are always miscut and misperforated.

1962-67   **Untagged**
TDB8 TBC12A $1 **blue,** 4 #TDB8a   200.00
  a.   TDP6 **black,** pane of 6 stamps of type
        TE55   35.00

Horiz. gum breakers are 5 ½mm apart and alternating vert. gum breakers are 22 ½mm and 8 ½mm apart on No. TDB8a. No. TDB8 has 4 silicone interleaves, 1 behind each pane, and staples at left. Some panes may show a joint line and/or EE markings.

"DUMMY" — TDBC1

1962-67
TDB9   TDBC1 **black** 2 #TDB9a   90.00
  a.   TDP1 Pane of 6   —
TDB10 TDBC1 **red** 2 #TDB9a   *200.00*

Horiz. gum breakers are 11 ½mm apart, and alternating vert. gum breakers are 14mm and 8 ½mm apart on No. TDB9a. Nos. TDB9 and TDB10 have 2 glassine interleaves, 1 behind each pane.

Mr. Zip With "DUMMY" — TBC13A

1963-66
    Black or Violet "Dummy" Handstamp
TDB11 TBC13A $1 **blue,** 4 #TDB9a   125.00
  a.   TDP1 Pane of 6   10.00
  b.   As #TDB11, with 4 #TDB11a   125.00
    55x7 ½mm Red "Dummy" Overprint
TDB12 TBC13A $1 **blue,** 4 #TDB9a   50.00
  a.   As #TDB12, with different inside front
        cover   15.00

Alternating horiz. gum breakers are 4 ½mm and 6 ½mm apart, and alternating vert. gum breakers are 14mm and 8 ½mm apart on No. TDB11a.

No. TDB12 has inside front cover reading "Domestic Postage Rates." No. TDB12a has inside front cover reading "Minute Man — Buy — HOLD US Savings Bonds."

Nos. TDB11-TDB12a have 4 silicone interleaves, 1 behind each pane.

Post Office Seal With Violet "DUMMY"
Handstamp — TBC14A

For Testing Purposes Only — TDP7

No. TDP7 panes were made from coil stock and therefore are always miscut and misperforated.

1967-68   **Tagged**   *Perf. 11¼x10½*
TDB13 TBC14A $2 **brown,** 5 #TDB13a   200.00
  a.   TDP7 **black,** pane of 8 stamps of
        type TE55   35.00

Horiz. gum breakers are 11mm apart and alternating vert. gum breakers are 14mm and 8 ½mm apart on No. TDB13a. No. TDB13 has 5 silicone interleaves, 1 behind each pane, and staples at left. Some booklets and panes have felt pen markings along the top and bottom edges placed by the technicians for machine adjustments.

On Nos. TDB14, TDB15, TDB16 and TDB17, the perforation gauge is measured with the staple position at left, and the gum breakers are measured with the staple position at top.

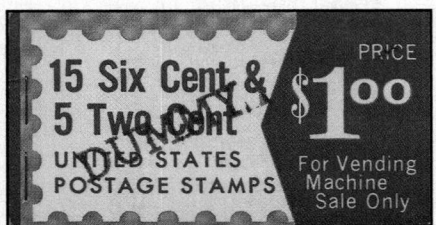

Stamp Silhouette With Violet "DUMMY" Handstamp — TBC15

1960s-72   Tagged   Perf. 10½x11¼
TDB14   TBC15 $1 brown, 4 #TDB14a   150.00
  a.   TDP6 black, pane of 6 stamps of
    type TE55, staple position at top   35.00

Horiz. gum breakers are 11mm apart and vert. gum breakers are 22mm apart on No. TDB14a. No. TDB14 has 4 silicone interleaves, 1 behind each pane, and staples at left. "Dummy" handstamp is 34½x6½mm. Some booklets and panes have felt pen markings on the front and/or back covers.

TDP6A

TDB15   TBC15 $1 blue, 4 #TDB15a   150.00
  a.   TDP6A black, pane of 6 stamps of
    type TE55, staple position at top   35.00

Horiz. gum breakers are 11mm apart on No. TDB15a. No. TDB15 has 4 silicone interleaves, 1 behind each pane, and staples at left. "Dummy" handstamp is 34½x6½mm. Panes are upside down relative to covers. Some booklets and panes have felt pen markings on the front and/or back covers.

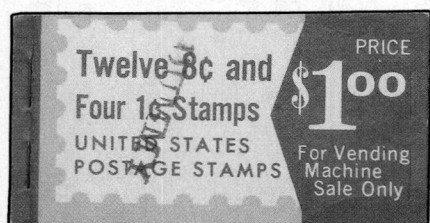

TBC15A

TDB16   TBC15A $1 claret, 3 #TDB16a   250.00
  a.   TDP6A black, pane of 6 stamps of
    type TE55, staple position at top   35.00
  b.   As #TDB16, with 34½x6½mm
    "Dummy" handstamp   250.00

Horiz. gum breakers are 11mm apart on No. TDB16a. No. TDB16 has 3 silicone interleaves, 1 behind each pane, and staples at left. "Dummy" handstamp is 29½x4½mm on No. TDB16.

TBC15B

TDB17   TBC15B $1 red, 2 #TDB17a   175.00
  a.   TDP6B or TDP6A black, pane of 6
    stamps of type TE55, staple posi-
    tion at top   35.00
  b.   As #TDB17, with 34½x6½mm
    "Dummy" handstamp   175.00

Horiz. gum breakers are 11mm apart, and alternating vert. gum breakers are 14 and 8½mm apart on No. TDB17a. Some panes do not show vertical gum breakers. No. TDB17 has 2 silicone interleaves, 1 behind each pane, and staples at left. "Dummy" handstamp is 29½x4½mm on No. TDB17. Some

booklets and panes have felt pen markings on the front and/or back covers.

Eisenhower With Violet "DUMMY" Handstamp — TBC16

1970-71   Tagged   Perf. 11¼x10½
TDB18   TBC16 $2 blue, 5 #TDB18a   200.00
  a.   TDP7 black, pane of 8 stamps of
    type TE55   35.00
  b.   As #TDB18, with 34½x6½mm "Dum-
    my" handstamp   200.00

Horiz. gum breakers are 11mm apart and vert. gum breakers are 22mm apart on No. TDB18a. No. TDB18 has 5 silicone interleaves, 1 behind each pane, and staples at left. "Dummy" handstamp is 29½x4½mm on No. TDB18.

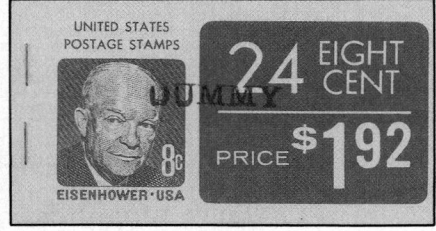

TBC17

With Red "Dummy" Handstamp
TDB19   TBC17 $1.92 claret, 3 #TDB13a   150.00
  a.   TDP7 black, pane of 8 stamps of type
    TE55   35.00
  b.   As #TDB19, with violet 34½x6½mm
    "Dummy" handstamp   150.00

No. TDB19 has 3 silicone interleaves, 1 behind each pane, and staples at left. "Dummy" handstamp is 29½x4½mm on No. TDB19.

FOLDED AND GLUED BOOKLETS

Blank Cover
TBC20

Blank
Pane of 8
TDP10

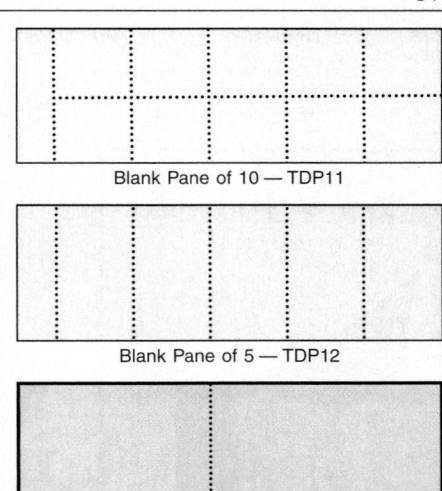

Blank Pane of 10 — TDP11

Blank Pane of 5 — TDP12

Blank Pane of 2 — TDP12a

Produced by Bureau of Engraving and Printing.

1970s-80s   Untagged   Perf. 11x10½
TDB25   TBC20   blank, #TDB25a   400.00
  a.   TDP10   Pane of 8   —

Perf. 10x9¾
TDB26   TBC20   blank, 2 #TDB26a   80.00
  a.   TDP11   Pane of 10, 43x137mm   —

Perf. 10 Horiz.
TDB27   TBC20   blank, #TDB27a   50.00
  a.   TDP12   Pane of 5, 43x137mm, dull
    gum   —
TDB28   TBC20   blank, 2 #TDB28a   30.00
  a.   TDP12   Pane of 5, 43x135mm, dull
    gum   —
  b.   As #TDB28, with 2 #TDB28a, shiny
    gum   —

Produced by KCS Industries
Imperf
TDB29   TBC20   blank, 2 #TDB29a   50.00
  a.   TDP12   Pane of 5, 43x135mm, dull
    gum   —

Panes in No. TDB29 are fastened to each other and to the booklet cover at the top tab with 3 glue spots. The booklet cover of No. TDB29 is not scored at the pane fold location.

Perf. 11 Horiz.
TDB30   TBC20   blank, 2 #TDB30a   125.00
  a.   TDP12a   Pane of 2, 43x137mm, dull
    gum   —
  b.   As #TDB30, with inverted pane
    (perfs unaligned with cover fold)   —

Panes in No. TDB30 are fastened to each other with 3 glue spots and bottom pane is fastened to booklet cover with a 1mm wide glue line. Covers are known with handstamps "A1" (black), "A2" (orange), "B1" (red), or "B2" (violet) on the front and back cover panels.

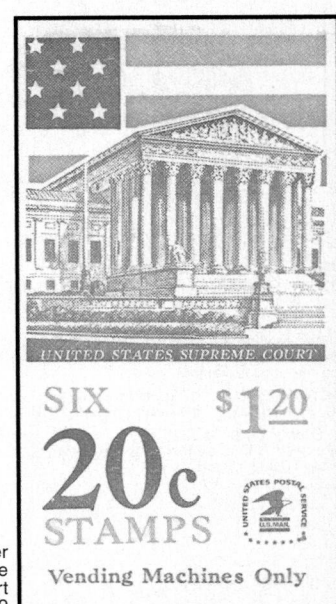

Flag Over
Supreme
Court
BC29

Printed by Bureau of Engraving & Printing.

1985   **Untagged**   *Perf. 10 Horiz.*
TDB31 BC29 $1.20 **red & blue**, #TDB31a   450.00
   a.   TDP12 Pane of 5, 43x133mm, dull
       gum
       Tab selvage is 9mm high.

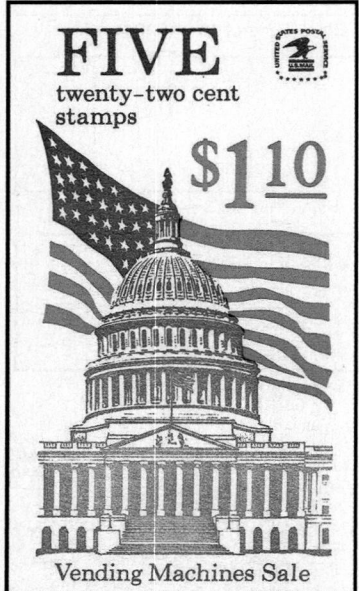

Flag Over
Capitol
BC33C

Printed by Bureau of Engraving & Printing.

1985   **Untagged**   *Perf. 10 Horiz.*
TDB32 BC33C $1.10 **red & blue**, #TDB32a   20.00
   a.   TDP12 Pane of 5, 43x130mm, dull
       gum   —
       Tab selvage is 9 or 12mm high.

Seashells — BC33A

Seashells Without Text — TBC21

Printed by Bureau of Engraving & Printing.

1985   **Untagged**   *Perf. 10x9¾*
TDB33 BC33A $4.40 **multicolored**, 2 #TDB33a   350.00
   a.   TDP11 Pane of 10, 43x135mm, dull
       gum   —

Tab selvage is 11mm high. Panes are scored at all horizontal perforation rows. Some booklet covers have red felt pen marks on the outside front cover.

TDB34 TBC21   **multicolored**, 2 #TDB33a   350.00
TDB35 TBC21   **multicolored**, 2 #TDB28a   250.00

Scoring on No. TDB35 varies. Seven adjacent booklet covers are needed to show the complete design of all 25 seashells for Nos. TDB33-TDB35.

Jack London — TBC22

Rectangles and Numeral — TDP13

Printed by Bureau of Engraving & Printing.

1988   **Untagged**   *Perf. 11x9¾*
TDB36 TBC22 $5 **multicolored**, 2 #TDB36a   —
   a.   TDP13 **blue**, pane of 10, 43x135mm,
       shiny gum   —

Tab selvage is 11½mm high. Panes are scored at all horizontal perforation rows. No. TDB36 booklet covers have a small printed number in the lower right corner that matches the large number on the booklet panes on the inside. Some booklet covers have red felt pen marks on the outside front cover. Numeral on No. TDB36a is "3." An unpublished quote from George Washington is printed on inside front cover and unissued "American Garden" printed on inside back cover.

Hummingbird
BC80

Printed by American Bank Note Company.

1994   **Untagged**   *Perf. 11 Horiz.*
TDB37 BC80 $5.80 **multicolored**, 2 #TDB37a   —
   a.   TDP12 Pane of 5, 41x137mm, glossy
       gum   —

Outside front covers have 2 green felt pen marks.

Flag
BC106

Printed by American Bank Note Company.

1994   **Untagged**   *Perf. 10*
TDB38 BC106 G **multicolored**, 2 #TDB38a   —
   a.   TDP12 Pane of 5, 43x137mm, glossy
       gum   —

Front covers have felt pen marks.

Daffodils —
TBC23

Rectangles — TDP14

Rectangles — TBP14a

Rectangles (Large Stamps) — TDP15

Printed by Bureau of Engraving and Printing.

1990s		Untagged	Perf. 11x9¾
TDB39	TBC23	multicolored, 2 #TDB39a	
a.		TDP14 blue, pane of 10, 43x135mm, shiny gum	—
TDB40	TBC23	multicolored, 4 #TDB40a	
a.		TDP13 blue, pane of 10, 43x135mm, shiny gum	—
TDB40B	TBC23	multicolored, 2 #TDB40Bc	
c.		TDP13 blue, pane of 10, 43x135mm, shiny gum	—
TDB41	TBC23	multicolored, 4 #TDB41a	
a.		TDP14 dark blue, pane of 10, 43x135mm, shiny gum	—
TDB42	TBC23	multicolored, 4 #TDB42a	
a.		TDP14a dark blue, pane of 10, 43x135mm, shiny gum	—
TDB43	TBC23	multicolored, 2 #TDB43a	
a.		TDP15 black, pane of 10, 66x137mm, shiny gum	—

Tab selvage is 12mm high on Nos. TDB39-TDB43. Numerals shown on Nos. TDB40a, TDB42a are "11." Numeral shown on No. TDB40Bc is "6." Nos. TDB42 and TDB43 lack printing on inside covers found on Nos. TDB39-TDB41. Booklet cover of No. TDB43 is larger and shows a 3mm tall "6" in the lower right corner of the outside front cover. Other covers of type TBC23 show a 3mm "12" there.

SELF-ADHESIVE FOLDED & GLUED BOOKLETS
Blank Cover and Pane Types

1990s ?		Untagged	Perf. 11 Horiz.
TDB60	TBC20	blank, 2 #TDB60a	—
a.		TDP12 blank, pane of 2, self-adhesive, 44x132mm	—

Blank Convertible Booklet Cover — TBC30

Serpentine Die Cut 10½x11, 11

1999			Overall Tagging
TDB61	TBC30	blank, self-adhesive blank pane of 10	150.00

Stamps in pane have same arrangement as that of the 1999 20c Pheasant booklet, No. BK242A.

ATM TEST SHEETLETS

Eagle and Flag Pane Cover — TBC40

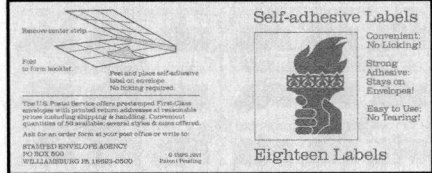

Stamp Layout — TBC40R

1989			Imperf.
		Self-Adhesive	
TDB80	TBC40	$3 multicolored, blue, pane of 12 (TBC40R)	1,500.
a.		With "Paper Corp" handwritten in right margin	2,250.
		Shiny, Water-Activated Gum	
TDB81	TBC40R	$3 multicolored, blue, pane of 12 (TBC40R)	2,250.

The backing paper serves as a booklet cover on No. TDB80. Sizes: No. TDB80, 61x157mm; No. TDB80a, 62½x178mm; No. TDB81, 66x160mm. No. TDB80 exists not fully trimmed, and measuring 62½x159mm. No. TDB81 does not have a cover, and does not require a backing paper.

Statue of Liberty Torch Pane Cover — TBC41

Stamp Layout — TBC41R

Printed by Avery Dennison.

1990		Untagged	Die Cut
		Self-Adhesive	
TDB82	TBC41	green, pane of 18 (TBC41R)	15.00

No. 2475a Overprinted in Black "SPECIMEN / FOR ATM TEST" on Each Stamp

Statue of Liberty Torch Pane Cover — TBC41AR

Printed by Avery Dennison.

1990		Untagged	Die Cut
		Self-Adhesive	
		Printed on Plastic	
TDB83	TBC41AR	25c dark red & dark blue, pane of 12	—

Representation of Stamp Layout — TBC42R

Produced by Dittler Brothers.

1992	**Untagged**	***Misaligned Die Cut***
	Self-Adhesive	
TDB84	blank, pane of 18 (TBC42R)	*500.00*

| 1992 | | ***No Die Cuts*** |
| TDB85 | **blank,** pane of 18 (TBC42R) | *300.00* |

Nos. TDB84 and TDB85 were printed on thick paper similar to regular postage No. 2596a and were used for testing Postal Buddy machines. Backing paper of Nos. TDB84 and TDB85 reads "SELF-ADHESIVE * DO NOT WET." A detailed illustration of No. TBC42R is difficult to reproduce.

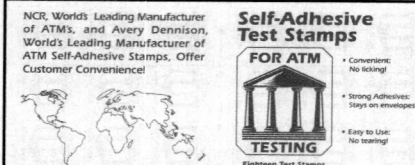

Temple Pane Cover — TBC43

Stamp Layout — TBC43R

Printed by Avery Dennison.

1997		***Die Cut***
	Self-Adhesive	
TDB86 TBC43	**dark blue,** pane of 18 (TBC43R), Plate #V1	250.00

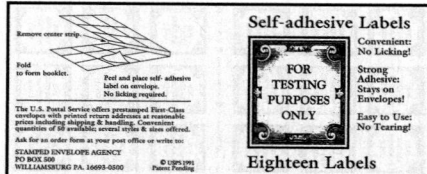

For Testing Purposes Only Pane Cover — TBC44

Stamp Layout — TBC44R

Printed by Avery Dennison.

1997		***Die Cut***
	Self-Adhesive	
TDB87 TBC44	**black,** pane of 18 black labels (TBC44R), Plate #V1	150.00
	Serpentine Die Cut 7¾	
TDB88 TBC44	**black,** pane of 18 black labels (TBC44R), Plate #V1	15.00
TDB89 TBC44	**blue,** pane of 18 magenta labels (TBC44R), Plate #V1	250.00

George Clinton — TBC46R

1998		***Serpentine Die Cut 11.2x11.6***
	Self-Adhesive	
TDB89A TBC46R	**blue gray**	35.00
	On cover	—

All known examples of No. TDB89A were affixed to envelope backs for use in testing.

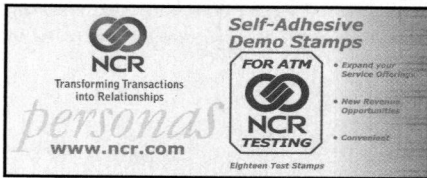

NCR Logo Pane Cover — TBC45

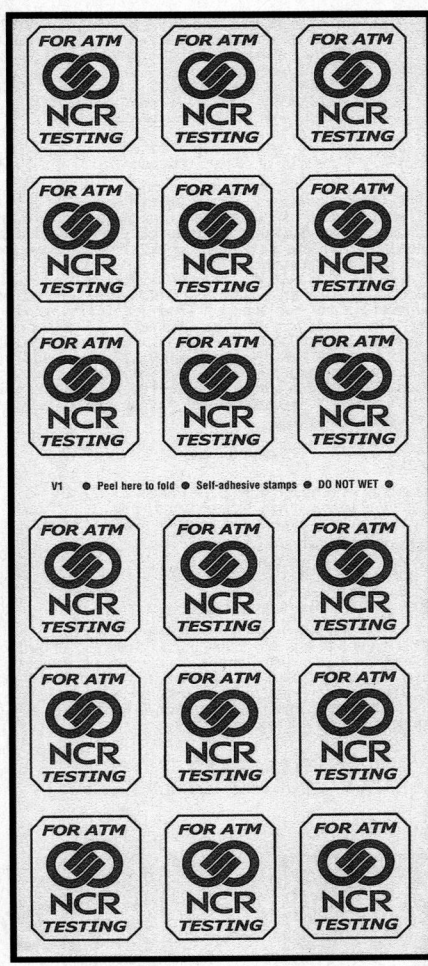

Stamp Layout — TBC45R

Printed by NCR.

2000   *Imperf.*

Without Gum

TDB90 TBC45   **multicolored,** pane of 18 black
labels (TBC45R), Plate #V1   50.00

CHRISTMAS SEALS

Issued by the American National Red Cross (1907-1919), the National Tuberculosis Association (1920-1967), the National Tuberculosis and Respiratory Disease Association (1968-1972) and the American Lung Association (1973-).

While the Christmas Seal is not a postage stamp, it has long been associated with the postal service because of its use on letters and packages.

Einar Holboell, an employee of the Danish Post Office, created the Christmas Seal. He believed that seal sales could raise money for charity. The post offices of Denmark, Iceland and Sweden began to sell such seals in the 1904 Christmas season. In the United States, Christmas Seals were first issued in 1907 under the guidance of Emily P. Bissell, following the suggestion of Jacob Riis, social service worker.

Until 1975, all seals (except those of 1907 and 1908 type I) were issued in sheets of 100. The grilled gum (1908) has small square depressions like a waffle. The broken gum (1922), devised to prevent paper curling, consists of depressed lines in the gum, ½mm. apart, forming squares. The vertical and horizontal broken gum (1922, 1923, 1925, 1927-1932) forms diamonds. The perf. 12.00 (1917-1919, 1923, 1925, 1931) has two larger and wider-spaced holes between every 11 smaller holes.

Values are for unused seals with original gum.

SEALS ISSUED BY THE DELAWARE CHAPTER OF THE AMERICAN NATIONAL RED CROSS

CS1 (Type II)

Designer — Emily P. Bissell.
Nearly $4,000 worth of seals were sold, $3,000 cleared.

Type I — "Merry Christmas" only.
Type II — "Merry Christmas" and "Happy New Year."

1907   *Perf. 14*
WX1   CS1   Type I   17.50
WX2   CS1   Type II   15.00

Types I and II litho. by Theo. Leonhardt & Son, Philadelphia, Pa. The 1st seals were sold Dec. 7, 1907, in Wilmington, Del.

Issued in sheets of 228 (19x12). Type II was issued to extend the sale of seals until New Year's Day, 1908.
Counterfeits of both types exist (perf. 12).

SEALS ISSUED BY THE AMERICAN NATIONAL RED CROSS

CS2 (Type II)

Designer — Howard Pyle. Sales $135,000.

Type I — frame lines with square corners, small "C" in "Christmas."

Type II — frame lines have rounded corners, large "C" in "Christmas," leaves veined.

1908   *Perf. 12, 14*
WX3   CS2   Type I, perf. 14, smooth gum   35.00
  a.   Perf. 12, smooth gum   45.00
  c.   Perf. 14, grilled gum   100.00
  d.   Perf. 12, grilled gum   50.00
  e.   As #WX3, bklt. pane of 6   250.00
  f.   As "c," bklt. pane of 6   250.00
  g.   As #WX3, bklt. pane of 3   250.00
WX4   CS2   Type II, perf. 12   30.00
  a.   Booklet pane of 6   175.00
  b.   Booklet pane of 3   125.00

Type I litho. by Theo. Leonhardt & Son. Sheets of 250 (14x18), with the 1st space in the 9th and 18th rows left blank.

Type II litho. by American Bank Note Co., New York, N.Y. in sheets of 100 (10x10).

Two sub-types of Type I, one with horn separated from the "8" (slightly more common) and the other with horn connected to the "8." Booklet panes are of the first sub-type.

Booklet panes have straight edges on 3 sides and perforated on left side where there is a stub, except No. WX4b which is a vert. strip of 3 with stub at top. Panes of 6 were made up in books of 24 and 48 and sold for 25c and 50c, and panes of 3 in books of 9 sold for 10c. The grilled gum has small square depressions like on a waffle.

CS3   CS4

Designer — Carl Wingate. Sales $250,000.

1909   ***Perf. 12***
WX5   CS3   One type only   1.25
Litho. by The Strobridge, Cincinnati, Ohio. Seals with a round
punched hole of 3½mm are printers' samples.

1910   ***Perf. 12***
Designer — Frances Thompson. Sales $300,000.
WX6   CS4   One type only   20.00
Lithographed by The Strobridge Lithographing Co.

SEALS ISSUED BY THE
AMERICAN NATIONAL RED CROSS
(But sold by the National Association for the Study
and Prevention of Tuberculosis)

*"The Old Home
Among the Cedars" —*
CS5 (Type II)   CS6

Designer — Anton Rudert under directions of F. D. Millet.
Sales $320,000.

Type I — diameter of circle 22mm, solid end in house.
Type II — same circle but thinner, lined end to house.
Type III — diameter of circle 20mm, lined end to house.

1911   ***Perf. 12***
WX7   CS5   Type I   50.00
WX8   CS5   Type II   120.00

COIL STAMP
Perf. 8½ Vertically
WX9   CS5   Type III   75.00
Typo. by Eureka, Scranton, Pa. Type I has name and address
of printer and union label in red in top margin. Type II has union
label only in green on left margin.

1912   ***Perf. 12***
Designer — John H. Zeh. Sales $402,256.
WX10   CS6   One type only   11.00
Lithographed by The Strobridge Lithographing Co.

CS7 (Type I)

Designer — C. J. Budd. Sales $449,505.

Type I — with Poinsettia flowers and green circles around red
crosses at either side.
Type II — the Poinsettia flowers have been removed.
Type III — the Poinsettia flowers and green circles have been
removed.

1913   ***Perf. 12***
WX11   CS7   Type I   1,400.
WX12   CS7   Type II   7.50
WX13   CS7   Type III   8.50
Lithographed by American Bank Note Co.

CS8   CS9

1914   ***Perf. 12***
WX15   CS8   One type only   10.00
Lithographed by The Strobridge Lithographing Co.

1915
Designer — Benjamin S. Nash. Sales $760,000.
WX16   CS9   Perf. 12½   10.00
       a.   Perf. 12   65.00
Lithographed by Andrew B. Graham Co., Washington, D.C.

CS10   CS11

Designer — T. M. Cleland. Sales $1,040,810.

1916
WX18   CS10   Perf. 12   5.00
       a.   Perf. 12x12½   6.00
       b.   Perf. 12½x12   15.00
       c.   Perf. 12½   14.00
Lithographed by the Strobridge Lithographing Co.

Seals of 1917-21 are on coated paper.

1917
Designer — T. M. Cleland. Sales $1,815,110.
WX19   CS11   Perf. 12   2.00
       a.   Perf. 12½   15.00
       b.   Perf. 12x12.00   2.00
       c.   Perf. 12x12½   20.00
Typographed by Eureka Specialty Printing Co.
Perf. 12.00 has two larger and wider-spaced holes between
every eleven smaller holes.
Sheets come with straight edged margins on all four sides
also with perforated margins at either right or left. Perforated
margins have the union label imprint in green.

SEALS ISSUED BY THE AMERICAN
NATIONAL RED CROSS
(Distributed by the National
Tuberculosis Association)

CS12   CS13 (Type I)

Designer — Charles A. Winter.
These seals were given to members and others in lots of 10,
the Natl. Tuberculosis Assoc. being subsidized by a gift of
$2,500,000 from the American National Red Cross.

Type I — "American Red Cross" 15mm long, heavy circles
between date.
Type II — "American Red Cross" 15½mm long, periods
between date.

1918
WX21   CS12   Type I, perf. 11½x12.00   7.50
       a.   Perf. 12   10.00
       b.   Perf. 12.00, booklet pane of 10   2.00
       c.   Perf. 12x12.00, booklet pane of 10   2.00
       d.   Perf. 12, booklet pane of 10   2.00
       e.   Perf. 12.00x12, booklet pane of 10   65.00
WX22   CS12   Type II, from booklet pane, perf.
              12½xRoulette 9½   .60
       a.   Perf. 12½, booklet pane of 10   1.50
       b.   Perf. 12½x12, bklt. pane of 10   —
       d.   Roulette 9½xPerf. 12½, bklt. pane of 10   —
       e.   Perf. 12½xRoulette 9½, bklt. pane of 10   20.00

---

       f.   Perf. 12½, booklet pane of 10   20.00
       h.   Roulette 9½xPerf. 12½ pane of 10   20.00
       i.   Roulette 9½xPerf. 12½ and Roulette
              12½, booklet pane of 10
       j.   Perf. 12½, booklet pane of 10   50.00
       k.   Perf. 12½x12½ and 12, bklt. pane of 10   —
       l.   Roulette 9½xPerf. 12½, booklet pane of
              10   —
       m.   Perf. 12½, booklet pane of 10   —
       n.   As "m," stub at bottom, bklt. pane of 10   50.00
For perf 12.00, see note following No. WX19.
Type I typographed by Eureka Specialty Printing Co.
Booklet panes of 10 (2x5) normally have straight edges on all
four sides. They were cut from the sheets of 100 and can be
plated by certain flaws which occur on both. Sheets have union
label imprint on top margin in brown.
Type II lithographed by Strobridge Lithographing Co.
Booklet panes of 10 are the same but normally have a perforated
margin at top and stub attached. These too can be plated by
flaws. One or both vert. sides are rouletted on #WX22e; perforated on #WX22f and WX22h. #WX22i is rouletted 12½ on left,
perf. 12½ on right. #WX22j, WX22k and WX22l are panes of 10
(5x2). #WX22m has a perforated margin at left.
Nos. WX21-WX21a are from sheet of 100, no straight edges.
The seal with "American Red Cross" 17¼mm long is believed
to be an essay.

1919
Designer — Ernest Hamlin Baker. Sales $3,872,534.
Type I — plume at right side of Santa's cap.
Type II — no plume but a white dot in center of band.
WX24   CS13   Type I, perf. 12   .40
       a.   Perf. 12x12.00   .60
       b.   Perf. 12½x12   .50
       c.   Perf. 12½x12.00   2.75
WX25   CS13   Type II, perf. 12½   .40
For perf 12.00, see note following No. WX19.
This is the first time the double barred cross, the emblem of
the National Tuberculosis Association, appeared in the design
of the seals. It is also the last time the red cross emblem of the
American National Red Cross was used on seals.
Type I typo. by Eureka, and has union label on margin at left
in dark blue. Type II litho. by Strobridge.

SEALS ISSUED BY THE
NATIONAL TUBERCULOSIS ASSOCIATION

CS14   CS15

Designer — Ernest Hamlin Baker. Sales $3,667,834.

Type I — size of seal 18x22mm.
Type II — seal 18½x23½mm, letters larger & numerals
heavier.
1920
WX26   CS14   Type I, perf. 12x12½   .50
       a.   Perf. 12   .40
       b.   Perf. 12½x12   13.50
       c.   Perf. 12½   15.00
WX27   CS14   Type II, perf. 12½   .50
Type I typo. by Eureka, and has union label imprint and rings
on margin at left in dark blue. Type II litho. & offset by
Strobridge.

1921
Designer — George V. Curtis. Sales $3,520,303.
Type I — dots in the chimney shading and faces are in diago-
nal lines, dots on chimney are separate except between the 2
top rows of bricks where they are solid.
Type II — dots in the chimney shading and faces are in horiz.
lines.
Type III — as Type I except red dots on chimney are mostly
joined forming lines, dots between the 2 top rows of bricks are
not a solid mass.
WX28   CS15   Type I, perf. 12½   .65
WX29   CS15   Type II, perf. 12½   .40
WX29A CS15   Type III, perf. 12   .50
Type I typo. by Eureka. Type II offset by Strobridge. Type III
typo. by Zeese-Wilkinson Co., Long Island City, N.Y.

CS16   CS17

Designer — T. M. Cleland. Sales $3,857,086.

1922

WX30	CS16	Perf. 12½, broken gum	.80
a.		Perf. 12, broken gum	3.00
b.		Perf. 12x12½, broken gum	7.50
c.		Perf. 12, smooth gum	3.00
d.		Perf. 12½, vertical broken gum	3.00

Typographed by Eureka Specialty Printing Co.

The broken gum, which was devised to prevent curling of paper, consists of depressed lines in the gum ½mm apart, forming squares, or vertical broken gum forming diamonds.

1923

Designer — Rudolph Ruzicka. Sales $4,259,660.

WX31	CS17	Perf. 12½, vertical broken gum	.30
a.		Perf. 12, horizontal broken gum	3.00
b.		Perf. 12x12.00, vertical broken gum	3.50
c.		Perf. 12½x12, vertical broken gum	6.50
d.		Perf. 12, vertical broken gum	.90
e.		Perf. 12.00x12, vertical broken gum	3.00

For perf 12.00, see note following No. WX19.

Typographed by Eureka Specialty Printing Co.

The broken gum on this and issues following printed by Eureka consists of very fine depressed lines forming diamonds.

CS18   CS19 (Type II)

Designer — George V. Curtis. Sales $4,479,656.

1924

WX32	CS18	One type only	.30

Offset by Strobridge, E.&D., and U.S.P.& L.

1925   Perf. 12½

Designer — Robert G. Eberhard. Sales $4,937,786.

Type I — red lines at each side of "1925" do not join red tablet below.

Type II — red lines, as in type I, join red tablet below.

Type III — as type I but shorter rays around flames and "ea" of "Health" smaller.

WX35	CS19	Type I, vert. broken gum	.30
a.		Perf. 12, vertical broken gum	3.50
b.		Perf. 12x12½ vertical broken gum	.60
c.		Perf. 12.00x12½ vert. broken gum	
WX36	CS19	Type I	.30
WX37	CS19	Type III	.75

For perf 12.00, see note following No. WX19.

Type I typo. by Eureka. Type II offset by E.&D. Type III litho. by Gugler Lithographing Co., Milwaukee.

CS20   CS21

Designer — George V. Curtis. Sales $5,121,872.

1926   Perf. 12½

WX38	CS20	One type only	.25

Offset by E.&D. and U.S.P.&L.

Printers' marks: E.&D. has a red dot at upper right on seal 91 on some sheets. U.S.P.&L. has a black dot at upper left on seal 56 on some sheets.

1927

Designer — John W. Evans. Sales $5,419,959.

WX39	CS21	Perf. 12, horizontal broken gum	.20
a.		Smooth gum (see footnote)	1.00
WX40	CS21	Perf. 12½, no dot	.20
WX41	CS21	Perf. 12½, one larger red dot in background 1mm above right post of dashboard on sleigh	.20

"Bonne Sante" added to design and #WX39a but with body of sleigh myrtle green instead of green were used in Canada.

Offset: #WX39, WX39a by Eureka. #WX40 by E.&D. #WX41 by U.S.P.&L.

Printer's marks: Eureka has no mark but can be identified by the perf. 12. E.&D. has red dot to left of knee of 1st reindeer on seal 92. U.S.P.&L. has 2 red dots in white gutter, one at lower left of seal 46 (and sometimes 41) and the other at upper right of seal 55. The perforations often strike out one of these dots.

The Gallant Ship "Argosy" — CS22   CS23

Designer — John W. Evans. Sales $5,465,738.

Type I — shading on sails broken, dots in flag regular.
Type II — shading on sails broken, dots in flag spotty.
Type III — shading on sails unbroken, dots in flag regular.

1928   Perf. 12½

WX44	CS22	Type I, vertical broken gum	.20
WX45	CS22	Type II	.20
WX46	CS22	Type III	.20

Seals inscribed "Bonne Annee 1929" or the same as type II but green in water, and black lines of ship heavier and deeper color were used in Canada.

Offset: Type I by Eureka, Type II by Strobridge, Type III by E.&D.

Printers' marks: Type I comes with and without a blue dash above seal 10, also with a blue and a black dash. Type II has 2 blue dashes below seal 100. Type III has red dot in crest of 1st wave on seal 92.

1929   Perf. 12½

Designer — George V. Curtis. Sales $5,546,147.

WX49	CS23	Vertical broken gum	.20
a.		Perf. 12, vertical broken gum	.50
b.		Perf. 12½x12, vertical broken gum	1.25
WX50	CS23	Smooth gum	.20

Seals inscribed "Bonne Sante 1929" or "Christmas Greetings 1929" were used in Canada.

Offset: #WX49-WX49b by Eureka, #WX50 by E.&D., U.S.P.&L., and R.R. Heywood Co., Inc., New York, N.Y.

Printers' marks: Eureka is without mark but identified by broken gum. E.&D. has a black dot in lower left corner of seal 92. U.S.P.&L. has blue dot above bell on seal 56. Heywood has a blue dot at lower right corner of seal 100.

CS24   CS25

Designer — Ernest Hamlin Baker, and redrawn by John W. Evans. Sales $5,309,352.

1930   Perf. 12½

WX55	CS24	Vertical broken gum	.20
a.		Perf. 12, vert. broken gum	.50
b.		Perf. 12.00x12, vert. broken gum	.25
c.		Perf. 12½x12, vertical broken gum	2.50
d.		Perf. 12, booklet pane of 10, horiz. broken gum	.50
WX56	CS24	Smooth gum	.20

Seals inscribed "Bonne Sante" or "Merry Christmas" on red border of seal were used in Canada.

Offset: #WX55-WX55d by Eureka, #WX56 by Strobridge, E.&D. and U.S.P.&L.

Printers' marks: Eureka has a dot between the left foot and middle of "M" of "Merry" on seal 1. Strobridge has 2 dashes below "ALL" on seal 100. E.&D. printed on Nashua paper has dot on coat just under elbow on seal 92, and on Gummed Products Co. paper has the dot on seals 91, 92. U.S.P.&L. has a dash which joins tree to top frame line just under "MA" of "Christmas" on seal 55.

The plate for booklet panes was made up from the left half of the regular plate and can be plated by certain flaws which occur on both.

1931   Perf. 12½

Designer — John W. Evans. Sales $4,526,189.

WX61	CS25	Horiz. broken gum (see footnote)	2.00
WX62	CS25	Horizontal broken gum	.20
a.		Perf. 12x12½, horiz. broken gum	.35
b.		Perf. 12.00x12½, horizontal broken gum	2.50
c.		Perf. 12, horizontal broken gum	1.00
g.		Perf. 12, vertical broken gum, booklet pane of 10	.50
h.		Perf. 12x12.00, vertical broken gum, booklet pane of 10	.60
WX63	CS25	Smooth gum	.20

For perf 12.00, see note following No. WX19.

Offset: #WX61-WX62h by Eureka, #WX63 by Strobridge. #WX61 has a green dash across inner green frame line at bottom center on each seal in sheet except those in 1st and last vertical rows and the 2 rows at bottom.

Printers' marks: Eureka has none. Strobridge has the usual 2 dashes under seal 100.

The plate for booklet panes was made up from transfers of 60 seals (12x5). The panes can be plated by minor flaws.

CS26   CS27

Designer — Edward F. Volkmann. Sales $3,470,637.

1932

WX64	CS26	Perf. 12½x12¾	.20
a.		Vertical broken gum	.50
WX65	CS26	Perf. 12	.20
WX66	CS26	Perf. 12½	.20
WX67	CS26	Perf. 12½	.20

Offset: #WX64 by Eureka, #WX65 by E.&D., #WX66 by U.S.P.&L., #WX67 by Columbian Bank Note Co., Chicago. #WX64, WX67 have a little red spur on bottom inner frame line of each seal, at left corner.

Printers' marks: Eureka has a red dash, in each corner of the sheet, which joins the red border to the red inner frame line. E.&D. has a blue dot in snow at lower left on seal 91. U.S.P.&L. has a blue dot on top of post on seal 56. Columbian Bank Note has small "C" in lower part of girl's coat on seal 82.

1933

Designer — Hans Axel Walleen. Sales $3,429,311.

WX68	CS27	Perf. 12	.20
WX69	CS27	Perf. 12½	.20

Offset: #WX68 by Eureka, #WX69 by Strobridge, U.S.P.&L., and the Columbian Bank Note Co.

Printers' marks: Eureka has rope joining elbow of figure to left on seals 11, 20, 91, 100. Strobridge has the usual 2 dashes under seal 100. U.S.P.&L. has green dot on tail of "s" of "Greetings" on seal 55. Columbian has white "c" on margin, under cross, on seal 93.

CS28   CS29

Designer — Herman D. Giesen. Sales $3,701,344.

1934

WX72	CS28	Perf. 12½x12¼	.20
WX73	CS28	Perf. 12½ (see footnote)	.20
WX74	CS28	Perf. 12½ (see footnote)	.20
WX75	CS28	Perf. 12½ (see footnote)	.20

Offset: #WX72 by Eureka, #WX73 by Strobridge, #WX74 by E.&D. and #WX75 by U.S.P.&L.

Cutting of blue plate for the under color: #WX72, WX73 (early printing) and WX74 have lettering and date cut slightly larger than ultramarine color. #WX73 (later printing) has square cutting around letters and date, like top part of letter "T". #WX75 has cutting around letters and date cut slightly larger.

Printers' marks: Eureka has 5 stars to right of cross on seal 10. Strobridge has 2 blue dashes in lower left corner of seal 91 or in lower right corner of seal 100. E.&D. has a red dot in lower left corner of seal 99. U.S.P.&L. has 5 stars to left of cross on seal 56.

Great Britain issued seals of this design which can be distinguished by the thinner and whiter paper. Sheets have perforated margins on all 4 sides but without any lettering on bottom margin, perf. 12½.

1935

Designer — Ernest Hamlin Baker. Sales $3,946,498.

WX76	CS29	Perf. 12½x12¼	.20
WX77	CS29	Perf. 12½	.20

Offset: #WX76 by Eureka, #WX77 by Strobridge, U.S.P.&L. and Columbian Bank Note Co.

Eureka recut their blue plate and eliminated the faint blue shading around cross, girl's head and at both sides of the upper part of post. U.S.P.& L. eliminated the 2 brown spurs which pointed to the base of cross, in all 4 corners of the sheet.

Printers' marks: Eureka has an extra vertical line of shading on girl's skirt on seal 60. Strobridge has 2 brown dashes in lower right corner of position 100 but sheets from an early printing are without this mark. U.S.P.&L. has a blue dot under post on seal 55. Columbian has a blue "c" under post on seal 99.

The corner seals carry slogans: "Help Fight Tuberculosis," "Protect Your Home from Tuberculosis," "Tuberculosis Is Preventable," "Tuberculosis Is Curable."

Printers' marks appear on seal 56 on sheets of 100 unless otherwise noted:

E Eureka Specialty Printing Co.
S Strobridge Lithographing Co. (1930-1958).
S Specialty Printers of America (1975-).
D Edwards & Deutsch Lithographing Co. (E.&D.)
U United States Printing & Lithographing Co. (U.S.P.&L.)
F Fleming-Potter Co., Inc.
W Western Lithograph Co.
B Berlin Lithographing Co. (1956-1969); I. S. Berlin Press (1970-1976); Barton-Cotton (1977-).
R Bradford-Robinson Printing Co.
N Sale-Niagara, Inc.
Seals from 1936 onward are printed by offset.
Seals with tropical gum (dull), starting in 1966, were used in Puerto Rico.

CS30   CS31

Designer — Walter I. Sasse. Sales $4,522,269.

1936

			Pair
WX80	CS30	Perf. 12½x12 (E)	.20
WX81	CS30	Perf. 12½ (S,D,U)	.20

Seals with red background and green cap-band alternate with seals showing green background and red cap-band. The corner seals carry the same slogans as those of 1935.

Two of the three Strobridge printings show vertical green dashes in margin below seal 100, besides "S" on seal 56.

1937

Designer — A. Robert Nelson. Sales $4,985,697.

WX88	CS31	Perf. 12x12½ (E)	.20
WX89	CS31	Perf. 12½ (S,D,U)	.20

Positions 23, 28, 73 and 78, carry slogans: "Health for all," "Protect your home," "Preventable" and "Curable."
The "U" printer's mark of U.S.P.&L. appears on seal 55. It is omitted on some sheets.

CS32   CS33

Designer — Lloyd Coe. Sales $5,239,526.

1938

WX92	CS32	Perf. 12½x12 (E)	.20
WX93	CS32	Perf. 12½ (S,D,U)	.20
a.		Miniature sheet, imperf.	2.50

The corner seals bear portraits of Rene T. H. Laennec, Robert Koch, Edward Livingston Trudeau and Einar Holboll.
No. WX93a contains the 4 corner seals, with the regular seal in the center. It sold for 25 cents.

1939

Designer — Rockwell Kent. Sales $5,593,399.

WX96	CS33	Perf. 12½x12 (E)	.20
a.		Booklet pane of 20, perf. 12	.50
WX97	CS33	Perf. 12½ (S,D,U)	.20

The center seals, positions 45, 46, 55, 56, carry slogans: "Health to All," "Protect Your Home," "Tuberculosis Preventable" and "Holiday Greetings."
Printers' marks appear on seal 57.

CS34   CS35

Designer — Felix L. Martini. Sales $6,305,979.

1940

WX100	CS34	Perf. 12½x12 (E)	.20
WX101	CS34	Perf. 12½x13 (E)	.20
WX103	CS34	Perf. 12½ (S,D,U)	.20

Seals 23, 32 and 34 carry the slogan "Protect Us from Tuberculosis." Each slogan seal shows one of the 3 children.

1941

Designer — Stevan Dohanos. Sales $7,530,496.

WX104	CS35	Perf. 12½x12 (E)	.20
WX105	CS35	Perf. 12½ (S,D,U)	.20

"S" and "U" printers' marks exist on same sheet.

CS36   CS37

Designer — Dale Nichols. Sales $9,390,117.

1942

WX108	CS36	Perf. 12x12½ (E)	.20
WX109	CS36	Perf. 12½ (S,D,U)	.20

1943

Designer — Andre Dugo. Sales $12,521,494.

			Pair
WX112	CS37	Perf. 12½x12 (E)	.20
WX113	CS37	Perf. 12½ (S,D,U)	.20

On alternate seals, the vert. frame colors (blue & red) are transposed as are the horiz. frame colors (buff & black).
Seals where "Joyeux Noel" replaces "Greetings 1943" and "1943" added on curtain or the same as #WX113 but darker colors were used in Canada.

CS38   CS39

Designer — Spence Wildey. Sales $14,966,227.

1944

WX118	CS38	Perf. 12½x12 (E)	.20
WX119	CS38	Perf. 12½ (S,D,U)	.20

Seals with "USA" omitted are for Canada.

1945   "USA" at Lower Right Corner

Designer — Park Phipps. Sales $15,638,755.

WX124	CS39	Perf. 12½x12 (E)	.20
WX125	CS39	Perf. 12½ (S,D,U)	.20

Seals with "USA" omitted are for Canada.

CS40   CS41

Designer — Mary Louise Estes and Lloyd Coe. Sales $17,075,608.

1946   "USA" at Left of Red Cross

WX130	CS40	Perf. 12½x12 (E)	.20
WX131	CS40	Perf. 12½ (S,D,U)	.20

Seals with "USA" omitted are for Canada and Bermuda.
Printers' marks are on seal 86.
The center seals (45, 46, 55, 56) bear portraits of Jacob Riis, Emily P. Bissell, E. A. Van Valkenburg and Leigh Mitchell Hodges.

1947

Designer — Raymond H. Lufkin. Sales $18,665,523.

WX135	CS41	Perf. 12x12½ (E)	.20
WX136	CS41	Perf. 12½ (S,D,U)	.20

Seals with "USA" omitted are for Canada and Great Britain.
The "U" printer's mark of U.S.P.&L. appears on seal 46.

CS42   CS43

Designer — Jean Barry Bart. Sales $20,153,834.

1948

WX140	CS42	Perf. 12x12½ (E)	.20
WX141	CS42	Perf. 12½ (S,D,U)	.20

Seals with "USA" omitted are for Canada and Great Britain.

1949

Designer — Herbert Meyers. Sales $20,226,794.

WX145	CS43	Perf. 12x12½ (E)	.20
WX146	CS43	Perf. 12½ (S,D,U)	.20

Seals with "USA" omitted are for Canada & Great Britain.

CS44   CS45

Designer — Andre Dugo. Sales $20,981,540.

1950

WX150	CS44	Perf. 12½x12 (E)	.20
WX151	CS44	Perf. 12½ (S,D,U,F)	.20

Seals with "USA" omitted are for Canada & Great Britain.

1951

Designer — Robert K. Stephens. Sales $21,717,953.

WX155	CS45	Perf. 12½x12 (E)	.20
WX156	CS45	Perf. 12½ (S,D,U,F)	.20

Seals with "USA" omitted are for Canada.

 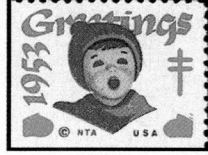

CS46   CS47

Designer — Tom Darling. Sales $23,238,148.

1952
WX159 CS46 Perf. 12½x12 (E) .20
WX160 CS46 Perf. 12½ (S,D,U,F) .20

For Nos. WX159-WX160 overprinted "Ryukyus" in Japanese characters, see Ryukyu Islands Nos. WX1 and WX1a.

1953
Designers — Elmer Jacobs and E. Willis Jones. Sales $23,889,044.

WX164 CS47 Perf. 13 (E) .20
WX165 CS47 Perf. 12½ (S,D,U,F) .20

CS48

Designer — Jorgen Hansen. Sales $24,670,202.

1954   Block of 4
WX168 CS48 Perf. 13 (E) .40
WX169 CS48 Perf. 12½ (S,U,F,W) .40
WX170 CS48 Perf. 11 (D) .50

CS49

Designer — Jean Simpson. Sales $25,780,365.

1955   Pair
WX173 CS49 Perf. 13 (E) .25
WX174 CS49 Perf. 12½ (S,U,F,W) .25
WX175 CS49 Perf. 11 (D) .25

CS50

Designer — Heidi Brandt. Sales $26,310,491.

1956   Block of 4
WX178 CS50 Perf. 12½x12 (E) .40
WX179 CS50 Perf. 12½ (E,S,U,F,W) .50
WX180 CS50 Perf. 11 (D,B) .40
WX183 CS50 "Puerto Rico," perf. 12½ 3.00

CS51

Designer — Clinton Bradley. Sales $25,959,998.

1957   Block of 4
WX184 CS51 Perf. 13 (E) .40
WX185 CS51 Perf. 12½ (S,U,F,W,R) .40
WX186 CS51 Perf. 11 (D,B) .50
WX187 CS51 Perf. 10½x11 (D) .75
WX188 CS51 Perf. 10½ (D) 3.00
WX190 CS51 "Puerto Rico," perf. 13 3.00

CS52

Designer — Alfred Guerra. Sales $25,955,390.

1958   Pair
WX191 CS52 Perf. 13 (E) .25
WX192 CS52 Perf. 12½ (S,U,F,W,R) .25
WX193 CS52 Perf. 10½x11 (B,D) .50
WX194 CS52 Perf. 11 (B,D) .35
WX196 CS52 "Puerto Rico," perf. 13 1.50

CS53

Designer — Katherine Rowe. Sales $26,740,906.

1959   Pair
WX197 CS53 Perf. 13 (E) .25
WX198 CS53 Perf. 12½ (F,R,W) .25
  a.   Horiz. pair, imperf. btwn. (D) 1.50
WX199 CS53 Perf. 10½x11 (B) .40
WX200 CS53 Perf. 11 (B,D) .25
WX201 CS53 Perf. 10½ (B) 2.00
WX203 CS53 "Puerto Rico," perf. 13 1.25

E.&D. omitted every other vertical row of perforation on a number of sheets which were widely distributed as an experiment. #WX198a (shown above in illustration) is from these sheets.

CS54

Designer — Philip Richard Costigan. Sales $26,259,030.

1960   Block of 4
WX204 CS54 Perf. 12½ (E,F,R,W) .35
WX205 CS54 Perf. 12½x12 (E) 1.00
WX206 CS54 Perf. 11x10½ (B) .35
WX207 CS54 Perf. 11 (D) .35

Puerto Rico used No. WX204 (E).

CS55

Designer — Heidi Brandt. Sales $26,529,517.

1961   Block of 4
WX209   CS55 Perf. 12½ (E,F,R,W) .35
WX209A CS55 Perf. 12½x12 (E) 2.00
WX210   CS55 Perf. 11x10½ (B) .35
WX211   CS55 Perf. 11 (D) .35

Puerto Rico used No. WX209 (E).

CS56

Designer — Paul Dohanos. Sales $27,429,202.

1962   Block of 4
WX213 CS56 Perf. 12½ (F,R,W) .35
WX214 CS56 Perf. 13 (E) .35
WX215 CS56 Perf. 10½x11 (B) .35
WX216 CS56 Perf. 11 (D,B) .35

Puerto Rico used No. WX214.

CS57

Designer — Judith Campbell Piussi. Sales $27,411,806.

1963   Block of 4
WX218 CS57 Perf. 12½ (E,F,R,W) .35
WX219 CS57 Perf. 11 (B,D) .35

Puerto Rico used No. WX218 (E).

CS58

Designer — Gaetano di Palma. Sales $28,784,043.

1964			Block of 4
WX220	CS58	Perf. 12½ (E,F,R,W)	.35
WX221	CS58	Perf. 11 (B,D)	.35

Puerto Rico used No. WX221 (B).

CS59

Designer — Frede Salomonsen. Sales $29,721,878.

1965			Block of 4
WX222	CS59	Perf. 12½ (F,W)	.35
WX223	CS59	Perf. 11 (B,D)	.35
WX224	CS59	Perf. 13 (E)	.35

Puerto Rico used No. WX223 (B).

CS60

Designer — Heidi Brandt. Sales $30,776,586.

1966			Block of 8
WX225	CS60	Perf. 12½ (E,F,W)	.65
WX226	CS60	Perf. 10½x11 (B)	.65
WX227	CS60	Perf. 11 (D)	.65

Blocks of four seals with yellow green and white backgrounds alternate in sheet in checkerboard style.
Puerto Rico used No. WX226.

Holiday Train — CS61

Designer — L. Gerald Snyder. Sales $31,876,773.

The seals come in 10 designs showing a train filled with Christmas gifts and symbols. The direction of the train is reversed in alternating rows as are the inscriptions "Christmas 1967" and "Greetings 1967." The illustration shows first 2 seals of top row.

1967			Block of 20 (10x2)
WX228	CS61	Perf. 13 (E)	.65
WX229	CS61	Perf. 12½ (F,W)	.65
WX230	CS61	Perf. 10½ (B)	1.50
WX231	CS61	Perf. 11 (D)	.75
WX232	CS61	Perf. 11x10½ (B)	.75

Puerto Rico used No. WX229 (F).

SEALS ISSUED BY NATIONAL TUBERCULOSIS AND RESPIRATORY DISEASE ASSOCIATION

CS62

Designer — William Eisele. Sales $33,059,107.

1968			Block of 4
WX233	CS62	Perf. 13 (E)	.50
WX234	CS62	Perf. 10½x11 (B)	.50
WX234A	CS62	Perf. 10½ (B)	.50
WX235	CS62	Perf. 11 (D)	.50
WX236	CS62	Perf. 12½ (F,W)	.50

Pairs of seals with bluish green and yellow backgrounds alternate in sheet in checkerboard style.
Puerto Rico used No. WX236 (F).

CS63

Designer — Bernice Kochan. Sales $34,437,591.

1969			Block of 4
WX237	CS63	Perf. 13 (E)	.35
WX238	CS63	Perf. 12½ (F,W)	.35
WX239	CS63	Perf. 10½x11 (B)	.50
WX240	CS63	Perf. 11 (B)	.50

Puerto Rico used No. WX238 (F).

CS64

Designer — L. Gerald Snyder. Sales $36,237,977.
Sheets contain 100 different designs, Christmas symbols, toys, decorated windows; inscribed alternately "Christmas 1970" and "Greetings 1970." The illustration shows 6 seals from the center of the sheet.

1970			Sheet of 100 (10x10)
WX242	CS64	Perf. 12½ (E,F,W)	1.25
WX243	CS64	Perf. 11 (B)	1.25
WX244	CS64	Perf. 11x10½ (B)	1.25

Puerto Rico used No. WX242 (F).

CS65

Designer — James Clarke. Sales $36,120,000.

1971			Block of 8 (2x4)
WX245	CS65	Perf. 12½ (E,F)	.50
WX246	CS65	Perf. 11 (B)	.50

The 4 illustrated seals each come in a 2nd design arrangement: cross at left, inscriptions transposed, and reversed bugler, candle and tree ornaments. Each sheet of 100 has 6 horiz. rows as shown and 4 rows with 2nd designs.
Puerto Rico used No. WX245 (F).
Eureka printings are found with large "E," small "E" and without "E."

CS66

Designer — Linda Layman. Sales $38,000,557.
The seals come in 10 designs showing various holiday scenes with decorated country and city houses, carolers, Christmas trees and snowman. Inscribed alternately "1972 Christmas" and "Greetings 1972." Shown are seals from center of row.

1972			Strip of 10
WX247	CS66	Perf. 13 (E)	.50
WX248	CS66	Perf. 12½ (F)	.75
WX249	CS66	Perf. 11 (B)	.50

Seal 100 has designer's name. Puerto Rico used No. WX248.

SEALS ISSUED BY AMERICAN LUNG ASSOCIATION

CS67

Designer — Cheri Johnson. Sales $36,902,439.
The seals are in 12 designs representing "The 12 Days of Christmas." Inscribed alternately "Christmas 1973" and "Greetings 1973." Shown is block from center of top 2 rows.

1973			Block of 12
WX250	CS67	Perf. 12½ (F), 18x22mm	.50
a.		Size 16½x20½mm (E)	.50
WX251	CS67	Perf. 11 (B,W)	.50

Seal 100 has designer's name. Puerto Rico used #WX250 (F).

CS68

Designer — Rubidoux. Sales $37,761,745.

1974   **Block of 4**
WX252 CS68   Perf. 12½ (E,F)   .35
WX253 CS68   Perf. 11 (B)   .35
Seal 99 has designer's name. Puerto Rico used #WX252 (F).

CS69

Children's paintings of holiday scenes. Different design for each state or territory. Paintings by elementary school children were selected in a nationwide campaign ending in Jan., 1974. Sales $34,710,107.

1975   **Sheet of 54 (6x9)**
WX254 CS69   Perf. 12½ (S,F)   1.25
WX255 CS69   Perf. 11 (B)   1.25

Printers' marks are on seal 28 (New Mexico). Specialty Printers' seals (S) carry union labels: "Scranton 4," "Scranton 7," "E. Stroudsburg."
Puerto Rico used No. WX254 (F).

CS70

Continuous village picture covers sheet with Christmas activities and Santa crossing the sky with sleigh and reindeer. No inscription on 34 seals. Others inscribed "Christmas 1976," "Greetings 1976," and (on 9 bottom-row seals) "American Lung Association." Illustration shows seals 11-12, 20-21.
Sales $36,489,207.

1976   **Sheet of 54 (9x6)**
WX256 CS70   Perf. 12½ (F,N)   1.25
WX257 CS70   Perf. 11 (B)   1.25
WX258 CS70   Perf. 13 (S)   1.25

Printers' marks (N, B, S) on seal 32 and (F) on seal 23.
Puerto Rico used No. WX256 (F).

CS71

Children's paintings of holiday scenes. Different design for each state or territory.

Sales $37,583,883.

1977   **Sheet of 54 (6x9)**
WX259 CS71   Perf. 12½ (F)   1.25
WX260 CS71   Perf. 11 (B)   1.25
WX261 CS71   Perf. 13 (S)   1.50

Printers' marks on seal 28 (Georgia).
Puerto Rico used No. WX259.

CS72

Children's paintings of holiday scenes. Different design for each state or territory.
Sales $37,621,466.

1978   **Sheet of 54 (6x9)**
WX262 CS72   Perf. 12½ (F)   1.25
WX263 CS72   Perf. 11 (B)   1.25
WX264 CS72   Perf. 13 (S)   1.25

Printers' marks on seal 29 (New Hampshire).
Puerto Rico used No. WX262.

Type of 1978 Inscribed 1979
1979   **Sheet of 54 (6x9)**
WX265 CS72   Perf. 12½ (F)   1.25
WX266 CS72   Perf. 11 (B)   1.25
WX267 CS72   Perf. 13 (S)   1.25

Printer's marks on seal 22 (Virgin Islands). Puerto Rico used No. WX265.

Beginning in 1979 there is no longer one national issue. Additional designs are issued on a limited basis as test seals to determine the designs to be used the following year.

SANITARY FAIR

The United States Sanitary Commission was authorized by the Secretary of War on June 9, 1861, and approved by President Lincoln on June 13, 1861. It was a committee of inquiry, advice and aid dealing with the health and general comfort of Union troops, supported by public contributions.

Many Sanitary Fairs were held to raise funds for the Commission, and eight issued stamps. The first took place in 1863 at Chicago, where no stamp was issued. Some Sanitary Fairs advertised on envelopes.

Sanitary Fair stamps occupy a position midway between United States semi-official carrier stamps and the private local posts. Although Sanitary Fair stamps were not valid for U.S. postal service, they were prepared for, sold and used at the fair post offices, usually with the approval and participation of the local postmaster.

The Commission undertook to forward soldiers' unpaid and postage due letters. These letters were handstamped "Forwarded by the U.S. Sanitary Commission."

Details about the Sanitary Fair stamps may be found in the following publications:

American Journal of Philately, Jan. 1889, by J. W. Scott

The Collector's Journal, Aug-Sept. 1909, by C. E. Severn

Scott's Monthly Journal, Jan. 1927 (reprint, Apr. 1973), by Elliott Perry

Stamps, April 24th, 1937, by Harry M. Konwiser

Pat Paragraphs, July, 1939, by Elliott Perry

Covers, Aug. 1952, by George B. Wray

Sanitary Fairs, 1992, by Alvin and Marjorie Kantor

The listings were compiled originally by H. M. Konwiser and Dorsey F. Wheless.

SF1

Albany, New York
Army Relief Bazaar

Setting A: narrow spacing, pane of 12.
Setting B: wider spacing, sheet of 25.

1864, Feb. 22-Mar. 30		Litho.		*Imperf.*
		Thin White Paper		
WV1	SF1 10c	**rose**		125.
		Used on cover (tied "Albany")		9,500.
		Block of 4, setting A		1,200.
		Pane of 12, setting A		4,800.
		Block of 4, setting B		500.
		Sheet of 25, setting B		3,000.
WV2	SF1 10c	**black**		700.
		Block of 5, setting A		4,500.
		Vert. pair, setting B		1,500.

The No. WV1 tied by Albany cancel on cover is unique. One other cover exists in private hands with the stamp uncanceled and slightly damaged.

Vert. pair is only setting B multiple of No. WV2.

Imitations are typographed in red, blue, black or green on a thin white or ordinary white paper, also on colored papers and are:

(a) Eagle with topknot, printed in sheets of 30 (6x5).
(b) Eagle without shading around it.
(c) Eagle with shading around it, but with a period instead of a circle in "C" of "Cents," and "Ten Cents" is smaller.

SF2

Boston, Mass.
National Sailors' Fair

1864, Nov. 9-22		Die Cut		Litho.
WV3	SF2 10c	**green**		350.

Brooklyn, N.Y.
Brooklyn Sanitary Fair
Sheets of 25 (WV4)

SF3

1864, Feb. 22-Mar. 8		Litho.		*Imperf.*
WV4	SF3 (15c)	**green**	1,000.	3,600.
		On cover, Fair postmark on envelope		3,000.
		Block of 4	6,500.	
		Block of 6	10,000.	
WV5	SF3 (25c)	**black**	4,750.	
		On cover, with 1c local #28L2, Fair postmark on envelope		36,000.

No. WV4 used is valued canceled by the Fair postmark. Two or more examples also exist with a manuscript cancel. No. WV5 unused is unique as is the usage on cover.

Imitations: (a) Typographed and shows "Sanitary" with a heavy cross bar to "T" and second "A" with a long left leg. (b) Is a rough typograph print without shading in letters of "Fair."

SF4

SF5

1863, Dec.		Typeset		*Imperf.*
WV6	SF4	5c **black**, *rosy buff*	800.	200.
WV7	SF5	10c **green**	1,100.	
		Tete beche pair	9,000.	

No. WV6 used is believed to be unique. It has a manuscript cancel and is faulty. It is valued thus.

SF6

SF7

New York, N.Y.
Metropolitan Fair

1864, Apr. 4-27		Engr.		*Imperf.*
		Thin White Paper		
WV8	SF6 10c	**blue**		325.
		Sheet of 4		1,750.
WV9	SF6 10c	**red**		1,900.
		Pair		4,500.
WV10	SF6 10c	**black**		18,000.

Engraved and printed by John E. Gavit of Albany, N.Y. from a steel plate composed of four stamps, 2x2. Can be plated by the positions of scrolls and dots around "Ten Cents."

No. WV10 is unique.

Philadelphia, Pa.
Great Central Fair

1864, June 7-28		Engr.		*Perf. 12*
		Printed by Butler & Carpenter, Philadelphia		
		Sheets of 126 (14x9)		
WV11	SF7 10c	**blue**	40.00	525.00
		On cover tied with Fair postmark		2,250.
		On cover with 3c #65, Fair and Philadelphia postmarks		36,000.
		On cover with 3c #65, New York postmark		42,500.
		Block of 4	250.00	
WV12	SF7 20c	**green**	27.50	500.00
		On cover tied with Fair postmark		1,500.
		Block of 4	135.00	
		Block of 12	475.00	
WV13	SF7 30c	**black**	35.00	400.00
		On cover tied with Fair postmark		1,500.
		Nos. WV11-WV13 on single cover, Fair postmark		7,500.
		Block of 4	160.00	
		Block of 6	240.00	

Imprint "Engraved by Butler & Carpenter, Philadelphia" on right margin adjoining three stamps.

Used examples of Nos. WV11-WV13 have Fair cancellation. The No. WV11 covers used with 3c #65 are each unique. The New York usage is on a Metropolitan Fair illustrated envelope.

Imitation of No. WV13 comes typographed in blue or green on thick paper.

White and amber envelopes were sold by the fair inscribed "Great Central Fair for the Sanitary Commission," showing picture in several colors of wounded soldier, doctors and ambulance marked "U.S. Sanitary Commission." Same design and inscription are known on U.S. envelope No. U46.

SF8

SF9

Springfield, Mass.
Soldiers' Fair

1864, Dec. 19-24		Typo.		*Imperf.*
WV14	SF8 10c	**lilac**		225.00
		On unaddressed cover, Fair postmark on envelope		750.00
		Horizontal strip of 4		1,000.

Design by Thomas Chubbuck, engraver of the postmaster provisional stamp of Brattleboro, Vt.

One cover exists pencil-addressed to Wm. Ingersoll, Springfield Armory; value slightly more than an unaddressed cover.

Imitations: (a) Without designer's name in lower right corner, in lilac on laid paper. (b) With designer's name, but roughly typographed, in lilac on white wove paper. Originals show 5 buttons on uniform.

Stamford, Conn.
Soldiers' Fair

1864, July 27-29				
WV15	SF9 15c	**pale brown**	2,000.	5,750.

Originals have tassels at ends of ribbon inscribed "SOLDIERS FAIR." Imitations have leaning "S" in "CENTS" and come in lilac, brown, green, also black on white paper, green on pinkish paper and other colors.

ESSAY
Great Central Fair, Philadelphia

1864				
WV11-E1		Design as issued but value tablets blank, greenish black on glazed paper (unique)		—

PROOFS
Metropolitan Fair, New York

1864				
WV10P	10c	**black,** plate on India, mounted on card		900.

Great Central Fair, Philadelphia

WV11P	10c	**blue,** card	32.50
		Block of 4	150.00
WV11TC/WV13TC	10c and 30c	**grnsh blk,** se-tenant, glazed paper, large die	—
WV12P	20c	**green,** card	35.00
		Block of 4	175.00
WV12TC	20c	**carmine,** wove, perf.	35.00
		Block of 4	175.00
WV12TC	20c	**vermilion,** India on card, large die	275.00
WV12TC	20c	**vermilion,** wove, imperf.	22.50
		Block of 4	115.00
WV12TC	20c	**vermilion,** wove, perf.	35.00
		Block of 4	175.00
WV12TC	20c	**orange,** wove, imperf.	22.50
		Block of 4	115.00
WV12TC	20c	**brown orange,** opaque paper	22.50
		Block of 4	115.00
WV12TC	20c	**red brown,** wove, perf.	35.00
		Block of 4	175.00
WV12TC	20c	**black brown,** wove, imperf.	25.00
		Block of 4	125.00
WV12TC	20c	**olive,** wove, imperf.	22.50
		Block of 4	100.00
WV12TC	20c	**yellow green,** wove, imperf.	22.50
		Block of 4	125.00
WV12TC	20c	**light green,** wove, perf.	35.00
		Block of 4	175.00
WV12TC	20c	**blue,** India on card, large die	275.00
WV12TC	20c	**blue,** wove, perf.	175.00
WV12TC	20c	**bright blue,** wove, imperf.	22.50
		Block of 4	125.00
WV12TC	20c	**bright blue,** wove, perf.	35.00
		Block of 4	175.00
WV12TC	20c	**lt. ultramarine,** wove, imperf.	22.50
		Block of 4	125.00
WV12TC	20c	**purple,** wove, imperf.	22.50
		Block of 4	125.00
WV12TC	20c	**claret,** wove, imperf.	35.00
		Block of 4	200.00

WV12TC	20c **brown black,** wove,		
	perf.		35.00
	Block of 4		175.00
WV12TC	20c **greenish black,** glazed		
	paper, large die		225.00
WV12TC	20c **gray black,** opaque		
	paper, wove, imperf.		22.50
	Block of 4		125.00
WV12TC	20c **gray black,** wove, perf.		35.00
	Block of 4		175.00
WV12TC	20c **black,** experimental		
	double paper, wove,		
	imperf.		25.00
	Block of 4		140.00
WV13P	30c **black,** card		35.00
	Block of 4		175.00
WV13TC	30c **blue,** imperf		35.00

Reprints (1903?) exist of WV11TC-WV13TC, se-tenant vertically, large die on glazed white, pink or yellow card and small die on India paper (mounted se-tenant) in carmine, red carmine, vermilion, orange, brown, yellow brown, olive, yellow green, blue green, gray blue, ultramarine, light violet, violet, claret and gray black.

There also exist large die essay reprints on India paper, green bond paper and glazed cardboard without denomination or with 20c. The 20c value has an added line below the center shield.

ENCASED POSTAGE STAMPS

In early 1862, months after the beginning of the American Civil War, people were conserving resources in anticipation of hard times and shortages ahead. Coins were one of the most hoarded resources, and as a result of this hoarding, coins began to command a premium over paper money. The public was reluctant to spend their coins, fearing the premiums for coins might increase, and a loss might result. Many millions of dollars in gold and silver coins, even copper-nickel cents, disappeared into private hands.

The U.S. Mint began coining copper-nickel cents almost exclusively, but could not meet demand. In response, the public turned to postage stamps to meet small obligations, and shopkeepers were forced to accept stamps as change. Envelopes stating the amount of stamps contained within and cards bearing stamps were sometimes used to keep the stamps from sticking and becoming destroyed, and printers sold advertisements on large numbers of these envelopes. By July 1862, the government had authorized the monetizing of postage stamps and began printing stamp impressions on bank note paper.

On August 12, 1862, John Gault was issued a patent for a "Design for Encasing Government Stamps" to be used as the equivalent of currency. Gault's plans called for a postage stamp to have its corners wrapped around a cardboard circle and show through a thin mica covering. An outer metal frame would hold these items secure, and a heavier brass backing would complete the piece. The brass backing would be suitable for advertising purposes. The resulting piece was about the size of a quarter, but much lighter in weight. The stamps placed in the new encased postage were the 1c, 3c, 5c, 10c, 12c, 24c, 30c and 90c stamps of the 1861 issue. Of course, Gault sold his encased postage at a small markup over the value of the stamp enclosed and the cost of production.

On August 21, 1862, the government issued postage currency in 5c, 10c, 25c and 50c denominations, and fractional currency was issued in 1863. These policies, plus the increased production of brass and copper-nickel coinage in 1863, effectively ended Gault's enterprise. Still, encased postage proved very popular, because it solved the major problems of stamp damage and the necessity of opening stamp envelopes to count the contents. At least 30 companies took advantage of the advertising possibilities and had their ads stamped on the brass backing. Perhaps $50,000 or a little more in encased postage eventually was sold and circulated, not nearly enough by itself to solve the nation's small change crisis. Of the approximately 750,000 pieces sold, only 3,500-7,000 are believed to have survived for collectors.

Values are for very fine examples with mica intact, although signs of circulation and handling are to be expected.

Grading encompasses three areas: 1. Case will show signs of wear or handling and signs of original toning. 2. Mica will be intact with no pieces missing. 3. Stamp will be fresh with no signs of toning or wrinkling.

Examples that came with silvered cases and still have some or all of the original silvering will sell for more than the values shown.

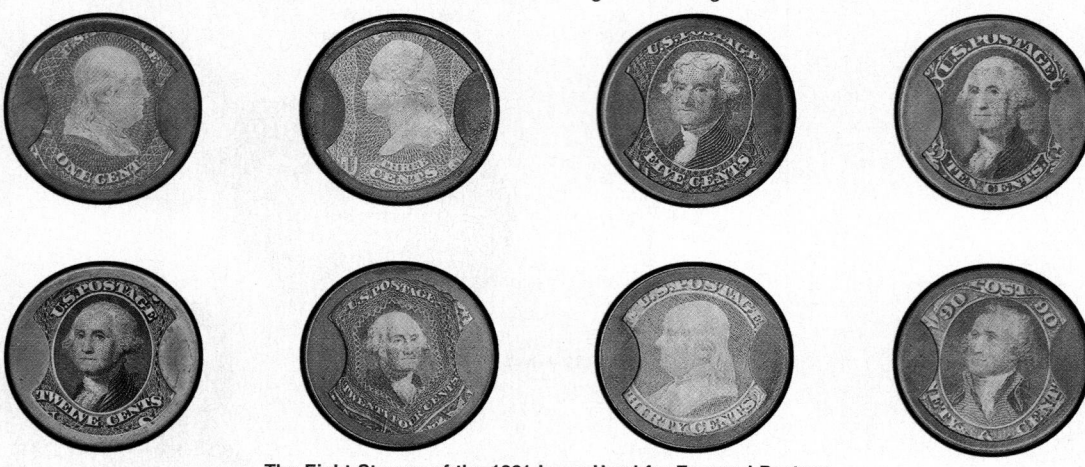

The Eight Stamps of the 1861 Issue Used for Encased Postage

Aerated Bread Co., New York

EP1	1c	*7,000.*
EP1A	5c	*15,000.*

No. EP1A is unique.

Ayer's Cathartic Pills, Lowell, Mass.

Varieties with long and short arrows below legend occur on all denominations.

EP2	1c	500.
EP3	3c	425.
EP4	5c	1,000.
EP5	10c	1,000.
EP6	12c	2,500.
EP7	24c	*3,500.*

Take Ayer's Pills

EP8	1c	500.
EP9	3c	400.
EP10	5c	1,000.
a.	Ribbed frame	*3,000.*
EP11	10c	1,250.
a.	Ribbed frame	*5,000.*
EP12	12c	2,500.
EP12A	30c	*5,000.*

Nos. EP11a and EP12A each are unique.

Ayer's Sarsaparilla

Three varieties: "AYER'S" small, medium or large. Example illustrated is the medium variety.

EP13	1c medium "Ayer's"	500.
a.	Small	750.
EP15	3c medium "Ayer's"	400.
a.	Small	650.
b.	Large	450.
c.	Ribbed frame, medium	2,000.
EP16	5c medium "Ayer's"	2,000.
a.	Large	1,500.
EP17	10c medium "Ayer's"	550.
a.	Ribbed frame, medium	1,750.
b.	Small	1,250.
c.	Large	1,100.
EP18	12c medium "Ayer's"	2,250.
a.	Small	2,750.
EP19	24c medium "Ayer's"	1,900.
EP20	30c medium "Ayer's"	*4,500.*

Bailey & Co., Philadelphia

EP21	1c	1,100.
EP22	3c	1,200.
EP23	5c	*2,250.*
EP24	10c	*2,250.*
EP25	12c	*3,000.*

"FANCYGOODS" as one word

"FANCY GOODS" as two words

Joseph L. Bates, Boston

EP26	1c one word	450.
a.	Two words	600.
EP27	3c one word	2,000.
a.	Two words	1,000.
EP28	5c two words	1,250.
a.	One word	1,500.
b.	Ribbed frame, one word	2,750.
EP29	10c two words	1,750.
a.	One word	1,500.
b.	Ribbed frame, one word	2,500.
EP30	12c two words	4,000.

Brown's Bronchial Troches

EP31	1c	2,250.
EP32	3c	650.
EP33	5c	450.
EP34	10c	1,000.
EP35	12c	2,750.
EP36	24c	3,250.
EP37	30c	4,000.

F. Buhl & Co., Detroit

EP38	1c	2,750.
EP39	3c	9,000.
EP40	5c	2,000.
EP41	10c	1,750.
EP42	12c	6,000.
EP43	24c	5,750.

No. EP39 is unique.

Burnett's Cocoaine Kalliston

EP44	1c	750.
EP45	3c	750.
EP46	5c	650.
EP47	10c	700.
EP48	12c	3,750.
EP49	24c	5,000.
EP50	30c	4,000.
EP51	90c	7,500.

Burnett's Cooking Extracts

EP52	1c	450.
EP53	3c	500.
EP54	5c	500.
EP55	10c	750.
a.	Ribbed frame	4,000.
EP56	12c	2,000.
EP57	24c	5,000.
EP58	30c	5,500.
EP58A	90c	5,500.

No. EP58A is unique.

A. M. Claflin, Hopkinton, Mass.

EP59	1c	*11,000.*
EP60	3c	—
EP61	5c	*15,000.*
EP62	10c	*7,500.*
EP63	12c	*16,000.*

No. EP60 is unique.

H. A. Cook, Evansville, Ind.

EP64	5c	*4,000.*
EP65	10c	*3,000.*

Dougan, Hatter, New York

EP66	1c	*2,500.*
EP67	3c	*2,500.*
EP68	5c	*3,750.*
EP69	10c	*3,750.*

Drake's Plantation Bitters

EP70	1c	500.
EP71	3c	500.
EP72	5c	600.
a.	Ribbed frame	*2,500.*
EP73	10c	650.
a.	Ribbed frame	*2,500.*
EP74	12c	2,000.
EP75	24c	*3,500.*
EP76	30c	*3,500.*
EP77	90c	*11,000.*

Ellis, McAlpin & Co., Cincinnati

EP78	1c	—
EP79	3c	*2,250.*
EP80	5c	1,250.
EP81	10c	1,100.
EP82	12c	*3,500.*
EP83	24c	*2,750.*

Specialists have questioned the existence of No. EP78. The editors would like to see authenticated evidence of this listing.

G. G. Evans, Philadelphia

EP84	1c	1,250.
EP85	3c	1,500.
EP86	5c	—
EP87	10c	*7,000.*

Gage Bros. & Drake, Tremont House, Chicago

EP88	1c	1,200.
EP89	3c	600.
EP90	5c	750.
EP91	10c	1,100.
a.	Ribbed frame	*4,000.*
EP92	12c	*3,000.*

Only one example of No. EP91a is available to collectors.

J. Gault

EP93	1c	600.
a.	Ribbed frame	—
EP95	3c	600.
a.	Ribbed frame	1,400.
EP96	5c	350.
a.	Ribbed frame	600.
EP97	10c	750.
a.	Ribbed frame	650.
EP98	12c	900.
a.	Ribbed frame	*2,500.*
EP99	24c	1,850.
a.	Ribbed frame	*2,750.*
EP100	30c	*2,750.*
a.	Ribbed frame	*3,750.*
EP101	90c	*9,000.*

L. C. Hopkins & Co., Cincinnati

EP102	1c	2,500.
EP103	3c	5,500.
EP104	5c	7,000.
EP105	10c	6,000.

Hunt & Nash, Irving House, New York

EP106	1c	2,000.
EP107	3c	2,000.
a.	Ribbed frame	3,000.
EP108	5c	900.
a.	Ribbed frame	950.
EP109	10c	1,400.
a.	Ribbed frame	1,000.
EP110	12c	2,000.
a.	Ribbed frame	3,000.
EP111	24c	3,750.
a.	Ribbed frame	4,500.
EP112	30c	6,000.

No. EP112 is unique.

Kirkpatrick & Gault, New York

EP113	1c	500.
EP114	3c	700.
EP115	5c	500.
EP116	10c	500.
EP117	12c	1,250.
EP118	24c	1,750.
EP119	30c	2,750.
EP120	90c	10,000.

Lord & Taylor, New York

EP121	1c	1,250.
EP122	3c	1,500.
EP123	5c	1,100.
EP124	10c	1,250.
EP125	12c	2,500.
EP126	24c	2,750.
EP127	30c	3,750.
EP128	90c	10,000.

Mendum's Family Wine Emporium, New York

EP129	1c	1,000.
EP130	3c	1,200.
EP131	5c	1,500.
EP132	10c	3,000.
a.	Ribbed frame	2,750.
EP133	12c	3,500.

B. F. Miles, Peoria

EP134	1c	25,000.
EP135	5c	15,000.

John W. Norris, Chicago

EP136	1c	3,750.
EP137	3c	3,750.
EP138	5c	3,250.
EP139	10c	3,500.

"INSURANCE" Curved　　　"INSURANCE" Straight

North America Life Insurance Co., N. Y.

EP140	1c Curved	475.
a.	Straight	525.
EP141	3c Straight	800.
a.	Curved	1,750.
EP142	5c Straight	675.
a.	Straight, ribbed frame	1,100.
b.	Curved	3,000.
EP143	10c Straight	900.
a.	Straight, ribbed frame	3,250.
b.	Curved	1,750.
c.	Curved, ribbed frame	2,250.
EP144	12c Straight	2,500.
a.	Curved	3,500.

No. EP142b is unique. Nos. EP143a and EP144a each may be unique.

Pearce, Tolle & Holton, Cincinnati

EP145	1c	3,250.
EP146	3c	3,000.
EP147	5c	3,000.
EP148	10c	7,000.
EP149	12c	4,250.
EP150	24c	—

No. EP149 is unique.
The existence of No. EP150 has been questioned by specialists. The editors would like to see authenticated evidence of its existence.

Sands' Ale

EP151	5c	3,750.
EP152	10c	4,500.
EP153	12c	
EP154	30c	—

No. EP154 is unique. The case of the known example has been opened. It is possible that the 30c stamp has been substituted for the original stamp and/or the mica has been replaced.

Schapker & Bussing, Evansville, Ind.

EP155	1c	2,000.
EP156	3c	1,750.
EP157	5c	850.
EP158	10c	750.
EP159	12c	5,000.

John Shillito & Co., Cincinnati

EP160	1c	3,000.
EP161	3c	1,100.
EP162	5c	600.
EP163	10c	950.
EP164	12c	5,500.

S. Steinfeld, New York

EP165	1c	3,750.
EP166	5c	7,000.
EP167	10c	6,000.
EP168	12c	6,000.

N. G. Taylor & Co., Philadelphia

EP169	1c	3,700.
EP170	3c	3,500.
EP171	5c	3,250.
EP172	10c	3,500.
EP173	12c	3,750.

No. EP173 is unique.

Weir and Larminie, Montreal		
EP174	1c	4,000.
EP175	3c	15,000.
EP176	5c	4,250.
EP177	10c	3,000.

White, the Hatter, New York		
EP178	1c	3,750.
EP179	3c	2,750.
EP180	5c	5,000.
EP181	10c	5,000.

POSTAGE CURRENCY

Small coins disappeared from circulation in 1861-62 as cash was hoarded. To ease business transactions, merchants issued notes of credit, promises to pay, tokens, store cards, etc. U.S. Treasurer Francis E. Spinner made a substitute for small currency by affixing postage stamps, singly and in multiples, to Treasury paper. He arranged with the Post office to replace worn stamps with new when necessary.

The next step was to print the stamps on Treasury paper. On July 17, 1862, Congress authorized the issue of such "Postage Currency." It remained in use until May 27, 1863. It was not money, but a means of making stamps negotiable.

On Oct. 10, 1863 a second issue was released. These, and the later three issues, did not show stamps and are called Fractional Currency. In 1876 Congress authorized the minting of silver coins to redeem the outstanding fractional currency.

Values quoted are for notes in crisp, new condition, not creased or worn.
Creased or worn notes sell for 25 percent to 75 percent less.
Items valued with a dash are believed to be unique.

Illustrations reduced.
Front Engraved and Printed by the National Bank Note Co.
Back Engraved and Printed in Black by the American Bank Note Co.
"A B Co." on Back

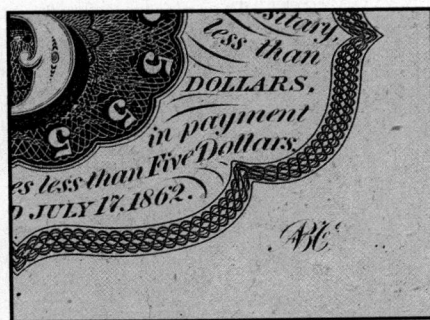

"ABCo." imprint, lower right corner of back (#1-8)

1862, Aug. 21

Perforated Edges-Perf. 12

PC1	5c Bust of Jefferson on 5c stamp, brown	190.00
a.	Inverted back	*950.00*
PC2	10c Bust of Washington on 10c stamp, green	160.00
PC3	25c Five 5c stamps, brown	240.00
PC4	50c Five 10c stamps, green	290.00
a.	Inverted back	*950.00*

Imperforate Edges

PC5	5c Bust of Jefferson on 5c stamp	75.00
a.	Inverted back	*525.00*
PC6	10c Bust of Washington on 10c stamp	75.00
a.	Inverted back	*675.00*
PC7	25c Five 5c stamps	135.00
a.	Inverted back	*600.00*
PC8	50c Five 10c stamps	160.00
a.	Inverted back	*750.00*

No. PC8 exists perforated 14, privately produced.

Front and Back Engraved and Printed by the National Bank Note Co.

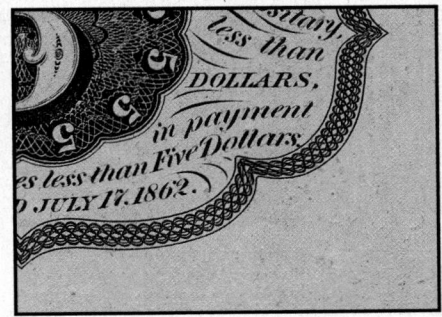

Without "A B Co." on Back

Perforated Edges-Perf. 12

PC9	5c Bust of Jefferson on 5c stamp	230.00
a.	Inverted back	—
PC10	10c Bust of Washington on 10c stamp	250.00
a.	Inverted back	—
PC11	25c Five 5c stamps	340.00
a.	Inverted back	*1,100.*
PC12	50c Five 10c stamps	450.00
a.	Inverted back	—

Imperforate Edges

PC13	5c Bust of Jefferson on 5c stamp	210.00
a.	Inverted back	—
PC14	10c Bust of Washington on 10c stamp	320.00
a.	Inverted back	*1,100.*
PC15	25c Five 5c stamps	425.00
PC16	50c Five 10c stamps	750.00
a.	Inverted back	—

CONFEDERATE STATES OF AMERICA

3¢ 1861 POSTMASTERS' PROVISIONALS

With the secession of South Carolina from the Union on Dec. 20, 1860, a new era began in U.S. history as well as its postal history. Other Southern states quickly followed South Carolina's lead, which in turn led to the formation of the provisional government of the Confederate States of America on Feb. 4, 1861.

President Jefferson Davis' cabinet was completed Mar. 6, 1861, with the acceptance of the position of Postmaster General by John H. Reagan of Texas. The provisional government had already passed regulations that required payment for postage in cash and that effectively carried over the U.S. 3c rate until the new Confederate Post Office Department took over control of the system.

Soon after entering on his duties, Reagan directed the postmasters in the Confederate States and in the newly seceded states to "continue the performance of their duties as such, and render all accounts and pay all moneys (sic) to the order of the Government of the U.S. as they have heretofore done, until the Government of the Confederate States shall be prepared to assume control of its postal affairs."

As coinage was becoming scarce, postal patrons began having problems buying individual stamps or paying for letters individually, especially as stamp stocks started to run short in certain areas. Even though the U.S. Post Office Department was technically in control of the postal system and southern postmasters were operating under Federal authority, the U.S.P.O. was hesitant in re-supplying seceded states with additional stamps and stamped envelopes.

The U.S. government had made the issuance of postmasters' provisionals illegal many years before, but the southern postmasters had to do what they felt was necessary to allow patrons to pay for postage and make the system work. Therefore, a few postmasters took it upon themselves to issue provisional stamps in the 3c rate then in effect. Interestingly, these were stamps and envelopes that the U.S. government did not recognize as legal, but they did do postal duty unchallenged in the Confederate States. Yet the proceeds were to be remitted to the U.S. government in Washington! Six authenticated postmasters' provisionals in the 3c rate have been recorded.

On May 13, 1861, Postmaster General Reagan issued his proclamation "assuming control and direction of postal service within the limits of the Confederate States of America on and after the first day of June," with new postage rates and regulations. The Federal government suspended operations in the Confederate States (except for western Virginia and the seceding state of Tennessee) by a proclamation issued by Postmaster General Montgomery Blair on May 27, 1861, effective from May 31, 1861, and June 10 for western and middle Tennessee. As Tennessee did not join the Confederacy until July 2, 1861, the unissued 3c Nashville provisional was produced in a state that was in the process of seceding, while the other provisionals were used in the Confederacy before the June 1 assumption of control of postal service by the Confederate States of America.

HILLSBORO, N.C.

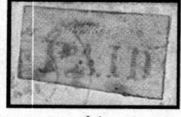

A1

Handstamped Adhesive

1AX1 A1 3c **bluish black,** on cover   —

No. 1AX1 is unique. This is the same handstamp as used for No. 39X1. 3c usage is determined from the May 27, 1861 circular date stamp.

Cancellation: black town.

JACKSON, MISS.

E1

Handstamped Envelope

2AXU1 E1 3c **black**   *2,500.*

See Nos. 43XU1-43XU4.

MADISON COURT HOUSE, FLA.

A1   "CNETS"

Typeset Adhesive

3AX1	A1	3c **gold**	— 10,000.
		On cover	65,000.
a.		"CNETS"	14,000.

No. 3AX1 on cover and No. 3AX1a are each unique.

Cancellations: black town, oblong paid, ms "Paid in Money," manuscript.

See No. 137XU1.

NASHVILLE, TENN.

A1

Typeset Adhesive (5 varieties)

4AX1	A1	3c **carmine**	200.
		Horizontal strip of 5 showing all varieties	1,500.

No. 4AX1 was prepared by Postmaster McNish with the U.S. rate, but the stamp was never issued.

Fakes exist of the horizontal strips. Expertization is recommended.

See Nos. 61X2-61XU2.

SELMA, ALA.

E1

Handstamped Envelope

5AXU1 E1 3c **black**   *2,500.*

See Nos. 77XU1-77XU3.

TUSCUMBIA, ALA.

E1

Handstamped Envelope, impression at upper right

6AXU1 E1 3c **dull red,** *buff*   *17,500.*

No. 6AXU1 also exists with a 3c 1857 stamp affixed at upper right over the provisional handstamp, tied by black circular "TUSCUMBIA, ALA." town postmark. Value $15,000.

Dangerous forgeries exist of No. 6AXU1.

See Nos. 84XU1-84XU3.

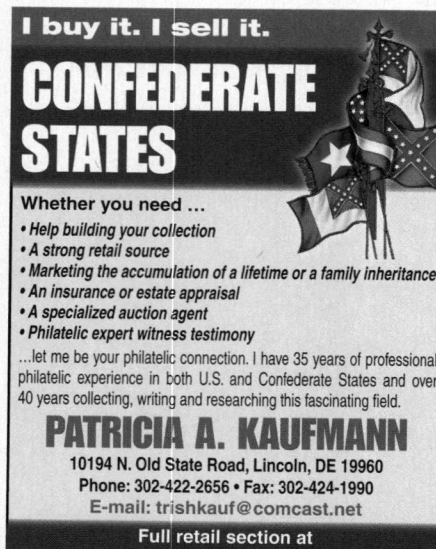

CONFEDERATE POSTMASTERS' PROVISIONALS

These stamps and envelopes were issued by individual postmasters generally during the interim between June 1, 1861, when the use of United States stamps stopped in the Confederacy, and October 16, 1861, when the first Confederate Government stamps were issued. They were occasionally issued at later periods, especially in Texas, when regular issues of government stamps were unavailable.

Canceling stamps of the post offices were often used to produce envelopes, some of which were supplied in advance by private citizens. These envelopes and other stationery therefore may be found in a wide variety of papers, colors, sizes and shapes, including patriotic and semi-official types. It is often difficult to determine whether the impression made by the canceling stamp indicates provisional usage or merely postage paid at the time the letter was deposited in the post office. Occasionally the same mark was used for both purposes.

The *press-printed* **provisional envelopes are in a different category. They were produced in quantity, using envelopes procured in advance by the postmaster, such as those of Charleston, Lynchburg, Memphis, etc.** The **press-printed** *envelopes are listed and valued on all known papers.*

The **handstamped** *provisional envelopes are listed and valued according to type and variety of handstamp, but not according to paper. Many exist on such a variety of papers that they defy accurate, complete listing. The value of a handstamped provisional envelope is determined primarily by the clarity of the markings and its overall condition and attractiveness, rather than the type of paper.*

All handstamped provisional envelopes, when used, should also show the postmark of the town of issue.

Most handstamps are impressed at top right, although they exist from some towns in other positions.

Many illustrations in this section are reduced in size.

Values for envelopes are for entires. Values for stamps of provisional issues are for examples with little or no gum; original gum over a large portion of the stamp will increase the value substantially.

ABERDEEN, MISS.

E1

Handstamped Envelopes

1XU1	E1	5c **black**		6,000.
a.		10c (ms.) on 5c **black**		12,500.

No. 1XU1a is unique.

ABINGDON, VA.

E1

Handstamped Envelopes

2XU1	E1	2c **black**		11,000.
2XU2	E1	5c **black**		1,400.
		On patriotic cover		3,000.
2XU3	E1	10c **black**	2,200.	3,500.

The unused No. 2XU3 is a unique mint example, and the value represents the price realized in a 1997 auction sale. No. 2XU3 used also is unique.

ALBANY, GA.

E1

E2

E3

E4

Handstamped Envelopes

3XU1	E1	5c **greenish blue**	900.
		On patriotic cover	
3XU2	E2	10c **greenish blue**	2,000.
a.		10c on 5c **greenish blue**	3,500.
3XU5	E3	5c **greenish blue**	
3XU6	E4	10c **greenish blue**	2,500.

The "10" in the No. 3XU2 marking is larger than the "10" in the No. 3XU3 marking.

Only one example each recorded of Nos. 3XU2, 3XU2a and 3XU6. No. 3XU2a is the unique Confederate example of one provisional marking revaluing another.

The existence of No. 3XU5 is in question. The editors would like to see an authenticated example of this marking.

ANDERSON COURT HOUSE, S.C.

E1

Handstamped Envelopes

4XU1	E1	5c **black**	500.	2,250.
4XU2	E1	10c (ms.) **black**		3,000.
4XU3	E1	(2c) **black,** denomination omitted (circular rate)		2,250.

ATHENS, GA

A1 (Type I)

A1 (Type II)

**Typographed Adhesives
(from woodcuts of two types)**

Pairs, both horizontal and vertical, always show one of each type.

5X1	A1	5c **purple** (shades)	1,000.	1,500.
		Pair		4,000.
		On cover		2,500.
		Pair on cover		5,500.
		Strip of 4 on cover (horiz.)		10,000.
a.		Tete beche pair (vertical)		7,500.
		Tete beche pair on cover		22,500.
5X2	A1	5c **red**		4,750.
		On cover		20,000.
		Pair on cover		

Cancellations in black: grid, town, "PAID."

The colorless ornaments in the four corners of No. 5X2 were recut making them wider than those in No. 5X1.

Dangerous fakes exist of Nos. 5X1 and 5X2. Certificates of authenticity from recognized committees are strongly recommended.

The existence of a pair on cover of No. 5X2 is in question. The editors would like to see an example of this usage.

ATLANTA, GA.

E1

E2

Handstamped Envelopes

6XU1	E1	5c	**red**		3,500.
6XU2	E1	5c	**black**	175.	700.
			On patriotic cover		3,500.
a.		10c on 5c	**black**		2,500.
6XU4	E2	2c	**black**		3,000.
6XU5	E2	5c	**black**		1,500.
			On patriotic cover		3,500.
a.		10c on 5c	**black**		2,500.
6XU6	E2	10c	**black**		950.
			On patriotic cover		—

Only one example recorded of No. 6XU1.

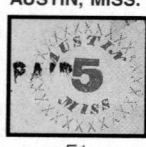

E3

Handstamped Envelopes

6XU8	E3	5c	**black**		3,500.
6XU9	E3	10c	**black** ("10" upright)		2,750.

Only one example recorded of No. 6XU8.

AUSTIN, MISS.

E1

Press-printed Envelope (typeset)

8XU1	E1	5c	**red,** *amber*	75,000.

One example recorded.

Cancellation: black "Paid."

AUSTIN, TEX.

E1a

Handstamped Adhesive

9X1	E1a	10c	**black**	
			On cover, uncanceled	1,500.
			On cover, tied	—

Only one example of No. 9X1 tied on cover is recorded.

Handstamped Envelope

9XU1	E1a	10c	**black**	1,750.

Cancellation on Nos. 9X1 and 9XU1: black town.

AUTAUGAVILLE, ALA.

E1

E2

Handstamped Envelopes

10XU1	E1	5c	**black**	10,000.
10XU2	E2	5c	**black**	12,500.

No. 10XU2 is unique.

BALCONY FALLS, VA.

E1

Handstamped Envelope

122XU1	E1	10c	**blue**	2,000.

The use of No. 122XU1 as a provisional marking is in question. The editors would like to see authenticated evidence of its use as a provisional.

BARNWELL COURT HOUSE, S. C.

E1

Handstamped Envelope

123XU1	E1	5c	**black**	2,500.

These are two separate handstamps.

BATON ROUGE, LA.

A1

A2

Typeset Adhesives
Ten varieties of each

11X1	A1	2c	**green**	8,000.	5,000.
			On cover		20,000.
a.			"McCcrmick"	37,500.	35,000.
			On cover		—
11X2	A2	5c	**green & carmine** (Maltese cross border)	1,500.	1,400.
			On cover		3,000.
			Strip of 3		5,000.
			Strip of 5		22,500.
			Canceled in New Orleans, on cover		20,000.
a.			"McCcrmick"	—	2,000.
			On cover		7,000.

Only one example each is recorded of No. 11X1a unused, used and on cover.

The "Canceled in New Orleans" examples entered the mails in New Orleans after having been placed (uncanceled) on riverboats in Baton Rouge. Two such covers are recorded.

A3

 (sub-position)

A4

Ten varieties of each

11X3	A3	5c	**green & carmine** (crisscross border)	4,500.	2,750.
			On cover		10,000.
a.			"McCcrmick"		3,500.
11X4	A4	10c	**blue**		14,000.
			On cover		75,000.

No. 11X4 on cover is unique.

Cancellation on Nos. 11X1-11X4: black town.

BEAUMONT, TEX.

A1

A2

Typeset Adhesives
Several varieties of each

12X1	A1	10c	**black,** *yellow*		12,500.
			On cover		55,000.
12X2	A1	10c	**black,** *pink*		12,500.
			On cover		30,000.
12X3	A2	10c	**black,** *yellow,* on cover		90,000.

One example recorded of No. 12X3.

Cancellations: black pen; black town.

BLUFFTON, S. C.

E1

Handstamped Envelope

124XU1	E1	5c	**black**	8,000.

Only one example recorded of No. 124XU1.

BRIDGEVILLE, ALA.

A1

Handstamped Adhesive in black within red pen-ruled squares

13X1	A1	5c	**black & red,** pair on cover	20,000.

Cancellation is black pen.

CAMDEN, S. C.

E1

E2

Handstamped Envelopes

125XU1	E1	5c	black	4,500.
125XU2	E2	10c	black	450.

No. 125XU2 unused was privately carried and is addressed but has no postal markings. No. 125XU2 is indistinguishable from a handstamp paid cover when used.

CANTON, MISS.

E1

"P" in star is initial of Postmaster William Priestly.

Handstamped Envelopes

14XU1	E1	5c	black	2,750.
a.		10c (ms.) on 5c	black	5,000.

CAROLINA CITY, N. C.

E1

Handstamped Envelope

118XU1	E1	5c	black	3,500.

CARTERSVILLE, GA.

E1

Handstamped Envelope

126XU1	E1	(5c)	red	1,250.

CHAPEL HILL, N. C.

E1

Handstamped Envelope

15XU1	E1	5c	black	3,250.
		On patriotic cover		5,000.

CHARLESTON, S. C.

A1

E1

E2

Lithographed Adhesive

16X1	A1	5c	blue	1,200.	850.
		Pair		2,500.	2,200.
		On cover			2,500.
		On patriotic cover			5,000.
		Pair, on cover			5,000.
		On cover with No. 112XU1			—
		Used on cover with C.S.A. 5c			
		#6 to make 10c rate			—

Values are for stamps showing parts of the outer frame lines on at least 3 sides.

Cancellation: black town (two types).

Press-printed Envelopes
(typographed from woodcut)

16XU1	E1	5c	blue	1,250.	4,000.
16XU2	E1	5c	blue, *amber*	1,250.	4,000.
16XU3	E1	5c	blue, *orange*	1,250.	4,000.
16XU4	E1	5c	blue, *buff*	1,250.	4,000.
16XU5	E1	5c	blue, *blue*	1,250.	4,000.
16XU6	E2	10c	blue, *orange*		77,500.

The No. 16XU6 used entire is unique; value based on 1997 auction sale.
Beware of fakes of the E1 design.

Handstamped Cut Square

16XU7	E2	10c	black	3,000.

There is only one example of No. 16XU7. It is a cutout, not an entire. It may not have been mailed from Charleston, and it may not have paid postage.

CHARLOTTE, N. C.

146XU1	5c	blue, "5" in circle and straight line "PAID"	—

CHARLOTTESVILLE, VA.

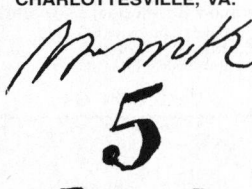

E1

Handstamped Envelopes, Manuscript Initials

127XU1	E1	5c	blue	—
127XU2	E1	10c	blue	—

CHATTANOOGA, TENN.

E1

E1a

Handstamped Envelopes

17XU2	E1	5c	black	2,500.
17XU3	E1a	5c on 2c	black	4,250.

CHRISTIANSBURG, VA.

E1

Handstamped Envelopes
Impressed at top right

99XU1	E1	5c	black	2,250.
99XU2	E1	5c	blue	2,000.
99XU4	E1	5c	green on U.S. envelope No. U27	4,500.
99XU5	E1	10c	blue	3,500.

The absence of 5c and 10c handstamped paid markings from this town suggests that Nos. 99XU1-99XU5 were used as both provisional and handstamped paid markings.

COLAPARCHEE, GA.

E1   Control

Handstamped Envelope

119XU1	E1	5c	black	3,500.

There are only two recorded examples of No. 119XU1, and both are used with general issue stamp from Savannah.

COLUMBIA, S. C.

E1

E2

Handstamped Envelopes

18XU1	E1	5c	blue	550.	900.
		Used on cover with C.S.A. 5c			
		#1 or #1c to make 10c rate			3,000.
		Used on cover with C.S.A. 5c			
		#7 to make 10c rate			7,500.
a.		10c on 5c	blue		3,500.
18XU2	E1	5c	black	600.	1,250.

Three types of "PAID," one in circle

18XU4	E2	5c	blue, seal on front	2,500.
a.		Seal on back		1,250.
18XU5	E2	10c	blue, seal on back	2,750.

Three types of "PAID" for Nos. 18XU4-18XU5, one in circle.

Circular Seal similar to E2, 27mm diameter

18XU6	E2	5c	blue (seal on back)	4,000.

COLUMBIA, TENN.

E1

Handstamped Envelope

113XU1	E1	5c	red	7,000.
		One example recorded.		

COLUMBUS, GA.

E1

Handstamped Envelopes

19XU1	E1	5c	blue	1,000.
19XU2	E1	10c	red	2,250.

COURTLAND, ALA.

E1

Handstamped Envelopes (from woodcut)

103XU1	E1	5c	red	10,000.

DALTON, GA

E1

Handstamped Envelopes

20XU1	E1	5c	black	750.
a.		Denomination omitted (5c rate)		875.
b.		10c (ms.) on 5c	black	1,500.
c.		20c (ms.) on 5c	black	—
20XU2	E1	10c	black	1,250.

DANVILLE, VA.

A1

E1

E2

E3

E4

Typeset Adhesive
Wove Paper

21X1	A1	5c	red	5,500.
		On cover		—
		Cut to shape		4,000.
		On cover, cut to shape		10,000.

Two varieties known.

Cancellation: blue town.

Laid Paper

21X2	A1	5c	red	10,000.

Cancellation: black town.

No. 21X2 is unique.

Press-printed Envelopes (typographed)
Two types: "SOUTHERN" in straight or curved line
Impressed (usually) at top left

21XU1	E1	5c	black	6,000.
21XU2	E1	5c	black, *amber*	—
21XU3	E1	5c	black, *dark buff*	6,000.

The existence of No. 21XU2 is in question. The editors would like to see authenticated evidence of its existence.

Unissued 10c envelopes (type E1, in red) are known. All recorded examples are envelopes on which added stamps paid the postage.

Dangerous forgeries exist of No. 21XU1.

Handstamped Envelopes

21XU3A	E4	5c	black (ms "WBP" initials)	1,000.
21XU4	E2	10c	black	2,500.
21XU6	E3	10c	black	2,750.
21XU7	E4	10c	black (ms "WBP" initials)	—

Types E2 and E3 both exist on one cover.

DEMOPOLIS, ALA.

E1

Handstamped Envelopes, Signature in ms.

22XU1	E1	5c	black ("Jno. Y. Hall")	3,500.
22XU2	E1	5c	black ("J. Y. Hall")	3,500.
22XU3	E1	5c	(ms.) black ("J. Y. Hall")	4,000.

EATONTON, GA.

E1

E2

Handstamped Envelopes

23XU1	E1	5c	black	3,000.
23XU2	E2	5c + 5c	black	5,000.

EMORY, VA.

A1

Handstamped Adhesives ("PAID" and "5" in circle on selvage of U.S. 1c 1857 issue)
Perf. 15 on three sides

24X1	A1	5c	blue, on cover, ms. tied	15,000.

Also known with "5" above "PAID."

Cancellation: blue town.

E1   E2

Handstamped Envelopes

24XU1	E1	5c	blue	2,000.
24XU2	E2	10c	blue	10,000.

Only one example recorded of No. 24XU2.

FINCASTLE, VA.

E1

Press-printed Envelope (typeset)
Impressed at top right

104XU1	E1	10c	black	20,000.

One example recorded of No. 104XU1.

FORSYTH, GA.

E1

Handstamped Envelope

120XU1	E1	10c	black	2,000.

Only one example recorded of No. 120XU1.

FRANKLIN, N. C.

E1

Press-printed Envelope (typeset)
Impressed at top right

25XU1	E1	5c	blue, *buff*	30,000.
25XU2		5c	black, large "5" woodcut in 31mm circular town mark	2,500.

The one known No. 25XU1 envelope shows black circular Franklin postmark with manuscript date.

FRAZIERSVILLE, S. C.

E1

Handstamped Envelope, "5" manuscript

128XU1	E1	5c	black	3,000.

Only one example recorded of No. 128XU1.

FREDERICKSBURG, VA.

A1

Sheets of 20, two panes of 10 varieties each

Typeset Adhesives
Thin bluish paper

26X1	A1	5c	**blue,** *bluish*	450.	850.
			Block of 4	2,250.	
			Sheet of 20	12,500.	
			On cover		5,000.
			Pair on cover		12,000.
26X2	A1	10c	**red,** *bluish*	1,250.	
			Brown red, *bluish*	1,500.	
			Block of 4	—	

Cancellation: black town.

GAINESVILLE, ALA.

E1

E2

Handstamped Envelopes

27XU1	E1	5c	**black**	4,500.
27XU2	E2	10c	("01") **black**	6,000.

Postmark spells town name "Gainsville."

GALVESTON, TEX.

E1

Handstamped Envelopes

98XU1	E1	5c	**black**	500.	1,500.
98XU2	E1	10c	**black**		2,000.

E2

Handstamped Envelopes

98XU3	E2	10c	**black**	550.	2,400.
98XU4	E2	20c	**black**		3,500.
98XU5	E3	5c	**black,** "5" in double line "Gal-veston/Tex" postmark with straightline "PAID"		—

GASTON, N. C.

E1

Handstamped Envelope

129XU1	E1	5c	**black**	6,000.

Only one example recorded of No. 129XU1.

GEORGETOWN, S. C.

E1

Control

Handstamped Envelopes

28XU1	E1	5c	**black**		1,200.
28XU2	E1	5c	**black,** separate "5" and straightline "PAID" hand-stamps, control on reverse	—	2,000.

GOLIAD, TEX.

A1

A2

Typeset Adhesives

29X1	A1	5c	**black**		12,000.
29X2	A1	5c	**black,** *gray*		11,500.
29X3	A1	5c	**black,** *rose*		12,000.
			On cover front		50,000.
29X4	A1	10c	**black**	—	12,000.
29X5	A1	10c	**black,** *rose*		12,000.

Type A1 stamps are signed "Clarke-P.M." vertically in black or red.

29X6	A2	5c	**black,** *gray*		10,000.
a.			"GOILAD"		12,000.
			Pair, left stamp the error		—
29X7	A2	10c	**black,** *gray*		12,000.
			On cover		25,000.
a.			"GOILAD"		15,000.
			On cover		30,000.
29X8	A2	5c	**black,** *dark blue,* on cover		7,000.
29X9	A2	10c	**black,** *dark blue*		20,000.

Cancellations in black: pen, town, "Paid"

GONZALES, TEX.

Colman & Law were booksellers when John B. Law (of the firm) was appointed Postmaster. The firm used a small lithographed label on drugs and on the front or inside of books they sold.

A1

Lithographed Adhesives
on colored glazed paper

30X1	A1	(5c)	**gold,** *dark blue,* pair on cov-er, *1861*	15,000.
30X2	A1	(10c)	**gold,** *garnet,* on cover, *1864*	12,500.
30X3	A1	(10c)	**gold,** *black,* on cover, *1865*	—

Cancellations: black town, black pen. No. 30X1 must bear double-circle town cancel as validating control. The control was applied to the labels in the sheet before their sale as stamps. When used, the stamps bear an additional Gonzales double-circle postmark.

GREENSBORO, ALA.

E1

GREENSBORO, ALA. (right column)

E2

Handstamped Envelopes

31XU1	E1	5c	**black**	3,000.
31XU2	E1	10c	**black**	2,750.
31XU3	E2	10c	**black**	6,000.

GREENSBORO, N. C.

E1

Handstamped Envelope

32XU1	E1	10c	**red**	1,250.

GREENVILLE, ALA.

A1

A2

Typeset Adhesives
On pinkish surface-colored glazed paper.

33X1	A1	5c	**blue & red**	25,000.	
			On cover	—	40,000.
33X2	A2	10c	**red & blue**		
			On cover		40,000.

Two used examples each are known of Nos. 33X1-33X2, and all are on covers. Covers bear a postmark but it was not used to cancel the stamps.
The former No. 33X1a has been identified as a counterfeit.

GREENVILLE, TENN.

E1

144XU1	E1	5c	**black**	—

Only one example of No. 144XU1 is recorded.

GREENVILLE COURT HOUSE, S. C.

PAID 5 E1

E1a

Control

Handstamped Envelopes (Several types)

34XU1	E1	5c **black**	2,000.
34XU2	E1a	10c **black**	2,000.
a.		20c (ms.) on 10c **black**	3,000.

Envelopes must bear the black control on the back.

GREENWOOD DEPOT, VA.

A1

"PAID" Handstamped Adhesive ("PAID" with value and signature in ms.)
Laid Paper

35X1	A1	10c **black**, *gray blue*, uncanceled, on cover	
		On cover, tied	20,000.

Six examples recorded of No. 35X1, all on covers. One of these is in the British Library collection. Of the remaining five, only one has the stamp tied to the cover.

Cancellation: black town.

GRIFFIN, GA.

E1

Handstamped Envelopes

102XU1	E1	5c **black**	2,250.
102XU2	E1	10c **black**	

No. 102XU2 is on a large piece of an envelope with July 25 postmark at left.

GROVE HILL, ALA.

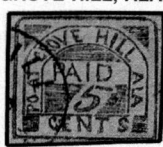

A1

Handstamped Adhesive (from woodcut)

36X1	A1	5c **black**	—
		On cover, tied	75,000.

Two examples are recorded. One is on cover tied by the postmark. The other is canceled by magenta pen on a cover front.

Cancellations: black town, magenta pen.

HALLETTSVILLE, TEX.

A1

Handstamped Adhesive
Ruled Letter Paper

37X1	A1	10c **black**, *gray blue*, on cover	15,000.
		One example known.	

Cancellation: black ms.

HAMBURGH, S. C.

E1

Handstamped Envelope

112XU1	E1	5c **black**	9,000.
		On cover with #16X1 (forwarded)	—

HARRISBURGH (Harrisburg), TEX.

E1

Handstamped Envelope

130XU1	E1	5c **black**	—

No. 130XU1 is indistinguishable from a handstamp paid cover when used.

HELENA, TEX.

A1

Typeset Adhesives
Several varieties

38X1	A1	5c **black**, *buff*	7,500.	6,000.
38X2	A1	10c **black**, *gray*		5,000.

On 10c "Helena" is in upper and lower case italics.
Used examples are valued with small faults or repairs, as all recorded have faults.

Cancellation: black town.

HILLSBORO, N. C.

A1

Handstamped Adhesive

39X1	A1	5c **black**, on cover	15,000.

No. 39X1 is unique.
See 3c 1861 Postmasters' Provisional No. 1AX1.

Cancellation: black town.

Ms./Handstamped Envelope

39XU1	10c "paid 10" in manuscript with undated blue town cancel as control on face	

HOLLANDALE, TEX.

E1

Handstamped Envelope

132XU1	E1	5c **black**	—

HOUSTON, TEX.

E1

Handstamped Envelopes

40XU1	E1	5c **red**	—	750.
		On patriotic cover		
a.		10c (ms.) on 5c **red**		3,000.
40XU2	E1	10c **red**	—	1,500.
40XU3	E1	10c **black**		2,250.
40XU4	E1	5c +10c **red**		2,500.
40XU5	E1	10c +10c **red**		2,500.

Nos. 40XU2-40XU5 show "TEX" instead of "TXS."

HUNTSVILLE, TEX.

E1   Control

Handstamped Envelope

92XU1	E1	5c **black**	5,000.

No. 92XU1 exists with "5" outside or within control circle.

INDEPENDENCE, TEX.

A1

Handstamped Adhesives

41X1	A1	10c **black**, *buff*, on cover, un-canceled, cut to shape	
41X2	A1	10c **black**, *dull rose*, on cover	20,000.

With small "10" and "Pd" in manuscript

41X3	A1	10c **black**, *buff*, on cover, un-canceled, cut to shape	32,500.
		On cover, uncanceled, cut square	—

No. 41X1 is unique.
All known examples of Nos. 41X1-41X3 are uncanceled on covers with black "INDEPENDANCE TEX." (sic) postmark.
The existence of No. 41X2 has been questioned by specialists. The editors would like to see authenticated evidence of the existence of this item.

ISABELLA, GA.

E1

Handstamped Envelope, "5" Manuscript

133XU1	E1	5c **black**	2,000.

Only one example recorded of No. 133XU1.

IUKA, MISS.

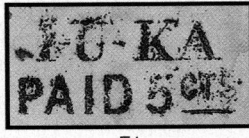

E1

Handstamped Envelope

42XU1	E1	5c **black**		1,750.
		On patriotic cover		4,000.

JACKSON, MISS.

E1a

Handstamped Envelopes
Two types of numeral

43XU1	E1a	5c **black**		750.
		On patriotic cover		3,000.
a.		10c on 5c **black**		2,750.
43XU2	E1a	10c **black**		2,000.
43XU4	E1a	10c on 5c **blue**		2,750.

The 5c also exists on a lettersheet.
See 3c 1861 Postmasters' Provisional No. 2AXU1.

JACKSONVILLE, ALA.

E1

Handstamped Envelope

110XU1	E1	5c **black**	—	3,000.

JACKSONVILLE, FLA.

E1

Handstamped Envelope

134XU1	E1	5c **black**		—

Undated double circle postmark control on reverse.

JETERSVILLE, VA.

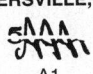

A1

Handstamped Adhesive
("5" with ms. "AHA." initials)
Laid Paper

44X1	A1	5c **black,** vertical pair on cover, uncanceled	16,000.

Initials are those of Postmaster A. H. Atwood.

Cancellation: black town.

JONESBORO, TENN.

E1

Handstamped Envelopes

45XU1	E1	5c **black**	7,000.
45XU2	E1	5c **dark blue**	7,000.

KINGSTON, GA.

E1   E2

E3

E4

Typeset Envelopes
(design types E1-E2, E4 are handstamps; typeset design E3 probably impressed by hand but possibly press printed)

46XU1	E1	5c **black**	2,250.
46XU2	E2	5c **black**	3,250.
46XU4	E3	5c **black**	13,000.
46XU5	E4	5c **black**	2,000.

There is only one recorded example of No. 46XU4.

KNOXVILLE, TENN.

A1

Typographed Adhesives
(stereotype from woodcut)
Grayish Laid Paper

47X1	A1	5c **brick red**	1,400.	1,400.
		Manuscript cancel		350.
		Horizontal pair	4,000.	3,000.
		Vertical pair	3,500.	
		Vertical strip of 3	6,500.	
		On cover, tied by handstamp		7,000.
		On cover, manuscript cancel		2,100.
		Pair on cover		7,500.
47X2	A1	5c **carmine**	1,900.	2,250.
		Manuscript cancel		1,000.
		Vertical strip of 3		—
		On cover, tied by handstamp		7,500.
		On cover, manuscript cancel		2,100.
47X3	A1	10c **green,** on cover		57,750.

The #47X3 cover is unique. Value is based on 1997 auction sale.

Cancellations in black: town, bars, pen or pencil.

E1   E2

Press-printed Envelopes (typographed)

47XU1	E1	5c **blue**	750.	2,000.
47XU2	E1	5c **blue,** orange	750.	2,250.
47XU3	E1	10c **red** (cut to shape)		4,000.
47XU4	E1	10c **red,** orange (cut to shape)		4,000.

Only one example each recorded of Nos. 47XU3 and 47XU4.
Dangerous fakes exist of Nos. 47XU1 and 47XU2.

Handstamped Envelopes

47XU5	E2	5c **black**	750.	1,500.
		On patriotic cover		3,750.
a.		10c on 5c **black**		3,500.

Type E2 exists with "5" above or below "PAID."

LA GRANGE, TEX.

E1

Handstamped Envelopes

48XU1	E1	5c **black**	—	2,250.
48XU2	E1	10c **black**		3,000.

LAKE CITY, FLA.

E1

Control

Handstamped Envelope

96XU1	E1	10c **black**	2,000.

Envelopes have black circle control mark, or printed name of E. R. Ives, postmaster, on face or back.

LAURENS COURT HOUSE, S. C.

E1

Handstamped Envelope

116XU1	E1	5c **black**	1,750.

LENOIR, N. C.

A1

E1

Handstamped Adhesive (from woodcut)
White wove paper with cross-ruled orange lines

49X1	A1	5c **blue & orange**	7,250.	6,750.
		On cover, pen canceled		12,500.
		On cover, tied by handstamp		25,000.

Cancellations: blue town, blue "Paid" in circle, black pen.

Handstamped Envelopes

49XU1	A1	5c **blue**	3,500.
49XU2	A1	10c (5c+5c) **blue**	25,000.
49XU3	E1	5c **blue**	4,500.
49XU4	E1	5c **black**	3,500.

No. 49XU2 is unique. A variety of No. 49XU3 is recorded with two light strikes of the provisional handstamp, one in blue and one in black.

LEXINGTON, MISS.

E1

Handstamped Envelopes

50XU1	E1	5c	black	5,000.
50XU2	E1	10c	black	5,000.

LEXINGTON, VA.

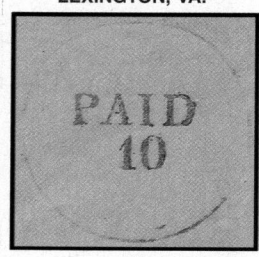

E1

Handstamped Envelopes

135XU1	E1	5c	blue	500.
		Used with 5c #6 to make 10c rate		
135XU2	E1	10c	blue	750.

Nos. 135XU1-135XU2 by themselves are indistinguishable from a handstamp paid cover when used.

LIBERTY, VA. (and Salem, Va.)

A1

Typeset Adhesive (probably impressed by hand)
Laid Paper

74X1	A1	5c	black, on cover, uncanceled, with Liberty postmark	35,000.
			On cover, uncanceled, with Salem postmark	40,000.

Two known on covers with Liberty, Va. postmark; one cover known with the nearby Salem, Va. office postmark.

LIMESTONE SPRINGS, S. C.

A1

Handstamped Adhesive

121X1	A1	5c	black, light blue, on cover	10,000.
			Two on cover	15,000.
121X2	A1	5c	black, white, on cover	30,000.
			Two on cover	

Stamps are cut round or rectangular. Covers are not postmarked.

LIVINGSTON, ALA.

A1

Lithographed Adhesive

51X1	A1	5c	blue	14,000.
			On cover	60,000.
			Pair on cover	120,000.

The pair on cover is unique.

Cancellation: black town.

LYNCHBURG, VA.

A1   E1

Typographed Adhesive
(stereotype from woodcut)

52X1	A1	5c	blue (shades)	1,800.	1,350.
			Pair		3,000.
			On cover		5,000.
			Pair on cover		20,000.

Cancellations: black town, blue town.

Press-printed Envelopes (typographed)
Impressed at top right or left

52XU1	E1	5c	black		3,000.
52XU2	E1	5c	black, amber	650.	3,000.
52XU3	E1	5c	black, buff		3,000.
52XU4	E1	5c	black, brown	900.	3,000.
			On patriotic cover		—

MACON, GA.

A1   A2

(Below these, two more images)

FIVE CENTS. (A3)   TWO CENTS (A4)

A3   A4

Typeset Adhesives
Several varieties of type A1, 10 of A2, 5 of A3
Wove Paper

53X1	A1	5c	black, light blue green (shades)	900.	700.
			On cover		6,000.
			Pair on cover		14,000.
			Comma after "OFFICE"	950.	1,100.
			Comma after "OFFICE," on cover		7,500.

Warning: Dangerous forgeries exist of the normal variety and the Comma after "OFFICE" variety. Certificates of authenticity from recognized committees are strongly recommended.

53X3	A2	5c	black, yellow	2,500.	850.
			On cover		6,500.
			Pair on cover		11,000.
			Pair on patriotic cover		25,000.
53X4	A3	5c	black, yellow (shades)	3,000.	1,400.
			On cover		6,000.
			Pair on cover		10,000.
a.			Vertical tête bêche pair		—
53X5	A4	2c	black, gray green		—
			On cover		60,000.

Laid Paper

53X6	A2	5c	black, yellow	6,000.	3,500.
			On cover		6,000.
53X7	A3	5c	black, yellow	6,000.	
			On cover		9,000.
53X8	A1	5c	black, light blue green	1,750.	2,250.
			On cover		4,500.

No. 53X4a is unique.

Cancellations: black town, black "PAID" (2 types).

E1

Handstamped Envelope

Two types: "PAID" over "5," "5" over "PAID"

53XU1	E1	5c	black	250.	575.
			On patriotic cover		1,900.

Values are for "PAID" over "5" variety. "5" over "PAID" is much scarcer.

MADISON, GA.

E1

Handstamped Envelope

136XU1	E1	5c	red	500.

No. 136XU1 is indistinguishable from a handstamp paid cover when used.

MADISON COURT HOUSE, FLA.

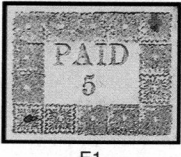

E1

Typeset Envelope

137XU1	E1	5c	black, yellow	23,000.

No. 137XU1 is unique.
See 3c 1861 Postmasters' Provisional No. 3AX1.

MARIETTA, GA.

E1   Control

E2

Handstamped Envelopes

54XU1	E1	5c	black	500.
a.		10c on 5c	black	1,750.

With Double Circle Control

54XU3	E1	10c	black	
54XU4	E2	5c	black	2,000.

The existence of No. 54XU3 has been questioned by specialists. The editors would like to see authenticated evidence that verifies this listing.

MARION, VA.

A1

Adhesives with Typeset frame and Handstamped numeral in center

55X1	A1	5c	black		7,500.
			On cover		20,000.
55X2	A1	10c	black	16,500.	10,000.
			On cover		60,000.
55X3	A1	5c	black, bluish, laid paper	—	—

The 2c, 3c, 15c and 20c are believed to be bogus items printed later using the original typeset frame.
Cancellations: black town, black "PAID."

MARS BLUFF, S. C.

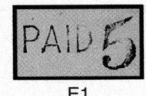

E1

145XU1 E1 5c **black**   —

The No. 145XU1 marking is a provisional only when unused, used from another town or used under a general issue.

MEMPHIS, TENN.

A1   A2

Typographed Adhesives (stereotyped from woodcut)

Plate of 50 (5x10) for the 2c. The stereotypes for the 5c stamps were set in 5 vertical rows of 8, with at least 2 rows set sideways to the right (see Thomas H. Pratt's monograph, "The Postmaster's Provisionals of Memphis").

56X1	A1	2c	**blue** (shades)	100.	1,250.
			Block of 4	550.	
			On cover		10,000.
			Cracked plate (16, 17, 18)	160.	1,350.

The "cracking off" (breaking off) of the plate at right edge caused incomplete printing of stamps in positions 5, 10, 15, 20, and 50. Poor make-ready also caused incomplete printing in position 50.

56X2	A2	5c	**red** (shades)	150.	190.
			Pair	340.	475.
			Block of 4	1,000.	
			On cover		1,750.
			Pair on cover		3,500.
			Strip of 4 on cover		7,000.
			On patriotic cover		5,000.
a.			Tête bêche pair		1,500.
			Pair on cover		10,000.
b.			Pair, one sideways		2,500.
c.			Pelure paper	—	—

Cancellation on Nos. 56X1-56X2: black town.

Press-printed Envelopes (typographed)

56XU1	A2	5c	**red** (shades)	2,500.
			Used with 5c #56X2 to make 10c rate	6,000.
56XU2	A2	5c	**red,** *amber*	2,500.
			Used with C.S.A. 5c #1 to make 10c rate	7,500.
56XU3	A2	5c	**red,** *orange*	2,500.
			On patriotic cover	

MICANOPY, FLA.

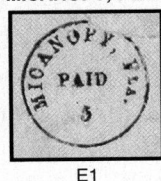

E1

Handstamped Envelope

105XU1	E1	5c	**black**	11,500.

One example recorded.

MILLEDGEVILLE, GA.

E1

E2   E3

Handstamped Envelopes

Two types of No. 57XU5: Type I, tall, thin "1" and "0" of "10"; Type II, short, fat "1" and "0" of "10."

57XU1	E1	5c	**black**		500.
a.			Wide spacing between "I" and "D" of "PAID"		600.
b.			10c on 5c **black**		1,000.
57XU2	E1	5c	**blue**		800.
57XU4	E2	10c	**black**	375.	1,000.
a.			Wide spacing between "I" and "D" of "PAID"		1,000.
57XU5	E3	10c	**black,** type I	125.	800.
a.			Type II		1,500.

On No. 57XU4, the "PAID/10" virtually always falls outside the Milledgeville control marking (as in illustration E1).

The existence of No. 57XU2 as a provisional has been questioned by specialists. The editors would like to see authenticated evidence of provisional use of this marking.

MILTON, N. C.

E1

Handstamped Envelope, "5" Manuscript

138XU1	E1	5c	**black**	2,500.

MOBILE, ALA.

A1

Lithographed Adhesives

58X1	A1	2c	**black**	2,250.	1,100.
			Pair	—	2,100.
			On cover		5,000.
			Pair on cover		20,000.
			Three singles on one cover		20,000.
			Five stamps on one cover		20,000.
58X2	A1	5c	**blue**	350.	400.
			Pair	900.	950.
			On cover		1,800.
			On cover, canceled in Claiborne, Ala.		—
			On cover, canceled in Montgomery, Ala.		—
			Pair on cover		2,400.
			Strip of 3 on cover		14,000.
			Strip of 4 on cover		—
			Strip of 5 on cover		—
			Line through "O" of "Office" (plate scratch)		—

Cancellations: black town, express company.

The existence of a strip of 5 of No. 58X2 has been questioned by specialists. The editors would like to see authenticated evidence of the existence of this strip either on or off cover.

MONTGOMERY, ALA.

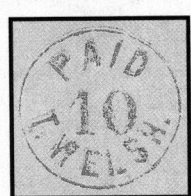

E1

Handstamped Envelopes

59XU1	E1	5c	**red**		1,100.
a.			10c on 5c **red**		2,750.
59XU2	E1	5c	**blue**	400.	900.
59XU3	E1	10c	**red**		850.
59XU4	E1	10c	**blue**		1,500.
59XU5	E1	10c	**black**		850.

The 10c design is larger than the 5c.

The absence of 5c and 10c handstamped paid markings from this town suggests that Nos. 59XU1-59XU5 were used as both provisional and handstamped paid markings.

E2   E3

59XU7	E2	2c	**red**		2,500.
59XU7A	E2	2c	**blue**		3,500.
59XU8	E2	5c	**black**		2,250.
59XU9	E3	10c	**black**		3,250.
59XU10	E3	10c	**red**		1,750.

MT. LEBANON, LA.

A1

Woodcut Adhesive (mirror image of design)

60X1	A1	5c	**red brown,** on cover	385,000.

One example known. Value is based on 1999 auction sale.

Cancellation: black pen.

NASHVILLE, TENN.

A2

Typographed Adhesives (stereotyped from woodcut)
Gray Blue Ribbed Paper

61X2	A2	5c	**carmine** (shades)	1,000.	600.
			Pair		2,000.
			On cover		3,000.
			On patriotic cover		4,500.
			Pair on cover		6,000.
			On cover with U.S. 3c 1857 (express)		25,000.
a.			Vertical tête bêche pair		4,000.
			On cover		30,000.
61X3	A2	5c	**brick red** (shades)	1,000.	700.
			Pair		1,750.
			On cover		3,500.
			On patriotic cover		6,000.
			Pair on cover		7,500.
			On U.S. #U26 (express)		35,000.
			On U.S. #U27 with #26 (express)		25,000.
61X4	A2	5c	**gray** (shades)	1,250.	1,000.
			On cover		5,750.
			On patriotic cover		12,000.
			Pair on cover		7,500.
			Strip of 5 on cover front		8,750.
61X5	A2	5c	**violet brown** (shades)	1,100.	750.
			Block of 4		
			On cover		4,500.
			On patriotic cover		
			Pair on cover		6,000.
a.			Vertical tete beche pair	5,000.	4,000.
			Pair on cover		
61X6	A2	10c	**green**		5,500.
			On cover		22,500.
			On cover with U.S. 3c 1857 (express)		75,000.
			On U.S. #U26 (express)		100,000.
			On cover with No. 61X2		27,500.

Cancellations

Blue "Paid"
Blue "Postage Paid"
Blue town
Blue numeral "5"
Blue numeral "10"
Blue express company
Black express company

For the former 61X1, see No. 4AX1 in the 3c 1861 Postmasters' Provisional section.

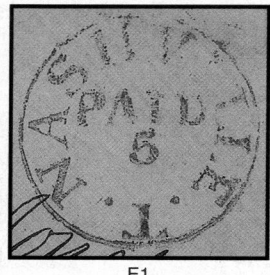

E1

Handstamped Envelopes

61XU1	E1	5c	**blue**	900.
			On patriotic envelope	1,900.
61XU2	E1	5c +10c	**blue**	2,750.

NEW ORLEANS, LA.

A1   A2

Typographed Adhesives
(stereotyped from woodcut)
Plate of 40

62X1	A1	2c	**blue**, *July 14, 1861*	200.	550.
			Pair	600.	1,150.
			Block of 4	6,500.	
			On cover		4,250.
			On patriotic cover		8,000.
			Pair on cover		10,000.
			Three singles on one cover		20,000.
			Strip of 5 on cover		30,000.
a.			Printed on both sides	—	
			On cover		7,500.
62X2	A1	2c	**red** (shades), *Jan. 6, 1862*	175.	1,000.
			Pair	450.	
			Block of 4	1,750.	
			On cover		25,000.
62X3	A2	5c	**brown**, *white, June 12, 1861*	275.	200.
			Pair	575.	425.
			Block of 4	1,750.	
			On cover		450.
			On cover from town other than N.O.		5,000.
			On patriotic cover		5,500.
			Pair on cover		850.
			Strip of 5 on cover		5,000.
			On cover with U.S. #26 (Southern Letter Unpaid)		150,000.
			On cover with U.S. No. 30A		—
a.			Printed on both sides		2,250.
			On cover		7,500.
b.		5c	**ocher**, *June 18, 1861*	700.	625.
			Pair		1,500.
			On cover		2,750.
			On patriotic cover		6,000.
			Pair on cover		3,500.
c.		5c	**chocolate brown**, *white*		1,500.

The editors would like to see authenticated evidence of the existence of No. 62X3a on cover.

62X4	A2	5c	**red brn**, *bluish, Aug. 22, 1861*	300.	200.
			Pair	675.	475.
			Horizontal strip of 6		3,500.
			Block of 4	2,200.	
			On cover		425.
			On patriotic cover		5,500.
			Pair on cover		700.
			Block of 4 on cover		5,000.
			Used on cover with C.S.A. 5c #1 to make 10c rate		27,500.
a.			Printed on both sides		2,750.
			On cover		9,000.
62X5	A2	5c	**yel brn**, *off-white, Dec. 3, 1861*	150.	240.
			Pair	325.	525.
			Block of 4	700.	
			On cover		850.
			On patriotic cover		3,000.
			Pair on cover		1,200.
			Strip of 5 on cover		
62X6	A2	5c	**red**	—	7,500.
62X7	A2	5c	**red**, *bluish*		15,000.

Cancellations

Black town (single or double circle New Orleans)
Red town (double circle New Orleans)
Town other than New Orleans
Postmaster's handstamp
Black "Paid"
Express Company
Packet boat, cover "STEAM"

E1

These provisional handstamps were applied at the riverfront postal station.

Handstamped Envelopes

62XU1	E1	5c	**black**	4,500.
62XU2	E1	10c	**black**	12,500.

"J. L. RIDDELL, P. M." omitted

62XU3	E1	2c	**black**	9,500.

NEW SMYRNA, FLA.

A1

Handstamped Adhesive
On white paper with blue ruled lines

63X1	A1	10c ("O1") on 5c	**black**	45,000.

One example known. It is uncanceled on a postmarked patriotic cover.

NORFOLK, VA.

E1

Handstamped Envelopes
Ms Signature on Front or Back

139XU1	E1	5c	**blue**	— 1,250.
139XU2	E1	10c	**blue**	1,750.

OAKWAY, S. C.

A1

Handstamped Adhesive (from woodcut)

115X1	A1	5c	**black**, on cover	66,000.

Two used examples of No. 115X1 are recorded, both on cover. Value represents 1997 auction realization for the cover on which the stamp is tied by manuscript "Paid."

PENSACOLA, FLA.

E1

Handstamped Envelopes

106XU1	E1	5c	**black**	3,750.
a.		10c (ms.) on 5c	**black**	4,250.
			On patriotic cover	13,500.

PETERSBURG, VA.

A1

Typeset Adhesive
Ten varieties
Thick white paper

65X1	A1	5c	**red** (shades)	2,250.	750.
			Pair	5,000.	2,000.
			Block of 4	11,000.	
			On cover		2,500.
			On patriotic cover		—
			Pair on cover		8,000.
			Used on cover with C.S.A. 5c #1 to make 10c rate		57,500.

Cancellation: blue town.

PITTSYLVANIA COURT HOUSE, VA.

A1

Typeset Adhesives

66X1	A1	5c	**dull red**, wove paper	7,000.	6,000.
			Octagonally cut		5,000.
			On cover		55,000.
			On cover, octagonally cut		20,000.
66X2	A1	5c	**dull red**, laid paper	6,500.	
			Octagonally cut		5,500.
			On cover		55,000.
			On cover, octagonally cut		40,000.

Cancellation: black town.

PLAINS OF DURA, GA.

E1

Handstamped Envelopes, Ms. Initials

140XU1	E1	5c	**black**	—
140XU2	E1	10c	**black**	3,000.

No. 140XU2 is unique.

PLEASANT SHADE, VA.

A1

Typeset Adhesive
Five varieties

67X1	A1	5c	**blue**	2,750.	20,000.
			On cover		27,500.
			Pair	8,000.	
			Pair on cover		55,000.
			Block of 6	25,000.	

Cancellation: blue town.

PLUM CREEK, TEX.

E1

Manuscript Adhesive

141X1 E1 10c **black,** *blue,* on cover   —

The ruled lines and "10" are done by hand. Size and shape of the stamp varies.

PORT GIBSON, MISS.

E1

Handstamped Envelope, Ms Signature

142XU1 E1 5c **black**   —

PORT LAVACA, TEX.

A1

Typeset Adhesive

107X1 A1 10c **black,** on cover   *25,000.*

One example known. It is uncanceled on a postmarked cover.

RALEIGH, N. C.

E1

Handstamped Envelopes

68XU1	E1	5c **red**	600.
		On patriotic cover	4,000.
68XU2	E1	5c **blue**	3,000.

RHEATOWN, TENN.

A1

Typeset Adhesive
Three varieties

69X1	A1	5c **red**	*6,000.*	*7,500.*
		On cover, ms. cancel		*20,000.*
		On cover, tied by handstamp		*37,500.*
		Pair	*6,000.*	

Stamps normally were canceled in manuscript. One cover is known with stamp tied by red town postmark.

Cancellations: red town or black pen.

RICHMOND, TEX.

E1

Handstamped Envelopes or Letter Sheets

70XU1	E1	5c **red**	2,500.
a.		10c on 5c **red**	5,000.
70XU2	E1	10c **red**	2,000.
a.		15c (ms.) on 10c **red**	5,000.

RINGGOLD, GA.

E1

Handstamped Envelope

71XU1 E1 5c **blue black**   8,000.

RUTHERFORDTON, N. C.

A1

Handstamped Adhesive, Ms. "Paid 5cts"

72X1 A1 5c **black,** cut round, on cover (un-
    canceled)   *25,000.*

No. 72X1 is unique.

SALEM, N. C.

E1

E2

Handstamped Envelopes

73XU1	E1	5c **black**	1,750.
73XU2	E1	10c **black**	2,250.
73XU3	E2	5c **black**	2,250.
a.		10c on 5c **black**	2,800.

Reprints exist on various papers. They either lack the "Paid" and value or have them counterfeited.

Salem, Va.
See No. 74X1 under Liberty, Va.

SALISBURY, N. C.

E1

Press-printed Envelope (typeset)
Impressed at top left

75XU1 E1 5c **black,** *greenish*   *5,000.*

One example known. Part of envelope is torn away, leaving part of design missing. Illustration E1 partly suppositional.

SAN ANTONIO, TEX.

E1   E2

Control

Handstamped Envelopes

76XU1	E1	10c **black**	275.	2,000.
76XU1A	E2	5c **black**		1,500.
76XU2	E2	10c **black**		2,500.

Black circle control mark is on front or back.

SAVANNAH, GA.

E1

Control

PAID 10

E2

Handstamped Envelopes

101XU1	E1	5c **black**	400.
		On patriotic cover	—
a.		10c on 5c **black**	1,500.
101XU2	E2	5c **black**	600.
a.		20c on 5c **black**	2,000.
101XU3	E1	10c **black**	750.
101XU4	E2	10c **black**	750.

Envelopes must have octagonal control mark. One example is known of No.101XU2a.

SELMA, ALA.

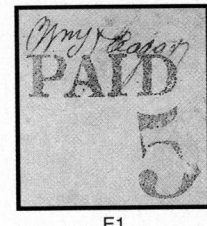

E1

Handstamped Envelopes; Signature in Ms.

77XU1	E1	5c **black**	1,250.
a.		10c on 5c **black**	3,000.
77XU2	E1	10c **black**	2,500.

Signature is that of Postmaster William H. Eagar. See 3c 1861 Postmasters' Provisional No. 5AX1.

SPARTA, GA.

E1a

Handstamped Envelopes

93XU1	E1a	5c **red**	—	2,000.
93XU2	E1a	10c **red**		2,500.

Only one example recorded of No. 93XU2.

SPARTANBURG, S. C.

A1   A2

Handstamped Adhesives
(on ruled or plain wove paper)

78X1	A1	5c **black**		3,500.
		On cover		25,000.
		Pair on cover		30,000.
		On patriotic cover		30,000.
a.		"5" omitted (on cover)		
78X2	A2	5c **black,** *bluish*		4,000.
		On cover		15,000.
78X3	A2	5c **black,** *brown*		4,000.
		On cover		18,000.

Most examples of Nos. 78X1-78X3 are cut round. Cut square examples in sound condition are worth much more. The only recorded pair of No. 78X1 is on cover. The stamps are cut round, but are still connected.

Cancellations: black "PAID," black town.

E1

Control

78XU1   E1   10c **black** (control on reverse)   —

STATESVILLE, N. C.

E1

Handstamped Envelopes

79XU1	E1	5c **black**	250.	675.
a.		10c on 5c **black**		2,250.

Fakes exist of No. 79XU1 unused.

SUMTER, S. C.

E1

Handstamped Envelopes

80XU1	E1	5c **black**		400.
a.		10c on 5c **black**		800.
80XU2	E1	10c **black**		500.
a.		2c (ms.) on 10c **black**		1,100.

Used examples of Nos. 80XU1-80XU2 are indistinguishable from handstamped "Paid" covers.

TALBOTTON, GA.

E1

Handstamped Envelopes

94XU1	E1	5c **black**		1,000.
a.		10c on 5c **black**		2,000.
94XU2	E1	10c **black**		1,000.

TALLADEGA, ALA.

E1

Handstamped Envelopes

143XU1	E1	5c **black**	1,200.	—
143XU2	E1	10c **black**	1,200.	—

TELLICO PLAINS, TENN.

A1

Typeset Adhesives
Settings of two 5c and one 10c
Laid Paper

81X1	A1	5c **red**	1,750.	—
		On cover		50,000.
81X2	A1	10c **red**	3,250.	
		Se-tenant with 5c		5,500.
		Strip of 3 (5c+5c+10c)		9,500.

Cancellation: black pen.

THOMASVILLE, GA.

E1

Control

Handstamped Envelopes
82XU1   E1   5c **black**   575.
     On patriotic cover   2,300.

On No. 82XU1, the control is on the reverse of the cover. The dated control is known with four different dates.

E2

82XU2   E2   5c **black**   900.

TULLAHOMA, TENN.

E1   Control

Handstamped Envelope
111XU1   E1   10c **black**   3,000.

TUSCALOOSA, ALA.

PAID
5

E1

Handstamped Envelopes
83XU1   E1   5c **black**   250.
83XU2   E1   10c **black**   250.

Used examples of Nos. 83XU1-83XU2 are indistinguishable from handstamped "Paid" covers. Some authorities question the use of E1 to produce provisional envelopes.

TUSCUMBIA, ALA.

E1

Handstamped Envelopes

84XU1	E1	5c **black**	2,250.	—
		On patriotic cover		
84XU2	E1	5c **red**		3,000.
84XU3	E1	10c **black**		3,500.

See 3c 1861 Postmasters' Provisional No. 6AXU1.

UNIONTOWN, ALA.

A1

Typeset Adhesives
(settings of 4 (2x2), 4 varieties of each value)
Laid Paper

86X1	A1	2c **dark blue,** *gray blue,* on cover	—	
86X2	A1	2c **dark blue,** sheet of 4	57,500.	
86X3	A1	5c **green,** *gray blue*	4,000.	3,250.
		Pair		
		On cover		9,000.

86X4   A1   5c **green**   4,000.   3,250.
              On cover   7,500.
              Pair on cover   20,000.
86X5   A1   10c **red,** *gray blue*
              On cover   37,500.

Two examples known of No. 86X1, both on cover (drop letters), one uncanceled and one pen canceled.
The only recorded examples of No. 86X2 are in a unique sheet of 4.
The item listed as No. 86X5 used is an uncanceled stamp on a large piece with part of addressee's name in manuscript.

Cancellation on Nos. 86X3-86X5: black town.

UNIONVILLE, S. C.

A1

Handstamped Adhesive
"PAID" and "5" applied separately
Paper with Blue Ruled Lines
87X1   A1   5c **black,** *grayish*   —
              On cover, uncanceled   17,500.
              On cover, tied
              Pair on patriotic cover   32,500.

The pair on patriotic cover is the only pair recorded.

Cancellation: black town.

VALDOSTA, GA.

E1   Control

Handstamped Envelopes
100XU1   E1   10c **black**   2,000.
100XU2   E1   5c +5c **black**

The black circle control must appear on front of the No. 100XU2 envelope and on the back of the No. 100XU1 envelope.
There is one recorded cover each of Nos. 100XU1-100XU2.

VICTORIA, TEX.

A1   A2

Typeset Adhesives
Surface colored paper
88X1   A1   5c **red brown,** *green*   17,500.
88X2   A1   10c **red brown,** *green*   22,500.
              On cover   125,000.
88X3   A2   10c **red brown,** *green,* pelure
              paper   27,500.   22,500.

WALTERBOROUGH, S. C.

E1

Handstamped Envelopes
108XU1   E1   10c **black,** *buff*   —
108XU2   E1   10c **carmine**   4,250.

The existence of No. 108XU1 is in question. The editors would like to see authenticated evidence of its existence.

WARRENTON, GA.

E1

Handstamped Envelopes
89XU1   E1   5c **black**   1,250.
   a.   10c (ms.) on 5c **black**   1,000.

Fakes of the Warrenton provisional marking based on the illustration shown are known on addressed but postally unused covers.

WASHINGTON, GA.

E1

Handstamped Envelope
117XU1   E1   10c **black**   2,000.

Envelopes must have black circle postmark control on the back. Examples with the undated control on the front are not considered provisional unless a dated postmark is also present.

WEATHERFORD, TEX.

E1

Handstamped Envelopes
(woodcut with "PAID" inserted in type)
109XU1   E1   5c **black**   2,000.
109XU2   E1   5c +5c **black**   11,000.

One example is known of No. 109XU2.

WINNSBOROUGH, S. C.

 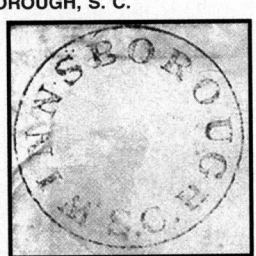

E1   Control

Handstamped Envelopes
97XU1   E1   5c **black**   1,750.
97XU2   E1   10c **black**   3,500.

Envelopes must have black circle control on front or back.

WYTHEVILLE, VA.

 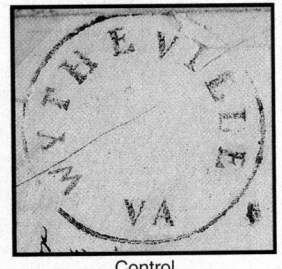

E1   Control

Handstamped Envelope
114XU1   E1   5c **black**   900.

For later additions, listed out of numerical sequence, see:
#74X1, Liberty, Va.
#92XU1, Huntsville, Tex.
#93XU1, Sparta, Ga.
#94XU1, Talbotton, Ga.

#96XU1, Lake City, Fla.
#97XU1, Winnsborough, S. C.
#98XU1, Galveston, Tex.
#99XU1, Christiansburg, Va.
#100XU1, Valdosta, Ga.
#101XU1, Savannah, Ga.
#102XU1, Griffin, Ga.
#103XU1, Courtland, Ala.
#104XU1, Fincastle, Va.
#105XU1, Micanopy, Fla.
#106XU1, Pensacola, Fla.
#107X1, Port Lavaca, Tex.
#108XU1, Walterborough, S. C.
#109XU1, Weatherford, Tex.
#110XU1, Jacksonville, Ala.
#111XU1, Tullahoma, Tenn.
#112XU1, Hamburgh, S. C.
#113XU1, Columbia, Tenn.
#114XU1, Wytheville, Va.
#115X1, Oakway, S. C.
#116XU1, Laurens Court House, S. C.
#117XU1, Washington, Ga.
#118XU1, Carolina City, N.C.
#119XU1, Colaparchee, Ga.
#120XU1, Forsyth, Ga.
#121XU1, Limestone Springs, S.C.
#122XU1, Balcony Falls, Va.
#123XU1, Barnwell Court House, S.C.
#124XU1, Bluffton, S.C.
#125XU1, Camden, S.C.
#126XU1, Cartersville, Ga.
#127XU1, Charlottesville, Va.
#128XU1, Fraziersville, S.C.
#129XU1, Gaston, N.C.
#130XU1, Harrisburgh, Tex.
#132XU1, Hollandale, Tex.
#133XU1, Isabella, Ga.
#134XU1, Jacksonville, Fla.
#135XU1, Lexington, Va.
#136XU1, Madison, Ga.
#137XU1, Madison Court House, Fla.
#138XU1, Milton, N.C.
#139XU1, Norfolk, Va.
#140XU1, Plains of Dura, Ga.
#141X1, Plum Creek, Tex.
#142XU1, Port Gibson, Miss.
#143XU1, Talladega, Ala.
#144XU1, Greenville, Tenn.
#145XU1, Mars Bluff, S.C.
#146XU1, Charlotte, N.C.

CONFEDERATE STATES OF AMERICA, GENERAL ISSUES

The general issues are valued in the very fine grade, and unused stamps are valued both with and without original gum. As noted in the catalogue introduction, "original gum" for this era is defined as at least a majority part original gum, that is, at least 51% original gum. Stamps with substantially more than 51% original gum may be expected to sell for more than the values given, and stamps with less than a majority part original gum will sell for somewhat less.

For explanations of various terms used see the notes at the end of the postage listings.

Jefferson Davis — A1

1861　　Litho.　　Soft Porous Paper　　*Imperf.*

All 5c Lithographs were printed by Hoyer & Ludwig, of Richmond, Va.

Stones A or B — First stones used. Earliest dated cancellation October 16, 1861. Plating not completed hence size of sheets unknown. These stones had imprints. Stamps from Stones A or B are nearly all in the olive green shade. Sharp, clear impressions. Distinctive marks are few and minute.

Stone 1 — Earliest dated cancellation October 18, 1861. Plating completed. Sheet consists of four groups of fifty varieties arranged in two panes of one hundred each without imprint. The first small printing was in olive green and later small printings appeared in light and dark green; the typical shade, however, is an intermediate shade of bright green. The impressions are clear though not as sharp as those from Stones A or B. Distinctive marks are discernible.

Stone 2 — Earliest dated cancellation December 2, 1861. Plating completed. Sheet consists of four groups of fifty varieties arranged in two panes of one hundred each without imprint. All shades other than olive green are known from this stone, the most common being a dull green. Poor impressions. Many noticeable distinctive marks.

Stone 2

1	A1	5c	**green** (shades)	275.	175.
			No gum	175.	
			bright green	325.	185.
			dull green	275.	175.

CONRAD L. BUSH
JOHN L. KIMBROUGH

On cover		300.
Single on cover (overpaid drop letter)		500.
On wallpaper cover		*1,500.*
On prisoner's cover		—
On prisoner's cover with U.S. #65		—
On prisoner's cover with U.S. #U34		—
On patriotic cover		2,500.
Pair	600.	425.
Pair on cover		500.
Block of 4	1,450.	1,300.
Pair with full horiz. gutter between		
a.　5c **light green**	275.	175.
No gum	175.	
b.　5c **dark green**	350.	225.
No gum	210.	

VARIETIES

Spur on upper left scroll (Pos. 21)	425.	275.
Side margin copy showing initials (Pos. 41 or 50)	—	—
Misplaced transfer (clear twin impressions of lower left scrolls — pos. 1 entered over pos. 10)	—	—
Rouletted unofficially	500.	850.
On cover		*1,750.*
Pair on cover		*3,750.*

Cancellations

Blue town	+10.
Red town	+125.
Violet town	+150.
Green town	+175.
Orange town	+225.
Texas town	+35.
Arkansas town	+100.
Florida town	+110.
Kentucky town	+300.
Blue gridiron	+5.
Red gridiron	+50.
Blue concentric	+5.
Star or flowers	+125.
Numeral	+50.
"Paid"	+50.
"Steamboat"	+150.
Express Co.	+350.
Railroad	+300.
Pen	60.

Stone 1

1	A1	5c	**green**	300.	200.
			No gum	200.	
			bright green	300.	200.
			dull green	275.	200.
a.		5c	**light green**	275.	200.
			No gum	175.	
b.		5c	**dark green**	325.	225.
			No gum	210.	
c.		5c	**olive green**	375.	250.
			No gum	225.	
			On cover		300.
			On patriotic cover		2,500.
			Pair	750.	475.
			Pair on cover		600.
			Block of 4	1,650.	1,250.

VARIETIES

Acid flaw	350.	200.
Arrow between panes	600.	325.
Flaw on "at" of "States" (Pos. 38)	325.	225.

Cancellations

Blue town	+10.
Red town	+80.
Green town	+225.
Texas town	+35.
Arkansas town	+90.
Florida town	+110.
Kentucky town	+300.
October, 1861, year date	+40.
Blue gridiron	+5.
Red gridiron	+75.
Blue concentric	+5.
Numeral	+50.
"Paid"	+50.
"Steam"	+150.
"Steamboat"	+150.
Express Company	+350.
Railroad	+300.
Pen	70.

Stones A or B

1c	A1	5c	**olive green**	400.	200.
			No gum	250.	
			On cover		400.
			On patriotic cover		1,400.
			Pair	850.	450.
			Pair on cover		700.
			Block of 4	2,250.	1,300.

VARIETIES

White curl back of head	425.	275.
Imprint	775.	475.

Cancellations

Blue town	+10.
Red town	+150.
October, 1861, year date	+50.
Blue gridiron	+5.
Blue concentric	+5.
Numeral	+60.
"Paid"	+50.
"Steam"	+150.
Express Co.	+400.
Pen	90.

Thomas Jefferson — A2

1861-62　　Litho.　　Soft Porous Paper

Hoyer & Ludwig — First stone used. Earliest dated cancellation November 8, 1861. Sheet believed to consist of four groups of fifty varieties each arranged in two panes of one hundred each with imprint at bottom of each pane. Two different imprints are known. Hoyer & Ludwig printings are always in a uniform shade of dark blue. Impressions are clear and distinct, especially so in the early printings. Plating marks are distinct.

J. T. Paterson & Co. — Earliest dated cancellation July 25, 1862. Sheet consists of four groups of fifty varieties each arranged in two panes of one hundred each with imprint at bottom of each pane. Two different imprints are known and at least one pane is known without an imprint. Wide range of shades. Impressions are less clear than those from the Hoyer & Ludwig stone. Paterson stamps show small vertical colored dash below the lowest point of the upper left triangle.

Stone "Y" — Supposedly made by J. T. Paterson & Co., as it shows the distinctive mark of that firm. Plating not completed hence size of sheet unknown. No imprint found. Color is either a light milky blue or a greenish blue. Impressions are very poor and have a blurred appearance. Stone Y stamps invariably show a large flaw at the back of the head as well as small vertical colored dash beneath the upper left triangle.

Paterson

2	A2	10c	**blue**	300.	200.
			No gum	180.	
			On cover		325.
			On wallpaper cover		1,500.
			On patriotic cover		2,250.
			On prisoner's cover with U.S. #65		—
			Pair	750.	475.
			Pair on cover		950.
			Strip of 3 on cover		—
			Block of 4	1,850.	
			Horiz. pair, gutter btwn.	1,500.	
a.		10c	**light blue**	300.	200.
			No gum	175.	
b.		10c	**dark blue**	700.	275.
			No gum	425.	
c.		10c	**indigo**	*3,000.*	*2,500.*
			No gum	*2,000.*	
d.		Printed on both sides		—

VARIETIES

Malformed "O" of "POSTAGE" (Pos. 25)	425.	240.
J. T. Paterson & Co. imprint	1,250.	1,250.

Cancellations

Blue town	+10.
Red town	+100.
Green town	+200.
Violet town	—
Texas town	+125.
Arkansas town	+275.
Florida town	+325.
July, 1862, date	+300.
Straight line town	+500.
Blue gridiron	+10.
Red gridiron	+75.
Blue concentric	+10.
Numeral	+80.
"Paid"	+75.
Star or flower	+150.
Railroad	+350.
Express Co.	+300.
Pen	75.

Hoyer

2b	A2 10c **dark blue**	700.	275.
	No gum	425.	
	On cover		450.
	On wallpaper cover		2,000.
	On patriotic cover		3,000.
	On prisoner's cover with U.S. #65		
	Pair	1,300.	850.
	Pair on cover		1,500.
	Strip of 3 on cover		3,500.
	Block of 4	2,900.	
d.	Printed on both sides		—

VARIETIES

Malformed "T" of "TEN" (Pos. 4)	750.	300.
"G" and "E" of "POSTAGE" joined (Pos. 10)	750.	300.
Circular flaw, upper left star (Pos. 11)	750.	300.
Third spiked ornament at right, white (Pos. 45)	750.	350.
Hoyer & Ludwig imprint	1,000.	825.
Rouletted unofficially, on cover		3,000.

Cancellations

Blue town	+30.
Red town	+100.
Texas town	+125.
Arkansas town	+275.
Florida town	+325.
Kentucky town	+400.
Nov., 1861, date	+300.
Straight line town	+500.
Blue gridiron	+10.
Red gridiron	+75.
Blue concentric	+10.
Numeral	+75.
"Paid"	+50.
Railroad	+350.
Express Company	+300.
Pen	85.

Stone Y

2e	A2 10c **greenish blue**	1,100.	375.
	No gum	650.	
	light milky blue	1,100.	375.
	No gum	650.	
	On cover		550.
	On wallpaper cover		1,000.
	On patriotic cover		2,100.
	Pair	2,750.	
	Block of 4	—	2,500.

Cancellations

Blue town	+10.
Red town	+125.
Violet town	+75.
Green town	+300.
Texas town	+125.
Arkansas town	+275.
Florida town	—
Straight line town	+500.
Blue gridiron	+10.
Red gridiron	+75.
Blue concentric	+10.
Numeral	+100.
"Paid"	+100.
Pen	120.

Andrew Jackson — A3

Sheet consists of four groups of fifty varieties arranged in two panes of 100 each.

One stone only was used. Printed by Hoyer & Ludwig, of Richmond, Va. Issued to prepay drop letter and circular rates. Strips of five used to prepay regular 10c rate, which was changed from 5c on July 1, 1862. Earliest known cancellation, March 21, 1862.

1862 (March?)   Soft Porous Paper   Litho.

3	A3 2c **green**	900.	750.
	light green	900.	750.
	dark green	900.	800.
	No gum	550.	
	dull yellow green	1,300.	900.
	No gum	850.	
	On cover		2,750.
	Pair on cover (double circular rate)		3,250.
	Strip of 5 on cover		13,500.
	On patriotic cover		—
	Pair	2,000.	
	Block of 4	5,500.	5,000.
	Block of 5	6,500.	5,500.
a.	2c **bright yellow green**	2,000.	
	No gum	1,300.	
	On cover		4,000.
	Pair		

VARIETIES

Diagonal half used as 1c with unsevered pair, on cover		—
Horiz. pair, vert. gutter between	—	

Pair, mark between stamps (btwn. Pos. 4 and 5)	2,100.	2,100.
Mark above upper right corner (Pos. 30)	1,000.	850.
Mark above upper left corner (Pos. 31)	1,000.	850.
Acid flaw	1,000.	700.

Cancellations

Blue town	+500.
Red town	+800.
Arkansas town	—
Texas town	+1,250.
Blue gridiron	+250.
"Paid"	—
Express Company	—
Railroad	+3,000.
Pen	350.

1862   Soft Porous Paper   Litho.

Stone 2 — First stone used for printing in blue. Plating is the same as Stone 2 in green. Earliest dated cancellation Feb. 26, 1862. Printings from Stone 2 are found in all shades of blue. Rough, coarse impressions are typical of printings from Stone 2.

Stone 3 — A new stone used for printings in blue only. Earliest dated cancellation April 10, 1862. Sheet consists of four groups of fifty varieties each arranged in two panes of one hundred each without imprint. Impressions are clear and sharp, often having a proof-like appearance, especially in the deep blue printing. Plating marks, while not so large as on Stone 2 are distinct and clearly defined.

Stone 2

4	A1 5c **blue**	225.	125.
	No gum	130.	
	light blue	250.	140.
	No gum	150.	
	Pair	625.	450.
	Block of 4	1,300.	2,000.
	Horiz. pair, wide gutter between	1,250.	
	Vert. pair, narrow gutter between	—	
	On cover		275.
	Single on cover (overpaid drop letter)		400.
	Pair on cover		450.
	On wallpaper cover		1,250.
	On patriotic cover		2,500.
	On prisoner's cover		—
	On prisoner's cover with U.S. #65		—
a.	5c **dark blue**	250.	175.
	No gum	150.	
b.	5c **light milky blue**	300.	200.
	No gum	180.	

VARIETIES

Spur on upper left scroll (Pos. 21)	250.	150.
Thin hard paper		140.
Misplaced transfer (faint twin impression of second lower left scroll at left — pos. 2 entered over pos. 10)		—

Cancellations

Blue town	+20.
Red town	+100.
Orange town	+400.
Texas town	+300.
Arkansas town	+325.
Florida town	+200.
Straight line town	+300.
Blue gridiron	+10.
Red gridiron	+85.
Star or Flowers	+125.
Numeral	+85.
Railroad	—
"Paid"	+25.
"Steamboat"	+400.
Express Company	—
"Way"	+250.
Pen	65.

Stone 3

4	A1 5c **blue**	750.	250.
	No gum	500.	
a.	5c **dark blue**	800.	275.
	No gum	550.	
b.	5c **light milky blue**	750.	250.
	No gum	500.	
	Pair	1750.	550.
	Block of 4	4,500.	2,000.
	On cover		500.
	Pair on cover		625.
	On patriotic cover		2,750.
	Horiz. pair, wide gutter btwn.	—	
	Vert. pair, narrow gutter between	—	

Stone 3 stamps can be positively identified by plating only. Color or shade is not a determinant.

VARIETIES

Tops of "C" and "E" of "cents" joined by flaw (Pos. 33)	850.	325.
"Flying bird" above lower left corner ornament (Pos. 19)	850.	325.

Cancellations

Blue town	+40.
Red town	+100.
Texas town	+300.
Arkansas town	+325.
Straight line town	+325.
Blue gridiron	+10.
Star or Flowers	+125.
"Paid"	+50.
Pen	80.

1862 (March?)   Soft Porous Paper   Litho.

Settings of fifty varieties repeated.

Printed by Hoyer & Ludwig, of Richmond, Va. One stone used, being the same as that used for the Hoyer & Ludwig 10c value in blue. Color change occured probably in March, 1862.

There are many shades of this stamp. The carmine is a very dark, bright color and should not be confused with the deeper shade of rose.

Earliest known cancellation, March 10, 1862. The earliest date of usage of the carmine shade is May 1, 1862.

5	A2 10c **rose** (shades)	1,500.	500.
	No gum	900.	
	dull rose	1,350.	500.
	brown rose	1,850.	1,000.
	deep rose	1,600.	650.
	carmine rose	1,850.	875.
	On cover		800.
	On wallpaper cover		2,000.
	On patriotic cover		3,000.

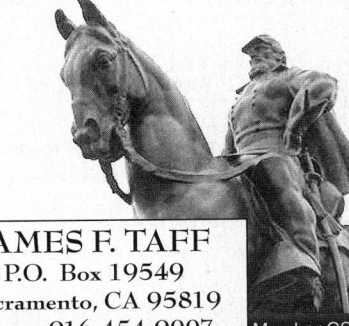

On prisoner's cover		*5,500.*
On prisoner's cover with U.S. #65		—
Pair	3,350.	2,250.
Strip of 3	—	4,000.
Block of 4	11,000.	6,500.
a. 10c carmine	3,500.	1,900.
No gum	2,100.	
On cover		4,500.

VARIETIES

Malformed "T" of "TEN" (Pos. 4)	1,850.	600.
"G" and "E" of "POSTAGE" joined (Pos. 10)	1,850.	600.
Circular flaw, upper left star (Pos. 11)	1,950.	675.
Third spiked ornament at right, white (Pos. 45)	1,950.	675.
Scratched stone (occurring on Pos. 40, 39, 49 and 48, one pane)	1,950.	925.
Imprint	1,750.	
Horiz. pair, vert. gutter between		—
Side margin copy, initials (Pos. 41)	1,500.	

Cancellations

Blue town	+50.
Red town	+125.
Green town	+350.
Texas town	+150.
Arkansas town	—
Straight line town	+500.
April, 1862, year date	—
Blue gridiron	+50.
Black concentric	+50.
Blue concentric	+50.
"Paid"	—
Railroad	—
Express Company	—
Pen	200.

Jefferson Davis — A4

Plate of 400 in four panes of 100 each. No imprint.
No. 6 represents London printings from De La Rue & Co., a number of sheets being sent over by blockade runners. Fine clear impressions. The gum is light and evenly distributed. Exact date of issue unknown. Earliest known cancellation, April 16, 1862.

Typographed by De La Rue & Co. in London, England

1862 (April)　　　　Hard Medium Paper

6	A4 5c light blue	15.00	27.50
	No gum	7.50	
	Single on cover used before July 1, 1862		150.00
	Single on cover (overpaid drop letter)		275.00
	Single on patriotic cover used before July 1, 1862		2,000.
	Single on prisoner's cover used before July 1, 1862		—
	On wallpaper cover		800.00
	On patriotic cover		1,200.
	On prisoner's cover		—
	On prisoner's cover with U.S. #65		—
	Pair	35.00	75.00
	Pair on cover		100.00
	Pair on patriotic cover		1,300.
	Block of 4	80.00	290.00
	Block of 4 on cover		900.00

Cancellations

Blue town	+2.00
Red town	+55.00
Green town	+75.00
Texas town	+65.00
Arkansas town	+100.00
Straight line town	+150.00
Blue gridiron	+2.00
Red gridiron	+35.00
Blue concentric	+2.00
Express Company	+350.00
Railroad	+250.00
"Paid"	+50.00

1862 (July)　　Typo.　　Thin to Thick Paper

Plate of 400 in four panes of 100 each. No imprint.
Locally printed by Archer & Daly of Richmond, Va., from plates made in London, England, by De La Rue & Co. Printed on both imported English and local papers. Earliest known cancellation, July 15, 1862.
No. 7 shows coarser impressions than No. 6, and the color is duller and often blurred. Gum is light or dark and unevenly distributed.

7	A4 5c blue	18.00	20.00
	No gum	9.00	
	Single on cover (overpaid drop letter)		200.00
	On wallpaper cover		800.00
	On patriotic cover		1,200.

On prisoner's cover		—
On prisoner's cover with U.S. #65		—
Pair	40.00	47.50
Pair on cover		95.00
Block of 4	90.00	350.00
Block of 4 on cover		800.00
Eight on cover (Trans-Miss. rate)		—
a. 5c deep blue	22.50	35.00
No gum	11.00	
b. Printed on both sides	2,500.	1,500.
Pair		3,250.
Pair on cover		4,000.

VARIETIES

White tie (U.R. 30)	150.00	150.00
White tie on cover		350.00
De La Rue paper (thin)	27.50	45.00
No gum	15.00	
White tie, De La Rue paper	200.00	250.00
Thick paper	22.50	*35.00*
Horiz. pair, vert. gutter between	200.00	

Cancellations

Blue town	+2.00
Red town	+75.00
Brown town	+30.00
Violet town	+110.00
Green town	+150.00
Texas town	+90.00
Arkansas town	+110.00
Florida town	+140.00
Straight line town	+140.00
Blue gridiron	+2.00
Red gridiron	+60.00
Blue concentric	+2.00
Railroad	+250.00
Express Company	+400.00
Design (stars, etc.)	+75.00
"Paid"	+50.00

The unissued 10c design A4 was privately printed in various colors for philatelic purposes. (See note below No. 14.)
Counterfeits of the 10c exist.

Andrew Jackson — A5

Sheet of 200 (two panes of 100 each).
One plate. Printed by Archer & Daly of Richmond, Va. Earliest known cancellation. Apr. 21, 1863. Issued to prepay drop letter and circular rates. Strips of five used to prepay regular 10c rate.

1863 (April)　　Soft Porous Paper　　Engraved

8	A5 2c brown red	70.	*350.*
	No gum	40.	
a.	2c pale red	90.	*450.*
	No gum	45.	
	Single on cover		*1,500.*
	On prisoner's cover		—
	On prisoner's cover with U.S. #65		—
	Pair	150.	*1,000.*
	Pair on cover		*3,250.*
	On wallpaper cover		—
	Block of 4	350.	—
	Block of 5		—
	Strip of 5 on cover		*4,500.*
	Strip of 5 on wallpaper cover		—
	Strip of 10 on cover		—
	Double transfer	125.	*450.*
	Horiz. pair, vert. gutter between	325.	

Cancellations

Blue town	+35.
Red town	+225.
Violet town	+300.
Army of Tenn.	—
Blue gridiron	+35.
Black numeral	—
Railroad	+325.

Jefferson Davis "TEN CENTS" — A6

One plate of 200 subjects all of which were probably recut as every example examined to date shows distinct recutting. Plating not completed.
Printed by Archer & Daly of Richmond, Va. First printings in milky blue. First issued in April, 1863. Earliest known cancellation, April 23, 1863.

1863, Apr.　　Soft Porous Paper　　Engraved

9	A6 10c blue	900.	550.
	No gum	575.	
a.	10c milky blue (first printing)	900.	550.
	No gum	575.	
b.	10c gray blue	950.	650.
	No gum	625.	
	On cover		1,600.
	On wallpaper cover		3,000.
	On patriotic cover		3,500.
	On prisoner's cover		—
	On prisoner's cover with U.S. #65		—
	Pair	2,000.	2,200.
	Pair on cover		3,000.
	Block of 4	5,250.	
	Four stamps on one cover (Trans-Mississippi rate)		13,500.
	Curved lines outside the labels at top and bottom are broken in the middle (Pos. 63R)	1,050.	775.
	Double transfer	1,100.	1,000.
	Damaged plate	1,200.	1,100.

Cancellations

Blue town	+25.
Red town	+150.
Green town	+600.
Violet town	—
Straight line town	+500.
April, 1863, year date	—
Black gridiron	+25.
Blue gridiron	+50.
Red gridiron	+200.
Railroad	+400.
Circle of wedges	+1,250.
Pen	350.

Frame Line "10 CENTS" — A6a

Printed by Archer & Daly of Richmond, Va.
One copper plate of 100 subjects, all but one of which were recut. Earliest known use April 19, 1863.
Stamp design same as Die A (Pos. 11).
Values are for stamps showing parts of lines on at least 3 of 4 sides. Used stamps showing 4 complete lines sell for 200%-300% of the values given. Unused stamps showing 4 complete lines are exceedingly rare (only two recorded), and the sound example is valued at $25,000.

1863, Apr.　　Soft Porous Paper　　Engraved

10	A6a 10c blue	5,000.	1,800.
	No gum	3,500.	
a.	10c milky blue	5,000.	1,800.
	No gum	3,500.	
b.	10c greenish blue	5,500.	1,900.
	No gum	4,000.	
c.	10c dark blue	5,500.	1,900.
	No gum	4,000.	
	On cover		3,000.
	On wallpaper cover		4,750.
	On patriotic cover		10,000.
	On prisoner's cover		7,000.
	On prisoner's cover with U.S. #65		—
	Pair	11,500.	6,000.
	Pair on cover		7,000.
	Block of 4	27,500.	
	Strip of 4	26,000.	
	Strip of 6		20,000.
	Strip of 7	42,500.	
	Double transfer (Pos. 74)	5,500.	1,900.

Cancellations

Blue town	+100.
Red town	+500.
Straight line town	+750.
April, 1863, year date	—
Blue gridiron	+100.
Pen	800.

No Frame Line "10 CENTS" (Die A) — A7

There are many slight differences between A7 (Die A) and A8 (Die B), the most noticeable being the additional line outside the ornaments at the four corners of A8 (Die B).
Stamps were first printed by Archer & Daly, of Richmond, Va. In 1864 the plates were transferred to the firm of Keatinge & Ball in Columbia, S. C., who made further printings from them. Two plates, each with two panes of 100, numbered 1 and 2. First state shows numbers only, later states show various styles

of Archer & Daly imprints, and latest show Keatinge & Ball imprints. Archer & Daly stamps show uniformly clear impressions and a good quality of gum evenly distributed (Earliest known cancellation, April 21, 1863); Keatinge & Ball stamps generally show filled in impressions in a deep blue, and the gum is brown and unevenly distributed. (Earliest known cancellation, Oct. 4, 1864.) The so-called laid paper is probably due to thick streaky gum. (These notes also apply to No. 12.)

1863-64 — Thick or Thin Paper — Engraved

11	A7	10c blue		15.00	20.00
		No gum		7.50	
		deep blue, Keatinge & Ball ('64)		15.00	35.00
		No gum		9.00	
		On cover			100.00
		Single on cover (overpaid drop letter)			200.00
		On wallpaper cover			800.00
		On patriotic cover			1,000.
		On prisoner's cover			750.00
		On prisoner's cover with U.S. #65			2,500.
		On cover, dp. blue (K. & B.) ('64)			200.00
		On wallpaper cover (K. & B.)			1,250.
		On prisoner's cover (K. & B.) with U.S. #65 ('64)			—
		Pair		35.00	45.00
		Pair on cover			275.00
		Block of 4		80.00	350.00
		Strip of 4 on cover (Trans-Mississippi rate)			—
		Margin block of 12, Archer & Daly impt. & P#		450.00	
		Margin block of 12, Keatinge & Ball impt. & P#		425.00	
		Horiz. pair, vert. gutter between		125.00	
a.		10c milky blue		45.00	47.50
		No gum		25.00	
b.		10c dark blue		22.50	25.00
		No gum		12.50	
c.		10c greenish blue		30.00	20.00
		No gum		17.50	
d.		10c green		60.00	80.00
		No gum		40.00	
e.		Officially perforated 12½ (A. & D.)		325.00	275.00
		On cover			750.00
		On wallpaper cover			
		Pair		650.00	600.00
		Pair on cover			2,750.
		Block of 4		1,500.	4,250.

VARIETIES

Double transfer	75.00	100.00
Rouletted unofficially		500.00
On cover		800.00

Cancellations

Blue town	+5.00
Red town	+35.00
Orange town	+110.00
Brown town	+60.00
Green town	+175.00
Violet town	+100.00
Texas town	+60.00
Arkansas town	+125.00
Florida town	+200.00
Straight line town	+350.00
Army of Tenn.	+300.00
April, 1863 year date	+75.00
"FREE"	+250.00
Blue gridiron	+5.00
Black concentric circles	+10.00
Star	+100.00
Crossroads	+150.00
"Paid"	+100.00
Numeral	+100.00
Railroad	+175.00
Steamboat	+1,500.

Jefferson Davis (Die B) — A8

Plates bore Nos. 3 and 4, otherwise notes on No. 11 apply. Earliest known use: Archer & Daly — May 1, 1863; Keatinge & Ball — Sept. 4, 1864.

1863-64 — Thick or Thin Paper — Engraved

12	A8	10c blue		18.00	20.00
		No gum		9.00	
		deep blue, Keatinge & Ball ('64)		17.50	40.00
		No gum		10.00	
		On cover			90.00
		Single on cover (overpaid drop letter)			200.00
		On wallpaper cover			800.00
		On patriotic cover			1,250.
		On prisoner's cover			750.00
		On prisoner's cover with U.S. #65			2,500.
		On cover, dp. blue (K. & B.) ('64)			130.00
		Pair		40.00	52.50
		Pair on cover			200.00

Block of 4		90.00	300.00
Strip of 4 on cover (Trans-Mississippi rate)			
Margin block of 12, Archer & Daly impt. & P#		475.00	
Margin block of 12, Keatinge & Ball impt. & P#		425.00	
Horiz. pair, vert. gutter between		125.00	
a.	10c milky blue	45.00	47.50
	No gum	25.00	
b.	10c light blue	17.50	20.00
	No gum	9.00	
c.	10c greenish blue	35.00	55.00
	No gum	20.00	
d.	10c dark blue	18.00	22.50
	No gum	9.00	
e.	10c green	125.00	140.00
	No gum	75.00	
f.	Officially perforated 12½ (A. & D.)	350.00	300.00
	On cover		750.00
	Pair	750.00	600.00
	Pair on cover		
	Block of 4	1,900.	

VARIETIES

Double transfer	95.00	110.00
Rouletted unofficially	—	375.00
On cover		850.00

Cancellations

Blue town	+5.00
Red town	+35.00
Brown town	+90.00
Green town	+120.00
Violet town	+85.00
Texas town	+125.00
Arkansas town	+150.00
Florida town	+200.00
Straight line town	+400.00
Army of Tenn.	+350.00
May, 1863, year date	+60.00
Blue gridiron	+5.00
Black concentric circles	+10.00
Railroad	+175.00

George Washington — A9

1863 (June?) — Engraved by Archer & Daly

One plate which consisted of two panes of 100 each. First printings were from plates with imprint in Old English type under each pane, which was later removed. Printed on paper of varying thickness and in many shades of green. This stamp was also used as currency. Earliest known cancellation, June 1, 1863. Forged cancellations exist.

13	A9	20c green		40.00	400.
		No gum		25.00	
		On cover			1,250.
		On wallpaper cover			1,750.
		On prisoner's cover			4,000.
		On prisoner's cover with U.S. #65			5,000.
		Pair		85.00	900.
		Horizontal pair with gutter between		350.00	
		Pair on cover (non-Trans-Mississippi rate)			4,500.
		Pair on cover (Trans-Mississippi rate)			
		Block of 4		200.00	3,500.
		Strip of 4 with imprint		425.00	
		Block of 8 with imprint		1,050.	
a.		20c yellow green		70.00	450.
		No gum		45.00	
b.		20c dark green		65.00	500.
		No gum		40.00	
c.		20c bluish green		100.00	—
		No gum		65.00	
d.		Diagonal half used as 10c on cover			2,000.
		Diagonal half on prisoner's cover			—
e.		Horizontal half used as 10c on cover			3,500.

VARIETIES

Double transfer, 20 doubled (Pos. 24L and 35R)	300.	—
"20" on forehead	3,000.	—
Rouletted unofficially		1,100.
On cover		3,750.

Cancellations

Blue town	+50.
Red town	+200.
Violet town	
Texas town	+100.
Arkansas town	+400.
Tennessee town	+1,000.
Railroad	

John C. Calhoun — A10

Typographed by De La Rue & Co., London, England

1862

14	A10	1c orange		110.00
		No gum		65.00
		Pair		230.00
		Block of 4		475.00
a.		1c deep orange		130.00
		No gum		80.00

This stamp was never put in use.

Upon orders from the Confederate Government, De La Rue & Co. of London, England, prepared Two Cents and Ten Cents typographed plates by altering the One Cent (No. 14) and the Five Cents (Nos. 6-7) designs previously made by them. Stamps were never officially printed from these plates although privately made prints exist in various colors.

Explanatory Notes

The following notes by Lawrence L. Shenfield explain the various routes, rates and usages of the general issue Confederate stamps.

"Across the Lines"
Letters Carried by Private Express Companies

Adams Express Co. and American Letter Express Company Handstamps Used on "Across the Lines" Letters

PRIVATE LETTER MAIL.
Direct each letter to your correspondent as usual, envelope that with 15 cents in money and direct to
B. WHITESIDES,
Franklin, Ky.
Letters exceeding half an ounce or going over 500 miles must have additional amount enclosed. For single Newspapers enclose 10 cents.

B. Whitesides Label

About two months after the outbreak of the Civil War, in June, 1861, postal service between North and South and vice versa was carried on largely by Adams Express Company, and the American Letter Express Company. Northern terminus for the traffic was Louisville, Ky.; Southern terminus was Nashville, Tenn. Letters for transmission were delivered to any office of the express company, together with a fee, usually 20c or 25c per ½ ounce to cover carriage. The express company messengers carried letters across the lines and delivered them to their office on the other side, where they were deposited in the Government mail for transmission to addressees, postage paid out of the fee charged. Letters from North to South, always enclosed in 3c U.S. envelopes, usually bear the handstamp of the Louisville office of the express company, and in addition the postmark and "Paid 5" of Nashville, Tenn., indicating its acceptance for delivery at the Nashville Post Office. Letters from South to North sometimes bear the origin postmark of a Southern post office, but more often merely the handstamp of the Louisville express company office applied as the letters cleared through Louisville. The B. Whitesides South to North cover bears a "Private Letter Mail" label. In addition, these covers bear the 3c 1857 U.S. adhesive stamp, cancelled with the postmark and grid of Louisville, Ky., where they went into the Government mail for delivery. Some across-the-lines letters show the handstamp of various express company offices, according to the particular routing the letters followed. On August 26, 1861, the traffic ceased by order of the U.S. Post Office Dept. (Values are for full covers bearing the usual Louisville, Ky., or Nashville, Tenn., handstamps of the express company. Unusual express office markings are rarer and worth more.)

North to South 3c U.S. Envelope, Adams Exp. Co. Louisville, Ky., handstamp   1,500.
North to South 3c U.S. Envelope, American Letter Express Co., Ky., handstamp   2,100.
South to North 3c 1857, Adams Exp. Co., Louisville, Ky., handstamp   1,750.
South to North 3c 1857, American Letter Exp. 250, Nashville, Tenn., handstamp   2,500.
South to North 3c 1861, Adams Exp. Co., Louisville, Ky., handstamp   3,250.
South to North 3c 1857, B. Whitesides, Franklin, Ky., label   16,500.

Blockade-Run Letters from Europe to the Confederate States

Charleston "STEAM-SHIP" in Oval Handstamp

As the Federal Fleet gradually extended its blockade of the Confederate States coastal regions, the South was forced to resort to blockade runners to carry letters to and from outside ports. These letters were all private-ship letters and never bore a foreign stamp if from Europe, nor a Confederate stamp if to Europe. The usual route from Europe was via a West Indies port, Nassau, Bahamas; Hamilton, Bermuda, or Havana, into the Southern ports of Wilmington, N.C. and Charleston, S.C. More rarely letters came in to Savannah, Mobile and New Orleans. Letters from Europe are the only ones which are surely identified by their markings. They bore either the postmark of Wilmington, N.C., straightline "SHIP" and "12", "22", "32", etc., in manuscript; or the postmark of Charleston, S. C., "STEAMSHIP" in oval, and "12", "22", "32", etc., in manuscript. Very rarely Charleston used a straightline "SHIP" instead of "STEAMSHIP" in oval. All such letters were postage due; the single letter rate of 12c being made up of 2c for the private ship captain plus 10c for the regular single letter Confederate States rate. Over-weight letters were 22c (due), 32c, 42c, etc. A few examples are known on which Confederate General Issue stamps were used, usually as payment for forwarding postage. Covers with such stamps, or with the higher rate markings, 22c, 32, etc., are worth more.
Values are for full covers in fine condition.

Charleston, S.C. "6" handstamp   2,500.
Charleston, S.C., postmark, "STEAMSHIP," and "12" in ms.   3,000.

Charleston, S.C., postmark, "SHIP," and "12" in ms.   3,000.
Wilmington, N.C., postmark, "SHIP," and "12" in ms.   3,000.
Savannah, Ga., postmark "SHIP," and "7" in ms. (*)   4,000.
New Orleans, La. postmark, "SHIP," and "10" in ms.   5,000.

(* 7c rate: 5c postage before July 1, 1862, plus 2c for ship captain.)

Express Company Mail in the Confederacy

Southern Express Company Handstamps
Shortly after the outbreak of war in 1861, the Adams Express Company divisions operating in the South were forced to suspend operations and turned their Southern lines over to a new company organized under the title Southern Express Company. This express did the bulk of the express business in the Confederacy despite the continued opposition of the Post Office Dept. of the C.S.A. and the ravages of the contending armies upon railroads. Other companies operating in the Confederacy were: South Western Express Co. (New Orleans), Pioneer Express Company, White's Southern Express (only one example known) and some local expresses of limited operation. The first three used handstamps of various designs usually bearing the city name of the office. Postal regulation necessitated the payment of regular Confederate postal rates on letters carried by express companies, express charges being paid in addition. Important letters, particularly money letters, were entrusted to these express companies as well as goods and wares of all kinds. The express rates charged for letters are not known; probably they varied depending upon the difficulty and risk of transmittal. Covers bearing stamps and express company handstamps are very rare.

Prisoner-of-War and Flag-of-Truce Letters

Prison Censor Handstamps
By agreement between the United States and the Confederate States, military prisoners and imprisoned civilians of both sides were permitted to send censored letters to their respective countries. Such letters, if from North to South, usually bore a U.S. 3c 1861 adhesive, postmarked at a city near the prison, to pay the postage to the exchange ground near Old Point Comfort, Va.; and a 10c Confederate stamp, canceled at Richmond, Va. (or "due" handstamp) to pay the Confederate postage to destination. If from South to North, letters usually bore a 10c Confederate stamp canceled at a Southern city (or "paid" handstamp) and a U. S. 3c 1861 adhesive (or "due 3" marking) and the postmark of Old Point Comfort, Va. In addition, prison censor markings, handstamped or manuscript, the name and rank of the soldier, and "Flag of Truce, via Fortress Monroe" in manuscript usually appear on these covers. Federal prison censor handstamps of various designs are known from these prisons:
Camp Chase, Columbus, O.
David's Island, Pelham, N.Y.
Fort Delaware, Delaware City, Del.
Camp Douglas, Chicago, Ill.
Elmira Prison, Elmira, N.Y.
Johnson's Island, Sandusky, O.
Fort McHenry, Baltimore, Md.
Camp Morton, Indianapolis, Ind.
Fort Oglethorpe, Macon, Ga.
Old Capitol Prison, Washington, D.C.
Point Lookout Prison, Point Lookout, Md.
Fort Pulaski, Savannah, Ga.
Rock Island Prison, Rock Island, Ill.
Ship Island, New Orleans, La.
West's Hospital, Baltimore, Md.
U.S. General Hospital, Gettysburg, Pa.
Several other Federal prisons used manuscript censor markings.
Southern prison censor markings are always in manuscript, and do not identify the prison. The principal Southern prisons were at Richmond and Danville, Va.; Andersonville and Savannah, Ga.; Charleston, Columbia and Florence S.C.; Salisbury, N.C.; Hempstead and Tyler, Tex.
Civilians residing in both the North and the South were also, under exceptional circumstances, permitted to send Flag of Truce letters across the lines. Such covers bore no censor marking nor prison markings, but were always endorsed "via Flag of Truce".
Values will be found under various individual stamps for "on prisoner's cover" and are for the larger prisons. Prisoners' letters from the smaller prisons are much rarer. Only a very small percentage of prisoners' covers bore *both* a U.S. stamp and a Confederate stamp.

The "SOUTHERN LETTER UNPAID" Marking On Northbound Letters of Confederate Origin

DUE 3

SOUTHᴺ LETTER UNPAID.

By mid-May, 1861, correspondence between the North and South was difficult. In the South, postmasters were resigning and closing their accounts with Washington as the Confederacy prepared to organize its own postal system by June 1. From that date on, town marks and "paid" handstamps (and later postmasters' provisional stamps) were used in all post offices of the seceded states. The three most important Southern cities for clearing mail to the North were Memphis, Nashville and Richmond. The Richmond-Washington route was closed in April; Memphis was closed by June 1st, and mail attempting to cross the lines at these points generally ended up at the dead letter office. However, at Louisville, Kentucky, mail from the South via Nashville continued to arrive in June, July and August. On June 24, 1861, the Post Office Department advised the Louisville post office, "You will forward letters from the South for the Loyal States as unpaid, after removing postage stamps, but foreign letters in which prepayment is compulsory must come to the Dead Letter Office." However, Louisville avoided the task of "removing postage stamps," and instead prepared the "Southern Letter Unpaid" handstamp and special "due 3" markers for use. These markings were applied in the greenish-blue color of the Louisville office to letters of Southern origin that had accumulated, in addition to the usual town mark and grid of Louisville. The letters were delivered in the North as unpaid. Probably Louisville continued to forward such unpaid mail until about July 15. The marking is very rare. Other Southern mail was forwarded from Louisville as late as Aug. 27.

For listings see under U.S. 1857-61 issue, Nos. 26, 35-38. Values shown there are generally for this marking on off-cover stamps. Complete covers bearing stamps showing the full markings are valued from $10,000 upward depending upon the stamps, other postal markings and unusual usages, and condition. Fraudulent covers exist.

Trans-Mississippi Express Mail-the 40c Rate

From the fall of New Orleans on April 24, 1862, the entire reach of the Mississippi River was threatened by the Federal fleets. Late in 1862 the Confederacy experienced difficulty in maintaining regular mail routes trans-Mississippi to the Western states. Private express companies began to carry some mail, but by early 1863 when the Meridian-Jackson-Vicksburg-Shreveport route was seriously menaced, the Post Office Department of the Confederate States was forced to inaugurate an express mail service by contracting with a private company the name of which remains undisclosed. The eastern termini were at Meridian and Brandon, Miss.; the western at Shreveport and Alexandria, La. Letters, usually endorsed "via Meridian (or Brandon)" if going West; "via Shreveport (or Alexandria)" if going East were deposited in any Confederate post office. The rate was 40c per ½ ounce or less. Such Trans-Mississippi Express Mail upon arrival at a terminus was carried by couriers in a devious route across the Mississippi and returned to the regular mails at the nearest terminus on the other side of the river. The precise date of the beginning of the Trans-Mississippi service is not known. The earliest date of use so far seen is November 2, 1863 and the latest use February 9, 1865. These covers can be identified by the written endorsement of the route, but particularly by the rate since many bore no route endorsements.

Strips of four of 10c engraved stamps, pairs of the 20c stamp and various combinations of 10c stamps and the 5c London or Local prints are known; also handstamped Paid 40c marking. No identifying handstamps were used, merely the postmark of the office which received the letter originally. Values for Trans-Mississippi Express covers will be found under various stamps of the General Issues.

A 50c Preferred Mail Express rate, announced in April, 1863, preceded the Trans-Mississippi Express Mail 40c rate. One cover showing this rate is known.

Packet and Steamboat Covers and Markings

Letters carried on Confederate packets operating on coastal routes or up and down the inland waterways were usually handstamped with the name of the packet or marked STEAM or STEAMBOAT. Either United States stamps of the 1857 issue or stamped envelopes of the 1853 or 1860 issues have been found so used, as well as Confederate Postmasters' Provisional and General Issue stamps. Some specially designed pictorial or imprinted packet boat covers also exist. All are scarce and command values from $1,000 upward for handstamped United States envelopes and from $1,500 up for covers bearing Confederate stamps.

TABLE OF SECESSION

	Ordinance of Secession	Admitted to Confederacy	Period for Use of U.S. Stamps As Independent State	Total to 5/31/1861*
SC	12/20/1860	2/4/1861	46 days	163 days
MS	1/9/1861	2/4/1861	26 days	143 days
FL	1/10/1861	2/4/1861	25 days	142 days
AL	1/11/1861	2/4/1861	24 days	141 days
GA	1/19/1861	2/4/1861	16 days	133 days
LA	1/26/1861	2/4/1861	9 days	126 days
TX	2/1/1861	3/6/1861	33 days	120 days
VA	4/17/1861	5/7/1861	20 days	45 days
AR	5/6/1861	5/18/1861	12 days	26 days
TN	5/6/1861	7/2/1861	57 days	26 days
NC	5/20/1861	5/27/1861	7 days	12 days

* The use of United States stamps in the seceded States was prohibited after May 31, 1861.

TX — Ordinance of Secession adopted Feb. 1. Popular vote to secede Feb. 23, effective Mar. 2, 1861.

VA — Ordinance of Secession adopted. Admitted to Confederacy May 7. Scheduled election of May 23 ratified the Ordinance of Secession.

TN — Ordinance passed to "submit to vote of the people a Declaration of Independence, and for other purposes." Adopted May 6. Election took place June 8. General Assembly ratified election June 24.

The Confederate postal laws did not provide the franking privilege for any mail except official correspondence of the Post Office Department. Such letters could be sent free only when enclosed in officially imprinted envelopes individually signed by the official using them. These envelopes were prepared and issued for Post Office Department use.

The imprints were on United States envelopes of 1853-61 issue, and also on commercial envelopes of various sizes and colors. When officially signed and mailed, they were postmarked, usually at Richmond, Va., with printed or handstamped "FREE". Envelopes are occasionally found unused and unsigned, and more rarely, signed but unused. When such official envelopes were used on other than official Post Office Department business, Confederate stamps were used.

Semi-official envelopes also exist bearing imprints of other government departments, offices, armies, states, etc. Regular postage was required to carry such envelopes through the mails.

CONFEDERATE STATES OF AMERICA,
POST OFFICE DEPARTMENT,
OFFICIAL BUSINESS,

John H. Reagan

POSTMASTER GENERAL.

Confederate States of America,
POST OFFICE DEPARTMENT,
OFFICIAL BUSINESS

John B. A. Dimitry

Act. CHIEF CLERK P. O. DEPARTMENT

Typical Imprints of Official Envelopes of the Post Office Department. (Many variations of type, style and wording exist.)

Office	Signature
Postmaster General	John H. Reagan
Chief of the Contract Bureau	H. St. Geo. Offutt
Chief of the Appointment Bureau	B. N. Clements
Chief of the Finance Bureau	Jno. L. Harrell
Chief of the Finance Bureau	J. L. Lancaster
Chief of the Finance Bureau	A. Dimitry
Dead Letter Office	A. Dimitry
Dead Letter Office	Jno. L. Harrell
Chief Clerk, P. O. Department	B. Fuller
Chief Clerk	W. D. Miller
Auditor's Office	W. W. Lester
Auditor's Office	B. Baker
Auditor's Office	J. W. Robertson
First Auditor's Office, Treasury Department	J. W. Robertson
First Auditor's Office, Treasury Department	B. Baker
Third Auditor's Office	A. Moise
Third Auditor's Office	I. W. M. Harris
Agency, Post Office Dept. Trans-Miss.	Jas. H. Starr

PROOFS

1861

(1) — Die on Glazed Card

(1a) — Die on Wove Paper

(5) — Plate on Wove Paper

(6) — Plate on Thin Card

(7) — Plate on Thick Ribbed Paper

1P	(5)	5c **green,** plate on wove paper	1,500.
2P	(5)	10c **blue,** plate on wove paper	1,500.
2TC	(5)	10c **black,** plate on wove paper (stone Y)	3,000.

1862

6P	(1)	5c **light blue,** die on glazed card	600.
6P, 14P	(1)	5c **blue & 1c orange,** composite die proof, 20x90mm card	6,000.
6P	(5)	5c **light blue,** plate on wove paper	150.
		Pair with gutter between	375.
6TC	(1a)	5c **dark blue,** die on woven paper	600.
6TC	(5)	5c **gray blue,** plate on wove paper	600.
6TC	(1)	5c **black,** die on glazed card	900.
6TC	(5)	5c **black,** plate on wove paper	1,000.
6TC	(1)	5c **pink,** die on glazed card	900.
7TC	(5)	5c **carmine,** plate on wove paper	850.
7TC	(6)	5c **carmine,** plate on thin card	750.

1863

8TC	(1a)	2c **black,** die on wove paper	1,750.
9TC	(1a)	10c **black,** die on wove paper	1,500.
11TC	(1a)	10c **black,** die on wove paper	1,100.
12P	(7)	10c **deep blue,** plate on thick ribbed paper	750.
13P	(1a)	20c **green,** die on wove paper	4,000.
13TC	(1a)	20c **red brown,** die on wove paper	4,000.

1862

14P	(1)	1c **orange,** die on glazed card	2,000.
14TC	(1)	1c **black,** die on glazed card	2,500.
14TC	(5)	1c **light yellow brown,** plate on wove paper	800.

Essay Die Proofs

In working up the final dies, proofs of incomplete designs in various stages were made. Usually dated in typeset lines, they are very rare. Others, of the 10c (No. 12) and the 20c (No. 13) were proofs made as essays from the dies. They are deeply engraved and printed in deep shades of the issued colors, but show only small differences from the stamps as finally issued. All are very rare.

Specimen Overprints

The De La Rue typographed 5c and 1c are known with "SPECIMEN" overprinted diagonally, also horizontally for 1c.

Counterfeits

In 1935 a set of 12 lithographed imitations, later known as the "Springfield facsimiles," appeared in plate form. They are in approximately normal colors on yellowish soft wove paper of modern manufacture.

CANAL ZONE

The Canal Zone, a strip of territory with an area of about 552 square miles following generally the line of the Canal, was under the jurisdiction of the United States, 1904-1979, and under the joint jurisdiction of the United States and Panama, 1979-1999, when the Canal, in its entirety, reverted to Panama.

The Canal organization underwent two distinct and fundamental changes. The construction of the Canal and the general administration of civil affairs were performed by the Isthmian Canal Commission under the provisions of the Spooner Act. This was supplanted in April, 1914, by the Panama Canal Act which established the organization known as The Panama Canal. This was an independent government agency which included both the operation and maintenance of the waterway and civil government in the Canal Zone. Most of the quasi-business enterprises relating to the Canal operation were conducted by the Panama Railroad, an adjunct of The Panama Canal.

A basic change in the mode of operations took effect July 1, 1951, under provisions of Public Law 841 of the 81st Congress. This in effect transferred the Canal operations to the Panama Railroad Co., which had been made a federal government corporation in 1948, and changed its name to the Panama Canal Co. Simultaneously the civil government functions of The Panama Canal, including the postal service, were renamed the Canal Zone Government. The organization therefore consisted of two units — the Panama Canal Co. and Canal Zone Government — headed by an individual who was president of the company and governor of the Canal Zone. His appointment as governor was made by the president of the United States, subject to confirmation by the Senate, and he was ex-officio president of the company.

The Canal Zone Government functioned as an independent government agency, and was under direct supervision of the president of the United States who delegated this authority to the Secretary of the Army.

The Panama Canal is 50 miles long from deep water in the Atlantic to deep water in the Pacific. It runs from northwest to southeast with the Atlantic entrance being 33.5 miles north and 27 miles west of the Pacific entrance. The airline distance between the two entrances is 43 miles. It requires about eight hours for an average ship to transit the Canal. Transportation between the Atlantic and Pacific sides of the Isthmus is available by railway, highway or air.

The Canal Zone Postal Service began operating June 24, 1904, when nine post offices were opened in connection with the construction of the Panama Canal. It ceased Sept. 30, 1979, and the Panama Postal Service took over.

Italicized numbers in parentheses indicate quantity issued.

100 CENTAVOS = 1 PESO

100 CENTESIMOS = 1 BALBOA

100 CENTS = 1 DOLLAR

Catalogue values for unused stamps are for Never Hinged items beginning with No. 118 in the regular postage section and No. C6 in the airpost section.

Map of Panama — A1

Violet to Violet Blue Handstamp on Panama Nos. 72, 72a-72c, 78, 79.

On the 2c "PANAMA" is normally 13mm long. On the 5c and 10c it measures about 15mm.

On the 2c, "PANAMA" reads up on the upper half of the sheet and down on the lower half. On the 5c and 10c, "PANAMA" reads up at left and down at right on each stamp.

On the 2c only, varieties exist with inverted "V" for "A," accent on "A," inverted "N," etc., in "PANAMA."

1904, June 24		**Engr.**	**Unwmk.**	**Perf. 12**	
1	A1	2c **rose,** both "PANAMA" reading up or down *(2600)*		650.	425.
		Single on post card			*1,650.*
		Strip of 3 on cover			*1,500.*
		Block of 4		3,000.	2,100.
		"PANAMA" 15mm long *(260)*		700.	600.

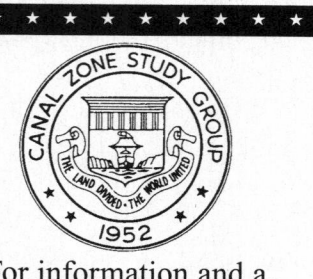

		"P NAMA"	700.	600.
a.		"CANAL ZONE" inverted *(100)*	1,000.	850.
b.		"CANAL ZONE" double	3,250.	2,000.
c.		"CANAL ZONE" double, both inverted	20,000.	
d.		"PANAMA" reading down and up *(52)*	750.	650.
e.		As "d," "CANAL ZONE" invtd.	9,000.	7,000.
f.		Vert. pair, "PANAMA" reading up on top 2c, down on other	2,100.	2,100.
g.		As "f," "CANAL ZONE" inverted	20,000.	
2	A1	5c **blue** *(7800)*	300.	200.
		On cover		250.
		First day cover		7,500.
		Block of 4	1,400.	1,000.
		Left "PANAMA" 2¼mm below bar *(156)*	575.	500.
		Colon between right "PANAMA" and bar *(156)*	575.	500.
a.		"CANAL ZONE" inverted	775.	600.
		On cover		800.
b.		"CANAL ZONE" double	2,250.	1,500.
c.		Pair, one without "CANAL ZONE" overprint	5,000.	5,000.
d.		"CANAL ZONE" overprint diagonal, reading down to right	800.	700.
3	A1	10c **yellow** *(4946)*	400.	250.
		On cover		325.
		First day cover		5,000.
		Block of 4	1,750.	1,150.
		Left "PANAMA" 2¼mm below bar *(100)*	675.	575.
		Colon between right "PANAMA" and bar *(100)*	650.	550.
a.		"CANAL ZONE" inverted *(200)*	775.	600.
		On cover		800.
b.		"CANAL ZONE" double		15,000.
c.		Pair, one without "CANAL ZONE" overprint	6,000.	5,000.

Cancellations consist of town and/or bars in magenta or black, or a mixture of both colors.

Nos. 1-3 were withdrawn July 17, 1904.

Forgeries of the "Canal Zone" overprint and cancellations are numerous.

United States Nos. 300, 319, 304, 306 and 307 Overprinted in Black

1904, July 18				**Wmk. 191**	
4	A115	1c **blue green** *(43,738)*		40.00	22.50
		green		40.00	22.50
		On cover			75.00
		Block of 4		175.00	140.00
		P# strip of 3, Impt.		160.00	
		P# block of 6, Impt.		925.00	
5	A129	2c **carmine** *(68,414)*		35.00	25.00
		On cover			75.00
		Block of 4		150.00	125.00
		P# strip of 3, Impt.		150.00	
		P# block of 6, Impt.		1,200.	
a.		2c **scarlet**		35.00	30.00

6	A119	5c **blue** *(20,858)*		110.00	65.00
		On cover			275.00
		Block of 4		525.00	325.00
		P# strip of 3, Impt.		475.00	
		P# block of 6, Impt.		1,450.	
7	A121	8c **violet black** *(7932)*		160.00	85.00
		On cover			500.00
		Block of 4		750.00	450.00
		P# strip of 3, Impt.		675.00	
		P# block of 6, Impt.		3,250.	
8	A122	10c **pale red brown** *(7856)*		150.00	90.00
		On cover			500.00
		Block of 4		650.00	475.00
		P# strip of 3, Impt.		625.00	
		P# block of 6, Impt.		2,750.	
		Nos. 4-8 *(5)*		495.00	287.50

Nos. 4-8 frequently show minor broken letters.

Cancellations consist of circular town and/or bars in black, blue or magenta.

Beware of fake overprints.

A2

A3

CANAL
ZONE
Regular Type

CANAL
ZONE
Antique Type

The Canal Zone overprint on stamps Nos. 9-15 and 18-20 was made with a plate which had six different stages, each with its peculiar faults and errors. Stage 1: Broken CA-L, broken L, A-L spaced, on Nos. 9, 10, 12-15. Stage 2: broken L, Z, N, E, on Nos. 9, 10, 12-14. Stage 3: same as 2 with additional antique ZONE, on Nos. 9, 11-14, 18. Stage 4: same as 3 with additional antique CANAL on Nos. 9, 12, 13. Stage 5: broken E and letters L, Z, N, and words CANAL and ZONE in antique type on Nos. 12-14, 19, 20. Stage 6: same as 5 except for additional antique Z on stamp which had antique L, on No. 12. The Panama overprints can be distinguished by the different shades of the red overprint, the width of the bar, and the word PANAMA. No. 11 has two different Panama overprints; No. 12 has six; No. 13 five; No. 14 two; and Nos. 15, 18-20, one each. In the "8cts" surcharge of Nos. 14 and 15, there are three varieties of the figure "8." The bar is sometimes misplaced so that it appears on the bottom of the stamp instead of the top.

1904-06   Unwmk.
Black Overprint on Stamps of Panama

9	A2	1c **green** (319,800) Dec. 12, 1904	2.75	2.25
		On cover		12.50
		Block of 4	12.00	12.00
		Spaced "A L" in "CANAL" (700)	110.00	100.00
		"ON" of "ZONE" dropped	300.00	275.00
a.		"CANAL" in antique type (500)	100.00	100.00
b.		"ZONE" in antique type (1500)	70.00	70.00
c.		Inverted overprint	5,500.	4,000.
d.		Double overprint	2,750.	2,000.
10	A2	2c **rose** (367,500) Dec. 12, 1904	4.50	4.50
		On cover		17.50
		Block of 4	21.00	17.50
		Spaced "A L" of "CANAL" (1700)	85.00	85.00
		"ON" of "ZONE" dropped	400.00	400.00
a.		Inverted overprint	225.00	275.00
b.		"L" of "CANAL" sideways	2,500.	2,500.

"PANAMA" (15mm long) reading up at left, down at right
Overprint "CANAL ZONE" in Black, "PANAMA" and Bar in Red

11	A3	2c **rose** (150,000) Dec. 9, 1905	7.00	5.00
		On cover		50.00
		Block of 4	32.50	27.50
		Inverted "M" in "PANAMA" (3,000)	45.00	40.00
		"PANAMA" 16mm long (3000)	45.00	40.00
a.		"ZONE" in antique type (1500)	200.00	200.00
b.		"PANAMA" overprint inverted, bar at bottom (200)	675.00	675.00
12	A3	5c **blue** (400,000) Dec. 12, 1904	8.00	3.75
		On cover		100.00
		Block of 4	35.00	25.00
		Spaced "A L" in "CANAL" (300)	90.00	80.00
		"PAMANA" reading up (2800)	75.00	70.00
		"PAMANA" reading down (400)	200.00	180.00
		"PANAMA" 16mm long (1300)	40.00	37.50
		Inverted "M" in "PANAMA" (1300)	40.00	37.50
		Right "PANAMA" 5mm below bar (600)	75.00	70.00
		"PANAM"	70.00	65.00
		"PANAAM" at right	950.00	900.00
		"PAN MA"	75.00	70.00
		"ANAMA"	80.00	75.00
a.		"CANAL" in antique type (2750)	75.00	65.00
b.		"ZONE" in antique type (2950)	75.00	65.00
c.		"CANAL ZONE" double (200)	800.00	800.00
d.		"PANAMA" double (120)	1,050.	1,000.
e.		"PANAMA" inverted, bar at bottom		2,000.
13	A3	10c **yellow** (64,900) Dec. 12, 1904	21.00	12.50
		On cover		125.00
		Block of 4	105.00	62.50
		Spaced "A L" in "CANAL" (200)	200.00	180.00
		"PANAMA" 16mm long (400)	75.00	65.00
		"PAMANA" reading down (200)	200.00	180.00
		Invtd. "M" in "PANAMA" (400)	100.00	90.00
		Right "PANAMA" 5mm below bar (398)	150.00	140.00
		Left "PANAMA" touches bar (400)	200.00	160.00
a.		"CANAL" in antique type (200)	200.00	200.00
b.		"ZONE" in antique type (400)	175.00	160.00
c.		"PANAMA" ovpt. double (80)	650.00	650.00
d.		"PANAMA" overprint in red brown (5000)	27.50	27.50
		"PANAMA" ovpt. in orange red	32.50	32.50

With Added Surcharge in Red

a

There are three varieties of "8" in the surcharge on #14-15.

14	A3	8c on 50c **bister brown** (27,900) Dec. 12, 1904	32.50	22.50
		On cover		200.00
		Block of 4	190.00	140.00
		Spaced "A L" in "CANAL" (194)	175.00	160.00
		Right "PANAMA" 5mm below bar (438)	200.00	175.00
a.		"ZONE" in antique type (25)	1,150.	1,150.
b.		"CANAL ZONE" inverted (200)	450.00	425.00
c.		"PANAMA" overprint in rose brown (6000)	40.00	40.00
d.		As "c," "CANAL" in antique type (10)	2,000.	
e.		As "c," "ZONE" in antique type (10)	2,000.	

f.		As "c," "8 cts" double (30)	1,100.	
g.		As "c," "8" omitted	4,250.	
h.		As "c," "cts 8"		

Nos. 11-14 are overprinted or surcharged on Panama Nos. 77, 77e, 78, 78c, 78d, 78f, 78g, 78h, 79 79c, 79e, 79g and 81 respectively.

Panama No. 74a, 74b Overprinted "CANAL ZONE" in Regular Type in Black and Surcharged Type "a" in Red
Both "PANAMA" (13mm long) Reading Up

15	A3(a)	8c on 50c **bister brown** (435) Dec. 12, 1904	2,750.	4,750.
		On cover		10,000.
		Block of 4	12,000.	
		"PANAMA" 15mm long (50)	2,900.	5,000.
		"P NAMA"	5,000.	
		Spaced "A L" in "CANAL" (5)	5,000.	
a.		"PANAMA" reading down and up (10)	7,500.	—

On No. 15 with original gum, the gum is almost always disturbed. Unused stamps are valued thus.

Map of Panama — A4

Panama Nos. 19 and 21 Surcharged in Black:

a   b

c   d

e   f

1906

There were three printings of each denomination, differing principally in the relative position of the various parts of the surcharges. Varieties occur with inverted "V" for the final "A" in "PANAMA," "CA" spaced, "ZO" spaced, "2c" spaced, accents in various positions, and with bars shifted so that two bars appear on top or bottom of the stamp (either with or without the corresponding bar on top or bottom) and sometimes with only one bar at top or bottom.

16	A4	1c on 20c **violet,** type a (100,000) Mar.	2.00	1.60
		On cover		10.00
		Block of 4	9.00	7.50
a.		Type b (100,000) May	2.00	1.60
		On cover		10.00
		Block of 4	9.00	7.50
b.		Type c (300,000) Sept.	2.00	1.60
		On cover		10.00
		Block of 4	10.50	7.50
		Spaced C A	13.00	12.50
c.		As No. 16, double surcharge		2,000.
17	A4	2c on 1p **lake,** type d (200,000) Mar.	2.75	2.75
		On cover		12.00
		Block of 4	14.00	12.50
a.		Type e (200,000) May	2.75	2.75
		On cover		12.00
		Block of 4	14.00	12.50
b.		Type f (50,000) Sept.	20.00	20.00
		On cover		75.00
		Block of 4	90.00	90.00

Panama Nos. 74, 74a and 74b Overprinted "CANAL ZONE" in Regular Type in Black and Surcharged in Red

b   c

1905-06
Both "PANAMA" Reading Up

18	A3(b)	8c on 50c **bister brown** (17,500) Nov. 1905	55.00	50.00
		On cover		225.00
		Block of 4	250.00	230.00
		"PANAMA" 15mm long (1750)	90.00	80.00
		"P NAMA"	125.00	110.00
a.		"ZONE" in antique type (175)	200.00	180.00
b.		"PANAMA" reading down and up (350)	175.00	160.00
19	A3(c)	8c on 50c **bister brown** (19,000) Apr. 23, 1906	55.00	50.00
		On cover		275.00
		Block of 4	250.00	200.00
		"PANAMA" 15mm long (1900)	85.00	70.00
		"P NAMA"	90.00	
a.		"CANAL" in antique type (190)	210.00	180.00
b.		"ZONE" in antique type (190)	210.00	180.00
c.		"8 cts" double	1,100.	1,100.
d.		"PANAMA" reading down and up (380)	110.00	90.00

On Nos. 18-19 with original gum, the gum is usually disturbed. Unused stamps are valued thus.

Panama No. 81 Overprinted "CANAL ZONE" in Regular Type in Black and Surcharged in Red Type "c" plus Period
"PANAMA" reading up and down

20	A3(c)	8c on 50c **bister brown** (19,600) Sept. 1906	42.50	40.00
		On cover		200.00
		Block of 4	175.00	175.00
		"PANAMA" reading up (392)	120.00	110.00
a.		"CANAL" antique type (196)	200.00	180.00
b.		"ZONE" in antique type (196)	200.00	180.00

c. "8 cts" omitted *(50)* — 800.00 800.00
d. "8 cts" double — 1,500.
e. "cts 8" — —

Nos. 14 and 18-20 exist without CANAL ZONE overprint but were not regularly issued and are considered printer's waste. Forgeries of the overprint varieties of Nos. 9-15 and 18-20 are known.

Vasco Núñez de Balboa — A5

Fernández de Córdoba — A6

Justo Arosemena — A7

Manuel J. Hurtado — A8

José de Obaldía — A9

Engraved by Hamilton Bank Note Co.
Overprinted in Black by Isthmian Canal Commission Press.

1906-07   **Unwmk.**   **Perf. 12**
Overprint Reading Up

21 A6 2c **red & black** *(50,000)* Oct. 29, 1906 — 27.50 27.50
   On cover — 55.00
   Block of 4 — 140.00 190.00
a. "CANAL" only — 4,000.

Overprint Reading Down

22 A5 1c **green & black** *(2,000,000)* Jan. 14, 1907 — 2.50 1.10
   dull green & black — 2.50 1.10
   On cover — 5.00
   Block of 4 — 11.00 7.50
   "ANA" for "CANAL" *(1000)* — 70.00 70.00
   "CAN L" for "CANAL" — 80.00 80.00
   "ONE" for "ZONE" *(3000)* — 80.00 80.00
a. Horiz. pair, imperf. btwn. *(50)* — 1,100. 1,100.
b. Vert. pair, imperf. btwn. *(20)* — 2,000. 1,750.
c. Vert. pair, imperf. horiz. *(20)* — 2,250. 1,750.
d. Inverted overprint reading up *(100)* — 550.00 550.00
e. Double overprint *(300)* — 275.00 275.00
f. Double overprint, one inverted — 1,750. 1,600.
g. Invtd. center, ovpt. reading up — 5,000. 5,000.
   Pair on cover — 12,500.
h. Horiz. pair, imperf vert. — —

23 A6 2c **red & black** *(2,370,000)* Nov. 25, 1906 — 3.25 1.40
   scarlet & black, 1907 — 3.25 1.40
   On cover — 6.00
   Block of 4 — 14.00 9.00
   "CAN L" for "CANAL" — 45.00
a. Horizontal pair, imperf. between *(20)* — 2,000. 1,750.
b. Vertical pair, one without overprint — 2,500. 2,500.
c. Double overprint *(100)* — 700.00 700.00
d. Double overprint, one diagonal — 800.00 800.00
e. Double overprint, one diagonal, in pair with normal — 2,500.
f. 2c carmine red & black, Sept. 9, 1907 — 5.00 2.75
g. As "f," inverted center and overprint reading up — 6,000.
   On cover — 12,000.
h. As "d," one "ZONE CANAL" — 4,000.
i. "CANAL" double — 4,000.

24 A7 5c **ultramarine & black** *(1,390,000)* Dec. 1906 — 6.00 2.25
   light ultramarine & black — 6.00 2.25
   blue & black, Sept. 16, 1907 — 6.00 2.25
   dark blue & black — 6.00 2.25
   dull blue & black — 6.00 2.25
   light blue & black — 6.00 2.25
   On cover — 40.00

   Block of 4 — 26.00 20.00
   "CAN L" for "CANAL" — 60.00
c. Double overprint *(200)* — 500.00 400.00
d. "CANAL" only *(10)* — 4,000.
e. "ZONE CANAL" — 4,500.
25 A8 8c **purple & black** *(170,000)* Dec. 1906 — 21.00 8.00
   On cover — 100.00
   Block of 4 — 115.00 55.00
a. Horizontal pair, imperf. between and at left margin *(34)* — 2,000. 4,000.
26 A9 10c **violet & black** *(250,000)* Dec. 1906 — 20.00 8.00
   On cover — 100.00
   Block of 4 — 110.00 50.00
a. Dbl. ovpt., one reading up *(10)* — 5,000.
b. Overprint reading up — 5,500.
   Nos. 22-26 *(5)* — 52.75 20.75

The early printings of this series were issued on soft, thick, porous-textured paper, while later printings of all except No. 25 appear on hard, thin, smooth-textured paper.
Normal spacing of the early printings is 7¼mm between the words; later printings, 6¾mm. Nos. 22 and 26 exist imperf. between stamp and sheet margin. Nos. 22-25 occur with "CA" of "CANAL" spaced ½mm further apart on position No. 50 of the setting.
The used pair of No. 25a is unique.

Córdoba — A11

Arosemena — A12

Hurtado — A13

José de Obaldía — A14

Engraved by American Bank Note Co.

1909
Overprint Reading Down

27 A11 2c **vermilion & black** *(500,000)* May 11, 1909 — 12.50 5.50
   On cover — 15.00
   First day cover — 750.00
   Block of 4 — 57.50 30.00
a. Horizontal pair, one without overprint — 2,600.
b. Vert. pair, one without ovpt. — 3,500.
28 A12 5c **deep blue & black** *(200,000)* May 28, 1909 — 45.00 12.50
   On cover — 60.00
   Block of 4 — 200.00 60.00
29 A13 8c **violet & black** *(50,000)* May 25, 1909 — 42.50 14.00
   On cover — 90.00
   Block of 4 — 210.00 82.50
30 A14 10c **violet & black** *(100,000)* Jan. 19, 1909 — 40.00 15.00
   On cover — 85.00
   Block of 4 — 200.00 85.00
a. Horizontal pair, one with "ZONE" omitted — 2,400.
b. Vertical pair, one without overprint — 3,000.

Nos. 27-30 occur with "CA" spaced (position 50).
Do not confuse No. 27 with Nos. 39d or 53a.
On No. 30a, the stamp with "ZONE" omitted is also missing most of "CANAL."

Vasco Núñez de Balboa — A15

Engraved, Printed and Overprinted by American Bank Note Co.
Black Overprint Reading Up

Type I

Type I Overprint: "C" with serifs both top and bottom. "L," "Z" and "E" with slanting serifs.
Compare Type I overprint with Types II to V illustrated before Nos. 38, 46, 52 and 55.

1909-10
31 A15 1c **dark green & black** *(4,000,000)* Nov. 8, 1909 — 4.00 1.25
   On cover — 5.00
   Block of 4 — 17.00 6.75
a. Inverted center and overprint reading down — 22,500.
c. Bklt. pane of 6, handmade, perf. margins — 575.00
32 A11 2c **vermilion & black** *(4,000,000)* Nov. 8, 1909 — 4.50 1.25
   On cover — 5.00
   Block of 4 — 20.00 6.75
a. Vert. pair, imperf. horiz. — 1,000. 1,000.
c. Bklt. pane of 6, handmade, perf. margins — 875.00
d. Double overprint — —
33 A12 5c **deep blue & black** *(2,000,000)* Nov. 8, 1909 — 17.00 4.00
   On cover — 40.00
   Block of 4 — 80.00 20.00
a. Double overprint *(200)* — 375.00 375.00
   On cover — 1,000.
34 A13 8c **violet & black** *(200,000)* Mar. 18, 1910 — 12.00 6.00
   On cover — 75.00
   Block of 4 — 55.00 30.00
a. Vertical pair, one without overprint *(10)* — 1,750.
35 A14 10c **violet & black** *(100,000)* Nov. 8, 1909 — 50.00 20.00
   On cover — 100.00
   Block of 4 — 225.00 100.00
   Nos. 31-35 *(5)* — 87.50 32.50

Normal spacing between words of overprint on No. 31 is 10mm and on Nos. 32 to 35, 8½mm. Minor spacing variations are known.

A16

A17

1911, Jan. 14
36 A16 10c on 13c **gray** *(476,700)* — 6.00 2.25
   On cover — 50.00
   Block of 4 — 30.00 15.00
a. "10 cts" inverted — 350.00 300.00
b. "10 cts" omitted — 350.00

The "10 cts" surcharge was applied by the Isthmian Canal Commission Press after the overprinted stamps were received from the American Bank Note Co.
Many used stamps offered as No. 36b are merely No. 36 from which the surcharge has been removed with chemicals.

1914, Jan. 6
37 A17 10c **gray** *(200,000)* — 50.00 12.50
   On cover — 85.00
   Block of 4 — 210.00 65.00

Black Overprint Reading Up

Type II

Type II Overprint: "C" with serif at top only. "L" and "E" with vertical serifs. "O" tilts to left.

1912-16

38	A15	1c	**green & black** *(3,000,000)*		
			July 1913	11.00	3.00
			On cover		5.50
			Block of 4	50.00	20.00
a.			Vertical pair, one without overprint	1,750.	1,750.
			On cover		*2,250.*
b.			Booklet pane of 6, imperf. margins *(120,000)*	625.00	
c.			Booklet pane of 6, handmade, perf. margins	*1,000.*	
39	A11	2c	**vermilion & black** *(7,500,000)* Dec. 1912	8.00	1.10
			orange vermilion & black, *1916*	8.00	1.10
			On cover		5.00
			Block of 4	40.00	6.50
a.			Horiz. pair, right stamp without overprint *(20)*	1,500.	
b.			Horiz. pair, left stamp without overprint *(10)*	2,000.	
c.			Booklet pane of 6, imperf. margins *(194,868)*	550.00	
d.			Overprint reading down	200.00	
e.			As "d," inverted center	650.00	750.00
f.			As "e," booklet pane of 6, handmade, perf. margins	*8,000.*	
g.			As "c," handmade, perf. margins	1,000.	
h.			As No. 39, "CANAL" only		1,100.
40	A12	5c	**deep blue & black** *(2,300,000)* Dec. 1912	22.50	2.75
			On cover		35.00
			Block of 4	105.00	13.00
a.			With Cordoba portrait of 2c	*10,000.*	
41	A14	10c	**violet & black** *(200,000)* *Feb. 1916*	52.50	8.50
			On cover		80.00
			Block of 4	260.00	40.00

Normal spacing between words of overprint on the first printing of Nos. 38-40 is 8½mm and on the second printing 9¼mm. The spacing of the single printing of No. 41 and the imperf. margin booklet pane printings of Nos. 38 and 39 is 7¾mm. Minor spacing variations are known.

Map of Panama Canal — A18

Balboa Taking Possession of the Pacific Ocean — A19

Gatun Locks — A20

Culebra Cut — A21

Engraved, Printed and Overprinted by American Bank Note Co.

1915, Mar. 1

Blue Overprint, Type II

42	A18	1c	**dark green & black** *(100,000)*	9.00	6.50
			On cover		17.50
			Block of 4	40.00	30.00
			First day cover		200.00
43	A19	2c	**carmine & black**	12.00	4.25
			vermilion & black	12.00	4.25
			On cover		25.00
			First day cover		150.00

			Block of 4	50.00	21.00
44	A20	5c	**blue & black** *(100,000)*	11.00	5.75
			On cover		55.00
			Block of 4	50.00	29.00
			First day cover		500.00
45	A21	10c	**orange & black** *(50,000)*	22.50	11.00
			On cover		70.00
			Block of 4	95.00	55.00
			First day cover		500.00

Normal spacing between words of overprint is 9¼mm on all four values except position No. 61 which is 10mm.

Black Overprint Reading Up

Type III

Type III Overprint: Similar to Type I but letters appear thinner, particularly the lower bar of "L," "Z" and "E." Impressions are often light, rough and irregular, and not centered.

Engraved and Printed by American Bank Note Co.
Overprint applied by
Panama Canal Press, Mount Hope, C.Z.

1915-20

46	A15	1c	**green & black,** *Dec. 1915*	160.00	125.00
			light green & black, *1920*	225.00	180.00
			On cover		160.00
			Pair on cover		500.00
			Block of 4	725.00	650.00
a.			Overprint reading down *(200)*	375.00	
b.			Double overprint *(180)*	350.00	
c.			"ZONE" double *(2)*	4,250.	
d.			Double overprint, one reads "ZONE CANAL" *(18)*	2,000.	
47	A11	2c	**orange vermilion & black,** *Aug. 1920*	3,250.	75.00
			On cover		375.00
			Block of 4	13,500.	600.00
48	A12	5c	**deep blue & black,** *Dec. 1915*	500.00	175.00
			On cover		1,000.
			Block of 4	2,400.	850.00

Normal spacing between words of overprint on Nos. 46-48 is 9¼mm. This should not be confused with an abnormal 9¼mm spacing of the 2c and 5c values of type I, which are decidedly scarce in singles, particularly used. Blocks of the abnormal spacing are rare.

A22

S. S. "Panama" in Culebra Cut — A23

S. S. "Cristobal" in Gatun Locks — A24

Engraved, Printed and Overprinted by American Bank Note Co.

1917, Jan. 23

Blue Overprint, Type II

49	A22	12c	**purple & black** *(314,914)*	17.50	5.50
			On cover		50.00
			First day cover		—
			Block of 4	87.50	30.00
50	A23	15c	**bright blue & black**	52.50	25.00
			On cover		135.00
			Block of 4	240.00	125.00

51	A24	24c	**yellow brown & black**	42.50	14.00
			On cover		325.00
			Block of 4	200.00	85.00

Normal spacing between words of overprint is 11¼mm.

Black Overprint Reading Up

Type IV

Type IV Overprint: "C" thick at bottom, "E" with center bar same length as top and bottom bars.

Engraved, Printed and Overprinted by American Bank Note Co.

1918-20

52	A15	1c	**green & black** *(2,000,000)*		
			Jan. 1918	32.50	11.00
			On cover		12.50
			Block of 4	150.00	47.50
a.			Overprint reading down	175.00	—
b.			Booklet pane of 6 *(60,000)*	650.00	
c.			Booklet pane of 6, left vertical row of 3 without overprint	*7,500.*	
d.			Booklet pane of 6, right vertical row of 3 with double overprint	*7,500.*	
e.			Horiz. bklt. pair, left stamp without overprint	*3,000.*	
f.			Horiz. bklt. pair, right stamp with double overprint	*3,000.*	
g.			Double overprint, booklet single		3,000.
53	A11	2c	**vermilion & black** *(2,000,000)*		
			Nov. 1918	110.00	7.00
			On cover		10.00
			Block of 4	500.00	35.00
a.			Overprint reading down	150.00	150.00
b.			Horiz. pair, right stamp without ovpt.	2,000.	
c.			Booklet pane of 6 *(34,000)*	1,050.	
d.			Booklet pane of 6, left vertical row of 3 without overprint	*15,000.*	
e.			Horiz. bklt. pair, left stamp without overprint	*3,000.*	
			On cover (unique)		*4,500.*
54	A12	5c	**deep blue & black** *(500,000)*		
			Apr. 1920	150.00	35.00
			On cover		200.00
			Block of 4	825.00	160.00

Normal spacing between words of overprint on Nos. 52 and 53 is 9¼mm. On No. 54 and the booklet printings of Nos. 52 and 53, the normal spacing is 9mm. Minor spacing varieties are known.

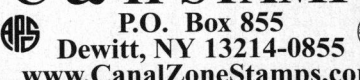

Black Overprint Reading Up

Type V

Type V Overprint: Smaller block type 1¾mm high. "A" with flat top.

1920-21

55	A15	1c	**light green & black,** *Apr.*		
			1921	22.50	3.50
			On cover		8.00
			Block of 4	100.00	17.50
a.			Overprint reading down	300.00	225.00
b.			Horiz. pair, right stamp without ovpt. (10)		1,750.
c.			Horiz. pair, left stamp without ovpt. (21)		1,000.
d.			"ZONE" only	4,250.	—
e.			Booklet pane of 6	2,250.	
f.			As No. 55, "CANAL" double (10)	2,000.	
56	A11	2c	**orange vermilion & black,** *Sept. 1920*	8.50	2.00
			On cover		7.00
			Block of 4	37.50	9.50
a.			Double overprint *(100)*	600.00	
b.			Double overprint, one reading down *(100)*	650.00	
c.			Horiz. pair, right stamp without overprint (11)	1,500.	
d.			Horiz. pair, left stamp without overprint (20)	1,250.	
e.			Vertical pair, one without overprint	1,500.	
f.			"ZONE" double	1,250.	
g.			Booklet pane of 6	850.00	
h.			As No. 56, "CANAL" double	1,000.	
57	A12	5c	**deep blue & black,** *Apr. 1921*	300.00	55.00
			On cover		225.00
			Block of 4	1,350.	250.00
a.			Horiz. pair, right stamp without overprint (10)	2,500.	
b.			Horiz. pair, left stamp without overprint (10)	2,500.	

Normal spacing between words of overprint on Nos. 55-57 is 9½mm. On booklet printings of Nos. 55 and 56 the normal spacing is 9¼mm.

Drydock at Balboa — A25

U.S.S. "Nereus" in Pedro Miguel Locks — A26

1920, Sept.

Black Overprint Type V

58	A25	50c	**orange & black**	260.00	160.00
			On cover		1,000.
			Block of 4	1,300.	800.00
59	A26	1b	**dark violet & black** *(23,014)*	175.00	65.00
			On cover		1,000.
			Block of 4	825.00	325.00

José Vallarino — A27

"Land Gate" — A28

Bolívar's Tribute — A29

Municipal Building in 1821 and 1921 — A30

Statue of Balboa — A31

Tomás Herrera — A32

José de Fábrega — A33

Engraved, Printed and Overprinted by American Bank Note Co.

Type V overprinted in black, reading up, on all values except the 5c which is overprinted with larger type in red

1921, Nov. 13

60	A27	1c	**green**	4.00	1.50
			On cover		6.00
			Block of 4	19.00	7.25
a.			"CANAL" double	2,500.	
b.			Booklet pane of 6	1,000.	
61	A28	2c	**carmine**	3.00	1.25
			On cover		15.00
			Block of 4	13.50	5.50
a.			Overprint reading down	200.00	225.00
b.			Double overprint	900.00	
c.			Vertical pair, one without overprint	3,500.	
d.			"CANAL" double	1,900.	
f.			Booklet pane of 6	2,100.	
62	A29	5c	**blue** (R)	11.00	3.50
			On cover		30.00
			Block of 4	50.00	20.00
a.			Overprint reading down (R)	60.00	
63	A30	10c	**violet**	18.00	7.50
			On cover		60.00
			Block of 4	100.00	35.00
a.			Overprint, reading down	90.00	
64	A31	15c	**light blue**	50.00	17.50
			On cover		175.00
			Block of 4	240.00	95.00
65	A32	24c	**black brown**	70.00	22.50
			On cover		600.00
			Block of 4	375.00	125.00
66	A33	50c	**black**	150.00	95.00
			On cover		600.00
			Block of 4	725.00	450.00
			Nos. 60-66 (7)	306.00	148.75

Experts question the status of the 5c with a small type V overprint in red or black.

Type III overprint in black, reading up, applied by the Panama Canal Press, Mount Hope, C. Z.
Engraved and printed by the American Bank Note Co.

1924, Jan. 28

67	A27	1c	**green**	500.	200.
			On cover		350.
			Block of 4	2,250.	900.
a.			"ZONE CANAL" reading down	850.	
b.			"ZONE" only, reading down	1,900.	
c.			Se-tenant pair, #67a and 67b	2,750.	

Arms of Panama — A34

1924, Feb.

68	A34	1c	**dark green**	10.00	4.50
			On cover		12.00
			Block of 4	50.00	24.00
69	A34	2c	**carmine**	7.50	2.75
			carmine rose	7.50	2.75
			On cover		15.00
			Block of 4	32.50	12.50

The following were prepared for use, but not issued.

A34	5c	**dark blue** *(600)*	350.
		Block of 4	1,750.
A34	10c	**dark violet** *(600)*	350.
		Block of 4	1,750.
A34	12c	**olive green** *(600)*	350.
		Block of 4	1,750.
A34	15c	**ultramarine** *(600)*	350.
		Block of 4	1,750.
A34	24c	**yellow brown** *(600)*	350.
		Block of 4	1,750.
A34	50c	**orange** *(600)*	350.
		Block of 4	1,750.
A34	1b	**black** *(600)*	350.
		Block of 4	1,750.

The 5c to 1b values were prepared for use but never issued due to abrogation of the Taft Agreement which required the Canal Zone to use overprinted Panama stamps. Six hundred of each denomination were not destroyed, as they were forwarded to the Director General of Posts of Panama for transmission to the UPU which then required about 400 sets. Only a small number of sets appear to have reached the public market.

All Panama stamps overprinted "CANAL ZONE" were withdrawn from sale June 30, 1924, and were no longer valid for postage after Aug. 31, 1924.

United States Nos. 551-554, 557, 562, 564-566, 569, 570 and 571 Overprinted in Red (No. 70) or Black (all others)

Printed and Overprinted by the U.S. Bureau of Engraving and Printing.
Type A
Letters "A" with Flat Tops

1924-25			**Unwmk.**		***Perf. 11***
70	A154	½c	**olive brown** *(399,500) Apr. 15, 1925*	1.50	.75
			Never hinged	3.75	
			On cover		4.00
			First day cover		75.00
			Block of 4	6.50	3.50
			P# block of 6	21.00	
71	A155	1c	**deep green** *(1,985,000) July 1, 1924*	1.40	1.00
			Never hinged	2.60	
			On cover		4.00
			First day cover		75.00
			Block of 4	6.00	4.25
			P# block of 6	30.00	
a.			Inverted overprint	500.00	500.00
b.			"ZONE" inverted	350.00	325.00
c.			"CANAL" only *(20)*	1,750.	
d.			"ZONE CANAL" *(180)*	500.00	
e.			Booklet pane of 6 *(43,152)*	80.00	
72	A156	1½c	**yellow brown** *(180,599) Apr. 15, 1925*	2.00	1.70
			brown	2.00	1.70
			Never hinged	3.25	
			First day cover, Nos. 70, 72		80.00
			Block of 4	8.75	9.50
			P# block of 6	37.50	
73	A157	2c	**carmine** *(2,975,000) July 1, 1924*	7.00	1.70
			Never hinged	11.00	
			First day cover		80.00
			Block of 4	32.50	8.00
			P# block of 6	160.00	
a.			Booklet pane of 6 *(140,000)*	175.00	
74	A160	5c	**dark blue** *(500,000) July 1, 1924*	19.00	7.50
			Never hinged	29.00	
			On cover		20.00
			Block of 4	80.00	37.50
			P# block of 6	325.00	
75	A165	10c	**orange** *(60,000) July 1, 1924*	42.50	20.00
			Never hinged	62.50	
			On cover		45.00
			First day cover		500.00
			Block of 4	200.00	105.00
			P# block of 6	875.00	

76 A167	12c **brown violet** (80,000) July 1, 1924	35.00	32.50
	Never hinged	67.50	
	First day cover		750.00
	Block of 4	150.00	140.00
	P# block of 6	475.00	
a.	"ZONE" inverted	3,750.	3,000.
77 A168	14c **dark blue** (100,000) June 27, 1925	30.00	22.50
	Never hinged	45.00	
	On cover		50.00
	Block of 4	130.00	140.00
	P# block of 6	425.00	
78 A169	15c **gray** (55,000) July 1, 1924	47.50	37.50
	Never hinged	75.00	
	On cover		52.50
	Block of 4	210.00	190.00
	P# block of 6	825.00	
79 A172	30c **olive brown** (40,000) July 1, 1924	37.50	22.50
	Never hinged	60.00	
	On cover		50.00
	Block of 4	160.00	110.00
	P# block of 6	600.00	
80 A173	50c **lilac** (25,000) July 1, 1924	75.00	45.00
	Never hinged	150.00	
	On cover		500.00
	Block of 4	325.00	225.00
	P# block of 6	3,000.	
81 A174	$1 **violet brown** (10,000) July 1, 1924	225.00	95.00
	Never hinged	350.00	
	On cover		1,000.
	Block of 4	1,000.	500.00
	Margin block of 4, arrow, top or bottom	1,250.	
	P# block of 6	4,250.	
	Nos. 70-81 (12)	523.40	287.65

Normal spacing between words of the overprint is 9¼mm. Minor spacing variations are known. The overprint of the early printings used on all values of this series except No. 77 is a sharp, clear impression. The overprint of the late printings, used only on Nos. 70, 71, 73, 76, 77, 78 and 80 is heavy and smudged, with many of the letters, particularly the "A" practically filled.

Booklet panes Nos. 71e, 73a, 84d, 97b, 101a, 106a and 117a were made from 360 subject plates. The handmade booklet panes Nos. 102a, 115c and a provisional lot of 117b were made from Post Office panes from regular 400-subject plates.

United States Nos. 554, 555, 557, 562, 564-567, 569, 570, 571, 623 Overprinted in Red (No. 91) or Black (all others)

Type B
Letters "A" with Sharp Pointed Tops

1925-28			**Perf. 11**
84 A157	2c **carmine** (1,110,000) May 1926	30.00	8.00
	Never hinged	45.00	
	On cover		11.00
	Block of 4	125.00	37.50
	P# block of 6	375.00	
	P# block of 6 & large 5 point star, side only	2,000.	
a.	"CANAL" only (20)	2,750.	
b.	"ZONE CANAL" (180)	500.00	
c.	Horizontal pair, one without overprint	3,500.	
d.	Booklet pane of 6 (82,000)	175.00	
e.	Vertical pair, "a" and "b" se-tenant	3,500.	
85 A158	3c **violet** (199,200) June 27, 1925	3.75	3.25
	Never hinged	6.00	
	On cover		6.00
	Block of 4	16.50	13.50
	P# block of 6	165.00	
a.	"ZONE ZONE"	600.00	550.00
86 A160	5c **dark blue** (1,343,147) Jan. 7, 1926	3.75	3.00
	Never hinged	6.00	
	On cover		20.00
	Block of 4	16.50	13.00
	P# block of 6	165.00	
	Double transfer (15571 UL 86)	—	—
a.	"ZONE ZONE" (LR18)	1,250.	
b.	"CANAL" inverted (LR7)	950.00	
c.	Inverted overprint (80)	500.00	
d.	Horizontal pair, one without overprint	3,250.	
e.	Overprinted "ZONE CANAL" (90)	350.00	
f.	"ZONE" only (10)	2,000.	
g.	Vertical pair, one without overprint, other overprint inverted (10)	2,500.	
h.	"CANAL" only	2,250.	
87 A165	10c **orange** (99,510) Aug. 1925	35.00	12.00
	Never hinged	52.50	
	On cover		40.00
	Block of 4	160.00	72.50
	P# block of 6	500.00	
a.	"ZONE ZONE" (LR18)	3,000.	
88 A167	12c **brown violet** (58,062) Feb. 1926	22.50	14.00
	Never hinged	34.00	
	On cover		45.00
	Block of 4	110.00	62.50
	P# block of 6	375.00	
a.	"ZONE ZONE" (LR18)	5,250.	

89 A168	14c **dark blue** (55,700) Dec. 1928	27.50	16.00
	Never hinged	42.50	
	On cover		50.00
	Block of 4	125.00	75.00
	P# block of 6	350.00	
90 A169	15c **gray** (204,138) Nov. 1925	7.50	4.50
	Never hinged	11.50	
	On cover		15.00
	Block of 4	35.00	21.00
	P# block of 6	200.00	
	P# block of 4, large 5 point star, side only	3,000.	
a.	"ZONE ZONE" (LR18)	5,500.	

It is believed that the four recorded P# blocks of 4 with large 5-point star are the largest known P# multiples from the plate that shows the star.

91 A187	17c **black** (199,500) Apr. 5, 1926	4.50	3.00
	Never hinged	7.50	
	On cover		12.50
	Block of 4	19.00	14.00
	P# block of 6	190.00	
a.	"ZONE" only (20)	1,200.	
b.	"CANAL" only	1,700.	
c.	"ZONE CANAL" (270)	300.00	
92 A170	20c **carmine rose** (259,807) Apr. 5, 1926	7.25	3.25
	Never hinged	11.00	
	On cover		32.50
	Block of 4	32.50	14.00
	P# block of 6	175.00	
a.	"CANAL" inverted (UR48)	4,000.	
b.	"ZONE" inverted (LL76)	4,250.	
c.	"ZONE CANAL" (LL91)	3,600.	

Double transfer (14438 LR79)

93 A172	30c **olive brown** (154,700) Dec. 1925	5.75	3.75
	Never hinged	8.50	
	On cover		60.00
	Block of 4	25.00	19.00
	P# block of 6	250.00	
	Double transfer (14438 LR79)	550.00	
94 A173	50c **lilac** (13,533) July 1928	240.00	165.00
	Never hinged	375.00	
	On cover		500.00
	Block of 4	1,200.	750.00
	P# block of 6	2,500.	
95 A174	$1 **violet brown** (20,000) Apr. 1926	125.00	55.00
	Never hinged	275.00	
	On cover		1,000.
	Block of 4	600.00	250.00
	Margin block of 4, arrow, top or bottom	625.00	
	P# block of 6	2,000.	
	Nos. 84-95 (12)	512.50	290.75

Nos. 85-88, 90 and 93-95 exist with wrong-font "CANAL" and "ZONE." Positions are: Nos. 85-88 and 90, UL51 (CANAL) and UL82 (ZONE); Nos. 93-95, U51 (CANAL) and U82 (ZONE).

Normal spacing between words of the overprint is 11mm on No. 84; 9mm on Nos. 85-88, 90, first printing of No. 91 and the first, third and fourth printing of No. 92; 7mm on the second printings of Nos. 91-92. Minor spacing varieties exist on Nos. 84-88, 90-92.

Overprint Type B on U.S. Sesquicentennial Stamp No. 627

1926			
96 A188	2c **carmine rose** (300,000) July 6, 1926	5.00	3.75
	Never hinged	7.50	
	First day cover		60.00
	Block of 4	22.50	18.00
	P# block of 6	85.00	

On this stamp there is a space of 5mm instead of 9mm between the two words of the overprint.

The authorized date, July 4, fell on a Sunday with the next day also a holiday, so No. 96 was not regularly issued until July 6. But the postmaster sold some stamps and canceled some covers on July 4 for a few favored collectors.

Overprint Type B in Black on U.S. Nos. 583, 584, 591

1926-27	**Rotary Press Printings**		**Perf. 10**
97 A157	2c **carmine** (1,290,000) Dec. 1926	50.00	11.00
	Never hinged	85.00	
	On cover		14.00
	Block of 4	250.00	50.00

a.	P# block of 4	475.00	
b.	Pair, one without overprint (10)	3,250.	
c.	Booklet pane of 6 (58,000)	525.00	
d.	"CANAL" only (10)	2,000.	
	"ZONE" only (10)	2,750.	
98 A158	3c **violet** (239,600) May 9, 1927	8.00	4.25
	Never hinged	12.00	
	On cover		12.00
	Block of 4	35.00	19.00
	P# block of 4	120.00	
99 A165	10c **orange** (128,400) May 9, 1927	18.00	7.50
	Never hinged	27.50	
	On cover		35.00
	Block of 4	82.50	40.00
	P# block of 4	225.00	

No. 97d is valued in the grade of fine. Very fine examples are not known.

Overprint Type B in Black on U.S. Nos. 632, 634 (Type I), 635, 637, 642

1927-31	**Rotary Press Printings**		**Perf. 11x10½**
100 A155	1c **green** (434,892) June 28, 1927	1.75	1.40
	Never hinged	3.50	
	On cover		3.00
	Block of 4	8.00	6.75
	P# block of 4	17.00	
a.	Vertical pair, one without overprint (10)	5,500.	
101 A157	2c **carmine** (1,628,195) June 28, 1927	2.50	1.00
	Never hinged	3.75	
	On cover		3.00
	Block of 4	11.00	4.75
	P# block of 4	24.00	
a.	Booklet pane of 6 (82,108)	200.00	
102 A158	3c **violet** (1,250,000) Feb., 1931	4.50	2.75
	Never hinged	6.75	
	On cover		5.00
	Block of 4	22.50	13.50
	P# block of 4	90.00	
a.	Booklet pane of 6, handmade, perf. margins	6,500.	
103 A160	5c **dark blue** (60,000) Dec. 13, 1927	32.50	10.00
	Never hinged	55.00	
	On cover		30.00
	Block of 4	140.00	42.50
	P# block of 4	210.00	
104 A165	10c **orange** (119,800) July, 1930	17.50	10.00
	Never hinged	26.00	
	On cover		35.00
	Block of 4	77.50	45.00
	P# block of 4	190.00	
	Nos. 100-104 (5)	58.75	25.15

Wet and Dry Printings
Canal Zone stamps printed by both the "wet" and "dry" process are Nos. 105, 108-109, 111-114, 117, 138-140, C21-C24, C26, J25, J27. Starting with Nos. 147 and C27, the Bureau of Engraving and Printing used the "dry" method exclusively, except for Nos. 152, 157 and 164.
See note on Wet and Dry Printings following U.S. No. 1029.

Maj. Gen. William Crawford Gorgas — A35

Maj. Gen. George Washington Goethals — A36

Gaillard Cut — A37

Maj. Gen. Harry Foote Hodges — A38

Lt. Col. David Du Bose Gaillard — A39

Maj. Gen. William
Luther Sibert — A40

Jackson
Smith — A41

Rear Adm. Harry
Harwood
Rousseau — A42

Col. Sydney Bacon
Williamson — A43

Joseph Clay Styles
Blackburn — A44

Printed by the U. S. Bureau of Engraving and Printing.
Plates of 400 subjects (except 5c), issued in panes of 100.
The 5c was printed from plate of 200 subjects, issued in panes
of 50. The 400-subject sheets were originally cut by knife into
Post Office panes of 100, but beginning in 1948 they were
separated by perforations to eliminate straight edges.

1928-40		Flat Plate Printing	Unwmk.	Perf. 11	
105	A35	1c **green** *(22,392,147)*		.20	.20
		Never hinged		.25	
		P# block of 6		2.50	—
a.		Wet printing, yel grn, *Oct. 3, 1928*		.20	.20
		Never hinged		.25	
		First day cover			17.50
		P# block of 6		4.25	—
106	A36	2c **carmine** *(7,191,600) Oct. 1, 1928*		.20	.20
		Never hinged		.25	
		First day cover			17.50
		P# block of 6		2.75	—
a.		Booklet pane of 6 *(284,640)*		15.00	20.00
		Never hinged		22.50	
107	A37	5c **blue** *(4,187,028) June 25, 1929*		1.00	.40
		Never hinged		1.30	
		First day cover			5.00
		P# block of 6		13.00	—
108	A38	10c **orange** *(4,559,788)*		.20	.20
		Never hinged		.25	
		P# block of 6		4.75	—
a.		Wet printing, *Jan. 11, 1932*		.40	.25
		Never hinged		.50	
		First day cover			40.00
		P# block of 6		6.00	—
109	A39	12c **brown violet** *(844,635)*		.75	.60
		Never hinged		1.00	
		P# block of 6		12.00	—
a.		Wet printing, violet brown, *July 1, 1929*		1.50	1.00
		Never hinged		2.00	
		First day cover			60.00
		P# block of 6		21.00	—
110	A40	14c **blue** *(406,131) Sept. 27, 1937*		.85	.85
		Never hinged		1.20	
		First day cover			5.00
		P# block of 6		16.00	—
111	A41	15c **gray black** *(3,356,500)*		.40	.35
		Never hinged		.55	
		P# block of 6		9.00	—
a.		Wet printing, gray, *Jan. 11, 1932*		.80	.50
		Never hinged		1.10	
		First day cover			45.00
		P# block of 6		12.50	5.00
112	A42	20c **dark brown** *(3,619,080)*		.60	.20
		Never hinged		.80	
		P# block of 6		9.00	—
a.		Wet printing, olive brown, *Jan. 11, 1932*		1.00	.30
		Never hinged		1.30	
		First day cover			45.00
		P# block of 6		16.00	—
113	A43	30c **black** *(2,376,491)*		.80	.70
		Never hinged		1.10	
		P# block of 6		12.00	—
a.		Wet printing, brn blk, *Apr. 15, 1940*		1.25	1.00
		Never hinged		1.60	
		First day cover			10.00
		P# block of 6		22.50	—
114	A44	50c **rose lilac** *(1,...)*		1.50	.65
		Never hinged		2.00	
		P# block of 6		18.00	—
a.		Wet printing, lilac, *July 1, 1929*		2.50	.85

		Never hinged	3.50	
		First day cover		150.00
		P# block of 6	35.00	—
		Nos. 105-114 (10)	6.50	4.35

Nos. 105, 108, 112, 113 and 114 exist with both shiny gum
and dull gum.
Coils are listed as Nos. 160-161.

United States Nos. 720 and 695 Overprinted type B

Rotary Press Printing

1933, Jan. 14			Perf. 11x10½	
115	A226	3c **deep violet** *(3,150,000)*	2.75	.25
		Never hinged	4.00	
		First day cover		12.00
		P# block of 4	35.00	—
b.		"CANAL" only	2,600.	
c.		Booklet pane of 6, handmade, perf. margins	175.00	—
116	A168	14c **dark blue** *(104,800)*	4.50	3.50
		Never hinged	7.00	
		First day cover		20.00
		P# block of 4	60.00	—
a.		"ZONE CANAL" *(16)*	1,500.	

Maj. Gen. George Washington
Goethals — A45

20th anniversary of the opening of the Panama Canal.

Flat Plate Printing

1934, Aug. 15		Unwmk.		Perf. 11	
117	A45	3c **red violet**		.20	.20
		Never hinged		.25	
		First day cover			3.00
		P# block of 6		1.00	—
a.		Booklet pane of 6		30.00	32.50
		Never hinged		60.00	
b.		As "a," handmade, perf. margins		160.00	—
c.		Wet printing, violet		.20	.20
		P# block of 6		1.00	—

Coil is listed as No. 153.

> **Catalogue values for unused stamps in this section, from this point to the end, are for Never Hinged items.**

United States Nos. 803 and
805 Overprinted in Black

Rotary Press Printing

1939, Sept. 1		Unwmk.	Perf. 11x10½	
118	A275	½c **red orange** *(1,030,000)*	.20	.20
		First day cover		1.00
		P# block of 4	2.75	—
119	A277	1½c **bister brown** *(935,000)*	.20	.20
		brown	.20	.20
		First day cover		1.00
		P# block of 4	2.25	—

Balboa-Before
A46

Balboa-After
A47

Gaillard Cut-
Before
A48

Gaillard Cut-
After
A49

Bas Obispo-
Before
A50

Bas Obispo-
After
A51

Gatun Locks-
Before
A52

Gatun Locks-
After
A53

Canal Channel-
Before
A54

Canal Channel-
After
A55

Gamboa-Before
A56

Gamboa-After
A57

Pedro Miguel
Locks-Before
A58

Pedro Miguel
Locks-After
A59

Gatun Spillway-
Before
A60

Gatun Spillway-
After
A61

25th anniversary of the opening of the Panama Canal.
Withdrawn Feb. 28, 1941; remainders burned Apr. 12, 1941.

Flat Plate Printing

1939, Aug. 15   Unwmk.   *Perf. 11*
120	A46	1c **yellow green** *(1,019,482)*		.65	.30
		First day cover			2.00
		P# block of 6		17.50	—
121	A47	2c **rose carmine** *(227,065)*		.75	.35
		First day cover			2.00
		P# block of 6		17.50	—
122	A48	3c **purple** *(2,523,735)*		.75	.20
		First day cover			2.00
		P# block of 6		17.50	—
123	A49	5c **dark blue** *(460,213)*		2.50	1.25
		First day cover			2.50
		P# block of 6		30.00	—
124	A50	6c **red orange** *(68,290)*		5.00	3.00
		First day cover			6.00
		P# block of 6		75.00	—
125	A51	7c **black** *(71,235)*		5.50	3.00
		First day cover			6.00
		P# block of 6		75.00	—
126	A52	8c **green** *(41,576)*		7.00	3.50
		First day cover			6.00
		P# block of 6		85.00	—
127	A53	10c **ultramarine** *(83,571)*		6.00	5.00
		First day cover			6.00
		P# block of 6		85.00	—
128	A54	11c **blue green** *(34,010)*		11.00	8.00
		First day cover			10.00
		P# block of 6		175.00	—
129	A55	12c **brown carmine** *(66,735)*		11.00	7.50
		First day cover			10.00
		P# block of 6		150.00	—
130	A56	14c **dark violet** *(37,365)*		11.00	7.50
		First day cover			10.00
		P# block of 6		175.00	—

131	A57	15c **olive green** *(105,058)*		15.00	6.00
		First day cover			10.00
		P# block of 6		200.00	—
132	A58	18c **rose pink** *(39,255)*		16.00	8.50
		First day cover			10.00
		P# block of 6		190.00	—
133	A59	20c **brown** *(100,244)*		17.50	7.50
		First day cover			10.00
		P# block of 6		225.00	—
134	A60	25c **orange** *(34,283)*		25.00	17.50
		First day cover			20.00
		P# block of 6		400.00	—
135	A61	50c **violet brown** *(91,576)*		30.00	6.00
		First day cover			20.00
		P# block of 6		450.00	—
		Nos. 120-135 (16)		164.65	85.10

Maj. Gen. George
W. Davis — A62

Gov. Charles E.
Magoon — A63

Theodore
Roosevelt — A64

John F.
Stevens — A65

John F. Wallace — A66

1946-49   Unwmk.   *Perf. 11*
Size: 19x22mm
136	A62	½c **bright red** *(1,020,000)* Aug. 16, 1948		.40	.25
		First day cover			1.25
		P# block of 6		2.50	—
137	A63	1½c **chocolate** *(603,600)* Aug. 16, 1948		.40	.25
		First day cover			1.25
		P# block of 6		2.50	—
138	A64	2c **light rose carmine** *(6,951,755)*		.20	.20
		P# block of 6		.65	—
a.		Wet printing, rose carmine, *Oct. 27, 1949*		.20	.20
		First day cover			1.00
		P# block of 6		1.00	—
139	A65	5c **dark blue**		.35	.20
		P# block of 6		2.25	—
a.		Wet printing, deep blue, *Apr. 25, 1946*		.60	.20
		First day cover			1.00
		P# block of 6		4.00	—
140	A66	25c **green** *(1,520,000)*		.85	.55
		P# block of 6		7.00	—
a.		Wet printing, yel grn, *Aug. 16, 1948*		3.00	1.00
		First day cover			3.50
		P# block of 6		20.00	—
		Nos. 136-140 (5)		2.20	1.45

See Nos. 155, 162, 164.

Map of
Biological Area
and Coati-
mundi
A67

25th anniversary of the establishment of the Canal Zone Biological Area on Barro Colorado Island.
Withdrawn Mar. 30, 1951, and remainders destroyed Apr. 10,
1951.

1948, Apr. 17   Unwmk.   *Perf. 11*
141	A67	10c **black** *(521,200)*		1.75	.80
		First day cover			3.00
		P# block of 6		15.00	—

"Forty-niners"
Arriving at
Chagres — A68

Journeying in
"Bungo" to Las
Cruces — A69

Las Cruces Trail to
Panama — A70

Departure for San
Francisco — A71

Centenary of the California Gold Rush.
Stocks on hand were processed for destruction on Aug. 11,
1952 and destroyed Aug. 13, 1952.

1949, June 1   Unwmk.   *Perf. 11*
142	A68	3c **blue** *(500,000)*		.65	.25
		First day cover			1.00
		P# block of 6		6.50	—
143	A69	6c **violet** *(481,600)*		.65	.30
		First day cover			1.00
		P# block of 6		6.50	—
144	A70	12c **bright blue green** *(230,200)*		1.75	.90
		First day cover			2.00
		P# block of 6		21.00	—
145	A71	18c **deep red lilac** *(240,200)*		2.00	1.50
		First day cover			3.25
		P# block of 6		20.00	—
		Nos. 142-145 (4)		5.05	2.95

Workers in Culebra
Cut — A72

Early Railroad
Scene — A73

Contribution of West Indian laborers in the construction of the
Panama Canal.
Entire issue sold, none withdrawn and destroyed.

1951, Aug. 15   Unwmk.   *Perf. 11*
146	A72	10c **carmine** *(480,000)*		3.00	1.50
		First day cover			3.00
		P# block of 6		25.00	—

Centenary of the completion of the Panama Railroad and the
first transcontinental railroad trip in the Americas.

1955, Jan. 28   Unwmk.   *Perf. 11*
147	A73	3c **violet** *(994,000)*		1.00	.60
		First day cover			1.50
		P# block of 6		7.25	—

Gorgas
Hospital and
Ancon
Hill — A74

75th anniversary of Gorgas Hospital.

1957, Nov. 17   Unwmk.   *Perf. 11*
148	A74	3c **black**, *dull blue green* *(1,010,000)*		.45	.35
		Light blue green paper		.40	.35
		First day cover			1.00
		P# block of 4		4.25	—

S.S.
Ancon — A75

1958, Aug. 30   Unwmk.   Perf. 11
149 A75 4c greenish blue *(1,749,700)*   .40   .30
   First day cover   1.00
   P# block of 4   3.25   —

Roosevelt
Medal and
Canal Zone
Map — A76

Centenary of the birth of Theodore Roosevelt (1858-1919).

1958, Nov. 15   Unwmk.   Perf. 11
150 A76 4c brown *(1,060,000)*   .60   .30
   First day cover   1.00
   P# block of 4   3.50   —

Boy Scout
Badge — A77

Administration Building,
Balboa Heights — A78

50th anniversary of the Boy Scouts of America.

Giori Press Printing
1960, Feb. 8   Unwmk.   Perf. 11
151 A77 4c dark blue, red & bister
   (654,933)   .55   .40
   First day cover   1.50
   P# block of 4   4.50   —

1960, Nov. 1   Unwmk.   Perf. 11
152 A78 4c rose lilac *(2,486,725)*   .20   .20
   First day cover   1.00
   P# block of 4   .90   —

Types of 1934, 1960 and 1946
Coil Stamps
1960-62   Unwmk.   Perf. 10 Vertically
153 A45 3c deep violet *(3,743,959)* Nov. 1,
   1960   .20   .20
   First day cover   1.00
   Pair   .40   .25
   Joint line pair   1.10   —

Perf. 10 Horizontally
154 A78 4c dull rose lilac *(2,776,273)* Nov.
   1, 1960   .20   .20
   First day cover   1.00
   Pair   .40   .25
   Joint line pair   1.10   —

Perf. 10 Vertically
155 A65 5c deep blue *(3,288,264)* Feb. 10,
   1962   .25   .20
   First day cover   1.00
   Pair   .50   .50
   Joint line pair   1.25   —
   Nos. 153-155 (3)   .65   .60

Girl Scout
Badge and
Camp at
Gatun
Lake — A79

50th anniversary of the Girl Scouts.

Giori Press Printing
1962, Mar. 12   Unwmk.   Perf. 11
156 A79 4c blue, dark green & bister
   (640,000)   .40   .30
   First day cover *(83,717)*   1.25
   P# block of 4   2.75   —

Thatcher Ferry
Bridge and
Map of
Western
Hemisphere
A80

Opening of the Thatcher Ferry Bridge, spanning the Panama Canal.

Giori Press Printing
1962, Oct. 12   Unwmk.   Perf. 11
157 A80 4c black & silver *(775,000)*   .35   .25
   First day cover *(65,833)*   1.00
   P# block of 4, 2P#   3.75
  a. Silver (bridge) omitted *(50)*   7,500.
   Hinged   5,500.
   P# block of 6, black P# only   52,500.

Goethals Memorial,
Balboa — A81

Fort San
Lorenzo — A82

1968-71   Giori Press Printing   Perf. 11
158 A81 6c green & ultra. *(1,890,000)* Mar.
   15, 1968   .30   .30
   First day cover   1.00
   P# block of 4   2.00   —
159 A82 8c slate green, blue, dark brown
   & ocher *(3,460,000)* July 14,
   1971   .35   .20
   First day cover   1.00
   P# block of 4   2.75   —

Types of 1928, 1932 and 1948
Coil Stamps
1975, Feb. 14   Unwmk.   Perf. 10 Vertically
160 A35 1c green *(1,090,958)*   .20   .20
   First day cover   1.00
   Pair   .40   .30
   Joint line pair   1.00   —
161 A38 10c orange *(590,658)*   .70   .40
   First day cover   1.00
   Pair   1.40   .80
   Joint line pair   5.00   —
162 A66 25c yellow green *(129,831)*   2.75   2.75
   First day cover   3.00
   Pair   5.50   5.50
   Joint line pair   20.00   —
   Nos. 160-162 (3)   3.65   3.35

Dredge
Cascadas
A83

1976, Feb. 23   Giori Press Printing   Perf. 11
163 A83 13c multicolored *(3,653,950)*   .35   .20
   First day cover   1.00
   P# block of 4   2.00   —
  a. Booklet pane of 4 *(1,032,400)* Apr. 19   3.00   —

No. 163a exists with and without staple holes in selvage tab.

Stevens Type of 1946
1977   Rotary Press Printing   Perf. 11x10½
Size: 19x22½mm
164 A65 5c deep blue *(1,009,612)*   .60   .85
   P# block of 4   3.50   —
  a. Tagged, dull gum   12.00   15.00
   P# block of 4   125.00

No. 164 exists with both shiny gum and dull gum.
No. 164a exists even though there was no equipment in the Canal Zone to detect tagging.

Towing
Locomotive,
Ship in Lock,
by Alwyn
Sprague
A84

1978, Oct. 25   Perf. 11
165 A84 15c dp grn & bl grn *(2,921,083)*   .35   .20
   First day cover *(81,405)*   1.00
   P# block of 4   2.00   —

AIR POST STAMPS

Regular Issue of 1928
Surcharged in Dark Blue

Type I — Flag of "5" pointing up **15**

15 Type II — Flag of "5" curved

1929-31   Flat Plate Printing   Unwmk.   Perf. 11
C1 A35 15c on 1c green, type I, Apr. 1,
   1929   8.00   5.50
   Never hinged   12.00
   First day cover   25.00
   Block of 4   35.00   25.00
   P# block of 6   120.00   —
C2 A35 15c on 1c yellow green, type II,
   Mar. 1931   70.00   47.50
   Never hinged   120.00
   On cover   175.00
   Block of 4   340.00   340.00
   P# block of 6   900.00   —
C3 A36 25c on 2c carmine *(223,880)* Jan.
   11, 1929   3.50   2.00
   Never hinged   5.25
   First day cover   17.50
   Block of 4   15.00   9.00
   P# block of 6   115.00   —

Nos. 114 and 106 Surcharged
in Black

1929, Dec. 31
C4 A44 10c on 50c lilac *(116,666)*   8.50   6.00
   Never hinged   12.00
   First day cover   25.00
   Block of 4   37.50   26.00
   P# block of 6   120.00   —
C5 A36 20c on 2c carmine *(638,395)*   4.75   1.50
   Never hinged   7.50
   First day cover   20.00
   Block of 4   19.00   7.00
   P# block of 6   110.00
  a. Dropped "2" in surcharge *(7,000)*   85.00   60.00

> Catalogue values for unused stamps in this
> section, from this point to the end, are for Never
> Hinged items.

Gaillard
Cut — AP1

Printed by the U. S. Bureau of Engraving and Printing.
Plates of 200 subjects, issued in panes of 50.

1931-49		Unwmk.		Perf. 11
C6	AP1	4c **red violet** (525,000) Jan. 3, 1949	.75	.65
		First day cover		2.00
		P# block of 6	5.25	
C7	AP1	5c **yellow green** (9,935,500) Nov. 18, 1931	.60	.30
		green	.60	.30
		First day cover		10.00
		P# block of 6	4.50	
C8	AP1	6c **yellow brown** (9,399,500) Feb. 15, 1946	.75	.35
		First day cover		2.00
		P# block of 6	5.25	
C9	AP1	10c **orange** (5,079,000) Nov. 18, 1931	1.00	.35
		First day cover		10.00
		P# block of 6	10.00	
C10	AP1	15c **blue** (11,072,700) Nov. 18, 1931	1.25	.30
		pale blue	1.25	.30
		First day cover		15.00
		P# block of 6	11.00	
C11	AP1	20c **red violet** (3,184,100) Nov. 18, 1931	2.00	.25
		deep violet	2.00	.30
		First day cover		35.00
		P# block of 6	20.00	
C12	AP1	30c **rose lake** (1,119,500) July 15, 1941	4.50	1.00
		dull rose	4.50	1.00
		First day cover		22.50
		P# block of 6	37.50	
C13	AP1	40c **yellow** (795,600) Nov. 18, 1931	3.50	1.10
		lemon	3.50	1.10
		First day cover		75.00
		P# block of 6	32.50	
C14	AP1	$1 **black** (372,500) Nov. 18, 1931	9.00	1.60
		First day cover		150.00
		P# block of 6	85.00	
		Nos. C6-C14 (9)	23.35	5.90

Douglas Plane over Sosa Hill — AP2

Planes and Map of Central America AP3

Pan American Clipper and Scene near Fort Amador — AP4

Pan American Clipper at Cristobal Harbor — AP5

Pan American Clipper over Gaillard Cut — AP6

Pan American Clipper Landing — AP7

10th anniversary of Air Mail service and the 25th anniversary of the opening of the Panama Canal.
Withdrawn Feb. 28, 1941, remainders burned Apr. 12, 1941.

Flat Plate Printing

1939, July 15		Unwmk.		Perf. 11
C15	AP2	5c **greenish black** (86,576)	4.50	2.25
		First day cover		5.00
		P# block of 6	47.50	
C16	AP3	10c **dull violet** (117,644)	4.00	3.00
		First day cover		5.00
		P# block of 6	50.00	
C17	AP4	15c **light brown** (883,742)	5.50	1.00
		First day cover		3.00
		P# block of 6	57.50	
C18	AP5	25c **blue** (82,126)	16.00	8.00
		First day cover		17.50
		P# block of 6	275.00	
C19	AP6	30c **rose carmine** (121,382)	16.00	7.75
		First day cover		15.00
		P# block of 6	175.00	
C20	AP7	$1 **green** (40,051)	40.00	27.50
		First day cover		60.00
		P# block of 6	500.00	
		Nos. C15-C20 (6)	86.00	49.50

Globe and Wing — AP8

Flat Plate Printing

1951, July 16		Unwmk.		Perf. 11
C21	AP8	4c **lt red violet** (1,315,000)	.75	.35
		P# block of 6	7.00	
a.		Wet printing, red violet	1.25	.40
		1st day card, Balboa Heights		1.50
		P# block of 6	10.00	
C22	AP8	6c **lt brown** (22,657,625)	.50	.25
		P# block of 6	5.00	
a.		Wet printing, brown	.95	.35
		1st day cover, Balboa Heights		1.00
		P# block of 6	7.50	
C23	AP8	10c **lt red orange** (1,049,130)	.90	.35
		P# block of 6	8.00	
a.		Wet printing, red orange	2.00	.50
		1st day cover, Balboa Heights		2.00
		P# block of 6	16.00	
C24	AP8	21c **lt blue** (1,460,000)	7.50	4.00
		P# block of 6	70.00	
a.		Wet printing, blue	15.00	5.00
		1st day cover, Balboa Heights		7.50
		P# block of 6	125.00	
C25	AP8	31c **cerise** (375,000)	7.50	3.75
		1st day cover, Balboa Heights		7.50
		P# block of 6	70.00	
a.		Horiz. pair, imperf. vert. (98)	1,250.	—
C26	AP8	80c **lt gray black** (827,696)	4.50	1.50
		P# block of 6	35.00	
a.		Wet printing, gray black	12.50	1.65
		1st day cover, Balboa Heights		12.50
		1st day cover, Balboa Heights, #C21-C26		20.00
		P# block of 6	100.00	
		Nos. C21-C26 (6)	21.65	10.20

See note after No. 114. Total number of first day covers with one or more of Nos. C21-C26, about 12,000.

Flat Plate Printing

1958, Aug. 16		Unwmk.		Perf. 11
C27	AP8	5c **yellow green** (899,923)	1.00	.60
		First day cover (2,176)		4.50
		P# block of 4	6.00	
C28	AP8	7c **olive** (9,381,797)	1.00	.45
		First day cover (2,815)		4.50
		P# block of 4	6.00	
C29	AP8	15c **brown violet** (359,923)	5.00	2.75
		First day cover (2,040)		6.00
		P# block of 4	40.00	
C30	AP8	25c **orange yellow** (600,000)	12.50	2.75
		First day cover (2,115)		9.00
		P# block of 4	125.00	
C31	AP8	35c **dark blue** (283,032)	10.00	2.75
		First day cover (1,868)		11.00
		P# block of 4	65.00	
		Nos. C27-C31 (5)	29.50	9.30
		Nos. C21-C31 (11)	51.15	19.50

Emblem of US Army Caribbean School — AP9

US Army Caribbean School for Latin America at Fort Gulick.

Giori Press Printing

1961, Nov. 21		Unwmk.		Perf. 11
C32	AP9	15c **red & blue** (560,000)	1.75	.75
		First day cover (25,949)		1.75
		P# block of 4	10.00	

Malaria Eradication Emblem and Mosquito AP10

World Health Organization drive to eradicate malaria.

Giori Press Printing

1962, Sept. 24		Unwmk.		Perf. 11
C33	AP10	7c **yellow & black** (862,349)	.50	.40
		First day cover (44,433)		1.00
		P# block of 4	3.00	

Globe-Wing Type of 1951

Rotary Press Printing

1963, Jan. 7				Perf. 10½x11
C34	AP8	8c **carmine** (5,054,727)	.75	.30
		First day cover (19,128)		1.00
		P# block of 4	4.00	

Alliance for Progress Emblem AP11

2nd anniv. of the Alliance for Progress, which aims to stimulate economic growth and raise living standards in Latin America.

Giori Press Printing

1963, Aug. 17		Unwmk.		Perf. 11
C35	AP11	15c **gray, grn & dk ultra** (405,000)	1.50	.85
		First day cover (29,594)		1.50
		P# block of 4	12.50	

Jet over Canal Zone Views — AP12

50th anniversary of the opening of the Panama Canal.
Designs: 6c, Cristobal. 8c, Gatun Locks. 15c, Madden Dam. 20c, Gaillard Cut. 30c, Miraflores Locks. 80c, Balboa.

Giori Press Printing

1964, Aug. 15		Unwmk.		Perf. 11
C36	AP12	6c **green & black** (257,193)	.60	.35
		1st day cover, Balboa		1.50
		P# block of 4	3.75	
C37	AP12	8c **rose red & black** (3,924,283)	.60	.35
		1st day cover, Balboa		1.00
		P# block of 4	4.00	
C38	AP12	15c **blue & black** (472,666)	1.25	.75
		1st day cover, Balboa		1.00
		P# block of 4	9.25	
C39	AP12	20c **rose lilac & black** (399,784)	1.60	1.00
		1st day cover, Balboa		2.00
		P# block of 4	10.00	
C40	AP12	30c **reddish brown & black** (204,524)	2.75	2.25
		1st day cover, Balboa		3.00
		P# block of 4	17.50	
C41	AP12	80c **olive bister & black** (186,809)	4.25	3.00

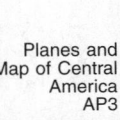

1st day cover, Balboa		4.00
1st day cover, Balboa, #C36-C41		10.00
P# block of 4	24.00	
Nos. C36-C41 (6)	11.05	7.70

There were 57,822 first day covers with one or more of Nos. C36-C41.
No. C40 exists with dull gum.

Canal Zone Seal and Jet Plane — AP13

Giori Press Printing

1965, July 15   Unwmk.   Perf. 11

C42	AP13	6c **green & black** (548,250)	.50	.30
		First day cover, Balboa		2.00
		P# block of 4	3.25	
C43	AP13	8c **rose red & black** (8,357,700)	.45	.20
		First day cover, Balboa		1.00
		P# block of 4	3.00	
C44	AP13	15c **blue & black** (2,385,000)	.75	.20
		First day cover, Balboa		1.00
		P# block of 4	7.00	
C45	AP13	20c **lilac & black** (2,290,699)	.80	.30
		First day cover, Balboa		1.25
		P# block of 4	4.25	
C46	AP13	30c **redsh brn & blk** (2,332,255)	1.10	.30
		First day cover, Balboa		1.25
		P# block of 4	4.75	
C47	AP13	80c **bister & black** (1,456,596)	2.50	.75
		First day cover, Balboa		2.50
		First day cover, Balboa, #C42-C47		7.00
		P# block of 4	18.00	
		Nos. C42-C47 (6)	6.10	2.05

There were 35,389 first day covers with one or more of Nos. C42-C47.

1968-76

C48	AP13	10c **dull orange & black** (10,055,000) Mar. 15, 1968	.35	.20
		First day cover, Balboa (7,779)		1.00
		P# block of 4	3.50	
a.		Booklet pane of 4 (713,390) Feb. 18, 1970	4.25	
		First day cover, Balboa (5,054)		5.00
C49	AP13	11c **olive & black** (3,335,000) Sept. 24, 1971	.35	.20
		First day cover, Balboa (10,916)		1.00
		P# block of 4	3.50	
a.		Booklet pane of 4 (1,277,760) Sept. 24, 1971	3.50	
		First day cover, Balboa (2,460)		5.00
C50	AP13	13c **emerald & black** (1,865,000) Feb. 11, 1974	.85	.25
		First day cover, Balboa (7,646)		1.00
		P# block of 4	5.00	
a.		Booklet pane of 4 (619,200) Feb. 11, 1974	6.00	
		First day cover, Balboa (3,660)		5.00
C51	AP13	22c **vio & blk** (363,720) May 10, 1976	1.10	2.00
		First day cover, Balboa		2.50
		P# block of 4	6.25	
C52	AP13	25c **pale yellow green & black** (1,640,441) Mar. 15, 1968	.80	.70
		First day cover, Balboa		1.00
		P# block of 4	5.50	
C53	AP13	35c **salmon & black** (573,822) May 10, 1976	1.25	2.00
		First day cover, Balboa		2.50
		P# block of 4	10.00	
		Nos. C48-C53 (6)	4.70	5.35

No. C50a exists with and without staple holes in selvage tab.
There were 5,047 first day covers with one or more of Nos. C51, C53.

AIR POST OFFICIAL STAMPS

Beginning in March 1915, stamps for use on official mail were identified by a large "P" perforated through each stamp. These were replaced by overprinted issues in 1941. The use of official stamps was discontinued December 31, 1951. During their currency, they were not for sale in mint condition and were sold to the public only when canceled with a parcel post rotary canceler reading "Balboa Heights, Canal Zone" between two wavy lines.

After having been withdrawn from use, mint stamps (except Nos. CO8-CO12 and O3, O8) were made available to the public at face value for three months

beginning Jan. 2, 1952. **Values for used examples of Nos. CO1-CO7, CO14, O1-O2, O4-O9, are for canceled-to-order stamps with original gum, postally used stamps being worth more.** Sheet margins were removed to facilitate overprinting and plate numbers are, therefore, unknown.

Air Post Stamps of 1931-41 Overprinted in Black

Two types of overprint.

Type I — "PANAMA CANAL" 19-20mm long

1941-42   Unwmk.   Perf. 11

CO1	AP1	5c **yellow green** (42,754) Mar. 31, 1941	5.50	1.50
		green	5.50	1.50
		On cover		50.00
		Block of 4	25.00	6.00
CO2	AP1	10c **orange** (49,723) Mar. 31, 1941	8.50	1.75
		On cover		25.00
		Block of 4	37.50	8.00
CO3	AP1	15c **blue** (56,898) Mar. 31, 1941	11.00	1.75
		On cover		25.00
		Block of 4	47.50	15.00
CO4	AP1	20c **red violet** (22,107) Mar. 31, 1941	13.00	4.00
		deep violet	13.00	4.00
		On cover		110.00
		Block of 4	62.50	22.50
CO5	AP1	30c **rose lake** (22,100) June, 4, 1942	17.50	5.00
		dull rose	17.50	4.50
		On cover		40.00
		Block of 4	80.00	22.50
CO6	AP1	40c **yellow** (22,875) Mar. 31, 1941	17.50	7.50
		lemon yellow	17.50	7.50
		On cover		75.00
		Block of 4	80.00	37.50
CO7	AP1	$1 **black** (29,525) Mar. 31, 1941	20.00	10.00
		On cover		150.00
		Block of 4	90.00	45.00
		Nos. CO1-CO7 (7)	93.00	31.50

Overprint varieties occur on Nos. CO1-CO7 and CO14: "O" of "OFFICIAL" over "N" of "PANAMA" (entire third row). "O" of "OFFICIAL" broken at top (position 31). "O" of "OFFICIAL" over second "A" of "PANAMA" (position 45). First "F" of "OFFICIAL" over second "A" of "PANAMA" (position 50).

1941, Sept. 22

Type II — "PANAMA CANAL" 17mm long

CO8	AP1	5c **yellow green** (2,000)	—	160.00
		On cover		500.00
		Block of 4		925.00
CO9	AP1	10c **orange** (2,000)	—	275.00
		On cover		400.00
		Block of 4		1,650.
CO10	AP1	20c **red violet** (2,000)	—	175.00
		On cover		
		Block of 4		1,050.
CO11	AP1	30c **rose lake** (5,000)	1,250.	65.00
		On cover		125.00
		Block of 4		325.00
CO12	AP1	40c **yellow** (2,000)	—	180.00
		On cover		500.00
		Block of 4		1,100.
		Nos. CO8-CO12 (5)		855.00

1947, Nov.

Type I — "PANAMA CANAL" 19-20mm long

CO14	AP1	6c **yellow brown** (33,450)	12.50	5.00
		On cover		50.00
		Block of 4	57.50	25.00
a.		Inverted overprint (50)		2,750.

POSTAGE DUE STAMPS

Prior to 1914, many of the postal issues were handstamped "Postage Due" and used as postage due stamps.

Postage Due Stamps of the United States Nos. J45a, J46a, and J49a Overprinted in Black

1914, Mar.   Wmk. 190   Perf. 12

J1	D2	1c **rose carmine** (23,533)	85.	15.
		On cover		275.
		Block of 4 (2mm spacing)	425.	70.

		Block of 4 (3mm spacing)	450.	80.
		P# block of 6, impt. & star	1,000.	
J2	D2	2c **rose carmine** (32,312)	250.	42.50
		On cover		275.
		Block of 4	1,250.	200.
		P# block of 6	2,000.	
J3	D2	10c **rose carmine** (92,493)	1,000.	40.
		On cover		900.
		Block of 4 (2mm spacing)	4,250.	170.
		Block of 4 (3mm spacing)	4,250.	170.
		P# block of 6, Impt. & star	8,500.	

Many examples of Nos. J1-J3 show one or more letters of the overprint out of alignment, principally the "E."

San Geronimo Castle Gate, Portobelo (See footnote) — D1

Statue of Columbus — D2

Pedro J. Sosa — D3

1915, Mar.   Unwmk.   Perf. 12

Blue Overprint, Type II, on Postage Due Stamps of Panama

J4	D1	1c **olive brown** (50,000)	12.50	5.00
		On cover		150.00
		Block of 4	55.00	22.50
J5	D2	2c **olive brown** (50,000)	225.00	17.50
		On cover		425.00
		Block of 4	975.00	90.00
J6	D3	10c **olive brown** (200,000)	50.00	10.00
		On cover		175.00
		Block of 4	225.00	45.00

Type D1 was intended to show a gate of San Lorenzo Castle, Chagres, and is so labeled. By error the stamp actually shows the main gate of San Geronimo Castle, Portobelo.

Surcharged in Red

CANAL 2 ZONE

1915, Nov.   Unwmk.   Perf. 12

J7	D1	1c on 1c **olive brown** (60,614)	110.00	15.00
		On cover		160.00
		Block of 4	500.00	70.00
J8	D2	2c on 2c **olive brown**	25.00	7.50
		On cover		225.00
		Block of 4	110.00	37.50
J9	D3	10c on 10c **olive brown** (175,548)	22.50	5.00
		On cover		300.00
		Block of 4	100.00	25.00

One of the printings of No. J9 shows wider spacing between "1" and "0." Both spacings occur on the same sheet.

D4

Capitol, Panama — D5

1919, Dec.

Surcharged in Carmine at Mount Hope

J10	D4	2c on 2c **olive brown**	30.00	12.50
		On cover		110.00
		Block of 4	130.00	55.00
J11	D5	4c on 4c **olive brown** (35,695)	35.00	15.00
		On cover		190.00
		Block of 4	160.00	75.00
a.		"ZONE" omitted		8,250.
b.		"4" omitted		8,250.

Blue Overprint, Type V, on Postage Due Stamp of Panama

1922
J11C D1 1c **dark olive brown** — 10.00
  d. "CANAL ZONE" reading down 200.00

United States Postage Due Stamps Nos. J61, J62b and J65b Overprinted

Type A
Letters "A" with Flat Tops

1924, July 1   **Perf. 11**
J12 D2 1c **carmine rose** (10,000) 110.00 27.50
  On cover 100.00
  Block of 4 475.00 125.00
  P# block of 6 1,250.
J13 D2 2c **deep claret** (25,000) 55.00 15.00
  On cover 110.00
  Block of 4 275.00 65.00
  P# block of 6 725.00
J14 D2 10c **deep claret** (30,000) 250.00 50.00
  On cover 225.00
  Block of 4 (2mm spacing) 1,250. 210.00
  Block of 4 (3mm spacing) 1,250. 210.00
  Margin block of 6, imprint, star and P# 3,500. —

Values for Nos. J12-J29 on cover are for philatelically contrived items. Commercial usages on cover are much more valuable.

United States Nos. 552, 554 and 562 Overprinted Type A and Additionally Overprinted at Mount Hope in Red or Blue

1925, Feb.   **Perf. 11**
J15 A155 1c **deep green** (R) (15,000) 90.00 15.00
  On cover 110.00
  Block of 4 400.00 62.50
  P# block of 6 900.00
J16 A157 2c **carmine** (Bl) (21,335) 22.50 7.00
  On cover 67.50
  Block of 4 100.00 30.00
  P# block of 6 225.00
J17 A165 10c **orange** (R) (39,819) 50.00 11.00
  On cover 90.00
  Block of 4 250.00 47.50
  P# block of 6 500.00
  a. "POSTAGE DUE" double 800.00
  b. "E" of "POSTAGE" omitted 750.00
  c. As "b," "POSTAGE DUE" double 3,250.

Overprinted Type B
Letters "A" with Sharp Pointed Tops
On U.S. Postage Due Stamps Nos. J61, J62, J65, J65a

1925, June 24
J18 D2 1c **carmine rose** (80,000) 8.00 3.00
  On cover 65.00
  Block of 4 35.00 15.00
  P# block of 6 90.00
  a. "ZONE ZONE" (LR18) 1,750.
J19 D2 2c **carmine rose** (146,430) 15.00 4.00
  On cover 47.50
  Block of 4 65.00 17.50
  P# block of 6 160.00
  a. "ZONE ZONE" (LR18) 1,750.
J20 D2 10c **carmine rose** (153,980) 150.00 20.00
  On cover 300.00
  Block of 4, 2mm spacing 650.00 85.00
  Block of 4, 3mm spacing 675.00 90.00
  P# block of 6, Impt. & Star 1,250.
  a. Vert. pair, one without ovpt. (10) 3,500.
  P# block of 6, Impt. & Star 18,000.
  b. 10c rose red 250.00 150.00
  On cover
  c. As "b," double overprint 450.00 —

Nos. J18-J20 exist with wrong font "CANAL" (UL51) and "ZONE" (UL82).

Regular Issue of 1928-29 Surcharged

1929-30
J21 A37 1c on 5c blue (35,990) Mar. 20, 1930 4.00 1.75
  Never hinged 9.00
  On cover 37.50
  P# block of 6 42.50
  a. "POSTAGE DUE" omitted (5) 5,500.
J22 A37 2c on 5c blue (40,207) Oct. 18, 1930 7.50 2.50
  Never hinged 15.00
  On cover 32.50
  P# block of 6 75.00
J23 A37 5c on 5c blue (35,464) Dec. 1, 1930 7.50 2.75
  Never hinged 15.00
  On cover 32.50
  P# block of 6 75.00
J24 A37 10c on 5c blue (90,504) Dec. 16, 1929 7.50 2.75
  Never hinged 15.00
  On cover 32.50
  P# block of 6 75.00

On No. J23 the three short horizontal bars in the lower corners of the surcharge are omitted.

Canal Zone Seal — D6

Printed by the U.S. Bureau of Engraving and Printing.
Plates of 400 subjects, issued in panes of 100.

1932-41   **Flat Plate Printing**
J25 D6 1c **claret** (378,300) Jan. 2, 1932 .20 .20
  Never hinged .25
  On cover 30.00
  P# block of 6 2.00
  a. Dry printing, red violet .25 .20
  Never hinged .30
  On cover 32.50
  P# block of 6 3.00
J26 D6 2c **claret** (413,800) Jan. 2, 1932 .20 .20
  Never hinged .25
  On cover 22.50
  P# block of 6 3.00
J27 D6 5c **claret** Jan. 2, 1932 .35 .20
  Never hinged .40
  On cover 25.00
  P# block of 6 3.50
  a. Dry printing, red violet 1.00 .30
  Never hinged 1.30
  On cover 22.50
  P# block of 6 10.00
J28 D6 10c **claret** (400,600) Jan. 2, 1932 1.40 1.50
  Never hinged 2.00
  On cover 32.50
  P# block of 6 15.00
J29 D6 15c **claret** Apr. 21, 1941 1.10 1.00
  Never hinged 1.50
  On cover 37.50
  P# block of 6 12.00
  Nos. J25-J29 (5) 3.25 3.10

See note after No. J14.

OFFICIAL STAMPS

See note at beginning of Air Post Official Stamps
Regular Issues of 1928-34 Overprinted in Black by the Panama Canal Press, Mount Hope, C.Z.

	OFFICIAL
Type 1	PANAMA CANAL Type 2

Type 1 — "PANAMA" 10mm long
Type 1a — "PANAMA" 9mm long

1941, Mar. 31   **Unwmk.**   **Perf. 11**
O1 A35 1c **yellow green**, type 1 (87,198) 2.00 .40
  Never hinged 2.75
  On cover 70.00
O2 A45 3c **deep violet**, type 1 (34,958) 3.75 .75
  Never hinged 5.25
  On cover 90.00
O3 A37 5c **blue**, type 2 (19,105) 1,000. 32.50
  On cover 110.00
O4 A38 10c **orange**, type 1 (18,776) 7.50 1.90
  Never hinged 10.00
  On cover 200.00
O5 A41 15c **gray black**, type 1 (16,888) 13.00 2.25
  Never hinged 17.50
  gray 2.25
  On cover 140.00
O6 A42 20c **olive brown**, type 1 (20,264) 15.00 2.75
  Never hinged 22.50
  On cover 100.00
O7 A44 50c **lilac**, type 1 (19,175) 37.50 5.50
  Never hinged 52.50
  rose lilac 5.50
  On cover
O8 A44 50c **rose lilac**, type 1a (1000) 650.00

No. O3 exists with "O" directly over "N" of "PANAMA."

No. 139 Overprinted in Black

1947, Feb.
O9 A65 5c **deep blue**, type 1 (21,639) 9.00 3.75
  Never hinged 15.00
  On cover 75.00

POST OFFICE SEALS

POS1

Issued in panes of 8 (2 x 4), without gum, imperforate outer margins.

1907   **Typo.**   **Unwmk.**   **Perf. 11½**
OX1 POS1 **blue** 35.00 50.00
  On cover 1,500.
  Block of 4 150.00
  Pane of 8 750.00
  a. Wmkd. seal of U.S. in sheet 75.00 125.00
  Block of 4 425.00
  Pane of 8 1,250.

No. OX1 clichés are spaced 3½mm apart both horizontally and vertically.

1910
OX2 POS1 **ultramarine** 50.00 65.00
  On cover 1,750.
  Block of 4, cliches ½mm apart horiz. and vert. 225.00
  Pane of 8 1,000.
  Block of 4, cliches 1½mm apart horiz., 4mm vert. 275.00
  Pane of 8 1,100.
  a. Wmkd. "Rolleston Mills" in sheet (½mm spacing) 80.00 100.00
  Block of 4 350.00
  b. Wmkd. U.S. Seal in sheet (1½mm x 4mm spacing) 85.00 100.00
  Block of 4 350.00
  Pane of 8 1,500.

POS2

Printed by the Panama Canal Press, Mount Hope, C.Z.
Issued in panes of 25 (5 x 5), without gum, imperforate outer margins at top, bottom, and left.
Rouletted 6 horizontally in color of seal, vertically without color

1917, Sept. 22
OX3 POS2 **slate violet** (shades) 4.00 4.00
  On cover 250.00
  Block of 4 17.50

	Pane of 25	250.00	
a.	Wmkd. double lined letters in sheet ("Sylvania")	17.50	25.00
	Block of 4	85.00	
	Pane of 25	600.00	

POS3

1945   *Rouletted 6, without color*

Issued in panes of 20 (4 x 5), without gum, imperforate outer margins.

OX4	POS3	**deep violet blue** (shades)	7.00	10.00
		On cover		300.00
		Block of 4	35.00	
		Pane of 20	300.00	

POS4

Typographed by the Panama Canal Press. Issued in panes of 32 (4 x 8), without gum, imperforate margins except at top of pane.

Size: 46x27mm
Seal Diameter: 13mm

1954, Mar. 8   Unwmk.   *Perf. 12½*

OX5	POS4	**black** (16,000)	5.00	5.00
		On cover		200.00
		Block of 4	20.00	
		Pane of 32	200.00	
a.		Wmkd. Seal of U. S. in sheet	12.50	12.50
		Block of 4	60.00	
		Pane of 32	500.00	
b.		Double impression	45.00	
c.		As "a," double impression	75.00	

POS5

Seal Diameter: 11½mm

1961, May 16   *Perf. 12½*

OX6	POS5	**black** (48,000)	3.00	5.00
		On cover		175.00
		Block of 4	12.00	
		Pane of 32	125.00	
a.		Wmkd. Seal of U.S. in sheet, perf. 12½	7.50	7.50
		Block of 4	35.00	
		Pane of 32	300.00	

No. OX6 exists in approximately equal proportions on three types of paper: very thin tissue-like, medium, and heavy opaque.

1974, July 1   *Rouletted 5*

OX7	POS5	**black**	2.50	5.00
		On cover		150.00
		Block of 4	11.00	
		Pane of 32	100.00	

ENVELOPES

Values for cut squares are for examples with fine margins on all sides. Values for unused entires are for those without printed or manuscript address. A "full

corner" includes back and side flaps and commands a premium.

Vasco Núñez de Balboa — U1

Fernandez de Córdoba — U2

Envelopes of Panama Lithographed and Overprinted by American Bank Note Co.

1916, Apr. 24

On White Paper

U1	U1	1c	**green & black**	15.00	10.00
			Entire	95.00	35.00
a.			Head and overprint only	2,000.	2,000.
			Entire		
b.			Frame only	1,500.	2,500.
			Entire		
U2	U2	2c	**carmine & black**	12.50	4.50
			Entire	90.00	25.00
a.			2c **red & black**	12.50	4.50
			Entire	85.00	45.00
b.			Head and overprint only		
			Entire	1,500.	2,000.
c.			Frame only (red)		
			Entire	1,000.	2,000.
d.			Frame double (carmine)		
			Entire	2,500.	2,250.

José Vallarino — U3

"The Land Gate" — U4

1921, Nov. 13

On White Paper

U3	U3	1c	**green**	140.00	100.00
			Entire	700.00	375.00
U4	U4	2c	**red**	35.00	20.00
			Entire	275.00	125.00

Arms of Panama — U5

Typographed and embossed by American Bank Note Co. with "CANAL ZONE" in color of stamp.

1923, Dec. 15

On White Paper

U5	U5	2c **carmine**	55.00	32.50
		Entire	200.00	125.00

U.S. Nos. U420 and U429 Overprinted in Black by Bureau of Engraving and Printing, Washington, D.C.

1924, July 1

U6	U92	1c **green** (50,000)	5.00	3.00
		Entire	30.00	19.00
		Entire, 1st day cancel		125.00

U7	U93	2c **carmine** (100,000)	5.00	3.00
		Entire	30.00	19.00
		Entire, 1st day cancel		125.00

Seal of Canal Zone — U6

Printed by the Panama Canal Press, Mount Hope, C.Z.

1924, Oct.

On White Paper

U8	U6	1c **green** (205,000)	2.00	1.00
		Entire	24.00	15.00
U9	U6	2c **carmine** (1,997,658)	.75	.40
		Entire	27.50	15.00

Gorgas — U7

Goethals — U8

Typographed and Embossed by International Envelope Corp., Dayton, O.

1932, Apr. 8

U10	U7	1c **green** (1,300,000)	.20	.20
		Entire	3.00	1.10
		Entire, 1st day cancel		35.00
U11	U8	2c **carmine** (400,250)	.25	.20
		Entire	3.50	1.75
		Entire, 1st day cancel		35.00

No. U9 Surcharged in Violet by Panama Canal Press, Mount Hope, C.Z. Numerals 3mm high

1932, July 20

U12	U6	3c on 2c **carmine** (20,000)	17.50	6.75
		Entire	225.00	125.00

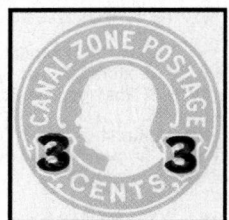

No. U11 Surcharged in Violet, Numerals 5mm high

1932, July 20

U13	U8	3c on 2c **carmine** (320,000)	2.00	1.00
		Entire	25.00	15.00
		Entire, 1st day cancel		75.00

1934, Jan. 17

Numerals with Serifs

U14	U6	3c on 2c **carmine** (Numerals 4mm high) (8,000)	115.00	60.00
		Entire	450.00	525.00
U15	U8	3c on 2c **carmine** (Numerals 5mm high) (23,000)	25.00	15.00
		Entire	250.00	150.00

Typographed and Embossed by International Envelope Corp., Dayton, O.

1934, June 18

U16	U8	3c **purple** (2,450,000)	.20	.20
		Entire	1.20	1.40

1958, Nov. 1
U17 U8 4c **blue** *(596,725)* .20 .25
    Entire 1.25 1.25
    Entire, 1st day cancel, Cristobal 2.00

Surcharged at Left of Stamp in Ultra. as No. UX13

1969, Apr. 28
U18 U8 4c +1c **blue** *(93,850)* .20 .25
    Entire 1.25 1.60
    Entire, 1st day cancel 1.50
U19 U8 4c +2c **blue** *(23,125)* .50 .65
    Entire 2.50 4.00
    Entire, 1st day cancel 1.50

Ship Passing
through Gaillard
Cut — U9

Typographed and Embossed by United States
Envelope Co., Williamsburg, Pa.

1971, Nov. 17
U20 U9 8c **emerald** *(121,500)* .25 .30
    Entire .75 .65
    Entire, 1st day cancel, Balboa
    (9,650) 1.50

Surcharged at Left of Stamp in Emerald as #UX13

1974, Mar. 2
U21 U9 8c +2c **emerald** .30 .35
    Entire 1.00 2.00
    Entire, 1st day cancel 1.25

1976, Feb. 23
U22 U9 13c **violet** *(638,350)* .35 .40
    Entire .85 .85
    Entire, 1st day cancel, Balboa
    (9,181) 1.25

**Surcharged at Left of Stamp in Violet as No.
UX13**

1978, July 5
U23 U9 13c +2c **violet** *(245,041)* .35 .40
    Entire .85 2.00
    Entire, 1st day cancel 1.25

AIR POST ENVELOPES

No. U9 Overprinted with Horizontal Blue and Red
Bars Across Entire Face. Overprinted by Panama
Canal Press, Mount Hope. Boxed inscription in lower
left with nine lines of instructions. Additional
adhesives required for air post rate.

1928, May 21
UC1 U6 2c **red**, entire *(15,000)* 135.00 65.00
    First day cancel 175.00

No. U9 with Similar Overprint of Blue and Red Bars,
and "VIA AIR MAIL" in Blue, At Left, no box.

1929
UC2 U6 2c **red**, entire *(60,200)* 65.00 27.50
  a. Inscription centered *(10,000)* Jan. 11 325.00 190.00
    Earliest known use of No. UC2 is Feb. 6.

DC-4
Skymaster
UC1

Typographed and Embossed by International
Envelope Corp., Dayton, O.

1949, Jan. 3
UC3 UC1 6c **blue** *(4,400,000)* .25 .25
    Entire 4.00 3.00
    Entire, 1st day cancel 2.00

1958, Nov. 1
UC4 UC1 7c **carmine** *(1,000,000)* .25 .20
    Entire 4.00 3.50
    Entire, 1st day cancel 1.50

No. U16 Surcharged at
Left of Stamp and
Imprinted "VIA AIR MAIL"
in Dark Blue

Surcharged by Panama Canal Press, Mount Hope,
C.Z.

1963, June 22
UC5 U8 3c + 5c **purple** *(105,000)* 1.00 1.00
    Entire 6.00 8.00
    Entire, 1st day cancel 5.00
  a. Double surcharge 1,250.

Jet Liner and
Tail Assembly
UC2

Typographed and Embossed by International
Envelope Corp., Dayton, O.

1964, Jan. 6
UC6 UC2 8c **deep carmine** *(600,000)* .35 .35
    Entire 2.25 2.50
    Entire, 1st day cancel, Balboa *(3,855)* 2.25

No. U17 Surcharged at Left of Stamp as No. UC5
and Imprinted "VIA AIR MAIL" in Vermilion
Surcharged by Canal Zone Press, La Boca, C.Z.

1965, Oct. 15
UC7 U8 4c + 4c **blue** *(100,000)* .50 .40
    Entire 4.50 7.50
    Entire, 1st day cancel 5.00

Jet Liner and Tail
Assembly — UC3

Typographed and Embossed by United States
Envelope Co., Williamsburg, Pa.

1966, Feb.
UC8 UC3 8c **carmine** *(224,000)* .50 .45
    Entire 5.00 5.00
    Earliest known use: Feb. 23.

No. UC8 Surcharged at Left of Stamp as No. UX13
in Vermilion
Surcharged by Canal Zone Press, La Boca, C.Z.

1968, Jan. 18
UC9 UC3 8c + 2c **carmine** *(376,000)* .40 .35
    Entire 2.75 5.00
    Entire, 1st day cancel 4.50

No. UC7 with Additional Surcharge at Left
of Stamp as No. UX13 and Imprinted
"VIA AIR MAIL" in Vermilion
Surcharged by Canal Zone Press, La Boca, C.Z.

1968, Feb. 12
UC10 U8 4c + 4c + 2c **blue** *(224,150)* .60 .50
    Entire 2.25 6.00
    Entire, 1st day cancel 5.00

Type of 1966
Typographed and Engraved by United States
Envelope Co., Williamsburg, Pa.

1969, Apr. 1

Luminescent Ink
UC11 UC3 10c **ultramarine** *(448,000)* .60 .40
    Entire 4.00 5.00
    Entire, 1st day cancel, Balboa *(9,583)* 2.00

No. U17 Surcharged at Left of Stamp as Nos. UC5
and UX13, and Imprinted "VIA AIR MAIL"
in Vermilion

1971, May 17
UC12 U8 4c + 5c + 2c **blue** *(55,775)* .75 .50
    Entire 4.00 6.00
    Entire, 1st day cancel 5.00

No. UC11 Surcharged in Ultra. at Left of Stamp as
No. UX13

1971, May 17

Luminescent Ink
UC13 UC3 10c + 1c **ultramarine** *(152,000)* .45 .40
    Entire 4.00 7.00
    Entire, 1st day cancel 3.50

Type of 1966
Typographed and Engraved by United States
Envelope Co., Williamsburg, Pa.

1971, Nov. 17
UC14 UC3 11c **rose red** *(258,000)* .30 .20
    Entire 1.10 1.25
    Entire, 1st day cancel, Balboa *(3,451)* 1.50
  a. 11c **carmine,** stamp tagged, *(395,000)* .30 .20
    Entire 1.10 1.25
    Entire, 1st day cancel, Balboa *(5,971)* 1.50

The red diamonds around the envelope edges are luminescent on both Nos. UC14 and UC14a. No. UC14 is size 10, No. UC14a size 6¾.

Surcharged at Left of Stamp in Rose Red as No.
UX13

1974, Mar. 2
UC15 UC3 11c + 2c **carmine,** tagged, *(305,000)* .35 .30
    Entire 1.50 3.00
    Entire, 1st day cancel 1.25
  a. 11c + 2c **rose red,** untagged, *(87,000)* .35 .25
    Entire 1.75 2.00

No. U21 with Additional Surcharge in Vermilion
at Left of Stamp as No. UX13 and Imprinted
"VIA AIR MAIL" in Vermilion

1975, May 3
UC16 U9 8c + 2c + 3c **emerald** *(75,000)* .50 .30
    Entire 1.25 2.50
    Entire, 1st day cancel 1.50

REGISTRATION ENVELOPES

RE1

Panama Registration Envelope surcharged
by Panama Canal Press, Mount Hope, C.Z.

1918, Oct.   **8mm between CANAL & ZONE**
UF1 RE1 10c on 5c **black & red,** *cream*
    (10,000), entire 1,750. 2,000.
  a. 9¼mm between CANAL & ZONE
    (25,000), entire *('19)* 1,300. 2,000.

Stamped envelopes inscribed "Diez Centésimos," surcharged with numerals "5" and with solid blocks printed over "Canal Zone," were issued by the Republic of Panama after being rejected by the Canal Zone. Parts of "Canal Zone" are often legible under the surcharge blocks. These envelopes exist without surcharge.

POSTAL CARDS

Values are for Entires

Map of Panama — PC1

Panama Card Lithographed by American
Bank Note Co., revalued and surcharged in black
by the Isthmian Canal Commission.

1907, Feb. 9
UX1 PC1 1c on 2c **carmine,** "CANAL"
          15mm *(50,000)*   40.   25.
  a. Double surcharge   1,500. 2,000.
  b. Double surcharge, one reading down   2,750.
  c. Triple surcharge, one reading down   3,300.
  d. "CANAL" 13mm *(10,000)*   250.   200.
  e. As "d," double surcharge   2,400.

Balboa — PC2

Panama card lithographed by Hamilton Bank
Note Co. Overprinted in black by Isthmian
Canal Commission.
At least six types of overprint, reading down.

1908, Mar. 3
UX2 PC2 1c **green & black,** "CANAL"
          13mm *(295,000)*   190.   80.
  a. Double overprint   2,000. 2,000.
  b. Triple overprint   1,750.   —
  c. Period after "ZONE" *(40,000)*   200.   125.
  d. "CANAL" 15mm *(30,000)*   200.   125.
  e. "ZONE CANAL", reading up   4,000.

Balboa
PC3   PC4
Lithographed by Hamilton Bank Note Co.
Overprinted in Black by Panama Canal Press, Mount
Hope, C.Z.

1910, Nov. 10
UX3 PC3 1c **green & black** *(40,000)*   190.   70.
  a. Double overprint   4,250.

This card, with overprint reading up, is actually the fourth of
seven settings of UX2.

Lithographed and Overprinted by American Bank
Note Co.

1913, Mar. 27
UX4 PC4 1c **green & black** *(634,000)*   160.   60.

Design of Canal Zone Envelopes
Overprinted in black by the American Bank Note Co.

1921, Oct.
UX5 U3 1c **green**   1,100.   450.

Typographed and embossed by American Bank
Note Co. with "CANAL ZONE" in color of stamp.

1924, Jan.
UX6 U5 1c **green**   1,050. *1,100.*

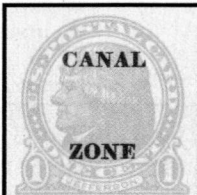

U.S. No. UX27 Overprinted
by U.S. Gov't. Printing
Office at Washington, D.C.

1924, July 1
UX7 PC17 1c **green,** buff *(Jefferson)*
           (50,000)   85.   35.

Design of Canal Zone Envelope
Printed by Panama Canal Press.

1925, Jan.
UX8 U6 1c **green,** buff *(25,000)*   80.   35.
  a. Background only   1,800.

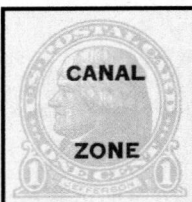

U.S. No. UX27 Overprinted

1925, May
UX9 PC17 1c **green,** buff *(Jefferson)*
           (850,000)   8.50   5.00

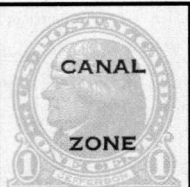

U.S. No. UX27 Overprinted

1935, Oct.
UX10 PC17 1c **green,** buff *(Jefferson)*
            (2,900,000)   1.80   1.80
  a. Double overprint   1,900.

**Used values are for contemporaneous usage
without additional postage applied.**

Same on U.S. No. UX38

1952, May 1
UX11 PC22 2c **carmine rose,** buff *(Franklin)*
            (800,000)   2.00   2.00
            1st day cancel, Balboa Heights   3.50

Ship in
Lock — PC5

Printed by Bureau of Engraving & Printing,
Washington, D.C.

1958, Nov. 1
UX12 PC5 3c **dark blue,** buff *(335,116)*   2.00   *3.00*
           First day cancel, Cristobal   1.25

No. UX12 Surcharged at Left of
Stamp in Green by Panama Canal
Press, Mount Hope, C.Z.

1963, July 27
UX13 PC5 3c + 1c **dark blue,** buff *(78,000)* 4.00 *6.00*
           First day cancel   3.50

Ship Passing through
Panama Canal — PC6

Printed by Panama Canal Press, Mount Hope, C.Z.

1964, Dec. 1
UX14 PC6 4c **violet blue,** buff *(74,200)*   3.75   *7.50*
           1st day cancel, Cristobal
           (19,260)   3.50

Ship in Lock
(Towing
locomotive at
right
redrawn) — PC7

Printed by Bureau of Engraving & Printing,
Washington, D.C.

1965, Aug. 12
UX15 PC7 4c **emerald** *(95,500)*   1.10   *2.00*
           1st day cancel, Cristobal
           (20,366)   1.00

No. UX15 Surcharged at Left of Stamp in Green
as No. UX13 by Canal Zone Press, La Boca, C.Z.

1968, Feb. 12
UX16 PC7 4c + 1c **emerald** *(94,775)*   1.10   *4.00*
           First day cancel   1.00

Ship-in-Lock Type of 1965

1969, Apr. 1
UX17 PC7 5c **light ultramarine** *(63,000)*   1.00   *2.50*
           1st day cancel, Balboa *(11,835)*   1.00

No. UX17 Surcharged at Left of Stamp in Light
Ultramarine as No. UX13

1971, May 24
UX18 PC7 5c + 1c **light ultramarine** *(100,500)* .90 *3.50*
           First day cancel   1.00

Ship-in-Lock Type of 1965
Printed by Bureau of Engraving & Printing,
Washington, D.C.

1974, Feb. 11
UX19 PC7 8c **brown** *(90,895)*   1.00   *2.00*
           1st day cancel, Balboa *(10,375)*   1.00

No. UX19 Surcharged at Left of Stamp in Brown as
No. UX13

1976, June 1
UX20 PC7 8c + 1c **brown** *(60,249)*   .65   *4.00*
           First day cancel   1.00

No. UX19 Surcharged at Left of Stamp in Brown as
No. UX13

1978, July 5
UX21 PC7 8c + 2c **brown** *(74,847)*   1.00   *4.00*
           First day cancel   1.00

AIR POST POSTAL CARDS

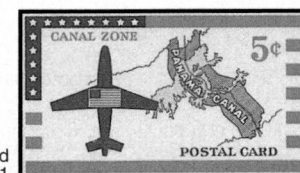

Plane, Flag and
Map — APC1

Printed by Bureau of Engraving & Printing,
Washington, D.C.

1958, Nov. 1
UXC1 APC1 5c **blue & carmine rose**
            (104,957)   3.75   *7.50*
            1st day cancel, Balboa   3.75

No. UXC1 Surcharged at Left of Stamp in Green
as No. UX13 by Panama Canal Press,
Mount Hope, C.Z.

1963, July 27
UXC2 APC1 5c + 1c **blue & carmine rose**
            (48,000)   10.00 *18.00*
  a. Inverted surcharge   1,500.
            First day cancel   5.00

No. UX15 Surcharged at Left of Stamp as
No. UX13 and Imprinted "AIR MAIL" in Vermilion

1965, Aug. 18
UXC3 PC7 4c + 2c **emerald** *(41,700)*   4.00 *20.00*
           First day cancel   6.00

No. UX15 Surcharged at Left of Stamp as No. UC5
and Imprinted "AIR MAIL" in Vermilion
by Canal Zone Press, La Boca, C.Z.

1968, Feb. 12
UXC4 PC7 4c + 4c **emerald** *(60,100)*   3.00 *16.00*
           First day cancel   6.00

No. UX17 Surcharged at Left of Stamp as No. UC5
and Imprinted "AIR MAIL" in Vermilion

1971, May 24
UXC5 PC7 5c + 4c **light ultramarine**
           (68,000)   1.00 *15.00*
           First day cancel   6.00

PROOFS

1928-40

Column (1) — Large Die
Column (2) — Small Die

106TC	2c	black	1,300.	
113P	30c	brown black		975.

1934

117P	3c	deep violet (8)		475.

1939

120P	1c	yellow green	1,300.	875.
121P	2c	rose carmine		875.
122P	3c	purple	1,300.	875.
123P	5c	dark blue	1,300.	875.
124P	6c	red orange		875.
125P	7c	black		875.
126P	8c	green	1,300.	875.
127P	10c	ultramarine	1,300.	875.
128P	11c	blue green	1,300.	875.
129P	12c	brown carmine	1,300.	875.
130P	14c	dark violet		875.
131P	15c	olive green		875.

132P	18c	rose pink		875.
133P	20c	brown	1,300.	875.
134P	25c	orange	1,300.	875.
135P	50c	violet brown	1,300.	875.

1946-48

136P	½c	bright red	1,300.
137P	1½c	chocolate	1,300.
139P	5c	deep blue	1,300.
140P	25c	yellow green	1,300.
141P	10c	black	825.

1949

142P	3c	blue	1,150.
143P	6c	violet	1,150.
144P	12c	bright blue green	1,150.
145P	18c	deep red lilac	1,150.

1951

146P	10c	carmine	1,500.

1955

147P	3c	violet	1,500.

Air Post

1931-49

C6P	4c	red violet	1,600.
C7P	5c	light green	1,600.
C8P	6c	yellow brown	1,600.
C13TC	40c	orange	1,600.

1939

C15P	5c	greenish black		925.
C15TC	5c	scarlet	1,300.	
C16P	10c	dull violet	1,300.	925.
C17P	15c	light brown	1,300.	925.
C18P	25c	blue		925.
C19P	30c	rose carmine	1,300.	925.
C20P	$1	green	1,300.	925.

1951

C21P	4c	red violet	1,300.

The Small Die proofs listed are on soft yellowish wove paper. Only No. 117P has more than two examples reported in private collections.

CUBA

After the U.S. battleship "Maine" was destroyed in Havana harbor with a loss of 266 lives in February, 1898, the United States demanded the withdrawal of Spanish troops from Cuba. The Spanish-American War followed. With the peace treaty of Dec. 10, 1898, Spain relinquished Cuba to the United States in trust for its inhabitants. On Jan. 1, 1899, Spanish authority was succeeded by U.S. military rule which lasted until May 20, 1902, when Cuba, as a republic, assumed self-government.

The listings in this catalogue cover the U.S. Administration issue of 1899, the Republic's 1899-1902 issues under U.S. military rule and the Puerto Principe issue of provincial provisionals.

Values for Nos. 176-220 are for stamps in the grade of fine and in sound condition where such exist. Values for Nos. 221-UX2b are for very fine examples.

100 CENTS = 1 DOLLAR

Puerto Principe Issue

In December, 1898, Puerto Principe, a provincial capital now called Camagüey, ran short of 1c, 2c, 3c, 5c and 10c stamps. The Postmaster ordered Cuban stamps to be surcharged on Dec. 19, 1898.

The surcharging was done to horizontal strips of five stamps, so vertical pairs and blocks do not exist. Five types are found in each setting, and five printings were made. Counterfeits are plentiful.

First Printing

Black Surcharge, 17½mm high

Surcharge measures 17½mm high and is roughly printed in dull black ink.

HABILITADO HABILITADO HABILITADO

2 **2** **2**

cents. cents. cents.
Position 1   Position 2   Position 3

HABILITADO   HABILITADO

2   **2**

cents.   cents.
Position 4   Position 5

Position 1	— No serif at right of "t"
Position 2	— Thin numeral except on 1c on 1m No. 176
Position 3	— Broken right foot of "n"
Position 4	— Up-stroke of "t" broken
Position 5	— Broken "DO"

This printing consisted of the following stamps:

176	1c on 1m orange brown, Pos. 1, 2, 3, 4 and 5
178	2c on 2m orange brown, Pos. 1, 3, 4 and 5
179	2c on 2m orange brown, Pos. 2
180	3c on 3m orange brown, Pos. 1, 3, 4 and 5
181	3c on 3m orange brown, Pos. 2
188	5c on 5m orange brown, Pos. 1, 3, 4 and 5
189	5c on 5m orange brown, Pos. 2

Second Printing

Black Surcharge, 17½mm high

This printing was from the same setting as used for the first printing, but the impression is much clearer and the ink quite shiny.

The printing consisted of the following stamps:

179F	3c on 2m orange brown, Pos. 1, 3, 4 and 5
179G	3c on 2m orange brown, Pos. 2
182	5c on 1m orange brown, Pos. 1, 3, 4 and 5
183	5c on 1m orange brown, Pos. 2
184	5c on 2m orange brown, Pos. 1, 3, 4 and 5

185	5c on 2m orange brown, Pos. 2
186	5c on 3m orange brown, Pos. 1, 3, 4 and 5
187	5c on 3m orange brown, Pos. 2
188	5c on 5m orange brown, Pos. 1, 3, 4 and 5
189	5c on 5m orange brown, Pos. 2
190	5c on ½m blue green, Pos. 1, 3, 4 and 5
191	5c on ½m blue green, Pos. 2

Third Printing

Red Surcharge, 20mm high

The same setting as for the first and second was used for the third printing. The 10c denomination first appeared in this printing and position 2 of that value has numerals same as on positions 1, 3, 4 and 5, while position 4 has broken "1" in "10."

The printing consisted of the following stamps:

196	3c on 1c black violet, Pos. 1, 3, 4 and 5
197	3c on 1c black violet, Pos. 2
198	5c on 1c black violet, Pos. 1, 3, 4 and 5
199	5c on 1c black violet, Pos. 2
200	10c on 1c black violet, Pos. 1, 2, 3 and 5
200a	10c on 1c black violet, Pos. 4

Fourth Printing

Black Surcharge, 19½mm high

The same type as before but spaced between so that the surcharge is 2mm taller. Clear impression, shiny ink.

HABILITADO HABILITADO HABILITADO

1 **1** **1**

cents. cents. cents.
Position 1   Position 2   Position 3

HABILITADO   HABILITADO

1   **1**

cents.   cents.
Position 4   Position 5

Position 1	— No serif at right of "t"
Position 2	— Broken "1" on No. 177
Position 2	— Thin numerals on 5c stamps
Position 3	— Broken right foot of "n"
Position 4	— Up-stroke of "t" broken
Position 4	— Thin numeral on 3c stamps
Position 5	— Broken "DO"

This printing consisted of the following stamps:

177	1c on 1m orange brn, Pos. 1, 3, 4 and 5
177a	1c on 1m orange brn, Pos. 2
179B	3c on 1m orange brn, Pos. 1, 2, 3 and 5

179D	3c on 1m orange brn, Pos. 4
183B	5c on 1m orange brn, Pos. 1, 3, 4 and 5
189C	5c on 5m orange brn, Pos. 1, 3, 4 and 5
192	5c on ½m blue green, Pos. 1, 3, 4 and 5
193	5c on ½m blue green, Pos. 2

Fifth Printing

Black Surcharge, 19½mm high

HABILITADO HABILITADO HABILITADO

3 **3** **3**

cents. cents. eents.
Position 1   Position 2   Position 3

HABILITADO   HABILITADO

3   **3**

cents.   cents.
Position 4   Position 5

Position 1	— Nick in bottom of "e"and lower serif of "s"
Position 2	— Normal surcharge
Position 3	— "eents"
Position 4	— Thin numeral
Position 5	— Nick in upper part of right stroke of "n"

This printing consisted of the following stamps:

201	3c on 1m blue green, Pos. 1, 2 and 5
201b	3c on 1m blue green, Pos. 3
202	3c on 1m blue green, Pos. 4
203	3c on 2m blue green, Pos. 1, 2 and 5
203a	3c on 2m blue green, Pos. 3
204	3c on 2m blue green, Pos. 4
205	3c on 3m blue green, Pos. 1, 2 and 5
205b	3c on 3m blue green, Pos. 3
206	3c on 3m blue green, Pos. 4
211	5c on 1m blue green, Pos. 1, 2 and 5
211a	5c on 1m blue green, Pos. 3
212	5c on 1m blue green, Pos. 4
213	5c on 2m blue green, Pos. 1, 2 and 5
213a	5c on 2m blue green, Pos. 3
214	5c on 2m blue green, Pos. 4
215	5c on 3m blue green, Pos. 1, 2 and 5
215a	5c on 3m blue green, Pos. 3
216	5c on 3m blue green, Pos. 4
217	5c on 4m blue green, Pos. 1, 2 and 5
217a	5c on 4m blue green, Pos. 3
218	5c on 4m blue green, Pos. 4
219	5c on 8m blue green, Pos. 1, 2 and 5
219b	5c on 8m blue green, Pos. 3
220	5c on 8m blue green, Pos. 4

Counterfeits exist of all Puerto Principe surcharges. Illustrations have been altered to discourage further counterfeiting.

Regular Issues of Cuba of 1896 and 1898
Surcharged:

HABILITADO
1
cent.
a

HABILITADO
1
cents.
b

Numeral in ( ) after color indicates printing.

1898-99
Black Surcharge on Nos. 156-158, 160

176	(a)	1 cent on 1m **orange brn** (1)	50.00	30.00
177	(b)	1 cents on 1m **org brn** (4)	45.00	35.00
a.		Broken figure "1"	75.00	65.00
b.		Inverted surcharge		200.00
d.		Same as "a" inverted		*250.00*

HABILITADO
2
cents.
c

HABILITADO
2
cents.
d

178	(c)	2c on 2m **orange brown** (1)	24.00	20.00
a.		Inverted surcharge	250.00	50.00
179	(d)	2c on 2m **orange brown** (1)	40.00	35.00
a.		Inverted surcharge	350.00	100.00

HABILITADO
3
cents.
k

HABILITADO
3
cents.
l

179B	(k)	3c on 1m **orange brown** (4)	300.	175.
c.		Double surcharge	1,500.	750.
		An unused copy is known with "cents" omitted.		
179D	(l)	3c on 1m **orange brown** (4)	*1,500.*	*750.*
e.		Double surcharge	—	—

HABILITADO
3
cents.
e

HABILITADO
3
cents.
f

179F	(e)	3c on 2m **orange brown** (2)		*1,500.*
		Value is for copy with minor faults.		
179G	(f)	3c on 2m **orange brown** (2)	—	*2,000.*
		Value is for copy with minor faults.		
180	(e)	3c on 3m **orange brown** (1)	30.	30.
a.		Inverted surcharge		110.
181	(f)	3c on 3m **orange brown** (1)	75.	75.
a.		Inverted surcharge		*200.*

HABILITADO
5
cents.
g

HABILITADO
5
cents.
h

HABILITADO
5
cents.
i

HABILITADO
5
cents.
j

182	(g)	5c on 1m **orange brown** (2)	700.	200.
a.		Inverted surcharge		500.
183	(h)	5c on 1m **orange brown** (2)	*1,300.*	500.
a.		Inverted surcharge		700.
184	(g)	5c on 2m **orange brown** (2)	750.	250.
185	(h)	5c on 2m **orange brown** (2)	1,500.	500.

186	(g)	5c on 3m **orange brown** (2)	650.	175.
a.		Inverted surcharge	1,200.	700.
187	(h)	5c an 3m **orange brown** (2)		400.
a.		Inverted surcharge		1,000.
188	(g)	5c on 5m **orange brown** (1) (2)	80.	60.
a.		Inverted surcharge	400.	200.
b.		Double surcharge	—	—
189	(h)	5c on 5m **orange brown** (1) (2)	350.	250.
a.		Inverted surcharge		400.
b.		Double surcharge	—	—
189C	(i)	5c on 5m **orange brown** (4)		*7,500.*

Values for Nos. 188, 189 are for the first printing.

Black Surcharge on No. P25

190	(g)	5c on ½m **blue green** (2)	250.	75.
a.		Inverted surcharge	500.	150.
b.		Pair, one without surcharge		500.
191	(h)	5c on ½m **blue green** (2)	300.	90.
a.		Inverted surcharge		200.
192	(i)	5c on ½m **blue green** (4)	550.	200.
a.		Double surcharge, one diagonal		*11,500.*

Value for No. 190b is for pair with unsurcharged stamp at right. One pair with unsurcharged stamp at left is known.
No. 192a is unique.

193	(j)	5c on ½m **blue green** (4)	800.	300.

Red Surcharge on No. 161

196	(k)	3c on 1c **black violet** (3)	65.	35.
a.		Inverted surcharge		325.
197	(l)	3c on 1c **black violet** (3)	125.	55.
a.		Inverted surcharge		400.
198	(i)	5c on 1c **black violet** (3)	25.	30.
a.		Inverted surcharge		125.
b.		Vertical surcharge		*3,500.*
c.		Double surcharge	*400.*	*600.*
d.		Double inverted surcharge		—
199	(j)	5c on 1c **black violet** (3)	55.	55.
a.		Inverted surcharge		*250.*
b.		Vertical surcharge		*2,000.*
c.		Double surcharge	1,000.	700.

Value for No. 198b is for surcharge reading up. One example is known with surcharge reading down.

HABILITADO
10
cents.
m

200	(m)	10c on 1c **black violet** (3)	20.	50.
a.		Broken figure "1"	40.	100.

Black Surcharge on Nos. P26-P30

201	(k)	3c on 1m **blue green** (5)	350.	350.
a.		Inverted surcharge		450.
b.		"EENTS"	550.	450.
c.		As "b," inverted		850.
202	(l)	3c on 1m **blue green** (5)	550.	400.
a.		Inverted surcharge		850.
203	(k)	3c on 2m **blue green** (5)	850.	400.
a.		"EENTS"	1,250.	500.
b.		Inverted surcharge		850.
c.		As "a," inverted		950.
204	(l)	3c on 2m **blue green** (5)	1,250.	600.
a.		Inverted surcharge		750.
205	(k)	3c on 3m **blue green** (5)	900.	400.
a.		Inverted surcharge		500.
b.		"EENTS"	1,250.	450.
c.		As "b," inverted		700.
206	(l)	3c on 3m **blue green** (5)	1,200.	550.
a.		Inverted surcharge		700.
211	(i)	5c on 1m **blue green** (5)		1,800.
a.		"EENTS"		2,500.
212	(j)	5c on 1m **blue green** (5)		2,250.
213	(i)	5c on 2m **blue green** (5)		1,800.
a.		"EENTS"		1,900.
214	(j)	5c on 2m **blue green** (5)		1,750.
215	(i)	5c on 3m **blue green** (5)		550.
a.		"EENTS"		1,000.
216	(j)	5c on 3m **blue green** (5)	—	1,000.
217	(i)	5c on 4m **blue green** (5)	2,500.	900.
a.		"EENTS"	3,000.	1,500.
b.		Inverted surcharge		2,000.
c.		As "a," inverted		2,000.
218	(j)	5c on 4m **blue green** (5)		1,500.
a.		Inverted surcharge		2,000.
219	(i)	5c on 8m **blue green** (5)	2,500.	1,250.
a.		Inverted surcharge		1,800.
b.		"EENTS"	—	1,800.
c.		As "b," inverted		2,500.
220	(j)	5c on 8m **blue green** (5)	2,000.	2,000.
a.		Inverted surcharge		2,500.

Puerto Principe pairs, strips and stamps properly canceled on cover are scarce and command high premiums.

Most copies of all but the most common varieties are faulty or have tropical toning. Values are for sound copies where they exist.

United States Stamps Nos. 279, 267, 267b, 279Bf, 279Bh, 268, 281, 282C and 283 Surcharged in Black

1899		**Wmk. 191**		*Perf. 12*
221	A87	1c on 1c **yellow green**	5.25	.40
		On cover		15.00
		Block of 4	27.50	4.50
		P# strip of 3, Impt.	57.50	
		P# block of 6, Impt.	300.00	
222	A88	2c on 2c **reddish carmine,** type III, *Feb.*	10.00	.75
		On cover		22.50
		Block of 4	55.00	8.00
		P# strip of 3, Impt.	115.00	
		P# block of 6, Impt.	650.00	
b.		2c on 2c **vermilion,** type III, *Feb.*	10.00	.75
222A	A88	2c on 2c **reddish carmine,** type IV, *Feb.*	6.00	.40
		On cover		12.50
		Block of 4	30.00	4.50
		P# strip of 3, Impt.	65.00	
		P# block of 6, Impt.	600.00	
		"CUBA" at bottom	600.00	
		"CUPA" (broken letter, pos. 99)	175.00	
c.		2c on 2c **vermilion,** type IV, *Feb.*	6.00	.40
d.		As No. 222A, inverted surcharge	5,500.	5,000.
223	A88	2½c on 2c **reddish carmine,** type III, *Jan. 2*	5.00	.80
		On cover		20.00
		Block of 4	27.50	8.00
		P# strip of 3, Impt.	90.00	
		P# block of 6, Impt.	350.00	
b.		2½ on 2c **vermilion,** type III, *Jan. 2*	5.00	.80
223A	A88	2½c on 2c **reddish carmine,** type IV, *Jan. 2*	3.50	.50
		On cover		12.50
		Block of 4	20.00	4.50
		P# strip of 3, Impt.	62.50	
		P# block of 6, Impt.	250.00	
c.		2½c on 2c **vermilion,** type IV, *Jan. 2*	3.50	.50

All 2½c stamps were sold and used as 2 centavo stamps.

224	A89	3c on 3c **purple**	14.00	1.75
		On cover		25.00
		Block of 4	65.00	14.00
		P# strip of 3, Impt.	110.00	
		P# block of 6, Impt.	675.00	
a.		Period between "B" and "A"	40.00	35.00

Two types of surcharge
I — "3" directly over "P"
II — "3" to left over "P"

225	A91	5c on 5c **blue**	14.00	2.00
		On cover		30.00
		Block of 4	65.00	15.00
		P# strip of 3, Impt.	190.00	
		P# block of 6, Impt.	800.00	
		"CUBA" at bottom	—	—
		"CUPA" (broken letter)	80.00	40.00
226	A94	10c on 10c **brown,** type I	25.00	6.50
		On cover		110.00
		Block of 4	115.00	45.00
		P# strip of 3, Impt.	260.00	
		P# block of 6, Impt.	1,000.	
		"CUBA" at bottom	400.00	550.00
b.		"CUBA" omitted	5,500.	4,000.
226A	A94	10c on 10c **brown,** type II	6,500.	
		Block of 4	—	
		Nos. 221-226 (8)	*82.75*	*13.10*

No. 226A exists only in the special printing.
The No. 225 "CUPA" variety always has a straight edge at the right.

Special Printing

In March 1900, one pane of 100 each of Nos. 221-225, 226A, J1-J4 and two panes of 50 of No. E1, were specially overprinted for displays at the Paris Exposition (1900) and Pan American Exposition (1901). The 2c pane was light red, type IV. Copies were hand-stamped type E "Specimen" in black ink by H. G. Mandel and mounted by him in separate displays for the two Expositions. Additional stamps from each pane were also handstamped "specimen," but most were destroyed after the Expositions. Nearly all examples remaining bear impression of a dealer's hand-stamp reading "Special Surcharge" in red ink on the back. Value: Nos. 221-225, J1-J4, each $625; No. E1, $1,000.

Issues of the Republic under US Military Rule

Statue of
Columbus — A20

Royal Palms — A21

Allegory,
"Cuba" — A22

Ocean Liner — A23

Cane Field — A24

Re-engraved

The re-engraved stamps issued by the Republic of Cuba in 1905-07 may be distinguished from the Issue of 1899 as follows:
Nos. 227-231 are watermarked U S-C
The re-engraved stamps are unwatermarked.

1c: The ends of the label inscribed "Centavo" are rounded instead of square.
2c: The foliate ornaments, inside the oval disks bearing the numerals of value, have been removed.
5c: Two lines forming a right angle have been added in the upper corners of the label bearing the word "Cuba."
10c: A small ball has been added to each of the square ends of the label bearing the word "Cuba."

No. 227

Re-engraved

No. 228

Re-engraved

No. 230

Re-engraved

No. 231

Re-engraved

Printed by the U.S. Bureau of Engraving and Printing

1899		Wmk. US-C (191C)		Perf. 12
227	A20	1c **yellow green**	3.50	.20
		On cover		2.00
		Block of 4	15.00	1.00
		P# block of 10, Impt., type VII	225.00	—
228	A21	2c **carmine**	3.50	.20
		On cover		2.00
		Block of 4	15.00	1.00
		P# block of 10, Impt., type VII	180.00	—
a.		2c **scarlet**	3.50	.20
b.		Booklet pane of 6	3,750.	
229	A22	3c **purple**	3.50	.20
		On cover		4.00
		Block of 4	15.00	2.50

		P# block of 10, Impt., type VII	275.00	—
230	A23	5c **blue**	4.50	.20
		On cover		4.00
		Block of 4	21.00	2.50
		P# block of 10, Impt., type VII	450.00	—
231	A24	10c **brown**	11.00	.50
		On cover		6.50
		Block of 4	52.50	5.50
		P# block of 10, Impt., type VII	1,200.	—
		Nos. 227-231 (5)	26.00	1.30

SPECIAL DELIVERY STAMPS

Issued under Administration of the United States

Special Delivery Stamp of the United States No. E5 Surcharged in Red

1899		Wmk. 191		Perf. 12
E1	SD3	10c on 10c **blue**	130.	100.
		On cover		450.
		Block of 4	575.	
		Margin block of 4, arrow	650.	
		P# strip of 3, Impt.	1,000.	
		P# block of 6, Impt.	6,000.	
		Five dots in curved frame above messenger's head (Pl. 882)	—	
a.		No period after "CUBA"	575.	400.

Issue of the Republic under US Military Rule

Special Delivery Messenger SD2

Printed by the US Bureau of Engraving and Printing

1899		Wmk. US-C (191C)		
		Inscribed: "Immediata"		
E2	SD2	10c **orange**	50.00	15.00
		On cover		150.00
		Block of 4	250.00	
		P# strip of 3, Impt., type VII	300.00	
		P# block of 6, Impt., type VII	1,000.	

Re-engraved

In 1902 the Republic of Cuba issued a stamp of design SD2 re-engraved with word correctly spelled "Inmediata." The corrected die was made in 1899 (See No. E3P). It was printed by the U.S. Bureau of Engraving and Printing.

POSTAGE DUE STAMPS

Issued under Administration of the United States Postage Due Stamps of the United States Nos. J38, J39, J41 and J42 Surcharged in Black Like Regular Issue of Same Date

1899		Wmk. 191		Perf. 12
J1	D2	1c on 1c **deep claret**	45.00	5.25
		Block of 4	210.00	45.00
		P# block of 6, Impt.	900.00	
J2	D2	2c on 2c **deep claret**	45.00	5.25
		Block of 4	200.00	30.00
		P# block of 6, Impt.	900.00	
a.		Inverted surcharge		4,000.
J3	D2	5c on 5c **deep claret**	45.00	5.25
		Block of 4	220.00	45.00
		P# block of 6, Impt.	900.00	
		"CUPA" (broken letter)	150.00	140.00

J4	D2	10c on 10c **deep claret**	27.50	2.50
		Block of 4	125.00	27.50
		P# block of 6, Impt.	800.00	

The No. J3 "CUPA" variety always has a straight edge at right.

ENVELOPES

Values are for Cut Squares
US Envelopes of 1887-99 Surcharged

a

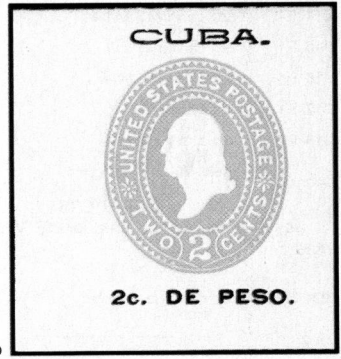
b

1899

U1	U77 (a)	1c on 1c **green**, *oriental buff* (No. U354)	5.00	3.50
		Entire	12.00	15.00
U2	U77 (a)	1c on 1c **green**, *blue* (No. U355)	3.25	2.50
		Entire	5.00	6.50
a.		Double surcharge, entire	5,250.	
U3	U71 (b)	2c on 2c **green** (No. U311)	1.50	1.10
		Entire	3.00	3.50
a.		Double surcharge, entire	4,500.	6,500.
b.		Inverted surcharge at lower left, entire	—	4,250.
U4	U71 (b)	2c on 2c **green**, *amber* (No. U312)	2.75	1.65
		Entire	5.25	6.00
a.		Double surcharge, entire	5,250.	
U5	U71 (a)	2c on 2c **green**, *oriental buff* (No. U313)	17.50	8.00
		Entire	47.50	47.50
U6	U79 (a)	2c on 2c **carmine**, *amber* (No. U363)	17.50	17.50
		Entire	47.50	47.50
U7	U79 (a)	2c on 2c **carmine**, *oriental buff* (No. U364)	25.00	25.00
		Entire	100.00	80.00
U8	U79 (a)	2c on 2c **carmine**, *blue* (No. U365)	3.00	2.00
		Entire	7.00	8.00
a.		Double surcharge, entire	6,750.	
		Nos. U1-U8 (8)	75.50	61.25

In addition to the envelopes listed above, several others are known but were not regularly issued. They are:
1c on 1c green
1c on 1c green, *manila*
2c on 2c carmine
4c on 4c brown
5c on 5c blue

Issue of the Republic under US Military Rule

Columbus — E1

Similar envelopes without watermark on white and amber papers, were issued by the Republic after Military Rule ended in 1902.

1899   Wmk. "US POD '99" in Monogram

U9	E1	1c **green**	.75	.65
		Entire	4.00	4.00
U10	E1	1c **green**, *amber*	1.00	.65
		Entire	4.00	4.00
U11	E1	1c **green**, *buff*	17.50	13.00
		Entire	85.00	42.50
U12	E1	1c **green**, *blue*	25.00	15.00
		Entire	85.00	42.50
U13	E1	2c **carmine**	1.00	.70
		Entire	3.75	3.00
U14	E1	2c **carmine**, *amber*	1.00	.70
		Entire	3.75	3.00
U15	E1	2c **carmine**, *buff*	9.00	7.75
		Entire	35.00	21.00
U16	E1	2c **carmine**, *blue*	25.00	18.00
		Entire	60.00	52.50
U17	E1	5c **blue**	3.25	2.25
		Entire	5.00	2.75
U18	E1	5c **blue**, *amber*	6.00	4.00
		Entire	9.00	5.75
		Nos. U9-U18 (10)	89.50	62.70

WRAPPERS
Issue of the Republic under US Military Rule
1899

W1	E1	1c **green**, *manila*	4.00	10.00
		Entire	11.00	50.00
W2	E1	2c **carmine**, *manila*	12.00	10.00
		Entire	25.00	50.00

POSTAL CARDS

Values are for Entires

U.S. Postal
Cards Nos.
UX14, UX16
Surcharged

CUBA.—1c. de Peso.

UX1	PC8	1c on 1c **black**, buff, Jefferson		
		(1,000,000)	15.00	16.50
a.		No period after "1c"	40.00	75.00
b.		No period after "Peso"	35.00	
c.		Surcharge "2c" (error)	6,500.	
UX2	PC3	2c on 2c **black**, buff, Liberty		
		(583,000)	15.00	16.50
a.		No period after "Peso"	40.00	75.00
b.		Double surcharge	—	

In 1904 the Republic of Cuba revalued remaining stocks of No. UX2 by means of a perforated numeral "1."

PROOFS
1899

Column (1) — Large Die
Column (2) — Small Die

227P	1c yellow green	160.	160.
227TC	1c blue green	375.	
227TC	1c black	625.	
228P	2c carmine	160.	160.
228TC	2c black	625.	
229P	3c purple	160.	160.
229TC	3c black	375.	
230P	5c blue	160.	160.
230TC	5c black	625.	
231P	10c brown	160.	160.
231TC	10c gray	625.	
231TC	10c black	625.	

Special Delivery

E2TC	10c	blue	1,500.	
E3P	10c	orange	375.	325.

SPECIMEN STAMPS

Handstamped U.S. Type E in Purple

1899

221S	E	1c on 1c **yellow green**	200.	
222AS	E	2c on 2c **reddish carmine**, type IV	200.	
223AS	E	2½c on 2c **reddish carmine**, type IV	200.	
224S	E	3c on 3c **purple**	200.	
225S	E	5c on 5c **blue**	200.	
226S	E	10c on 10c **brown**, type I	200.	
226AS	E	10c on 10c **brown**, type II	4,000.	

See note after No. 226A for Special Printings with black "Specimen" overprints.

1899

227S	E	1c **yellow green**	225.	
228S	E	2c **carmine**	225.	
229S	E	3c **purple**	225.	
230S	E	5c **blue**	225.	
231S	E	10c **brown**	225.	

Special Delivery

1899

E1S	E	10c on 10c **blue**	550.	
a.		Five dots in curved frame above messenger's head	1,750.	
E2S	E	10c **orange**	1,000.	

Postage Due

1899

J1S	E	1c on 1c **deep claret**	275.	
J2S	E	2c on 2c **deep claret**	275.	
J3S	E	5c on 5c **deep claret**	275.	
J4S	E	10c on 10c **deep claret**	275.	

Black "Specimen" overprint known on all stamps of the Special Printing.

DANISH WEST INDIES

Formerly a Danish colony, these islands were purchased by the United States on March 31, 1917 and have since been known as the U.S. Virgin Islands. They lie east of Puerto Rico, have an area of 132 square miles and had a population of 27,086 in 1911. The capital is Charlotte Amalie (also called St. Thomas). Stamps of Danish West Indies were replaced by those of the United States in 1917. However, for the first six months of U.S. ownership, until September 30, 1917, a postal transition period existed. During this period, either U.S., D.W.I. or mixed frankings could be used. The domestic printed matter or postcard rate was 5 bits or 1 cent, and the foreign printed matter or postcard rate was 10 bits, 2 cents, or 5 bits + 1 cent. The domestic minimum weight letter rate was 10 bits, 2 cents, or 5 bits + 1 cent, while the foreign minimum letter rate was 25 bits, 5 cents, or any combination of U.S. and D.W.I. stamps that together totalled 25 bits or 5 cents.

Letters posted to foreign destinations during the transition period are rare because of World War I. Values for covers listed here are for the period before the transition. Transition-period covers, including those with mixed franking, sell for much more.

100 CENTS = 1 DOLLAR
100 BIT = 1 FRANC (1905)

Coat of
Arms — A1

Wmk. 111 —
Small Crown

1856   Typo.   Wmk. 111   Imperf.
Yellowish Paper
Yellow Wavy-line Burelage, UL to LR

1	A1	3c **dark carmine**, brown gum	200.	275.
		On cover		3,000.
		Block of 4	1,300.	
a.		3c **dark carmine**, yellow gum	220.	275.
		On cover		3,000.
		Block of 4	2,850.	
b.		3c **carmine**, white gum	4,250.	—
		On cover		—

The brown and yellow gums were applied locally.
Reprint: 1981, carmine, back-printed across two stamps ("Reprint by Dansk Post og Telegrafmuseum 1978"), value, pair, $10.

1866
White Paper
Yellow Wavy-line Burelage UR to LL

2	A1	3c **rose**	40.	75.
		On cover		3,000.
		Block of 4	200.	350.
		Rouletted 4½ privately	350.	175.
		On cover, rouletted 4½		
		Rouletted 9	450.	200.

The value for used blocks is for favor cancel (CTO).
No. 2 reprints, unwatermarked: 1930, carmine, value $100. 1942, rose carmine, back-printed across each row ("Nytryk 1942 G. A. Hagemann Danmark og Dansk Vestindiens Frimaerker Bind 2"), value $50.

1872   Perf. 12½

3	A1	3c **rose**	92.50	275.
		On cover		7,500.
		Block of 4	525.	

1873
Without Burelage

4	A1	4c **dull blue**	250.	475.
		On cover		
		Block of 4	1,300.	
a.		Imperf., pair	775.	
b.		Horiz. pair, imperf. vert.	575.	

The 1930 reprint of No. 4 is ultramarine, unwatermarked and imperf., value $100.
The 1942 4c reprint is blue, unwatermarked, imperf. and has printing on back (see note below No. 2), value $60.

Numeral of Value — A2

NORMAL
FRAME

INVERTED
FRAME

The arabesques in the corners have a main stem and a branch. When the frame is in normal position, in the upper left corner the branch leaves the main stem half way between two little leaflets. In the lower right corner the branch starts at the foot of the second leaflet. When the frame is inverted the corner designs are, of course, transposed.

The central element in the fan-shaped scrollwork at the outside of the lower left corner of Nos. 5a, 6a, 7b and 11a looks like an elongated diamond.

Wmk. 112 — Crown

1874-79   Wmk. 112   Perf. 14x13½

White Wove Paper, Printings 1-3 Thin, 4-7 Medium, 8-9 Thick
1c	Nine printings
3c	Eight printings
4c	Two printings
5c	Six printings
7c	Two printings
10c	Seven printings
12c	Two printings
14c	One printing
50c	Two printings

Values for inverted frames, covers and blocks are for the cheapest variety.

5	A2	1c **green & brown red**	20.00	30.00
		On cover		250.00
		Block of 4	90.00	240.00
a.		1c **green & rose lilac,** thin paper	80.00	125.00
b.		1c **green & red violet,** medium paper	45.00	65.00
c.		1c **green & claret,** thick paper	20.00	30.00
e.		As "c," inverted frame	20.00	30.00
f.		As "a," inverted frame	475.00	

No. 5 exists with "b" surcharge, "10 CENTS 1895." See note below No. 15.

6	A2	3c **blue & carmine**	25.00	20.00
		On cover		225.00
		Block of 4	110.00	
		White "wedge" flaw	50.00	50.00
a.		3c **light blue & rose carmine,** thin paper	65.00	50.00
b.		3c **deep blue & dark carmine,** medium paper	40.00	17.00
c.		3c **greenish blue & lake,** thick paper	32.50	17.00
d.		Imperf., pair	375.00	
e.		Inverted frame, thick paper	21.00	15.00
f.		As "a," inverted frame	350.00	
7	A2	4c **brown & dull blue**	16.00	19.00
		On cover		225.00
		Block of 4	75.00	
b.		4c **brown & ultramarine,** thin paper	190.00	225.00
c.		Diagonal half used as 2c on cover		140.00
d.		As "b," inverted frame	825.00	1,400.
8	A2	5c **green & gray**	30.00	25.00
		On cover		250.00
		Block of 4	130.00	
a.		5c **yellow green & dark gray,** thin paper	55.00	37.50
b.		Inverted frame, thick paper	27.50	25.00
9	A2	7c **lilac & orange**	32.50	95.00
		On cover		1,100.
		Block of 4	160.00	
a.		7c **lilac & yellow**	90.00	100.00
b.		Inverted frame	60.00	150.00
10	A2	10c **blue & brown**	25.00	30.00
		On cover		300.00
		Block of 4	115.00	
a.		10c **dark blue & black brown,** thin paper	70.00	45.00
b.		Period between "t" & "s" of "cents"	30.00	30.00
c.		Inverted frame	27.50	32.50
11	A2	12c **red lilac & yellow green**	42.50	175.00
		On cover		1,750.
		Block of 4	230.00	
a.		12c **lilac & deep green**	150.00	200.00
12	A2	14c **lilac & green**	650.00	1,100.
		On cover		4,000.
		Block of 4		
a.		Inverted frame	2,500.	3,500.
13	A2	50c **violet,** thin paper	175.00	300.00
		On cover		2,500.
		Block of 4	1,250.	
a.		50c **gray violet,** thick paper	225.00	350.00

Issue dates: 1c, 3c, 4c, 14c, Jan. 15, 1874. 7c, July 22, 1874. 5c, 10c, 1876; 12c, 1877; 50c, 1879. Colors of major numbers are generally those of the least expensive of two or more shades, and do not indicate the shade of the first printing.

Nos. 9 and 13 Surcharged in Black:

a

b

1887
14	A2 (a)	1c on 7c **lilac & orange**	100.00	200.00
		On cover		3,000.
		Block of 4	450.00	
a.		1c on 7c **lilac & yellow**	100.00	225.00
b.		Double surcharge	250.00	500.00
c.		Inverted frame	110.00	350.00

1895
15	A2 (b)	10c on 50c **violet,** thin paper	42.50	67.50
		On cover		275.00
		Block of 4	275.00	

The "b" surcharge also exists on No. 5, with "10" found in two sizes. These are essays.

1896-1901   Perf. 13
16	A2	1c **green & red violet,** inverted frame ('98)	13.00	22.50
		On cover		150.00
		Block of 4	65.00	
a.		Normal frame	290.00	425.00
17	A2	3c **blue & lake,** inverted frame ('98)	12.00	17.50
		On cover		150.00
		Block of 4	55.00	
		White "wedge" flaw	35.00	45.00
a.		Normal frame	250.00	425.00
18	A2	4c **bister & dull blue** ('01)	17.50	15.00
		On cover		150.00
		Block of 4	77.50	
a.		Diagonal half used as 2c on cover		100.00
b.		Inverted frame	55.00	85.00
		On cover		250.00
c.		As "b," diagonal half used as 2c on cover		350.00
19	A2	5c **green & gray,** inverted frame	35.00	35.00
		Block of 4	160.00	325.00
a.		Normal frame	750.00	1,100.
20	A2	10c **blue & brown** ('01)	80.00	150.00
		On cover		1,150.
		Block of 4	475.00	
a.		Inverted frame	925.00	1,600.
b.		Period between "t" and "s" of "cents"	170.00	160.00
		Nos. 16-20 (5)	157.50	240.00

Two printings each of Nos. 18-19.

Arms — A5

1900
21	A5	1c **light green**	3.00	3.00
		On cover, pair		80.00
		On cover, single franking		300.00
		Block of 4	12.50	12.50
22	A5	5c **light blue**	17.50	25.00
		On cover		300.00
		Block of 4	80.00	

Nos. 6, 17 and 20 Surcharged in Black — c

1902   Perf. 14x13½
23	A2	2c on 3c **blue & carmine,** inverted frame	575.00	725.00
		On cover		4,000.
		Block of 4	3,000.	
a.		"2" in date with straight tail	650.00	800.00
b.		Normal frame	4,000.	

Perf. 13
24	A2	2c on 3c **blue & lake,** inverted frame	10.00	27.50
		On cover		160.00
		Block of 4	45.00	

		White "wedge" flaw	55.00	55.00
a.		"2" in date with straight tail	12.00	32.50
b.		Dated "1901"	600.00	650.00
c.		Normal frame	175.00	250.00
d.		Dark green surcharge	2,000.	
e.		As "d" & "a"	—	
f.		As "d" & "c"	—	

One example recorded of No. 24f.

25	A2	8c on 10c **blue & brown**	25.00	42.50
		On cover		225.00
		Block of 4	105.00	
a.		"2" with straight tail	30.00	45.00
b.		On No. 20b	32.50	45.00
c.		Inverted frame	250.00	425.00

Nos. 17 and 20 Surcharged in Black — d

1902   Perf. 13
27	A2	2c on 3c **blue & lake,** inverted frame	12.00	40.00
		On cover		500.00
		Block of 4	52.50	
		White "wedge" flaw	40.00	55.00
a.		Normal frame	240.00	425.00
28	A2	8c on 10c **blue & brown**	12.00	14.00
		On cover		175.00
		Block of 4	52.50	
a.		On No. 20b	18.50	25.00
b.		Inverted frame	225.00	400.00

Wmk. 113 — Crown

1903			Wmk. 113		
29	A5	2c carmine		8.00	22.50
		On cover			125.00
		Block of 4		35.00	
30	A5	8c brown		27.50	30.00
		On cover			250.00
		Block of 4		115.00	

King Christian IX — A8   St. Thomas Harbor — A9

1905			Typo.	Perf. 12½	
31	A8	5b green		3.75	3.25
		On cover			35.00
		Block of 4		17.00	
32	A8	10b red		3.75	3.25
		On cover			35.00
		Block of 4		16.00	
33	A8	20b green & blue		8.75	8.25
		On cover			150.00
		Block of 4		40.00	
34	A8	25b ultramarine		8.75	10.50
		On cover			85.00
		Block of 4		40.00	
35	A8	40b red & gray		8.25	8.25
		On cover			225.00
		Block of 4		37.50	
36	A8	50b yellow & gray		10.00	12.00
		On cover			250.00
		Block of 4		42.50	

Perf. 12
Wmk. Two Crowns (113)
Frame Typographed, Center Engraved

37	A9	1fr green & blue		17.50	45.00
		On cover			625.00
		Block of 4		75.00	
38	A9	2fr orange red & brown		30.00	60.00
		On cover			1,100.
		Block of 4		150.00	
39	A9	5fr yellow & brown		77.50	275.00
		On cover			1,750.
		Block of 4		375.00	
		Nos. 31-39 (9)		168.25	425.50

On cover values are for commercial usages, usually parcel address cards. Philatelic covers are valued at approximately 25% of these figures.

Nos. 18, 22 and 30 Surcharged in Black

5 BIT 1905

1905			Wmk. 112	Perf. 13	
40	A2	5b on 4c bister & dull blue		16.00	45.00
		On cover			250.00
		Block of 4		77.50	
a.		Inverted frame		45.00	82.50
41	A5	5b on 5c light blue		14.00	37.50
		On cover			250.00
		Block of 4		65.00	

Wmk. 113

42	A5	5b on 8c brown		14.00	37.50
		On cover			250.00
		Block of 4		60.00	

Favor cancels exist on Nos. 40-42. Value 25% less.

King Frederik VIII — A10

Frame Typographed, Center Engraved
1908			Wmk. 113	Perf. 13	
43	A10	5b green		1.90	1.90
		On cover			22.50
		Block of 4		9.50	
		Number block of 6		18.50	
44	A10	10b red		1.90	1.90
		On cover			22.50
		Block of 4		9.50	

45	A10	15b violet & brown		3.75	4.50
		On cover			125.00
		Block of 4		19.00	
		Number block of 6		52.50	
46	A10	20b green & blue		30.00	27.50
		On cover			110.00
		Block of 4		130.00	
		Number block of 6		375.00	
47	A10	25b blue & dark blue		1.90	2.50
		On cover			35.00
		Block of 4		9.00	
		Number block of 6		18.50	
48	A10	30b claret & slate		50.00	52.50
		On cover			350.00
		Block of 4		220.00	240.00
		Number block of 6		525.00	
49	A10	40b vermilion & gray		5.75	9.50
		On cover			210.00
		Block of 4		25.00	
		Number block of 6		55.00	
50	A10	50b yellow & brown		5.75	14.00
		On cover			210.00
		Block of 4		25.00	
		Number block of 6		70.00	
		Nos. 43-50 (8)		100.95	114.30

Printing numbers appear in the selvage, once per pane, in Roman or Arabic numerals.

King Christian X — A11   Wmk. 114 — Multiple Crosses

Frame Typographed, Center Engraved
1915			Wmk. 114	Perf. 14x14½	
51	A11	5b yellow green		4.00	4.25
		On cover			45.00
		Block of 4		17.50	
		Number block of 4		40.00	
52	A11	10b red		4.00	42.50
		On cover			100.00
		Block of 4		17.50	
		Number block of 4		40.00	
53	A11	15b lilac & red brown		4.00	47.50
		On cover			300.00
		Block of 4		17.50	
		Number block of 4		40.00	
54	A11	20b green & blue		4.00	47.50
		On cover			350.00
		Block of 4		17.50	
		Number block of 4		40.00	
55	A11	25b blue & dark blue		4.00	12.50
		On cover			100.00
		Block of 4		17.50	
		Number block of 4		40.00	
56	A11	30b claret & black		4.00	85.00
		On cover			900.00
		Block of 4		17.50	
		Number block of 4		40.00	
57	A11	40b orange & black		4.00	85.00
		On cover			550.00
		Block of 4		18.50	
		Number block of 4		40.00	
58	A11	50b yellow & brown		4.00	85.00
		On cover			650.00
		Block of 4		18.50	
		Number block of 4		40.00	
		Nos. 51-58 (8)		32.00	409.25

Forged and favor cancellations exist.

Plate identifications 11-D, 50-D or 50-O are located in the selvage in all four corners of the pane. The 50-D is on all denominations. 11-D, all but the 50b, 50-O, all but 15b, 20b, 25b.

POSTAGE DUE STAMPS

Royal Cipher "Christian Rex" — D1   Numeral of Value — D2

1902			Litho.	Unwmk.	Perf. 11½	
J1	D1	1c dark blue			4.50	17.50
		On cover				400.00
		Block of 4			22.50	
J2	D1	4c dark blue			11.50	22.50
		On cover				350.00
		Block of 4			50.00	

J3	D1	6c dark blue		19.00	60.00
		On cover			450.00
		Block of 4		92.50	
J4	D1	10c dark blue		18.00	65.00
		On cover			400.00
		Block of 4		87.50	

There are five types of each value. On the 4c they may be distinguished by differences in the figure "4"; on the other values differences are minute.

Used values of Nos. J1-J8 are for canceled stamps. Uncanceled stamps without gum have probably been used. Value 60% of unused. On cover values are for stamps tied by cancellation.

Excellent counterfeits of Nos. J1-J4 exist.

1905-13				Perf. 13	
J5	D2	5b red & gray		4.50	6.75
		On cover			450.00
		Block of 4		20.00	
J6	D2	20b red & gray		7.50	14.00
		On cover			450.00
		Block of 4		32.50	
J7	D2	30b red & gray		6.75	14.00
		On cover			450.00
		Block of 4		30.00	
J8	D2	50b red & gray		6.00	35.00
		On cover			900.00
		Block of 4		27.50	
a.		Perf. 14x14½ ('13)		37.50	140.00
		Block of 4		175.00	
b.		Perf. 11½		325.00	

Nos. J5-J8 are known imperforate but were not regularly issued. Excellent counterfeits exist.
See notes following No. J4 for canceled stamps.

ENVELOPES

E1

1877-78				On White Paper	
U1	E1	2c light blue ('78)		5.50	14.00
		Entire		22.50	65.00
a.		2c ultramarine		20.00	200.00
		Entire		100.00	800.00
U2	E1	3c orange		5.50	12.50
		Entire		22.50	65.00
a.		3c red orange		5.50	12.50
		Entire		22.50	65.00

Three different Crown watermarks are found on entires of No. U1, four on entires of No. U2. Envelope watermarks do not show on cut squares.

POSTAL CARDS
Values are for entire cards.
Italicized numbers in parentheses indicate quantities issued.
Designs of Adhesive Stamps
"BREV-KORT" at top

1877					
		Inscription in Three Lines			
UX1	A2	6c violet		40.00	1,400.

Used value is for card to foreign destination postmarked before April 1, 1879.

1878-85					
		Inscription in Four Lines			
UX2	A2	2c light blue (8,800)		22.50	50.00
UX3	A2	3c carmine rose (17,700)		17.50	35.00

1888					
		Inscription in Five Lines			
UX4	A2	2c light blue (30,500)		20.00	32.50
UX5	A2	3c red (26,500)		12.50	22.50

Card No. UX5 Locally Surcharged with type "c" but with date "1901"

1901					
UX6	A2	1c on 3c red (2,000)		50.00	200.00

Card No. UX4 Locally Surcharged with type "c"

1902					
UX7	A2	1c on 2c light blue (3,000)		37.50	160.00

Card No. UX5 Surcharged similar to type "c" but heavy letters

1902					
UX8	A2	1c on 3c red (7,175)		12.50	150.00

1903

UX9	A5	1c **light green** (10,000)	12.50	30.00
UX10	A5	2c **carmine** (10,000)	19.00	70.00

1905

UX11	A8	5b **green** (16,000)	12.50	22.50
UX12	A8	10b **red** (14,000)	12.50	35.00

1907-08 Unwmk.

UX13	A10	5b **green** ('08) (30,750)	9.50	30.00
UX14	A10	10b **red** (19,750)	12.50	40.00

1913 Wmk. Wood-grain

UX15	A10	5b **green** (10,000)	90.00	210.00
UX16	A10	10b **red** (10,000)	100.00	325.00

1915-16 Wmk. Wood-grain

UX17	A11	5b **yellow green** (8,200)	80.00	250.00
UX18	A11	10b **red** ('16) (2,000)	100.00	—

PAID REPLY POSTAL CARDS

Designs similar to Nos. UX2 and UX3 with added
inscriptions in Danish and French:
Message Card-Four lines at lower left.
Reply Card-Fifth line centered, "Svar. Réponse."
Italicized numbers in parentheses indicate quantities
issued.

1883

UY1	A2	2c +2c **light blue**, unsevered		
		(2,600)	25.00	250.00
m.		Message card, detached	12.50	35.00
r.		Reply card, detached	12.50	35.00
UY2	A2	3c +3c **carmine rose**, unsevered	21.00	150.00
m.		Message card, detached	12.50	20.00
r.		Reply card, detached	12.50	25.00

Designs similar to Nos. UX4 and UX5 with added
inscription in fifth line, centered in French:
Message Card-"Carte postale avec réponse payée."
Reply Card-"Carte postale-réponse."

1888

UY3	A2	2c +2c **light blue**, unsevered		
		(26,000)	25.00	125.00
m.		Message card, detached	10.00	20.00
r.		Reply card, detached	10.00	100.00
UY4	A2	3c +3c **carmine rose**, unsevered (5,000)	22.50	175.00
m.		Message card, detached	11.00	35.00
r.		Reply card, detached	11.00	125.00

No. UY4 Locally Surcharged with type "c" but with
date "1901"

1902

UY5	A2	1c on 3c+1c on 3c **carmine rose**, unsevered (1,000)	35.00	300.00
m.		Message card, detached	12.50	50.00
r.		Reply card, detached	14.00	75.00

No. UY4 Surcharged in Copenhagen with type
similar to "c" but heavy letters

UY6	A2	1c on 3c+1c on 3c **carmine rose**, unsevered (975)	50.00	350.00
m.		Message card, detached	20.00	60.00
r.		Reply card, detached	20.00	75.00

Designs similar to Nos. UX9 and UX10 with added
inscriptions in Danish and English

1903

UY7	A5	1c +1c **light green**, unsevered (5,000)	35.00	75.00
m.		Message card, detached	11.00	20.00
r.		Reply card, detached	11.00	25.00
UY8	A5	2c +2c **carmine**, unsevered (5,000)	40.00	400.00
m.		Message card, detached	15.00	50.00
r.		Reply card, detached	15.00	75.00

Designs similar to Nos. UX11 and UX12 with added
inscriptions

1905

UY9	A8	5b +5b **green**, unsevered (5,000)	21.00	75.00
m.		Message card, detached	10.00	20.00
r.		Reply card, detached	10.00	30.00
UY10	A8	10b +10b **red**, unsevered (4,000)	30.00	90.00
m.		Message card, detached	12.50	25.00
r.		Reply card, detached	15.00	35.00

Designs similar to Nos. UX13, UX14 and UX15 with
added inscriptions

1908 Unwmk.

UY11	A10	5b +5b **green**, unsevered (7,150)	25.00	100.00
m.		Message card, detached	11.00	30.00
r.		Reply card, detached	11.00	35.00
UY12	A10	10b +10b **red**, unsevered (6,750)	25.00	100.00
m.		Message card, detached	12.50	30.00
r.		Reply card, detached	11.00	40.00

1913 Wmk. Wood-grain

UY13	A10	5b +5b **green**, unsevered (5,000)	—	
m.		Message card, detached	—	
r.		Reply card, detached	—	

The 10b + 10b red type A10 with wood-grain watermark was
authorized and possibly printed, but no example is known.

REVENUE STAMPS

PLAYING CARDS

These stamps were overprinted by the Bureau of
Engraving and Printing. Shipments of 10,000 each of

Nos. RFV1-RFV3 were sent to the Virgin Islands on
June 17, 1920, Jan. 16, 1926, and Mar. 5, 1934,
respectively.

U.S. Playing Card Stamp No.
RF3 Overprinted in Carmine

1920 Engr. Wmk. 191R Rouletted 7

RFV1	RF2	4c on 2c **blue**	225.00

U.S. Playing Card Stamp No.
RF17 Overprinted in Carmine

1926 Rouletted 7

RFV2	RF4	4c on (8c) **blue**	60.00

RFV2 was surcharged with new value in "Bits" for use in
collecting a tobacco tax.

Same Overprint on U.S. Type RF4

1934 Perf. 11

RFV3	RF4	4c on (8c) **light blue**	225.00	125.00

The above stamp with perforation 11 was not issued in the
United States without the overprint.

GUAM

A former Spanish island possession in the Pacific Ocean, one of the Mariana group, about 1,450 miles east of the Philippines. Captured June 20, 1898, and ceded to the United States by treaty after the Spanish-American War. Stamps overprinted "Guam" were used while the post office was under the jurisdiction of the Navy Department from July 7, 1899, until March 29, 1901, when a Postal Agent was appointed by the Post Office Department and the postal service passed under that Department's control. From this date on Guam was supplied with regular United States postage stamps, although the overprints remained in use for several more years.

Italicized numbers in parentheses indicate quantities issued.

Population 9,000 (est. 1899).

100 CENTS = 1 DOLLAR

United States Nos. 279, 279B, 279Bc, 268, 280a,
281, 282, 272, 282C, 283, 284, 275, 275a, 276 and
276A Overprinted

1899 Wmk. 191 Perf. 12
Black Overprint

1	A87	1c **deep green** (25,000)	20.00	25.00
		Never hinged	40.00	
		On cover		200.00

		Block of 4	90.00	140.00
		P# strip of 3, Impt.	90.00	
		P# block of 6, Impt.	350.00	
		A bogus inverted overprint exists.		
2	A88	2c **red**, type IV, *Dec.* (105,000)	17.50	25.00
		light red, type IV	17.50	25.00
		On cover		200.00
		Never hinged	35.00	
		Block of 4	85.00	140.00
		P# strip of 3, Impt.	75.00	
		P# block of 6, Impt.	300.00	
a.		2c **rose carmine**, type IV, *Aug. 15*	30.00	30.00
		Never hinged	60.00	
		On cover		225.00
		Block of 4	125.00	175.00
		P# strip of 3, Impt.	100.00	
		P# block of 6, Impt.	375.00	
3	A89	3c **purple** (5000)	140.00	175.00
		Never hinged	275.00	
		On cover		400.00
		Block of 4	600.00	850.00
		P# strip of 3, Impt.	575.00	
		P# block of 6, Impt.	1,600.	
4	A90	4c **lilac brown** (5000)	135.00	175.00
		Never hinged	270.00	
		On cover		450.00
		Block of 4	600.00	825.00

		P# strip of 3, Impt.	550.00	
		P# block of 6, Impt.	2,000.	
		Extra frame line at top (Plate 793 R62)	—	
5	A91	5c **blue** (20,000)	32.50	45.00
		Never hinged	65.00	
		On cover		200.00
		Block of 4	140.00	250.00
		P# strip of 3, Impt.	140.00	
		P# block of 6, Impt.	775.00	
6	A92	6c **lake** (5000)	125.00	200.00
		Never hinged	250.00	
		On cover		450.00
		Block of 4	550.00	1,000.
		P# strip of 3, Impt.	500.00	
		P# block of 6, Impt.	1,600.	
7	A93	8c **violet brown** (5000)	140.00	200.00
		Never hinged	275.00	
		On cover		450.00
		Block of 4	600.00	1,000.
		P# strip of 3, Impt.	600.00	
		P# block of 6, Impt.	1,700.	
8	A94	10c **brown**, type I (10,000)	47.50	55.00
		Never hinged	95.00	
		On cover		275.00
		Block of 4	210.00	300.00
		P# strip of 3, Impt.	225.00	
		P# block of 6, Impt.	1,000.	

9	A94	10c **brown**, type II	4,000.	—	
		Never hinged	7,000.		
		Pair	—		
10	A95	15c **olive green** (5000)	150.00	175.00	
		Never hinged	300.00		
		On cover		900.00	
		Block of 4	650.00	875.00	
		P# strip of 3, Impt.	600.00		
		P# block of 6, Impt.	2,200.		
11	A96	50c **orange** (4000)	350.00	425.00	
		Never hinged	700.00		
		On cover		1,500.	
		Block of 4	1,600.	2,000.	
		P# strip of 3, Impt.	1,600.		
		P# block of 6, Impt.	4,500.		
a.		50c **red orange**	550.00	—	
		Never hinged	1,100.		

Red Overprint

12	A97	$1 **black**, type I (3000)	350.00	400.00
		Never hinged	700.00	
		On cover		3,500.
		Block of 4	1,750.	1,750.
		P# strip of 3, Impt.	1,750.	
		P# block of 6, Impt.	16,000.	
13	A97	$1 **black**, type II	4,500.	—
		Never hinged	—	
		Block of 4	—	
		Nos. 1-8, 10-12 (11)	1,507.	1,900.

Counterfeits of overprint exist.
No. 13 exists only in the special printing.

Special Printing

In March 1900, one pane of 100 stamps of each of Nos. 1-8, 10-12 and two panes of 50 stamps of No. E1 were specially overprinted for displays at the Paris Exposition (1900) and Pan American Exposition (1901). The 2c pane was light red, type IV.

Stamps were handstamped type E "Specimen" in black ink by H. G. Mandel and mounted by him in separate displays for the two Expositions. Additional stamps from each pane were also handstamped "Specimen" but most were destroyed after the Expositions.

J. M. Bartels, a stamp dealer, signed some stamps from these panes "Special Surcharge" in pencil on the gum to authenticate them as coming from the "Mandel" Special Printing panes. In 1904 or later, he handstamped additional surviving examples "Special Surcharge" in red ink on the back as his guarantee. Some of these guaranteed stamps had Mandel's "Specimen" handstamp on the face while others did not. Value (with or without "Specimen" handstamp): Nos. 1-8, 10, each $1,000; Nos. 11, E1, each $1,250; No. 12, $2,000.

SPECIAL DELIVERY STAMP

Special Delivery Stamp of the United States, No. E5 Overprinted diagonally in Red

1899		**Wmk. 191**	**Perf. 12**	
E1	SD3	10c **blue** (5000)	150.	200.
		Never hinged	275.	
		On cover		1,500.
		Block of 4	650.	
		Margin block of 4, arrow	750.	
		P# strip of 3, Impt.	900.	
		P# block of 6, Impt.	4,000.	
a.		Dots in curved frame above messenger (Plate 882)	200.	
		Never hinged	400.	
		P# block of 6, Impt. (Plate 882)	4,250.	

Counterfeits of overprint exist.
The special stamps for Guam were replaced by the regular issues of the United States.

GUAM GUARD MAIL
LOCAL POSTAL SERVICE

Inaugurated April 8, 1930, by Commander Willis W. Bradley, Jr., U.S.N., Governor of Guam, for the conveyance of mail between Agaña and the other smaller towns.

Philippines Nos. 290 and 291 Overprinted

1930, Apr. 8		**Unwmk.**		**Perf. 11**	
M1	A40	2c **green** (2,000)	400.	300.
		Never hinged	575.	
		On cover		600.
		Block of 4	1,700.	
		P# block of 6	—	
M2	A40	4c **carmine** (3,000)	225.	150.
		Never hinged	325.	
		On cover		400.
		Block of 4	950.	
		P# block of 6	—	

Counterfeits of overprint exist.

Seal of Guam — A1

1930, July		**Unwmk.**		**Perf. 12**	
		Without Gum			
M3	A1	1c **red & black** (1,000)	125.00	150.00
		On cover		225.00
		Block of 4	525.00	
M4	A1	2c **black & red** (4,000)	75.00	95.00
		On cover		250.00
		Block of 4	325.00	
a.		Block of 4 with extra impression of vignette covering the intersection of the block	10,000.	

Examples are often found showing parts of watermark "CLEVELAND BOND."

Philippines Nos. 290 and 291
Overprinted in Black

1930, Aug. 10		**Unwmk.**		**Perf. 11**	
M5	A40	2c **green** (20,000)	2.75	4.50
		Never hinged	4.00	
		On cover		75.00
		Block of 4	12.00	
		P# block of 6	125.00	
a.		2c **yellow green**	2.50	4.50
M6	A40	4c **carmine** (80,000)	.50	1.75
		Never hinged	.75	
		On cover		75.00
		Block of 4	2.25	
		P# block of 6	90.00	

Same Overprint in Red on Philippines Nos. 290, 291, 292, 293a, and 294

1930, Dec.					
M7	A40	2c **green** (50,000)	.80	2.00
		Never hinged	1.20	
		On cover		50.00
		Block of 4	3.50	
		P# block of 6	125.00	
a.		GRAUD (Pos. 63) (500)	425.00	
b.		MIAL (Pos. 84) (500)	425.00	
M8	A40	4c **carmine** (50,000)	.85	1.50
		Never hinged	1.30	
		On cover		50.00
		Block of 4	3.50	
		P# block of 6	90.00	
M9	A40	6c **deep violet** (25,000)	2.50	4.50
		Never hinged	3.75	
		On cover		60.00
		Block of 4	11.00	
		P# block of 10, Impt.	250.00	
M10	A40	8c **orange brown** (25,000)	2.50	4.50
		Never hinged	3.75	
		On cover		60.00
		Block of 4	11.00	
		P# block of 10, Impt.	300.00	
M11	A40	10c **deep blue** (25,000)	2.75	4.50
		Never hinged	4.00	
		On cover		60.00
		Block of 4	11.00	
		P# block of 10, Impt.	350.00	

The local postal service was discontinued April 8th, 1931, and replaced by the service of the United States Post Office Department.

SPECIMEN STAMPS

Handstamped U.S. Type E in Purple   *Specimen.*

1899					
1S	E	1c **deep green**	175.00	
2aS	E	2c **rose carmine**, type IV	175.00	
3S	E	3c **purple**	175.00	
4S	E	4c **lilac brown**	175.00	
5S	E	5c **blue**	175.00	
6S	E	6c **lake**	175.00	
7S	E	8c **violet brown**	175.00	
8S	E	10c **brown**, type I	175.00	
10S	E	15c **olive green**	175.00	
11S	E	50c **orange**	350.00	
12S	E	$1 **black**, type I	350.00	
13S	E	$1 **black**, type II	—	

Special Delivery

1899				
E1S	E	10c **blue**	500.00	

Values for specimen stamps are for fine-very fine appearing examples with minor faults.
See note after No. 13 for Special Printings with black "Specimen" overprints.

HAWAII

Until 1893, Hawaii was an independent kingdom. From 1893-1898 it was a republic. The United States annexed Hawaii in 1898, and it became a Territory on June 14, 1900. Hawaiian stamps remained in use through June 13, 1900, and were replaced by U.S. stamps on June 14. In 1959 Hawaii became the 50th State of the Union. Hawaii consists of about 20 islands in the mid-Pacific, about 2,300 miles southwest of San Francisco. The area is 6,434 square miles and the population was estimated at 150,000 in 1899. Honolulu is the capital.

100 CENTS = 1 DOLLAR

Values of Hawaii stamps vary considerably according to condition. Quotations for Nos. 5-82 are for very fine examples. Extremely fine to superb stamps sell at much higher prices, and inferior or poor stamps sell at reduced prices, depending on the condition of the individual example.

A1

A2

A3

1851-52 Unwmk. Typeset Pelure Paper Imperf.

1	A1	2c **blue**	660,000.	250,000.
		On cover		2,100,000.
2	A1	5c **blue**	55,000.	32,500.
		On cover		80,000.
3	A2	13c **blue**	37,000.	28,000.
		On cover		75,000.
4	A3	13c **blue**	52,500.	37,500.
		On cover		80,000.

Nos. 1-4 are known as the "Missionaries."
Two varieties of each. Nos. 1-4, off cover, are almost invariably damaged. Values are for examples with minor damage which has been skillfully repaired.
No. 1 unused and on cover are each unique; the on-cover value is based on a 1995 auction sale.

A4

King
Kamehameha
III — A5

Printed in Sheets of 20 (4x5)

1853 Thick White Wove Paper Engr.

5	A4	5c **blue**	1,000.	1,700.
		On cover		4,000.
		On cover with U.S. #17		12,000.
		Pair	3,850.	4,500.
a.		Line through "Honolulu" (Pos. 2)	3,000.	3,000.
6	A5	13c **dark red**	750.	1,600.
		On cover		32,500.
		On cover with #5		10,000.
		On cover with U.S. #11 (pair)		25,000.
		On cover with U.S. #17		35,000.
		On cover with #5 and U.S. #17		35,000.
		On cover with #8 and U.S. #36b		38,500.
		Pair	2,000.	4,750.
		Block of 4		4,000.

Black Manuscript Surcharge on Scott 6

1857

7	A6	5c on 13c **dark red**	7,000.	10,000.
		On cover with pair U.S. #7 and 15		57,500.
		On cover with pair U.S. #11, 14		55,000.
		On cover with U.S. #14		50,000.
		On cover with U.S. #17		40,000.

1857

Thin White Wove Paper

8	A4	5c **blue**	675.	750.
		On cover		2,800.
		On cover with U.S. #11		—
		On cover with U.S. #7, 15		—
		On cover with U.S. #17		10,000.
		On cover with U.S. #26		—
		On cover with U.S. #35		11,000.
		On cover with U.S. #36		10,000.
		On cover with U.S. #69		12,500.
		On cover with U.S. #76		—
		Pair	1,650.	
		Pair on cover		15,000.
a.		Line through "Honolulu" (Pos. 2)	1,250.	1,250.
		On cover with U.S. #17		6,500.
b.		Double impression	3,500.	4,750.

1861

Thin Bluish Wove Paper

9	A4	5c **blue**	375.	375.
		On cover		4,000.
		On cover with U.S. #36b		3,250.
		On cover with U.S. #65		3,000.
		On cover with U.S. #65, 73		6,500.
		On cover with U.S. #68		4,250.
		On cover with U.S. #76		7,000.
		Block of 4	2,000.	
a.		Line through "Honolulu" (Pos. 2)	800.	1,000.

1868

RE-ISSUE

Ordinary White Wove Paper

10	A4	5c **blue**		25.
		Block of 4		125.
a.		Line through "Honolulu" (Pos. 2)		55.
		In pair with #10		350.
11	A5	13c **dull rose**		300.
		Block of 4		1,400.

Remainders of Nos. 10 and 11 were overprinted "SPECIMEN." See Nos. 10S-11Sb.
Nos. 10 and 11 were never placed in use but stamps (both with and without overprint) were sold at face value at the Honolulu post office.

REPRINTS (Official Imitations) 1889

5c Originals have two small dots near the left side of the square in the upper right corner. These dots are missing in the reprints.
13c The bottom of the 3 of 13 in the upper left corner is flattened in the originals and rounded in the reprints. The "t" of "Cts" on the left side is as tall as the "C" in the reprints, but shorter in the originals.

10R	A4	5c **blue**		60.
		Block of 4		275.
11R	A5	13c **orange red**		300.
		Block of 4		1,400.

On August 19, 1892, the remaining supply of reprints was overprinted in black "REPRINT." The reprints (both with and without overprint) were sold at face value.
Quantities sold (including overprints) were 5c-3634 and 13c-1696. See Nos. 10R-S and 11R-S.

Values for the Numeral stamps, Nos. 12-26, are for four-margin examples. Unused values are for stamps without gum.

A7

A8

A9

1859-62 Typeset from settings of 10 varieties

12	A7	1c **light blue**, *bluish white*	17,500.	15,000.
		Pair		37,500.
a.		"1 Ce" omitted		22,500.
b.		"nt" omitted		—
13	A7	2c **light blue**, *bluish white*	6,250.	5,000.
		On cover		12,500.
		Block of 4	27,500.	
a.		2c **dark blue**, *grayish white*	6,750.	5,000.
		On cover		12,500.
b.		Comma after "Cents"	—	6,750.
		On cover		12,500.
c.		No period after "LETA"	—	—
14	A7	2c **black**, *greenish blue* ('62)	8,000.	5,750.
		On cover		10,000.
a.		"2-Cents."	—	—

1862-63

15	A7	1c **black**, *grayish* ('63)	650.	2,750.
		On cover		3,250.
a.		Tête bêche pair	9,000.	
b.		"NTER"		—
c.		Period omitted after "Postage"	850.	
16	A7	2c **black**, *grayish*	1,000.	800.
		On cover		5,000.
		Pair	—	
a.		"2" at top of rectangle	3,750.	3,750.
		On cover		13,500.
b.		Printed on both sides	—	21,000.
c.		"NTER"	3,250.	6,500.
d.		2c **black**, *grayish white*	1,000.	725.
e.		Period omitted after "Cents"	—	
f.		Overlapping impressions	—	—
g.		"TAGE"	—	
17	A7	2c **dark blue**, *bluish* ('63)	12,000.	8,750.
		Pair	25,000.	
a.		"ISL"	—	
18	A7	2c **black**, *blue gray* ('63)	3,500.	6,000.
		On cover		18,000.
		Pair	—	13,500.
		Thick paper	—	

1864-65

19	A7	1c **black**	550.	10,000.
		Pair	1,150.	
		Block of 4	2,750.	
20	A7	2c **black**	775.	1,500.
		On cover		19,000.
		Pair	1,600.	
		Block of 4	4,000.	
21	A8	5c **blue**, *blue* ('65)	900.	700.
		On cover (pair)		13,000.
		On cover with U.S. #65		—
		On cover with U.S. #68		—
		On cover with U.S. #76		8,250.
		Block of 4	3,600.	
a.		Tête bêche pair	10,500.	
b.		5c **bluish black**, *grayish white*	12,500.	3,500.

No. 21b unused is unique. Value based on 1995 auction sale. No. 21b used is also unique but defective. Value based on 2007 auction sale.

22	A9	5c **blue**, *blue* ('65)	575.	900.
		On cover with U.S. #76		9,250.
		On cover with U.S. #63 and 76		—
		Block of 4	2,600.	
a.		Tête bêche pair	20,000.	
b.		5c **blue**, *grayish white*	—	
c.		Overlapping impressions	—	—

1864
Laid Paper
23	A7	1c black	300.	2,500.
		On cover with U.S. #76		12,000.
		Block of 4	1,250.	
a.		"HA" instead of "HAWAIIAN"	3,750.	
b.		Tête bêche pair	6,250.	
c.		Tête bêche pair, Nos. 23, 23a	18,000.	
24	A7	2c black	325.	1,050.
		Block of 4	1,350.	
a.		"NTER"	3,750.	
b.		"S" of "POSTAGE" omitted	1,500.	
c.		Tête bêche pair	5,500.	

A10

King Kamehameha IV — A11

1865
Wove Paper
25	A10	1c dark blue	350.	
		Block of 4	1,450.	
a.		Double impression	—	
b.		With inverted impression of No. 21 on face	18,500.	
26	A10	2c dark blue	350.	
		Block of 4	1,450.	

Nos. 12 to 26 were typeset and were printed in sheets of 50 (5 settings of 10 varieties each). The sheets were cut into panes of 25 (5x5) before distribution to the post offices.

1861-63   Litho.
Horizontally Laid Paper
27	A11	2c pale rose	325.	300.
		On cover		1,000.
		Pair		
a.		2c carmine rose ('63)	3,000.	2,500.

Vertically Laid Paper
28	A11	2c pale rose	325.	325.
		On cover		1,500.
		Block of 4	1,750.	1,650.
a.		2c carmine rose ('63)	350.	375.
		On cover		2,000.
		Block of 4	1,700.	

RE-ISSUE
1869   Engr.   Thin Wove Paper
29	A11	2c red	45.00	—
		Block of 4	225.00	

No. 29 was not issued for postal purposes although canceled examples are known. It was sold only at the Honolulu post office, at first without overprint and later with overprint "CANCELLED." See No. 29S.
See note following No. 51.

Princess Victoria Kamamalu — A12

King Kamehameha IV — A13

King Kamehameha V — A14

Kamehameha V — A15

Mataio Kekuanaoa — A16

1864-86   Engr.   Wove Paper   Perf. 12
30	A12	1c purple ('86)	11.00	8.00
		Never hinged	27.50	
		On cover		150.00
		Block of 4	55.00	
a.		1c mauve ('71)	60.00	20.00
		Never hinged	100.00	
		Block of 4	300.00	
b.		1c violet ('78)	20.00	10.00
		Never hinged	50.00	
		Block of 4	160.00	200.00
31	A13	2c rose vermilion	65.00	9.00
		Never hinged	160.00	
		On cover		200.00
		On cover with U.S. #76		1,000.
		Block of 4	275.00	400.00
a.		2c vermilion ('86)	45.00	20.00
		Never hinged	110.00	
		On cover		150.00
b.		Half used as 1c on cover with #32		8,500.
		As "b," with U.S. #117		18,000.
32	A14	5c blue ('66)	175.00	30.00
		Never hinged	400.00	
		On cover		250.00
		On cover with any U.S. issues of 1861-67		4,000.
		On cover with U.S. #116		17,500.
		On cover with U.S. #116 and 69		25,000.
		Block of 4	800.00	175.00
33	A15	6c yellow green ('71)	45.00	9.00
		Never hinged	110.00	
		On cover		300.00
a.		6c bluish green ('78)	35.00	9.00
		Never hinged	87.50	
		On cover		300.00
		On cover with U.S. #179		1,500.
		On cover with U.S. #183 + #184		1,750.
		On cover with U.S. #185		800.00
		Block of 4	160.00	500.00
b.		As "a," horiz. pair, imperf.	2,250.	
34	A16	18c dull rose ('71)	95.00	37.50
		Never hinged	230.00	
		On cover		350.00
		On cover with No. 36		
		On cover with No. 36 and U.S. No. 179		2,000.
		On cover with U.S. No. 161		—
		On cover with U.S. No. 163		—
		On cover with U.S. No. 185		10,000.
		Block of 4	475.00	
		Nos. 30-34 (5)	391.00	93.50
		Set, never hinged	927.50	

Half of No. 31 was used with a 5c stamp to make up the 6-cent rate to the United States.
No. 32 has traces of rectangular frame lines surrounding the design. Nos. 39 and 52C have no such frame lines.

King David Kalakaua — A17

Prince William Pitt Leleiohoku — A18

1875
35	A17	2c brown	9.00	3.00
		Never hinged	22.00	
		On cover		200.00
		Block of 4	45.00	40.00
36	A18	12c black	65.00	27.50
		Never hinged	165.00	
		On cover		400.00
		On cover with U.S. No. 161		—
		On cover with U.S. No. 179b		—
		Block of 4	350.00	

Princess Likelike — A19

King David Kalakaua — A20

Queen Kapiolani — A21

Statue of King Kamehameha I — A22

King William Lunalilo — A23

Queen Emma Kaleleonalani — A24

1882
37	A19	1c blue	11.00	6.00
		Never hinged	29.00	
		On cover		60.00
		Block of 4	55.00	50.00
38	A17	2c lilac rose	125.00	45.00
		Never hinged	275.00	
		On cover		150.00
		Block of 4	625.00	
39	A14	5c ultramarine	15.00	3.25
		Never hinged	37.50	
		On cover		27.50
		Block of 4	75.00	60.00
a.		Vert. pair, imperf. horiz.	5,000.	6,000.

40	A20	10c	**black**	47.50	22.50
			Never hinged	120.00	
			On cover		160.00
			Block of 4	200.00	140.00
41	A21	15c	**red brown**	65.00	25.00
			Never hinged	160.00	
			On cover		200.00
			Block of 4	300.00	200.00
			Nos. 37-41 (5)	263.50	101.75
			Set, never hinged	621.00	

1883-86

42	A19	1c	**green**	3.25	2.00
			Never hinged	8.00	
			On cover		25.00
			Block of 4	15.00	14.00
43	A17	2c	**rose** ('86)	4.50	1.00
			Never hinged	11.00	
			On cover		25.00
			Block of 4	22.50	12.50
a.		2c	**dull red**	62.50	21.00
			Never hinged	140.00	
			Block of 4	310.00	
44	A20	10c	**red brown** ('84)	37.50	10.00
			Never hinged	95.00	
			On cover		125.00
			Block of 4	175.00	100.00
45	A20	10c	**vermilion**	42.50	12.50
			Never hinged	105.00	
			On cover		125.00
			Block of 4	200.00	80.00
46	A18	12c	**red lilac**	85.00	32.50
			Never hinged	225.00	
			On cover		425.00
			Block of 4	425.00	240.00
47	A22	25c	**dark violet**	150.00	60.00
			Never hinged	350.00	
			On cover		375.00
			Block of 4	675.00	350.00
48	A23	50c	**red**	190.00	85.00

			Never hinged	425.00	
			On cover		525.00
			Block of 4	950.00	250.00
49	A24	$1	**rose red**	275.00	250.00
			Never hinged	625.00	
			On cover		8,000.
			Block of 4	1,450.	
			Maltese cross cancellation		100.00
			Nos. 42-49 (8)	787.75	453.00
			Set, never hinged	1,884.	

Other fiscal cancellations exist on No. 49.
Nos. 48-49 are valued used with postal cancels. Canceled-to-order cancels exist and are worth less.

REPRODUCTION and REPRINT
Yellowish Wove Paper

1886-89			Engr.		*Imperf.*
50	A11	2c	orange vermilion	160.00	
			Never hinged	275.00	
			Block of 4	800.00	
51	A11	2c	carmine ('89)	30.00	
			Never hinged	50.00	
			Block of 4	140.00	

In 1885 the Postmaster General wished to have on sale complete sets of Hawaii's portrait stamps, but was unable to find either the stone from which Nos. 27 and 28, or the plate from which No. 29 was printed. He therefore sent a copy of No. 29 to the American Bank Note Company, with an order to engrave a new plate like it and print 10,000 stamps therefrom, of which 5000 were overprinted "SPECIMEN" in blue.

The original No. 29 was printed in sheets of fifteen (5x3), but the plate of these "Official Imitations" was made up of fifty stamps (10x5). Later, in 1887, the original die for No. 29 was discovered and, after retouching, a new plate was made and 37,500 stamps were printed (No. 51). These, like the originals, were printed in sheets of fifteen. They were delivered during 1889 and 1890. In 1892 all remaining unsold in the Post Office were overprinted "Reprint".

No. 29 is red in color, and printed on very thin white wove paper. No. 50 is orange vermilion in color, on medium, white to buff paper. In No. 50 the vertical line on the left side of the portrait touches the horizontal line over the label "Elua Keneta", while in the other two varieties, Nos. 29 and 51, it does not touch the horizontal line by half a millimeter. In No. 51 there are three parallel lines on the left side of the King's nose, while in No. 29 and No. 50 there are no such lines. No. 51 is carmine in color and printed on thick, yellowish to buff, wove paper.

It is claimed that both Nos. 50 and 51 were available for postage, although not made to fill a postal requirement. They exist with favor cancellation. No. 51 also is known postally used. See Nos. 50S-51S.

Queen Liliuokalani — A25

1890-91					*Perf. 12*
52	A25	2c	**dull violet** ('91)	5.00	1.50
			Never hinged	12.50	
			On cover		25.00
			Block of 4	25.00	12.00
a.			Vert. pair, imperf. horiz.	4,000.	
52C	A14	5c	**deep indigo**	120.00	150.00
			Never hinged	275.00	
			On cover		500.00
			Block of 4	575.00	

Stamps of 1864-91
Overprinted in Red

Three categories of double overprints:
I. Both overprints heavy.
II. One overprint heavy, one of moderate strength.
III. One overprint heavy, one of light or weak strength.

1893

53	A12	1c	**purple**	8.50	12.50
			Never hinged	21.50	
			On cover		35.00
			Block of 4	42.50	70.00
a.			"189" instead of "1893"	575.00	—
b.			No period after "GOVT"	265.00	250.00
f.			Double overprint (III)	600.00	
54	A19	1c	**blue**	8.50	12.50
			Never hinged	22.50	
			On cover		40.00
			Block of 4	45.00	67.50
b.			No period after "GOVT"	140.00	140.00
e.			Double overprint (II)	1,500.	
f.			Double overprint (III)	400.00	

55	A19	1c	**green**	1.75	*3.00*
			Never hinged	4.50	
			On cover		25.00
			Block of 4	8.00	15.00
d.			Double overprint (I)	625.00	450.00
f.			Double overprint (III)	200.00	250.00
g.			Pair, one without ovpt.	10,000.	
56	A17	2c	**brown**	12.00	*20.00*
			Never hinged	28.50	
			On cover		60.00
			Block of 4	60.00	120.00
b.			No period after "GOVT"	300.00	
57	A25	2c	**dull violet**	1.50	1.25
			Never hinged	3.50	
			On cover		25.00
			Block of 4	6.50	6.50
a.			"18 3" instead of "1893"	850.00	850.00
d.			Double overprint (I)	1,300.	650.00
f.			Double overprint (III)	175.00	175.00
g.			Inverted overprint	4,000.	4,500.
58	A14	5c	**deep indigo**	13.00	*25.00*
			Never hinged	32.00	
			On cover		100.00
			Block of 4	65.00	140.00
b.			No period after "GOVT"	250.00	250.00
f.			Double overprint (III)	1,250.	650.00
59	A14	5c	**ultramarine**	6.50	2.50
			Never hinged	15.00	
			On cover		40.00
			Block of 4	32.50	20.00
d.			Double overprint (I)	6,500.	
e.			Double overprint (II)	4,000.	4,000.
f.			Double overprint (III)		600.00
g.			Inverted overprint	1,500.	1,500.
60	A15	6c	**green**	17.50	*25.00*
			Never hinged	40.00	
			On cover		140.00
			Block of 4	85.00	125.00
e.			Double overprint (II)	1,000.	
61	A20	10c	**black**	12.00	*15.00*
			Never hinged	30.00	
			On cover		125.00
			Block of 4	60.00	82.50
e.			Double overprint (II)	900.00	650.00
f.			Double overprint (III)	200.00	
61B	A20	10c	**red brown**	14,000.	*29,000.*
			Block of 4	60,000.	
			Strip of 5, plate imprint	75,000.	
62	A18	12c	**black**	12.00	*17.50*
			Never hinged	30.00	
			On cover		150.00
			Block of 4	62.50	110.00
d.			Double overprint (I)	2,000.	
e.			Double overprint (II)	1,750.	
63	A18	12c	**red lilac**	165.00	*250.00*
			Never hinged	400.00	
			On cover		550.00
			Block of 4	950.00	—
64	A22	25c	**dark violet**	32.00	*40.00*
			Never hinged	72.00	
			On cover		225.00
			Block of 4	150.00	200.00
b.			No period after "GOVT"	350.00	350.00
f.			Double overprint (III)	1,000.	
			Nos. 53-61,62-64 (12)	290.25	424.25
			Nos. 53-61, 62-64 never hinged	699.50	

Virtually all known examples of No. 61B are cut in at the top.

Overprinted in Black

65	A13	2c	**vermilion**	80.00	*75.00*
			Never hinged	200.00	
			On cover		450.00
			Block of 4	350.00	500.00
b.			No period after "GOVT"	260.00	260.00
66	A17	2c	**rose**	1.25	*2.25*
			Never hinged	3.00	
			On cover		25.00
			Block of 4	6.50	11.00
b.			No period after "GOVT"	50.00	60.00
d.			Double overprint (I)	4,000.	
e.			Double overprint (II)	2,750.	
f.			Double overprint (III)	300.00	
66C	A15	6c	**green**	14,000.	*29,000.*
			On cover		—
			Block of 4	60,000.	
67	A20	10c	**vermilion**	20.00	*30.00*
			Never hinged	50.00	
			On cover		125.00
			Block of 4	100.00	180.00
f.			Double overprint (III)	1,250.	
68	A20	10c	**red brown**	10.00	*13.00*
			Never hinged	25.00	
			On cover		100.00
			Block of 4	50.00	75.00
f.			Double overprint (III)	4,000.	
69	A18	12c	**red lilac**	325.00	*500.00*
			Never hinged	575.00	
			On cover		950.00
			Block of 4	1,500.	2,400.
70	A21	15c	**red brown**	22.50	*30.00*
			Never hinged	50.00	
			On cover		300.00
			Block of 4	110.00	150.00
e.			Double overprint (II)	2,000.	
71	A16	18c	**dull rose**	35.00	*35.00*
			Never hinged	75.00	
			On cover		225.00
			Block of 4	160.00	175.00
a.			"18 3" instead of "1893"	500.00	500.00
b.			No period after "GOVT"	300.00	300.00
d.			Double overprint (I)	600.00	
f.			Double overprint (III)	250.00	
g.			Pair, one without ovpt.	3,500.	
h.			As "b," double overprint (II)	1,750.	
72	A23	50c	**red**	75.00	*90.00*
			Never hinged	175.00	
			On cover		600.00

	Block of 4	350.00	*500.00*
b.	No period after "GOVT"	*450.00*	*450.00*
	Never hinged	675.00	
f.	Double overprint (III)	*1,000.*	
73 A24	$1 **rose red**	140.00	*175.00*
	Never hinged	300.00	
	On cover		775.00
	Block of 4	600.00	*875.00*
b.	No period after "GOVT"	*450.00*	*425.00*
	Nos. 65-66,67-73 (9)	*708.75*	*950.25*
	Nos. 65-66, 67-73 never hinged	1,453.	

Coat of Arms — A26

View of Honolulu — A27

Statue of Kamehameha I — A28

Stars and Palms — A29

S. S. "Arawa" — A30

Pres. Sanford Ballard Dole — A31

"CENTS" Added — A32

1894

74	A26	1c **yellow**	2.25	1.50
		Never hinged	6.00	
		On cover		25.00
		Block of 4	10.00	8.50
75	A27	2c **brown**	2.25	.60
		Never hinged	6.00	
		On cover		25.00
		Block of 4	9.00	7.00
		"Flying goose" flaw (48 LR 2)	550.00	400.00
		Never hinged	*1,400.*	
		Double transfer	5.00	5.00
76	A28	5c **rose lake**	5.00	2.00
		Never hinged	13.00	
		On cover		25.00
		Block of 4	25.00	15.00
77	A29	10c **yellow green**	7.50	5.00
		Never hinged	20.00	
		On cover		45.00
		Block of 4	35.00	25.00
78	A30	12c **blue**	15.00	*17.50*
		Never hinged	40.00	
		On cover		150.00
		Block of 4	65.00	*80.00*
		Double transfer	22.50	25.00
79	A31	25c **deep blue**	20.00	13.50
		Never hinged	52.50	

	On cover		100.00
	Block of 4	100.00	—
	Nos. 74-79 (6)	52.00	*40.10*
Set, never hinged		137.50	

Numerous double transfers exist on Nos. 75 and 81.

1899

80	A26	1c **dark green**	2.00	1.50
		Never hinged	5.00	
		On cover		25.00
		Block of 4	9.50	7.00
81	A27	2c **rose**	1.40	1.00
		Never hinged	3.50	
		On cover		20.00
		Block of 4	6.00	6.00
		Double transfer	—	—
		"Flying goose" flaw (48 LR 2)	350.00	350.00
		Never hinged	850.00	
a.		2c **salmon**	1.50	1.25
		Never hinged	4.00	
b.		Vert. pair, imperf. horiz.	4,500.	
82	A32	5c **blue**	8.00	3.25
		Never hinged	20.00	
		On cover		25.00
		Block of 4	40.00	55.00
Set, never hinged		28.50	

OFFICIAL STAMPS

Lorrin Andrews Thurston — O1

1896		Engr.	Unwmk.	*Perf. 12*	
O1	O1	2c **green**		45.00	19.00
		Never hinged		110.00	
		On cover			400.00
		Block of 4		200.00	
O2	O1	5c **black brown**		45.00	19.00
		Never hinged		110.00	
		On cover			450.00
		Block of 4		200.00	
O3	O1	6c **deep ultramarine**		45.00	19.00
		Never hinged		110.00	
		On cover			—
		Block of 4		200.00	
O4	O1	10c **bright rose**		45.00	19.00
		Never hinged		110.00	
		On cover			500.00
		Block of 4		200.00	
O5	O1	12c **orange**		55.00	19.00
		Never hinged		135.00	
		On cover			—
		Block of 4		260.00	
O6	O1	25c **gray violet**		65.00	19.00
		Never hinged		160.00	
		On cover			—
		Block of 4		300.00	
		Nos. O1-O6 (6)		300.00	114.00
		Set, never hinged		735.00	

Used values for Nos. O1-O6 are for stamps canceled-to-order "FOREIGN OFFICE/HONOLULU H.I." in double circle without date. Values of postally used stamps: Nos. O1-O2, O4, $35 each; No. O3, $100; No. O5, $125; No. O6, $150.

ENVELOPES

Italicized numbers in parentheses indicate quantities issued.
All printed by American Bank Note Co., N.Y.

View of Honolulu Harbor — E1

Envelopes of White Paper, Outside and Inside

1884				
U1	E1	1c **light green** *(109,000)*	2.50	3.00
		Entire	6.00	*15.00*
a.		1c **green** *(10,000)*	6.00	15.00

		Entire	15.00	*90.00*
b.		1c **dark green**	10.00	10.00
		Entire	25.00	75.00
U2	E1	2c **carmine** *(386,000 including U2a, U2b)*	2.50	4.00
		Entire	5.00	*17.50*
a.		2c **red**	2.50	4.00
		Entire	5.00	*17.50*
b.		2c **rose**	2.50	4.00
		Entire	5.00	*17.50*
c.		2c **pale pink** *(5,000)*	30.00	30.00
		Entire	90.00	100.00
U3	E1	4c **red** *(18,000)*	25.00	30.00
		Entire	50.00	150.00
U4	E1	5c **blue** *(90,775)*	6.50	7.50
		Entire	17.50	*30.00*
U5	E1	10c **black** *(3,500 plus)*	37.50	37.50
		Entire	100.00	*150.00*

Envelopes White Outside, Blue Inside

U6	E1	2c **rose**	175.00	225.00
		Entire	475.00	*1,500.*
U7	E1	4c **red**	175.00	225.00
		Entire	475.00	—
U8	E1	5c **blue**	175.00	225.00
		Entire	475.00	*1,250.*
U9	E1	10c **black**	300.00	450.00
		Entire	500.00	—
		Nos. U1-U9 (9)	899.00	*1,207.*

Nos. U1, U2, U4 & U5 Overprinted Locally "Provisional Government 1893" in Red or Black

1893				
U10	E1	1c **light green** (R) *(16,000)*	6.00	11.00
		Entire	12.00	*30.00*
a.		Double overprint	*1,750.*	
		Entire	*6,000.*	
U11	E1	2c **carmine** (Bk) *(37,000)*	3.00	4.00
		Entire	6.00	20.00
a.		Double overprint	500.00	
		Entire	*1,100.*	*1,250.*
b.		Double overprint, one inverted, entire	*1,500.*	

No. U11 is known as an unused entire with a triple overprint, two of the overprints being at the bottom right portion of the envelope. Unique. Value, $9,500.

U12	E1	5c **blue** (R) *(34,891)*	5.00	5.00
		Entire	10.00	15.00
a.		Double overprint	375.00	*400.00*
		Entire	600.00	*3,000.*
b.		Triple overprint, entire	*7,500.*	
U13	E1	10c **black** (R) *(17,707 incl. No. U14)*	15.00	20.00
		Entire	27.50	*125.00*
a.		Double overprint, entire	*1,800.*	*2,000.*

Envelope No. U9 with same overprint

U14	E1	10c **black** (R)	325.	750.00
		Entire	*1,100.*	—

SPECIAL DELIVERY ENVELOPE

Value is for Entire.
Envelope No. U5 with added inscription "Special Despatch Letter" etc. in red at top left corner

1885			
UE1	E1	10c **black** *(2,000)*	225.

Envelope No. UE1 was prepared for use but never issued for postal purposes. Postally used examples exist, but no special delivery service was performed. Favor cancellations exist.

POSTAL CARDS

All printed by American Bank Note Co., N.Y.
Values are for entires.

Queen Liliuokalani — PC1

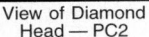

View of Diamond
Head — PC2

Royal
Emblems — PC3

1882-92				Engr.
UX1	PC1	1c **red**, *buff* (125,000)	30.00	75.00
UX2	PC2	2c **black** (45,000)	50.00	90.00
a.		Lithographed ('92)	150.00	250.00
UX3	PC3	3c **blue green** (21,426)	60.00	125.00

1889				Litho.
UX4	PC1	1c **red**, *buff* (171,240)	25.00	50.00

Cards Nos. UX4, UX2a and UX3 overprinted locally
"Provisional Government 1893" in red or black

1893				
UX5	PC1	1c **red**, *buff* (Bk) (28,760)	30.00	75.00
a.		Double overprint	4,000.	3,500.
UX6	PC2	2c **black** (R) (10,000)	55.00	95.00

No. UX6 is known unused with double overprint, one inverted
at lower left of card. Unique. Value, $16,000.

UX7	PC3	3c **blue green** (R) (8,574)	65.00	250.00
a.		Double overprint	1,750.	

Iolani
Palace — PC4

Map of Pacific Ocean, Mercator's Projection — PC5

1894-97				Litho.
		Border Frame 131½x72½mm		
UX8	PC4	1c **red**, *buff* (100,000)	20.00	40.00
a.		Border frame 132½x74mm ('97) (200,000)	20.00	40.00
UX9	PC5	2c **green** (60,000)	45.00	80.00
a.		Border frame 132½x74mm ('97) (190,000)	45.00	80.00

PAID REPLY POSTAL CARDS
Double cards, same designs as postal cards
with added inscriptions on reply cards.

1883				Litho.
UY1	PC1	1c +1c **purple**, *buff*, unsevered (5,000)	400.00	450.00
m.		Message card, detached	35.00	100.00
r.		Reply card, detached	35.00	100.00
UY2	PC2	2c +2c **dark blue**, unsevered (5,000)	450.00	500.00
m.		Message card, detached	55.00	140.00
r.		Reply card, detached	55.00	140.00

1889				
UY3	PC1	1c +1c **gray violet**, *buff*, unsevered (5,000)	400.00	450.00
m.		Message card, detached	35.00	100.00
r.		Reply card, detached	35.00	100.00

UY4	PC2	2c +2c **sapphire**, unsevered (5,000)	400.00	450.00
m.		Message card, detached	35.00	80.00
r.		Reply card, detached	35.00	80.00

Values for unused unsevered Paid Reply Postal Cards are for
cards which have not been folded. Folded cards sell for about
33% of these values.

Detached card used values are for canceled cards with
printed messages on the back.

REVENUE STAMPS

R1

R2

R3

R4

R5

R6

Printed by the American Bank Note Co.
Sheets of 70

1877		Engr.	Unwmk.	Rouletted 8
R1	R1	25c **green** (160,000)	15.00	16.00
		Never hinged	37.50	
R2	R2	50c **yellow orange** (190,000)	35.00	15.00
		Never hinged	85.00	
R3	R3	$1 **black** (580,000)	35.00	9.00
		Never hinged	85.00	
a.		$1 gray	35.00	9.00
		Never hinged	85.00	

Denominations Typo.

R4	R4	$5 **vermilion & violet blue** (21,000)	145.00	50.00
		Never hinged	350.00	

R5	R5	$10 **reddish brown & green** (14,000)	145.00	50.00
		Never hinged	350.00	
R6	R6	$50 **slate blue & carmine** (3,500)	1,050.	400.00

No. R6 unused is valued without gum, as all known examples
come thus.

Unused values for all revenues except No. R6 are for
stamps with original gum. Apparently unused stamps without gum sell for less.

No. R1 Surcharged in Black or Gold

a

b

1893-94				
R7	R1 (a)	20c on 25c **green**	45.00	27.50
		Never hinged	90.00	
a.		Inverted surcharge	1,250.	900.00
R8	R1 (b)	20c on 25c **green** (G)	90.00	90.00
		Never hinged	175.00	
a.		Inverted surcharge	—	
b.		Double surcharge	—	—
c.		Double surcharge, one black, one gold	—	1,500.
d.		Double surcharge, one gold, one red in different font	—	
e.		Double surcharge, with a single added letter "c"	—	
f.		Double surcharge with two "c" letters added	—	

On No. R8b, one surcharge is always diagonal. On No. R8c,
the black surcharge is 20mm wide, while the normal gold
surcharge is 15mm wide.

R7

Kamehameha I — R8

Sheets of 50

1894		Litho.		Perf. 14
R9	R7	20c **red** (10,000)	350.00	375.00
		Never hinged	850.00	
a.		Imperf. (25,000)	700.00	1,200.
		Never hinged	1,700.	
		Pair	1,600.	
		Never hinged	3,600.	

No. R9a is known in an unused pair on paper with "DENNIS"
papermaker's watermark.

R10	R7	25c **violet brown**	1,300.	1,000.
		Never hinged	2,400.	
a.		Imperf.	1,900.	
		Never hinged	3,800.	—
		Pair	4,250.	
		Never hinged	7,900.	
b.		As "a," tete beche pair		

Printed by the American Bank Note Co.
Sheets of 100

1897		Engr.		Perf. 12
R11	R8	$1 **dark blue** (60,000)	10.00	9.00
		Never hinged	20.00	

R9

1901   *Rouletted 8*

R12	R9	$50	**slate blue & carmine** *(7,000)*	60.00 65.00
			Never hinged	130.00

Types of 1877
Printed by the American Bank Note Co.
Sheets of 70

1910-13   Engr.   *Perf. 12*

R13	R2	50c	**yellow orange** ('13) *(70,000)*	15.00 30.00
			Never hinged	32.50
R14	R3	$1	**black** ('13) *(35,000)*	21.00 *35.00*
			Never hinged	45.00
R15	R4	$5	**vermilion & violet blue** *(14,000)*	40.00 *60.00*
			Never hinged	90.00
a.			Denomination inverted	—
R16	R5	$10	**reddish brown & green** *(14,000)*	40.00 *60.00*
			Never hinged	90.00

PROOFS and TRIAL COLOR PROOFS

The large die proofs range in size and format from die impressions on India die sunk on cards generally up to 6x9 inches, through die impressions on India on or off card in medium to stamp size. Many individual listings are known in more than one size and format. Values reflect the size and format most commonly seen.

			DIE	PLATE
			(1) Large	(3) India (4) Card

1853

5TC	5c	**black** on wove		*6,000.*
6TC	13c	**black** on wove		*6,000.*

1868-89

10TC	5c	**orange red**	*1,000.*	
11TC	13c	**orange red**	*1,000.*	800.
11RP	13c	**orange red**	*2,500.*	800.

1861-63

27TC	2c	**black**		*1,000.*

1864-71

30P	1c	**purple**	900.	350.
		Block of 4		1,000.
31P	2c	**rose vermilion**	900.	350. 350.
		Block of 4		—
31TC	2c	**green**	*1,700.*	
32P	5c	**blue**	900.	350. 350.
32TC	5c	**black**	*1,250.*	
32TC	5c	**dark red**		350.
32TC	5c	**orange red**		350.
32TC	5c	**orange**		350.
32TC	5c	**red brown**		350.
		Block of 4		1,800.
32TC	5c	**green**		350.
		Block of 4		1,800.
32TC	5c	**dark violet**		350.
		Block of 4		1,800.
33P	6c	**green**	900.	350.
		Block of 4		1,800.
34P	18c	**dull rose**	900.	350. 350.
		Block of 4		1,800.
34TC	18c	**orange red**	900.	650.
34TC	18c	**dark orange**	900.	

1875

35P	2c	**brown**	900.	350. 350.
		Block of 4		1,800.
35TC	2c	**black**	*2,600.*	
36P	12c	**black**	900.	350. 350.
36TC	12c	**violet blue**	900.	

1882

37P	1c	**blue**		350.
		Block of 4		1,800.
37TC	1c	**black**	*3,750.*	
39P	5c	**ultramarine**	900.	350.
40P	10c	**black**	900.	350.
		Block of 4		1,800.
41P	15c	**red brown**		190. 350.
		Block of 4		1,800.

1883-86

42P	1c	**green**		350. 350.
		Block of 4		1,800.
43P	2c	**rose**		350. 350.

		Block of 4		1,800.	
47P	25c	**dark violet**	900.	190.	
		Block of 4		1,800.	
47TC	25c	**black**	*1,000.*		
48P	50c	**red**	1,000.	230.	
		Block of 4		1,800.	
48TC	50c	**lake**	*1,300.*	500.	
49P	$1	**rose red**	*2,100.*	350.	500.
		Block of 4		1,800.	
49TC	$1	**black**		190.	
49TC	$1	**orange red**	1,000.	*1,000.*	
49TC	$1	**carmine**		*1,000.*	
49TC	$1	**vermilion**		*1,000.*	
		Block of 4		*1,800.*	

1886-89

50P	2c	**orange vermilion**	1,000.	500.	
51P	2c	**carmine**	1,000.		

1890-91

52P	2c	**dull violet**	*4,000.*	500.	500.
52CP	5c	**deep indigo**		500.	

1894

74P	1c	**yellow**	1,000.	350.	350.
75P	2c	**brown**	1,000.	350.	
75TC	2c	**dark green**	1,000.		
76P	5c	**rose lake**	1,000.	350.	350.
77P	10c	**yellow green**	1,000.	350.	350.
		Block of 4		1,800.	
77TC	10c	**deep blue green**	1,000.		
78P	12c	**blue**	1,000.	300.	350.
79P	25c	**deep blue**	1,000.	300.	350.

1899

82P	5c	**blue**		190.	350.
		Block of 4		1,800.	

Official

1896

O1P	2c		1,000.	500.	350.
O2P	5c	**black brown**	1,000.	500.	350.
O3P	6c	**deep ultramarine**	1,000.	500.	350.
O4P	10c	**bright rose**	1,000.	—	350.
		Block of 4			
O4TC	10c	**black**	1,000.		
O5P	12c	**orange**	1,000.	500.	350.
O5TC	12c	**black**	1,000.		
O6P	25c	**gray violet**	1,000.	500.	350.
O6TC	25c	**black**	1,000.		

Envelopes
Uncleared indicia only

1884

U1P	1c	**green**	*1,000.*
U1TC	1c	**black**	*1,000.*
U1TC	1c	**orange**	*1,000.*
U2P	2c	**carmine**	*1,000.*
U2TC	2c	**black**	*1,000.*
U2TC	2c	**blue**	*1,000.*
U3P	4c	**red**	*1,000.*
U3TC	4c	**black**	*1,000.*
U4P	5c	**blue**	*1,000.*
U4TC	5c	**black**	*1,000.*
U5P	10c	**black**	*1,000.*

Postal Cards
Large die proofs are of indicia only, India proofs are entire card.

1882-95

UX1P	1c	**red**	*3,500.*	*2,000.*
UX1TC	1c	**green**		*2,000.*
UX2P	2c	**black**		*2,000.*
UX3P	3c	**blue green**		*3,000.*
UX8TC	1c	**orange**		*3,000.*
UX8TC	1c	**brown**		*3,000.*

Revenues

			DIE	PLATE	
			(1) Large	(3) India	(4) Card

1877-97

R1P	25c	**green**		*600.*	600.
		Block of 4		*2,750.*	
R1TC	25c	**blue green**	*1,150.*		
R1TC	25c	**black**	*1,150.*		
R1TC	25c	**brown red**	*1,150.*		
R1TC	25c	**brown**	*1,150.*		
R1TC	25c	**grayish blue**	*1,150.*		
R2P	50c	**yellow orange**		*600.*	600.
		Block of 4		*2,800.*	
R2TC	50c	**blue green**	*1,150.*		
R2TC	50c	**black**	*1,150.*		
R2TC	50c	**brown red**	*1,150.*		
R2TC	50c	**brown**	*1,150.*		
R2TC	50c	**grayish blue**	*1,150.*		
R3P	$1	**black**	*1,150.*		600.
		Block of 4		*2,750.*	
R3TC	$1	**blue green**	*1,150.*		
R3TC	$1	**brown red**	*1,150.*		
R3TC	$1	**brown**	*1,150.*		
R3TC	$1	**grayish blue**	*1,150.*		
R4P	$5	**vermilion & violet blue**			350.
				2,750.	
R5P	$10	**reddish brown & green**		*600.*	600.
		Block of 4		*2,750.*	

			DIE	PLATE	
			(1) Large	(3) India	(4) Card

R6P	$50	**slate blue & carmine**			800.
		Block of 4		*2,750.*	
R11P	$1	**dark blue**	*1,250.*	800.	700.

SPECIMEN STAMPS

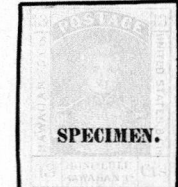

Overprinted in Black or Red — Type A

1868

10S	A	5c	**blue** (R)	25.
			Block of 4	125.
a.			Line through "Honolulu" (Pos. 2)	100.
11S	A	13c	**dull rose**	25.
			Block of 4	125.

Overprinted in Black — Type B

11S	B	13c	**dull rose**	275.
			Block of 4	1,250.
a.			Double overprint, as #11S A, one as #11S B	*4,000.*
b.			Period omitted (Pos. 18, 20)	575.

Overprinted in Black — Type C

1889

10RS	C	5c	**blue**	60.
			Block of 4	250.
11RS	C	13c	**orange red**	225.
			Block of 4	950.

Overprinted in Black — Type D

1869

29S	D	2c	**red**	50.
			Block of 4	250.

Overprinted in Blue — Type E

1886

50S	E	2c	**orange vermilion**	60.
			Block of 4	250.

Overprinted in Black — Type C

1889				
51S	C	2c	carmine	30.
			Block of 4	150.

PHILIPPINES

Issued under U.S. Administration

Following the American occupation of the Philippines, May 1, 1898, after Admiral Dewey's fleet entered Manila Bay, an order was issued by the U. S. Postmaster General (No. 201, May 24, 1898) establishing postal facilities with rates similar to the domestic rates.

Military postal stations were established as branch post offices, each such station being placed within the jurisdiction of the nearest regular post office. Supplies were issued to these military stations through the regular post office of which they were branches.

Several post office clerks were sent to the Philippines and the San Francisco post office was made the nearest regular office for the early Philippine mail and the postmarks of the period point out this fact.

U.S. stamps overprinted "PHILIPPINES" were placed on sale in Manila June 30, 1899. Regular U.S. stamps had been in use from early March, and at the Manila post office Spanish stamps were also acceptable.

The first regular post office was established at Cavite on July 30, 1898, as a branch of the San Francisco post office. The first cancellation was a dated handstamp with "PHILIPPINE STATION" and "SAN FRANCISCO, CAL."

On May 1, 1899, the entire Philippine postal service was separated from San Francisco and numerous varieties of postmarks resulted. Many of the early used stamps show postmarks and cancellations of the Military Station, Camp or R.P.O. types, together with "Killers" of the types employed in the U.S. at the time.

The Philippines became a commonwealth of the United States on November 15, 1935, the High Commissioner of the United States taking office on the same day. The official name of the government was "Commonwealth of the Philippines" as provided by Article 17 of the Constitution. Upon the final and complete withdrawal of sovereignty of the United States and the proclamation of Philippine independence on July 4, 1946, the Commonwealth of the Philippines became the "Republic of the Philippines."

Italicized numbers in parentheses indicate quantities issued.

Authority for dates of issue, stamps from 1899 to 1911, and some quantities issued-"The Postal Issues of the Philippines," by F. L. Palmer (New York, 1912). Authority for quantities issued — "NAPP's Numbers, Volume 2," by Joseph M. Napp (2001).

100 CENTS = 1 DOLLAR

100 CENTAVOS = 1 PESO (1906)

Regular Issues of the United
States Overprinted in Black

Printed and overprinted by the U.S. Bureau of
Engraving and Printing.

1899, June 30   Unwmk.   Perf. 12

On U.S. Stamp No. 260

212	A96	50c	**orange**	325.	225.
			Never hinged	775.	
			On cover		—
			Block of 4	1,550.	—
			P# strip of 3, Impt.	1,450.	
			P# block of 6, Impt.	12,500.	

On U.S. Stamps

Nos. 279, 279B, 279Bd, 279Be, 279Bf, 279Bc, 268,
281, 282C, 283, 284, 275, 275a

Wmk. Double-lined USPS (191)

213	A87	1c	**yellow green**		
			(5,500,000)	4.00	.60
			Never hinged	10.00	
			On cover		10.00
			Block of 4	20.00	5.00
			P# strip of 3, Impt.	40.00	
			P# block of 6, Impt.	225.00	
a.			Inverted overprint	32,500.	
214	A88	2c	**red,** type IV *(6,970,000)*	1.75	.60
			light red	1.75	.60
			Never hinged	4.25	
			On cover		10.00
			Block of 4	7.00	4.00
			P# strip of 3, Impt.	25.00	
			P# block of 6, Impt.	175.00	
a.			2c **orange red,** type IV, *1901*	1.75	.60
			pale orange red	1.75	.60
			deep orange red, *1903*	1.75	.60
			Never hinged	4.25	
b.			Booklet pane of 6, red, type IV		
			1900	250.00	300.00
			orange red, *1901*	250.00	300.00
			Never hinged	600.00	
c.			2c **reddish carmine,** type IV	2.50	1.00
			Never hinged	6.00	
			On cover		12.50
			Block of 4	11.00	7.50
			P# strip of 3, Impt.	35.00	

			P# block of 6, Impt.	225.00	
d.			2c **rose carmine,** type IV	3.00	1.10
			Never hinged	7.25	
			On cover		15.00
			Block of 4	14.00	8.50
			P# strip of 3, Impt.	40.00	
			P# block of 6, Impt.	260.00	
215	A89	3c	**purple** *(673,814)*	9.00	1.25
			Never hinged	21.50	
			On cover		30.00
			Block of 4	42.50	13.50
			P# strip of 3, Impt.	85.00	
			P# block of 6, Impt.	475.00	
216	A91	5c	**blue** *(1,700,000)*	9.00	1.00
			Never hinged	21.50	
			On cover		20.00
			Block of 4	42.50	9.00
			P# strip of 3, Impt.	85.00	
			P# block of 6, Impt.	500.00	
a.			Inverted overprint		3,750.

No. 216a is valued in the grade of fine.

217	A94	10c	**brown,** type I		
			(750,000)+	35.00	4.00
			Never hinged	80.00	
			On cover		60.00
			Block of 4	160.00	55.00
			P# strip of 3, Impt.	175.00	
			P# block of 6, Impt.	700.00	

(+ Quantity includes Nos. 217, 217A)

217A	A94	10c	**orange brown,** type II	125.00	27.50
			Never hinged	325.00	
			On cover		160.00
			Block of 4	600.00	190.00
			P# strip of 3, Impt.	900.00	
			P# block of 6, Impt.	3,000.	
218	A95	15c	**olive green** *(200,000)*	40.00	8.00
			light olive green	37.50	8.50
			Never hinged	95.00	
			On cover		110.00
			Block of 4	175.00	52.50
			P# strip of 3, Impt.	200.00	
			P# block of 6, Impt.	1,250.	
219	A96	50c	**orange** *(50,000)+*	125.00	37.50
			Never hinged	300.00	
			On cover		400.00
			Block of 4	575.00	250.00
			P# strip of 3, Impt.	575.00	
			P# block of 6, Impt.	5,000.	
a.			50 **red orange**	250.00	55.00
			Never hinged	600.00	
			Block of 4	1,700.	
			Nos. 213-219 (8)	348.75	80.45

(+ Quantity includes Nos. 212, 219, 219a)

Special Printing

In March 1900 one pane of 100 stamps of each of Nos. 213-217, 218, 219 and J1-J5 were specially overprinted for displays at the Paris Exposition (1900) and Pan American Exposition (1901). The 2c pane was light red, type IV.

Stamps were handstampd type E "Specimen" in black ink on the face by H. G. Mandel and mounted by him in separate displays for the two Expositions. Additional stamps from each pane were also handstamped "Specimen" but most were destroyed after the Expositions.

J. M. Bartels, a stamp dealer, signed some stamps from these panes "Special Surcharge" in pencil on the gum to authenticate them as coming from the "Mandel" Special Printing panes. In 1904 or later, he handstamped additional surviving examples "Special Surcharge" in red ink on the back as his guarantee. Some of these guaranteed stamps had Mandel's "Specimen" handstamp on the face while others did not. Value, each $775.

Regular Issue

1901, Aug. 30
Same Overprint in Black On U.S. Stamps Nos.
280b, 282 and 272

220	A90	4c	**orange brown**		
			(404,907)	30.00	5.00
			Never hinged	75.00	
			On cover		50.00
			Block of 4	140.00	50.00
			P# strip of 3, Impt.	160.00	
			P# block of 6, Impt.	725.00	
221	A92	6c	**lake** *(223,465)*	35.00	7.00
			Never hinged	90.00	
			On cover		65.00
			Block of 4	175.00	50.00
			P# strip of 3, Impt.	175.00	
			P# block of 6, Impt.	900.00	
222	A93	8c	**violet brown** *(248,000)*	37.50	7.50
			Never hinged	90.00	
			On cover		50.00
			Block of 4	190.00	55.00
			P# strip of 3, Impt.	190.00	
			P# block of 6, Impt.	950.00	

Same Overprint in Red On U.S. Stamps Nos. 276,
276A, 277a and 278

223	A97	$1	**black,** type I *(3,000)+*	350.00	250.00
			Never hinged	1,150.	
			On cover		800.00
			Block of 4	1,600.	

				1,750.	
	P# strip of 3, Impt.			1,750.	
	P# block of 6, Impt.			—	
	Horiz. pair, types I & II			3,750.	

(+ Quantity includes Nos. 223, 223A)

223A	A97	$1	**black,** type II	2,400.	750.00
			Never hinged	5,750.	
			On cover		—
			Block of 4	10,500.	—
			P# strip of 3, Impt., one stamp No. 223	8,500.	
			P# block of 6, Impt., two stamps No. 223	—	

Specialists have questioned the existence of the plate block of 6 of No. 223A. The editors would like to see evidence of its existence.

224	A98	$2	**dark blue** (1800)	350.00	325.00
			Never hinged	1,150.	
			On cover		3,250.
			Block of 4	1,600.	—
			P# strip of 3, Impt.	2,250.	
			P# block of 6, Impt.	—	
225	A99	$5	**dark green** (782)	700.00	825.00
			Never hinged	1,700.	
			On cover		12,500.
			Block of 4	3,000.	—
			P# strip of 3, Impt.	3,750.	
			P# block of 6, Impt.	—	

Special Printing

Special printings exist of Nos. 227, 221, 223-225, made from defaced plates. These were made for display at the St. Louis Exposition. All but a few copies were destroyed. Most of the existing copies have the handstamp "Special Printing" on the back. Value: Nos. 227, 221, each $775; No. 223, $1,200; No. 224, $1,650; No. 225, $2,500.

Regular Issue

1903-04

Same Overprint in Black On U.S. Stamps Nos. 300 to 310 and shades

226	A115	1c	**blue green** (9,631,172)	7.00	.40
			Never hinged	15.50	
			On cover		8.25
			Block of 4	32.50	4.25
			P# strip of 3, Impt.	25.00	
			P# block of 6, Impt.	260.00	
227	A116	2c	**carmine** (850,000)	9.00	1.10
			Never hinged	20.00	
			On cover		10.00
			Block of 4	42.50	6.00
			P# strip of 3, Impt.	42.50	
			P# block of 6, Impt.	325.00	
228	A117	3c	**bright violet** (14,500)	67.50	12.50
			Never hinged	150.00	
			On cover		55.00
			Block of 4	275.00	85.00
			P# strip of 3, Impt.	275.00	
			P# block of 6, Impt.	1,650.	
229	A118	4c	**brown** (13,000)	80.00	22.50
			Never hinged	175.00	
a.			4c orange brown	80.00	20.00
			Never hinged	175.00	
			On cover		40.00
			Block of 4	350.00	150.00
			P# strip of 3, Impt.	325.00	
			P# block of 6, Impt.	1,950.	
230	A119	5c	**blue** (1,211,844)	17.50	1.00
			Never hinged	40.00	
			On cover		22.50
			Block of 4	80.00	7.50
			P# strip of 3, Impt.	70.00	
			P# block of 6, Impt.	425.00	
231	A120	6c	**brownish lake** (11,500)	85.00	22.50
			Never hinged	190.00	
			On cover		65.00
			Block of 4	350.00	150.00
			P# strip of 3, Impt.	350.00	
			P# block of 6, Impt.	2,100.	
232	A121	8c	**violet black** (49,033)	50.00	15.00
			Never hinged	125.00	
			On cover		300.00
			Block of 4	250.00	100.00
			P# strip of 3, Impt.	275.00	
			P# block of 6, Impt.	1,500.	
233	A122	10c	**pale red brown** (300,179)	35.00	2.25
			Never hinged	80.00	
			On cover		27.50
			Block of 4	160.00	20.00
			P# strip of 3, Impt.	175.00	
			P# block of 6, Impt.	1,000.	
a.			10c red brown	30.00	3.00
			Never hinged	70.00	
			On cover		35.00
			Block of 4	140.00	32.50
			P# strip of 3, Impt.	150.00	
			P# block of 6, Impt.	1,200.	
b.			Pair, one without overprint		1,500.
234	A123	13c	**purple black** (91,341)	35.00	17.50
			Never hinged	80.00	
a.			13c brown violet	35.00	17.50
			Never hinged	80.00	
			On cover		55.00
			Block of 4	150.00	110.00
			P# strip of 3, Impt.	175.00	
			P# block of 6, Impt.	1,350.	
235	A124	15c	**olive green** (183,965)	60.00	15.00
			Never hinged	135.00	
			On cover		100.00
			Block of 4	275.00	100.00
			P# strip of 3, Impt.	300.00	
			P# block of 6, Impt.	2,000.	
236	A125	50c	**orange** (57,641)	125.00	35.00
			Never hinged	275.00	
			On cover		300.00

			Block of 4	575.00	275.00
			P# strip of 3, Impt.	575.00	
			P# block of 6, Impt.	17,500.	
	Nos. 226-236 (11)			571.00	144.75

Same Overprint in Red On U.S. Stamps Nos. 311, 312 and 313

237	A126	$1	**black** (5617)	375.00	250.00
			Never hinged	1,000.	
			On cover		750.00
			Block of 4	1,750.	1,850.
			P# strip of 3, Impt.	1,750.	
			P# block of 6, Impt.	8,500.	
238	A127	$2	**dark blue** (695)	700.00	800.00
			Never hinged	1,650.	
			Block of 4	3,250.	—
			P# strip of 3, Impt.	3,500.	
			P# block of 6, Impt.	16,000.	
239	A128	$5	**dark green** (746)	900.00	5,000.
			Never hinged	2,000.	
			Block of 4	4,000.	—
			P# strip of 3, Impt.	4,500.	
			P# block of 6, Impt.		

Same Overprint in Black On U.S. Stamp No. 319

240	A129	2c	**carmine** (862,245)	8.00	2.25
			Never hinged	17.50	
			On cover		3.50
			Block of 4	35.00	15.00
			P# strip of 3, Impt.	45.00	
			P# block of 6, Impt.	350.00	
a.			Booklet pane of 6	2,000.	
b.			2c scarlet	8.00	2.75
			Never hinged	19.00	
			On cover		4.00
			Block of 4	35.00	17.50
			P# strip of 3, Impt.	47.50	
			P# block of 6, Impt.	375.00	
c.			As "b," booklet pane of 6	—	

Dates of issue:
Sept. 20, 1903, Nos. 226, 227, 236.
Jan. 4, 1904, Nos. 230, 234, 235, 237, 240a.
Nov. 1, 1904, Nos. 228, 229, 231, 232, 233, 238, 239, 240.
Nos. 212 to 240 became obsolete on Sept. 8, 1906, the remainders being destroyed.

Special Printing

Two sets of special printings exist of the 1903-04 issue. The first consists of Nos. 226, 230, 234, 235, 236, 237 and 240. These were made for display at the St. Louis Exposition. All but a few stamps were destroyed. Most of the existing examples have the handstamp "Special Surcharge" on the back. Value: No. 237, $1,550; others $900; J6, J7, $1,150.

In 1907 the entire set Nos. 226, 228 to 240, J1 to J7 were specially printed for the Bureau of Insular Affairs on very white paper. They are difficult to distinguish from the ordinary stamps except the Special Delivery stamp which is on U.S. No. E6 (see Philippines No. E2A). Value: No. 237, $1,300; No. 238, $2,600; No. 239, $3,500; others, $775.

Regular Issue

José Rizal — A40

Printed by the U.S. Bureau of Engraving and Printing.

Plates of 400 subjects in four panes of 100 each.

Booklet panes Nos. 240a, 241b, 242b, 261a, 262b, 276a, 277a, 285a, 286a, 290e, 291b and 292c were made from plates of 180 subjects. No. 214b came from plates of 360 subjects.

Designs: 4c, McKinley. 6c, Ferdinand Magellan. 8c, Miguel Lopez de Legaspi. 10c, Gen. Henry W. Lawton. 12c, Lincoln. 16c, Adm. William T. Sampson. 20c, Washington. 26c, Francisco Carriedo. 30c, Franklin. 1p-10p, Arms of City of Manila.

Wmk. Double-lined PIPS (191)

1906, Sept. 8 **Perf. 12**

241	A40	2c	**deep green** (51,000,019)	.40	.20
			Never hinged	1.00	
			Block of 4	1.75	.20
a.			2c yellow green ('10)	.60	.20
			Never hinged	1.50	
			Double transfer		40.00
b.			Booklet pane of 6 (720,120)	750.00	800.00
			Never hinged	1,500.	
242	A40	4c	**carmine** (11,000,019)	.50	.20
			Never hinged	1.25	
			Block of 4	2.25	.20
a.			4c carmine lake ('10)	1.00	.20
			Never hinged	2.50	
b.			Booklet pane of 6 (300,600)	650.00	700.00
			Never hinged	1,250.	
243	A40	6c	**violet** (1,980,019)	2.50	.20
			Never hinged	6.25	
			Block of 4	11.00	.85
244	A40	8c	**brown** (770,019)	4.50	.90
			Never hinged	11.00	
			Block of 4	20.00	6.00
245	A40	10c	**blue** (5,500,019)	3.50	.30
			Never hinged	8.75	
a.			10c dark blue	3.50	.30
			Never hinged	8.75	
			Block of 4	15.00	1.25
246	A40	12c	**brown lake** (670,019)	9.00	2.50

			Never hinged	22.50	
			Block of 4	42.50	17.00
247	A40	16c	**violet black** (1,300,019)	6.00	.35
			Never hinged	15.00	
			Block of 4	30.00	2.00
248	A40	20c	**orange brown** (2,100,019)	7.00	.35
			Never hinged	17.50	
			Block of 4	35.00	2.25
249	A40	26c	**violet brown** (428,000)	11.00	3.00
			Never hinged	27.50	
			Block of 4	50.00	20.00
250	A40	30c	**olive green** (1,256,019)	6.50	1.75
			Never hinged	16.00	
			Block of 4	32.50	8.75
251	A40	1p	**orange** (200,019)	45.00	7.50
			Never hinged	110.00	
			Block of 4	200.00	40.00
252	A40	2p	**black** (100,000)	55.00	1.75
			Never hinged	140.00	
			Block of 4	250.00	10.00
253	A40	4p	**dark blue** (10,000)	160.00	20.00
			Never hinged	375.00	
			Block of 4	700.00	90.00
254	A40	10p	**dark green** (6,019)	275.00	80.00
			Never hinged	675.00	
			Block of 4	1,250.	400.00
	Nos. 241-254 (14)			585.90	119.00

1909

Change of Colors

255	A40	12c	**red orange** (300,000)	11.00	3.00
			Never hinged	27.50	
			Block of 4	52.50	15.00
256	A40	16c	**olive green** (500,000)	6.00	.75
			Never hinged	15.00	
			Block of 4	27.50	3.50
257	A40	20c	**yellow** (800,000)	9.00	1.25
			Never hinged	22.50	
			Block of 4	42.50	7.50
258	A40	26c	**blue green** (250,000)	3.50	.75
			Never hinged	8.75	
			Block of 4	16.00	4.00
259	A40	30c	**ultramarine** (600,000)	13.00	3.50
			Never hinged	32.50	
			Block of 4	60.00	22.50
260	A40	1p	**pale violet** (100,000)	45.00	5.00
			Never hinged	110.00	
			Block of 4	225.00	32.50
260A	A40	2p	**violet brown** (50,000)	100.00	4.00
			Never hinged	250.00	
			Block of 4	475.00	25.00
	Nos. 255-260A (7)			187.50	18.25

1911 **Wmk. Single-lined PIPS (190)** **Perf. 12**

261	A40	2c	**green** (44,000,000)	.75	.20
			Never hinged	1.80	
			Block of 4	5.00	.35
a.			Booklet pane of 6 (896,160)	800.00	900.00
			Never hinged	1,400.	
262	A40	4c	**carmine lake** (6,000,000)	3.00	.20
			Never hinged	6.75	
			Block of 4	14.00	.35
a.			4c carmine		
b.			Booklet pane of 6 (100,020)	600.00	700.00
			Never hinged	1,100.	
263	A40	6c	**deep violet** (3,200,000)	3.00	.20
			Never hinged	6.75	
			Block of 4	13.00	.30
264	A40	8c	**brown** (1,400,000)	9.50	.50
			Never hinged	21.50	
			Block of 4	45.00	2.25
265	A40	10c	**blue** (3,700,000)	4.00	.20
			Never hinged	9.00	
			Block of 4	19.00	.30
266	A40	12c	**orange** (1,320,000)	4.00	.45
			Never hinged	9.00	
			Block of 4	17.50	2.10
267	A40	16c	**olive green** (1,000,000)	4.50	.40
			Never hinged	10.00	
a.			16c pale olive green	4.50	.50
			Never hinged	10.00	
			Block of 4	20.00	1.60
268	A40	20c	**yellow** (3,000,000)	3.50	.20
			Never hinged	7.75	
			Block of 4	15.00	.65
a.			20c orange	4.00	.30
			Never hinged	9.00	
			Block of 4	17.00	1.40
269	A40	26c	**blue green** (249,900)	6.00	.30
			Never hinged	13.50	
			Block of 4	27.50	1.50
270	A40	30c	**ultramarine** (1,000,000)	6.00	.50
			Never hinged	13.50	
			Block of 4	27.50	2.50
271	A40	1p	**pale violet** (694,000)	27.50	.60
			Never hinged	62.50	
			Block of 4	140.00	3.00
272	A40	2p	**violet brown** (100,000)	45.00	1.00
			Never hinged	100.00	
			Block of 4	200.00	6.25
273	A40	4p	**deep blue** (10,000)	700.00	110.00
			Never hinged	1,400.	
			Block of 4	3,250.	550.00
274	A40	10p	**deep green** (20,000)	250.00	30.00
			Never hinged	500.00	
			Block of 4	1,100.	150.00
	Nos. 261-274 (14)			1,066.	144.75

1914

275	A40	30c	**gray** (700,000)	12.00	.50
			Never hinged	27.50	
			Block of 4	57.50	3.00

1914   **Perf. 10**
276   A40   2c **green** *(60,000,000)*   2.00   .20
       Never hinged   4.50
       Block of 4   8.50   .45
  a.   Booklet pane of 6 *(400,080)*   750.00   800.00
       Never hinged   1,250.
277   A40   4c **carmine** *(2,500,000)*   3.50   .30
       Never hinged   8.50
       Block of 4   15.00   .85
  a.   Booklet pane of 6 *(56,040)*   750.00
       Never hinged   1,300.
278   A40   6c **light violet** *(700,000)*   45.00   9.50
       Never hinged   100.00
       Block of 4   210.00   55.00
  a.   6c **deep violet**   50.00   6.25
       Never hinged   110.00
       Block of 4   220.00   35.00
279   A40   8c **brown** *(200,000)*   50.00   10.50
       Never hinged   110.00
       Block of 4   220.00   57.50
280   A40   10c **dark blue** *(2,000,000)*   30.00   .20
       Never hinged   67.50
       Block of 4   130.00   1.00
281   A40   16c **olive green** *(700,000)*   100.00   5.00
       Never hinged   225.00
       Block of 4   450.00   29.00
282   A40   20c **orange** *(2,000,000)*   32.50   1.00
       Never hinged   75.00
       Block of 4   150.00   5.75
283   A40   30c **gray** *(1,300,000)*   70.00   4.50
       Never hinged   150.00
       Block of 4   300.00   17.50
284   A40   1p **pale violet** *(198,000)*   140.00   3.75
       Never hinged   300.00
       Block of 4   600.00   22.50
       Nos. 276-284 (9)   473.00   34.95

1918   **Perf. 11**
285   A40   2c **green** *(40,000,000)*   21.00   4.25
       Never hinged   40.00
       Block of 4   92.50   18.00
  a.   Booklet pane of 6 *(50,040)*   750.00   800.00
       Never hinged   1,300.
286   A40   4c **carmine** *(3,000,000)*   26.00   2.50
       Never hinged   55.00
       Block of 4   115.00   12.50
  a.   Booklet pane of 6   1,350.   2,000.
287   A40   6c **deep violet** *(1,000,000)*   40.00   1.75
       Never hinged   90.00
       Block of 4   175.00   8.50
287A   A40   8c **light brown** *(200,000)*   220.00   25.00
       Never hinged   400.00
       Block of 4   925.00   160.00
288   A40   10c **dark blue** *(2,000,000)*   60.00   1.50
       Never hinged   140.00
       Block of 4   260.00   8.00
289   A40   16c **olive green** *(700,000)*   110.00   7.50
       Never hinged   250.00
       Block of 4   525.00   32.50
289A   A40   20c **orange** *(1,000,000)*   85.00   8.00
       Never hinged   200.00
       Block of 4   400.00   42.50
289C   A40   30c **gray** *(500,000)*   95.00   13.00
       Never hinged   215.00
       Block of 4   400.00   62.50
289D   A40   1p **pale violet** *(200,000)*   100.00   17.50
       Never hinged   225.00
       Block of 4   425.00   92.50
       Nos. 285-289D (9)   757.00   81.00

1917   **Unwmk.**   **Perf. 11**
290   A40   2c **yellow green** *(444,746,800)*   .25   .20
       Never hinged   .55
       Block of 4   1.10   .20
  a.   2c **dark green**   .30   .20
       Never hinged   .65
       green   .20   .20
       Double transfer
  b.   Vert. pair, imperf. horiz.   1,500.
  c.   Horiz. pair, imperf. between   1,500.   —
  d.   Vertical pair, imperf. btwn.   1,750.   1,000.
  e.   Booklet pane of 6 *(3,251,080)*   27.50   30.00
       Never hinged   60.00
291   A40   4c **carmine** *(50,579,100)*   .30   .20
       Never hinged   .65
       Block of 4   1.35   .30
  a.   4c **light rose**   .30   .20
       Never hinged   .65
       Block of 4   1.25   .20
  b.   Booklet pane of 6 *(500,820)*   20.00   22.50
       Never hinged   35.00
292   A40   6c **deep violet** *(8,803,600)*   .35   .20
       Never hinged   .70
       Block of 4   1.50   .30
  a.   6c **lilac**   .40   .20
       Never hinged   .80
  b.   6c **red violet**   .40   .20
       Never hinged   .70
  c.   Booklet pane of 6 *(75)*   550.00   800.00
       Never hinged   900.00
293   A40   8c **yellow brown** *(6,036,700)*   .25   .20
       Never hinged   .45
  a.   8c **orange brown**   .25   .20
       Never hinged   .45
       Block of 4   1.75   .35
294   A40   10c **deep blue** *(15,848,800)*   .30   .20
       Never hinged   .65
       Block of 4   1.25   .25
295   A40   12c **red orange** *(3,396,500)*   .35   .20
       Never hinged   .75
       Block of 4   1.50   .50
296   A40   16c **light olive green** *(3,249,600)* 65.00   .25
       Never hinged   130.00
       Block of 4   300.00   1.25
  a.   16c **olive bister**   65.00   .50
       Never hinged   130.00
297   A40   20c **orange yellow** *(10,814,600)*   .35   .20

Never hinged   .75
Block of 4   2.25   .30
298   A40   26c **green** *(1,595,400)*   .50   .45
       Never hinged   1.10
       Block of 4   2.25   2.10
  a.   26c **blue green**   .60   .25
       Never hinged   1.35
299   A40   30c **gray** *(6,031,300)*   .55   .20
       Never hinged   1.35
       Block of 4   2.60   .35
       Dark gray   .55   .20
300   A40   1p **pale violet** *(1,173,200)*   40.00   1.00
       Never hinged   90.00
       Block of 4   175.00   4.50
  a.   1p **red lilac**   40.00   1.00
       Never hinged   90.00
       Block of 4   175.00   4.50
  b.   1p **pale rose lilac**   40.00   1.10
       Never hinged   90.00
       Block of 4   175.00   4.50
301   A40   2p **violet brown** *(475,300)*   35.00   1.00
       Never hinged   77.50
       Block of 4   160.00   4.75
302   A40   4p **blue** *(541,800)*   32.50   .50
       Never hinged   72.50
       Block of 4   150.00   2.25
  a.   4p **dark blue**   35.00   .55
       Never hinged   77.50
       Nos. 290-302 (13)   175.70   4.80

1923-26
303   A40   16c **olive bister** *(Adm. George*
              Dewey) (13,524,300)   1.00   .20
       Never hinged   2.25
       Block of 4   4.75   .45
  a.   16c **olive green**   1.25   .20
       Never hinged   2.75
304   A40   10p **deep green** *('26) (32,400)*   50.00   6.00
       Never hinged   110.00
       Block of 4   210.00   27.50

Legislative Palace Issue
Issued to commemorate the opening of the Legislative Palace.

Legislative Palace — A42

Printed by the Philippine Bureau of Printing.
1926, Dec. 20   **Unwmk.**   **Perf. 12**
319   A42   2c **green & black** *(502,300)*   .50   .25
       Never hinged   1.25
       First day cover   3.50
       Block of 4   2.25   1.10
  a.   Horiz. pair, imperf. between   300.00
  b.   Vert. pair, imperf. between   575.00
320   A42   4c **carmine & black** *(304,150)*   .55   .40
       Never hinged   1.20
       First day cover   3.50
       Block of 4   2.50   1.60
  a.   Horiz. pair, imperf. between   325.00
  b.   Vert. pair, imperf. between   600.00
321   A42   16c **olive green & black**
              (203,500)   1.00   .65
       Never hinged   2.25
       First day cover   10.00
       Block of 4   5.00   3.00
  a.   Horiz. pair, imperf. between   350.00
  b.   Vert. pair, imperf. between   625.00
  c.   Double impression of center   675.00
322   A42   18c **light brown & black**
              (103,700)   1.10   .50
       Never hinged   2.50
       First day cover   10.00
       Block of 4   5.00   2.25
  a.   Double impression of center *(150)*   1,250.
  b.   Vertical pair, imperf. between   675.00
323   A42   20c **orange & black** *(103,200)*   2.00   1.00
       Never hinged   4.50
       Block of 4   8.50   5.00
  a.   20c **orange & brown** *(100)*   600.00   —
  b.   As No. 323, imperf., pair *(50)*   575.00   575.00
  c.   As "a," imperf., pair *(100)*   1,750.
  d.   Vert. pair, imperf. between   700.00
324   A42   24c **gray & black** *(103,100)*   1.00   .55
       Never hinged   2.25
       Block of 4   4.50   2.50
  a.   Vert. pair, imperf. between   700.00
325   A42   1p **rose lilac & black** *(10,800)* 47.50   32.50
       Never hinged   70.00
       Block of 4   200.00   150.00
  a.   Vert. pair, imperf. between   700.00
       First day cover, #319-325   400.00
       Nos. 319-325 (7)   53.65   35.85

No. 322a is valued in the grade of fine.

Coil Stamp
Rizal Type of 1906
Printed by the U.S. Bureau of Engraving and Printing.
1928   **Unwmk.**   **Perf. 11 Vertically**
326   A40   2c **green** *(110,000)*   7.50   12.50
       Never hinged   18.75
       Pair   17.50   32.50
       Line pair   55.00   100.00
       Never hinged   140.00

Types of 1906-1923
1925-31   **Unwmk.**   **Imperf.**
340   A40   2c **yellow green** *('31) (99,986)*   .40   .40
       Never hinged   .90
       Block of 4   1.75   1.75
  a.   2c **green** *('25) (51,000)*   .80   .60
       Never hinged   1.80
341   A40   4c **carmine rose** *('31) (49,855)*   .45   .40
       Never hinged   1.00
       Block of 4   2.00   1.75
  a.   4c **carmine** *('25) (25,500)*   1.20   .60
       Never hinged   2.75
       Block of 4   5.25   4.00
342   A40   6c **violet** *('31) (10,000)*   2.00   1.75
       Never hinged   4.00
       Block of 4   8.50   7.50
  a.   6c **deep violet** *('25) (5,200)*   12.00   6.00
       Never hinged   13.50
343   A40   8c **brown** *('31) (10,000)*   2.00   2.00
       Never hinged   4.00
       Block of 4   8.50   8.25
  a.   8c **yellow brown** *('25) (5,200)*   12.00   6.00
       Never hinged   13.50
344   A40   10c **blue** *('31) (7,000)*   3.75   3.00
       Never hinged   7.50
       Block of 4   16.00   11.00
  a.   10c **deep blue** *('25) (2,200)*   45.00   16.00
       Never hinged   100.00
345   A40   12c **deep orange** *('31) (7,000)*   6.00   4.00
       Never hinged   13.00
       Block of 4   25.00   17.00
  a.   12c **red orange** *('25) (2,200)*   55.00   30.00
       Never hinged   125.00
346   A40   16c **olive green** *(Dewey) ('31)*
              (7,000)   4.00   3.00
       Never hinged   8.00
       Block of 4   17.00   12.50
  a.   16c **bister green** *('25) (2,200)*   40.00   12.50
       Never hinged   90.00
347   A40   20c **deep yellow orange** *('31)*
              (7,000)   4.50   3.00
       Never hinged   9.00
       Block of 4   19.00   12.50
  a.   20c **yellow orange** *('25) (2,200)*   42.50   15.00
       Never hinged   95.00
348   A40   26c **green** *('31) (7,000)*   4.50   3.50
       Never hinged   9.00
       Block of 4   19.00   12.50
  a.   26c **blue green** *('25) (2,200)*   45.00   16.00
       Never hinged   100.00
349   A40   30c **light gray** *('31) (7,000)*   6.00   4.00
       Never hinged   12.00
       Block of 4   25.00   13.00
  a.   30c **gray** *('25) (2,200)*   45.00   16.00
       Never hinged   100.00
350   A40   1p **light violet** *('31) (6,395)*   8.00   7.00
       Never hinged   16.00
       Block of 4   37.50   29.00
  a.   1p **violet** *('25) (2,100)*   175.00   85.00
       Never hinged   375.00
351   A40   2p **brown violet** *('31) (3,612)*   20.00   15.00
       Never hinged   40.00
       Block of 4   85.00   62.50
  a.   2p **violet brown** *('25) (600)*   375.00   200.00
       Never hinged   625.00
352   A40   4p **blue** *('31) (2,570)*   70.00   55.00
       Never hinged   140.00
       Block of 4   325.00   —
  a.   4p **deep blue** *('25) (300)*   2,000.   875.00
       Never hinged   3,350.
353   A40   10p **green** *('31) (2,208)*   150.00   130.00
       Never hinged   250.00
       Block of 4   650.00
  a.   10p **deep green** *('25) (200)*   2,875.   1,550.
       Never hinged   4,750.
       Nos. 340-353 (14)   281.60   232.05

Nos. 340a-353a were the original post office issue. These were reprinted twice in 1931 for sale to collectors (Nos. 340-353).

Mount Mayon, Luzon — A43

Post Office, Manila — A44

Pier No. 7, Manila Bay — A45

Vernal Falls, Yosemite Park, California (See Footnote) — A46

Rice Planting — A47

Rice Terraces — A48

Baguio Zigzag — A49

1932, May 3   Unwmk.   Perf. 11

354	A43	2c **yellow green** (5,432,000)	.60	.30
		Never hinged	.90	
		First day cover		2.00
		Block of 4	3.00	1.25
355	A44	4c **rose carmine** (1,602,800)	.60	.30
		Never hinged	.90	
		First day cover		2.00
		Block of 4	3.00	1.25
356	A45	12c **orange** (483,000)	.75	.60
		Never hinged	1.10	
		First day cover		6.50
		Block of 4	3.25	2.25
357	A46	18c **red orange** (983,400)	32.50	10.00
		Never hinged	50.00	
		First day cover		16.00
		Block of 4	130.00	45.00
358	A47	20c **yellow** (441,000)	1.00	.65
		Never hinged	1.50	
		First day cover		6.50
		Block of 4	4.25	2.50
359	A48	24c **deep violet** (425,000)	1.50	.80
		Never hinged	2.25	
		First day cover		6.50
		Block of 4	6.25	4.75
360	A49	32c **olive brown** (510,600)	1.40	.80
		Never hinged	2.10	
		First day cover		6.50

	Block of 4	6.00	4.75
	First day cover, #354-360		50.00
	Nos. 354-360 (7)	38.35	13.45

The 18c vignette was intended to show Pagsanjan Falls in Laguna, central Luzon, and is so labeled. Through error the stamp pictures Vernal Falls in Yosemite National Park, California.

Nos. 302, 302a Surcharged in Orange or Red

1932

368	A40	1p on 4p **blue** (O) (134,000)	5.00	.75
		Never hinged	7.75	
		On cover		.60
		Block of 4	22.50	3.50
a.		1p on 4p **dark blue** (O)	5.00	1.50
		Never hinged	7.75	
369	A40	2p on 4p **dark blue** (R) (80,000)	7.50	1.00
		Never hinged	11.00	
a.		2p on 4p **blue** (R)	7.50	1.00
		Never hinged	12.00	
		On cover		.90
		Block of 4	35.00	4.75

Far Eastern Championship

Issued in commemoration of the Tenth Far Eastern Championship Games.

Baseball Players — A50

Tennis Player — A51

Basketball Players — A52

Printed by the Philippine Bureau of Printing.

1934, Apr. 14   Unwmk.   Perf. 11½

380	A50	2c **yellow brown** (999,985)	1.50	.80
		brown	1.50	.80
		Never hinged	2.25	
		First day cover		2.00
		"T" of "Eastern" malformed	2.00	1.25
381	A51	6c **ultramarine** (800,000)	.25	.20
		pale ultramarine	.25	.20
		Never hinged	.30	
		First day cover		1.60
a.		Vertical pair, imperf. between	1,250.	
382	A52	16c **violet brown** (500,000)	.50	.50
		dark violet	.50	.50
		Never hinged	.75	
		First day cover		2.25
a.		Vert. pair, imperf. horiz.	1,750.	
		Nos. 380-382 (3)	2.25	1.50

José Rizal — A53

Woman and Carabao — A54

La Filipina — A55

Pearl Fishing — A56

Fort Santiago — A57

Salt Spring — A58

Magellan's Landing, 1521 — A59

"Juan de la Cruz" — A60

Rice Terraces — A61

Miguel Lopez de Legaspi and Chief Sikatuna Signing "Blood Compact," 1565 — A62

Barasoain Church, Malolos A63

Battle of Manila Bay, 1898 — A64

Montalban Gorge — A65

George Washington — A66

Printed by U.S. Bureau of Engraving and Printing.

		1935, Feb. 15	**Unwmk.**		**Perf. 11**	
383	A53	2c	rose (62,183,400)		.20	.20
			Never hinged		.25	
			First day cover			1.00
384	A54	4c	yellow green (14,238,193)		.20	.20
			Light yellow green		.20	.20
			Never hinged		.25	
			First day cover			1.00
385	A55	6c	dark brown (1,958,928)		.25	.20
			Never hinged		.35	
			First day cover			1.00
386	A56	8c	violet (792,000)		.25	.20
			Never hinged		.35	
			First day cover			1.60
387	A57	10c	rose carmine (341,400)		.30	.20
			Never hinged		.45	
			First day cover			1.60
388	A58	12c	black (319,500)		.35	.20
			Never hinged		.50	
			First day cover			1.60
389	A59	16c	dark blue (2,422,778)		.35	.20
			Never hinged		.55	
			First day cover			1.60
390	A60	20c	light olive green (1,061,400)		.35	.20
			Never hinged		.45	
			First day cover			2.25
391	A61	26c	indigo (212,000)		.40	.25
			Never hinged		.60	
			First day cover			3.00
392	A62	30c	orange red (171,200)		.40	.25
			Never hinged		.60	
			First day cover			3.00
393	A63	1p	red orange & black (80,000)		2.00	1.25
			Never hinged		3.00	
			First day cover			8.25

394	A64	2p	bister brown & black		8.00	1.25
			(61,100)			
			Never hinged		11.00	
			First day cover			14.00
395	A65	4p	blue & black (59,000)		7.00	3.50
			Never hinged		10.50	
			First day cover			20.00
396	A66	5p	green & black (54,000)		20.00	3.50
			Never hinged		30.00	
			First day cover			27.50
			Nos. 383-396 (14)		40.05	11.60

USED VALUES

Used values in italics are for postally used examples with cancels of the proper function during the correct period of use.

Issues of the Commonwealth
Commonwealth Inauguration Issue

Issued to commemorate the inauguration of the Philippine Commonwealth, Nov. 15, 1935.

"The Temples of Human Progress" A67

		1935, Nov. 15	**Unwmk.**		**Perf. 11**	
397	A67	2c	carmine rose (1,531,000)		.25	.20
			Never hinged		.30	
			First day cover			1.00
398	A67	6c	deep violet (523,000)		.25	.20
			Never hinged		.30	
			First day cover			1.00
399	A67	16c	blue (313,500)		.25	.20
			Never hinged		.35	
			First day cover			1.00
400	A67	36c	yellow green (261,000)		.40	.30
			Never hinged		.60	
			First day cover			1.40
401	A67	50c	brown (218,500)		.60	.55
			Never hinged		.90	
			First day cover			2.00
			Nos. 397-401 (5)		1.75	1.45

Jose Rizal Issue

75th anniversary of the birth of Jose Rizal (1861-1896), national hero of the Filipinos.

Jose Rizal — A68

Printed by the Philippine Bureau of Printing.

		1936, June 19	**Unwmk.**		**Perf. 12**	
402	A68	2c	yellow brown (500,000)		.20	.20
			light yellow brown		.20	.20
			Never hinged		.25	
			First day cover			1.00
403	A68	6c	slate blue (300,000)		.20	.20
			light slate green		.20	.20
			Never hinged		.25	
			First day cover			1.00
a.			Imperf. vertically, pair		1,350.	
			Never hinged		1,950.	
404	A68	36c	red brown (200,000)		.50	.45
			light red brown		.50	.45
			Never hinged		.75	
			First day cover			2.25
			Nos. 402-404 (3)		.90	.85

Commonwealth Anniversary Issue

Issued in commemoration of the first anniversary of the Commonwealth.

President Manuel L. Quezon — A69

Printed by U.S. Bureau of Engraving and Printing.

		1936, Nov. 15	**Unwmk.**		**Perf. 11**	
408	A69	2c	orange brown (4,946,816)		.20	
			Never hinged		.30	
			First day cover			1.00
409	A69	6c	yellow green (1,019,900)		.20	.20
			Never hinged		.30	
			First day cover			1.00
410	A69	12c	ultramarine (527,600)		.20	.20
			Never hinged		.30	
			First day cover			1.50
			Nos. 408-410 (3)		.60	.60

Stamps of 1935 Overprinted in Black

a

b

		1936-37	**Unwmk.**		**Perf. 11**	
411	A53(a)	2c	rose, Dec. 28, 1936		.20	.20
			(84,092,400)			
			Never hinged		.25	
			First day cover			35.00
a.			Bklt. pane of 6, Jan. 15 1937		2.50	2.00
			(239,492)			
			Never hinged		4.00	
			First day cover			40.00
b.			Hyphen omitted		125.00	100.00
412	A54(b)	4c	yellow green, Mar. 29,		.50	4.00
			1937 (100,000)			
			Never hinged		.75	
413	A55(a)	6c	dark brown, Oct. 7, 1936		.20	.20
			(2,230,394)			
			Never hinged		.25	
			On cover			.20
414	A56(b)	8c	violet, Mar. 29, 1937		.25	.20
			(627,500)			
			Never hinged		.35	
			On cover			.25
415	A57(b)	10c	rose carmine, Dec. 28,		.20	.20
			1936 (1,687,550)			
			Never hinged		.25	
			First day cover			35.00
a.			"COMMONWEALT"		20.00	—
			Never hinged		30.00	
416	A58(b)	12c	black, Mar. 29, 1937		.20	.20
			(2,118,600)			
			Never hinged		.30	
			On cover			.20
417	A59(b)	16c	dark blue, Oct. 7, 1936		.30	.20
			(597,300)			
			Never hinged		.45	
			On cover			.20
418	A60(a)	20c	lt olive green, Mar. 29,		1.00	.40
			1937 (100,000)			
			Never hinged		1.60	
						.45
419	A61(b)	26c	indigo, Mar. 29, 1937		.90	.35
			(100,000)			
			Never hinged		1.50	
			On cover			.40
420	A62(b)	30c	orange red, Dec. 28, 1936		.50	.20
			(836,252)			
			Never hinged		.80	
			First day cover			35.00
421	A63(b)	1p	red org & blk, Oct. 7, 1936		1.00	.25
			(319,250)			
			Never hinged		1.60	
			On cover			.40
422	A64(b)	2p	bis brn & blk, Mar. 29,		10.00	3.00
			1937 (50,000)			
			Never hinged		15.00	
						3.50
423	A65(b)	4p	blue & blk, Mar. 29, 1937		35.00	6.50
			(30,000)			
			Never hinged		55.00	
			On cover			50.00
424	A66(b)	5p	green & blk, Mar. 29, 1937		10.00	2.50
			(60,500)			
			Never hinged		15.00	
			On cover			35.00
			Nos. 411-424 (14)		60.25	18.40
			Set, Never hinged		93.10	

Eucharistic Congress Issue
Issued to commemorate the 33rd International Eucharistic Congress held at Manila, Feb. 3-7, 1937.

Map, Symbolical of the Eucharistic Congress Spreading Light of Christianity — A70

FLAT PLATE PRINTING
Plates of 256 subjects in four panes of 64 each.

1937, Feb. 3	Unwmk.	Perf. 11	
425 A70	2c yellow green (4,102,848)	.20	.20
	Never hinged	.25	
	First day cover		1.00
426 A70	6c light brown (2,626,240)	.20	.20
	Never hinged	.25	
	First day cover		1.00
427 A70	12c sapphire (2,165,440)	.20	.20
	Never hinged	.25	
	First day cover		1.00
428 A70	20c deep orange (1,640,640)	.30	.20
	Never hinged	.50	
	First day cover		1.00
429 A70	36c deep violet (1,115,840)	.55	.40
	Never hinged	.80	
	First day cover		1.40
430 A70	50c carmine (1,115,840)	.70	.35
	Never hinged	1.10	
	First day cover		2.00
	Nos. 425-430 (6)	2.15	1.55
	Set, Never hinged	3.15	

Arms of City of Manila — A71

1937, Aug. 27	Unwmk.	Perf. 11	
431 A71	10p gray (70,000)	6.00	2.00
	Never hinged	8.50	
432 A71	20p henna brown (90,600)	5.00	1.40
	Never hinged	8.00	
	First day cover, #431-432		50.00

Stamps of 1935 Overprinted in Black:

a

b

1938-40	Unwmk.	Perf. 11	
433 A53(a)	2c rose, 1939 (103,549,959)	.20	.20
	Never hinged	.25	
a.	Booklet pane of 6 (157,176)	3.50	3.50
	Never hinged	5.50	
b.	As "a," lower left-hand stamp overprinted "WEALTH COMMON-" (24)	4,000.	
c.	Hyphen omitted	100.00	50.00
434 A54(b)	4c yellow green, 1940 (72,500)	3.00	30.00
	Never hinged	4.75	
435 A55(a)	6c dark brown, May 12, 1939 (4,013,440)	.25	.20
	Never hinged	.40	
	First day cover		35.00
a.	6c golden brown	.25	.20
	Never hinged	.40	
436 A56(b)	8c violet, 1939 (1,583,357)	.20	.20
	Never hinged	.25	
a.	"COMMONWEALT" (LR 31)	90.00	
	Never hinged	140.00	
437 A57(b)	10c rose carmine, May 12, 1939 (2,695,242)	.20	.20
	Never hinged	.25	
a.	"COMMONWEALT" (LR 31)	65.00	—

438 A58(b)	12c black, 1940 (3,765,000)	.20	.20
	Never hinged	.25	
439 A59(b)	16c dark blue (1,415,700)	.20	.20
	Never hinged	.25	
440 A60(a)	20c light olive green, 1939 (1,663,799)	.20	.20
	Never hinged	.25	
441 A61(b)	26c indigo, 1940 (597,500)	1.00	.20
	Never hinged	1.50	
442 A62(b)	30c orange red, May 23, 1939 (643,100)	2.50	.70
	Never hinged	4.00	
443 A63(b)	1p red org & blk, Aug. 29, 1938 (1,065,629)	.50	.20
	Never hinged	.80	
	First day cover		40.00
444 A64(b)	2p bister brown & black, 1939 (98,000)	6.00	.75
	Never hinged	9.00	
445 A65(b)	4p blue & black, 1940 (6,500)	275.00	300.00
	Never hinged	450.00	
	On cover		500.00
446 A66(b)	5p green & black, 1940 (31,500)	16.00	4.00
	Never hinged	26.00	
	Nos. 433-446 (14)	305.45	337.25
	Set, Never hinged	496.90	

Overprint "b" measures 18½x1¾mm.
No. 433b occurs in booklet pane, No. 433a, position 5; all examples are straight-edged, left and bottom.

First Foreign Trade Week Issue
Nos. 384, 298a and 432 Surcharged in Red, Violet or Black:

a

b

c

1939, July 5			
449 A54(a)	2c on 4c yellow green (R) (500,000)	.20	.20
	Never hinged	.35	
	First day cover		1.40
450 A40(b)	6c on 26c blue green (V) (166,700)	.20	.20
	Never hinged	.35	
	First day cover		2.00
a.	6c on 26c green	2.00	.30
	Never hinged	2.50	
451 A71(c)	50c on 20p henna brown (Bk) (60,000)	1.25	1.00
	Never hinged	2.00	
	First day cover		5.00
	Nos. 449-451 (3)	1.65	1.40
	Set, Never hinged	2.70	

Commonwealth 4th Anniversary Issue (#452-460)

Triumphal Arch — A72

Printed by U.S. Bureau of Engraving and Printing.

1939, Nov. 15	Unwmk.	Perf. 11	
452 A72	2c yellow green (1,562,352)	.20	.20
	Never hinged	.25	
	First day cover		1.00
453 A72	6c carmine (1,267,717)	.20	.20
	Never hinged	.25	
	First day cover		1.00
454 A72	12c bright blue (971,724)	.20	.20
	Never hinged	.25	
	First day cover		1.40
	Nos. 452-454 (3)	.60	.60
	Set, Never hinged	.75	

Malacañan Palace — A73

1939, Nov. 15	Unwmk.	Perf. 11	
455 A73	2c green (1,578,600)	.20	.20
	Never hinged	.25	
	First day cover		1.00
456 A73	6c orange (1,252,859)	.20	.20
	Never hinged	.25	
	First day cover		1.00
457 A73	12c carmine (935,800)	.20	.20
	Never hinged	.25	
	First day cover		1.40
	Nos. 455-457 (3)	.60	.60
	Set, Never hinged	.75	

President Quezon Taking Oath of Office — A74

1940, Feb. 8	Unwmk.	Perf. 11	
458 A74	2c dark orange (1,572,400)	.20	.20
	Never hinged	.25	
	First day cover		1.00
459 A74	6c dark green (1,257,900)	.20	.20
	Never hinged	.25	
	First day cover		1.00
460 A74	12c purple (980,779)	.25	.20
	Never hinged	.30	
	First day cover		1.40
	Nos. 458-460 (3)	.65	.60
	Set, Never hinged	.80	

José Rizal — A75

ROTARY PRESS PRINTING

1941, Apr. 14	Unwmk.	Perf. 11x10½	
	Size: 19x22½mm		
461 A75	2c apple green (59,915,600)	.20	.50
	Never hinged	.25	
	First day cover		1.00
	P# block of 4	1.00	

FLAT PLATE PRINTING

1941-43	Unwmk. Size: 18¾x22mm	Perf. 11	
462 A75	2c apple green	.20	5.00
	Never hinged	.25	
a.	2c pale apple green ('41)	.20	.50
	Never hinged	.25	
b.	As No. 462, booklet pane of 6 (24,000)	1.25	50.00
	Never hinged	2.00	
c.	As "a," booklet pane of 6 ('41) (114,960)	2.50	7.50
	Never hinged	4.00	

This stamp was issued only in booklet panes and all examples have one or two straight edges.
Further printings were made in 1942 and 1943 in different shades from the first supply of stamps sent to the islands.

Stamps of 1935-41 Handstamped in Violet

1944	Unwmk.	Perf. 11, 11x10½	
463 A53	2c rose (On 411), Dec. 3 (168)	325.00	160.00
a.	Booklet pane of 6 (28)	12,500.	
463B A53	2c rose (On 433), Dec. 14 (41)	2,000.	1,750.

464	A75	2c	**apple green** (On 461), *Nov. 8 (24,400)*	10.00	8.00
			Never hinged	17.50	
			On cover		17.50
465	A54	4c	**yellow green** (On 384), *Nov. 8 (807)*	42.50	42.50
			Never hinged	70.00	—
			On cover		—
466	A55	6c	**dark brown** (On 385), *Dec. 14 (64)*	3,500.	2,000.
467	A69	6c	**yellow green** (On 409), *Dec. 3*	225.00	150.00
			Never hinged	400.00	—
			On cover		—
468	A55	6c	**dark brown** (On 413), *Dec. 28 (206)*	4,750.	825.00
469	A72	6c	**carmine** (On 453), *Nov. 8 (235)*	350.00	125.00
			On cover		—
470	A73	6c	**yellow green** (On 456), *Dec. 14 (141)*	1,750.	725.00
			On cover		—
471	A74	6c	**dark green** (On 459), *Nov. 8*	275.00	225.00
			On cover		—
472	A56	8c	**violet** (On 436), *Nov. 8 (1,643)*	17.50	24.00
			Never hinged	30.00	—
			On cover		—
473	A57	10c	**carmine rose** (On 415), *Nov. 8 (450)*	300.00	150.00
			On cover		—
474	A57	10c	**carmine rose** (On 437), *Nov. 8 (358)*	275.00	200.00
			Never hinged	475.00	—
			On cover		—
475	A69	12c	**ultramarine** (On 410), *Dec. 3*	1,100.	400.00
			On cover		—
476	A72	12c	**bright blue** (On 454), *Nov. 8 (36)*	6,000.	2,500.
			On cover		—
477	A74	12c	**purple** (On 460), *Nov. 8*	375.00	275.00
			On cover		—
478	A59	16c	**dark blue** (On 389), *Dec. 3 (122)*	2,250.	
479	A59	16c	**dark blue** (On 417), *Nov. 8 (200)*	1,250.	1,000.
			On cover		—
480	A59	16c	**dark blue** (On 439), *Nov. 8 (500)*	500.00	200.00
			On cover		—
481	A60	20c	**light olive green** (On 440), *Nov. 8 (1,401)*	110.00	35.00
			Never hinged	185.00	—
482	A62	30c	**orange red** (On 420), *Dec. 3 (248)*	450.00	1,500.
			On cover		—
483	A62	30c	**orange red** (On 442), *Dec. 3 (200)*	750.00	375.00
			On cover		—
484	A63	1p	**red orange & black** (On 443) *Dec. 3 (21)*	6,250.	4,500.

Nos. 463-484 are valued in the grade of fine to very fine.
No. 463 comes only from the booklet pane. All examples have one or two straight edges.

Types of 1935-37 Overprinted

a

b

c

1945			**Unwmk.**		***Perf. 11***
485	A53(a)	2c	**rose**, *Jan. 19 (65,816,000)*	.20	.20
			Never hinged	.20	
			First day cover		2.50
486	A54(b)	4c	**yellow green**, *Jan. 19 (4,986,800)*	.20	.20
			Never hinged	.20	
			First day cover		2.50
487	A55(a)	6c	**golden brown**, *Jan. 19 (4,381,440)*	.20	.20
			Never hinged	.20	
			First day cover		2.50
488	A56(b)	8c	**violet**, *Jan. 19 (535,000)*	.20	.20
			Never hinged	.25	
			First day cover		3.00
489	A57(b)	10c	**rose carmine**, *Jan. 19 (1,060,000)*	.20	.20
			Never hinged	.20	
			First day cover		3.00
490	A58(b)	12c	**black**, *Jan. 19 (3,214,200)*	.20	.20
			Never hinged	.20	
			First day cover		3.50
491	A59(b)	16c	**dark blue**, *Jan. 19 (1,060,000)*	.25	.20
			Never hinged	.30	
			First day cover		4.00
492	A60(a)	20c	**light olive green**, *Jan. 19 (976,800)*	.30	.20
			Never hinged	.40	
			First day cover		4.25
493	A62(b)	30c	**orange red**, *May 1 (535,000)*	.50	.35
			Never hinged	.75	
			First day cover		2.50
494	A63(b)	1p	**red orange & black**, *Jan. 19 (1,434,400)*	1.10	.25
			Never hinged	1.60	
			First day cover		6.50
495	A71(c)	10p	**gray**, *May 1 (22,000)*	45.00	13.50
			Never hinged	70.00	
			First day cover		20.00
496	A71(c)	20p	**henna brown**, *May 1 (42,500)*	35.00	15.00
			Never hinged	55.00	
			First day cover		25.00
			Nos. 485-496 (12)	83.35	30.70
			Set, Never hinged	129.30	

José Rizal — A76

ROTARY PRESS PRINTING

1946, May 28			**Unwmk.**		***Perf. 11x10½***
497	A76	2c	**sepia** *(53,560,000)*	.20	.20
			Never hinged	.20	
			P# block of 4	.50	

Later issues, released by the Philippine Republic on July 4, 1946, and thereafter, are listed in Scott's Standard Postage Stamp Catalogue, Vol. 5.

AIR POST STAMPS

Madrid-Manila Flight Issue

Issued to commemorate the flight of Spanish aviators Gallarza and Loriga from Madrid to Manila.

Regular Issue of 1917-26
Overprinted in Red or Violet by
the Philippine Bureau of
Printing

1926, May 13			**Unwmk.**		***Perf. 11***
C1	A40	2c	**green** (R) *(9,900)*	18.00	15.00
			Never hinged	40.00	
			First day cover		26.00
			Block of 4	80.00	67.50
C2	A40	4c	**carmine** (V) *(8,900)*	20.00	17.50
			Never hinged	45.00	
			First day cover		26.00
			Block of 4	90.00	80.00
a.			Inverted overprint *(100)*	4,000.	—
C3	A40	6c	**lilac** (R) *(5,000)*	55.00	55.00
			Never hinged	125.00	
			First day cover		40.00
			Block of 4	240.00	
C4	A40	8c	**orange brown** (V) *(5,000)*	57.50	50.00
			Never hinged	130.00	
			First day cover		40.00
			Block of 4	250.00	
C5	A40	10c	**deep blue** (R) *(5,000)*	57.50	50.00
			Never hinged	130.00	

			First day cover		40.00
			Block of 4	250.00	
C6	A40	12c	**red orange** (V) *(4,000)*	65.00	50.00
			Never hinged	145.00	
			First day cover		42.50
			Block of 4	275.00	
C7	A40	16c	**light olive green** (Sampson) (V) *(300)*	3,250.	1,600.
			Block of 4		
C8	A40	16c	**olive bister** (Sampson) (R) *(100)*	5,000.	3,000.
			Block of 4		
C9	A40	16c	**olive green** (Dewey) (V) *(3,600)*	70.00	50.00
			Never hinged	160.00	
			First day cover		42.50
			Block of 4	325.00	
C10	A40	20c	**orange yellow** (V) *(4,000)*	65.00	65.00
			Never hinged	160.00	
			First day cover		42.50
			Block of 4	300.00	
C11	A40	26c	**blue green** (V) *(3,900)*	70.00	65.00
			Never hinged	155.00	
			First day cover		45.00
			Block of 4	325.00	
C12	A40	30c	**gray** (V) *(4,000)*	65.00	65.00
			Never hinged	155.00	
			First day cover		45.00
			Block of 4	300.00	
C13	A40	2p	**violet brown** (R) *(900)*	650.00	300.00
			Never hinged	1,200.	
			On cover		350.00
			Block of 4	—	
C14	A40	4p	**dark blue** (R) *(700)*	750.00	500.00
			Never hinged	1,300.	
			On cover		575.00
			Block of 4	—	
C15	A40	10p	**deep green** (V) *(500)*	1,350.	700.00
			On cover		775.00
			Block of 4		

Same Overprint on No. 269
Wmk. Single-lined PIPS (190)
Perf. 12

| C16 | A40 | 26c | **blue green** (V) *(100)* | 6,250. | |
| | | | Block of 4 | | |

Same Overprint on No. 284
Perf. 10

C17	A40	1p	**pale violet** (V) *(2,000)*	225.00	175.00
			Never hinged	450.00	
			On cover		200.00
			First day cover		225.00
			Block of 4	950.00	

Overprintings of Nos. C1-C6, C9-C15 and C17 were made from two plates. Position No. 89 of the first printing shows broken left blade of propeller.

London-Orient Flight Issue
Issued Nov. 9, 1928, to celebrate the arrival of a British squadron of hydroplanes.

Regular Issue of 1917-25
Overprinted in Red

1928, Nov. 9			**Unwmk.**		***Perf. 11***
C18	A40	2c	**green** *(101,200)*	1.00	.50
			Never hinged	1.75	
			First day cover		7.75
C19	A40	4c	**carmine** *(50,500)*	1.10	.75
			Never hinged	2.00	
			First day cover		9.50
C20	A40	6c	**violet** *(12,600)*	3.50	2.25
			Never hinged	6.25	
			On cover		2.50
C21	A40	8c	**orange brown** *(10,000)*	4.00	2.50
			Never hinged	7.00	
			On cover		3.00
C22	A40	10c	**deep blue** *(10,000)*	4.00	2.50
			Never hinged	7.00	
			On cover		3.00
C23	A40	12c	**red orange** *(8,000)*	5.00	3.25
			Never hinged	8.75	
			On cover		3.75
C24	A40	16c	**olive green** (No. 303a) *(12,600)*	4.50	2.50
			Never hinged	7.75	
			On cover		3.00
C25	A40	20c	**orange yellow** *(8,000)*	6.00	3.25
			Never hinged	10.50	
			On cover		4.00
C26	A40	26c	**blue green** *(7,000)*	16.00	7.25
			Never hinged	28.00	
			On cover		9.25
C27	A40	30c	**gray** *(7,000)*	16.00	7.25
			Never hinged	28.00	
			On cover		9.25

Same Overprint on No. 271
Wmk. Single-lined PIPS (190)
Perf. 12

C28	A40	1p **pale violet** (6,000)	55.00	30.00
		Never hinged	90.00	
		On cover		34.00
		Nos. C18-C28 (11)	116.10	62.00
		Set, never hinged	197.00	

Von Gronau Issue
Issued commemoration of the visit of Capt. Wolfgang von Gronau's airplane on its round-the-world flight.

Nos. 354-360 Overprinted by the Philippine Bureau of Printing

1932, Sept. 27   **Unwmk.**   *Perf. 11*

C29	A43	2c **yellow green** (100,000)	.90	.30
		Never hinged	1.40	
		First day cover		2.00
C30	A44	4c **rose carmine** (80,000)	.90	.40
		Never hinged	1.40	
		First day cover		2.00
C31	A45	12c **orange** (55,000)	1.25	.65
		Never hinged	2.00	
		On cover		1.00
C32	A46	18c **red orange** (25,305)	5.00	3.25
		Never hinged	8.00	
		On cover		3.50
C33	A47	20c **yellow** (30,000)	4.00	2.00
		Never hinged	6.50	
		On cover		2.25
C34	A48	24c **deep violet** (30,000)	4.00	2.00
		Never hinged	6.50	
		On cover		2.25
C35	A49	32c **olive brown** (30,000)	3.50	2.00
		Never hinged	5.75	
		On cover		2.25
		First day cover, #C29-C35		35.00
		Nos. C29-C35 (7)	19.55	10.60
		Set, never hinged	31.75	

Rein Issue
Commemorating the flight from Madrid to Manila of the Spanish aviator Fernando Rein y Loring.

Regular Issue of 1917-25 Overprinted in Black

1933, Apr. 11

C36	A40	2c **green** (95,000)	.75	.45
		Never hinged	1.10	
		First day cover		1.60
C37	A40	4c **carmine** (75,000)	.90	.45
		Never hinged	1.40	
		First day cover		—
C38	A40	6c **deep violet** (65,000)	1.10	.80
		Never hinged	1.75	
		First day cover		3.00
C39	A40	8c **orange brown** (35,000)	3.75	1.75
		Never hinged	5.75	
C40	A40	10c **dark blue** (35,000)	3.75	1.25
		Never hinged	5.75	
C41	A40	12c **orange** (35,000)	3.75	1.25
		Never hinged	5.75	
C42	A40	16c **olive green** (Dewey) (35,000)	3.50	1.25
		Never hinged	5.25	
C43	A40	20c **yellow** (35,000)	3.75	1.25
		Never hinged	5.75	
C44	A40	26c **green** (35,000)	3.75	1.75
		Never hinged	5.75	
a.		26c **blue green**	4.00	2.00
		Never hinged	6.00	
C45	A40	30c **gray** (30,000)	4.00	2.00
		Never hinged	6.00	
		First day cover, #C36-C45		40.00
		Nos. C36-C45 (10)	29.00	12.20
		Set, never hinged	44.25	

Stamp of 1917 Overprinted by the Philippine Bureau of Printing

1933, May 26   **Unwmk.**   *Perf. 11*

C46	A40	2c **green** (500,000)	.65	.40
		Never hinged	1.00	

Regular Issue of 1932 Overprinted

C47	A44	4c **rose carmine** (799,878)	.30	.20
		Never hinged	.45	
C48	A45	12c **orange** (500,000)	.60	.20
		Never hinged	.90	
C49	A47	20c **yellow** (500,000)	.60	.20
		Never hinged	.90	
C50	A48	24c **deep violet** (500,000)	.65	.25
		Never hinged	1.00	
C51	A49	32c **olive brown** (500,000)	.85	.35
		Never hinged	1.40	
		First day cover, #C46-C51		35.00
		Nos. C46-C51 (6)	3.65	1.60
		Set, never hinged	4.65	

Transpacific Issue
Issued to commemorate the China Clipper flight from Manila to San Francisco, Dec. 2-5, 1935.

Nos. 387, 392 Overprinted in Gold

1935, Dec. 2   **Unwmk.**   *Perf. 11*

C52	A57	10c **rose carmine** (500,000)	.40	.20
		Never hinged	.60	
		First day cover		2.00
C53	A62	30c **orange red** (300,000)	.60	.35
		Never hinged	.90	
		First day cover		3.00

Manila-Madrid Flight Issue
Issued to commemorate the Manila-Madrid flight by aviators Antonio Arnaiz and Juan Calvo.

Nos. 291, 295, 298a, 298 Surcharged in Various Colors by Philippine Bureau of Printing

1936, Sept. 6

C54	A40	2c on 4c **carmine** (Bl)		
		(2,000,000)	.20	.20
		Never hinged	.25	
		First day cover		1.00
C55	A40	6c on 12c **red orange** (V)		
		(500,000)	.20	.20
		Never hinged	.30	
		First day cover		3.00
C56	A40	16c on 26c **blue green** (Bk)		
		(300,000)	.25	.20
		Never hinged	.40	
		First day cover		5.00
a.		16c on 26c **green**	2.00	.70
		Never hinged	3.00	
		Nos. C54-C56 (3)	.65	.60
		Set, never hinged	.95	

Air Mail Exhibition Issue
Issued to commemorate the first Air Mail Exhibition, held Feb. 17-19, 1939.

Nos. 298a, 298, 431 Surcharged in Black or Red by Philippine Bureau of Printing

1939, Feb. 17

C57	A40	8c on 26c **blue green** (Bk)		
		(200,000)	1.00	.40
		Never hinged	1.50	

		First day cover		3.50
a.		8c on 26c **green** (Bk)	3.50	.55
		Never hinged	5.25	
C58	A71	1p on 10p **gray** (R) (30,000)	3.25	2.25
		Never hinged	4.75	
		First day cover		8.00

Moro Vinta and Clipper — AP1

Printed by the US Bureau of Engraving and Printing.

1941, June 30   **Unwmk.**   *Perf. 11*

C59	AP1	8c **carmine** (210,000)	2.00	.60
		Never hinged	2.75	
		First day cover		2.00
C60	AP1	20c **ultramarine** (25,000)	3.00	.50
		Never hinged	4.00	
		First day cover		2.50
C61	AP1	60c **blue green** (50,000)	3.00	1.00
		Never hinged	4.00	
		First day cover		3.50
C62	AP1	1p **sepia** (1,110,000)	.70	.50
		Never hinged	1.00	
		First day cover		2.25
		Nos. C59-C62 (4)	8.70	2.60
		Set, never hinged	10.75	

No. C47 Handstamped in Violet

1944, Dec. 3   **Unwmk.**   *Perf. 11*

C63	A44	4c **rose carmine** (122)	3,750.	2,750.
		On cover		—

SPECIAL DELIVERY STAMPS

U.S. No. E5 Overprinted in Red

a

Printed by U.S. Bureau of Engraving & Printing
Wmk. Double-lined USPS (191)

1901, Oct. 15   *Perf. 12*

E1	SD3	10c **dark blue** (14,998)	100.	80.
		Never hinged	185.	
		On cover		350.
		Block of 4	500.	
		P# strip of 3, Impt.	500.	
		P# block of 6, Impt.	5,000.	
a.		Dots in curved frame above messen-		
		ger (Pl. 882)	175.	160.
		P# block of 6, Impt. (Pl. 882)	5,500.	

Special Delivery Messenger SD2

Wmk. Double-lined PIPS (191)

1906, Sept. 8   *Perf. 12*

E2	SD2	20c **deep ultramarine** (40,019)	45.00	8.00
		Never hinged	90.00	
		On cover		17.50
		Block of 4	200.00	
b.		20c **pale ultramarine**	35.00	8.00
		Never hinged	70.00	
		On cover		17.50
		Block of 4	150.00	

SPECIAL PRINTING
U.S. No. E6 Overprinted Type "a" in Red

1907   **Wmk. Double-lined USPS (191)**   *Perf. 12*
E2A   SD4   10c   **ultramarine**   *2,750.*
     Block of 4   *11,500.*
     P# block of 6, Impt.   *38,500.*

This stamp was part of the set specially printed for the Bureau of Insular Affairs in 1907. See note following No. 240. There is only one intact plate block of No. E2A. It is fine and is valued thus.

1911, Apr.   **Wmk. Single-lined PIPS (190)**   *Perf. 12*
E3   SD2   20c   **deep ultramarine** *(200,000)*   22.00   1.75
     Never hinged   42.00
     On cover   12.50
     Block of 4   90.00

1916   *Perf. 10*
E4   SD2   20c   **deep ultramarine** *(200,000)*   175.00   75.00
     Never hinged   275.00
     On cover   100.00
     Block of 4   825.00
     pale ultramarine

Early in 1919 the supply of Special Delivery stamps in the Manila area was exhausted. A Government decree permitted the use of regular issue postage stamps for payment of the special delivery fee when so noted on the cover. This usage was permitted until the new supply of Special Delivery stamps arrived.

1919   **Unwmk.**   *Perf. 11*
E5   SD2   20c   **ultramarine** *(4,195,862)*   .60   .20
     Never hinged   .90
     On cover   5.00
     Block of 4   2.50
a.   20c **pale blue**   .75   .20
     Never hinged   1.00
     On cover   5.25
     Block of 4   3.00
b.   20c **dull violet**   .60   .20
     Never hinged   .90
     On cover   5.00
     Block of 4   2.50

Type of 1906 Issue
1925-31   **Unwmk.**   *Imperf.*
E6   SD2   20c   **dull violet** *('31) (6,500)*   30.00   75.00
     Never hinged   45.00
     On cover   250.00
     Block of 4   130.00
     P# block of 6   400.00
a.   20c **violet blue** *('25) (2,100)*   50.00   —
     Never hinged   80.00
     On cover   —
     Block of 4   250.00
     P# block of 6   750.00

Type of 1919 Overprinted in Black

1939, Apr. 27   **Unwmk.**   *Perf. 11*
E7   SD2   20c   **blue violet** *(1,253,250)*   .25   .20
     Never hinged   .40
     First day cover   35.00

Nos. E5b and E7 Handstamped in Violet

1944   **Unwmk.**   *Perf. 11*
E8   SD2   20c   **dull violet** *(On E5b) (138)*   1,400.   550.00
E9   SD2   20c   **blue violet** *(On E7), Nov. 8*   550.00   250.00
     (600)
     On cover   —

Type SD2 Overprinted "VICTORY" As No. 486

1945, May 1   **Unwmk.**   *Perf. 11*
E10   SD2   20c   **blue violet** *(578,600)*   .70   .55
     Never hinged   1.10
     First day cover   10.00
a.   "IC" close together   3.25   2.75
     Never hinged   4.75

SPECIAL DELIVERY OFFICIAL STAMP

Type of 1906 Issue Overprinted

1931   **Unwmk.**   *Perf. 11*
EO1   SD2   20c   **dull violet** *(46,750)*   3.00   75.00
     Never hinged   4.50
a.   No period after "B"   50.00   250.00
     Never hinged   75.00
b.   Double overprint   —

It is strongly recommended that expert opinion be acquired for No. EO1 used.

POSTAGE DUE STAMPS

U.S. Nos. J38-J44 Overprinted in Black

Printed by the U.S. Bureau of Engraving and Printing.

Wmk. Double-lined USPS (191)
1899, Aug. 16   *Perf. 12*
J1   D2   1c   **deep claret** *(340,892)*   7.50   2.50
     Never hinged   15.00
     On cover   30.00
     On cover, used as regular postage   110.00
     P# strip of 3, Impt.   125.00
     P# block of 6, Impt.   650.00
J2   D2   2c   **deep claret** *(306,983)*   7.50   2.50
     Never hinged   15.00
     On cover   37.50
     P# strip of 3, Impt.   125.00
     P# block of 6, Impt.   650.00
J3   D2   5c   **deep claret** *(34,565)*   15.00   2.50
     Never hinged   30.00
     On cover   70.00
     P# strip of 3, Impt.   200.00
     P# block of 6, Impt.   1,500.
J4   D2   10c   **deep claret** *(15,848)*   19.00   5.50
     Never hinged   37.50
     On cover   100.00
     P# strip of 3, Impt.   175.00
     P# block of 6, Impt.   1,100.
J5   D2   50c   **deep claret** *(6,168)*   200.00   100.00
     Never hinged   335.00
     On cover   —
     P# strip of 3, Impt.   1,100.
     P# block of 6, Impt.   4,000.

No. J1 was used to pay regular postage Sept. 5-19, 1902.

1901, Aug. 31
J6   D2   3c   **deep claret** *(14,885)*   17.50   7.00
     Never hinged   35.00
     On cover   60.00
     P# strip of 3, Impt.   175.00
     P# block of 6, Impt.   875.00
J7   D2   30c   **deep claret** *(2,140)*   250.00   110.00
     Never hinged   415.00
     On cover   —
     P# strip of 3, Impt.   1,000.
     P# block of 6, Impt.   4,000.
     Nos. J1-J7 (7)   516.50   230.00
     Set, never hinged   882.50

Post Office Clerk — D3

1928, Aug. 21   **Unwmk.**   *Perf. 11*
J8   D3   4c   **brown red** *(948,054)*   .20   .20
     Never hinged   .25
J9   D3   6c   **brown red** *(255,490)*   .30   .75
     Never hinged   .45
J10   D3   8c   **brown red** *(508,621)*   .25   .75
     Never hinged   .35
J11   D3   10c   **brown red** *(254,195)*   .30   .75
     Never hinged   .45
J12   D3   12c   **brown red** *(407,457)*   .25   .75
     Never hinged   .35
J13   D3   16c   **brown red** *(253,215)*   .30   .75
     Never hinged   .45
J14   D3   20c   **brown red** *(259,665)*   .30   .75
     Never hinged   .45
     Nos. J8-J14 (7)   1.90   4.70
     Set, never hinged   2.75

No. J8 Surcharged in Blue

1937, July 29   **Unwmk.**   *Perf. 11*
J15   D3   3c on 4c   **brown red**   .25   .20
     Never hinged   .35
     First day cover   35.00
     See note after No. NJ1.

Nos. J8-J14 Handstamped in Violet

1944, Dec. 3   **Unwmk.**   *Perf. 11*
J16   D3   4c   **brown red** *(306)*   150.00   —
J17   D3   6c   **brown red** *(390)*   90.00   —
J18   D3   8c   **brown red** *(379)*   95.00   —
J19   D3   10c   **brown red** *(405)*   90.00   —
J20   D3   12c   **brown red** *(423)*   90.00   —
J21   D3   16c   **brown red** *(425)*   95.00   —
J22   D3   20c   **brown red** *(375)*   95.00   —
     Nos. J16-J22 (7)   705.00

OFFICIAL STAMPS

Official Handstamped Overprints

"Officers purchasing stamps for government business may, if they so desire, surcharge them with the letters O.B. either in writing with black ink or by rubber stamps but in such a manner as not to obliterate the stamp that postmasters will be unable to determine whether the stamps have been previously used." C.M. Cotterman, Director of Posts, December 26, 1905.

Beginning January 1, 1906, all branches of the Insular Government used postage stamps to prepay postage instead of franking them as before. Some officials used manuscript, some utilized the typewriting machines but by far the larger number provided themselves with rubber stamps. The majority of these read "O.B." but other forms were: "OFFICIAL BUSINESS" or "OFFICIAL MAIL" in two lines, with variations on many of these.

These "O.B." overprints are known on U.S. 1899-1901 stamps; on 1903-06 stamps in red and blue; on 1906 stamps in red, blue, black, yellow and green.

"O.B." overprints were also made on the centavo and peso stamps of the Philippines, per order of May 25, 1907.

Beginning in 1926 the Bureau of Posts issued press-printed official stamps, but many government offices continued to handstamp ordinary postage stamps "O.B."

During the Japanese occupation period 1942-45, the same system of handstamped official overprints prevailed, but the handstamp usually consisted of "K.P.", initials of the Tagalog words, "Kagamitang Pampamahalaan" (Official Business), and the two Japanese characters used in the printed overprint on Nos. NO1 to NO4.

Legislative Palace Issue of 1926 Overprinted in Red

Printed and overprinted by the Philippine Bureau of Printing.

1926, Dec. 20   Unwmk.   Perf. 12

O1	A42	2c	green & black (90,500)	3.00	1.00
			Never hinged	4.50	
			On cover		2.00
			Block of 4	13.00	5.50
O2	A42	4c	carmine & black (90,450)	3.00	1.25
			Never hinged	4.50	
			On cover		2.00
			First day cover		10.00
			Block of 4	13.00	5.50
a.			Vertical pair, imperf. between	750.00	
O3	A42	18c	light brown & black (70,000)	8.00	4.00
			Never hinged	12.00	
			On cover		6.50
			Block of 4	36.00	20.00
O4	A42	20c	orange & black (70,250)	7.75	1.75
			Never hinged	11.50	
			On cover		2.25
			Block of 4	36.00	8.25
			First day cover, #O1-O4		50.00
			Nos. O1-O4 (4)	21.75	8.00
			Set, never hinged	32.50	

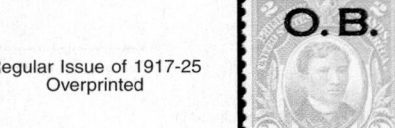

Regular Issue of 1917-25
Overprinted

Printed and overprinted by the U.S. Bureau of Engraving and Printing.

1931   Unwmk.   Perf. 11

O5	A40	2c	green (22,940,100)	.40	.20
			Never hinged	.65	
a.			No period after "B"	17.50	17.50
			Never hinged	27.50	
b.			No period after "O"	40.00	30.00
O6	A40	4c	carmine (5,377,000)	.45	.20
			Never hinged	.70	
a.			No period after "B"	40.00	20.00
			Never hinged	60.00	
O7	A40	6c	deep violet (616,500)	.75	.20
			Never hinged	1.25	
O8	A40	8c	yellow brown (706,700)	.75	.20
			Never hinged	1.25	
O9	A40	10c	deep blue (1,006,800)	1.20	.20
			Never hinged	1.90	
O10	A40	12c	red orange (158,050)	2.00	.20
			Never hinged	3.00	
a.			No period after "B"	80.00	80.00
			Never hinged	120.00	
O11	A40	16c	light olive green (Dewey) (824,400)	1.00	.20
			Never hinged	1.50	
a.			16c olive bister	2.00	.20
			Never hinged	3.00	
O12	A40	20c	orange yellow (509,050)	1.25	.20
			Never hinged	1.90	
a.			No period after "B"	80.00	80.00
			Never hinged	120.00	
O13	A40	26c	green (68,600)	2.00	.30
			Never hinged	3.25	
a.			26c blue green	2.50	.65
			Never hinged	4.00	
O14	A40	30c	gray (199,400)	2.00	.25
			Never hinged	3.25	
			Nos. O5-O14 (10)	11.80	2.15
			Set, never hinged	18.65	

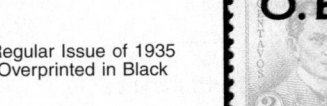

Regular Issue of 1935
Overprinted in Black

1935   Unwmk.   Perf. 11

O15	A53	2c	rose (7,927,800)	.20	.20
			Never hinged	.25	
a.			No period after "B"	15.00	10.00
			Never hinged	22.50	
O16	A54	4c	yellow green (5,079,266)	.20	.20
			Never hinged	.25	
a.			No period after "B"	15.00	40.00
			Never hinged	22.50	
O17	A55	6c	dark brown (786,896)	.25	.20
			Never hinged	.40	
a.			No period after "B"	35.00	35.00
			Never hinged	52.50	
O18	A56	8c	violet (656,200)	.30	.20
			Never hinged	.45	
O19	A57	10c	rose carmine (756,100)	.30	.20
			Never hinged	.45	
O20	A58	12c	black (104,500)	.75	.20
			Never hinged	1.10	
O21	A59	16c	dark blue (254,800)	.55	.20
			Never hinged	.85	
O22	A60	20c	light olive green (203,079)	.60	.20
			Never hinged	.90	

O23	A61	26c	indigo (67,750)	.90	.25
			Never hinged	1.50	
O24	A62	30c	orange red (83,500)	.80	.20
			Never hinged	1.20	
			Nos. O15-O24 (10)	4.85	2.05
			Set, never hinged	7.35	

Nos. 411 and 418 with
Additional Overprint in Black

1937-38   Unwmk.   Perf. 11

O25	A53	2c	rose, Apr. 10, 1937 (11,580,800)	.20	.20
			Never hinged	.20	
			First day cover		50.00
a.			No period after "B"	25.00	25.00
			Never hinged	45.00	
b.			Period after "B" raised (UL 4)	150.00	
O26	A60	20c	light olive green, Apr. 26, 1938 (174,929)	.70	.50
			Never hinged	1.10	

Regular Issue of 1935 Overprinted In Black:

a

b

1938-40   Unwmk.   Perf. 11

O27	A53(a)	2c	rose (23,239,872)	.20	.20
			Never hinged	.20	
a.			Hyphen omitted	10.00	10.00
			Never hinged	15.00	
b.			No period after "B"	20.00	30.00
			Never hinged	30.00	
O28	A54(b)	4c	yellow green (85,000)	.75	.25
			Never hinged	1.10	
O29	A55(a)	6c	dark brown (393,549)	.30	.20
			Never hinged	.45	
O30	A56(b)	8c	violet (82,000)	.75	.25
			Never hinged	1.10	
O31	A57(b)	10c	rose carmine (1,188,735)	.20	.20
			Never hinged	.20	
a.			No period after "O"	50.00	40.00
			Never hinged	75.00	
O32	A58(b)	12c	black (340,000)	.30	.20
			Never hinged	.45	
O33	A59(b)	16c	dark blue (490,000)	.30	.20
			Never hinged	.45	
O34	A60(a)	20c	light olive green ('40) (162,000)	.55	.25
			Never hinged	.85	
O35	A61(b)	26c	indigo (77,000)	.75	.30
			Never hinged	1.10	
O36	A62(b)	30c	orange red (82,000)	.75	.25
			Never hinged	1.10	
			Nos. O27-O36 (10)	4.85	2.30
			Set, never hinged	7.00	

No. 461 Overprinted in Black

c

ROTARY PRESS PRINTING

1941, Apr. 14   Unwmk.   Perf. 11x10½

O37	A75	2c	apple green (21,087,900)	.20	.40
			Never hinged	.20	
			First day cover		3.50
			Margin block of 4, P#	.25	

Nos. O27, O37, O16, O29,
O31, O22 and O26
Handstamped in Violet

1944   Unwmk.   Perf. 11, 11x10½

O38	A53	2c	rose (On O27) (128)	375.00	150.00
O39	A75	2c	apple green (On O37) (13,100)	10.00	10.00
			Never hinged	15.00	
			On cover		25.00
			Block of 4	47.50	—
O40	A54	4c	yellow green (On O16) (2,634)	42.50	30.00
			Never hinged	75.00	
			Block of 4	190.00	
O40A	A55	6c	dark brown (On O29)	8,000.	—
O41	A57	10c	rose carmine (On O31) (665)	500.00	—
			Block of 4	2,100.	
a.			No period after "O"	4,000.	
O42	A60	20c	light olive green (On O22)	8,000.	
O43	A60	20c	light olive green (On O26)	1,750.	

No. 497 Overprinted Type "c" in Black

1946, June 19   Unwmk.   Perf. 11x10½

O44	A76	2c	sepia (10,470,000)	.20	.20
			Never hinged	.20	
			Margin block of 4, P#	.40	

POST OFFICE SEALS

POS1

1906   Litho.   Unwmk.   Perf. 12

OX1	POS1	light brown	75.00	75.00
		On cover		1,750.

Wmk. "PIRS" in Double-lined Capitals

1907   Perf. 12

OX2	POS1	light brown	95.00	95.00
		On cover		2,250.

Hyphen-hole Perf. 7

OX3	POS1	orange brown	40.00	45.00

1911   Hyphen-hole Perf. 7

OX4	POS1	yellow brown	40.00	45.00
		On cover		1,750.
OX5	POS1	olive bister	75.00	75.00
		On cover		1,750.
a.		Unwatermarked	—	
OX6	POS1	yellow	75.00	75.00
		On cover		1,750.

1913   Unwmk.   Hyphen-hole Perf. 7

OX7	POS1	lemon yellow	3.00	15.00
		On cover		250.00

Perf. 12

OX8	POS1	yellow	150.00	200.00
		On cover		2,000.

Wmk. "USPS" in Single-lined Capitals
Hyphen-hole Perf. 7

OX9	POS1	yellow	80.00	50.00
		On cover		1,500.

1934   Unwmk.   Rouletted

OX10	POS1	dark blue	3.00	10.00
		On cover		450.00

POS2

OX11 POS2 **dark blue** 6.00 *7.50*
On cover *300.00*

POS3

1938 *Hyphen-hole Perf. 7*
OX12 POS3 **dark blue** 3.00 *4.00*
On cover *175.00*

ENVELOPES

U.S. Envelopes of 1899 Issue Overprinted below stamp in color of the stamp, except where noted

1899-1900

Note: Many envelopes for which there was no obvious need were issued in small quantities. Anyone residing in the Islands could, by depositing with his postmaster the required amount, order any envelopes in quantities of 500, or multiples thereof, provided it was on the schedule of U.S. envelopes.

Such special orders are indicated by a plus sign after the quantity.

U1	U77	1c **green** (#U352) *(370,000)*	3.00 2.00
		Entire	8.75 9.50
U2	U77	1c **green**, *amber* (#U353) *(1,000)*+	18.00 14.00
		Entire	40.00 40.00
U3	U77	1c **green**, *amber* (#U353) red overprint *(500)*+	22.50 20.00
		Entire	60.00 57.50
U4	U77	1c **green**, *oriental buff* (#U354) *(1,000)*+	14.00 14.00
		Entire	30.00 30.00
U5	U77	1c **green**, *oriental buff* (#U354) red overprint *(500)*+	35.00 35.00
		Entire	72.50 *72.50*
U6	U77	1c **green**, *blue* (#U355) *(1,000)*+	9.00 9.00
		Entire	30.00 30.00
U7	U77	1c **green**, *blue* (#U355) red overprint *(500)*+	20.00 19.00
		Entire	72.50 67.50
U8	U79	2c **carmine** (#U362) *(1,180,000)*	1.50 1.50
		Entire	4.00 3.00
U9	U79	2c **carmine**, *amber* (#U363) *(21,000)*	5.25 5.00
		Entire	15.00 12.50
U10	U79	2c **carmine**, *oriental buff* (#U364) *(10,000)*	5.25 4.75
		Entire	17.00 13.50

U11	U79	2c **carmine**, *blue* (#U365) *(10,000)*	4.75 6.25
		Entire	12.50 12.00
U12	U81	4c **brown**, *amber* (#U372) *(500)*	40.00 35.00
		Entire	85.00 92.50
a.		Double overprint	—
		Entire	4,000.
U13	U83	4c **brown** (#U374) *(10,500)*	12.50 9.00
		Entire	30.00 40.00
U14	U83	4c **brown**, *amber* (#U375) *(500)*	55.00 50.00
		Entire	175.00 125.00
U15	U84	5c **blue** (#U377) *(20,000)*	6.25 6.00
		Entire	13.00 13.00
U16	U84	5c **blue**, *amber* (#U378) *(500)*+	35.00 35.00
		Entire	87.50 *110.00*
		Nos. U1-U16 (16)	287.00 265.50

1903 **Same Overprint on U.S. Issue of 1903**

U17	U85	1c **green** (#U379) *(300,000)*	1.50 1.25
		Entire	4.25 4.25
U18	U85	1c **green**, *amber* (#U380) *(1,000)*+	12.50 12.00
		Entire	22.50 25.00
U19	U85	1c **green**, *oriental buff* (#U381) *(1,000)*+	14.50 12.50
		Entire	26.00 24.00
U20	U85	1c **green**, *blue* (#U382) *(1,500)*+	12.00 11.00
		Entire	26.00 26.00
U21	U85	1c **green**, *manila* (#U383) *(500)*+	20.00 20.00
		Entire	45.00 47.50
U22	U86	2c **carmine** (#U385) *(150,500)*	5.00 3.50
		Entire	7.50 7.00
U23	U86	2c **carmine**, *amber* (#U386) *(500)*+	17.50 14.00
		Entire	35.00 42.50
U24	U86	2c **carmine**, *oriental buff* (#U387) *(500)*+	17.50 *25.00*
		Entire	45.00
U25	U86	2c **carmine**, *blue* (#U388) *(500)*+	17.50 17.50
		Entire	40.00
U26	U87	4c **chocolate**, *amber* (#U391) *(500)*+	55.00 *75.00*
		Entire	140.00 190.00
a.		Double overprint, entire	7,000.
U27	U88	5c **blue**, *amber* (#U394) *(500)*+	55.00 —
		Entire	125.00 125.00
		Nos. U17-U27 (11)	228.00 191.75

1906 **Same Overprint on Re-cut U.S. issue of 1904**

U28	U89	2c **carmine** (#U395)	42.50 27.50
		Entire	150.00 125.00
U29	U89	2c **carmine**, *Oriental buff* (#U397)	67.50 *110.00*
		Entire	225.00 275.00

Rizal —E1

E2, McKinley.

1908

U30	E1	2c **green**	.50 .25
		Entire	.85 1.50
U31	E1	2c **green**, *amber*	4.00 2.25
		Entire	9.00 8.00
U32	E1	2c **green**, *oriental buff*	5.00 3.00
		Entire	9.00 9.00
U33	E1	2c **green**, *blue*	5.00 3.00
		Entire	9.00 9.00
U34	E1	2c **green**, *manila (500)*	7.25 —
		Entire	15.00 20.00
U35	E2	4c **carmine**	.50 .25
		Entire	1.40 1.25
U36	E2	4c **carmine**, *amber*	4.00 2.50
		Entire	9.00 7.00
U37	E2	4c **carmine**, *oriental buff*	4.25 3.50
		Entire	9.00 17.00
U38	E2	4c **carmine**, *blue*	4.00 3.00
		Entire	8.50 8.50
U39	E2	4c **carmine**, *manila (500)*	9.00 —
		Entire	20.00 30.00
		Nos. U30-U39 (10)	43.50 17.75

Rizal — E3

"Juan de la Cruz" — E4

1927, Apr. 5

U40	E3	2c **green**	11.50 9.50
		Entire	30.00 25.00
		Entire, 1st day cancel	*37.50*

1935, June 19

U41	E4	2c **carmine**	.35 .25
		Entire	1.25 .75
U42	E4	4c **olive green**	.50 .30
		Entire	1.65 1.10

For surcharges see Nos. NU1-NU2.

Nos. U30, U35, U41 and U42 Handstamped in Violet

1944

U42A	E1	2c **green** (On U30), Entire	—
U43	E4	2c **carmine** (On U41)	17.50 14.00
		Entire	47.50 *77.00*
U44	E2	4c **carmine**, *McKinley* (On U35)	950.00 *950.00*
		Entire	—
U45	E4	4c **olive green** (On U42)	82.50 70.00
		Entire	140.00 175.00

WRAPPERS

U.S. Wrappers Overprinted in Color of Stamp

1901

W1	U77	1c **green**, *manila* (No. W357) *(320,000)*	1.50 1.25
		Entire	5.00 *10.00*

1905

W2	U85	1c **green**, *manila* (No. W384)	9.00 9.00
		Entire	22.50 25.00
a.		Double overprint, entire	4,500.
W3	U86	2c **carmine**, *manila* (No. W389)	11.00 10.50
		Entire	22.50 27.50

Design of Philippine Envelopes

1908

W4	E1	2c **green**, *manila*	2.00 2.00
		Entire	11.00 15.00

POSTAL CARDS

Values are for Entires.
U.S. Cards Overprinted in Black below Stamp
a **PHILIPPINES.**

1900, Feb.

UX1	(a)	1c **black** (Jefferson) (UX14) *(100,000)*	17.50 15.00
a.		Without period	47.50 75.00
UX2	(a)	2c **black** (Liberty) (UX16) *(20,000)*	40.00 30.00
a.		With double "PHILIPPINES" overprint	*20,000.*

b

1903, Sept. 15
UX3	(b)	1c **black** (McKinley) (UX18)		1,350.	1,150.
UX4	(b)	2c **black** (Liberty) (UX16)		800.	700.

c   PHILIPPINES.

1903, Nov. 10
UX5	(c)	1c **black** (McKinley) (UX18)		47.50	40.00
UX6	(c)	2c **black** (Liberty) (UX16)		60.00	55.00

d   PHILIPPINES

1906
UX7	(d)	1c **black** (McKinley) (UX18)		275.	300.
UX8	(d)	2c **black** (Liberty) (UX16)		2,000.	1,500.

Designs same as postage issue of 1906

1907
UX9	A40	2c **black**, *buff* (Rizal)		10.00	8.00
UX10	A40	4c **black**, *buff* (McKinley)		25.00	20.00

Color changes

1911
UX11	A40	2c **blue**, *light blue* (Rizal)		8.00	8.00
a.		2c blue on white		20.00	20.00
UX12	A40	4c **blue**, *light blue* (McKinley)		25.00	25.00

An impression of No. UX11 exists on the back of a U.S. No. UX21.

1915
UX13	A40	2c **green**, *buff* (Rizal)		3.00	2.00
UX14	A40	2c **yellow green**, *amber*		3.50	1.50
UX15	A40	4c **green**, *buff* (McKinley)		20.00	15.00

Design of postage issue of 1935

1935
UX16	A53	2c **red**, *pale buff* (Rizal)		2.50	1.60

No. UX16 Overprinted at left of Stamp   **COMMONWEALTH**

1938
UX17	A53	2c **red**, *pale buff*		2.50	1.60

No. UX16 Overprinted   **COMMONWEALTH**

UX18	A53	2c **red**, *pale buff*		45.00	45.00

No. UX16 Overprinted   **COMMONWEALTH**

UX19	A53	2c **red**, *pale buff*		4.00	4.00

Nos. UX13, UX18 and UX19 Handstamped in Violet

1944
UX20	A40	2c **green**, *buff, Rizal* (On UX13)		180.00	225.00
UX21	A53	2c **red**, *pale buff* (On UX18)		650.00	—
UX22	A53	2c **red**, *pale buff* (On UX19)		285.00	550.00

Overprinted in Black at left   **VICTORY**

1945, Jan. 19
UX23	A76	2c **gray brown**, *pale buff*		1.25	.75
		First day cancel			3.25
a.		"IC" of "Victory" very close		5.00	3.00

This card was not issued without overprint.

PAID REPLY POSTAL CARDS
U.S. Paid Reply Cards of 1892-93 issues
Overprinted with type "a" in blue

1900, Feb.
UY1		2c +2c **blue**, unsevered (5,000)		160.00	500.00
m.		PM2 Message card, detached		27.50	50.00
r.		PR2 Reply card, detached		27.50	50.00
s.		As No. UY1, double impression of overprint on message card		—	

Overprinted type "c" in black

1903
UY2		1c + 1c **black**, *buff*, unsevered (20,000)		150.00	375.00
m.		PM1 Message card, detached		22.50	25.00
r.		PR1 Reply card, detached		22.50	25.00
UY3		2c + 2c **blue**, unsevered (20,000)		300.00	700.00
m.		PM2, Message card, detached		55.00	50.00
r.		PR2, Reply card, detached		55.00	50.00

OFFICIAL CARDS

Overprinted at left of stamp

1925   **On postal card No. UX13**
UZ1	A40	2c **green**, *buff* (Rizal)	35.00	35.00

1935   **On postal card No. UX16**
UZ2	A53	2c **red**, *pale buff*	14.00	17.50

Overprinted at Left of Stamp   **O. B.**

1938   **On postal card No. UX19**
UZ3	A53	2c **red**, *pale buff*	13.00	17.50

Overprinted Below Stamp   **O. B.**

1941   **Design of postage issue of 1941**
UZ4	A75	2c **light green**, *pale buff*	160.00	200.00

This card was not issued without overprint.

Postal Card No. UX19 Overprinted at Left of Stamp   **O. B.**

1941
UZ5	A53	2c **red**, *pale buff*	20.00	25.00

OCCUPATION STAMPS

Issued Under Japanese Occupation
Nos. 461, 438 and 439 Overprinted with Bars in Black

1942-43		Unwmk.	Perf. 11x10½, 11		
N1	A75	2c **apple green**, *Mar. 4, 1942* (3,000,000)		.20	1.00
		Never hinged		.20	
		P# block of 4		.25	
a.		Pair, one without overprint		—	
N2	A58	12c **black**, *Apr. 30, 1943* (310,000)		.25	2.00
		Never hinged		.40	
N3	A59	16c **dark blue**, *Mar. 4, 1942* (160,000)		5.00	3.75
		Never hinged		7.50	
		Nos. N1-N3 (3)		5.45	6.75
		Set, never hinged		8.10	

Nos. 435a, 435, 442, 443, and 423 Surcharged in Black

1942-43			Perf. 11		
N4	A55(a)	5(c) on 6c **golden brown** *Sept. 1, 1942* (800,000)		.20	.75
		Never hinged		.35	
		First day cover, Manila			4.00
a.		Top bar shorter and thinner (200,000)		.20	1.00
		Never hinged		.35	
b.		5(c) on 6c **dark brown**		.20	.85
		Never hinged		.35	
c.		As "b," top bar shorter and thinner		.20	1.00
		Never hinged		.35	
N5	A62(b)	16(c) on 30c **orange red**, *Jan. 11, 1943* (210,000)		.25	.60
		Never hinged		.45	
		First day cover			5.00
N6	A63(c)	50c on 1p **red orange & black**, *Apr. 30, 1943* (20,000)		.75	1.25
		Never hinged		1.10	
a.		Double surcharge			300.00
N7	A65(d)	1p on 4p **blue & black**, *Apr. 30, 1943* (19,975)		100.00	175.00
		Never hinged		155.00	
		Inverted "S" in "PESO," position 4		150.00	225.00
		Nos. N4-N7 (4)		101.20	177.60
		Set, never hinged		156.85	

On Nos. N4 and N4b, the top bar measures 1 ½x22 ½mm. On Nos. N4a and N4c, the top bar measures 1x21mm and the "5" is smaller and thinner.

The used value for No. N7 is for postal cancellation. Used stamps exist with first day cancellations. They are worth somewhat less.

1942, May 18
N8	A54	2(c) on 4c **yellow green** (100,000)		6.00	6.00
		Never hinged		8.75	
		First day cover			6.00

Issued to commemorate Japan's capture of Bataan and Corregidor. The American-Filipino forces finally surrendered May 7, 1942. No. N8 exists with "R" for "B" in BATAAN.

No. 384
Surcharged in
Black

1942, Dec. 8

N9	A54	5(c) on 4c **yellow green**		
		(400,000)	.50	1.00
		Never hinged	.75	
		First day cover		3.00

1st anniversary of the "Greater East Asia War."

Nos. C59 and
C62 Surcharged
in Black

1943, Jan. 23

N10	AP1	2(c) on 8c **carmine** (400,000)	.25	1.00
		Never hinged	.35	
N11	AP1	5c on 1p **sepia** (300,000)	.50	1.50
		Never hinged	.75	
		First day cover, #N10-N11		4.00

1st anniv. of the Philippine Executive Commission.

Nipa
Hut — OS1

Rice
Planting — OS2

Mt. Mayon and Mt.
Fuji — OS3

Moro
Vinta — OS4

Wmk. 257

The "c" currency is indicated by four Japanese characters,
"p" currency by two.

Engraved; Typographed (2c, 6c, 25c)

1943-44		**Wmk. 257**	**Perf. 13**	
N12	OS1	1c **deep orange**, June 7,		
		1943	.20	.20
		Never hinged	.25	
N13	OS2	2c **bright green**, Apr. 1, 1943	.20	.20
		Never hinged	.25	
N14	OS1	4c **slate green**, June 7, 1943	.20	.20
		Never hinged	.25	
N15	OS3	5c **orange brown**, Apr. 1,		
		1943	.20	.20
		Never hinged	.25	
N16	OS2	6c **red**, July 14, 1943	.20	.20
		Never hinged	.25	
N17	OS3	10c **blue green**, July 14, 1943	.20	.20
		Never hinged	.25	
N18	OS4	12c **steel blue**, July 14, 1943	1.00	1.00
		Never hinged	1.50	
N19	OS4	16c **dark brown**, July 14, 1943	.20	.20
		Never hinged	.25	
N20	OS1	20c **rose violet**, Aug. 16, 1943	1.25	1.25
		Never hinged	1.90	
N21	OS3	21c **violet**, Aug. 16, 1943	.20	.20
		Never hinged	.35	
N22	OS2	25c **pale brown**, Aug. 16, 1943	.20	.20
		Never hinged	.35	
N23	OS3	1p **deep carmine**, June 7,		
		1943	.75	.75
		Never hinged	1.15	

N24	OS4	2p **dull violet**, Sept. 16, 1943	5.50	5.50
		Never hinged	8.25	
		First day cover		14.00
N25	OS4	5p **dark olive**, Apr. 10, 1944	14.00	14.00
		Never hinged	21.00	
		First day cover		14.00
		Nos. N12-N25 (14)	24.40	24.30
		Set, never hinged	35.25	

Map of Manila Bay
Showing Bataan and
Corregidor — OS5

1943, May 7   Photo.   Unwmk.

N26	OS5	2c **carmine red**	.20	.75
		Never hinged	.30	
N27	OS5	5c **bright green**	.25	1.00
		Never hinged	.35	
		Colorless dot after left "5"	4.00	—
		First day cover, #N26-N27,		
		Manila		4.00

1st anniversary of the fall of Bataan and Corregidor.

No. 440 Surcharged in Black

1943, June 20   Engr.   Perf. 11

N28	A60	12(c) on 20c **light olive green**		
		(350,000)	.25	.75
		Never hinged	.35	
		First day cover		6.00
a.		Double surcharge	—	

350th anniversary of the printing press in the Philippines.
"Limbagan" is Tagalog for "printing press."

Rizal Monument,
Filipina and Philippine
Flag — OS6

1943, Oct. 14   Photo.   Unwmk.   Perf. 12

N29	OS6	5c **light blue**	.20	.90
		Never hinged	.20	
a.		Imperf.	.20	.90
N30	OS6	12c **orange**	.20	.90
		Never hinged	.25	
a.		Imperf.	.20	.90
N31	OS6	17c **rose pink**	.20	.90
		Never hinged	.30	
		First day cover, #N29-N31, Manila		3.00
a.		Imperf.	.20	.90
		First day cover, #N29a-N31a, Ma-		
		nila		3.00
		Nos. N29-N31 (3)	.60	2.70
		Set, never hinged	.75	

"Independence of the Philippines." Japan granted "independence" Oct. 14, 1943, when the puppet republic was founded.
The imperforate stamps were issued without gum.

José
Rizal — OS7

Rev. José
Burgos — OS8

Apolinario Mabini — OS9

1944, Feb. 17   Litho.   Unwmk.   Perf. 12

N32	OS7	5c **blue**	.20	1.00
		Never hinged	.20	
a.		Imperf.	.35	1.00
		Never hinged	.20	
N33	OS8	12c **carmine**	.20	1.00
		Never hinged	.25	
a.		Imperf.	.20	1.00
		Never hinged	.35	
N34	OS9	17c **deep orange**	.20	1.00
		Never hinged	.30	
		First day cover, #N32-N34, Manila		1.00
a.		Imperf.	.20	1.00
		Never hinged	.35	
		First day cover, #N32a-N34a, Apr.		
		17, Manila		3.00
		Nos. N32-N34 (3)	.60	3.00
		Set, never hinged	.75	

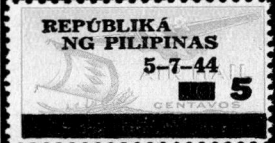

Nos. C60 and C61
Surcharged in
Black

1944, May 7   Unwmk.   Perf. 11

N35	AP1	5(c) on 20c **ultramarine**	.50	1.00
		Never hinged	.75	
N36	AP1	12(c) on 60c **blue green** (165,000)	1.75	1.75
		Never hinged	2.50	
		First day cover, #N35-N36		4.00

2nd anniversary of the fall of Bataan and Corregidor.

José P. Laurel — OS10

1945, Jan. 12   Litho.   Unwmk.   Imperf.
Without Gum

N37	OS10	5c **dull violet brown**	.20	.50
N38	OS10	7c **blue green**	.20	.50
N39	OS10	20c **chalky blue**	.20	.50
		First day cover, #N37-N39		3.00
		Nos. N37-N39 (3)		1.50

Issued belatedly on Jan. 12, 1945, to commemorate the first
anniversary of the puppet Philippine Republic, Oct. 14, 1944.
"S" stands for "sentimos."

The special cancellation devices prepared for use on Oct. 14,
1944, were employed on "First Day" covers Jan. 12, 1945.

OCCUPATION SEMI-POSTAL STAMPS

Woman, Farming and
Cannery — OSP1

1942, Nov. 12   Litho.   Unwmk.   Perf. 12

NB1	OSP1	2c + 1c **pale violet**	.20	.60
		Never hinged	.20	
NB2	OSP1	5c + 1c **bright green**	.25	1.00
		Never hinged	.30	
NB3	OSP1	16c + 2c **orange**	30.00	32.50
		Never hinged	42.00	
		First day cover, #NB1-NB3		37.50
		Nos. NB1-NB3 (3)	30.45	34.10
		Set, never hinged	42.50	

Issued to promote the campaign to produce and conserve
food. The surtax aided the Red Cross.

Souvenir Sheet

OSP2

Illustration reduced.

1943, Oct. 14   **Without Gum**   *Imperf.*
NB4 OSP2 Sheet of 3   75.00   17.50
     Sheet with first day cancel and
     cachet, Manila   17.50
     First day cover, Manila   17.50

"Independence of the Philippines."

No. NB4 contains one each of Nos. N29a-N31a. Marginal inscription is from Rizal's "Last Farewell." Sold for 2.50p.

The value of No. NB4 used is for a sheet from a first day cover. Commercially used sheets are extremely scarce and worth much more.

Nos. N18, N20 and N21
Surcharged in Black

1943, Dec. 8   **Wmk. 257**   *Perf. 13*
NB5 OS4 12c + 21c **steel blue**   .20   1.50
     Never hinged   .30
NB6 OS1 20c + 36c **rose violet**   .20   1.50
     Never hinged   .30
NB7 OS3 21c + 40c **violet**   .20   2.00
     Never hinged   .30
     First day cover, #NB5-NB7   2.50
     Nos. NB5-NB7 (3)   .60   5.00
     Set, never hinged   .90

The surtax was for the benefit of victims of a Luzon flood. "Baha" is Tagalog for "flood."

Souvenir Sheet

OSP3

Illustration reduced.

1944, Feb. 9   **Litho.**   **Unwmk.**   *Imperf.*
             Without Gum
NB8 OSP3 Sheet of 3   6.50   3.50
     First day cover   4.00

No. NB8 contains one each of Nos. N32a-N34a. The sheet sold for 1p, the surtax going to a fund for the care of heroes' monuments. Size: 101x143mm. No. NB8 exists with 5c inverted.

OCCUPATION POSTAGE DUE

No. J15 Overprinted with Bar in Blue

1942, Oct. 14   **Unwmk.**   *Perf. 11*
NJ1 D3 3c on 4c **brown red** *(40,000)*   25.00   20.00
     Never hinged   37.50
     First day cover   35.00
     Double bar

On examples of No. J15, two lines were drawn in India ink with a ruling pen across "United States of America" by employees of the Short Paid Section of the Manila Post Office to make a provisional 3c postage due stamp which was used from Sept. 1, 1942 (when the letter rate was raised from 2c to 5c) until Oct. 14 when No. NJ1 went on sale. Value on cover, $125.

OCCUPATION OFFICIAL STAMPS

Nos. 461, 413, 435, 435a and
442 Overprinted or Surcharged
in Black with Bars and

1943-44   **Unwmk.**   *Perf. 11x10½, 11*
NO1 A75   2c **apple green**, *Apr. 7, 1943*
     (200,000)   .20   .75
     Never hinged   .30
     P# block of 4   .25
   a.   Double overprint   400.00
     Never hinged   600.00
     On cover (double overprint)   1,250.
NO2 A55   5(c) on 6c **dark brown** (On No.
     413), *June 26, 1944*
     (23,049)   40.00   45.00
     Never hinged   55.00
     First day cover   125.00
NO3 A55   5(c) on 6c **golden brown** (On No.
     435a), *Apr. 7, 1943*
     (250,000)   .20   .90
     Never hinged   .35
   a.   Narrower spacing between bars
     (249,951)   .20   .90
     Never hinged   .35
   b.   5(c) on 6c dark brown (On No. 435)   .20   .90
     Never hinged   .35
   c.   As "b," narrower spacing between bars   .20   .90

   d.   Double overprint   .35
NO4 A62 16(c) on 30c **orange red**, *Apr. 7,*
     1943 (100,000)   .30   1.25
     Never hinged   .45
   a.   Wider spacing between bars   .30   1.25
     Never hinged   .45
     First day cover, Nos. NO1,
     NO3-NO4   35.00
     Nos. NO1-NO4 (4)   40.70   47.90
     Set, never hinged   56.05

On Nos. NO3 and NO3b the bar deleting "United States of America" is 9¾ to 10mm above the bar deleting "Common." On Nos. NO3a and NO3c, the spacing is 8 to 8½mm.

On No. NO4, the center bar is 19mm long, 3½mm below the top bar and 6mm above the Japanese characters. On No. NO4a, the center bar is 20½mm long, 9mm below the top bar and 1mm above the Japanese characters.

"K.P." stands for Kagamitang Pampamahalaan, "Official Business" in Tagalog.

Nos. 435 and 435a
Surcharged in Black

1944, Aug. 28   **Unwmk.**   *Perf. 11*
NO5 A55 (5c) on 6c **golden brown** *(500,000)*   .30   .40
     Never hinged   .45
   a.   5(c) on 6c **dark brown**   .30   .40
     Never hinged   .45

Nos. O34 and C62 Overprinted in Black

a

b

NO6 A60(a) 20c **light olive green** *(200,000)*   .40   .50
     Never hinged   .60
NO7 AP1(b) 1p **sepia** *(100,000)*   .90   1.00
     Never hinged   1.45
     First day cover, #NO5-NO7   4.00
     Nos. NO5-NO7 (3)   1.60   1.90
     Set, never hinged   2.50

OCCUPATION ENVELOPES

No. U41 Surcharged in Black **5**   **5**

1943, Apr. 1
NU1 E4 5c on 2c **carmine**   .50   .30
     Entire   3.00   3.00
     Entire, 1st day cancel   4.00

No. U41 Surcharged in Black

1944, Feb. 17

NU2	E4	5c on 2c **carmine**	.75	.50
		Entire	3.50	5.00
		Entire, 1st day cancel		7.50
a.	Inverted surcharged	—		
b.	Double surcharge	—		
c.	Both 5's missing	—		

OCCUPATION POSTAL CARDS

Values are for entire cards.

Nos. UX19 and UZ4 Overprinted with Bars in Black

1942

NUX1	A53	2c **red,** *pale buff,* Mar. 4, 1942	15.00	15.00
		First day cancel		85.00
a.	Vertical obliteration bars reversed	140.00		
NUX2	A75	2c **light green,** *pale buff,* Dec. 12, 1942	3.00	2.00
		First day cancel		6.00

Rice Planting — A77

1943, May 17

NUX3	A77	2c **green**	1.00	1.00
		First day cancel, Manila		2.00

OCCUPATION OFFICIAL CARDS

Nos. UX19, UX17 and UX18 Overprinted in Black with Bars and 公用 (K. P.)

1943, Apr. 7

NUZ1	A53	2c **red,** *pale buff*	5.00	5.00
		First day cancel		100.00
a.	On No. UX17	—		
b.	On No. UX18	—		

No. NUX3 Overprinted in Black

REPUBLIKA NG PILIPINAS (K. P.)

1944, Aug. 28

NUZ2	A77	2c **green**	1.50	1.00
		First day cancel		2.00
a.	Double overprint	—		

FILIPINO REVOLUTIONARY GOVERNMENT

Following the defeat of the Spanish fleet by U.S. Commodore Dewey in Manila on May 1, 1898, which essentially ended the Spanish-American War in the Philippines, postal services were disrupted throughout the Philippines. Postal service was reestablished through U.S. Army military stations, beginning in June 1898 near Manila, continuing province by province until culminating at Zamboanga and other cities in the southern areas in late 1899.

Provisional stamps were prepared for use in the central part of the island of Luzon at Malolos in late 1898 under the leadership of General Emilio Aguinaldo, who had proclaimed the Philippine Republic on June 12, 1898. Later, other provisional stamps were prepared by local Filipino insurgents at Iloilo (Panay Island), Bohol, Cebu and Negros, and Spanish period stamps were overprinted and/or surcharged for use by postal officials at Zamboanga and La Union.

The most familiar of these provisionals were the "Aguinaldo" issues of the Filipino Revolutionary Government in central Luzon near Manila. The letters "KKK," the initials of the revolutionary society, "Kataas-

taasang, Kagalang-galang Katipunan nang Mañga Anak nang Bayan," meaning "Sovereign Worshipful Association of the Sons of the Country," readily identify the Aguinaldo provisionals. Hostilities broke out between the Aguinaldo regime and the occupying American administration in February 1899, and the Filipino-American War continued until the American capture of Aguinaldo on March 23, 1901.

The Aguinaldo regular postage, registration, revenue, newspaper and telegraph stamps were in use in Luzon as early as November 10, 1898, and continued in use through early 1901. Although the postal regulations specified that these stamps be used for their inscribed purpose, they were commonly used interchangeably.

POSTAGE ISSUES

A1

A2

Coat of Arms — A3

1898-99   Unwmk.   Perf. 11½

Y1	A1	2c **red**	175.00	125.00
		On cover		1,500.
a.	Double impression	225.00		
Y2	A2	2c **red**	.25	.25
		On cover		450.00
b.	Double impression	—		
d.	Horiz. pair, imperf. between	—		
e.	Vert. pair, imperf. between	200.00		
Y3	A3	2c **red**	150.00	200.00
		On cover		2,000.

Imperf pairs and pairs, imperf horizontally, have been created from No. Y2e.

RS1

N1

REGISTRATION STAMP

YF1	RS1	8c **green**	3.50	10.00
		On cover with #Y2		3,500.
a.	Imperf., pair	400.00		
b.	Imperf. vertically, pair	—		

NEWSPAPER STAMP

YP1	N1	1m **black**	1.00	10.00
a.	Imperf., pair	1.00	10.00

PROOFS

1906

			(1) Large	DIE (2) Small	(2a)
241P	2c	yellow green		500.	750.
242P	4c	carmine lake	600.	500.	750.
243P	6c	violet	600.	500.	750.
244P	8c	brown	600.	500.	750.
245P	10c	dark blue		500.	750.
246P	12c	brown lake		500.	750.
247P	16c	violet black	600.	500.	750.
248P	20c	orange brown		500.	750.
249P	26c	violet brown		500.	750.
250P	30c	olive green	600.	500.	750.
251P	1p	orange		500.	750.
252P	2p	black		500.	750.
253P	4p	dark blue		500.	750.
254P	10p	dark green		500.	750.

1909-13

255P	12c	red orange	600.	625.
256P	16c	olive green	600.	625.
257P	20c	yellow	600.	625.
258P	26c	blue green	600.	625.
259P	30c	ultramarine	600.	625.
260P	1p	pale violet	600.	625.
260AP	2p	violet brown	600.	625.
275P	30c	gray	600.	625.

1923

303P	16c	olive bister	450.
303TC	16c	olive green	450.

1926

322P	18c	light brown & black, plate, glazed card	350.

1932

357P	18c	red orange	450.
357TC	18c	orange red	450.
360TC	32c	green	450.
360TC	18c	olive green	450.

1935

383P	2c	rose	600.
384P	4c	yellow green	600.
385P	6c	dark brown	600.
386P	8c	violet	600.
387P	10c	rose carmine	600.
388P	12c	black	600.
389P	16c	dark blue	600.
390P	20c	light olive green	600.
390TC	20c	black	—
391P	26c	indigo	600.
392P	30c	orange red	600.
393P	1p	red orange & black	600.
394P	2p	bister brown & black	600.
395P	4p	blue & black	600.
396P	5p	green & black	600.

1936

408P	2c	orange brown	450.
408TC	2c	yellow green	450.

1937

425P	2c	yellow green	500.

1939

452P	2c	yellow green	500.
453P	6c	carmine	500.
454P	12c	bright blue	500.

1939

455P	2c	green	750.	500.
456P	6c	orange		500.
457P	12c	carmine		500.

1940

458P	2c	dark orange	1,000.	600.
459P	6c	dark green		600.
460P	12c	purple		600.

1941

461P	2c	apple green	600.

1946

497P	2c	sepia	—

AIR POST

1941

C59P	8c	carmine	500.
C60P	20c	ultramarine	500.
C61P	60c	blue green	500.
C62P	1p	sepia	500.

SPECIAL DELIVERY

1906

E2P	20c	ultramarine	1,000.	1,000.	850.
E2TC	20c	green		1,000.	

POSTAGE DUE

1899

J1P	1c	deep claret	1,100.
J2P	2c	deep claret	1,100.
J3P	5c	deep claret	1,100.
J4P	10c	deep claret	1,100.
J5P	50c	deep claret	1,100.

1901

J6P	3c	deep claret	1,100.
J7P	30c	deep claret	1,100.

SPECIMEN STAMPS

Handstamped US Type E in Purple   Specimen.

1899

213S E	1c	yellow green	175.00
214dS E	2c	rose carmine, type IV	175.00
215S E	3c	purple	175.00
216S E	5c	blue	175.00

217S E	10c	brown, type I	175.00
218S E	15c	olive brown	175.00
219S E	50c	orange	175.00

See note after No. 219 for Special Printings with black "Specimen" overprints.

Overprinted US Type R in Black *Specimen*

1917-25

290S R	2c	green	40.00
291S R	4c	carmine	40.00
292S R	6c	deep violet	40.00
293S R	8c	yellow brown	40.00
294S R	10c	deep blue	40.00
295S R	12c	red orange	40.00
297S R	20c	orange yellow	40.00
298S R	26c	green	40.00
299S R	30c	gray	40.00
300S R	1p	pale violet	40.00
301S R	2p	violet brown	40.00
302S R	4p	blue	40.00

1923-26

303S R	16c	olive bister	25.00
304S R	10p	deep green	25.00

1926   **Overprinted Type R in Red**

319S R	2c	green & black	65.00
320S R	4c	carmine & black	65.00
321S R	16c	olive green & black	65.00
322S R	18c	light brown & black	65.00
323S R	20c	orange & black	65.00
324S R	24c	gray & black	65.00
325S R	1p	rose lilac & black	65.00

Overprinted US Type S in Red *Cancelled*

1926

319S S	2c	green & black	65.00
320S S	4c	carmine & black	65.00
321S S	16c	olive green & black	65.00
322S S	18c	light brown & black	65.00
323S S	20c	orange & black	65.00
324S S	24c	gray & black	65.00
325S S	1p	rose lilac & black	65.00

Imperforate examples of this set, on glazed cards with centers in brown, are known with the "Cancelled" overprint. Value, $2,250 for set.

Handstamped "SPECIMEN" in Red Capitals, 13x3mm

1925

340S S	2c	green	75.00
341S S	4c	carmine	75.00
342S S	6c	deep violet	75.00
343S S	8c	yellow brown	100.00
344S S	10c	deep blue	100.00
345S S	12c	red orange	100.00
346S S	16c	olive bister	100.00
347S S	20c	yellow	100.00
348S S	26c	blue green	100.00
349S S	30c	gray	100.00
350S S	1p	violet	100.00
351S S	2p	violet brown	100.00
352S S	4p	deep blue	150.00
353S S	10p	deep green	250.00

SPECIAL DELIVERY

1919   **Overprinted Type R in Black**

E5S R	20c	ultramarine	200.00
E5bS R	20c	dull violet	—

Handstamped "SPECIMEN" in Red Capitals, 13x3mm

1925

E6aS	20c	violet blue	300.00

POSTAGE DUE

1899   **Overprinted Type E in Black**

J1S E	1c	deep claret	225.00
J2S E	2c	deep claret	225.00
J3S E	5c	deep claret	225.00
J4S E	10c	deep claret	225.00
J5S E	50c	deep claret	225.00

OFFICIAL

1926   **Overprinted Type R in Red**

O1S R	2c	green & black	30.00
O2S R	4c	carmine & black	30.00
O3S R	18c	light brown & black	30.00
O4S R	20c	orange & black	30.00

1926   **Overprinted Type S in Red**

O1S S	2c	green & black	30.00
O2S S	4c	carmine & black	30.00
O3S S	18c	light brown & black	30.00
O4S S	20c	orange & black	30.00

PUERTO RICO

(Porto Rico)

United States troops landed at Guanica Bay, Puerto Rico, on July 25, 1898, and mail service between various points in Puerto Rico began soon after under the authority of General Wilson, acting governor of the conquered territory, who authorized a provisional service early in August, 1898. The first Military Postal Station was opened at La Playa de Ponce on August 3, 1898. Control of the island passed formally to the United States on October 18, 1898. Twenty-one military stations operating under the administration of the Military Postal Service were authorized in Puerto Rico after the Spanish-American war. After the overprinted provisional issue of 1900, unoverprinted stamps of the United States replaced those of Puerto Rico.

Name changed to Puerto Rico by Act of Congress, approved May 17, 1932.

Italicized numbers in parentheses indicate quantities issued.

100 CENTS = 1 DOLLAR.

PROVISIONAL ISSUES
Ponce Issue

A11

1898   **Unwmk.**   **Handstamped**   *Imperf.*

200	A11	5c	violet, *yellowish*	7,500. —

The only way No. 200 is known used is handstamped on envelopes. Both unused stamps and used envelopes have a violet control mark.

Uses on 2c U.S. stamps on cover were strictly as a cancellation, not as provisional postage.

Dangerous counterfeits exist.

Coamo Issue

CORREOS	CORREOS	CORREOS	CORREOS	CORREOS
5 CTS.	**5 CTS.**	**5 CTS.**	**5 CTS.**	**5 CTS.**
COAMO	COAMO	COAMO	COAMO	COAMO
CORREOS	CORREOS	CORREOS	CORREOS	CORREOS
5 CTS.	**5 CTS.**	**5 CTS.**	**5 CTS.**	**5 CTS.**
COAMO	COAMO	COAMO	COAMO	COAMO

A12

Types of "5":
I — Curved flag. Pos. 2, 3, 4, 5.
II — Flag turns down at right. Pos. 1, 9, 10.
III — Fancy outlined "5." Pos. 6, 7.
IV — Flag curls into ball at right. Pos. 8.

Typeset, setting of 10

1898, Aug.   **Unwmk.**   *Imperf.*

201	A12	5c	**black**, Type I	650. *1,050.*
			Type II	700. *1,100.*
			Type III	775. *1,200.*
			Type IV	850. *1,350.*
			Irregular "block" of 4 showing one of each type	3,750.
			Sheet of 10	10,000.
			On cover	*32,500.*
			Pair on cover	—

Blocks not showing all four types and pairs normally sell for 10-20% over the value of the individual stamps.

The stamps bear the control mark "F. Santiago" in violet. About 500 were issued.

Dangerous counterfeits exist.

Regular Issue

United States Nos. 279, 279Bf, 281, 272 and 282C Overprinted in Black at 36 degree Angle

[stamp illustration: PORTO RICO]

1899		**Wmk. 191**		*Perf. 12*
210	A87	1c	yellow green, *Mar. 15*	5.00 1.40
			On cover	50.00
			First day cover	—
			Block of 4	25.00 10.00
			P# strip of 3, Impt.	45.00
			P# block of 6, Impt.	275.00
a.			Overprint at 25 degree angle	7.00 2.25
			Pair, 36 degree and 25 degree angles	25.00
			"PORTO RICU"	35.00 —
211	A88	2c	**reddish carmine**, type IV, *Mar. 15*	4.25 1.25
			On cover	50.00
			Block of 4	22.50 10.00
			P# strip of 3, Impt.	37.50

		P# block of 6, Impt.	350.00	
		"FORTO RICO" (pos. 77)	—	
a.		Overprint at 25 degree angle, *Mar. 15*	5.50	2.25
		On cover		50.00
		First day cover	—	
		Block of 4	27.50	17.50
		P# strip of 3, Impt.	45.00	
		P# block of 6, Impt.	275.00	
		Pair, 36 degree and 25 degree angles	25.00	
		P# strip of 3, Impt.	95.00	
		P# block of 6, Impt.	700.00	
		"PORTU RICO" (pos. 46)	50.00	20.00
		"PORTO RICU" (pos. 3)	—	
		"PURTO RICO"	—	
		"FURTU RICO"	—	
212	A91 5c	blue	12.50	2.50
		On cover		50.00
		Block of 4	55.00	27.50
		P# strip of 3, Impt.	70.00	
		P# block of 6, Impt.	350.00	
213	A93 8c	violet brown	35.00	17.50
		On cover		125.00
		Block of 4	160.00	110.00
		P# strip of 3, Impt.	250.00	
		P# block of 6, Impt.	*2,250.*	
		"FORTO RICO"	90.00	60.00
a.		Overprint at 25 degree angle	40.00	19.00
		Pair, 36 degree and 25 degree angles	100.00	
c.		"PORTO RIC"	150.00	110.00
214	A94 10c	**brown**, type I	22.50	6.00
		On cover		120.00
		Block of 4	100.00	45.00
		P# strip of 3, Impt.	150.00	
		P# block of 6, Impt.	1,250.	
		"FORTO RICO"	85.00	70.00
		Nos. 210-214 (5)	79.25	28.65

Misspellings of the overprint on Nos. 210-214 (PORTO RICU, PORTU RICO, FORTO RICO) are actually broken letters.

United States Nos. 279 and 279B Overprinted in Black

1900

215	A87	1c	**yellow green**	6.50	1.40
			On cover		50.00
			Block of 4	27.50	10.00
			P# strip of 3, Impt.	30.00	
			P# block of 6, Impt.	175.00	
216	A88	2c	**red**, type IV, *Apr. 2*	4.75	2.00
			On cover		50.00
			Block of 4	22.50	15.00
			P# strip of 3, Impt.	32.50	
			P# block of 6, Impt.	175.00	
b.			Inverted overprint		*8,250.*

Special Printing

In March 1900 one pane of 100 stamps of each of the 1c (No. 215), 2c (No. 216) and 5c, 8c and 10c values, as well as 1c, 2c and 10c postage due stamps were specially overprinted for displays at the Paris Exposition (1900) and Pan American Exposition (1901). These last six items were never regularly issued with the PUERTO RICO overprint and therefore have no Scott catalogue number. The 2c pane was light red, type IV.

Stamps were handstampd type E "Specimen" in black ink by H. G. Mandel and mounted by him in separate displays for the two Expositions. Additional stamps from each pane were also handstamped "Specimen," but most were destroyed after the Expositions.

J. M. Bartels, a stamp dealer, signed some stamps from these panes "Special Surcharge" in pencil on the gum to authenticate them as coming from the "Mandel" Special Printing panes. In 1904 or later, he handstamped additional surviving examples "Special Surcharge" in red ink on the back as his guarantee. Some of these guaranteed stamps had Mandel's "Specimen" handstamp on the face while others did not. Value, each $1,750.

No Special Printing panes overprinted "Porto Rico" were produced by the government. Stamps do exist with a black type E "Specimen" handstamp, but it is believed that H. G. Mandel applied such handstamps to regularly issued overprinted "Porto Rico" stamps from his personal collection. Examples are known of the 2c type IV, in reddish carmine, 25 degree angle.

AIR POST

In 1938 a series of eight labels, two of which were surcharged, was offered to the public as "Semi-Official Air Post Stamps", the claim being that they had been authorized by the "Puerto Rican postal officials". These labels, printed by the Ever Ready Label Co. of New York, were a private issue of Aerovias Nacionales Puerto Rico, operating a passenger and air express service. Instead of having been authorized by the postal officials, they were at first forbidden but later tolerated by the Post Office Department at Washington.

In 1941 a further set of eight triangular labels was prepared and offered to collectors, and again the Post Office Department officials at Washington objected and forbade their use after September 16, 1941.

These labels represent only the charge for service rendered by a private enterprise for transporting matter outside the mails by plane. Their use did not not eliminate the payment of postage on letters carried by air express, which must in every instance be paid by United States postage stamps.

POSTAGE DUE STAMPS

United States Nos. J38, J39 and J42 Overprinted in Black at 36 degree Angle

1899   **Wmk. 191**   *Perf. 12*

J1	D2	1c	**deep claret**	22.50	5.50
			On cover		125.00
			Block of 4	100.00	35.00
			P# strip of 3, Impt.	120.00	
			P# block of 6, Impt.	*625.00*	
a.			Overprint at 25 degree angle	22.50	7.50

			Pair, 36 degree and 25 degree angles	65.00	
			P# strip of 3, Impt.	150.00	
			P# block of 6, Impt.	*750.00*	
J2	D2	2c	**deep claret**	20.00	6.00
			On cover		250.00
			Block of 4	80.00	37.50
			P# strip of 3, Impt.	120.00	
			P# block of 6, Impt.	*800.00*	
a.			Overprint at 25 degree angle	20.00	7.00
			Pair, 36 degree and 25 degree angles	60.00	
			P# strip of 3, Impt.	140.00	
			P# block of 6, Impt.	*900.00*	
J3	D2	10c	**deep claret**	190.00	60.00
			On cover		—
			Block of 4	800.00	
			P# strip of 3, Impt.	*1,250.*	
			P# block of 6, Impt.	*3,750.*	
a.			Overprint at 25 degree angle	175.00	85.00
			Pair, 36 degree and 25 degree angles	650.00	

ENVELOPES

U.S. Envelopes of 1887 Issue Overprinted in Black

PORTO RICO.

20mm long

1899-1900

Note: Some envelopes for which there was no obvious need were issued in small quantities. Anyone residing in Puerto Rico could, by depositing with his postmaster the required amount, order any envelope in quantities of 500, or multiples thereof, provided it was on the schedule of U.S. envelopes. Such special orders are indicated by a plus sign, i. e., Nos. U15 and U18, and half the quantities of Nos. U16 and U17.

U1	U71	2c	**green** (No. U311) *(3,000)*	16.00	*20.00*
			Entire	40.00	*350.00*
a.			Double overprint, entire	*3,500.*	
U2	U74	5c	**blue** (No. U330) *(1,000)*	20.00	20.00
			Entire	55.00	*350.00*
a.			Double overprint, entire	—	

U.S. Envelopes of 1899 Overprinted in color of the stamp

PORTO RICO.

21mm long

U3	U79	2c	**carmine** (No. U362) *(100,000)*	3.00	3.00
			Entire	10.00	*12.00*
U4	U84	5c	**blue** (No. U377) *(10,000)*	8.00	*9.00*
			Entire	17.50	*32.50*

Overprinted in Black   **PORTO RICO,**

19mm long

U5	U77	1c	**green**, *blue* (No. U355) *(1,000)*		750.
			Entire		1,900.
U6	U79	2c	**carmine**, *amber* (No. U363), Die 2 *(500)*	450.	500.
			Entire	1,100.	1,250.
U7	U79	2c	**carmine**, *oriental buff* (No. U364), Die 2 *(500)*		500.
			Entire		1,250.
U8	U80	2c	**carmine**, *oriental buff* (No. U369), Die 3 *(500)*		600.
			Entire		1,300.
U9	U79	2c	**carmine**, *blue* (No. U365), Die 2		4,000.
			Entire		
U10	U83	4c	**brown** (No. U374), Die 3 *(500)*	200.	500.
			Entire	500.	900.

U.S. Envelopes of 1899 Issue Overprinted

PUERTO RICO.

23mm long

U11	U79	2c	**carmine** (No. U362) red overprint *(100,000)*	4.00	3.00
			Entire	10.00	11.00
U12	U79	2c	**carmine**, *oriental buff* (No. U364), Die 2, black overprint *(1,000)*	—	325.00
			Entire	1,200.	1,300.
U13	U80	2c	**carmine**, *oriental buff* (No. U369), Die 3, black overprint *(1,000)*		375.00
			Entire		1,750.
U14	U84	5c	**blue** (No. U377) blue overprint *(10,000)*	14.00	14.00
			Entire	42.50	50.00

Overprinted in Black   **PUERTO RICO.**

U15	U77	1c	**green**, *oriental buff* (No. U354) *(500)+*	20.00	50.00
			Entire	75.00	80.00
U16	U77	1c	**green**, *blue* (No. U355) *(1,000)+*	25.00	50.00
			Entire	95.00	125.00
U17	U79	2c	**carmine**, *oriental buff* (No. U364) *(1,000)+*	20.00	50.00

			Entire	95.00	*135.00*
U18	U79	2c	**carmine**, *blue* (No. U365)		
			(500)+	20.00	*50.00*
			Entire	75.00	*135.00*

There were two settings of the overprint, with minor differences, which are found on Nos. U16 and U17.

WRAPPER

U.S. Wrapper of 1899 Issue Overprinted in Green

PORTO RICO.

21mm long

W1	U77	1c	**green**, *manila* (No. W357)		
			(15,000)	8.00	*35.00*
			Entire	17.00	*110.00*

POSTAL CARDS

Values are for Entires.

Imprinted below stamp   **PORTO RICO.**

1899-1900   **U.S. Postal Card No. UX14**

UX1	PC8	1c	**black**, *buff*, imprint 21mm long	165.	*175.*
b.			Double imprint	*2,250.*	

Imprinted below stamp   **PORTO RICO.**

UX1A	PC8	1c	**black**, *buff*, imprint 20mm long	1,200.	*1,300.*

Imprinted below stamp   **PORTO RICO.**

UX2	PC8	1c	**black**, *buff*, imprint 26mm long	165.	*190.*

Imprinted below stamp   **PUERTO RICO.**

UX3	PC8	1c	**black**, *buff*	150.	*200.*

REVENUE STAMPS

U.S. Revenue Stamps Nos. R163, R168-R169, R171 and Type of 1898 Surcharged in Black or Dark Blue

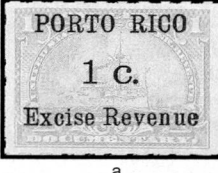

a   b

1901   **Wmk. 191R**   *Hyphen-hole Roulette 7*

R1	R15(a)	1c on 1c	**pale blue** (Bk)	10.00	8.75
R2	R15(a)	10c on 10c	**dark brown**	12.50	11.00
R3	R15(a)	25c on 25c	**purple brown**	15.00	11.00
R4	R15(a)	50c on 50c	**slate violet**	25.00	16.50
R5	R16(b)	$1 on $1	**pale greenish gray**	62.50	22.50
R6	R16(b)	$3 on $3	**pale greenish gray**	70.00	32.50
R7	R16(b)	$5 on $5	**pale greenish gray**	85.00	37.50
R8	R16(b)	$10 on $10	**pale greenish gray**	120.00	70.00
R9	R16(b)	$50 on $50	**pale greenish gray**	325.00	160.00
		Nos. R1-R9 (9)		725.00	369.75

Lines of 1c surcharge spaced farther apart; total depth of surcharge 15¾mm instead of 11mm.

RECTIFIED SPIRITS

U.S. Wine Stamps of 1933-34 Overprinted in Red or Carmine

RECTIFIED

SPIRITS

1934   **Offset Printing**   **Wmk. 191R**   *Roulletted 7*
Overprint Lines 14mm Apart, Second Line 25mm Long

RE1	RE5	2c	**green**	15.00
RE2	RE5	3c	**green**	55.00
RE3	RE5	4c	**green**	17.50
RE4	RE5	5c	**green**	15.00
RE5	RE5	6c	**green**	17.50

Overprint Lines 21½mm Apart, Second Line 23½mm Long

RE6	RE2	50c **green**	27.50
RE7	RE2	60c **green**	25.00

Handstamped overprints are also found on U.S. Wine stamps of 1933-34.

U.S. Wine Stamps of 1933-34 Overprinted in Black

RECTIFIED

RECTIFIED

SPIRITS
a

SPIRITS
b

1934 Offset Printing Wmk. 191R Rouletted 7

RE8	RE5(a)	1c **green**	22.50
RE9	RE5(a)	2c **green**	12.50
RE10	RE5(a)	3c **green**	60.00
RE11	RE5(a)	5c **green**	12.50
RE12	RE5(a)	6c **green**	15.00
RE13	RE2(b)	50c **green**	17.50
RE14	RE2(b)	60c **green**	15.00
RE15	RE2(b)	72c **green**	75.00
RE16	RE2(b)	80c **green**	40.00

RECTIFIED SPIRITS

PUERTO RICO

U.S. Wine Stamps of 1933-34 Overprinted in Black

1934 Offset Printing Wmk. 191R Rouletted 7

RE17	RE5	½c **green**		2.50
RE18	RE5	1c **green**	50.00	.60
RE19	RE5	2c **green**	50.00	.50
RE20	RE5	3c **green**	100.00	3.50
RE21	RE5	4c **green**		.75

RE22	RE5	5c **green**	50.00	1.00
RE23	RE5	6c **green**	50.00	1.25
RE24	RE5	10c **green**	100.00	3.50
RE25	RE5	30c **green**		30.00

Overprint Lines 12½mm Apart

RE26	RE2	36c **green**		6.00
RE27	RE2	40c **green**	150.00	5.00
RE28	RE2	50c **green**	150.00	2.50
RE29	RE2	60c **green**	110.00	.50
a.		Inverted overprint		—
RE30	RE2	72c **green**	150.00	4.00
RE31	RE2	80c **green**	150.00	4.00
RE32	RE2	$1 **green**	175.00	7.50

George Sewall Boutwell

Engr. (8c & 58c); Litho.
1942-57		Wmk. 191	Roulatted 7

Without Gum

RE33	R1	½c **carmine**	3.50	1.25
RE34	R1	1c **sepia**	8.25	3.50
RE35	R1	2c **bright yellow green**	1.10	.20
RE36	R1	3c **lilac**	70.00	35.00
RE37	R1	4c **olive**	2.25	.50
RE38	R1	5c **orange**	5.50	1.00
RE39	R1	6c **red brown**	4.00	1.25
RE40	R1	8c **bright pink** ('57)	8.25	3.50
RE41	R1	10c **bright purple**	12.50	5.00

RE41A	R1	30c **vermilion**	175.00	
RE42	R1	36c **dull yellow**	250.00	70.00
RE43	R1	40c **deep claret**	20.00	7.00
RE44	R1	50c **green**	11.00	4.00
RE45	R1	58c **red orange**	87.50	7.00
RE46	R1	60c **brown**	1.40	.20
RE47	R1	62c **black**	3.50	.70
RE48	R1	72c **blue**	40.00	1.00
RE49	R1	77½c **olive gray**	11.00	3.50
RE50	R1	80c **brownish black**	14.00	6.00
RE51	R1	$1 **violet**	87.50	25.00
	Nos. RE33-RE51 (20)		816.25	175.60

The 30c is believed not to have been placed in use.

SPECIMEN STAMPS

Handstamped U.S. Type E in Purple **Specimen.**

1899
210S	E	1c **yellow green**	180.00
211S	E	2c **reddish carmine**, type IV	180.00
212S	E	5c **blue**	180.00
213S	E	8c **violet brown**	180.00
214S	E	10c **brown**	180.00

See note after No. 216 for Special Printings with **black** "Specimen" overprint.

Postage Due

1899
J1S	E	1c **deep claret**	225.00
J2S	E	2c **deep claret**	225.00
J3S	E	10c **deep claret**	225.00

Revenue

R1S	E	1c on 1c **pale blue**	40.00
R2S	E	10c on 10c **dark brown**	40.00
R3S	E	25c on 25c **purple brown**	40.00
R4S	E	50c on 50c **state violet**	40.00
R5S	E	$1 on $1 **pale greenish gray**	40.00
R6S	E	$3 on $3 **pale greenish gray**	40.00
R7S	E	$5 on $5 **pale greenish gray**	40.00
R8S	E	$10 on $10 **pale greenish gray**	40.00
R9S	E	$50 on $50 **pale greenish gray**	40.00

RYUKYU ISLANDS

LOCATION — Chain of 63 islands between Japan and Formosa, separating the East China Sea from the Pacific Ocean.
GOVT. — Semi-autonomous under United States administration.
AREA — 848 sq. mi.
POP. — 945,465 (1970)
CAPITAL — Naha, Okinawa
The Ryukyus were part of Japan until American forces occupied them in 1945. The islands reverted to Japan May 15, 1972.

100 Sen = 1 Yen
100 Cents = 1 Dollar (1958).

In the Provisional Issues and Postal Stationery sections, italicized numbers in parentheses indicate quantity sold.
Values for First Day Covers are for unaddressed, cacheted covers. Values are for official cachets for Scott 1-26, C1-C3 and E1; and for commercial cachets for all others. Early cachets from the Japanese Philatelic Society command substantial premiums.

> Catalogue values for unused stamps are for Never Hinged items beginning with Scott 1 in the regular postage section, Scott C1 in the air post section, Scott E1 in the special delivery section, Scott R1 in the revenue section, Scott 91S in the specimen section and Scott RQ1 in the unemployment insurance section.

Cycad — A1

Lily — A2

Sailing Ship — A3

Farmer — A4

Wmk. 257

1948-49 Typo. Wmk. 257 Perf. 13
Second Printing, July 18, 1949

1	A1	5s **magenta**	2.50	2.50
		Imprint block of 10	37.50	
2	A2	10s **yellow green**	6.00	5.50
		Imprint block of 10	90.00	
3	A1	20s **yellow green**	3.50	3.50
		Imprint block of 10	55.00	
4	A3	30s **vermilion**	1.50	1.50
		Imprint block of 10	25.00	
5	A2	40s **magenta**	1.50	1.50
		Imprint block of 10	25.00	
6	A3	50s **ultramarine**	6.00	4.00
		Imprint block of 10	90.00	
7	A4	1y **ultramarine**	6.00	5.50
		Imprint block of 10	90.00	
		Nos. 1-7 (7)	27.00	24.00

First Printing, July 1, 1948

1a	A1	5s **magenta**	3.00	*3.50*
		First day cover		250.00
		Imprint block of 10	45.00	
2a	A2	10s **yellow green**	2.00	*2.00*
		First day cover		250.00
		Imprint block of 10	30.00	
3a	A1	20s **yellow green**	2.00	*2.00*
		First day cover		250.00
		Imprint block of 10	30.00	
4a	A3	30s **vermilion**	4.00	*3.50*
		First day cover		250.00
		Imprint block of 10	45.00	
5a	A2	40s **magenta**	60.00	60.00
		First day cover		250.00
		Imprint block of 10	900.00	
6a	A3	50s **ultramarine**	4.00	4.00
		First day cover		250.00
		Imprint block of 10	55.00	
7a	A4	1y **ultramarine**	475.00	350.00
		First day cover		250.00
		Imprint block of 10	*7,000.*	
		Nos. 1a-7a (7)	550.00	425.00

First printing: thick yellow gum, dull colors, rough perforations, grayish paper. Second printing: white gum, sharp colors, cleancut perforations, white paper.

A5   Ryukyu University — A6

Designs: 50s, Tile rooftop & Shishi. 1y, Ryukyu girl. 2y, Shuri Castle. 3y, Guardian dragon. 4y, Two women. 5y, Sea shells.

1950, Jan. 21   Photo.   Unwmk.   Perf. 13x13½
Off-white Paper

8	A5	50s dark carmine rose	.20	.20
		First day cover		20.00
		Imprint block of 6	2.00	
a.		White paper, third printing, Sept. 6, 1958	.50	.50
		First day cover		27.50
		Imprint block of 10	6.50	
b.		"White Sky" variety (pos. 76)	3.50	3.50
9	A5	1y deep blue	4.00	3.00
		First day cover		20.00
		Imprint block of 6	35.00	
10	A5	2y rose violet	12.00	6.00
		First day cover		20.00
		Imprint block of 6	100.00	
11	A5	3y carmine rose	30.00	11.00
		First day cover		20.00
		Imprint block of 6	275.00	
12	A5	4y greenish gray	15.00	11.00
		First day cover		20.00
		Imprint block of 6	110.00	
13	A5	5y blue green	8.00	6.00
		First day cover		20.00
		Imprint block of 6	60.00	
		First day cover, #8-13		200.00
		Nos. 8-13 (6)	69.20	37.20

No. 8a has colorless gum and an 8-character imprint in the sheet margin. The original 1950 first two printings on off-white paper have yellowish gum and a 5-character imprint.

For No. 8b, a defect in pos. 76 of the plates used for the first two printings resulted in the sky above the tile roof being predominantly white. A new master negative and plate was made for the third printing, so pos. 76 for this printing does not have the "white sky" variety.

For surcharges see Nos. 16-17.

1951, Feb. 12   Perf. 13½x13

14	A6	3y red brown	60.00	25.00
		First day cover		60.00
		Imprint block of 6	450.00	

Opening of Ryukyu University, Feb. 12.

Pine Tree — A7

1951, Feb. 19   Perf. 13

15	A7	3y dark green	55.00	25.00
		First day cover		60.00
		Imprint block of 6	450.00	

Reforestation Week, Feb. 18-24.

No. 8 surcharged in Black

16A Type I   16 Type II   16B Type III

There are three types of 10y surcharge:

Type I: narrow-spaced rules, "10" normal spacing, "Kai Tei" characters in 9-point type. First printing, Jan. 1, 1952.
Type II: wide-spaced rules, "10" normal spacing, "Kai Tei" characters in 9-point type. Second printing, June 5, 1952.
Type III: rules and "10" both wide-spaced, "Kai Tei" characters in 8-point type. Third printing, Dec. 8, 1952.

9 Point Kai Tei   8 Point Kai Tei

Both eight and nine point type were used in overprinting Nos. 16-17. In the varieties listed below, the first number indicates the size of the "Kai" character, and the second number is the size of the "Tei" character.

1952   Perf. 13½x13

16	A5	10y on 50s dark carmine rose (II)	10.00	10.00
		Imprint block of 6	90.00	
		Top imprint block of 4, Higa Seal (pos. 8, 9, 18, 19)	75.00	
c.		8/8 point Kai Tei	10.00	10.00
d.		9/8 point Kai Tei	90.00	90.00
		9/9-9/8-8/8 se-tenant (horiz. strip of all 3 varieties)	150.00	150.00
		8/8-9/9 horiz. se-tenant pair	30.00	30.00
		9/9-8/8 horiz. se-tenant pair	30.00	30.00
e.		Surcharge transposed	900.00	—
f.		Legend of surcharge only (no obliteration bars)	1,200.	
g.		Wrong font for "0" (pos. 59)	150.00	150.00
h.		Wrong font for "Yen" symbol (pos. 69)	150.00	150.00
i.		Surcharge on "white sky" variety (No. 8b) (pos. 76)	150.00	150.00

On No. 16e, the entire obliteration-bars portion of the surcharge normally under the 10 Yen must be visible at the top of the stamp. Ten examples of No. 16e exist (pos. 91-100) with the full obliteration bars also in the bottom selvage.

Forgeries to defraud the Postal Agency of revenue are known, used only, at the Gusikawa Post Office. Two types. Value, $500 each.

16A	A5	10y on 50s dark carmine rose (I)	40.00	40.00
		Imprint block of 6	350.00	
a.		8/8 point Kai Tei	40.00	40.00
		8/8-9/9 horiz. se-tenant pair (pos. 23-24)	200.00	250.00
		9/9-8/8 horiz. se-tenant pair	110.00	110.00
b.		Bottom two bars inverted (pos. 17)	150.00	150.00
c.		Wrong font for "0" (pos. 73)	250.00	250.00
d.		Surcharge on "white sky" variety (No. 8b) (pos. 76)	250.00	250.00
e.		Wide spaced obliterating bars (pos. 72)	150.00	150.00
f.		Wide spaced bottom obliterating bars (pos. 86, 95)	80.00	80.00
16B	A5	10y on 50s dark carmine rose (III)	50.00	40.00
		Imprint block of 6	450.00	
a.		Wrong font for "Yen" symbol (pos. 25, 35, 85)	200.00	200.00
b.		Wrong font for "Tei" (pos. 26)	350.00	350.00
c.		Asterisk missing (pos. 54)	—	—
d.		"Kai Tei" 1.25mm above asterisk (pos. 54)	350.00	350.00
e.		"Kai" omitted (pos. 71)	—	
f.		Narrow spaced "10" (pos. 96)	350.00	350.00
		Strip of 3, narrow spaced "10" in center (pos. 95-97)	450.00	
g.		Surcharge on "white sky" variety (No. 8b)	350.00	350.00
h.		Extra wide spaced "10" (pos. 60)	200.00	200.00
i.		Asterisk within 2.0mm of "Kai Tei" (pos. 87)	200.00	200.00

The Kai Tei of the third printing measures the same as the 8-point type in the earlier printings but has differing characteristics. The Top curved line of the Kai is shorter and the lower curved line is also much shorter.

No. 10 surcharged 100y in black

17	A5	100y on 2y rose violet, Kai Tei characters in 9/9-point type, June 16, 1952	2,200.	1,600.
		Hinged	1,600.	
		Imprint block of 6	18,500.	
		Top imprint block of 4, Higa Seal (pos. 7, 8, 17, 18)	10,000.	
a.		8/8 point Kai Tei	2,200.	1,600.
b.		9/8 point Kai Tei	3,500.	3,500.
		9/9-9/8-8/8 se-tenant (horiz. strip of all 3 varieties)	9,750.	9,750.
		8/8-9/9 horiz. se-tenant pair	5,000.	5,000.
		9/9-8/8 horiz. se-tenant pair	7,000.	7,000.
c.		Center "0" in wrong font, stamp with 9/9 Kai Tei (pos. 42)	5,000.	5,000.
d.		Center "0" in wrong font, stamp with 8/8 Kai Tei (pos. 67, 86)	3,500.	3,500.
e.		Center "0" in wrong font, stamp with 9/8 Kai Tei (pos. 53)	5,000.	5,000.
f.		Wrong font for last "0" (pos. 59)	5,000.	5,000.
g.		Wrong font for "yen" symbol (pos. 69)	5,000.	5,000.

Varieties of shifted and damaged surcharge characters exist, most notably a damaged ("clipped") Kai.

See note after 16B to differentiate between 8-point and 9-point charaters.
Surcharge forgeries are known. Authentication by competant experts is recommended.

Dove, Bean Sprout and Map — A8   Madanbashi Bridge — A9

1952, Apr. 1   Perf. 13½x13

18	A8	3y deep plum	120.00	40.00
		First day cover		80.00
		Imprint block of 10	1,800.	

Establishment of the Government of the Ryukyu Islands (GRI), April 1, 1952.

1952-53

Designs: 2y, Main Hall, Shuri Castle. 3y, Shurei Gate. 6y, Stone Gate, Soenji Temple, Naha. 10y, Benzaiten-do Temple. 30y, Sonohan Utaki (altar) at Shuri Castle. 50y, Tamaudun (royal mausoleum). Shuri. 100y, Stone Bridge, Hosho Pond, Enkaku Temple.

19	A9	1y red, Nov. 20, 1952	.30	.30
		Imprint block of 10	4.50	
20	A9	2y green, Nov. 20, 1952	.40	.40
		Imprint block of 10	6.00	
21	A9	3y aquamarine, Nov. 20, 1952	.50	.50
		First day cover, #19-21		40.00
		Imprint block of 10	7.50	
22	A9	6y blue, Jan. 20, 1953	3.00	3.00
		First day cover		27.50
		Imprint block of 10	45.00	
23	A9	10y crimson rose, Jan. 20, 1953	4.00	1.50
		First day cover		47.50
		Imprint block of 10	60.00	
24	A9	30y olive green, Jan. 20, 1953	15.00	10.00
		First day cover		75.00
		Imprint block of 10	225.00	
a.		30y light olive green, 1958	60.00	
		Imprint block of 10	850.00	
25	A9	50y rose violet, Jan. 20, 1953	20.00	12.00
		First day cover		125.00
		Imprint block of 10	275.00	
26	A9	100y claret, Jan. 20, 1953	25.00	6.50
		First day cover		190.00
		Imprint block of 10	325.00	
		First day cover, #22-26		550.00
		Nos. 19-26 (8)	68.20	34.20

Issued: 1y, 2y and 3y, Nov. 20, 1952. Others, Jan. 20, 1953.

Reception at Shuri Castle — A10

Perry and American Fleet — A11

1953, May 26   Perf. 13½x13, 13x13½

27	A10	3y deep magenta	14.00	6.50
		Imprint block of 6	120.00	
28	A11	6y dull blue	1.50	1.50
		First day cover, #27-28		15.00
		Imprint block of 6	12.00	

Centenary of the arrival of Commodore Matthew Calbraith Perry at Naha, Okinawa.

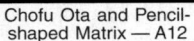

Chofu Ota and Pencil-
shaped Matrix — A12

Shigo Toma and
Pen — A13

1953, Oct. 1   *Perf. 13½x13*

29	A12	4y yellow brown	12.00	5.00
		First day cover		20.00
		Imprint block of 10	150.00	

Third Newspaper Week.

1954, Oct. 1

30	A13	4y blue	14.00	7.50
		First day cover		25.00
		Imprint block of 10	175.00	

Fourth Newspaper Week.

Ryukyu
Pottery — A14

Noguni Shrine and
Sweet Potato
Plant — A15

Designs: 15y, Lacquerware. 20y, Textile design.

1954-55   **Photo.**   *Perf. 13*

31	A14	4y brown, *June 25,*		
		1954	1.00	.60
		First day cover		10.00
		Imprint block of 10	11.00	
32	A14	15y vermilion, *June 20,*		
		1955	5.00	4.00
		First day cover		12.50
		Imprint block of 10	75.00	
33	A14	20y yellow orange, *June*		
		20, 1955	3.00	2.50
		First day cover		12.50
		Imprint block of 10	45.00	
		First day cover, #32-33		35.00
		Nos. 31-33 (3)	9.00	7.10

For surcharges see Nos. C19, C21, C23.

1955, Nov. 26

34	A15	4y blue	14.00	7.00
		First day cover		22.50
		Imprint block of 10	175.00	

350th anniv. of the introduction of the sweet potato to the Ryukyu Islands.

Stylized Trees — A16

Willow
Dance — A17

1956, Feb. 18   **Unwmk.**

35	A16	4y bluish green	12.00	6.00
		First day cover		20.00
		Imprint block of 6	100.00	

Arbor Week, Feb. 18-24.

1956, May 1   *Perf. 13*

8y, Straw hat dance. 14y, Dancer in warrior costume with fan.

36	A17	5y rose lilac	1.00	.60
		First day cover		6.50
		Imprint block of 10	15.00	
37	A17	8y violet blue	2.50	2.00
		First day cover		6.50
		Imprint block of 10	37.50	
38	A17	14y reddish brown	4.00	3.00
		First day cover		6.50
		Imprint block of 10	55.00	
		First day cover, #36-38		35.00
		Nos. 36-38 (3)	7.50	5.60

For surcharges see Nos. C20, C22.

Telephone
A18

1956, June 8

39	A18	4y violet blue	15.00	8.00
		First day cover		20.00
		Imprint block of 6	120.00	

Establishment of dial telephone system.

Garland of Pine,
Bamboo and
Plum — A19

Map of Okinawa and
Pencil Rocket — A20

1956, Dec. 1   *Perf. 13½x13*

40	A19	2y multicolored	2.00	2.00
		First day cover		3.50
		Imprint block of 10	27.50	

New Year, 1957.

1957, Oct. 1   **Photo.**   *Perf. 13½x13*

41	A20	4y deep violet blue	1.00	1.00
		First day cover		6.00
		Imprint block of 10	12.50	

7th annual Newspaper Week, Oct. 1-7.

Phoenix — A21

1957, Dec. 1   **Unwmk.**   *Perf. 13*

42	A21	2y multicolored	.25	.25
		First day cover		1.50
		Imprint block of 10	3.50	

New Year, 1958.

Ryukyu Stamps — A22

1958, July 1   *Perf. 13½*

43	A22	4y multicolored	.80	.80
		First day cover		1.25
		Imprint block of 4	4.00	

10th anniv. of 1st Ryukyu stamps.

Yen Symbol and Dollar
Sign — A23

Perf. 10.3, 10.8, 11.1 & Compound

1958, Sept. 16   *Typo.*

          Without Gum

44	A23	½c orange	.90	.90
		Imprint block of 6	8.00	
a.		Imperf., pair	1,750.	
b.		Horiz. pair, imperf. between	150.00	
c.		Vert. pair, imperf. between	200.00	
d.		Vert. strip of 4, imperf. between	800.00	
45	A23	1c yellow green	1.40	1.40
		Imprint block of 6	11.00	
a.		Horiz. pair, imperf. between	200.00	
b.		Vert. pair, imperf. between	150.00	
c.		Vert. strip of 3, imperf. between	700.00	
d.		Vert. strip of 4, imperf. between	800.00	

e.	Block of 4, imperf. btwn. vert. & horiz.	10,000.	
46	A23	**2c dark blue**	2.25	2.25

46 A23 2c **dark blue** 2.25 / 2.25
Imprint block of 6 17.50
a. Horiz. pair, imperf. between 200.00
b. Vert. pair, imperf. between 2,000.
c. Horiz. strip of 3, imperf. between 450.00
d. Horiz. strip of 4, imperf. between 800.00
47 A23 3c **deep carmine** 1.75 / 1.50
Imprint block of 6 14.00
a. Horiz. pair, imperf. between 200.00
b. Vert. pair, imperf. between 150.00
c. Vert. strip of 3, imperf. between 450.00
d. Vert. strip of 4, imperf. between 800.00
e. Block of 4, imperf. btwn. vert. & horiz. 10,000.
48 A23 4c **bright green** 2.25 / 2.25
Imprint block of 6 17.50
a. Horiz. pair, imperf. between 500.00
b. Vert. pair, imperf. between 200.00
49 A23 5c **orange** 4.25 / 3.75
Imprint block of 6 35.00
a. Horiz. pair, imperf. between 225.00
b. Vert. pair, imperf. between 850.00
50 A23 10c **aquamarine** 5.75 / 4.75
Imprint block of 6 42.50
a. Horiz. pair, imperf. between 300.00
b. Vert. pair, imperf. between 200.00
c. Vert. strip of 3, imperf. between 800.00
51 A23 25c **bright violet blue** 8.00 / 6.00
Imprint block of 6 62.50
a. Gummed paper, perf. 10.3 ('61) 15.00 / 15.00
Imprint block of 6 95.00
b. Horiz. pair, imperf. between 2,000.
c. Vert. pair, imperf. between 5,000.
d. Vert. strip of 3, imperf. between 900.00
52 A23 50c **gray** 17.50 / 10.00
Imprint block of 6 140.00
a. Gummed paper, perf. 10.3 ('61) 15.00 / 15.00
Imprint block of 6 150.00
First day cover, #51a-52a 35.00
b. Horiz. pair, imperf. between 1,750.
53 A23 $1 **rose lilac** 12.50 / 5.50
Imprint block of 6 100.00
a. Horiz. pair, imperf. between 500.00
b. Vert. pair, imperf. between 2,500.
Nos. 44-53 (10) 56.55 / 38.30

Printed locally. Perforation, paper and shade varieties exist. Nos. 51a and 52a are on off-white paper and perf 10.3.

First day covers come with various combinations of stamps: Nos. 44-48, 49-53, 44-53 etc. Values $20 for short set of low values (Nos. 44-48) to $60 for full set on one cover.

Gate of Courtesy — A24

1958, Oct. 15   Photo.   Perf. 13½
54 A24 3c **multicolored** 1.25 / 1.25
First day cover 1.50
Imprint block of 4 6.25

Restoration of Shureimon, Gate of Courtesy, on road leading to Shuri City.

Imitations of this stamp were distributed in 1972 to discourage speculation in Ryukyuan stamps. The imitations were printed without gum and have a lengthy message in light blue printed on the back. A second type exists, with printed black perforations and three Japanese characters on the back ("Mozo Hin" — imitation) in black. Value, sheet of 10 $15.

Lion Dance — A25

Trees and Mountains — A26

1958, Dec. 10   Unwmk.   Perf. 13½
55 A25 1½c **multicolored** .30 / .30
First day cover 1.50
Imprint block of 6 2.00

New Year, 1959.

1959, Apr. 30   Litho.   Perf. 13½x13
56 A26 3c **blue, yellow green, green & red** .70 / .60
First day cover 1.00
Imprint block of 6 5.50

"Make the Ryukyus Green" movement.

Yonaguni Moth — A27

1959, July 23   Photo.   Perf. 13
57 A27 3c **multicolored** 1.20 / 1.00
First day cover 1.50
Imprint block of 6 9.00

Meeting of the Japanese Biological Education Society in Okinawa.

Hibiscus — A28

Toy (Yakaji) — A29

Designs: 3c, Fish (Moorish idol). 8c, Sea shell (Phalium bandatum). 13c, Butterfly (Kallinia Inachus Eucerca), denomination at left, butterfly going up. 17c, Jellyfish (Dactylometra pacifera Goette).

Inscribed:
琉球郵便

Perforation and Paper Varieties of Ryukyu Islands Scott 44-53

Perforation	Perf. ID#	1/2¢ (No. 44) 1 2 3 4	1¢ (No. 45) 1 2 3 4	2¢ (No. 46) 1 2 3 4	3¢ (No. 47) 1 2 3 4	4¢ (No. 48) 1 2 3 4	5¢ (No. 49) 1 2 3 4	10¢ (No. 50) 1 2 3 4	25¢ (No. 51) 1 2 3 4	50¢ (No. 52) 1 2 3 4	$1 (No. 53) 1 2 3 4
11.1 x 11.1	M	* _ * _	* * _ _	* _ _ _	* * _ _	* _ _ _	* * _ _	* * _ _	* _ _ _	* _ _ _	* _ _ _
11.1 x 10.8	N	* _ * _	* * _ _	* _ _ _	* * _ _	* * _ ∞	* _ ? _	* _ * _	* _ _ _	* _ _ _	* _ * _
11.1 x 10.3	O	* _ _ *	? * _ _	* _ _ _	* * _ _	* _ _ _	* _ _ _	* _ * _	* _ _ _	_ _ _ _	* _ * _
10.8 x 11.1	P	* _ _ _	* * _ _	* _ _ _	* * _ _	* * _ _	* * _ _	* * _ _	* _ _ _	* _ _ _	* _ _ _
10.8 x 10.8	Q	* _ * _	* * _ _	* _ _ _	* * _ _	* * _ _	_ _ _ _	* * _ _	* * _ *	* _ _ _	* _ _ _
10.8 x 10.3	R	* _ _ *	* * _ _	* _ _ _	? * _ _	* * _ _	_ _ _ _	* * _ _	* _ _ _	_ _ _ _	* _ _ _
10.3 x 11.1	S	* _ _ _	_ * * _	* _ _ _	* * _ _	* _ _ *	? * _ _	* _ _ _	* _ _ _	_ _ _ _	_ _ _ _
10.3 x 10.8	T	* _ _ _	* * _ _	* * _ _	* * _ _	* * _ _	* * _ _	? * * _	_ _ _ _	_ _ _ _	* _ * _
10.3 x 10.3	U	* _ _ _	? * _ _	* _ _ _	* * _ _	? * _ _	_ _ _ _	* * _ _	? * _ _	_ _ _ \	_ _ _ _

Paper Legend: 1= off-white; 2= white; 3= ivory; 4= thick

Specialists use a shorthand to refer to perf. and paper types: e.g., 50M3 =10¢ stamp, perf. 11.1 x 11.1, ivory paper.

Notes:
* = Verified variety
? = Reported in literature, but unverified variety.
∞ = 48N4 is unknown; however, a single example of 48N exists on a thick white paper unknown used for any other issue.
\ = These particular perf/paper combinations are known only in stamps of the Second (1961) Printing (51a and 52a)

The following are known unused only: 45R1, 45T2, 47O1, 48N4, 53O1.
The following are known used only: 47N4, 47T4, 50M3, 50Q2, 50R2, 50T2, 51P3, 51S1, 53T3.
Chart classifications and data supplied by courtesy of the Ryukyu Philatelic Specialist Society.

1959, Aug. 10 — **Perf. 13x13½**

58	A28	½c multicolored	.30	.20
		Imprint block of 10	3.50	
59	A28	3c multicolored	.75	.40
		Imprint block of 10	9.00	
60	A28	8c light ultramarine, black & ocher	15.00	5.50
		Imprint block of 10	225.00	
61	A28	13c light blue, gray & orange	2.50	1.75
		Imprint block of 10	32.50	
62	A28	17c violet blue, red & yellow	25.00	9.00
		Imprint block of 10	375.00	
		First day cover, #58-62		17.50
		Nos. 58-62 (5)	43.55	16.85

Four-character inscription measures 10x2mm on ½c; 12x3mm on 3c, 8c; 8½x2mm on 13c, 17c. See Nos. 76-80.

1959, Dec. 1 — **Litho.**

63	A29	1½c gold & multicolored	.55	.45
		First day cover		1.50
		Imprint block of 10	8.00	

New Year, 1960.

University Badge A30

1960, May 22 — **Photo.** — **Perf. 13**

64	A30	3c multicolored	.95	.75
		First day cover		1.25
		Imprint block of 6	7.25	

10th anniv. opening of Ryukyu University.

Dancer — A31

Designs: Various Ryukyu Dances.

1960, Nov. 1 — **Photo.** — **Perf. 13**
Dark Gray Background

65	A31	1c yellow, red & violet	2.00	.80
		Imprint block of 10	22.00	
66	A31	2½c crimson, blue & yellow	3.00	1.00
		Imprint block of 10	37.50	
67	A31	5c dark blue, yellow & red	1.00	.50
		Imprint block of 10	11.00	
68	A31	10c dark blue, yellow & red	1.00	.70
		Imprint block of 10	12.00	
		First day cover, #65-68		5.50
		Nos. 65-68 (4)	7.00	3.00

See Nos. 81-87, 220.

Torch and Nago Bay — A32

Runners at Starting Line — A33

1960, Nov. 8

72	A32	3c light blue, green & red	6.00	3.00
		First day cover		3.50
		Imprint block of 6	45.00	
73	A33	8c orange & slate green	1.00	.75
		First day cover		1.50
		Imprint block of 6	7.50	
		First day cover, #72-73		5.00

8th Kyushu Inter-Prefectural Athletic Meet, Nago, Northern Okinawa, Nov. 6-7.

Little Egret and Rising Sun — A34

1960, Dec. 1 — **Unwmk.** — **Perf. 13**

74	A34	3c reddish brown	5.50	3.50
		First day cover		4.00
		Imprint block of 6	42.50	

National census.

Okinawa Bull Fight — A35

1960, Dec. 10 — **Perf. 13½**

75	A35	1½c bister, dark blue & red brown	1.75	1.50
		First day cover		2.00
		Imprint block of 6	12.50	

New Year, 1961.

Type of 1959 With Japanese Inscription Redrawn:

A28a

1960-61 — **Photo.** — **Perf. 13x13½**

76	A28a	½c multicolored, *Oct. 1961*	.75	.45
		Imprint block of 10	8.00	
77	A28a	3c multicolored, *Aug. 23, 1961*	1.25	.35
		First day cover		1.50
		Imprint block of 10	14.00	
78	A28a	8c light ultramarine, black & ocher, *July 1, 1960*	1.50	.80
		Imprint block of 10	17.50	
79	A28a	13c blue, brown & red, *July 1, 1960*	1.75	.90
		Imprint block of 10	19.00	
80	A28a	17c violet blue, red & yellow, *July 1, 1960*	15.00	6.00
		Imprint block of 10	190.00	
		First day cover, #78-80		15.00
		Nos. 76-80 (5)	20.25	8.50

Size of Japanese inscription on Nos. 78-80 is 10½x1½mm. On No. 79 the denomination is at right, butterfly going down.

Dancer Type of 1960 with "RYUKYUS" Added in English

1961-64 — **Perf. 13**

81	A31	1c multicolored, *Dec. 5, 1961*	.20	.20
		First day cover		1.00
		Imprint block of 10	2.00	
82	A31	2½c multicolored, *June 20, 1962*	.20	.20
		Imprint block of 10	2.25	
83	A31	5c multicolored, *June 20, 1962*	.25	.25
		Imprint block of 10	3.00	
84	A31	10c multicolored, *June 20, 1962*	.45	.40
		First day cover, #82-84		1.50
		Imprint block of 10	5.75	
84A	A31	20c multicolored, *Jan. 20, 1964*	3.25	1.40
		First day cover		2.50
		Imprint block of 10	37.50	
85	A31	25c multicolored, *Feb. 1, 1962*	1.00	.90
		First day cover		2.00

		Imprint block of 10	13.00	
86	A31	50c multicolored, *Sept. 1, 1961*	2.50	1.40
		Imprint block of 10	32.50	
87	A31	$1 multicolored, *Sept. 1, 1961*	6.00	.25
		Imprint block of 10	70.00	
		First day cover, #86-87		35.00
		Nos. 81-87 (8)	13.85	5.00

Pine Tree — A36

1961, May 1 — **Photo.** — **Perf. 13**

88	A36	3c yellow green & red	1.80	1.25
		First day cover		1.50
		Imprint block of 6	15.00	

"Make the Ryukyus Green" movement.

Naha, Steamer and Sailboat A37

1961, May 20

89	A37	3c aquamarine	2.25	1.50
		First day cover		1.75
		Imprint block of 6	18.00	

40th anniv. of Naha.

White Silver Temple — A38

Books and Bird — A39

1961, Oct. 1 — **Typo.** — **Unwmk.** — **Perf. 11**

90	A38	3c red brown	2.50	2.00
		First day cover		2.00
		Imprint block of 6	18.00	
a.		Horiz. pair, imperf. between	1,000.	
b.		Vert. pair, imperf. between	700.00	

Merger of townships Takamine, Kanegushiku and Miwa with Itoman.

A 3-cent stamp to commemorate the merger of two cities, Shimoji-cho and Hirara-shi of Miyako Island, was scheduled to be issued on Oct. 30, 1961. However, the merger was called off and the stamp never issued. It features a white chaplet on Kiyako linen on a blue background.

1961, Nov. 12 — **Litho.** — **Perf. 13**

91	A39	3c multicolored	1.10	.90
		First day cover		1.25
		Imprint block of 6	10.00	

Book Week.

Rising Sun and Eagles — A40

Symbolic Steps, Trees and Government Building — A41

1961, Dec. 10   **Photo.**   *Perf. 13½*
92   A40   1½c   **gold, vermilion & black**   2.00   2.00
    First day cover   3.00
    Imprint block of 6   16.00

New Year, 1962.

1962, Apr. 1   **Unwmk.**   *Perf. 13½*
Design: 3c, Government Building.
93   A41   1½c   **multicolored**   .60   .60
    Imprint block of 6   4.75
94   A41   3c   **bright green, red & gray**   .80   .80
    Imprint block of 6   6.50
    First day cover, #93-94   2.00

10th anniv. of the Government of the Ryukyu Islands (GRI).

Anopheles Hyrcanus Sinensis — A42

Design: 8c, Malaria eradication emblem and Shurei gate.

1962, Apr. 7   *Perf. 13½x13*
95   A42   3c   **multicolored**   .60   .60
    Imprint block of 6   4.50
96   A42   8c   **multicolored**   .90   .75
    Imprint block of 6   7.50
    First day cover, #95-96   2.25

World Health Organization drive to eradicate malaria.

Dolls and Toys — A43

Linden or Sea Hibiscus — A44

1962, May 5   **Litho.**   *Perf. 13½*
97   A43   3c   **red, black, blue & buff**   1.10   1.00
    First day cover   1.50
    Imprint block of 6   9.00

Children's Day, 1962.

1962, June 1   **Photo.**
Flowers: 3c, Indian coral tree. 8c, Iju (Schima liukiuensis Nakai). 13c, Touch-me-not (garden balsam). 17c, Shell flower (Alpinia speciosa).

98   A44   ½c   **multicolored**   .40   .20
    Imprint block of 10   4.50
99   A44   3c   **multicolored**   .35   .20
    Imprint block of 10   4.75
100 A44   8c   **multicolored**   .60   .45
    Imprint block of 10   6.50
101 A44   13c   **multicolored**   .80   .60

    Imprint block of 10   9.00
102 A44   17c   **multicolored**   1.40   .80
    Imprint block of 10   15.00
    First day cover, #98-102   3.75
    Nos. 98-102 (5)   3.55   2.25

See Nos. 107 and 114 for 1½c and 15c flower stamps. For surcharge see No. 190.

Earthenware A45

1962, July 5   *Perf. 13½x13*
103 A45   3c   **multicolored**   3.50   2.50
    First day cover   2.75
    Imprint block of 6   26.00

Philatelic Week.

Japanese Fencing (Kendo) A46

1962, July 25   *Perf. 13*
104 A46   3c   **multicolored**   4.00   3.00
    First day cover   3.50
    Imprint block of 6   30.00

All-Japan Kendo Meeting in Okinawa, July 25, 1962.

Rabbit Playing near Water, Bingata Cloth Design — A47

Young Man and Woman, Stone Relief — A48

1962, Dec. 10   *Perf. 13x13½*
105 A47   1½c   **gold & multicolored**   1.00   .80
    First day cover   1.50
    Imprint block of 10   12.50

New Year, 1963.

1963, Jan. 15   **Photo.**   *Perf. 13½*
106 A48   3c   **gold, black & blue**   .90   .80
    First day cover   1.50
    Imprint block of 6   6.75

Gooseneck Cactus — A49

Trees and Wooded Hills — A50

1963, Apr. 5   *Perf. 13x13½*
107 A49   1½c   **dark blue green, yellow & pink**   .20   .20
    First day cover   1.25
    Imprint block of 10   1.50

1963, Mar. 25   *Perf. 13½x13*
108 A50   3c   **ultramarine, green & red brown**   1.00   .80
    First day cover   1.25
    Imprint block of 6   7.00

"Make the Ryukyus Green" movement.

Map of Okinawa — A51

Hawks over Islands — A52

1963, Apr. 30   **Unwmk.**   *Perf. 13½*
109 A51   3c   **multicolored**   1.25   1.00
    First day cover   1.50
    Imprint block of 6   9.00

Opening of the Round Road on Okinawa.

1963, May 10   **Photo.**
110 A52   3c   **multicolored**   1.10   .95
    First day cover   1.50
    Imprint block of 6   9.00

Bird Day, May 10.

Shioya Bridge — A53

1963, June 5
111 A53   3c   **multicolored**   1.10   .95
    First day cover   1.40
    Imprint block of 6   8.25

Opening of Shioya Bridge over Shioya Bay.

Tsuikin-wan Lacquerware Bowl — A54

1963, July 1   **Unwmk.**   *Perf. 13½*
112 A54   3c   **multicolored**   3.00   2.50
    First day cover   2.75
    Imprint block of 6   22.50

Map of Far East and JCI Emblem — A55

1963, Sept. 16   **Photo.**   *Perf. 13½*
113 A55   3c multicolored   .70   .70
     First day cover   1.25
     Imprint block of 6   6.00

Meeting of the International Junior Chamber of Commerce (JCI), Naha, Okinawa, Sept. 16-19.

Mamaomoto — A56

Site of Nakagusuku Castle — A57

1963, Oct. 15   *Perf. 13x13½*
114 A56   15c multicolored   2.00   .80
     First day cover   1.25
     Imprint block of 10   25.00

1963, Nov. 1   *Perf. 13½x13*
115 A57   3c multicolored   .70   .60
     First day cover   1.25
     Imprint block of 6   5.25

Protection of national cultural treasures.

Flame — A58

Dragon (Bingata Pattern) — A59

1963, Dec. 10   *Perf. 13½*
116 A58   3c red, dark blue & yellow   .70   .60
     First day cover   1.25
     Imprint block of 6   5.25

15th anniv. of the Universal Declaration of Human Rights.

1963, Dec. 10   **Photo.**
117 A59   1½c multicolored   .60   .60
     First day cover   1.50
     Imprint block of 10   7.50

New Year, 1964.

Carnation — A60

Pineapples and Sugar Cane — A61

1964, May 10   *Perf. 13½*
118 A60   3c blue, yellow, black & car-
     mine   .40   .35
     First day cover   1.25
     Imprint block of 6   3.00

Mothers Day.

1964, June 1   *Perf. 13½*
119 A61   3c multicolored   .40   .35
     First day cover   1.25
     Imprint block of 6   3.00

Agricultural census.

Minsah Obi (Sash Woven of Kapok) — A62

1964, July 1   **Unwmk.**   *Perf. 13½*
120 A62   3c deep blue, rose pink & ocher   .55   .50
     First day cover   2.25
     Imprint block of 6   4.50
     a.   3c deep blue, deep carmine & ocher   .70   .65
       First day cover   2.75
       Imprint block of 6   5.25

Philatelic Week.

Girl Scout and Emblem — A63

1964, Aug. 31   **Photo.**
121 A63   3c multicolored   .40   .35
     First day cover   1.25
     Imprint block of 6   3.00

10th anniv. of Ryukyuan Girl Scouts.

Shuri Relay Station — A64

Parabolic Antenna and Map — A65

1964, Sept. 1   **Unwmk.**   *Perf. 13½*
Black Overprint
122 A64   3c deep green   .65   .65
     Imprint block of 6   5.50
     a.   Figure "1" inverted   35.00   35.00
     b.   Overprint inverted   *1,500.*
     c.   Overprint missing   *3,500.*

123 A65   8c ultramarine   1.25   1.25
     Imprint block of 6   10.00
     First day cover, #122-123   4.75
     a.   Overprint missing   *3,500.*

Opening of the Ryukyu Islands-Japan microwave system carrying telephone and telegraph messages. The overprints indicate the system was not actually opened until 1964.

Many of the stamps with overprint errors listed above are damaged. The values listed here are for stamps in very fine condition.

A number of different overprint shifts also exist with the shifts to greater and lesser degrees.

Gate of Courtesy, Olympic Torch and Emblem — A66

1964, Sept. 7   **Photo.**   *Perf. 13½x13*
124 A66   3c ultramarine, yellow & red   .30   .20
     First day cover (Sept. 7)   1.25
     First day cover (Sept. 6 & 7)   25.00
     Imprint block of 6   2.50

Relaying the Olympic torch on Okinawa en route to Tokyo. Torch arrival was scheduled for Sept. 6. A typhoon delayed arrival until Sept. 7. A small number of covers received both Sept. 6 and 7 cancels.

"Naihanchi," Karate Stance — A67

"Makiwara," Strengthening Hands and Feet — A68

"Kumite," Simulated Combat — A69

1964-65   **Photo.**   *Perf. 13½*
125 A67   3c dull claret, yel & blk, *Oct. 5,*
     1964   .50   .45
     First day cover   1.25
     Imprint block of 6   3.25
126 A68   3c yel & multi, *Feb. 5, 1965*   .40   .40
     First day cover   1.25
     Imprint block of 6   3.00
     Incomplete vertical stroke in
     "cent" sign   17.50   17.50
     First day cover   25.00
127 A69   3c gray, red & blk, *June 5, 1965*   .40   .40
     First day cover   1.25
     Imprint block of 6   3.00
     Nos. 125-127 (3)   1.30   1.25

Karate, Ryukyuan self-defense sport.

Miyara
Dunchi — A70

Snake and Iris
(Bingata) — A71

1964, Nov. 1   **Perf. 13½**
128 A70 3c **multicolored**   .30   .25
        First day cover   1.25
        Imprint block of 6   2.25

Protection of national cultural treasures. Miyara Dunchi was
built as a residence by Miyara-pechin Toen in 1819.

1964, Dec. 10   **Photo.**
129 A71 1½c **multicolored**   .30   .25
        First day cover   2.00
        Imprint block of 10   4.00

New Year, 1965.

Boy Scouts — A72

1965, Feb. 6   **Perf. 13½**
130 A72 3c **light blue & multi**   .45   .40
        First day cover   1.50
        Imprint block of 6   4.00

10th anniv. of Ryukyuan Boy Scouts.

Main
Stadium,
Onoyama
A73

1965, July 1   **Perf. 13x13½**
131 A73 3c **multicolored**   .25   .25
        First day cover   1.00
        Imprint block of 6   2.00

Inauguration of the main stadium of the Onoyama athletic
facilities.

Samisen of King
Shoko — A74

1965, July 1   **Photo.**   **Perf. 13½**
132 A74 3c **buff & multicolored**   .45   .40
        First day cover   1.25
        Imprint block of 6   3.25

Philatelic Week.

Kin Power Plant — A75

ICY Emblem, Ryukyu
Map — A76

1965, July 1
133 A75 3c **green & multicolored**   .25   .25
        First day cover   1.00
        Imprint block of 6   2.00

Completion of Kin power plant.

1965, Aug. 24   **Photo.**   **Perf. 13½**
134 A76 3c **multicolored**   .20   .20
        First day cover   1.00
        Imprint block of 6   1.75

20th anniv. of the UN and International Cooperation Year,
1964-65.

Naha City
Hall — A77

1965, Sept. 18   **Unwmk.**   **Perf. 13½**
135 A77 3c **blue & multicolored**   .20   .20
        First day cover   1.00
        Imprint block of 6   1.75

Completion of Naha City Hall.

Chinese Box
Turtle — A78

Horse (Bingata) — A79

Turtles: No. 137, Hawksbill turtle (denomination at top, country name at bottom). No. 138, Asian terrapin (denomination and
country name on top).

1965-66   **Photo.**   **Perf. 13½**
136 A78 3c **golden brown & multi,** *Oct. 20,*
        1965   .30   .30
        First day cover   1.00
        Imprint block of 6   2.50
137 A78 3c **black, yel & brown,** *Jan. 20,*
        1966   .30   .30
        First day cover   1.00
        Imprint block of 6   2.50
138 A78 3c **gray & multicolored,** *Apr. 20,*
        1966   .30   .30
        First day cover   1.00
        Imprint block of 6   2.50
        Nos. 136-138 (3)   .90   .90

1965, Dec. 10   **Photo.**   **Perf. 13½**
139 A79 1½c **multicolored**   .20   .20
        First day cover   1.50
        Imprint block of 10   2.25
 a.   Gold omitted   1,200. 2,000.

New Year, 1966.

There are 92 unused and 2 used examples of No. 139a
known.

NATURE CONSERVATION ISSUE

Noguchi's Okinawa
Woodpecker — A80

Sika Deer — A81

Design: No. 142, Dugong.

1966   **Photo.**   **Perf. 13½**
140 A80 3c **blue green & multi,** *Feb. 15*   .20   .20
        First day cover   1.00
        Imprint block of 6   1.65
141 A81 3c **blue, red, black, brown & green,**
        Mar. 15   .25   .25
        First day cover   1.00
        Imprint block of 6   1.75
142 A81 3c **blue, yellow green, black & red,**
        Apr. 20   .25   .25
        First day cover   1.00
        Imprint block of 6   1.75
        Nos. 140-142 (3)   .70   .70

Ryukyu Bungalow
Swallow — A82

1966, May 10   **Photo.**   **Perf. 13½**
143 A82 3c **sky blue, black & brown**   .20   .20
        First day cover   1.00
        Imprint block of 6   1.10

4th Bird Week, May 10-16.

Lilies and
Ruins
A83

1966, June 23   **Perf. 13x13½**
144 A83 3c **multicolored**   .20   .20
        First day cover   1.00
        Imprint block of 6   1.00

Memorial Day, end of the Battle of Okinawa, June 23, 1945.

University of
the Ryukyus
A84

1966, July 1
145 A84 3c **multicolored**   .20   .20
    First day cover   1.00
    Imprint block of 6   1.00

Transfer of the University of the Ryukyus from U.S. authority
to the Ryukyu Government.

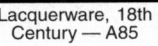

Lacquerware, 18th
Century — A85

Tile-Roofed House and
UNESCO
Emblem — A86

1966, Aug. 1   *Perf. 13½*
146 A85 3c **gray & multicolored**   .20   .20
    First day cover   1.50
    Imprint block of 6   1.30

Philatelic Week.

1966, Sept. 20   **Photo.**   *Perf. 13½*
147 A86 3c **multicolored**   .20   .20
    First day cover   1.00
    Imprint block of 6   1.10

20th anniv. of UNESCO.

Government
Museum and
Dragon
Statue — A87

1966, Oct. 6
148 A87 3c **multicolored**   .20   .20
    First day cover   1.00
    Imprint block of 6   1.00

Completion of the GRI (Government of the Ryukyu Islands)
Museum, Shuri.

Tomb of
Nakasone-Tuimya
Genga, Ruler of
Miyako — A88

1966, Nov. 1   **Photo.**   *Perf. 13½*
149 A88 3c **multicolored**   .20   .20
    First day cover   1.00
    Imprint block of 6   1.00

Protection of national cultural treasures.

Ram in Iris Wreath — A89

Clown Fish — A90

1966, Dec. 10   **Photo.**   *Perf. 13½*
150 A89 1½c **dark blue & multicolored**   .20   .20
    First day cover   1.50
    Imprint block of 10   1.10

New Year, 1967.

1966-67

Fish: No. 152, Young boxfish (white numeral at lower left). No.
153, Forceps fish (pale buff numeral at lower right). No. 154,
Spotted triggerfish (orange numeral). No. 155, Saddleback butterflyfish (carmine numeral, lower left).

151 A90 3c **orange red & multi,** *Dec. 20,*
    1966   .20   .20
    First day cover   1.00
    Imprint block of 6   1.75
152 A90 3c **orange yellow & multi,** *Jan. 10,*
    1967   .25   .20
    First day cover   1.00
    Imprint block of 6   1.75
153 A90 3c **multicolored,** *Apr. 10, 1967*   .40   .25
    First day cover   1.00
    Imprint block of 6   2.75
154 A90 3c **multicolored,** *May 25, 1967*   .35   .25
    First day cover   1.00
    Imprint block of 6   2.25
155 A90 3c **multicolored,** *June 10, 1967*   .30   .25
    First day cover   1.00
    Imprint block of 6   1.90
    Nos. 151-155 (5)   1.50   1.15

A 3-cent stamp to commemorate Japanese-Ameri-
can-Ryukyuan Joint Arbor Day was scheduled for
release on March 16, 1967. However, it was not
released. The stamp in light blue and white features
American and Japanese flags joined by a shield containing a tree.

Tsuboya Urn — A91

Episcopal Miter — A92

1967, Apr. 20
156 A91 3c **yellow & multicolored**   .20   .20
    First day cover   1.25
    Imprint block of 6   1.65

Philatelic Week.

1967-68   **Photo.**   *Perf. 13½*

Seashells: No. 158, Venus comb murex. No. 159, Chiragra
spider. No. 160, Green truban. No. 161, Euprotomus bulla.

157 A92 3c **light green & multi,** *July 20, 1967*   .20   .20
    First day cover   1.00
    Imprint block of 6   1.25
158 A92 3c **greenish blue & multi,** *Aug. 30,*
    1968   .25   .20
    First day cover   1.00
    Imprint block of 6   1.75
159 A92 3c **emerald & multi,** *Jan. 18, 1968*   .25   .20
    First day cover   1.00
    Imprint block of 6   1.65
160 A92 3c **light blue & multi,** *Feb. 20, 1968*   .30   .25
    First day cover   1.00
    Imprint block of 6   1.65
161 A92 3c **bright blue & multi,** *June 5, 1968*   .60   .50
    First day cover   1.00
    Imprint block of 6   4.00
    Nos. 157-161 (5)   1.60   1.35

Red-tiled Roofs
and ITY
Emblem — A93

1967, Sept. 11   **Photo.**   *Perf. 13½*
162 A93 3c **multicolored**   .20   .20
    First day cover   1.00
    Imprint block of 6   1.25

International Tourist Year.

Mobile TB
Clinic — A94

1967, Oct. 13   **Photo.**   *Perf. 13½*
163 A94 3c **lilac & multicolored**   .20   .20
    First day cover   1.00
    Imprint block of 6   1.25

15th anniv. of the Anti-Tuberculosis Society.

Hojo Bridge,
Enkaku Temple,
1498 — A95

1967, Nov. 1
164 A95 3c **blue green & multicolored**   .20   .20
    First day cover   1.00
    Imprint block of 6   1.50

Protection of national cultural treasures.

Monkey
(Bingata) — A96

TV Tower and
Map — A97

1967, Dec. 11   **Photo.**   *Perf. 13½*
165 A96 1½c **silver & multicolored**   .25   .20
    First day cover   1.50
    Imprint block of 10   3.00

New Year, 1968.

1967, Dec. 22
166 A97 3c **multicolored**   .25 .25
         First day cover   1.00
         Imprint block of 6   1.50
Opening of Miyako and Yaeyama television stations.

Dr. Kijin Nakachi and   Pill Box (Inro) — A99
Helper — A98

1968, Mar. 15   **Photo.**   *Perf. 13½*
167 A98 3c **multicolored**   .30 .25
         First day cover   1.00
         Imprint block of 6   1.75
120th anniv. of the first vaccination in the Ryukyu Islands, by
Dr. Kijin Nakachi.

1968, Apr. 18
168 A99 3c **gray & multicolored**   .45 .45
         First day cover   1.25
         Imprint block of 6   3.50
Philatelic Week.

Young Man,
Library, Book and
Map of Ryukyu
Islands — A100

1968, May 13
169 A100 3c **multicolored**   .30 .25
         First day cover   1.00
         Imprint block of 6   1.75
10th International Library Week.

Mailmen's
Uniforms
and Stamp
of 1948
A101

1968, July 1   **Photo.**   *Perf. 13x13½*
170 A101 3c **multicolored**   .30 .25
         First day cover   1.00
         Imprint block of 6   1.75
First Ryukyuan postage stamps, 20th anniv.

Main Gate,
Enkaku
Temple — A102

1968, July 15   **Photo. & Engr.**   *Perf. 13½*
171 A102 3c **multicolored**   .30 .25
         First day cover   1.00
         Imprint block of 6   1.75
Restoration of the main gate Enkaku Temple, built 1492-
1495, destroyed during World War II.

Old Man's Dance — A103

Mictyris
Longicarpus — A104

1968, Sept. 15   **Photo.**   *Perf. 13½*
172 A103 3c **gold & multicolored**   .30 .25
         First day cover   1.00
         Imprint block of 6   2.00
Old People's Day.

1968-69   **Photo.**   *Perf. 13½*
Crabs: No. 174, Uca dubia stimpson. No. 175, Baptozius
vinosus. No. 176, Cardisoma carnifex. No. 177, Ocypode cer-
atophthalma pallas.
173 A104 3c **blue, ocher & black,** *Oct. 10,*
         1968   .30 .25
         First day cover   1.25
         Imprint block of 6   2.50
174 A104 3c **light blue green & multi,** *Feb. 5,*
         1969   .35 .30
         First day cover   1.25
         Imprint block of 6   2.75
175 A104 3c **light green & multi,** *Mar. 5, 1969* .35 .30
         First day cover   1.25
         Imprint block of 6   2.75
176 A104 3c **light ultra & multi,** *May 15, 1969* .45 .40
         First day cover   1.25
         Imprint block of 6   3.25
177 A104 3c **light ultra & multi,** *June 2, 1969* .45 .40
         First day cover   1.25
         Imprint block of 6   3.25
         Nos. 173-177 (5)   1.90 1.65

Saraswati
Pavilion — A105

1968, Nov. 1   **Photo.**   *Perf. 13½*
178 A105 3c **multicolored**   .30 .25
         First day cover   1.00
         Imprint block of 6   2.00
Restoration of the Sarawati Pavilion (in front of Enkaku Temple), destroyed during World War II.

Tennis Player — A106   Cock and Iris
                            (Bingata) — A107

1968, Nov. 23   **Photo.**   *Perf. 13½*
179 A106 3c **green & multicolored**   .40 .35
         First day cover   1.00
         Imprint block of 6   3.25
35th All-Japan East-West Men's Soft-ball Tennis Tournament,
Naha City, Nov. 23-24.

1968, Dec. 10
180 A107 1½c **orange & multicolored**   .25 .20
         First day cover   1.50
         Imprint block of 10   3.50
New Year, 1969.

Boxer — A108   Ink Slab
                    Screen — A109

1969, Jan. 3
181 A108 3c **gray & multicolored**   .40 .30
         First day cover   1.00
         Imprint block of 6   2.75
20th All-Japan Amateur Boxing Championships held at the
University of the Ryukyus, Jan. 3-5.

1969, Apr. 17   **Photo.**   *Perf. 13½*
182 A109 3c **salmon, indigo & red**   .40 .35
         First day cover   1.50
         Imprint block of 6   2.75
Philatelic Week.

Box Antennas and Map   Gate of Courtesy and
of Radio Link — A110   Emblems — A111

1969, July 1   **Photo.**   *Perf. 13½*
183 A110 3c **multicolored**   .30 .25
         First day cover   1.00
         Imprint block of 6   2.25
Opening of the UHF (radio) circuit system between Okinawa
and the outlying Miyako-Yaeyama Islands.

1969, Aug. 1   **Photo.**   *Perf. 13½*
184 A111 3c **Prussian blue, gold & vermil-
         ion**   .30 .25
         First day cover   1.00
         Imprint block of 6   2.25
22nd All-Japan Formative Education Study Conf., Naha, Aug.
1-3.

FOLKLORE ISSUE

Tug of War
Festival
A112

Hari Boat
Race
A113

Izaiho Ceremony, Kudaka Island A114

Mortardrum Dance A115

Sea God Dance A116

1969-70 **Photo.** **Perf. 13**
185 A112 3c **multicolored,** *Aug. 1, 1969* .30 .25
    First day cover 1.50
    Imprint block of 6 2.25
186 A113 3c **multicolored,** *Sept. 5, 1969* .35 .30
    First day cover 1.50
    Imprint block of 6 2.25
187 A114 3c **multicolored,** *Oct. 3, 1969* .35 .30
    First day cover 1.50
    Imprint block of 6 2.25
188 A115 3c **multicolored,** *Jan. 20, 1970* .50 .45
    First day cover 1.50
    Imprint block of 6 3.50
189 A116 3c **multicolored,** *Feb. 27, 1970* .50 .45
    First day cover 1.50
    Imprint block of 6 3.50
    Nos. 185-189 (5) 2.00 1.75

No. 99 Surcharged

1969, Oct. 15 **Photo.** **Perf. 13½**
190 A44 ½c on 3c **multicolored** 1.00 1.00
    First day cover 3.00
    Imprint block of 10 13.50
   a. "1/2c" only surcharge 950.00

No. 190a are right margin stamps from a pane with a leftward misregistration of the surcharging plate.

Nakamura-ke Farm House, Built 1713-51 — A117

1969, Nov. 1 **Photo.** **Perf. 13½**
191 A117 3c **multicolored** .25 .20
    First day cover 1.00
    Imprint block of 6 1.50

Protection of national cultural treasures.

Statue of Kyuzo Toyama, Maps of Hawaiian and Ryukyu Islands — A118

1969, Dec. 5 **Photo.** **Perf. 13½**
192 A118 3c **light ultra & multi** .50 .50
    First day cover 1.50
    Imprint block of 6 3.75
   a. Without overprint 3,000.
   b. Wide-spaced bars 750.00

70th anniv. of Ryukyu-Hawaii emigration led by Kyuzo Toyama.
    The overprint "1969" at lower left and bars across "1970" at upper right was applied before No. 192 was issued.

Dog and Flowers (Bingata) — A119

Sake Flask Made from Coconut — A120

1969, Dec. 10
193 A119 1½c **pink & multicolored** .20 .20
    First day cover 1.50
    Imprint block of 10 2.75

New Year, 1970.

1970, Apr. 15 **Photo.** **Perf. 13½**
194 A120 3c **multicolored** .25 .25
    First day cover 1.25
    Imprint block of 6 1.75

Philatelic Week, 1970.

CLASSIC OPERA ISSUE

"The Bell" (Shushin Kaneiri) — A121

Child and Kidnapper (Chu-nusudu) A122

Robe of Feathers (Mekarushi) A123

Vengeance of Two Young Sons (Nidotichiuchi) A124

The Virgin and the Dragon (Kokonomaki) A125

1970 **Photo.** **Perf. 13½**
195 A121 3c **dull blue & multi,** *Apr. 28* .60 .40
    First day cover 1.75
    Imprint block of 6 4.00
   a. Souvenir sheet of 4 5.00 5.00
    First day cover 5.00
196 A122 3c **light blue & multi,** *May 29* .60 .40
    First day cover 1.75
    Imprint block of 6 4.00
   a. Souvenir sheet of 4 5.00 5.00
    First day cover 5.00
197 A123 3c **bluish green & multi,** *June 30* .60 .40
    First day cover 1.75
    Imprint block of 6 4.00
   a. Souvenir sheet of 4 5.00 5.00
    First day cover 5.00
198 A124 3c **dull blue green & multi,** *July 30* .60 .40
    First day cover 1.75
    Imprint block of 6 4.00
   a. Souvenir sheet of 4 5.00 5.00
    First day cover 5.00
199 A125 3c **multicolored,** *Aug. 25* .60 .40
    First day cover 1.75
    Imprint block of 6 4.00
   a. Souvenir sheet of 4 5.00 5.00
    First day cover 5.00
    Nos. 195-199 (5) 3.00 2.00
    Nos. 195a-199a (5) 25.00 25.00

Underwater Observatory and Tropical Fish — A126

1970, May 22
200 A126 3c **blue green & multi** .30 .25
    First day cover 1.25
    Imprint block of 6 2.00

Completion of the underwater observatory of Busena-Misaki, Nago.

Noboru Jahana (1865-1908), Politician — A127

Map of Okinawa and People — A128

Portraits: No. 202, Saion Gushichan Bunjaku (1682-1761), statesman. No. 203, Choho Giwan (1823-1876), regent and poet.

1970-71 **Engr.** **Perf. 13½**
201 A127 3c **rose claret,** *Sept. 25, 1970* .50 .45
    First day cover 2.50
    Imprint block of 6 3.50
202 A127 3c **dull blue green,** *Dec. 22, 1970* .75 .65
    First day cover 2.50
    Imprint block of 6 6.00
203 A127 3c **black,** *Jan. 22, 1971* .50 .45
    First day cover 2.50
    Imprint block of 6 3.50

1970, Oct. 1   **Photo.**
204 A128 3c **red & multicolored**   .25   .25
           First day cover   1.00
           Imprint block of 6   1.75

Oct. 1, 1970 census.

Great Cycad of
Une — A129

1970, Nov. 2   **Photo.**   **Perf. 13½**
205 A129 3c **gold & multicolored**   .25   .25
           First day cover   1.00
           Imprint block of 6   1.75

Protection of national treasures.

Japanese Flag,
Diet and Map of
Ryukyus — A130

Wild Boar and Cherry
Blossoms (Bingata) — A131

1970, Nov. 15   **Photo.**   **Perf. 13½**
206 A130 3c **ultramarine & multicolored** .80   .75
           First day cover   2.00
           Imprint block of 6   6.00

Citizen's participation in national administration to Japanese
law of Apr. 24, 1970.

1970, Dec. 10
207 A131 1½c **multicolored**   .20   .20
           First day cover   1.50
           Imprint block of 10   2.40

New Year, 1971.

Low Hand Loom
(Jibata) — A132

Farmer Wearing
Palm Bark
Raincoat and
Kuba Leaf
Hat — A133

Fisherman's
Wooden Box and
Scoop — A134

Designs: No. 209, Woman running a filature (reel). No. 211,
Woman hulling rice with cylindrical "Shiri-ushi."

1971   **Photo.**   **Perf. 13½**
208 A132 3c **light blue & multi,** *Feb. 16*   .30   .25
           First day cover   1.25
           Imprint block of 6   2.00
209 A132 3c **pale green & multi,** *Mar. 16*   .30   .25
           First day cover   1.25
           Imprint block of 6   2.00
210 A133 3c **light blue & multi,** *Apr. 30*   .35   .30
           First day cover   1.25
           Imprint block of 6   2.25
211 A132 3c **yellow & multi,** *May 20*   .40   .25
           First day cover   1.25
           Imprint block of 6   3.00
212 A134 3c **gray & multi,** *June 15*   .35   .30
           First day cover   1.25
           Imprint block of 6   2.25
           Nos. 208-212 (5)   1.70 1.45

Water Carrier
(Taku) — A135

1971, Apr. 15   **Photo.**   **Perf. 13½**
213 A135 3c **blue green & multicolored**   .35   .30
           First day cover   1.50
           Imprint block of 6   2.75

Philatelic Week, 1971.

Old and
New Naha,
and City
Emblem
A136

1971, May 20   **Perf. 13**
214 A136 3c **ultramarine & multicolored** .25   .20
           First day cover   1.00
           Imprint block of 6   1.75

50th anniv. of Naha as a municipality.

Caesalpinia
Pulcherrima — A137

Design: 2c, Madder (Sandanka).

1971   **Photo.**   **Perf. 13**
215 A137 2c **gray & multicolored,** *Sept. 30* .25 .20
           First day cover   1.00
           Imprint block of 10   3.00
216 A137 3c **gray & multicolored,** *May 10*   .25 .20
           First day cover   1.00
           Imprint block of 10   3.00

GOVERNMENT PARK SERIES

View from Mabuni
Hill — A138

Mt. Arashi from
Haneji
Sea — A139

Yabuchi Island
from Yakena
Port — A140

1971-72
217 A138 3c **green & multi,** *July 30, 1971* .20 .20
           First day cover   1.25
           Imprint block of 6   1.50
218 A139 3c **blue & multi,** *Aug. 30, 1971*   .20 .20
           First day cover   1.25
           Imprint block of 6   1.50
219 A140 4c **multicolored,** *Jan. 20, 1972*   .25 .20
           First day cover   1.25
           Imprint block of 6   1.75
           Nos. 217-219 (3)   .65   .60

For the 4-cent unissued "stamp" picturing Iriomote
Park, originally planned for issue in 1971 but never
released, see the note after No. R31.

Dancer — A141

Deva King, Torinji
Temple — A142

1971, Nov. 1   **Photo.**   **Perf. 13**
220 A141 4c **Prussian blue & multicolored** .20 .20
           First day cover   1.00
           Imprint block of 10   2.50

1971, Dec. 1
221 A142 4c **deep blue & multicolored**   .20   .20
           First day cover   1.00
           Imprint block of 6   1.50

Protection of national cultural treasures.

Rat and
Chrysanthemums
A143

Student Nurse
A144

1971, Dec. 10
222 A143 2c **brown orange & multi**   .20   .20
           First day cover   1.50
           Imprint block of 10   2.50

New Year, 1972.

1971, Dec. 24
223 A144 4c **lilac & multicolored**   .20   .20
           First day cover   1.00
           Imprint block of 6   1.50

Nurses' training, 25th anniversary.

A145　　　　A147

Coral Reef — A146

1972   **Photo.**   *Perf. 13*

224	A145	5c **bright blue & multi**, *Apr. 14*	.40	.35
		First day cover		1.25
		Imprint block of 6	2.75	
225	A146	5c **gray & multi**, *Mar. 30*	.40	.35
		First day cover		1.25
		Imprint block of 6	2.75	
226	A147	5c **ocher & multi**, *Mar. 21*	.40	.35
		First day cover		1.25
		Imprint block of 6	2.75	
		Nos. 224-226 (3)	1.20	1.05

Dove, U.S. and Japanese Flags — A148

1972, Apr. 17   **Photo.**   *Perf. 13*

227	A148	5c **bright blue & multi**	.80	.80
		First day cover		1.50
		Imprint block of 6	5.50	

Antique Sake Pot (Yushibin) — A149

1972, Apr. 20

228	A149	5c **ultramarine & multicolored**	.60	.60
		First day cover		1.25
		Imprint block of 6	4.50	

Ryukyu stamps were replaced by those of Japan after May 15, 1972.

AIR POST STAMPS

Catalogue values for all unused stamps in this section are for Never Hinged items.

Dove and Map of Ryukyus — AP1

1950, Feb. 15   **Photo.**   **Unwmk.**   *Perf. 13x13½*

C1	AP1	8y **bright blue**	150.00	60.00
		First day cover		35.00
		Imprint block of 6	1,250.	
C2	AP1	12y **green**	35.00	30.00
		First day cover		35.00
		Imprint block of 6	275.00	
C3	AP1	16y **rose carmine**	20.00	20.00
		First day cover		35.00
		Imprint block of 6	125.00	
		First day cover, #C1-C3		200.00
		Nos. C1-C3 (3)	205.00	110.00

Heavenly Maiden AP2

1951-54

C4	AP2	13y **blue**, *Oct. 1, 1951*	3.00	2.00
		First day cover		60.00
		Imprint block of 6, 5-character	300.00	
		Imprint block of 6, 8-character	37.50	
C5	AP2	18y **green**, *Oct. 1, 1951*	4.00	3.00
		First day cover		60.00
		Imprint block of 6, 5-character	55.00	
		Imprint block of 6, 8-character	45.00	
C6	AP2	30y **cerise**, *Oct. 1, 1951*	6.00	1.50
		First day cover		60.00
		First day cover, #C4-C6		250.00
		Imprint block of 6, 5-character	70.00	
		Imprint block of 6, 8-character	150.00	
C7	AP2	40y **red violet**, *Aug. 16, 1954*	8.00	7.00
		First day cover		35.00
		Imprint block of 6	90.00	
C8	AP2	50y **yellow orange**, *Aug. 16, 1954*	9.00	8.00
		First day cover		35.00
		Imprint block of 6	100.00	
		First day cover, #C7-C8		125.00
		Nos. C4-C8 (5)	30.00	21.50

Heavenly Maiden Playing Flute — AP3

1957, Aug. 1   **Engr.**   *Perf. 13½*

C9	AP3	15y **blue green**	9.00	4.00
		Imprint block of 6	65.00	
C10	AP3	20y **rose carmine**	15.00	7.00
		Imprint block of 6	100.00	
C11	AP3	35y **yellow green**	17.00	8.00
		Imprint block of 6	130.00	
a.		35y light yellow green, *1958*	150.00	
C12	AP3	45y **reddish brown**	20.00	10.00
		Imprint block of 6	150.00	
C13	AP3	60y **gray**	24.00	12.00
		Imprint block of 6	210.00	
		First day cover, #C9-C13		45.00
		Nos. C9-C13 (5)	85.00	41.00

On one printing of No. C10, position 49 shows an added spur on the right side of the second character from the left. Value unused, $175.

Same Surcharged in Brown Red or Light Ultramarine

1959, Dec. 20

C14	AP3	9c on 15y **blue green** (BrR)	3.00	2.00
		Imprint block of 6	22.50	
a.		Inverted surcharge	950.00	
		Imprint block of 6	6,750.	
C15	AP3	14c on 20y **rose carmine** (L.U.)	4.00	4.00
		Imprint block of 6	30.00	
C16	AP3	19c on 35y **light yellow green** (BrR)	8.00	6.00
		Imprint block of 6	57.50	
C17	AP3	27c on 45y **reddish brown** (L.U.)	19.00	6.00

		Imprint block of 6	150.00	
C18	AP3	35c on 60y **gray** (BrR)	16.00	9.00
		Imprint block of 6	125.00	
		First day cover, #C14-C18		35.00
		Nos. C14-C18 (5)	50.00	27.00

No. C15 is found with the variety described below No. C13. Value unused, $125.

Nos. 31-33, 36 and 38 Surcharged in Black, Brown, Red, Blue or Green

1960, Aug. 3   **Photo.**   *Perf. 13*

C19	A14	9c on 4y **brown**	4.00	1.00
		Imprint block of 10	50.00	
a.		Surcharge inverted and transposed	15,000.	15,000.
b.		Inverted surcharge (legend only)	12,000.	
c.		Surcharge transposed	1,500.	
d.		Legend of surcharge only	4,000.	
e.		Vert. pair, one without surcharge	6,000.	

Nos. C19c and C19d are from a single sheet of 100 with surcharge shifted downward. Ten examples of No. C19c exist with "9c" also in bottom selvage. No. C19d is from the top row of the sheet.
No. C19e is unique, pos. 100, caused by paper foldover.

C20	A17	14c on 5y **rose lilac** (Br)	5.00	3.00
		Imprint block of 10	65.00	
C21	A14	19c on 15y **vermilion** (R)	3.50	3.00
		Imprint block of 10	45.00	
C22	A17	27c on 14y **reddish brown** (Bl)	10.50	2.50
		Imprint block of 10	150.00	
C23	A14	35c on 20y **yellow orange** (G)	7.50	5.00
		Imprint block of 10	90.00	
		First day cover, #C19-C23		25.00
		Nos. C19-C23 (5)	30.50	14.50

Wind God — AP4

Designs: 9c, Heavenly Maiden (as on AP2). 14c, Heavenly Maiden (as on AP3). 27c, Wind God at right. 35c, Heavenly Maiden over treetops.

1961, Sept. 21   **Unwmk.**   *Perf. 13½*

C24	AP4	9c **multicolored**	.30	.20
		Imprint block of 6	2.25	
C25	AP4	14c **multicolored**	.80	.80
		Imprint block of 6	6.00	
C26	AP4	19c **multicolored**	.90	.90
		Imprint block of 6	6.50	
C27	AP4	27c **multicolored**	3.50	.60
		Imprint block of 6	27.50	
C28	AP4	35c **multicolored**	2.50	1.25
		Imprint block of 6	20.00	
		First day cover, #C24-C28		35.00
		Nos. C24-C28 (5)	8.00	3.75

AP5　　　　AP6

1963, Aug. 28   *Perf. 13x13½*

C29	AP5	5½c **multicolored**	.25	.25
		Imprint block of 10	3.00	
C30	AP6	7c **multicolored**	.30	.30
		First day cover		1.00
		First day cover, #C29-C30		2.50
		Imprint block of 10	3.50	

SPECIAL DELIVERY STAMP

Catalogue value for the unused stamp in this section is for a Never Hinged item.

Sea Horse and Map of
Ryukyus — SD1

1950, Feb. 15   Unwmk.   Photo.   Perf. 13x13½

E1   SD1   5y bright blue   35.00   20.00
       First day cover   100.00
       Imprint block of 6   350.00

QUANTITIES ISSUED

Regular Postage and Commemorative Stamps

Cat. No.	Quantity	Cat. No.	Quantity
1	90,214	87	3,019,000
2	55,901	88	298,966
3	94,663	89	298,966
4	55,413	90	398,901
5	76,387	91	398,992
6	117,321	92	1,498,970
7	291,403	93	598,989
1a	61,000	94	398,998
2a-4a	181,000	95	398,993
5a	29,936	96	298,993
6a	99,300	97	398,997
7a	46,000	98	9,699,000
8	2,559,000	99	10,991,500
8a	300,000	100	1,549,000
9	1,198,989	101	799,000
10	589,000	102	1,299,000
11	479,000	103	398,995
12	598,999	104	298,892
13	397,855	105	1,598,949
14	499,000	106	348,989
15	498,960	107	10,099,000
16	199,197	108	348,865
16A	199,900	109	348,937
16B	39,900	110	348,962
17	9,800	111	348,974
18	299,500	112	398,974
19	3,014,427	113	398,911
20	3,141,777	114	1,199,000
21	2,970,827	115	398,948
22	191,917	116	398,943
23	1,118,617	117	1,698,912
24	276,218	118	550,000
24a	ca. 1,300	119	549,000
25	231,717	120	749,000
26	220,130	121	799,000
27	398,993	122	389,000
28	386,421	123	319,000
29	498,854	124	1,999,000
30	298,994	125-127	999,000
31	4,768,413	128	799,000
32	1,202,297	129	1,699,000
33	500,059	130-131	799,000
34	298,994	132	849,000
35	199,000	133	799,000
36	455,896	134	1,299,000
37	160,518	135	1,099,000
38	198,720	136	1,299,000
39	198,199	137-138	1,598,000
40	599,000	139	3,098,000
41	598,075	140-142	1,598,000
42	1,198,179	143-148	2,498,000
43	1,625,406	149	2,298,000
44	994,880	150	3,798,000
45	997,759	151	2,298,000
46	996,759	152-156	1,998,000
47	2,705,955	157-158	1,698,000
48	997,542	159-160	1,298,000
49	996,609	161	898,000
50	996,928	162	1,498,000
51	499,000	163-164	1,298,000
52	249,000	165	3,998,000
52a	78,415	166-167	1,298,000
53	248,700	168	998,000
54	1,498,991	169-179	898,000
55	2,498,897	180	3,198,000
56	1,098,972	181-189	898,000
57	998,918	190	1,773,050
58	2,699,000	191	898,000
59	2,499,000	192	864,960
60	199,000	193	3,198,000
61	499,000	194	898,000
62	199,000	195-199	598,000
63	1,498,931	195a-199a	124,500
64	798,953	200-206	898,000
65-68	999,000	207	3,198,000
72	598,912	208-210	1,098,000
73	398,990	211-212	1,298,000
74	598,936	213	1,098,000
75	1,998,992	214	1,298,000
76	1,000,000	215-216	4,998,000
77	2,000,000	217	1,498,000
78	500,000	218-219	1,798,000
79-80	400,000	220	2,998,000
81	12,599,000	221	1,798,000
82	11,979,000	222	4,998,000
83	6,850,000	223	1,798,000
84	5,099,000	224-226	2,498,000
84A	1,699,000	227	2,998,000
85	4,749,000	228	3,998,000
86	2,099,000		

AIR POST STAMPS

Cat. No.	Quantity	Cat. No.	Quantity
C1-C3	198,000	C18	96,650
C4	1,952,348	C19	1,033,900
C5	331,360	C19a	100

Cat. No.	Quantity	Cat. No.	Quantity
C6	762,530	C20	230,000
C7	76,166	C21	185,000
C8	122,816	C22	191,000
C9	708,319	C23	190,000
C10	108,824	C24	17,199,000
C11	164,147	C25	1,999,000
C12	50,335	C26	1,250,000
C13	69,092	C27	3,499,000
C14	597,103	C28	1,699,000
C15	77,951	C29	1,199,000
C16	97,635	C30	1,949,000
C17	98,353		

SPECIAL DELIVERY STAMP

E1	198,804

PROVISIONAL ISSUES

Stamps of Japan Overprinted by Postmasters in Four
Island Districts

Trading Ship —
A82

Rice Harvest —
A83

Gen. Maresuke
Nogi — A84

Admiral
Heihachiro Togo
— A86

Garambi
Lighthouse,
Taiwan — A88

Meiji Shrine,
Tokyo — A90

Plane and Map
of Japan — A92

Kasuga Shrine,
Nara — A93

Mount Fuji and
Cherry
Blossoms —
A94

Horyu Temple,
Nara — A95

Miyajima Torii,
Itsukushima
Shrine — A96

Golden Pavilion,
Kyoto — A97

Great Budda,
Kamakura —
A98

Kamatari
Fujiwara — A99

War Factory Girl
— A144

Hyuga
Monument & Mt.
Fuji — A146

War Worker &
Planes — A147

Palms and Map
of "Greater East
Asia" — A148

Aviator Saluting
& Japanese Flag
— A150

Torii of Yasukuni
Shrine — A151

Mt. Fuji and
Cherry Blossoms
— A152

Torii of Miyajima
— A153

Garambi
Lighthouse,
Taiwan — A154

Sun & Cherry
Blossoms —
A161

Sunrise at Sea
& Plane — A162

Coal Miners —
A163

Yasukuni Shrine
— A164

"Thunderstorm
below Fuji," by
Hokusai — A167

KUME ISLAND

Values are for unused stamps. Used stamps sell for considerably more, should be expertized and are preferred on cover or document.

A1

Mimeographed
Seal Handstamped in Vermilion

1945, Oct. 1   Without Gum   Unwmk.   Imperf.

1X1	A1	7s **black**, *cream (2,400)*	3,200.	—
		On cover		
a.		"7" & "SEN" one letter space to left	3,500.	

Printed on legal-size U.S. military mimeograph paper and validated by the official seal of the Kume Island postmaster, Norifume Kikuzato. Valid until May 4, 1946.
Cancellations "20.10.1" (Oct. 1, 1945) or "20.10.6" (Oct. 6, 1945) are by favor. See proofs section for stamps on white watermarked U.S. official bond paper.

AMAMI DISTRICT

Inspection Seal ("Ken," abbreviation for *kensa zumi*, inspected or examined; five types and five colors)

Stamps of Japan 1937-46 Handstamped in
Black, Blue, Purple, Vermilion or Red
Typographed, Lithographed, Engraved

1947-48   Wmk. 257   Perf. 13, Imperf

2X1	A82	½s **purple**, #257	1,000.	
2X2	A83	1s **fawn**, #258		
2X3	A144	2s **orange brown**, #325	1,750.	
2X4	A84	2s **crimson**, #259	600.	
a.		2s **vermilion**, #259c		
2X5	A84	2s **rose red**, imperf., #351	2,000.	
2X6	A85	3s **green**, #260	1,700.	
2X7	A84	3s **brown**, #329		
2X8	A161	3s **rose carmine**, imperf., #352	1,800.	
2X9	A146	4s **emerald**, #330	700.	
2X10	A86	5s **brown lake**, #331	700.	
2X11	A162	5s **green**, imperf., #353	1,500.	
2X12	A147	6s **light ultramarine**, #332	1,250.	
2X13	A86	7s **orange vermilion**, #333	1,250.	
2X14	A90	8s **dark purple & pale violet**, #265	1,500.	
2X15	A148	10s **crimson & dull rose**, #344	600.	
2X16	A152	10s **red orange**, #355 (48)	2,500.	
2X17	A93	14s **rose lake & pale rose**, #268		
2X18	A150	15s **dull blue**, #336	600.	
2X19	A151	17s **gray violet**, #337	1,750.	
2X20	A94	20s **ultramarine**, #269	1,750.	
2X21	A152	20s **blue**, #338	600.	
2X22	A152	20s **ultramarine**, imperf., #356 (48)	1,750.	
2X23	A95	25s **dark brown & pale brown**, #270	900.	
2X24	A151	27s **rose brown**, #339	—	
2X25	A153	30s **bluish green**, #340		
2X26	A153	30s **bright blue**, imperf., #357	2,000.	
2X27	A88	40s **dull violet**, #341	1,750.	
2X28	A154	40s **dark violet**, #342	1,750.	
2X29	A97	50s **olive & pale olive**, #272	—	
2X30	A163	50s **dark brown**, imperf., #358 (48)	2,000.	

2X31	A164	1y **deep olive green**, imperf., #359		
2X32	A167	1y **deep ultramarine**, imperf., #364	2,500.	
2X33	A99	5y **deep gray green**, #274	—	
2X34	A99	5y **deep gray green**, imperf., #360	—	

Nos. 2X5, 2X8, 2X11, 2X16, 2X22, 2X26, 2X30, 2X31, 2X32 and 2X34 were issued without gum.

MIYAKO DISTRICT

Personal Seal of Postmaster
Jojin Tomiyama

Stamps of Japan 1937-46 Handstamped in Vermilion or Red
Typographed, Lithographed, Engraved

1946-47   Wmk. 257   Perf. 13

3X1	A144	1s **orange brown**, #325	175.	
3X2	A84	2s **crimson**, #259	125.	—
a.		2s **vermilion** #259c ('47)	150.	
b.		2s **pink** #259b ('47)	550.	
3X3	A84	3s **brown**, #329	100.	—
3X4	A86	4s **dark green**, #261	100.	
3X5	A86	5s **brown lake**, #331	550.	—
		On cover with #3X17		—
3X6	A88	6s **orange**, #263	100.	
3X7	A90	8s **dark purple & pale violet**, #265	100.	—
3X8	A148	10s **crimson & dull rose**, #334	100.	—
		On cover with #3X15		—
3X9	A152	10s **red orange**, imperf., #355 ('47) (1,000)	150.	
3X10	A92	12s **indigo**, #267	100.	—
3X11	A93	14s **rose lake & pale rose**, #268	100.	
3X12	A150	15s **dull blue**, #336	100.	—
3X13	A151	17s **gray violet**, #337	100.	—
3X14	A94	20s **ultramarine**, #269		—
3X15	A152	20s **blue**, #338	100.	—
3X16	A152	20s **ultramarine**, imperf., #356 ('47)	200.	
3X17	A95	25s **dark brown & pale brown**, #270	100.	—
3X18	A153	30s **bluish green**, #340	100.	—
3X19	A88	40s **dull violet**, #341	250.	
3X20	A154	40s **dark violet**, #342	100.	—
3X21	A97	50s **olive & pale olive**, #272	100.	—
3X22	A163	50s **dark brown**, #358 ('47) (750)	250.	—
3X23	A98	1y **brown & pale brown**, #273		9,000.
3X24	A167	1y **deep ultramarine**, #364 ('47) (500)	1,500.	600.

Nos. 3X9, 3X16, 3X22 and 3X24 were issued without gum. Nos. 3X22 and 3X24 have sewing machine perf.; No. 3X16 exists with that perf. also.

Nos. 3X1-3X2, 3X2a, 3X3-3X5, 3X8 Handstamp
Surcharged with 2 Japanese Characters

1946-47

3X25	A144	1y on 1s **orange brown**	140.	—
3X26	A84	1y on 2s **crimson**	3,000.	
3X27	A84	1y on 3s **brown** ('47)	3,000.	
3X28	A84	2y on 2s **crimson**	175.	—
a.		2y on 2s **vermilion** ('47)	175.	
3X29	A86	4y on 4s **dark green**	140.	—
3X30	A86	5y on 5s **brown lake**	140.	
3X31	A148	10y on 10s **crimson & dull rose**	140.	

The overwhelming majority of used examples of Miyako District stamps were used on Bulk Mailing Records documents and Letter Content Certification Records documents. Stamps affixed to such documents command a substantial premium above off-document used stamps.
Cancellation: black Miyako cds.

OKINAWA DISTRICT

Personal Seal of
Postmaster Shiichi
Hirata

R1

Japan Nos. 355-356, 358, 364 Overprinted in Black
1947, Nov. 1   Wmk. 257   Litho.   Imperf.
Without Gum

4X1	A152	10s **red orange** (13,997)	1,200.	1,000.
		On cover, strip of 3		9,500.
		On cover with #4X2		7,500.
4X2	A152	20s **ultramarine** (13,611)	600.	1,000.
4X3	A163	50s **dark brown** (6,276)	900.	700.
4X4	A167	1y **deep ultramarine** (1,947)	1,750.	1,000.

On Revenue Stamp of Japan

4X5	R1	30s **brown** (14,000)	3,500.	3,500.
		On cover		7,500.

No. 4X5 is on Japan's current 30s revenue stamp. The Hirata seal validated it for postal use.
Nos. 4X1-4X5 are known with rough sewing machine perforations, full or partial.

YAEYAMA DISTRICT

Personal Seal of Postmaster
Kenpuku Miyara

Stamps of Japan 1937-46 Handstamped in Black
Typographed, Engraved, Lithographed

1948   Wmk. 257   Perf. 13

5X1	A86	4s **dark green**, #261	1,200.	
5X2	A86	5s **brown lake**, #331	1,200.	
5X3	A86	7s **orange vermilion**, #333	800.	
5X4	A148	10s **crimson & dull rose**, #334	5,000.	
5X5	A94	20s **ultramarine**, #269	150.	—
		On cover with 2 #5X8		—
5X6	A96	30s **peacock blue**, #271	1,000.	
5X7	A88	40s **dull violet**, #341	80.	
5X8	A97	50s **olive & pale olive**, #272	100.	
5X9	A163	50s **dark brown**, imperf., #358 (250)	1,350.	
5X10	A99	5y **deep gray green**, #274	2,000.	

No. 5X9 was issued without gum.
This handstamp exists double, triple, inverted and in pair, one stamp without overprint.

Provisional postal stationery of the four districts also exists.

LETTER SHEETS

Values are for entires.

Stylized Deigo
Blossom — US1

Banyan
Tree — US2

Typographed by Japan Printing Bureau.
Stamp is in upper left corner.

Designer: Shutaro Higa

1948-49

U1	US1	50s **vermilion**, *cream, July 18, 1949 (250,000)*	50.00	60.00
		First day cancel		
a.		50s **orange red**, *gray, July 1, 1948 (1,000)*	1,500.	—

Designer: Ken Yabu

1950, Jan. 21

U2	US2	1y **carmine red**, *cream (250,000)*	40.00	50.00
		First day cancel		

AIR LETTER SHEETS

DC-4 Skymaster and
Shurei Gate — UC1

UC2

Designer: Chosho Ashitomi
"PAR AVION" (Bilingual) below Stamp

Litho. & Typo. by Japan Printing Bureau

1952-53

UC1	UC1 12y **light rose**, *pale blue green*, *Mar. 9, 1953 (76,000)*	20.00	12.50
a.	12y **dull rose**, *pale blue green, Nov. 1, 1952 (50,000)*	30.00	15.00
	First day cancel, No. UC1a	80.00	

No. UC1a is on tinted paper with colorless overall inscription "RYUKYU FOREIGN AIRMAIL," repeated in parallel vertical lines, light and indistinct. Dull rose ink of imprinted design and legend "AIR LETTER" appears to bleed. No. UC1 has overall inscription darker and more distinct. Light rose ink of design and legend does not bleed. Model: U.S. No. UC16.

**Litho. & Typo. by Nippon Toppan K.K.
"AEROGRAMME" below Stamp**

1955, Sept. 10

UC2	UC2 15y **violet blue & bright red**, *pale yellow green (89,300)*	30.00	15.00
	First day cancel	60.00	
a.	15y **violet blue & dull red**, *pale blue green, Oct. 1957 (33,742)*	45.00	25.00

Printing on the envelope stamp is heavier on No. UC2a than on No. UC2.

No. UC2 surcharged in Red

"13" & "¢" aligned at bot.;
2 thick bars — a

"¢" raised; 2 thick bars —
b

"13" & "¢" as in "a"; 4 thin
bars — c

"¢" raised; 4 thin bars —
d

Printers: Type "a," Nakamura Printing Co., "b" and "d," Okinawa Printing Co., "c," Sun Printing Co.

1958-60

UC3	UC2 13c on 15y type "a," *Sept. 16, 1958 (60,000)*	20.00	18.00
	First day cancel	60.00	
a.	Type "b," on No. UC2, *June 1, 1959 (2,000)*	40.00	30.00
b.	Type "b," on No. UC2a *(7,000)*	50.00	30.00

c.	Type "c," on No. UC2, *Sept. 22, 1959 (1,000)*	80.00	80.00
d.	As "c," small wrong font "¢" sign	1,000.	
e.	Type "c," on No. UC2a *(1,000)*	80.00	80.00
f.	As "e," double surcharge, one on reverse	2,000.	
g.	Type "b" and No. 46 on No. UC2a, *Aug. 22, 1960 (1,000)*	500.00	—
h.	Type "d" and Nos. 55, 58 on No. UC2, *Oct. 1, 1960 (1,000)*	450.00	450.00
i.	Type "d" and Nos. 55, 58 on No. UC2a *(2,000)*	300.00	300.00

For Nos. UC3g, UC3h and UC3i, additional stamps have been affixed to make up the 15c rate.

UC3

Lithographed by Japan Printing Bureau

1959, Nov. 10

UC4	UC3 15c **dark blue**, *pale blue (560,000)*	4.00	2.50
	First day cancel		10.00

POSTAL CARDS

Values are for entire cards.
Nos. UX1-UX9 are typo., others litho.
Printed by Japan Printing Bureau unless otherwise stated.
Quantities in parentheses; "E" means estimated.

Deigo Blossom Type

Designer: Shutaro Higa

1948, July 1

UX1	US1 10s **dull red**, *grayish tan (100,000)*	50.00	60.00

1949, July 1

UX2	US1 15s **orange red**, *gray (E 175,000)*	40.00	70.00
	First day cancel		—
a.	15s **vermilion**, *tan (E 50,000)*	110.00	125.00

Banyan Tree Type

Designer: Ken Yabu

1950, Jan. 21

UX3	US2 50s **carmine red**, *light tan (E 200,000)*	10.00	10.00
	First day cancel		60.00
a.	Grayish tan card (E 25,000)	25.00	50.00

Nos. UX2, UX2a Handstamp Surcharged in Vermilion

19-21x23-25mm —
a

22-23x26-27mm — b

20-21x24-24½mm
— c

22-23½x25-26mm — d

1951

UX4	US1 (c) 15s + 85s on #UX2 (E 35,000)	100.	100.
a.	Type "c" on #UX2a (E 5,000)	150.	150.
b.	Type "a" on #UX2 (E 39,000)	75.	100.
c.	Type "a" on #UX2a	1,000.	—
d.	Type "b" on #UX2	1,000.	1,000.
e.	Type "d" on #UX2 (E 4,000)	150.	200.
f.	Type "d" on #UX2a (E 1,000)	250.	300.

Type "a" exists on the 15s cherry blossom postal card of Japan. Value $100.

Crown, Leaf Ornaments

Naha die 21x22mm
PC3

Tokyo die
18½x19mm
PC4

Designer: Masayoshi Adaniya Koshun Printing Co.

1952

UX5	PC3 1y **vermilion**, *tan, Feb. 8 (400,600)*	50.00	30.00
UX6	PC4 1y **vermilion**, *off-white, Oct. 6 (1,295,000)*	25.00	14.00
a.	Tan card, coarse (50,000)	30.00	20.00
b.	Tan card, smooth (16,000)	500.00	150.00

Naminoue Shrine

PC5	PC6
Naha die 23x25½mm	Tokyo die 22x24½mm

Designer: Gensei Agena

1953-57

UX7	PC5 2y **green**, *off-white, Dec. 2, 1953 (1,799,400)*	60.00	20.00
	First day cancel		80.00
a.	Printed both sides	500.00	
UX8	PC6 2y **green**, *off-white, 1955 (2,799,400)*	15.00	6.00
a.	2y **deep blue green**, *1956 (300,000)*	30.00	16.50
b.	2y **yellow green**, *1957 (2,400,000)*	12.50	3.50
c.	As "a," printed on both sides	500.00	
d.	As "b," printed on both sides	500.00	

Stylized Pine,
Bamboo, Plum
Blossoms — PC7

1956 New Year Card

Designer: Koya Oshiro Kotsura and Koshun Printing Companies

1955, Dec. 1
UX9 PC7 2y **red,** *cream* 100.00 45.00
First day cancel 125.00

No. UX9 was printed on rough card (43,400) and smooth-finish card (356,600)

Sun — PC8   Temple Lion — PC9

1957 New Year Card

Designer: Seikichi Tamanaha Kobundo Printing Co.

1956, Dec. 1
UX10 PC8 2y **brown carmine & yellow,** *off-white (600,000)* 6.00 3.75
First day cancel 10.00

1958 New Year Card

Designer: Shin Isagawa Fukuryu Printing Co.

1957, Dec. 1
UX11 PC9 2y **lilac rose,** *off-white (1,000,000)* 1.75 2.25
First day cancel 4.00
a. "1" omitted in right date 75.00 75.00
b. Printed on both sides 250.00 300.00

Nos. UX8, UX8a and UX8b "Revalued" in Red, Cherry or Pink by Three Naha Printeries

a   b

c

1958-59
UX12 PC6 1½c on 2y **green,** type "a," *Sept. 16 (600,000)* 5.00 5.00
First day cancel 10.00
a. Shrine stamp omitted 750.00 1,000.
b. Bar of ½ omitted, top of 2 broken 75.00 100.00
c. Type "b," *Nov. (1,000,000)* 10.00 12.50
d. Type "c," *1959 (200,000)* 15.00 22.50
e. Wrong font "c," type "c" 30.00 45.00
f. "c" omitted, type "c" 1,500. 1,500.
g. Double surcharge, type "c" 1,000. —

Multicolor Yarn Ball Toy Pony
PC10   19½x23mm
PC11

1959 New Year Card

Designer: Masayoshi Adaniya Kobundo Printing Co.

1958, Dec. 10
UX13 PC10 1½c **black, red, yellow & gray blue,** *off-white (1,514,000)* 1.50 1.90
First day cancel 2.00
a. Black omitted —

1959, June 20
Designer: Seikichi Tamanaha Kobundo Printing Co.

UX14 PC11 1½c **dark blue & brown** *(1,140,000)* 1.50 1.25
First day cancel 1.50
a. Dark blue omitted 500.00

Toy Carp and   Toy Pony
Boy — PC12   21x25mm — PC13

1960 New Year Card

Designer: Masayoshi Adaniya

1959, Dec. 1
UX15 PC12 1½c **violet blue, red & black,** *cream (2,000,000)* 1.25 1.50
First day cancel 1.75

1959, Dec. 30
UX16 PC13 1½c **gray violet & brown,** *cream (3,500,000)* 3.00 .75
First day cancel 2.75

Household   Coral Head — PC15
Altar — PC14

1961 New Year Card

Designer: Shin Isagawa

1960, Nov. 20
UX17 PC14 1½c **gray, carmine, yellow & black,** *off-white (2,647,591)* 1.50 1.50
First day cancel 1.50

Summer Greeting Card

Designer: Shinzan Yamada Kidekuni Printing Co.

1961, July 5
UX18 PC15 1½c **ultramarine & cerise,** *off-white (264,900)* 2.25 3.75
First day cancel 4.00

Tiger — PC16   Inscribed "RYUKYUS" — PC17

1962 New Year Card

Designer: Shin Isagawa

1961, Nov. 15
UX19 PC16 1½c **ocher, black & red,** *off-white (2,891,626)* 1.50 2.50
First day cancel 1.65
a. Red omitted 750.00 —
b. Red inverted 500.00 —
c. Red omitted on face, inverted on back 500.00 —
d. Double impression of red, one inverted 500.00 —

e. Double impression of ocher & black, red inverted 500.00 —
f. Double impression of ocher & black, one inverted 500.00 —

1961-67
Designer: Seikichi Tamanaha
UX20 PC17 1½c **gray violet & brown,** *white ('67) (18,600,000)* 1.00 .50
a. Off-white card ('66) (4,000,000) 1.50 .75
b. Cream card, *Dec. 23 (12,500,000)* 1.00 .50
First day cancel 1.35

Ie Island — PC18   New Year Offerings — PC19

Summer Greeting Card

Designer: Shinzan Yamada Sakai Printing Co.

1962, July 10
UX21 PC18 1½c **bright blue, yellow & brown,** *off-white (221,500)* 1.50 2.50
First day cancel 3.00
Square notch at left 40.00 45.00

1963 New Year Card; Precanceled

Designer: Shin Isagawa Sakai Printing Co.

1962, Nov. 15
UX22 PC19 1½c **olive brown, carmine & black** *(3,000,000)* 1.50 3.00
First day cancel 2.25
a. Yellow brown background —
b. Brown ocher background —

Ryukyu Temple Dog and Wine Flask Silhouette PC20

Water Strider — PC21

International Postal Card

Designer: Shin Isagawa

1963, Feb. 15
UX23 PC20 5c **vermilion, emerald & black,** *pale yellow (150,000)* 1.75 2.75
First day cancel 1.65
a. Black & emerald omitted 450.00

Summer Greeting Card

Designer: Seikichi Tamanaha

1963, June 20
UX24 PC21 1½c **Prussian green & black,** *off-white (250,000)* 4.00 4.25
First day cancel 3.50

Princess
Doll — PC22

Bitter Melon
Vine — PC23

1964 New Year Card; Precanceled
Designer: Koya Oshiro

1963, Nov. 15
UX25 PC22 1½c **orange red, yellow & ultra,**
　　　　　off-white (3,200,000)　　2.00 2.00
　　　　　First day cancel　　　　　　　　2.00

Summer Greeting Card
Designer: Shinzan Yamada

1964, June 20
UX26 PC23 1½c **multicolored,** *off-white*
　　　　　(285,410)　　　　　　1.40 2.25
　　　　　First day cancel　　　　　　1.75

Fighting Kite with
Rider — PC24

Palm-leaf Fan — PC25

1965 New Year Card; Precanceled
Designer: Koya Oshiro

1964, Nov. 15
UX27 PC24 1½c **multicolored,** *off-white*
　　　　　(4,876,618)　　　　　1.25 1.75
　　　　　First day cancel　　　　　　2.00

Summer Greeting Card
Designer: Koya Oshiro

1965, June 20
UX28 PC25 1½c **multicolored,** *off-white*
　　　　　(340,604)　　　　　　1.40 2.50
　　　　　First day cancel　　　　　　1.65

Toy Pony
Rider — PC26

Fan Palm
Dipper — PC27

1966 New Year Card; Precanceled
Designer: Seikichi Tamanaha

1965, Nov. 15
UX29 PC26 1½c **multicolored,** *off-white*
　　　　　(5,224,622)　　　　　1.25 1.75
　　　　　First day cancel　　　　　　1.40
　　a.　Silver (background) omitted　250.00

Summer Greeting Card
Designer: Seikichi Tamanaha

1966, June 20
UX30 PC27 1½c **multicolored,** *off-white*
　　　　　(339,880)　　　　　　1.25 2.00
　　　　　First day cancel　　　　　　1.40

Toy Dove — PC28

Cycad Insect Cage and
Praying Mantis — PC29

1967 New Year Card; Precanceled
Designer: Seikichi Tamanaha

1966, Nov. 15
UX31 PC28 1½c **multicolored,** *off-white*
　　　　　(5,500,000)　　　　　1.25 1.75
　　　　　First day cancel　　　　　　1.65
　　a.　Silver (background) omitted　500.00
　　b.　Gray blue & green omitted　750.00

Summer Greeting Card
Designer: Shin Isagawa

1967, June 20
UX32 PC29 1½c **multicolored,** *off-white*
　　　　　(350.000)　　　　　　1.50 2.50
　　　　　First day cancel　　　　　　1.75

Paper Doll
Royalty — PC30

Pandanus
Drupe — PC31

1968 New Year Card; Precanceled
Designer: Shin Isagawa

1967, Nov. 15
UX33 PC30 1½c **multicolored,** *off-white*
　　　　　(6,200,000)　　　　　1.10 1.50
　　　　　First day cancel　　　　　　1.75
　　a.　Gold omitted　　　　　　500.00

Summer Greeting Card
Designer: Seikan Omine

1968, June 20
UX34 PC31 1½c **multicolored,** *off-white*
　　　　　(350,000)　　　　　　1.25 2.25
　　　　　First day cancel　　　　　　1.75

Toy Lion — PC32

Ryukyu Trading
Ship — PC33

1969 New Year Card; Precanceled
Designer: Teruyoshi Kinjo

1968, Nov. 15
UX35 PC32 1½c **multicolored,** *off-white*
　　　　　(7,000,000)　　　　　1.10 1.50
　　　　　First day cancel　　　　　　1.50

Summer Greeting Card
Designer: Seikichi Tamanaha

1969, June 20
UX36 PC33 1½c **multicolored,** *(349,800)*　1.25 2.25
　　　　　First day cancel　　　　　　1.75

Toy Devil
Mask — PC34

Ripe Litchis — PC35

1970 New Year Card; Precanceled
Designer: Teruyoshi Kinjo

1969, Nov. 15
UX37 PC34 1½c **multicolored** *97,200,000)*　1.10 1.50
　　　　　First day cancel　　　　　　1.25

Summer Greeting Card
Designer: Kensei Miyagi

1970, June 20
UX38 PC35 1½c **multicolored** *(400,000)*　1.40 2.25
　　　　　First day cancel　　　　　　1.50

Thread-winding
Implements for
Dance — PC36

Ripe
Guavas — PC37

1971 New Year Card; Precanceled
Designer: Yoshinori Arakai

1970, Nov. 16
UX39 PC36 1½c **multicolored** *(7,500,000)*　1.10 1.50
　　　　　First day cancel　　　　　　1.25

Summer Greeting Card
Designer: Kensei Miyagi

1971, July 10
UX40 PC37 1½c **multicolored** *(400,000)*　1.25 2.25
　　　　　First day cancel　　　　　　1.25

Pony Type of 1961
Zip Code Boxes in Vermilion

1971, July 10
UX41 PC17 1½c **gray violet & brown**
　　　　　(3,000,000)　　　　　1.25 3.50
　　　　　First day cancel　　　　　　2.00

No. UX41 Surcharged below
Stamp in Vermilion

"Revalued 2¢" applied by Nakamura Printing Co.

1971, Sept. 1
UX42 PC17 2c on 1½c **gray violet & brown**
　　　　　(1,699,569)　　　　　1.10 2.25
　　　　　First day cancel　　　　　　2.00
　　a.　Inverted surcharge　　　500.00
　　b.　Double surcharge　　　　500.00
　　c.　Surcharge on back　　　500.00
　　e.　Surcharge on back, inverted　500.00

1972 New Year Card; Precanceled

Tasseled Castanets — PC38

Zip Code Boxes in Vermilion
Designer: Yoshinori Arakaki

1971, Nov. 15
UX43 PC38 2c **multicolored** *(8,000,000)*　1.00 1.50
　　　　　First day cancel　　　　　　1.25

Type of 1961
Zip Code Boxes in Vermilion

1971, Dec. 15

UX44 PC17 2c gray violet & brown (3,500,000) 1.25 1.75
      First day cancel   1.65

PAID REPLY POSTAL CARDS

Sold as two attached cards, one for message, one for reply. The major listings are of unsevered cards except Nos. UY4-UY6.

   Message   Reply

1948, July 1

UY1 US1 10s + 10s **dull red**, *grayish tan*
            (1,000)   2,000.   —
   m.   Message card   600. 1,000.
   r.   Reply card   600. 1,000.

1949, July 18

UY2 US1 15s + 15s **vermilion**, *tan (E 150,000)*   30.00 *40.00*
   a.   Gray card (E 75,000)   75.00   —
           First day cancel
   m.   Message card   8.00 *16.50*
   r.   Reply card   8.00 *16.50*

1950, Jan. 21

UY3 US2 50s + 50s **carmine red**, *gray cream (E 130,000)*   25.00 *40.00*
   a.   Double impression of message card
   b.   Light tan card (E 96,000)   15.00   —
           First day cancel
   m.   Message card   3.50 *13.50*
   r.   Reply card   3.50 *13.50*

No. UY2a Handstamp Surcharged in Vermilion

1951

UY4 US1 1y (15s+85s) message, type
            "b" (E 3,000)   350.   350.
   a.   Reply, type "b" (E 3,000)   350.   350.
   b.   Message, type "a" (E 300)   600.   —
   c.   Reply, type "a" (E 300)   600.   —
   d.   Message, type "d" (E 200)   500.   —
   e.   Reply, type "d" (E 200)   500.   —
   f.   Message, UY2, type "a" (E 3,000)   150.   225.
   g.   Reply, UY2, type "a" (E 3,000)   150.   225.
   h.   Message, UY2, type "b" (E 2,500)   275.   275.
   i.   Reply, UY2, type "b" (E 2,500)   275.   275.
   j.   Message, UY2, type "d" (E 2,800)   150.   250.
   k.   Reply, UY2, type "d" (E 2,800)   150.   250.
   l.   1y + 1y unsevered, type "b"   850.
   m.   1y + 1y unsevered, type "a"   1,450.
   n.   1y + 1y unsevered, type "d"   1,200.
   o.   1y + 1y unsevered, UY2, type "a"   360.
   p.   1y + 1y unsevered, UY2, type "b"   650.
   q.   1y + 1y unsevered, UY2, type "d"   360.
   r.   1y + 1y unsevered, UY2, type "c"   3, 500.
   s.   Message, UY2, type "c,"   —
   t.   Reply, UY2, type "c"   —
   u.   Message, type "c"   —
   v.   Reply, type "c"   —

Types are illustrated above No. UX4.

     e   f

     g   h

Typographed Surcharge in Vermilion on No. UY2a

UY5 US1 1y (15s+85s) message, type
            "f" (E 20,000)   125.   125.
   a.   Reply, type "f" (E 20,000)   125.   125.
   b.   Message, type "e" (E 12,500)   225.   225.
   c.   Reply, type "e" (E 12,500)   225.   225.
   d.   Message, type "g" (E 500)   1,000.   1,000.
   e.   Reply, type "g" (E 500)   1,000.   1,000.
   f.   Message, UY2, type "e" (E 15,000)   125.   125.
   g.   Reply, UY2, type "e" (E 15,000)   125.   125.
   h.   Message, UY2, type "f" (E 9,000)   125.   125.
   i.   Reply, UY2, type "f" (E 9,000)   125.   125.
   j.   Message, UY2, type "g" (E 500)   1,000.   1,000.
   k.   Reply, UY2, type "g" (E 500)   1,000.   1,000.
   l.   1y + 1y unsevered, type "e"   675.
   m.   1y + 1y unsevered, UY2, type "e"   375.

Typographed Surcharge Type "h" in Vermilion on No. UY3

UY6 US2 1y (50s+50s) message (E 35,000)   125.00 *150.00*
   a.   Reply (E 35,000)   125.00 *150.00*
   b.   Message, UY3b (E 10,000)   125.00 *150.00*
   c.   Reply, UY3b (E 10,000)   125.00 *150.00*

No. UY6 is unknown as a joined card.

Smooth or Coarse Card

1952, Feb. 8

UY7 PC3 1y + 1y vermilion, *gray tan (60,000)*   120.00 *140.00*
           First day cancel   *250.00*
   m.   Message card   25.00 *50.00*
   r.   Reply card   25.00 *50.00*

1953

UY8 PC4 1y + 1y **vermilion**, *tan (22,900)*   30.00 *40.00*
           First day cancel
   a.   Off-white card (13,800)   40.00 *50.00*
   m.   Message card   7.50 *19.00*
   r.   Reply card   7.50 *26.50*

Off-white or Light Cream Card

1953, Dec. 2

UY9 PC5 2y + 2y **green** (50,000)   100.00 *90.00*
           First day cancel   *150.00*
   m.   Message card   15.00 *25.00*
   r.   Reply card   15.00 *35.00*

1955, May

UY10 PC6 2y + 2y **green**, *off-white (280,000)*   10.00   —
   a.   Reply card blank   500.00
   m.   Message card   3.25 *11.00*
   r.   Reply card   3.25 *15.00*

No. UY10 Surcharged in Red

1958, Sept. 16

UY11 PC6 1½c on 2y, 1½c on 2y (95,000)   8.00
           First day cancel   *22.50*
   a.   Surcharge on reply card only   500.00
   b.   Surcharge on message card only   500.00
   c.   Reply card double surcharge   750.00
   d.   Reply card stamp omitted (surcharge only)   1,000.   —
   m.   Message card   2.75 *10.00*
   r.   Reply card   2.75 *16.50*

Surcharge varieties include: "1" omitted; wrong font "2".

Pony Types

1959, June 20

UY12 PC11 1½c + 1½c **dark blue & brown** (366,000)   3.50
           First day cancel   *4.00*
   m.   Message card   .65 *3.50*
   r.   Reply card   .65 *3.50*

1960, Mar. 10

UY13 PC13 1½c + 1½c **gray violet & brown**, (150,000)   7.00   —
           First day cancel   *5.00*
   m.   Message card   1.50 *5.00*
   r.   Reply card   1.50 *5.00*

International Type

1963, Feb. 15

UY14 PC20 5c + 5c **vermilion, emerald & black**, *pale yellow (70,000)*   2.50
           First day cancel   *3.00*
   m.   Message card   .75 *3.75*
   r.   Reply card   .75 *3.75*

Pony ("RYUKYUS") Type

1963-69

UY15 PC17 1½c + 1½c **gray violet & brown**, *cream, Mar. 15, (800,000)*   2.00
           First day cancel   *2.50*
   a.   Off-white card, Mar. 13, 1967 (100,000)   2.25   —
   b.   White card, Nov. 22, 1969 (700,000)   1.75   —
   m.   Message card detached   .40 *4.00*
   r.   Reply card detached   .40 *4.00*

No. UY14 Surcharged below Stamp in Vermilion

1971, Sept. 1

UY16 PC17 2c on 1½c + 2c on 1½c **gray violet & brown** (80,000)   2.00   —
           First day cancel   *2.25*
   m.   Message card   .50 *2.50*
   r.   Reply card   .50 *2.50*

Pony ("RYUKYUS") Type
Zip Code Boxes in Vermilion

1971, Nov. 1

UY17 PC17 2c + 2c **gray violet & brown** (150,000)   2.00   —
           First day cancel   *2.50*
   m.   Message card   .50 *2.50*
   r.   Reply card   .50 *2.50*

OFFICIAL STAMPS ELECTION POSTAL CARDS

Official election free-mail postal cards were authorized by the United States Civil Administration of the Ryukyus, Ordinance 57, Dec. 18, 1951, as a measure to ensure equal access to voters for each candidate standing in district or general elections in the islands. Under the terms of the ordinance and the local enabling legislation, each candidate, on request, could receive a fixed number of cards per election, which were serviced with no mailing costs to the candidate.

Until the issuance of No. UZE15 in 1960, cards were processed without canceling; beginning with that issue, they were treated as regular postal cards and canceled.

With the exception of pieces bearing emergency handstamp or machine-cancel indicia, the cards were special-order printings (incorporating the election indicium) of designs and types of postal cards concurrently in use as regular postal cards (though at times in different colors).

ELECTION INDICIA

   Type I   Type II

Type I: Typographed, Size: 18x45mm
Type II: Typographed, Size: 17½x48-49mm

   Type III   Type IV

Type III: Typographed, Size: 17½x49-51mm
Type IV: Typographed, Size: 16½x62mm

Type IVa

Type V

Type IVa: Like Type IV but with second character from bottom ("SEN") having one stroke at upper left instead of two
Type V: Typographed, Size: 16-17x61-63mm (similar to Type IV, but with different bottom character)

Type X   **Type XI**

Type X: Typographed, Size: 17½x51-51½mm (similar to Type VIII, but with different appearance of five smaller characters at top)
Type XI: Typographed, Size: 10x31½mm

Type XV

Type XVI

Type XV: Typographed, Size: 18x50-50½mm
Type XVI: Machine cancel, Circle diameter: 20mm, Height of legend box: 23½mm

Type VI

Type VII

Type VI: Typographed, Size: 17½x51-52mm
Type VII: Typographed, Size: 17½x51-52mm (similar to Type VI, but with different bottom character)

Type XII

Type XIII

Type XII: Handstamped, Size: 17½-18x49½-51½mm, Thick characters
Type XIII: Handstamped, Size: 17½-18x50¼-51mm, Thin characters

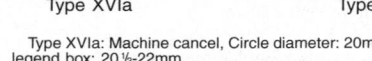
Type XVIa   **Type XVII**

Type XVIa: Machine cancel, Circle diameter: 20mm, Height of legend box: 20½-22mm
Type XVII: Typographed, Size: 18½x48½-50mm

Type VIII

Type IX

Type VIII: Typographed, Size: 17¼-17½x 52mm (similar to Type VII but with second character from bottom ("SEN") having one stroke at upper left instead of two)
Type IX: Handstamped, Size: 17½x51mm

Type XIIIa

Type XIV

Type XIIIa: Handstamped, Size: 17½-18x50¼x51mm, Thick characters, with shorter lvertical line at lower left.
Type XIV: Typographed, Size: 18x50-50½mm

Type XVIII

Type XVIII: Machine cancel, Circle diameter: 20mm, Height of legend box: 20½-22 mm

UZE1

1952, Feb. 2   First General Election
UZE1   PC3   1y **vermilion,** *tan* coarse (Naha
     die) + Type I *(345,000)*   300.00   —
   a.   Postmarked (error)

1952, July 26   1st District Special Election
UZE2   PC3   1y **vermilion,** *tan* coarse (Naha die)
     + Type II *(est. 25,000)*   50.00   —
   a.   2nd character from bottom in indicium
       (SEN) inverted

Used cards or unused with campaign messages must have reference to the 1st District (Kasari, Amami Gunto) election.

1953, Mar. 3   4th District Special Election
UZE3   PC4   1y **vermilion,** *tan* coarse (Tokyo die) +
     Type II *(est. 10,000)*   —
   a.   Postmarked (error)

Identifiable only when postmarked (in error, with dates between Mar. 3-Mar.31, 1953) and/or with campaign message in reference to 4th District election (Motobu, Okinawa Gunto).

1953, Mar. 27   3rd District Special Election
UZE4   PC4   1y **vermilion,** *tan* coarse (Tokyo die) +
     Type II *(est. 10,000)*   —
   a.   Postmarked (error)

Identifiable only when postmarked (in error, with dates between Mar. 27-Apr. 1953) and/or with campaign message in reference to 3rd District election (Yagaji, Okinawa Gunto).

UZE5

1954, Feb. 23   Second General Election
UZE5   PC5   2y **rose red,** *off white* (Naha die) +
     Type III *(70,000)*   50.00   —
   a.   Postmarked (error)

1954, Nov. 19   18th District Special Election
UZE6   PC6   2y **red,** *off white* (Tokyo die) +
     Type IV   500.00   —
   a.   Postmarked (error)   —
UZE6A   PC6   2y **red,** *off white* (Tokyo die) +
     Type V   500.00   —
   a.   Postmarked (error)

Postal records show receipt of 4,000 total cards of Nos. UZE6 and UZE6A, undefined as to type.

1955, Feb. 15   20th District Special Election
UZE7   PC6   2y **dark purple,** *off white* (Tokyo
     die) + Type IV *(2,000)*   500.00   —

1955, Mar. 8   23rd District Special Election
UZE8   PC6   2y **turquoise blue,** *off white* (Tokyo
     die) + Type V *(2,000)*   500.00   —
   a.   Postmarked (error)

1955, June 28   22nd District Special Election
UZE9   PC6   2y **dull brown,** *gray cream* (Tokyo
     die) + Type V *(3,030)*   400.00   —
   a.   Postmarked (error)

1956, Feb. 20   Third General Election
UZE10   PC6   2y **pale blue green,** *off white*
     (Tokyo die) + Type VI   75.00   150.00
   a.   Postmarked (error)   —
UZE10A   PC6   2y **pale blue green,** *off white*
     (Tokyo die) + Type VII   75.00   150.00
   a.   Postmarked (error)

Postal records show receipt of 65,000 total cards of Nos. UZE10 and UZE10A, undefined as to type.

1956, Oct. 26   25th District Special Election
UZE11   PC6   2y **brown red,** *off white* (Tokyo
     die) + Type IV   300.00   —
UZE11A   PC6   2y **brown red,** *off white* (Tokyo
     die) + Type V   180.00   350.00

Postal records show a total quantity of 3,030 examples of Nos. UZE11 and UZE11A prepared, unidentified as to type, of which 2,000 were issued.

1957, Aug. 5   18th District Special Election
UZE12   PC6   2y **lilac,** *off white* (Tokyo die) +
     Type IVa *(3,030)*   250.00   —

1958, Feb. 25   Fourth General Election
UZE13   PC6   2y **deep blue,** *off white* (Tokyo
     die) + Type VI (bold face
     print)   130.00   70.00
UZE13A   PC6   2y **deep blue,** *off white* (Tokyo
     die) + Type VI (light face
     print)   130.00   70.00
UZE13B   PC6   2y **deep blue,** *off white* (Tokyo
     die) + Type VII (bold face
     print)   130.00   70.00
UZE13C   PC6   2y **deep blue,** *off white* (Tokyo
     die) + Type VII (light face
     print)   90.00   70.00

Postal records show a total of 140,300 cards of Nos. UZE13-UZE13C prepared in two printings, undefined as to types.

UZE14

1959, July 23   26th District Special Election
UZE14   PC6   1 ½c on 2y **lemon,** *white* (Tokyo
     die) + Type VIII *(4,100)*   450.00   —

UZE15

1960, Oct. 24   Fifth General Election
UZE15   PC11   1 ½c **indigo & claret brown,**
     white (Naha die) + Type
     VIII *(150,000)*   70.00   70.00
UZE16   PC13   1 ½c **violet gray & claret brown,**
     cream (Tokyo die) + Type
     IX in LL corner *(10,000)*   —

1962, Oct. 22   Sixth General Election
UZE17   PC17   1 ½c **violet gray & claret**
     brown, *cream* + Type VIII   50.00   —
UZE17A   PC17   1 ½c **violet gray & claret**
     brown, *cream* + Type X   50.00   —

Postal records show a total of 116,000 cards of Nos. UZE17-UZE17A prepared, undefined as to type.

1962, Oct. 22
Sixth General Election Emergency Issue
UZE18   PC17   1 ½c **violet gray & claret brown,**
     cream + Type IX *(6,000)*   250.00   —
   a.   Indicium inverted   —

1965, Oct. 25   Seventh General Election
UZE19   PC17   1 ½c **violet gray & claret brown,**
     cream + Type XI *(134,000)*   20.00   90.00

1966, Aug. 1   3rd District Special Election
UZE20   PC17   1 ½c **violet gray & claret brown,**
     cream + Type XI *(est. 3,800)*   —

No. UZE20 is a remainder copy of No. UZE19, identifiable only when canceled at the Nakijin Post Office between Aug. 1-Aug. 20, 1966.

1966, Aug. 11
3rd District Special Election Emergency Issue
UZE21   PC17   1 ½c **violet gray & claret brown,**
     cream + Type XII *(est. 200)*   —
UZE22   PC17   1 ½c **violet gray & claret brown,**
     cream + Type XIII   225.00   —

1968, Oct. 21   First Chief Executive Election
UZE23   PC17   1 ½c **violet gray & claret brown,**
     white + Type XIV *(300,000)*   30.00   25.00

1968, Oct. 21   Eighth General Election
UZE24   PC17   1 ½c **violet gray & claret brown,**
     white + Type XV *(142,000)*   30.00   35.00

1970, Oct. 12   1st District Special Election
UZE25   PC17   1 ½c **violet gray & claret brown,**
     white + Type XV *(4,000)*   —

No. UZE25 is a remainder card of No. UZE24, identifiable only when canceled at the Higashi, Kunigami, Ogimi or Oku Post Offices between Oct. 12-Oct. 31, 1970.

UZE26A

1970, Oct. 23
First General Election for Coucilors and
Representatives to the Japanese Diet
UZE26　PC17　1½c **violet gray & claret**
　　　　　　brown, *white +* Type
　　　　　　XVI (*300,000*)　　250.00　30.00
UZE26A　PC17　1½c **violet gray & claret**
　　　　　　brown, *white +* Type
　　　　　　XVIa (*300,000*)　　250.00　30.00

Postal records show a total of 171,000 examples of Nos. UZE26-UZE26A prepared, undefined as to type.

Emergency Commercial Card Issue for First
General Japanese Diet Election
UZE27　*white or light gray blue +* Type XVI　— 30.00
UZE27A　*white or light gray blue +* Type XVIa　— 30.00

Postal records show a total of 79,000 commercial cards were acquired for official issue as Nos. UZE27-UZE27A after validating. Some of the cards show an imprinted black square, while others show nothing.

1970, Nov. 16　　**21st District Special Election**
UZE28　PC17　1½c **violet gray & claret brown,**
　　　　　white + Type XVII (8,000)　— 180.00

島本「ケン」は言う
「政治は相互の理解と協調と和の中にあり、抵抗や反抗はいたずらに憎悪の感情を起し、混乱を招くだけではない。抵抗と反抗はいたずらに憎悪の感情を起し、混乱を招くだけで、常に現実を踏まえて、前向きに誠実で勇気をもって実践する人、島本「ケン」でありまする人、島本「ケン」こそは新沖縄建設に必要な人でありますの。島本「ケン」こそは新沖縄建設の為に第二十二区本「ケン」こそは新沖縄建設の為に第二十二区げると共に絶対自信をもって「ケン」を推薦致します。

昭和四十五年十一月　日
　　　　　　　　推薦状
那覇市古波蔵二四四
島本ケン選挙本部
推薦者　〔署名〕

UZE29

1970, Nov. 16　　**22nd District Special Election**
UZE29　PC17　1½c **violet gray & claret**
　　　　　　brown, *white +* Type XVII
　　　　　　(2,000)　　　　— 350.00

No. UZE29 is a remainder card of No. UZE28, identifiable only with the imprinted message shown above of candidate Shimamoto Ken.

UZE30　PC17　1½c **violet gray & claret**
　　　　　　brown, *white +* Type XIII
UZE30A　PC17　1½c **violet gray & claret**
　　　　　　brown, *white +* Type XIIIa

Postal records show a total of 2,000 of Nos. UZE30-UZE30A prepared, undefined as to type.

1971, Feb. 15　　**7th District Special Election**
UZE31　PC17　1½c **violet gray & claret brown,**
　　　　　white + Type XV (4,000)　— —

1971, June 4
Second General Election for Coucilors and
Representatives to the Japanese Diet
UZE32　PC17　1½c **violet gray & claret brown,**
　　　　　white + Type XVIII (25,000)　— 45.00
Emergency Commercial Card Issue for Second
General Japanese Diet Election
UZE33　*white* + Type XVIII, 100x148mm
　　　　(25,000)　　　　　　　— 20.00
　a.　Double strike of election indicia, one in-
　　　verted in LR corner　　　　— —
UZE33A　*white +* Type XVIII, 104x150mm
　　　　(25,000)　　　　　　　— 50.00

REVENUE STAMPS

Upon its establishment Apr. 1, 1952, the government of the Ryukyu Islands assumed responsibility for the issuing of and the profit from revenue stamps. The various series served indiscriminately as evidence of payment of the required fees for various legal, realty and general commercial transactions.

1 yen — R1

　　3　　　5　　　10　　　50

　100　　500　　1000

Litho. by Japan Printing Bureau.
Designer: Eizo Yonamine

		1952-54	**Wmk. 257**	*Perf. 13x13½*	
R1	R1	1y	**brown**	15.00	10.00
R2	R1	3y	**carmine**	20.00	12.00
R3	R1	5y	**green**	25.00	15.00
R4	R1	10y	**blue**	30.00	20.00
R5	R1	50y	**purple**	35.00	25.00
R6	R1	100y	**yellow brown**	80.00	30.00
R7	R1	500y	**dark green**	350.00	100.00
R8	R1	1,000y	**carmine**	300.00	150.00
		Nos. R1-R8 (8)		855.00	362.00

Issued: #R1-R6, July 15, 1952; #R7-R8, Apr. 16, 1954.

Denomination Vertical

"Cent"

"Dollar"

Litho. by Kobundo Printing Co., Naha
Perf. 10, 10½, 11 and combinations

		1958, Sept. 16	**Without Gum**	**Unwmk.**	
R9	R1	1c	**red brown**	30.00	25.00
a.		Horiz. pair, imperf. between		500.00	
R10	R1	3c	**red**	40.00	35.00
a.		Horiz. pair, imperf. between		500.00	
R11	R1	5c	**green**	50.00	45.00
R12	R1	10c	**blue**	70.00	65.00
a.		Horiz. pair, imperf. between		500.00	
R13	R1	50c	**purple**	135.00	120.00
R14	R1	$1	**sepia**	200.00	175.00
R15	R1	$5	**dark green**	400.00	350.00
R16	R1	$10	**carmine**	450.00	400.00
		Nos. R9-R16 (8)		1,375.	1,215.

R2　　　　　　　　　　R3

R4

Litho. by Japan Printing Bureau.

		1959-69	**Wmk. 257**	*Perf. 13x13½*	
R17	R2	1c	**brown**	3.00	1.90
R18	R2	3c	**red**	3.00	1.10
R19	R2	5c	**purple**	5.50	3.25
R20	R2	10c	**green**	10.00	6.00
R21	R2	20c	**sepia** ('69)	80.00	55.00
R22	R2	30c	**light olive** ('69)	100.00	65.00
R23	R2	50c	**blue**	40.00	14.00
			Engr.		
R24	R3	$1	**olive**	45.00	12.50
R25	R3	$2	**vermilion** ('69)	250.00	50.00
R26	R3	$3	**purple** ('69)	450.00	60.00
R27	R3	$5	**orange**	120.00	45.00
R28	R3	$10	**dark green**	180.00	60.00
R29	R4	$20	**carmine** ('69)	2,000.	200.00
R30	R4	$30	**blue** ('69)	2,500.	—
R31	R4	$50	**black** ('69)	3,000.	—
		Nos. R17-R28 (12)		1,286.	373.75

UNEMPLOYMENT INSURANCE

These stamps, when affixed in an official booklet and canceled, certified a one-day contract for a day laborer. They were available to employers at certain post offices on various islands.

Dove — RQ1　　　Shield — RQ2

Lithographed in Naha

		1961, Jan. 10	**Without Gum**	**Unwmk.**	*Rouletted*
RQ1	RQ1	2c	**pale red**	800.00	
RQ2	RQ2	4c	**violet**	60.00	60.00

Redrawn
Lithographed by Japan Printing Bureau

		1966, Feb.	**Unwmk.**	*Perf. 13x13½*	
RQ3	RQ1	2c	**pale red**		
RQ4	RQ2	4c	**violet**	30.00	30.00

Redrawn stamps have bolder numerals and inscriptions, and fewer, stronger lines of shading in background.

Cycad — RQ3

Lithographed by Japan Printing Bureau

		1968, Apr. 19	**Wmk. 257**	*Perf. 13x13½*	
RQ5	RQ3	8c	**brown**	35.00	35.00

Nos. RQ3-RQ4 Surcharged with New Values and 2 Bars

		1967-72			
RQ6	RQ1	8c on 2c	**pale red**	70.00	70.00
RQ7	RQ2	8c on 4c	**violet** ('72)	35.00	35.00
RQ8	RQ2	12c on 4c	**violet** ('71)	30.00	30.00

A 4-cent "stamp" picturing Iriomote Park was originally planned for postage in 1971. Its use was changed, and it became a label that was used on the "Ryukyu Islands Emergency Conversion Confirmation Certificate." Value, $150 unused, $250 on document.

PROVISIONAL ISSUES MIYAKO

Stamps of Japan 1938-42 Handstamped in Black, Red or Orange

1948	Typo., Litho., Engr.	Wmk. 257	Perf. 13	
3XR1 A84	3s brown, #329	75.00	—
3XR2 A86	5s brown lake, #331	75.00	—
3XR3 A152	20s blue, #338 (R)	60.00	—
3XR4 A95	25s dark brown & pale brown, #270 (R)	60.00	—
a.	Black overprint	600.00	—
3XR5 A96	30s peacock blue, #271 (R)	60.00	—
3XR6 A154	40s dark violet, #342 (R)	60.00	—
3XR7 A97	50s olive & pale olive, #272 (R)	135.00	—
a.	Orange overprint	500.00	—

Doubled handstamps are known on all values and pairs with one stamp without handstamp exist on the 5s and 20s.

PROVISIONAL ISSUES YAEYAMA

In addition to the continued use of the then-current Japanese revenue stamps in stock from the wartime period, the varying authorities of the Yaeyama Gunto issued three district-specific revenue series, with a total of 28 values. Only those values at present verified by surviving examples are indicated. Numbers are reserved for other values believed to have been issued, but as yet not seen and verified.

No. 5XR2 — R5

No. 5XR3 — R6

No. 5XR5 — R7

No. 5XR27 — R8

1946 (?)	Without Gum	Imperf.
Value printed, frame handstamped
5XR1 R5	3s vermilion & black	—
5XR2 R5	10s vermilion & black	—
Validating handstamp below
5XR3 R6	1y vermilion & black	—

Civil Administration Issues
| 1947 (?) | Without Gum | Imperf. |
Value printed, frame handstamped
Cream Paper
| 5XR5 R7 | 10s vermilion & black | — |
| 5XR6 R7 | 50s vermilion & black | — |

Gunto Government Issues
| 1950 (?) | Without Gum | Imperf. |
Value printed, frame handstamped
Cream Paper
5XR17 R8	10s vermilion & black	—
5XR18 R8	50s vermilion & black	—
a.	50s vermilion & blue	—

5XR20 R8	1.50y vermilion & black	—
5XR22 R8	5y vermilion & black	—
5XR24 R8	20y vermilion & black	—
5XR27 R8	100y vermilion & black	—

Nos. 5XR17-5XR27 are known with rough perforations, full or partial.

SPECIMEN STAMPS

Regular stamps and postal cards of 1958-65 overprinted with three cursive syllabics mi-ho-n ("specimen").

Type A

1961-64	Overprinted in Black	
91S	3c multicolored (1,000)	250.00
118S	3c multicolored (1,100)	450.00
119S	3c multicolored (1,100)	400.00

Type B

1964-65	Overprinted in Red or Black	
120aS	3c deep blue, deep carmine & ocher (R) (1,500)	200.00
121S	3c multicolored (R) (1,500)	175.00
124S	3c ultra, yel & red (R) (5,000)	35.00
125S	3s dull claret, yel & black (1,500)	70.00
126S	3c yellow & multi (2,000)	60.00
127S	3c gray, red & black (2,000)	60.00
128S	3c multicolored (1,500)	70.00
129S	1½c multicolored (R) (1,500)	70.00
130S	3c light blue & multi (R) (1,500)	200.00
131S	3c multicolored (R) (1,500)	60.00
132S	3c buff & multicolored (2,000)	60.00
133S	3c green & multi (R) (2,000)	50.00
134S	3c multicolored (2,000)	50.00
135S	3c blue & multicolored (2,000)	50.00
136S	3c golden brown & multi (2,000)	50.00
139S	1½c multicolored (R) (2,500)	50.00

Postal Cards
1964-65	Overprinted Type A or B in Black or Red		
UX26S	A	1½c multicolored (1,000)	500.00
UX27S	B	1½c multicolored (1,000)	350.00
UX28S	A	1½c multicolored (1,000)	300.00
UX29S	A	1½c multicolored (1,100)	250.00

See also Nos. 46TCS and 48TCS following Proofs and Trial Color Proofs.

PROOFS AND TRIAL COLOR PROOFS

1948	Salmon Paper, Imperf.	
1aP	5s magenta	—
2aP	10s yellow green	—
3aP	20s yellow green	—
5aP	40s magenta	—
6aP	50s ultramarine	—
7aP	1y ultramarine	—

Between the printing of Nos. 1a-7a and Nos. 1-7 essay sheets of the series were prepared in Tokyo and overprinted with a swirl-pattern of blue or red dots. These essays sell for about $800 each.

Except for No. 12TC 4y olive, the trial color proofs of Nos. 8-13, 18, C1-C3 and E1 are from blocks of 9.

| 1950 | Soft White Paper, Imperf. | |
Proofs are Gummed, Trial Color Proofs are Without Gum
8P	50s dark carmine rose	1,500.
8TC	50s rose	1,750.
8TC	50s green	1,750.
9P	1y deep blue	1,500.
9TC	1y rose	1,750.
9TC	1y green	1,750.
10P	2y rose violet	1,500.
10TC	2y rose	1,750.
10TC	2y green	1,750.
11P	3y carmine rose	1,500.
11TC	3y rose	1,750.
11TC	3y green	1,750.
12P	4y greenish gray	1,500.
12TC	4y rose	1,750.
12TC	4y olive	1,750.
13P	5y blue green	1,500.
13TC	5y rose	1,750.
13TC	5y green	1,750.

1951	Soft White Paper, Imperf., Without Gum	
14P	3y red brown	1,000.
15P	3y dark green	800.

1952	Whitish Paper, Imperf., With Gum	
18TC	3y pale salmon	1,750.
18TC	3y scarlet	1,750.
18TC	3y red orange	1,900.

Perforated, gummed proof sheets of Nos. 18, 27 and 28 with oversized, untrimmed selvage were printed for display purposes.

1958	Off White Paper, Imperf., Without Gum	
46TC	2c black (100)	800.
48TC	4c black (100)	800.

AIR POST
| 1950 | Soft White Paper, Imperf. | |
Proofs are Gummed, Trial Color Proofs are Without Gum
C1P	8y bright blue	1,500.
C1TC	8y rose	1,750.
C1TC	8y light green	1,750.
C2P	12y green	1,500.
C2TC	12y rose	1,750.
C2TC	12y light green	1,750.
C3P	16y rose carmine	1,500.
C3TC	16y rose	1,750.

1951	Soft White Paper, Imperf., Without Gum	
C4P	13y blue	1,000.
C5P	18y green	1,000.
C6P	30y cerise	800.

SPECIAL DELIVERY
| 1950 | Soft White Paper, Imperf. | |
Proofs are Gummed, Trial Color Proofs are Without Gum
E1P	5y bright blue	1,500.
E1TC	5y rose	1,750.
E1TC	5y green	1,750.

Official proof folders contain one each of Nos. 8P-13P, 12TC in olive, C1P-C3P and E1P. The stamps are securely adhered to the folder. Value, $9,000.

Similar folders exist containing photographs of die proofs in black of the same issues and mockups of Nos. U2, UX3 and UY3.

KUME ISLAND
| 1945 | U.S. Official Watermarked White Bond Paper | |
Seal Handstamped in Vermilion Without Gum
| 1X1P | 7s black | 3,000. |
| a. | "7" and "SEN" one letter space to left, pos. 8 | 4,000. |

SPECIMEN OVERPRINTS ON TRIAL COLOR PROOFS
1961	Overprinted in Vermillion	
46TCS	2c black (100)	1,000.
48TCS	4c black (100)	1,000.

Cursive type used for these two trial color proofs is different from the mihon overprints.

TUBERCULOSIS PREVENTION SEALS

Issued by the Ryukyu Tuberculosis Prevention Association (1952-71) in panes of 100 (Nos. WX1 and WX5) and 20 (Nos. WX2-WX4 and WX6-WX20). The sale of seals provided income beyond government funding for treatment. Seals were sold by the pane for the price of 1 Yen (1952-58) or 1¢ (1959-71) per seal.

Nos. WX1 and WX1a are overprinted U.S. Christmas seals (Nos. WX159-WX160). Nos. WX2-WX20 were printed for the Ryukyu Tuberculosis Prevention Association by the Japan Printing Bureau. Nos. WX2-WX20 bear a year date and the word "GREETINGS." Nos. WX2-WX4 show "RYUKYUS" in kanji, and Nos. WX5-WX20 show "RYUKYUS" in both kanji and English.

Nos. WX1-WX20 were printed on unwatermarked paper. Values are for unused seals with original gum.

Designer — Tom Darling.

1952　　　　　Perf. 12½x12
Overprinted in Black

WX1	CS46	green, red, yellow & black	
		(600,000)	4.00
		Pane of 100	450.00
		Imprint single	10.00
		Imprint block of 4	25.00
a.		Perf 12½	4.00
		Pane of 100	450.00
		Imprint single	10.00
		Imprint block of 4	25.00

Lithographed by Eureka Specialty Co. (No. WX1) and United States Printing and Lithographing Co. (No. WX1a).

Panes of the 1952 Christmas seals (U.S. Nos. WX159 and WX160) were donated by the National Tuberculosis Association and overprinted "Ryu-Kyu" in kanji by the Koshun Insatsusho in Naha. Printer's marks appear on seal 56 in each pane of 100: "E" for Eureka Specialty Printing Co.; "U" for United States Printing and Lithographing Co. Panes printed by the Strobridge Lithographing Co. ("S"), Edwards & Deutch Lithographing Co. ("D") and the Fleming-Potter Co., Inc. ("F") may also have been overprinted, but these have not been verified.

Imprint appears in selvage below seal 100; imprint of Union Local No. 41 on No. WX1, and imprint of Union Local No. 1 on No. WX1a.

TBS1

Designer — Adaniya Masayoshi.

1953　　　　　Perf. 13x13¼

WX2	TBS1	green, red, & buff (780,000)	2.00
		Pane of 20, perf through top and bottom selvage	30.00
		Imprint single, type I	5.00
		Imprint block of 6	15.00
		Pane of 20, perf through top selvage only	30.00
		Imprint single, type I	5.00
		Imprint block of 6	15.00
a.		Imperf (20,000)	100.00
		Pane of 20	2,500.
		Imprint single, type I	150.00
		Imprint block of 6	750.00

Imprint appears in selvage below seal 19.

TBS2

...niya Masayoshi.

1954

WX3	TBS2	light green, red, & black	
		(780,000)	2.00
		Pane of 20, perf through top and bottom selvage	30.00
		Imprint single	5.00
		Imprint block of 6	15.00
		Pane of 20, perf through top selvage only	30.00
		Imprint single, type I	5.00
		Imprint block of 6	15.00
a.		Imperf (20,000)	—
		Pane of 20	—
		Imprint single, type I	—
		Imprint block of 6	—

Imprint appears in selvage below seal 19.

TBS3

Designer — Adaniya Masayoshi.

1955

WX4	TBS3	carmine red, apple green & black (1,180,000)	2.00
		Pane of 20, perf through top and bottom selvage	20.00
		Imprint single, type I	5.00
		Imprint block of 6	10.00
		Pane of 20, perf through top selvage only	20.00
		Imprint single, type I	5.00
		Imprint block of 6	10.00
a.		Imperf (20,000)	3.00
		Pane of 20	50.00
		Imprint single, type I	5.00
		Imprint block of 6	20.00

Imprint appears in selvage below seal 19.

TBS4

Designer — Adaniya Masayoshi.

1956

WX5	TBS4	cobalt, carmine red, yellow & black (1,460,000)	2.00
		Pane of 100, perf through top and bottom selvage	150.00
		Imprint single, type I	5.00
		Imprint block of 10	40.00
		Control No. strip of 3	15.00
a.		Imperf (40,000)	5.00
		Pane of 100	300.00
		Imprint single, type I	20.00
		Imprint block of 10	80.00
		Control No. strip of 3	80.00

Imprint appears in selvage below seal 98. Five-digit control number appear in right selvage next to seals 20 and 30, or 20, 30 and 40.

Two types of Marginal Imprint on Nos. WX6-WX20

Type I	Type II

TBS5

Designer — Yamazato Keiichi.

1957

WX6	TBS5	orange yellow, black, red & light blue (1,750,000)	1.00
		Pane of 20, perf through top and bottom selvage	15.00
		Imprint single, type I	2.00
		Imprint block of 4, type I	4.00
		Imprint single, type II	2.00
		Imprint block of 4, type II	4.00
a.		Imperf (50,000)	2.00
		Pane of 20	20.00
		Imprint single, type I	4.00
		Imprint block of 4, type I	10.00
		Imprint single, type II	4.00
		Imprint block of 4, type II	10.00

Imprint type I appears in selvage below seal 20; imprint type II appears in selvage below seal 17. Legend printed in Japanese in right selvage.

TBS6

Designer — Adaniya Masayoshi.

1958　　　　　Perf. 13¼x13

WX7	TBS6	yellow, blue, carmine red & black (1,900,000)	.50
		Pane of 20, perf through left and right selvage	8.00
		Imprint single, type I	2.00
		Imprint block of 4, type I	3.00
		Imprint single, type II	2.00
		Imprint block of 4, type II	3.00
a.		Imperf (80,000)	2.00
		Pane of 20	20.00
		Imprint single, type I	4.00
		Imprint block of 4, type I	10.00
		Imprint single, type II	4.00
		Imprint block of 4, type II	10.00
b.		Perf 11 (20,000)	10.00
		Pane of 20	200.00
		Imprint single, type I	25.00
		Imprint block of 4, type I	75.00
		Imprint single, type II	25.00
		Imprint block of 4, type II	75.00

Imprint type I appears in selvage below seal 20; imprint type II appears in selvage below seal 16. Legend printed in Japanese in top selvage. A total of 1,000 imperforate sheets were later perforated (No. WX7b), by order of the Ryukyu Tuberculosis Prevention Association.

TBS7

Designer — Tamanaha Seikichi.

1959　　　　　Perf. 13x13¼

WX8	TBS7	vermilion, mauve, ultramarine & indigo (2,100,000)	.50
		Pane of 20, perf through top and bottom selvage	8.00
		Imprint single, type I	2.00
		Imprint block of 4, type I	3.00
		Imprint single, type II	2.00
		Imprint block of 4, type II	3.00
a.		Imperf (200,000)	2.00
		Pane of 20	20.00
		Imprint single, type I	4.00
		Imprint block of 4, type I	10.00
		Imprint single, type II	4.00
		Imprint block of 4, type II	10.00

Imprint type I appears in selvage below seal 20; imprint type II appears in selvage below seal 17. Legend printed in Japanese in right selvage.

TBS8

Designer — Oshiro Kohya.

1960   *Perf. 13¼x13*
WX9   TBS8 **scarlet, orange, cobalt, bright
           blue & black** *(2,450,000)*   .50
           Pane of 20, perf through left and right
              selvage   8.00
           Imprint single, type I   2.00
           Imprint block of 4, type I   3.00
           Imprint single, type II   2.00
           Imprint block of 4, type II   3.00
  a.   *Imperf* *(50,000)*   2.00
           Pane of 20   20.00
           Imprint single, type I   4.00
           Imprint block of 4, type I   10.00
           Imprint single, type II   4.00
           Imprint block of 4, type II   10.00

Imprint type I appears in selvage below seal 20; imprint type II appears in selvage below seal 16. Legend printed in Japanese in top selvage.

TBS9

Designer — Omine Seikan.

1961   *Perf. 13x13¼*
WX10   TBS9 **multicolored** *(3,450,000)*   .30
           Pane of 20, perf through top and bot-
              tom selvage   6.00
           Imprint single, type I   .80
           Imprint block of 4, type I   2.00
           Imprint single, type II   .80
           Imprint block of 4, type II   2.00
  a.   *Imperf* *(50,000)*   1.00
           Pane of 20   12.00
           Imprint single, type I   3.00
           Imprint block of 4, type I   6.00
           Imprint single, type II   3.00
           Imprint block of 4, type II   6.00

Imprint type I appears in selvage below seal 20; imprint type II appears in selvage below seal 17. Legend printed in Japanese in right selvage.

TBS10

Designer — Kabira Choshin.

1962   *Perf. 13¼*
WX11   TBS10 **multicolored** *(3,450,000)*   .30
           Pane of 20, perf through top and bot-
              tom selvage   5.00
           Imprint single, type I   .60
           Imprint block of 6, type I   1.50
           Imprint single, type II   .60
           Imprint block of 6, type II   1.50
  a.   *Imperf* *(50,000)*   .50
           Pane of 20   7.00
           Imprint single, type I   1.00
           Imprint block of 6, type I   2.50
           Imprint single, type II   1.00
           Imprint block of 6, type II   2.50

Imprint type I appears in selvage below seal 19; imprint type II appears in selvage below seal 17. Legend printed in English in left selvage and in Japanese in right selvage.

TBS11

Designer — Kabira Choshin.

1963   *Perf. 13x13¼*
WX12   TBS11 **multicolored** *(3,450,000)*   .30
           Pane of 20, perf through top and bot-
              tom selvage   5.00
           Imprint single, type I   .60
           Imprint block of 4, type I   1.50

           Imprint single, type II   .60
           Imprint block of 4, type II   1.50
  a.   *Imperf* *(50,000)*   .50
           Pane of 20   7.00
           Imprint single, type I   1.00
           Imprint block of 4, type I   2.50
           Imprint single, type II   1.00
           Imprint block of 4, type II   2.50

Imprint type I appears in selvage below seal 20; imprint type II appears in selvage below seal 17. Legend printed in Japanese in right selvage.

TBS12

Designer — Kabira Choshin.

1964
WX13   TBS12 **multicolored** *(3,650,000)*   .30
           Pane of 20, perf through top and bot-
              tom selvage   5.00
           Imprint single, type I   .60
           Imprint block of 4, type I   1.50
           Imprint single, type II   .60
           Imprint block of 4, type II   1.50
  a.   *Imperf* *(50,000)*   .50
           Pane of 20   7.00
           Imprint single, type I   1.00
           Imprint block of 4, type I   2.50
           Imprint single, type II   1.00
           Imprint block of 4, type II   2.50

Imprint type I appears in selvage below seal 20; imprint type II appears in selvage below seal 17. Legend printed in English in left selvage and in Japanese in right selvage.

TBS13

Designer — Oyama Masaru.

1965   *Perf. 13¼x13*
WX14   TBS13 **dark blue, light green, carmine
           & pink** *(3,700,000)*   .30
           Pane of 20, perf through left and right
              selvage   5.00
           Imprint single, type I   .60
           Imprint block of 4, type I   1.50
           Imprint single, type II   .60
           Imprint block of 4, type II   1.50
  a.   *Imperf* *(100,000)*   .50
           Pane of 20   7.00
           Imprint single, type I   1.00
           Imprint block of 4, type I   2.50
           Imprint single, type II   1.00
           Imprint block of 4, type II   2.50

Imprint type I appears in selvage below seal 20; imprint type II appears in selvage below seal 16. Legend printed in English in top selvage and in Japanese in top and bottom selvage.

TBS14

Designer — Kabira Choshin.

1966   *Perf. 13x13¼*
WX15   TBS14 **dark green, yellow & carmine**
           (3,700,000)   .30
           Pane of 20, perf through top and bot-
              tom selvage   5.00
           Imprint single, type I   .60
           Imprint block of 4, type I   1.50
           Imprint single, type II   .60
           Imprint block of 4, type II   1.50
  a.   *Imperf* *(100,000)*   .50
           Pane of 20   7.00
           Imprint single, type I   1.00

           Imprint block of 4, type I   2.50
           Imprint single, type II   1.00
           Imprint block of 4, type II   2.50

Imprint type I appears in selvage below seal 20; imprint type II appears in selvage below seal 17. Legend printed in English in left selvage and in Japanese in right selvage.

TBS15

Designer — Kabira Choshin.

1967
WX16   TBS15 **blue, carmine, yellow & black**
           (4,100,000)   .30
           Pane of 20, perf through top and bot-
              tom selvage   5.00
           Imprint single, type I   .60
           Imprint block of 4, type I   1.50
           Imprint single, type II   .60
           Imprint block of 4, type II   1.50
  a.   *Imperf* *(100,000)*   .50
           Pane of 20   7.00
           Imprint single, type I   1.00
           Imprint block of 4, type I   2.50
           Imprint single, type II   1.00
           Imprint block of 4, type II   2.50

Imprint type I appears in selvage below seal 20; imprint type II appears in selvage below seal 17. Legend printed in English in left selvage and in Japanese in right selvage.

TBS16

Designer — Kabira Choshin.

1968
WX17   TBS16 **blue, carmine & black**
           (4,400,000)   .30
           Pane of 20, perf through top and bot-
              tom selvage   5.00
           Imprint single, type I   .60
           Imprint block of 4, type I   1.50
           Imprint single, type II   .60
           Imprint block of 4, type II   1.50
  a.   *Imperf* *(100,000)*   .50
           Pane of 20   7.00
           Imprint single, type I   1.00
           Imprint block of 4, type I   2.50
           Imprint single, type II   1.00
           Imprint block of 4, type II   2.50

Imprint type I appears in selvage below seal 20; imprint type II appears in selvage below seal 17. Legend printed in English in left selvage and in Japanese in right selvage.

TBS17

Designer — Oshiro Kohya.

1969
WX18   TBS17 **multicolored** *(4,600,000)*   .30
           Pane of 20, perf through top and bot-
              tom selvage   5.00
           Imprint single, type I   .60
           Imprint block of 4, type I   1.50
           Imprint single, type II   .60
           Imprint block of 4, type II   1.50
  a.   *Imperf* *(100,000)*   .50
           Pane of 20   7.00
           Imprint single, type I   1.00

Imprint block of 4, type I	2.50
Imprint single, type II	1.00
Imprint block of 4, type II	2.50

Imprint type I appears in selvage below seal 20; imprint type II appears in selvage below seal 17. Legend printed in English in left selvage and in Japanese in right selvage.

TBS18

Designer — Kabira Choshin.

1970
WX19   TBS18 **multicolored** *(4,650,000)*   .30
     Pane of 20, perf through top and bottom selvage   5.00

Imprint single, type I	.60
Imprint block of 4, type I	1.50
Imprint single, type II	.60
Imprint block of 4, type II	1.50
a. Imperf *(50,000)*	.50
Pane of 20	7.00
Imprint single, type I	1.00
Imprint block of 4, type I	2.50
Imprint single, type II	1.00
Imprint block of 4, type II	2.50

Imprint type I appears in selvage below seal 20; imprint type II appears in selvage below seal 17. Legend printed in English in left selvage and in Japanese in right selvage.

TBS19

Designer — Ashimine Kinsei.

1971
WX20   TBS19 **multicolored** *(4,650,000)*   .30
     Pane of 20, perf through top and bottom selvage   5.00

Imprint single, type I	.60
Imprint block of 4, type I	1.50
Imprint single, type II	.60
Imprint block of 4, type II	1.50
a. Imperf *(50,000)*	.50
Pane of 20	7.00
Imprint single, type I	1.00
Imprint block of 4, type I	2.50
Imprint single, type II	1.00
Imprint block of 4, type II	2.50

Imprint type I appears in selvage below seal 20; imprint type II appears in selvage below seal 17. Legend printed in English in left selvage and in Japanese in right selvage.

UNITED NATIONS

United Nations stamps are used on UN official mail sent from UN Headquarters in New York City, the UN European Office in Geneva, Switzerland, or from the Donaupark Vienna International Center or Atomic Energy Agency in Vienna, Austria to points throughout the world. They may be used on private correspondence sent through the UN post offices.

UN mail is carried by the US, Swiss and Austrian postal systems.

See Switzerland official stamp listings in the Scott *Standard Postage Stamp Catalogue* for stamps issued by the Swiss Government for official use of the UN European Office and other UN affiliated organizations. See France official stamp listings for stamps issued by the French Government for official use of UNESCO.

+: When following the quantity, this indicates the total printed to date. Unless otherwise noted, these are the initial printing order. Final quantities frequently are not given for definitives and air post stamps. The total printed is shown here.

Blocks of four generally sell for four times the single stamp value.

Values for first day covers are for cacheted and unaddressed covers. Addressed covers sell for much less, and addressed and uncacheted first day covers sell for very little.

For imperforate stamps, see the Proofs section following U.N. Souvenir Cards.

Catalogue values for all unused stamps in this section are for Never Hinged items.

Peoples of the World — A1

UN Headquarters Building — A2

"Peace, Justice, Security" — A3

UN Flag — A4

UN International Children's Emergency Fund — A5

World Unity — A6

Printed by Thomas De La Rue & Co., Ltd., London (1c, 3c, 10c, 15c, 20c, 25c), and Joh. Enschedé and Sons, Haarlem, Netherlands (1½c, 2c, 5c, 50c, $1). The 3c, 15c and 25c have frame engraved, center photogravure; other denominations are engraved. Panes of 50. Designed by O. C. Meronti (A1), Leon Helguera (A2), J. F. Doeve (A3), Ole Hamann (A4), S. L. Hartz (5c) and Hubert Woyty-Wimmer (20c).

Perf. 13x12½, 12½x13

1951   **Engr. and Photo.**   **Unwmk.**

1	A1	1c **magenta**, *Oct. 24*		
		(8,000,000)	.20	.20
		First day cover		1.00
		Margin block of 4, UN seal	.20	
2	A2	1½c **blue green**, *Oct. 24*		
		(7,450,000)	.20	.20
		First day cover		1.00
		Margin block of 4, UN seal	.20	—
		Precanceled *(361,700)*		55.00
3	A3	2c **purple**, *Nov. 16 (8,470,000)*	.20	.20
		First day cover		1.00

4	A4	3c **magenta & blue**, *Oct. 24*		
		(8,250,000)	.20	.20
		First day cover		1.00
		Margin block of 4, UN seal	.25	—
5	A5	5c **blue**, *Oct. 24 (6,000,000)*	.20	.20
		First day cover		1.75
		Margin block of 4, UN seal	.25	—
6	A1	10c **chocolate**, *Nov. 16*		
		(2,600,000)	.30	.25
		First day cover		2.00
		Margin block of 4, UN seal	.40	—
7	A4	15c **violet & blue**, *Nov. 16*		
		(2,300,000)	.35	.25
		First day cover		2.00
		Margin block of 4, UN seal	1.50	—
8	A6	20c **dark brown**, *Nov. 16*		
		(2,100,000)	.50	.30
		First day cover		2.00
		Margin block of 4, UN seal	1.50	—
9	A4	25c **olive gray & blue**, *Oct. 24*		
		(2,100,000)	.60	.30
		First day cover		2.00
		Margin block of 4, UN seal	2.40	—
10	A2	50c **indigo**, *Nov. 16 (1,785,000)*	5.75	2.25
		First day cover		8.00
		Margin block of 4, UN seal	2.75	—
11	A3	$1 **red**, *Oct. 24 (2,252,500)*	2.40	1.25
		First day cover		8.00
		Margin block of 4, UN seal	27.50	—
		Nos. 1-11 (11)	11.50	—
			10.90	5.60

First day covers of Nos. 1-11 and C1-C4 total 1,113,216.

The various printings of Nos. 1-11 vary in sheet marginal perforation. Some were perforated through left or right margins, or both; some through all margins.

Sheets of this issue carry a marginal inscription consisting of the UN seal and "First UN/Issue 1951." This inscription appears four times on each sheet. The listing "Margin block of 4, UN seal" or "Inscription block of 4" in this and following issues refers to a corner block.

Sheets of the 1½c, 2c, 50c and $1 have a cut-out of different shape in one margin. The printer trimmed this off entirely on most of the 1½c third printing, and partially on the 1½c fourth printing and $1 fifth and sixth printings.

See UN Offices in Geneva Nos. 4, 14.

Forgeries of the 1½c precancel abound. Examination by a competent authority is necessary.

Veterans' War
Memorial
Building, San
Francisco
A7

Issued to mark the 7th anniversary of the signing of the
United Nations Charter.
Engraved and printed by the American Bank Note Co., New
York. Panes of 50. Designed by Jean Van Noten.

1952, Oct. 24   **Perf. 12**
12   A7   5c blue (1,274,670)   .80   .35
                 First day cover (160,117)   1.00
                 Inscription block of 4   4.00   —

Globe and
Encircled
Flame — A8

4th anniversary of the adoption of the Universal Declaration
of Human Rights.
Engraved and printed by Thomas De La Rue & Co., Ltd.,
London. Panes of 50. Designed by Hubert Woyty-Wimmer.

1952, Dec. 10   **Perf. 13½x14**
13   A8   3c deep green (1,554,312)   .50   .35
                 First day cover   1.50
                 Inscription block of 4   2.25   —
14   A8   5c blue (1,126,371)   .60   .40
                 First day cover   2.00
                 First day cover, #13-14   5.75
                 Inscription block of 4   2.50   —

First day covers of Nos. 13 and 14 total 299,309.

Refugee Family — A9

Issued to publicize "Protection for Refugees."
Engraved and printed by Thomas De La Rue & Co., Ltd.,
London. Panes of 50. Designed by Olav Mathiesen.

1953, Apr. 24   **Perf. 12½x13**
15   A9   3c dark red brown & rose
                  brown (1,299,793)   .25   .25
                 First day cover   2.25
                 Inscription block of 4   1.00   —
16   A9   5c indigo & blue (969,224)   .50   .40
                 First day cover   3.25
                 First day cover, #15-16   7.50
                 Inscription block of 4   2.75   —

First day covers of Nos. 15 and 16 total 234,082.

Envelope, UN
Emblem and
Map — A10

Issued to honor the Universal Postal Union.
Engraved and printed by Thomas De La Rue & Co., Ltd.,
London. Panes of 50. Designed by Hubert Woyty-Wimmer.

1953, June 12   **Perf. 13**
17   A10   3c black brown (1,259,689)   .40   .40
                 First day cover   5.00
                 Inscription block of 4   1.60   —
18   A10   5c dark blue (907,312)   1.25   1.00

First day cover   4.50
First day cover, #17-18   9.50
Inscription block of 4   5.00

First day covers of Nos. 17 and 18 total 231,627.
Plate number ("1A" or "1B") in color of stamp appears below
47th stamp of sheet.

Gearwheels and UN Emblem — A11

Hands Reaching Toward Flame — A12

Issued to publicize United Nations activities in the field of technical assistance.
Engraved and printed by Thomas De La Rue & Co. Ltd. London. Panes of 50. Designed by Olav Mathiesen.

1953, Oct. 24   **Perf. 13x12½**

19	A11	3c **dark gray** (1,184,348)	.30	.25
		First day cover	2.00	
		Inscription block of 4	1.25	—
20	A11	5c **dark green** (968,182)	.50	.45
		First day cover	5.00	
		First day cover, #19-20	9.00	
		Inscription block of 4	2.75	—

First day covers of Nos. 19 and 20 total 229,211.

1953, Dec. 10   **Perf. 12½x13**

Issued to publicize Human Rights Day.
Engraved and printed by Thomas De La Rue & Co., Ltd., London. Panes of 50. Designed by León Helguera.

21	A12	3c **bright blue** (1,456,928)	.35	.30
		First day cover	2.00	
		Inscription block of 4	1.40	—
22	A12	5c **rose red** (983,831)	1.40	1.00
		First day cover	4.00	
		First day cover, #21-22	8.00	
		Inscription block of 4	5.50	—

First day covers of Nos. 21 and 22 total 265,186.

Ear of Wheat — A13

UN Emblem and Anvil Inscribed "ILO" — A14

Issued to honor the Food and Agriculture Organization and printed by Thomas De La Rue & Co., Ltd., London. Panes of 50. Designed by Dirk Van Gelder.

1954, Feb. 11   **Perf. 12½x13**

23	A13	3c **dark green & yellow** (1,250,000)	.30	.20
		First day cover	2.00	
		Inscription block of 4	1.75	—
24	A13	8c **indigo & yellow** (949,718)	.75	.50
		First day cover	4.00	
		First day cover, #23-24	5.00	
		Inscription block of 4	4.00	—

First day covers of Nos. 23 and 24 total 272,312.

1954, May 10   **Perf. 12½x13**

Design: 8c, inscribed "OIT."
Issued to honor the International Labor Organization.
Engraved and printed by Thomas De La Rue & Co., Ltd., London. Panes of 50. Designed by José Renau.

25	A14	3c **brown** (1,085,651)	.20	.20
		First day cover	2.00	
		Inscription block of 4	.50	—
26	A14	8c **magenta** (903,561)	1.25	.85

First day cover	4.00	
First day cover, #25-26	4.75	
Inscription block of 4	5.25	—

First day covers of Nos. 25 and 26 total 252,796.

UN European Office, Geneva — A15

Issued on the occasion of United Nations Day.
Engraved and printed by Thomas De La Rue & Co., Ltd., London. Panes of 50. Designed by Earl W. Purdy.

1954, Oct. 25   **Perf. 14**

27	A15	3c **dark blue violet** (1,000,000)	1.75	1.25
		First day cover	1.75	
		Inscription block of 4	8.50	—
28	A15	8c **red** (1,000,000)	.35	.30
		First day cover	2.25	
		First day cover, #27-28	3.50	
		Inscription block of 4	1.75	—

First day covers of Nos. 27 and 28 total 233,544.

Mother and Child — A16

Issued to publicize Human Rights Day.
Engraved and printed by Thomas De La Rue & Co., Ltd. London. Panes of 50. Designed by Leonard C. Mitchell.

1954, Dec. 10   **Perf. 14**

29	A16	3c **red orange** (1,000,000)	12.00	4.00
		First day cover	2.75	
		Inscription block of 4	55.00	—
30	A16	8c **olive green** (1,000,000)	.75	.35
		First day cover	3.25	
		First day cover, #29-30	7.50	
		Inscription block of 4	4.50	—

First day covers of Nos. 29 and 30 total 276,333.

Symbol of Flight — A17

Design: 8c, inscribed "OACI."
Issued to honor the International Civil Aviation Organization.
Engraved and printed by Waterlow & Sons, Ltd., London. Panes of 50. Designed by Angel Medina Medina.

1955, Feb. 9   **Perf. 13½x14**

31	A17	3c **blue** (1,000,000)	1.25	.75
		First day cover	7.00	
		Inscription block of 4	7.00	—
32	A17	8c **rose carmine** (1,000,000)	.75	.65
		First day cover	3.00	
		First day cover, #31-32	5.50	
		Inscription block of 4	3.50	—

First day covers of Nos. 31 and 32 total 237,131.

UNESCO Emblem — A18

Issued to honor the UN Educational, Scientific and Cultural Organization.
Engraved and printed by Waterlow & Sons, Ltd., London. Panes of 50. Designed by George Hamori.

1955, May 11   **Perf. 13½x14**

33	A18	3c **lilac rose** (1,000,000)	.40	.30
		First day cover	2.00	
		Inscription block of 4	2.50	—
34	A18	8c **light blue** (1,000,000)	.35	.30
		First day cover	3.00	
		First day cover, #33-34	5.00	
		Inscription block of 4	1.75	—

First day covers of Nos. 33 and 34 total 255,326.

United Nations Charter — A19

Design: 4c, Spanish inscription. 8c, French inscription.
10th anniversary of the United Nations.
Engraved and printed by Waterlow & Sons, Ltd., London. Panes of 50. Designed by Claude Bottiau.

1955, Oct. 24   **Perf. 13½x14**

35	A19	3c **deep plum** (1,000,000)	.90	.55
		First day cover	3.00	
		Inscription block of 4	4.00	—
36	A19	4c **dull green** (1,000,000)	.50	.50
		First day cover	3.00	
		Inscription block of 4	2.75	—
37	A19	8c **bluish black** (1,000,000)	.35	.25
		First day cover	4.00	
		First day cover, #35-37	11.00	
		Inscription block of 4	2.25	—
		Nos. 35-37 (3)	1.75	1.15

Wmk. 309 — Wavy Lines

Souvenir Sheet

1955, Oct. 24   **Wmk. 309**   *Imperf.*

38	A19	Sheet of 3 (250,000)	95.00	18.00
		Hinged	55.00	
a.		3c **deep plum**	3.00	.50
b.		4c **dull green**	3.00	.50
c.		8c **bluish black**	3.00	.50
		First day cover	18.00	
		Sheet with retouch on 8c	105.00	42.50

No. 38 measures 108x83mm and has marginal inscriptions in deep plum.
Two printings were made of No. 38. The first (200,000) may be distinguished by the broken line of background shading on the 8c. It leaves a small white spot below the left leg of the "n" of "Unies." For the second printing (50,000), the broken line was retouched, eliminating the white spot. The 4c was also retouched.
First day covers of Nos. 35-38 total 455,791.
Examples of No. 38 are known with the 4c and 8c stamps misaligned.

First day cover 1.00
First day cover, #59-60 1.00
Inscription block of 4 .85 —

First day covers of Nos. 59 and 60 total 504,832.

Central Hall, UN Seal — A31
Westminster — A30

Design: 8c, French inscription.
Central Hall, Westminster, London, was the site of the first session of the United Nations General Assembly, 1946.
Engraved and printed by the American Bank Note Co., New York. Panes of 50. Designed by Olav Mathiesen.

1958, Apr. 14 *Perf. 12*
61 A30 3c violet blue (3,353,716) .20 .20
First day cover 1.00
Inscription block of 4 .25 —
62 A30 8c rose claret (2,836,747) .20 .20
First day cover 1.00
First day cover, #61-62 2.00
Inscription block of 4 .60 —

First day covers of Nos. 61 and 62 total 449,401.

1958, Oct. 24 *Perf. 13½x14*
Engraved and printed by Bradbury, Wilkinson & Co., Ltd., England. Panes of 50. Designed by Herbert M. Sanborn.
63 A31 4c red orange (9,000,000) .20 .20
First day cover 1.00
First day cover of #63 also
bearing #64 75.00
Inscription block of 4 .20 —

1958, June 2 *Perf. 13x14*
64 A31 8c bright blue (5,000,000) .20 .20
First day cover (219,422) 1.00
Inscription block of 4 .55 —
Margin block of 4, Bradbury,
Wilkinson imprint 3.00 —

Gearwheels — A32

Hands Upholding
Globe — A33

Design: 8c, French inscription.
Issued to honor the Economic and Social Council.
Engraved and printed by the American Bank Note Co., New York. Panes of 50. Designed by Ole Hamann.

1958, Oct. 24 **Unwmk.** *Perf. 12*
65 A32 4c dark blue green (2,556,784) .20 .20
First day cover 1.00
Inscription block of 4 .30 —
66 A32 8c vermilion (2,175,117) .20 .20
First day cover 1.00
First day cover, #65-66 1.00
Inscription block of 4 .60 —

First day covers of Nos. 63, 65 and 66 total 626,236.

1958, Dec. 10 **Unwmk.** *Perf. 12*
Issued for Human Rights Day and to commemorate the 10th anniversary of the signing of the Universal Declaration of Human Rights.

Engraved and printed by the American Bank Note Co., New York. Panes of 50. Designed by Leonard C. Mitchell.
67 A33 4c yellow green (2,644,340) .20 .20
First day cover 1.00
Inscription block of 4 .40 —
68 A33 8c red brown (2,216,838) .20 .20
First day cover 1.00
First day cover, #67-68 1.00
Inscription block of 4 .75 —

First day covers of Nos. 67 and 68 total 618,124.

New York City
Building,
Flushing
Meadows
A34

Design: 8c, French inscription.
New York City Building at Flushing Meadows, New York, was the site of many General Assembly meetings, 1946-50.
Engraved and printed by Canadian Bank Note Company, Ltd., Ottawa. Panes of 50. Designed by Robert Perrot.

1959, Mar. 30 **Unwmk.** *Perf. 12*
69 A34 4c light lilac rose (2,035,011) .20 .20
First day cover 1.00
Inscription block of 4 .30 —
70 A34 8c aquamarine (1,627,281) .20 .20
First day cover 1.00
First day cover, #69-70 1.75
Inscription block of 4 .70 —

First day covers of Nos. 69 and 70 total 440,955.

A35 A36

Design: UN emblem and symbols of agriculture, industry and trade.
Issued to honor the Economic Commission for Europe.
Engraved and printed by Canadian Bank Note Company, Ltd., Ottawa. Panes of 50. Designed by Ole Hamann.

1959, May 18 **Unwmk.** *Perf. 12*
71 A35 4c blue (1,743,502) .20 .20
First day cover 1.00
Inscription block of 4 .60 —
72 A35 8c red orange (1,482,898) .20 .20
First day cover 1.00
First day cover, #71-72 1.25
Inscription block of 4 .75 —

First day covers of Nos. 71 and 72 total 433,549.

1959, Oct. 23 **Unwmk.** *Perf. 12*
Designs: 4c, Figure Adapted from Rodin's "Age of Bronze." 8c, same, French inscription.
Issued to honor the Trusteeship Council.
Engraved and printed by Canadian Bank Note Co., Ltd., Ottawa. Panes of 50. Designed by León Helguera; lettering by Ole Hamann.
73 A36 4c bright red (1,929,677) .20 .20
First day cover 1.00
Inscription block of 4 .30 —
74 A36 8c dark olive green (1,587,647) .20 .20
First day cover 1.00
First day cover, #73-74 1.50
Inscription block of 4 1.00 —

First day covers of Nos. 73 and 74 total 466,053.

World Refugee Year
Emblem — A37

Chaillot Palace,
Paris — A38

Design: 8c, French inscription.
Issued to publicize World Refugee Year, July 1, 1959-June 30, 1960.
Engraved and printed by Canadian Bank Note Co., Ltd., Ottawa. Panes of 50. Designed by Olav Mathiesen.

1959, Dec. 10 **Unwmk.** *Perf. 12*
75 A37 4c olive & red (2,168,963) .20 .20
First day cover 1.00
Inscription block of 4 .35 —
76 A37 8c olive & bright greenish blue
(1,843,886) .20 .20
First day cover 1.00
First day cover, #75-76 2.00
Inscription block of 4 .75 —

First day covers of Nos. 75 and 76 total 502,262.

1960, Feb. 29 **Unwmk.** *Perf. 14*
Design: 8c, French inscription.
Chaillot Palace in Paris was the site of General Assembly meetings in 1948 and 1951.
Engraved and printed by Thomas De La Rue & Co., Ltd., London. Panes of 50. Designed by Hubert Woyty-Wimmer.
77 A38 4c rose lilac & blue (2,276,678) .20 .20
First day cover 1.00
Inscription block of 4 .20 —
78 A38 8c dull green & brown (1,930,869) .20 .20
First day cover 1.00
First day cover, #77-78 2.50
Inscription block of 4 .70 —

First day covers of Nos. 77 and 78 total 446,815.

Map of Far
East and Steel
Beam — A39

Design: 8c, French inscription.
Issued to honor the Economic Commission for Asia and the Far East (ECAFE).
Printed by the Government Printing Bureau, Tokyo. Panes of 50. Designed by Hubert Woyty-Wimmer.

1960, Apr. 11 **Photo.** **Unwmk.** *Perf. 13x13½*
79 A39 4c deep claret, blue green & dull yellow
(2,195,945) .20 .20
First day cover 1.00
Inscription block of 4 .20 —
80 A39 8c olive green, blue & rose (1,897,902) .20 .20
First day cover 1.00
First day cover, #79-80 2.00
Inscription block of 4 .75 —

First day covers of Nos. 79 and 80 total 415,127.

Tree, FAO and UN
Emblems — A40

UN Headquarters
and Preamble to UN
Charter — A41

Design: 8c, French inscription.
Issued to commemorate the Fifth World Forestry Congress,
Seattle, Washington, Aug. 29-Sept. 10.
Printed by the Government Printing Bureau, Tokyo. Panes of
50. Designed by Ole Hamann.

1960, Aug. 29   Photo.   Unwmk.   Perf. 13½
81 A40 4c dark blue, green & orange
            (2,188,293)   .20   .20
        First day cover   1.00
        Inscription block of 4   .35
82 A40 8c yellow green, black & orange
            (1,837,778)   .20   .20
        First day cover   1.00
        First day cover, #81-82   2.00
        Inscription block of 4   .65
    First day covers of Nos. 81 and 82 total 434,129.

1960, Oct. 24   Unwmk.   Perf. 11
Design: 8c, French inscription.
Issued to commemorate the 15th anniversary of the United
Nations.
Engraved and printed by the British American Bank Note Co.,
Ltd., Ottawa, Canada. Panes of 50. Designed by Robert Perrot.

83 A41 4c blue (2,631,593)   .20   .20
        First day cover   1.00
        Inscription block of 4   .35
84 A41 8c gray (2,278,022)   .20   .20
        First day cover   1.00
        First day cover, #83-84   1.50
        Inscription block of 4   .65

Souvenir Sheet
Imperf
85   Sheet of 2 (1,000,000)   1.25 1.25
    a. A41 4c blue   .55   .55
    b. A41 8c gray   .55   .55
        First day cover (256,699)   .50

No. 85 has dark gray marginal inscription. Size: 92x71mm.
Broken "I" and "V" flaws occur in "ANNIVERSARY" in marginal
inscription. Value $40. Examples are known with the two
stamps misaligned.

Block and Tackle — A42

Scales of Justice from
Raphael's Stanze — A43

Design: 8c, French inscription.
Issued to honor the International Bank for Reconstruction and
Development.
Printed by the Government Printing Bureau, Tokyo. Panes of
50. Designed by Angel Medina Medina.

1960, Dec. 9   Photo.   Unwmk.   Perf. 13½x13
86 A42 4c multicolored (2,286,117)   .20   .20
        First day cover   1.00
        Inscription block of 4   .35
87 A42 8c multicolored (1,882,019)   .20   .20
        First day cover   1.00
        First day cover, #86-87   1.25
        Inscription block of 4   .65
    First day covers of Nos. 86 and 87 total 559,708.

1961, Feb. 13   Photo.   Unwmk.   Perf. 13½x13
Design: 8c, French inscription.
Issued to honor the International Court of Justice.
Printed by the Government Printing Bureau, Tokyo, Japan.
Panes of 50. Designed by Kurt Plowitz.

88 A43 4c yellow, orange brown & black
            (2,234,588)   .20   .20
        First day cover   1.00
        Inscription block of 4   .35
89 A43 8c yellow, green & black (2,023,968) .20 .20

        First day cover   1.00
        First day cover, #88-89   1.00
        Inscription block of 4   .65
    First day covers of Nos. 88 and 89 total 447,467.

Seal of
International
Monetary
Fund — A44

Design: 7c, French inscription.
Issued to honor the International Monetary Fund.
Printed by the Government Printing Bureau, Tokyo, Japan.
Panes of 50. Designed by Roy E. Carlson and Hordur Karlsson,
Iceland.

1961, Apr. 17   Photo.   Unwmk.   Perf. 13x13½
90 A44 4c bright bluish green (2,305,010) .20   .20
        First day cover   1.00
        Inscription block of 4   .35
91 A44 7c terra cotta & yellow (2,147,201) .20   .20
        First day cover   1.00
        First day cover, #90-91   1.00
        Inscription block of 4   .65
    First day covers of Nos. 90 and 91 total 448,729.

Abstract Group of
Flags — A45

Printed by Courvoisier S.A., La Chaux-de-Fonds, Switzerland. Panes of 50. Designed by Herbert M. Sanborn.

1961, June 5   Photo.   Unwmk.   Perf. 11½
92 A45 30c multicolored (3,370,000)   .45   .20
        First day cover (182,949)   1.00
        Inscription block of 4   2.00
    See UN Offices in Geneva No. 10.

Cogwheel and Map of
Latin America — A46

Design: 11c, Spanish inscription.
Issued to honor the Economic Commission for Latin America.
Printed by the Government Printing Bureau, Tokyo. Panes of
50. Designed by Robert Perrot.

1961, Sept. 18   Photo.   Unwmk.   Perf. 13½
93 A46 4c blue, red & citron (2,037,912)   .20   .20
        First day cover   1.00
        Inscription block of 4   .45
94 A46 11c green, lilac & orange vermilion
            (1,835,097)   .25   .20
        First day cover   1.00
        First day cover, #93-94   1.00
        Inscription block of 4   1.25
    First day covers of Nos. 93 and 94 total 435,820.

Africa House,
Addis Ababa, and
Map — A47

Design: 11c, English inscription.
Issued to honor the Economic Commission for Africa.
Printed by Courvoisier S.A., La Chaux-de-Fonds, Switzer-
land. Panes of 50. Designed by Robert Perrot.

1961, Oct. 24   Photo.   Unwmk.   Perf. 11½
95 A47 4c ultramarine, orange, yellow &
            brown (2,044,842)   .20   .20
        First day cover   1.00
        Inscription block of 4   .30
96 A47 11c emerald, orange, yellow & brown
            (1,790,894)   .25   .20
        First day cover   1.00
        First day cover, #95-96   1.00
        Inscription block of 4   1.10
    First day covers of Nos. 95 and 96 total 435,131.

Mother Bird Feeding Young
and UNICEF Seal — A48

Designs: 3c, Spanish inscription. 13c, French inscription.
15th anniversary of the United Nations Children's Fund.
Printed by Courvoisier S.A., La Chaux-de-Fonds, Switzerland. Panes of 50. Designed by Minoru Hisano.

1961, Dec. 4   Photo.   Unwmk.   Perf. 11½
97 A48 3c brown, gold, orange & yellow
            (2,867,456)   .20   .20
        First day cover   1.00
        Inscription block of 4   .25
98 A48 4c brown, gold, blue & emerald
            (2,735,899)   .20   .20
        First day cover   1.00
        Inscription block of 4   .35
99 A48 13c deep green, gold, purple & pink
            (1,951,715)   .20   .20
        First day cover   1.00
        First day cover, #97-99   1.40
        Inscription block of 4   1.25
        Nos. 97-99 (3)   .60   .60
    First day covers of Nos. 97-99 total 752,979.

Family and
Symbolic
Buildings
A49

Design: 7c, inscribed "Services Collectifs".
Issued to publicize the UN program for housing and urban
development, and in connection with the expert committee
meeting at UN headquarters, Feb. 7-21.
Printed by Harrison and Sons, Ltd., London, England. Panes
of 50. Designed by Olav Mathiesen.

1962, Feb. 28   Photo.   Unwmk.   Perf. 14½x14
Central design multicolored
100 A49 4c bright blue (2,204,190)   .20   .20
        First day cover   1.00
        Inscription block of 4   .35
    a. Black omitted   200.00
    b. Yellow omitted   —
    c. Brown omitted   —
101 A49 7c orange brown (1,845,821)   .20   .20
        First day cover   1.00
        First day cover, #100-101   1.25
        Inscription block of 4   .65
    a. Red omitted   —
    b. Black omitted   —
    c. Gold omitted   —
    First day covers of Nos. 100-101 total 466,178.

"The World Against
Malaria" — A50

Issued in honor of the World Health Organization and to call attention to the international campaign to eradicate malaria from the world.

Printed by Harrison and Sons, Ltd., London, England. Panes of 50. Designed by Rashid-ud Din.

1962, Mar. 30   Photo.   Unwmk.   *Perf. 14x14½*
Word frame in gray

102	A50	4c	**orange, yellow, brown, green & black** *(2,047,000)*	.20 .20
			First day cover	1.00
			Inscription block of 4	.35
103	A50	11c	**green, yellow, brown & indigo** *(1,683,766)*	.25 .20
			First day cover	1.00
			First day cover, #102-103	1.50
			Inscription block of 4	1.10 —

First day covers of Nos. 102-103 total 522,450.

"Peace" — A51

UN Flag — A52

Hands Combining "UN" and Globe — A53

UN Emblem over Globe — A54

Printed by Harrison & Sons, Ltd. London, England (1c, 3c and 11c), and by Canadian Bank Note Co., Ltd., Ottawa (5c). Panes of 50. Designed by Kurt Plowitz (1c), Ole Hamann (3c), Renato Ferrini (5c) and Olav Mathiesen (11c).

Photo.; Engr. (5c)

1962, May 25   Unwmk.   *Perf. 14x14½*

104	A51	1c	**vermilion, blue, black & gray** *(5,000,000)*	.20 .20
			First day cover	1.00
			Inscription block of 4	.25
105	A52	3c	**light green, Prussian blue, yellow & gray** *(5,000,000)*	.20 .20
			First day cover	1.00
			Inscription block of 4	.25

Perf. 12

106	A53	5c	**dark carmine rose** *(4,000,000)*	.20 .20
			First day cover	1.00
			Inscription block of 4	.65

Perf. 12½

107	A54	11c	**dark & light blue & gold** *(4,400,000)*	.25 .20
			First day cover	1.00
			First day cover, #104-107	6.00
			Inscription block of 4	1.10 —
			Nos. 104-107 (4)	.85 .80

First day covers of Nos. 104-107 total 738,985.
Size of 5c, No. 106: 36½x23½mm.
See No. 167. See UN Offices in Geneva Nos. 2 and 6.

Flag at Half-mast and UN Headquarters — A55

World Map Showing Congo — A56

Issued on the 1st anniversary of the death of Dag Hammarskjold, Secretary General of the United Nations 1953-61, in memory of those who died in the service of the United Nations.

Printed by Courvoisier S. A., La Chaux-de-Fonds, Switzerland. Panes of 50. Designed by Ole Hamann.

1962, Sept. 17   Photo.   Unwmk.   *Perf. 11½*

108	A55	5c	**black, light blue & blue** *(2,195,707)*	.20 .20
			First day cover	1.00
			Inscription block of 4	.50
109	A55	15c	**black, gray olive & blue** *(1,155,047)*	.20 .20
			First day cover	1.00
			First day cover, #108-109	2.00
			Inscription block of 4	.85

First day covers of Nos. 108-109 total 513,963.

1962, Oct. 24   Photo.   Unwmk.   *Perf. 11½*

Design: 11c inscribed "Operation des Nations Unies au Congo."

Issued to commemorate the United Nations Operation in the Congo.

Printed by Courvoisier S. A., La Chaux-de-Fonds, Switzerland. Panes of 50. Designed by George Hamori.

110	A56	4c	**olive, orange, black & yellow** *(1,477,958)*	.20 .20
			First day cover	1.00
			Inscription block of 4	.50
111	A56	11c	**blue green, orange, black & yellow** *(1,171,255)*	.20 .20
			First day cover	1.00
			First day cover, #110-111	1.75
			Inscription block of 4	.95

First day covers of Nos. 110-111 total 460,675.

Globe in Universe and Palm Frond — A57

Development Decade Emblem — A58

Design: 4c, English inscription.
Issued to honor the Committee on Peaceful Uses of Outer Space.

Printed by Bradbury, Wilkinson and Co., Ltd., England. Panes of 50. Designed by Kurt Plowitz.

1962, Dec. 3   Engr.   Unwmk.   *Perf. 14x13½*

112	A57	4c	**violet blue** *(2,263,876)*	.20 .20
			First day cover	1.00
			Inscription block of 4	.35
113	A57	11c	**rose claret** *(1,681,584)*	.25 .20
			First day cover	1.00
			First day cover, #112-113	2.00
			Inscription block of 4	1.25

First day covers of Nos. 112-113 total 529,780.

1963, Feb. 4   Photo.   Unwmk.   *Perf. 11½*

Design: 11c, French inscription.
UN Development Decade and UN Conference on the Application of Science and Technology for the Benefit of the Less Developed Areas, Geneva, Feb. 4-20.

Printed by Courvoisier S. A., La Chaux-de-Fonds, Switzerland. Panes of 50. Designed by Rashid-ud Din.

114	A58	5c	**pale green, maroon, dark blue & Prussian blue** *(1,802,406)*	.20 .20
			First day cover	1.00
			Inscription block of 4	.35

115	A58	11c	**yellow, maroon, dark blue & Prussian blue** *(1,530,190)*	.20 .20
			First day cover	1.00
			First day cover, #114-115	1.50
			Inscription block of 4	.90

First day covers of Nos. 114-115 total 460,877.

Stalks of Wheat — A59

Design: 11c, French inscription.
Issued for the "Freedom from Hunger" campaign of the Food and Agriculture Organization.

Printed by Courvoisier S. A., La Chaux-de-Fonds, Switzerland. Panes of 50. Designed by Ole Hamann.

1963, Mar. 22   Photo.   Unwmk.   *Perf. 11½*

116	A59	5c	**vermilion, green & yellow** *(1,666,178)*	.20 .20
			First day cover	1.00
			Inscription block of 4	.35 —
117	A59	11c	**vermilion, deep claret & yellow** *(1,563,023)*	.25 .20
			First day cover	1.00
			First day cover, #116-117	1.50
			Inscription block of 4	1.10 —

First day covers of Nos. 116-117 total 461,868.

Bridge over Map of New Guinea — A60

1st anniversary of the United Nations Temporary Executive Authority (UNTEA) in West New Guinea (West Irian).

Printed by Courvoisier S.A., La Chaux-de-Fonds, Switzerland. Panes of 50. Designed by Henry Bencsath.

1963, Oct. 1   Photo.   Unwmk.   *Perf. 11½*

118	A60	25c	**blue, green & gray** *(1,427,747)*	.50 .30
			First day cover *(222,280)*	1.00
			Inscription block of 4	2.25 —

General Assembly Building, New York — A61

Design: 11c, French inscription.
Since October 1955 all sessions of the General Assembly have been held in the General Assembly Hall, UN Headquarters, NY.

Printed by the Government Printing Bureau, Tokyo. Panes of 50. Designed by Kurt Plowitz.

1963, Nov. 4   Photo.   Unwmk.   *Perf. 13*

119	A61	5c	**violet blue, blue, yellow green & red** *(1,892,539)*	.20 .20
			First day cover	1.00
			Inscription block of 4	.35 —
120	A61	11c	**green, yellow green, blue, yellow & red** *(1,435,079)*	.20 .20
			First day cover	1.00
			First day cover, #119-120	1.25
			Inscription block of 4	.85 —

First day covers of Nos. 119-120 total 410,306.

Flame — A62

Design: 11c inscribed "15e Anniversaire."
15th anniversary of the signing of the Universal Declaration of Human Rights.
Printed by the Government Printing Bureau, Tokyo. Panes of 50. Designed by Rashid-ud Din.

1963, Dec. 10   Photo.   Unwmk.   Perf. 13
121 A62 5c green, gold, red & yellow
    (2,208,008)   .20 .20
  First day cover 1.00
  Inscription block of 4 .55
122 A62 11c carmine, gold, blue & yellow
    (1,501,125)   .20 .20
  First day cover 1.00
  First day cover, #121-122 1.00
  Inscription block of 4 .70

First day covers of Nos. 121-122 total 567,907.

Ships at Sea and IMCO Emblem — A63

Design: 11c, inscribed "OMCI."
Issued to honor the Intergovernmental Maritime Consultative Organization.
Printed by Courvoisier S.A., La Chaux-de-Fonds, Switzerland. Panes of 50. Designed by Henry Bencsath; emblem by Olav Mathiesen.

1964, Jan. 13   Photo.   Unwmk.   Perf. 11½
123 A63 5c blue, olive, ocher & yellow
    (1,805,750)   .20 .20
  First day cover 1.00
  Inscription block of 4 .35
124 A63 11c dark blue, dark green, emerald & yellow (1,583,848) .20 .20
  First day cover 1.00
  First day cover, #123-124 1.00
  Inscription block of 4 .85

First day covers of Nos. 123-124 total 442,696.

World Map, Sinusoidal Projection — A64

UN Emblem — A65

Three Men United Before Globe — A66

Stylized Globe and Weather Vane — A67

Printed by Thomas De La Rue & Co. Ltd., London (2c) and Courvoisier S.A., La Chaux-de-Fonds, Switzerland (7c, 10c and 50c). Panes of 50.
Designed by Ole Hamann (2c), George Hamori (7c, 10c) and Hatim El Mekki (50c).

1964-71   Photo.   Unwmk.   Perf. 14
125 A64 2c light & dark blue, orange & yellow green (3,800,000) .20 .20
  First day cover 1.00
  Inscription block of 4 .20
 a. Perf. 13x13½, Feb. 24, 1971 (1,500,000) .20 .20

Perf. 11½
126 A65 7c dark blue, orange brown & black
    (2,700,000)   .20 .20
  First day cover 1.00

  Inscription block of 4 .80
127 A66 10c blue green, olive green & black
    (3,200,000)   .20 .25
  First day cover 1.00
  First day cover, #125-127 5.00
  Inscription block of 4 .80
128 A67 50c multicolored (2,520,000) .75 .45
  First day cover (210,713) 1.00
  Inscription block of 4 3.75
  Nos. 125-128 (4) 1.35 1.10

Issue dates: 50c, Mar. 6; 2c, 7c, 10c, May 29, 1964.
First day covers of 2c, 7c and 10c total 524,073.
See UN Offices in Geneva Nos. 3 and 12.

Arrows Showing Global Flow of Trade — A68

Design: 5c, English inscription.
Issued to commemorate the UN Conference on Trade and Development, Geneva, Mar. 23-June 15.
Printed by Thomas De La Rue & Co., Ltd., London. Panes of 50. Designed by Herbert M. Sanborn and Ole Hamann.

1964, June 15   Photo.   Unwmk.   Perf. 13
129 A68 5c black, red & yellow (1,791,211) .20 .20
  First day cover 1.00
  Inscription block of 4 .35
130 A68 11c black, olive & yellow (1,529,526) .20 .20
  First day cover 1.00
  First day cover, #129-130 1.50
  Inscription block of 4 .85

First day covers of Nos. 129-130 total 422,358.

Poppy Capsule and Reaching Hands — A69

Design: 11c, Inscribed "Echec au Stupéfiants."
Issued to honor international efforts and achievements in the control of narcotics.
Printed by the Canadian Bank Note Co., Ottawa. Panes of 50. Designed by Kurt Plowitz.

1964, Sept. 21   Engr.   Unwmk.   Perf. 12
131 A69 5c rose red & black (1,508,999) .20 .20
  First day cover 1.00
  Inscription block of 4 .45
132 A69 11c emerald & black (1,340,691) .20 .20
  First day cover 1.00
  First day cover, #131-132 1.75
  Inscription block of 4 1.10

First day covers of Nos. 131-132 total 445,274.

Padlocked Atomic Blast — A70

Education for Progress — A71

Signing of the nuclear test ban treaty pledging an end to nuclear explosions in the atmosphere, outer space and under water.
Printed by Artia, Prague, Czechoslovakia. Panes of 50. Designed by Ole Hamann.

Litho. and Engr.
1964, Oct. 23   Unwmk.   Perf. 11x11½
133 A70 5c dark red & dark brown (2,422,789) .20 .20
  First day cover (298,652) 1.00
  Inscription block of 4 .45

1964, Dec. 7   Photo.   Unwmk.   Perf. 12½
Design: 11c, French inscription.
Issued to publicize the UNESCO world campaign for universal literacy and for free compulsory primary education.
Printed by Courvoisier, S. A., La Chaux-de-Fonds, Switzerland. Panes of 50. Designed by Kurt Plowitz.

134 A71 4c orange, red, bister, green & blue
    (2,375,181)   .20 .20
  First day cover 1.00
  Inscription block of 4 .40
135 A71 5c bister, red, dark & light blue
    (2,496,877)   .20 .20
  First day cover 1.00
  Inscription block of 4 .50
136 A71 11c green, light blue, black & rose
    (1,773,645)   .20 .20
  First day cover 1.00
  First day cover, #134-136 1.25
  Inscription block of 4 1.25
  Nos. 134-136 (3) .60 .60

First day covers of Nos. 134-136 total 727,875.

Progress Chart of Special Fund, Key and Globe — A72

UN Emblem, Stylized Leaves and View of Cyprus — A73

Design: 11c, French inscription.
Issued to publicize the Special Fund program to speed economic growth and social advancement in low-income countries.
Printed by the Government Printing Bureau, Tokyo. Panes of 50. Designed by Rashid-ud Din, Pakistan.

1965, Jan. 25   Photo.   Unwmk.   Perf. 13½x13
137 A72 5c dull blue, dark blue, yellow & red
    (1,949,274)   .20 .20
  First day cover 1.00
  Inscription block of 4 .40
138 A72 11c yellow green, dark blue, yellow & red (1,690,908) .20 .20
  First day cover 1.00
  First day cover, #137-138 1.25
  Inscription block of 4 .85
 a. Black omitted (UN emblem on key)

First day covers of Nos. 137-138 total 490,608.

1965, Mar. 4   Photo.   Unwmk.   Perf. 11½
Design: 11c, French inscription.
Issued to honor the United Nations Peace-keeping Force on Cyprus.
Printed by Courvoisier S.A., Switzerland. Panes of 50. Designed by George Hamori, Australia.

139 A73 5c orange, olive & black (1,887,042) .20 .20
  First day cover 1.00
  Inscription block of 4 .40
140 A73 11c yellow green, blue green & black
    (1,691,767)   .20 .20
  First day cover 1.00
  First day cover, #139-140 1.25
  Inscription block of 4 .80

First day covers of Nos. 139-140 total 438,059.

"From Semaphore to Satellite" — A74

Design: 11c, French inscription.
Centenary of the International Telecommunication Union.
Printed by Courvoisier S.A., Switzerland. Panes of 50.
Designed by Kurt Plowitz, United States.

1965, May 17   Photo.   Unwmk.   Perf. 11½
141 A74 5c **aquamarine, orange, blue & purple**
            (2,432,407)   .20 .20
         First day cover   1.00
         Inscription block of 4   .40   —
142 A74 11c **light violet, red orange, bister &**
            bright green (1,731,070)   .20 .20
         First day cover   1.00
         First day cover, #141-142   1.25
         Inscription block of 4   .80   —

First day covers of Nos. 141-142 total 434,393.

ICY Emblem — A75

Design: 15c, French inscription.
20th anniversary of the United Nations and International
Cooperation Year.
Printed by Bradbury, Wilkinson and Co., Ltd., England. Panes
of 50. Designed by Olav Mathiesen, Denmark.

1965, June 26   Engr.   Unwmk.   Perf. 14x13½
143 A75 5c **dark blue** (2,282,452)   .20 .20
         First day cover   1.00
         Inscription block of 4   .40   —
144 A75 15c **lilac rose** (1,993,562)   .20 .20
         First day cover   1.00
         First day cover, #143-144   1.00
         Inscription block of 4   1.00   —

Souvenir Sheet
145 A75 Sheet of two (1,928,366)   .35 .35
         First day cover   1.00

No. 145 contains one each of Nos. 143-144 with dark blue
and ocher marginal inscription, ocher edging. Size: 92x70mm.
First day covers of Nos. 143-145 total: New York, 748,876;
San Francisco, 301,435.

"Peace" — A76

Opening Words, UN
Charter — A77

UN Headquarters and
Emblem — A78

UN Emblem — A79

UN Emblem
Encircled — A80

Printed by Government Printing Bureau, Tokyo (1c); Govern-
ment Printing Office, Austria (15c, 20c); Government Printing
Office (Bundesdruckerei), Berlin (25c), and Courvoisier S.A.,
Switzerland ($1). Panes of 50.

Designed by Kurt Plowitz US (1c); Olav S. Mathiesen, Denmark (15c); Vergniaud Pierre-Noel, US (20c); Rashid-ud Din,
Pakistan (25c), and Ole Hamann, Denmark ($1).

1965-66   Photo.   Unwmk.   Perf. 13½x13
146 A76 1c **vermilion, blue, black & gray**
            (7,000,000)   .20 .20
         First day cover   1.00
         Inscription block of 4   .20   —

Perf. 14
147 A77 15c **olive bister, dull yellow, black &**
            deep claret (2,500,000)   .25 .20
         First day cover   1.00
         Inscription block of 4   1.10   —

Perf. 12
148 A78 20c **dark blue, blue, red & yellow**
            (3,000,000)   .30 .25
         First day cover   1.00
         First day cover, #147-148   1.25
         Inscription block of 4   1.25   —
   a.   Yellow omitted   —

Litho. and Embossed
Perf. 14
149 A79 25c **light & dark blue** (3,200,000) .35 .30
         First day cover   1.25
         First day cover, #146, 149   1.50
         Inscription block of 4   1.50   —
         Inscription block of 6,
            "Bundesdruckerei Berlin" imprint   20.00
         First day cover, "Bundesdrucker-
            ei," margin block of 6   32.50
   a.   Tagged (Berlin printing)   10.00 10.00

Photo.
Perf. 11½
150 A80 $1 **aquamarine & sapphire**
            (2,570,000)   1.75 1.60
         First day cover (181,510)   2.00
         Inscription block of 4   7.75   —
         Nos. 146-150 (5)   2.85 2.55

Issued: 1c, 25c, Sept. 20, 1965; 15c, 20c, Oct. 25, 1965; $1,
Mar. 25, 1966.
First day covers of Nos. 146 and 149 total 443,964. Those of
Nos. 147-148 total 457,596.
The 25c has the marginal inscription (UN emblem and
"1965") in two sizes: 1st printing (with Bundesdruckerei imprint),
6mm in diameter; 2nd printing, 8mm. In 1st printing, "halo" of
UN emblem is larger, overlapping "25c."
See UN Offices in Geneva Nos. 5, 9 and 11.

Fields and
People — A81

Globe and Flags of UN
Members — A82

Design: 11c, French inscription.
Issued to emphasize the importance of the world's population
growth and its problems and to call attention to population
trends and development.
Printed by Government Printing Office, Austria. Panes of 50.
Designed by Olav S. Mathiesen, Denmark.

1965, Nov. 29   Photo.   Unwmk.   Perf. 12
151 A81 4c **multicolored** (1,966,033)   .20 .20
         First day cover   1.00
         Inscription block of 4   .25   —
152 A81 5c **multicolored** (2,298,731)   .20 .20
         First day cover   1.00
         Inscription block of 4   .30   —
153 A81 11c **multicolored** (1,557,589)   .20 .20
         First day cover   1.00
         First day cover, #151-153   1.75
         Inscription block of 4   .90   —
         Nos. 151-153 (3)   .60 .60

First day covers of Nos. 151-153 total 710,507.

1966, Jan. 31   Photo.   Unwmk.   Perf. 11½
Design: 15c, French inscription.
Issued to honor the World Federation of United Nations
Associations.

Printed by Courvoisier S.A., Switzerland. Panes of 50.
Designed by Olav S. Mathiesen, Denmark.

154 A82 5c **multicolored** (2,462,215)   .20 .20
         First day cover   1.00
         Inscription block of 4   .35   —
155 A82 15c **multicolored** (1,643,661)   .20 .20
         First day cover   1.00
         First day cover, #154-155   1.25
         Inscription block of 4   .90   —

First day covers of Nos. 154-155 total 474,154.

WHO Headquarters,
Geneva — A83

Design: 11c, French inscription.
Issued to commemorate the opening of the World Health
Organization Headquarters, Geneva.
Printed by Courvoisier, S.A., Switzerland. Panes of 50.
Designed by Rashid-ud Din.

1966, May 26   Photo.   Perf. 12½x12
Granite Paper
156 A83 5c **lt & dk blue, orange, green & bis-**
            ter (2,079,893)   .20 .20
         First day cover   1.00
         Inscription block of 4   .45   —
157 A83 11c **orange, lt & dark blue, green &**
            bister (1,879,879)   .20 .20
         First day cover   1.00
         First day cover, #156-157   1.25
         Inscription block of 4   .90   —

First day covers of Nos. 156-157 total 466,171.

Coffee — A84

UN Observer — A85

Design: 11c, Spanish inscription.
Issued to commemorate the International Coffee Agreement
of 1962.
Printed by the Government Printing Bureau, Tokyo. Panes of
50. Designed by Rashid-ud Din, Pakistan.

1966, Sept. 19   Photo.   Perf. 13½x13
158 A84 5c **orange, lt blue, green, red & dk**
            brown (2,020,308)   .20 .20
         First day cover   1.00
         Inscription block of 4   .40   —
159 A84 11c **lt blue, yellow, green, red & dk**
            brown (1,888,682)   .20 .20
         First day cover   1.00
         First day cover, #158-159   1.00
         Inscription block of 4   .90   —

First day covers of Nos. 158-159 total 435,886.

1966, Oct. 24   Photo.   Perf. 11½
Issued to honor the Peace Keeping United Nation Observers.
Printed by Courvoisier, S.A. Panes of 50. Designed by Ole S.
Hamann.

Granite Paper
160 A85 15c **steel blue, orange, black & green**
            (1,889,809)   .25 .20
         First day cover (255,326)   1.00
         Inscription block of 4   1.40   —

Children of Various Races — A86

Designs: 5c, Children riding in locomotive and tender. 11c, Children in open railroad car playing medical team (French inscription).

20th anniversary of the United Nations Children's Fund (UNICEF).

Printed by Thomas De La Rue & Co., Ltd. Panes of 50. Designed by Kurt Plowitz.

1966, Nov. 28   Litho.   Perf. 13x13½

161	A86	4c	pink & multi (2,334,989)	.20 .20
			First day cover	1.00
			Inscription block of 4	.30 —
162	A86	5c	pale green & multi (2,746,941)	.20 .20
			First day cover	1.00
			Inscription block of 4	.35 —
a.			Yellow omitted	— —
163	A86	11c	light ultramarine & multi (2,123,841)	.20 .20
			First day cover	1.00
			First day cover, #161-163	1.00
			Inscription block of 4	.85 —
b.			Dark blue omitted	—
			Nos. 161-163 (3)	.60 .60

First day covers of Nos. 161-163 total 987,271.

Hand Rolling up Sleeve and Chart Showing Progress — A87

Design: 11c, French inscription.

United Nations Development Program.

Printed by Courvoisier, S.A. Panes of 50. Designed by Olav S. Mathiesen.

1967, Jan. 23   Photo.   Perf. 12½

164	A87	5c	green, yellow, purple & orange (2,204,679)	.20 .20
			First day cover	1.00
			Inscription block of 4	.35 —
165	A87	11c	blue, chocolate, light green & orange (1,946,159)	.20 .20
			First day cover	1.00
			First day cover, #164-165	1.00
			Inscription block of 4	1.00 —

First day covers of Nos. 164-165 total 406,011.

Type of 1962 and

UN Headquarters, NY, and World Map — A88

Printed by Courvoisier, S.A. Panes of 50. Designed by Jozsef Vertel, Hungary (1½c); Renato Ferrini, Italy (5c).

1967   Photo.   Perf. 11½

166	A88	1½c	ultramarine, black, orange & ocher (4,000,000)	.20 .20
			First day cover (199,751)	1.00
			Inscription block of 4	.20 —

Size: 33x23mm

167	A53	5c	red brown, brown & orange yellow (5,500,000)	.20 .20
			First day cover (212,544)	1.00
			Inscription block of 4	.40 —

Issue dates: 1½c, Mar. 17; 5c, Jan. 23.
For 5c of type A88, see UN Offices in Geneva No. 1.

Fireworks — A89

Design: 11c, French inscription.

Issued to honor all nations which gained independence since 1945.

Printed by Harrison & Sons, Ltd. Panes of 50. Designed by Rashid-ud Din.

1967, Mar. 17   Photo.   Perf. 14x14½

168	A89	5c	dark blue & multi (2,445,955)	.20 .20
			First day cover	1.00
			Inscription block of 4	.35 —
169	A89	11c	brown lake & multi (2,011,004)	.20 .20
			First day cover	1.00
			First day cover, #168-169	1.00
			Inscription block of 4	.85 —

First day covers of Nos. 168-169 total 390,499.

"Peace" — A90

UN Pavilion, EXPO '67 — A91

Designs: 5c, Justice. 10c, Fraternity. 15c, Truth.

EXPO '67, International Exhibition, Montreal, Apr. 28-Oct. 27, 1967.

Under special agreement with the Canadian Government Nos. 170-174 were valid for postage only on mail posted at the UN pavilion during the Fair. The denominations are expressed in Canadian currency.

Printed by British American Bank Note Co., Ltd., Ottawa. The 8c was designed by Olav S. Mathiesen after a photograph by Michael Drummond. The others were adapted by Ole S. Hamann from reliefs by Ernest Cormier on doors of General Assembly Hall, presented to UN by Canada.

1967, Apr. 28   Engr. & Litho.   Perf. 11

170	A90	4c	red & red brown (2,464,813)	.20 .20
			First day cover	1.00
			Inscription block of 4	.30 —
171	A90	5c	blue & red brown (2,177,073)	.20 .20
			First day cover	1.00
			Inscription block of 4	.30 —

Litho.

172	A91	8c	multicolored (2,285,440)	.20 .20
			First day cover	1.00
			Inscription block of 4	.50 —

Engr. and Litho.

173	A90	10c	green & red brown (1,955,352)	.20 .20
			First day cover	1.00
			Inscription block of 4	.75 —
174	A90	15c	dark brown & red brown (1,899,185)	.20 .20
			First day cover	1.00
			First day cover, #170-174	1.25
			Inscription block of 4	.85 —
			Nos. 170-174 (5)	1.00 1.00

First day covers of Nos. 170-174 total 901,625.

Luggage Tags and UN Emblem A92

Issued to publicize International Tourist Year, 1967.

Printed by Government Printing Office, Berlin. Panes of 50. Designed by David Dewhurst.

1967, June 19   Litho.   Perf. 14

175	A92	5c	reddish brown & multi (2,593,782)	.20 .20
			First day cover	1.00
			Inscription block of 4	.35 —
176	A92	15c	ultramarine & multi (1,940,457)	.25 .20
			First day cover	1.00
			First day cover, #175-176	1.25
			Inscription block of 4	1.10 —

First day covers of Nos. 175-176 total 382,886.

Quotation from Isaiah 2:4 — A93

Design: 13c, French inscription.

Issued to publicize the UN General Assembly's resolutions on general and complete disarmament and for suspension of nuclear and thermonuclear tests.

Printed by Heraclio Fournier S.A., Spain. Panes of 50. Designed by Ole Hamann.

1967, Oct. 24   Photo.   Perf. 14

177	A93	6c	ultramarine, yellow, gray & brown (2,462,277)	.20 .20
			First day cover	1.00
			Inscription block of 4	.45 —
178	A93	13c	magenta, yellow, gray & brown (2,055,541)	.20 .20
			First day cover	1.00
			First day cover, #177-178	1.00
			Inscription block of 4	.95 —

First day covers of Nos. 177-178 total 403,414.

Art at UN Issue
Miniature Sheet

Stained Glass Memorial Window by Marc Chagall, at UN Headquarters — A94

"The Kiss of Peace" by Marc Chagall — A95

Printed by Joh. Enschede and Sons, Netherlands. No. 180 issued in panes of 50. Design adapted by Ole Hamann from photograph by Hans Lippmann.

Sizes: a, 41x46mm. b, 24x46mm. c, 41x33½mm. d, 36x33½mm. e, 29x33½mm. f, 41½x47mm.

1967, Nov. 17 — Litho. — *Rouletted 9*

179 A94 6c Sheet of 6, #a.-f. *(3,178,656)* .40 .40
First day cover 1.00

Perf. 13x13½

180 A95 6c **multicolored** *(3,438,497)* .20 .20
First day cover 1.00
Inscription block of 4 .50 —

No. 179 contains six 6c stamps, each rouletted on 3 sides, imperf. on fourth side. Size: 124x80mm. On Nos. 179a-179c, "United Nations 6c" appears at top; on Nos. 179d-179f, at bottom. No. 179f includes name "Marc Chagall."

First day covers of Nos. 179-180 total 617,225.

Globe and Major UN Organs — A96

Statue by Henrik Starcke — A97

Design: 13c, French inscriptions.

Issued to honor the United Nations Secretariat.

Printed by Courvoisier, S. A., Switzerland. Panes of 50. Designed by Rashid-ud Din.

1968, Jan. 16 — Photo. — *Perf. 11½*

181 A96 6c **multicolored** *(2,772,965)* .20 .20
First day cover 1.00
Inscription block of 4 .40 —
182 A96 13c **multicolored** *(2,461,992)* .20 .20
First day cover 1.00
First day cover, #181-182 1.00
Inscription block of 4 1.00 —

First day covers of Nos. 181-182 total 411,119.

Art at UN Issue

The 6c is part of the "Art at the UN" series. The 75c belongs to the regular definitive series. The teakwood Starcke statue, which stands in the Trusteeship Council Chamber, represents mankind's search for freedom and happiness.

Printed by Courvoisier, S.A., Switzerland. Panes of 50.

1968, Mar. 1 — Photo. — *Perf. 11½*

183 A97 6c **blue & multi** *(2,537,320)* .20 .20
First day cover 1.00
Inscription block of 4 .50 —
184 A97 75c **rose lake & multi** *(2,300,000)* 1.10 .90
First day cover 1.25
First day cover, #183-184 5.00
Inscription block of 4 5.00 —

First day covers of Nos. 183-184 total 413,286.

See UN Offices in Geneva No. 13.

Factories and Chart — A98

UN Headquarters — A99

Design: 13c, French inscription ("ONUDI," etc.).

Issued to publicize the UN Industrial Development Organization.

Printed by Canadian Bank Note Co., Ltd., Ottawa. Panes of 50. Designed by Ole Hamann.

1968, Apr. 18 — Litho. — *Perf. 12*

185 A98 6c **greenish blue, lt greenish blue, black & dull claret** *(2,439,656)* .20 .20
First day cover 1.00
Inscription block of 4 .35 —
186 A98 13c **dull red brown, light red brown, black & ultra** *(2,192,453)* .20 .20
First day cover 1.00
First day cover, #185-186 1.00
Inscription block of 4 .80 —

First day covers of Nos. 185-186 total 396,447.

1968, May 31 — Litho. — *Perf. 12x13½*

Printed by Aspioti Elka-Chrome Mines, Ltd., Athens. Panes of 50. Designed by Olav S. Mathiesen.

187 A99 6c **green, blue, black & gray** *(4,000,000)* .20 .20
First day cover *(241,179)* 1.00
Inscription block of 4 .50 —

Radarscope and Globe — A100

Design: 20c, French inscription.

Issued to publicize World Weather Watch, a new weather system directed by the World Meteorological Organization.

Printed by the Government Printing Bureau, Tokyo. Designed by George A. Gundersen and George Fanais, Canada.

1968, Sept. 19 — Photo. — *Perf. 13x13½*

188 A100 6c **green, black, ocher, red & blue** *(2,245,078)* .20 .20
First day cover 1.00
Inscription block of 4 .40 —
189 A100 20c **lilac, black, ocher, red & blue** *(2,069,966)* .30 .20
First day cover 1.00
First day cover, #188-189 1.25
Inscription block of 4 1.40 —

First day covers of Nos. 188-189 total 620,510.

Human Rights Flame — A101

Books and UN Emblem — A102

Design: 13c, French inscription.

Issued for International Human Rights Year, 1968.

Printed by Harrison & Sons, Ltd., England. Designed by Robert Perrot, France.

1968, Nov. 22 — Photo.; Foil Embossed — *Perf. 12½*

190 A101 6c **bright blue, deep ultra & gold** *(2,394,235)* .20 .20
First day cover 1.00
Inscription block of 4 .40 —
191 A101 13c **rose red, dark red & gold** *(2,284,838)* .20 .20
First day cover 1.00
First day cover, #190-191 1.00
Inscription block of 4 .85 —

First day covers of Nos. 190-191 total 519,012.

1969, Feb. 10 — Litho. — *Perf. 13½*

Design: 13c, French inscription in center, denomination panel at bottom.

United Nations Institute for Training and Research (UNITAR).

Printed by the Government Printing Bureau, Tokyo. Panes of 50. Designed by Olav S. Mathiesen.

192 A102 6c **yellow green & multi** *(2,436,559)* .20 .20
First day cover 1.00
Inscription block of 4 .35 —
193 A102 13c **bluish lilac & multi** *(1,935,151)* .25 .20
First day cover 1.00
First day cover, #192-193 1.00
Inscription block of 4 1.00 —

First day covers of Nos. 192-193 total 439,606.

UN Building, Santiago, Chile A103

Design: 15c, Spanish inscription.

The UN Building in Santiago, Chile, is the seat of the UN Economic Commission for Latin America and of the Latin American Institute for Economic and Social Planning.

Printed by Government Printing Office, Berlin. Panes of 50. Design by Ole Hamann, adapted from a photograph.

1969, Mar. 14 — Litho. — *Perf. 14*

194 A103 6c **light blue, violet blue & light green** *(2,543,992)* .20 .20
First day cover 1.00
Inscription block of 4 .35 —
195 A103 15c **pink, cream & red brown** *(2,030,733)* .25 .20
First day cover 1.00
First day cover, #194-195 1.00
Inscription block of 4 1.10 —

First day covers of Nos. 194-195 total 398,227.

"UN" and UN Emblem — A104

UN Emblem and Scales of — A105

Printed by Government Printing Bureau, Tokyo. Panes of 50. Designed by Leszek Holdanowicz and Marek Freudenreich, Poland.

1969, Mar. 14   Photo.   *Perf. 13½*

196	A104 13c **bright blue, black & gold**		
	(*4,000,000*)	.20	.20
	First day cover (*177,793*)		1.00
	Inscription block of 4	.90	—

See UN Offices in Geneva No. 7.

1969, Apr. 21   Photo.   *Perf. 11½*

Design: 13c, French inscription.
20th anniversary session of the UN International Law Commission.
Printed by Courvoisier S.A., Switzerland. Panes of 50. Designed by Robert Perrot, France.

Granite Paper

197	A105 6c **bright green, ultra & gold**	.20	.20
	First day cover		1.00
	Inscription block of 4	.40	—
198	A105 13c **crimson, lilac & gold** (*1,966,994*)	.20	.20
	First day cover		1.00
	First day cover, #197-198		1.00
	Inscription block of 4	.90	—

First day covers of Nos. 197-198 total 439,324.

Allegory of Labor, Emblems of UN and ILO — A106

Design: 20c, French inscription.
Printed by Government Printing Bureau, Tokyo. Panes of 50. Designed by Nejat M. Gur, Turkey.
Issued to publicize "Labor and Development" and to commemorate the 50th anniversary of the International Labor Organization.

1969, June 5   Photo.   *Perf. 13*

199	A106 6c **blue, deep blue, yellow & gold**		
	(*2,078,381*)	.20	.20
	First day cover		1.00
	Inscription block of 4	.40	—
200	A106 20c **orange vermilion, magenta, yellow & gold** (*1,751,100*)	.25	.25
	First day cover		1.00
	First day cover, #199-200		1.25
	Inscription block of 4	1.40	—

First day covers of Nos. 199-200 total 514,155.

Art at UN Issue

Ostrich, Tunisian Mosaic, 3rd Century — A107

Design: 13c, Pheasant; French inscription.
The mosaic "The Four Seasons and the Genius of the Year" was found at Haidra, Tunisia. It is now at the Delegates' North Lounge, UN Headquarters, New York.
Printed by Heraclio Fournier, S. A., Spain. Panes of 50. Designed by Olav S. Mathiesen.

1969, Nov. 21   Photo.   *Perf. 14*

201	A107 6c **blue & multi** (*2,280,702*)	.20	.20
	First day cover		1.00
	Inscription block of 4	.35	—
202	A107 13c **red & multi** (*1,918,554*)	.20	.20
	First day cover		1.00
	First day cover, #201-202		1.00
	Inscription block of 4	.90	—

First day covers of Nos. 201-202 total 612,981.

Art at UN Issue

Peace Bell, Gift of Japanese — A108

Design: 25c, French inscription.
The Peace Bell was a gift of the people of Japan in 1954, cast from donated coins and metals. It is housed in a Japanese cypress structure at UN Headquarters, New York.
Printed by Government Printing Bureau, Tokyo. Panes of 50. Designed by Ole Hamann.

1970, Mar. 13   Photo.   *Perf. 13½x13*

203	A108 6c **violet blue & multi** (*2,604,253*)	.20	.20
	First day cover		1.00
	Inscription block of 4	.40	—
204	A108 25c **claret & multi** (*2,090,185*)	.35	.25
	First day cover		1.25
	First day cover, #203-204		1.25
	Inscription block of 4	1.75	—

First day covers of Nos. 203-204 total 502,384.

Mekong River, Power Lines and Map of Mekong Delta — A109

Design: 13c, French inscription.
Issued to publicize the Lower Mekong Basin Development project under UN auspices.
Printed by Heraclio Fournier, S.A., Spain. Panes of 50. Designed by Ole Hamann.

1970, Mar. 13   *Perf. 14*

205	A109 6c **dark blue & multi** (*2,207,309*)	.20	.20
	First day cover		1.00
	Inscription block of 4	.35	—
206	A109 13c **deep plum & multi** (*1,889,023*)	.20	.20
	First day cover		1.00
	First day cover, #205-206		1.00
	Inscription block of 4	.90	—

First day covers of Nos. 205-206 total 522,218.

"Fight Cancer" — A110

Design: 13c, French inscription.
Issued to publicize the fight against cancer in connection with the 10th International Cancer Congress of the International Union Against Cancer, Houston, Texas, May 22-29.
Printed by Government Printing Office, Berlin. Panes of 50. Designed by Leonard Mitchell.

1970, May 22   Litho.   *Perf. 14*

207	A110 6c **blue & black** (*2,157,742*)	.20	.20
	First day cover		1.00
	Inscription block of 4	.35	—
208	A110 13c **olive & black** (*1,824,714*)	.20	.20
	First day cover		1.00
	First day cover, #207-208		1.00
	Inscription block of 4	.85	—

First day covers of Nos. 207-208 total 444,449.

UN Emblem and Olive Branch — A111

UN Emblem — A112

Design: 13c, French inscription.
25th anniv. of the UN. First day covers were postmarked at UN Headquarters, NY, and at San Francisco.
Printed by Courvoisier, S.A., Switzerland. Designed by Ole Hamann and Olav S. Mathiesen (souvenir sheet).

1970, June 26   Photo.   *Perf. 11½*

209	A111 6c **red, gold, dark & light blue**		
	(*2,365,229*)	.20	.20
	First day cover		1.00
	Inscription block of 4	.35	—
210	A111 13c **dark blue, gold, green & red**		
	(*1,861,613*)	.20	.20
	First day cover		1.00
	Inscription block of 4	.80	—

Perf. 12½

211	A112 25c **dark blue, gold & light blue**		
	(*1,844,669*)	.35	.25
	First day cover		1.25
	First day cover, #209-211		1.50
	Inscription block of 4	1.50	—
	Nos. 209-211 (3)	.75	.65

Souvenir Sheet
Imperf

212	Sheet of 3 (*1,923,639*)	.75	.75
a.	A111 6c **red, gold & multicolored**	.20	.20
b.	A111 13c **violet blue, gold & multi**	.20	.20
c.	A112 25c **violet blue, gold & light blue**	.35	.35
	First day cover		1.25

No. 212 contains 3 imperf. stamps, gold border and violet blue marginal inscription. Size: 94½x78mm.
First day covers of Nos. 209-212 total: New York, 846,389; San Francisco, 471,100.

Scales, Olive Branch and Symbol of Progress — A113

Sea Bed, School of Fish and Underwater Research — A114

Design: 13c, French inscription.
Issued to publicize "Peace, Justice and Progress" in connection with the 25th anniversary of the United Nations.
Printed by Government Printing Bureau, Tokyo. Panes of 50. Designed by Ole Hamann.

1970, Nov. 20   Photo.   *Perf. 13½*

213	A113 6c **gold & multi** (*1,921,441*)	.20	.20
	First day cover		1.00
	Inscription block of 4	.40	—
214	A113 13c **silver & multi** (*1,663,669*)	.20	.20
	First day cover		1.00
	First day cover, #213-214		1.00
	Inscription block of 4	1.00	—

First day covers of Nos. 213-214 total 521,419.

1971, Jan. 25   Photo. & Engr.   *Perf. 13*

Issued to publicize peaceful uses of the sea bed.
Printed by Setelipaino, Finland. Panes of 50. Designed by Pentti Rahikainen, Finland.

215	A114 6c **blue & multi** (*2,354,179*)	.20	.20
	First day cover (*405,554*)		1.00
	Inscription block of 4	.50	—

See UN Offices in Geneva No. 15.

Refugees, Sculpture by Kaare K. Nygaard — A115

Wheat and Globe — A116

International support for refugees.
Printed by Joh. Enschede and Sons, Netherlands. Panes of 50. Designed by Dr. Kaare K. Nygaard and Martin J. Weber.

1971, Mar. 2   Litho.   Perf. 13x12½
216 A115 6c **brown, ocher & black** (2,247,232)   .20   .20
    First day cover   1.00
    Inscription block of 4   .30   —
217 A115 13c **ultramarine, greenish blue &**
    black (1,890,048)   .20   .20
    First day cover   1.00
    First day cover, #216-217   1.00
    Inscription block of 4   .90   —

  First day covers of Nos. 216-217 total 564,785.
  See UN Offices in Geneva No. 16.

1971, Apr. 13   Photo.   Perf. 14

Publicizing the UN World Food Program.
Printed by Heraclio Fournier, S.A., Spain. Panes of 50. Designed by Olav S. Mathiesen.

218 A116 13c **red & multicolored** (1,968,542)   .20   .20
    First day cover (409,404)   1.00
    Inscription block of 4   .90   —

    See UN Offices in Geneva No. 17.

UPU Headquarters, Bern — A117

Opening of new Universal Postal Union Headquarters, Bern. Printed by Courvoisier, S.A. Panes of 50. Designed by Olav S. Mathiesen.

1971, May 28   Photo.   Perf. 11½
219 A117 20c **brown orange & multi** (1,857,841)   .35   .25
    First day cover (375,119)   1.00
    Inscription block of 4   1.40   —

    See UN Offices in Geneva No. 18.

A118

"Eliminate Racial Discrimination" A119

International Year Against Racial Discrimination.
Printed by Government Printing Bureau, Tokyo. Panes of 50. Designers: Daniel Gonzague (8c); Ole Hamann (13c).

1971, Sept. 21   Photo.   Perf. 13½
220 A118 8c **yellow green & multi** (2,324,349)   .20   .20
    First day cover   1.00
    Inscription block of 4   .60   —
221 A119 13c **blue & multi** (1,852,093)   .20   .20
    First day cover   1.00
    First day cover, #220-221   1.00
    Inscription block of 4   .90   —

  First day covers of Nos. 220-221 total 461,103.
  See UN Offices in Geneva Nos. 19-20.

UN Headquarters, New York — A120

UN Emblem and Symbolic Flags — A121

No. 222 printed by Heraclio Fournier, S.A., Spain. No. 223 printed by Government Printing Bureau, Tokyo. Panes of 50. Designers: O. S. Mathiesen (8c); Robert Perrot (60c).

1971, Oct. 22   Photo.   Perf. 13½
222 A120 8c **violet blue & multi** (5,600,000)   .20   .20
    First day cover   1.00
    Inscription block of 4   .60   —

Perf. 13
223 A121 60c **ultra & multi** (3,500,000)+   .80   .80
    First day cover   1.25
    First day cover, #222-223   3.00
    Inscription block of 4   4.00   —

  First day covers of Nos. 222-223 total 336,013.

Maia, by Pablo Picasso — A122

To publicize the UN International School.
Printed by Courvoisier, S.A. Panes of 50. Designed by Ole Hamann.

1971, Nov. 19   Photo.   Perf. 11½
224 A122 8c **olive & multi** (2,668,214)   .20   .20
    First day cover   1.00
    Inscription block of 4   .45   —
225 A122 21c **ultra & multi** (2,040,754)   .30   .20
    First day cover   1.00
    First day cover, #224-225   1.75
    Inscription block of 4   1.50   —

  First day covers of Nos. 224-225 total 579,594.
  See UN Offices in Geneva No. 21.

Letter Changing Hands A123

Printed by Bundesdruckerei, Berlin. Panes of 50. Designed by Olav S. Mathiesen.

1972, Jan. 5   Litho.   Perf. 14
226 A123 95c **carmine & multi** (2,000,000)   1.30 1.10
    First day cover (188,193)   1.25
    Inscription block of 4   6.00   —

"No More Nuclear Weapons" A124

To promote non-proliferation of nuclear weapons.
Printed by Heraclio Fournier, S. A., Spain. Panes of 50. Designed by Arne Johnson, Norway.

1972, Feb. 14   Photo.   Perf. 13½x14
227 A124 8c **dull rose, black, blue & gray**
    (2,311,515)   .20   .20
    First day cover (268,789)   1.00
    Inscription block of 4   .55   —

    See UN Offices in Geneva No. 23.

Proportions of Man, by Leonardo da Vinci — A125

"Human Environment" — A126

World Health Day, Apr. 7.
Printed by Setelipaino, Finland. Panes of 50. Designed by George Hamori.

1972, Apr. 7   Litho. & Engr.   Perf. 13x13½
228 A125 15c **black & multi** (1,788,962)   .25   .20
    First day cover (322,724)   1.00
    Inscription block of 4   1.00   —

    See UN Offices in Geneva No. 24.

1972, June 5   Litho. & Embossed   Perf. 12½x14

UN Conf. on Human Environment, Stockholm, June 5-16, 1972.
Printed by Joh. Enschede and Sons, Netherlands. Panes of 50. Designed by Robert Perrot.

229 A126 8c **red, buff, green & blue**
    (2,124,604)   .20   .20
    First day cover   1.00
    Inscription block of 4   .50   —
230 A126 15c **blue green, buff, green & blue**
    (1,589,943)   .25   .20
    First day cover   1.00
    First day cover, #229-230   1.00
    Inscription block of 4   1.25   —

  First day covers of Nos. 229-230 total 437,222.
  See UN Offices in Geneva Nos. 25-26.

"Europe" and UN
Emblem — A127

The Five Continents by
José Maria Sert — A128

Economic Commission for Europe, 25th anniversary.
Printed by Government Printing Bureau, Tokyo. Panes of 50.
Designed by Angel Medina Medina.

1972, Sept. 11   **Litho.**   **Perf. 13x13½**
231 A127 21c yellow brown & multi (1,748,675) .35 .25
    First day cover (271,128) 1.00
    Inscription block of 4 1.60 —

See UN Offices in Geneva No. 27.

Art at UN Issue

Design shows part of ceiling mural of the Council Hall, Palais des Nations, Geneva. It depicts the five continents joining in space.
Printed by Courvoisier, S. A. Panes of 50. Designed by Ole Hamann.

1972, Nov. 17   **Photo.**   **Perf. 12x12½**
232 A128 8c gold, brown & golden brown
    (2,573,478) .20 .20
    First day cover 1.00
    Inscription block of 4 .50 —
233 A128 15c gold, blue green & brown
    (1,768,432) .30 .25
    First day cover 1.00
    First day cover, #232-233 1.00
    Inscription block of 4 1.25 —

First day covers of Nos. 232-233 total 589,817.
See UN Offices in Geneva Nos. 28-29.

Olive Branch and
Broken
Sword — A129

Poppy Capsule and
Skull — A130

Disarmament Decade, 1970-79.
Printed by Ajans-Turk, Turkey. Panes of 50. Designed by Kurt Plowitz.

1973, Mar. 9   **Litho.**   **Perf. 13½x13**
234 A129 8c blue & multi (2,272,716) .20 .20
    First day cover 1.00
    Inscription block of 4 .50 —
235 A129 15c lilac rose & multi (1,643,712) .35 .25
    First day cover 1.00
    First day cover, #234-235 1.00
    Inscription block of 4 1.50 —

First day covers of Nos. 234-235 total 548,336.
See UN Offices in Geneva Nos. 30-31.

1973, Apr. 13   **Photo.**   **Perf. 13½**
Fight against drug abuse.
Printed by Heraclio Fournier, S.A., Spain. Panes of 50. Designed by George Hamori.

236 A130 8c deep orange & multi (1,846,780) .20 .20
    First day cover 1.00
    Inscription block of 4 .60 —
237 A130 15c pink & multi (1,466,806) .35 .25

    First day cover 1.00
    First day cover, #236-237 1.00
    Inscription block of 4 1.50 —

First day covers of Nos. 236-237 total 394,468.
See UN Offices in Geneva No. 32.

Honeycomb — A131

5th anniversary of the United Nations Volunteer Program.
Designed by Courvoisier, S.A.

1973, May 25   **Photo.**   **Perf. 14**
238 A131 8c olive bister & multi (1,868,176) .20 .20
    First day cover 1.00
    Inscription block of 4 .50 —
239 A131 21c gray blue & multi (1,530,114) .35 .25
    First day cover 1.00
    First day cover, #238-239 1.25
    Inscription block of 4 1.50 —

First day covers of Nos. 238-239 total 396,517.
See UN Offices in Geneva No. 33.

Map of Africa with
Namibia — A132

To publicize Namibia (South-West Africa) for which the UN General Assembly ended the mandate of South Africa and established the UN Council for Namibia to administer the territory until independence.
Printed by Heraclio Fournier, S.A., Spain. Panes of 50. Designed by George Hamori.

1973, Oct. 1   **Photo.**   **Perf. 14**
240 A132 8c emerald & multi (1,775,260) .20 .20
    First day cover 1.00
    Inscription block of 4 .50 —
241 A132 15c bright rose & multi (1,687,782) .35 .25
    First day cover 1.00
    First day cover, #240-241 1.00
    Inscription block of 4 1.50 —

First day covers of Nos. 240-241 total 385,292.
See UN Offices in Geneva No. 34.

UN Emblem and
Human Rights
Flame — A133

25th anniversary of the adoption and proclamation of the Universal Declaration of Human Rights.
Printed by Government Printing Bureau, Tokyo. Panes of 50. Designed by Alfred Guerra.

1973, Nov. 16   **Photo.**   **Perf. 13½**
242 A133 8c deep carmine & multi (2,026,245) .20 .20
    First day cover 1.00
    Inscription block of 4 .50 —
243 A133 21c blue green & multi (1,558,201) .35 .25
    First day cover 1.00
    First day cover, #242-243 1.25
    Inscription block of 4 1.50 —

First day covers of Nos. 242-243 total 398,511.
See UN Offices in Geneva Nos. 35-36.

ILO Headquarters,
Geneva — A134

New Headquarters of International Labor Organization.
Printed by Heraclio Fournier, S.A., Spain. Panes of 50. Designed by Henry Bencsath.

1974, Jan. 11   **Photo.**   **Perf. 14**
244 A134 10c ultra & multi (1,734,423) .20 .20
    First day cover 1.00
    Inscription block of 4 .90 —
245 A134 21c blue green & multi (1,264,447) .35 .25
    First day cover 1.00
    First day cover, #244-245 1.25
    Inscription block of 4 1.75 —

First day covers of Nos. 244-245 total 282,284.
See UN Offices in Geneva Nos. 37-38.

UPU Emblem
and Post Horn
Encircling
Globe — A135

Centenary of Universal Postal Union.
Printed by Ashton-Potter Ltd., Canada. Panes of 50. Designed by Arne Johnson.

1974, Mar. 22   **Litho.**   **Perf. 12½**
246 A135 10c gold & multi (2,104,919) .25 .20
    First day cover (342,774) 1.00
    Inscription block of 4 1.10 —

See UN Offices in Geneva Nos. 39-40.

Art at UN Issue

Peace Mural, by
Candido
Portinari — A136

The mural, a gift of Brazil, is in the Delegates' Lobby, General Assembly Building.
Printed by Heraclio Fournier, S.A., Spain. Panes of 50. Design adapted by Ole Hamann.

1974, May 6   **Photo.**   **Perf. 14**
247 A136 10c gold & multi (1,769,342) .20 .20
    First day cover 1.00
    Inscription block of 4 .75 —
248 A136 18c ultra & multi (1,477,500) .40 .30
    First day cover 1.00
    First day cover, #247-248 1.25
    Inscription block of 4 1.50 —

First day covers of Nos. 247-248 total 271,440.
See UN Offices in Geneva Nos. 41-42.

Dove and UN
Emblem — A137

UN
Headquarters — A138

Globe, UN Emblem,
Flags — A139

Printed by Heraclio Fournier, S.A., Spain. Panes of 50.
Designed by Nejut M. Gur (2c); Olav S. Mathiesen (10c); Henry Bencsath (18c).

1974, June 10   Photo.   *Perf. 14*
249 A137 2c dark & light blue *(6,900,000)* .20 .20
First day cover 1.00
Inscription block of 4 .25
250 A138 10c multicolored *(4,000,000)* .20 .20
First day cover 1.00
Inscription block of 4 .70
251 A139 18c multicolored *(2,300,000)* .30 .20
First day cover 1.00
First day cover, #249-251 1.25
Inscription block of 4 1.50 —
Nos. 249-251 (3) .70 .60
First day covers of Nos. 249-251 total 307,402.
+ Printing orders to Feb. 1990.

Children of the World — A140   Law of the Sea — A141

World Population Year
Printed by Heraclio Fournier, S.A., Spain. Panes of 50. Designed by Henry Bencsath.

1974, Oct. 18   Photo.   *Perf. 14*
252 A140 10c light blue & multi *(1,762,595)* .20 .20
First day cover 1.00
Inscription block of 4 1.00
253 A140 18c lilac & multi *(1,321,574)* .40 .25
First day cover 1.00
First day cover, #252-253 1.25
Inscription block of 4 1.75
First day covers of Nos. 253-254 total 354,306.
See UN Offices in Geneva Nos. 43-44.

1974, Nov. 22   Photo.   *Perf. 14*
Declaration of UN General Assembly that the sea bed is common heritage of mankind, reserved for peaceful purposes.
Printed by Heraclio Fournier, S.A., Spain. Panes of 50. Designed by Asher Kalderon.
254 A141 10c green & multi *(1,621,328)* .20 .20
First day cover 1.00
Inscription block of 4 .80
255 A141 26c orange red & multi *(1,293,084)* .40 .30
First day cover 1.25
First day cover, #254-255 1.40
Inscription block of 4 1.90 —
First day covers of Nos. 254-255 total 280,686.
See UN Offices in Geneva No. 45.

Satellite and Globe — A142

Peaceful uses (meteorology, industry, fishing, communications) of outer space.
Printed by Setelipaino, Finland. Panes of 50. Designed by Henry Bencsath.

1975, Mar. 14   Litho.   *Perf. 13*
256 A142 10c multicolored *(1,681,115)* .20 .20
First day cover 1.00
Inscription block of 4 .85
257 A142 26c multicolored *(1,463,130)* .40 .30
First day cover 1.25
First day cover, #256-257 1.40
Inscription block of 4 1.75
First day covers of Nos. 256-257 total 330,316.
See UN Offices in Geneva Nos. 46-47.

Equality Between Men and Women — A143

UN Flag and "XXX" — A144

International Women's Year
Printed by Questa Colour Security Printers, Ltd., England. Panes of 50. Designed by Asher Kalderon and Esther Kurti.

1975, May 9   Litho.   *Perf. 15*
258 A143 10c multicolored *(1,402,542)* .20 .20
First day cover 1.00
Inscription block of 4 .80
259 A143 18c multicolored *(1,182,321)* .40 .30
First day cover 1.00
First day cover, #258-259 1.25
Inscription block of 4 1.75
First day covers of Nos. 258-259 total 285,466.
See UN Offices in Geneva Nos. 48-49.

1975, June 26   Litho.   *Perf. 13*
30th anniversary of the United Nations.
Printed by Ashton-Potter, Ltd., Canada. Nos. 260-261 panes of 50. Stamps designed by Asher Calderon, sheets by Olav S. Mathiesen.
260 A144 10c olive bister & multi *(1,904,545)* .20 .20
First day cover 1.00
Inscription block of 4 .70
261 A144 26c purple & multi *(1,547,766)* .50 .35
First day cover 1.25
First day cover, #260-261 1.40
Inscription block of 4 2.25

Souvenir Sheet
Imperf
262 Sheet of 2 *(1,196,578)* .65 .50
a. A144 10c olive bister & multicolored .20 .20
b. A144 26c purple & multicolored .40 .25
First day cover 1.25
No. 262 has blue and bister margin with inscription and UN emblem.
First day covers of Nos. 260-262 total: New York 477,912; San Francisco, 237,159.
See Offices in Geneva Nos. 50-52.

Hand Reaching up over Map of Africa and Namibia — A145   Wild Rose Growing from Barbed Wire — A146

"Namibia-United Nations direct responsibility." See note after No. 241.
Printed by Heraclio Fournier S.A., Spain. Panes of 50. Designed by Henry Bencsath.

1975, Sept. 22   Photo.   *Perf. 13½*
263 A145 10c multicolored *(1,354,374)* .20 .20
First day cover 1.00
Inscription block of 4 .80
264 A145 18c multicolored *(1,243,157)* .35 .30
First day cover 1.00
First day cover, #263-264 1.25
Inscription block of 4 1.60
First day covers of Nos. 263-264 total 281,631.
See UN Offices in Geneva Nos. 53-54.

1975, Nov. 21   Engr.   *Perf. 12½*
United Nations Peace-keeping Operations
Printed by Setelipaino, Finland. Panes of 50. Designed by Mrs. Eeva Oivo.
265 A146 13c ultramarine *(1,628,039)* .25 .20
First day cover 1.00
Inscription block of 4 1.00
266 A146 26c rose carmine *(1,195,580)* .50 .40

First day cover 1.25
First day cover, #265-266 1.40
Inscription block of 4 2.00
First day covers of Nos. 265-266 total 303,711.
See UN Offices in Geneva Nos. 55-56.

Symbolic Flags Forming Dove — A147   UN Emblem — A149

People of All Races A148

United Nations Flag — A150   Dove and Rainbow — A151

Printed by Ashton-Potter, Ltd., Canada (3c, 4c, 30c, 50c), and Questa Colour Security Printers, Ltd., England (9c). Panes of 50.
Designed by Waldemar Andrzesewski (3c); Arne Johnson (4c); George Hamori (9c, 30c); Arthur Congdon (50c).

1976   Litho.   *Perf. 13x13½, 13½x13*
267 A147 3c multicolored *(4,000,000)* .20 .20
First day cover 1.00
Inscription block of 4 .30
268 A148 4c multicolored *(4,000,000)* .20 .20
First day cover 1.00
Inscription block of 4 .35
Photo.
Perf. 14
269 A149 9c multicolored *(3,270,000)+* .20 .20
First day cover 1.00
Inscription block of 4 .65
Litho.
Perf. 13x13½
270 A150 30c blue, emerald & black *(2,500,000)* .40 .35
First day cover 2.00
Inscription block of 4 2.00
271 A151 50c yellow green & multi *(2,000,000)* .70 .65
First day cover 1.25
First day cover, #267-268, 270-271 1.50
Inscription block of 4 3.75
Nos. 267-271 (5) 1.70 1.60
Issue dates: 3c, 4c, 30c, 50c, Jan. 6; 9c, Nov. 19.
First day covers of Nos. 267-268, 270-271 total 355,165; of Nos. 269 and 280 total 366,556.
See UN Offices in Vienna No. 8.

Interlocking Bands and UN Emblem — A152

13c United Nations

World Federation of United Nations Associations.
Printed by Heraclio Fournier, S.A., Spain. Panes of 50. Designed by George Hamori.

1976, Mar. 12   Photo.   Perf. 14
272 A152 13c blue, green & black *(1,331,556)*   .20   .20
 First day cover   1.00
 Inscription block of 4   .80   —
273 A152 26c green & multi *(1,050,145)*   .35   .30
 First day cover   1.25
 First day cover, #272-273   1.25
 Inscription block of 4   1.60   —

First day covers of Nos. 272-273 total 300,775.
See UN Offices in Geneva No. 57.

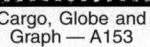

Cargo, Globe and Graph — A153

Houses Around Globe — A154

UN Conference on Trade and Development (UNCTAD), Nairobi, Kenya, May 1976.
Printed by Courvoisier, S.A. Panes of 50. Designed by Henry Bencsath.

1976, Apr. 23   Photo.   Perf. 11½
274 A153 13c deep magenta & multi *(1,317,900)*   .20   .20
 First day cover   1.00
 Inscription block of 4   .80   —
275 A153 31c dull blue & multi *(1,216,959)*   .40   .30
 First day cover   1.25
 First day cover, #274-275   1.40
 Inscription block of 4   2.00   —

First day covers of Nos. 274-275 total 234,657.
See UN Offices in Geneva No. 58.

1976, May 28   Photo.   Perf. 14
Habitat, UN Conference on Human Settlements, Vancouver, Canada, May 31-June 11.
Printed by Heraclio Fournier, S.A., Spain. Panes of 50. Designed by Eliezer Weishoff.

276 A154 13c red brown & multi *(1,346,589)*   .20   .20
 First day cover   1.00
 Inscription block of 4   .75   —
277 A154 25c green & multi *(1,057,924)*   .40   .30
 First day cover   1.25
 First day cover, #276-277   1.40
 Inscription block of 4   1.75   —

First day covers of Nos. 276-277 total 232,754.
See UN Offices in Geneva Nos. 59-60.

Magnifying Glass, Sheet of Stamps, UN Emblem — A155

13¢ UNITED NATIONS

Grain — A156

United Nations Postal Administration, 25th anniversary.
Printed by Courvoisier, S.A. Designed by Henry Bencsath.

1976, Oct. 8   Photo.   Perf. 11½
278 A155 13c blue & multi *(1,996,309)*   .20   .20
 First day cover   1.00
 Inscription block of 4   .90   —
279 A155 31c green & multi *(1,767,465)*   1.40 1.40
 First day cover   2.00
 First day cover, #278-279   2.50
 Inscription block of 4   6.25   —
 Panes of 20, #278-279   27.50   —

First day covers of Nos. 278-279 total 366,784.
Upper margin blocks are inscribed "XXV ANNIVERSARY"; lower margin blocks "UNITED NATIONS POSTAL ADMINISTRATIONS."
See UN Offices in Geneva Nos. 61-62.

1976, Nov. 19   Litho.   Perf. 14½
World Food Council.
Printed by Questa Colour Security Printers, Ltd., England. Panes of 50. Designed by Eliezer Weishoff.

280 A156 13c multicolored *(1,515,573)*   .25   .20
 First day cover   1.00
 Inscription block of 4   1.10   —

See UN Offices in Geneva No. 63.

WIPO Headquarters, Geneva A157

World Intellectual Property Organization (WIPO).
Printed by Heraclio Fournier, S. A., Spain. Panes of 50. Designed by Eliezer Weishoff.

1977, Mar. 11   Photo.   Perf. 14
281 A157 13c citron & multi *(1,330,272)*   .20   .20
 First day cover   1.00
 Inscription block of 4   .75   —
282 A157 31c bright green & multi *(1,115,406)*   .45   .35
 First day cover   1.25
 First day cover, #281-282   1.25
 Inscription block of 4   2.00   —

First day covers of Nos. 281-282 total 364,184.
See UN Offices in Geneva No. 64.

Drops of Water Falling into Funnel — A158

UN Water Conference, Mar del Plata, Argentina, Mar. 14-25.
Printed by Government Printing Bureau, Tokyo. Panes of 50. Designed by Elio Tomei.

1977, Apr. 22   Photo.   Perf. 13½x13
283 A158 13c yellow & multi *(1,317,536)*   .20   .20
 First day cover   1.00
 Inscription block of 4   .75   —
284 A158 25c salmon & multi *(1,077,424)*   .45   .35
 First day cover   1.25
 First day cover, #283-284   1.40
 Inscription block of 4   2.00   —

First day covers of Nos. 283-284 total 321,585.
See UN Offices in Geneva Nos. 65-66.

Burning Fuse Severed — A159

UN Security Council.
Printed by Heraclio Fournier, S.A., Spain. Panes of 50. Designed by Witold Janowski and Marek Freudenreich.

1977, May 27   Photo.   Perf. 14
285 A159 13c purple & multi *(1,321,527)*   .20   .20
 First day cover   1.00
 Inscription block of 4   .75   —
286 A159 31c dark blue & multi *(1,137,195)*   .45   .30
 First day cover   1.25
 First day cover, #285-286   1.40
 Inscription block of 4   2.00   —

First day covers of Nos. 285-286 total 309,610.
See UN Offices in Geneva Nos. 67-68.

"Combat Racism" — A160

United Nations 13c

Fight against racial discrimination.
Printed by Setelipaino, Finland. Panes of 50. Designed by Bruno K. Wiese.

1977, Sept. 19   Litho.   Perf. 13½x13
287 A160 13c black & yellow *(1,195,739)*   .20   .20
 First day cover   1.00
 Inscription block of 4   .75   —
288 A160 25c black & vermilion *(1,074,639)*   .40   .30
 First day cover   1.25
 First day cover, #287-288   1.40
 Inscription block of 4   1.75   —

First day covers of Nos. 287-288 total 356,193.
See UN Offices in Geneva Nos. 60-70.

Atom, Grain, Fruit and Factory — A161

Peaceful uses of atomic energy.
Printed by Heraclio Fournier, S.A., Spain. Panes of 50. Designed by Henry Bencsath.

1977, Nov. 18   Photo.   Perf. 14
289 A161 13c yellow bister & multi *(1,316,473)*   .20   .20
 First day cover   1.00
 Inscription block of 4   .90   —
290 A161 18c dull green & multi *(1,072,246)*   .35   .25
 First day cover   1.00
 First day cover, #289-290   1.25
 Inscription block of 4   1.50   —

First day covers of Nos. 289-290 total 325,348.
See UN Offices in Geneva Nos. 71-72.

Opening Words of UN Charter — A162

"Live Together in Peace" — A163

People of the World — A164

Printed by Questa Colour Security Printers, United Kingdom. Panes of 50. Designed by Salahattin Kanidinc (1c); Elio Tomei (25c); Paula Schmidt ($1).

1978, Jan. 27   Litho.   Perf. 14½

291	A162	1c	gold, brown & red (4,800,000)+	.20	.20
			First day cover		1.00
			Inscription block of 4	.25	—
292	A163	25c	multicolored (3,000,000)+	.35	.30
			First day cover		1.25
			Inscription block of 4	1.50	—
293	A164	$1	multicolored (3,400,000)+	1.25	1.25
			First day cover		1.50
			First day cover, #291-293		1.75
			Inscription block of 4	5.50	—
			Nos. 291-293 (3)	1.80	1.75

+ Printing orders to Sept. 1989.
First day covers of Nos. 291-293 total 264,782.
See UN Offices in Geneva No. 73.

Smallpox Virus — A165

Global eradication of smallpox.
Printed by Courvoisier, S.A. Panes of 50. Designed by Herbert Auchli.

1978, Mar. 31   Photo.   Perf. 12x11½

294	A165	13c	rose & black (1,188,239)	.20	.20
			First day cover		1.00
			Inscription block of 4	.75	—
295	A165	31c	blue & black (1,058,688)	.45	.40
			First day cover		1.25
			First day cover, #294-295		1.40
			Inscription block of 4	2.00	—

First day covers of Nos. 294-295 total 306,626.
See UN Offices in Geneva Nos. 74-75.

Open Handcuff — A166

Multicolored Bands and Clouds — A167

Liberation, justice and cooperation for Namibia.
Printed by Government Printing Office, Austria. Panes of 50. Designed by Cafiro Tomei.

1978, May 5   Photo.   Perf. 12

296	A166	13c	multicolored (1,203,079)	.20	.20
			First day cover		1.00
			Inscription block of 4	1.00	—
297	A166	18c	multicolored (1,066,738)	.30	.25
			First day cover		1.00
			First day cover, #296-297		1.25
			Inscription block of 4	1.40	—

First day covers of Nos. 296-297 total 324,471.
See UN Offices in Geneva No. 76.

1978, June 12   Photo.   Perf. 14

International Civil Aviation Organization for "Safety in the Air." Printed by Heraclio Fournier, S.A., Spain. Panes of 50. Designed by Cemalettin Mutver.

298	A167	13c	multicolored (1,295,617)	.20	.20
			First day cover		1.00
			Inscription block of 4	.85	—
299	A167	25c	multicolored (1,101,256)	.40	.30
			First day cover		1.25
			First day cover, #298-299		1.40
			Inscription block of 4	1.75	—

First day covers of Nos. 298-299 total 329,995.
See UN Offices in Geneva Nos. 77-78.

General Assembly — A168

Printed by Government Printing Bureau, Tokyo. Panes of 50. Designed by Jozsef Vertel.

1978, Sept. 15   Photo.   Perf. 13½

300	A168	13c	multicolored (1,093,005)	.20	.20
			First day cover		1.00
			Inscription block of 4	1.00	—
301	A168	18c	multicolored (1,065,934)	.35	.30
			First day cover		1.00
			First day cover, #300-301		1.25
			Inscription block of 4	1.50	—

First day covers of Nos. 300-301 total 283,220.
See UN Offices in Geneva Nos. 79-80.

Hemispheres as Cogwheels A169

Technical Cooperation Among Developing Countries Conference, Buenos Aires, Argentina, Sept. 1978.
Printed by Heraclio Fournier, S.A., Spain. Panes of 50. Designed by Simon Keter and David Pesach.

1978, Nov. 17   Photo.   Perf. 14

302	A169	13c	multicolored (1,251,272)	.20	.20
			First day cover		1.00
			Inscription block of 4	1.00	—
303	A169	31c	multicolored (1,185,213)	.50	.40
			First day cover		1.25
			First day cover, #302-303		1.40
			Inscription block of 4	2.25	—

First day covers of Nos. 302-303 total 272,556.
See UN Offices in Geneva No. 81.

Hand Holding Olive Branch — A170

Various Races Tree — A171

Globe, Dove with Olive Branch — A172

Birds and Globe — A173

Printed by Heraclio Fournier, S.A., Spain. Panes of 50. Designed by Raymon Müller (5c); Alrun Fricke (14c); Eliezer Weishoff (15c); Young Sun Hahn (20c).

1979, Jan. 19   Photo.   Perf. 14

304	A170	5c	multicolored (3,000,000)	.20	.20
			First day cover		1.00
			Inscription block of 4	.35	—
305	A171	14c	multicolored (3,000,000)+	.20	.20
			First day cover		1.00
			Inscription block of 4	.90	—
306	A172	15c	multicolored (3,000,000)+	.30	.25
			First day cover		1.00
			Inscription block of 4	1.40	—
307	A173	20c	multicolored (3,400,000)+	.30	.25
			First day cover		1.00
			First day cover, #304-307		1.75
			Inscription block of 4	1.40	—
			Nos. 304-307 (4)	1.00	.90

First day covers of Nos. 304-307 total 295,927.
+ Printing orders to June 1990.

UNDRO Against Fire and Water — A174

Office of the UN Disaster Relief Coordinator (UNDRO). Printed by Heraclio Fournier, S.A., Spain. Panes of 50. Designed by Gidon Sagi.

1979, Mar. 9   Photo.   Perf. 14

308	A174	15c	multicolored (1,448,600)	.25	.20
			First day cover		1.00
			Inscription block of 4	1.00	—
309	A174	20c	multicolored (1,126,295)	.35	.30
			First day cover		1.25
			First day cover, #308-309		1.25
			Inscription block of 4	1.50	—

First day covers of Nos. 308-309 total 266,694.
See UN Offices in Geneva Nos. 82-83.

Child and IYC Emblem — A175

International Year of the Child.
Printed by Heraclio Fournier, S.A., Spain. Panes of 20 (5x4). Designed by Helena Matuszewska (15c) and Krystyna Tarkowska-Gruszecka (31c).

1979, May 4   Photo.   Perf. 14

310	A175	15c	multicolored (2,290,329)	.20	.20
			First day cover		1.00
			Inscription block of 4	1.00	—
311	A175	31c	multicolored (2,192,136)	.35	.35
			First day cover		1.25
			First day cover, #310-311		2.25
			Inscription block of 4	1.60	—
			Panes of 20, #310-311	13.00	

First day covers of Nos. 310-311 total 380,022.
See UN Offices in Geneva Nos. 84-85.

Map of Namibia, Olive Branch — A176

Scales and Sword of Justice — A177

For a free and independent Namibia.
Printed by Ashton-Potter Ltd., Canada. Panes of 50.
Designed by Eliezer Weishoff.

1979, Oct. 5   **Litho.**   **Perf. 13½**
312 A176 15c multicolored (1,470,231) .20 .20
     First day cover 1.00
     Inscription block of 4 .95 —
313 A176 31c multicolored (1,355,323) .40 .35
     First day cover 1.25
     First day cover, #312-313 1.50
     Inscription block of 4 1.75 —

    First day covers of Nos. 312-313 total 250,371.
    See UN Offices in Geneva No. 86.

1979, Nov. 9   **Litho.**   **Perf. 13x13½**
International Court of Justice, The Hague, Netherlands.
Printed by Setelipaino, Finland. Panes of 50. Designed by Henning Simon.

314 A177 15c multicolored (1,244,972) .20 .20
     First day cover 1.00
     Inscription block of 4 .85 —
315 A177 20c multicolored (1,084,483) .40 .35
     First day cover 1.00
     First day cover, #314-315 1.25
     Inscription block of 4 1.75 —

    First day covers of Nos. 314-315 total 322,901.
    See UN Offices in Geneva Nos. 87-88.

Graph of Economic Trends — A178

Key — A179

New International Economic Order.
Printed by Questa Colour Security Printers, United Kingdom.
Panes of 50. Designed by Cemalettin Mutver (15c), George Hamori (31c).

1980, Jan. 11   **Litho.**   **Perf. 15x14½**
316 A178 15c multicolored (1,163,801) .20 .20
     First day cover 1.00
     Inscription block of 4 .85 —
317 A179 31c multicolored (1,103,560) .50 .35
     First day cover 1.25
     First day cover, #316-317 1.40
     Inscription block of 4 2.25 —

    First day covers of Nos. 316-317 total 211,945.
    See UN Offices in Geneva No. 89; Vienna No. 7.

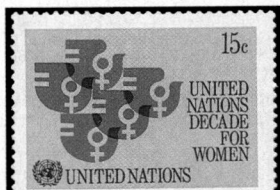

Women's Year Emblem — A180

United Nations Decade for Women.
Printed by Questa Colour Security Printers, United Kingdom.
Panes of 50. Designed by Susanne Rottenfusser.

1980, Mar. 7   **Litho.**   **Perf. 14½x15**
318 A180 15c multicolored (1,409,350) .20 .20
     First day cover 1.00
     Inscription block of 4 1.00 —
319 A180 20c multicolored (1,182,016) .30 .25

     First day cover 1.00
     First day cover, #318-319 1.25
     Inscription block of 4 2.00 —

    First day covers of Nos. 318-319 total 289,314.
    See UN Offices in Geneva Nos. 90-91; Vienna Nos. 9-10.

UN Emblem and "UN" on Helmet — A181

Arrows and UN Emblem — A182

United Nations Peace-keeping Operations.
Printed by Joh. Enschede en Zonen, Netherlands. Panes of 50. Designed by Bruno K. Wiese (15c), James Gardiner (31c)

1980, May 16   **Litho.**   **Perf. 14x13**
320 A181 15c blue & black (1,245,521) .25 .20
     First day cover 1.00
     Inscription block of 4 1.00 —
321 A182 31c multicolored (1,191,009) .40 .40
     First day cover 1.25
     First day cover, #320-321 1.40
     Inscription block of 4 2.25 —

    First day covers of Nos. 320-321 total 208,442.
    See UN Offices in Geneva No. 92; Vienna No. 11.

"35" and Flags — A183

Globe and Laurel — A184

35th Anniversary of the United Nations.
Printed by Ashton-Potter Ltd, Canada. Nos. 322-323, panes of 50. Designed by Cemalettin Matver (15c), Mian Mohammad Saeed (31c).

1980, June 26   **Litho.**   **Perf. 13x13½**
322 A183 15c multicolored (1,554,514) .20 .20
     First day cover 1.00
     Inscription block of 4 1.00 —
323 A184 31c multicolored (1,389,606) .40 .35
     First day cover 1.25
     First day cover, #322-323 1.40
     Inscription block of 4 2.00 —

Souvenir Sheet
Imperf
324   Sheet of 2 (1,215,505) .70 .60
 a.   A183 15c multicolored .20 .20
 b.   A184 31c multicolored .40 .40
     First day cover 1.25

    First day covers of Nos. 322-324 total: New York, 369,345; San Francisco, 203,701.
    See UN Offices in Geneva Nos. 93-95; Vienna Nos. 12-14.

Flag of Turkey — A185

Printed by Courvoisier, S.A., Switzerland. Panes of 16. Designed by Ole Hamann.

Each pane contains 4 blocks of 4 (Nos. 325-328, 329-332, 333-336, 337-340). A se-tenant block of 4 designs centers each pane.

1980, Sept. 26   **Litho.**   **Perf. 12**
Granite Paper
325 A185 15c shown (3,490,725) .20 .20
326 A185 15c Luxembourg (3,490,725) .20 .20
327 A185 15c Fiji (3,490,725) .20 .20
328 A185 15c Viet Nam (3,490,725) .20 .20
 a.   Se-tenant block of 4, #325-328 .80 .75
329 A185 15c Guinea (3,442,633) .20 .20
330 A185 15c Surinam (3,442,633) .20 .20
331 A185 15c Bangladesh (3,442,633) .20 .20
332 A185 15c Mali (3,442,633) .20 .20
 a.   Se-tenant block of 4, #329-332 .80 .75
333 A185 15c Yugoslavia (3,416,292) .20 .20
334 A185 15c France (3,416,292) .20 .20
335 A185 15c Venezuela (3,416,292) .20 .20
336 A185 15c El Salvador (3,416,292) .20 .20
 a.   Se-tenant block of 4, #333-336 .80 .75
337 A185 15c Madagascar (3,442,497) .20 .20
338 A185 15c Cameroon (3,442,497) .20 .20
339 A185 15c Rwanda (3,442,497) .20 .20
340 A185 15c Hungary (3,442,497) .20 .20
 a.   Se-tenant block of 4, #337-340 .80 .75
     First day covers of Nos. 325-340, each .45
     Set of 4 diff. panes of 16 8.00
     Nos. 325-340 (16) 3.20 3.20

    First day covers of Nos. 325-340 total 6,145,595.
    See Nos. 350-365, 374-389, 399-414, 425-440, 450-465, 477-492, 499-514, 528-543, 554-569, 690-697, 719-726, 744-751.

Symbolic Flowers — A186

Symbols of Progress — A187

Printed by Ashton-Potter Ltd., Canada. Panes of 50. Designed by Eliezer Weishoff (15c), Dietman Kowall (20c).

1980, Nov. 21   **Litho.**   **Perf. 13½x13**
341 A186 15c multicolored (1,192,165) .25 .25
     First day cover 1.00
     Inscription block of 4 1.25 —
342 A187 20c multicolored (1,011,382) .40 .35
     First day cover 1.00
     First day cover, #341-342 1.40
     Inscription block of 4 1.75 —

    First day covers of Nos. 341-342 total 232,149.
    See UN Offices in Geneva, Nos. 96-97; Vienna Nos. 15-16.

Inalienable Rights of the Palestinian People — A188

Printed by Courvoisier S.A., Switzerland. Panes of 50. Designed by David Dewhurst.

1981, Jan. 30   **Photo.**   **Perf. 12x11½**
343 A188 15c multicolored (993,489) .25 .20
     First day cover (127,187) 1.00
     Inscription block of 4 1.25 —

    See UN Offices in Geneva No. 98; Vienna No. 17.

Interlocking Puzzle
Pieces — A189

Stylized Person — A190

International Year of the Disabled.
Printed by Heraclio Fournier S.A., Spain. Panes of 50.
Designed by Sophia Van Heeswijk (20c) and G.P. Van der Hyde (35c).

1981, Mar. 6		**Photo.**	**Perf. 14**
344 A189 20c multicolored *(1,218,371)*		.25	.20
First day cover			1.00
Inscription block of 4		1.25	—
345 A190 35c black & orange *(1,107,298)*		.50	.45
First day cover			1.25
First day cover, #344-345			1.40
Inscription block of 4		2.25	—

First day covers of Nos. 344-345 total 204,891.
See UN Offices in Geneva Nos. 99-100; Vienna Nos. 18-19.

Desislava and
Sebastocrator Kaloyan,
Bulgarian Mural, 1259,
Boyana Church,
Sofia — A191

Art at UN Issue
Printed by Courvoisier. Panes of 50. Designed by Ole Hamann.

1981, Apr. 15		**Photo.**	**Perf. 11½**
		Granite Paper	
346 A191 20c multicolored *(1,252,648)*		.25	.25
First day cover			1.00
Inscription block of 4		1.40	—
347 A191 31c multicolored *(1,061,056)*		.45	.45
First day cover			1.25
First day cover, #346-347			1.40
Inscription block of 4		2.00	—

First day covers of Nos. 346-347 total 210,978.
See UN Offices in Geneva No. 101; Vienna No. 20.

Solar
Energy — A192

Conference
Emblem — A193

Conference on New and Renewable Sources of Energy, Nairobi, Aug. 10-21.
Printed by Setelipaino, Finland. Panes of 50. Designed by Ulrike Dreyer (20c); Robert Perrot (40c).

1981, May 29		**Litho.**	**Perf. 13**
348 A192 20c multicolored *(1,132,877)*		.30	.25
First day cover			1.00
Inscription block of 4		1.40	—
349 A193 40c multicolored *(1,158,319)*		.55	.50

First day cover		1.25
First day cover, #348-349		1.40
Inscription block of 4	2.50	—

First day covers of Nos. 348-349 total 240,205.
See UN Offices in Geneva No. 102; Vienna No. 21.

Flag Type of 1980

Printed by Courvoisier, S.A., Switzerland. Panes of 16. Designed by Ole Hamann.
Each pane contains 4 blocks of 4 (Nos. 350-353, 354-357, 358-361, 362-365). A se-tenant block of 4 designs centers each pane.

1981, Sept. 25			**Litho.**
		Granite Paper	
350 A185 20c Djibouti *(2,342,224)*		.25	.20
351 A185 20c Sri Lanka *(2,342,224)*		.25	.20
352 A185 20c Bolivia *(2,342,224)*		.25	.20
353 A185 20c Equatorial Guinea *(2,342,224)*		.25	.20
a. Se-tenant block of 4, #350-353		1.50	1.40
354 A185 20c Malta *(2,360,297)*		.25	.20
355 A185 20c Czechoslovakia *(2,360,297)*		.25	.20
356 A185 20c Thailand *(2,360,297)*		.25	.20
357 A185 20c Trinidad & Tobago *(2,360,297)*		.25	.20
a. Se-tenant block of 4, #354-357		1.50	1.40
358 A185 20c Ukrainian SSR *(2,344,755)*		.25	.20
359 A185 20c Kuwait *(2,344,755)*		.25	.20
360 A185 20c Sudan *(2,344,755)*		.25	.20
361 A185 20c Egypt *(2,344,755)*		.25	.20
a. Se-tenant block of 4, #358-361		1.50	1.40
362 A185 20c US *(2,450,537)*		.25	.20
363 A185 20c Singapore *(2,450,537)*		.25	.20
364 A185 20c Panama *(2,450,537)*		.25	.20
365 A185 20c Costa Rica *(2,450,537)*		.25	.20
a. Se-tenant block of 4, #362-365		1.50	1.40
First day covers, #350-365, each			.60
Set of 4 diff. panes of 16		11.50	
Nos. 350-365 (16)		4.00	3.20

First day covers of Nos. 350-365 total 3,961,237.

Seedling and Tree
Cross-section
A194

"10" and Symbols
of
Progress — A195

United Nations Volunteers Program, 10th anniv.
Printed by Walsall Security Printers, Ltd., United Kingdom.
Pane of 50. Designed by Gabriele Nussgen (18c), Angel Medina Medina (28c).

1981, Nov. 13			**Litho.**
366 A194 18c multicolored *(1,246,833)*		.30	.25
First day cover			1.00
Inscription block of 4		1.50	—
367 A195 28c multicolored *(1,282,868)*		.60	.55
First day cover			1.25
First day cover, #366-367			1.40
Inscription block of 4		2.75	—

First day covers of Nos. 366-367 total 221,106.
See UN Offices in Geneva Nos. 103-104; Vienna Nos. 22-23.

A196

A197

A198

Respect for Human Rights (17c), Independence of Colonial Countries and People (28c), Second Disarmament Decade (40c).
Printed by Courvoisier, S.A., Switzerland. Panes of 50. Designed by Rolf Christianson (17c); George Hamori (28c); Marek Kwiatkowski (40c).

1982, Jan. 22			**Perf. 11½x12**
368 A196 17c multicolored *(3,000,000)+*		.30	.25
First day cover			1.00
Inscription block of 4		1.25	—
369 A197 28c multicolored *(3,000,000)+*		.50	.40
First day cover			1.25
Inscription block of 4		2.25	—
370 A198 40c multicolored *(3,000,000)*		.80	.70
First day cover			1.25
First day cover, #368-370			1.25
Inscription block of 4		3.50	—
Nos. 368-370 (3)		1.60	1.35

First day covers of Nos. 368-370 total 243,073.

Sun and Hand Holding
Seedling — A199

Sun, Plant Land and
Water — A200

10th Anniversary of United Nations Environment Program.
Printed by Joh. Enschede En Zonen, Netherlands. Panes of 50. Designed by Philine Hartert (20c); Peer-Ulrich Bremer (40c).

1982, Mar. 19		**Litho.**	**Perf. 13½x13**
371 A199 20c multicolored *(1,017,117)*		.25	.25
First day cover			1.00
Inscription block of 4		1.25	—
372 A200 40c multicolored *(884,798)*		.70	.65
First day cover			1.25
First day cover, #371-372			1.40
Inscription block of 4		3.25	—

First day covers of Nos. 371-372 total 288,721.
See UN Offices in Geneva Nos. 107-108; Vienna Nos. 25-26.

UN Emblem and
Olive Branch in
Outer
Space — A201

Exploration and Peaceful Uses of Outer Space.
Printed By Enschede. Panes of 50. Designed by Wiktor C. Nerwinski.

1982, June 11		**Litho.**	**Perf. 13x13½**
373 A201 20c multicolored *(1,083,426)*		.55	.45
First day cover *(156,965)*			1.00
Inscription block of 4		2.40	—

See UN Offices in Geneva Nos. 109-110; Vienna No. 27.

Flag Type of 1980

Printed by Courvoisier. Panes of 16. Designed by Ole Hamann.
Issued in 4 panes of 16. Each pane contains 4 blocks of four (Nos. 374-377, 378-381, 383-385, 386-389). A se-tenant block of 4 designs centers each pane.

1982, Sept. 24   **Litho.**   *Perf. 12*
Granite Paper

374	A185	20c Austria *(2,314,006)*	.25	.20
375	A185	20c Malaysia *(2,314,006)*	.25	.20
376	A185	20c Seychelles *(2,314,006)*	.25	.20
377	A185	20c Ireland *(2,314,006)*	.25	.20
a.		Se-tenant block of 4, #374-377	1.50	1.40
378	A185	20c Mozambique *(2,300,958)*	.25	.20
379	A185	20c Albania *(2,300,958)*	.25	.20
380	A185	20c Dominica *(2,300,958)*	.25	.20
381	A185	20c Solomon Islnads *(2,300,958)*	.25	.20
a.		Se-tenant block of 4, #378-381	1.50	1.40
382	A185	20c Philippines *(2,288,589)*	.25	.20
383	A185	20c Swaziland *(2,288,589)*	.25	.20
384	A185	20c Nicaragua *(2,288,589)*	.25	.20
385	A185	20c Burma *(2,288,589)*	.25	.20
a.		Se-tenant block of 4, #382-385	1.50	1.40
386	A185	20c Cape Verde *(2,285,848)*	.25	.20
387	A185	20c Guyana *(2,285,848)*	.25	.20
388	A185	20c Belgium *(2,285,848)*	.25	.20
389	A185	20c Nigeria *(2,285,848)*	.25	.20
a.		Se-tenant block of 4, #386-389	1.50	1.40
		First day cover, #374-389, each		.75
		Set of 4 diff. panes of 16	14.00	
		Nos. 374-389 (16)	4.00	3.20

First day covers of Nos. 374-389 total 3,202,744.

Conservation and
Protection of
Nature — A202

Printed by Fournier. Panes of 50. Designed by Hamori.

1982, Nov. 19   **Photo.**   *Perf. 14*

390	A202	20c Leaf *(1,110,027)*	.35	.30
		First day cover		1.00
		margin block of 4, inscription	1.75	—
391	A202	28c Butterfly *(848,772)*	.60	.60
		First day cover		1.25
		First day cover, #390-391		1.40
		Inscription block of 4	2.50	—

First day covers of Nos. 390-391 total 214,148.
See UN Offices in Geneva Nos. 111-112; Vienna Nos. 28-29.

A203

A204

World Communications Year
Printed by Walsall. Panes of 50. Designed by Hanns Lohrer
(A203) and Lorena Berengo (A204).

1983, Jan. 28   **Litho.**   *Perf. 13*

392	A203	20c multicolored *(1,282,079)*	.25	.25
		First day cover		1.00
		Inscription block of 4	1.25	—
393	A204	40c multicolored *(931,903)*	.70	.65
		First day cover		1.25
		First day cover, #392-393		1.40
		Inscription block of 4	3.50	—

First day covers of Nos. 392-393 total 183,499.
See UN Offices in Geneva No. 113; Vienna No. 30.

A205

A206

Safety at Sea.
Printed by Questa. Panes of 50. Designed by Jean-Marie
Lenfant (A205), Ari Ron (A206).

1983, Mar. 18   **Litho.**   *Perf. 14½*

394	A205	20c multicolored *(1,252,456)*	.30	.25
		First day cover		1.00
		Inscription block of 4	1.50	
395	A206	37c multicolored *(939,910)*	.60	.55
		First day cover		1.25
		First day cover, #394-395		1.40
		Inscription block of 4	2.75	

First day covers of Nos. 394-395 total 199,962.
See UN Offices in Geneva Nos. 114-115; Vienna Nos. 31-32.

World Food
Program — A207

Printed by Government Printers Bureau, Japan. Designed by
Marek Kwiatkowski.

1983, Apr. 22   **Engr.**   *Perf. 13½*

396	A207	20c rose lake *(1,238,997)*	.35	.35
		First day cover *(180,704)*		1.00
		Inscription block of 4	1.60	—

See UN Offices in Geneva No. 116; Vienna Nos. 33-34.

A208

A209

UN Conference on Trade and Development.
Printed by Carl Uberreuter Druck and Verlag M. Salzer, Austria. Panes of 50. Designed by Dietmar Braklow (A208), Gabriel
Genz (A209).

1983, June 6   **Litho.**   *Perf. 14*

397	A208	20c multicolored *(1,060,053)*	.35	.35
		First day cover		1.10
		Inscription block of 4	1.50	—
398	A209	28c multicolored *(948,981)*	.70	.65
		First day cover		1.40
		First day cover, #397-398		1.50
		Inscription block of 4	2.90	—

First day covers of Nos. 397-398 total 200,131.
See UN Offices in Geneva Nos. 117-118; Vienna Nos. 35-36.

Flag Type of 1980

Printed by Courvoisier. Panes of 16. Designed by Ole
Hamann.
Issued in 4 panes of 16. Each pane contains 4 blocks of four
(Nos. 399-402, 403-406, 407-410, 411-414). A se-tenant block
of 4 designs centers each pane.

1983, Sept. 23   **Photo.**
Granite Paper   *Perf. 12*

399	A185	20c Great Britain *(2,490,599)*	.25	.20
400	A185	20c Barbados *(2,490,599)*	.25	.20
401	A185	20c Nepal *(2,490,599)*	.25	.20
402	A185	20c Israel *(2,490,599)*	.25	.20
a.		Se-tenant block of 4, #399-402	1.75	1.50
403	A185	20c Malawi *(2,483,010)*	.25	.20
404	A185	20c Byelorussian SSR *(2,483,010)*	.25	.20
405	A185	20c Jamaica *(2,483,010)*	.25	.20
406	A185	20c Kenya *(2,483,010)*	.25	.20
a.		Se-tenant block of 4, #403-406	1.75	1.50
407	A185	20c People's Republic of China *(2,474,140)*	.25	.20
408	A185	20c Peru *(2,474,140)*	.25	.20
409	A185	20c Bulgaria *(2,474,140)*	.25	.20
410	A185	20c Canada *(2,474,140)*	.25	.20
a.		Se-tenant block of 4, #407-410	1.75	1.50
411	A185	20c Somalia *(2,482,070)*	.25	.20
412	A185	20c Senegal *(2,482,070)*	.25	.20
413	A185	20c Brazil *(2,482,070)*	.25	.20
414	A185	20c Sweden *(2,482,070)*	.25	.20
a.		Se-tenant block of 4, #411-414	1.75	1.50
		First day cover, #399-414, each		.75
		Set of 4 diff. panes of 16	15.00	
		Nos. 399-414 (16)	4.00	3.20

First day covers of Nos. 399-414 total 2,214,134.

Window
Right — A210

Peace Treaty with
Nature — A211

35th Anniversary of the Universal Declaration of Human
Rights.
Printed by Government Printing Office, Austria. Panes of 16
(4x4). Designed by Friedensreich Hundertwasser, Austria.

1983, Dec. 9   **Photo. & Engr.**   *Perf. 13½*

415	A210	20c multicolored *(1,591,102)*	.30	.25
		First day cover		1.00
		Inscription block of 4	1.25	—
416	A211	40c multicolored *(1,566,789)*	.70	.65
		First day cover		1.25
		First day cover, #415-416		1.50
		Inscription block of 4	3.00	—
		Panes of 16, #415-416	16.00	

First day covers of Nos. 415-416 total 176,269.
See UN Offices in Geneva Nos. 119-120; Vienna Nos. 37-38.

International
Conference on
Population — A212

Printed by Bundesdruckerei, Federal Republic of Germany.
Panes of 50. Designed by Marina Langer-Rosa and Helmut
Langer, Federal Republic of Germany.

1984, Feb. 3   **Litho.**   *Perf. 14*

417	A212	20c multicolored *(905,320)*	.30	.25
		First day cover		1.00
		Inscription block of 4	1.40	—
418	A212	40c multicolored *(717,084)*	.65	.55
		First day cover		1.25
		First day cover, #417-418		1.40
		Inscription block of 4	2.50	—

First day covers of Nos. 417-418 total 118,068.
See UN Offices in Geneva No. 121; Vienna No. 39.

Tractor
Plowing
A213

Rice Paddy
A214

World Food Day, Oct. 16
Printed by Walsall Security Printers, Ltd., United Kingdom. Panes of 50. Designed by Adth Vanooijen, Netherlands.

1984, Mar. 15   Litho.   Perf. 14½
419 A213 20c **multicolored** (853,641)   .35   .30
       First day cover   1.25
       Inscription block of 4   1.60   —
420 A214 40c **multicolored** (727,165)   .65   .65
       First day cover   1.50
       First day cover, #419-420   1.75
       Inscription block of 4   2.75   —

First day covers of Nos. 419-420 total 116,009.
See UN Offices in Geneva Nos. 122-123; Vienna Nos. 40-41.

Grand
Canyon — A215

Ancient City of
Polonnaruwa, Sri
Lanka — A216

World Heritage
Printed by Harrison and Sons, United Kingdom. Panes of 50. Designs adapted by Rocco J. Callari, U.S., and Thomas Lee, China.

1984, Apr. 18   Litho.   Perf. 14
421 A215 20c **multicolored** (814,316)   .25   .20
       First day cover   1.00
       Inscription block of 4   1.10   —
422 A216 50c **multicolored** (579,136)   .75   .75
       First day cover   1.25
       First day cover, #421-422   1.40
       Inscription block of 4   3.50   —

First day covers of Nos. 421-422 total 112,036.
See Nos. 601-602, UN Offices in Geneva Nos. 124-125, 211-212; Vienna Nos. 42-43, 125-126.

A217   A218

Future for Refugees
Printed by Courvoisier. Panes of 50. Designed by Hans Erni, Switzerland.

1984, May 29   Photo.   Perf. 11½
423 A217 20c **multicolored** (956,743)   .35   .35
       First day cover   1.00
       Inscription block of 4   1.50   —
424 A218 50c **multicolored** (729,036)   1.00   .85
       First day cover   1.25
       First day cover, #423-424   1.40
       Inscription block of 4   4.25   —

First day covers of Nos. 423-424 total 115,789.
See UN Offices in Geneva Nos. 126-127; Vienna Nos. 44-45.

Flag Type of 1980

Printed by Courvoisier. Panes of 16. Designed by Ole Hamann.
Issued in 4 panes of 16. Each pane contains 4 blocks of four (Nos. 425-428, 429-432, 433-436, 437-440). A se-tenant block of 4 designs centers each pane.

1984, Sept. 21   Photo.   Perf. 12
Granite Paper
425 A185 20c Burundi (1,941,471)   .50   .45
426 A185 20c Pakistan (1,941,471)   .50   .45
427 A185 20c Benin (1,941,471)   .50   .45
428 A185 20c Italy (1,941,471)   .50   .45
  a.   Se-tenant block of 4, #425-428   2.75 2.50
429 A185 20c Tanzania (1,969,051)   .50   .45
430 A185 20c United Arab Emirates (1,969,051)   .50   .45
431 A185 20c Ecuador (1,969,051)   .50   .45
432 A185 20c Bahamas (1,969,051)   .50   .45
  a.   Se-tenant block of 4, #429-432   2.75 2.50
433 A185 20c Poland (2,001,091)   .50   .45
434 A185 20c Papua New Guinea (2,001,091)   .50   .45
435 A185 20c Uruguay (2,001,091)   .50   .45
436 A185 20c Chile (2,001,091)   .50   .45
  a.   Se-tenant block of 4, #433-436   2.75 2.50
437 A185 20c Paraguay (1,969,875)   .50   .45
438 A185 20c Bhutan (1,969,875)   .50   .45
439 A185 20c Central African Republic
                (1,969,875)   .50   .45
440 A185 20c Australia (1,969,875)   .50   .45
  a.   Se-tenant block of 4, #437-440   2.75 2.50
            First day cover, #425-440, each   1.00
            Set of 4 diff. panes of 16   27.50
            Nos. 425-440 (16)   8.00 7.20

First day covers of Nos. 425-440 total 1,914,972.

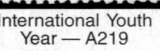

International Youth
Year — A219

ILO Turin
Center — A220

Printed by Waddingtons Ltd., United Kingdom. Panes of 50. Designed by Ramon Mueller, Federal Republic of Germany.

1984, Nov. 15   Litho.   Perf. 13½
441 A219 20c **multicolored** (884,962)   .40   .35
       First day cover   1.00
       Inscription block of 4   1.75   —
442 A219 35c **multicolored** (740,023)   1.10 1.10
       First day cover   1.25
       First day cover, #441-442   1.40
       Inscription block of 4   5.25   —

First day covers of Nos. 441-442 total 125,315.
See UN Offices in Geneva No. 128; Vienna Nos. 46-47.

1985, Feb. 1   Engr.   Perf. 13½
Printed by the Government Printing Bureau, Japan. Panes of 50. Engraved by Mamoru Iwakuni and Hiroshi Ozaki, Japan.

443 A220 23c **blue** (612,942)   .55   .45
       First day cover (76,541)   1.00
       Inscription block of 4   2.50   —

See UN Offices in Geneva Nos. 129-130; Vienna No. 48.

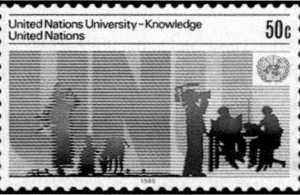

UN University
A221

Printed by Helio Courvoiser, Switzerland. Panes of 50. Designed by Moshe Pereg, Israel, and Hinedi Geluda, Brazil.

1985, Mar. 15   Photo.   Perf. 13½
444 A221 50c Farmer plowing, discussion group
                (625,043)   1.00   .85
       First day cover (77,271)   1.25
       Inscription block of 4   4.50   —

See UN Offices in Geneva Nos. 131-132; Vienna No. 49.

Peoples of the
World
United — A222

Painting UN
Emblem — A223

Printed by Carl Ueberreuter Druck and Verlag M. Salzer, Austria. Panes of 50. Designed by Fritz Henry Oerter, Federal Republic of Germany (22c), and Rimondi Rino, Italy ($3).

1985, May 10   Litho.   Perf. 14
445 A222 22c **multicolored** (2,000,000)+   .35   .30
       First day cover   1.00
       Inscription block of 4   1.50   —
446 A223 $3   **multicolored** (2,000,000)+   4.00 1.00
       First day cover   4.50
       First day cover, #445-446   6.50
       Inscription block of 4   17.00   —

First day covers of Nos. 445-446 total 88,613.
See UN Offices in Geneva Nos. 133-134; Vienna Nos. 50-51.

The Corner,
1947 — A224

Alvaro Raking
Hay,
1953 — A225

UN 40th anniversary. Oil paintings (details) by American artist Andrew Wyeth (b. 1917). Printed by Helio Courvoisier, Switzerland. Nos. 447-448 panes of 50. Designed by Rocco J. Callari, U.S., and Thomas Lee, China (#449).

1985, June 26   Photo.   Perf. 12 x 11½
447 A224 22c **multicolored** (944,960)   .40   .35
       First day cover   1.00
       Inscription block of 4   1.25   —
448 A225 45c **multicolored** (680,079)   1.10   .85
       First day cover   1.25
       First day cover, #447-448   1.50
       Inscription block of 4   4.25   —
       Souvenir Sheet
       Imperf
449   Sheet of 2 (506,004)   1.50 1.40
  a. A224 22c **multicolored**   .50   .40
  b. A225 45c **multicolored**   .75   .90
       First day cover   .75

First day covers of Nos. 447-449 total; New York, 210,189; San Francisco, 92,804.
See UN Offices in Geneva Nos. 135-137; Vienna Nos. 52-54.

Flag Type of 1980

Printed by Helio Courvoisier, Switzerland. Designed by Ole Hamann.
Issued in panes of 16; each contains 4 blocks of four (Nos. 450-453, 454-457, 458-461, 462-465). A se-tenant block of 4 designs is at the center of each pane.

1985, Sept. 20   Photo.   Perf. 12
Granite Paper

450	A185	22c Grenada (1,270,755)	.55	.50
451	A185	22c Federal Republic of Germany (1,270,755)	.55	.50
452	A185	22c Saudi Arabia (1,270,755)	.55	.50
453	A185	22c Mexico (1,270,755)	.55	.50
a.		Se-tenant block of 4, #450-453	3.25	2.75
454	A185	22c Uganda (1,216,878)	.55	.50
455	A185	22c St. Thomas & Prince (1,216,878)	.55	.50
456	A185	22c USSR (1,216,878)	.55	.50
457	A185	22c India (1,216,878)	.55	.50
a.		Se-tenant block of 4, #454-457	3.25	2.75
458	A185	22c Liberia (1,213,231)	.55	.50
459	A185	22c Mauritius (1,213,231)	.55	.50
460	A185	22c Chad (1,213,231)	.55	.50
461	A185	22c Dominican Republic (1,213,231)	.55	.50
a.		Se-tenant block of 4, #458-461	3.25	2.75
462	A185	22c Sultanate of Oman (1,215,533)	.55	.50
463	A185	22c Ghana (1,215,533)	.55	.50
464	A185	22c Sierra Leone (1,215,533)	.55	.50
465	A185	22c Finland (1,215,533)	.55	.50
a.		Se-tenant block of 4, #462-465	3.25	2.75
		First day covers, #460-465, each		1.00
		Set of 4 diff. panes of 16	30.00	
		Nos. 450-465 (16)	8.80	8.00

First day covers of Nos. 450-465 total 1,774,193.

UNICEF Child Survival Campaign — A226

Africa in Crisis — A227

Printed by the Government Printing Bureau, Japan. Panes of 50. Designed by Mel Harris, United Kingdom (#466) and Dipok Deyi, India (#467).

1985, Nov. 22   Photo. & Engr.   Perf. 13½

466	A226	22c Asian Toddler (823,724)	.35	.30
		First day cover		1.00
		Inscription block of 4	1.50	—
467	A226	33c Breastfeeding (632,753)	.65	.60
		First day cover		1.25
		First day cover, #466-467		1.75
		Inscription block of 4	3.00	—

First day covers of Nos. 466-467 total 206,923.
See UN Offices in Geneva Nos. 138-139; Vienna Nos. 55-56.

1986, Jan. 31   Photo.   Perf. 11½x12

Printed by Helio Courvoisier, Switzerland. Pane of 50. Designed by Wosene Kosrof, Ethiopia.

468	A227	22c multicolored (708,169)	.45	.40
		First day cover (80,588)		1.75
		Inscription block of 4	2.00	—

Campaign against hunger. See UN Offices in Geneva No. 140; Vienna No. 57.

Water Resources A228

Printed by the Government Printing Bureau, Japan. Pane of 40, 2 blocks of 4 horizontal by 5 blocks of 4 vertical. Designed by Thomas Lee, China.

1986, Mar. 14   Photo.   Perf. 13½

469	A228	22c Dam (525,839)	1.00	.80
470	A228	22c Irrigation (525,839)	1.00	.80
471	A228	22c Hygiene (525,839)	1.00	.80
472	A228	22c Well (525,839)	1.00	.80
a.		Block of 4, #469-472	4.00	3.75
		First day cover, #472a		6.50
		First day cover, #469-472, each		2.00
		Inscription block of 4, #469-472	5.00	—
		Pane of 40, #469-472	45.00	

UN Development Program. No. 472a has continuous design.
First day covers of Nos. 469-472 total 199,347.
See UN Offices in Geneva Nos. 141-144; Vienna Nos. 58-61.

Human Rights Stamp of 1954 — A229

Stamp collecting: 44c, Engraver. Printed by the Swedish Post Office, Sweden. Panes of 50. Designed by Czeslaw Slania and Ingalill Axelsson, Sweden.

1986, May 22   Engr.   Perf. 12½

473	A229	22c dark violet & bright blue (825,782)	.30	.25
		First day cover		1.00
		Inscription block of 4	1.50	—
474	A229	44c brown & emerald green (738,552)	.80	.70
		First day cover		1.25
		First day cover, #473-474		1.50
		Inscription block of 4	3.25	—

First day covers of Nos. 473-474 total: New York, 121,143; Chicago, 89,557.
See UN Offices in Geneva Nos. 146-147; Vienna Nos. 62-63.

Bird's Nest in Tree — A230

Peace in Seven Languages A231

Printed by the Government Printing Bureau, Japan. Panes of 50. Designed by Akira Iriguchi, Japan (#475), and Henryk Chylinski, Poland (#476).

1986, June 20   Photo. & Embossed   Perf. 13½

475	A230	22c multicolored (836,160)	.50	.40
		First day cover		1.00
		Inscription block of 4	2.25	—
476	A231	33c multicolored (663,882)	1.25	1.25
		First day cover		2.00
		First day cover, #475-476		4.50
		Inscription block of 4	6.00	—

International Peace Year.
First day covers of Nos. 475-476 total 149,976.
See UN Offices in Geneva Nos. 148-149; Vienna Nos. 64-65.

Flag Type of 1980

Printed by Helio Courvoisier, Switzerland. Designed by Ole Hamann. Issued in panes of 16; each contains 4 blocks of four (Nos. 477-480, 481-484, 485-488, 489-492). A se-tenant block of 4 designs centers each pane.

1986, Sept. 19   Photo.   Perf. 12
Granite Paper

477	A185	22c New Zealand (1,150,584)	.55	.50
478	A185	22c Lao PDR (1,150,584)	.55	.50
479	A185	22c Burkina Faso (1,150,584)	.55	.50
480	A185	22c Gambia (1,150,584)	.55	.50
a.		Se-tenant block of 4, #477-480	3.25	2.75
481	A185	22c Maldives (1,154,870)	.55	.50
482	A185	22c Ethiopia (1,154,870)	.55	.50
483	A185	22c Jordan (1,154,870)	.55	.50
484	A185	22c Zambia (1,154,870)	.55	.50
a.		Se-tenant block of 4, #481-484	3.25	2.75
485	A185	22c Iceland (1,152,740)	.55	.50
486	A185	22c Antigua & Barbuda (1,152,740)	.55	.50
487	A185	22c Angola (1,152,740)	.55	.50
488	A185	22c Botswana (1,152,740)	.55	.50
a.		Se-tenant block of 4, #485-488	3.25	2.75
489	A185	22c Romania (1,150,412)	.55	.50
490	A185	22c Togo (1,150,412)	.55	.50
491	A185	22c Mauritania (1,150,412)	.55	.50
492	A185	22c Colombia (1,150,412)	.55	.50
a.		Se-tenant block of 4, #489-492	3.25	2.75
		First day covers, #477-492, each		1.00
		Set of 4 diff. panes of 16	31.00	
		Nos. 477-492 (16)	8.80	8.00

First day covers of Nos. 477-492 total 1,442,284.

World Federation of UN Associations, 40th anniv. — A232

Printed by Johann Enschede and Sons, Netherlands. Designed by Rocco J. Callari, U.S.
Designs: 22c, Mother Earth, by Edna Hibel, U.S. 33c, Watercolor by Salvador Dali (b. 1904), Spain. 39c, New Dawn, by Dong Kingman, U.S. 44c, Watercolor by Chaim Gross, U.S.

1986, Nov. 14   Litho.   Perf. 13x13½
Souvenir Sheet

493		Sheet of 4 (433,888)	3.25	3.25
a.	A232	22c multicolored	.40	.40
b.	A232	33c multicolored	.50	.40
c.	A232	39c multicolored	.75	.50
d.	A232	44c multicolored	1.10	.90
		First day cover (106,194)		2.00

No. 493 has inscribed margin picturing UN and WFUNA emblems.
See UN Offices in Geneva No. 150; Vienna No. 66.

Trygve Halvdan Lie (1896-1968), first Secretary-General — A233

1987, Jan. 30   Photo. & Engr.   Perf. 13½

Printed by the Government Printing Office, Austria. Panes of 50. Designed by Rocco J. Callari, U.S., from a portrait by Harald Dal, Norway.

494	A233	22c multicolored (596,440)	.80	.80
		First day cover (84,819)		1.75
		Inscription block of 4	3.75	—

See Offices in Geneva No. 151; Vienna No. 67.

International Year of Shelter for the Homeless A234

Printed by Johann Enschede and Sons, Netherlands. Panes of 50. Designed by Wladyslaw Brykczynski, Poland.
Designs: 22c, Surveying and blueprinting. 44c, Cutting lumber.

1987, Mar. 13   Litho.   Perf. 13½x12½

495	A234	22c multicolored (620,627)	.40	.35
		First day cover		1.60
		Inscription block of 4	1.60	—
496	A234	44c multicolored (538,096)	1.10	1.10
		First day cover		1.90
		First day cover, #495-496		2.75
		Inscription block of 4	4.75	—

First day covers of Nos. 495-496 total 94,090.
See Offices in Geneva Nos. 154-155; Vienna Nos. 68-69.

Fight Drug Abuse — A235

Printed by the House of Questa, United Kingdom. Panes of 50. Designed by Susan Borgen and Noel Werrett, U.S.
Designs: 22c, Construction. 33c, Education.

1987, June 12   Litho.   Perf. 14½x15

497	A235 22c multicolored (674,563)	.55	.45
	First day cover		1.00
	Inscription block of 4	2.25	—
498	A235 33c multicolored (643,153)	1.00	.90
	First day cover		1.00
	First day cover, #497-498		1.75
	Inscription block of 4	4.50	—

First day covers of Nos. 497-498 total 106,941.
See Offices in Geneva Nos. 156-157; Vienna Nos. 70-71.

Flag Type of 1980

Printed by Courvoisier. Designed by Ole Hamann.
Issued in panes of 16; each contains 4 block of four (Nos. 499-502, 503-506, 507-510, 511-514). A se-tenant block of 4 designs centers each pane.

1987, Sept. 18   Photo.   Perf. 12
Granite Paper

499	A185 22c Comoros (1,235,828)	.55	.35
500	A185 22c Yemen PDR (1,235,828)	.55	.35
501	A185 22c Mongolia (1,235,828)	.55	.35
502	A185 22c Vanuatu (1,235,828)	.55	.35
a.	Se-tenant block of 4, #499-502	3.25	2.75
503	A185 22c Japan (1,244,534)	.55	.35
504	A185 22c Gabon (1,244,534)	.55	.35
505	A185 22c Zimbabwe (1,244,534)	.55	.35
506	A185 22c Iraq (1,244,534)	.55	.35
a.	Se-tenant block of 4, #503-506	3.25	2.75
507	A185 22c Argentina (1,238,065)	.55	.35
508	A185 22c Congo (1,238,065)	.55	.35
509	A185 22c Niger (1,238,065)	.55	.35
510	A185 22c St. Lucia (1,238,065)	.55	.35
a.	Se-tenant block of 4, #507-510	3.25	2.75
511	A185 22c Bahrain (1,239,323)	.55	.35
512	A185 22c Haiti (1,239,323)	.55	.35
513	A185 22c Afghanistan (1,239,323)	.55	.35
514	A185 22c Greece (1,239,323)	.55	.35
a.	Se-tenant block of 4, #511-514	3.25	2.75
	First day covers, #499-514, each		1.00
	Set of 4 diff. panes of 16	32.50	
	Nos. 499-514 (16)	8.80	5.60

United Nations
Day — A236

Printed by The House of Questa, United Kingdom. Panes of 12. Designed by Elisabeth von Janota-Bzowski (#515) and Fritz Henry Oerter (#516), Federal Republic of Germany.
Designs: Multinational people in various occupations.

1987, Oct. 23   Litho.   Perf. 14½x15

515	A236 22c multicolored (1,119,286)	.40	.35
	First day cover		1.00
	Inscription block of 4	2.00	—
516	A236 39c multicolored (1,065,468)	.60	.65
	First day cover		2.00
	First day cover, #515-516		1.60
	Inscription block of 4	2.50	—
	Panes of 12, #515-516	12.00	

See Offices in Geneva Nos. 158-159; Vienna Nos. 74-75.

Immunize Every
Child — A237

Printed by The House of Questa, United Kingdom. Panes of 50. Designed by Seymour Chwast, U.S.
Designs: 22c, Measles. 44c, Tetanus.

1987, Nov. 20   Litho.   Perf. 15x14½

517	A237 22c multicolored (660,495)	1.00	.50
	First day cover		2.00
	Inscription block of 4	3.00	—
518	A237 44c multicolored (606,049)	1.75	1.25
	First day cover		2.25
	First day cover, #517-518		3.50
	Inscription block of 4	9.00	—

See Offices in Geneva Nos. 160-161; Vienna Nos. 76-77.

Intl. Fund for
Agricultural
Development
(IFAD)
A238

Printed by CPE Australia Ltd., Australia. Panes of 50. Designed by Santiago Arolas, Switzerland.
Designs: 22c, Fishing. 33c, Farming.

1988, Jan. 29   Litho.   Perf. 13½

519	A238 22c multicolored (392,649)	.40	.35
	First day cover		1.00
	Inscription block of 4	2.00	—
520	A238 33c multicolored (475,185)	.85	.75
	First day cover		1.25
	First day cover, #519-520		3.00
	Inscription block of 4	4.00	—

See Offices in Geneva Nos. 162-163; Vienna Nos. 78-79.

A239

Printed by Heraclio Fournier, S.A., Spain. Panes of 50. Designed by David Ben-Hador, Israel.

1988, Jan. 29   Photo.   Perf. 13½x14

521	A239 3c multicolored (3,000,000)+	.20	.20
	First day cover		1.00
	Inscription block of 4	.75	—

Survival of the
Forests — A240

Printed by The House of Questa, United Kingdom. Panes of six se-tenant pairs. Designed by Braldt Bralds, the Netherlands.
Tropical rain forest: 25c, Treetops. 44c, Ground vegetation and tree trunks. Printed se-tenant in a continuous design.

1988, Mar. 18   Litho.   Perf. 14x15

522	A240 25c multicolored (647,360)	.90	.90
	First day cover		3.50
523	A240 44c multicolored (647,360)	1.50	1.50
	First day cover		6.50
a.	Pair, #522-523	3.25	3.25
	First day cover, #523a		7.00
	Inscription block of 4	6.75	
	Pane of 12, #522-523	19.00	

See Offices in Geneva Nos. 165-166; Vienna Nos. 80-81.

Intl. Volunteer Day — A241

Printed by Johann Enschede and Sons, the Netherlands. Panes of 50. Designed by James E. Tennison, U.S.
Designs: 25c, Eduraphon. 50c, Vocational training, horiz.

1988, May 6   Litho.   Perf. 13x14, 14x13

524	A241 25c multicolored (688,444)	.50	.45
	First day cover		1.00
	Inscription block of 4	2.25	—
525	A241 50c multicolored (447,784)	1.10	1.00
	First day cover		1.75
	First day cover, #524-525		2.00
	Inscription block of 4	4.50	—

See Offices in Geneva Nos. 167-168; Vienna Nos. 82-83.

Health in
Sports
A242

Printed by the Government Printing Bureau, Japan. Panes of 50. Paintings by LeRoy Neiman, American sports artist.
Designs: 25c, Cycling, vert. 35c, Marathon.

1988, June 17   Litho.   Perf. 13½x13, 13x13½

526	A242 25c multicolored (658,991)	.50	.45
	First day cover		2.25
	Inscription block of 4	2.50	—
527	A242 38c multicolored (420,421)	1.10	1.10
	First day cover		2.50
	First day cover, #526-527		3.75
	Inscription block of 4	6.50	—

See Offices in Geneva Nos. 169-170; Vienna Nos. 84-85.

Flag Type of 1980

Printed by Helio Courvoisier, Switzerland. Designed by Ole Hamann, Denmark. Issued in panes of 16; each contains 4 blocks of four (Nos. 528-531, 532-535, 536-539 and 540-543). A se-tenant block of 4 centers each pane.

1988, Sept. 15   Photo.   Perf. 12
Granite Paper

528	A185 25c Spain (1,029,443)	.60	.50
529	A185 25c St. Vincent & Grenadines (1,029,443)	.60	.50
530	A185 25c Ivory Coast (1,029,443)	.60	.50
531	A185 25c Lebanon (1,029,443)	.60	.50
a.	Se-tenant block of 4, #528-531	3.25	2.75
532	A185 25c Yemen (Arab Republic) (1,010,774)	.60	.50
533	A185 25c Cuba (1,010,774)	.60	.50
534	A185 25c Denmark (1,010,774)	.60	.50
535	A185 25c Libya (1,010,774)	.60	.50
a.	Se-tenant block of 4, #532-535	3.25	2.75
536	A185 25c Qatar (1,016,941)	.60	.50
537	A185 25c Zaire (1,016,941)	.60	.50
538	A185 25c Norway (1,016,941)	.60	.50
539	A185 25c German Democratic Republic (1,016,941)	.60	.50
a.	Se-tenant block of 4, #536-539	3.25	2.75
540	A185 25c Iran (1,009,234)	.60	.50
541	A185 25c Tunisia (1,009,234)	.60	.50
542	A185 25c Samoa (1,009,234)	.60	.50
543	A185 25c Belize (1,009,234)	.60	.50
a.	Se-tenant block of 4, #540-543	3.25	2.75
	First day covers, #528-543, each		1.25
	Set of 4 diff. panes of 16	32.50	
	Nos. 528-543 (16)	9.60	8.00

Universal Declaration of
Human Rights, 40th.
Anniv. — A243

Printed by Helio Couvoisier, Switzerland. Panes of 50. Designed by Rocco J. Callari, U.S.

1988, Dec. 9   Photo. & Engr.   Perf. 11x11½

544	A243 25c multicolored (893,706)	.50	.45
	First day cover		2.25
	Inscription block of 4	2.40	—

Souvenir Sheet

545	A243 $1 multicolored (411,863)	1.50	1.50
	First day cover		2.75

No. 545 has multicolored decorative margin inscribed with the preamble to the human rights declaration in English.
See Offices in Geneva Nos. 171-172; Vienna Nos. 86-87.

World Bank — A244

A245

Printed by Johann Enschede and Sons, the Netherlands. Panes of 50. Designed by Saturnino Lumboy, Philippines.

1989, Jan. 27		Litho.	Perf. 13x14	
546	A244	25c Energy and nature (612,114)	.65	.40
		First day cover		1.25
		Inscription block of 4	2.75	—
547	A244	45c Agriculture (528,184)	1.25	.95
		First day cover		1.50
		First day cover, #546-547		2.00
		Inscription block of 4	6.00	—

First day covers of Nos. 546-547 total 103,087 (NYC), 56,501 (Washington).
See Offices in Geneva Nos. 173-174; Vienna Nos. 88-89.

1989, Mar. 17		Litho.	Perf. 14x13½	

UN Peace-Keeping Force, awarded 1988 Nobel Peace Prize. Printed by CPE Australia, Ltd., Australia. Panes of 50. Designed by Tom Bland, Australia.

548	A245	25c multicolored (808,842)	.50	.40
		First day cover (52,115)		1.50
		Inscription block of 4	2.00	—

See Offices in Geneva No. 175; Vienna No. 90.

Aerial Photograph of New York
Headquarters — A246

Printed by Johann Enschede and Sons, the Netherlands. Panes of 25. Designed by Rocco J. Callari, United States, from a photograph by Simon Nathan.

1989, Mar. 17		Litho.	Perf. 14½x14	
549	A246	45c multicolored (2,000,000)+	.75	.65
		First day cover (41,610)		1.50
		Inscription block of 4	3.00	—

World Weather Watch,
25th Anniv. (in
1988) — A247

Printed by Johann Enschede and Sons, the Netherlands. Panes of 50.
Satellite photographs: 25c, Storm system off the U.S. east coast. 36c, Typhoon Abby in the north-west Pacific.

1989, Apr. 21		Litho.	Perf. 13x14	
550	A247	25c multicolored (849,819)	.60	.50
		First day cover		1.25
		Inscription block of 4	2.50	—
551	A247	36c multicolored (826,547)	1.25	1.00
		First day cover		1.75
		First day cover, #550-551		2.00
		Inscription block of 4	6.00	—

First day covers of Nos. 550-551 total 92,013.
See Offices in Geneva Nos. 176-177; Vienna Nos. 91-92.

Offices in Vienna, 10th Anniv.
A248   A249

Printed by the Government Printing Office, Austria. Panes of 25. Designed by Paul Flora (25c) and Rudolf Hausner (90c), Austria.

Photo. & Engr., Photo. (90c)

1989, Aug. 23			Perf. 14	
552	A248	25c multicolored (580,663)	1.50	1.00
		First day cover		2.25
		Inscription block of 4	11.00	—
553	A249	90c multicolored (505,776)	2.00	.75
		First day cover		2.25
		First day cover, #552-553		8.50
		Inscription block of 4	8.00	—
		Panes of 25, #552-553	125.00	

First day covers of Nos. 552-553 total 89,068.
See Offices in Geneva Nos. 178-179; Vienna Nos. 93-94.

Flag Type of 1980

Printed by Helio Courvoisier, Switzerland. Designed by Ole Hamann, Denmark. Issued in panes of 16; each contains 4 blocks of 4 (Nos. 554-557, 558-561, 562-565, 566-569). A se-tenant block of 4 designs centers each pane.

1989, Sept. 22		Photo.	Perf. 12	
		Granite Paper		
554	A185	25c Indonesia (959,076)	.60	.55
555	A185	25c Lesotho (959,076)	.60	.55
556	A185	25c Guatemala (959,076)	.60	.55
557	A185	25c Netherlands (959,076)	.60	.55
a.		Se-tenant block of 4, #554-557	3.50	3.00
558	A185	25c South Africa (960,502)	.60	.55
559	A185	25c Portugal (960,502)	.60	.55
560	A185	25c Morocco (960,502)	.60	.55
561	A185	25c Syrian Arab Republic (960,502)	.60	.55
a.		Se-tenant block of 4, #558-561	3.50	3.00
562	A185	25c Honduras (959,814)	.60	.55
563	A185	25c Kampuchea (959,814)	.60	.55
564	A185	25c Guinea-Bissau (959,814)	.60	.55
565	A185	25c Cyprus (959,814)	.60	.55
a.		Se-tenant block of 4, #562-565	3.50	3.00
566	A185	25c Algeria (959,805)	.60	.55
567	A185	25c Brunei (959,805)	.60	.55
568	A185	25c St. Kitts and Nevis (959,805)	.60	.55
569	A185	25c United Nations (959,805)	.60	.55
a.		Se-tenant block of 4, #566-569	3.50	3.00
		First day covers, #554-569, each		1.25
		Set of 4 diff. panes of 16	35.00	
		Nos. 554-569 (16)	9.60	8.80

First day covers of Nos. 554-569 total 794,934.

Declaration of
Human Rights, 40th
Anniv. (in
1988) — A250

Printed by Johann Enschede and Sons, the Netherlands. Panes of 12+12 se-tenant labels containing Articles 1 (25c) or 2 (45c) inscribed in English, French or German. Designed by Rocco J. Callari and Robert Stein, US.
Paintings: 25c, The Table of Universal Brotherhood, by Jose Clemente Orozco. 45c, Study for Composition II, by Vassily Kandinsky.

1989, Nov. 17		Litho.	Perf. 13½	
570	A250	25c multicolored (1,934,135)	.40	.30
		First day cover		1.50
		Inscription block of 3 + 3 labels	1.25	—
571	A250	45c multicolored (1,922,171)	.90	.80
		First day cover		1.75
		First day cover, #570-571		1.50
		Inscription block of 3 + 3 labels	2.75	—
		Panes of 12, #570-571	14.00	

First day covers of Nos. 570-571 total 146,489 (NYC), 46,774 (Washington).
See Nos. 582-583, 599-600, 616-617, 627-628; Offices in Geneva Nos. 180-181, 193-194, 209-210, 224-225, 234-235; Vienna Nos. 95-96, 108-109, 123-124, 139-140, 150-151.

Intl. Trade
Center — A251

Printed by House of Questa, United Kingdom. Panes of 50. Designed by Richard Bernstein, US.

1990, Feb. 2		Litho.	Perf. 14½x15	
572	A251	25c multicolored (429,081)	1.25	1.00
		First day cover (52,614)		1.75
		Inscription block of 4	5.50	—

See Offices in Geneva No. 182; Vienna No. 97.

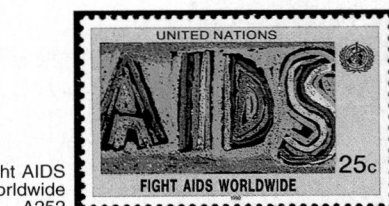

Fight AIDS
Worldwide
A252

Printed by Johann Enschede and Sons, the Netherlands. Panes of 50. Designed by Jacek Tofil, Poland (25c) and Fritz Henry Oerter, Federal Republic of Germany (40c).
Design: 40c, Shadow over crowd.

1990, Mar. 16		Litho.	Perf. 13½x12½	
573	A252	25c multicolored (492,078)	.40	.35
		First day cover		1.50
		Inscription block of 4	1.75	—
574	A252	40c multicolored (394,149)	1.25	1.00
		First day cover		2.00
		First day cover, #573-574		4.00
		Inscription block of 4	5.50	—

First day covers of Nos. 573-574 total 95,854.
See Offices in Geneva Nos. 184-185, Vienna Nos. 99-100.

Medicinal Plants — A253

Printed by Helio Courvoisier, Switzerland. Panes of 50. Designed by Rocco J. Callari & Robert Stein, US from illustrations from "Curtis's Botanical Magazine".

1990, May 4		Photo.	Granite Paper	Perf. 11½	
575	A253	25c Catharanthus roseus (796,792)		.55	.50
		First day cover			1.25
		Inscription block of 4		2.25	—
576	A253	90c Panax quinquefolium (605,617)		1.60	1.40
		First day cover			1.50
		First day cover, #575-576			3.00
		Inscription block of 4		7.00	—

First day covers of Nos. 575-576 total 100,548.
See Offices in Geneva Nos. 186-187, Vienna Nos. 101-102.

United
Nations, 45th
Anniv.
A254

Printed by Johann Enschede and Sons, the Netherlands. Panes of 50. Designed by Kris Geysen, Belgium (25c), Nejat M. Gur, Turkey (45c), Robert Stein, US (No. 579).
Design: 45c, "45," emblem.

1990, June 26		Litho.	Perf. 14½x13	
577	A254	25c multicolored (581,718)	.65	.60
		First day cover		1.00
		Inscription block of 4	2.75	—
578	A254	45c multicolored (582,769)	2.25	2.00
		First day cover		1.00

First day cover, #577-578   2.00
Inscription block of 4   10.00

Souvenir Sheet

579   Sheet of 2, #577-578 (315,946)   4.75   3.50
First day cover   3.50

First day covers of Nos. 577-579 total 129,011.
See Offices in Geneva Nos. 188-190; Vienna Nos. 103-105.

Crime Prevention — A255

Printed by Heraclio Fournier, S.A. Spain. Panes of 50.
Designed by Josef Ryzec, Czechoslovakia.

1990, Sept. 13   **Photo.**   *Perf. 14*
580 A255 25c Crimes of youth (533,089)   .80   .65
First day cover   1.50
Inscription block of 4   3.50
581 A255 36c Organized crime (427,215)   1.75   1.50
First day cover   1.75
First day cover, #580-581   3.00
Inscription block of 4   7.25

First day covers of Nos. 580-581 total 68,660.
See Offices in Geneva Nos. 191-192; Vienna Nos. 106-107.

Human Rights Type of 1989

Printed by Johann Enschede and Sons, the Netherlands.
Panes of 12+12 se-tenant labels containing Articles 7 (25c) or 8
(45c) inscribed in English, French or German. Designed by
Rocco J. Callari and Robert Stein, US.
    Artwork: 25c, Fragment from the sarcophagus of Plotinus, c.
270 A.D. 45c, Combined Chambers of the High Court of Appeal
by Charles Paul Renouard.

1990, Nov. 16   **Litho.**   *Perf. 13½*
582 A250 25c **black, gray & tan** (1,492,950)   .40   .35
First day cover   1.50
Inscription block of 3 + 3 labels   1.25 —
583 A250 45c **black & brown** (1,490,934)   .80   .65
First day cover   2.25
First day cover, #582-583   2.00
Inscription block of 3 + 3 labels   3.00 —
Panes of 12, #582-583   15.00

First day covers of Nos. 582-583 total 108,560.
See Offices in Geneva Nos. 193-194; Vienna Nos. 108-109.

Economic
Commission for
Europe — A256

Printed by Heraclio Fournier, S.A., Spain. Panes of 40.
Designed by Carlos Ochagavia, Argentina.

1991, Mar. 15   **Litho.**   *Perf. 14*
584 A256 30c Two storks (590,102)   1.10   .80
585 A256 30c Woodpecker, ibex (590,102)   1.10   .80
586 A256 30c Capercaille, plover (590,102)   1.10   .80
587 A256 30c Falcon, marmot (590,102)   1.10   .80
   a.   Block of 4, #584-587   4.50   3.25
First day cover, #587a   4.00
First day cover, #584-587, any single   4.50
Inscription block of 4, #587a   5.00 —
Pane of 40, #584-587   45.00

First day covers of Nos. 584-587 total 53,502.
See Offices in Geneva Nos. 195-198; Vienna Nos. 110-113.

Namibian
Independence
A257

Printed by Heraclio Fournier, S.A., Spain. Designed by Rocco
J. Callari, US, from photographs by John Isaac, India.

1991, May 10   **Litho.**   *Perf. 14*
588 A257 30c Dunes, Namib Desert (360,825)   .65   .50
First day cover   1.25
Inscription block of 4   3.00
589 A257 50c Savanna (415,648)   1.25   1.00
First day cover   1.75
First day cover, #588-589   3.00
Inscription block of 4   5.50 —

First day covers of Nos. 588-589 total 114,258.
See Offices in Geneva Nos. 199-200; Vienna Nos. 114-115.

A258

The Golden Rule by
Norman Rockwell — A259

UN Headquarters, New
York — A260

Printed by Johann Enschede and Sons, the Netherlands
(30c), Helio Courvoisier, S.A., Switzerland (50c), and by Government Printing Bureau, Japan ($2). Panes of 50. Designed by
Rocco J. Callari (30c), Norman Rockwell, US (50c), Rocco J.
Callari and Robert Stein, US ($2).

1991   **Litho.**   *Perf. 13½*
590 A258 30c **multi,** Sept. 11, (2,000,000)+   .65   .50
First day cover   1.25
Inscription block of 4   2.75

Photo.
Perf. 12x11½
591 A259 50c **multi,** Sept. 11, (2,000,000)+   1.25   1.00
First day cover   1.50
Inscription block of 4   5.75

Engr.
592 A260 $2 **dark blue,** May 10, (2,000,000)+   2.75   2.50
First day cover   3.75
Inscription block of 4   11.00 —

First day covers of Nos. 590-591 total 66,016, No. 592,
36,022.
See Offices in Geneva Nos. 199-200; Vienna Nos. 114-115.

Rights of the
Child — A261

Printed by The House of Questa, United Kingdom. Panes of
50. Designed by Nicole Delia Legnani, US (30c) and Alissa
Duffy, US (70c).

1991, June 14   **Litho.**   *Perf. 14½*
593 A261 30c Children, globe (440,151)   1.00   .75
First day cover   1.50
Inscription block of 4   4.50
594 A261 70c House, rainbow (447,803)   2.00   1.75
First day cover   3.00
First day cover, #593-594   3.00
Inscription block of 4   9.00 —

First day covers of Nos. 593-594 total 96,324.
See Offices in Geneva Nos. 203-204; Vienna Nos. 117-118.

Banning of
Chemical
Weapons
A262

Printed by Heraclio Fournier, S.A., Spain. Panes of 50.
Designed by Oscar Asboth, Austria (30c), Michael Granger,
France (90c).
    Design: 90c, Hand holding back chemical drums.

1991, Sept. 11   **Litho.**   *Perf. 13½*
595 A262 30c **multicolored** (367,548)   .90   .75
First day cover   1.25
Inscription block of 4   3.75
596 A262 90c **multicolored** (346,161)   2.50   2.00
First day cover   1.75
First day cover, #595-596   2.50
Inscription block of 4   11.00 —

First day covers of Nos. 595-596 total 91,552.
See Offices in Geneva Nos. 205-206; Vienna Nos. 119-120.

UN Postal
Administration, 40th
Anniv. — A263

Printed by The House of Questa, United Kingdom. Panes of
25. Designed by Rocco J. Callari, US.

1991, Oct. 24   **Litho.**   *Perf. 14x15*
597 A263 30c No. 1 (442,548)   .75   .65
First day cover   1.00
Inscription block of 4   3.00
598 A263 40c No. 3 (419,127)   1.00   .85
First day cover   1.00
First day cover, #597-598   1.50
Inscription block of 4   4.75 —
Panes of 25, #597-598   50.00

First day covers of Nos. 597-598 total 81,177 (New York),
58,501 (State College, PA).
See Offices in Geneva Nos. 207-208; Vienna Nos. 121-122.

Human Rights Type of 1989

Printed by Johann Enschede and Sons, the Netherlands.
Panes of 12+12 se-tenant labels containing Articles 13 (30c) or
14 (50c) inscribed in English, French or German. Designed by
Robert Stein, US.
    Artwork: 30c, The Last of England, by Ford Madox Brown.
40c, The Emigration to the East, by Tito Salas.

1991, Nov. 20   **Litho.**   *Perf. 13½*
599 A250 30c **multicolored** (1,261,198)   .50   .45
First day cover   1.25
Inscription block of 3 + 3 labels   2.10 —
600 A250 50c **multicolored** (1,255,077)   1.10   1.00
First day cover   1.75
First day cover, #599-600   2.25
Inscription block of 3 + 3 labels   4.00 —
Panes of 12, #599-600   16.00

First day covers of Nos. 599-600 total 136,605.
See Offices in Geneva Nos. 209-210; Vienna Nos. 123-124.

World Heritage Type of 1984

Printed by Cartor S.A., France. Panes of 50. Designed by
Robert Stein, U.S.
    Designs: 30c, Uluru Natl. Park, Australia. 50c, The Great Wall
of China.

1992, Jan. 24   **Litho.**   *Perf. 13*
Size: 35x28mm
601 A215 30c **multicolored** (337,717)   .65   .50
First day cover   1.25
Inscription block of 4   2.60
602 A215 50c **multicolored** (358,000)   1.00   .90
First day cover   1.75
First day cover, #601-602   2.75
Inscription block of 4   4.75 —

First day covers of Nos. 601-602 total 62,733.
See Offices in Geneva Nos. 211-212; Vienna Nos. 125-126.

Clean
Oceans — A264

Printed by The House of Questa, United Kingdom. Panes of
12. Designed by Braldt Bralds, Netherlands.

1992, Mar. 13   **Litho.**   **Perf. 14**
603 A264 29c Ocean surface *(983,126)*   .60   .55
604 A264 29c Ocean bottom *(983,126)*   .60   .55
   a.   Pair, #603-604   1.25   1.10
     First day cover, #604a   3.00
     First day cover, #603-604, any sin-
     gle   1.50
     Inscription block of 4, #603-604   3.50
     Pane of 12, #603-604   8.50

First day covers of Nos. 603-604 total 75,511.
See Offices in Geneva Nos. 214-215, Vienna Nos. 127-128.

Earth
Summit — A265

Printed by Helio Courvoisier S.A., Switzerland. Panes of 40.
Designed by Peter Max, US.
Designs: No. 605, Globe at LR. No. 606, Globe at LL. No.
607, Globe at UR. No. 608, Globe at UL.

1992, May 22   **Photo.**   **Perf. 11½**
605 A265 29c **multicolored** *(806,268)*   .65   .60
606 A265 29c **multicolored** *(806,268)*   .65   .60
607 A265 29c **multicolored** *(806,268)*   .65   .60
608 A265 29c **multicolored** *(806,268)*   .65   .60
   a.   Block of 4, #605-608   4.00   3.50
     First day cover, #608a   3.50
     First day cover, #605-608, each   3.50
     Inscription block of 4, #608a   5.00
     Pane of 40, #605-608   27.50

First day covers of Nos. 605-608a total 110,577.
See Offices in Geneva Nos. 216-219, Vienna Nos. 129-132.

Mission to Planet Earth — A266

Printed by Helio Courvoisier, S.A., Switzerland. Designed by
Attilla Hejja, US.
Designs: No. 609, Satellites over city, sailboats, fishing boat.
No. 610, Satellite over coast, passenger liner, dolphins, whale,
volcano.

1992, Sept. 4   **Photo.**   **Rouletted 8**
         Granite Paper
609 A266 29c **multicolored** *(643,647)*   1.50   1.25
610 A266 29c **multicolored** *(643,647)*   1.50   1.25
   a.   Pair, #609-610   4.75   4.75
     First day cover, #610a   2.00
     First day cover, #609-610, each   9.00
     Inscription block of 4   10.00
     Pane of 10, #609-610   24.00

First day covers of Nos. 609-610a total 69,343.
See Offices in Geneva Nos. 220-221, Vienna Nos. 133-134.

Science and
Technology for
Development
A267

Printed by Unicover Corp., US. Designed by Saul Mandel,
US.
Design: 50c, Animal, man drinking.

1992, Oct. 2   **Litho.**   **Perf. 14**
611 A267 29c **multicolored** *(453,365)*   .45   .35
     First day cover   1.50
     Inscription block of 4   2.00
612 A267 50c **multicolored** *(377,377)*   .80   .60
     First day cover   1.50
     First day cover, #611-612   4.75
     Inscription block of 4   3.75

First day covers of Nos. 611-612 total 69,195.
See Offices in Geneva Nos. 222-223, Vienna Nos. 135-136.

UN
University
Building,
Tokyo
A268

UN Headquarters,
New York — A269

Printed by Cartor SA, France (4c, 40c), Walsall Security
Printers, Ltd., UK (29c). Designed by Banks and Miles, UK (4c,
40c), Robert Stein, US (29c).
Design: 40c, UN University Building, Tokyo, diff.

1992, Oct. 2   **Litho.**   **Perf. 14, 13½x13 (29c)**
613 A268 4c **multicolored** *(1,500,000)+*   .20   .20
     First day cover   1.25
     Inscription block of 4   .80   —
614 A269 29c **multicolored** *(1,750,000)+*   .60   .45
     First day cover   1.25
     Inscription block of 4   2.50   —
615 A268 40c **multicolored** *(1,500,000)+*   .80   .60
     First day cover   1.25
     First day cover, #613-615   2.00
     Inscription block of 4   4.00   —
     Nos. 613-615 (3)   1.60   1.25

First day covers of Nos. 613-615 total 62,697.

Human Rights Type of 1989

Printed by Johann Enschede and Sons, the Netherlands.
Panes of 12+12 se-tenant labels containing Articles 19 (29c)
and 20 (50c) inscribed in English, French or German. Designed
by Robert Stein, US.
Artwork: 29c, Lady Writing a Letter with her Maid, by
Vermeer. 50c, The Meeting, by Ester Almqvist.

1992, Nov. 20   **Litho.**   **Perf. 13½**
616 A250 29c **multicolored,** *(1,184,531)*   .60   .50
     First day cover   3.00
     Inscription block of 3 + 3 labels   2.00   —
617 A250 50c **multicolored,** *(1,107,044)*   .75   .65
     First day cover   6.00
     First day cover, #616-617   2.75
     Inscription block of 3 + 3 labels   3.00   —
     Panes of 12, #616-617   14.00

First day covers of Nos. 616-617 total 104,470.
See Offices in Geneva Nos. 224-225; Vienna Nos. 139-140.

Aging With Dignity — A270

Printed by Cartor SA, France. Designed by C.M. Dudash, US.
Designs: 29c, Elderly couple, family. 52c, Old man, physician,
woman holding fruit basket.

1993, Feb. 5   **Litho.**   **Perf. 13**
618 A270 29c **multicolored** *(336,933)*   .60   .50
     First day cover   1.00
     Inscription block of 4   3.00   —
619 A270 52c **multicolored** *(308,080)*   1.25   1.00
     First day cover   1.25
     First day cover, #618-619   1.75
     Inscription block of 4   6.00   —

First day covers of Nos. 618-619 total 52,932.
See Offices in Geneva Nos. 226-227; Vienna Nos. 141-142.

Endangered
Species
A271

Printed by Johann Enschede and Sons, the Netherlands.
Designed by Rocco J. Callari and Norman Adams, US.
Designs: No. 620, Hairy-nosed wombat. No. 621, Whooping
crane. No. 622, Giant clam. No. 623, Giant sable antelope.

1993, Mar. 2   **Litho.**   **Perf. 13x12½**
620 A271 29c **multicolored** *(1,200,000)+*   .55   .50
621 A271 29c **multicolored** *(1,200,000)+*   .55   .50
622 A271 29c **multicolored** *(1,200,000)+*   .55   .50
623 A271 29c **multicolored** *(1,200,000)+*   .55   .50
   a.   Block of 4, #620-623   2.25   2.25
     First day cover, #623a   3.75
     First day cover, #620-623, each   1.75
     Inscription block of 4, #623a   2.40   —
     Pane of 16, #620-623   10.50

First day covers of Nos. 620-623a total 64,794.
See Nos. 639-642, 657-660, 674-677, 700-703, 730-733,
757-760, 773-776; Offices in Geneva Nos. 228-231, 246-249,
264-267, 280-283, 298-301, 318-321, 336-339, 352-355;
Vienna Nos. 143-146, 162-165, 180-183, 196-199, 214-217,
235-238, 253-256, 269-272.

Healthy
Environment
A272

Printed by Leigh-Mardon Pty. Limited, Australia. Designed by
Milton Glaser, US.
Designs: 29c, Personal. 50c, Family.

1993, May 7   **Litho.**   **Perf. 15x14½**
624 A272 29c Man *(430,463)*   .60   .50
     First day cover   1.00
     Inscription block of 4   2.50   —
625 A272 50c Family *(326,692)*   1.00   .90
     First day cover   1.50
     First day cover, #624-625   2.00
     Inscription block of 4   4.25   —

WHO, 45th anniv. First day covers of Nos. 624-625 total
55,139.
See Offices in Geneva Nos. 232-233; Vienna Nos. 147-148.

A273

Printed by House of Questa, Ltd., United Kingdom. Designed by Salahattin Kanidinc, US.

1993, May 7	Litho.	Perf. 15x14	
626 A273 5c **multicolored** (1,500,000)+		.20	.20
First day cover (23,452)			1.00
Inscription block of 4		.70	—

Human Rights Type of 1989

Printed by Johann Enschede and Sons, the Netherlands. Panes of 12 + 12 se-tenant labels containing Articles 25 (29c) and 26 (35c) inscribed in English, French or German. Designed by Robert Stein, US.

Artwork: 29c, Shocking Corn, by Thomas Hart Benton. 35c, The Library, by Jacob Lawrence.

1993, June 11	Litho.	Perf. 13½	
627 A250 29c **multicolored** (1,049,134)		.50	.40
First day cover			1.00
Inscription block of 3 + 3 labels		2.00	—
628 A250 35c **multicolored** (1,045,346)		.60	.45
First day cover			1.25
First day cover, #627-628			2.00
Inscription block of 3 + 3 labels		2.75	—
Panes of 12, #627-628		16.00	

First day covers of Nos. 627-628 total 77,719.
See Offices in Geneva Nos. 234-235; Vienna Nos. 150-151.

Intl. Peace Day — A274

Printed by the PTT, Switzerland. Designed by Hans Erni, Switzerland.
Denomination at: #629, UL. #630, UR. #631, LL. #632, LR.

1993, Sept. 21	Litho. & Engr.	Rouletted 12½	
629 A274 29c **blue & multi** (298,367)		1.40	1.25
630 A274 29c **blue & multi** (298,367)		1.40	1.25
631 A274 29c **blue & multi** (298,367)		1.40	1.25
632 A274 29c **blue & multi** (298,367)		1.40	1.25
a. Block of 4, #629-632		6.00	5.50
First day cover, #629-632, each			3.50
First day cover, #632a			3.50
Inscription block of 4, #632a		7.50	—
Pane of 40, #629-632		80.00	

First day covers of Nos. 629-632a total 41,743.
See Offices in Geneva Nos. 236-239; Vienna Nos. 152-155.

Environment-Climate — A275

Printed by House of Questa, Ltd., United Kingdom. Designed by Braldt Bralds, Netherlands.

Designs: #633, Chameleon. #634, Palm trees, top of funnel cloud. #635, Bottom of funnel cloud, deer, antelope. #636, Bird of paradise.

1993, Oct. 29	Litho.	Perf. 14½	
633 A275 29c **multicolored** (383,434)		.75	.50
634 A275 29c **multicolored** (383,434)		.75	.50
635 A275 29c **multicolored** (383,434)		.75	.50
636 A275 29c **multicolored** (383,434)		.75	.50
a. Strip of 4, #633-636		3.50	2.50
First day cover, #636a			2.75
First day cover, #633-636, each			3.75
Inscription block, 2 #636a		8.50	—
Pane of 24, #633-636		23.50	

First day covers of Nos. 633-636a total 38,182.
See Offices in Geneva Nos. 240-243; Vienna Nos. 156-159.

Intl. Year of the Family — A276

Printed by Cartor S.A., France. Designed by Rocco J. Callari, US.

Designs: 29c, Mother holding child, two children, woman. 45c, People tending crops.

1994, Feb. 4	Litho.	Perf. 13.1	
637 A276 29c **green & multi** (590,000)+		.85	.75
First day cover			1.00
Inscription block of 4		3.75	—
638 A276 45c **blue & multi** (540,000)+		1.00	.90
First day cover			1.25
First day cover, #637-638			1.75
Inscription block of 4		4.75	—

First day covers of Nos. 637-638 total 47,982. See Offices in Geneva Nos. 244-245; Vienna Nos. 160-161.

Endangered Species Type of 1993

Printed by Johann Enschede and Sons, the Netherlands. Designed by Rocco J. Callari, US (frame), and Kerrie Maddeford, Australia (stamps).

Designs: No. 639, Chimpanzee. No. 640, St. Lucia Amazon. No. 641, American crocodile. No. 642, Dama gazelle.

1994, Mar. 18	Litho.	Perf. 12.7	
639 A271 29c **multicolored** (1,200,000)+		.50	.50
640 A271 29c **multicolored** (1,200,000)+		.50	.50
641 A271 29c **multicolored** (1,200,000)+		.50	.50
642 A271 29c **multicolored** (1,200,000)+		.50	.50
a. Block of 4, #639-642		2.00	2.00
First day cover, #642a			3.50
First day cover, #639-642, each			1.75
Inscription block of 4, #642a		2.50	—
Pane of 16, #639-642		10.00	

First day covers of Nos. 639-642 total 79,599. See Offices in Geneva Nos. 246-249; Vienna Nos. 162-165.

Protection for Refugees — A277

Printed by Leigh-Mardon Pty. Limited, Australia. Designed by Francoise Peyroux, France.

1994, Apr. 29	Litho.	Perf. 14.3x14.8	
643 A277 50c **multicolored** (600,000)+		1.00	.90
First day cover (33,558)			1.75
Inscription block of 4		5.00	—

See Offices in Geneva No. 250; Vienna No. 166.

Dove of Peace — A278

Sleeping Child, by Stanislaw Wyspianski — A279

Mourning Owl, by Vanessa Isitt — A280

Printed by Cartor S.A., France, and Norges Banks Seddeltrykkeri, Norway (#646).

1994, Apr. 29	Litho.	Perf. 12.9	
644 A278 10c **multicolored** (1,000,000)+		.20	.20
First day cover			1.00
Inscription block of 4		.80	—
645 A279 19c **multicolored** (1,000,000)+		.40	.35
First day cover			1.75
Inscription block of 4		1.75	—

	Engr.		
	Perf. 13.1		
646 A280 $1 **red brown** (1,000,000)+		1.75	1.75
First day cover			3.00
Inscription block of 4		7.50	—
Nos. 644-646 (3)		2.35	2.30

First day covers of Nos. 644-646 total 48,946.

Intl. Decade for Natural Disaster Reduction — A281

Printed by The House of Questa, UK. Designed by Kenji Koga, Japan.

Earth seen from space, outline map of: #647, North America. #648, Eurasia. #649, South America, #650, Australia and South Asia.

1994, May 27	Litho.	Perf. 13.9x14.2	
647 A281 29c **multicolored** (630,000)+		1.50	1.00
648 A281 29c **multicolored** (630,000)+		1.50	1.00
649 A281 29c **multicolored** (630,000)+		1.50	1.00
650 A281 29c **multicolored** (630,000)+		1.50	1.00
a. Block of 4, #647-650		8.00	4.50
First day cover, #650a			4.50
First day cover, #647-650, each			2.50
Inscription block of 4, #650a		9.00	—
Pane of 40, #647-650		77.50	

First day covers of Nos. 647-650 total 37,135. See Offices in Geneva Nos. 251-254; Vienna Nos. 170-173.

Population and Development A282

Printed by Johann Enschede and Sons, the Netherlands. Designed by Jerry Smath, US.

Designs: 29c, Children playing. 52c, Family with house, car, other possessions.

1994, Sept. 1	Litho.	Perf. 13.2x13.6	
651 A282 29c **multicolored** (590,000)+		.50	.40
First day cover			1.00
Inscription block of 4		2.25	—
652 A282 52c **multicolored** (540,000)+		1.00	.90
First day cover			1.25
First day cover, #651-652			2.25
Inscription block of 4		4.25	—

First day covers of Nos. 651-652 total 45,256.
See Offices in Geneva Nos. 258-259; Vienna Nos. 174-175.

UNCTAD, 30th Anniv. — A283

Printed by Johann Enschede and Sons, the Netherlands. Designed by Luis Sarda, Spain.

1994, Oct. 28
653	A283 29c **multicolored** (590,000)+		.45	.35
	First day cover			1.00
	Inscription block of 4		2.00	—
654	A283 50c **multi, diff.** (540,000)+		.90	.65
	First day cover			1.25
	First day cover, #653-654			1.75
	Inscription block of 4		3.75	

First day covers of Nos. 653-654 total 42,763. See Offices in Geneva Nos. 260-261; Vienna Nos. 176-177.

UN, 50th Anniv. — A284

Printed by Swiss Postal Service. Designed by Rocco J. Callari, US.

1995, Jan. 1   Litho. & Engr.   Perf. 13.4
655	A284 32c **multicolored** (938,644)		1.00	1.00
	First day cover (39,817)			1.50
	Inscription block of 4		4.25	—

See Offices in Geneva No. 262; Vienna No. 178.

Social Summit, Copenhagen — A285

1995, Feb. 3   Photo. & Engr.   Perf. 13.6x13.9
Printed by Austrian Government Printing Office. Designed by Friedensreich Hundertwasser.
656	A285 50c **multicolored** (495,388)		1.00	.90
	First day cover (31,797)			2.00
	Inscription block of 4		4.00	—

See Offices in Geneva No. 263; Vienna No. 179.

Endangered Species Type of 1993

Printed by Johann Enschede and Sons, the Netherlands. Designed by Chris Calle, US.
Designs: No. 657, Giant armadillo. No. 658, American bald eagle. No. 659, Fijian/Tongan banded iguana. No. 660, Giant panda.

1995, Mar. 24   Litho.   Perf. 13x12½
657	A271 32c **multicolored** (756,000)+		.45	.45
658	A271 32c **multicolored** (756,000)+		.45	.45
659	A271 32c **multicolored** (756,000)+		.45	.45
660	A271 32c **multicolored** (756,000)+		.45	.45
a.	Block of 4, 657-660		2.25	2.25
	First day cover #660a			2.25
	First day cover, #657-660, each			1.75
	Inscription block of 4, #660a		2.50	—
	Pane of 16, #657-660		10.00	

First day covers of Nos. 657-660 total 67,311. See Offices in Geneva Nos. 264-267; Vienna Nos. 180-183.

Intl. Youth Year, 10th Anniv. — A286

Printed by The House of Questa (UK). Designed by Gottfried Kumpf, Austria.
Designs: 32c, Seated child. 55c, Children cycling.

1995, May 26   Litho.   Perf. 14.4x14.7
661	A286 32c **multicolored** (358,695)		.70	.55
	First day cover			1.00
	Inscription block of 4		3.00	
662	A286 55c **multicolored** (288,424)		1.10	.90
	First day cover			1.25
	First day cover, #661-662			2.00
	Inscription block of 4		4.50	

First day covers of Nos. 661-662 total 42,846. See Offices in Geneva Nos. 268-269; Vienna Nos. 184-185.

UN, 50th Anniv. — A287

Printed by Johann Enschede Security Printing, the Netherlands. Designed by Paul and Chris Calle, US.
Designs: 32c, Hand with pen signing UN Charter, flags. 50c, Veterans' War Memorial, Opera House, San Francisco.

1995, June 26   Engr.   Perf. 13.3x13.6
663	A287 32c **black** (501,961)		.65	.55
	First day cover			1.00
	Inscription block of 4		2.50	
664	A287 50c **maroon** (419,932)		1.10	1.00
	First day cover			1.00
	First day cover, #663-664			2.00
	Inscription block of 4		4.50	—

Souvenir Sheet
Litho. & Engr.
Imperf
665	Sheet of 2, #663-664 (347,963)+		2.75	2.50
a.	A287 32c **black**		1.10	.95
b.	A287 50c **maroon**		1.50	1.40
	First day cover			3.50

First day covers of Nos. 663-665 total: New York, 69,263; San Francisco, 53,354.
No. 665 exists with gold China 1996 overprint. Value $20.
See Offices in Geneva Nos. 270-272; Vienna Nos. 186-188.

4th World Conference on Women, Beijing — A288

Printed by Postage Stamp Printing House, MPT, People's Republic of China. Designed by Ting Shao Kuang, People's Republic of China.
Designs: 32c, Mother and child. 40c, Seated woman, cranes flying above.

1995, Sept. 5   Photo.   Perf. 12
666	A288 32c **multicolored** (561,847)		.60	.45
	First day cover			1.25
	Inscription block of 4		2.50	—

Size: 28x50mm
667	A288 40c **multicolored** (499,850)		.90	.80
	First day cover			1.25
	First day cover, #666-667			2.50
	Inscription block of 4		4.00	—

First day covers of Nos. 666-667 total 103,963. See Offices in Geneva Nos. 273-274; Vienna Nos. 189-190.

UN Headquarters A289

Designed by John B. De Santis, Jr. US.

1995, Sept. 5   Litho.   Perf. 15
668	A289 20c **multicolored** (18,326)		.40	.30
	First day cover			2.00
	Inscription block of 4		2.00	—

Miniature Sheet

United Nations, 50th Anniv. — A290

Designed by Ben Verkaaik, Netherlands.
Printed by House of Questa, UK.
Designs: #669a-669 l, Various people in continuous design (2 blocks of six stamps with gutter between).

1995, Oct. 24   Litho.   Perf. 14
669	Sheet of 12 (214,639 sheets)		14.00	7.50
	First day cover			15.00
a.-l.	A290 32c any single		1.00	.60
	First day cover, #669a-669l, each			7.00
670	Souvenir booklet (85,256 booklets)		16.00	
a.	A290 32c Booklet pane of 3, vert. strip of 3 from UL of sheet		4.00	4.00
b.	A290 32c Booklet pane of 3, vert. strip of 3 from UR of sheet		4.00	4.00
c.	A290 32c Booklet pane of 3, vert. strip of 3 from LL of sheet		4.00	4.00
d.	A290 32c Booklet pane of 3, vert. strip of 3 from LR of sheet		4.00	4.00
	First day covers, #670a-670d, set booklet tab singles			140.00

First day covers of Nos. 669-670 total 47,632. See Offices in Geneva Nos. 275-276; Vienna Nos. 191-192.

WFUNA, 50th Anniv. — A291

Designed by Rudolf Mirer, Switzerland.
Printed by Johann Enschede and Sons, the Netherlands.

1996, Feb. 2   Litho.   Perf. 13x13½
671	A291 32c **multicolored** (580,000)+		.55	.45
	First day cover			1.25
	Inscription block of 4		2.25	—

See Offices in Geneva No. 277; Vienna No. 193.

Mural, by Fernand Leger — A292

Designed by Fernand Leger, France.
Printed by House of Questa, UK.

1996, Feb. 2   Litho.   Perf. 14½x15
672	A292 32c **multicolored** (780,000)+		.50	.40
	First day cover			1.25
	Inscription block of 4		2.25	—
673	A292 60c **multi, diff.** (680,000)+		1.00	.80
	First day cover			1.75
	First day cover, #672-673			2.25
	Inscription block of 4		4.25	—

Endangered Species Type of 1993

Printed by Johann Enschede and Sons, the Netherlands. Designed by Diane Bruyninckx, Belgium.

Designs: No. 674, Masdevallia veitchiana. No. 675, Saguaro cactus. No. 676, West Australian pitcher plant. No. 677, Encephalartos horridus.

1996, Mar. 14		**Litho.**		***Perf. 12½***	
674	A271	32c	**multicolored**	*(640,000)+*	.50 .50
675	A271	32c	**multicolored**	*(640,000)+*	.50 .50
676	A271	32c	**multicolored**	*(640,000)+*	.50 .50
677	A271	32c	**multicolored**	*(640,000)+*	.50 .50
a.	Block of 4, #674-677				2.40 2.40
	First day cover, #677a				3.25
	First day cover, #674-677, each				1.75
	Inscription block of 4, #677a				—
	Pane of 16, #674-677				11.00

See Offices in Geneva Nos. 280-283; Vienna Nos. 196-199.

City Summit (Habitat II) — A293

Printed by Johann Enschede and Sons, the Netherlands. Designed by Teresa Fasolino, US.

Designs: No. 678, Deer. No. 679, Man, child, dog sitting on hill, overlooking town. No. 680, People walking in park, city skyline. No. 681, Tropical park, Polynesian woman, boy. No. 682, Polynesian village, orchids, bird.

1996, June 3		**Litho.**		***Perf. 14x13½***	
678	A293	32c	**multicolored**	*(475,000)+*	.90 .75
679	A293	32c	**multicolored**	*(475,000)+*	.90 .75
680	A293	32c	**multicolored**	*(475,000)+*	.90 .75
681	A293	32c	**multicolored**	*(475,000)+*	.90 .75
682	A293	32c	**multicolored**	*(475,000)+*	.90 .75
a.	Strip of 5, #678-682				6.25 6.25
	First day cover, #682a				6.00
	First day cover, #678-682, each				5.50
	Inscription block of 10, 2 #682a				11.00
	Sheet of 25				32.50

See Offices in Geneva Nos. 284-288; Vienna Nos. 200-204.

Sport and the Environment — A294

Printed by The House of Questa, UK. Designed by LeRoy Neiman, US.

Designs: 32c, Men's basketball. 50c, Women's volleyball, horiz.

1996, July 19		**Litho.**		***Perf. 14x14½, 14½x14***	
683	A294	32c	**multicolored**	*(680,000)+*	.75 .60
	First day cover				1.25
	Inscription block of 4				3.25
684	A294	50c	**multicolored**	*(680,000)+*	1.50 1.50
	First day cover				1.50
	First day cover, #683-684				2.00
	Inscription block of 4				7.75

Souvenir Sheet

685	A294	Sheet of 2, #683-684 *(370,000)+*		2.50 2.50
	First day cover			3.50

See Offices in Geneva Nos. 289-291; Vienna Nos. 205-207.
1996 Summer Olympic Games, Atlanta, GA.

Plea for Peace — A295

Printed by House of Questa, UK.
Designed by: 32c, Peng Yue, China. 60c, Cao Chenyu, China.

Designs: 32c, Doves. 60c, Stylized dove.

1996, Sept. 17		**Litho.**		***Perf. 14½x15***	
686	A295	32c	**multicolored**	*(580,000)+*	.55 .40
	First day cover				1.00
	Inscription block of 4				2.25
687	A295	60c	**multicolored**	*(580,000)+*	1.00 .80
	First day cover				1.25
	First day cover, #686-687				2.00
	Inscription block of 4				4.25

See Offices in Geneva Nos. 292-293; Vienna Nos. 208-209.

UNICEF, 50th Anniv. — A296

Printed by The House of Questa, UK. Designed by The Walt Disney Co.

Fairy Tales: 32c, Yeh-Shen, China. 60c, The Ugly Duckling, by Hans Christian Andersen.

1996, Nov. 20		**Litho.**		***Perf. 14½x15***	
688	A296	32c	**multicolored**	*(1,000,000)+*	.50 .40
	First day cover				1.25
	Pane of 8 + label				4.50
689	A296	60c	**multicolored**	*(1,000,000)+*	1.25 1.00
	First day cover				1.50
	First day cover, #688-689				2.50
	Pane of 8 + label				12.50

See Offices in Geneva Nos. 294-295; Vienna Nos. 210-211.

Flag Type of 1980

Printed by Helio Courvoisier, S.A., Switzerland. Designed by Oliver Corwin, US, and Robert Stein, UN. Each pane contains 4 blocks of 4 (Nos. 690-693, 694-697). A se-tenant block of 4 designs centers each pane.

1997, Feb. 12		**Photo.**		***Perf. 12***	
Granite Paper					
690	A185	32c	Tadjikistan *(940,000)+*		1.00 .75
691	A185	32c	Georgia *(940,000)+*		1.00 .75
692	A185	32c	Armenia *(940,000)+*		1.00 .75
693	A185	32c	Namibia *(940,000)+*		1.00 .75
a.	Block of 4, #690-693				5.00 4.00
694	A185	32c	Liechtenstein *(940,000)+*		1.00 .75
695	A185	32c	Republic of Korea *(940,000)+*		1.00 .75
696	A185	32c	Kazakhstan *(940,000)+*		1.00 .75
697	A185	32c	Latvia *(940,000)+*		1.00 .75
a.	Block of 4, #694-697				5.00 4.00
	First day cover, #690-697, each				3.00
	Set of 2 panes of 16				25.00

First day covers of Nos. 690-697 total 136,114.

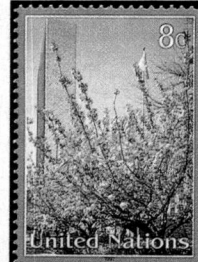

Cherry Blossoms, UN Headquarters — A297

Peace Rose — A298

Printed by The House of Questa, Ltd., UK.

1997, Feb. 12		**Litho.**		***Perf. 14½***	
698	A297	8c	**multicolored**	*(700,000)+*	.20 .20
	First day cover				1.00
	Inscription block of 4				.80
699	A298	55c	**multicolored**	*(700,000)+*	1.00 .90
	First day cover				1.25
	First day cover, #698-699				2.50
	Inscription block of 4				4.25

First day covers of Nos. 698-699 total 34,794.

Endangered Species Type of 1993

Printed by Johann Enschedé and Sons, the Netherlands. Designed by Rocco J. Callari, US.
Designs: No. 700, African elephant. No. 701, Major Mitchell's cockatoo. No. 702, Black-footed ferret. No. 703, Cougar.

1997, Mar. 13		**Litho.**		***Perf. 12½***	
700	A271	32c	**multicolored**	*(532,000)+*	.45 .45
701	A271	32c	**multicolored**	*(532,000)+*	.45 .45
702	A271	32c	**multicolored**	*(532,000)+*	.45 .45
703	A271	32c	**multicolored**	*(532,000)+*	.45 .45
a.	Block of 4, #700-703				2.40 2.40
	First day cover, #703a				3.00
	First day cover, #700-703, each				2.50
	Inscription block of 4, #703a				2.75
	Pane of 16				10.00

First day covers of Nos. 700-703 total 66,863.
See Offices in Geneva Nos. 298-301; Vienna Nos. 214-217.

Earth Summit, 5th Anniv. — A299

Printed by Helio Courvoisier SA, Switzerland. Designed by Peter Max, US.
Designs: No. 704, Sailboat. No. 705, Three sailboats. No. 706, Two people watching sailboat, sun. No. 707, Person, sailboat.
$1, Combined design similar to Nos. 704-707.

1997, May 30		**Photo.**		***Perf. 11.5***	
Granite Paper					
704	A299	32c	**multicolored**	*(328,566)*	.75 .50
705	A299	32c	**multicolored**	*(328,566)*	.75 .50
706	A299	32c	**multicolored**	*(328,566)*	.75 .50
707	A299	32c	**multicolored**	*(328,566)*	.75 .50
a.	Block of 4, #704-707				4.00 2.50
	First day cover, #707a				2.50
	First day cover, #704-707, each				6.00
	Inscription block of 4, #707a				4.50

Souvenir Sheet

708	A299	$1 **multicolored** *(181,667)*		2.75 2.75
	First day cover			3.00
a.	Ovptd. in sheet margin *(154,435)*			18.00 18.00
	First day cover, #708a			16.50

First day covers of Nos. 704-708 total: New York, 52,528; San Francisco, 49,197.
See Offices in Geneva Nos. 302-306; Vienna Nos. 218-222.
No. 708 contains one 60x43mm stamp. Overprint in sheet margin of No. 708a reads "PACIFIC 97 / World Philatelic Exhibition / San Francisco, California / 29 May - 8 June 1997".

Transportation — A300

Printed by The House of Questa, UK. Panes of 20.
Designed by Michael Cockcroft, UK.

Ships: No. 709, Clipper ship. No. 710, Paddle steamer. No. 711, Ocean liner. No. 712, Hovercraft. No. 713, Hydrofoil.

1997, Aug. 29		**Litho.**	**Perf. 14x14½**	
709	A300 32c	multicolored (303,767)	.50	.35
710	A300 32c	multicolored (303,767)	.50	.35
711	A300 32c	multicolored (303,767)	.50	.35
712	A300 32c	multicolored (303,767)	.50	.35
713	A300 32c	multicolored (303,767)	.50	.35
a.		Strip of 5, #709-713	3.25	2.25
		First day cover, #713a		4.00
		First day cover, #709-713, each		5.75
		Inscription block of 10, 2#713a	8.00	
		Sheet of 20	15.00	

First day covers of Nos. 709-713 total 29,287.
See Offices in Geneva Nos. 307-311; Vienna Nos. 223-227.
No. 713a has continuous design.

Philately — A301

Printed by Joh. Enschedé and Sons, the Netherlands. Panes of 20. Designed by Robert Stein, US.
Designs: 32c, No. 473. 50c, No. 474.

1997, Oct. 14		**Litho.**	**Perf. 13½x14**	
714	A301 32c	multicolored (363,237)	.75	.75
		First day cover		1.25
		Inscription block of 4	3.50	—
715	A301 50c	multicolored (294,967)	1.75	1.75
		First day cover		1.50
		First day cover, #714-715		2.50
		Inscription block of 4	9.50	—

First day covers of Nos. 714-715 total 43,684.
See Offices in Geneva Nos. 312-313; Vienna Nos. 228-229.

World Heritage
Convention, 25th
Anniv. — A302

Printed by Government Printing Office, Austria. Panes of 20. Designed by Robert Stein, US, based on photographs by Guo Youmin, People's Republic of China.
Terracotta warriors of Xian: 32c, Single warrior. 60c, Massed warriors. No. 718a, like #716. No. 718b, like #717. No. 718c, like Geneva #314. No. 718d, like Geneva #315. No. 718e, like Vienna #230. No. 718f, like Vienna #231.

1997, Nov. 19		**Litho.**	**Perf. 13½**	
716	A302 32c	multicolored (549,095)	.75	.60
		First day cover		1.25
		Inscription block of 4	3.25	—
717	A302 60c	multicolored (505,265)	1.25	1.00
		First day cover		1.75
		First day cover, #716-717		2.75
		Inscription block of 4	5.25	—
718		Souvenir booklet (304,406 booklets)	10.00	
a.-f.		A302 8c any single	.40	.40
g.		Booklet pane of 4 #718a	1.60	1.60
h.		Booklet pane of 4 #718b	1.60	1.60
i.		Booklet pane of 4 #718c	1.60	1.60
j.		Booklet pane of 4 #718d	1.60	1.60
k.		Booklet pane of 4 #718e	1.60	1.60
l.		Booklet pane of 4 #718f	1.60	1.60

First day covers of Nos. 716-718 total 33,386.
See Offices in Geneva Nos. 314-316; Vienna Nos. 230-232.

Flag Type of 1980

Printed by Helio Courvoisier, S.A., Switzerland. Designed by Oliver Corwin, and Robert Stein, US. Each pane contains 4 blocks of 4 (Nos. 719-722, 723-726). A se-tenant block of 4 designs centers each pane.

1998, Feb. 13		**Photo.**	**Perf. 12**	
		Granite Paper		
719	A185 32c	Micronesia (718,000)+	.80	.50
720	A185 32c	Slovakia (718,000)+	.80	.50
721	A185 32c	Democratic People's Republic of Korea (718,000)+	.80	.50
722	A185 32c	Azerbaijan (718,000)+	.80	.50
a.		Block of 4, #719-722	5.50	5.00
723	A185 32c	Uzbekistan (718,000)+	.80	.50
724	A185 32c	Monaco (718,000)+	.80	.50
725	A185 32c	Czech Republic (718,000)+	.80	.50
726	A185 32c	Estonia (718,000)+	.80	.50
a.		Block of 4, #723-726	5.50	5.00
		First day cover, #719-726, each		2.00
		Set of 2 panes of 16	25.00	
		Nos. 719-726 (8)	6.40	4.00

A303

A304

A305

Printed by The House of Questa, UK. Designed by Zhang Le Lu, China (1c), Robert Stein, US (2c), Gregory Halili, Philippines (21c). Panes of 20.

1998, Feb. 13		**Litho.**	**Perf. 14½x15, 15x14½**	
727	A303 1c	multicolored (1,000,000)+	.20	.20
		First day cover		1.00
		Inscription block of 4	.20	
728	A304 2c	multicolored (1,000,000)+	.20	.20
		First day cover		1.00
		Inscription block of 4	.20	
729	A305 21c	multicolored (1,000,000)+	.40	.30
		First day cover		1.00
		First day cover, #727-729		3.00
		Inscription block of 4	1.75	
		Nos. 727-729 (3)	.80	.70

Endangered Species Type of 1993

Printed by Johann Enschedé and Sons, the Netherlands. Designed by Rocco J. Callari, US and Pat Medearis-Altman, New Zealand.
Designs: No. 730, Lesser galago. No. 731, Hawaiian goose. No. 732, Golden birdwing. No. 733, Sun bear.

1998, Mar. 13		**Litho.**	**Perf. 12½**	
730	A271 32c	multicolored (502,000)+	.50	.45
731	A271 32c	multicolored (502,000)+	.50	.45
732	A271 32c	multicolored (502,000)+	.50	.45
733	A271 32c	multicolored (502,000)+	.50	.45
a.		Block of 4, #730-733	2.40	2.40
		First day cover, #733a		3.50
		First day cover, #730-733, each		3.50
		Inscription block of 4, #733a	2.75	
		Pane of 16	11.00	

See Offices in Geneva Nos. 318-321; Vienna Nos. 235-238.

Intl. Year of the Ocean — A306

Printed by Johann Enschedé and Sons, the Netherlands. Designed by Larry Taugher, US.

1998, May 20		**Litho.**	**Perf. 13x13½**	
734	A306	Sheet of 12 (280,000)+	10.00	9.00
		First day cover		9.00
a.-l.		32c any single	.80	.55
		First day cover, #734a-734l, each		4.00

See Offices in Geneva No. 322; Vienna No. 239.

Rain Forests
A307

Printed by Government Printing Bureau, Japan. Designed by Rick Garcia, US.

1998, June 19		**Litho.**	**Perf. 13x13½**	
735	A307 32c	Jaguar (570,000)+	.60	.60
		First day cover		2.50
		Inscription block of 4	2.75	—
		Souvenir Sheet		
736	A307 $2	like #735 (280,000)+	3.00	2.00
		First day cover		3.00

See Offices in Geneva Nos. 323-324; Vienna Nos. 240-241.

U.N.
Peacekeeping
Forces, 50th
Anniv. — A308

Printed by Helio Courvoisier, S.A. (Switzerland). Designed by Andrew Davidson, UK.
Designs: 33c, Commander with binoculars. 40c, Two soldiers on vehicle.

1998, Sept. 15		**Photo.**	**Perf. 12**	
737	A308 33c	multicolored (485,000)+	.50	.40
		First day cover		1.25
		Inscription block of 4	2.25	—
738	A308 40c	multicolored (445,000)+	.80	.70
		First day cover		1.25
		First day cover, #737-738		2.00
		Inscription block of 4	3.75	—

See Offices in Geneva Nos. 325-326; Vienna Nos. 242-243.

Universal Declaration of Human Rights, 50th Anniv. — A309

Printed by Cartor Security Printing (France). Designed by Jean-Michel Folon, France.
Stylized people: 32c, Carrying flag. 55c, Carrying pens.

1998, Oct. 27		Litho. & Photo.		Perf. 13	
739	A309 32c multicolored (485,000)+			.50	.40
	First day cover				1.25
	Inscription block of 4			2.25	—
740	A309 55c multicolored (445,000)+			.95	.85
	First day cover				1.50
	First day cover, #739-740				2.50
	Inscription block of 4			4.00	—

See Offices in Geneva Nos. 327-328; Vienna Nos. 244-245.

Schönbrunn Palace, Vienna — A310

Printed by the House of Questa, UK. Panes of 20. Designed by Robert Stein, US.
Designs: 33c, #743f, The Gloriette. 60c, #743b, Wall painting on fabric (detail), by Johann Wenzl Bergl, vert. No. 743a, Blue porcelain vase, vert. No. 743c, Porcelain stove, vert. No. 743d, Palace. No. 743e, Great Palm House (conservatory).

1998, Dec. 4		Litho.		Perf. 14	
741	A310 33c multicolored (485,000)+			.60	.55
	First day cover				1.25
	Inscription block of 4			2.75	—
742	A310 60c multicolored (445,000)+			1.25	1.00
	First day cover				1.50
	First day cover, #741-742				2.50
	Inscription block of 4			5.25	—

Souvenir Booklet

743	Booklet (110,000)+		15.00	
a.-c.	A310 11c any single		.45	.45
d.-f.	A310 15c any single		.60	.60
g.	Booklet pane of 4 #743d		2.40	2.40
h.	Booklet pane of 3 #743a		1.40	1.40
i.	Booklet pane of 3 #743b		1.40	1.40
j.	Booklet pane of 3 #743c		1.40	1.40
k.	Booklet pane of 4 #743e		2.40	2.40
l.	Booklet pane of 4 #743f		2.40	2.40

See Offices in Geneva Nos. 329-331; Vienna Nos. 246-248.

Flag Type of 1980

Printed by Helio Courvoisier S.A., Switzerland. Designed by Oliver Corwin, Robert Stein and Blake Tarpley, US. Each pane contains 4 blocks of 4 designs (Nos. 744-747, 748-751). A se-tenant block of 4 designs centers each pane.

1999, Feb. 5		Photo.		Perf. 12	
744	A185 33c multicolored (524,000)+			.80	.60
745	A185 33c multicolored (524,000)+			.80	.60
746	A185 33c multicolored (524,000)+			.80	.60
747	A185 33c multicolored (524,000)+			.80	.60
a.	Block of 4, #744-747			6.00	5.00
748	A185 33c multicolored (524,000)+			.80	.60
749	A185 33c multicolored (524,000)+			.80	.60
750	A185 33c multicolored Bosnia & Herzegovina (524,000)+			.80	.60
751	A185 33c multicolored (524,000)+			.80	.60
a.	Block of 4, #748-751			6.00	5.00
	First day cover, #744-751, each				2.50
	Set of 2 panes of 16			22.50	
	Nos. 744-751 (8)			6.40	4.80

First day covers of Nos. 744-751 total 102,040.

Flags and Globe — A311

Roses — A312

Designed by Blake Tarpley (#752), Rorie Katz, (#753), US. Printed by Johann Enschedé and Sons, the Netherlands (#752), Helio Courvoisier SA, Switzerland (#753).

1999, Feb. 5		Litho.		Perf. 14x13½	
752	A311 33c multicolored (960,000)+			.50	.40
	First day cover				1.00
	Inscription block of 4			2.25	—

Photo.
Granite Paper
Perf. 11½x12

753	A312 $5 multicolored (420,000)+			5.75	1.00
	First day cover				5.50
	First day cover, #752-753				6.50
	Inscription block of 4			23.00	—

First day covers of Nos. 752-753 total 32,142.

World Heritage Sites, Australia A313

Printed by House of Questa, UK. Panes of 20. Designed by Passmore Design, Australia.
Designs: 33c, #756f, Willandra Lakes region. 60c, #756b, Wet tropics of Queensland. No. 756a, Tasmanian wilderness. No. 756c, Great Barrier Reef. No. 756d, Uluru-Kata Tjuta Natl. Park. No. 756e, Kakadu Natl. Park.

1999, Mar. 19		Litho.		Perf. 13	
754	A313 33c multicolored (480,000)+			.60	.75
	First day cover				1.25
	Inscription block of 4			3.00	—
755	A313 60c multicolored (440,000)+			1.25	1.50
	First day cover				1.50
	First day cover, #754-755				2.50
	Inscription block of 4			6.00	—

Souvenir Booklet

756	Booklet (97,000)+		12.00	
a.-c.	A313 5c any single		.20	.20
d.-f.	A313 15c any single		.60	.60
g.	Booklet pane of 4 #756a		.70	.70
h.	Booklet pane of 4 #756d		2.50	2.50
i.	Booklet pane of 4 #756b		.70	.70
j.	Booklet pane of 4 #756e		2.50	2.50
k.	Booklet pane of 4 #756c		.70	.70
l.	Booklet pane of 4 #756f		2.50	2.50

First day covers of Nos. 754-756 total 42,385.
See Offices in Geneva Nos. 333-335; Vienna Nos. 250-252.

Endangered Species Type of 1993

Printed by Johann Enschedé and Sons, the Netherlands. Designed by Jimmy Wang, China.
Designs: No. 757, Tiger. No. 758, Secretary bird. No. 759, Green tree python. No. 760, Long-tailed chinchilla.

1999, Apr. 22		Litho.		Perf. 12½	
757	A271 33c multicolored (494,000)+			.50	.40
758	A271 33c multicolored (494,000)+			.50	.40
759	A271 33c multicolored (494,000)+			.50	.40

760	A271 33c multicolored (494,000)+			.50	.40
a.	Block of 4, #757-760			2.50	2.50
	First day cover, #760a				3.50
	First day cover, #757-760, each				2.00
	Inscription block of 4, #760a			2.75	—
	Pane of 16			11.00	

First day covers of Nos. 757-760 total 49,656.
See Offices in Geneva Nos. 336-339; Vienna Nos. 253-256.

UNISPACE III, Vienna — A314

Printed by Helio Courvoisier SA, Switzerland. Designed by Attila Hejja, US.
Designs: No. 761, Probe on planet's surface. No. 762, Planetary rover. No. 763, Composite of #761-762.

1999, July 7		Photo.		Rouletted 8	
761	A314 33c multicolored (1,000,000)+			.50	.45
762	A314 33c multicolored (1,000,000)+			.50	.45
a.	Pair, #761-762			1.75	1.50
	First day cover, #762a				2.00
	First day cover, #761-762, each				3.75
	Inscription block of 4			4.00	—
	Pane of 10, #761-762			9.00	—

Souvenir Sheet
Perf. 14½

763	A314 $2 multicolored (530,000)+			4.00	2.50
	First day cover				3.00
a.	Ovptd. in sheet margin			16.00	8.00
	First day cover				8.00

No. 763a was issued 7/7/00 and is overprinted in violet blue "WORLD STAMP EXPO 2000 / ANAHEIM, CALIFORNIA / U.S.A./ 7-16 JULY 2000."
First day covers of Nos. 761-763 total 48,190.
See Offices in Geneva #340-342; Vienna #257-259.

UPU, 125th Anniv. — A315

Printed by Helio Courvoisier S.A., Switzerland. Panes of 24. Designed by Mark Hess, US.

Various people, 19th century methods of mail transportation, denomination at: No. 764, UL. No. 765, UR. No. 766, LL. No. 767, LR.

1999, Aug. 23		Photo.		Perf. 11¾	
764	A315 33c multicolored (378,000)+			.50	.40
765	A315 33c multicolored (378,000)+			.50	.40
766	A315 33c multicolored (378,000)+			.50	.40
767	A315 33c multicolored (378,000)+			.50	.40
a.	Block of 4, #764-767			2.75	2.00
	Inscription block of 4			3.25	
	First day cover, #767a				2.25
	First day cover, #764-767, each				6.00
	Sheet of 20			17.00	

First day covers of Nos. 764-767 total 25,294.
See Offices in Geneva Nos. 343-346; Vienna Nos. 260-263.

In Memoriam — A316

Printed by Walsall Security Printers, Ltd., United Kingdom. Panes of 20. Designed by Robert Stein, US.

Designs: 33c, $1, UN Headquarters. Size of $1 stamp: 34x63mm.

1999, Sept. 21   Litho.   Perf. 14½x14
768 A316 33c multicolored (550,000)+   1.00 1.00
     Inscription block of 4   4.50
     First day cover   1.25

Souvenir Sheet
Perf. 14
769 A316 $1 multicolored (235,000)+   2.00 1.50
     First day cover   1.75

First day covers of Nos. 768-769 total 42,130.
See Offices in Geneva #347-348, Vienna #264-265.

Education, Keystone to the 21st Century — A317

Printed by Government Printing Office, Austria. Panes of 20.
Designed by Romero Britto, Brazil.

1999, Nov. 18   Litho.   Perf. 13½x13¾
770 A317 33c Two readers (450,000)+   .55 .30
     First day cover   1.25
     Inscription block of 4   2.40
771 A317 60c Heart (430,000)+   1.10 .60
     First day cover   1.50
     First day cover, #770-771   2.50
     Inscription block of 4   4.75

First day covers of Nos. 770-771 total 34,679.
See Offices in Geneva Nos. 349-350, Vienna Nos. 266-267.

International Year of
Thanksgiving — A318

Printed by Cartor Security Printing, France. Panes of 20.
Designed by Rorie Katz, US.

2000, Jan. 1   Litho.   Perf. 13¼x13½
772 A318 33c multicolored (550,000)+   .65 .60
     First day cover   1.25
     Inscription block of 4   3.25

On No. 772 parts of the design were applied by a thermographic process producing a shiny, raised effect. See Offices in Geneva No. 351, Vienna No. 268.

Endangered Species Type of 1993

Printed by Johann Enschedé and Sons, the Netherlands.
Designed by Suzanne Duranceau, Canada.
    Designs: No. 773, Brown bear. No. 774, Black-bellied bustard. No. 775, Chinese crocodile lizard. No. 776, Pygmy chimpanzee.

2000, Apr. 6   Litho.   Perf. 12¾x12½
773 A271 33c multicolored (490,000)+   .50 .30
774 A271 33c multicolored (490,000)+   .50 .30
775 A271 33c multicolored (490,000)+   .50 .30
776 A271 33c multicolored (490,000)+   .50 .30
  a.   Block of 4, #773-776   2.50 2.50
       First day cover, #776a   3.50
       First day cover, #773-776, each   1.75
       Inscription block of 4, #776a   2.75
       Pane of 16   10.50

See Offices in Geneva Nos. 352-355; Vienna Nos. 269-272.

Our World
2000 — A319

Printed by Cartor Security Printing, France. Panes of 20.
Designed by Robert Stein, US.
    Winning artwork in Millennium painting competition: 33c, Crawling Toward the Millennium, by Sam Yeates, US. 60c, Crossing, by Masakazu Takahata, Japan, vert.

2000, May 30   Litho.   Perf. 13x13½, 13½x13
777 A319 33c multicolored (400,000)+   .60 .30
     First day cover   1.25
     Inscription block of 4   2.50
778 A319 60c multicolored (360,000)+   1.00 .60
     First day cover   1.50
     First day cover, #777-778   2.50
     Inscription block of 4   4.50

See Offices in Geneva No. 356-357, Vienna No. 273-274.

UN, 55th
Anniv. — A320

Printed by Cartor Security Printing, France. Panes of 20.
Designed by Rorie Katz, US.
    Designs: 33c, Workmen removing decorative discs in General Assembly Hall, 1956. 55c, UN Building in 1951.

2000, July 7   Litho.   Perf. 13¼x13
779 A320 33c multicolored (400,000)+   .60 .30
     First day cover   1.25
     Inscription block of 4   2.50
780 A320 55c multicolored (360,000)+   1.00 .55
     First day cover   1.50
     First day cover, #779-780   2.25
     Inscription block of 4   4.25

Souvenir Sheet
781 A320 Sheet of 2, #779-780 (277,000)+   2.50 2.50
     First day cover   3.00

See Offices in Geneva No. 358-360, Vienna No. 275-277.

International
Flag of
Peace — A321

Printed by House of Questa, UK. Panes of 20.
Designed by Mateja Prunk, Slovenia.

2000, Sept. 15   Litho.   Perf. 14½x14
782 A321 33c multicolored (400,000)+   .65 .30
     First day cover   1.25
     Inscription block of 4   2.60

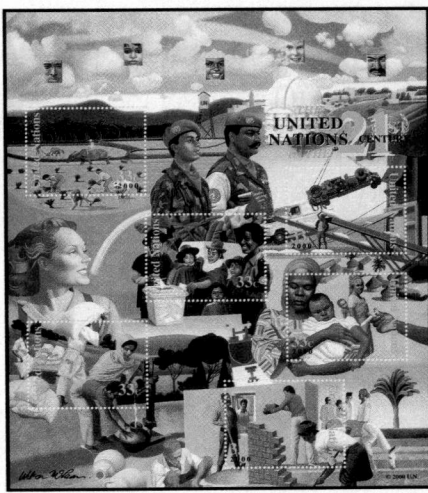
The UN in the 21st Century — A322

Printed by Government Printing Office, Austria.
Designed by Wilson McLean, UK.

No. 783: a, Farmers, animals in rice paddy. b, Vehicle chassis being lifted. c, People voting. d, Baby receiving inoculation. e, Woman, man at pump. f, Mason, construction workers.

2000, Sept. 15   Litho.   Perf. 14
783 A322 Sheet of 6 (274,000)+   7.50 5.00
     First day cover   7.50
  a.-f. 33c any single   1.25 .30
       First day covers, each   6.00

See Offices in Geneva No. 361; Vienna No. 278.

World Heritage Sites, Spain — A323

Printed by House of Questa, UK. Panes of 20. Designed by Robert Stein, US.
    Designs: Nos. 784, 786a, Alhambra, Generalife and Albayzín, Granada. Nos. 785, 786d, Amphitheater of Mérida. #786b, Walled Town of Cuenca. #786c, Aqueduct of Segovia. #786e, Toledo. #786f, Güell Park, Barcelona.

2000, Oct. 6   Litho.   Perf. 14¾x14½
784 A323 33c multicolored (400,000)+   .55 .30
     First day cover   1.25
     Inscription block of 4   2.60
785 A323 60c multicolored (360,000)+   1.10 .60
     First day cover   1.50
     First day cover, #784-785   2.50
     Inscription block of 4   5.00

Souvenir Booklet
786   Booklet (63,000)+   9.00
  a.-c.   A323 5c any single   .20 .20
  d.-f.   A323 15c any single   .50 .50
  g.   Booklet pane of 4, #786a   .80 .80
  h.   Booklet pane of 4, #786d   2.00 2.00
  i.   Booklet pane of 4, #786b   .80 .80
  j.   Booklet pane of 4, #786e   2.00 2.00
  k.   Booklet pane of 4, #786c   .80 .80
  l.   Booklet pane of 4, #786f   2.00 2.00

See Offices in Geneva Nos. 362-364, Vienna Nos. 279-281.

Respect for Refugees — A324

Printed by Johann Enschedé and Sons, the Netherlands. Panes of 20. Designed by Yuri Gevorgian, Armenia.

2000, Nov. 9		**Litho.**	**Perf. 13¼x12¾**	
787	A324	33c multicolored *(540,000)+*	.65	.30
		First day cover		1.25
		Inscription block of 4	3.00	—

Souvenir Sheet

788	A324	$1 multicolored *(225,000)+*	2.00	1.50
		First day cover		2.00

See Offices in Geneva Nos. 365-366, Vienna Nos. 282-283.

Endangered Species Type of 1993

Printed by Johann Enschedé and Sons, the Netherlands. Designed by Grace DeVito, US.
Designs: No. 789, Common spotted cuscus. No. 790, Resplendent quetzal. No. 791, Gila monster. No. 792, Guereza.

2001, Feb. 1		**Litho.**	**Perf. 12¾x12½**	
789	A271	34c multicolored *(430,000)+*	.50	.30
790	A271	34c multicolored *(430,000)+*	.50	.30
791	A271	34c multicolored *(430,000)+*	.50	.30
792	A271	34c multicolored *(430,000)+*	.50	.30
a.		Block of 4, #789-792	2.60	2.50
		First day cover, #792a		3.50
		First day cover, #789-792 each		1.25
		Inscription block of 4, #792a	2.75	—
		Pane of 16	10.50	

See Offices in Geneva Nos. 367-370; Vienna Nos. 284-287.

Intl. Volunteers Year — A325

Printed by Johann Enschedé and Sons, the Netherlands. Panes of 20. Designed by Rorie Katz and Robert Stein, US.
Paintings by: 34c, Jose Zaragoza, Brazil. 80c, John Terry, Australia.

2001, Mar. 29		**Litho.**	**Perf. 13¼**	
793	A325	34c multicolored *(390,000)+*	.65	.30
		First day cover		1.25
		Inscription block of 4	2.60	
794	A325	80c multicolored *(360,000)+*	1.60	.80
		First day cover		1.75
		First day cover, #793-794		2.50
		Inscription block of 4	6.50	

See Offices in Geneva Nos. 371-372; Vienna Nos. 288-289.

Flag Type of 1980

Printed by Helio Courvoisier, Switzerland. Designed by Ole Hamann. Issued in panes of 16; each contains 4 blocks of 4 (Nos. 795-798, 799-802). A se-tenant block of 4 designs centers each pane.

2001, May 25		**Photo.**	**Perf. 12**	
		Granite Paper		
795	A185	34c Slovenia *(460,000)+*	1.00	.30
796	A185	34c Palau *(460,000)+*	1.00	.30
797	A185	34c Tonga *(460,000)+*	1.00	.30
798	A185	34c Croatia *(460,000)+*	1.00	.30
a.		Block of 4, #795-798	10.00	5.00
799	A185	34c Former Yugoslav Republic of		
		Macedonia *(460,000)+*	1.00	.30
800	A185	34c Kiribati *(460,000)+*	1.00	.30
801	A185	34c Andorra *(460,000)+*	1.00	.30
802	A185	34c Nauru *(460,000)+*	1.00	.30
a.		Block of 4, #799-802	10.00	5.00
		First day cover, #795-802, each		1.25
		Set of 2 panes of 16	30.00	
		Nos. 795-802 (8)	8.00	2.40

Sunflower — A326

Rose — A327

Printed by Johann Enschedé and Sons, the Netherlands. Panes of 20. Designed by Rorie Katz, US.

2001, May 25		**Litho.**	**Perf. 13¼x13¾**	
803	A326	7c multicolored *(550,000)+*	.20	.20
		First day cover		1.25
		Margin block of 4, inscription	.50	—
804	A327	34c multicolored *(650,000)+*	.60	.30
		First day cover		1.25
		First day cover, #803-804		1.40
		Margin block of 4, inscription	3.00	—

World Heritage Sites, Japan — A328

Printed by Johann Enschedé and Sons, the Netherlands. Panes of 20. Designed by Rorie Katz, US.
Designs: 34c, #807a, Kyoto. 70c, #807d, Shirakawa-Go and Gokayama. #807b, Nara. #807c, Himeji-Jo. #807e, Itsukushima Shinto Shrine. #807f, Nikko.

2001, Aug. 1		**Litho.**	**Perf. 12¾x13¼**	
805	A328	34c multicolored *(380,000)+*	.60	.30
		First day cover		1.25
		Inscription block of 4	2.50	—
806	A328	70c multicolored *(360,000)+*	1.25	.70
		First day cover		2.10
		First day cover, #805-806		2.75
		Inscription block of 4	5.50	—

Souvenir Booklet

807		Booklet *(51,000)+*	11.00	
a.-c.		A328 5c any single	.25	.25
d.-f.		A328 20c any single	.60	.60
g.		Booklet pane of 4, #807a	1.00	1.00
h.		Booklet pane of 4, #807d	2.50	2.50
i.		Booklet pane of 4, #807b	1.00	1.00
j.		Booklet pane of 4, #807e	2.50	2.50
k.		Booklet pane of 4, #807c	1.00	1.00
l.		Booklet pane of 4, #807f	2.50	2.50

See Offices in Geneva Nos. 373-375, Vienna Nos. 290-292.

Dag Hammarskjöld (1905-61), UN Secretary General — A329

Printed by Banknote Corporation of America, US. Panes of 20. Designed by Robert Stein, US.

2001, Sept. 18		**Engr.**	**Perf. 11x11¼**	
808	A329	80c blue *(530,000)+*	1.50	.75
		First day cover		2.25
		Inscription block of 4	6.00	—

See Offices in Geneva No. 376, Vienna No. 293.

A330

UN Postal Administration, 50th Anniv. — A331

Printed by Johann Enschedé and Sons, the Netherlands. Panes of 20. Designed by Rorie Katz, US.

2001, Oct. 18		**Litho.**	**Perf. 13½**	
809	A330	34c Stamps, streamers *(350,000)+*	.60	.50
		First day cover		1.25
		Inscription block of 4	3.00	—
810	A330	80c Stamps, gifts *(310,000)+*	1.60	1.25
		First day cover		2.25
		First day cover, #809-810		3.00
		Inscription block of 4	7.00	—

Souvenir Sheet

811	A331	Sheet of 2 #811a *(180,000)+*	6.00	2.50
a.		$1 blue & light blue, 38mm diameter	3.00	1.25
		First day cover		10.00

See Offices in Geneva Nos. 377-379, Vienna Nos. 294-296.

Climate Change — A332

Printed by Walsall Security Printers Limited, UK. Panes of 24. Designed by Robert Giusti, US.
Designs: No. 812, Canada geese, greenhouses, butterfly, thistle. No. 813, Canada geese, iceberg, penguins, tomato plant. No. 814, Palm tree, solar collector. No. 815, Hand planting ginkgo cutting.

2001, Nov. 16   Litho.   Perf. 13¼

812	A332	34c **multicolored** (70,500)+	.75	.45
813	A332	34c **multicolored** (70,500)+	.75	.45
814	A332	34c **multicolored** (70,500)+	.75	.45
815	A332	34c **multicolored** (70,500)+	.75	.45
a.		Horiz. strip, #812-815	3.00	3.00
		Inscription block of 8	6.00	
		First day cover, #815a		2.75
		First day cover, #812-815, each		9.00
		Pane of 24	18.00	—

See Offices in Geneva Nos. 380-383, Vienna Nos. 297-300.

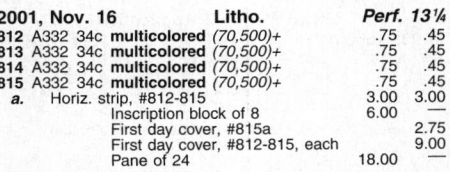

Awarding of Nobel Peace Prize to Secretary General Kofi Annan and UN — A333

Printed by Cartor S. A., France. Panes of 12. Designed by Robert Stein, US.

2001, Dec. 10   Litho.   Perf. 13¼

816	A333	34c **multicolored** (840,000)+	.70	.60
		Inscription block of 4	3.50	
		First day cover		1.25
		Pane of 12	11.50	—

See Offices in Geneva Nos. 384, Vienna Nos. 301.

Children and Stamps — A334

Printed by Government Printing Office, Austria. Panes of 20. Designed by Jerry Smath, US.

2002, Mar. 1   Litho.   Perf. 13¾

817	A334	80c **multicolored** (420,000)+	1.40	.80
		First day cover		2.25
		Inscription block of 4	6.50	

Endangered Species Type of 1993

Printed by Johann Enschedé and Sons, the Netherlands. Designed by Teresa Fasolino, US.

Designs: No. 818, Hoffmann's two-toed sloth. No. 819, Bighorn sheep. No. 820, Cheetah. No. 821, San Esteban Island chuckwalla.

2002, Apr. 4   Litho.   Perf. 12¾x12½

818	A271	34c **multicolored** (414,000)+	.60	.40
819	A271	34c **multicolored** (414,000)+	.60	.40
820	A271	34c **multicolored** (414,000)+	.60	.40
821	A271	34c **multicolored** (414,000)+	.60	.40
a.		Block of 4, #818-821	2.50	2.50
		First day cover, #821a		3.50
		First day cover, #818-821 each		1.50
		Inscription block of 4, #821a	2.75	
		Pane of 16	10.00	—

See Offices in Geneva Nos. 386-389; Vienna 308-311.

Independence of East Timor — A335

Printed by The House of Questa, UK. Designed by Karen Kelleher, US. Panes of 20

Designs: 34c, Wooden ritual mask. 57c, Decorative door panel.

2002, May 20   Litho.   Perf. 14x14½

822	A335	34c **multicolored** (355,000)+	.70	.40
		First day cover		1.25
		Inscription block of 4	3.00	
823	A335	57c **multicolored** (325,000)+	1.20	.70
		First day cover		1.90
		First day cover, #822-823		2.50
		Inscription block of 4	5.00	

See Offices in Geneva Nos. 390-391; Vienna Nos. 312-313.

Intl. Year of Mountains A336

Printed by Cartor Security Printing, France. Designed by Robert Stein and Rorie Katz, US.

Designs: No. 824, Khan Tengri, Kyrgyzstan. No. 825, Mt. Kilimanjaro, Tanzania. No. 826, Mt. Foraker, US. No. 827, Paine Grande, Chile.

2002, May 24   Litho.   Perf. 13x13¼

824	A336	34c **multicolored** (1,362,000)+	.85	.40
		First day cover		3.00
825	A336	34c **multicolored** (1,362,000)+	.85	.40
		First day cover		3.00
826	A336	80c **multicolored** (1,362,000)+	2.10	1.00
		First day cover		5.00
		First day cover, #824, 826		3.25
827	A336	80c **multicolored** (1,362,000)+	2.10	1.00
a.		Vert. strip or block of four, #824-827	7.00	4.00
		First day cover		5.00
		First day cover, #825, 827		3.25
		First day cover, #823-827		3.00
		Pane of 12, 3 each #824-827	17.50	—

See Offices in Geneva Nos. 392-395; Vienna Nos. 314-317.

World Summit on Sustainable Development, Johannesburg A337

Printed by The House of Questa, UK. Designed by Peter Max, US.

Designs: No. 828, Sun, Earth, planets, stars. No. 829, Three women. No. 830, Sailboat. No. 831, Three faceless people.

2002, June 27   Litho.   Perf. 14½x14

828	A337	37c **multicolored** (1,350,000)+	.80	.40
		First day cover		1.25
829	A337	37c **multicolored** (1,350,000)+	.80	.40
		First day cover		1.25
830	A337	60c **multicolored** (1,350,000)+	2.00	.80
		First day cover		2.00
		First day cover, #828, 830		2.25
831	A337	60c **multicolored** (1,350,000)+	2.00	.80
a.		Vert. strip or block of four, #828-831	6.00	3.50
		First day cover		2.00
		First day cover, #829, 831		2.25
		First day cover, #828-831		4.50
		Pane of 12, 3 each #828-831	17.00	—

See Offices in Geneva Nos. 396-399; Vienna Nos. 318-321.

World Heritage Sites, Italy — A338

Printed by Cartor Security Printing, France. Panes of 20. Designed by Rorie Katz, US.

Designs: 37c, #834d, Florence. 70c, #834a, Amalfi Coast. #834b, Aeolian Islands. #834c, Rome. #834e, Pisa. #834f, Pompeii.

2002, Aug. 30   Litho.   Perf. 13½x13¼

832	A338	37c **multicolored** (365,000)+	.70	.40
		First day cover		1.25
		Inscription block of 4	3.00	
833	A338	70c **multicolored** (345,000)+	1.40	.80
		First day cover		2.40
		First day cover, #832-833		3.00
		Inscription block of 4	6.00	—

Souvenir Booklet

834		Booklet (52,000)+	9.00	
a.-c.		A338 5c any single	.25	.25
d.-f.		A338 15c any single	.50	.50
g.		Booklet pane of 4, #834d	2.00	2.00
h.		Booklet pane of 4, #834a	1.00	1.00
i.		Booklet pane of 4, #834e	2.00	2.00
j.		Booklet pane of 4, #834b	1.00	1.00
k.		Booklet pane of 4, #834f	2.00	2.00
l.		Booklet pane of 4, #834c	1.00	1.00

See Offices in Geneva Nos. 400-402, Vienna Nos. 322-324.
See Italy Nos. 2506-2507.

AIDS Awareness — A339

Printed by Walsall Security Printers Limited, UK. Panes of 20. Designed by Rorie Katz, US.

2002, Oct. 24   Litho.   Perf. 13½

835	A339	70c **multicolored** (365,000)+	1.40	.80
		Inscription block of 4	5.75	
		First day cover, #835		2.10
		Pane of 20	30.00	—

See No. B1, Offices in Geneva Nos. 403, B1, Vienna Nos. 325, B1.

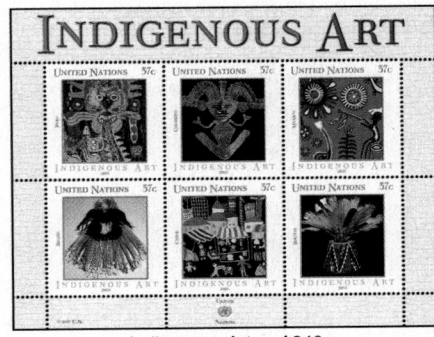

Indigenous Art — A340

Printed by House of Questa, UK.
Designed by Rorie Katz and Robert Stein, US.

No. 836: a, Detail of Paracas textile, Peru. b, Sinu culture anthropo-zoomorphic pendant, Colombia. c, Hicholi Indian embroidery, Mexico. d, Rigpaktsa back ornament, Brazil. e, Wool crafts, Chile. f, Huari feathered woven hat, Bolivia.

2003, Jan. 31   Litho.   Perf. 14¼
836 A340   Sheet of 6 (165,000)+   6.00 2.75
             First day cover   6.25
a.-f.   37c Any single   .85   .40
See Offies in Geneva No. 405; Vienna No. 326.

Clasped
Hands — A341

UN
Emblem — A342

UN Headquarters
A343

Printed by House of Questa, UK (23c, 37c); Walsall Security Printers Ltd., UK (70c). Designed by Rorie Katz, US (23c, 37c), Robert Stein and Rorie Katz (70c). Panes of 20.

2003, Mar. 28   Litho.   Perf. 14¼
837 A341   23c multicolored (870,000)+   .45   .30
             First day cover   1.25
             Inscription block of 4   1.80   —

Litho. with Foil Application
838 A342   37c gold & multicolored (870,000)+ .75 .50
             First day cover   1.25
             Inscription block of 4   3.00   —

Litho. with Hologram
839 A343   70c multicolored (910,000)+   1.40   .90
             First day cover   2.50
             First day cover, #837-839   3.25
             Inscription block of 4   5.60   —

Powered Flight, Cent. — A344

Printed by Government Printing Office, Austria. Designed by Robert Stein, US. Panes of 16 (eight pairs).

2003, Mar. 28   Litho.   Perf. 13½x13¾
840 23c multicolored (175,000)+   .50   .35
841 70c multicolored (175,000)+   1.50   .90
a.   A344 Tete beche pair, #840-841   2.00 1.25
     First day cover, #841a   2.60
     Inscription block of 4   3.75

Endangered Species Type of 1993
Printed by Johann Enschedé and Sons, the Netherlands. Designed by Joseph Hautman, US.
Designs: No. 842, Great hornbill. No. 843, Scarlet ibis. No. 844, Knob-billed goose. No. 845, White-faced whistling duck.

2003, Apr. 3   Litho.   Perf. 12¾x12½
842 A271 37c multicolored (364,000)+   .75   .40
843 A271 37c multicolored (364,000)+   .75   .40
844 A271 37c multicolored (364,000)+   .75   .40
845 A271 37c multicolored (364,000)+   .75   .40
a.   Block of 4, #842-845   2.50 2.50
     First day cover, #845a   3.75
     First day cover, #842-845 each   1.25
     Inscription block of 4, #845a   2.75   —
     Pane of 16   11.00   —
See Offices in Geneva Nos. 407-410; Vienna 329-332.

Intl. Year of
Freshwater
A345

Printed by De La Rue Global Services, United Kingdom. Panes of 20. Designed by Rick Garcia, US.

2003, June 20   Litho.   Perf. 14¼x14½
846 A345 23c Wildlife, garbage (211,000)+ .70   .35
847 A345 37c Trees, canoe (211,000)+   1.10   .40
a.   Horiz. pair, #846-847   2.25   .75
     First day cover, #847a   3.00
     Inscription block of 4   4.50   —
See Offices in Geneva, Nos. 411-412; Vienna Nos. 333-334.

Ralph Bunche (1903-
71), Diplomat — A346

Printed by Johann Enschedé and Sons, the Netherlands. Panes of 20. Designed by Rorie Katz, US.

Litho. With Foil Application
2003, Aug. 7   Perf. 13½x14
848 A346 37c blue & multicolored (405,000)+ .75 .40
     First day cover   1.25
     Inscription block of 4   3.00   —
     Pane of 20   15.00   —
See Offices in Geneva No. 413; Vienna No. 336.

In Memoriam of Victims
of Aug. 19 Bombing of
UN Complex in
Baghdad, Iraq — A347

Printed by Cartor Security Printing, France. Panes of 20. Designed by Jenny J. Karia and Robert Stein, US.

2003, Oct. 24   Litho.   Perf. 13¼x13
849 A347 60c multicolored (850,000)+   1.25   .75
     First day cover   1.90
     Inscription block of 4   5.00   —
     Pane of 20   25.00   —
See Offices in Geneva No. 414, Vienna No. 337.

World
Heritage
Sites,
United
States
A348

Printed by De La Rue Global Services, United Kingdom. Panes of 20. Designed by Rorie Katz, US.
Designs: 37c, #852a, Yosemite National Park. 60c, #852d, Hawaii Volcanoes National Park. #852b, Great Smoky Mountains National Park. #852c, Olympic National Park. #852e, Everglades National Park. #852f, Yellowstone National Park.

2003, Oct. 24   Litho.   Perf. 14½x14¼
850 A348 37c multicolored (303,000)+   .90   .50
     First day cover   1.25
     Inscription block of 4   3.75   —
851 A348 60c multicolored (193,000)+   1.50   .90
     First day cover   2.10
     First day cover, #850-851   2.75
     Inscription block of 4   6.50   —

Souvenir Booklet
852   Booklet (38,500)+   10.00
a.-c.   A348 10c any single   .25   .25
d.-f.   A348 20c any single   .55   .55
g.   Booklet pane of 4 #852a   1.00 1.00
h.   Booklet pane of 4 #852d   2.25 2.25
i.   Booklet pane of 4 #852b   1.00 1.00
j.   Booklet pane of 4 #852e   2.25 2.25
k.   Booklet pane of 4 #852c   1.00 1.00
l.   Booklet pane of 4 #852f   2.25 2.25
See Offices in Geneva Nos. 415-417, Vienna Nos. 338-340.

UN Security Council — A349

UN Emblem — A350

UN General Assembly — A351

Flags — A352

UN Headquarters — A353

Road
Safety — A354

Printed by Cartor Security Printing. Panes of 20. Designed by Michel Granger, France.
Road map art with: 37c, Automobile with road signs, city skyline. 70c, Automobile, hand, vert.

2004, Apr. 7		**Litho.**	**Perf. 13x13¼, 13¼x13**	
863	A354	37c multicolored *(266,000)*+	.70	.35
		First day cover		1.25
		Inscription block of 4	2.75	—
864	A354	70c multicolored *(196,000)*+	1.25	.70
		First day cover		2.40
		First day cover, #863-864		3.00
		Inscription block of 4	5.25	—

See Offices in Geneva Nos. 423-424, Vienna Nos. 347-348.

Japanese Peace Bell, 50th Anniv. — A355

Printed by Imprimerie des Timbres-Poste, France. Panes of 20. Designed by Martin Mörck, Norway.

2004, June 3		**Litho. & Engr.**	**Perf. 13¼x13**	
865	A355	80c multicolored *(376,000)*+	1.50	.80
		First day cover		2.25
		Inscription block of 4	6.25	—
		Pane of 20	30.00	—

See Offices in Geneva No. 425; Vienna No. 349.

World Heritage Sites, Greece — A356

Printed by Johann Enschedé and Sons, the Netherlands. Panes of 20. Designed by Rorie Katz, US.
Designs: No. 866, Acropolis, Athens. Nos. 867, 868e, Delos. No. 868a, Delphi. No. 868b, Pythagoreion and Heraion of Samos. No. 868c, Olympia. No. 868d, Mycenae and Tiryns.

2004, Aug. 12		**Litho.**	**Perf. 14x13¼**	
866	A356	37c multicolored *(275,000)*+	.70	.35
		First day cover		1.25
		Inscription block of 4	2.75	—
a.		Booklet pane of 4	3.00	—
867	A356	60c multicolored *(195,000)*+	1.10	.60
		First day cover		2.10
		First day cover, #866-867		2.75
		Inscription block of 4	4.75	—

Souvenir Booklet

868		Booklet, #866a, 868f-868j *(31,000)*+	13.00	
a.-d.	A356	23c any single	.55	.50
e.	A356	37c multi	1.00	1.00
f.		Booklet pane of 4 #868a	2.20	2.20
g.		Booklet pane of 4 #868b	2.20	2.20
h.		Booklet pane of 4 #868c	2.20	2.20
i.		Booklet pane of 4 #868d	2.20	2.20
j.		Booklet pane of 4 #868e	4.00	4.00

See Offices in Geneva Nos. 426-428, Vienna Nos. 350-352.
No. 868 sold for $7.20.

2003, Nov. 26		**Litho.**	**Perf. 13¼**	
853	A349	37c multicolored + label	5.00	5.00
854	A350	37c multicolored + label	5.00	5.00
855	A351	37c multicolored + label	5.00	5.00
856	A352	37c multicolored + label	5.00	5.00
857	A353	37c multicolored + label	5.00	5.00
a.		Vert. strip of 5, #853-857, + 5 labels	25.00	25.00
		Sheet, 4 #857a	100.00	—
		First day cover, #857a		—
		First day cover, #853-857, each		3.75

The full sheet sold for $14.95 with or without personalized labels. The personalization of labels was available only at UN Headquarters, and not through mail order.
One thousand full sheets with sheet margins inscribed "Hong Kong Stamp Expo" were sold only at that venue. Value $125. Also exists with sheet margins inscribed "Essen." Value $100.
A sheet containing two strips of five stamps similar to Nos. 853-857 but dated "2005" and ten labels sold for $4.95. These sheets were only available canceled. Value $50. An imperforate error of this sheet is known.

Endangered Species Type of 1993

Printed by Johann Enschedé and Sons, the Netherlands. Designed by Yuan Lee, U.S.
Designs: No. 858, American black bear. No. 859, Musk deer. No. 860, Golden snub-nosed monkey. No. 861, Wild yak.

2004, Jan. 29		**Litho.**	**Perf. 12¾x12½**	
858	A271	37c multicolored *(316,000)*+	.75	.35
859	A271	37c multicolored *(316,000)*+	.75	.35
860	A271	37c multicolored *(316,000)*+	.75	.35
861	A271	37c multicolored *(316,000)*+	.75	.35
a.		Block of 4, #858-861	2.50	2.50
		First day cover, #861a		3.75
		First day cover, #858-861, each		1.25
		Inscription block of 4, #861a	2.75	—
		Pane of 16	11.00	—

See Offices in Geneva Nos. 418-421; Vienna Nos. 342-345.

Indigenous Art Type of 2003

Printed by Johann Enschedé and Sons, the Netherlands. Designed by Rorie Katz and Robert Stein, US.
No. 862: a, Viking wood carving depicting Saga of Sigurd Favnesbane, Norway. b, Stele, Italy. c, Detail of matador's suit, Spain. d, Amphora, Greece. e, Bronze figurine of bull, Czech Republic. f, Detail of lacquer box illustration depicting scene from "On the Seashore," by Alexander Pushkin, Russia.

2004, Mar. 4		**Litho.**	**Perf. 13¼**	
862	A340	Sheet of 6 *(134,000)*+	4.50	3.50
		First day cover		6.25
a.-f.		37c Any single	.70	.35
		First day cover, a.-f., each		3.00

See Offices in Geneva No. 422; Vienna No. 346.

My Dream for
Peace — A357

Printed by Government Printing Office, Austria. Panes of 20. Winning designs of Lions Club International children's global peace poster contest by: 37c, Sittichok Pariyaket, Thailand. 80c, Bayan Fais Abu Bial, Israel.

2004, Sept. 21		**Litho.**	**Perf. 14**	
869	A357	37c multicolored *(276,000)*+	.75	.35
		First day cover		1.25
		Inscription block of 4	3.00	—
		Pane of 20	15.00	—
870	A357	80c multicolored *(206,000)*+	1.60	.80
		First day cover		2.40
		First day cover, #869-870		3.00
		Inscription block of 4	6.50	—
		Pane of 20	32.00	—

See Offices in Geneva Nos. 429-430, Vienna Nos. 353-354.

A358

Human
Rights — A359

Printed by Banknote Corportation of America, US. Designed by Yuri Gervorgian, Armenia.

2004, Oct. 14		**Litho.**	**Perf. 11¼**	
871	A358	37c multicolored *(464,000)*+	.75	.35
		First day cover		1.25
		Pane of 8	6.00	—
872	A359	70c multicolored *(464,000)*+	1.40	1.40
		First day cover		2.40
		First day cover, #871-872		3.00
		Pane of 8	11.50	—

See Offices in Geneva Nos. 431-432, Vienna Nos. 355-356.

Disarmament
A360

Printed by Government Printing Office, Austria. Designed by Michel Granger, France.

2004, Oct. 15   Litho.   Perf. 13¾
873 A360 37c multicolored (270,000)+   .70   .70
         First day cover   1.25
         Inscription block of 4   3.00
         Pane of 20   15.00

The U.N. Postal Administration announced that it would begin offering canceled-to-order stamps at the same price as mint stamps, effective Feb. 4, 2005. It has been reliably reported that this did not happen.

United Nations, 60th Anniv. — A361

Printed by Banknote Corporation of America, US. Designed by Czeslaw Slania, Sweden.

2005, Feb. 4   Litho. & Engr.   Perf. 11x11¼
874 A361 80c multicolored (395,000)+   1.60   1.60
         First day cover   2.50
         Inscription block of 4   6.50
         Pane of 20   32.50

Souvenir Sheet
Litho.
Imperf
875 A361 $1 multicolored (135,000)+   17.50   5.00
         First day cover   12.00

See Offices in Geneva Nos. 434-435; Vienna Nos. 357-358.

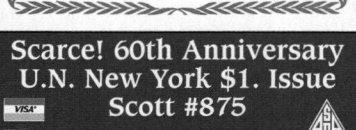
Endangered Species Type of 1993

Printed by Johann Enschedé and Sons, the Netherlands. Designed by Boris Zlotsky, US.

Designs: No. 876, Blue orchid. No. 877, Swan orchid. No. 878, Christmas orchid. No. 879, Aerangis modesta.

2005, Mar. 3   Litho.   Perf. 12¾x12½
876 A271 37c multicolored (248,000)+   .75   .75
877 A271 37c multicolored (248,000)+   .75   .75
878 A271 37c multicolored (248,000)+   .75   .75
879 A271 37c multicolored (248,000)+   .75   .75
  a.   Block of 4, #876-879   2.50   3.00
         First day cover, #879a   4.25
         First day cover #876-879, each   1.75
         Inscription block of 4, #879a   2.75
         Pane of 16   10.00

See Offices in Geneva Nos. 436-439; Vienna Nos. 360-363.

Non-Violence, Sculpture by Carl Fredrik Reuterswärd, New York — A362

Armillary Sphere, Sculpture by Paul Manship, Geneva — A363

Terra Cotta Warriors, Vienna — A364

Single Form, Sculpture by Barbara Hepworth, New York — A365

Sphere Within a Sphere, Sculpture by Arnaldo Pomodoro, New York — A366

2005, Mar. 3   Litho.   Perf. 13¼
880 A362 80c multicolored + label   20.00   20.00
881 A363 80c multicolored + label   20.00   20.00
882 A364 80c multicolored + label   20.00   20.00
883 A365 80c multicolored + label   20.00   20.00

884 A366 80c multicolored + label   20.00   20.00
  a.   Vert. strip of 5, #880-884, + 5 labels 100.00 100.00
         Sheet, 2 #884a   200.00   —
         First day cover, #884a
         First day cover, #880-884,
           each   4.00
  b.   Sheet of 10, both #884 37c (error)   —

The full sheet sold for $14.95 with or without personalized labels. The personalization of labels was available only at UN Headquarters, and not through mail order.
The full sheet exists with sheet margins and labels commemorating the Riccione 2005 Philatelic Exhibition. This sheet went on sale 8/20/05 and was also sold for $14.95. Value $150.

Nature's Wisdom — A367

Printed by Cartor Security Printing, France. Panes of 20. Designed by Robert Stein, US.
Designs: 37c, Ice climber, Norway. 80c, Egret, Japan.

2005, Apr. 21   Litho.   Perf. 13½x13¼
885 A367 37c multicolored (280,000)+   .65   .65
         First day cover   1.40
         Inscription block of 4   2.75
         Pane of 20   13.00
886 A367 80c multicolored (200,000)+   1.50   1.50
         First day cover   3.00
         First day cover, #885-886   3.50
         Inscription block of 4   6.00
         Pane of 20   30.00

See Offices in Geneva Nos. 440-441, Vienna Nos. 364-365.

Intl. Year of Sport — A368

Printed by Cartor Security Printing, France. Designed by Roland Hirter, Switzerland.

2005, June 3   Litho.   Perf. 13x13¼
887 A368 37c Sailing (255,000)+   .65   .65
         First day cover   1.50
         Inscription block of 4   2.75
         Pane of 20   13.00
888 A368 70c Running (185,000)+   1.25   1.25
         First day cover   2.75
         First day cover, #887-888   3.50
         Inscription block of 4   5.25
         Pane of 20   25.00

See Offices in Geneva Nos. 442-443; Vienna Nos. 366-367.

World Heritage Sites, Egypt — A369

Printed by Johann Enschedé and Sons, the Netherlands. Panes of 20. Designed by Rorie Katz, US.
Designs: Nos. 889, 891a, Memphis and its Necropolis. Nos. 890, 891b, Ancient Thebes. No. 891b, Philae. No. 891c, Abu Mena. No. 891e, Islamic Cairo. No. 891f, St. Catherine area.

2005, Aug. 4   Litho.   Perf. 14x13¼
889 A369 37c multicolored (275,000)+   .60   .60
         First day cover   1.40
         Inscription block of 4   2.75
890 A369 80c multicolored (195,000)+   1.40   1.40
         First day cover   3.00

	First day cover, #889-890		3.50
	Inscription block of 4	6.00	

Souvenir Booklet

891		Booklet, #891g-891l (29,000)+	12.00	
a.-c.	A369	23c any single	.40	.40
d.-f.	A369	37c any single	.65	.65
g.		Booklet pane of 4 #891a	1.75	—
h.		Booklet pane of 4 #891b	1.75	—
i.		Booklet pane of 4 #891c	1.75	—
j.		Booklet pane of 4 #891d	2.50	—
k.		Booklet pane of 4 #891e	2.50	—
l.		Booklet pane of 4 #891e	2.50	—

See Offices in Geneva Nos. 444-446, Vienna Nos. 368-370.

My Dream for Peace Type of 2004

Printed by Government Printing Office, Austria. Panes of 20.

Winning designs of Lions Club International children's global peace poster contest by: 37c, Vittoria Sansebastiano, Italy. 80c, Jordan Harris, US.

2005, Sept. 21		Litho.	Perf. 14	
892	A357	37c multicolored (270,000)+	.60	.60
		First day cover		1.40
		Inscription block of 4	2.75	
		Pane of 20	12.00	
893	A357	80c multicolored (200,000)+	1.40	1.40
		First day cover		3.00
		First day cover, #892-893		3.50
		Inscription block of 4	5.75	
		Pane of 20	28.00	

See Offices in Geneva Nos. 447-448, Vienna Nos. 371-372.

Food
for
Life
A370

Printed by Government Printing Office, Austria. Designed by Andrew Davidson, United Kingdom.

Designs: 37c, Oats, children and adults. 80c, Wheat, mothers breastfeeding babies.

2005, Oct. 20		Litho.	Perf. 13¾	
894	A370	37c multicolored (245,000)+	.60	.60
		First day cover		1.25
		Inscription block of 4	2.75	
		Pane of 20	12.00	
895	A370	80c multicolored (185,000)+	1.40	1.40
		First day cover		2.75
		First day cover, #894-895		3.25
		Inscription block of 4	5.75	
		Pane of 20	28.00	

See Offices in Geneva Nos. 449-450; Vienna Nos. 373-374.

Stylized Flags
in Heart and
Hands — A371

Printed by Cartor Security Printing, France. Panes of 20. Designed by Eliezer Weishoff, Israel.

2006, Feb. 3		Litho.	Perf. 13x13¼	
896	A371	25c multicolored (670,000)+	.50	.50
		First day cover		1.75
		Inscription block of 4	2.00	
		Pane of 20	10.00	

Indigenous Art Type of 2003

Printed by Johann Enschedé and Sons, the Netherlands. Designed by Robert Stein, US.

No. 897 — Musical instruments: a, Drum, Ivory Coast. b, Drum, Tunisia. c, Stringed instruments, Morocco. d, Drums, Sudan. e, Instruments, Cameroun. f, Harp, Congo.

2006, Feb. 3		Litho.	Perf. 13¼	
897	A340	Sheet of 6 (88,000)+	5.00	4.50
		First day cover		6.25
a.-f.		37c Any single	.80	.75

See Offices in Geneva No. 452; Vienna No. 375.

UN Symbols Type of 2003

2006, Mar. 6		Litho.	Perf. 13¼	
898	A349	39c multicolored + label	2.50	1.75
899	A350	39c multicolored + label	2.50	1.75
900	A351	39c multicolored + label	2.50	1.75
901	A352	39c multicolored + label	2.50	1.75
902	A353	39c multicolored + label	2.50	1.75
a.		Vert. strip of 5, #898-902, + 5 labels	12.50	8.75
		Sheet, 4 #902a	50.00	—

The full sheet sold for $14.95 with or without personalized labels. The personalization of labels was available only at UN Headquarters, and not through mail order.

Sculpture Type of 2005

2006, Mar. 6		Litho.	Perf. 13¼	
903	A362	84c multicolored + label	4.00	4.00
a.		Perf. 14½x14 + label	10.00	10.00
904	A363	84c multicolored + label	4.00	4.00
a.		Perf. 14½x14 + label	10.00	10.00
905	A364	84c multicolored + label	4.00	4.00
a.		Perf. 14½x14 + label	10.00	10.00
906	A365	84c multicolored + label	4.00	4.00
a.		Perf. 14½x14 + label	10.00	10.00
907	A366	84c multicolored + label	4.00	4.00
a.		Vert. strip of 5, #903-907, + 5 labels	20.00	20.00
		Sheet, 2 #907a	40.00	40.00
b.		Perf. 14½x14 + label	10.00	10.00
c.		Vert. strip of 5, #903a-906a, 907b, + 5 labels	50.00	50.00
		Sheet, 2 #907c	110.00	110.00

The full sheet sold for $14.95 with or without personalized labels. The personalization of labels was available only at UN Headquarters, and not through mail order.

Nos. 903a-906a, 907b, issued 9/21/06. Nos. 903a-906a, 907a were from sheet for 2006 Berlin Stamp Show. The year "2006" is slightly larger on Nos. 903a-906a, 907b than on Nos. 903-907.

Full sheets with different margins were sold at the Washington 2006 World Philatelic Exhibition, where the labels could be personalized.

Endangered Species Type of 1993

Printed by Johann Enschedé and Sons, the Netherlands. Designed by John D. Dawson, US.

Designs: No. 908, Golden mantella. No. 909, Panther chameleon. No. 910, Peruvian rainbow boa. No. 911, Dyeing poison frog.

2006, Mar. 16		Litho.	Perf. 12¾x12½	
908	A271	39c multicolored (212,000)+	.60	.60
909	A271	39c multicolored (212,000)+	.60	.60
910	A271	39c multicolored (212,000)+	.60	.60
911	A271	39c multicolored (212,000)+	.60	.60
a.		Block of 4, #908-911	2.75	2.75
		First day cover #911a		4.50
		First day cover, #908-911, each		2.00
		Inscription block of 4, #911a	3.00	—
		Pane of 16	11.50	—

See Offices in Geneva Nos. 453-456; Vienna Nos. 376-379.

Dove Between War and Peace — A372

Designed by Armando Milani, Italy.

2006, Apr. 10		Litho.	Perf. 13¼	
912	A372	75c multicolored + label	2.75	2.75
		Sheet of 10 + 10 labels	25.00	—

The full sheet sold for $14.95 with or without personalized labels. The personalization of labels was available only at UN Headquarters, and not through mail order.

Intl. Day of
Families
A373

Printed by Johann Enschedé and Sons, the Netherlands. Designed by Shelly Bartek, US.

Designs: 39c, Family harvesting grapes. 84c, Children playing with toy sailboats.

2006, May 27		Litho.	Perf. 14x13½	
913	A373	39c multicolored (226,000)+	.70	.70
		First day cover		1.50
		Inscription block of 4	3.00	
		Pane of 20	14.00	
914	A373	84c multicolored (186,000)+	1.50	1.50
		First day cover		3.25
		First day cover, #913-914		3.75
		Inscription block of 4	6.25	
		Pane of 20	30.00	

See Offices in Geneva Nos. 457-458; Vienna Nos. 380-381.

World Heritage Sites, France — A374

Printed by Cartor Security Printing, France. Panes of 20. Designed by Robert Stein, US.

Eiffel Tower and: Nos. 915, 917a, Banks of the Seine. Nos. 916, 917d, Roman Aqueduct. No. 917b, Provins. No. 917c, Carcasonne. No. 917e, Mont-Saint-Michel. No. 917f, Chateau de Chambord.

Litho. & Embossed with Foil Application

2006, June 17			Perf. 13½x13¼	
915	A374	39c multicolored (260,000)+	.70	.70
		First day cover		1.50
		Inscription block of 4	3.00	
916	A374	84c multicolored (180,000)+	1.50	1.50
		First day cover		3.25
		First day cover, #889-890		3.75
		Inscription block of 4	6.25	

Souvenir Booklet

917		Booklet, #917g-917l (28,000)+	14.00	
a.-c.	A374	24c any single	.40	.40
d.-f.	A374	39c any single	.70	.70
g.		Booklet pane of 4 #917a	1.60	—
h.		Booklet pane of 4 #917b	1.60	—
i.		Booklet pane of 4 #917c	1.60	—
j.		Booklet pane of 4 #917d	3.00	—
k.		Booklet pane of 4 #917e	3.00	—
l.		Booklet pane of 4 #917f	3.00	—

See Offices in Geneva Nos. 459-461, Vienna Nos. 382-384.

My Dream for Peace Type of 2004

Printed by Cartor Security Printing, France. Panes of 20. Winning designs of Lions Club International children's global peace poster contest by: 39c, Cheuk Tat Li, Hong Kong. 84c, Kosshapan Paitoon, Thailand.

2006, Sept. 21		Litho.	Perf. 13½x13	
918	A357	39c multicolored (246,000)+	.80	.80
		First day cover		1.50
		Inscription block of 4	3.20	
		Pane of 20	16.00	
919	A357	84c multicolored (186,000)+	1.75	1.75
		First day cover		3.25
		First day cover, #918-919		3.75
		Inscription block of 4	7.00	
		Pane of 20	35.00	

See Offices in Geneva Nos. 462-463; Vienna Nos. 385-386.

Flags and
Coins — A375

Printed by Cartor Security Printing, France. Designed by Rorie Katz, US.

No. 920 — Flag of: a, People's Republic of China, 1 yuan coin. b, Australia, 1 dollar coin. c, Ghana, 50 cedi coin. d, Israel, 10 agorot coin. e, Russia, 1 ruble coin. f, Mexico, 10 peso coin. g, Japan, 10 yen coin. h, Cambodia, 200 riel coin.

2006, Oct. 5 — Litho. — Perf. 13¼x13
920　Sheet of 8　　　　　　　　6.50 6.50
a.-h. A375 39c Any single　　　　　.80   .80
　　　First day cover　　　　　　　　　9.00

A column of rouletting in the middle of the sheet separates it into two parts. See Offices in Geneva No. 464; Vienna No. 387.

Flag Type of 1980

Printed by Government Printing Office, Austria. Designed by Rorie Katz, US. Issued in panes of 16; each pane contains 4 blocks of 4. A se-tenant block of 4 designs centers each pane.

2007, Feb. 2 — Litho. — Perf. 14
921　A185 39c Tuvalu (275,000)+　　　　.80   .80
922　A185 39c Switzerland (275,000)+　　.80   .80
923　A185 39c Timor-Leste (275,000)+　　.80   .80
924　A185 39c Montenegro (275,000)+　　.80   .80
a.　　Block of 4, #921-924　　　　3.20 3.20
　　　First day cover, #921-924, each　　1.90
　　　Pane of 16　　　　　　　13.00
　　　Nos. 921-924 (4)　　　　3.20 3.20

Endangered Species Type of 1993

Printed by Johann Enschedé and Sons, the Netherlands. Designed by John Rowe, US.
Designs: No. 925, Drill. No. 926, Common squirrel monkey. No. 927, Ring-tailed lemur. No. 928, Collared mangabey.

2007, Mar. 15 — Litho. — Perf. 12¾x12½
925　A271 39c multicolored (212,000)+　.80   .80
926　A271 39c multicolored (212,000)+　.80   .80
927　A271 39c multicolored (212,000)+　.80   .80
928　A271 39c multicolored (212,000)+　.80   .80
a.　　Block of 4, #925-928　　　　3.20 3.20
　　　First day cover　　　　　　　　　4.50
　　　First day cover, #925-928, each　　2.00
　　　Inscription block of 4, #928a　　3.20 —
　　　Pane of 16　　　　　　　13.00

See Offices in Geneva Nos. 465-468; Vienna Nos. 388-391.

UN Emblem — A376

Designed by Robert Stein.

2007, Feb. 5 — Litho. — Perf. 14½x14
929　A376 84c dark blue + label　　15.00 15.00
　　　Sheet of 10 + 10 labels　　135.00

The full sheet sold for $14.95. The sheet has two each of five different labels that could not be personalized. The sheet was distributed to members of the Japanese mission on Sept. 21, 2006, but it was not sold to the public until 2007. The sheet's availability to the public was not announced through press releases or on the UNPA website prior to the day of issue or afterward. It was sent to standing order customers in May 2007. Compare with Type A377.

Flags and Coins Type of 2006

Printed by Cartor Security Printing, France. Designed by Rorie Katz, US.
No. 930 — Flag of: a, Brazil, 50 centavo coin. b, Thailand, 1 baht coin. c, Viet Nam, 5,000 dong coin. d, Ecuador, 10 centavo coin. e, India, 5 rupee coin. f, South Africa, 5 cent coin. g, Barbados, 25 cent coin. h, Republic of Korea, 500 won coin.

2007, May 3 — Litho. — Perf. 13¼x13
930　Sheet of 8 (125,000)+　　　　6.50 6.50
a.-h. A375 39c Any single　　　　　.80   .80
　　　First day cover　　　　　　　　　9.00

A column of rouletting in the middle of the sheet separates it into two parts. See Offices in Geneva No. 469; Vienna No. 392.

UN Emblem — A377

2007, June 1 — Litho. — Perf. 13¼
931　A377 84c blue + label　　　　4.00 3.00
　　　Sheet of 10 + 10 labels　　40.00

The full sheet sold for $14.95. The sheet has two each of five different labels that could not be personalized.

Compare with Type A376.

Peaceful Visions — A378

Printed by Lowe-Martin Company, Canada. Designed by Slavka Kolesar, Canada. Panes of 20.
Designs: 39c, "Nest." 84c, "Sisters Weave the Olive Branch."

2007, June 1 — Litho. — Perf. 13x12½
932　A378 39c multicolored (264,000)+　　.80   .80
　　　First day cover　　　　　　　　　1.50
　　　Inscription block of 4　　　　3.20
　　　Pane of 20　　　　　　　16.00
933　A378 84c multicolored (214,000)+　1.75 1.75
　　　First day cover　　　　　　　　　3.25
　　　First day cover, #932-933　　　　3.75
　　　Inscription block of 4　　　　7.00
　　　Pane of 20　　　　　　　35.00

See Offices in Geneva Nos. 470-471; Vienna Nos. 398-399.

UN Symbols Type of 2003

2007, May 14 — Litho. — Perf. 13¼
934　A349 41c multicolored + label　　3.00 3.00
935　A350 41c multicolored + label　　3.00 3.00
936　A351 41c multicolored + label　　3.00 3.00
937　A352 41c multicolored + label　　3.00 3.00
938　A353 41c multicolored + label　　3.00 3.00
a.　　Vert. strip of 5, #934-938, + 5 labels　15.00 15.00
　　　Sheet, 4 #938a　　　　　　60.00

The full sheet sold for $14.95 with or without personalized labels. The personalization of labels was available only at UN Headquarters, and not through mail order.

UN Flag — A379

2007, May 14 — Litho. — Perf. 13¼
939　A379 90c blue + label　　　　5.00 3.00
　　　Sheet of 10 + 10 labels　　50.00

The full sheet sold for $14.95. The sheet has two each of five different labels that could not be personalized.
A second printing of No. 939 has the "U" and "N" more closely spaced.

Helmet of UN Peacekeeper — A380

Printed by Lowe-Martin Group, Canada. Panes of 20.

2007, Aug. 9 — Litho. — Perf. 12½x13¼
940　A380 90c multicolored (550,000)+　1.90 1.90
　　　First day cover　　　　　　　　　3.00
　　　Inscription block of 4　　　　7.60
　　　Pane of 20　　　　　　　38.00

World Heritage Sites, South America — A381

Printed by Lowe-Martin Group, Canada. Panes of 20. Designed by Rorie Katz, US.
Designs: No. 941, Galapagos Islands, Ecuador. Nos. 942, 943a, Rapa Nui, Chile. No. 943b, Cueva de las Manos, Argentina. No. 943c, Machu Picchu, Peru. No. 943d, Tiwanaku, Bolivia. No. 943e, Iguaçu National Park, Brazil.

2007, Aug. 9 — Litho. — Perf. 13¼x13
941　A381 41c multicolored (254,000)+　　.85   .85
　　　First day cover　　　　　　　　　1.50
　　　Inscription block of 4　　　　3.40
a.　　Booklet pane of 4　　　　　3.40   —
942　A381 90c multicolored (254,000)+　1.90 1.90
　　　First day cover　　　　　　　　　3.25
　　　First day cover, #941-942　　　　4.00
　　　Inscription block of 4　　　　7.60

Souvenir Booklet

943　　Booklet, #941a, 943f-943j (26,500)+　17.00
a.-c.　A381 26c Any single　　　　　.55   .55
d.-e.　A381 41c Either single　　　　.85   .85
f.　　Booklet pane of 4 #943a　　　2.20
g.　　Booklet pane of 4 #943b　　　2.20
h.　　Booklet pane of 4 #943c　　　2.20
i.　　Booklet pane of 4 #943d　　　3.40
j.　　Booklet pane of 4 #943e　　　3.40

See Offices in Geneva Nos. 472-474, Vienna Nos. 400-402. No. 943 sold for $8.50.

Humanitarian Mail — A382

Printed by Lowe-Martin Group, Canada. Panes of 10.

2007, Sept. 6 — Litho. — Perf. 12½x13¼
944　A382 90c multicolored (288,000)+　1.90 1.90
　　　First day cover　　　　　　　　　3.00
　　　Inscription block of 4　　　　7.60
　　　Pane of 10　　　　　　　19.00

See Offices in Geneva No. 475, Vienna No. 403, Switzerland No. 9O21.

Space for Humanity A383

Printed by Johann Enschedé and Sons, the Netherlands. Panes of 6. Designed by Donato Giancola, US.
Designs: 41c, Space Shuttle. 90c, Astronauts spacewalking. $1, International Space Station.

2007, Oct. 25 — Litho. — Perf. 13½x14
945　A383 41c multicolored (264,000)+　　.85   .85
　　　First day cover　　　　　　　　　1.50
　　　Inscription block of 4　　　　3.40
　　　Sheet of 6　　　　　　　5.10
946　A383 90c multicolored (264,000)+　1.90 1.90
　　　First day cover　　　　　　　　　3.25
　　　First day cover, #945-946　　　　4.00
　　　Inscription block of 4　　　　7.60
　　　Sheet of 6　　　　　　11.40

Souvenir Sheet

947　A383 $1 multicolored (110,000)+　2.25 2.00
　　　First day cover　　　　　　　　　3.25
a.　　With World Space Week emblem in margin
　　　(110,000)+　　　　　　　2.25 2.00
　　　First day cover　　　　　　　　　3.25

See Offices in Geneva Nos. 476-478, Vienna Nos. 409-411.

Intl. Holocaust Remembrance Day — A384

Printed by Lowe-Martin Company, Canada. Panes of 9. Designed by Matías Delfino, Argentina.

2008, Jan. 27		Litho.		**Perf. 13**	
948	A384 41c **multicolored** (495,000)+			.85	.85
	First day cover				1.90
	Sheet of 9			7.75	

See Offices in Geneva No. 479, Vienna No. 412, Israel No. 1715.

Endangered Species Type of 1993

Printed by Johann Enschedé and Sons, the Netherlands. Designed by Suzanne Duranceau, Canada.
Designs: No. 949, South African fur seal. No. 950, Orange cup coral. No. 951, Longsnout seahorse. No. 952, Gray whale.

2008, Mar. 6		Litho.		**Perf. 12¾x12½**	
949	A271 41c **multicolored** (164,000)+			.85	.85
950	A271 41c **multicolored** (164,000)+			.85	.85
941	A271 41c **multicolored** (164,000)+			.85	.85
952	A271 41c **multicolored** (164,000)+			.85	.85
a.	Block of 4, #949-952			3.40	3.40
	First day cover, #952a				4.75
	First day cover, #949-952, each				2.00
	Inscription block of 4, #952a			3.40	—
	Pane of 16			14.00	—

See Offices in Geneva Nos. 480-483; Vienna Nos. 417-420.

Flags and Coins Type of 2006

Printed by Cartor Security Printing, France. Designed by Rorie Katz, US.
No. 953 - Flag of: a, United Kingdom, 2 pound coin. b, Singapore, 5 dollar coin. c, Colombia, 500 peso coin. d, Sri Lanka, 10 rupee coin. e, Philippines, 1 peso coin. f, Indonesia, 500 rupiah coin. g, United Arab Emirates, 1 dirham coin. h, Libya, 50 dinar coin.

2008, May 8		Litho.		**Perf. 13¼x13**	
953		Sheet of 8 (100,000)+		7.00	7.00
a.-h.	A375 41c Any single			.85	.85
	First day cover				9.25

A column of rouletting in the middle of the sheet separates it into two parts. See Offices in Geneva No. 484; Vienna No. 421.

Sculpture and Flags — A385

UN Flag — A386

UN General Assembly — A387

Flags — A388

UN Headquarters — A389

Designed by Rorie Katz, US.

2008, May 12		Litho.		**Perf. 13¼**	
954	A385 42c **multicolored** + label			1.50	1.50
955	A386 42c **multicolored** + label			1.50	1.50
956	A387 42c **multicolored** + label			1.50	1.50
957	A388 42c **multicolored** + label			1.50	1.50
958	A389 42c **multicolored** + label			1.50	1.50
a.	Vert. strip of 5, #954-958, + 5 labels			8.75	8.75
	Sheet, 4 #958a			35.00	—

The full sheet sold for $14.95 with or without personalized labels. The personalization of labels was available only at UN Headquarters, and not through mail order.

UN Emblem — A390

Designed by Rorie Katz, US.

2008, May 12		Litho.		**Perf. 13¼**	
959	A390 94c **blue** + label			3.00	3.00
	Sheet of 10 + 10 labels			30.00	—

The full sheet sold for $14.95 with or without labels that could be personalized. There are five non-personalized labels. The personalization of labels was available only at UN Headquarters, and not through mail order.

Wheelchair Accessibility Symbol — A391

"UN" in Braille — A392

Printed by Johann Enschedé and Sons, the Netherlands. Panes of 20. Designed by Rorie Katz, US.

2008, June 6		Litho. & Embossed		**Perf. 14x13¼**	
960	A391 42c **blue & yellow** (224,000)+			.85	.85
	First day cover				1.60
	Inscription block of 4			3.40	—
	Sheet of 20			17.00	—
961	A392 94c **yellow & blue** (174,000)+			1.90	1.90
	First day cover				3.50
	First day cover, #960-961				4.00
	Inscription block of 4			7.60	—
	Sheet of 20			38.00	—

Convention on the Rights of Persons with Disabilities. See Offices in Geneva Nos. 485-486, Vienna Nos. 427-428.

Sport for Peace — A393

Printed by Johann Enschedé and Sons, the Netherlands. Panes of 9 (#962-963). Designed by Romero Britto, Brazil.
Designs: 42c, $1.25, Sprinter. 94c, Hurdler.

2008, Aug. 8		Litho.		**Perf. 14½**	
962	A393 42c **multicolored** (389,700)+			.85	.85
	First day cover				1.60
	Inscription block of 4			3.40	—
	Pane of 9			7.75	—
963	A393 94c **multicolored** (389,700)+			1.90	1.90
	First day cover				3.50
	First day cover, #962-963				4.00
	Inscription block of 4			7.60	—
	Pane of 9			17.50	—

Souvenir Sheet
Perf. 12¾x13¼

964	A393 $1.25 **multicolored** (150,000)+			2.50	2.50
	First day cover				3.75

2008 Summer Olympics, Beijing. See Offices in Geneva Nos. 487-489, Vienna Nos. 429-431.

Sport for Peace — A394

2008, Aug. 8		Litho.		**Perf. 13¼**	
965	A394 94c **multicolored** + label			3.00	3.00
	Pane of 10 + 10 labels			30.00	—

2008 Summer Olympics, Beijing. The full pane sold for $14.95 with or without personalized labels. There are two non-personalized labels. The personalization of labels was available only at UN Headquarters, and not through mail order.

"We Can End Poverty" — A395

Printed by Sweden Post, Sweden. Panes of 20.
Winning designs in children's art contest by: 42c, Grace
Tsang, Hong Kong. 94c, Bryan Jevoncia, Indonesia, vert.

2008, Sept. 18	Litho.		Perf. 12¾x12½	
966	A395	42c multicolored (225,000)+	.85	.85
		First day cover		1.60
		Inscription block of 4	3.40	
		Sheet of 20	17.00	—
		Perf. 12½x12¾		
967	A395	94c multicolored (165,000)+	1.90	1.90
		First day cover		3.50
		First day cover, #966-967		4.00
		Inscription block of 4	7.60	
		Sheet of 20	38.00	—

See Offices in Geneva Nos. 490-491, Vienna Nos. 432-433.

Climate Change Types of Geneva and Vienna and

A396

Climate Change — A397

Printed by Lowe-Martin Group, Canada. Panes of 4.
Designed by Rorie Katz, US.
No. 968 - Parched ground and snail shell with quarter of
Earth in: a, LR. b, LL. c, UR. d, UL.
No. 969 - Coral reef with quarter of Earth in: a, LR. b, LL. c,
UR. d, UL.
No. 970: a, Like #969a. b, Like #969b. c, Like #969c. d, Like
#969d. e, Like Geneva #493a. f, Like Geneva #493b. g, Like
Geneva #493c. h, Like Geneva #493d. i, Like Vienna #434a. j,
Like Vienna #434b. k, Like Vienna #434c. l, Like Vienna #434d.
m, Like Geneva #492a. n, Like Geneva #492b. o, Like Geneva
#492c. p, Like Geneva #492d. q, Like Vienna #435a. r, Like
Vienna #435b. s, Like Vienna #435c. t, Like Vienna #435d.
All stamps have blue panels inscribed "Climate Change."

2008, Oct. 23	Litho.		Perf. 13¼x13	
968	Sheet of 4 (100,000)+		3.40	3.40
a.-d.	A396 42c Any single		.85	.85
e.	Booklet pane of 4, #968a-968d		3.50	
	First day cover			4.50
969	Sheet of 4 (100,000)+		7.60	7.60
a.-d.	A397 94c Any single		1.90	1.90
	First day cover			9.75
	First day cover, #968-969			14.00

Souvenir Booklet

970	Booklet, #968e, 970u-970y (22,500)+	18.00	
a.-d.	A397 27c Any single	.55	.55
e.-h.	G77 27c Any single	.55	.55
i.-l.	V72 27c Any single	.55	.55
m.-p.	G76 42c Any single	.85	.85
q.-t.	V73 42c Any single	.85	.85
u.	Booklet pane of 4, #970a-970d	2.40	—
v.	Booklet pane of 4, #970e-970h	2.40	—
w.	Booklet pane of 4, #970i-970l	2.40	—
x.	Booklet pane of 4, #970m-970p	3.50	—
y.	Booklet pane of 4, #970q-970t	3.50	—

No. 970 sold for $9. See Offices in Geneva Nos. 492-494,
Vienna Nos. 434-436.

Paintings of Flowers by Jaime
Arredondo — A398

Printed by Lowe-Martin Company, Inc., Canada. Panes of 20.
Designs: 1c, Cielo rosado. 9c, Rosa de sangre. 10c, Espíritu
de mujer.

2009, Feb. 6	Litho.		Perf. 13¼	
971	A398	1c multicolored (570,000)+	.20	.20
		First day cover		1.90
		Inscription block of 4	.20	
		Sheet of 20	.40	—
972	A398	9c multicolored (570,000)+	.20	.20
		First day cover		1.90
		Inscription block of 4	.80	
		Sheet of 20	4.00	—
973	A398	10c multicolored (570,000)+	.20	.20
		First day cover		1.90
		First day cover, #971-973		1.90
		Inscription block of 4	.80	
		Sheet of 20	4.00	—
		Nos. 971-973 (3)	.60	.60

U Thant (1909-74), Secretary
General — A399

Printed by Johann Enschedé and Sons, the Netherlands.
Panes of 20.

Litho. With Foil Application

2009, Feb. 6			Perf. 14x13½	
974	A399 94c purple & multicolored			
	(255,000)+		1.90	1.90
	First day cover			3.00
	Inscription block of 4		7.60	
	Sheet of 20		38.00	—

See Offices in Geneva No. 495, Vienna No. 437.

Endangered Species Type of 1993

Printed by Johann Enschedé and Sons, the Netherlands.
Designed by Roger Kent, United Kingdom.
Designs: No. 975, Emperor dragonfly. No. 976, Southern
wood ant. No. 977, Rosalia longicorn. No. 978, Apollo butterfly.

2009, Apr. 16	Litho.		Perf. 12¾x12½	
975	A271	42c multicolored (156,000)+	.85	.85
976	A271	42c multicolored (156,000)+	.85	.85
977	A271	42c multicolored (156,000)+	.85	.85
978	A271	42c multicolored (156,000)+	.85	.85
a.	Block of 4, #975-978		3.40	3.40

First day cover, #978a		4.75
First day cover, #975-978, each		2.00
Inscription block of 4, #978a	3.40	—
Pane of 16	14.00	—

See Offices in Geneva Nos. 496-499; Vienna Nos. 438-441.

World Heritage Sites, Germany — A400

Printed by Johann Enschedé and Sons, the Netherlands.
Panes of 20. Designed by Grit Fiedler, Germany.
Designs: Nos. 979, 981a, Town Hall and Roland on the Marketplace, Bremen. Nos. 980, 981d, Aachen Cathedral. No.
981b, Wartburg Castle. No. 981c, Palaces and Parks of Potsdam and Berlin. No. 981e, Luther Memorials in Eisleben and
Wittenberg. No. 981f, Monastic Island of Reichenau.

2009, May 7	Litho.		Perf. 14x13½	
979	A400	44c multicolored (220,000)+	.90	.90
		First day cover		1.60
		Inscription block of 4	3.60	
980	A400	98c multicolored (220,000)+	2.00	2.00
		First day cover		3.50
		First day cover, #979-980		4.25
		Inscription block of 4	8.00	—

Souvenir Booklet

981	Booklet, #981g-981l (21,000)+	17.50	
a.-c.	A400 27c any single	.55	.55
d.-f.	A400 42c any single	.85	.85
g.	Booklet pane of 4 #981a	2.25	—
h.	Booklet pane of 4 #981b	2.25	—
i.	Booklet pane of 4 #981c	2.25	—
j.	Booklet pane of 4 #981d	3.50	—
k.	Booklet pane of 4 #981e	3.50	—
l.	Booklet pane of 4 #981f	3.50	—

See Offices in Geneva Nos. 500-502, Vienna Nos. 442-444.

2009 END-OF-YEAR ISSUES

The UNPA has announced that the following items
will be released in late 2009. Dates and denominations
are tentative.
New York personalized stamps, *June 5.*
New York surcharged postal stationery, *June 5.*
ECOSOC *Aug. 6,* 42c, 94c stamps; Geneva 1f,
1.80fr stamps; Vienna 55c, 75c stamps.
UN Millennium Goals *Sept. 25,* 42c stamp;
Geneva 1.80fr stamp; Vienna €1.15 stamp.
International Day of Non-Violence *Oct. 2,* $1
stamp.
Indigenous People *Oct. 8,* sheet of six 42c stamps;
Geneva sheet of 6 1.30fr stamps; Viena sheet of 6 65c
stamps.
Listings as of 10AM, Aug. 4, 2009.

SEMI-POSTAL STAMPS

Souvenir Sheet

AIDS Awareness — SP1

Printed by Walsall Security Printers Limited, UK. Designed by
Rorie Katz, US.

2002, Oct. 24   Litho.   Perf. 14½
B1 SP1 37c + 6c **multicolored** *(175,000)+*   2.50 2.50
   First day cover, #B1   3.00

See Offices in Geneva No. B1, Vienna No. B1.

AIR POST STAMPS

Plane and Gull — AP1

Swallows and UN Emblem AP2

Engraved and printed by Thomas De La Rue & Co., Ltd., London. Panes of 50. Designed by Ole Hamann (AP1) and Olav Mathiesen (AP2).

1951, Dec. 14   Unwmk.   Perf. 14
C1 AP1 6c **henna brown** *(2,500,000)*   .20   .20
   First day cover   2.00
   Inscription block of 4   .25
C2 AP1 10c **bright blue green** *(2,750,000)* .30   .20
   First day cover   2.00
   Inscription block of 4   1.10
C3 AP2 15c **deep ultramarine** *(3,250,000)*   .40   .25
   First day cover   3.00
   Inscription block of 4   1.60
a.   15c **Prussian blue**   75.00
C4 AP2 25c **gray black** *(2,250,000)*   .85   .50
   First day cover   7.50
   First day cover, #C1-C4   30.00
   Inscription block of 4   4.75
   Nos. C1-C4 (4)   1.75 1.15

First day covers of Nos. 1-11 and C1-C4 total 1,113,216.
Early printings of Nos. C1-C4 have wide, imperforate sheet margins on three sides. Later printings were perforated through all margins.

Airplane Wing and Globe — AP3

Engraved and printed by Thomas De La Rue & Co., Ltd., London. Panes of 50. Designed by W. W. Wind.

1957, May 27   Perf. 12½x14
C5 AP3 4c **maroon** *(5,000,000)*   .20   .20
   First day cover *(282,933)*   1.00
   Inscription block of 4   .30

For 5c see No. C6.

Type of 1957 and

UN Flag and Plane — AP4

Engraved and printed by Waterlow & Sons, Ltd., London. Panes of 50. Designed by W. W. Wind (5c) and Olav Mathiesen (7c).

1959, Feb. 9   Unwmk.   Perf. 12½x13½
C6 AP3 5c **rose red** *(4,000,000)*   .20   .20
   First day cover   1.00
   Inscription block of 4   .50
Perf. 13½x14
C7 AP4 7c **ultramarine** *(4,000,000)*   .20   .20
   First day cover   1.00
   First day cover, #C6-C7   17.50
   Inscription block of 4   .75

First day covers of Nos. C6 and C7 total 413,556.

Outer Space — AP5

UN Emblem — AP6

Bird of Laurel Leaves — AP7

Printed by Courvoisier S.A., La Chaux-de-Fonds, Switzerland. Panes of 50. Designed by Claude Bottiau (6c), George Hamori (8c) and Kurt Plowitz (13c).

1963, June 17   Photo.   Unwmk.   Perf. 11½
C8 AP5 6c **black, blue & yellow green**
        (4,000,000)   .20   .20
   First day cover   1.00
   Inscription block of 4   .45
C9 AP6 8c **yellow, olive green & red**
        (4,000,000)   .20   .20
   First day cover   1.00
   Inscription block of 4   .60
Perf. 12½x12
C10 AP7 13c **ultra, aquamarine, gray &**
        carmine *(2,700,000)*   .20   .20
   First day cover   1.00
   First day cover, #C8-C10   8.50
   Inscription block of 4   .90

First day covers of Nos. C8-C10 total 535,824.

"Flight Across the Globe" — AP8

Jet Plane and Envelope — AP9

Printed by the Austrian Government Printing Office, Vienna, Austria. Panes of 50. Designed by Ole Hamann (15c) and George Hamori (25c).

Perf. 11½x12, 12x11½
1964, May 1   Photo.   Unwmk.
C11 AP8 15c **violet, buff, gray & pale**
        green *(3,000,000)*   .30   .20
   First day cover   1.00
   Inscription block of 4   1.40
a.   Gray omitted
C12 AP9 25c **yellow, orange, gray, blue &**
        red *(2,000,000)*   .50   .30
   First day cover   1.00
   First day cover, #C11-C12   8.00
   Inscription block of 4   2.50
   Nos. C8-C12 (5)   1.40 1.10

First day covers of Nos. C11-C12 total 353,696.
For 75c in type AP8, see UN Offices in Geneva No. 8.

Jet Plane and UN Emblem — AP10

Printed by Setelipaino, Finland. Panes of 50. Designed by Ole Hamann.

1968, Apr. 18   Litho.   Perf. 13
C13 AP10 20c **multicolored** *(3,000,000)*   .35   .25
   First day cover *(225,378)*   1.00
   Inscription block of 4   1.60

Wings, Envelopes and UN Emblem — AP11

Printed by Setelipaino, Finland. Panes of 50. Designed by Olav S. Mathiesen.

1969, Apr. 21   Litho.   Perf. 13
C14 AP11 10c **orange vermilion, orange,**
        yellow & black *(4,000,000)*   .20   .20
   First day cover *(132,686)*   1.00
   Inscription block of 4   .75

UN Emblem and Stylized Wing — AP12

Birds in Flight — AP13

Clouds AP14

"UN" and
Plane — AP15

Printed by Government Printing Bureau, Japan (9c); Heraclio Fournier, S. A., Spain (11c, 17c); Setelipaino, Finland (21c). Panes of 50. Designed by Lyell L. Dolan (9c), Arne Johnson (11c), British American Bank Note Co. (17c) and Asher Kalderon (21c).

1972, May 1		**Litho. & Engr.**		**Perf. 13x13½**	
C15	AP12	9c	light blue, dark red & violet		
			blue *(3,000,000)*+	.20	.20
			First day cover		1.00
			Inscription block of 4	.50	
			Photo.		
			Perf. 14x13½		
C16	AP13	11c	blue & multicolored		
			(3,000,000)+	.20	.20
			First day cover		1.00
			Inscription block of 4	.75	—
			Perf. 13½x14		
C17	AP14	17c	yellow, red & orange		
			(3,000,000)+	.25	.20
			First day cover		1.00
			Inscription block of 4	1.10	—
			Perf. 13		
C18	AP15	21c	silver & multi *(3,500,000)*	.25	.25
			First day cover		1.00
			First day cover, #C15-C18		3.50
			Inscription block of 4	1.25	—
			Nos. C15-C18 *(4)*	.90	.85

First day covers of Nos. C15-C18 total 553,535.

Globe and
Jet — AP16

Pathways
Radiating
from UN
Emblem
AP17

Bird in Flight, UN
Headquarters
AP18

Printed by Setelipaino, Finland. Panes of 50. Designed by George Hamori (13c), Shamir Bros. (18c) and Ölav S. Mathiesen (26c).

1974, Sept. 16		**Litho.**	**Perf. 13, 12½x13 (18c)**		
C19	AP16	13c	multicolored *(2,500,000)*+	.20	.20
			First day cover		1.00
			Inscription block of 4	.80	—
C20	AP17	18c	gray olive & multicolored		
			(2,000,000)	.25	.20
			First day cover		1.00
			Inscription block of 4	1.10	—
C21	AP18	26c	blue & multi *(2,000,000)*	.35	.30
			First day cover		1.25
			First day cover, #C19-C21		2.50
			Inscription block of 4	1.60	—
			Nos. C19-C21 *(3)*	.80	.70

First day covers of Nos. C19-C21 total 309,610.

Winged Airmail
Letter — AP19

Symbolic Globe
and Plane — AP20

Printed by Heraclio Fournier, S.A. Panes of 50. Designed by Eliezer Weishoff (25c) and Alan L. Pollock (31c).

1977, June 27		**Photo.**		**Perf. 14**	
C22	AP19	25c	greenish blue & multi		
			(2,000,000)+	.40	.25
			First day cover		1.25
			Inscription block of 4	1.75	—
C23	AP20	31c	magenta *(2,000,000)*	.45	.30
			First day cover		1.25
			First day cover, #C22-C23		1.50
			Inscription block of 4	2.10	—

First day covers of Nos. C22-C23 total 209,060.

ENVELOPES

Used values for all postal stationery are for non-philatelic contemporaneous usages.

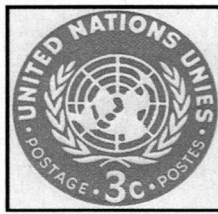

Emblem of United
Nations — U1

Printed by the International Envelope Corp., Dayton, Ohio. Die engraved by the American Bank Note Co., New York.

1953, Sept. 15				**Embossed**	
U1	U1	3c	blue, entire *(555,000)*	.40	.40
			Entire, first day cancel *(102,278)*		1.00

Printed by International Envelope Corp., Dayton, Ohio.

1958, Sept. 22				**Embossed**	
U2	U1	4c	ultramarine, entire *(1,000,000)*	.40	.40
			Entire, first day cancel *(213,621)*		1.00

Stylized Globe
and Weather
Vane — U2

Printed by United States Envelope Co., Springfield, Mass. Designed by Hatim El Mekki.

1963, Apr. 26				**Litho.**	
U3	U2	5c	multicolored, entire *(1,115,888)*	.25	.25
			Entire, first day cancel *(165,188)*		1.00

Printed by Setelipaino, Finland.

1969, Jan. 8				**Litho.**	
U4	U2	6c	black, blue, magenta & dull yellow, entire *(850,000)*	.25	.25
			Entire, first day cancel *(152,593)*		1.00

Headquarters Type of Regular Issue, 1968
Printed by Eureka Co., a division of Litton Industries.

1973, Jan. 12				**Litho.**	
U5	A99	8c	sepia, blue & olive, entire		
			(700,000)	.50	.50
			Entire, first day cancel *(145,510)*		1.00

Headquarters Type of Regular Issue, 1974
Printed by United States Envelope Co., Springfield, Mass.

1975, Jan. 10				**Litho.**	
U6	A138	10c	blue, olive bister & multi, entire		
			(547,500)	.40	.40
			Entire, first day cancel *(122,000)*		1.00

UNITED NATIONS 22c   Bouquet of Ribbons — U3

Printed by Carl Ueberreuter Druck and Verlag M. Salzer, Austria. Designed by George Hamori, Australia.

1985, May 10				**Litho.**	
U7	U3	22c	multicolored, entire *(250,000)*	8.50	3.50
			Entire, first day cancel *(28,600)*		3.50

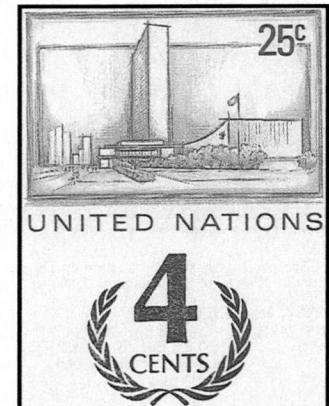

New York
Headquarters
U4

Printed by Mercury Walch, Australia. Designed by Rocco J. Callari, United States.

1989, Mar. 17				**Litho.**	
U8	U4	25c	multicolored, entire *(350,000)*	2.75	2.75
			Entire, first day cancel *(28,567)*		6.00

For surcharge see No. U9A.

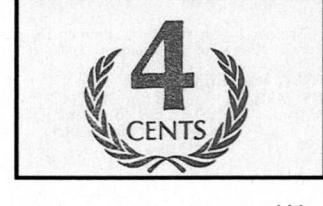

No. U8
Surcharged

1991, Apr. 15				**Litho.**	
U9	U4	25c +4c	multicolored, entire *(50,000)*+	2.75	4.00
			Entire, first day cover		5.50

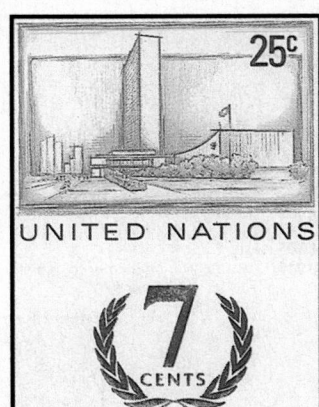

No. U8
Surcharged

1995 **Litho.**
U9A U4 25c +7c **multicolored,** entire 3.00 4.50
Entire, first day cover 6.00

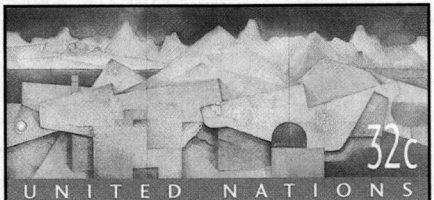

Cripticandina, by Alfredo La Placa — U5

Illustration reduced.
Design sizes: No. U10, 79x38mm. No. U11, 89x44mm.

1997, Feb. 12 **Litho.**
U10 U5 32c **multicolored,** #6¾, entire *(65,000)+* 3.00 2.00
Entire, first day cancel 5.50
U11 U5 32c **multicolored,** #10, entire *(80,000)+* 3.00 2.00
Entire, first day cancel 5.50

Nos. U10-U11 Surcharged

1999, Jan. 10 **Litho.**
U12 U5 32c +1c **multicolored,** on #U10, entire 2.00 2.00
First day cancel, entire 2.50
U13 U5 32c +1c **multicolored,** on #U11, entire 2.25 2.25
First day cancel, entire 2.50

New York
Headquarters — U6

Design sizes: No. U14, 34x34mm. No. U15, 36x36mm.

2001, May 25 **Litho.**
U14 U6 34c **multicolored,** #6¾, entire .90 .90
Entire, first day cancel 1.25
U15 U6 34c **multicolored,** #10, entire .90 .90
Entire, first day cancel 1.25

Nos. U14-U15 Surcharged

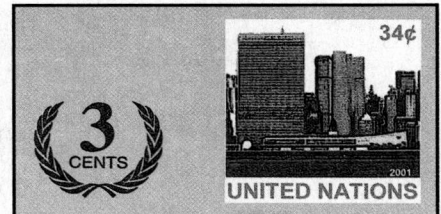

2002, June 30 **Litho.**
U16 U6 34c +3c **multicolored,** entire (#U14) 1.75 1.75
Entire, first day cancel 2.00
U17 U6 34c +3c **multicolored,** entire (#U15) 1.75 1.75
Entire, first day cancel 2.00

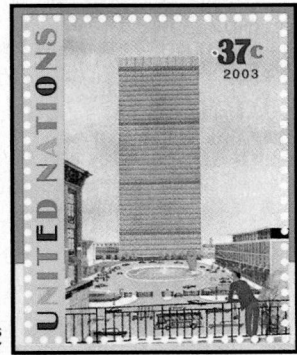

UN Headquarters
U7

Printed by Australia Post Spintpak, Australia.
Design sizes: No. U18, 37x47mm. No. U19, 40x52mm.

2003, Mar. 28 **Litho.**
U18 U7 37c **multicolored,** #6¾, entire *(62,000)+* 1.00 .50
Entire, first day cancel 1.25
U19 U7 37c **multicolored,** #10, entire *(72,000)+* 1.00 .50
Entire, first day cancel 1.25

Nos. U18-U19 Surcharged

2006, Jan. 8 **Litho.**
U20 U7 37c +2c **multicolored,** entire (#U18) 1.50 1.75
Entire, first day cancel 1.25
U21 U7 37c +2c **multicolored,** entire (#U19) 1.50 1.75
Entire, first day cancel 1.25

Nos. U18-U19 Surcharged Like No. U20
2007, May 14 **Litho.**
U22 U7 37c +4c **multicolored,** entire (#U18) 1.75 1.10
Entire, first day cancel 2.10
U23 U7 37c +4c **multicolored,** entire (#U19) 1.75 1.10
Entire, first day cancel 2.10

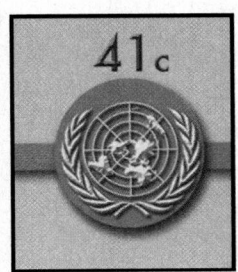

United Nations
Emblem — U8

Printed by Lowe-Martin Group, Canada. Designed by Robert
Stein, US.
Design sizes: No. U24, 22x28mm. No. U25, 29x38mm.

2007, Aug. 9 **Litho.**
U24 U8 41c **multicolored,** #6¾, entire *(35,000)+* 1.50 1.10
Entire, first day cancel 2.10
U25 U8 41c **multicolored,** #10, entire *(35,000)+* 1.50 1.10
Entire, first day cancel 2.10

Nos. U24-U25 Surcharged Like No. U20
2008, May 12 **Litho.**
U26 U8 41c +1c **multicolored,** entire (#U24) 1.50 1.10
Entire, first day cancel 2.10
U27 U8 41c +1c **multicolored,** entire (#U25) 1.50 1.10
Entire, first day cancel 2.10

AIR POST ENVELOPES AND AIR LETTER SHEETS

Used values for all postal stationery are for non-
philatelic contemporaneous usages.

Letter Sheet
Type of Air Post Stamp of 1951
Inscribed "Air Letter" at Left
Printed by Dennison & Sons, Long Island City, NY.

1952, Aug. 29 **Litho.**
UC1 AP2 10c **blue,** *bluish,* entire *(187,000)* 22.50 *20.00*
Entire, 1st day cancel *(57,274)* 2.50
Designed by C. Mutver.

Letter Sheet
Inscribed "Air Letter" and "Aerogramme" at Left

1954, Sept. 14 **Litho.**
UC2 AP2 10c **royal blue,** *bluish,* entire,
(207,000) 9.50 5.00
Entire, 1st day cancel 200.00
a. No white border, *1958 (148,800)* 7.00 *8.00*

No. UC2 was printed with a narrow white border (½ to 1mm
wide) surrounding the stamp. On No. UC2a, this border has
been partly or entirely eliminated.

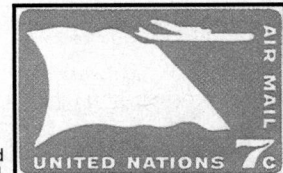

UN Flag and
Plane — UC1

(UN Emblem Emblossed)

Printed by International Envelope Corp., Dayton, O.
Die engraved by American Bank Note Co., New York.

1959, Sept. 21 **Embossed**
UC3 UC1 7c **blue,** entire *(550,000)* 1.00 *1.25*
Entire, 1st day cancel *(172,107)* 1.00

Letter Sheet
Type of Air Post Stamp of 1959
Printed by Thomas De La Rue & Co., Ltd., London

1960, Jan. 18 **Litho.**
UC4 AP4 10c **ultramarine,** *bluish,* entire
(405,000) .65 .65
Entire, 1st day cancel *(122,425)* .50

Printed on protective tinted paper containing colorless
inscription "United Nations" in the five official languages of the
UN.

Letter Sheet
Type of Air Post Stamp of 1951
Inscribed "Correo Aereo" instead of "Poste Aerienne"
Printed by Thomas De La Rue & Co., Ltd., London

1961, June 26 **Litho.**
UC5 AP1 11c **ultramarine,** *bluish,* entire
(550,000) .50 .50
Entire, 1st day cancel *(128,557)* .50
a. 11c **dark blue,** *green* entire, *July 16, 1965*
(419,000) 1.25 —

Printed on protective tinted paper containing colorless
inscription "United Nations" in the five official languages of the
UN.

UN Emblem — UC2

Printed by United States Envelope Co., Springfield, Mass. Designed by George Hamori.

1963, Apr. 26   **Litho.**
UC6 UC2 8c **multicolored,** entire *(880,000)*   .30 .30
        Entire, 1st day cancel *(165,208)*   1.00

Letter Sheet

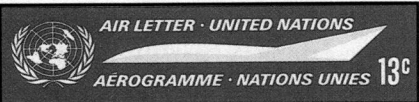

UN Emblem and Stylized Plane — UC3

Printed by Setelipaino, Finland. Designed by Robert Perrot.

1968, May 31   **Litho.**
UC7 UC3 13c **violet blue & light blue,** entire
        (750,000)   .30 .30
        Entire, 1st day cancel *(106,700)*   .50

Type of 1963
Printed by Setelipaino, Finland.

1969, Jan. 8   **Litho.**
UC8 UC2 10c **pink, Prussian blue, orange & sepia,** entire *(750,000)*   .35 .35
        Entire, 1st day cancel *(153,472)*   .50

Letter Sheet

UN Emblem, "UN," Globe and Plane — UC4

Printed by Joh. Enschede and Sons. Designed by Edmondo Calivis, Egypt. Sheet surface printed in greenish blue.

1972, Oct. 16   **Litho.**
UC9 UC4 15c **violet blue & greenish blue,** entire
        (500,000)   .60 .60
        Entire, 1st day cancel *(85,500)*   1.00

Bird Type of Air Post Stamp, 1972
Printed by Eureka Co., a division of Litton Industries

1973, Jan. 12   **Litho.**
UC10 AP13 11c **blue & multicolored,** entire
        (700,000)   .40 .40
        Entire, 1st day cancel *(134,500)*   1.00

Globe and Jet Air Post Type of 1974
Printed by United States Envelope Co., Springfield, Mass.

1975, Jan. 10   **Litho.**
UC11 AP16 13c **blue & multicolored,** entire
        (555,539)   .60 .60
        Entire, 1st day cancel *(122,000)*   1.00

Letter Sheet
Headquarters Type of Regular Issue, 1971
Printed by Joh. Enschede and Sons, Netherlands

1975, Jan. 10   **Photo.**
UC12 A120 18c **blue & multicolored,** entire
        (400,000)   .60 .60
        Entire, 1st day cancel *(70,500)*   1.00

Letter Sheet

"UN" Emblem and Birds UC5

Printed by Joh. Enschede and Sons. Designed by Angel Medina Medina.

1977, June 27   **Litho.**
UC13 UC5 22c **multicolored,** entire *(400,000)*   .65 .60
        Entire, 1st day cancel *(70,000)*   1.00

Letter Sheet

Paper Airplane UC6

Printed by Joh. Enschede and Sons.
Designed by Margaret-Ann Champion.

1982, Apr. 28   **Litho.**
UC14 UC6 30c **black,** *pale green,* entire
        (400,000)   1.50 1.50
        Entire, 1st day cancel *(61,400)*   1.25

Letter Sheet No. UC14 Surcharged

1987, July 7   **Litho.**
UC15 UC6 30c + 6c **black,** *green,* entire
        (43,000)   47.50 45.00
        Entire, 1st day cancel   20.00

New York Headquarters UC7

Printed by Mercury Walch, Australia. Designed by Thomas Lee, China.

1989, Mar. 17   **Litho.**
UC16 UC7 39c **multicolored,** entire *(350,000)*   3.00 3.00
        Entire, 1st day cancel *(14,798)*   9.50

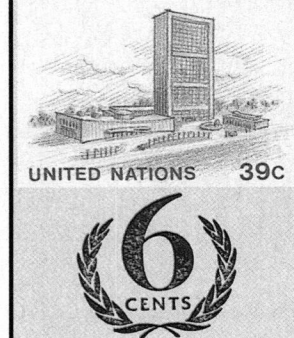

No. UC16 Surcharged

1991, Feb. 12   **Litho.**
UC17 UC7 39c + 6c **multicolored,** entire
        (35,563)   16.00 25.00
        Entire, first day cancel   8.50

UC8

Designed by Robert Stein. Printed by Mercury-Walch, Australia.

1992, Sept. 4   **Litho.**
UC18 UC8 45c **multicolored,** entire, *(185,000)+* 2.75 3.00
        First day cancel   10.00

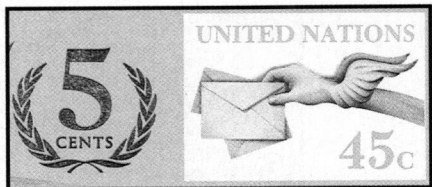

Letter Sheet No. UC18 Surcharged

1995, July 9   **Litho.**
UC19 UC8 45c +5c **multicolored,** entire   4.75 7.50
        First day cover   9.00

Cherry Blossoms — UC9

1997, Mar. 13   **Litho.**
UC20 UC9 50c **multicolored,** entire *(115,000)+* 2.50 2.00
        Entire, first day cancel   2.50

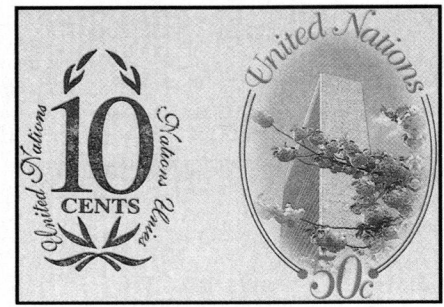

No. UC20 Surcharged

1999, Aug. 23   **Litho.**
UC21 UC9 50c +10c **multicolored,** entire   2.25 2.75
        Entire, first day cancel   2.00

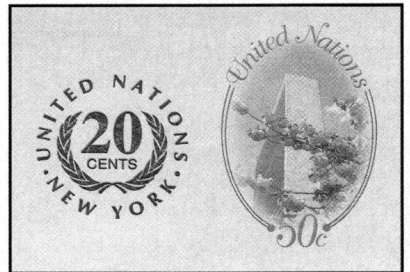

No. UC20 Surcharged

2001, Jan. 9   **Litho.**
UC22 UC9 50c +20c **multicolored,** entire   2.25 2.75
        Entire, first day cancel   2.00

Cherry Blossoms at New York Headquarters UC10

2001, May 25   **Litho.**
UC23 UC10 70c **multicolored,** entire   1.75 1.75
Entire, first day cancel   1.75

No. UC23 Surcharged

2006, Jan. 8   **Litho.**
UC24 UC10 70c +5c **multicolored,** entire   2.00 3.00
Entire, first day cancel   1.50

No. UC23 Surcharged Like No. UC24

2007, May 14   **Litho.**
UC25 UC10 70c +20c **multicolored,** entire   2.50 2.25
Entire, first day cancel   3.00

United Nations Emblem and Airplane UC11

Printed by Sprintpak, Australia. Designed by Robert Stein, US.

2007, Aug. 9   **Litho.**
UC26 UC11 90c **multicolored,** entire *(40,000)+*   2.75 2.75
Entire, first day cancel   3.00

No. UC26 Surcharged Like No. UC24

2008, May 12   **Litho.**
UC27 UC11 90c +4c **multicolored,** entire   2.25 2.00
Entire, first day cancel   3.00

POSTAL CARDS

Values are for entire cards.

Type of Postage Issue of 1951
Printed by Dennison & Sons, Long Island City, N.Y.

1952, July 18   **Litho.**
UX1 A2 2c **blue,** buff *(899,415)*   .20 .20
First day cancel *(116,023)*   .50

Printed by British American Bank Note Co., Ltd., Ottawa, Canada

1958, Sept. 22   **Litho.**
UX2 A2 3c **gray olive,** buff *(575,000)*   .20 .20
First day cancel *(145,557)*   .50

World Map, Sinusoidal Projection — PC1

Printed by Eureka Specialty Printing Co., Scranton, Pa.

1963, Apr. 26   **Litho.**
UX3 PC1 4c **light blue, violet blue, orange & bright citron** *(784,000)*   .25 .20
First day cancel *(112,280)*   .50
a. Bright citron omitted   —

UN Emblem and Post Horn — PC2

"UN" — PC3

Printed by Canadian Bank Note Co., Ltd., Ottawa. Designed by John Mason.

1969, Jan. 8   **Litho.**
UX4 PC2 5c **blue & black** *(500,000)*   .25 .20
First day cancel *(95,975)*   .50

1973, Jan. 12   **Litho.**
Printed by Government Printing Bureau, Tokyo. Designed by Asher Kalderon.

UX5 PC3 6c **gray & multicolored** *(500,000)*   .20 .20
First day cancel *(84,500)*   .50

Type of 1973
Printed by Setelipaino, Finland.

1975, Jan. 10   **Litho.**
UX6 PC3 8c **light green & multi** *(450,000)*   .60 .60
First day cancel *(72,500)*   .50

UN Emblem — PC4

Printed by Setelipaino, Finland. Designed by George Hamori.

1977, June 27   **Litho.**
UX7 PC4 9c **multicolored** *(350,000)*   .60 .60
First day cancel *(70,000)*   .50

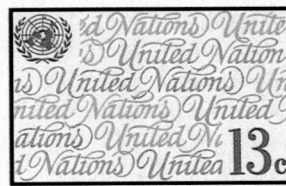

PC5

Printed by Courvoisier. Designed by Salahattin Kanidinc.

1982, Apr. 28   **Photo.**
UX8 PC5 13c **multicolored** *(350,000)*   .50 .50
First day cancel *(59,200)*   1.00

Views of New York Headquarters PC6

Designs: No. UX9, Spring at U.N. Headquarters, vert. No. UX10, Cherry Blossoms, U.N. Gardens, vert. No. UXC11, Row of Flags of member states. No. UX12, U.N. General Assembly. No. UX13, River view, U.N. Headquarters. No. UX14, U.N. Headquarters, vert. No. UX15, Row of flags of member states, vert. No. UX16, Night view, U.N. Headquarters, vert. No. UX17, U.N. Security Council. No. UX18, U.N. Gardens.

Printed by Johann Enschede and Sons, the Netherlands. Designed by Thomas Lee, China, from photographs.

1989, Mar. 17   **Litho.**
UX9 PC6 15c **multicolored** *(120,000)+*   .65 1.00
First day cancel   2.25
UX10 PC6 15c **multicolored** *(120,000)+*   .65 1.00
First day cancel   2.25
UX11 PC6 15c **multicolored** *(120,000)+*   .65 1.00
First day cancel   2.25
UX12 PC6 15c **multicolored** *(120,000)+*   .65 1.00
First day cancel   2.25
UX13 PC6 15c **multicolored** *(120,000)+*   .65 1.00
First day cancel   2.25
UX14 PC6 36c **multicolored** *(120,000)+*   .90 1.50
First day cancel   2.50
UX15 PC6 36c **multicolored** *(120,000)+*   .90 1.50
First day cancel   2.50
UX16 PC6 36c **multicolored** *(120,000)+*   .90 1.50
First day cancel   2.50
UX17 PC6 36c **multicolored** *(120,000)+*   .90 1.50
First day cancel   2.50
UX18 PC6 36c **multicolored** *(120,000)+*   .90 1.50
First day cancel   2.50
Nos. UX9-UX18 (10)   7.75 12.50

Nos. UX9-UX13 and UX14-UX18 sold only in sets. Nos. UX9-UX13 sold for $2 and Nos. UX14-UX18 sold for $3.
First day cancels of Nos. UX9-UX18 total 125,526.

New York Headquarters Type of 1991
Printed by Mercury-Walch, Australia.

1992, Sept. 4   **Litho.**
UX19 A260 40c **blue** *(150,000)+*   3.50 4.00
First day cancel *(9,603)*   12.50

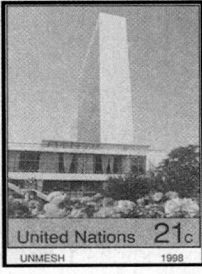

Secretariat Building, Roses — PC7

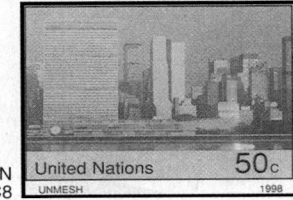

UN Complex — PC8

Printed by Mercury-Walch, Australia.

1998, May 20   **Litho.**
UX20 PC7 21c **multicolored** *(150,000)+*   1.25 1.25
First day cancel   1.75
UX21 PC8 50c **multicolored** *(150,000)+*   2.00 2.00
First day cancel   2.25

Illustrations of the buildings and other scenes are shown on the back of each card.

New York Headquarters PC9

2001, May 25   **Litho.**
UX22 PC9 70c **multicolored**   1.75 1.75
Entire, first day cancel   1.75

No. UX20 Surcharged

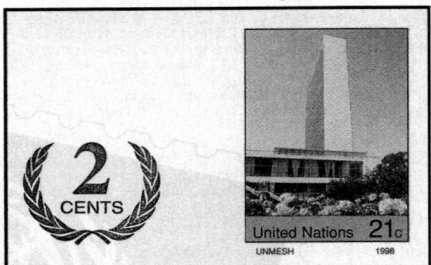

2002, June 30   Litho.
UX23 PC7 21c +2c **multicolored**   1.10 1.25
       First day cancel   1.25

PC10

PC11

PC12

PC13

PC14

PC15

PC16   PC17

PC18

UNITED NATIONS 70c

Illustrations from *This is the United Nations*, by M. Sasek — PC19

Printed by Banknote Corporation of America, US.

2003, Mar. 28   Litho.
UX24 PC10 23c **multicolored** *(61,500)+*   .45   .45
       Entire, first day cancel   1.00
UX25 PC11 23c **multicolored** *(61,500)+*   .45   .45
       Entire, first day cancel   1.00
UX26 PC12 23c **multicolored** *(61,500)+*   .45   .45
       Entire, first day cancel   1.00
UX27 PC13 23c **multicolored** *(61,500)+*   .45   .45
       Entire, first day cancel   1.00
UX28 PC14 23c **multicolored** *(61,500)+*   .45   .45
       Entire, first day cancel   1.00
UX29 PC15 70c **multicolored** *(86,500)+*   1.40 1.40
       Entire, first day cancel   1.40
UX30 PC16 70c **multicolored** *(86,500)+*   1.40 1.40
       Entire, first day cancel   1.40
UX31 PC17 70c **multicolored** *(86,500)+*   1.40 1.40
       Entire, first day cancel   1.40
UX32 PC18 70c **multicolored** *(86,500)+*   1.40 1.40
       Entire, first day cancel   1.40
UX33 PC19 70c **multicolored** *(86,500)+*   1.40 1.40
       Entire, first day cancel   1.40
          Nos. UX24-UX33 (10)   9.25 9.25

Nos. UX24-UX28 and UX29-UX33 were sold only in shrink-wrapped sets.

AIR POST POSTAL CARDS

Values are for entire cards.

Type of Air Post Stamp of 1957
Printed by British American Bank Note Co., Ltd., Ottawa.

1957, May 27   Litho.
UXC1 AP3 4c **maroon**, *buff (631,000)*   .25   .30
       First day cancel *(260,005)*   1.00

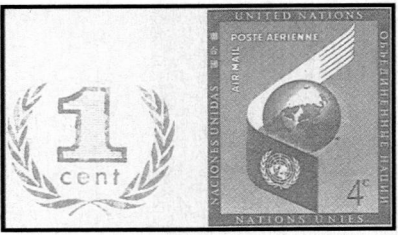

No. UXC1 Surcharged in Maroon at Left of Stamp

1959, June 5   Litho.
UXC2 AP3 4c + 1c **maroon**, *buff (1,119,000)* .30   .50
       Cancel first day of public use,
       June 8   300.00
  a. Double surcharge   —
  b. Inverted surcharge   —
  c. Double surcharge, one inverted   —
   This surcharge also exists on a No. U1 envelope. Status uncertain.

Type of Air Post Stamp, 1957
Printed by Eureka Specialty Printing Co., Scranton, Pa.

1959, Sept. 21   Litho.
UXC3 AP3 5c **crimson**, *buff (500,000)*   .65   .65
       First day cancel *(119,479)*   .50

Outer Space — APC1

Printed by Eureka Specialty Printing Co., Scranton, Pa.

1963, Apr. 26   Litho.
UXC4 APC1 6c **black & blue** *(350,000)*   .60   .60
       First day cancel *(109,236)*   .50

APC2

Printed by Eureka-Carlisle Co., Scranton, Pa. Designed by Olav S. Mathiesen.

1966, June 9   Litho.
UXC5 APC2 11c **dark red, rose, yellow &**
              brown *(764,500)*   .30   .30
       First day cancel *(162,588)*   .50

1968, May 31   Litho.
UXC6 APC2 13c **dark green, bright green &**
              yellow *(829,000)*   .40   .40
       First day cancel *(106,500)*   1.00

UN Emblem and Stylized Planes — APC3

Printed by Canadian Bank Note Co., Ltd., Ottawa. Designed by Lawrence Kurtz.

1969, Jan. 8   Litho.
UXC7 APC3 8c **gray, dull yellow, lt blue, indi-**
              go & red *(500,000)*   .65   .65
       First day cancel *(94,037)*   .50

Type of Air Post Stamp of 1972
Printed by Government Printing Bureau, Tokyo. Designed by L. L. Dolan.

1972, Oct. 16   Litho.
UXC8 AP12 9c **orange, red, gray & green**
              (500,000)   .45   .45
       First day cancel *(85,600)*   .50

Type of 1969
Printed by Government Printing Bureau, Tokyo

1972, Oct. 16   **Litho.**
UXC9 APC3 15c **lilac, light blue, pink & carmine** *(500,000)*   .50   .50
       First day cancel *(84,800)*   .50

Types of Air Post Stamps, 1972-74
Printed by Setelipaino, Finland.

1975, Jan. 10   **Litho.**
UXC10 AP14 11c **greenish blue, blue & dark blue** *(250,000)*   .50   .50
       First day cancel *(70,500)*   .50
UXC11 AP17 18c **gray & multicolored** *(250,000)*   .50   .50
       First day cancel *(70,500)*   .50

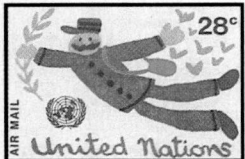

Flying
Mailman — APC4

Printed by Courvoisier. Designed by Arieh Glaser.

1982, Apr. 28   **Photo.**
UXC12 APC4 28c **multicolored** *(350,000)*   .45   .50
       First day cancel *(58,700)*   1.40

STOCKBOOKS

Stockbooks are a classic and convenient storage alternative for many collectors. These Lighthouse stockbooks feature heavyweight archival quality paper with 9 pockets on each page. The 9" x 12" pages are bound inside a handsome leatherette grain cover and include double glassine interleaving between the pages for added protection.

Item	Color	Pg Count	Retail	AA*
LS4/8BL	Blue	16 pgs	$14.90	$12.99
LS4/8GR	Green	16 pgs	$14.90	$12.99
LS4/8RD	Red	16 pgs	$14.90	$12.99
LS4/16GR	Green	32 pgs	$21.90	$18.99
LS4/16RD	Red	32 pgs	$21.90	$18.99
LS4/24BK	Black	48 pgs	$34.90	$29.99
LS4/24BL	Blue	48 pgs	$34.90	$29.99
LS4/24GR	Green	48 pgs	$34.90	$29.99
LS4/24RD	Red	48 pgs	$34.90	$29.99
LS4/32BK	Black	64 pgs	$41.90	$35.99
LS4/32BL	Blue	64 pgs	$41.90	$35.99
LS4/32GR	Green	64 pgs	$41.90	$35.99
LS4/32RD	Red	64 pgs	$41.90	$35.99

OFFICES IN GENEVA, SWITZERLAND

For use only on mail posted at the Palais des Nations (UN European Office), Geneva. Inscribed in French unless otherwise stated.

100 Centimes = 1 Franc

Types of United Nations Issues 1961-69 and

United
Nations
European
Office,
Geneva — G1

Printed by Setelipaino, Finland (5c, 70c, 80c, 90c, 2fr, 10fr), Courvoisier, S.A., Switzerland (10c, 20c, 30c, 50c, 60c, 3fr). Government Printing Office, Austria (75c) and Government Printing Office, Federal Republic of Germany (1fr).
Panes of 50. 30c designed by Ole Hamann, others as before.

Designs: 5c, UN Headquarters, New York, and world map. 10c, UN flag. 20c, Three men united before globe. 50c, Opening words of UN Charter. 60c, UN emblem over globe. 70c, "un" and UN emblem. 75c, "Flight Across Globe." 80c, UN Headquarters and emblem. 90c, Abstract group of flags. 1fr, UN emblem. 2fr, Stylized globe and weather vane. 3fr, Statue by Henrik Starcke. 10fr, "Peace, Justice, Security."
The 20c, 80c and 90c are inscribed in French. The 75c and 10fr carry French inscription at top, English at bottom.

1969-70   **Photo.**   **Unwmk.**

Perf. 13 (5c, 70c, 90c); 12½x12 (10c);

1	A88	5c purple & multi, Oct. 4, 1969 (3,300,000)	.20 .20
		First day cover	1.00
		Inscription block of 4	.25 —
a.		Green omitted	—
2	A52	10c salmon & multi, Oct. 4, 1969 (4,300,000)+	.20 .20
		First day cover	1.00
		Inscription block of 4	.25 —

Perf. 11½ (20c-60c, 3fr)

3	A66	20c black & multi, Oct. 4, 1969 (4,500,000)	.20 .20
		First day cover	1.00
		Inscription block of 4	.45 —
4	G1	30c dark blue & multi, Oct. 4, 1969 (3,000,000)	.20 .20
		First day cover	1.00
		Inscription block of 4	.60 —
5	A77	50c ultra & multi, Oct. 4, 1969 (3,300,000)	.30 .30
		First day cover	1.25
		Inscription block of 4	.80 —
6	A54	60c dark brown, salmon & gold, Apr. 17, 1970 (3,300,000)+	.35 .35
		First day cover	1.00
		Inscription block of 4	1.50 —
7	A104	70c red, black & gold, Sept. 22, 1970 (3,300,000)+	.40 .40
		First day cover	1.00
		Inscription block of 4	1.75 —

Perf. 11½x12 (75c)

8	AP8	75c carmine rose & multi, Oct. 4, 1969 (3,300,000)+	.45 .45
		First day cover	1.00
		Inscription block of 4	1.90 —

Perf. 13½x14 (80c)

9	A78	80c blue green, red & yellow, Sept. 22, 1970 (3,300,000)	.45 .45
		First day cover	1.00
		Inscription block of 4	1.90 —
10	A45	90c blue & multi, Sept. 22, 1970 (3,300,000)	.50 .50
		First day cover	1.00
		Inscription block of 4	2.10 —

Litho. & Embossed
Perf. 14 (1fr)

11	A79	1fr light & dark green, Oct. 4, 1969 (3,000,000)	.55 .55
		First day cover	1.00
		Inscription block of 4	2.40 —

Photo.
Perf. 12x11½ (2fr)

12	A67	2fr blue & multi, Sept. 22, 1970 (3,000,000)+	1.10 1.10
		First day cover	2.00
		Inscription block of 4	4.50 —
13	A97	3fr olive & multi, Oct. 4, 1969 (3,000,000)+	1.75 1.75
		First day cover	2.25
		Inscription block of 4	7.50 —

Engr.
Perf. 12 (10fr)

14	A3	10fr dark blue, Apr. 17, 1970 (2,250,000)+	5.75 5.75
		First day cover	8.50
		Inscription block of 4	24.00 —
		Nos. 1-14 (14)	12.40 12.40

+ Printing orders to June 1984.
First day covers of Nos. 1-5, 8, 11, 13 total 607,578; of Nos. 6 and 14, 148,055; of Nos. 7, 9-10 and 12, 226,000.

Sea Bed Type of UN

1971, Jan. 25   **Photo. & Engr.**   *Perf. 13*

15	A114	30c green & multi (1,935,871)	.20 .20
		First day cover (152,590)	1.00
		Inscription block of 4	.65 —

Refugee Type of UN

1971, Mar. 12   **Litho.**   *Perf. 13x12½*

16	A115	50c deep carmine, deep orange & black (1,820,114)	.25 .25
		First day cover (148,220)	1.00
		Inscription block of 4	1.05 —

World Food Program Type of UN

1971, Apr. 13   **Photo.**   *Perf. 14*

17	A116	50c dark violet & multi (1,824,170)	.25 .25
		First day cover (151,580)	1.00
		Inscription block of 4	1.05 —

UPU Headquarters Type of UN

1971, May 28   **Photo.**   *Perf. 11½*

18	A117	75c green & multi (1,821,878)	.35 .35
		First day cover (140,679)	1.00
		Inscription block of 4	1.60 —

Eliminate Racial Discrimination Types of UN

Designed by Daniel Gonzague (30c) and Ole Hamann (50c).

1971, Sept. 21   **Photo.**   *Perf. 13½*

19	A118	30c blue & multi (1,838,474)	.20 .20
		First day cover	1.00
		Inscription block of 4	.75 —
20	A119	50c yellow green & multi (1,804,126)	.25 .25
		First day cover	1.00
		First day cover, #19-20	1.25
		Inscription block of 4	1.10 —

First day covers of Nos. 19-20 total 308,420.

Picasso Type of UN

1971, Nov. 19   **Photo.**   *Perf. 11½*

21	A122	1.10fr multicolored (1,467,993)	.75 .75
		First day cover (195,215)	1.25
		Inscription block of 4	3.00 —

Palais des
Nations,
Geneva — G2

Printed by Courvoisier, S. A. Panes of 50. Designed by Ole Hamann.

1972, Jan. 5   **Photo.**   *Perf. 11½*

22	G2	40c olive, blue, salmon & dark green (3,500,000)+	.25 .25
		First day cover (152,300)	1.00
		Inscription block of 4	1.05 —

+ Initial printing order.

Nuclear Weapons Type of UN

1972, Feb. 14   **Photo.**   *Perf. 13½x14*

23	A124	40c yellow, green, black, rose & gray (1,567,305)	.25 .25
		First day cover (151,350)	1.00
		Inscription block of 4	1.25 —

World Health Day Type of UN

1972, Apr. 7   **Litho. & Engr.**   *Perf. 13x13½*

24	A125	80c black & multi (1,543,368)	.45 .45
		First day cover (192,600)	1.00
		Inscription block of 4	2.00 —

Human Environment Type of UN

Lithographed & Embossed

1972, June 5   *Perf. 12½x14*

25	A126	40c olive, lemon, green & blue (1,594,089)	.25 .25
		First day cover	1.00
		Inscription block of 4	1.00 —
26	A126	80c ultra, pink, green & blue (1,568,009)	.45 .45
		First day cover	1.40
		First day cover, #25-26	1.75
		Inscription block of 4	1.80 —

First day covers of Nos. 25-26 total 296,700.

Economic Commission for Europe Type of UN

1972, Sept. 11   **Litho.**   *Perf. 13x13½*

27	A127	1.10fr red & multi (1,604,082)	1.00 1.00
		First day cover (149,630)	1.75
		Inscription block of 4	4.25 —

Art at UN (Sert) Type of UN

1972, Nov. 17   **Photo.**   *Perf. 12x12½*

28	A128	40c gold, red & brown (1,932,428)	.30 .30
		First day cover	1.00
		Inscription block of 4	1.25 —
29	A128	80c gold, brown & olive (1,759,600)	.60 .60
		First day cover	1.25
		First day cover, #28-29	1.75
		Inscription block of 4	2.50 —

First day covers of Nos. 28-29 total 295,470.

Disarmament Decade Type of UN

1973, Mar. 9   **Litho.**   *Perf. 13½x13*

30	A129	60c violet & multi (1,586,845)	.40 .40
		First day cover	1.00
		Inscription block of 4	1.60 —
31	A129	1.10fr olive & multi (1,408,169)	.85 .85
		First day cover	1.40
		First day cover, #30-31	1.75
		Inscription block of 4	3.50 —

First day covers of Nos. 30-31 total 260,680.

Drug Abuse Type of UN

1973, Apr. 13   **Photo.**   *Perf. 13½*

32	A130	60c blue & multi (1,481,432)	.45 .45
		First day cover (144,760)	1.00
		Inscription block of 4	1.90 —

Volunteers Type of UN

1973, May 25   **Photo.**   *Perf. 14*

33	A131	80c gray green & multi (1,443,519)	.35 .35
		First day cover (143,430)	1.10
		Inscription block of 4	1.50 —

Namibia Type of UN

1973, Oct. 1   **Photo.**   *Perf. 13½*

34	A132	60c red & multi (1,673,898)	.35 .35
		First day cover (148,077)	1.00
		Inscription block of 4	1.50 —

Human Rights Type of UN

1973, Nov. 16   **Photo.**   *Perf. 13½*

35	A133	40c ultramarine & multi (1,480,791)	.30 .30
		First day cover	1.00
		Inscription block of 4	1.25 —
36	A133	80c olive & multi (1,343,349)	.50 .50
		First day cover	1.25
		First day cover, #35-36	1.75
		Inscription block of 4	2.10 —

First day covers of Nos. 35-36 total 438,260.

ILO Headquarters Type of UN

1974, Jan. 11   **Photo.**   *Perf. 14*

37	A134	60c violet & multi (1,212,703)	.45 .45
		First day cover	1.00
		Inscription block of 4	1.90 —
38	A134	80c brown & multi (1,229,851)	.65 .65
		First day cover	1.10
		First day cover, #37-38	1.25
		Inscription block of 4	2.75 —

First day covers of Nos. 37-38 total 240,660.

Centenary of UPU Type of UN

1974, Mar. 22   **Litho.**   *Perf. 12½*

39	A135	30c gold & multi (1,567,517)	.25 .25
		First day cover	1.00
		Inscription block of 4	1.25 —
40	A135	60c gold & multi (1,430,839)	.60 .60
		First day cover	1.25
		First day cover, #39-40	1.50
		Inscription block of 4	2.50 —

First day covers of Nos. 39-40 total 231,840.

Art at UN (Portinari) Type of UN

1974, May 6   Photo.   *Perf. 14*
41   A136   60c   **dark red & multi** *(1,202,357)*   .40   .40
    First day cover   1.00
    Inscription block of 4   1.75
42   A136   1fr   **green & multi** *(1,230,045)*   .70   .70
    First day cover   1.20
    First day cover, #41-42   1.50
    Inscription block of 4   3.00
First day covers of Nos. 41-42 total 249,130.

World Population Year Type of UN

1974, Oct. 18   Photo.   *Perf. 14*
43   A140   60c   **bright green & multi** *(1,292,954)*   .50   .50
    First day cover   1.00
    Inscription block of 4   2.25
44   A140   80c   **brown & multi** *(1,221,288)*   .70   .70
    First day cover   1.00
    First day cover, #43-44   1.25
    Inscription block of 4   3.25
First day covers of Nos. 43-44 total 189,597.

Law of the Sea Type of UN

1974, Nov. 22   Photo.   *Perf. 14*
45   A141   1.30fr   **blue & multicolored** *(1,266,270)*   1.00   1.00
    First day cover *(181,000)*   1.25
    Inscription block of 4   4.00

Outer Space Type of UN

1975, Mar. 14   Litho.   *Perf. 13*
46   A142   60c   **multicolored** *(1,339,704)*   .50   .50
    First day cover   1.00
    Inscription block of 4   2.00
47   A142   90c   **multicolored** *(1,383,888)*   .75   .75
    First day cover   1.00
    First day cover, #46-47   1.50
    Inscription block of 4   3.25
First day covers of Nos. 46-47 total 250,400.

International Women's Year Type of UN

1975, May 9   Litho.   *Perf. 15*
48   A143   60c   **multicolored** *(1,176,080)*   .40   .40
    First day cover   1.00
    Inscription block of 4   1.90
49   A143   90c   **multicolored** *(1,167,863)*   .70   .70
    First day cover   1.00
    First day cover, #48-49   1.50
    Inscription block of 4   3.25
First day covers of Nos. 48-49 total 250,660.

30th Anniversary Type of UN

1975, June 26   Litho.   *Perf. 13*
50   A144   60c   **green & multi** *(1,442,075)*   .40   .40
    First day cover   1.00
    Inscription block of 4   2.00
51   A144   90c   **violet & multi** *(1,612,411)*   .70   .70
    First day cover   1.00
    First day cover, #50-51   1.25
    Inscription block of 4   3.25

Souvenir Sheet
Imperf
52   Sheet of 2 *(1,210,148)*   1.00   1.00
a.   A144   60c   **green & multicolored**   .30   .30
b.   A144   90c   **violet & multicolored**   .60   .60
    First day cover   1.25
No. 52 has blue and bister margin with inscription and UN emblem. Size: 92x70mm.
First day covers of Nos. 50-52 total 402,500.

Namibia Type of UN

1975, Sept. 22   Photo.   *Perf. 13½*
53   A145   50c   **multicolored** *(1,261,019)*   .30   .30
    First day cover   1.00
    Inscription block of 4   1.25
54   A145   1.30fr   **multicolored** *(1,241,990)*   .85   .85
    First day cover   1.10
    First day cover, #53-54   1.25
    Inscription block of 4   4.00
First day covers of Nos. 53-54 total 226,260.

Peace-keeping Operations Type of UN

1975, Nov. 21   Engr.   *Perf. 12½*
55   A146   60c   **greenish blue** *(1,249,305)*   .35   .35
    First day cover   1.00
    Inscription block of 4   1.50
56   A146   70c   **bright violet** *(1,249,935)*   .65   .65
    First day cover   1.00
    First day cover, #55-56   1.25
    Inscription block of 4   2.75
First day covers of Nos. 55-56 total 229,245.

WFUNA Type of UN

1976, Mar. 12   Photo.   *Perf. 14*
57   A152   90c   **multicolored** *(1,186,563)*   .90   .90
    First day cover   1.00
    Inscription block of 4   4.00
First day covers of No. 57 total 121,645.

UNCTAD Type of UN

1976, Apr. 23   Photo.   *Perf. 11½*
58   A153   1.10fr   **sepia & multi** *(1,167,284)*   .90   .90
    First day cover *(107,030)*   1.25
    Inscription block of 4   4.00

Habitat Type of UN

1976, May 28   Photo.   *Perf. 14*
59   A154   40c   **dull blue & multi** *(1,258,986)*   .20   .20
    First day cover   1.00
    Inscription block of 4   1.00
60   A154   1.50fr   **violet & multi** *(1,110,507)*   .75   .75
    First day cover   1.25
    First day cover, #59-60   1.60
    Inscription block of 4   3.50
First day covers of Nos. 59-60 total 242,530.

UN Emblem, Post Horn and Rainbow — G3

UN Postal Administration, 25th anniversary.
Printed by Courvoisier, S.A. Panes of 20 (5x4). Designed by Hector Viola.

1976, Oct. 8   Photo.   *Perf. 11½*
61   G3   80c   **tan & multicolored** *(1,794,009)*   .50   .50
    First day cover   2.00
    Inscription block of 4   2.50
62   A3   1.10fr   **light green & multi** *(1,751,178)*   1.60   1.60
    First day cover   2.00
    Inscription block of 4   8.00
    First day cover, #61-62   3.00
    Panes of 20, #61-62   37.50
Upper margin blocks are inscribed "XXVe ANNIVERSAIRE"; lower margin blocks "ADMINISTRATION POSTALE DES NATIONS UNIES."
First day covers of Nos. 61-62 total 152,450.

World Food Council Type of UN

1976, Nov. 19   Litho.   *Perf. 14½*
63   A156   70c   **multicolored** *(1,507,630)*   .50   .50
    First day cover *(170,540)*   1.00
    Inscription block of 4   2.25

WIPO Type of UN

1977, Mar. 11   Photo.   *Perf. 14*
64   A157   80c   **red & multi** *(1,232,664)*   .60   .60
    First day cover *(212,470)*   1.00
    Inscription block of 4   2.75

Drop of Water and Globe — G4

UN Water Conference, Mar del Plata, Argentina, Mar. 14-25.
Printed by Government Printing Bureau, Tokyo. Panes of 50. Designed by Eliezer Weishoff.

1977, Apr. 22   Photo.   *Perf. 13½x13*
65   G4   80c   **ultramarine & multi** *(1,146,650)*   .50   .50
    First day cover   1.00
    Inscription block of 4   2.25
66   G4   1.10fr   **dark carmine & multi** *(1,138,236)*   .80   .80
    First day cover   1.25
    First day cover, #65-66   1.75
    Inscription block of 4   3.50
First day covers of Nos. 65-66 total 289,836.

Hands Protecting UN Emblem — G5

UN Security Council.

Printed by Heraclio Fournier, S.A., Spain. Panes of 50. Designed by George Hamori.

1977, May 27   Photo.   *Perf. 11*
67   G5   80c   **blue & multi** *(1,096,030)*   .50   .50
    Inscription block of 4   2.25
68   G5   1.10fr   **emerald & multi** *(1,075,925)*   .80   .80
    First day cover   1.25
    First day cover, #67-68   1.75
    Inscription block of 4   3.50
First day covers of Nos. 67-68 total 305,349.

Colors of Five Races Spun into One Firm Rope — G6

Fight against racial discrimination.
Printed by Setelipaino, Finland. Panes of 50. Designed by M. A. Munnawar.

1977, Sept. 19   Litho.   *Perf. 13½x13*
69   G6   40c   **multicolored** *(1,218,834)*   .25   .25
    First day cover   1.00
    Inscription block of 4   1.10
70   G6   1.10fr   **multicolored** *(1,138,250)*   .65   .65
    First day cover   1.25
    First day cover, #69-70   1.75
    Inscription block of 4   2.75
First day covers of Nos. 69-70 total 308,722.

Atomic Energy Turning Partly into Olive Branch — G7

Peaceful uses of atomic energy.
Printed by Heraclio Fournier, S.A., Spain. Panes of 50. Designed by Witold Janowski and Marek Freudenreich.

1977, Nov. 18   Photo.   *Perf. 14*
71   G7   80c   **dark carmine & multi** *(1,147,787)*   .55   .55
    First day cover   1.00
    Inscription block of 4   2.50
72   G7   1.10fr   **Prussian blue & multi** *(1,121,209)*   .75   .75
    First day cover   1.20
    First day cover, #71-72   1.50
    Inscription block of 4   3.50
First day covers of Nos. 71-72 total 298,075.

"Tree" of Doves — G8

Printed by Questa Colour Security Printers, United Kingdom. Panes of 50. Designed by M. Hioki.

1978, Jan. 27   Litho.   *Perf. 14½*
73   G8   35c   **multicolored** *(3,000,000)+*   .20   .20
    First day cover *(259,735)*   1.00
    Inscription block of 4   .75

Globes with Smallpox Distribution — G9

Global eradication of smallpox.

Printed by Courvoisier, S.A. Panes of 50. Designed by Eliezer Weishoff.

1978, Mar. 31		Photo.		Perf. 12x11½	
74	G9	80c yellow & multi (1,116,044)		.60	.60
		First day cover			1.00
		Inscription block of 4		2.50	—
75	G9	1.10fr light green & multi (1,109,946)		.90	.90
		First day cover			1.25
		First day cover, #74-75			2.00
		Inscription block of 4		3.75	—

First day covers of Nos. 74-75 total 254,700.

Namibia Type of UN

1978, May 5		Photo.		Perf. 12	
76	A166	80c multicolored (1,183,208)		.85	.85
		First day cover (316,610)			1.00
		Inscription block of 4		3.50	—

Jets and Flight Patterns — G10

International Civil Aviation Organization for "Safety in the Air." Printed by Heraclio Fournier, S.A., Spain. Panes of 50. Designed by Tomas Savrda.

1978, June 12		Photo.		Perf. 14	
77	G10	70c multicolored (1,275,106)		.40	.40
		First day cover			1.00
		Inscription block of 4		1.75	—
78	G10	80c multicolored (1,144,339)		.70	.70
		First day cover			1.00
		First day cover, #77-78			1.60
		Inscription block of 4		3.00	—

First day covers of Nos. 77-78 total 255,700.

General Assembly, Flags and Globe — G11

Printed by Government Printing Bureau, Tokyo. Panes of 50. Designed by Henry Bencsath.

1978, Sept. 15		Photo.		Perf. 13½	
79	G11	70c multicolored (1,204,441)		.45	.45
		First day cover			1.00
		Inscription block of 4		2.25	—
80	G11	1.10fr multicolored (1,183,889)		.85	.85
		First day cover			1.25
		First day cover, #79-80			1.75
		Inscription block of 4		3.75	—

First day covers of Nos. 79-80 total 245,600.

Technical Cooperation Type of UN

1978, Nov. 17		Photo.		Perf. 14	
81	A169	80c multicolored (1,173,220)		.70	.70
		First day cover (264,700)			1.00
		Inscription block of 4		3.25	—

Seismograph Recording Earthquake — G12

Office of the UN Disaster Relief Coordinator (UNDRO). Printed by Heraclio Fournier, S.A., Spain. Panes of 50. Designed by Michael Klutmann.

1979, Mar. 9		Photo.		Perf. 14	
82	G12	80c multicolored (1,183,155)		.50	.50
		First day cover			1.00
		Inscription block of 4		2.00	—
83	G12	1.50fr multicolored (1,168,121)		.80	.80

		First day cover			1.40
		First day cover, #82-83			1.90
		Inscription block of 4		3.50	—

First day covers of Nos. 82-83 total 162,070.

Children and Rainbow — G13

International Year of the Child. Printed by Heraclio Fournier, S.A., Spain. Panes of 20 (5x4). Designed by Arieh Glaser.

1979, May 4		Photo.		Perf. 14	
84	G13	80c multicolored (2,251,623)		.35	.35
		First day cover			1.25
		Inscription block of 4		1.60	—
85	G13	1.10fr multicolored (2,220,463)		.65	.65
		Inscription block of 4		2.75	—
		First day cover, #84-85			1.75
		Panes of 20, #84-85		20.00	1.25

First day covers of Nos. 84-85 total 176,120.

Namibia Type of UN

1979, Oct. 5		Litho.		Perf. 13½	
86	A176	1.10fr multicolored (1,229,830)		.60	.60
		First day cover (134,160)			1.25
		Inscription block of 4		2.25	—

International Court of Justice, Scales — G14

International Court of Justice, The Hague, Netherlands. Printed by Setelipaino, Finland. Panes of 50. Designed by Kyohei Maeno.

1979, Nov. 9		Litho.		Perf. 13x13½	
87	G14	80c multicolored (1,123,193)		.40	.40
		First day cover			1.00
		Inscription block of 4		1.75	—
88	G14	1.10fr multicolored (1,063,067)		.60	.60
		First day cover			1.25
		First day cover, #87-88			1.75
		Inscription block of 4		2.75	—

First day covers of Nos. 87-88 total 158,170.

New Economic Order Type of UN

1980, Jan. 11		Litho.		Perf. 15x14½	
89	A179	80c multicolored (1,315,918)		.85	.85
		First day cover (176,250)			1.00
		Inscription block of 4		3.50	—

Women's Year Emblem — G15

United Nations Decade for Women. Printed by Questa Colour Security Printers, United Kingdom. Panes of 50. Designed by M.A. Munnawar.

1980, Mar. 7		Litho.		Perf. 14½x15	
90	G15	40c multicolored (1,265,221)		.30	.30
		First day cover			1.00
		Inscription block of 4		1.40	—
91	G15	70c multicolored (1,240,375)		.70	.70
		First day cover			1.10
		First day cover, #90-91			1.25
		Inscription block of 4		3.50	—

First day covers of Nos. 90-91 total 204,350.

Peace-keeping Operations Type of UN

1980, May 16		Litho.		Perf. 14x13	
92	A181	1.10fr blue & green (1,335,391)		.85	.85
		First day cover (184,700)			1.00
		Inscription block of 4		3.50	—

35th Anniversary Type of UN and Dove and "35" — G16

35th Anniversary of the United Nations. Printed by Ashton-Potter Ltd., Canada. Panes of 50. Designed by Gidon Sagi (40c), Cemalattin Mutver (70c).

1980, June 26		Litho.		Perf. 13x13½	
93	G16	40c blue green & black (1,462,005)		.35	.30
		First day cover			1.00
		Inscription block of 4		1.40	—
94	A183	70c multicolored (1,444,639)		.65	.65
		First day cover			1.00
		First day cover, #93-94			1.50
		Inscription block of 4		3.00	—

Souvenir Sheet
Imperf

95		Sheet of 2 (1,235,200)		1.10	1.10
a.		G16 40c blue green & black		.30	.30
b.		A183 70c multicolored		.80	.80
		First day cover			1.00

First day covers of Nos. 93-95 total 379,800.

ECOSOC Type of UN and

Family Climbing Line Graph — G17

Printed by Ashton-Potter Ltd., Canada. Panes of 50. Designed by Eliezer Weishoff (40c), A. Medina Medina (70c).

1980, Nov. 21		Litho.		Perf. 13½x13	
96	A186	40c multicolored (986,435)		.30	.30
		First day cover			1.00
		Inscription block of 4		1.25	—
97	G17	70c multicolored (1,016,462)		.60	.60
		First day cover			1.00
		First day cover #96-97			1.50
		Inscription block of 4		2.50	—

Economic and Social Council.
First day covers of Nos. 96-97 total 210,460.

Palestinian Rights

Printed by Courvoisier S.A., Switzerland. Panes of 50. Designed by David Dewhurst.

1981, Jan. 30		Photo.		Perf. 12x11½	
98	A188	80c multicolored (1,031,737)		.55	.55
		First day cover (117,480)			1.00
		Inscription block of 4		2.75	—

International Year of the Disabled.

Printed by Heraclio Fournier S.A., Spain. Panes of 50. Designed by G.P. Van der Hyde (40c) and Sophia van Hees-wijk (1.50fr).

1981, Mar. 6		Photo.		Perf. 14	
99	A190	40c black & blue (1,057,909)		.25	.25
		First day cover			1.00
		Inscription block of 4		1.00	—
100	V4	1.50fr black & red (994,748)		1.00	1.00
		First day cover			1.25
		First day cover, #99-100			1.75
		Inscription block of 4		4.00	—

First day covers of Nos. 99-100 total 202,853.

Art Type of UN

1981, Apr. 15		Photo.		Perf. 11½	
		Granite Paper			
101	A191	80c multicolored (1,128,782)		.80	.80
		First day cover (121,383)			1.00
		Inscription block of 4		3.75	—

Energy Type of 1981

1981, May 29		Litho.		Perf. 13	
102	A192	1.10fr **multicolored** *(1,096,806)*		.75	.75
		First day cover *(113,700)*			1.25
		Inscription block of 4		3.50	—

Volunteers Program Type and

Symbols of Science, Agriculture and Industry — G18

Printed by Walsall Security Printers, Ltd., United Kingdom. Panes of 50.
Designed by Gabriele Nussgen (40c), Bernd Mirbach (70c).

1981, Nov. 13		Litho.			
103	A194	40c **multicolored** *(1,032,700)*		.45	.45
		First day cover			1.00
		Inscription block of 4		2.25	—
104	G18	70c **multicolored** *(1,123,672)*		.90	.90
		First day cover			1.00
		First day cover, #103-104			1.50
		Inscription block of 4		4.25	—

First day covers of Nos. 103-104 total 190,667.

Fight against Apartheid — G19

Flower of Flags — G20

Printed by Courvoisier, S.A., Switzerland. Panes of 50.
Designed by Tomas Savrda (30c); Dietmar Kowall (1fr).

1982, Jan. 22			Perf. 11½x12		
105	G19	30c **multicolored** *(3,000,000)+*		.25	.25
		First day cover			1.00
		Inscription block of 4		1.10	—
106	G20	1fr **multicolored** *(3,000,000)+*		.80	.80
		First day cover			1.00
		First day cover, #105-106			1.25
		Inscription block of 4		3.25	—

First day covers of Nos. 105-106 total 199,347.

Human Environment Type of UN and:

Sun and Leaves — G21

10th Anniversary of United Nations Environment Program.
Printed by Joh. Enschede en Zonen, Netherlands. Panes of 50. Designed by Sybille Brunner (40c); Philine Hartert (1.20fr).

1982, Mar. 19		Litho.		Perf. 13½x13	
107	G21	40c **multicolored** *(948,743)*		.30	.30
		First day cover			1.00
		Inscription block of 4		1.50	—
108	A199	1.20fr **multicolored** *(901,096)*		1.10	1.25
		First day cover			1.10
		First day cover, #107-108			1.40
		Inscription block of 4		5.25	—

First day covers of Nos. 107-108 total 190,155.

Outer Space Type of UN and:

Satellite, Applications of Space Technology G22

Exploration and Peaceful Uses of Outer Space.
Printed by Enschede. Panes of 50. Designed by Wiktor C. Nerwinski (80c) and George Hamori (1fr).

1982, June 11		Litho.		Perf. 13x13½	
109	A201	80c **multicolored** *(964,593)*		.60	.60
		First day cover			1.00
		Inscription block of 4		3.00	—
110	G22	1fr **multicolored** *(898,367)*		.80	.80
		First day cover			1.25
		First day cover, #109-110			1.50
		Inscription block of 4		3.75	—

First day covers of Nos. 109-110 total 205,815.

Conservation & Protection of Nature

1982, Nov. 19		Photo.		Perf. 14	
111	A202	40c **Bird** *(928,143)*		.45	.40
		First day cover			1.00
		Inscription block of 4		2.10	—
112	A202	1.50fr **Reptile** *(847,173)*		1.10	1.10
		First day cover			1.25
		First day cover, #111-112			1.75
		Inscription block of 4		5.25	—

First day covers of Nos. 111-112 total 198,504.

World Communications Year

1983, Jan. 28		Litho.		Perf. 13	
113	A204	1.20fr **multicolored** *(894,025)*		1.25	1.25
		First day cover *(131,075)*			1.25
		Inscription block of 4		5.25	—

Safety at Sea Type of UN and

G23

Designed by Valentin Wurnitsch (A22).

1983, Mar. 18		Litho.		Perf. 14½	
114	A205	40c **multicolored** *(892,365)*		.40	.40
		First day cover			1.00
		Inscription block of 4		1.75	—
115	G23	80c **multicolored** *(882,720)*		.80	.80
		First day cover			1.00
		First day cover, #114-115			1.50
		Inscription block of 4		3.50	—

First day covers of Nos. 114-115 total 219,592.

World Food Program

1983, Apr. 22		Engr.		Perf. 13½	
116	A207	1.50fr **blue** *(876,591)*		1.25	1.25
		First day cover			1.25
		Inscription block of 4		5.25	—

Trade Type of UN and

G24

Designed by Wladyslaw Brykczynski (A23).

1983, June 6		Litho.		Perf. 14	
117	A208	80c **multicolored** *(902,495)*		.50	.50
		First day cover			1.00
		Inscription block of 4		2.50	—
118	G24	1.10fr **multicolored** *(921,424)*		.90	.90
		First day cover			1.00
		First day cover, #117-118			1.40
		Inscription block of 4		4.00	—

First day covers of Nos. 117-118 total 146,507.

Homo Humus Humanitas — G25

Right to Create — G26

35th Anniversary of the Universal Declaration of Human Rights.
Printed by Government Printing Office, Austria. Designed by Friedensreich Hundertwasser, Austria. Panes of 16 (4x4).

1983, Dec. 9		Photo. & Engr.		Perf. 13½	
119	G25	40c **multicolored** *(1,770,921)*		.45	.45
		First day cover			1.00
		Inscription block of 4		2.00	—
120	G26	1.20fr **multicolored** *(1,746,735)*		.95	.95
		First day cover			1.10
		Inscription block of 4		4.25	—
		First day cover, #119-120			1.40
		Panes of 16, #119-120		22.50	—

First day covers of Nos. 119-120 total 315,052.

International Conference on Population Type

1984, Feb. 3		Litho.		Perf. 14	
121	A212	1.20fr **multicolored** *(776,879)*		.90	.90
		First day cover *(105,377)*			1.00
		Inscription block of 4		4.00	—

Fishing G27

Women Farm Workers, Africa — G28

World Food Day, Oct. 16
Printed by Walsall Security Printers, Ltd., United Kingdom. Panes of 50. Designed by Adth Vanooijen, Netherlands.

1984, Mar. 15		Litho.		Perf. 14½	
122	G27	50c **multicolored** *(744,506)*		.30	.30
		First day cover			1.00
		Inscription block of 4		1.60	—
123	G28	80c **multicolored** *(784,047)*		.60	.60

First day cover   1.25
First day cover, #122-123   1.75
Inscription block of 4   2.75 —

First day covers of Nos. 122-123 total 155,234.

Valletta,
Malta — G29

Los Glaciares
National Park,
Argentina — G30

World Heritage

Printed by Harrison and Sons, United Kingdom. Panes of 50. Designs adapted by Rocco J. Callari, US, and Thomas Lee, China.

1984, Apr. 18	Litho.	Perf. 14	
124 G29 50c **multicolored** (763,627)		.60	.60
First day cover			1.00
Inscription block of 4		2.50	—
125 G30 70c **multicolored** (784,489)		.85	.85
First day cover			1.25
First day cover, #124-125			1.75
Inscription block of 4		4.50	—

First day covers of Nos. 124-125 total 164,498.

G31

G32

Future for Refugees

Printed by Courvoisier. Panes of 50. Designed by Hans Erni, Switzerland.

1984, May 29	Photo.	Perf. 11½	
126 G31 35c **multicolored** (880,762)		.30	.30
First day cover			1.00
Inscription block of 4		1.50	—
127 G32 1.50fr **multicolored** (829,895)		1.10	1.10
First day cover			1.25
First day cover, #126-127			1.75
Inscription block of 4		5.00	—

First day covers of Nos. 126-127 total 170,306.

International Youth
Year — G33

Printed by Waddingtons Ltd., United Kingdom. Panes of 50. Designed by Eliezer Weishoff, Israel.

1984, Nov. 15	Litho.	Perf. 13½	
128 G33 1.20fr **multicolored** (755,622)		1.25	1.25
First day cover (96,680)			1.00
Inscription block of 4		5.50	—

ILO Type of UN and

ILO Turin
Center — G34

Printed by the Government Printing Bureau, Japan. Panes of 50. Engraved by Mamoru Iwakuni and Hiroshi Ozaki, Japan (#129) and adapted from photographs by Rocco J. Callari, US, and Thomas Lee, China (#130).

1985, Feb. 1	Engr.	Perf. 13½	
129 A220 80c **dull red** (654,431)		.70	.70
First day cover			1.00
Inscription block of 4		3.00	—
130 G34 1.20fr U Thant Pavilion (609,493)		1.10	1.10
First day cover			1.50
First day cover, #129-130			2.25
Inscription block of 4		4.75	—

First day covers of Nos. 129-130 total 118,467.

UN University Type

1985, Mar. 15	Photo.	Perf. 13½	
131 A221 50c Pastoral scene, advanced communications (625,087)		.60	.60
First day cover			1.00
Inscription block of 4		2.75	—
132 A221 80c like No. 131 (712,674)		1.00	1.00
First day cover			1.25
First day cover, #131-132			1.75
Inscription block of 4		4.50	—

First day covers of Nos. 131-132 total 93,324.

Flying
Postman — G35

NATIONS UNIES   Interlocked Peace
Doves — G36

Printed by Carl Ueberreuter Druck and Verlag M. Salzer, Austria. Panes of 50. Designed by Arieh Glaser, Israel (#133), and Carol Sliwka, Poland (#134).

1985, May 10	Litho.	Perf. 14	
133 G35 20c **multicolored** (2,000,000)+		.25	.25
First day cover			1.00
Inscription block of 4		1.25	—
134 G36 1.20fr **multicolored** (2,000,000)+		1.25	1.25
First day cover			1.50
First day cover, #133-134			2.00
Inscription block of 4		6.00	—

First day covers of Nos. 133-134 total 103,165.

40th Anniversary Type

Designed by Rocco J. Callari, U.S., and Thomas Lee, China (No. 137).

1985, June 26	Photo.	Perf. 12 x 11½	
135 A224 50c **multicolored** (764,924)		.60	.60
First day cover			1.00
Inscription block of 4		2.50	—
136 A225 70c **multicolored** (779,074)		.90	.90
First day cover			1.25
First day cover, #135-136			2.00
Inscription block of 4		4.00	—

Souvenir Sheet

Imperf

137	Sheet of 2 (498,041)	2.25	2.25
a.	A224 50c **multicolored**	.85	.85
b.	A225 70c **multicolored**	1.10	1.10
	First day cover		1.25

First day covers of Nos. 135-137 total 252,418.

UNICEF Child Survival Campaign Type

Printed by the Government Printing Bureau, Japan. Panes of 50. Designed by Mel Harris, United Kingdom (#138) and Adth Vanooijen, Netherlands (#139).

1985, Nov. 22	Photo. & Engr.	Perf. 13½	
138 A226 50c Three girls (657,409)		.40	.40
First day cover			1.00
Inscription block of 4		2.00	—
139 A226 1.20fr Infant drinking (593,568)		1.10	1.10
First day cover			1.25
First day cover, #138-139			1.75
Inscription block of 4		4.50	—

First day covers of Nos. 138-139 total 217,696.

Africa in Crisis Type

Printed by Helio Courvoisier, Switzerland. Panes of 50. Designed by Alemayehou Gabremedhiu, Ethiopia.

1986, Jan. 31	Photo.	Perf. 11½x12	
140 A227 1.40fr Mother, hungry children (590,576)		1.25	1.25
First day cover (80,159)			2.00
Inscription block of 4		5.25	—

UN Development Program Type

Forestry. Printed by the Government Printing Bureau, Japan. Pane of 40, 2 blocks of 4 horizontal and 5 blocks of 4 vertical. Designed by Thomas Lee, China.

1986, Mar. 14	Photo.	Perf. 13½	
141 A228 35c Erosion control (547,567)		1.75	1.75
142 A228 35c Logging (547,567)		1.75	1.75
143 A228 35c Lumber transport (547,567)		1.75	1.75
144 A228 35c Nursery (547,567)		1.75	1.75
a.	Block of 4, #141-144	7.50	7.50
	First day cover, #144a		8.50
	First day cover, #141-144, each		2.50
	Inscription block of 4, #144a	8.50	—
	Pane of 40, #141-144	80.00	

No. 144a has a continuous design.
First day covers of Nos. 141-144 total 200,212.

Dove and Sun — G37

Printed by Questa Color Security Printers, Ltd., United Kingdom. Panes of 50. Designed by Ramon Alcantara Rodriguez, Mexico.

1986, Mar. 14	Litho.	Perf. 15x14½	
145 G37 5c **multicolored** (2,000,000)+		.20	.20
First day cover (58,908)			1.00
Inscription block of 4		.50	—

Stamp Collecting Type

Designs: 50c, UN Human Rights stamp. 80c, UN stamps. Printed by the Swedish Post Office, Sweden. Panes of 50. Designed by Czeslaw Slania and Ingalill Axelsson, Sweden.

1986, May 22	Engr.	Perf. 12½	
146 A229 50c **dark green & henna brown** (722,015)		.60	.60
First day cover			1.50
Inscription block of 4		2.50	—
147 A229 80c **dark green & yellow orange** (750,945)		.90	.90
First day cover			1.50
First day cover, #146-147			1.75
Inscription block of 4		3.75	—

First day covers of Nos. 146-147 total 137,653.

Flags and Globe as Dove — G38

Peace in French — G39

International Peace Year. Printed by the Government Printing Bureau, Japan. Panes of 50. Designed by Renato Ferrini, Italy (#148), and Salahattin Kanidinc, US (#149).

1986, June 20   Photo. & Embossed   Perf. 13½
148 G38   45c **multicolored** *(620,978)*   .60   .60
   First day cover   1.00
   Inscription block of 4   2.75   —
149 G39   1.40fr **multicolored** *(559,658)*   1.25 1.25
   First day cover   1.60
   First day cover, #148-149   3.00   —
   Inscription block of 4   5.50   —

First day covers of Nos. 148-149 total 123,542.

WFUNA Anniversary Type
Souvenir Sheet

Printed by Johann Enschede and Sons, Netherlands. Designed by Rocco J. Callari, US.
Designs: 35c, Abstract by Benigno Gomez, Honduras. 45c, Abstract by Alexander Calder (1898-1976), US. 50c, Abstract by Joan Miro (b. 1893), Spain. 70c, Sextet with Dove, by Ole Hamann, Denmark.

1986, Nov. 14   Litho.   Perf. 13x13½
150   Sheet of 4 *(478,833)*   3.75 3.75
  a. A232 35c **multicolored**   .50   .50
  b. A232 45c **multicolored**   .70   .70
  c. A232 50c **multicolored**   .90   .90
  d. A232 70c **multicolored**   1.25 1.25
   First day cover *(58,452)*   2.00

No. 150 has inscribed margin picturing UN and WFUNA emblems.

Trygve Lie Type
1987, Jan. 30   Photo. & Engr.   Perf. 13½
151 A233 1.40fr **multicolored** *(516,605)*   1.10 1.10
   First day cover *(76,152)*   1.50
   Inscription block of 4   5.50   —

Sheaf of Colored Bands, by Georges Mathieu — G40

Armillary Sphere, Palais des Nations — G41

Printed by Helio Courvoisier, Switzerland (#152), and the Government Printing Bureau, Japan (#153). Panes of 50. Designed by Georges Mathieu (#152) and Rocco J. Callari (#153), US.

Photo., Photo. & Engr. (#153)
1987, Jan. 30   Perf. 11½x12, 13½
152 G40   90c **multicolored** *(1,600,000)+*   .65   .65
   First day cover   1.00
   Inscription block of 4   3.00   —
153 G41   1.40fr **multicolored** *(1,600,000)+*   1.25 1.25
   First day cover   1.00
   First day cover, #152-153   2.00
   Inscription block of 4   5.00   —

First day covers of Nos. 152-153 total 85,737.

Shelter for the Homeless Type

Designs: 50c, Cement-making and brick-making. 90c, Interior construction and decorating.

1987, Mar. 13   Litho.   Perf. 13½x12½
154 A234 50c **multicolored** *(564,445)*   .50   .50
   First day cover   1.00
   Inscription block of 4   2.50   —
155 A234 90c **multicolored** *(526,646)*   1.00 1.00
   First day cover   1.10
   First day cover, #154-155   2.00
   Inscription block of 4   4.25   —

First day covers of Nos. 154-155 total 100,366.

Fight Drug Abuse Type

Designs: 80c, Mother and child. 1.20fr, Workers in rice paddy.

1987, June 12   Litho.   Perf. 14½x15
156 A235 80c **multicolored** *(634,776)*   .50   .50
   First day cover   1.25
   Inscription block of 4   3.00   —
157 A235 1.20fr **multicolored** *(609,475)*   1.00 1.00
   First day cover   1.75
   First day cover, #156-157   2.50
   Inscription block of 4   4.75   —

First day covers of Nos. 156-157 total 95,247.

UN Day Type

Designed by Elisabeth von Janota-Bzowski (35c) and Fritz Oerter (50c).
Designs: Multinational people in various occupations.

1987, Oct. 23   Litho.   Perf. 14½x15
158 A236 35c **multicolored** *(1,114,756)*   .55   .55
   First day cover   1.60
   Inscription block of 4   2.50   —
159 A236 50c **multicolored** *(1,117,464)*   .80   .80
   First day cover   1.90
   Inscription block of 4   3.50   —
   First day cover, #158-159   2.50
   Panes of 12, #158-159   15.00

Immunize Every Child Type

Designs: 90c, Whooping cough. 1.70fr, Tuberculosis.

1987, Nov. 20   Litho.   Perf. 15x14½
160 A237 90c **multicolored** *(634,614)*   1.50 1.50
   First day cover   1.00
   Inscription block of 4   6.25   —
161 A237 1.70fr **multicolored** *(607,725)*   2.75 2.75
   First day cover   1.25
   First day cover, #160-161   2.50
   Inscription block of 4   11.50   —

IFAD Type

Designs: 35c, Flocks, dairy products. 1.40fr, Fruit.

1988, Jan. 29   Litho.   Perf. 13½
162 A238 35c **multicolored** *(524,817)*   .35   .35
   First day cover   1.00
   Inscription block of 4   1.90   —
163 A238 1.40fr **multicolored** *(499,103)*   1.40 1.40
   First day cover   1.50
   First day cover, #162-163   2.00
   Inscription block of 4   7.00   —

G42

Printed by Heraclio Fournier, S.A., Spain. Panes of 50. Designed by Bjorn Wiinblad, Denmark.

1988, Jan. 29   Photo.   Perf. 14
164 G42   50c **multicolored** *(1,600,000)+*   .80   .80
   First day cover   2.00
   Inscription block of 4   3.75   —

Survival of the Forests Type

Pine forest: 50c, Treetops, mountains. 1.10fr, Lake, tree trunks. Printed se-tenant in a continuous design.

1988, Mar. 18   Litho.   Perf. 14x15
165 A240 50c **multicolored** *(728,569)*   1.25 1.25
   First day cover   4.00
166 A240 1.10fr **multicolored** *(728,569)*   3.50 3.50
   First day cover   6.00
  a. Pair, #165-166   5.50 5.25
   First day cover, #166a   10.00
   Inscription block of 4, 2 #166a   12.50   —
   Pane of 12, #165-166   30.00   —

Intl. Volunteer Day Type
Designed by Christopher Magadini, US.
Designs: 80c, Agriculture. vert. 90c, Veterinary medicine.

1988, May 6   Litho.   Perf. 13x14, 14x13
167 A241 80c **multicolored** *(612,166)*   .80   .80
   First day cover   1.50
   Inscription block of 4   4.00   —
168 A241 90c **multicolored** *(467,334)*   1.00 1.00
   First day cover   1.75
   First day cover, #167-168   3.50
   Inscription block of 4   4.25   —

Health in Sports Type
Paintings by LeRoy Neiman, American sports artist: 50c, Soccer. vert. 1.40fr, Swimming.

1988, June 17   Litho.   Perf. 13½x13, 13x13½
169 A242 50c **multicolored** *(541,421)*   .40   .40
   First day cover   1.25
   Inscription block of 4   3.00   —
170 A242 1.40fr **multicolored** *(475,445)*   1.40 1.40
   First day cover   2.40
   First day cover, #169-170   3.00
   Inscription block of 4   10.00   —

Universal Declaration of Human Rights 40th Anniv. Type
1988, Dec. 9   Photo. & Engr.   Perf. 12
171 A243 90c **multicolored** *(745,508)*   .70   .70
   First day cover   2.50
   Inscription block of 4   3.25   —
Souvenir Sheet
172 A243 2fr **multicolored** *(517,453)*   2.75 2.75
   First day cover   4.00

World Bank Type
1989, Jan. 27   Litho.   Perf. 13x14
173 A244 80c Telecommunications *(524,056)*   1.00 1.00
   First day cover   1.50
   Inscription block of 4   4.50   —
174 A244 1.40fr Industry *(488,058)*   2.00 2.00
   First day cover   2.40
   First day cover, #173-174   3.50
   Inscription block of 4   9.00   —

First day covers of Nos. 173-174 total 111,004.

Peace-Keeping Force Type
1989, Mar. 17   Perf. 14x13½
175 A245 90c **multicolored** *(684,566)*   1.25 1.25
   First day cover *(52,463)*   1.00
   Inscription block of 4   6.75   —

World Weather Watch Type
Satellite photographs: 90c, Europe under the influence of Arctic air. 1.10fr, Surface temperatures of sea, ice and land surrounding the Kattegat between Denmark and Sweden.

1989, Apr. 21   Litho.   Perf. 13x14
176 A247 90c **multicolored** *(864,409)*   1.25 1.25
   First day cover   1.50
   Inscription block of 4   5.50   —
177 A247 1.10fr **multicolored** *(853,556)*   2.00 2.00
   First day cover   1.90
   First day cover, #176-177   3.00
   Inscription block of 4   9.00   —

First day covers of Nos. 176-177 total 83,343.

Offices in Geneva, 10th Anniv.
G43   G44

Printed by Government Printing Office, Austria. Panes of 25. Designed by Anton Lehmden (50c) and Arik Brauer (2fr), Austria.

Photo., Photo. & Engr. (2fr)
1989, Aug. 23   Perf. 14
178 G43   50c **multicolored** *(605,382)*   1.00 1.00
   First day cover   1.25
   Inscription block of 4   5.00   —

179	G44	2fr	**multicolored** (538,140)	3.50	3.50
			First day cover		2.75
			Inscription block of 4	15.00	—
			First day cover, #178-179		3.25
			Panes of 25, #178-179	110.00	

First day covers of Nos. 178-179 total 83,304.

Human Rights Type of 1989

Printed by Johann Enschede and Sons, the Netherlands. Panes of 12+12 se-tenant labels containing Articles 3 (35c) or 4 (80c) inscribed in English, French or German. Designed by Rocco J. Callari and Robert Stein, US.
Artwork: 35c, Young Mother Sewing, by Mary Cassatt. 80c, The Unknown Slave, sculpture by Albert Mangones.

1989, Nov. 17			**Litho.**	**Perf. 13½**	
180	A250	35c	**multicolored** (1,923,818)	.35	.35
			First day cover		1.25
			Inscription block of 3 + 3 labels	1.60	—
181	A250	80c	**multicolored** (1,917,953)	1.00	1.00
			First day cover		3.00
			Inscription block of 3 + 3 labels	4.50	—
			First day cover, #180-181		4.50
			Panes of 12, #180-181	17.50	

First day covers of Nos. 180-181 total 134,469.
See Nos. 193-194, 209-210, 234-235.

Intl. Trade Center Type

1990, Feb. 2			**Litho.**	**Perf. 14½x15**	
182	A251	1.50fr	**multicolored** (409,561)	2.25	2.25
			First day cover (61,098)		3.50
			Inscription block of 4	11.00	

G45

Printed by Heraclio Fournier, S.A., Spain. Designed by Guy Breniaux, France and Elizabeth White, US.

1990, Feb. 2			**Photo.**	**Perf. 14x13½**	
183	G45	5fr	**multicolored** (1,600,000)+	4.75	4.75
			First day cover (54,462)		7.00
			Inscription block of 4	21.00	

Fight AIDS
Worldwide —
G46a

Fight AIDS Type

Designed by Jacek Tofil, Poland (50c) and Lee Keun Moon, Korea (80c).
Designs: 50c, "SIDA." 80c, Proportional drawing of man like the illustration by Leonardo da Vinci.

1990, Mar. 16			**Litho.**	**Perf. 13½x12½**	
184	G46	50c	**multicolored** (480,625)	1.00	1.00
			First day cover		1.25
			Inscription block of 4	5.00	—
185	G46a	80c	**multicolored** (602,721)	1.75	1.75
			First day cover		1.50
			First day cover, #184-185		2.00
			Inscription block of 4	7.75	—

First day covers of Nos. 184-185 total 108,364.

Medicinal Plants Type

1990, May 4	**Photo.**	**Granite Paper**		**Perf. 11½**	
186	A253	90c	Plumeria rubra (625,522)	1.00	1.00
			First day cover		1.40
			Inscription block of 4	5.00	—
187	A253	1.40fr	Cinchona officinalis (648,619)	2.00	2.00
			First day cover		2.25
			First day cover, #186-187		3.50
			Inscription block of 4	9.50	—

First day covers of Nos. 186-187 total 114,062.

UN 45th Anniv. Type

Designed by Fritz Henry Oerter and Ruth Schmidthammer, Federal Republic of Germany (90c), Michiel Mertens, Belgium (1.10fr), Robert Stein, US (No. 190).
"45," emblem and: 90c, Symbols of clean environment, transportation and industry. 1.10fr, Dove in silhouette.

1990, June 26			**Litho.**	**Perf. 14½x13**	
188	A254	90c	**multicolored** (557,253)	1.10	1.10
			First day cover		1.40
			Inscription block of 4	5.25	—
189	A254	1.10fr	**multicolored** (519,635)	2.25	2.25
			First day cover		2.00
			First day cover, #188-189		3.00
			Inscription block of 4	9.50	—

Souvenir Sheet

190			Sheet of 2, #188-189 (401,027)	6.00	6.00
			First day cover		4.50

First day covers of Nos. 188-190 total 148,975.

Crime Prevention Type

1990, Sept. 13			**Photo.**	**Perf. 14**	
191	A255	50c	Official corruption (494,876)	1.25	1.25
			First day cover		1.40
			Inscription block of 4	5.50	—
192	A255	2fr	Environmental crime (417,033)	3.00	3.00
			First day cover		3.25
			First day cover, #191-192		4.50
			Inscription block of 4	15.00	—

First day covers of Nos. 191-192 total 76,605.

Human Rights Type of 1989

Panes of 12+12 se-tenant labels containing Articles 9 (35c) or 10 (90c) inscribed in French, German or English.
Artwork: 35c, The Prison Courtyard by Vincent Van Gogh. 90c, Katho's Son Redeems the Evil Doer From Execution by Albrecht Durer.

1990, Nov. 16			**Litho.**	**Perf. 13½**	
193	A250	35c	**multicolored** (1,578,828)	.45	.45
			First day cover		2.75
			Inscription block of 3 + 3 labels	1.75	—
194	A250	90c	**black & brown** (1,540,200)	1.25	1.25
			First day cover		6.00
			Inscription block of 3 + 3 labels	4.50	—
			First day cover, #193-194		2.50
			Panes of 12, #193-194	20.00	

First day covers of Nos. 193-194 total 100,282.

Economic Commission for Europe Type

1991, Mar. 15			**Litho.**	**Perf. 14**	
195	A256	90c	Owl, gull (643,143)+	1.25	1.25
			First day cover		3.00
196	A256	90c	Bittern, otter (643,143)+	1.25	1.25
			First day cover		3.00
197	A256	90c	Swan, lizard (643,143)+	1.25	1.25
			First day cover		3.00
198	A256	90c	Great crested grebe (643,143)+	1.25	1.25
			First day cover		3.00
a.			Block of 4, #195-198	5.00	5.00
			First day cover, #198a		5.50
			Inscription block of 4, #198a	6.50	—
			Pane of 40, #195-198	52.50	

First day covers of Nos. 195-198a total 75,759.

Namibian Independence Type

1991, May 10			**Litho.**	**Perf. 14**	
199	A257	70c	Mountains (328,014)	1.25	1.25
			First day cover		1.60
			Inscription block of 4	5.50	—
200	A257	90c	Baobab tree (395,362)	2.25	2.25
			First day cover		2.25
			First day cover, #199-200		5.00
			Inscription block of 4	10.00	—

First day covers of Nos. 199-200 total 94,201.

Ballots Filling Ballot
Box — G47

UN Emblem — G48

Printed by House of Questa, United Kingdom. Designed by Ran Banda Mawilmada, Sri Lanka (80c), Maurice Gouju, France (1.50fr).

1991, May 10			**Litho.**	**Perf. 15x14½**	
201	G47	80c	**multicolored** (1,600,000)+	1.00	1.00
			First day cover		1.75
			Inscription block of 4	4.50	—
202	G48	1.50fr	**multicolored** (1,600,000)+	2.25	2.25

			First day cover		3.25
			First day cover, #201-202		3.75
			Inscription block of 4	10.00	—

First day covers of Nos. 201-202 total 77,590.

G49

Rights of the
Child — G50

Printed by The House of Questa. Panes of 50. Designed by Ryuta Nakajima, Japan (80c) and David Popper, Switzerland (1.10fr).

1991, June 14			**Litho.**	**Perf. 14½**	
203	G49	80c	Hands holding infant (469,962)	1.25	1.25
			First day cover		1.75
			Inscription block of 4	6.25	—
204	G50	1.10fr	Children, flowers (494,382)	2.00	2.00
			First day cover		2.25
			First day cover, #203-204		3.25
			Inscription block of 4	9.50	—

First day covers of Nos. 203-204 total 97,732.

G51

Banning of
Chemical
Weapons
G52

Printed by Heraclio Fournier S.A. Panes of 50. Designed by Oscar Asboth, Austria (80c), Michel Granger, France (1.40fr).

1991, Sept. 11			**Litho.**	**Perf. 13½**	
205	G51	80c	**multicolored** (345,658)	2.25	2.25
			First day cover		1.75
			Inscription block of 4	9.50	—
206	G52	1.40fr	**multicolored** (366,076)	3.75	3.75
			First day cover		2.50
			First day cover, #205-206		3.50
			Inscription block of 4	16.50	—

First day covers of Nos. 205-206 total 91,887.

UN Postal Administration, 40th Anniv. Type

1991, Oct. 24				**Perf. 14x15**	
207	A263	50c	UN NY No. 7 (506,839)	1.00	1.00
			First day cover		1.25
			Inscription block of 4	4.50	—
208	A263	1.60fr	UN NY No. 10 (580,493)	2.50	2.50
			First day cover		3.00
			Inscription block of 4	11.00	—
			First day cover, #207-208		3.25
			Panes of 25, #207-208	75.00	

First day covers of Nos. 207-208 total 88,784.

Human Rights Type of 1989

Panes of 12+12 se-tenant labels containing Articles 15 (50c) or 16 (90c) inscribed in French, German or English.
Artwork: 50c, Early Morning in Rio...1925, by Paul Klee. 90c, Marriage of Giovanni (?) Arnolfini and Giovanna Cenami (?), by Jan Van Eyck.

1991, Nov. 20   Litho.   Perf. 13½

209	A250	50c	multicolored (1,295,172)	.85	.85
			First day cover		3.25
			Inscription block of 3 + 3 labels	2.75	
210	A250	90c	multicolored (1,324,091)	1.50	1.50
			First day cover		6.75
			Inscription block of 3 + 3 labels	4.50	
			First day cover, #209-210		2.00
			Panes of 12, #209-210	27.50	

First day covers of Nos. 209-210 total 139,904.

World Heritage Type of 1984

Designs: 50c, Sagarmatha Natl. Park, Nepal. 1.10fr, Stonehenge, United Kingdom.

1992, Jan. 24   Litho.   Perf. 13
Size: 35x28mm

211	G29	50c	multicolored (468,647)	1.10	1.10
			First day cover		1.25
			Inscription block of 4	4.75	
212	G29	1.10fr	multicolored (369,345)	2.25	2.25
			First day cover		2.25
			First day cover, #211-212		3.00
			Inscription block of 4	9.50	

First day covers of Nos. 211-212 total 77,034.

F.S.3,00   NATIONS UNIES   G53

Printed by The House of Questa. Panes of 50. Designed by Nestor Jose Martin, Argentina.

1992, Jan. 24   Litho.   Perf. 15x14½

213	G53	3fr	multicolored (1,600,000)+	3.50	3.50
			First day cover (36,135)		4.00
			Inscription block of 4	14.00	

Clean Oceans Type

1992, Mar. 13   Litho.   Perf. 14

214	A264	80c	Ocean surface, diff. (850,699)	.90	.90
215	A264	80c	Ocean bottom, diff. (850,699)	.90	.90
a.			Pair, #214-215	1.80	2.00
			First day cover, #215a		2.75
			First day cover, #214-215, each		1.75
			Inscription block of 4, 2 #215a	5.00	
			Pane of 12, #214-215	11.00	

First day covers of Nos. 214-215a total 90,725.

Earth Summit Type

Designs: No. 216, Rainbow. No. 217, Two clouds shaped as faces. No. 218, Two sailboats. No. 219, Woman with parasol, boat, flowers.

1992, May 22   Photo.   Perf. 11½

216	A265	75c	multicolored (826,543)	1.25	1.25
217	A265	75c	multicolored (826,543)	1.25	1.25
218	A265	75c	multicolored (826,543)	1.25	1.25
219	A265	75c	multicolored (826,543)	1.25	1.25
a.			Block of 4, #216-219	5.25	5.25
			First day cover, #219a		4.00
			First day cover, #216-219, each		6.00
			Inscription block of 4, #216-219	5.75	
			Pane of 40, #216-219	55.00	

First day covers of Nos. 216-219a total 74,629.

Mission to Planet Earth Type

Designs: No. 220, Space station. No. 221, Probes near Jupiter.

1992, Sept. 4   Photo.   Rouletted 8
Granite Paper

220	A266	1.10fr	multicolored (668,241)	2.50	2.50
221	A266	1.10fr	multicolored (668,241)	2.50	2.50
a.			Pair, #220-221	5.00	5.00
			First day cover, #221a		5.00
			First day cover, #220-221, each		9.00
			Inscription block of 4, 2 #220-221	11.00	
			Pane of 10, #220-221	25.00	

First day covers of Nos. 220-221 total 76,060.

Science and Technology Type of 1992

Designs: 90c, Doctor, nurse. 1.60fr, Graduate seated before computer.

1992, Oct. 2   Litho.   Perf. 14

222	A267	90c	multicolored (438,943)	1.50	1.50
			First day cover		1.60
			Inscription block of 4	6.00	
223	A267	1.60fr	multicolored (400,701)	3.50	3.50
			First day cover		2.50
			First day cover, #222-223		3.25
			Inscription block of 4	14.00	

First day covers of Nos. 222-223 total 75,882.

Human Rights Type of 1989

Panes of 12+12 se-tenant labels containing Articles 21 (50c) and 22 (90c) inscribed in French, German or English.
Artwork: 50c, The Oath of the Tennis Court, by Jacques Louis David. 90c, Rocking Chair I, by Henry Moore.

1992, Nov. 20   Litho.   Perf. 13½

224	A250	50c	multicolored, (1,201,788)	.80	.80
			First day cover		7.00
			Inscription block of 3 + 3 labels	3.00	
225	A250	90c	multicolored, (1,179,294)	1.50	1.50
			First day cover		7.00
			Inscription block of 3 + 3 labels	5.00	
			First day cover, #224-225		1.75
			Panes of 12, #224-225	26.00	

First day covers of Nos. 224-225 total 104,491.

Aging With Dignity Type

Designs: 50c, Older man coaching soccer. 1.60fr, Older man working at computer terminal.

1993, Feb. 5   Litho.   Perf. 13

226	A270	50c	multicolored (483,452)	.70	.70
			First day cover		1.00
			Inscription block of 4	3.50	
227	A270	1.60fr	multicolored (331,008)	2.25	2.25
			First day cover		2.75
			First day cover, #226-227		3.00
			Inscription block of 4	10.50	

First day covers of Nos. 226-227 total 61,361.

Endangered Species Type

Designed by Rocco J. Callari, US, and Betina Ogden, Australia.
Designs: No. 228, Pongidae (gorilla). No. 229, Falco peregrinus (peregrine falcon). No. 230, Trichechus inunguis (Amazonian manatee). No. 231, Panthera uncia (snow leopard).

1993, Mar. 2   Litho.   Perf. 13x12½

228	A271	80c	multicolored (1,200,000)+	1.10	1.10
229	A271	80c	multicolored (1,200,000)+	1.10	1.10
230	A271	80c	multicolored (1,200,000)+	1.10	1.10
231	A271	80c	multicolored (1,200,000)+	1.10	1.10
a.			Block of 4, #228-231	4.50	4.50
			First day cover, #231a		5.00
			First day cover, #228-231, each		2.00
			Inscription block of 4, #228-231	4.50	
			Pane of 16, #228-231	19.00	

First day covers of Nos. 228-231a total 75,363.

Healthy Environment Type

1993, May 7   Litho.   Perf. 15x14½

232	A272	60c	Neighborhood (456,304)	1.10	1.10
			First day cover		1.25
			Inscription block of 4	4.75	
233	A272	1fr	Urban skyscrapers (392,015)	2.25	2.25
			First day cover		2.00
			First day cover, #232-233		3.25
			Inscription block of 4	9.50	

First day covers of Nos. 232-233 total 59,790.

Human Rights Type of 1989

Printed in panes of 12 + 12 se-tenant labels containing Article 27 (50c) and 28 (90c) inscribed in French, German or English.
Artwork: 50c, Three Musicians, by Pablo Picasso. 90c, Voice of Space, by Rene Magritte.

1993, June 11   Litho.   Perf. 13½

234	A250	50c	multicolored (1,166,286)	.85	.85
			First day cover		3.50
			Inscription block of 3 + 3 labels	2.75	
235	A250	90c	multicolored (1,122,348)	2.00	2.00
			First day cover		4.50
			Inscription block of 3 + 3 labels	6.25	
			First day cover, #234-235		2.00
			Panes of 12, #234-235	26.00	

First day covers of Nos. 234-235 total 83,432.

Intl. Peace Day Type

Denomination at: #236, UL. #237, UR. #238, LL. #239, LR.

1993, Sept. 21   Litho. & Engr.   Rouletted 12½

236	A274	60c	purple & multi (357,760)	2.00	2.00
237	A274	60c	purple & multi (357,760)	2.00	2.00
238	A274	60c	purple & multi (357,760)	2.00	2.00
239	A274	60c	purple & multi (357,760)	2.00	2.00
a.			Block of 4, #236-239	8.00	8.00
			First day cover, #239a		5.50
			First day cover, #236-239, each		5.00
			Inscription block of 4, #239a	9.50	
			Pane of 40, #236-239	75.00	

First day covers of Nos. 236-239a total 47,207.

Environment-Climate Type

1993, Oct. 29   Litho.   Perf. 14½

240	A275	1.10fr	Polar bears (391,593)	2.00	2.00
241	A275	1.10fr	Whale sounding (391,593)	2.00	2.00
242	A275	1.10fr	Elephant seal (391,593)	2.00	2.00
243	A275	1.10fr	Penguins (391,593)	2.00	2.00
a.			Strip of 4, #240-243	8.00	8.00
			First day cover, #243a		7.25
			First day cover, #240-243, each		6.00
			Inscription block of 8, 2 #243a	22.50	
			Pane of 24, #240-243	52.50	

First day covers of Nos. 240-243a total 41,819.

Intl. Year of the Family Type of 1993

Designs: 80c, Parents teaching child to walk. 1fr, Two women and child picking plants.

1994, Feb. 4   Litho.   Perf. 13.1

244	A276	80c	rose violet & multi (535,000)+	1.20	1.20
			First day cover		1.75
			Inscription block of 4	5.75	
245	A276	1fr	brown & multi (535,000)+	1.60	1.60
			First day cover		2.00
			First day cover, #244-245		3.25
			Inscription block of 4	7.25	

First day covers of Nos. 244-245 total 50,080.

Endangered Species Type of 1993

Designed by Rocco J. Callari (frame) and Leon Parson, US (stamps).
Designs: No. 246, Mexican prairie dog. No. 247, Jabiru. No. 248, Blue whale. No. 249, Golden lion tamarin.

1994, Mar. 18   Litho.   Perf. 12.7

246	A271	80c	multicolored (1,200,000)+	1.10	1.10
247	A271	80c	multicolored (1,200,000)+	1.10	1.10
248	A271	80c	multicolored (1,200,000)+	1.10	1.10
249	A271	80c	multicolored (1,200,000)+	1.10	1.10
a.			Block of 4, #246-249	4.50	4.50
			First day cover, #249a		5.50
			First day cover, #246-249, each		1.75
			Inscription block of 4, #246-249	4.75	
			Pane of 16, #246-249	20.00	

First day covers of Nos. 246-249a total 82,043.

Protection for Refugees Type of 1994

Design: 1.20fr, Hand lifting figure over chasm.

1994, Apr. 29   Litho.   Perf. 14.3x14.8

250	A277	1.20fr	multicolored (550,000)+	2.50	2.50
			First day cover (33,805)		2.50
			Inscription block of 4	11.00	

Intl. Decade for Natural Disaster Reduction Type of 1994

Earth seen from space, outline map of: No. 251, North America. No. 252, Eurasia. No. 253, South America. No. 254, Australia and South Pacific region.

1994, May 27   Litho.   Perf. 13.9x14.2

251	A281	60c	multicolored (570,000)+	1.75	1.75
252	A281	60c	multicolored (570,000)+	1.75	1.75
253	A281	60c	multicolored (570,000)+	1.75	1.75
254	A281	60c	multicolored (570,000)+	1.75	1.75
a.			Block of 4, #251-254	7.00	7.00
			First day cover, #254a		7.00
			First day cover, #251-254, each		5.00
			Inscription block of 4, #254a	9.50	
			Pane of 40, #251-254	75.00	

First day covers of Nos. 251-254a total 37,595.

Palais des Nations, Geneva — G54

Creation of the World, by Oili Maki — G55

Printed by House of Questa, United Kingdom. Designed by Rocco J. Callari, US.

1994, Sept. 1   Litho.   Perf. 14.3x14.6

255	G54	60c	multicolored (1,075,000)+	.75	.75
			First day cover		1.10
			Inscription block of 4	3.25	
256	G55	80c	multicolored (1,075,000)+	1.00	1.00
			First day cover		1.50
			Inscription block of 4	4.25	
257	G54	1.80fr	multi, diff. (1,075,000)+	2.25	2.25
			First day cover		2.75
			Inscription block of 4	9.50	
			First day cover, #255-257		4.50

First day covers of Nos. 255-257 total 51,637.

Population and Development Type of 1994

Designs: 60c, People shopping at open-air market. 80c, People on vacation crossing bridge.

1994, Sept. 1		**Litho.**		**Perf. 13.2x13.6**	
258	A282	60c	multicolored (535,000)+	1.10	1.10
			First day cover		1.25
			Inscription block of 4	5.00	—
259	A282	80c	multicolored (535,000)+	1.50	1.50
			First day cover		1.75
			Inscription block of 4	7.50	—
			First day cover, #258-259		3.00

First day covers of Nos. 258-259 total 50,443.

UNCTAD Type of 1994

1994, Oct. 28					
260	A283	80c	multi, diff. (535,000)+	1.25	1.25
			First day cover		1.75
			Inscription block of 4	5.50	—
261	A283	1fr	multi, diff. (535,000)+	1.75	1.75
			First day cover		2.00
			Inscription block of 4	7.75	—
			First day cover, #260-261		3.50
a.			Grayish green omitted		—
			Inscription block of 4		—

First day covers of Nos. 260-261 total 48,122.

UN 50th Anniv. Type of 1995

1995, Jan. 1		**Litho. & Engr.**		**Perf. 13.4**	
262	A284	80c	multicolored (823,827)	1.25	1.25
			First day cover (38,988)		3.00
			Inscription block of 4	5.75	—

Social Summit Type of 1995

1995, Feb. 3		**Photo. & Engr.**		**Perf. 13.6x13.9**	
263	A285	1fr	multi, diff. (452,116)	1.50	1.50
			First day cover (35,246)		2.00
			Inscription block of 4	7.00	—

Endangered Species Type of 1993

Designed by Sibylle Erni, Switzerland.
Designs: No. 264, Crowned lemur, Lemur coronatus. No. 265, Giant Scops owl, Otus gurneyi. No. 266, Zetek's frog, Atelopus varius zeteki. No. 267, Wood bison, Bison bison athabascae.

1995, Mar. 24		**Litho.**		**Perf. 13x12½**	
264	A271	80c	multicolored (730,000)+	1.25	1.25
265	A271	80c	multicolored (730,000)+	1.25	1.25
266	A271	80c	multicolored (730,000)+	1.25	1.25
267	A271	80c	multicolored (730,000)+	1.25	1.25
a.			Block of 4, 264-267	5.00	5.00
			First day cover, #267a		4.50
			First day cover, #264-267, each		1.60
			Inscription block of 4, #267a	5.75	—
			Pane of 16, #264-267	19.00	

First day covers of Nos. 264-267a total 71,907.

Intl. Youth Year Type of 1995

Designs: 80c, Farmer on tractor, fields at harvest time. 1fr, Couple standing by fields at night.

1995, May 26		**Litho.**		**Perf. 14.4x14.7**	
268	A286	80c	multicolored (294,987)	1.60	1.60
			First day cover		1.75
			Inscription block of 4	7.00	—
269	A286	1fr	multicolored (264,823)	2.75	2.75
			First day cover		2.00
			First day cover, #268-269		4.00
			Inscription block of 4	12.00	—

First day covers of Nos. 268-269 total 45,665.

UN, 50th Anniv. Type of 1995

Designs: 60c, Like No. 663. 1.80fr, Like No. 664.

1995, June 26		**Engr.**		**Perf. 13.3x13.6**	
270	A287	60c	maroon (352,336)	1.00	1.00
			First day cover		.90
			Inscription block of 4	4.50	—
271	A287	1.80fr	green (377,391)	3.25	3.25
			First day cover		3.00
			First day cover, #270-271		4.00
			Inscription block of 4	14.00	—

Souvenir Sheet
Litho. & Engr.
Imperf

272			Sheet of 2, #270-271 (251,272)	4.25	4.25
a.	A287	60c	maroon	1.00	1.00
b.	A287	1.80fr	green	3.25	3.25
			First day cover		8.00

First day covers of Nos. 270-272 total 72,666.

Conference on Women Type of 1995

Designs: 60c, Black woman, cranes flying above. 1fr, Women, dove.

1995, Sept. 5		**Photo.**		**Perf. 12**	
273	A288	60c	multicolored (342,336)	1.40	1.40
			First day cover		1.25
			Inscription block of 4	6.00	—

Size: 28x50mm

274	A288	1fr	multicolored (345,489)	2.50	2.00
			First day cover		2.25
			First day cover, #273-274		3.25
			Inscription block of 4	11.00	—

First day covers of Nos. 273-274 total 57,542.

UN People, 50th Anniv. Type of 1995

1995, Oct. 24		**Litho.**		**Perf. 14**	
275			Sheet of 12 (216,832 sheets)	17.00	12.50
			First day cover		20.00
a.-l.	A290	30c	each	1.30	1.25
			First day cover, #275a-275l, each		7.00
276			Souvenir booklet, (74,151 booklets)	17.00	
a.	A290	30c	Booklet pane of 3, vert. strip of 3 from UL of sheet	4.25	4.25
b.	A290	30c	Booklet pane of 3, vert. strip of 3 from UR of sheet	4.25	4.25
c.	A290	30c	Booklet pane of 3, vert. strip of 3 from LL of sheet	4.25	4.25
d.	A290	30c	Booklet pane of 3, vert. strip of 3 from LR of sheet	4.25	4.25

First day covers of Nos. 275-276d total 53,245.

WFUNA, 50th Anniv. Type

Design: 80c, Fishing boat, fish in net.

1996, Feb. 2		**Litho.**		**Perf. 13x13½**	
277	A291	80c	multicolored (550,000)+	1.25	1.25
			First day cover		2.00
			Inscription block of 4	6.50	—

The Galloping Horse Treading on a Flying Swallow, Chinese Bronzework, Eastern Han Dynasty (25-220 A.D.) — G56

Palais des Nations, Geneva — G57

Printed by House of Questa, UK.

1996, Feb. 2		**Litho.**		**Perf. 14½x15**	
278	G56	40c	multicolored (1,125,000)+	.50	.50
			First day cover		1.25
			Inscription block of 4	2.50	—
279	G57	70c	multicolored (1,125,000+)	1.10	1.10
			First day cover		1.50
			First day cover, #278-279		3.50
			Inscription block of 4	4.75	—

Endangered Species Type of 1993

Designs: No. 280, Paphiopedilum delenatii. No. 281, Pachypodium baronii. No. 282, Sternbergia lutea. No. 283, Darlingtonia californica.

1996, Mar. 14		**Litho.**		**Perf. 12½**	
280	A271	80c	multicolored (680,000)+	1.10	1.10
281	A271	80c	multicolored (680,000)+	1.10	1.10
282	A271	80c	multicolored (680,000)+	1.10	1.10
283	A271	80c	multicolored (680,000)+	1.10	1.10
a.			Block of 4, #280-283	4.50	4.50
			First day cover, #280-283, each		2.00
			First day cover, #283a		4.50
			Inscription block of 4, #283a	4.75	—
			Pane of 16, #280-283	18.00	

City Summit Type of 1996

Designs: No. 284, Asian family. No. 285, Oriental garden. No. 286, Fruit, vegetable vendor, mosque. No. 287, Boys playing ball. No. 288, Couple reading newspaper.

1996, June 3		**Litho.**		**Perf. 14x13½**	
284	A293	70c	multicolored (420,000)+	1.50	1.50
285	A293	70c	multicolored (420,000)+	1.50	1.50
286	A293	70c	multicolored (420,000)+	1.50	1.50
287	A293	70c	multicolored (420,000)+	1.50	1.50
288	A293	70c	multicolored (420,000)+	1.50	1.50
a.			Strip of 5, #284-288	7.50	7.50
			First day cover, #288a		11.00
			First day cover, #284-288, each		5.00
			Inscription block of 10, 2 #288a	20.00	

Sport and the Environment Type

Designs: 70c, Cycling, vert. 1.10fr, Sprinters.

1996, July 19		**Litho.**		**Perf. 14x14½, 14½x14**	
289	A294	70c	multicolored (625,000)+	1.25	1.25
			First day cover		1.50
			Inscription block of 4	5.75	—

290	A294	1.10fr	multicolored (625,000)+	1.75	1.75
			First day cover		2.25
			First day cover, #289-290		4.50
			Inscription block of 4	8.75	—

Souvenir Sheet

291	A294		Sheet of 2, #289-290 (345,000)+	3.00	3.00
			First day cover		12.00

Plea for Peace Type

Designed by: 90c, Chen Yu, China. 1.10fr, Zhou Jing, China.

Designs: 90c, Tree filled with birds, vert. 1.10fr, Bouquet of flowers in rocket tail vase, vert.

1996, Sept. 17		**Litho.**		**Perf. 15x14½**	
292	A295	90c	multicolored (550,000)+	1.50	1.50
			First day cover		1.50
			Inscription block of 4	6.50	—
293	A295	1.10fr	multicolored (550,000)+	2.00	2.00
			First day cover		2.25
			First day cover, #292-293		3.75
			Inscription block of 4	10.00	—

UNICEF Type

Fairy Tales: 70c, The Sun and the Moon, South America. 1.80fr, Ananse, Africa.

1996, Nov. 20		**Litho.**		**Perf. 14½x15**	
294	A296	70c	multicolored (1,000,000)+	1.00	1.00
			First day cover		1.50
			Pane of 8 + label	8.50	
295	A296	1.80fr	multicolored (1,000,000)+	2.40	2.40
			First day cover		3.00
			First day cover, #294-295		4.00
			Pane of 8 + label	21.00	

UN Flag — G58

Palais des Nations Under Construction by Massimo Campigli — G59

Printed by The House of Questa, Ltd., UK.

1997, Feb. 12		**Litho.**		**Perf. 14½**	
296	G58	10c	multicolored (600,000)+	.20	.20
			First day cover		1.25
			Inscription block of 4	.55	—
297	G59	1.10fr	multicolored (700,000)+	1.50	1.50
			First day cover		2.25
			First day cover, #296-297		3.50
			Inscription block of 4	6.00	—

First day covers of Nos. 296-297 total 41,186.

Endangered Species Type of 1993

Designs: No. 298, Ursus maritimus (polar bear). No. 299, Goura cristata (blue-crowned pigeon). No. 300, Amblyrhynchus cristatus (marine iguana). No. 301, Lama guanicoe (guanaco).

1997, Mar. 13		**Litho.**		**Perf. 12½**	
298	A271	80c	multicolored (620,000)+	1.00	1.00
299	A271	80c	multicolored (620,000)+	1.00	1.00
300	A271	80c	multicolored (620,000)+	1.00	1.00
301	A271	80c	multicolored (620,000)+	1.00	1.00
a.			Block of 4, #298-301	4.00	4.00
			First day cover, #301a		5.00
			First day cover, #298-301, each		2.50
			Inscription block of 4, #301a	4.50	
			Pane of 16	17.00	

First day covers of Nos. 298-301 total 71,905.

Earth Summit Anniv. Type

Designs: No. 302, Person flying over mountain. No. 303, Mountain, person's face. No. 304, Person standing on mountain, sailboats. No. 305, Person, mountain, trees. 1.10fr, Combined design similar to Nos. 302-305.

1997, May 30		**Photo.**		**Perf. 11½**	
			Granite Paper		
302	A299	45c	multicolored (227,187)	1.00	1.00
303	A299	45c	multicolored (227,187)	1.00	1.00
304	A299	45c	multicolored (227,187)	1.00	1.00
305	A299	45c	multicolored (227,187)	1.00	1.00
a.			Block of 4, #302-305	4.00	4.00
			First day cover, #305a		8.00
			First day cover, #302-305, each		6.00
			Inscription block of 4, #305a	6.25	

Souvenir Sheet

306	A299	1.10fr	multicolored (176,386)	3.50	3.50
			First day cover		5.00

First day covers of Nos. 302-306 total 55,389.

Transportation Type of 1997

Air transportation: No. 307, Zeppelin, Fokker tri-motor. No. 308, Boeing 314 Clipper, Lockheed Constellation. No. 309, DeHavilland Comet. No. 310, Boeing 747, Illyushin jet. No. 311, Concorde.

1997, Aug. 29			**Litho.**	**Perf. 14x14½**	
307	A300	70c	multicolored (271,575)	1.00	1.00
308	A300	70c	multicolored (271,575)	1.00	1.00
309	A300	70c	multicolored (271,575)	1.00	1.00
310	A300	70c	multicolored (271,575)	1.00	1.00
311	A300	70c	multicolored (271,575)	1.00	1.00
a.			Strip of 5, #307-311	5.00	5.00
			First day cover, #311a		7.00
			First day cover, #307-311, each		4.75
			Margin block of 10, 2#311a	12.50	

No. 311a has continuous design.
First day covers of Nos. 307-311 total 33,303.

Philately Type

Designs: 70c, No. 146. 1.10fr, No. 147.

1997, Oct. 14			**Litho.**	**Perf. 13½x14**	
312	A301	70c	multicolored (254,406)	.90	.90
			First day cover		1.75
			Inscription block of 4	3.50	—
313	A301	1.10fr	multicolored (303,125)	1.75	1.75
			First day cover		2.25
			First day cover, #312-313		6.00
			Inscription block of 4	7.00	—

First day covers of Nos. 312-313 total 47,528.

World Heritage Convention Type

Terracotta warriors of Xian: 45c, Single warrior. 70c, Massed warriors. No. 316a, like #716. No. 316b, like #717. No. 316c, like Geneva #314. No. 316d, like Geneva #315. No. 316e, like Vienna #230. No. 316f, like Vienna #231.

1997, Nov. 19			**Litho.**	**Perf. 13½**	
314	A302	45c	multicolored (409,820)	1.25	1.25
			First day cover		1.40
			Inscription block of 4	5.50	—
315	A302	70c	multicolored (414,059)	2.25	2.25
			First day cover		1.50
			First day cover, #314-315		4.00
			Inscription block of 4	9.50	—
316			Souvenir booklet (275,114 booklets)	11.00	
a.-f.			A302 10c any single	.45	.45
g.			Booklet pane of 4 #316a	1.80	1.80
h.			Booklet pane of 4 #316b	1.80	1.80
i.			Booklet pane of 4 #316c	1.80	1.80
j.			Booklet pane of 4 #316d	1.80	1.80
k.			Booklet pane of 4 #316e	1.80	1.80
l.			Booklet pane of 4 #316f	1.80	1.80

First day covers of Nos. 314-316 total 40,366.

Palais des Nations, Geneva — G60

Printed by The House of Questa, UK. Designed by UN (2fr).

1998, Feb. 13			**Litho.**	**Perf. 14½x15**	
317	G60	2fr	multicolored (550,000)+	1.75	1.75
			First day cover		6.00
			Inscription block of 4	7.00	

Endangered Species Type of 1993

Designed by Rocco J. Callari, US and Suzanne Duranceau, Canada.
Designs: No. 318, Macaca thibetana (short-tailed Tibetan macaque). No. 319, Phoenicopterus ruber (Caribbean flamingo). No. 320, Ornithoptera alexandrae (Queen Alexandra's birdwing). No. 321, Dama mesopotamica (Persian fallow deer).

1998, Mar. 13			**Litho.**	**Perf. 12½**	
318	A271	80c	multicolored (560,000)+	1.10	1.10
319	A271	80c	multicolored (560,000)+	1.10	1.10
320	A271	80c	multicolored (560,000)+	1.10	1.10
321	A271	80c	multicolored (560,000)+	1.10	1.10
a.			Block of 4, #318-321	4.50	4.50
			First day cover, #321a		6.00
			First day cover, #318-321, each		5.00
			Inscription block of 4, #321a	4.75	—
			Pane of 16	15.00	

Intl. Year of the Ocean — G61

Designed by Jon Ellis, US.

1998, May 20			**Litho.**	**Perf. 13x13½**	
322	G61		Pane of 12 (270,000)+	12.00	10.00
			First day cover		10.00
a.-l.			45c any single	.90	.90
			First day cover, #322a-322l, each		3.00

Rain Forests Type

1998, June 19				**Perf. 13x13½**	
323	A307	70c	Orangutans (430,000)+	.90	.90
			First day cover		5.00
			Inscription block of 4	4.00	—

Souvenir Sheet

324	A307	3fr	like #323 (250,000)+	5.00	7.00
			First day cover		7.00

Peacekeeping Type

Designs: 70c, Soldier with two children. 90c, Two soldiers, children.

1998, Sept. 15			**Photo.**	**Perf. 12**	
325	A308	70c	multicolored (400,000)+	.85	.85
			First day cover		1.50
			Inscription block of 4	3.50	—
326	A308	90c	multicolored (390,000)+	1.40	1.40
			First day cover		4.00
			First day cover, #325-326		5.00
			Inscription block of 4	6.00	—

Declaration of Human Rights Type of 1998

Designs: 90c, Stylized birds. 1.80fr, Stylized birds flying from hand.

1998, Oct. 27			**Litho. & Photo.**	**Perf. 13**	
327	A309	90c	multicolored (400,000)+	.95	.95
			First day cover		2.00
			Inscription block of 4	4.00	—
328	A309	1.80fr	multicolored (390,000)+	2.00	2.00
			First day cover		3.50
			First day cover, #327-328		5.00
			Inscription block of 4	8.00	—

Schönbrunn Palace Type

Designs: 70c, #331b, Great Palm House. 1.10fr, #331d, Blue porcelain vase, vert. No. 331a, Palace. No. 331c, The Gloriette (archway). No. 331e, Wall painting on fabric (detail), by Johann Wenzl Bergl, vert. No. 331f, Porcelain stove, vert.

1998, Dec. 4			**Litho.**	**Perf. 14**	
329	A310	70c	multicolored (375,000)+	1.25	1.25
			First day cover		1.50
			Inscription block of 4	4.00	—
330	A310	1.10fr	multicolored (375,000)+	1.50	1.50
			First day cover		2.25
			First day cover, #329-330		5.00
			Inscription block of 4	6.00	—

Souvenir Booklet

331			Booklet (100,000)+	12.00	
a.-c.			A310 10c any single	.25	.25
d.-f.			A310 30c any single	.75	.75
g.			Booklet pane of 4 #331a	1.00	1.00
h.			Booklet pane of 3 #331d	3.00	3.00
i.			Booklet pane of 3 #331e	3.00	3.00
j.			Booklet pane of 3 #331f	3.00	3.00
k.			Booklet pane of 4 #331b	1.00	1.00
l.			Booklet pane of 4 #331c	1.00	1.00

Palais Wilson, Geneva — G62

Designed and printed by Helio Courvoisier, SA, Switzerland.

1999, Feb. 5			**Photo.**	**Perf. 11½**	
			Granite Paper		
332	G62	1.70fr	brown red (600,000)+	2.00	2.00
			First day cover (25,568)		3.50
			Inscription block of 4	8.50	

World Heritage, Australia Type

Designs: 90c, #335e, Kakadu Natl. Park. 1.10fr, #335c, Great Barrier Reef. No. 335a, Tasmanian Wilderness. No. 335b, Wet tropics of Queensland. No. 335d, Uluru-Kata Tjuta Natl. Park. No. 335f, Willandra Lakes region.

1999, Mar. 19			**Litho.**	**Perf. 13**	
333	A313	90c	multicolored (420,000)+	1.40	1.40
			First day cover		2.00
			Inscription block of 4	5.75	—
334	A313	1.10fr	multicolored (420,000)+	1.50	1.50
			First day cover		2.25
			First day cover, #333-334		4.50
			Inscription block of 4	8.00	—

Souvenir Booklet

335			Booklet (90,000)+	9.75	
a.-c.			A313 10c any single	.25	.25
d.-f.			A313 20c any single	.55	.55
g.			Booklet pane of 4, #335a	1.00	1.00
h.			Booklet pane of 4, #335d	2.25	2.25
i.			Booklet pane of 4, #335b	1.00	1.00
j.			Booklet pane of 4, #335e	2.25	2.25
k.			Booklet pane of 4, #335c	1.00	1.00
l.			Booklet pane of 4, #335f	2.25	2.25

First day covers of Nos. 333-335 total 44,622.

Endangered Species Type of 1993

Designed by Tim Barrall, US.
Designs: No. 336, Equus hemionus (Asiatic wild ass). No. 337, Anodorhynchus hyacinthinus (hyacinth macaw). No. 338, Epicrates subflavus (Jamaican boa). No. 339, Dendrolagus bennettianus (Bennetts' tree kangaroo).

1999, Apr. 22			**Litho.**	**Perf. 12½**	
336	A271	90c	multicolored (488,000)+	1.25	1.25
337	A271	90c	multicolored (488,000)+	1.25	1.25
338	A271	90c	multicolored (488,000)+	1.25	1.25
339	A271	90c	multicolored (488,000)+	1.25	1.25
a.			Block of 4, #336-339	5.00	5.00
			First day cover, #339a		5.75
			First day cover, #336-339, each		2.00
			Inscription block of 4, #339a	6.00	—
			Pane of 16	19.00	

First day covers of Nos. 336-339 total 52,856.

UNISPACE III Type

Designs: No. 340, Farm, satellite dish. No. 341, City, satellite in orbit. No. 342, Composite of #340-341.

1999, July 7			**Photo.**	**Rouletted 8**	
340	A314	45c	multicolored (925,000)+	.90	.90
341	A314	45c	multicolored (925,000)+	.90	.90
a.			Pair, #340-341	2.00	2.00
			First day cover, #341a		2.25
			First day cover, #340-341, each		14.00
			Inscription block of 4	5.00	—
			Pane of 10, #340-341	9.50	—

Souvenir Sheet
Perf. 14½

342	A314	2fr	multicolored (275,000)+	4.50	4.50
			First day cover		6.00
a.			Ovptd. in sheet margin	9.50	9.50
			First day cover		19.00

No. 342a is ovptd. in violet blue "PHILEXFRANCE 99 / LE MONDIAL DU TIMBRE / PARIS / 2 AU 11 JUILLET 1999.
First day covers of Nos. 340-342 total 63,412.

UPU Type

Various people, early 20th century methods of mail transportation, denomination at: No. 343, UL. No. 344, UR. No. 345, LL. No. 346, LR.

1999, Aug. 23			**Photo.**	**Perf. 11¾**	
343	A315	70c	multicolored (336,000)+	1.00	1.00
344	A315	70c	multicolored (336,000)+	1.00	1.00
345	A315	70c	multicolored (336,000)+	1.00	1.00
346	A315	70c	multicolored (336,000)+	1.00	1.00
a.			Block of 4, #343-346	4.00	4.00
			First day cover, #346a		3.50
			First day cover, #343-346, each		1.50
			Inscription block of 4, #346a	4.25	

First day covers of Nos. 343-346 total 27,041.

In Memoriam Type

Designs: 1.10fr, 2fr, Armillary sphere, Palais de Nations. Size of 2fr stamp: 34x63mm.

1999, Sept. 21		Litho.	Perf. 14½x14	
347	A316	1.10fr multicolored (400,000)+	1.40	1.40
		First day cover		3.00
		Inscription block of 4	6.00	

Souvenir Sheet
Perf. 14

348	A316	2fr multicolored (225,000)+	3.00	3.00
		First day cover		3.50

First day covers of Nos. 347-348 total 46,527.

Education Type

1999, Nov. 18		Litho.	Perf. 13½x13¾	
349	A317	90c Rainbow over globe (350,000)+	.95	.95
		First day cover		1.75
		Inscription block of 4	4.00	
350	A317	1.80fr Fish, tree, globe, book (370,000)+	2.00	2.00
		First day cover		3.50
		First day cover, #349-350		4.50
		Inscription block of 4	8.25	—

First day covers of Nos. 349-350 total 37,925.

Intl. Year Of Thanksgiving Type

2000, Jan 1		Litho.	Perf. 13¼x13½	
351	A318	90c multicolored (450,000)+	1.25	1.25
		First day cover		3.00
		Inscription block of 4	5.50	

On No. 351 portions of the design were applied by a thermographic process producing a shiny, raised effect.

Endangered Species Type of 1993

Designed by Robert Hynes, US.
Designs: No. 352, Hippopotamus amphibius (hippopotamus). No. 353, Coscoroba coscoroba (Coscoroba swan). No. 354, Varanus prasinus (emerald monitor). No. 355, Enhydra lutris (sea otter).

2000, Apr. 6		Litho.	Perf. 12¾x12½	
352	A271	90c multicolored (488,000)+	1.25	1.25
353	A271	90c multicolored (488,000)+	1.25	1.25
354	A271	90c multicolored (488,000)+	1.25	1.25
355	A271	90c multicolored (488,000)+	1.25	1.25
a.		Block of 4, #352-355	5.00	5.00
		First day cover, #355a		5.00
		First day cover, #352-355, each		1.90
		Inscription block of 4, #355a	5.25	—
		Pane of 16	20.00	

Our World 2000 Type

Winning artwork in Millennium painting competition: 90c, The Embrace, by Rita Adaimy, Lebanon. 1.10fr, Living Single, by Richard Kimanthi, Kenya, vert.

2000, May 30		Litho.	Perf. 13x13½, 13½x13	
356	A319	90c multicolored (330,000)+	1.25	1.25
		First day cover		1.75
		Inscription block of 4	5.00	
357	A319	1.10fr multicolored (330,000)+	1.50	1.50
		First day cover		2.25
		First day cover, #356-357		3.50
		Inscription block of 4	6.00	—

55th Anniversary Type

Designs: 90c, Trygve Lie, Harry S Truman, workers at cornerstone dedication ceremony, 1949. 1.40fr, Window cleaner on Secretariat Building, General Assembly Hall under construction, 1951.

2000, July 7		Litho.	Perf. 13¼x13	
358	A320	90c multicolored (370,000)+	1.25	1.25
		First day cover		1.75
		Inscription block of 4	5.00	—
359	A320	1.40fr multicolored (370,000)+	2.00	2.00
		First day cover		2.60
		First day cover, #358-359		3.75
		Inscription block of 4	8.00	—

Souvenir Sheet

360	A320	Sheet of 2, #358-359 (235,000)+	3.25	3.25
		First day cover		3.25

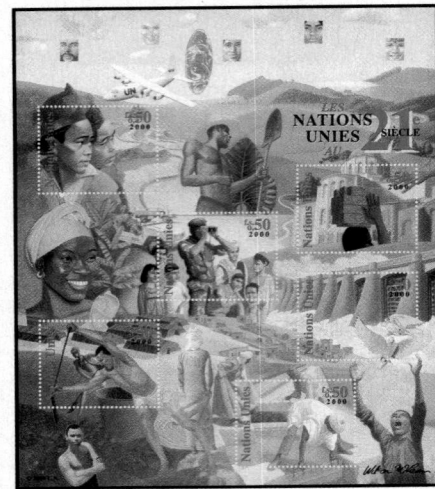

The UN in the 21st Century — G63

Printed by Government Printing Office, Austria. Designed by Wilson McLean, UK.

No. 361: a, Two people, terraced rice paddy. b, Man carrying bricks on head. c, UN Peacekeeper with binoculars. d, Dam, doves. e, Men with shovels. f, People working on irrigation system.

2000, Sept. 15		Litho.	Perf. 14	
361	G63	Pane of 6 (266,000)+	7.50	7.50
		First day cover		7.50
a.-f.		50c any single	1.25	1.25
		First day covers, each		5.00

World Heritage, Spain Type

Designs: Nos. 362, 364b, Walled Town of Cuenca. Nos. 363, 364e, Toledo. #364a, Alhambra, Generalife and Albayzin, Granada. #364c, Aqueduct of Segovia. #364d, Amphitheater of Mérida. #364f, Güell Park, Barcelona.

2000, Oct. 6		Litho.	Perf. 14¾x14½	
362	A323	1fr multicolored (340,000)+	1.40	1.40
		First day cover		1.90
		Inscription block of 4	5.75	—
363	A323	1.20fr multicolored (340,000)+	1.60	1.60
		First day cover		2.25
		First day cover, #362-363		3.50
		Inscription block of 4	6.50	—

Souvenir Booklet

364		Booklet (64,000)+	8.00	
a.-c.		A323 10c any single	.20	.20
d.-f.		A323 20c any single	.50	.50
g.		Booklet pane of 4, #364a	.70	.70
h.		Booklet pane of 4, #364d	2.00	2.00
i.		Booklet pane of 4, #364b	.70	.70
j.		Booklet pane of 4, #364e	2.00	2.00
k.		Booklet pane of 4, #364c	.70	.70
l.		Booklet pane of 4, #364f	2.00	2.00

Respect for Refugees Type

Designs: 80c, 1.80fr, Refugee with cane, four other refugees.

2000, Nov. 9		Litho.	Perf. 13¼x12¾	
365	A324	80c multicolored (400,000)+	1.25	1.25
		First day cover		1.75
		Inscription block of 4	4.50	—

Souvenir Sheet

366	A324	1.80fr multicolored (215,000)+	2.50	2.50
		First day cover		3.00

Endangered Species Type of 1993

Printed by Johann Enschedé and Sons, the Netherlands. Designed by Higgins Bond.
Designs: No. 367, Felis lynx canadensis (North American lynx). No. 368, Pavo muticus (green peafowl). No. 369, Geochelone elephantopus (Galapagos giant tortoise). No. 370, Lepilemur spp. (sportive lemur).

2001, Feb. 1		Litho.	Perf. 12¾x12½	
367	A271	90c multicolored (448,000)+	1.25	1.25
368	A271	90c multicolored (448,000)+	1.25	1.25
369	A271	90c multicolored (448,000)+	1.25	1.25
370	A271	90c multicolored (448,000)+	1.25	1.25
a.		Block of 4, #367-370	5.00	5.00
		First day cover, #370a		5.50
		First day cover, #367-370 each		1.90
		Inscription block of 4, #370a	5.25	—
		Pane of 16	20.00	

Intl. Volunteers Year — G64

Printed by Johann Enschedé and Sons, the Netherlands. Panes of 20. Designed by Rorie Katz and Robert Stein, US.
Paintings by: 90c, Ernest Pignon-Ernest, France. 1.30fr, Paul Siché, France.

2001, Mar. 29		Litho.	Perf. 13¼	
371	G64	90c multicolored (350,000)+	1.10	1.10
		First day cover		1.75
		Inscription block of 4	4.50	
372	G64	1.30fr multicolored (340,000)+	1.60	1.60
		First day cover		2.40
		First day cover, #371-372		3.50
		Inscription block of 4	6.50	

World Heritage, Japan Type

Designs: 1.10fr, #375b, Nara. 1.30fr, #375e, Itsukushima Shinto Shrine. #375a, Kyoto. #375c, Himeji-Jo. #375d, Shirakawa-Go and Gokayama. #375f, Nikko.

2001, Aug. 1		Litho.	Perf. 12¾x13¼	
373	A328	1.10fr multicolored (350,000)+	1.30	1.30
		First day cover		2.00
		Inscription block of 4	5.75	—
374	A328	1.30fr multicolored (350,000)+	1.50	1.50
		First day cover		2.40
		First day cover, #373-374		3.75
		Inscription block of 4	6.50	—

Souvenir Booklet

375		Booklet (52,000)+	8.50	
a.-c.		A328 10c any single	.25	.25
d.-f.		A328 30c any single	.50	.50
g.		Booklet pane of 4, #375a	.85	.85
h.		Booklet pane of 4, #375d	2.00	2.00
i.		Booklet pane of 4, #375b	.85	.85
j.		Booklet pane of 4, #375e	2.00	2.00
k.		Booklet pane of 4, #375c	.85	.85
l.		Booklet pane of 4, #375f	2.00	2.00

Dag Hammarskjöld Type

2001, Sept. 18		Engr.	Perf. 11x11¼	
376	A329	2fr carmine lake (380,000)+	2.50	2.50
		First day cover		3.25
		Inscription block of 4	10.00	—

UN Postal Administration, 50th Anniv. Types

2001, Oct. 18		Litho.	Perf. 13½	
377	A330	90c Stamps, globe (310,000)+	1.25	1.25
		First day cover		1.60
		Inscription block of 4	5.25	—
378	A330	1.30fr Stamps, horns (310,000)+	2.25	2.25
		First day cover		2.40
		First day cover, #377-378		3.50
		Inscription block of 4	9.25	—

Souvenir Sheet

379	A331	Sheet of 2 (175,000)+	5.00	4.00
a.		1.30fr red & light blue, 38mm diameter	1.75	1.75
b.		1.80fr red & light blue, 38mm diameter	2.25	2.25
		First day cover		8.00

Climate Change Type

Designs: No. 380, Lizard, flowers, shoreline. No. 381, Windmills, construction workers. No. 382, Non-polluting factory. No. 383, Solar oven, city, village, picnickers.

2001, Nov. 16		Litho.	Perf. 13¼	
380	A332	90c multicolored (73,500)+	1.10	1.10
381	A332	90c multicolored (73,500)+	1.10	1.10
382	A332	90c multicolored (73,500)+	1.10	1.10
383	A332	90c multicolored (73,500)+	1.10	1.10
a.		Horiz. strip, #380-383	4.50	4.50
		Inscription block of 8	9.00	—
		First day cover, #383a		5.25
		First day covers, #380-383, each		6.00
		Pane of 24	25.00	—

Nobel Peace Prize Type

2001, Dec. 10		Litho.	Perf. 13¼	
384	A333	90c multicolored (840,000)+	1.10	1.10
		Inscription block of 4	4.50	—
		First day cover		1.75
		Pane of 12	13.50	—

NATIONS UNIES — Palais des Nations — G65

Printed by Government Printing Office, Austria. Panes of 20. Designed by Robert Stein, US.

2002, Mar. 1	Litho.		Perf. 13¾	
385 G65	1.30fr multicolored (630,000)+		1.40	1.40
	First day cover			2.25
	Inscription block of 4		5.75	—

Endangered Species Type of 1993

Printed by Johann Enschedé and Sons, the Netherlands. Designed by Lori Anzalone, US.
Designs: No. 386, Cacajao calvus (white uakari). No. 387, Mellivora capensis (honey badger). No. 388, Otocolobus manul (manul). No. 389, Varanus exanthematicus (Bosc's monitor).

2002, Apr. 4	Litho.		Perf. 12¾x12½	
386 A271	90c multicolored (420,000)+		1.25	1.25
387 A271	90c multicolored (420,000)+		1.25	1.25
388 A271	90c multicolored (420,000)+		1.25	1.25
389 A271	90c multicolored (420,000)+		1.25	1.25
a.	Block of 4, #386-389		5.00	5.00
	First day cover, #389a			5.50
	First day cover, #386-389 each			1.90
	Inscription block of 4, #389a		5.25	—
	Pane of 16		20.00	—

Independence of East Timor Type

Designs: 90c, Wooden statue of male figure. 1.30fr, Carved wooden container.

2002, May 20	Litho.		Perf. 14x14½	
390 A335	90c multicolored (305,000)+		1.25	1.25
	First day cover			1.90
	Inscription block of 4		5.00	—
391 A335	1.30fr multicolored (295,000)+		1.75	1.75
	First day cover			2.60
	First day cover, #390-391			3.75
	Inscription block of 4		7.00	—

Intl. Year of Mountains Type

Designs: No. 392, Weisshorn, Switzerland. No. 393, Mt. Fuji, Japan. No. 394, Vinson Massif, Antarctica. No. 395, Mt. Kamet, India.

2002, May 24	Litho.		Perf. 13x13¼	
392 A336	70c multicolored (1,230,000)+		.90	.90
	First day cover			1.40
393 A336	70c multicolored (1,230,000)+		.90	.90
	First day cover			1.40
394 A336	1.20fr multicolored (1,230,000)+		1.60	1.60
	First day cover			2.40
	First day cover, #392, 394			3.25
395 A336	1.20fr multicolored (1,230,000)+		1.60	1.60
a.	Vert. strip or block of four, #392-395		5.75	5.75
	First day cover			2.40
	First day cover, #392, 395			3.25
	First day cover, #392-395			6.00
	Pane of 12, 3 each #392-395		19.00	—

World Summit on Sustainable Development (Peter Max) Type

Designs: No. 396, Sun, birds, flowers, heart. No. 397, Three faceless people, diff. No. 398, Three women, diff. No. 399, Sailboat, mountain.

2002, June 27	Litho.		Perf. 14½x14	
396 A337	90c multicolored (1,215,000)+		1.25	1.25
	First day cover			1.90
397 A337	90c multicolored (1,215,000)+		1.25	1.25
	First day cover			1.90
398 A337	1.80fr multicolored (1,215,000)+		2.50	2.50
	First day cover			3.50
	First day cover, #396, 398			4.00
399 A337	1.80fr multicolored (1,215,000)+		2.50	2.50
a.	Vert. strip or block of four, #396-399		8.00	8.00
	First day cover			3.50
	First day cover, #397, 399			4.00
	First day cover, #396-399			8.00
	Pane of 12, 3 each #396-399		23.50	—

World Heritage, Italy Type

Designs: 90c, #402e, Pisa. 1.30fr, #402b, Aeolian Islands. #402a, Amalfi Coast. #402c, Rome. #402d, Florence. #402f, Pompeii.

2002, Aug. 30	Litho.		Perf. 13½x13¼	
400 A338	90c multicolored (355,000)+		1.25	1.25
	First day cover			1.90
	Inscription block of 4		5.00	—
401 A338	1.30fr multicolored (355,000)+		2.00	2.00
	First day cover			2.75
	First day cover, #400-401			4.00
	Inscription block of 4		8.25	—

Souvenir Booklet

402	Booklet (51,000)+		22.50	
a.-c.	A338 10c any single		.50	.50
d.-f.	A338 20c any single		1.50	1.50
g.	Booklet pane of 4 #402d		6.00	6.00
h.	Booklet pane of 4 #402a		1.50	1.50
i.	Booklet pane of 4, #402e		6.00	6.00
j.	Booklet pane of 4, #402b		1.50	1.50
k.	Booklet pane of 4, #402f		6.00	6.00
l.	Booklet pane of 4, #402c		1.50	1.50

AIDS Awareness Type

2002, Oct. 24	Litho.		Perf. 13½	
403 A339	1.30fr multicolored (305,000)+		2.00	2.00
	Inscription block of 4		7.75	—
	First day cover #403			2.60
	Pane of 20		40.00	—

Entry of Switzerland into United Nations — G66

Printed by House of Questa, UK. Panes of 20. Designed by Thierry Clauson, Switzerland.

2002, Oct. 24	Litho.		Perf. 14½x14¾	
404 G66	3fr multicolored (580,000)+		4.25	4.25
	Inscription block of 4		17.00	—
	First day cover, #404			5.00
	Pane of 20		85.00	—

Indigenous Art — G67

Printed by House of Questa, UK.
Designed by Rorie Katz and Robert Stein, US.

No. 405: a, Detail of Inca poncho, Peru. b, Bahia culture seated figure, Brazil. c, Blanket, Ecuador. d, Mayan stone sculpture, Belize. e, Embroidered fabric, Guatemala. f, Colima terra-cotta dog sculpture, Mexico.

2003, Jan. 31	Litho.		Perf. 14¼	
405 G67	Pane of 6 (168,000)+		9.00	9.00
	First day cover			9.75
a.-f.	90c Any single		1.40	1.40
	First day cover, a.-f., each			2.50

New Inter-Parliamentary Union Headquarters, Geneva — G68

Printed by House of Questa, UK. Panes of 20. Designed by Cyril Wursten, Switzerland.

2003, Feb. 20	Litho.		Perf. 14½x14	
406 G68	90c multicolored (480,000)+		1.75	1.75
	Inscription block of 4		7.25	—
	First day cover			2.00
	Pane of 20		25.00	—

Endangered Species Type of 1993

Printed by Johann Enschedé and Sons, the Netherlands. Designed by James Hautman, US.
Designs: No. 407, Branta ruficollis (red-breasted goose). No. 408, Geronticus calvus (bald ibis). No. 409, Dendrocygna bicolor (fulvous whistling duck). No. 410, Ramphastos vitellinus (channel-billed toucan).

2003, Apr. 3	Litho.		Perf. 12¾x12½	
407 A271	90c multicolored (368,000)+		1.25	1.25
408 A271	90c multicolored (368,000)+		1.25	1.25
409 A271	90c multicolored (368,000)+		1.25	1.25
410 A271	90c multicolored (368,000)+		1.25	1.25
a.	Block of 4, #407-410		5.00	5.00
	First day cover, #410a			6.25

	First day cover, #407-410 each		2.10
	Inscription block of 4, #410a	5.60	—
	Pane of 16	22.50	—

International Year of Freshwater Type of 2003

2003, June 20	Litho.		Perf. 14¼x14½	
411 A345	70c Waterfall (255,000)+		1.00	1.00
412 A345	1.30fr People, mountain (255,000)+		2.00	2.00
a.	Horiz. pair, #411-412		4.00	4.00
	First day cover, #412a			3.75
	Inscription block of 4		8.25	—

Ralph Bunche Type
Litho. With Foil Application

2003, Aug. 7			Perf. 13½x14	
413 A346	1.80fr brown red & multicolored (300,000)+		2.75	2.75
	First day cover			3.50
	Inscription block of 4		12.50	—
	Pane of 20		55.00	—

In Memoriam Type of 2003

2003, Oct. 24	Litho.		Perf. 13¼x13	
414 A347	85c multicolored (700,000)+		1.50	1.50
	First day cover			2.10
	Inscription block of 4		8.75	—
	Pane of 20		30.00	—

World Heritage Sites, United States Type

Designs: 90c, #417b, Great Smoky Mountains National Park. 1.30fr, #417f, Yellowstone National Park. #417a, Yosemite National Park. #417c, Olympic National Park. #417d, Hawaii Volcanoes National Park. #417e, Everglades National Park.

2003, Oct. 24	Litho.		Perf. 14½x14¼	
415 A348	90c multicolored (205,000)+		1.50	1.50
	First day cover			2.10
	Inscription block of 4		6.25	—
416 A348	1.30fr multicolored (205,000)+		2.25	2.25
	First day cover			3.25
	First day cover, #415-416			4.50
	Inscription block of 4		9.25	—

Souvenir Booklet

417	Booklet (39,000)+		9.00	
a.-c.	A348 10c any single		.20	.20
d.-f.	A348 30c any single		.55	.55
g.	Booklet pane of 4 #417a		.70	.70
h.	Booklet pane of 4 #417d		2.25	2.25
i.	Booklet pane of 4 #417b		.70	.70
j.	Booklet pane of 4 #417e		2.25	2.25
k.	Booklet pane of 4 #417c		.70	.70
l.	Booklet pane of 4 #417f		2.25	2.25

Endangered Species Type of 1993

Printed by Johann Enschedé and Sons, the Netherlands. Designed by Yuan Lee, US.
Designs: No. 418, Ursus thibetanus (Asiatic black bear). No. 419, Hippocamelus antisensis (Northern Andean deer). No. 420, Macaca silenus (Lion-tailed macaque). No. 421, Bos gaurus (Gaur).

2004, Jan. 29	Litho.		Perf. 12¾x12½	
418 A271	1fr multicolored (300,000)+		1.40	1.40
419 A271	1fr multicolored (300,000)+		1.40	1.40
420 A271	1fr multicolored (300,000)+		1.40	1.40
421 A271	1fr multicolored (300,000)+		1.40	1.40
a.	Block of 4, #418-421		5.75	5.75
	First day cover, #421a			7.50
	First day cover, #418-421, each			2.50
	Inscription block of 4, #421a		6.25	—
	Pane of 16		28.00	—

Indigenous Art Type of 2003

Printed by Johann Enschedé and Sons, the Netherlands. Designed by Rorie Katz and Robert Stein, US.

No. 422: a, Decoration for cows, Switzerland. b, Stone Age terra cotta sculpture of seated woman, Romania. c, Butter stamps, France. d, Detail of herald's tabard, United Kingdom. e, Woodcut print of medieval Cologne, Germany. f, Mesolithic era terra cotta sculpture of mother and child, Serbia and Montenegro.

2004, Mar. 4	Litho.		Perf. 13¼	
422 G67	Sheet of 6 (102,000)+		9.00	9.00
	First day cover			12.00
a.-f.	1fr Any single		1.50	1.50

Road Safety Type

Road map art with: 85c, Man on hand. 1fr, Person, seat belt, vert.

2004, Apr. 7	Litho.	Perf. 13x13¼, 13¼x13		
423 A354	85c multicolored (185,000)+		1.40	1.40
	First day cover			2.10
	Inscription block of 4		6.00	—
424 A354	1fr multicolored (185,000)+		1.75	1.75
	First day cover			2.50
	First day cover, #423-424			4.00
	Inscription block of 4		7.25	—

See France No. 3011.

Japanese Peace Bell, 50th Anniv. Type

2004, June 3	Litho. & Engr.		Perf. 13¼x13	
425 A355	1.30fr multicolored (230,000)+		2.00	2.00
	First day cover			3.00
	Inscription block of 4		8.50	—
	Pane of 20		45.00	—

World Heritage Sites, Greece Type

Designs: 1fr, No. 428b, Delphi. 1.30fr, #428e, Pythagoreion and Heraion of Samos. No. 428a, Acropolis, Athens. No. 428c, Olympia. #428d, Delos. #428f, Mycenae and Tiryns.

2004, Aug. 12		**Litho.**	**Perf. 14x13¼**	
426	A356	1fr **multicolored** *(180,000)+*	1.50	1.50
		First day cover		2.25
		Inscription block of 4	6.50	—
427	A356	1.30fr **multicolored** *(180,000)+*	2.00	2.00
		First day cover		3.00
		First day cover, #426-427		4.50
		Inscription block of 4	8.50	—

Souvenir Booklet

428		Booklet *(33,000)+*	13.50	
a.-c.	A356	20c any single	.30	.30
d.-f.	A356	50c any single	.80	.80
g.		Booklet pane of 4 #428a	1.25	1.25
h.		Booklet pane of 4 #428b	1.25	1.25
i.		Booklet pane of 4 #428c	1.25	1.25
j.		Booklet pane of 4 #428d	3.25	3.25
k.		Booklet pane of 4 #428e	3.25	3.25
l.		Booklet pane of 4 #428f	3.25	3.25

My Dream for Peace Type

Winning designs of Lions Club International children's global peace poster contest by: 85c, Anggun Sita Rustinya, Indonesia. 1.20fr, Amanda Nunez, Belize.

2004, Sept. 21		**Litho.**	**Perf. 14**	
429	A357	85c **multicolored** *(195,000)+*	1.40	1.40
		First day cover		1.90
		Inscription block of 4	5.75	—
		Pane of 20	28.00	—
430	A357	1.20fr **multicolored** *(195,000)+*	2.00	2.00
		First day cover		2.75
		First day cover, #429-430		4.00
		Inscription block of 4	8.25	—
		Pane of 20	40.00	—

Human Rights — G70

Printed by Banknote Corportation of America, US. Designed by Yuri Gervorgian, Armenia. Panes of 8.

2004, Oct. 14		**Litho.**	**Perf. 11¼**	
431	G69	85c **multicolored** *(408,000)+*	1.25	1.25
		First day cover		2.10
		Pane of 8	10.00	—
432	G70	1.30fr **multicolored** *(408,000)+*	2.25	2.25
		First day cover		3.25
		First day cover, #431-432		4.50
		Pane of 8	18.00	—

Sports — G71

Printed by Cartor Security Printing, France. Designed by Roland Hirter, Switzerland. Panes of 20.

2004, Nov. 23		**Litho.**	**Perf. 13x13½**	
433	G71	180c **multicolored** *(216,000)+*	3.25	3.25
		First day cover		4.00
		Inscription block of 4	13.00	—
		Pane of 20	65.00	—

See Switzerland No. 1196.

United Nations, 60th Anniv. Type of 2005

Printed by Banknote Corporation of America, US. Designed by Czeslaw Slania, Sweden.

2005, Feb. 4		**Litho. & Engr.**	**Perf. 11x11¼**	
434	A361	1.30fr **multicolored** *(270,000)+*	2.50	2.50
		First day cover		3.50
		Inscription block of 4	10.00	—
		Pane of 20	50.00	—

Souvenir Sheet

Litho.

Imperf

435	A361	3fr **multicolored** *(125,000)+*	5.00	3.50
		First day cover		6.75

Endangered Species Type of 1993

Printed by Johann Enschedé and Sons, the Netherlands. Designed by Boris Zlotsky, US.

Designs: No. 436, Laelia milleri. No. 437, Psygmorchis pusilla. No. 438, Dendrobium cruentum. No. 439, Orchis purpurea.

2005, Mar. 3		**Litho.**	**Perf. 12¾x12½**	
436	A271	1fr **multicolored** *(248,000)+*	1.75	1.75
437	A271	1fr **multicolored** *(248,000)+*	1.75	1.75
438	A271	1fr **multicolored** *(248,000)+*	1.75	1.75
439	A271	1fr **multicolored** *(248,000)+*	1.75	1.75
a.		Block of 4, #436-439	7.00	7.00
		First day cover #439a		8.75
		First day cover, #436-439, each		3.00
		Inscription block of 4, #439a	7.75	—
		Pane of 16	27.50	

Nature's Wisdom — G72

Printed by Cartor Security Printing, France. Panes of 20. Designed by Robert Stein, US.

Designs: 1fr, Children collecting water, India. 80c, Ruby brittle star, Bahamas.

2005, Apr. 21		**Litho.**	**Perf. 13½x13¼**	
440	G72	1fr **multicolored** *(180,000)+*	1.75	1.75
		First day cover		2.75
		Inscription block of 4	7.25	—
		Pane of 20	35.00	—
441	G72	1.30fr **multicolored** *(180,000)+*	2.00	2.00
		First day cover		3.75
		First day cover, #440-441		5.50
		Inscription block of 4	9.25	—
		Pane of 20	40.00	—

Intl. Year of Sport Type

Printed by Cartor Security Printing, France. Designed by Roland Hirter, Switzerland.

2005, June 3		**Litho.**	**Perf. 13x13¼**	
442	A368	1fr Wheelchair racing *(185,000)+*	1.75	1.75
		First day cover		2.75
		Inscription block of 4	7.75	—
		Pane of 20	35.00	—
443	A368	1.30fr Cycling *(185,000)+*	2.25	2.25
		First day cover		3.75
		First day cover, #442-443		5.50
		Inscription block of 4	9.25	—
		Pane of 20	45.00	—

World Heritage Sites, Egypt Type

Printed by Johann Enschedé and Sons, the Netherlands. Panes of 20. Designed by Rorie Katz, US.

Designs: Nos. 444, 446b, Philae. Nos. 445, 446e, Islamic Cairo. No. 446a, Memphis and its Necropolis. No. 446c, Abu Mena. No. 446d, Ancient Thebes. No. 446f, St. Catherine area.

2005, Aug. 4		**Litho.**	**Perf. 14x13¼**	
444	A369	1fr **multicolored** *(180,000)+*	2.00	2.00
		First day cover		2.75
		Inscription block of 4	8.00	—
445	A369	1.30fr **multicolored** *(180,000)+*	2.50	2.50
		First day cover		3.75
		First day cover, #444-445		5.50
		Inscription block of 4	10.00	—

Souvenir Booklet

446		Booklet, #446g-446l *(31,000)+*	16.50	
a.-c.	A369	20c any single	.40	.40
d.-f.	A369	50c any single	.90	.90
g.		Booklet pane of 4 #446a	1.60	—
h.		Booklet pane of 4 #446b	1.60	—
i.		Booklet pane of 4 #446c	1.60	—
j.		Booklet pane of 4 #446d	3.75	—
k.		Booklet pane of 4 #446e	3.75	—
l.		Booklet pane of 4 #446f	3.75	—

My Dream for Peace Type

Winning designs of Lions Club International children's global peace poster contest by: 1fr, Marisa Harun, Indonesia. 1.30fr, Carlos Javier Parramón Teixidó, Spain.

2005, Sept. 21		**Litho.**	**Perf. 14**	
447	A357	1fr **multicolored** *(175,000)+*	1.75	1.75
		First day cover		2.60
		Inscription block of 4	7.25	—
		Pane of 20	35.00	—
448	A357	1.30fr **multicolored** *(175,000)+*	2.00	2.00
		First day cover		3.50
		First day cover, #447-448		5.00
		Inscription block of 4	8.25	—
		Pane of 20	40.00	—

Food for Life Type

Printed by Government Printing Office, Austria. Designed by Andrew Davidson, United Kingdom.

Designs: 1fr, Rye, airplane dropping parcels, camel caravan. 1.30fr, Sorghum, people carrying grain sacks, trucks.

2005, Oct. 20		**Litho.**	**Perf. 13¾**	
449	A370	1fr **multicolored** *(170,000)+*	1.90	1.90
		First day cover		2.60
		Inscription block of 4	7.75	—
		Pane of 20	38.00	—
450	A370	1.30fr **multicolored** *(170,000)+*	2.40	2.40
		First day cover		3.50
		First day cover, #449-450		5.00
		Inscription block of 4	9.75	—
		Pane of 20	48.00	—

Armillary Sphere, Palais des Nations — G73

Printed by Cartor Security Printing, France. Panes of 20. Designed by Rorie Katz, United States.

Litho. with Hologram

2006, Feb. 3			**Perf. 13¼x13½**	
451	G73	1.30fr **multicolored** *(280,000)+*	2.25	2.25
		First day cover		3.25
		Inscription block of 4	9.00	—
		Pane of 20	45.00	—

Indigenous Art Type of 2003

Printed by Johann Enschedé and Sons, the Netherlands. Designed by Robert Stein, US.

No. 452 — Musical instruments: a, Bell, Benin. b, Drum, Swaziland. c, Sanza, Congo. d, Stringed instruments, Cape Verde. e, Caixixi, Ghana. f, Bells, Central Africa.

2006, Feb. 3		**Litho.**	**Perf. 13¼**	
452	G67	Pane of 6 *(91,000)+*	12.00	12.00
		First day cover		14.00
a.-f.		1.20fr Any single	2.00	2.00

Endangered Species Type of 1993

Printed by Johann Enschedé and Sons, the Netherlands. Designed by John D. Dawson, US.

Designs: No. 453, Dyscophus antongilii. No. 454, Chamaeleo dilepsis. No. 455, Corallus caninus. No. 456, Phyllobates vittatus.

2006, Mar. 16	Litho.		Perf. 12¾x12½	
453 A271	1fr multicolored (228,000)+		1.75	1.75
454 A271	1fr multicolored (228,000)+		1.75	1.75
455 A271	1fr multicolored (228,000)+		1.75	1.75
456 A271	1fr multicolored (228,000)+		1.75	1.75
a.	Block of 4, #453-456		7.00	7.00
	First day cover, #456a			7.75
	First day cover, #453-456, each			2.60
	Inscription block of 4, #456a		7.00	—
	Pane of 16		28.00	

Intl. Day of Families Type

Printed by Johann Enschedé and Sons, the Netherlands. Designed by Shelly Bartek, US.
Designs: 1fr, Family reading together. 1.30fr, Family on motorcycle.

2006, May 27	Litho.		Perf. 14x13½	
457 A373	1fr multicolored (150,000)+		1.75	1.75
	First day cover			2.50
	Inscription block of 4		7.00	
	Pane of 20		35.00	—
458 A373	1.30fr multicolored (150,000)+		2.25	2.25
	First day cover			3.25
	First day cover, #457-458			5.00
	Inscription block of 4		7.00	
	Pane of 20		35.00	—

World Heritage Sites, France Type

Printed by Cartor Security Printing, France. Panes of 20. Designed by Robert Stein, US.
Eiffel Tower and: Nos. 459, 461b, Provins. Nos. 460, 461e, Mont Saint-Michel. No. 461a, Banks of the Seine. No. 461c, Carcasonne. No. 461d, Roman Aqueduct. No. 446f, Chateau de Chambord.

Litho. & Embossed with Foil Application

2006, June 17			Perf. 13½x13¼	
459 A374	1fr multicolored (280,000)+		1.75	1.75
	First day cover			2.50
	Inscription block of 4		7.00	
460 A374	1.30fr multicolored (280,000)+		2.25	2.25
	First day cover			3.25
	First day cover, #444-445			5.00
	Inscription block of 4		9.00	

Souvenir Booklet

461	Booklet, #461g-461l (29,000)+		15.00	
a.-c.	A374 20c any single		.35	.35
d.-f.	A374 50c any single		.85	.85
g.	Booklet pane of 4 #461a		1.40	—
h.	Booklet pane of 4 #461b		1.40	—
i.	Booklet pane of 4 #461c		1.40	—
j.	Booklet pane of 4 #461d		3.50	—
k.	Booklet pane of 4 #461e		3.50	—
l.	Booklet pane of 4 #461f		3.50	—

See France Nos. 3219-3220.

My Dream for Peace Type of 2004

Printed by Cartor Security Printing, France. Panes of 20. Winning designs of Lions Club International children's global peace poster contest by: 85c, Ariam Boaglio, Italy. 1.20fr, Sierra Spicer, US.

2006, Sept. 21	Litho.		Perf. 13½x13	
462 A357	85c multicolored (160,000)+		1.60	1.60
	First day cover			2.40
	Inscription block of 4		6.40	
	Pane of 20		32.00	—
463 A357	1.20fr multicolored (160,000)+		2.25	2.25
	First day cover			3.25
	First day cover, #462-463			4.75
	Inscription block of 4		9.00	
	Pane of 20		45.00	—

Flags and Coins Type

Printed by Cartor Security Printing, France. Designed by Rorie Katz, US.
No. 464 - Flag of: a, Uganda, 500 shilling coin. b, Luxembourg, 1 euro coin. c, Cape Verde, 20 escudo coin. d, Belgium, 1 euro coin. e, Italy, 1 euro coin. f, New Zealand, 1 dollar coin. g, Switzerland, 2 franc coin. h, Lebanon, 500 pound coin.

2006, Oct. 5	Litho.		Perf. 13¼x13	
464	Pane of 8		15.00	9.00
a.-h.	A375 85c Any single		1.50	1.50
	First day cover			14.50
	First day cover, #464a-464h, each			5.00

A column of rouletting in the middle of the pane separates it into two parts.

Endangered Species Type of 1993

Printed by Johann Enschedé and Sons, the Netherlands. Designed by John Rowe, US.
Designs: No. 465, Theropithecus gelada. No. 466, Cercopithecus neglectus. No. 467, Varecia variegata. No. 468, Hylobates moloch.

2007, Mar. 15	Litho.		Perf. 12¾x12½	
465 A271	1fr multicolored (208,000)+		1.75	1.75
466 A271	1fr multicolored (208,000)+		1.75	1.75
467 A271	1fr multicolored (208,000)+		1.75	1.75
468 A271	1fr multicolored (208,000)+		1.75	1.75
a.	Block of 4, #465-468		7.00	7.00

	First day cover, #468a		8.25	
	First day cover, #465-468, each		2.75	
	Inscription block of 4, #468a		7.00	—
	Pane of 16		28.00	

Flags and Coins Type of 2006

Printed by Cartor Security Printing, France. Designed by Rorie Katz, US.
No. 469 — Flag of: a, Burkina Faso, 500 franc coin. b, France, 50 cent coin. c, Moldova, 50 bani coin. d, Papua New Guinea, 1 kina coin. e, Bolivia, 1 boliviano coin. f, Myanmar, 100 kyat coin. g, Mali, 500 franc coin. h, Tunisia, 5 dinar coin.

2007, May 3	Litho.		Perf. 13¼x13	
469	Sheet of 8 (125,000)+		12.50	12.50
a.-h.	A375 85c Any single		1.50	1.50
	First day cover			14.50
	First day cover, #469a-469h, each			2.50

A column of rouletting in the middle of the sheet separates it into two parts.

Peaceful Visions Type of 2007

Printed by Lowe-Martin Company, Canada. Designed by Slavka Kolesar, Canada. Panes of 20.
Designs: 1.20fr, "Harvest for All." 1.80fr, "This Dream Has Wings."

2007, June 1	Litho.		Perf. 13x12½	
470 A378	1.20fr multicolored (156,000)+		2.25	2.25
	First day cover			3.00
	Inscription block of 4		9.00	
	Pane of 20		45.00	—
471 A378	1.80fr multicolored (156,000)+		3.25	3.25
	First day cover			4.50
	First day cover, #470-471			6.50
	Inscription block of 4		13.00	
	Pane of 20		65.00	—

World Heritage Sites, South America Type

Printed by Lowe-Martin Group, Canada. Panes of 20. Designed by Rorie Katz, US.
Designs: Nos. 472, 474a, Tiwanaku, Bolivia. Nos. 473, 474f, Machu Picchu, Peru. No. 474b, Iguaçu National Park, Brazil. No. 474c, Galapagos Islands, Ecuador. No. 474d, Rapa Nui, Chile. No. 474e, Cueva de las Manos, Argentina.

2007, Aug. 9	Litho.		Perf. 13¼x13	
472 A381	1fr multicolored (150,000)+		1.90	1.90
	First day cover			2.50
	Inscription block of 4		7.60	
473 A381	1.80fr multicolored (150,000)+		3.25	3.25
	First day cover			4.50
	First day cover, #472-473			6.00
	Inscription block of 4		13.00	

Souvenir Booklet

474	Booklet, #474g-474l (27,000)+		15.50	
a.-c.	A381 20c Any single		.35	.35
d.-f.	A381 50c Any single		.90	.90
g.	Booklet pane of 4 #474a		1.40	—
h.	Booklet pane of 4 #474b		1.40	—
i.	Booklet pane of 4 #474c		1.40	—
j.	Booklet pane of 4 #474d		3.60	—
k.	Booklet pane of 4 #474e		3.60	—
l.	Booklet pane of 4 #474f		3.60	—

Humanitarian Mail Type

Printed by Lowe-Martin Group, Canada. Panes of 10.

2007, Sept. 6	Litho.		Perf. 12½x13¼	
475 A382	1.80fr multicolored (320,000)+		3.25	3.25
	First day cover			4.25
	Inscription block of 4		13.00	
	Pane of 10		32.50	

Space for Humanity Type

Printed by Johann Enschedé and Sons, the Netherlands. Panes of 6. Designed by Donato Giancola, US.
Designs: 1fr, Astronaut spacewalking. 1.80fr, International Space Station, space probe, Jupiter.
3fr, Astronauts spacewalking.

2007, Oct. 25	Litho.		Perf. 13½x14	
476 A383	1fr multicolored (252,000)+		1.90	1.90
	First day cover			2.50
	Inscription block of 4		7.60	
	Pane of 6		11.40	
477 A383	1.80fr multicolored (252,000)+		3.25	3.25
	First day cover			4.50
	First day cover, #476-477			6.00
	Inscription block of 4		13.00	
	Pane of 6		19.50	

Souvenir Sheet

478 A383	3fr multicolored (110,000)+		5.50	5.50
	First day cover			6.50

Intl. Holocaust Remembrance Day Type

Printed by Lowe-Martin Company, Canada. Panes of 9. Designed by Matías Delfino, Argentina.

2008, Jan. 27	Litho.		Perf. 13	
479 A384	85c multicolored (495,000)+		1.75	1.75
	First day cover			2.75
	Pane of 9		16.00	

Endangered Species Type of 1993

Printed by Johann Enschedé and Sons, the Netherlands. Designed by Suzanne Duranceau, Canada.

Designs: No. 480, Odobenus rosmarus. No. 481, Platygyra daedalea. No. 482, Hippocampus bargibanti. No. 483, Delphinapterus leucas.

2008, Mar. 6	Litho.		Perf. 12¾x12½	
480 A271	1fr multicolored (172,000)+		2.00	2.00
481 A271	1fr multicolored (172,000)+		2.00	2.00
482 A271	1fr multicolored (172,000)+		2.00	2.00
483 A271	1fr multicolored (172,000)+		2.00	2.00
a.	Block of 4, #480-483		8.00	8.00
	First day cover, #483a			9.00
	First day cover, #480-483, each			3.00
	Inscription block of 4, #483a		8.00	—
	Pane of 16		32.00	—

Flags and Coins Type of 2006

Printed by Cartor Security Printing, France. Designed by Rorie Katz, US.
No. 484 — Flag of: a, Madagascar, 1 ariary coin. b, Rwanda, 50 franc coin. c, Benin, 10 franc coin. d, Iran, 500 rial coin. e, Namibia, 5 dollar coin. f, Maldives, 1 rufiyaa coin. g, Albania, 10 lek coin. h, Turkey, 1 lira coin.

2008, May 8	Litho.		Perf. 13¼x13	
484	Sheet of 8 (100,000)+		15.00	15.00
a.-h.	A375 85c Any single		1.75	1.75
	First day cover			17.00
	First day cover, #484a-484h			3.50

A column of rouletting in the middle of the sheet separates it into two parts.

Handshake — G74

Sign Language — G75

Printed by Johann Enschedé and Sons, the Netherlands. Panes of 20. Designed by Rorie Katz, US.

2008, June 6	Litho. & Embossed		Perf. 14x13¼	
485 G74	1fr orange & red (142,000)+		2.25	2.25
	First day cover			3.00
	Inscription block of 4		9.00	
	Sheet of 20		45.00	—
486 G75	1.80fr red & orange (142,000)+		4.00	4.00
	First day cover			5.25
	First day cover, #485-486			7.25
	Inscription block of 4		16.00	
	Sheet of 20		80.00	—

Convention on the Rights of Persons with Disabilities.

Sport for Peace Type of 2008

Printed by Johann Enschedé and Sons, the Netherlands. Panes of 9 (#487-488). Designed by Romero Britto, Brazil.
Designs: 1fr, 3fr, Gymnast. 1.80fr, Tennis player.

2008, Aug. 8	Litho.		Perf. 14½	
487 A393	1fr multicolored (330,030)+		2.25	2.25
	First day cover			3.00
	Inscription block of 4		9.00	
	Pane of 9		21.00	
488 A393	1.80fr multicolored (330,030)+		4.00	4.00
	First day cover			5.00
	First day cover, #487-488			7.00
	Inscription block of 4		16.00	
	Pane of 9		36.00	—

Souvenir Sheet
Perf. 12¾x13¼

489 A393	3fr multicolored (160,000)+		6.50	6.50
	First day cover			7.50

2008 Summer Olympics, Beijing.

"We Can End Poverty" Type of 2008

Printed by Sweden Post, Sweden. Panes of 20.
Winning designs in children's art contest by: 1fr, Ranajoy Banerjee, India, vert. 1.80fr, Elizabeth Elaine Chun Nig Au, Hong Kong, vert.

2008, Sept. 18		Litho.		Perf. 12½x12¾	
490	A395	1fr multicolored (130,000)+		2.25	2.25
		First day cover			3.00
		Inscription block of 4		9.00	—
		Sheet of 20		45.00	—
491	A395	1.80fr multicolored (130,000)+		3.75	3.75
		First day cover			5.00
		First day cover, #490-491			7.00
		Inscription block of 4		15.00	—
		Sheet of 20		75.00	—

Climate Change Types of New York and Vienna and

Changement de climat   G76

Climate Change — G77

Printed by Lowe-Martin Group, Canada. Panes of 4. Designed by Rorie Katz, US.
No. 492 - Polar bear with quarter of Earth in: a, LR. b, LL. c, UR. d, UL.
No. 493 - Ship and sea ice with quarter of Earth in: a, LR. b, LL. c, UR. d, UL.
No. 494: a, Like New York #969a. b, Like New York #969b. c, Like New York #969c. d, Like New York #969d. e, Like Geneva #493a. f, Like Geneva #493b. g, Like Geneva #493c. h, Like Geneva #493d. i, Like Vienna #434a. j, Like Vienna #434b. k, Like Vienna #434c. l, Like Vienna #434d. m, Like New York #968a. n, Like New York #968b. o, Like New York #968c. p, Like New York #968d. q, Like Geneva #492a. r, Like Geneva #492b. s, Like Geneva #492c. t, Like Geneva #492d. u, Like Vienna #435a. v, Like Vienna #435b. w, Like Vienna #435c. x, Like Vienna #435d.
All stamps have red panels inscribed "Changement de climat."

2008, Oct. 23		Litho.	Perf. 13¼x13	
492		Sheet of 4 (100,000)+	10.50	10.50
a.-d.		G76 1.20fr Any single	2.60	2.60
		First day cover		11.00
493		Sheet of 4 (100,000)+	15.50	15.50
a.-d.		G77 1.80fr Any single	3.75	3.75
		First day cover		16.50
		First day cover, #492-493		27.50

Souvenir Booklet

494		Booklet, #494y-494ad (22,000)+	22.00	
a.-d.		A397 35c Any single	.75	.75
e.-h.		G77 35c Any single	.75	.75
i.-l.		V72 35c Any single	.75	.75
m.-p.		A396 50c Any single	1.00	1.00
q.-t.		G76 50c Any single	1.00	1.00
u.-x.		V73 50c Any single	1.00	1.00
y.		Booklet pane of 4, #494a-494d	3.00	—
z.		Booklet pane of 4, #494e-494h	3.00	—
aa.		Booklet pane of 4, #494i-494l	3.00	—
ab.		Booklet pane of 4, #494m-494p	4.25	—
ac.		Booklet pane of 4, #494q-494t	4.25	—
ad.		Booklet pane of 4, #494u-494x	4.25	—

U Thant Type of 2009

Printed by Johann Enschedé and Sons, the Netherlands. Panes of 20.

Litho. With Foil Application

2009, Feb. 6			Perf. 14x13½	
495	A399	1.30fr red & multicolored (150,000)+	2.40	2.40
		First day cover		3.50
		Inscription block of 4	9.60	—
		Sheet of 20	48.00	—

Endangered Species Type of 1993

Printed by Johann Enschedé and Sons, the Netherlands. Designed by Roger Kent, United Kingdom.

Designs: No. 496, Maculinea arion. No. 497, Dolomedes plantarius. No. 498, Cerambyx cerdo. No. 499, Coenagrion mercuriale.

2009, Apr. 16		Litho.		Perf. 12¾x12½	
496	A271	1fr multicolored (144,000)+		1.90	1.90
497	A271	1fr multicolored (144,000)+		1.90	1.90
498	A271	1fr multicolored (144,000)+		1.90	1.90
499	A271	1fr multicolored (144,000)+		1.90	1.90
a.		Block of 4, #496-499		7.75	7.75
		First day cover, #499a			8.50
		First day cover, #496-499, each			2.75
		Inscription block of 4, #499a		7.75	—
		Pane of 16		31.00	—

World Heritage Sites, Germany Type of 2009

Printed by Johann Enschedé and Sons, the Netherlands. Panes of 20. Designed by Grit Fiedler, Germany.
Designs: Nos. 500, 502b, Wartburg Castle. Nos. 501, 502f, Monastic Island of Reichenau. No. 502a, Town Hall and Roland on the Marketplace, Bremen. No. 502c, Palaces and Parks of Potsdam and Berlin. No. 502d, Aachen Cathedral. No. 502e, Luther Memorials in Eisleben and Wittenberg.

2009, May 7		Litho.	Perf. 14x13½	
500	A400	1fr multicolored (155,000)+	1.90	1.90
		First day cover		2.75
		Inscription block of 4	7.75	
501	A400	1.30fr multicolored (155,000)+	2.50	2.50
		First day cover		3.50
		First day cover, #500-501		5.50
		Inscription block of 4	10.00	—

Souvenir Booklet

502		Booklet, #502g-502l (22,000)+	18.00	
a.-c.		A400 30c any single	.55	.55
d.-f.		A400 50c any single	.90	.90
g.		Booklet pane of 4 #502a	2.25	—
h.		Booklet pane of 4 #502b	2.25	—
i.		Booklet pane of 4 #502c	2.25	—
j.		Booklet pane of 4 #502d	3.75	—
k.		Booklet pane of 4 #502e	3.75	—
l.		Booklet pane of 4 #502f	3.75	—

2009 END-OF-YEAR ISSUES
See end of New York postage listings.

SEMI-POSTAL STAMP

AIDS Awareness Semi-postal Type
Souvenir Sheet

2002, Oct. 24		Litho.	Perf. 14½	
B1	SP1	90c + 30c multicolored (171,000)+	3.00	3.00
		First day cover, #B1		5.00

AIR LETTER SHEET

Used values for all postal stationery are for non-philatelic contemporaneous usages.

UN Type of 1968
Printed by Setelipaino, Finland. Designed by Robert Perrot.

1969, Oct. 4			Litho.	
UC1	UC3	65c ultra & light blue, entire (350,000)	.50	1.50
		Entire, first day cancel (52,000)		.75

POSTAL CARDS

UN Type of 1969 and Type of Air Post Postal Card, 1966
Printed by Courvoisier, S.A., Switzerland. Designed by John Mason (20c) and Olav S. Mathiesen (30c).
Wmk. Post Horn, Swiss Cross, "S" or "Z"

1969, Oct. 4			Litho.	
UX1	PC2	20c olive green & black, buff (415,000)	.25	.30
		First day cancel (51,500)		.50
UX2	APC2	30c violet blue, blue, light & dark green, buff (275,000)	.25	.30
		First day cancel (49,000)		.50

No. UX2, although of design APC2, is not inscribed "Poste Aerienne" or "Air Mail."

UN Emblem — GPC1

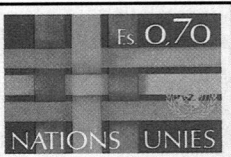

UN Emblem and Ribbons — GPC2

Printed by Setelipaino, Finland. Designed by Veronique Crombez (40c) and Lieve Baeten (70c).

1977, June 27			Litho.	
UX3	GPC1	40c multicolored (500,000)	.30	.30
		First day cancel (65,000)		1.00
UX4	GPC2	70c multicolored (300,000)	.40	.40
		First day cancel (65,000)		.50

A second printing of No. UX3 was made in 1984. It was released after the Swiss postal card rate had been increased to 50c so instructions were issued that all cards must have a 10c stamp affixed before being sold. A few were sold in NY without the added stamp. The card stock differs from the original printing.

Emblem of the United Nations — GPC3

Peace Dove — GPC4

Printed by Johann Enschede en Zonen, Netherlands. Designed by George Hamori, Australia (50c) and Ryszard Dudzicki, Poland (70c).

1985, May 10			Litho.	
UX5	GPC3	50c multicolored (300,000)	1.00	3.50
		First day cancel (34,700)		1.00
UX6	GPC4	70c multicolored (300,000)	3.25	3.25
		First day cancel (34,700)		4.50

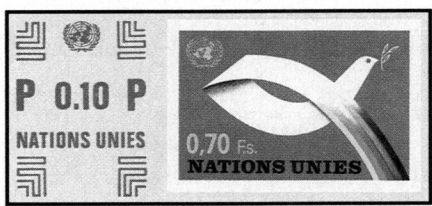

No. UX6 Surcharged in Lake

1986, Jan. 2			Litho.	
UX7	GPC4	70c + 10c multi (90,500)	2.50	2.50
		First day cancel (8,000 est.)		10.00

Type of 1990
Printed by Mercury-Walch, Australia.

1992, Sept. 4			Litho.	
UX8	G45	90c multicolored (150,000)+	1.75	1.75
		First day cancel (12,385)		6.00

No. UX5 Surcharged in Lake like No. UX7

1993, May 7			Litho.	
UX9	GPC3	50c +10c multicolored (47,000)+	1.50	1.50
		First day cancel		20.00

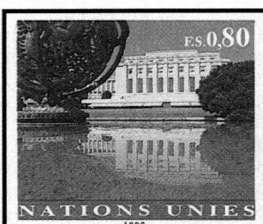

Palais des Nations — GPC5

Printed by Leigh Mardon Pty. Limited, Australia.

1993, May 7   Litho.
UX10 GPC5 80c **multicolored** (200,000)+   3.00 3.00
     First day cancel   7.50

#UX5, UX10 Surcharged in Carmine like #UX7
1996, Mar. 22   Litho.
UX11 GPC3 50c +20c **multi**   3.00 3.00
     First day cancel   4.00
UX12 GPC5 80c +30c **multi**   3.00 3.00
     First day cancel   4.00

Assembly
Hall — GPC6

Palais des
Nations — GPC7

Printed by Mercury-Walsh, Australia.

1998, May 20   Litho.
UX13 GPC6 70c **multicolored** (80,000)+   2.00 2.00
     First day cancel   3.00
UX14 GPC7 1.10fr **multicolored** (80,000)+   3.00 3.00
     First day cancel   3.25

Illustrations of the buildings are shown on the back of each card.

Type of 2002
Printed by Johann Enschedé and Sons, the Netherlands.

2002, Mar. 1   Litho.
UX15 G65 1.30fr **multicolored** (68,000)+   1.75 1.75
     First day cancel   2.00

Nos. UX8, UX13 and UX14 Surcharged Like No. UX7, But With Serifed Numerals
2004, Sept. 21   Litho.
UX16 GPC6 70c +15c **multicolored**   2.00 2.00
     First day cancel   2.00
UX17 G45 90c +10c **multicolored**   2.10 2.10
     First day cancel   2.10
UX18 GPC7 1.10fr +10c **multicolored**   2.25 2.25
     First day cancel   2.25

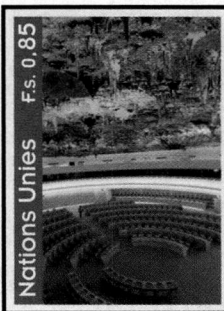

Ceiling Sculpture,
Human Rights and
Alliance of Civilization
Chamber — GPC8

The Broken
Chair Memorial
GPC9

League of
Nations
Building
GPC10

2009, May 7   Litho.
UX19 GPC8 85c **multicolored**   2.10 2.10
     First day cancel   2.10
UX20 GPC9 1fr **multicolored**   2.40 2.40
     First day cancel   2.40
UX21 GPC10 1.80fr **multicolored**   3.50 3.50
     First day cancel   3.50

OFFICES IN VIENNA, AUSTRIA

For use only on mail posted at the Vienna International Center for the UN and the International Atomic Energy Agency.

100 Groschen = 1 Schilling
100 Cents = 1 Euro (2002)

Type of Geneva, 1978, UN Types of 1961-72 and

Donaupark,
Vienna — V1

Aerial View — V2

Printed by Helio Courvoisier S.A., Switzerland. Panes of 50. Designed by Henryk Chylinski (4s); Jozsef Vertel (6s).

1979, Aug. 24   **Photo.**   **Perf. 11½**
Granite Paper
1 G8 50g **multicolored** (3,500,000)+   .20 .20
     First day cover   1.00
     Inscription block of 4   .20
2 A52 1s **multicolored** (3,800,000)+   .20 .20
     First day cover   1.00
     Inscription block of 4   .40
3 V1 4s **multicolored** (3,500,000)+   .25 .25
     First day cover   1.00
     Inscription block of 4   1.10
4 AP13 5s **multicolored** (3,500,000)+   .30 .30
     First day cover   1.00

5 V2 6s **multicolored** (4,500,000)+   .35 .35
     First day cover   1.25
     Inscription block of 4   1.40 —
6 A45 10s **multicolored** (3,500,000)+   .60 .60
     First day cover   2.00
     Inscription block of 4   3.25 —
     Nos. 1-6 (6)   1.90 1.90

+ Printing orders to Mar. 1993.
No. 4 is not inscribed "Air Mail," No. 6 has no frame.
First day covers of Nos. 1-6 total 1,026,575.

New Economic Order Type of UN
1980, Jan. 11   **Litho.**   **Perf. 15x14½**
7 A178 4s **multicolored** (1,418,418)   .60 .60
     First day cover   1.25
     Inscription block of 4   9.00 —

Value for margin inscription block is for one from bottom of sheet. One from top is about twice the value shown.

Dove Type of UN
1980, Jan. 11   **Litho.**   **Perf. 14x13½**
8 A147 2.50s **multicolored** (3,500,000)+   .25 .25
     First day cover   1.00
     Inscription block of 4   1.25 —

First day covers of Nos. 7-8 total 336,229.

Women's Year
Emblem on World
Map — V3

United Nations Decade for Women.
Printed by Questa Colour Security Printers, United Kingdom. Panes of 50. Designed by Gunnar Janssen.

1980, Mar. 7   **Litho.**   **Perf. 14½x15**
9 V3 4s **light green & dark green** (1,569,080)   .40 .40
     First day cover   1.00
     Inscription block of 4   1.75 —
10 V3 6s **bister brown** (1,556,016)   .75 .75
     First day cover   1.25
     First day cover, #9-10   1.50
     Inscription block of 4   3.25 —

First day covers of Nos. 9-10 total 443,893.

Peace-keeping Operations Type of UN
1980, May 16   **Litho.**   **Perf. 14x13**
11 A182 6s **multicolored** (1,719,852)   .40 .40
     First day cover (323,923)   1.00
     Inscription block of 4   2.00 —

35th Anniversary Types of Geneva and UN
1980, June 26   **Litho.**   **Perf. 13x13½**
12 G16 4s **carmine rose & black** (1,626,582)   .35 .35
     First day cover   1.00
     Inscription block of 4   1.60 —
13 A184 6s **multicolored** (1,625,400)   .60 .60
     First day cover   1.25
     Inscription block of 4   2.75 —

Souvenir Sheet
Imperf
14   Sheet of 2 (1,675,191)   .90 .90
a.   G16 4s carmine rose & black   .25 .25
b.   A184 6s multicolored   .65 .65
     First day cover   1.00

First day covers of Nos. 12-14 total 657,402.

ECOSOC Types of UN and Geneva
Printed by Ashton-Potter Ltd., Canada. Panes of 50. Designed by Dietman Kowall (4s), Angel Medina Medina (6s).

1980, Nov. 21   **Perf. 13½x13**
15 A187 4s **multicolored** (1,811,218)   .30 .30
     First day cover   1.00
     Inscription block of 4   1.50 —
16 G17 6s **multicolored** (1,258,420)   .60 .60

First day cover 1.00
First day cover #15-16 1.25
Inscription block of 4 2.50

Economic and Social Council (ECOSOC).
First day covers of Nos. 15-16 total 224,631.

Palestinian Rights Type of UN

Printed by Courvoisier, S.A., Switzerland. Panes of 50.
Designed by David Dewhurst.

1981, Jan. 30	Photo.	Perf. 12x11½	
17 A188 4s multicolored (1,673,310)		.45	.45
First day cover (208,812)			1.00
Inscription block of 4		2.00	—

Disabled Type of UN and

Interlocking Stitches — V4

International Year of the Disabled.
Printed by Heraclio Fournier S.A., Spain. Panes of 50.
Designed by Sophia van Heeswijk.

1981, Mar. 6	Photo.	Perf. 14	
18 A189 4s multicolored (1,508,719)		.40	.40
First day cover			1.00
Inscription block of 4		1.75	—
19 V4 6s black & orange (1,569,385)		.60	.60
First day cover			1.00
First day cover, #18-19			1.25
Inscription block of 4		2.75	—

First day covers of Nos. 18-19 total 290,603.

Art Type of UN

1981, Apr. 15	Photo.	Perf. 11½	
	Granite Paper		
20 A191 6s multicolored (1,643,527)		.75	.75
First day cover (196,916)			1.00
Inscription block of 4		3.25	—

Energy Type of UN

1981, May 29	Litho.	Perf. 13	
21 A193 7.50s multicolored (1,611,130)		.70	.70
First day cover (216,197)			1.00
Inscription block of 4		3.00	—

Volunteers Program Types

1981, Nov. 13	Litho.		
22 A195 5s multicolored (1,582,780)		.40	.40
First day cover			1.00
Inscription block of 4		2.25	—
23 G18 7s multicolored (1,516,139)		.90	.90
First day cover			1.00
First day cover, #22-23			1.00
Inscription block of 4		4.25	—

First day covers of Nos. 22-23 total 282,414.

"For a Better World" — V5

Printed by Courvoisier, S.A., Switzerland. Sheets of 50.
Designed by Eliezer Weishoff.

1982, Jan. 22		Perf. 11½x12	
24 V5 3s multicolored (3,300,000)+		.35	.35
First day cover (203,872)			1.00
Inscription block of 4		1.75	

Human Environment Types of UN

10th Anniversary of United Nations Environment Program.
Printed by Joh. Enschede en Zonen, Netherlands. Panes of 50.
Designed by Peer-Ulrich Bremer (5s); Sybille Brunner (7s).

1982, Mar. 19	Litho.	Perf. 13½x13	
25 A200 5s multicolored (1,312,765)		.40	.40
First day cover			1.00
Inscription block of 4		1.90	—
26 G21 7s multicolored (1,357,513)		.80	.80
First day cover			1.00
First day cover, #25-26			1.25
Inscription block of 4		3.75	—

First day covers of Nos. 25-26 total 248,576.

Outer Space Type of UN

Exploration and Peaceful Uses of Outer Space. Printed by
Enschede. Panes of 50. Designed by George Hamori.

1982, June 11	Litho.	Perf. 13x13½	
27 G22 5s multicolored (1,339,038)		.60	.60
First day cover (150,845)			1.75
Inscription block of 4		3.00	—

Conservation & Protection of Nature Type

1982, Nov. 16	Photo.	Perf. 14	
28 A202 5s Fish (1,202,694)		.50	.50
First day cover			1.00
Inscription block of 4		2.50	—
29 A202 7s Animal (1,194,403)		.70	.70
First day cover			1.00
First day cover, #28-29			1.40
Inscription block of 4		3.00	—

First day covers of Nos. 28-29 total 243,548.

World Communications Year Type

1983, Jan. 28	Litho.	Perf. 13	
30 A203 4s multicolored (1,517,443)		.40	.40
First day cover (150,541)			1.40
Inscription block of 4		2.10	—

Safety at Sea Type

1983, Mar. 18	Litho.	Perf. 14½	
31 G23 4s multicolored (1,506,052)		.40	.40
First day cover			1.00
Inscription block of 4		2.00	—
32 A206 6s multicolored (1,527,990)		.65	.65
First day cover			1.00
First day cover, #31-32			2.25
Inscription block of 4		2.75	—

First day covers of Nos. 31-32 total 219,118.

World Food Program Type

1983, Apr. 22	Engr.	Perf. 13½	
33 A207 5s green (1,419,237)		.45	.45
First day cover			1.00
Inscription block of 4		2.25	—
34 A207 7s brown (1,454,227)		.70	.70
First day cover			1.00
First day cover, #33-34			1.25
Inscription block of 4		2.75	—

First day covers of Nos. 33-34 total 212,267.

UN Conference on Trade and Development Type

1983, June 6	Litho.	Perf. 14	
35 G24 4s multicolored (1,544,973)		.30	.30
First day cover			1.00
Inscription block of 4		1.90	—
36 A209 8.50s multicolored (1,423,172)		.75	.75
First day cover			1.00
First day cover, #35-36			1.25
Inscription block of 4		3.25	—

First day covers of Nos. 35-36 total 184,023.

The Second
Skin — V6

Right to Think — V7

35th Anniversary of the Universal Declaration of Human Rights

Printed by Government Printing Office, Austria. Designed by
Friedensreich Hundertwasser, Austria. Panes of 16 (4x4).

1983, Dec. 9	Photo. & Engr.	Perf. 13½	
37 V6 5s multicolored (2,163,419)		.45	.45
First day cover			1.25
Inscription block of 4		2.25	
38 V7 7s multicolored (2,163,542)		.70	.70
First day cover			1.25
First day cover, #37-38			2.25
Inscription block of 4		3.25	
Panes of 16, #37-38		18.00	

First day covers of Nos. 37-38 total 246,440.

International Conference on Population Type

Printed by Bundesdruckerei, Federal Republic of Germany.
Panes of 50. Designed by Marina Langer-Rosa and Helmut
Langer, Federal Republic of Germany.

1984, Feb. 3	Litho.	Perf. 14	
39 A212 7s multicolored (1,135,791)		.65	.65
First day cover (80,570)			1.50
Inscription block of 4		2.75	—

Field Irrigation
V8

Harvesting
Machines
V9

World Food Day, Oct. 16

Printed by Walsall Security Printers, Ltd., United Kingdom.
Panes of 50. Designed by Adth Vanooijen, Netherlands.

1984, Mar. 15	Litho.	Perf. 14½	
40 V8 4.50s multicolored (994,106)		.40	.40
First day cover			1.00
Inscription block of 4		2.00	—
41 V9 6s multicolored (1,027,115)		.65	.65
First day cover			1.00
First day cover #40-41			2.25
Inscription block of 4		2.50	—

First day covers of Nos. 40-41 total 194,546.

Serengeti Park,
Tanzania — V10

Ancient City of
Shiban, People's
Democratic Rep.
of Yemen — V11

World Heritage

Printed by Harrison and Sons, United Kingdom. Panes of 50.
Designs adapted by Rocco J. Callari, US, and Thomas Lee,
China.

1984, Mar. 15		Litho.		Perf. 14
42	V10	3.50s multicolored (957,518)	.25	.25
		First day cover		1.25
		Inscription block of 4	1.25	
43	V11	15s multicolored (928,794)	1.25	1.25
		First day cover		1.75
		First day cover, #42-43		2.50
		Inscription block of 4	5.75	—

First day covers of Nos. 42-43 total 193,845.

V12

V13

Future for Refugees

Designed by Hans Erni, Switzerland.
Printed by Courvoisier. Panes of 50.

1984, Mar. 29		Photo.		Perf. 11½
44	V12	4.50s multicolored (1,086,393)	.45	.45
		First day cover		1.25
		Inscription block of 4	2.25	
45	V13	8.50s multicolored (1,109,865)	1.25	1.25
		First day cover		1.75
		First day cover, #44-45		2.25
		Inscription block of 4	5.75	—

First day covers of Nos. 44-45 total 185,349.

International Youth
Year — V14

Printed by Waddingtons Ltd., United Kingdom. Panes of 50.
Designed by Ruel A. Mayo, Phillipines.

1984, Nov. 15		Litho.		Perf. 13½
46	V14	3.50s multicolored (1,178,833)	.45	.45
		First day cover		1.25
		Inscription block of 4	2.10	
47	V14	6.50s multicolored (1,109,337)	.70	.70
		First day cover		1.50
		First day cover, #46-47		2.25
		Inscription block of 4	3.25	—

First day covers of Nos. 46-47 total 165,762.

ILO Type of Geneva

Printed by the Government Printing Bureau, Japan. Panes of
50. Adapted from photographs by Rocco J. Callari, US, and
Thomas Lee, China.

1985, Feb. 1		Engr.		Perf. 13½
48	G34	7.50s U Thant Pavilion (948,317)	.75	.75
		First day cover (115,916)		1.75
		Inscription block of 4	3.50	

UN University Type

Printed by Helio Courvoisier, Switzerland. Panes of 50.
Designed by Moshe Pereg, Israel, and Hinedi Geluda, Brazil.

1985, Mar. 15		Photo.		Perf. 13½
49	A221	8.50s Rural scene, lab researcher (863,673)	.75	.75
		First day cover (108,479)		1.75
		Inscription block of 4	3.75	

Ship of Peace — V15   Shelter under UN
                               Umbrella — V16

Printed by Carl Ueberreuter Druck and Verlag M. Salzer,
Austria. Panes of 50. Designed by Ran Banda Mawilmada, Sri
Lanka (4.50s), and Sophia van Heeswijk, Federal Republic of
Germany (15s).

1985, May 10		Litho.		Perf. 14
50	V15	4.50s multicolored (2,000,000)+	.30	.30
		First day cover		.75
		Inscription block of 4	1.50	
51	V16	15s multicolored (2,000,000)+	2.00	2.00
		First day cover		2.75
		First day cover, #50-51		3.50
		Inscription block of 4	9.50	—

First day covers of Nos. 50-51 total 142,687.

40th Anniversary Type

Designed by Rocco J. Callari, U.S., and Thomas Lee, China
(No. 54).

1985, June 26		Photo.		Perf. 12 x 11½
52	A224	6.50s multicolored (984,820)	.90	.90
		First day cover		1.25
		Inscription block of 4	4.25	
53	A225	8.50s multicolored (914,347)	1.40	1.40
		First day cover		1.75
		First day cover, #52-53		2.50
		Inscription block of 4	6.25	

Souvenir Sheet
Imperf

54		Sheet of 2 (676,648)	2.50	2.50
a.	A224	6.50s multi	1.00	1.00
b.	A225	8.50s multi	1.40	1.40
		First day cover		2.50

First day covers of Nos. 52-54 total 317,652.

UNICEF Child Survival Campaign Type

Printed by the Government Printing Bureau, Japan. Panes of
50. Designed by Mel Harris, United Kingdom (No. 55) and Vreni
Wyss-Fischer, Switzerland (No. 56).

1985, Nov. 22		Photo. & Engr.		Perf. 13½
55	A226	4s Spoonfeeding children (889,918)	.75	.75
		First day cover		1.50
		Inscription block of 4	3.50	
56	A226	6s Mother hugging infant (852,958)	1.40	1.40
		First day cover		1.50
		First day cover, #55-56		2.50
		Inscription block of 4	6.00	

First day covers of Nos. 55-56 total 239,532.

Africa in Crisis Type

Printed by Helio Courvoisier, Switzerland. Panes of 50.
Designed by Tesfaye Tessema, Ethiopia.

1986, Jan. 31		Photo.		Perf. 11½x12
57	A227	8s multicolored (809,854)	.80	.80
		First day cover (99,996)		2.75
		Inscription block of 4	3.50	

UN Development Program Type

Agriculture. Printed by the Government Printing Bureau,
Japan. Panes of 40, 2 blocks of 4 horizontal and 5 blocks of 4
vertical. Designed by Thomas Lee, China.

1986, Mar. 14		Photo.		Perf. 13½
58	A228	4.50s Developing crop strains (730,691)	1.50	1.50
59	A228	4.50s Animal husbandry (730,691)	1.50	1.50
60	A228	4.50s Technical instruction (730,691)	1.50	1.50
61	A228	4.50s Nutrition education (730,691)	1.50	1.50
a.		Block of 4, #58-61	6.25	6.25
		First day cover, #61a		6.75
		First day cover, #58-61, each		2.00
		Inscription block of 4, #58-61	7.00	
		Pane of 40, #58-61	87.50	

No. 61a has a continuous design.
First day covers of Nos. 58-61 total 227,664.

Stamp Collecting Type

Designs: 3.50s, UN stamps. 6.50s, Engraver. Printed by the
Swedish Post Office, Sweden. Panes of 50. Designed by Czeslaw Slania and Ingalill Axelsson, Sweden.

1986, May 22		Engr.		Perf. 12½
62	A229	3.50s dk ultra & dk brown (874,119)	.40	.40
		First day cover		1.50
		Inscription block of 4	2.25	
63	A229	6.50s int blue & brt rose (877,284)	.90	.90
		First day cover		1.50
		First day cover, #62-63		2.25
		Inscription block of 4	4.50	

First day covers of Nos. 62-63 total 150,836.

Olive Branch,
Rainbow,
Earth — V17

International Peace Year. Printed by the Government Printing
Bureau, Japan. Panes of 50. Designed by Milo Schor, Israel
(No. 64), and Mohammad Sardar, Pakistan (No. 65).

Photogravure & Embossed

1986, June 20				Perf. 13½
64	V17	5s shown (914,699)	.75	.75
		First day cover		1.50
		Inscription block of 4	3.75	
65	V17	6s Doves, UN emblem (818,386)	1.00	1.00
		First day cover		1.50
		First day cover, #64-65		2.50
		Inscription block of 4	4.50	—

First day covers of Nos. 64-65 total 169,551.

WFUNA Anniversary Type
Souvenir Sheet

Printed by Johann Enschede and Sons, Netherlands.
Designed by Rocco J. Callari, US.

Designs: 4s, White stallion by Elisabeth von Janota-Bzowski,
Germany. 5s, Surrealistic landscape by Ernst Fuchs, Austria.
6s, Geometric abstract by Victor Vasarely (b. 1908), France. 7s,
Mythological abstract by Wolfgang Hutter (b. 1928), Austria.

1986, Nov. 14		Litho.		Perf. 13x13½
66		Sheet of 4 (668,264)	4.00	4.00
a.	A232	4s multicolored	.75	.75
b.	A232	5s multicolored	.85	.85
c.	A232	6s multicolored	1.00	1.00
d.	A232	7s multicolored	1.25	1.25
		First day cover (121,852)		4.00

No. 66 has inscribed margin picturing UN and WFUNA
emblems.

Trygve Lie Type
Photogravure & Engraved

1987, Jan. 30				Perf. 13½
67	A233	8s multicolored (778,010)	.70	.70
		First day cover (94,112)		2.50
		Inscription block of 4	3.50	—

Shelter for the Homeless Type

Designs: 4s, Family and homes. 9.50s, Family entering
home.

1987, Mar. 13		Litho.		Perf. 13½x12½
68	A234	4s multicolored (704,922)	.50	.50
		First day cover		1.25
		Inscription block of 4	2.40	
69	A234	9.50s multicolored (671,200)	1.10	1.10
		First day cover		1.75
		First day cover, #68-69		2.75
		Inscription block of 4	4.75	—

First day covers of Nos. 68-69 total 117,941.

Fight Drug Abuse Type

Designs: 5s, Soccer players. 8s, Family.

1987, June 12		Litho.		Perf. 14½x15
70	A235	5s multicolored (869,875)	.40	.40
		First day cover		1.40
		Inscription block of 4	2.40	—

71 A235 8s multicolored (797,889)	.90	.90
First day cover		1.75
First day cover, #70-71		2.75
Inscription block of 4	4.00	—

First day covers of Nos. 70-71 total 117,964.

Donaupark,
Vienna — V18

Peace Embracing
the Earth — V19

Printed by The House of Questa, United Kingdom. Panes of 50. Designed by Henry Bencsath, US (2s), and Eliezer Weishoff, Israel (17s).

1987, June 12 Litho. Perf. 14½x15		
72 V18 2s multicolored (2,000,000)+	.30	.30
First day cover		1.25
Inscription block of 4	1.40	—
73 V19 17s multicolored (2,000,000)+	1.60	1.60
First day cover		2.50
First day cover, #72-73		3.50
Inscription block of 4	7.00	—

First day covers of Nos. 72-73 total 111,153.

UN Day Type

Designed by Elisabeth von Janota-Bzowski (5s) and Fritz Henry Oerter (6s), Federal Republic of Germany.
Designs: Multinational people in various occupations.

1987, Oct. 23 Litho. Perf. 14½x15		
74 A236 5s multicolored (1,575,731)	.75	.75
First day cover		1.40
Inscription block of 4	3.75	—
75 A236 6s multicolored (1,540,523)	.90	.90
First day cover		1.75
First day cover, #74-75		2.75
Inscription block of 4	4.25	—
Panes of 12, #74-75	22.00	

Immunize Every Child Type

Designs: 4s, Poliomyelitis. 9.50s, Diphtheria.

1987, Nov. 20 Litho. Perf. 15x14½		
76 A237 4s multicolored (793,716)	.75	.75
First day cover		1.00
Inscription block of 4	4.00	—
77 A237 9.50s multicolored (769,288)	2.00	2.00
First day cover		1.90
First day cover, #76-77		2.75
Inscription block of 4	8.25	—

IFAD Type

Designs: 4s, Grains. 6s, Vegetables.

1988, Jan. 29 Litho. Perf. 13½		
78 A238 4s multicolored (697,307)	.40	.40
First day cover		1.25
Inscription block of 4	2.75	—
79 A238 6s multicolored (701,521)	.90	.90
First day cover		1.75
First day cover, #78-79		2.75
Inscription block of 4	4.25	—

Survival of the Forests Type

Deciduous forest in fall: 4s, Treetops, hills and dales. 5s, Tree trunks. Printed se-tenant in a continuous design.

1988, Mar. 18 Litho. Perf. 14x15		
80 A240 4s multicolored (990,607)	2.25	2.25
First day cover		4.50
81 A240 5s multicolored (990,607)	3.00	3.00
First day cover		5.50
a. Pair, #80-81	5.25	5.25
First day cover, #81a		9.00
Inscription block of 4, #80-81	12.00	—
Pane of 12, #80-81	30.00	

Intl. Volunteer Day Type

Designed by George Fernandez, U.S.
Designs: 6s, Medical care, vert. 7.50s, Construction.

1988, May 6 Litho. Perf. 13x14, 14x13		
82 A241 6s multicolored (701,167)	.75	.75
First day cover		1.40
Inscription block of 4	4.00	—
83 A241 7.50s multicolored (638,240)	1.00	1.00

First day cover		1.60
First day cover, #82-83		3.00
Inscription block of 4	5.75	—

Health in Sports Type

Paintings by LeRoy Neiman, American Sports artist: 6s, Skiing, vert. 8s, Tennis.

1988, June 17 Litho. Perf. 13½x13, 13x13½		
84 A242 6s multicolored (668,902)	.90	.90
First day cover		1.40
Inscription block of 4	5.00	—
85 A242 8s multicolored (647,915)	1.40	1.40
First day cover		2.00
First day cover #84-85		4.00
Inscription block of 4	8.50	—

Universal Declaration of Human Rights 40th Anniv. Type

1988, Dec. 9 Photo. & Engr. Perf. 11½		
86 A243 5s multicolored (1,080,041)	.50	.50
First day cover		2.50
Inscription block of 4	3.00	—

Souvenir Sheet

87 A243 11s multicolored (688,994)	1.25	1.25
First day cover		4.75

No. 87 has multicolored decorative margin inscribed with preamble to the human rights declaration in German.

World Bank Type

1989, Jan. 27 Litho. Perf. 13x14		
88 A244 5.50s Transportation (682,124)	1.10	1.10
First day cover		1.40
Inscription block of 4	5.25	—
89 A244 8s Health care, education (628,649)	1.75	1.75
First day cover		2.00
First day cover, #88-89		3.00
Inscription block of 4	8.25	—

First day covers of Nos. 88-89 total 135,964.

Peace-Keeping Force Type

1989, Mar. 17 Litho. Perf. 14x13½		
90 A245 6s multicolored (912,731)	.85	.85
First day cover (81,837)		2.00
Inscription block of 4	4.00	—

World Weather Watch Type

Satellite photograph and radar image: 4s, Helical cloud formation over Italy, the eastern Alps, and parts of Yugoslavia. 9.50s, Rainfall in Tokyo, Japan.

1989, Apr. 21 Litho. Perf. 13x14		
91 A247 4s multicolored (948,680)	1.00	1.00
First day cover		1.40
Inscription block of 4	4.50	—
92 A247 9.50s multicolored (880,138)	2.10	2.10
First day cover		2.00
First day cover, #91-92		4.00
Inscription block of 4	10.50	—

First day covers of Nos. 91-92 total 116,846.

Offices in Vienna, 10th Anniv.
V20   V21

Printed by the Government Printing Office, Austria. Panes of 25. Designed by Gottfried Kumpf (5s) and Andre Heller (7.50s), Austria.

Photo. & Engr., Photo. (7.50s)

1989, Aug. 23 Perf. 14		
93 V20 5s multicolored (958,339)	2.25	2.25
First day cover		1.25
Inscription block of 4	11.50	—
94 V21 7.50s multicolored (785,517)	2.25	2.25
First day cover		3.00
First day cover, #93-94		4.00
Inscription block of 4	11.50	—
Panes of 25, #93-94	100.00	

First day covers of Nos. 93-94 total 210,746.

Human Rights Type of 1989

Panes of 12+12 se-tenant labels containing Articles 5 (4s) or 6 (6s) inscribed in German, English or French.
Paintings: 4s, The Prisoners, by Kathe Kollwitz. 6s, Justice, by Raphael.

1989, Nov. 17 Litho. Perf. 13½		
95 A250 4s multicolored (2,267,450)	.50	.50
First day cover		2.50
Inscription block of 3 + 3 labels	1.75	—
96 A250 6s multicolored (2,264,876)	.75	.75
First day cover		3.50
First day cover, #95-96		3.00
Inscription block of 3 + 3 labels	2.50	—
Panes of 12, #95-96	15.00	

First day covers of Nos. 95-96 total 183,199.
See Nos. 108-109, 123-124, 150-151.

Intl. Trade Center Type

1990, Feb. 2 Litho. Perf. 14½x15		
97 A251 12s multicolored (559,556)	1.25	1.25
First day cover (77,928)		4.00
Inscription block of 4	5.50	—

Painting by
Kurt Regschek
V22

Printed by the National Postage Stamps and Fiduciary Printing Works, France. Designed by Robert J. Stein, US.

1990, Feb. 2 Litho. Perf. 13x13½		
98 V22 1.50s multicolored (1,000,000)+	.30	.30
First day cover (64,622)		2.50
Inscription block of 4	1.40	—

Fight AIDS Type

Designed by Jacek Tofil, Poland (5s), Orlando Pelaez, Colombia (11s).
Designs: 5s, "SIDA." 11s, Stylized figures, ink blot.

1990, Mar. 16 Litho. Perf. 13½x12½		
99 A252 5s multicolored (623,155)	1.00	1.00
First day cover		1.50
Inscription block of 4	6.00	—
100 A252 11s multicolored (588,742)	2.25	2.25
First day cover		2.50
First day cover, #99-100		4.75
Inscription block of 4	11.50	—

First day covers of Nos. 99-100 total 123,657.

Medicinal Plants Type

1990, May 4 Photo. Granite Paper Perf. 11½		
101 A253 4.50s Bixa orellana (709,840)	1.25	1.25
First day cover		1.50
Inscription block of 4	5.50	—
102 A253 9.50s Momordica charantia (732,883)	2.50	2.50
First day cover		2.50
First day cover, #101-102		4.75
Inscription block of 4	10.50	—

First day covers of Nos. 101-102 total 117,545.

UN 45th Anniv. Type

Designed by Talib Nauman, Pakistan (7s), Marleen Bosmans (9s), Robert Stein, US (No. 105).
Designs: 7s, 9s, "45" and emblem.

1990, June 26 Litho. Perf. 14½x13		
103 A254 7s multicolored (604,878)	1.40	1.40
First day cover		1.75
Inscription block of 4	6.00	—
104 A254 9s multicolored, diff. (550,902)	2.40	2.40
First day cover		2.25
First day cover, #103-104		4.00
Inscription block of 4	10.50	—

Souvenir Sheet

105 Sheet of 2, #103-104 (423,370)	5.00	3.50
First day cover		3.50

First day covers of Nos. 103-105 total 181,174.

Crime Prevention Type

1990, Sept. 13 Photo. Perf. 14		
106 A255 6s Domestic violence (661,810)	1.00	1.00
First day cover		1.50
Inscription block of 4	5.50	—
107 A255 8s Crimes against cultural heritage (607,940)	2.25	2.25
First day cover		2.25
First day cover, #106-107		3.00
Inscription block of 4	11.00	—

First day covers of Nos. 106-107 total 112,193.

Human Rights Type of 1989

Panes of 12+12 se-tenant labels containing Articles 11 (4.50s) or 12 (7s) inscribed in German, English or French.
Paintings: 4.50s, Before the Judge, by Sandor Bihari. 7s, Young Man Greeted by a Woman Writing a Poem, by Suzuki Harunobu.

1990, Nov. 16   **Litho.**   **Perf. 13½**
108 A250 4.50s **multicolored** *(1,684,833)*   .30   .30
    First day cover   2.50
    Inscription block of 3 + 3 labels   1.25   —
109 A250 7s **multicolored** *(1,541,022)*   .90   .90
    First day cover   3.50
    First day cover, #108-109   2.50
    Inscription block of 3 + 3 labels   4.25   —
    Panes of 12, #108-109   20.00

First day covers of Nos. 108-109 total 168,831.

Economic Commission for Europe Type

1991, Mar. 15   **Litho.**   **Perf. 14**
110 A256 5s Weasel, hoopoe *(727,436)*   1.10   1.10
111 A256 5s Warbler, swans *(727,436)*   1.10   1.10
112 A256 5s Badgers, squirrel *(727,436)*   1.10   1.10
113 A256 5s Fish *(727,436)*   1.10   1.10
  a.   Block of 4, #110-113   4.50   4.50
    First day cover, No. 113a   5.00
    First day cover, Nos. 110-113, each   3.25
    Inscription block of 4, #110-113   5.50   —
    Pane of 40, #110-113   50.00

First day covers of Nos. 110-113 total 81,624.

Namibian Independence Type

1991, May 10   **Litho.**   **Perf. 14**
114 A257 6s Mountains, clouds *(531,789)*   1.25   1.50
    First day cover   2.50
    Inscription block of 4   5.25   —
115 A257 9.50s Dune, Namib Desert *(503,735)*   2.75   2.75
    First day cover   3.75
    First day cover, #114-115   4.50
    Inscription block of 4   11.50   —

First day covers of Nos. 114-115 total 111,184.

V24

Printed by House of Questa, United Kingdom. Designed by Marina Langer-Rosa, Germany.

1991, May 10   **Litho.**   **Perf. 15x14½**
116 V24 20s **multicolored** *(1,750,000)+*   2.50   2.50
    First day cover *(60,843)*   4.00
    Inscription block of 4   10.50   —

V25

Banning of
Chemical
Weapons
V28

Printed by Heraclio Fournier, S.A. Panes of 50. Designed by Oscar Asboth, Austria (5s), Michel Granger, France (10s).

1991, Sept. 11   **Litho.**   **Perf. 13½**
119 V27 5s **multicolored** *(469,454)*   1.00   1.00
    First day cover   1.40
    Inscription block of 4   4.50   —
120 V28 10s **multicolored** *(525,704)*   2.25   2.25
    First day cover   2.50
    First day cover, #119-120   3.00
    Inscription block of 4   10.00   —

First day covers of Nos. 119-120 total 116,862.

UN Postal Administration, 40th Anniv. Type

1991, Oct. 24   **Litho.**   **Perf. 14x15**
121 A263 5s UN NY No. 8 *(564,450)*   .75   .75
    First day cover   1.40
    Inscription block of 4   4.00   —
122 A263 8s UN NY No. 5 *(609,830)*   1.75   1.75
    First day cover   2.10
    First day cover, #121-122   3.25
    Inscription block of 4   9.00   —
    Panes of 25, #121-122   60.00

First day covers of Nos. 121-122 total 107,802.

Human Rights Type of 1989

Panes of 12+12 se-tenant labels containing Articles 17 (4.50s) or 18 (7s) inscribed in German, English or French. Artwork: 4.50s, Pre-columbian Mexican pottery. 7s, Windows, by Robert Delaunay.

1991, Nov. 20   **Litho.**   **Perf. 13½**
123 A250 4.50s **black & brown** *(1,717,097)*   .50   .50
    First day cover   2.75
    Inscription block of 3 + 3 labels   3.00   —
124 A250 7s **multicolored** *(1,717,738)*   .80   .80
    First day cover   5.00
    First day cover, #123-124   1.75
    Inscription block of 3 + 3 labels   5.00   —
    Panes of 12+12 labels, #123-124   25.00   25.00

First day covers of Nos. 123-124 total 204,854.

World Heritage Type of 1984

Designs: 5s, Iguacu Natl. Park, Brazil. 9s, Abu Simbel, Egypt.

1992, Jan. 24   **Litho.**   **Perf. 13**
          Size: 35x28mm
125 V10 5s **multicolored** *(586,738)*   1.25   1.25
    First day cancel   1.50
    Inscription block of 4   5.75   —
126 V10 9s **multicolored** *(476,965)*   2.25   2.25
    First day cancel   2.75
    First day cancel, #125-126   4.00
    Inscription block of 4   9.00   —

First day covers of Nos. 125-126 total 93,016.

Clean Oceans Type

1992, Mar. 13   **Litho.**   **Perf. 14**
127 A264 7s Ocean surface, diff. *(1,121,870)*   1.00   1.00
128 A264 7s Ocean bottom, diff. *(1,121,870)*   1.00   1.00
  a.   Pair, #127-128   2.25   2.25
    First day cover, #128a   3.25
    First day cover, #127-128, any single   2.00
    Inscription block of 4, 2 each #127-128   5.00   —
    Pane of 12, #127-128   14.00

First day covers of Nos. 127-128 total 128,478.

Earth Summit Type

1992, May 22   **Photo.**   **Perf. 11½**
129 A265 5.50s Man in space *(784,197)*   1.30   1.30
130 A265 5.50s Sun *(784,197)*   1.30   1.30
131 A265 5.50s Man fishing *(784,197)*   1.30   1.30
132 A265 5.50s Sailboat *(784,197)*   1.30   1.30
  a.   Block of 4, #129-132   5.50   5.50

    First day cover, #132a   6.00
    First day cover, #129-132, any single   4.00
    Inscription block of 4, #129-132   7.00   —
    Pane of 40, #129-132   60.00

First day covers of Nos. 129-132a total 82,920.

Mission to Planet Earth Type

Designs: No. 133, Satellite, person's mouth. No. 134, Satellite, person's ear.

1992, Sept. 4   **Photo.**   **Rouletted 8**
          Granite Paper
133 A266 10s **multicolored** *(881,716)*   2.50   2.50
134 A266 10s **multicolored** *(881,716)*   2.50   2.50
  a.   Pair, #133-134   5.00   5.00
    First day cover, #134a   4.50
    First day cover, #133-134, any single   9.00
    Inscription block of 4, #133-134   12.50   —
    Pane of 10, #133-134   30.00

First day covers of Nos. 133-134 total 99,459.

Science and Technology Type of 1992

Designs: 5.50s, Woman emerging from computer screen. 7s, Green thumb growing flowers.

1992, Oct. 2   **Litho.**   **Perf. 14**
135 A267 5.50s **multicolored** *(482,830)*   .75   .75
    First day cover   1.75
    Inscription block of 4   3.75   —
136 A267 7s **multicolored** *(500,517)*   1.40   1.40
    First day cover   2.00
    First day cover, #135-136   4.00
    Inscription block of 4   6.75   —

First day covers of Nos. 135-136 total 98,091.

V29

Intl. Center,
Vienna — V30

Printed by Walsall Security Printers, Ltd., UK. Designed by Gundi Groh, Austria (5.50s), Rocco J. Callari, US (7s).

1992, Oct. 2   **Litho.**   **Perf. 13x13½**
137 V29 5.50s **multicolored** *(2,100,000)+*   .90   .90
    First day cover   1.25
    Inscription block of 4   4.25   —
          Perf. 13½x13
138 V30 7s **multicolored** *(2,100,000)+*   1.25   1.25
    First day cover   2.00
    First day cover, #137-138   3.50
    Inscription block of 4   6.00   —

First day covers of Nos. 137-138 total 151,788.

Human Rights Type of 1989

Panes of 12+12 se-tenant labels containing Articles 23 (6s) and 24 (10s) inscribed in German, English or French. Artwork: 6s, Les Constructeurs, by Fernand Leger. 10s, Sunday Afternoon on the Island of Le Grande Jatte, by Georges Seurat.

1992, Nov. 20   **Litho.**   **Perf. 13½**
139 A250 6s **multicolored**, *(1,536,516)*   .75   .75
    First day cover   5.00
    Inscription block of 3 + 3 labels   3.00   —
140 A250 10s **multicolored**, *(1,527,861)*   1.25   1.25
    First day cover   11.00
    Inscription block of 3 + 3 labels   5.50   —
    First day cover, #139-140   2.00
    Panes of 12, #139-140   30.00   30.00

Aging With Dignity Type

Designs: 5.50s, Elderly couple, family working in garden. 7s, Older woman teaching.

Rights of the
Child — V26

Printed by The House of Questa. Panes of 50. Designed by Anna Harmer, Austria (7s) and Emiko Takegawa, Japan (9s).

1991, June 14   **Litho.**   **Perf. 14½**
117 V25 7s Stick drawings *(645,145)*   1.50   1.50
    First day cover   1.75
    Inscription block of 4   6.25   —
118 V26 9s Child, clock, fruit *(568,214)*   2.00   2.00
    First day cover   2.25
    First day cover, #117-118   3.50
    Inscription block of 4   8.50   —

First day covers of Nos. 117-118 total 120,619.

1993, Feb. 5   Litho.   *Perf. 13*
141 A270 5.50s multicolored *(428,886)*   .75 .75
          First day cover   1.60
          Inscription block of 4   4.50
142 A270   7s multicolored *(459,471)*   1.40 1.40
          First day cover   2.00
          First day cover, #141-142   3.00
          Inscription block of 4   7.50 —

First day covers of Nos. 141-142 total 87,052.

Endangered Species Type

Designed by Rocco J. Callari and Steve Brennan, US.
Designs: No. 143, Equus grevyi (Grevy's zebra). No. 144,
Spheniscus humboldti (Humboldt's penguins). No. 145,
Varanus griseus (desert monitor). No. 146, Canis lupus (gray
wolf).

1993, Mar. 2   Litho.   *Perf. 13x12½*
143 A271 7s multicolored *(1,200,000)+*   1.05 1.05
144 A271 7s multicolored *(1,200,000)+*   1.05 1.05
145 A271 7s multicolored *(1,200,000)+*   1.05 1.05
146 A271 7s multicolored *(1,200,000)+*   1.05 1.05
   a.   Block of 4, #143-146   4.25 4.25
          First day cover, #146a   5.25
          First day cover, #143-146, any sin-
            gle   1.75
          Inscription block of 4, #146a   5.00 —
          Pane of 16, #143-146   18.00

First day covers of Nos. 143-146a total 106,211.

Healthy Environment Type

1993, May 7   Litho.   *Perf. 15x14½*
147 A272   6s Wave in ocean *(517,433)*   1.25 1.25
          First day cover   1.50
          Inscription block of 4   5.25
148 A272 10s Globe *(453,123)*   2.00 2.00
          First day cover   2.25
          First day cover, #147-148   3.50
          Inscription block of 4   8.75 —

First day covers of Nos. 147-148 total 79,773.

V31

Designed by Marek Kwiatkowski, Poland. Printed by Helio
Courvoisier S.A., Switzerland.

1993, May 7   Photo.   *Perf. 11½*
                     Granite Paper
149 V31 13s multicolored *(1,500,000)+*   2.50 2.50
          Inscription block of 4   10.50 —

Human Rights Type of 1989

Printed in sheets of 12 + 12 se-tenant labels containing Article 29 (5s) and 30 (6s) inscribed in German, English or French.
Artwork: 5s, Lower Austrian Peasants' Wedding, by Ferdinand G. Waldmuller. 6s, Outback, by Sally Morgan.

1993, June 11   Litho.   *Perf. 13½*
150 A250 5s multicolored *(1,532,531)*   1.00 1.00
          First day cover   2.50
          Inscription block of 3 + 3 labels   4.00
151 A250 6s multicolored *(1,542,716)*   1.25 1.25
          First day cover   3.50
          First day cover, #150-151   1.50
          Inscription block of 3 + 3 labels   5.00 —
          Panes of 12, #150-151   28.00 25.00

First day covers of Nos. 150-151 total 128,687.

Intl. Peace Day Type

Denomination at: No. 152, UL. No. 153, UR. No. 154, LL. No.
155, LR.

1993, Sept. 21   Litho. & Engr.   *Rouletted 12½*
152 A274 5.50s green & multi *(445,699)*   1.80 1.80
153 A274 5.50s green & multi *(445,699)*   1.80 1.80
154 A274 5.50s green & multi *(445,699)*   1.80 1.80
155 A274 5.50s green & multi *(445,699)*   1.80 1.80
   a.   Block of 4, #152-155   7.25 7.25
          First day cover, #155a   4.00
          First day cover, #152-155, any
            single   2.25
          Inscription block of 4, #155a   8.75 —
          Pane of 40, #152-155   80.00

First day covers of Nos. 152-155a total 67,075.

Environment-Climate Type

Designs: No. 156, Monkeys. No. 157, Bluebird, industrial pollution, volcano. No. 158, Volcano, nuclear power plant, tree
stumps. No. 159, Cactus, tree stumps, owl.

1993, Oct. 29   Litho.   *Perf. 14½*
156 A275 7s multicolored *(484,517)*   2.00 2.00
157 A275 7s multicolored *(484,517)*   2.00 2.00
158 A275 7s multicolored *(484,517)*   2.00 2.00
159 A275 7s multicolored *(484,517)*   2.00 2.00
   a.   Strip of 4, #156-159   8.00 8.00
          First day cover, #159a   9.50
          First day cover, #156-159, any sin-
            gle   4.00
          Inscription block of 8, 2 #159a   21.00 —
          Pane of 24, #156-159   47.50

First day covers of Nos. 156-159a total 61,946.

Intl. Year of the Family Type of 1993

Designs: 5.50s, Adults, children holding hands. 8s, Two
adults, child planting crops.

1994, Feb. 4   Litho.   *Perf. 13.1*
160 A276 5.50s blue green & multi *(650,000)+*   1.20 1.20
          First day cover   1.60
          Inscription block of 4   5.00
161 A276   8s red & multi *(650,000)+*   1.80 1.80
          First day cover   2.25
          First day cover, #160-161   3.00
          Inscription block of 4   8.00 —

First day covers of Nos. 160-161 total 78,532.

Endangered Species Type of 1993

Designed by Rocco J. Callari, US (frame), and Paul
Margocsy, Australia (stamps).
Designs: No. 162, Ocelot. No. 163, White-breasted silver-
eye. No. 164, Mediterranean monk seal. No. 165, Asian
elephant.

1994, Mar. 18   Litho.   *Perf. 12.7*
162 A271 7s multicolored *(1,200,000)+*   1.30 1.30
163 A271 7s multicolored *(1,200,000)+*   1.30 1.30
164 A271 7s multicolored *(1,200,000)+*   1.30 1.30
165 A271 7s multicolored *(1,200,000)+*   1.30 1.30
   a.   Block of 4, #162-165   5.25 5.25
          First day cover, #165a   6.00
          First day cover, #162-165, each   2.25
          Inscription block of 4, #165a   5.75 —
          Pane of 16, #162-165   21.00

First day covers of Nos. 162-165a total 104,478.

Protection for Refugees Type

Design: 12s, Protective hands surround group of refugees.

1994, Apr. 29   Litho.   *Perf. 14.3x14.8*
166 A277 12s multicolored *(650,000)+*   1.50 1.50
          First day cover *(49,519)*   3.00
          Inscription block of 4   8.00 —

V32

V33

V34

Designed by Masatoshi Hioki, Japan (#167), Ramon
Alcantara Rodriguez, Mexico (#168), Eliezer Weishoff, Israel
(#169).
Printed by Cartor, S.A., France.

1994, Apr. 29   Litho.   *Perf. 12.9*
167 V32 50g multicolored *(1,450,000)+*   .20   .20
          First day cover   1.25
          Inscription block of 4   .40
168 V33   4s multicolored *(1,150,000)+*   .50   .50
          First day cover   1.25
          Inscription block of 4   2.75
169 V34 30s multicolored *(560,000)+*   4.50 4.50
          First day cover   5.00
          Inscription block of 4   20.00 —

First day covers of Nos. 167-169 total 74,558.

Intl. Decade for Natural Disaster Reduction Type

Earth seen from space, outline map of: No. 170, North
America. No. 171, Eurasia. No. 172, South America. No. 173,
Australia and South Asia.

1994, May 27   Litho.   *Perf. 13.9x14.2*
170 A281 6s multicolored *(690,000)+*   1.75 1.75
171 A281 6s multicolored *(690,000)+*   1.75 1.75
172 A281 6s multicolored *(690,000)+*   1.75 1.75
173 A281 6s multicolored *(690,000)+*   1.75 1.75
   a.   Block of 4, #170-173   7.00 7.00
          First day cover, #173a   6.00
          First day cover, #170-173, each   3.25
          Inscription block of 4, #173a   8.50
          Pane of 40, #170-173   82.50

First day covers of Nos. 170-173a total 52,502.

Population and Development Type

Designs: 5.50s, Women teaching, running machine tool,
coming home to family. 7s, Family on tropical island.

1994, Sept. 1   Litho.   *Perf. 13.2x13.6*
174 A282 5.50s multicolored *(650,000)+*   1.50 1.50
          First day cover   2.00
          Inscription block of 4   6.25
175 A282   7s multicolored *(650,000)+*   2.00 2.00
          First day cover   2.00
          First day cover, #174-175   5.00
          Inscription block of 4   8.50 —

First day covers of Nos. 174-175 total 67,423.

UNCTAD Type

1994, Oct. 28
176 A283 6s multi, diff. *(650,000)+*   1.25 1.25
          First day cover   1.25
          Inscription block of 4   6.25
177 A283 7s multi, diff. *(650,000)+*   1.50 1.50
          First day cover   1.75
          First day cover, #176-177   3.00
          Inscription block of 4   7.00 —

First day covers of Nos. 176-177 total 67,064.

UN 50th Anniv. Type

1995, Jan. 1   Litho. & Engr.   *Perf. 13.4*
178 A284 7s multicolored *(742,052)*   1.25 1.25
          First day cover *(118,537)*   2.00
          Inscription block of 4   5.50 —

Social Summit Type

1995, Feb. 3   Photo. & Engr.   *Perf. 13.6x13.9*
179 A285 14s multi, diff. *(595,554)*   2.25 2.25
          First day cover *(51,244)*   3.50
          Inscription block of 4   11.00 —

Endangered Species Type of 1993

Designed by Salvatore Catalano, US.
Designs: No. 180, Black rhinoceros, Diceros bicornis. No.
181, Golden conure, Aratinga guarouba. No. 182, Douc langur,
Pygathrix nemaeus. No. 183, Arabian oryx, Oryx leucoryx.

1995, Mar. 24   Litho.   *Perf. 13x12½*
180 A271 7s multicolored *(938,000)+*   1.00 1.00
181 A271 7s multicolored *(938,000)+*   1.00 1.00
182 A271 7s multicolored *(938,000)+*   1.00 1.00
183 A271 7s multicolored *(938,000)+*   1.00 1.00
   a.   Block of 4, 180-183   4.00 4.00
          First day cover, #183a   4.50
          First day cover, #180-183, each   2.00
          Inscription block of 4, #183a   5.00 —
          Pane of 16, #180-183   17.50

First day covers of Nos. 180-183a total 95,401.

Intl. Youth Year Type

Designs: 6s, Village in winter. 7s, Teepees.

1995, May 26   Litho.   *Perf. 14.4x14.7*
184 A286 6s multicolored *(437,462)*   1.50 1.50
          First day cover   1.50
          Inscription block of 4   6.00
185 A286 7s multicolored *(409,449)*   1.75 1.75
          First day cover   2.50
          First day cover, #184-185   4.25
          Inscription block of 4   7.50 —

First day covers of Nos. 184-185 total 60,979.

UN, 50th Anniv. Type

Designs: 7s, Like No. 663. 10s, Like No. 664.

1995, June 26   Engr.   *Perf. 13.3x13.6*
186 A287 7s green *(433,922)*   1.25 1.25
          First day cover   2.00
          Inscription block of 4   5.50 —
187 A287 10s black *(471,198)*   2.00 2.00
          First day cover   1.75
          First day cover, #186-187   4.00
          Inscription block of 4   9.00 —

Souvenir Sheet
Litho. & Engr.
Imperf

188	Sheet of 2, #186-187 *(367,773)*	4.50	4.50
a.	A287 7s **green**	1.75	1.75
b.	A287 10s **black**	2.50	2.50
	First day cover		6.50

First day covers of Nos. 186-188b total 171,765.

Conference on Women Type

Designs: 5.50s, Women amid tropical plants. 6s, Woman reading, swans on lake.

1995, Sept. 5   Photo.   *Perf. 12*

189	A288 5.50s **multicolored** *(549,951)*	1.25	1.25
	First day cover		1.50
	Inscription block of 4	5.25	—

Size: 28x50mm

190	A288 6s **multicolored** *(556,569)*	2.25	2.25
	First day cover		1.50
	First day cover, #189-190		3.50
	Inscription block of 4	9.50	—

First day covers of Nos. 189-190 total 71,976.

UN People, 50th Anniv. Type

1995, Oct. 24   Litho.   *Perf. 14*

191	Sheet of 12 *(280,528 sheets)*	17.00	10.00
	First day cover		16.00
a.-l.	A290 3s any single	1.30	1.30
	First day cover, #191a-191 l, each		1.25
192	Souvenir booklet, *(95,449 booklets)*	19.00	
a.	A290 3s Booklet pane of 3, vert. strip of 3 from UL of sheet	4.75	4.75
b.	A290 3s Booklet pane of 3, vert. strip of 3 from UR of sheet	4.75	4.75
c.	A290 3s Booklet pane of 3, vert. strip of 3 from LL of sheet	4.75	4.75
d.	A290 3s Booklet pane of 3, vert. strip of 3 from LR of sheet	4.75	4.75

First day covers of Nos. 191-192d total 107,436.

WFUNA, 50th Anniv. Type

Design: 7s, Harlequin holding dove.

1996, Feb. 2   Litho.   *Perf. 13x13½*

193	A291 7s **multicolored** *(655,000)+*	1.25	1.25
	First day cover		2.00
	Inscription block of 4	6.00	—

UN Flag — V35

Abstract, by Karl Korab — V36

Printed by House of Questa, UK.

1996, Feb. 2   Litho.   *Perf. 15x14½*

194	V35 1s **multicolored** *(1,180,000)+*	.20	.20
	First day cover		1.25
	Inscription block of 4	.80	—
195	V36 10s **multicolored** *(880,000)+*	1.60	1.60
	First day cover		2.75
	First day cover, #194-195		4.50
	Inscription block of 4	7.00	—

Endangered Species Type of 1993

Designs: No. 196, Cypripedium calceolus. No. 197, Aztekium ritteri. No. 198, Euphorbia cremersii. No. 199, Dracula bella.

1996, Mar. 14   Litho.   *Perf. 12½*

196	A271 7s **multicolored** *(846,000)+*	1.00	1.00
197	A271 7s **multicolored** *(846,000)+*	1.00	1.00
198	A271 7s **multicolored** *(846,000)+*	1.00	1.00
199	A271 7s **multicolored** *(846,000)+*	1.00	1.00
a.	Block of 4, #196-199	4.00	4.00
	First day cover, #199a		4.50
	First day cover, #196-199, each		2.00
	Inscription block of 4, #199a	5.50	—
	Pane of 16, #196-199	17.50	

City Summit Type

Designs: No. 200, Arab family selling fruits, vegetables. No. 201, Women beside stream, camels. No. 202, Woman carrying bundle on head, city skyline. No. 203, Woman threshing grain, yoke of oxen in field. No. 204, Native village, elephant.

1996, June 3   Litho.   *Perf. 14x13½*

200	A293 6s **multicolored** *(500,000)+*	1.50	1.50
201	A293 6s **multicolored** *(500,000)+*	1.50	1.50
202	A293 6s **multicolored** *(500,000)+*	1.50	1.50
203	A293 6s **multicolored** *(500,000)+*	1.50	1.50
204	A293 6s **multicolored** *(500,000)+*	1.50	1.50
a.	Strip of 5, #200-204	7.50	7.50
	First day cover, #204a		11.50
	First day cover, #200-204, each		4.50
	Inscription block of 10, 2 #204a	16.00	

Sport and the Environment Type

6s, Men's parallel bars (gymnastics), vert. 7s, Hurdles.

1996, July 19   Litho.   *Perf. 14x14½, 14½x14*

205	A294 6s **multicolored** *(730,000)+*	1.00	1.00
	First day cover		2.75
	Inscription block of 4	5.00	—
206	A294 7s **multicolored** *(730,000)+*	1.50	1.50
	First day cover		3.00
	First day cover, #205-206		6.00
	Inscription block of 4	7.00	—

Souvenir Sheet

207	A294 Sheet of 2, #205-206 *(500,000)+*	2.50	2.50
	First day cover		10.00

Plea for Peace Type

Designed by: 7s, Du Keqing, China. 10s, Xu Kangdeng, China.

Designs: 7s, Dove and butterflies. 10s, Stylized dove, diff.

1996, Sept. 17   Litho.   *Perf. 14½x15*

208	A295 7s **multicolored** *(655,000)+*	1.00	1.00
	First day cover		1.50
	Inscription block of 4	4.75	—
209	A295 10s **multicolored** *(655,000)+*	2.00	2.00
	First day cover		2.50
	First day cover, #208-209		5.00
	Inscription block of 4	9.00	—

UNICEF Type

Fairy Tales: 5.50s, Hansel and Gretel, by the Brothers Grimm. 8s, How Maui Stole Fire from the Gods, South Pacific.

1996, Nov. 20   Litho.   *Perf. 14½x15*

210	A296 5.50s **multicolored** *(1,160,000)+*	.90	.90
	First day cover		1.25
	Pane of 8 + label	8.00	
211	A296 8s **multicolored** *(1,160,000)+*	1.40	1.40
	First day cover		2.00
	First day cover, #210-211		4.00
	Pane of 8 + label	12.00	

V37

Phoenixes Flying Down (Detail), by Sagenji Yoshida — V38

Printed by The House of Questa, Ltd., UK.

1997, Feb. 12   Litho.   *Perf. 14½*

212	V37 5s **multicolored** *(750,000)+*	.80	.80
	First day cover		1.25
	Inscription block of 4	3.40	—
213	V38 6s **multicolored** *(1,050,000)+*	.90	.90
	First day cover		1.50
	First day cover, #212-213		4.00
	Inscription block of 4	4.00	—

First day covers of Nos. 212-213 total 156,021.

Endangered Species Type of 1993

Designs: No. 214, Macaca sylvanus (Barbary macaque). No. 215, Anthropoides paradisea (blue crane). No. 216, Equus przewalskii (Przewalski horse). No. 217, Myrmecophaga tridactyla (giant anteater).

1997, Mar. 13   Litho.   *Perf. 12½*

214	A271 7s **multicolored** *(710,000)+*	1.10	1.10
215	A271 7s **multicolored** *(710,000)+*	1.10	1.10
216	A271 7s **multicolored** *(710,000)+*	1.10	1.10
217	A271 7s **multicolored** *(710,000)+*	1.10	1.10
a.	Block of 4, #214-217	4.50	4.50
	First day cover, #217a		6.00
	First day cover, #214-217, each		3.75
	Inscription block of 4, #217a	6.25	
	Pane of 16	25.00	

First day covers of Nos. 214-217 total 86,406.

Earth Summit Anniv. Type

Designs: No. 218, Person running. No. 219, Hills, stream, trees. No. 220, Tree with orange leaves. No. 221, Tree with pink leaves.

11s, Combined design similar to Nos. 218-221.

1997, May 30   Photo.   *Perf. 11.5*
Granite Paper

218	A299 3.50s **multicolored** *(282,016)*	1.25	1.25
219	A299 3.50s **multicolored** *(282,016)*	1.25	1.25
220	A299 3.50s **multicolored** *(282,016)*	1.25	1.25
221	A299 3.50s **multicolored** *(282,016)*	1.25	1.25
a.	Block of 4, #218-221	5.00	5.00
	First day cover, #221a		10.00
	First day cover, #218-221, each		4.75
	Inscription block of 4, #221a	6.00	

Souvenir Sheet

222	A299 11s **multicolored** *(221,434)*	2.50	2.50
	First day cover		12.00

First day covers of Nos. 218-222 total 62,390.

Transportation Type

Ground transportation: No. 223, 1829 Rocket, 1901 Darraque. No. 224, Steam engine from Vladikawska Railway, trolley. No. 225, Double-decker bus. No. 226, 1950s diesel locomotive, semi-trailer. No. 227, High-speed train, electric car.

1997, Aug. 29   Litho.   *Perf. 14x14½*

223	A300 7s **multicolored** *(356,097)*	1.00	1.00
224	A300 7s **multicolored** *(356,097)*	1.00	1.00
225	A300 7s **multicolored** *(356,097)*	1.00	1.00
226	A300 7s **multicolored** *(356,097)*	1.00	1.00
227	A300 7s **multicolored** *(356,097)*	1.00	1.00
a.	Strip of 5, #223-227	5.00	5.00
	First day cover, #227a		16.00
	First day cover, #223-227, each		4.75
	Inscription block of 10, 2#227a	11.00	

No. 227a has continuous design.
First day covers of Nos. 223-227 total 44,877.

Philately Type

Designs: 6.50s, No. 62. 7s, No. 63.

1997, Oct. 14   Litho.   *Perf. 13½x14*

228	A301 6.50s **multicolored** *(379,767)*	1.00	1.00
	First day cover		2.50
	Inscription block of 4	5.25	—
229	A301 7s **multicolored** *(378,107)*	1.50	1.50
	First day cover		3.50
	First day cover, #228-229		6.00
	Inscription block of 4	7.00	—

First day covers of Nos. 228-229 total 57,651.

World Heritage Convention Type

Terracotta warriors of Xian: 3s, Single warrior. 6s, Massed warriors. No. 232a, like #716. No. 232b, like #717. No. 232c, like Geneva #314. No. 232d, like Geneva #315. No. 232e, like Vienna #230. No. 232f, like Vienna #231.

1997, Nov. 19   Litho.   *Perf. 13½*

230	A302 3s **multicolored** *(528,352)*	1.00	1.00
	First day cover		1.50
	Inscription block of 4	4.25	—
231	A302 6s **multicolored** *(530,947)*	2.00	2.00
	First day cover		2.75
	First day cover, #230-231		5.00
	Inscription block of 4	9.00	—
232	Souvenir booklet *(298,055 booklets)*	10.00	
a.-f.	A302 1s any single	.40	.40
g.	Booklet pane of 4 #232a	1.60	1.60
h.	Booklet pane of 4 #232b	1.60	1.60
i.	Booklet pane of 4 #232c	1.60	1.60
j.	Booklet pane of 4 #232d	1.60	1.60
k.	Booklet pane of 4 #232e	1.60	1.60
l.	Booklet pane of 4 #232f	1.60	1.60

First day covers of Nos. 230-232 total 71,708.

Japanese Peace Bell, Vienna — V39

Vienna Subway, Vienna Intl. Center — V40

Printed by The House of Questa, UK. Panes of 20.
Designed by Heinz Pfeifer, Austria (6.50s), Pigneter, Austria (9s).

1998, Feb. 13   Litho.   *Perf. 15x14½*

233	V39 6.50s **multicolored** *(670,000)+*	1.00	1.00
	First day cover		3.25
	Inscription block of 4	4.50	—
234	V40 9s **multicolored** *(770,000)+*	1.50	1.50
	First day cover		4.50
	First day cover, #233-234		3.00
	Inscription block of 4	6.25	—

Endangered Species Type of 1993

Designed by Rocco J. Callari, US and Robert Hynes, US.

Designs: No. 235, Chelonia mydas (green turtle). No. 236, Speotyto cunicularia (burrowing owl). No. 237, Trogonoptera brookiana (Rajah Brooke's birdwing). No. 238, Ailurus fulgens (lesser panda).

1998, Mar. 13		**Litho.**	**Perf. 12½**
235	A271 7s **multicolored** *(620,000)+*	1.10	1.10
236	A271 7s **multicolored** *(620,000)+*	1.10	1.10
237	A271 7s **multicolored** *(620,000)+*	1.10	1.10
238	A271 7s **multicolored** *(620,000)+*	1.10	1.10
a.	Block of 4, #235-238	4.50	4.50
	First day cover, #238a	5.00	
	First day cover, #235-238, each	2.50	
	Inscription block of 4, #238a	5.00	—
	Pane of 16	19.00	

Intl. Year of the Ocean — V41

Designed by Yuan Lee, China.

1998, May 20		**Litho.**	**Perf. 13x13½**
239	V41 Sheet of 12 *(345,000)*	13.00	13.00
a.-l.	3.50s any single	1.10	1.10
	First day cover, 3239	17.00	
	First day cover, #239a-239l, each	3.00	

Rain Forests Type

1998, June 19			**Perf. 13x13½**
240	A307 6.50s Ocelot *(590,000)+*	.90	.90
	First day cover	4.00	
	Inscription block of 4	4.75	

Souvenir Sheet

241	A307 22s like #240 *(340,000)+*	3.50	3.50
	First day cover	5.25	

Peacekeeping Type of 1998

Designs: 4s, Soldier passing out relief supplies. 7.50s, UN supervised voting.

1998, Sept. 15		**Photo.**	**Perf. 12**
242	A308 4s multicolored *(555,000)+*	.70	.70
	First day cover	1.25	
	Inscription block of 4	2.80	—
243	A308 7.50s multicolored *(545,000)+*	1.25	1.25
	First day cover	1.75	
	First day cover, #242-243	4.00	
	Inscription block of 4	5.25	—

Declaration of Human Rights Type

Designs: 4.50s, Stylized person. 7s, Gears.

1998, Oct. 27		**Litho. & Photo.**	**Perf. 13**
244	A309 4.50s multicolored *(555,000)+*	.80	.80
	First day cover	1.50	
	Inscription block of 4	3.25	—
245	A309 7s multicolored *(545,000)+*	1.25	1.25
	First day cover	2.75	
	First day cover, #244-245	4.00	
	Inscription block of 4	5.00	—

Schönbrunn Palace Type

Designs: 3.50s, #248d, Palace. 7s, #248c, Porcelain stove, vert. No. 248a, Blue porcelain vase, vert. No. 248b, Wall painting on fabric (detail), by Johann Wenzl Bergl, vert. No. 248e, Great Palm House (conservatory). No. 248f, The Gloriette (archway).

1998, Dec. 4		**Litho.**	**Perf. 14**
246	A310 3.50s **multicolored** *(615,000)+*	.60	.60
	First day cover	2.00	
	Inscription block of 4	2.50	—
247	A310 7s **multicolored** *(615,000)+*	1.10	1.10
	First day cover	2.75	
	First day cover, #246-247	4.00	
	Inscription block of 4	4.50	—

Souvenir Booklet

248	Booklet *(158,000)+*	11.00	
a.-c.	A310 1s any single	.35	.35
d.-f.	A310 2s any single	.60	.60
g.	Booklet pane of 4 #248d	2.40	2.40

---

h.	Booklet pane of 3 #248a	1.00	1.00
i.	Booklet pane of 3 #248b	1.00	1.00
j.	Booklet pane of 3 #248c	1.00	1.00
k.	Booklet pane of 4 #248e	2.40	2.40
l.	Booklet pane of 4 #248f	2.40	2.40

Volcanic Landscape — V42

Designed by Peter Pongratz, Austria. Printed by Johann Enschedé and Sons, the Netherlands.

1999, Feb. 5		**Litho.**	**Perf. 13x13½**
249	V42 8s **multicolored** *(660,000)+*	1.50	1.50
	First day cover *(33,022)*	4.00	
	Inscription block of 4	7.50	

World Heritage, Australia Type

Designs: 4.50s, #252d, Uluru-Kata Tjuta Natl. Park. 6.50s, #252a, Tasmanian Wilderness. No. 252b, Wet tropics of Queensland. No. 252c, Great Barrier Reef. No. 252e, Kakadu Natl. Park. No. 252f, Willandra Lakes region.

1999, Mar. 19			**Perf. 13**
250	A313 4.50s **multicolored** *(540,000)+*	.75	.75
	First day cover	1.25	
	Inscription block of 4	3.00	
251	A313 6.50s **multicolored** *(540,000)+*	1.10	1.10
	First day cover	1.50	
	First day cover, #250-251	4.50	
	Inscription block of 4	4.50	

Souvenir Booklet

252	Booklet *(116,000)+*	7.50	
a.-c.	A313 1s any single	.20	.20
d.-f.	A313 2s any single	.40	.40
g.	Booklet pane of 4, #252a	.80	.80
h.	Booklet pane of 4, #252d	1.60	1.60
i.	Booklet pane of 4, #252b	.80	.80
j.	Booklet pane of 4, #252e	1.60	1.60
k.	Booklet pane of 4, #252c	.80	.80
l.	Booklet pane of 4, #252f	1.60	1.60

First day covers of Nos. 250-252 total 65,123.

Endangered Species Type of 1993

Designed by Jeffrey Terreson, US.
Designs: No. 253, Pongo pygmaeus (oran-utan). No. 254, Pelecanus crispus (Dalmatian pelican). No. 255, Eunectes notaeus (yellow anaconda). No. 256, Caracal.

1999, Apr. 22		**Litho.**	**Perf. 12½**
253	A271 7s **multicolored** *(552,000)+*	1.00	1.00
254	A271 7s **multicolored** *(552,000)+*	1.00	1.00
255	A271 7s **multicolored** *(552,000)+*	1.00	1.00
256	A271 7s **multicolored** *(552,000)+*	1.00	1.00
a.	Block of 4, #253-256	4.00	4.00
	First day cover, #256a	6.00	
	First day cover, #253-256, each	2.25	
	Inscription block of 4, #256a	4.75	—
	Pane of 16	17.00	

First day covers of Nos. 253-256 total 66,733.

UNISPACE III Type

Designs: No. 257, Satellite over ships. No. 258, Satellite up close. No. 259, Composite of #257-258.

1999, July 7		**Photo.**	**Rouletted 8**
257	A314 3.50s **multicolored** *(1,200,000)+*	.75	.75
258	A314 3.50s **multicolored** *(1,200,000)+*	.75	.75
a.	Pair, #257-258	1.60	1.60
	First day cover, #258a	3.00	
	First day cover, #257-258, each	2.50	
	Inscription block of 4	6.50	—
	Pane of 10, #257-258	9.00	—

Souvenir Sheet
Perf. 14½

259	A314 13s **multicolored** *(350,000)+*	4.50	4.50
	First day cover	5.00	

First day covers of Nos. 257-259 total 72,143.

UPU Type

Various people, late 20th century methods of mail transportation, denomination at: No. 260, UL. No. 261, UR. No. 262, LL. No. 263, LR.

1999, Aug. 23		**Photo.**	**Perf. 11¾**
260	A315 6.50s **multicolored** *(417,000)+*	1.00	1.00
261	A315 6.50s **multicolored** *(417,000)+*	1.00	1.00
262	A315 6.50s **multicolored** *(417,000)+*	1.00	1.00
263	A315 6.50s **multicolored** *(417,000)+*	1.00	1.00
a.	Block of 4, #260-263	4.00	4.00

First day cover, #263a	4.50	
First day cover, #260-263, each	2.00	
Inscription block of 4	4.50	

First day covers of Nos. 260-263 total 38,453.

In Memoriam Type

Designs: 6.50s, 14s, Donaupark. Size of 14s stamp: 34x63mm.

1999, Sept. 21		**Litho.**	**Perf. 14½x14**
264	A316 6.50s **multicolored** *(530,000)+*	.90	.90
	First day cover	3.00	
	Inscription block of 4	4.50	

Souvenir Sheet
Perf. 14

265	A316 14s **multicolored** *(338,000)+*	2.40	2.40
	First day cover	4.00	

First day covers of Nos. 264-265 total 61,089.

Education Type

1999, Nov. 18		**Litho.**	**Perf. 13½x13¾**
266	A317 7s Boy, girl, book *(490,000)+*	1.00	1.00
	First day cover	1.60	
	Inscription block of 4	4.25	
267	A317 13s Group reading *(490,000)+*	2.00	2.00
	First day cover	3.00	
	First day cover, #266-267	4.00	
	Inscription block of 4	8.50	—

First day covers of Nos. 266-267 total 48,590.

Intl. Year of Thanksgiving Type

2000, Jan. 1		**Litho.**	**Perf. 13¼x13½**
268	A318 7s **multicolored** *(510,000)+*	1.00	1.00
	First day cover	3.00	
	Inscription block of 4	4.75	

On No. 268 parts of the design were applied by a thermographic process producing a shiny, raised effect.

Endangered Species Type of 1993

Designed by Lori Anzalone, US.
Designs: No. 269, Panthera pardus (leopard). No. 270, Platalea leucorodia (white spoonbill). No. 271, Hippocamelus bisulcus (huemal). No. 272, Orcinus orca (killer whale).

2000, Apr. 6		**Litho.**	**Perf. 12¾x12½**
269	A271 7s **multicolored** *(548,000)+*	1.10	1.10
270	A271 7s **multicolored** *(548,000)+*	1.10	1.10
271	A271 7s **multicolored** *(548,000)+*	1.10	1.10
272	A271 7s **multicolored** *(548,000)+*	1.10	1.10
a.	Block of 4, #269-272	4.50	4.50
	First day cover, #272a	6.00	
	First day cover, #269-272, each	2.00	
	Inscription block of 4, #272a	4.75	—
	Pane of 16	18.00	

Our World 2000 Type

Winning artwork in Millennium painting competition: 7s, Tomorrow's Dream, by Voltaire Perez, Philippines. 8s, Remembrance, by Dimitris Nalbandis, Greece, vert.

2000, May 30		**Litho.**	**Perf. 13x13½, 13½x13**
273	A319 7s **multicolored** *(430,000)+*	1.00	1.00
	First day cover	1.75	
	Inscription block of 4	4.50	
274	A319 8s **multicolored** *(430,000)+*	1.20	1.20
	First day cover	2.00	
	First day cover, #273-274	3.00	
	Inscription block of 4	5.00	—

55th Anniversary Type

Designs: 7s, Secretariat Building, unfinished dome of General Assembly Hall, 1951. 9s, Trygve Lie and Headquarters Advisory Committee at topping-out ceremony, 1949.

2000, July 7		**Litho.**	**Perf. 13¼x13**
275	A320 7s **multicolored** *(440,000)+*	.90	.90
	First day cover	1.75	
	Inscription block of 4	4.50	
276	A320 9s **multicolored** *(440,000)+*	1.25	1.25
	First day cover	2.25	
	First day cover, #275-276	3.00	
	Inscription block of 4	6.00	—

Souvenir Sheet

277	A320 Sheet of 2, #275-276 *(300,000)+*	2.75	2.75
	First day cover	3.25	

The UN in the 21st Century — V43

Printed by Government Printing Office, Austria. Designed by Wilson McLean, UK.

No. 278: a, Farm machinery. b, UN Peacekeepers and children. c, Oriental farm workers. d, Peacekeepers searching for mines. e, Medical research. f, Handicapped people.

2000, Sept. 15		Litho.		Perf. 14	
278	V43	Sheet of 6 (330,000)+		6.00	6.00
		First day cover			5.00
a.-f.		3.50s any single		1.00	1.00
		First day cover, #278a-278f, each			4.00

World Heritage, Spain Type

Designs: Nos. 279, 281c, Aqueduct of Segovia. Nos. 280, 281f, Güell Park, Barcelona. #281a, Alhambra, Generalife and Albayzin, Granada. #281b, Walled Town of Cuenca. #281d, Amphitheater of Mérida. #281e, Toledo.

2000, Oct. 6		Litho.		Perf. 14¾x14½	
279	A323	4.50s multicolored (430,000)+		.80	.80
		First day cover			1.25
		Inscription block of 4		3.00	
280	A323	6.50s multicolored (430,000)+		1.20	1.20
		First day cover			1.75
		First day cover, #279-280			2.40
		Inscription block of 4		4.00	—

Souvenir Booklet

281		Booklet (92,000)+		8.00	
a.-c.	A323	1s any single		.20	.20
d.-f.	A323	2s any single		.50	.50
g.		Booklet pane of 4, #281a		.65	.65
h.		Booklet pane of 4, #281d		2.00	2.00
i.		Booklet pane of 4, #281b		.65	.65
j.		Booklet pane of 4, #281e		2.00	2.00
k.		Booklet pane of 4, #281c		.65	.65
l.		Booklet pane of 4, #281f		2.00	2.00

Respect for Refugees Type

Designs: 7s, 25s, Refugee with hat, three other refugees.

2000, Nov. 9		Litho.		Perf. 13¼x12¾	
282	A324	7s multicolored (530,000)+		1.10	1.10
		First day cover			1.75
		Inscription block of 4		4.50	—

Souvenir Sheet

283	A324	25s multicolored (273,000)+		3.75	3.75
		First day cover			4.50

Endangered Species Type of 1993

Printed by Johann Enschedé and Sons, the Netherlands. Designed by Betina Ogden, Australia.
Designs: No. 284, Tremarctos ornatus (spectacled bear). No. 285, Anas laysanensis (Laysan duck). No. 286, Proteles cristatus (aardwolf). No. 287, Trachypithecus cristatus (silvered leaf monkey).

2001, Feb. 1		Litho.		Perf. 12¾x12½	
284	A271	7s multicolored (540,000)+		1.10	1.10
285	A271	7s multicolored (540,000)+		1.10	1.10
286	A271	7s multicolored (540,000)+		1.10	1.10
287	A271	7s multicolored (540,000)+		1.10	1.10
a.		Block of 4, #284-287		4.50	4.50
		First day cover, #287a			5.00
		First day cover, #284-287 each			1.75
		Inscription block of 4, #287a		4.25	—
		Pane of 16		16.00	

Intl. Volunteers Year — V44

Printed by Johann Enschedé and Sons, the Netherlands. Panes of 20. Designed by Rorie Katz and Robert Stein, US.
Paintings by: 10s, Nguyen Thanh Chuong, Viet Nam. 12s, Ikko Tanaka, Japan.

2001, Mar. 29		Litho.		Perf. 13¼	
288	V44	10s multicolored (440,000)+		1.40	1.40
		First day cover			2.00
		Inscription block of 4		5.75	
289	V44	12s multicolored (430,000)+		1.75	1.75
		First day cover			2.40
		First day cover, #288-289			3.75
		Inscription block of 4		7.00	

World Heritage, Japan Type

Designs: 7s, #290c, Himeji-Jo. 15s, #291f, Nikko. #292a, Kyoto. #292b, Nara. #292d, Shirakawa-Go and Gokayama. #292e, Itsukushima Shinto Shrine.

2001, Aug. 1		Litho.		Perf. 12¾x13¼	
290	A328	7s multicolored (440,000)+		1.00	1.00
		First day cover			1.40
		Inscription block of 4		4.00	
291	A328	15s multicolored (440,000)+		2.10	2.10
		First day cover			3.00
		First day cover, #290-291			3.75
		Inscription block of 4		8.50	

Souvenir Booklet

292		Booklet (78,000)+		9.00	
a.-c.	A328	1s any single		.25	.25
d.-f.	A328	2s any single		.50	.50
g.		Booklet pane of 4, #292a		1.00	1.00
h.		Booklet pane of 4, #292d		2.00	2.00
i.		Booklet pane of 4, #292b		1.00	1.00
j.		Booklet pane of 4, #292e		2.00	2.00
k.		Booklet pane of 4, #292c		1.00	1.00
l.		Booklet pane of 4, #292f		2.00	2.00

Dag Hammarskjöld Type

2001, Sept. 18		Engr.		Perf. 11x11¼	
293	A329	7s green (480,000)+		1.00	1.00
		First day cover			2.00
		Inscription block of 4		4.25	—

UN Postal Administration, 50th Anniv. Types

2001, Oct. 18		Litho.		Perf. 13½	
294	A330	7s Stamps, balloons (380,000)+		1.00	1.00
		First day cover			1.60
		Inscription block of 4		4.00	—
295	A330	8s Stamps, cake (380,000)+		1.10	1.10
		First day cover			1.75
		First day cover, #294-295			2.75
		Inscription block of 4		4.50	—

Souvenir Sheet

296	A331	Sheet of 2 (225,000)+		4.00	4.00
a.		7s green & light blue, 38mm diameter		1.00	1.00
b.		21s green & light blue, 38mm diameter		3.00	3.00
		First day cover			7.00

Climate Change Type

Designs: No. 297, Solar panels, automobile at pump. No. 298, Blimp, bicyclists, horse and rider. No. 299, Balloon, sailboat, lighthouse, train. No. 300, Bird, train, traffic signs.

2001, Nov. 16		Litho.		Perf. 13¼	
297	A332	7s multicolored (87,000)+		1.00	1.00
298	A332	7s multicolored (87,000)+		1.00	1.00
299	A332	7s multicolored (87,000)+		1.00	1.00
300	A332	7s multicolored (87,000)+		1.00	1.00
a.		Horiz. strip, #297-300		5.00	5.00
		Inscription block of 8		8.25	
		First day cover, #300a			4.50
		First day cover, #297-300 each		6.00	
		Pane of 24		30.00	—

Nobel Peace Prize Type

2001, Dec. 10		Litho.		Perf. 13¼	
301	A333	7s multicolored (1,260,000)+		1.00	.50
		Inscription block of 4		5.00	—
		First day cover			1.60
		Pane of 12		14.00	—

100 Cents = 1 Euro (€)

Austrian Tourist Attractions V45

Printed by House of Questa, UK. Panes of 20. Designed by Rorie Katz, US.
Designs: 7c, Semmering Railway. 51c, Pferdschwemme, Salzburg. 58c, Aggstein an der Donau Ruins. 73c, Hallstatt. 87c, Melk Abbey. €2.03, Kapitelschwemme, Salzburg.

2002, Mar. 1		Litho.		Perf. 14½x14	
302	V45	7c multicolored (860,000)+		.20	.20
		First day cover			1.25
		Inscription block of 4		.65	
303	V45	51c multicolored (960,000)+		1.10	1.10
		First day cover			1.40
		Inscription block of 4		4.50	
304	V45	58c multicolored (860,000)+		1.25	1.25
		First day cover			1.60
		Inscription block of 4		5.25	
305	V45	73c multicolored (760,000)+		1.50	1.50
		First day cover			2.00
		Inscription block of 4		6.75	
306	V45	87c multicolored (760,000)+		2.00	2.00
		First day cover			2.40
		Inscription block of 4		8.25	
307	V45	€2.03 multicolored (710,000)+		4.25	4.25
		First day cover			5.50
		First day cover, #288-289			10.50
		Inscription block of 4		18.00	—
Nos. 302-307 (6)				10.30	10.30

Endangered Species Type of 1993

Printed by Johann Enschedé and Sons, the Netherlands. Designed by Tim Barrall, US.
Designs: No. 308, Hylobates syndactylus (siamang). No. 309, Spheniscus demersus (jackass penguin). No. 310, Prionodon linsang (banded linsang). No. 311, Bufo retiformis (Sonoran green toad).

2002, Apr. 4		Litho.		Perf. 12¾x12½	
308	A271	51c multicolored (500,000)+		1.25	1.25
309	A271	51c multicolored (500,000)+		1.25	1.25
310	A271	51c multicolored (500,000)+		1.25	1.25
311	A271	51c multicolored (500,000)+		1.25	1.25
a.		Block of 4, #308-311		5.00	5.00
		First day cover, #311a			4.75
		First day cover, #308-311 each			1.75
		Inscription block of 4, #311a		5.25	
		Pane of 16		18.00	—

Independence of East Timor Type

Designs: 51c, Deer horn container with carved wooden stopper. €1.09, Carved wooden tai weaving loom.

2002, May 20		Litho.		Perf. 14x14½	
312	A335	51c multicolored (384,000)+		1.00	1.00
		First day cover			1.50
		Inscription block of 4		4.50	
313	A335	€1.09 multicolored (374,000)+		2.25	2.25
		First day cover			3.25
		First day cover, #312-313			4.00
		Inscription block of 4		9.50	

Intl. Year of Mountains Type

Designs: No. 314, Mt. Cook, New Zealand. No. 315, Mt. Robson, Canada. No. 316, Mt. Rakaposhi, Pakistan. No. 317, Mt. Everest (Sagarmatha), Nepal.

2002, May 24		Litho.		Perf. 13x13¼	
314	A336	22c multicolored (1,335,000)+		.50	.50
		First day cover			1.25
315	A336	22c multicolored (1,335,000)+		.50	.50
		First day cover			1.25
316	A336	51c multicolored (1,335,000)+		1.25	1.25
		First day cover			1.50
		First day cover, #314, 316			2.25
317	A336	51c multicolored (1,335,000)+		1.25	1.25
a.		Vert. strip or block of four, #314-317		4.00	4.00
		First day cover			1.50
		First day cover, #315, 317			2.25
		First day cover, #314-317			3.75
		Pane of 12, 3 each #314-317		12.00	—

World Summit on Sustainable Development (Peter Max) Type

Designs: No. 318, Rainbow. No. 319, Three women, diff. No. 320, Three faceless people. No. 321, Birds, wave.

2002, June 27		Litho.		Perf. 14½x14	
318	A337	51c multicolored (1,305,000)+		1.25	1.25
		First day cover			1.50
319	A337	51c multicolored (1,305,000)+		1.25	1.25
		First day cover			1.50
320	A337	58c multicolored (1,305,000)+		1.50	1.50
		First day cover			1.60
		First day cover, #318, 320			2.50
321	A337	58c multicolored (1,305,000)+		1.50	1.50
a.		Vert. strip or block of four, #318-321		5.50	5.50

	First day cover			1.60
	First day cover, #319, 321			2.50
	First day cover, #318-321			3.75
	Pane of 12, 3 each #318-321			14.50

World Heritage, Italy Type

Designs: 51c, #324f, Pompeii. 58c, #324c, Rome. #324a, Amalfi Coast. #324b, Aeolian Islands. #324d, Florence. #324e, Pisa.

2002, Aug. 30		Litho.	Perf. 13½x13¼	
322	A338	51c **multicolored** (400,000)+	1.10	1.10
		First day cover		1.75
		Inscription block of 4	4.50	—
323	A338	58c **multicolored** (400,000)+	1.25	1.25
		First day cover		2.00
		First day cover, #322-323		3.00
		Inscription block of 4	5.00	—

Souvenir Booklet

324		Booklet (71,000)+	9.25	
a.-c.	A338	7c any single	.25	.25
d.-f.	A338	15c any single	.60	.60
g.		Booklet pane of 4, #324d	2.40	2.40
h.		Booklet pane of 4, #324a	1.00	1.00
i.		Booklet pane of 4, #324e	2.40	2.40
j.		Booklet pane of 4, #324b	1.00	1.00
k.		Booklet pane of 4, #324f	2.40	2.40
l.		Booklet pane of 4, #324c	1.00	1.00

AIDS Awareness Type

2002, Oct. 24		Litho.	Perf. 13½	
325	A339	€1.53 **multicolored** (370,000)+	3.50	3.75
		Inscription block of 4	13.00	
		First day cover, #325		4.00
		Pane of 20	65.00	

Indigenous Art — V46

Printed by House of Questa, UK.
Designed by Rorie Katz and Robert Stein, US.

No. 326: a, Mola, Panama. b, Mochican llama-shaped spouted vessel, Peru. c, Tarabuco woven cloth, Bolivia. d, Masks, Cuba. e, Aztec priest's feather headdress, Mexico. f, Bird-shaped staff head, Colombia.

2003, Jan. 31		Litho.	Perf. 14¼	
326	V46	Sheet of 6 (212,000)+	8.00	8.00
		First day cover		8.25
a.-f.		51c Any single	1.30	1.30
		First day cover, a.-f., each		3.00

Austrian Tourist Attractions Type of 2002

Printed by House of Quest, UK. Designed by Rorie Katz, US. Panes of 20.
Designs: 25c, Kunsthistorisches Museum, Vienna. €1, Belvedere Palace, Vienna.

2003, Mar. 28		Litho.	Perf. 14½x14	
327	V45	25c **multicolored** (650,000)+	.55	.55
		First day cover		1.25
		Inscription block of 4	2.25	—
328	V45	€1 **multicolored** (650,000)+	2.25	2.25
		First day cover		3.25
		First day cover, #327-328		3.50
		Inscription block of 4	9.00	—

Endangered Species Type of 1993

Printed by Johann Enschedé and Sons, the Netherlands. Designed by Robert Hautman, US.
Designs: No. 329, Anas formosa (Baikal teal). No. 330, Bostrychia hagedash (Hadada ibis). No. 331, Ramphastos toco (toco toucan). No. 332, Alopochen aegyptiacus (Egyptian goose).

2003, Apr. 3		Litho.	Perf. 12¾x12½	
329	A271	51c **multicolored** (432,000)+	1.00	1.00
330	A271	51c **multicolored** (432,000)+	1.00	1.00
331	A271	51c **multicolored** (432,000)+	1.00	1.00
332	A271	51c **multicolored** (432,000)+	1.00	1.00
a.		Block of 4, #329-332	4.00	4.00
		First day cover, #332a		5.25
		First day cover, #329-332 each		1.90
		Inscription block of 4, #332a	4.50	—
		Pane of 16	18.00	—

International Year of Freshwater Type of 2003

2003, June 20		Litho.	Perf. 14¼x14½	
333	A345	55c Bridge, bird (316,000)+	1.40	1.40
334	A345	75c Horse, empty river (316,000)+	1.90	1.90
a.		Horiz. pair, #333-334	3.30	3.30
		First day cover, #334a		3.75
		Inscription block of 4	7.50	—

Austrian Tourist Attractions Type of 2002

Printed by Johann Enschedé and Sons, the Netherlands. Panes of 20. Designed by Rorie Katz, US.
Design: 4c, Schloss Eggenberg, Graz.

2003, Aug. 7		Litho.	Perf. 14x13¼	
335	V45	4c **multicolored** (650,000)+	.20	.20
		First day cover		1.25
		Inscription block of 4	.35	
		Pane of 20	1.60	

Ralph Bunche Type

Litho. With Foil Application

2003, Aug. 7			Perf. 13½x14	
336	A346	€2.10 **olive green & multicolored** (384,000)+	4.50	4.50
		First day cover		5.50
		Inscription block of 4	19.00	
		Pane of 20	95.00	

In Memoriam Type of 2003

2003, Oct. 24		Litho.	Perf. 13¼x13	
337	A347	€2.10 **multicolored** (670,000)+	5.00	5.00
		First day cover		6.25
		Inscription block of 4	22.00	—
		Pane of 20	110.00	

World Heritage Sites, United States Type

Designs: 55c, #340c, Olympic National Park. 75c, #340e, Everglades National Park. #340a, Yosemite National Park. #340b, Great Smoky Mountains National Park. #340d, Hawaii Volcanoes National Park. #340f, Yellowstone National Park.

2003, Oct. 24		Litho.	Perf. 14½x14¼	
338	A348	55c **multicolored** (275,000)+	1.50	.75
		First day cover		2.10
		Inscription block of 4	6.00	—
339	A348	75c **multicolored** (275,000)+	2.00	1.00
		First day cover		2.75
		First day cover, #338-339		4.25
		Inscription block of 4	8.00	—

Souvenir Booklet

340		Booklet (57,500)+	9.00	
a.-c.	A348	15c any single	.35	.35
d.-f.	A348	20c any single	.40	.40
g.		Booklet pane of 4 #340a	1.40	1.40
h.		Booklet pane of 4 #340d	1.60	1.60
i.		Booklet pane of 4 #340b	1.40	1.40
j.		Booklet pane of 4 #340e	1.60	1.60
k.		Booklet pane of 4 #340c	1.40	1.40
l.		Booklet pane of 4 #340f	1.60	1.60

Austrian Tourist Attractions Type of 2002

Printed by Imprimerie de Timbres-Poste, France.
Design: 55c, Schloss Schönbrunn, Vienna.

2004, Jan. 29		Litho.	Perf. 13x13¼	
341	V45	55c **multicolored** (740,000)+	1.50	1.50
		First day cover		2.10
		Inscription block of 4	6.00	—
		Pane of 20	30.00	

Endangered Species Type of 1993

Printed by Johann Enschedé and Sons, the Netherlands. Designed by Yuan Lee, U.S.
Designs: No. 342, Melursus ursinus (Sloth bear). No. 343, Cervus eldi (Eld's deer). No. 344, Cercocebus torquatus (Cherry-crowned mangabey). No. 345, Bubalus arnee (Wild water buffalo).

2004, Jan. 29		Litho.	Perf. 12¾x12½	
342	A271	55c **multicolored** (376,000)+	1.25	1.25
343	A271	55c **multicolored** (376,000)+	1.25	1.25
344	A271	55c **multicolored** (376,000)+	1.25	1.25
345	A271	55c **multicolored** (376,000)+	1.25	1.25
a.		Block of 4, #342-345	5.00	5.00
		First day cover, #345a		6.50
		First day cover, #342-345, each		2.25
		Inscription block of 4, #345a	6.00	—
		Pane of 16	24.00	—

Indigenous Art Type of 2003

Printed by Johann Enschedé and Sons, the Netherlands. Designed by Rorie Katz and Robert Stein, US.

No. 346: a, Illuminated illustration from the Book of Kells, Ireland. b, Easter eggs, Ukraine. c, Venus of Willendorf, Paleolithic age limestone statue, Austria. d, Flatatunga panel, Iceland. e, Neolithic era idol, Hungary. f, Illuminated illustration from medical treatise, Portugal.

2004, Mar. 4		Litho.	Perf. 13¼	
346	V46	Sheet of 6 (133,000)+	7.50	7.50
		First day cover		10.50
a.-f.		55c Any single	1.25	1.25
		First day cover, a.-f., each		2.75

Road Safety Type

Road map art with: 55c, Automobile, alcohol bottles. 75c, Road, clouds in traffic light colors, vert.

2004, Apr. 7		Litho.	Perf. 13x13¼, 13¼x13	
347	A354	55c **multicolored** (225,000)+	1.25	1.25
		First day cover		2.10
		Inscription block of 4	6.00	—
348	A354	75c **multicolored** (225,000)+	1.75	1.75
		First day cover		2.75
		First day cover, #338-339		4.25
		Inscription block of 4	8.00	—

Japanese Peace Bell, 50th Anniv. Type

2004, June 3		Litho. & Engr.	Perf. 13¼x13	
349	A355	€2.10 **multicolored** (280,000)+	4.50	4.50
		First day cover		6.25
		Inscription block of 4	22.00	—
		Pane of 20	110.00	

World Heritage Sites, Greece Type

Designs: 55c, No. 352f, Mycenae and Tiryns. 75c, No. 352e, Olympia. No. 352a, Acropolis, Athens. No. 352b, Delos. No. 352c, Delphi. No. 352d, Pythagoreion and Heraion of Samos.

2004, Aug. 12		Litho.	Perf. 14x13¼	
350	A356	55c **multicolored** (250,000)+	1.40	1.40
		First day cover		1.90
		Inscription block of 4	5.75	—
351	A356	75c **multicolored** (250,000)+	1.90	1.90
		First day cover		2.75
		First day cover, #350-351		4.00
		Inscription block of 4	7.75	—

Souvenir Booklet

352		Booklet (49,000)+	14.00	
a.-d.	A356	25c any single	.55	.55
e.-f.	A356	30c either single	.70	.70
g.		Booklet pane of 4 #352a	2.20	2.20
h.		Booklet pane of 4 #352b	2.20	2.20
i.		Booklet pane of 4 #352c	2.20	2.20
j.		Booklet pane of 4 #352d	2.20	2.20
k.		Booklet pane of 4 #352e	2.80	2.80
l.		Booklet pane of 4 #352f	2.80	2.80

My Dream for Peace Type

Winning designs of Lions Club International children's global peace poster contest by: 55c, Henry Ulfe Renteria, Peru. €1, Michelle Fortaliza, Philippines.

2004, Sept. 21		Litho.	Perf. 14	
353	A357	55c **multicolored** (235,000)+	1.40	1.40
		First day cover		1.90
		Inscription block of 4	5.75	
		Pane of 20	28.00	
354	A357	€1 **multicolored** (235,000)+	2.50	2.50
		First day cover		3.50
		First day cover, #353-354		4.50
		Inscription block of 4	10.00	
		Pane of 20	50.00	

V47

Human Rights — V48

Printed by Banknote Corporation of America, US. Designed by Yuri Gervorgian, Armenia. Panes of 8.

2004, Oct. 14		Litho.	Perf. 11¼	
355	V47	55c **multicolored** (480,000)+	1.00	1.00
		First day cover		2.00
		Pane of 8	12.00	—

356 V48 €1.25 **multicolored** (480,000)+   3.00 3.00
First day cover   4.50
First day cover, #355-356   5.75
Pane of 8   28.00 —

United Nations, 60th Anniv. Type of 2005
Printed by Banknote Corporation of America, US. Designed by Czeslaw Slania, Sweden.

2005, Feb. 4   **Litho. & Engr.**   **Perf. 11x11¼**
357 A361 55c **multicolored** (310,000)+   1.60 1.60
First day cover   2.60
Inscription block of 4   6.50 —
Pane of 20   32.50 —

Souvenir Sheet
Litho.
Imperf
358 A361 €2.10 **multicolored** (165,000)+   5.50 5.50
First day cover   6.25

International Center, Vienna — V49

Printed by Cartor Security Printing, France.

Litho. with Hologram
2005, Feb. 4   **Perf. 13½x13¼**
359 V49 75c **multicolored** (360,000)+   2.25 2.25
First day cover   3.25
Inscription block of 4   9.00 —
Pane of 20   45.00 —

Endangered Species Type of 1993
Designs: No. 360, Ansellia africana. No. 361, Phragmipedium kovachii. No. 362, Cymbidium ensifolium. No. 363, Renanthera imschootiana.

2005, Mar. 3   **Litho.**   **Perf. 12¾x12½**
360 A271 55c multicolored   1.40 1.40
361 A271 55c multicolored   1.40 1.40
362 A271 55c multicolored   1.40 1.40
363 A271 55c multicolored   1.40 1.40
a. Block of 4, #360-363   6.00 6.00
First day cover, #363a   7.00
First day cover, #360-363, each   2.25
Inscription block of 4, #363a   6.25 —
Pane of 16   19.00 —

Nature's Wisdom — V50

Printed by Cartor Security Printing, France. Panes of 20. Designed by Robert Stein, US.
Designs: 55c, Desert landscape, China. 80c, Cheetah family, Africa.

2005, Apr. 21   **Litho.**   **Perf. 13½x13¼**
364 V50 55c **multicolored** (230,000)+   1.60 1.60
First day cover   2.40
Inscription block of 4   6.50 —
Pane of 20   32.50 —
365 V50 75c **multicolored** (230,000)+   2.25 2.25
First day cover   3.50
First day cover, #364-365   4.75
Inscription block of 4   9.00 —
Pane of 20   45.00 —

Intl. Year of Sport Type
Printed by Cartor Security Printing, France. Designed by Roland Hirter, Switzerland.

2005, June 3   **Litho.**   **Perf. 13x13¼**
366 A368 55c Equestrian (245,000)+   1.60 1.60
First day cover   2.25
Inscription block of 4   6.50 —
Pane of 20   32.50 —
367 A368 €1.10 Soccer (245,000)+   3.25 3.25
First day cover   4.50

First day cover, #366-367   6.00
Inscription block of 4   13.00 —
Pane of 20   65.00 —

World Heritage Sites, Egypt Type
Printed by Johann Enschedé and Sons, the Netherlands. Panes of 20. Designed by Rorie Katz.
Designs: Nos. 368, 370c, Abu Mena. Nos. 369, 370f, St. Catherine area. No. 370a, Memphis and its Necropolis. No. 370b, Philae. No. 370d, Ancient Thebes. No. 370e, Islamic Cairo.

2005, Aug. 4   **Litho.**   **Perf. 14x13¼**
368 A369 55c **multicolored** (250,000)+   1.60 1.60
First day cover   2.40
Inscription block of 4   6.50 —
369 A369 75c **multicolored** (250,000)+   2.25 2.25
First day cover   3.25
First day cover, #368-369   4.75
Inscription block of 4   9.00 —

Souvenir Booklet
370 Booklet, #370g-370l (45,000)+   19.50
a.- A369 25c any single   .75 .75
c.
d.- A369 30c any single
f.   .85 .85
g. Booklet pane of 4 #370a   3.00 —
h. Booklet pane of 4 #370b   3.00 —
i. Booklet pane of 4 #370c   3.00 —
j. Booklet pane of 4 #370d   3.50 —
k. Booklet pane of 4 #370e   3.50 —
l. Booklet pane of 4 #370f   3.50 —

No. 370 sold for €6.80.

My Dream for Peace Type
Winning designs of Lions Club International children's global peace poster contest by: 55c, Lee Min Gi, Republic of Korea. €1, Natalie Chan, US.

2004, Sept. 21   **Litho.**   **Perf. 14**
371 A357 55c **multicolored** (225,000)+   1.60 1.60
First day cover   2.25
Inscription block of 4   6.50 —
Pane of 20   32.00 —
372 A357 €1 **multicolored** (225,000)+   2.75 2.75
First day cover   4.00
First day cover, #371-372   5.25
Inscription block of 4   11.00 —
Pane of 20   55.00 —

Food for Life Type
Printed by Government Printing Office, Austria. Designed by Andrew Davidson, United Kingdom.
Designs: 55c, Corn, people with food bowls, teacher and students. €1.25, Rice, helicopter dropping food, elephant caravan.

2005, Oct. 20   **Litho.**   **Perf. 13¾**
373 A370 55c **multicolored** (210,000)+   1.60 1.60
First day cover   2.10
Inscription block of 4   6.50 —
Pane of 20   32.00 —
374 A370 €1.25 **multicolored** (210,000)+   3.50 3.50
First day cover   4.75
First day cover, #373-374   6.00
Inscription block of 4   14.00 —
Pane of 20   70.00 —

Indigenous Art Type of 2003
Printed by Johann Enschedé and Sons, the Netherlands. Designed by Robert Stein, US.

No. 375 — Musical instruments: a, Drum, Guinea. b, Whistle, Congo. c, Horn, Botswana. d, Drums, Burundi. e, Harp, Gabon. f, Bell, Nigeria.

2006, Feb. 3   **Litho.**   **Perf. 13¼**
375 V46 Sheet of 6 (117,000)+   8.50 8.50
First day cover   10.50
a.-f. 55c Any single   1.40 1.40
First day cover, #375a-375f, each   5.00

Endangered Species Type of 1993
Printed by Johann Enschedé and Sons, the Netherlands. Designed by John D. Dawson, US.

Designs: No. 376, Dendrobates pumilio. No. 377, Furcifer lateralis. No. 378, Corallus hortulanus. No. 379, Dendrobates leucomelas.

2006, Mar. 16   **Litho.**   **Perf. 12¾x12½**
376 A271 55c **multicolored** (260,000)+   1.40 1.40
377 A271 55c **multicolored** (260,000)+   1.40 1.40
378 A271 55c **multicolored** (260,000)+   1.40 1.40
379 A271 55c **multicolored** (260,000)+   1.40 1.40
a. Block of 4, #376-379   5.75 5.75
First day cover, #379a   6.75
First day cover, #376-379, each   2.40
Inscription block of 4, #379a   5.75 —
Pane of 16   23.00 —

Intl. Day of Families Type
Printed by Johann Enschedé and Sons, the Netherlands. Designed by Shelly Bartek, US.
Designs: 55c, Family at water pump. €1.25, Family preparing food.

2006, May 27   **Litho.**   **Perf. 14x13½**
380 A373 55c **multicolored** (190,000)+   1.50 1.50
First day cover   2.00
Inscription block of 4   6.00 —
Pane of 20   30.00 —
381 A373 €1.25 **multicolored** (190,000)+   3.25 3.25
First day cover   4.50
First day cover, #380-381   5.75
Inscription block of 4   13.00 —
Pane of 20   65.00 —

World Heritage Sites, France Type
Printed by Cartor Security Printing, France. Panes of 20. Designed by Robert Stein, US.
Eiffel Tower and: Nos. 382, 384c, Carcasonne. Nos. 383, 384f, Chateau de Chambord. No. 384a, Banks of the Seine. No. 384b, Provins. No. 384d, Roman Aqueduct. No. 384e, Mont Saint-Michel.

Litho. & Embossed with Foil Application
2006, June 17   **Perf. 13½x13¼**
382 A374 55c **multicolored** (220,000)+   1.50 1.50
First day cover   2.25
Inscription block of 4   6.00 —
383 A374 75c **multicolored** (220,000)+   2.00 2.00
First day cover   3.00
First day cover, #368-369   4.50
Inscription block of 4   8.00 —

Souvenir Booklet
384 Booklet, #384g-384l (41,000)+   18.00
a.-c. A374 25c any single   .65 .65
d.-f. A374 30c any single   .80 .80
g. Booklet pane of 4 #384a   2.60 —
h. Booklet pane of 4 #384b   2.60 —
i. Booklet pane of 4 #384c   2.60 —
j. Booklet pane of 4 #384d   3.25 —
k. Booklet pane of 4 #384e   3.25 —
l. Booklet pane of 4 #384f   3.25 —

No. 384 sold for €6.80.

My Dream for Peace Type of 2004
Printed by Cartor Security Printing, France. Panes of 20. Winning designs of Lions Club International children's global peace poster contest by: 55c, Klara Thein, Germany. €1, Laurensia Levina, Indonesia.

2006, Sept. 21   **Litho.**   **Perf. 13½x13**
385 A357 55c **multicolored** (200,000)+   1.60 1.60
First day cover   2.25
Inscription block of 4   6.40 —
Pane of 20   32.00 —
386 A357 €1 **multicolored** (200,000)+   3.00 3.00
First day cover   4.00
First day cover, #385-386   5.50
Inscription block of 4   12.00 —
Pane of 20   60.00 —

Flags and Coins Type
Printed by Cartor Security Printing, France. Designed by Rorie Katz, US.
No. 387 — Flag of: a, Gambia, 1 dalasi coin. b, Pakistan, 1 rupee coin. c, Afghanistan, 2 afghani coin. d, Austria, 1 euro coin. e, Germany, 50 cent coin. f, Haiti, 50 centimes coin. g, Denmark, 20 krone coin. h, Netherlands, 1 euro coin.

2006, Oct. 5   **Litho.**   **Perf. 13¼x13**
387 Sheet of 8   12.50 12.50
a.-h. A375 55c Any single   1.50 1.50
First day cover   14.50
First day cover, #387a-387h, each   5.00

A column of rouletting in the middle of the sheet separates it into two parts.

Endangered Species Type of 1993
Printed by Johann Enschedé and Sons, the Netherlands. Designed by John Rowe, US.
Designs: No. 388, Chlorocebus aethiops. No. 389, Nasalis larvatus. No. 390, Papio hamadryas. No. 391, Erythrocebus patas.

2007, Mar. 15   **Litho.**   **Perf. 12¾x12½**
388 A271 55c **multicolored** (256,000)+   1.60 1.60
389 A271 55c **multicolored** (256,000)+   1.60 1.60
390 A271 55c **multicolored** (256,000)+   1.60 1.60
391 A271 55c **multicolored** (256,000)+   1.60 1.60
a. Block of 4, #388-391   6.40 6.40
First day cover, #391a   7.50
First day cover, #388-391, each   2.60
Inscription block of 4, #391a   6.40 —
Pane of 16   26.00 —

Flags and Coins Type of 2006
Printed by Cartor Security Printing, France. Designed by Rorie Katz, US.
No. 392 — Flag of: a, Trinidad and Tobago, 50 cent coin. b, Sierra Leone, 10 cent coin. c, Hungary, 100 forint coin. d, San Marino, 2 euro coin. e, Croatia, 1 kuna coin. f, Spain, 1 euro coin. g, Kazakhstan, 100 tenge coin. h, Ireland, 5 cent coin.

2007, May 3   **Litho.**   **Perf. 13¼x13**
392 Sheet of 8 (155,000)+   13.00 13.00
a.-h. A375 55c Any single   1.60 1.60
First day cover   15.00
First day cover, #392a-392h, each   5.00

A column of rouletting in the middle of the sheet separates it into two parts.

Peaceful Visions Type of 2007

Printed by Lowe-Martin Company, Canada. Designed by Slavka Kolesar. Panes of 20.
Designs: 55c, "The Sowers." €1.25, "We All Thrive Under the Same Sky."

2007, June 1			Litho.		Perf. 13x12½	
398	A378	55c	**multicolored** (200,000)+		1.60	1.60
			First day cover			2.25
			Inscription block of 4		6.40	
			Pane of 20		32.00	—
399	A378	€1.25	**multicolored** (200,000)+		3.75	3.75
			First day cover			5.00
			First day cover, #398-399			6.25
			Inscription block of 4		15.00	—
			Pane of 20		75.00	—

World Heritage Sites, South America Type

Printed by Lowe-Martin Group, Canada. Panes of 20. Designed by Rorie Katz, US.
Designs: Nos. 400, 402e, Iguaçu National Park, Brazil. Nos. 401, 402b, Cueva de las Manos, Argentina. No. 402a, Rapa Nui, Chile. No. 402c, Machu Picchu, Peru. No. 402d, Tiwanaku, Bolivia. No. 474f, Galapagos Islands, Ecuador.

2007, Aug. 9			Litho.		Perf. 13¼x13	
400	A381	55c	**multicolored** (210,000)+		1.75	1.75
			First day cover			2.50
			Inscription block of 4		7.00	
401	A381	75c	**multicolored** (210,000)+		2.25	2.25
			First day cover			3.50
			First day cover, #400-401			5.00
			Inscription block of 4		9.00	

Souvenir Booklet

402			Booklet, #402g-402l (37,000)+		20.00	
a.-c.	A381	25c	Any single		.75	.75
d.-f.	A381	30c	Any single		.90	.90
g.			Booklet pane of 4 #402a		3.00	—
h.			Booklet pane of 4 #402b		3.00	—
i.			Booklet pane of 4 #402c		3.00	—
j.			Booklet pane of 4 #402d		3.60	—
k.			Booklet pane of 4 #402e		3.60	—
l.			Booklet pane of 4 #402f		3.60	—

Humanitarian Mail Type

Printed by Lowe-Martin Group, Canada. Panes of 10.

2007, Sept. 6			Litho.		Perf. 12½x13¼	
403	A382	75c	**multicolored** (310,000)+		2.25	2.25
			First day cover			3.25
			Inscription block of 4		9.00	
			Pane of 10		22.50	—

Space for Humanity Type

Printed by Johann Enschedé and Sons, the Netherlands. Panes of 6. Designed by Donato Giancola, US.
Designs: 65c, Space stations. €1.15, Space Station. €2.10, Space probe, Jupiter.

2007, Oct. 25			Litho.		Perf. 13½x14	
409	A383	65c	**multicolored** (306,000)+		2.00	2.00
			First day cover			2.60
			Inscription block of 4		8.00	
			Pane of 6		12.00	—
410	A383	€1.15	**multicolored** (306,000)+		3.50	3.50
			First day cover			4.75
			First day cover, #409-410			6.25
			Inscription block of 4		14.00	—
			Pane of 6		21.00	—

Souvenir Sheet

411	A383	€2.10	**multicolored** (130,000)+		6.25	6.25
			First day cover			7.25

Intl. Holocaust Remembrance Day Type

Printed by Lowe-Martin Company, Canada. Panes of 9. Designed by Matías Delfino, Argentina.

2008, Jan. 27			Litho.		Perf. 13	
412	A384	65c	**multicolored** (540,000)+		2.25	2.25
			First day cover			3.25
			Pane of 9		21.00	—

Johann Strauss Memorial, Vienna — V61

Pallas Athene Fountain, Vienna — V62

Pegasus Fountain, Salzburg V63

Statue, Belvedere Palace Gardens, Vienna — V64

Printed by Johann Enschedé and Sons, the Netherlands. Panes of 20. Designed by Rorie Katz, US.

2008, Jan. 28			Litho.		Perf. 13½x14	
413	V61	10c	**black** (320,000)+		.35	.35
			First day cover			.50
			Inscription block of 4		1.40	—
			Pane of 20		7.00	—
			Perf. 14x13½			
414	V62	15c	**black** (320,000)+		.50	.50
			First day cover			.75
			Inscription block of 4		2.00	—
			Pane of 20		10.00	—
415	V63	65c	**black** (320,000)+		2.25	2.25
			First day cover			3.25
			Inscription block of 4		9.00	—
			Pane of 20		45.00	—
416	V64	€1.40	**black** (320,000)+		4.75	4.75
			First day cover			7.00
			Inscription block of 4		19.00	—
			Pane of 20		95.00	—
			Nos. 413-416 (4)		7.85	7.85

Endangered Species Type of 1993

Printed by Johann Enschedé and Sons, the Netherlands. Designed by Suzanne Duranceau, Canada.
Designs: No. 4170, Mirounga angustirostris. No. 418, Millepora alcicornis. No. 419, Hippocampus histrix. No. 420, Physeter catodon.

2008, Mar. 6			Litho.		Perf. 12¾x12½	
417	A271	65c	**multicolored** (212,000)+		2.10	2.10
418	A271	65c	**multicolored** (212,000)+		2.10	2.10
419	A271	65c	**multicolored** (212,000)+		2.10	2.10
420	A271	65c	**multicolored** (212,000)+		2.10	2.10
a.			Block of 4, #417-420		8.40	8.40
			First day cover, #420a			9.50
			First day cover, #417-420, each			3.25
			Inscription block of 4, #420a		8.40	
			Pane of 16		34.00	—

Flags and Coins Type of 2006

Printed by Cartor Security Printing, France. Designed by Rorie Katz, US.
No. 421 — Flag of: a, Poland, 5 zloty coin. b, Latvia, 1 lat coin. c, Portugal, 1 euro coin. d, Armenia, 500 dram coin. e, Sweden, 1 krona coin. f, Cyprus, 1 euro coin. g, Slovakia, 1 koruna coin. h, Qatar, 50 dirham coin.

2008, May 8			Litho.		Perf. 13¼x13	
421			Sheet of 8 (120,000)+		18.00	18.00
a.-h.	A375	65c	Any single		2.25	2.25
			First day cover			20.00

A column of rouletting in the middle of the sheet separates it into two parts.

Graduate — V70

Stylized Person, Heart, Brain, Hands — V71

Printed by Johann Enschedé and Sons, the Netherlands. Panes of 20. Designed by Rorie Katz, US.

2008, June 6			Litho. & Embossed		Perf. 14x13¼	
427	V70	55c	**green & violet** (186,000)+		2.00	2.00
			First day cover			2.50
			Inscription block of 4		8.00	—
			Sheet of 20		40.00	—
428	V71	€1.40	**violet & green** (186,000)+		5.00	5.00
			First day cover			6.50
			First day cover, #427-428			7.75
			Inscription block of 4		20.00	—
			Sheet of 20		100.00	—

Convention on the Rights of Persons with Disabilities.

Sport for Peace Type of 2008

Printed by Johann Enschedé and Sons, the Netherlands. Panes of 9 (#429-430). Designed by Romero Britto, Brazil.
Designs: 65c, Man on rings. €1.30, €2.10, Swimmer.

2008, Aug. 8			Litho.		Perf. 14½	
429	A393	65c	**multicolored** (435,600)+		2.25	2.25
			First day cover			3.00
			Inscription block of 4		9.00	—
			Pane of 9		21.00	—
430	A393	€1.30	**multicolored** (435,600)+		4.50	4.50
			First day cover			6.00
			First day cover, #429-430			7.75
			Inscription block of 4		18.00	—
			Pane of 9		41.00	—

Souvenir Sheet
Perf. 12¾x13¼

431	A393	€2.10	**multicolored** (200,000)+		7.25	7.25
			First day cover			8.25
a.			Overprinted in sheet margin		7.25	7.25
			First day cover			8.25

2008 Summer Olympics, Beijing. No. 431a is overprinted in black "Peking 2008" and medals with UN emblem.

"We Can End Poverty" Type of 2008

Printed by Sweden Post, Sweden. Panes of 20.
Winning designs in children's art contest: 65c, By Mariam Marukian, Armenia. 75c, By Rufaro Duri, Zimbabwe, vert.

2008, Sept. 18			Litho.		Perf. 12¾x12½	
432	A395	65c	**multicolored** (160,000)+		2.25	2.25
			First day cover			3.25
			Inscription block of 4		9.00	—
			Sheet of 20		45.00	—
			Perf. 12½x12¾			
433	A395	75c	**multicolored** (160,000)+		2.60	2.60
			First day cover			3.75
			First day cover, #432-433			5.75
			Inscription block of 4		10.50	—
			Sheet of 20		52.00	—

Climate Change Types of New York and Geneva and

V72

Climate Change — V73

Printed by Lowe-Martin Group, Canada. Panes of 4. Designed by Rorie Katz, US.
No. 434 — Smokestacks with quarter of Earth in: a, LR. b, LL. c, UR. d, UL.
No. 435 — Cut trees with quarter of Earth in: a, LR. b, LL. c, UR. d, UL.
No. 436: a, Like New York #969a. b, Like New York #969b. c, Like New York #969c. d, Like New York #969d. e, Like Geneva #493a. f, Like Geneva #493b. g, Like Geneva #493c. h, Like Geneva #493d. i, Like New York #434a. j, Like Vienna #434b. k, Like Vienna #434c. l, Like Vienna #434d. m, Like New York #968a. n, Like New York #968b. o, Like New York #968c. p, Like New York #968d. q, Like Geneva #492a. r, Like Geneva #492b. s, Like Geneva #492c. t, Like Geneva #492d. u, Like Vienna #435a. v, Like Vienna #435b. w, Like Vienna #435c. x, Like Vienna #435d.
All stamps have green panels inscribed "Klimawandel."

2008, Oct. 23	Litho.	Perf. 13¼x13	
434	Sheet of 4 (120,000)+	9.00	9.00
a.-d.	V72 65c Any single	2.25	2.25
	First day cover		9.75
435	Sheet of 4 (120,000)+	16.00	16.00
a.-d.	V73 €1.15 Any single	4.00	4.00
	First day cover		17.00
	First day cover, #434-435		27.00

Souvenir Booklet

436	Booklet, #436y-436ad (31,000)+	27.00	
a.-d.	A397 30c Any single	1.00	1.00
e.-h.	G77 30c Any single	1.00	1.00
i.-l.	V72 30c Any single	1.00	1.00
m.-p.	A396 35c Any single	1.10	1.10
q.-t.	G76 35c Any single	1.10	1.10
u.-x.	V73 35c Any single	1.10	1.10
y.	Booklet pane of 4, #436a-436d	4.25	—
z.	Booklet pane of 4, #436e-436h	4.25	—
aa.	Booklet pane of 4, #436i-436l	4.25	—
ab.	Booklet pane of 4, #436m-436p	4.75	—
ac.	Booklet pane of 4, #436q-436t	4.75	—
ad.	Booklet pane of 4, #436u-436x	4.75	—

U Thant Type of 2009

Printed by Johann Enschedé and Sons, the Netherlands. Panes of 20.

Litho. With Foil Application

2009, Feb. 6		Perf. 14x13½	
437 A399	€1.15 green & multicolored (180,000)+	3.50	3.50
	First day cover		4.25
	Inscription block of 4	14.00	—
	Sheet of 20	70.00	—

Endangered Species Type of 1993

Printed by Johann Enschedé and Sons, the Netherlands. Designed by Roger Kent, United Kingdom.
Designs: No. 438, Trogonoptera brookiana. No. 439, Pandinus imperator. No. 440, Carabus intricatus. No. 441, Brachypelma smithi.

2009, Apr. 16	Litho.	Perf. 12¾x12½	
438 A271	65c multicolored (184,000)+	1.90	1.90
439 A271	65c multicolored (184,000)+	1.90	1.90
440 A271	65c multicolored (184,000)+	1.90	1.90
441 A271	65c multicolored (184,000)+	1.90	1.90
a.	Block of 4, #438-441	7.75	7.75
	First day cover, #441a		8.50
	First day cover, #438-441, each		2.75
	Inscription block of 4, #441a	7.75	—
	Pane of 16	31.00	—

World Heritage Sites, Germany Type of 2009

Printed by Johann Enschedé and Sons, the Netherlands. Panes of 20. Designed by Grit Fiedler, Germany.
Designs: Nos. 442, 444c, Palaces and Parks of Potsdam and Berlin. Nos. 443, 444e, Luther Memorials in Eisleben and Wittenberg. No. 444a, Town Hall and Roland on the Marketplace, Bremen. No. 444b, Wartburg Castle. No. 444d, Aachen Cathedral. No. 444f, Monastic Island of Reichenau.

2009, May 7	Litho.	Perf. 14x13½	
442 A400	65c multicolored (190,000)+	1.90	1.90
	First day cover		2.50
	Inscription block of 4	7.75	
443 A400	€1.40 multicolored (320,000)+	4.00	4.00
	First day cover		5.25
	First day cover, #500-501		6.75
	Inscription block of 4	16.00	

Souvenir Booklet

444	Booklet, #444g-444l (32,000)+	22.50	
a.-c.	A400 30c any single	.85	.85
d.-f.	A400 35c any single	1.00	1.00
g.	Booklet pane of 4 #444a	3.50	—
h.	Booklet pane of 4 #444b	3.50	—
i.	Booklet pane of 4 #444c	3.50	—
j.	Booklet pane of 4 #444d	4.00	—
k.	Booklet pane of 4 #444e	4.00	—
l.	Booklet pane of 4 #444f	4.00	—

2009 END-OF-YEAR ISSUES
See end of New York postage listings.

SEMI-POSTAL STAMP

AIDS Awareness Semi-postal Type
Souvenir Sheet

2002, Oct. 24	Litho.	Perf. 14½	
B1 SP1	51c + 25c multicolored (220,000)+	3.00	3.00
	First day cover, #B1		3.50

ENVELOPES

Used values for all postal stationery are for non-philatelic contemporaneous usages.

Donaupark, Vienna — VU1

Printed by Mercury-Walch Pty. Ltd. (Australia). Designed by Hannes Margreiter (Austria).
Design: 7s, Landscape. Design at lower left shows Vienna landmarks (6s), river scene (7s).

1995, Feb. 3		Litho.	
U1 VU1	6s multicolored, entire (128,000)+	2.00	2.00
	First day cancel (14,132)		2.75
U2 VU1	7s multicolored, entire (128,000)+	2.00	2.00
	First day cancel (9,684)		3.50

VU2

Printed by Mercury-Walch Pty. Ltd. (Australia).

1998, Mar. 13		Litho.	
U3 VU2	13s multicolored, entire (87,000)+	3.50	3.00
	Entire, first day cancel		3.50

VU3

Vienna International Center — VU4

Printed by Australia Post Sprintpak (Australia). Designed by Robert Stein (US).

2002, June 27		Litho.	
U4 VU3	51c multicolored, entire (93,000)+	1.50	1.50
	Entire, first day cancel		2.00
U5 VU4	€1.09 multicolored, entire (88,000)+	2.60	2.60
	Entire, first day cancel		3.25

Nos. U4-U5 Surcharged

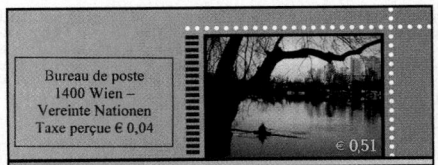

Bureau de poste
1400 Wien —
Vereinte Nationen
Taxe perçue € 0,04

2003, June 2		Litho.	
U6 VU3	51c +4c multicolored, entire	4.25	4.25
	Entire, first day cancel		3.75
U7 VU4	€1.09 +16c multicolored, entire	5.75	5.75
	Entire, first day cancel		4.75

UN Flag — VU5

Dove With Olive Branch — VU6

Printed by Government Printing Office, Austria. Designed by Rorie Katz, US.

2004, June 3		Litho.	
U8 VU5	55c multicolored, entire (53,000)+	2.10	1.40
	Entire, first day cancel		2.50
U9 VU6	€1.25 multicolored, entire (48,000)+	4.00	2.75
	Entire, first day cancel		4.50

Nos. U8-U9 Surcharged Like No. U6

2007, Sept. 3   **Litho.**
U10 VU5   55c +10c **multicolored**, entire   3.00   3.00
     Entire, first day cancel   3.75
U11 VU6   €1.25 +15c **multicolored**, entire   5.25   5.25
     Entire, first day cancel   6.00

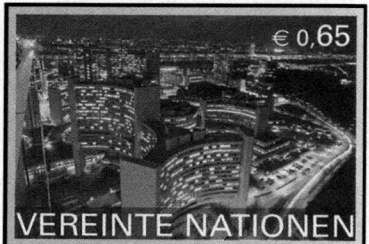

Vienna International Center — VU7

Vienna International Center — VU8

Designed by Rorie Katz, US.

2009, May 7   **Litho.**
U12 VU7   65c **multicolored**, entire   3.00   3.00
     Entire, first day cancel   3.00
U13 VU8   €1.40 **multicolored**, entire   5.00   5.00
     Entire, first day cancel   5.00

AIR LETTER SHEETS

VLS1

Printed by Joh. Enschede and Sons. Designed by Ingrid Ousland.

1982, Apr. 28   **Litho.**
UC1 VLS1   9s **multi**, *light green*, entire *(650,000)*   2.50   2.50
     First day cancel *(120,650)*   3.00

No. UC1 Surcharged in Lake

1986, Feb. 3   **Litho.**
UC2 VLS1   9s +2s **multi**, *light green*, entire
     (131,190)   52.50   60.00
     First day cancel *(18,500)*   26.00

Birds in Flight, UN Emblem VLS2

Printed by Mercury-Walch, Australia. Designed by Mieczyslaw Wasiliewski, Poland.

1987, Jan. 30   **Litho.**
UC3 VLS2   11s **bright blue**, entire *(414,000)*   3.00   3.00
     First day cancel *(48,348)*   4.00

No. UC3 Surcharged

1992, Jan. 1   **Litho.**
UC4 VLS2   11s +1s **bright blue**, entire *(80,000)*   52.50   60.00
     First day cancel   25.00

Donaupark, Vienna — VLS3

Designed by Rocco J. Callari. Printed by Mercury-Walch, Australia.

1992, Sept. 4   **Litho.**
UC5 VLS3   12s **multicolored**, entire *(200,000)+*   5.00   5.00
     First day cancel *(16,261)*   27.50

POSTAL CARDS

Olive Branch — VPC1

Bird Carrying Olive Branch — VPC2

Printed by Courvoisier. Designed by Rolf Christianson (3s), M.A. Munnawar (5s).

1982, Apr. 28   **Photo.**
UX1 VPC1   3s **multicolored**, *cream (500,000)*   1.00   1.00
     First day cancel *(93,010)*   1.65
UX2 VPC2   5s **multicolored** *(500,000)*   .75   1.00
     First day cancel *(89,502)*   1.65

Emblem of the United Nations — VPC3

Printed by Johann Enschede en Zonen, Netherlands. Designed by George Hamori, Australia.

1985, May 10   **Litho.**
UX3 VPC3   4s **multicolored** *(350,000)*   1.50   3.50
     First day cancel *(53,450)*   3.00

No. UX2 Surcharged Like No. UC4

1992, Jan. 1   **Photo.**
UX4 VPC2   5s +1s **multicolored** *(71,700)*   19.00   19.00
     First day cancel   17.00

Type of 1990
Printed by Mercury-Walch, Australia.

1992, Sept. 4   **Litho.**
UX5 V22   6s **multicolored** *(445,000)+*   2.00   3.00
     First day cancel *(16,359)*   10.00
     See No. UX9.

Type of 1985
Printed by Leigh Mardon Pty. Limited, Australia.

1993, May 7   **Litho.**
UX6 A222   5s **multicolored** *(450,000)*   16.00   16.00
     First day cancel   10.00

Donaupark, Vienna — VPC4

Printed by Leigh Mardon Pty. Limited, Australia.

1993, May 7   **Litho.**
UX7 VPC4   6s **multicolored** *(450,000)+*   4.00   4.00
     First day cancel   7.50
     See No. UX10.

No. UX6 with design of Vienna No.1 Added

1994, Jan. 1   **Litho.**
UX8 A222+G8   5s +50g **multi** *(350,000)*   2.50   4.00
     First day cancel   4.00

No. UX5 with design of Vienna #167 Added
1997, July 1   **Litho.**
UX9 V22+V32   6s +50g **multi**   2.50   2.50
     First day cancel   5.00

No. UX7 with design of Vienna #194 Added
1997, July 1
UX10 VPC4+V35   6s +1s **multi**   3.00   3.00
     First day cancel   5.00

VPC5

Designed by Günter Leidenfrost.

1998, May 20   **Litho.**
UX11 VPC5   6.50s **multicolored** *(137,000)+*   1.50   1.50
     First day cancel   2.00

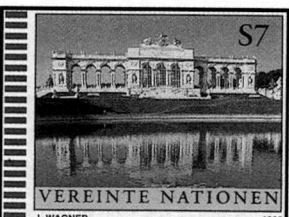

The Gloriette — VPC6

1999, Feb. 5   **Litho.**
UX12 VPC6   7s **multicolored** *(136,000)+*   2.00   2.00
     First day cancel   2.50

Type of 1983
2000, June 2   **Litho.**
UX13 V7   7s **multicolored**   2.25   2.25
     First day cancel   2.25

Clock Tower, Graz, Austria — VPC7

Printed by Johann Enschedé and Sons, the Netherlands. Designed by Robert Stein, US.

2002, Mar. 1 Litho.
UX14 VPC7 51c **multicolored** *(83,000)+* 1.00 1.00
    First day cancel 1.25

No. UX14 Surcharged

2003, June 2 Litho.
UX15 VPC7 51c +4c **multicolored** 2.75 2.75
    First day cancel 2.75

Vienna International Center — VPC8

Printed by Government Printing Office, Austria. Designed by Rorie Katz, US.

2004, June 3 Litho.
UX16 VPC8 55c **multicolored** *(63,000)+* 2.60 1.25
    First day cancel 3.00

No. UX16 Surcharged Like No. UX15

2007, Sept. 3 Litho.
UX17 VPC8 55c +10c **multicolored**, entire 3.75 3.75
    Entire, first day cancel 4.50

Vienna International Center — VPC9

2009, May 7 Litho.
UX18 VPC9 65c **multicolored** 3.50 3.50
    First day cancel 3.50

U.N. SOUVENIR CARDS

No. 39

These cards were issued by the United Nations Postal Administration and were not valid for postage.

Each card bears reproductions of UN stamps and a statement by the Secretary-General in English.

Values are for mint cards without cancels.

SC1 World Health Day, Apr. 7, 1972. Card of 5: #43, 102, 156, 207, 228. .65

A second printing shows several minor differences.

SC2 Art on UN Stamps, Nov. 17, 1972. Card of 11: #170, 171, 173, 174, 180, 183, 201, 202, 203, 224, 232. #201, 202 form a simulated setenant pair .45
SC3 Disarmament Decade, Mar. 9, 1973. Card of 5: #133, 147, 177, 227, 234. .50
SC4 Declaration of Human Rights, 25th Anniversary, Nov. 16, 1973. Card of 10: #13, 22, 29, 39, 47, 58, 68, 121, 190, 242 .75
SC5 UPU centenary, Mar. 22, 1974. Card of 7: #17, 18, 219, 246; Geneva 18, 39, 40. .75
SC6 World Population Year, Oct. 18, 1974. Card of 5: #151, 152, 153, 252, 253; Geneva 43, 44. 4.00
SC7 Peaceful Uses of Outer Space, Mar. 14, 1975. Card of 6: #112, 113, 256, 257; Geneva 46, 47. 2.00
SC8 UN Peace Keeping Operations, Nov. 21, 1975. Card of 9: #52, 111, 118, 139, 160, 265, 266; Geneva 55, 56. 2.00
SC9 World Federation of United Nations Associations, Mar. 12, 1976. Card of 5: #154, 155, 272, 273; Geneva 57. 2.00
SC10 World Food Council, Nov. 19, 1976. Card of 6: #116, 117, 218, 280; Geneva 17, 63. 2.50

SC11 World Intellectual Property Organization (WIPO), Mar. 11, 1977. Card of 15: #17, 23, 25, 31, 33, 41, 43, 49, 59, 86, 90, 123, 281, 282; Geneva 64. 2.50
SC12 Combat Racism, Sept. 19, 1977. Card of 8: #220, 221, 287, 288; Geneva 19, 20, 69, 70. 2.50
SC13 Namibia, May 5, 1978. Card of 10: #240, 241, 263, 264, 296, 297; Geneva 34, 53, 54, 76. 1.00
SC14 Intl. Civil Aviation Organization, June 12, 1978. Card of 6: #31, 32, 298, 299; Geneva 77, 78. 2.50
SC15 Intl. Year of the Child, May 4, 1979. Card of 9: #5, 97, 161, 162, 163, 310, 311; Geneva 84, 85. .75
SC16 Intl. Court of Justice, Nov. 9, 1979. Card of 6: #88, 89, 314, 315; Geneva 87, 88. .75
SC17 UN Decade for Women, Mar. 7, 1980. Card of 4: #258, 318; Geneva 90; Vienna 9. 10.00
SC18 Economic and Social Council, Nov. 7, 1980. Card of 8: #65, 66, 341, 342; Geneva 96, 97; Vienna 15, 16. .75
SC19 Intl. Year of Disabled Persons, Mar. 6, 1981. Card of 6: #344, 345; Geneva 99, 100; Vienna 18, 19. .65
SC20 New and Renewable Sources of Energy, May 29, 1981. Card of 4: #348, 349; Geneva 102; Vienna 21. 1.00
SC21 Human Environment, Mar. 19, 1982. Card of 5: #230, 371; Geneva 26, 107; Vienna 25 .75
SC22 Exploration and Peaceful Uses of Outer Space, June 11, 1982. Card of 7: #112, 256, 373; Geneva 46, 109, 110; Vienna 27. 1.40
SC23 Safety at Sea, Mar. 18, 1983. Card of 6: #123, 124, 394, 395; Geneva 114, 115; Vienna 31, 32. 1.10
SC24 Trade and Development, June 6, 1983. Card of 11: #129, 130, 274, 275, 397, 398; Geneva 58, 117, 118; Vienna 31, 32. 1.50
SC25 Intl. Conference on Population, Feb. 3, 1984. Card of 10: #151, 153, 252, 253, 417, 418; Geneva 43, 44, 121; Vienna 39. 2.00
SC26 Intl. Youth Year, Nov. 15, 1984. Card of 5: #441, 442; Geneva 128; Vienna 46, 47. 3.00
SC27 ILO Turin Center, Feb. 1, 1985. Card of 8: #25, 200, 244, 443; Geneva 37, 129, 130; Vienna 48. 2.75
SC28 Child Survival Campaign, Nov. 22, 1985. Card of 6: #466, 467; Geneva 138, 139; Vienna 55, 56. 3.00

SC29 Stamp Collecting, May 22, 1986. Card of 5: #278, 473; Geneva 61, 147; Vienna 63. 8.25

No. 29 with stitch marks has been removed from the Ameripex program. Value is one-half that of unstitched copy.

SC30 Intl. Peace Year, June 20, 1986. Card of 6: #475, 476; Geneva 148, 149; Vienna 64, 65. 4.00
SC31 Shelter for the Homeless, Mar. 13, 1987. Card of 6: #495, 496; Geneva 154, 155; Vienna 68, 69. 2.50
SC32 Immunize Every Child, Nov. 20, 1987. Card of 13: #44, 103, 157, 208, 294, 517, 518; Vienna 76, 77. 3.00
SC33 Intl. Volunteer Day, May 6, 1988. Card of 10: #239, 367, 524, 525; Geneva 103, 167, 168; Vienna 23, 82, 83. 4.00
SC34 Health in Sports, June 17, 1988. Card of 6: #526, 527; Geneva 169, 170; Vienna 84, 85. 5.00
SC35 World Bank, Jan. 27, 1989. Card of 8: #86-87, 546-547; Geneva 173-174; Vienna 88-89. 5.00
SC36 World Weather Watch, Apr. 21, 1989. Card of 10: #49-50, 188-189, 550-551; Geneva 176-177; Vienna 91-92. 5.00
SC37 Fight AIDS Worldwide, Mar. 16, 1990. Card of 6, #573-574; Geneva 184-185; Vienna 99-100 6.50
SC38 Crime Prevention, Sept. 13, 1990. Card of 6: #580-581; Geneva 191-192; Vienna 106-107. 6.00
SC39 Economic Commission for Europe, Mar. 15, 1991. Card of 12: #584-587; Geneva 195-198; Vienna 110-113. 6.00
SC40 Rights of the Child, June 14, 1991. Card of 6: #593-594; Geneva 203-204; Vienna 117-118. 7.00
SC41 Mission to Planet Earth, Sept. 4, 1992, Card of 6; #609-610; Geneva 220-221; Vienna 133-134 17.00
SC42 Science and Technology for Development, Oct. 2, 1992, Card of 6; #611-612; Geneva 222-223; Vienna 135-136 15.00
SC43 Healthy Environment, May 7, 1993, Card of 6; #624-625; Geneva #232-233; Vienna #147-148 17.50
SC44 Peace, Sept. 21, 1993, Card of 12, #629-632; Geneva #236-239; Vienna #152-155 16.00

No. 44 exists overprinted in gold with Hong Kong '94 emblem.

SC45 Intl. Year of the Family, Feb. 4, 1994, Card of 6; #637-638; Geneva #244-245; Vienna #160-161 13.50

SC46	Population & Development, 1994, Card of 9, #151, 651-652; Geneva #43, 258-259; Vienna #39, 174-175	12.50
SC47	World Summit for Social Development, 1995, Card of 3, #656; Geneva #263; Vienna #179	10.50
SC48	Intl. Youth Year, 1995, Card of 9, #441, 661-662; Geneva #128, 268-269; Vienna #46, 184-185	16.00
SC49	WFUNA, 1996, Card of 3, #671; Geneva #277; Vienna #193	14.00
SC50	UNICEF, 1996, Card of 6, #688-689; Geneva #294-295; Vienna #210-211	9.00
SC51	Philately, 1997, Card of 6, #714-715; Geneva #312-313; Vienna #228-229	12.50
SC52	Peacekeeping, #737-738; Geneva #325-326; Vienna #242-243	9.00

SC53	Universal Declaration of Human Rights, #739-740; Geneva #327-328; Vienna #244-245	9.00
SC54	UPU, #767a; Geneva #346a; Vienna #263a	5.00
SC55	Respect for Refugees, #787; Geneva #365; Vienna #282	6.00
SC56	Intl. Volunteers Year, #793-794; Geneva #371-372; Vienna #288-289	4.00
SC57	Johannesburg Summit on Sustainable Development, #828-831; Geneva #396-399; Vienna #318-321	5.00
SC58	International Year of Freshwater, #846-8471; Geneva #411-412; Vienna #333-334	4.00
SC59	Japanese Peace Bell, 50th Anniv., #865; Geneva #425; Vienna #349	4.00

SC60	Nature's Wisdom, #885-886; Geneva #440-441; Vienna #364-365	4.00
SC61	Intl. Day of Families, #913-914, Geneva #457-458, Vienna #380-381	4.00
SC62	As #SC61, with Washington 2006 World Philatelic Exhibition emblem and text	17.50
	No. SC62 was only sold canceled.	
SC63	Peaceful Visions, #932, Geneva #470-471, Vienna #398-399	4.00

A "souvenir card" depicting no stamps was released in 2008 with the "We Can End Poverty" set. It sold for $1.75.

U.N. PROOFS

Proofs of United Nations stamps are known in four basic types: Die Proofs, Trial Color Proofs, Progressive Color Proofs, and Imperforate Plate Proofs on gummed stamp paper.

Die Proofs (PD suffix) for United Nations stamps show the design of the issued stamp. They are usually imperforate singles printed on stamp paper, that are either affixed to a backing paper that is a component of a printer's card, or affixed directly to a printer's card. These cards usually have a handstamp denoting the status of the proof (approved, approved with corrections, not approved, etc.). Many cards have signatures of UN Postal Administration officials. Cards with an "approved" handstamp and/or signature do not always contain proofs having the designs of the actual stamp produced for sale. As most proof cards have a handstamp, the listings mention specific handstamps only when it is critical to distinguishing items. Items not affixed to cards that are indistinguishable from imperforate singles of the issued stamps are not listed, even though they may have come from "stock sheet style" proof cards that have approval handstamps. Items affixed to art boards available to the general public are not considered to be proofs unless they are identified, usually by handstamps, that they are proofs. Die proofs of sheet layouts showing marginal inscriptions only exist, but are beyond the scope of these listings.

Trial Color Proofs (TC suffix) show the design of the stamp, but with one or more colors differing from that of the actual stamp. Items will be listed as trial color proofs when they differ significantly from the issued color. As evidenced by printer's identification numbers on some trial color proof cards, shades of individual items may differ slightly, but two similar yet discrete shades may fall under one color description. Trial colors can sometimes be found on cards with die proofs.

Progressive Color Proofs (PP suffix) are a set of color proofs containing the number of items stated in the listing. Values, therefore, are for the set of singles (unless otherwise mentioned in the description), not a single progressive color proof from that set. Numbers in parentheses represent the total number of complete sets that were created. Partial sets are not listed if complete sets are known.

Imperforate Plate Proofs (PI suffix) are usually found on gummed stamp paper. Any exceptions are noted in the listing description. Numbers in parentheses represent the total number of imperforate proof stamps created. Many items have inked fingerprints on the reverse as a security device. Values are for pairs unless otherwise stated. Many gutter pairs will have creases. Some gutter pairs will have marginal inscriptions. These are worth more.

Organization of listings Listings have all of the New York, Geneva and Vienna stamps and souvenir cards for any set all together. The first part of an item's catalogue number is the same catalogue number as shown in the listings for stamps and postal stationery. The prefix "G" is before the catalogue number for items from Geneva; prefix "V" for items from Vienna. Items with prefix "SC" are souvenir cards, and catalogue numbers without prefix are from New York. The suffix describing the type of proof follows the catalogue number. Die proofs (suffix PD) are the first proof category in the listings, and will be followed by the other categories in the same order as listed above. Each proof category will list New York items first, followed by Geneva items, Vienna items, and then souvenir cards.

Often cards of proofs will contain all of the items in an issued set. The catalogue numbers for cards that contain New York, Geneva and Vienna proofs are organized by the highest New York catalogue number of the various die proof items in the set. If there are no New York items in the card, then the numbering will be organized by the highest Geneva or Vienna catalogue number in the card of die proofs. Cards that contain both die proofs and trial color proofs are catalogued under the die proofs.

Numbers in parentheses represent the total number of items created. The number of items coming in part or in total from printer's archives are approximations. Listings for single proofs affixed to cards do not usually mention that they are affixed to a card. Cards containing more than one proof will have a minor letter following the PD suffix, and the listing will detail the component parts, as some cards may in the future be broken down by owners into individual proof items. Cutting up cards, however, may destroy their value, as listings are often based on the presence of the handstamp. Removing proofs from the card will lower their value, as it may then be impossible to distinguish them from imperforate singles.

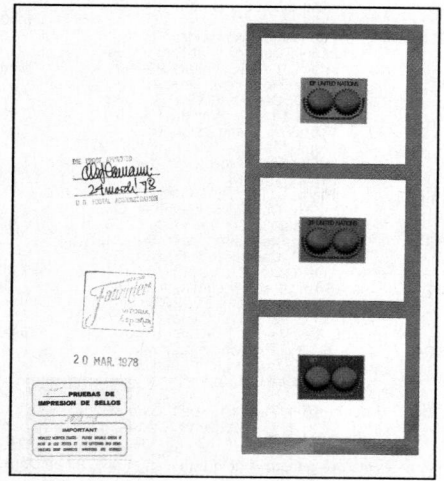

No. 303PDa — A Typical Die Proof Card

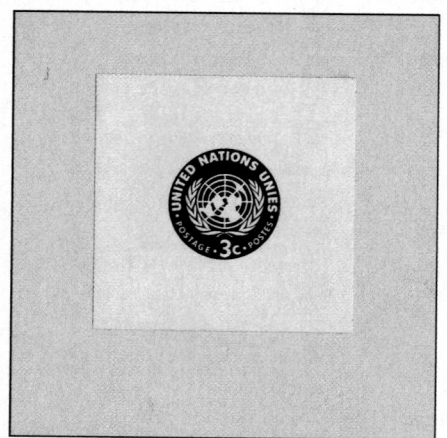

No. U1TC in Black — A Typical Trial Color Proof

Sheets of 50 of No. V1PP — A Typical Progressive Proof Set

No. 1PI — A Typical Pair of Imperforate Plate Proofs

New York #1-11
Definitives

1951

1PD	(1)	600.
2PD	(3)	500.
3PD	(3)	450.
3PDa	Card, #3PD, 3TC blue violet (1)	575.
4PD	(1)	600.
5PD	(1)	575.
5PDa	Card, #5PD, 5TC dark blue violet	1,150.
6PD	(1)	600.
6PDa	Card, #1PD, 6PD (3)	3,100.
7PD	(1)	600.
8PD	(4)	300.
9PD	(1)	600.
9PDa	Card, #4PD, 7PD, 9PD, essays of #7, 9 (1)	1,850.
9PDb	Card, #9PD, 9TC green (1)	825.
10PD	(1)	500.
11PD	(4)	475.
2TC	indigo (1)	—
3TC	red violet (2)	—
3TC	dark red (2)	350.
3TC	red orange (1)	450.
3TC	carmine (3)	—
3TC	orange red (3)	—
3TCa	Card, #3TC carmine, #3TC orange red (1)	700.
5TC	orange red (1)	750.
5TC	brown (1)	750.
5TC	bright blue (1)	—
5TC	light blue (1)	—
5TC	dark blue (1)	—
5TC	black (1)	—
5TC	red orange (1)	—
5TCa	Card, #5TC black, 5TC brown (1)	925.
10TC	black (1)	—
10TC	dark green (1)	—
10TCa	Card, #10TC blue green , #10TC yellow green (1)	—
11TC	dark red, 2 impressions side by side (1)	—
11TC	purple, 2 impressions side by side (1)	—
11TCa	dark blue (2 impressions side by side below two impressions of #5TC (1)	—
1PI	Pair (25)	1,000.
2PI	Pair (5)	—
5PI	Pair (42)	350.
	Vert. pair with horiz. gutter (8)	375.
6PI	Pair (25)	—
8PI	Pair (50)	500.
11PI	Pair (3)	800.

Imperforate printer's waste has impression of No. 6 with stamps of other countries.

New York #12
Signing of UN Charter, 7th Anniv.

1952

12PD	(3)	—
12TC	dark blue (2)	—
12TC	black (2)	—
12TC	green (2)	—
12TC	light blue (1)	—

New York #13-14
Universal Declaration of Human Rights, 4th Anniv.

1952

13PDa	Card, #13PD and two #13TC in slightly different shades (1)	975.
14PDa	Card, #14PD and two #14TC in slightly different shades (1)	975.
14PDb	Card, #13PD, 14PD (1)	—

New York #15-16
Protection for Refugees

1953

15PD	(1)	450.
16PD	(1)	450.
16PDa	Card, #15PD, 16PD (3)	775.
16PDb	Card, #15PD, 16PD, 16TC indigo (1)	875.
16PDc	Card, #16PDb and card, #15PD, 15TC, 16PD (some staining) (1)	575.

15PI	Pair (80)	400.
	Vert. pair with horiz. gutter (20)	400.
16PI	Pair (80)	—
	Vert. pair with horiz. gutter (20)	—

New York #17-18
Universal Postal Union

1953

17PDa	Card, #17PD, 17TC red brown, 17TC ultramarine, 17TC blue	2,000.
17PDb	Card, #17PD, 17TC violet brown (1)	—
18PDa	Card, #18PD, 18TC bright blue (1)	—
18PDb	Card, #17PDa, 18PDa (1)	—
17PI	Pair (82)	200.
	Horiz. pair with vert. gutter (8)	—
18PI	Pair (84)	200.
	Horiz. pair with vert. gutter (6)	—

Approximately half of PI items are stained and glued on cardboard. Imperforate printer's waste has No. 17 with No. 18 and impressions of other items on the reverse.

New York #19-20
Technical Assistance

1953

20PDa	Card, #19PD-20PD, #19TC-20TC in slightly different shades (2)	1,250.

New York #21-22
Human Rights Day

1953

22PDa	Card, #23PD-24PD, two #23TC, two #24TC in slightly different shades (2)	1,600.
21PI	Pair (40)	350.
	Vert. pair with horiz. gutter (10)	—
22PI	Pair (40)	350.
	Vert. pair with horiz. gutter (10)	—

New York #23-24
Food and Agricultural Organization

1954

24PDa	Card, #23PD-24PD, two #23TC-24TC in slightly different colors (2)	1,600.
23PI	Pair (40)	225.
	Vert. pair with horiz. gutter (10)	—
24PI	Pair (40)	225.
	Vert. pair with horiz. gutter (120)	—

New York #25-26
International Labor Organization

1954

25PDa	Card, #25PD, two #25TC in slightly different shades, three #26TC in purple shades (2)	2,400.
26PDa	Card, #25PD-26PD, #26TC in slightly different shade (2)	
25PI	Pair (40)	350.
	Vert. pair with horiz. gutter (10)	—
26PI	Pair (40)	350.
	Vert. pair with horiz. gutter (10)	—

New York #27-28
United Nations Day

1954

27PI	Pair (40)	300.
	Horiz. pair with vert. gutter (10)	—
28PI	Pair (40)	300.
	Horiz. pair with vert. gutter (10)	—

New York #29-30
Human Rights Day

1954

29PD	(5)	350.
30PD	(5)	350.
29PI	Pair (40)	350.
	Vert. pair with horiz. gutter (10)	—
30PI	Pair (40)	—
	Vert. pair with horiz. gutter (10)	—

New York #31-32
International Civil Aviation Organization

1955

31PDa	Card, #31PD, two #31TC in different blue shades (3)	
32PDa	Card, #32PD, three #32TC in different red shades (3)	1,400.
32PDb	Card, #31PD-32PD, #31TC-#32TC in different shades, three essays of #31-32 (1)	1,650.
31TC	black (1)	—
32TC	black (1)	—
31PI	Pair (171)	225.
	Horiz. pair with vert. gutter (26)	—
32PI	Pair (130)	225.
	Horiz. pair with vert. gutter (20)	—

No. 31PI exists with and without punch holes.

New York #33-34
UN Educational, Scientific and Cultural Organization

1955

33PD	(1)	—
33PDa	Card, #33PD, two #33TC in different shades (3)	700.
34PD	(1)	—

34PDa	Card, #34PD, two #34TC in different shades (3)	700.
33TC	black (1)	—
34TC	black (1)	—
33PI	Pair (128)	—
	Horiz. pair with vert. gutter (16)	—
34PI	Pair (90)	—
	Horiz. pair with vert. gutter (10)	—

No. 33PI exists with and without punch holes.

New York #35-38
UN, 10th Anniv.

1955

35PDa	Card, #35PD, two #35TC in different shades (2)	2,400.
35PDb	Card, #35PD, #35TC in lighter shade (1)	—
36PDa	Card, #36PD, two #36TC in different shades (3)	—
37PDa	Card, #37PD, two #37TC in different shades (3)	—
38PD	Sheet of #38 with security punches (2)	1,950.
38bPD	Watermarked sheet of nine #38b and nine #38c with security punches (1)	4,250.
38cPD	Watermarked sheet of nine #38c with security punches (1)	5,000.
35TC	carmine (1)	—
35TC	black (1)	—
36TC	black (1)	—
37TC	black (1)	—
38PP	4 items (9 souvenir sheets)	—
38PP	Retouch, 2 items (9 souvenir sheets)	—
35PI	Pair (130)	325.
	Horiz. pair with vert. gutter (20)	—
36PI	Pair (130)	325.
	Horiz. pair with vert. gutter (20)	—
37PI	Pair (180)	325.
	Horiz. pair with vert. gutter (30)	—
38PI	Pairs of souvenir sheets (16)	3,000.
	Single with sheet margin (4)	850.
	Retouch Pairs of souvenir sheets (4)	—
	Retouch, single with sheet margin (1)	—

No. 37PI exists with and without punch holes.

New York #39-40
Human Rights Day

1955

39PDa	Card, #39PD, two #39TC in different shades (2)	850.
40PDa	Card, #40PD, two #40TC in different shades (2)	850.
39TC	black (1)	—
40TC	black (1)	—
40TCa	Card, #39TC in aquamarine, #40TC in dark green and two essays (1)	1,250.
39PI	Pair (180)	425.
	Vert. pair with horiz. gutter (20)	—
40PI	Pair (130)	425.
	Vert. pair with horiz. gutter (20)	—

No. 39PI exists with and without punch holes.

New York #41-42
International Telecommunication Union

1956

41PD	(2)	300.
42PD	(2)	300.
41PI	Pair (40)	350.
	Horiz. pair with vert. gutter (10)	—
42PI	Pair (40)	350.
	Horiz. pair with vert. gutter (10)	—

New York #43-44
World Health Organization

1956

43PD	(2)	225.
44PD	(2)	225.
43PI	Pair (40)	250.
	Vert. pair with horiz. gutter (10)	—
44PI	Pair (40)	250.
	Vert. pair with horiz. gutter (10)	—

Nos. 43PI-44PI have "Colour approved" handstamped in margin.

New York #45-46
General Assembly

1956

45PD	(7)	275.
46PD	(7)	275.
45PI	Pair (40)	350.
	Horiz. pair with vert. gutter (10)	—
46PI	Pair (40)	350.
	Horiz. pair with vert. gutter (10)	—

New York #47-48
Human Rights Day

1956

47PD	(2)	375.
48PD	(2)	375.
47TC	red (3)	400.
47TC	carmine (3)	—
48TC	blue (6)	400.
47PI	Pair (40)	300.
	Horiz. pair with vert. gutter (10)	—
48PI	Pair (40)	300.
	Horiz. pair with vert. gutter (10)	—

New York #49-50
World Meteorological Organization

1957

49PD	(2)	275.
50PD	(2)	275.
49TC	blue (3)	250.
50TC	carmine rose (3)	250.
49PI	Pair (40)	—
	Vert. pair with horiz. gutter (10)	—
50PI	Pair (40)	—
	Vert. pair with horiz. gutter (10)	—

Nos. 49PI-50PI have "Colour approved" handstamped in margin.

New York #51-52
UN Emergency Force

1957

51PD	(7)	275.
52PD	(7)	275.
51PI	Pair (40)	—
	Horiz. pair with vert. gutter (10)	—
52PI	Pair (40)	—
	Horiz. pair with vert. gutter (10)	—

New York #55-56
Security Council

1957

55PD	(6)	275.
56PD	(11)	275.
55TC	golden brown (6)	—
55TC	brown (5)	—
55PI	Pair (40)	—
	Vert. pair with horiz. gutter (10)	—
56PI	Pair (40)	—
	Vert. pair with horiz. gutter (10)	—

New York #57-58
Human Rights Day

1957

57PD	(12)	275.
58PD	(9)	275.
57TC	light red brown (1)	300.
58TC	dark blue (3)	—
58TC	gray green (6)	300.
57PI	Pair (50)	—
58PI	Pair (50)	—

Nos. 57TC-58TC have handstamps with "Approved" crossed out.

New York #59-60
International Atomic Energy Agency

1958

59PD	(12)	250.
60PD	(13)	250.
59TC	emerald (7)	—
59TC	black (7)	350.
60TC	black (8)	350.
59PI	With security punch (358 pairs)	—
	Cross gutter block, with security punch (4)	—
	Horiz. pair with vert. gutter, with security punch (52)	—
	Vert. pair with horiz. gutter, with security punch (32)	—
60PI	Pair with security punch (358)	—
	Cross gutter block, with security punch (4)	—
	Horiz. pair with vert. gutter, with security punch (52)	—
	Vert. pair with horiz. gutter, with security punch (32)	—

New York #61-62
Central Hall, Site of First General Assembly Meeting

1958

61PD	(8)	275.
62PD	(8)	275.
61TC	black (3)	275.
62TC	black (3)	275.
61PI	With security punch (358 pairs)	—
	Cross gutter block, with security punch (4)	—
	Horiz. pair with vert. gutter, with security punch (32)	—
	Vert. pair with horiz. gutter, with security punch (52)	—
62PI	Pair with security punch (358)	—
	Cross gutter block, with security punch (4)	—
	Horiz. pair with vert. gutter, with security punch (32)	—
	Vert. pair with horiz. gutter, with security punch (52)	—

New York #63-64
UN Emblem

1958

63PD	(21)	250.
64PD	(7)	250.
64PDa	Card, #64PD, #64TC Prussian blue, #64TC ultramarine (2)	975.
63TC	brown orange (3)	300.
64TC	light blue (1)	300.
64TC	ultramarine (1)	500.
63PI	Pair (80)	—

	Vert. pair with horiz. gutter (20)	—
64PI	Pair (80)	—
	Vert. pair with horiz. gutter (20)	—

No. 63TC is affixed to cards inscribed "D."

New York #65-66
Economic and Social Council

1958

65PD	(8)	250.
66PD	(7)	250.
65TC	black (2)	325.
65TC	orange brown (1)	—
65TC	green (1)	—
65TC	red orange (1)	—
66TC	black (2)	325.
65PI	Pair with security punch (358)	—
	Cross gutter block, with security punch (4)	—
	Horiz. pair with vert. gutter, with security punch (32)	—
	Vert. pair with horiz. gutter, with security punch (52)	—
66PI	Pair with security punch (358)	—
	Cross gutter block, with security punch (4)	—
	Horiz. pair with vert. gutter, with security punch (32)	—
	Vert. pair with horiz. gutter, with security punch (52)	—

New York #67-68
Human Rights Day

1958

67PD	(5)	300.
68PD	(5)	300.
67TC	black (2)	425.
68TC	black (1)	425.
67PI	Pair (358)	—
	Cross gutter block, with security punch and "SPECIMEN" ovpt. (4)	—
	Horiz. pair with vert. gutter, with security punch and "SPECIMEN" ovpt. (52)	—
	Vert. pair with horiz. gutter, with security punch and "SPECIMEN" ovpt. (32)	—
68PI	Pair (358)	—
	Cross gutter block, with security punch and "SPECIMEN" ovpt. (4)	—
	Horiz. pair with vert. gutter, with security punch and "SPECIMEN" ovpt. (52)	—
	Vert. pair with horiz. gutter, with security punch and "SPECIMEN" ovpt. (32)	—

Essays of Nos. 67 and 68 without denominations exist in issued colors and black.

New York #69-70
New York City Building, Flushing Meadows

1959

69PD	(7)	300.
70PD	(7)	300.
69PI	Pair (216)	—
	Cross gutter block (3)	—
	Horiz. pair with vert. gutter (54)	—
	Vert. pair with horiz. gutter (24)	—
70PI	Pair (216)	—
	Cross gutter block (3)	—
	Horiz. pair with vert. gutter (54)	—
	Vert. pair with horiz. gutter (24)	—

New York #71-72
Economic Commission for Europe

1959

71PD	(7)	275.
72PD	(7)	275.
71PI	Pair (216)	—
	Cross gutter block (3)	—
	Horiz. pair with vert. gutter (24)	—
	Vert. pair with horiz. gutter (54)	—
72PI	Pair (216)	—
	Cross gutter block (3)	—
	Horiz. pair with vert. gutter (24)	—
	Vert. pair with horiz. gutter (54)	—

New York #73-74
Trusteeship Council

1959

73PD	(5)	300.
74PD	(5)	300.
73TC	orange red (2)	—
73PI	Pair (216)	—
	Cross gutter block (3)	—
	Horiz. pair with vert. gutter (24)	—
	Vert. pair with horiz. gutter (54)	—
74PI	Pair (216)	—
	Cross gutter block (3)	—
	Horiz. pair with vert. gutter (24)	—
	Vert. pair with horiz. gutter (54)	—

No. 73TC has handstamps with words "Color and" crossed out.

New York #75-76
World Refugee Year

1959

75PD	(6)	300.
76PD	(5)	300.
75TC	purple & red (3)	—
76TC	olive & Prussian blue (2)	—
76TC	purple & green (3)	—
75PI	Pair (216)	—

	Cross gutter block (3)	—
	Horiz. pair with vert. gutter (54)	—
	Vert. pair with horiz. gutter (24)	—
76PI	Pair (216)	—
	Cross gutter block (3)	—
	Horiz. pair with vert. gutter (54)	—
	Vert. pair with horiz. gutter (24)	—

New York #77-78
Chaillot Palace

1960

77PD	(4)	250.
78PD	(4)	250.
78TC	brown & blue green(1)	325.
78TC	blue & red (1)	325.
78TCa	Card, #78TC brown & blue green, #78TC blue &red (1)	—
77PI	Pair (25)	—
78PI	Pair (25)	—

New York #79-80
Economic Commission for Asia and the Far East

1960

79PD	(1)	—
80PDa	Card, #79PD, #80PD (1)	—
80PDb	Card, two #79PD, two #80PD (1)	1,250.
79PI	Pair (50)	—
80PI	Pair (50)	—

New York #81-82
World Forestry Congress

1960

81PD	(2)	425.
82PDa	Card, #81PD-82PD (3)	350.
81PI	Pair (100)	—
82PI	Pair (100)	—

New York #83-85
UN, 15th Anniv.

1960

83PD	(5)	325.
84PD	(6)	325.
85PD	(2)	700.
83TC	black (1)	—
83TC	bright blue (2)	—
83PI	Pair (144)	—
	Cross gutter block (2)	—
	Horiz. pair with vert. gutter (36)	—
	Vert. pair with horiz. gutter (16)	—
84PI	Pair (119)	—
	Cross gutter block (2)	—
	Horiz. pair with vert. gutter (36)	—
	Vert. pair with horiz. gutter (16)	—
85PI	Pair (16)	—
	Cross gutter block (2)	—
	Horiz. pair with vert. gutter (8)	—
	Vert. pair with horiz. gutter (8)	—

An essay in blue has diagonal lines in background rather than cross-hatching.

New York #86-87
International Bank for Reconstruction and Development

1960

87PDa	Card, 2 #86PD, 2 #87PD (2)	1,150.
87PDb	Card, #86PD-87PD with simulated perforations (1)	—
86PI	Pair (100)	—
87PI	Pair (100)	—

New York #88-89
International Court of Justice

1961

89PDa	Card, #88PD-89PD affixed, dated 10/31/61 (2)	450.
89PDb	Card, 2 #88PD, 2 #89PD, disapproved (2)	—
88PI	Pair (100)	—
89PI	Pair (100)	—

New York #90-91
International Monetary Fund

1961

91PDa	Card with 2 #90PD, 2 #91PD in slightly different shades (1)	1,300.
90PI	Pair (100)	—
91PI	Pair (50)	—

New York #92
Abstract Flags

1961

92PI	Pair (80)	—
	Horiz. pair with vert. gutter (20)	—

New York #93-94
Economic Commission for Latin America

1961

93PDa	Card, 2 #93PD, 2 essays of #94 (2)	—
94PDa	Card, 2 #94PD (1)	400.

Essays of No. 94 lack serifs in "1's."

New York #95-96
Economic Commission for Africa

1961

96PDa	Card with #95PD-96PD affixed (8)	500.
95PP	4 items (100)	—
96PP	8 items (100)	—
95PI	Pair (100)	—
96PI	Pair (100)	—

New York #97-99
UN Children's Fund (UNICEF)

1961

99PDa	Card, #97PD-99PD, with approval handstamp (3)	1,050.
99PDb	Card, #97PD-99PD, no approval handstamp (5)	600.
97PP	4 items (80)	—
	Vert. pair with horiz. gutter (10)	—
98PP	4 items (80)	—
	Vert. pair with horiz. gutter (10)	—
99PP	4 items (80)	—
	Vert. pair with horiz. gutter (10)	—
97PI	Pair (80)	—
	Vert. pair with horiz. gutter (20)	—
98PI	Pair (80)	—
	Vert. pair with horiz. gutter (20)	—
99PI	Pair (80)	—
	Vert. pair with horiz. gutter (20)	—

New York #100-101
Housing and Urban Development Program

1962

100PD	With approval handstamp (3)	200.
101PD	With approval handstamp (3)	200.
100PI	Pair with oval "Harrison's Photogravure Specimen" handstamp (25)	350.
101PI	Pair with oval "Harrison's Photogravure Specimen" handstamp (25)	350.

Three essays each of Nos. 100 and 101 have larger numerals than issued stamps are are on cards marked "disapproved."

New York #102-103
Malaria Eradication Campaign

1962

102PD	(5)	400.
103PD	(5)	400.

New York #104-107
Definitives

1962

104PD	(5)	400.
105PD	(7)	425.
106PD	With approval handstamp & signature (2)	400.
107PD		500.
104PI	Pair with oval "Harrison's Photogravure Specimen" handstamp (25)	250.
105PI	Pair with oval "Harrison's Photogravure Specimen" handstamp (25)	250.
107PI	Pair with oval "Harrison's Photogravure Specimen" handstamp (25)	250.
	Same, without handstamp (25)	400.

Three essays of No. 106 have indistinct line between "U" and "N," and are on cards marked "disapproved."

New York #108-109
Death of Dag Hammarskjold, 1st Anniv.

1962

108PDa	Card, #108PD, essay of #109 (1)	—
109PDa	Card, #109PD, essay of #108 (1)	—
109PDb	Card, #108PD-#109PD (2)	600.
108PI	Pair (80)	—
	Vert. pair with horiz. gutter (20)	—
109PI	Pair (80)	—
	Vert. pair with horiz. gutter (20)	—

Essays of Nos 108-109 lack denomination.

New York #110-111
UN Operation in the Congo

1962

111PDa	Card, 3 #110PD, 3 #111PD (1)	1,150.
111PDb	Card, #111PD, essay of #110 (2)	550.
110PP	4 items (80)	—
	Horiz. pair with vert. gutter (10)	—
111PP	4 items (80)	—
	Horiz. pair with vert. gutter (10)	—
110PI	Pair (80)	—
	Horiz. pair with vert. gutter (20)	—
111PI	Pair (80)	—
	Horiz. pair with vert. gutter (20)	—

Essays of No. 110 have 5c denomination.

New York #112-113
Committee on Peaceful Uses of Outer Space

1962

112PD	(2)	—
113PD	(1)	—
113PDa	Card, #112PD-113PD (3)	500.

Essays similar to Nos. 112PD-113PD have text in white panel below palm frond.

New York #114-115
UN Development Decade

1963

115PDa	Card, #114PD, 2 #115PD (one in slightly different shade) with approval handstamp (3)	875.
115PDb	Card, #114PD-115PD (3)	400.
114PP	4 items (80)	—
	Vert. pair with horiz. gutter (10)	—
115PP	4 items (80)	—
	Vert. pair with horiz. gutter (10)	—
114PI	Pair (80)	—
	Vert. pair with horiz. gutter (20)	—
115PI	Pair (80)	—
	Vert. pair with horiz. gutter (20)	—

New York #116-117
Freedom from Hunger Campaign

1963

116PD	(1)	—
117PD	(1)	—
117PDa	Card, #116PD-117PD (5)	500.
116PP	3 items (80)	—
	Horiz. pair with vert. gutter (10)	—
117PP	3 items (80)	—
	Horiz. pair with vert. gutter (10)	—
116PI	Pair (80)	—
	Horiz. pair with vert. gutter (20)	—
117PI	Pair (80)	—
	Horiz. pair with vert. gutter (20)	—

Essays similar to Nos. 116PD-117PD have taller numerals and lettering.

New York #118
UN Temporary Executive Authority in West New Guinea

1963

118PD	With approval handstamp (2)	400.
118PDa	Card, #118PD (approved), #118TC (not approved) (3)	500.
118TCa	Card, 2 #118TC (disapproved or with instructions to printer) (3)	500.
118PP	3 items (100)	—
	Horiz. pair with vert. gutter (10)	—
118PI	Pair (100)	—
	Horiz. pair with vert. gutter (20)	—

No. 118TC has right side of map in a lighter shade of green.

New York #119-120
General Assembly Building, New York

1963

120PDa	Card, #119PD-120PD (2)	400.

New York #121-122
Universal Declaration of Human Rights, 15th Anniv.

1963

121PD	(2)	250.
122PD	(2)	250.
121PI	Pair (100)	—
122PI	Pair (100)	—

Essays similar to Nos. 121PD-122PD have top line of frame text flush left rather than centered, and are on a disapproved card.

New York #123-124
Intergovernmental Maritime Consultative Organization

1964

124PDa	Card, #123PD-124PD (3)	550.
123PP	4 items (80)	—
	Horiz. pair with vert. gutter (10)	—
124PP	4 items (80)	—
	Horiz. pair with vert. gutter (10)	—
123PI	Pair (80)	—
	Horiz. pair with vert. gutter (20)	—
124PI	Pair (80)	—
	Horiz. pair with vert. gutter (20)	—

New York #125-128
Definitives

1964

125PD	(3)	275.
125PDa	Card, #125 perforated with approval handstamp (1)	—
126PD	(3)	240.
127PDa	Card, #126PD-127PD with approval handstamp (3)	550.
127PDb	Card, #127PD (approved), #127PD (not approved, in slightly different shade, #126PD (disapproved in slightly different shade) (3)	925.
128PD	(3)	240.
125PP	3 items (100)	—
126PP	3 items (80)	—
	Vert. pair with horiz. gutter (10)	—
127PP	4 items (80)	—
	Horiz. pair with vert. gutter (10)	—
128PP	4 items (80)	—
	Horiz. pair with vert. gutter (10)	—
125PI	Pair (65)	—
	Horiz. pair with vert. gutter (10)	—
126PI	Pair (80)	—
	Vert. pair with horiz. gutter (20)	—
127PI	Pair (80)	—
128PI	Horiz. pair with vert. gutter (20)	—
	Pair (80)	—
	Vert. pair with horiz. gutter (20)	—

Essays similar to No. 125PD have larger numerals and blue text.

New York #129-130
UN Conference on Trade and Development

1964

129PD	(6)	250.
130PD	(6)	250.
129PI	Pair (25)	—
130PI	Pair (25)	—

New York #131-132
Narcotics Control

1964

131PD	(2)	250.
132PD	(2)	250.
132PDa	Card, #131PD-132PD (3)	600.

New York #133
Nuclear Test Ban Treaty

1964

133TC	dark red & black, perforated, litho. & engr. (1)	300.
133TC	lilac, perforated, engr. (20)	
133TCa	Card, 2 #133TC dark red & dark brown, litho. & vignette essay, litho. (1)	—
133TCb	Card, #133TC dark red & black, engr. & 5 vignette essays, engr. (1)	—
133TCc	Card, 11 #133TC in red, claret, brown rose, brown, dark brown, dull blue, blue, blue violet, gray, dark gray, black, engr. (1)	—

New York #134-136
Education for Progress Campaign

1964

135PD	(1)	—
136PDa	Card, #134PD-136PD, with approval stamp (3)	—
136PDb	Card, #134PD-136PD, without approval stamp (2)	300.
136PDc	Card, #134PD, #136PD, without approval stamp (1)	450.
134PP	4 items (80)	—
	Horiz. pair with vert. gutter (10)	—
135PP	4 items (80)	—
	Horiz. pair with vert. gutter (10)	—
136PP	4 items (80)	—
	Horiz. pair with vert. gutter (10)	—
134PI	Pair (80)	—
	Horiz. pair with vert. gutter (20)	—
135PI	Pair (80)	—
	Horiz. pair with vert. gutter (20)	—
136PI	Pair (80)	—
	Horiz. pair with vert. gutter (20)	—

New York #137-138
Special Fund Program

1965

137PD	(2)	225.
138PD	(2)	225.
138PDa	Card, #137PD-138PD, with approval stamp (1)	500.
138PDb	Card, #137PD-138PD, without approval stamp (1)	—

New York #139-140
UN Peace-Keeping Force in Cyprus

1965

140PDa	Card #139PD-140PD, with approval stamp (5)	500.
140PP	3 items (80)	—
	Vert. pair with horiz. gutter (10)	—
139PI	Pair (40)	—
	Vert. pair with horiz. gutter (10)	—
140PI	Pair (40)	—
	Vert. pair with horiz. gutter (10)	—

Smaller-size essays (30x38mm) of Nos. 139-140 are in three cards with approval stamps.

New York #141-142
International Telecommunication Union

1965

142PDa	Card, #141PD-142PD, with approval stamp (3)	500.
142PDb	Card, #141PD-142PD, no approval stamp (3)	450.
142PDc	Card, #141PD-142PD, #141TC dated "8.2.65" (3)	925.
141PP	4 items (80)	—
	Horiz. pair with vert. gutter (10)	—
142PP	4 items (80)	—
	Horiz. pair with vert. gutter (10)	—
141PI	Pair (80)	—
	Horiz. pair with vert. gutter (20)	—
142PI	Pair (80)	—
	Horiz. pair with vert. gutter (20)	—

No. 141TC has orange yellow lines instead of orange lines.

New York #143-145
UN, 20th Anniv. and International Cooperation Year

1965

143PD	(3)	275.
143PDa	Card, #143PD, 144TC orange red (3)	825.
144PD	(3)	275.
144PDa	Card, #143PD-144PD, with approval stamp (7)	500.
145PD	Imperforate sheet with manuscript printer's instructions (4)	—
	Issued souvenir sheet, perforated (on printer's card) (1)	110.
145PDa	#143PD, #144PD affixed to #145 souvenir sheet margin (5)	600.

New York #146-150
Definitives

1965-66

146PD	(7)	200.
148PDa	Block of 12 perforated stamps with approval handstamp in margin (2)	140.
148PDb	Card, #147-148 perforated, with approval handstamp (3)	500.
149PD	Perforated, with approval handstamp (2)	250.
149PDa	Card, #149PD (2nd printing), #149PD, first printing, perforated, with approval handstamp (2)	600.
150PD	(3)	240.
149TC	Prussian blue & dark blue, perforated (1)	—
150PP	3 items (80), affixed on cards	—
	Horiz. pair with vert. gutter (10)	—
150PI	Pair (161)	375.
	Horiz. pair with vert. gutter (19)	—

Two cards without approval handstamp have perforated essays of both Nos. 147 and 148. The essay of No. 147 has larger numerals and the essay of No. 148 has bright yellow text at bottom. No. 150PI has had extra glue applied.

New York #151-153
Population Trends and Development

1965

152PDa	Card, #151PD-152PD, 153TC, perforated (2) with approval handstamp	825.

No. 153TC has "Nations Unies" in black instead of gray.

New York #154-155
World Federation of United Nations Associations

1966

155PDa	Card, #154-155PD with approval handstamp (3)	500.
154PP	4 items (80)	—
	Vert. pair with horiz. gutter (10)	—
155PP	4 items (80)	—
	Vert. pair with horiz. gutter (10)	—
154PI	Pair (80)	—
	Vert. pair with horiz. gutter (20)	—
155PI	Pair (80)	—
	Vert. pair with horiz. gutter (20)	—

New York #156-157
World Health Organization

1966

157TCa	Card, #156TC-157TC, with approval handstamp (3)	500.
156PP	4 items (50)	—
157PP	4 items (80)	—
	Horiz. pair with vert. gutter (10)	—
156PI	Pair (65)	—
	Horiz. pair with vert. gutter (10)	—
157PI	Pair (80)	—
	Horiz. pair with vert. gutter (20)	—

Nos. 156TC and 157TC have side and front of building the same shade of blue.

New York #158-159
International Coffee Agreement of 1962

1966

159PDa	Card, #158PD-159PD (3)	625.

New York #160
UN Observers

1964

160PD	(2) on cards dated "3.2.1966"	125.
160PP	4 items (50)	—
160PI	Pair (65)	—
	Vert. pair with horiz. gutter (10)	—

Two essays of No. 160 with white text lines larger and closer together are on cards dated "17.1.1966."

New York #161-163
UNICEF, 20th Anniv.

1966

161PD	(3)	250.
162PD	(3)	250.
163PD	(3)	250.
161PI	Pair (72)	—
	Cross gutter block (1)	—
	Horiz. pair with vert. gutter (18)	—
	Vert. pair with horiz. gutter (8)	—
162PI	Pair (72)	—
	Cross gutter block (1)	—
	Horiz. pair with vert. gutter (18)	—
	Vert. pair with horiz. gutter (8)	—
163PI	Pair (72)	—
	Cross gutter block (1)	—
	Horiz. pair with vert. gutter (18)	—
	Vert. pair with horiz. gutter (8)	—

New York #164-165
UN Development Program

1967

165PDa	Card, # 164PD-165PD, dated "6.9. 1966" (3)	725.
165PDb	Card, #165PD, 2 #164PD, with approval handstamp, dated "4.10.66" (6)	925.
164PI	Pair (40)	—
	Horiz. pair with vert. gutter (10)	—
165PI	Pair (40)	—
	Horiz. pair with vert. gutter (10)	—

New York #166-167
Definitives

1967

166PD	(6)	225.
166PDa	Card, 2 #166PD (3)	575.
167PD	(3)	200.
167TC	With brown line separating "UN" in vignette, on card dated "27.4.1966" (3)	250.
166PP	4 items (80)	—
	Vert. pair with horiz. gutter (10)	—
167PP	3 items (80)	—
	Horiz. pair with vert. gutter (10)	—
166PI	Pair (80)	—
	Vert. pair with horiz. gutter (20)	—
167PI	Pair (80)	—
	Horiz. pair with vert. gutter (20)	—

New York #168-169
Independence

1967

168PD	(2)	250.
169PD	(3)	250.

New York #170-174
EXPO '67

1967

170PD	(1)	300.
171PD	(1)	300.
172PD	(3)	300.
173PD	(1)	300.
174PD	(3)	300.
170PP	2 items (144)	—
	Cross gutter block (1)	—
	Horiz. pair with vert. gutter (8)	—
	Vert. pair with horiz. gutter (18)	—
171PP	2 items (144)	—
	Cross gutter block (1)	—
	Horiz. pair with vert. gutter (8)	—
	Vert. pair with horiz. gutter (18)	—
172PP	3 items (144)	—
	Cross gutter block (1)	—
	Horiz. pair with vert. gutter (18)	—
	Vert. pair with horiz. gutter (8)	—
173PP	2 items (144)	—
	Cross gutter block (1)	—
	Horiz. pair with vert. gutter (8)	—
	Vert. pair with horiz. gutter (18)	—
174PP	2 items (144)	—
	Cross gutter block (1)	—
	Horiz. pair with vert. gutter (8)	—
	Vert. pair with horiz. gutter (18)	—
170PI	Pair (72)	—
	Cross gutter block (1)	—
	Horiz. pair with vert. gutter (8)	—
	Vert. pair with horiz. gutter (18)	—
171PI	Pair (72)	—
	Cross gutter block (1)	—
	Horiz. pair with vert. gutter (8)	—
	Vert. pair with horiz. gutter (18)	—
172PI	Pair (72)	—
	Cross gutter block (1)	—
	Horiz. pair with vert. gutter (18)	—
	Vert. pair with horiz. gutter (8)	—
173PI	Pair (72)	—
	Cross gutter block (1)	—
	Horiz. pair with vert. gutter (8)	—
	Vert. pair with horiz. gutter (18)	—
174PI	Pair (72)	—
	Cross gutter block (1)	—
	Horiz. pair with vert. gutter (8)	—
	Vert. pair with horiz. gutter (18)	—

New York #175-176
International Tourist Year

1967

176PDa	#175-176, perforated, affixed to printer's card (2)	600.

New York #177-178
Towards Disarmament

1967

177PD	(3)	—
178PD	(3)	200.
178TC	Wall text in copper, gold lines in wall (1)	110.
178TC	Wall text in copper, blue gray lines in wall (3)	110.
178TC	Wall text in brown, silver lines in wall (1)	110.
178TC	Wall text in brown, blue gray lines in wall (3)	110.

New York #179-180
Chagall Stained Glass Windows

1967

179PP	8 items (29)	—
180PP	8 items (29)	—
179PI	Pair on card stock (24)	1,050.
180PI	Pair on card stock (135)	650.
	Horiz. pair with vert. gutter, on card stock (15)	—
180PI	Pair on stamp paper (75)	525.

Essays of Nos. 179-180 in 5c denomination exist.

New York #181-182
UN Secretariat

1968

181PD	(1)	110.
182PD	(1)	110.
182PDa	Card, #181PD-182PD (1)	—
181PP	5 items (160)	—
	Horiz. pair with vert. gutter (20)	—
182PP	5 items (160)	—
	Horiz. pair with vert. gutter (20)	—
181PI	Pair (80)	—
	Horiz. pair with vert. gutter (20)	—
182PI	Pair (80)	—
	Horiz. pair with vert. gutter (20)	—

New York #183-184
Art at the UN

1968

183PD	(1)	250.
184PD	(1)	250.
184PDa	Card, #183PD-184PD, dated "5.12.67" (2)	—
184TCa	Card, #183TC-184TC, dated "10.XI.67" (3)	725.
183PP	5 items (80)	—
	Vert. pair with horiz. gutter (10)	—
184PP	5 items (80)	—
	Vert. pair with horiz. gutter (10)	—
183PI	Pair (65)	—
	Vert. pair with horiz. gutter (10)	—
184PI	Pair (80)	—
	Vert. pair with horiz. gutter (20)	—

No. 183TC has a bright blue frame; No. 184TC a birght red frame.

New York #185-186
UN Industrial Development Orgainzation

1968

185PD	(4)	325.
186PD	(3)	500.
186TC	brown frame, deep blue "ONUDI" (2)	—
185PP	4 items, affixed to cards (3)	—
186PP	4 items, affixed to cards (3)	—
185PI	Pair with security punch (25)	250.
186PI	Pair with security punch (25)	250.

New York #187
UN Headquarters

1964

187TC	light gray roof in foreground, numbered 34 or 38, dated July 7, 1967 (2)	140.
187TC	With wide curved white line under window of General Assembly building, numbered 397 or 404, dated 11.8.1967 (2)	125.
187TC	With halo around UN emblem, dated Feb. 12, 1968 (2)	240.
187PP	11 items, on card with staple holes (3)	—
187PI	Pair with "Specimen" overprint (80)	250.
	Vert. pair with horiz. gutter, with "Specimen" overprint (20)	—
187PI	Pair without "Specimen" overprint (80)	375.
	Vert. pair with horiz. gutter, without "Specimen" overprint (20)	—

New York #188-189
World Weather Watch

1968

189PDa	Card, #188PD-189PD (1)	500.
188PP	5 items (100)	—
189PP	5 items (100)	—

New York #190-191
International Human Rights Year

1968

190PD	(6)	210.
191PD	(6)	210.
190PP	4 items (100)	—
191PP	4 items (100)	—
190PI	Pair (50)	—
191PI	Pair (50)	—

New York #192-193
UN Institute for Training and Research

1969
193PDa	Card, #192PD-193PD (2)	425.
192PP	6 items (50)	—
193PP	6 items (100)	—
192PI	Pair (15)	425.
193PI	Pair (15)	425.

New York #194-195
Economic Commission for Latin America

1969
195PDa	#194-195, perforated, affixed to printer's card (4)	425.

New York #196
"UN" and Emblem

1969
196PD	With approval handstamp (2)	250.
196TC	Card, #196PD, 196TC dark blue background (2)	—
196PP	3 items (100)	—

New York #197-198
UN International Law Commission

1969
198PDa	Card, #197PD-198PD (9)	650.
197PP	4 items (80)	—
	Horiz. pair with vert. gutter (10)	—
198PP	4 items (80)	—
	Horiz. pair with vert. gutter (10)	—
197PI	(40 pairs)	—
	Horiz. pair with vert. gutter (10)	—
198PI	(40 pairs)	—
	Horiz. pair with vert. gutter (10)	—

New York #199-200
Labor and Development

1969
199PD	With approval handstamp (1)	—
200PD	(1)	—
200PDa	Card, #199PD-200PD, with approval handstamp (1)	425.
199TC	Men in dark blue, perforated (3)	—
200TC	Rose pink background, perforated (3)	—
200PP	4 items (91)	—

Geneva #1-14
Definitives

1969-70
G1PD	(2)	200.
G3PD	(1)	—
G3PDa	Card, 2 #G3PD, with approval handstamp (2)	—
G4PD	(2)	—
G5PD	(3)	325.
G7PD	(1)	250.
G8PD	Perforated, on card with approval handstamp (2)	275.
G8PDa	Perforated layout sheet proof with 4 #G8PD affixed (1)	—
G8PDb	Partial perforated layout sheet proof with 2 #G8PD affixed (1)	—
G9PD	(1)	275.
G10PD	(1)	200.
G11PD	(1)	225.
G12PD	(1)	240.
G13PD	(4)	225.
G14PD	(3)	—
G1TC	Black panel behind "UN" (1)	—
G6TCa	Card, #G6PD, #G6TC pewter emblem, dated "7.10.69" (3)	—
G6TCb	Card, #G6TC silver emblem, 2 #G6PD dated "17.9.69" (3)	—
G6TCc	Card, #G6PD, #G6TC orange denomination, dated "27.8.69" (3)	—
G12TC	gray background, on card marked "Rejected" (2)	325.
G1PP	3 items, perforated (100)	—
G2PP	5 items (160)	—
	Horiz. pair with vert. gutter (20)	—
G3PP	5 items (160)	—
	Horiz. pair with vert. gutter (20)	—
G4PP	5 items (151)	—
	Horiz. pair with vert. gutter (20)	—
G5PP	4 items (160)	—
	Vert. pair with horiz. gutter (20)	—
G6PP	3 items (160)	—
	Horiz. pair with vert. gutter (20)	—
G7PP	4 items (100)	—
G8PP	8 items (150)	—
G9PP	6 items (100)	—
G10PP	8 items (100)	—
G12PP	6 items (100)	—
G13PP	5 items (160)	—
	Vert. pair with horiz. gutter (20)	—
G2PI	Pair (80)	—
	Horiz. pair with vert. gutter (20)	—
G3PI	Pair (80)	—
	Horiz. pair with vert. gutter (20)	—
G4PI	Pair (73)	—
	Horiz. pair with vert. gutter (20)	—
G5PI	Pair (80)	—
	Vert. pair with horiz. gutter (20)	—
G6PI	Pair (80)	—
	Horiz. pair with vert. gutter (20)	—
G7PI	Pair (80)	—
G8PI	Pair (75)	—
G9PI	Pair (50)	—

G10PI	Pair (50)	—
G13PI	Pair (80)	—
	Vert. pair with horiz. gutter (20)	—

Four essays of No. G2 exist, having "0" below "F" jutting out to left. Two essays of No. G10 with small "F.S." are on rejected cards.

New York #201-202
Mosaic Art at the UN

1969
201PD	(3)	210.
202PD	(3)	210.
202PDa	Card, #201PD-202PD (2)	—
201PP	8 items (100)	—
202PP	8 items (100)	—
201PI	Pair (50)	—
202PI	Pair (50)	—

New York #203-204
Peace Bell

1970
204PDa	Card, 2 each #203PD-204PD (2)	1,300.
203PP	5 items (100)	—
204PP	5 items (100)	—

About half of Nos. 203PP and 204PP have faults.

New York #205-206
Lower Mekong Basin Development Project

1970
205PD	(2)	250.
206PD	(2)	250.
205PP	10 items (100)	—
206PP	10 items (100)	—
205PI	Pair (50)	—
206PI	Pair (50)	—

New York #207-208
Fight Cancer

1970
207PD	Perforated, non-glossy paper, on piece of printer's card (1)	—
208PD	Perforated, non-glossy paper, on piece of printer's card (1)	—
208PDa	Card, #207PD-208PD, perforated, non-glossy paper (1)	—
208PDb	Card, 2 #207PD-208PD, perforated, non-glossy paper, with approval handstamp (1)	1,050.
208PDc	#207-208, perforated, glossy paper, on printer's card (2)	—
207PP	2 items (50)	—
208PP	2 items (50)	—
207PI	Pair (50)	—
208PI	Pair (50)	—

New York #209-212
UN, 25th Anniv.

1970
209PD	(2)	—
210PD	(2)	—
211PD	On card (3)	—
211PDa	Card, #209PD-211PD (2)	750.
212PD	(1)	275.
212PDa	Card, #209PD-212PD (1)	—
209PP	4 items (180)	—
	Horiz. pair with vert. gutter (10)	—
210PP	5 items (180)	—
	Horiz. pair with vert. gutter (10)	—
211PP	3 items (180)	—
	Vert. pair with horiz. gutter (10)	—
212PP	5 items (22)	—
209PI	Pair (80)	—
	Horiz. pair with vert. gutter (20)	—
210PI	Pair (80)	—
	Horiz. pair with vert. gutter (20)	—
211PI	Pair (80)	—
	Vert. pair with horiz. gutter (20)	—
212PI	Pair (12)	—

New York #213-214
Peace, Justice and Progress

1970
214PDa	Card, #213PD-214PD (3)	600.
214PDb	Card, 2 each #213PD-214PD (2)	1,300.
213PP	4 items (50)	—
214PP	4 items (50)	—

New York #215, Geneva #15
Peaceful Uses of the Sea Bed

1971
215PD	(2)	200.
G15PD	(1)	—
215PP	6 items (100)	—
G15PP	6 items (100)	—
215PI	Pair (50)	—
G15PI	Pair (50)	—

New York #216-217, Geneva #16
International Support for Refugees

1971
217PDa	Card, #216PD-217PD, #G16PD (2)	775.
216PP	4 items (80)	—
	Horiz. pair with vert. gutter (10)	—
217PP	4 items (80)	—
	Horiz. pair with vert. gutter (10)	—
G16PP	4 items (160)	—

216PI	Horiz. pair with vert. gutter (20)	—
	Pair (80)	—
	Horiz. pair with vert. gutter (20)	—
217PI	Pair (80)	—
	Horiz. pair with vert. gutter (20)	—
G16PI	Pair (80)	—
	Horiz. pair with vert. gutter (20)	—

New York #218, Geneva #17
World Food Program

1971
218PD	(4)	225.
G17PD	(4)	225.
G17TC	(1)	375.
218PP	6 items (100)	—
G17PP	6 items (100)	—
218PI	Pair (50)	—
G17PI	Pair (50)	—

New York #219, Geneva #18
Universal Postal Union

1971
219PDa	Card, #219PD, #G18PD (3)	550.
219PP	5 items (130)	—
	Horiz. pair with vert. gutter (10)	—
G18PP	5 items (150)	—
219PI	Pair (80)	—
	Horiz. pair with vert. gutter (20)	—
G18PI	Pair (80)	—
	Horiz. pair with vert. gutter (20)	—

New York #220-221, Geneva #19-20
International Year Against Racial Discrimination

1971
221PDa	Card, #220PD-221PD, #G19PD-G20PD and 4 similar items with slightly different colors (1)	2,400.
221PDb	Card with affixed plastic sheet with #220PD-221PD, #G19PD-G20PD affixed (1)	600.
221PDc	Cut-up card, #220PD-221PD, G19PD-G20PD (1)	—
220PP	5 items (100)	—
221PP	5 items (75)	—
G19PP	5 items (100)	—
G20PP	5 items (100)	—

New York #222-223
UN Headquarters, New York

1971
222PD	(4)	275.
223PD	(2)	275.
222PP	8 items (91)	—
223PP	5 items (92)	—
222PI	Pair (175)	—

Two sheets of 50 of No. 222PI are "approved."

New York #224-225, Geneva #21
UN International School

1971
225PDa	Card, #224PD-225PD, G21PD, with approval stamp (2)	750.
225PDb	Card or sheet, #224PD-225PD, 1fr essay of #G21 (3)	925.
224PP	5 items (180)	—
	Vert. pair with horiz. gutter (10)	—
225PP	5 items (100)	—
	Vert. pair with horiz. gutter (10)	—
G21PP	5 items (180)	—
	Vert. pair with horiz. gutter (10)	—
224PI	Pair (80)	—
	Vert. pair with horiz. gutter (20)	—
225PI	Pair (80)	—
	Vert. pair with horiz. gutter (20)	—
G21PI	Pair (80)	—
	Vert. pair with horiz. gutter (20)	—

New York #226, Geneva #22
Definitives

1972
226PD	Perforated on printer's card (3)	225.
G22PD	(5)	225.
226PP	4 items (100)	—
G22PP	4 items (180)	—
	Horiz. pair with vert. gutter (10)	—
226PI	Pair (50)	—
G22PI	Pair (80)	—
	Horiz. pair with vert. gutter (20)	—

New York #227, Geneva #23
Non-proliferation of Nuclear Weapons

1972
227PD	(2)	200.
G23PD	(2)	225.
227PP	6 items (100)	—
G23PP	6 items (100)	—
227PI	Pair (50)	—
G23PI	Pair (50)	—

Two essays each of Nos. 227 and G23 lacking strong gray billowing in center of cloud exist on cards dated "22.Set.1971."

New York #228, Geneva #24, Souvenir Card #1
World Health Day

1972

228PDa	Card, #228PD, #G24PD with approval handstamp (1)	500.
G24PD	(1)	—
SC1PD	Card with stamps with simulated perforations and cancels (2)	600.
228PP	8 items (80)	—
G24PP	8 items (160)	—
	Vert. pair with horiz. gutter (10)	—
G24PI	Pair (180)	—
	Vert. pair with horiz. gutter (20)	—

New York #229-230, Geneva #25-26
UN Conference on Human Environment

1972

229PD	(1)	—
230PDa	Card, #229PD-230PD, #G25PD-G26PD (3)	450.
230PDb	Card, #230PD, #G25PD-G26PD (1)	—
229PP	6 items (288)	—
	Cross gutter block (2)	—
	Horiz. pair with vert. gutter (16)	—
	Vert. pair with horiz. gutter (36)	—
230PP	6 items (288)	—
	Cross gutter block (2)	—
	Horiz. pair with vert. gutter (16)	—
	Vert. pair with horiz. gutter (36)	—
G25PP	6 items (288)	—
	Cross gutter block (2)	—
	Horiz. pair with vert. gutter (16)	—
	Vert. pair with horiz. gutter (36)	—
G26PP	6 items (288)	—
	Cross gutter block (2)	—
	Horiz. pair with vert. gutter (16)	—
	Vert. pair with horiz. gutter (36)	—
229PI	Pair (144)	—
	Cross gutter block (2)	—
	Horiz. pair with vert. gutter (16)	—
	Vert. pair with horiz. gutter (36)	—
230PI	Pair (144)	—
	Cross gutter block (2)	—
	Horiz. pair with vert. gutter (16)	—
	Vert. pair with horiz. gutter (36)	—
G25PI	Pair (144)	—
	Cross gutter block (2)	—
	Horiz. pair with vert. gutter (16)	—
	Vert. pair with horiz. gutter (36)	—
G26PI	Pair (144)	—
	Cross gutter block (2)	—
	Horiz. pair with vert. gutter (16)	—
	Vert. pair with horiz. gutter (36)	—

New York #231, Geneva #27
Economic Commission for Europe

1972

231PDa	Card, #231PD, #G27PD (4)	550.
231PP	8 items (100)	—
G27PP	8 items (50)	—

New York #232-233, Geneva #28-29, Souvenir Card #2
Art at the UN

1972

232PDa	Card, #232PD, #233TC text in dull blue green, #G28PD-G29PD (1)	975.
G28PD	(1)	—
G29PDa	Card, #G28PD-G29PD, #233TC text in dull blue green (1)	—
G29PDb	Card, #G29PD, #233TC text in dull blue green (1)	—
SC2PD	(25)	—
SC2PDa	Defaced card, with corrections marked in blue (8)	—
SC2TC	Untrimmed card, signature in light blue (3)	160.
G28PP	3 items (50)	—
G29PP	3 items (50)	—
232PI	Pair (80)	—
	Vert. pair with horiz. gutter (20)	—
233PI	Pair (80)	—
	Vert. pair with horiz. gutter (20)	—
G28PI	Pair (80)	—
	Vert. pair with horiz. gutter (20)	—
G29PI	Pair (80)	—
	Vert. pair with horiz. gutter (20)	—

New York #234-235, Geneva #30-31, Souvenir Card #3
Disarmament Decade

1973

235PDa	Card, #234PD-235PD, #G30PD-G31PD, with approval handstamp (1)	825.
SC3PD	With printer's stamp or approval handstamp (9)	110.
234PP	8 items (130)	—
235PP	8 items (100)	—
	Horiz. pair with vert. gutter (20)	—
G30PP	8 items (130)	—
	Horiz. pair with vert. gutter (20)	—
G31PP	8 items (100)	—
234PI	Pair (230)	—
	Horiz. pair with vert. gutter (20)	—
235PI	Pair (230)	—
	Horiz. pair with vert. gutter (20)	—
G30PI	Pair (205)	—

	Horiz. pair with vert. gutter (20)	—
G31PI	Pair (230)	—
	Horiz. pair with vert. gutter (20)	—

Two examples of #SC3PD are cut in half.

New York #236-237, Geneva #32
Fight Against Drug Abuse

1973

236PD	(1)	—
237PDa	Card, #236PD-237PD, #G32PD with approval handstamp (4)	725.
237PDb	Card, #237PD, #G32PD with approval handstamp (1)	—
237PDc	Card, #237PD, #G32PD, 9c essay of #236 (6)	—
236PP	8 items (75)	—
237PP	8 items (100)	—
G32PP	8 items (50)	—
236PI	Pair (50)	—
237PI	Pair (50)	—
G32PI	Pair (50)	—

New York #238-239, Geneva #33
UN Volunteer Program

1973

239PDa	Card, #238PD-239PD, #G33PD (9)	600.
238PP	8 items (80)	—
239PP	8 items (100)	—
G33PP	8 items (50)	—
238PI	Pair (50)	—
239PI	Pair (50)	—
G33PI	Pair (25)	—

New York #240-241, Geneva #34
Namibia

1973

241PDa	Card, #240PD-241PD, #G34PD (1)	—
241PDb	Card, #240PD-241PD, #G34PD, essays of 240-241, #G34 with Africa outlined in gold (3)	1,400.
240PP	8 items (100)	—
241PP	8 items (100)	—
G34PP	8 items (50)	—
240PI	Pair (50)	—
241PI	Pair (50)	—
G34PI	Pair (50)	—

Two cards containing only the essays exist.

New York #242-243, Geneva #35-36, Souvenir Card #4
Universal Declaration of Human Rights, 25th Anniv.

1973

242PD	(9)	275.
243PDa	Card, #242PD-243PD, #G35PD-G36PD (6)	1,300.
243PDb	Card, #242PD-243PD (9)	725.
243PDc	Card, #243PD, #G35PD-G36PD (1)	—
SC4PD	With approval handstamp (3)	—
242PP	5 items (100)	—
243PP	5 items (100)	—
G35PP	5 items (100)	—
G36PP	5 items (50)	—
SC4PP	2 items (1)	—
SC4PI	untrimmed card (1)	—

No. SC4PP may not be a complete set of progressive proofs.

New York #244-245, Geneva #37-38
New International Labor Organization Headquarters

1974

245PDa	Card, #245PD, #G37PD-G38PD, 8c essay of #244 (4)	1,200.
244PP	8 items (75)	—
245PP	8 items (75)	—
G37PP	8 items (50)	—
G38PP	8 items (50)	—
244PI	Pair (50)	—
245PI	Pair (50)	—
G37PI	Pair (50)	—
G38PI	Pair (50)	—

New York #246, Geneva #39-40, Souvenir Card #5
Universal Postal Union, Cent.

1974

246PD	(1)	—
246PDa	Card, #246PD, #G39PD-G40PD (7)	925.
G40PDa	Card, #G39PD-G40PD (1)	—
SC5PD	Affixed to card (5)	400.
SC5PDa	Card with printer instructions in ink (1)	—
SC5PDb	Progressive proof sheet with printer instructions in ink (1)	400.
246PP	6 items (100)	—
G39PP	5 items (50)	—
G40PP	5 items (50)	—
246PI	Pair (25)	—
G39PI	Pair (25)	—
G40PI	Pair (25)	—

New York #247-248, Geneva #41-42
Art at the UN

1974

247PDa	Card, #247PD, #G41PD-G42PD, 15c essay of #248 (5)	1,250.
248PDa	Card, #247PD-248PD, #G41PD-G42PD (3)	925.
247PP	8 items (100)	—
248PP	8 items (100)	—
G41PP	8 items (50)	—
G42PP	8 items (50)	—
247PI	Pair (50)	—
248PI	Pair (50)	—
G41PI	Pair (50)	—
G42PI	Pair (50)	—

New York #249-251
Definitives

1974

249PD	Affixed on perforated blank (1)	—
250PD	Affixed on perforated blank (1)	—
250PDa	Taped to card (1)	—
250PDb	Card, #250PD, 251TC with darker brown background, essay of #249 with flat top "S," with "21.DIC.1973" date and approval stamp (2)	—
251PD	Affixed on perforated blank (1)	125.
251PDa	Card, #249PD, #251PD, with "17.ENE.1974" date and approval stamp (3)	500.
251TCa	Darker brown background, on cards dated "21.DIC.1973" (3)	—
250PP	10 items (50)	—
251PP	8 items (35)	—
249PI	Pair (200)	—
250PI	Pair (50)	—
251PI	Pair (100)	—

New York #252-253, Geneva #43-44, Souvenir Card #6
World Population Year

1974

252PDa	Card, #252PD, #G44PD, 21c essay of #253, 40c essay of #G43 in se-tenant strip (5)	725.
253PDa	Card, #252PD-253PD, G44PD, 40c essay of #G43 in se-tenant strip (4)	800.
SC6PD	With approval handstamp (10)	—
252PP	10 items (50)	—
253PP	10 items (50)	—
G43PP	10 items (50)	—
G44PP	10 items (50)	—
252PI	Pair (50)	—
253PI	Pair (50)	—
G43PI	Pair (50)	—
G44PI	Pair (50)	—

All examples of No. SC6PD show the 40c essay.

New York #254-255, Geneva #45
Law of the Sea

1974

255PDa	Card, #254PD-255PD, #G45TC with blue green sky (3)	800.
254PP	10 items (50)	—
255PP	10 items (50)	—
G45PP	10 items (50)	—
254PI	Pair (50)	—
255PI	Pair (50)	—
G45PI	Pair (50)	—

New York #256-257, Geneva #46-47, Souvenir Card #7
Peaceful Uses of Outer Space

1975

256PDa	Card, #256PD, #G46PD-G47PD (1)	—
257PD	Cut from #256PDa (1)	—
257PDa	Card, #256PD-257PD, G46PD-G47PD (3)	825.
SC7PD	with approval handstamp (4)	—
256PP	8 items (150)	—
257PP	8 items (150)	—
G46PP	8 items (50)	—
G47PP	8 items (50)	—
256PI	Pair (100)	—
257PI	Pair (100)	—
G46PI	Pair (50)	—
G47PI	Pair (50)	—

New York #258-259, Geneva #48-49
International Women's Year

1975

258PD	On card dated "16 Oct. 1974" (4)	250.
259PD	(4)	250.
G48PD	On card dated "16 Oct. 1974" (4)	325.
G49PD	(4)	325.
258TC	bright blue background (on cards dated "17 Sep. 1974") (4)	—
G48TC	red brown background (on cards dated "17 Sep. 1974") (4)	—
258PP	6 items (50)	—
259PP	6 items (50)	—
G48PP	6 items (50)	—
G49PP	6 items (50)	—
258PI	Pair (50)	—

259PI	Pair (50)	—
G48PI	Pair (50)	—
G49PI	Pair (50)	—

Six essays of the 18c stamp with "Nations Unies" inscription, and six essays of the 90c stamp with "United Nations" inscription exist.

New York #260-262, Geneva #50-52
UN, 30th Anniv.

1975

261PDa	Card, #260PD-261PD, #G51PP, #G50TC in olive green, se-tenant (4)	1,200.
262PD	(5)	500.
G52PD	(1)	
G52TC	With #G52aTC olive green (5)	700.
260PP	6 items (50)	—
261PP	6 items (50)	—
262PP	10 items (6)	—
G50PP	6 items (50)	—
G51PP	6 items (50)	—
G52PP	10 items (6)	—
260PI	Pair (50)	—
261PI	Pair (50)	—
262PI	Pair of souvenir sheets (26)	—
G50PI	Pair (50)	—
G51PI	Pair (50)	—
G52PI	Pair of souvenir sheets (26)	—

New York #263-264, Geneva #53-54
Namibia

1975

264PDa	Card, #263PD-264PD, #G53PD-G54PD (9)	975.
263PP	8 items (50)	—
264PP	8 items (50)	—
G53PP	8 items (50)	—
G54PP	7 items (50)	—
263PI	Pair (50)	—
264PI	Pair (50)	—
G53PI	Pair (50)	—
G54PI	Pair (50)	—

New York #265-266, Geneva #55-56, Souvenir Card #8
UN Peacekeeping Operations

1975

266PDa	Card, #265PD-266PD, #G55PD-G56PD (3)	1,300.
266PDb	Card, #266PD, #G55PD-G56PD, 10c essay of #265 (5)	1,200.
SC8PD	With approval handstamp (5)	—
265PI	Pair (25)	—
266PI	Pair (25)	—
G55PI	Pair (25)	—
G56PI	Pair (25)	—

New York #267-271
Definitives

1976

267PD	(4)	225.
268PD	(3)	350.
269PD	(5)	110.
270PD	(8)	225.
271PD	(4)	200.
271TC	Dark green background (not approved cards dated "30 June 1975" (5)	—
267PP	10 items (25)	—
268PP	8 items (50)	—
269PP	3 items (50)	—
270PP	6 items (50)	—
271PP	10 items (25)	—
267PI	Pair (50)	—
268PI	Pair (50)	—
269PI	Pair (50)	—
270PI	Pair (50)	—
271PI	Pair (50)	—

New York #272-273, Geneva #57, Souvenir Card #9
World Federation of United Nations Associations

1976

273PDa	Card, #272PD-273PD, #G57PD (4)	825.
SC9PD	With approval handstamp dated "18 Sep 1975" (4)	—
SC9TC	With light blue denominations on 1966 stamp (not approved) (5)	—
272PP	6 items (50)	—
273PP	6 items (50)	—
G57PP	6 items (50)	—
272PI	Pair (50)	—
273PI	Pair (50)	—
G57PI	Pair (50)	—

New York #274-275, Geneva #58
UN Conference on Trade and Development

1976

G58PDa	Card, #G58PD, non-denominated essays of #274-275 (5)	725.
274PP	5 items (130)	—
	Vert. pair with horiz. gutter (10)	—
275PP	5 items (130)	—
	Vert. pair with horiz. gutter (10)	—
G58PP	5 items (150)	—
274PI	Pair (80)	—
	Vert. pair with horiz. gutter (20)	—
275PI	Pair (80)	—
	Vert. pair with horiz. gutter (20)	—
G58PI	Pair (80)	—
	Vert. pair with horiz. gutter (20)	—

New York #276-277, Geneva #59-60
UN Conference on Human Settlements

1976

277PDa	Card, #276PD-277PD, #G59PD-G60PD (4)	1,100.
276PP	12 items (50)	—
277PP	12 items (50)	—
G59PP	12 items (50)	—
G60PP	12 items (50)	—
276PI	Pair (50)	—
277PI	Pair (50)	—
G59PI	Pair (50)	—
G60PI	Pair (50)	—

New York #278-279, Geneva #61-62
UN Postal Administration, 25th Anniv.

1976

279PDa	Card, #278PD-279PD, #G61PD-G62PD (5)	700.
278PP	5 items (64)	—
	Horiz. pair with vert. gutter (4)	—
	Vert. pair with horiz. gutter (4)	—
279PP	5 items (64)	—
	Horiz. pair with vert. gutter (4)	—
	Vert. pair with horiz. gutter (4)	—
G61PP	5 items (72)	—
	Horiz. pair with vert. gutter (4)	—
G62PP	5 items (63)	—
	Horiz. pair with vert. gutter (4)	—
	Vert. pair with horiz. gutter (4)	—

New York #280, Geneva #63, Souvenir Card #10
World Food Council

1976

280PD	(5)	200.
63PD	(5)	200.
SC10PD	With approval handstamp (12)	—
280PP	2 items (50)	—
G63PP	2 items (50)	—
280PI	Pair (50)	—
G63PI	Pair (50)	—

New York #281-282, Geneva #64, Souvenir Card #11
World Intellectual Property Organization

1977

282PDa	Card, #281PD-282PD, #G64PD (4)	650.
SC11PD	With approval handstamp (4)	—
281PP	8 items (50)	—
282PP	8 items (50)	—
G64PP	8 items (50)	—
281PI	Pair (50)	—
282PI	Pair (50)	—
G64PI	Pair (50)	—

New York #283-284, Geneva #65-66
UN Water Conference

1977

283PD	Cut out from #284PDb (1)	—
284PDa	Card, #283PD-284PD, #G65PD-G66PD (2)	925.
284PDb	Card, #284PD, #G65PD-G66PD (1)	—
284PDc	Card, #284PD, #G66PD (1)	—
283PP	6 items (50)	—
284PP	6 items (50)	—
G65PP	5 items (50)	—
G66PP	5 items (50)	—
283PI	Pair (50)	—
284PI	Pair (50)	—
G65PI	Pair (50)	—
G66PI	Pair (50)	—

New York #285-286, Geneva #67-68
UN Security Council

1977

286PDa	Card, #285PD-286PD, essays of #G67-G68 with small top Chinese character (4)	975.
G68PDa	Card, #G67PD-G68PD (large Chinese character) (4)	450.
286PP	8 items (50)	—
G67PP	8 items (50)	—
G68PP	8 items (50)	—
285PI	Pair (50)	—
286PI	Pair (50)	—
G67PI	Pair (50)	—
G68PI	Pair (50)	—

A card with the two essays only (a cutout of No. 286PDa) with "not approved" handstamp exists.

New York #287-288, Geneva #69-70, Souvenir Card #12
Combat Racism

1977

288PDa	Card, #287PD-288PD (4)	425.
G70PDa	Card, #G69PD-G70PD (4)	500.
SC12PD	With approval handstamp and specimen perfin (5)	—
287PP	3 items (50)	—
288PP	3 items (50)	—
G69PP	6 items (150)	—
G70PP	6 items (150)	—
287PI	Pair (175)	—
288PI	Pair (175)	—
G69PI	Pair (225)	—
G70PI	Pair (225)	—

New York #289-290, Geneva #71-72
Peaceful Uses of Atomic Energy

1977

290PDa	Card, #289PD-290PD, #G71PD-G72PD (4)	1,100.
290PDb	Card, #289PD-290PD, #G71PD, essay of #G72 with capital "F" in "Fins" (5)	975.
289PP	8 items (50)	—
290PP	8 items (50)	—
G71PP	6 items (50)	—
G72PP	6 items (50)	—
289PI	Pair (50)	—
290PI	Pair (50)	—
G71PI	Pair (50)	—
G72PI	Pair (50)	—

New York #291-293, Geneva #73
Definitives

1978

291PD	(4)	200.
292PD	(5)	225.
293PD	(4)	200.
G73PD	With approval handstamp (4)	225.
G73TC	Tree in deep brown (with "not approved" handstamp (6)	175.
G73PP	6 items (50)	—
291PI	Pair (50)	—
292PI	Pair (50)	—
293PI	Pair (75)	—
G73PI	Pair (50)	—

Six essays of No. 293 having "C" in Naciones not even with "A" exist on card with "not approved" handstamp.

New York #294-295, Geneva #74-75
Global Eradication of Smallpox

1978

295PDa	Card, #294PD-295PD, #G74PD-G75PD (5)	1,000.
294PP	2 items (50)	—
295PP	2 items (50)	—
G74PP	4 items (50)	—
G75PP	4 items (50)	—
294PI	Pair (50)	—
295PI	Pair (50)	—
G74PI	Pair (50)	—
G75PI	Pair (50)	—

New York #296-297, Geneva #76, Souvenir Card #13
Liberation, Justice and Cooperation for Namibia

1978

296PD	On perforated sheet layout (2)	—
297PD	On perforated sheet layout (1)	—
297PDa	Card, #296-297, #G76, perforated (4)	725.
297PDb	Card, #296-297 perforated, essay of #G76 ("F." and "S." same size, not approved) (4)	725.
G76PD	On perforated sheet layout (9)	—
SC13PD	With approval handstamp (5)	110.
296PP	6 items (50)	—
297PP	6 items (50)	—
G76PP	6 items (50)	—
296PI	Pair (50)	—
297PI	Pair (50)	—
G76PI	Pair (50)	—

The essay of No. G76 exists on a not approved perforated sheet layout.

New York #298-299, Geneva #77-78, Souvenir Card #14
Safety in the Air

1978

298PDa	Card, #298PD, #G77PD-G78PD (1)	—
299PD	Cut out from #298PDa (1)	—
299PDa	Card, #298PD-299PD, #G77PD-G78PD (3)	875.
SC14PD	With approval handstamp (4)	—
298PP	10 items (50)	—
299PP	10 items (50)	—
G77PP	6 items (50)	—
G78PP	6 items (50)	—
298PI	Pair (50)	—
299PI	Pair (50)	—
G77PI	Pair (50)	—
G78PI	Pair (50)	—

New York #300-301, Geneva #79-80
UN General Assembly

1978

301PDa	Card, #300PD-301PD, #G79PD-G80PD (4)	975.
300PP	4 items (50)	—
301PP	5 items (50)	—
G79PP	6 items (50)	—
G80PP	6 items (50)	—
300PI	Pair (25)	—
301PI	Pair (25)	—
G79PI	Pair (25)	—
G80PI	Pair (25)	—

New York #302-303, Geneva #81
Technical Cooperation Conference

1978

303PDa	Card, #302PD-303PD, #G81PD (3)	975.
302PP	10 items (50)	—
303PP	10 items (50)	—
G81PP	8 items (50)	—
302PI	Pair (50)	—
303PI	Pair (50)	—
G81PI	Pair (50)	—

Five not approved cards have essays of the set showing black behind closer cogwheels and text close to bottom frame. Value $725.

New York #304-307
Definitives

1979

304PD	(1)	—
304PDa	Card, #304PD-307PD (9)	—
304PDb	Card, #304PD, essays of #305, 306, 307 with inked-in corrections for printer (2)	875.
307PDa	Card, #305PD-307PD (3)	725.
304PP	8 items (50)	—
305PP	8 items (50)	—
306PP	6 items (50)	—
307PP	4 items (50)	—
304PI	Pair (50)	—
305PI	Pair (50)	—
306PI	Pair (75)	—
307PI	Pair (75)	—

Three cut-up not approved cards exist containing the three essays with inked-in corrections.
Nos. 306PI and 307PI include 25 pairs of reprints.

New York #308-309, Geneva #82-83
UN Disaster Relief Coordinator

1979

309PDa	Card, #308PD-309PD (4)	425.
G83PDa	Card, #G82PD-G83PD (1)	—
G83PDb	Card, #G82PD-G83PD, essays of #308-309 with inked-in corrections for printer (3)	875.
308PP	9 items (50)	—
309PP	9 items (50)	—
G82PP	4 items (50)	—
G83PP	4 items (50)	—
308PI	Pair (50)	—
309PI	Pair (50)	—
G82PI	Pair (50)	—
G83PI	Pair (50)	—

Two not approved cards contain the essays with inked-in corrections for printer.

New York #310-311, Geneva #84-85, Souvenir Card #15
International Year of the Child

1979

310PDa	Card, #310PD, essays of #G84-G85 (with IYC emblem above bottom of children's feet) (1)	—
311PD	Cut out from #310PDa (1)	—
311PDa	Card, #310PD-311PD, essays #G84-G85 (2)	1,350.
G85PDa	Card, #G84PD-G85PD (4)	625.
SC15PD	With manuscript approval (4)	—
310PP	9 items (20)	—
311PP	9 items (20)	—
G84PP	8 items (20)	—
G85PP	10 items (20)	—
310PI	Pair (40)	140.
311PI	Pair (40)	140.
G84PI	Pair (20)	140.
G85PI	Pair (20)	140.

One cut up not approved card contains the two essays. Five essays of No. SC15 marked "not approved" show the stamp essays.

Vienna #1-6
Definitives

1979

V6PDa	Card, #V1PD-V6PD (5)	2,000.
V1PP	5 items (50)	—
V2PP	5 items (150)	—
V3PP	5 items (50)	—
V4PP	5 items (50)	—
V5PP	5 items (50)	—
V6PP	5 items (50)	—
V1PI	Pair (50)	—
V2PI	Pair (150)	—
V3PI	Pair (50)	—
V4PI	Pair (50)	—
V5PI	Pair (50)	—
V6PI	Pair (50)	—

New York #312-313, Geneva #86
Namibia

1979

313PDa	Card, #312PD-313PD, #G86PD (4)	825.
312PP	8 items (50)	—
313PP	8 items (50)	—
G86PP	8 items (50)	—
312PI	Pair (50)	—
313PI	Pair (50)	—
G86PI	Pair (50)	—

One card of No. 313PDa is badly damaged.

New York #314-315, Geneva #87-88, Souvenir Card #16
International Court of Justice

1979

315PDa	Card, #314PD-315PD, #G87PD-G88PD 2 each (4)	1,650.
SC16PD	With "not approved" handstamp and "Specimen" perfin (5)	—
314PP	4 items (50)	—
315PP	4 items (50)	—
G87PP	6 items (50)	—
G88PP	7 items (50)	—
314PI	Pair (50)	—
315PI	Pair (50)	—
G87PI	Pair (50)	—
G88PI	Pair (50)	—

New York #316-317, Geneva #89, Vienna #7
New International Economic Order

1980

316PD	(11)	225.
317PD	(5)	200.
G89PD	With approval handstamp (5)	175.
V7PD	(5)	225.
316PP	4 items (50)	—
317PP	4 items (50)	—
G89PP	4 items (50)	—
V7PP	5 items (50)	—
316PI	Pair (50)	—
317PI	Pair (50)	—
G89PI	Pair (50)	—
V7PI	Pair (50)	—

Five cards of No. 316PD are marked "not approved" but there are no discernable differences between it and approved proofs. Six "not approved" cards have essays of No. G89 with text "Nouvel International Economique Ordre." Six "not approved" cards have essays of No. V7 with the same text.

Vienna #8
Definitive

1980

V8PD	(4)	200.
V8PP	11 items, perforated (250)	—
V8PI	Pair (25)	—

New York #318-319, Geneva #90-91, Vienna #9-10, Souvenir Card #17
Decade for Women

1980

318PD	(13)	225.
319PD	(11)	200.
G90PD	(13)	225.
G91PD	(5)	225.
V9PD	(5)	175.
V10PD	(5)	200.
SC17PD	With approval handstamp (5)	175.
318PP	4 items (50)	—
319PP	4 items (50)	—
G90PP	4 items (50)	—
G91PP	4 items (50)	—
V9PP	3 items (50)	—
V10PP	2 items (50)	—
318PI	Pair (50)	—
319PI	Pair (50)	—
G90PI	Pair (50)	—
G91PI	Pair (50)	—
V9PI	Pair (50)	—
V10PI	Pair (50)	—

New York #320-321, Geneva #92, Vienna #11
UN Peace-keeping Operations

1980

321PDa	Card, #320PD-321PD, #V11PD, essay of #G92 with "de" on top line (3)	975.
G92PD	(4)	240.
320PP	2 items (50)	—
321PP	8 items (50)	—
G92PP	4 items (50)	—
V11PP	12 items (50)	—
320PI	Pair (50)	—
321PI	Pair (50)	—
G92PI	Pair (50)	—
V11PI	Pair (50)	—

New York #322-324, Geneva #93-95, Vienna #12-14
UN, 35th Anniv.

1980

324PDa	Card, #324PD, #G95D, #V14PD (4)	1,050.
324PDb	Card, #322PD-324PD, #G93PD-G94PD, #V12PD-V14PD, essay of #G95 with incomplete marginal inscription (3)	1,050.
322PP	8 items (50)	—
323PP	8 items (50)	—
G93PP	6 items (300)	—
G94PP	13 items (650)	—
V12PP	3 items (50)	—
V13PP	8 items (50)	—
322PI	Pair (100)	—
323PI	Pair (100)	—
G93PI	Pair (100)	—
G94PI	Pair (100)	—
V12PI	Pair (175)	—
V13PI	Pair (100)	—

New York #325-340
Flags

1980

325PD	Cut from #340PDa (1)	—
332PD	Cut from #340PDa (1)	—
340PDa	Card, #325PD-340PD (4)	3,500.
340PDb	Card, #326PD-331PD, #333PD-340PD (1)	—
325-340PP	Set of 20 sheets (1)	—
325-340PI	Set of 4 sheets (2)	—

On Nos. 325-340PP, there are five progressive proof sheets per issued sheet.

New York #341-342, Geneva #96-97, Vienna #15-16, Souvenir Card #18
Economic and Social Council

1980

342PDa	Sheet, #341PD-342PD, #G96PD-G97PD, #V15PD-V16PD (4)	110.
G96PD	(4)	—
G97PD	(4)	—
V15PD	(4)	—
V16PD	(4)	—
SC18PD	(4)	—
341PP	6 items (50)	—
342PP	6 items (50)	—
G96PP	6 items (50)	—
G97PP	6 items (50)	—
V15PP	6 items (50)	—
V16PP	6 items (50)	—
341PI	Pair (50)	—
342PI	Pair (50)	—
G96PI	Pair (50)	—
G97PI	Pair (50)	—
V15PI	Pair (50)	—
V16PI	Pair (50)	—

An essay of No. SC18 with curved cancel on 4s stamp has "not approved" handstamp.

New York #343, Geneva #98, Vienna #17
Inalienable Rights of the Palestinian People

1981

343TCa	Card, #343TC blue, #G98PD, #V17PD (1)	625.
G98PD	(5)	—
V17PD	(5)	—
343PP	4 items (50)	—
G98PP	5 items (50)	—
V17PP	4 items (50)	—
343PI	Pair (50)	—
G98PI	Pair (50)	—
V17PI	Pair (50)	—

New York #344-345, Geneva #99-100, Vienna #18-19, Souvenir Card #19
Intl. Year of the Disabled

1980

344PD	Cut out from #G100PDa (1)	—
344PDa	Card, #344PD, #G99PD-G100PD, #V18PD-V19PD, 31c essay of #345 (4)	1,450.
344PDb	Card, #344PD, #G100PD, #V18PD-V19PD (4)	—
G100PDa	Card, #G100PD, #V18PD-V19PD (1)	—
SC19PD	With "not approved" handstamp (9)	110.
344PP	6 items (50)	—
345PP	2 items (50)	—
G99PP	2 items (50)	—
G100PP	2 items (50)	—
V18PP	6 items (50)	—
V19PP	2 items (50)	—
344PI	Pair (50)	—
345PI	Pair (50)	—
G99PI	Pair (50)	—
G100PI	Pair (50)	—
V18PI	Pair (50)	—
V19PI	Pair (50)	—

All die proof cards are stamped "not approved." One example of No. SC19PD has "35c" covering "31c."

New York #346-347, Geneva #101, Vienna #20
Art at the UN

1981

347PDa	Card, #346PD-347PD, #G101PD, #V20PD (1)	1,050.
347PDb	Card, #347PD, #G101PD, #V20PD, 15c essay of #346 (not approved) (6)	—
346PP	5 items (50)	—
347PP	5 items (50)	—
G101PP	5 items (50)	—
V20PP	5 items (50)	—
346PI	Pair (50)	—
347PI	Pair (50)	—
G101PI	Pair (50)	—
V20PI	Pair (50)	—

New York #348-349, Geneva #102, Vienna #21, Souvenir Card #20
Conference on New and Renewable Sources of Energy

1981

348PDa	Card, #348PD, #G102PD, #V21PD, 31c essay of #349 (3)	925.
SC20PD	With approval and specimen handstamps (4)	—
348PP	6 items (50)	—
349PP	4 items (50)	—
G102PP	6 items (50)	—
V21PP	4 items (50)	—
348PI	Pair (50)	—
349PI	Pair (50)	—
G102PI	Pair (50)	—
V21PI	Pair (50)	—

All examples of No. SC20PD have the 31c essay.

New York #350-365
Flags

1981

357PDa	Card, #350PD-357PD (5)	—
365PDa	Card, #358PD-365PD (5)	2,300.
350-365PP	Set of 19 sheets (1)	—
350-365PI	Set of 4 sheets (2)	4,600.

On Nos. 350-365PP, there are four progressive sheets for the issued sheet containing Nos. 354-357, and five progressive proof sheets per issued sheet for the issued sheets containing Nos. 350-353, 358-361 and 362-365. Two sets of imperforate sheets of Nos. 350-353 and two sets of imperforate sheets of Nos. 354-357 exist with 15c denominations are essays.

New York #366-367, Geneva #103-104, Vienna #22-23
Volunteers Program, 10th Anniv.

1981

367PDa	Card, #367PD, #G103PD-G104PD, #V22PD-V23PD, 20c essay of #366 (3)	1,450.
G103TC	white background (1)	—
V22TC	white background (1)	—
V23TC	white background (1)	—
366PI	Pair (50)	—
367PI	Pair (50)	—
G103PI	Pair (50)	—
G104PI	Pair (50)	—
V22PI	Pair (50)	—
V23PI	Pair (50)	—

New York #368-370, Geneva #105-106, Vienna #24
Definitives

1982

370PDa	Card, #368PD-370PD, #G106PD, #V24PD, essay of #G105 with no "I" before "apartheid" (5)	1,450.
368PP	5 items (50)	—
369PP	5 items (50)	—
370PP	5 items (50)	—
G105PP	4 items (50)	—
G106PP	5 items (50)	—
V24PP	5 items (50)	—
368PI	Pair (50)	—
369PI	Pair (50)	—
370PI	Pair (50)	—
G105PI	Pair (50)	—
C106PI	Pair (50)	—
V24PI	Pair (50)	—

One example of No. 370PDa has all stamps canceled and #G105 altered.

New York #371-372, Geneva #107-108, Vienna #25-26, Souvenir Card #21
Environment Program, 10th Anniv.

1982

372PDa	Card, #371PD-372PD, #G107PD, #V25PD-V26PD, 1.30fr essay of #G108 (5)	1,600.
372PDb	Card, #372PD, #G107PD-G108PD, #V25PD-V26PD, 18c essay of #371 (4)	1,450.
SC21PD	(5)	—
371PP	8 items (50)	—
372PP	7 items (50)	—
G107PP	12 items (50)	—
G108PP	8 items (50)	—
V25PP	7 items (50)	—
V26PP	11 items (50)	—
371PI	Pair (50)	—
372PI	Pair (50)	—
G107PI	Pair (50)	—
G108PI	Pair (50)	—
V25PI	Pair (50)	—
V26PI	Pair (50)	—

One example of No. 372PDb has had some stamps defaced. Five essays of No. SC21PD show the 18c essay, with one altered to change 18c to 20c.

New York #373, Geneva #109-110, Vienna #27, Souvenir Card #22
Exploration and Peaceful Uses of Outer Space

1982

373PDa	Card, #373PD, #G109PD-G110PD, #V27PD (4)	925.
G109PD	(4)	—
G110PD	(4)	—
V27PD	(4)	—
SC22PD	(4)	—
373PP	6 items (50)	—
G109PP	6 items (50)	—
G110PP	14 items (50)	—
V27PP	14 items (50)	—
373PI	Pair (50)	—
G109PI	Pair (50)	—
G110PI	Pair (50)	—
V27PI	Pair (50)	—

New York #374-389
Flags

1982

381PDa	Card, #374PD-381PD (5)	2,000.
389PDa	Card, #382PD-389PD (4)	2,000.
374-389PP	Set of 20 sheets (1)	—
374-389PI	Set of 4 sheets (2)	5,250.

On Nos. 374-389PP, there are five progressive proof sheets per issued sheet.

New York #390-391, Geneva #111-112, Vienna #28-29
Conservation and Protection of Nature

1982

390PDa	Card, #390PD, #G111PD, #V29PD, essays of #G112 and #V28 (1)	—
391PD	(1)	—
391PDa	Card, #390PD-391PD, #G111PD, #V29PD, essays of #G112 and #V28 (3)	1,400.
G112PD	(3)	250.
V29PD	(3)	200.
390PP	10 items (50)	—
391PP	10 items (50)	—
G111PP	10 items (50)	—
G112PP	10 items (50)	—
V28PP	10 items (50)	—
V29PP	10 items (50)	—
390PI	Pair (50)	—
391PI	Pair (50)	—
G111PI	Pair (50)	—
G112PI	Pair (50)	—
V28PI	Pair (50)	—
V29PI	Pair (50)	—

Essays of No. G112 have snake with lighter stripes. Essays of No. V28 have umlaut missing one dot.

New York #392-393, Geneva #113, Vienna #30
World Communications Year

1983

392PD	(5)	225.
393PD	(4)	200.
G113PD	(4)	200.
V30PD	(5)	200.
392TC	Dark blue and green colors switched (4)	300.
V30TC	Dark blue and green colors switched (3)	325.
392PP	10 items (50)	—
393PP	15 items (50)	—
G113PP	15 items (50)	—
V30PP	10 items (50)	—
392PI	Pair (50)	—
393PI	Pair (50)	—
G113PI	Pair (50)	—
V30PI	Pair (50)	—

New York #394-395, Geneva #114-115, Vienna #31-32, Souvenir Card #23
Safety at Sea

1983

395PDa	Card, #394PD-395PD, #G114PD-G115PD, #V31PD-V32PD, #394TC-395TC, #G114TC (1)	—
395PDb	Card, #394PD-395PD, #G114PD (4)	750.
G115PDa	Card, #G115PD, #V31PD-V32PD, #394TC-395TC, #G114TC(10)	—
SC23PD	(5)	—
SC23TC	(6)	—
394PP	10 items (50)	—
395PP	8 items (50)	—
G114PP	11 items (50)	—
G115PP	5 items (50)	—
V31PP	5 items (50)	—
V32PP	8 items (50)	—
394PI	Pair (50)	—
395PI	Pair (50)	—
G114PI	Pair (50)	—
G115PI	Pair (50)	—
V31PI	Pair (50)	—
V32PI	Pair (50)	—

Nos. 394TC and G114TC have orange buoy lights instead of red, and No. 395TC has red violet line in ship instead of orange. These appear on No. SC23TC.

New York #396, Geneva #116, Vienna #33-34
World Food Program

1983

396PD	(3)	225.
G116PD	(3)	225.
V33PD	(3)	200.
V34PD	(3)	225.
396PI	Pair (25)	—
G116PI	Pair (25)	—
V33PI	Pair (25)	—
V34PI	Pair (25)	—

New York #397-398, Geneva #117-118, Vienna #35-36, Souvenir Card #24
UN Conference on Trade and Development

1983

398PDa	Card, #397PD-398PD, #G117PD-G118PD, #V35PD-V36PD, approval handstamp (4)	—
398PDb	Card, #397PD-398PD, #G117PD, #V36PD, essays of #G118 and #V35, (not approved, undated) (5)	1,300.
398PDc	As #398PDb, with red dot essays (not approved, dated) (5)	—
SC24PD	With approval handstamp (4)	—
SC24TC	With "not approved" handstamp (5)	—
397PP	5 items (50)	—
398PP	7 items (50)	—
G117PP	5 items (50)	—
G118PP	6 items (50)	—
V35PP	6 items (50)	—
V36PP	7 items (50)	—
397PI	Pair (50)	—
398PI	Pair (50)	—
G117PI	Pair (50)	—
G118PI	Pair (50)	—
V35PI	Pair (50)	—
V36PI	Pair (50)	—

Essays of Nos. G118 and V35 have blue rectangle instead of blue and yellow triangles on bottom row of flags, along with other differences. No. 398PDb has essays showing flag with green dot in 3rd row; 398PDc has red dot on this flag. No. SC24TC has Nos. G118 and V35 with lighter box bottom.

New York #399-414
Flags

1983

403PD	With approval handstamp (1)	240.
406PDa	Card, #399PD-402PD, 404PD-406PD, #403 essay (5)	1,600.
414PDa	Card, #407PD, 409PD-414PD, #408 essay (5)	2,100.
399-414PP	Set of 20 sheets (1)	—
399-414PI	Set of 4 sheets (2)	5,000.

The essay of No. 403 has fewer sun rays than on the issued stamp. The essay of No. 408 has incomplete ring above crest and thinner garlands at left and right. Nos. 413PD-414PD are marked "not approved" on No. 414PDa, but there is no appreciable difference between these and the issued stamps. On Nos. 399-414PP, there are five progressive proof sheets per issued sheet.

New York #415-416, Geneva #119-120, Vienna #37-38
Universal Declaration of Human Rights, 35th Anniv.

1983

415PD	mounted on presentation folder, perforated	450.
416PD	mounted on presentation folder, perforated	450.
G120PDa	Card, #G119PD-G120PD (10)	500.
V37PD	mounted on presentation folder, perforated	325.
V38PD	mounted on presentation folder, perforated	400.
415PP	7 items, with "Muster" overprint (32)	—
415PPa	6 items, without "Muster" overprint (24)	—
	Horiz. pair with vert. gutter, without "Muster" overprint (4)	—
416PP	7 items, with "Muster" overprint (24)	—
	Horiz. pair with vert. gutter, with "Muster" overprint (16)	—
416PPa	6 items, without "Muster" overprint (24)	—
	Horiz. pair with vert. gutter, without "Muster" overprint (4)	—
G119PP	7 items, with "Muster" overprint (24)	—
	Horiz. pair with vert. gutter, with "Muster" overprint (16)	—
G119PPa	6 items, without "Muster" overprint (24)	—
	Horiz. pair with vert. gutter, without "Muster" overprint (4)	—
G120PP	7 items, with "Muster" overprint (24)	—
	Horiz. pair with vert. gutter, with "Muster" overprint (16)	—
G120PPa	6 items, without "Muster" overprint (24)	—
	Horiz. pair with vert. gutter, without "Muster" overprint (4)	—
V37PP	7 items, with "Muster" overprint (24)	—
	Horiz. pair with vert. gutter, with "Muster" overprint (16)	—
V37PPa	6 items, without "Muster" overprint (24)	—
	Horiz. pair with vert. gutter, without "Muster" overprint (4)	—
V38PP	7 items, with "Muster" overprint (24)	—
	Horiz. pair with vert. gutter, with "Muster" overprint (16)	—
V38PPa	6 items, without "Muster" overprint (24)	—
	Horiz. pair with vert. gutter, without "Muster" overprint (4)	—
415PI	Pair (64)	—
	Horiz. pair with vert. gutter (16)	—
416PI	Pair (64)	—
	Horiz. pair with vert. gutter (16)	—
G119PI	Pair (64)	—
	Horiz. pair with vert. gutter (16)	—
G120PI	Pair (64)	—
	Horiz. pair with vert. gutter (16)	—

V37PI	Pair (64)	—
	Horiz. pair with vert. gutter (16)	—
V38PI	Pair (64)	—
	Horiz. pair with vert. gutter (16)	—

On Nos. 415PP-416PP, G119PP-G120PP, V37PP-V38PP, one of the items with "Muster" overprint is a finished imperforate.

New York #417-418, Geneva #121, Vienna #39, Souvenir Card #25
Intl. Conference on Population

1984

417PD	(4)	240.
418PD	(4)	250.
G121PD	(4)	250.
V39PD	(4)	250.
SC25PD	With "not approved" handstamp (9)	—
417PP	8 items (50)	—
418PP	7 items (50)	—
G121PP	8 items (50)	—
V39PP	8 items (50)	—
417PI	Pair (50)	—
418PI	Pair (50)	—
G121PI	Pair (50)	—
V39PI	Pair (50)	—

No. 418PP does not include the blue progressive proof found in No. 417PP.

New York #419-420, Geneva #122-123, Vienna #40-41
World Food Day

1984

419PD	(5)	—
420PDa	Card, #419PD-420PD, #G122PD-G123PD, #V40PD-V41PD with "not approved" handstamp (8)	1,500.
419PP	6 items (50)	—
420PP	6 items (50)	—
G122PP	6 items (50)	—
G123PP	6 items (50)	—
V40PP	6 items (50)	—
V41PP	6 items (50)	—
419PI	Pair (50)	—
420PI	Pair (50)	—
G122PI	Pair (50)	—
G123PI	Pair (50)	—
V40PI	Pair (50)	—
V41PI	Pair (50)	—

There is no appreciable difference between approved and not approved examples of No. 419PD.

New York #421-422, Geneva #124-125, Vienna #42-43
World Heritage Sites

1984

422PDa	Card, #421PD-422PD, with approval handstamp (4)	875.
G125PDa	Card, #G124PD-G125PD, with approval handstamp (4)	625.
V43PDa	Card, #V42PD-V43PD, with approval handstamp (4)	625.
V43TCa	Card, #V42PD (darker sky), V43PD prussian blue sky, "not approved" handstamp (8)	875.
421PP	6 items (80)	—
	Horiz. pair with vert. gutter (10)	—
422PP	6 items (80)	—
	Horiz. pair with vert. gutter (10)	—
G124PP	6 items (80)	—
	Horiz. pair with vert. gutter (10)	—
G125PP	6 items (80)	—
	Horiz. pair with vert. gutter (10)	—
V42PP	6 items (80)	—
	Horiz. pair with vert. gutter (10)	—
V43PP	6 items (80)	—
	Horiz. pair with vert. gutter (10)	—
421PI	Pair (80)	—
	Horiz. pair with vert. gutter (20)	—
422PI	Pair (80)	—
	Horiz. pair with vert. gutter (20)	—
G124PI	Pair (80)	—
	Horiz. pair with vert. gutter (20)	—
G125PI	Pair (80)	—
	Horiz. pair with vert. gutter (20)	—
V42PI	Pair (80)	—
	Horiz. pair with vert. gutter (20)	—
V43PI	Pair (80)	—
	Horiz. pair with vert. gutter (20)	—

Four cards like No. 422PDa with "not approved" handstamp contain essays with slightly different vignettes having taller sky area that is brighter blue and with less distinct designs. Four cards like No. G125PDa contain essays lacking "F.S." before denominations.

New York #423-424, Geneva #126-127, Vienna #44-45
Future for Refugees

1984

424PDa	Card, #423PD-424PD, #G126PD-G127PD, #V44PD-V45PD (2)	—
424PDb	Card, #423PD, #G127PD, 2 each #424PD, #G126PD, #V44PD-V45PD (3)	—
424PDc	Card, #423PD-424PD, #G126PD-G127PD, #V44PD-V45PD, #423TC-424TC, #G126TC-G127TC, V44TC-V45TC (5)	2,750.
424TCa	Card, #423TC-424TC, #G126TC-G127TC, #V44TC-V45TC (1)	—

423PP	2 items (50)	—
G126PP	2 items (50)	—
G127PP	2 items (50)	—
V44PP	2 items (50)	—
V45PP	2 items (50)	—
423PI	Pair (50)	—
424PI	Pair (25)	—
G126PI	Pair (50)	—
G127PI	Pair (50)	—
V44PI	Pair (50)	—
V45PI	Pair (50)	—

Trial color items have backgrounds in buff.

New York #425-440
Flags

1984

432PDa	Card, #429PD-432PD (1)	925.
432PDb	Card, 2 each #429PD-432PD (2)	—
436PDa	Card, #425PD, 427PD, 433PD-436PD, essays of #426, 428 (5)	1,850.
440PDa	Card, #437PD-440PD (1)	925.
440PDb	Card, 2 each #437PD-440PD (2)	—
425-440PP	Set of 21 sheets (1)	—
425-440PI	Set of 4 sheets (2)	4,250.

Essays of Nos. 426 and 428 have country name in smaller type. On Nos. 425-440PP, there are six progressive proof sheets for the issued sheet containing Nos. 429-432, and five progressive proof sheets for the issued sheets containing Nos. 425-428, 433-436 and 437-440.

New York #441-442, Geneva #128, Vienna #46-47, Souvenir Card #26
Intl. Youth Year

1984

441PD	With approval handstamp (4)	350.
442PD	With approval handstamp (3)	240.
G128PD	With approval handstamp (4)	300.
V46PD	(4)	250.
V47PD	(4)	300.
SC26PD	With approval handstamp (4)	—
G128TC	Greenish black strand in center (not approved) (5)	325.
SC26TC	With #G128TC "not approved" handstamp (5)	—
441PP	7 items (50)	—
442PP	9 items (50)	—
G128PP	9 items (50)	—
V46PP	7 items (50)	—
V47PP	7 items (50)	—
441PI	Pair (50)	—
442PI	Pair (50)	—
G128PI	Pair (50)	—
V46PI	Pair (50)	—
V47PI	Pair (50)	—

Five "not approved" essays of No. 441 and four of No. 442 have "N" in "Nations" not touching white frame at bottom. A card with a cutout version of the approved No. 442, but with a "not approved" handstamp, and a card with a cutout essay of No. 442 with an "approved" handstamp exist, probably in error.

New York #443, Geneva #129-130, Vienna #48, Souvenir Card #27
Intl. Labor Organization

1985

443PD	Card, imperforate sheet of 50 stamps (1)	—
443PDa	Card, #443PD (single), #G129PD (single) (4)	500.
G130PDa	Card, #G130PD (single), #V48PD (single) (4)	550.
V48PD	Card, imperforate sheet of 50 stamps (4)	—
SC27PD	With approval handstamp (4)	—
443PI	Pair (50)	—
G129PI	Pair (50)	—
G130PI	Pair (50)	—
V48PI	Pair (50)	—

Essays of No. SC27 exist which have the 1954 stamp with a buff background.

New York #444, Geneva #131-132, Vienna #49
UN University

1985

444PDa	Card, #444PD, #G131PD-G132PD, #V49PD, with approval handstamp (5)	1,150.
G132TC	Bright colors in background ("not approved" handstamp) (6)	400.
444PP	6 items (50)	—
G131PP	6 items (50)	—
G132PP	6 items (50)	—
V49PP	6 items (50)	—
444PI	Pair (50)	—
G131PI	Pair (50)	—
G132PI	Pair (50)	—
V49PI	Pair (50)	—

New York #445-446, Geneva #133-134, Vienna #50-51
Definitives

1985

445PDa	Card, #445PD, #G133PD-G134PD, #V50PD-V51PD, #446PD ("not approved handstamp") (4)	1,600.
446PDa	Card, #445PD-446PD, #G134PD (4)	775.
445PP	4 items (50)	—
446PP	5 items (50)	—

G133PP	7 items (50)	—
G134PP	3 items (50)	—
V50PP	5 items (50)	—
V51PP	5 items (50)	—
V50PI	Pair (50)	—
V51PI	Pair (50)	—

No. 446TC has a lighter blue emblem. Other items in No. 445PDa were declared "not approved," but do not have any appreciable difference from approved items.

New York #447-449, Geneva #135-137, Vienna #52-54
UN, 40th Anniv.

1985

447PDa	Card, 4 each #447PD, #G135PD, #V52PD (1)	—
448PDa	Card, 4 each #448PD, #G136PD, #V53PD (1)	—
449PDa	Card, #447PD-449PD, #G135PD-G137PD, #V52PD-V54PD (1)	1,850.
449PDb	Card, #449PD, #G137PD, #V54PD (4)	—
447PP	5 items (50)	—
448PP	5 items (50)	—
449PP	6 items (36)	—
G135PP	5 items (50)	—
G136PP	5 items (50)	—
G137PP	6 items (36)	—
V52PP	5 items (50)	—
V53PP	5 items (50)	—
V54PP	6 items (36)	—
447PI	Pair (50)	—
448PI	Pair (50)	—
449PI	Pair of souvenir sheets (27)	—
G135PI	Pair (50)	—
G136PI	Pair (50)	—
G137PI	Pair of souvenir sheets (27)	—
V52PI	Pair (50)	—
V53PI	Pair (50)	—
V54PI	Pair of souvenir sheets (27)	—

New York #450-465
Flags

1985

465PDa	Card, #450PD-455PD, 457PD-465PD, essay of #456 (5)	2,900.
450-465PP	Set of 24 sheets (1)	—
450-465PI	Set of 4 sheets (2)	4,000.

Essay of Nos. 456 has thin-lined star. On Nos. 425-440PP, there are six progressive proof sheets per issued sheet.

New York #466-467, Geneva #138-139, Vienna #55-56, Souvenir Card #28
UNICEF Child Survival Campaign

1985

466PD	(4)	300.
466PDa	Card, with cut-up pane of 50 (1)	—
467PD	(4)	—
467PDa	Card, with cut-up pane of 50 (1)	—
G138PD	(4)	300.
G138PDa	Card, with cut-up pane of 50 (1)	—
G139PD	(4)	225.
G139PDa	Card, with cut-up pane of 50 (1)	—
V55PD	(4)	300.
V55PDa	Card, with cut-up pane of 50 (1)	—
V56PD	(4)	250.
V56PDa	Card, with cut-up pane of 50 (1)	—
SC28PD	(4)	—
466PP	5 items (50)	—
467PP	5 items (50)	—
G138PP	5 items (50)	—
G139PP	5 items (50)	—
V55PP	5 items (50)	—
V56PP	5 items (50)	—
466PI	Pair (50)	—
467PI	Pair (50)	—
G138PI	Pair (50)	—
G139PI	Pair (50)	—
V55PI	Pair (50)	—
V56PI	Pair (50)	—

New York #468, Geneva #140, Vienna #57
Africa in Crisis

1986

468PDa	Card, #468PD, #G140PD, essay of #V57 (4)	—
468PP	5 items (50)	—
G140PP	4 items (50)	—
V57PP	4 items (50)	—
468PI	Pair (50)	—
G140PI	Pair (50)	—
V57PI	Pair (50)	—

One example of No. 468PDa has essay of No. V57 corrected to show small loop of "8" at top as in the issued stamp.

New York #472a, Geneva #144a, Vienna #61a
UN Development Program

1986

472aPD	(4)	825.
472aPDa	Card, pane of 10 blocks (2)	—
G144aPD	(4)	825.
G144aPDa	Card, pane of 10 blocks (2)	—
V61aPD	(4)	825.
V61aPDa	Card, pane of 10 blocks (2)	—
472aPP	6 items (10 blocks)	—
G144aPP	6 items (10 blocks)	—
V61aPP	6 items (10 blocks)	—

472aPI	Pair (20)	—
G144aPI	Pair (20)	—
V61aPI	Pair (20)	—

Geneva #145
Definitive

1986

G145PD	(5)	—
G145PP	5 items (50)	—
G145PI	Pair (50)	—

New York #473-474, Geneva #146-147, Vienna #62-63, Souvenir Card #29
Philately

1986

473PDa	Partial pane of 39 with approval handstamp on reverse (1)	—
473PDb	Full pane of 50 with approval handstamp on reverse (3)	—
474PDa	Imperforate pane of 50 with approval handstamp on reverse (4)	—
G146PDa	Imperforate pane of 50 with approval handstamp on reverse (4)	—
G147PDa	Partial pane of 41 with approval handstamp on reverse (1)	—
G147PDb	Full pane of 50 with approval handstamp on reverse (3)	—
V62PDa	Imperforate pane of 50 with approval handstamp on reverse (4)	—
V63PDa	Partial pane of 41 with approval handstamp on reverse (1)	—
V63PDb	Full pane of 50 with approval handstamp on reverse (4)	—
SC29PD	(3)	—
473TC	greenish black (5)	725.
474TC	purple (1)	725.
474TC	blue (1)	725.
474TC	red brown (1)	725.
474TC	olive brown (1)	725.
474TC	dark green (1)	725.
G146TC	purple (1)	725.
G146TC	blue (1)	725.
G146TC	reddish purple (1)	725.
G146TC	greenish black (1)	725.
G146TC	dark olive brown (1)	725.
G147TC	dark blue (5)	775.
V62TC	purple (1)	725.
V62TC	blue (1)	725.
V62TC	red brown (1)	725.
V62TC	greenish black (1)	725.
V62TC	dark olive brown (1)	725.
V63TC	greenish black (5)	775.

New York #475-476, Geneva #148-149, Vienna #64-65, Souvenir Card #30
International Peace Year

1986

475PD	(4)	300.
475PDa	Card, imperforate pane of 50 (1)	—
476PD	(4)	250.
476PDa	Card, imperforate pane of 50 (1)	—
G148PD	(4)	450.
G148PDa	Card, imperforate pane of 50 (1)	—
G149PD	(4)	250.
V64PD	(1)	300.
V65PD	(4)	—
V65PDa	Card, imperforate pane of 50 (1)	—
SC30PD	(4)	—
475PP	4 items (50)	—
476PP	4 items (50)	—
G148PP	4 items (50)	—
G149PP	4 items (50)	—
V64PP	4 items (50)	—
V65PP	3 items (50)	—
475PI	Pair (50)	—
476PI	Pair (50)	—
G148PI	Pair (50)	—
G149PI	Pair (50)	—
V64PI	Pair (50)	—
V65PI	Pair (50)	—

Essays of No. V64 with 7s denominations exist in three cards with singles and one card with an imperforate pane of 50.

New York #477-492
Flags

1986

492PDa	Card, #477PD-492PD (5)	3,250.
477-492PP	Set of 24 sheets (1)	—
477-492PI	Set of 4 sheets (2)	4,000.

On Nos. 477-492PP, there are six progressive proof sheets per issued sheet.

New York #493, Geneva #150, Vienna #66
World Federation of UN Associations, 40th Anniv.

1986

493PD	(3)	525.
493PDa	Imperforate souvenir sheet with cancel lines added (1)	—
G150PD	(3)	300.
G150PDa	Imperforate souvenir sheet with cancel lines added (1)	—
V66PD	(3)	400.
V66PDa	Imperforate souvenir sheet with cancel lines added (1)	—
493PP	8 items (16)	—
G150PP	11 items (16)	—
V66PP	6 items (16)	—
493PI	souvenir sheets (32)	—
G150PI	souvenir sheets (32)	—
V66PI	souvenir sheets (32)	—

New York #494, Geneva #151, Vienna #67
Trygve Lie

1987

494PD	On imperforate sheet layout (1)	—
494PDa	Card, #494PD, #G151PD, V67PD (4)	725.
G151PD	On imperforate sheet layout (1)	—
V67PD	On imperforate sheet layout (1)	—
494PP	10 items (50)	—
G151PP	10 items (50)	—
V67PP	10 items (50)	—
494PI	Pair (50)	—
G151PI	Pair (100)	—
V67PI	Pair (50)	—

Geneva #152-153
Definitives

1987

G152PD	(1)	375.
G153PD	(4)	—
G153TCa	Card, 2 #G153TC dark blue panel (5)	—
G153TCb	Card, imperforate pane of 50 #G153TC dark blue panel (2)	525.
G152PP	6 items (50)	—
G153PP	5 items (50)	—
G152PI	Pair (50)	—
G153PI	Pair (50)	—

Six essays of No. G152 with design 33mm high exist on cards marked "approved text only."

New York #495-496, Geneva #154-155, Vienna #68-69, Souvenir Card #31
International Year of Shelter for the Homeless

1987

496PDa	Card, #495PD-496PD, #G154PD-G155PD, #V68PD-V69PD (4)	1,350.
SC31PD	(3)	—
495PP	6 items (80)	—
	Horiz. pair with vert. gutter (10)	—
496PP	6 items (80)	—
	Horiz. pair with vert. gutter (10)	—
G154PP	6 items (80)	—
	Horiz. pair with vert. gutter (10)	—
G155PP	6 items (80)	—
	Horiz. pair with vert. gutter (10)	—
V68PP	6 items (80)	—
	Horiz. pair with vert. gutter (10)	—
V69PP	6 items (80)	—
	Horiz. pair with vert. gutter (10)	—
495PI	Pair (80)	—
	Horiz. pair with vert. gutter (20)	—
496PI	Pair (80)	—
	Horiz. pair with vert. gutter (20)	—
G154PI	Pair (80)	—
	Horiz. pair with vert. gutter (20)	—
G155PI	Pair (80)	—
	Horiz. pair with vert. gutter (20)	—
V68PI	Pair (80)	—
	Horiz. pair with vert. gutter (20)	—
V69PI	Pair (80)	—
	Horiz. pair with vert. gutter (20)	—

New York #497-498, Geneva #156-157, Vienna #70-71
Fight Drug Abuse

1987

498PDa	Card, #497PD-498PD, #G156PD-G157PD, #V70PD-V71PD with approval handstamp (5)	1,450.
497PP	8 items (50)	—
498PP	8 items (50)	—
G156PP	8 items (50)	—
G157PP	8 items (50)	—
V70PP	8 items (50)	—
V71PP	8 items (50)	—
497PI	Pair (100)	—
498PI	Pair (100)	—
G156PI	Pair (100)	—
G157PI	Pair (100)	—
V70PI	Pair (100)	—
V71PI	Pair (100)	—

Six "not approved" cards contain essays of the six stamps, each lacking the white line separating the halves of the vignette.

Vienna #72-73
Definitives

1987

V73PDa	Card, #V72PD-V73PD (5)	575.
V72PP	8 items (50)	—
V73PP	7 items (50)	—
V72PI	Pair (100)	—
V73PI	Pair (100)	—

New York #499-514
Flags

1987

511PDa	Card, #500PD, 501PD, 503PD, 507PD, 509PD, 511PD (1)	—
514PDa	Card, #499PD-514PD (5)	3,750.
514PDb	Card, #499PD, 500PD, 502PD, 504PD-506PD, 508PD, 510PD, 512PD-514PD (1)	—
499-514PP	Set of 24 sheets (1)	—
499-502PI	Sheet (2)	—
503-506PI	Sheet (2)	—

On Nos. 499-514PP, there are six progressive proof sheets per issued sheet.

New York #515-516, Geneva #158-159, Vienna #74-75
United Nations Day

1987

515PDa	Card, #515PD, #V74PD, essay of #G158 (1)	—
516PDa	Card, #516PD, #G159PD, #V75PD (1)	—
516PDb	Card, #515PD-516PD, #G159PD, #V74PD-V75PD, essay of #G158 (4)	1,250.
515PP	8 items (36)	—
	Cross gutter block (3)	—
	Horiz. pair with vert. gutter (6)	—
	Vert. pair with horiz. gutter (18)	—
516PP	8 items (36)	—
	Cross gutter block (3)	—
	Horiz. pair with vert. gutter (6)	—
	Vert. pair with horiz. gutter (18)	—
G158PP	8 items (36)	—
	Cross gutter block (3)	—
	Horiz. pair with vert. gutter (6)	—
	Vert. pair with horiz. gutter (18)	—
G159PP	8 items (36)	—
	Cross gutter block (3)	—
	Horiz. pair with vert. gutter (6)	—
	Vert. pair with horiz. gutter (18)	—
V74PP	8 items (36)	—
	Cross gutter block (3)	—
	Horiz. pair with vert. gutter (6)	—
	Vert. pair with horiz. gutter (18)	—
V75PP	8 items (36)	—
	Cross gutter block (3)	—
	Horiz. pair with vert. gutter (6)	—
	Vert. pair with horiz. gutter (18)	—
515PI	Pair (12)	—
516PI	Pair (12)	—
G158PI	Pair (28)	—
	Cross gutter block (3)	—
	Horiz. pair with vert. gutter (6)	—
	Vert. pair with horiz. gutter (18)	—
G159PI	Pair (28)	—
	Cross gutter block (3)	—
	Horiz. pair with vert. gutter (6)	—
	Vert. pair with horiz. gutter (18)	—
V74PI	Pair (28)	—
	Cross gutter block (3)	—
	Horiz. pair with vert. gutter (6)	—
	Vert. pair with horiz. gutter (18)	—
V75PI	Pair (28)	—
	Cross gutter block (3)	—
	Horiz. pair with vert. gutter (6)	—
	Vert. pair with horiz. gutter (18)	—

Essay of No. G158 lacks accent in "Journée."

New York #517-518, Geneva #160-161, Vienna #76-77, Souvenir Card #32
Immunize Every Child

1987

518PDa	Card, #517PD-518PD, #G161PD, #V76PD-V77PD, 35c essay of #G160 (11)	1,500.
SC32PD	(11)	—
517PP	11 items (50)	—
518PP	11 items (50)	—
G160PP	11 items (50)	—
G161PP	12 items (50)	—
V76PP	12 items (50)	—
V77PP	9 items (50)	—
517PI	Pair (50)	—
518PI	Pair (50)	—
G160PI	Pair (75)	—
G161PI	Pair (75)	—
V76PI	Pair (75)	—
V77PI	Pair (75)	—

All examples of No. SC32PD have the essay of No. G160. There is no appreciable difference between approved and not approved examples of Nos. 518PDa or SC32PD.

New York #519-520, Geneva #162-163, Vienna #78-79
International Fund for Agricultural Development

1988

520PDa	Card, #519PD-520PD, #G162PD-G163PD, #V78PD-V79PD (4)	1,550.
519PP	8 items (50)	—
520PP	8 items (50)	—
G162PP	9 items (50)	—
G163PP	9 items (50)	—
V78PP	9 items (50)	—
V79PP	9 items (50)	—
519PI	Pair (50)	—
520PI	Pair (50)	—
G162PI	Pair (50)	—
G163PI	Pair (50)	—
V78PI	Pair (50)	—
V79PI	Pair (50)	—

New York #521, Geneva #164
Definitives

1988

521PD	(4)	575.
G164PD	(6)	300.
521PP	6 items (50)	—
G164PP	11 items (50)	—
521PI	Pair (50)	—
G164PI	Pair (50)	—

New York #523a, Geneva #166a, Vienna #81a
Survival of the Forests

1988

523aPDa	Card, imperforate pane of 6 pairs with approval handstamp (6)	
523aPDb	Card, perforated pane of 6 pairs with approval handstamp (1)	2,750.
		—
G166aPDa	Card, imperforate pane of 6 pairs with approval handstamp (7)	2,400.
V81aPDa	Card, imperforate pane of 6 pairs with approval handstamp (7)	2,400.
523aPP	8 items (6 pairs)	—
G166aPP	8 items (6 pairs)	—
V81aPP	8 items (6 pairs)	—
523aPI	Pair (12)	—
G166aPI	Pair (24)	—
V81aPI	Pair (24)	—

Panes on Nos. 523aPDa, 523aPDb, G166aPDa, V81aPDa are not affixed to cards but are between stamp mounts.

New York #524-525, Geneva #167-168, Vienna #82-83, Souvenir Card #33
Intl. Volunteer Day

1988

524PDa	Card, #524PD, #G167PD-G168PD, #V82PD-V83PD with approval handstamp (4)	1,400.
525PDa	Card, #525PD, #G168PD, #V83PD, essays of #524, #G167, #V82 with "not approved" handstamp (4)	875.
SC33PD	(4)	—
SC33TC	light blue signature (4)	—
524PP	6 items (40)	—
525PP	6 items (40)	—
525PPa	Horiz. se-tenant pair with vert. gutter, #524PP-525PP (10)	—
G167PP	6 items (40)	—
G168PP	6 items (40)	—
G168PPa	Horiz. se-tenant pair with vert. gutter, #G167PP-G168PP (10)	—
V82PP	6 items (40)	—
V83PP	6 items (40)	—
V83PPa	Horiz. se-tenant pair with vert. gutter, #V82PP-V83PP (10)	—
524PI	Pair (70)	—
525PI	Pair (70)	—
G167PI	Pair (70)	—
G168PI	Pair (70)	—
V82PI	Pair (70)	—
V83PI	Pair (70)	—

Essays have incomplete dates at bottom.

New York #526-527, Geneva #169-170, Vienna #84-85, Souvenir Card #34
Health in Sports

1988

526PD	With approval handstamp(2)	250.
526PDa	Card, #526PD, #527TC (1)	—
526PDb	Card, imperforate pane of 50 #526PD (1)	—
527PD	(6)	150.
527PDa	Card, 2 #527PD (1)	—
527PDb	Card, imperforate pane of 50 #527PD (2)	—
G169PD	(6)	350.
G169PDa	Card, 2 #G169PD (1)	—
G169PDb	Card, imperforate pane of 50 #G169PD (2)	—
G170PD	With approval handstamp (2)	350.
G170PDa	Card, #G170PD, #G170TC (1)	—
G170PDb	Card, imperforate pane of 50 #G170PD (1)	—
V84PD	With approval handstamp (2)	450.
V84PDa	Card, #V84PD, #V84TC (1)	—
V84PDb	Card, imperforate pane of 50 #V84PD (1)	—
V85PD	(6)	450.
V85PDa	Card, 2 #V85PD (1)	—
V85PDb	Card, imperforate pane of 50 #V85PD (2)	—
SC34PD	With approval handstamp (5)	—
526TC	Card, darker brown in LL part of vignette (not approved) (4)	325.
526TCa	Card, imperforate pane of 50 #526TC (1)	—
G170TC	Card, black "F.S." (not approved) (4)	—
G170TCa	Card, imperforate pane of 50 #G170TC (1)	—
V84TC	Card, red splotches in UL of vignette (not approved) (4)	325.
V84TCa	Card, imperforate pane of 50 #V84TC (109)	—
SC34TC	With #526TC (not approved) (4)	—
526PP	4 items (50)	—
527PP	4 items (50)	—
G169PP	4 items (50)	—
G170PP	4 items (50)	—
V84PP	5 items (50)	—
V85PP	4 items (50)	—
526PI	Pair (50)	—
527PI	Pair (50)	—
G169PI	Pair (50)	—
G170PI	Pair (45)	—
V84PI	Pair (50)	—
V85PI	Pair (50)	—

There is no appreciable difference between approved and not approved examples of Nos. 527PD, G169PD and V85PD.

New York #528-543
Flags

1988

543PDa	Card, #540PD, 543PD (2)	425.
543PDb	Card, #540PD, 543PD, 22c essays of #528-539, 541-542 (2)	—
528-543PP	Set of 24 sheets (1)	—
528-543PI	Set of 4 sheets (2)	3,000.

Nine cards each containing 22c essays of Nos. 528-543 exist. Value $2,900 each. On Nos. 528-543PP, there are six progressive proof sheets per issued sheet.

New York #544-545, Geneva #171-172, Vienna #86-87
Universal Declaration of Human Rights, 40th Anniv.

1988

545PDa	Card, #544PD-545PD, #G171PD-G172PD, #V86PD-V87PD (5)	2,900.
G172PDa	Card, #172PD, 90c essay of #G172 (6)	775.
544PP	6 items (50)	—
545PP	6 items (1)	—
G171PP	6 items (50)	—
G172PP	6 items (1)	—
V86PP	6 items (50)	—
V87PP	6 items (1)	—
544PI	Pair (50)	—
545PI	souvenir sheets (2)	650.
G171PI	Pair (50)	—
G172PI	souvenir sheets (2)	975.
V86PI	Pair (50)	625.
V87PI	souvenir sheets (2)	—

New York #546-547, Geneva #173-174, Vienna #88-89, Souvenir Card #35
World Bank

1989

547PDa	Card, #546PD-547PD, #G173PD-G174PD, #V88PD-V89PD with approval handstamp (4)	1,250.
547PDb	Card, #547PD in slightly lighter colors, #V88PD, #G173TC, essays of #546, #G174, #V89 (5)	1,150.
SC35PD	With "29 Aug. 1988" handstamp on back (4)	—
546PP	6 items (40)	—
547PP	6 items (40)	—
547PPa	Vert. se-tenant pair with horiz. gutter, #546PP-547PP (10)	—
G173PP	6 items (40)	—
G174PP	6 items (40)	—
G174PPa	Vert. se-tenant pair with horiz. gutter, #G173PP-G174PP (10)	—
V88PP	6 items (40)	—
V89PP	6 items (40)	—
V89PPa	Vert. se-tenant pair with horiz. gutter, #V88PP-V89PP (10)	—
546PI	Pair (40)	—
547PI	Pair (40)	—
G173PI	Pair (70)	—
G174PI	Pair (70)	—
G174PIa	Vert. se-tenant pair with horiz. gutter, #G173PI-G174PI (10)	—
V88PI	Pair (50)	—
V89PI	Pair (50)	—

No. G173TC has lighter orange background. Essays of Nos. 546, G174, and V89 have incomplete years at bottom.

New York #548, Geneva #175, Vienna #90
UN Peace-keeping Force

1989

548PD	Imperforate pane of 50 with "not approved" handstamp (1)	—
548PDa	Card, #548PD, #G175PD, #V90PD (5)	—
G175PD	Imperforate pane of 50 with "not approved" handstamp (1)	—
V90PD	Imperforate pane of 50 with "not approved" handstamp (1)	—
548PP	6 items (90)	—
	Horiz. pair with vert. gutter (5)	—
G175PP	6 items (90)	—
	Horiz. pair with vert. gutter (5)	—
V90PP	6 items (90)	—
	Horiz. pair with vert. gutter (5)	—
548PI	Pair (70)	—
G175PI	Pair (138)	—
	Horiz. pair with vert. gutter (10)	—
V90PI	Pair (138)	—
	Horiz. pair with vert. gutter (10)	—

There is no appreciable difference between approved and not approved examples of No. 548PDa.

New York #549
Definitive

1989

549PD	(9)	—
549PP	6 items (64)	—
	Cross gutter block (1)	—
	Horiz. pair with vert. gutter (8)	—
	Vert. pair with horiz. gutter (8)	—
549PI	Pair (24)	—

There is no appreciable difference between approved and not approved examples of No. 549PD.

New York #550-551, Geneva #176-177, Vienna #91-92, Souvenir Card #36
World Weather Watch

1989

551PDa	Card, #550PD-551PD, #G176PD-G177PD, #V91PD-V92PD (9)	—
SC36PD	(4)	—
550PP	6 items (40)	—
551PP	6 items (40)	—
551PPa	Vert. se-tenant pair with horiz. gutter, #550PP-551PP (10)	—
G176PP	6 items (40)	—
G177PP	6 items (40)	—
G177PPa	Vert. se-tenant pair with horiz. gutter, #G176PP-G177PP (10)	—
V91PP	6 items (40)	—
V92PP	6 items (40)	—
V92PPa	Vert. se-tenant pair with horiz. gutter, #V91PP-V92PP (10)	—
550PI	(50 pairs)	—
551PI	(50 pairs)	—
G176PI	(70 pairs)	—
G177PI	(70 pairs)	—
G177PIa	Vert. se-tenant pair with horiz. gutter, #G176PI-G177PI (10)	—
V91PI	(50 pairs)	—
V92PI	(50 pairs)	—

There is no appreciable difference between approved and not approved examples of No. 551PDa.

New York #552-553, Geneva #178-179, Vienna #93-94
Offices in Vienna, 10th Anniv.

1989

552PD	With approval handstamp (4)	—
553PD	(4)	—
G178PD	(4)	—
G179PDa	Card, #G179PD, #G179TC orange background, #G179TC dull green background (4)	—
V93PD	(4)	—
V94PD	(9)	—
552PP	10 items (25)	—
553PP	12 items (25)	—
G178PP	10 items (25)	—
G179PP	10 items (25)	—
V93PP	10 items (25)	—
V94PP	10 items (25)	—
552PI	(24 pairs)	—
553PI	(24 pairs)	—
G178PI	(24 pairs)	—
G179PI	(24 pairs)	—
V93PI	(24 pairs)	—
V94PI	(24 pairs)	—

Five not approved essays of #552 have clearly defined cross-hatching in background. There is no appreciable difference between approved and not approved examples of No. V94PD. One item from No. G179PP and V93PP is blank as it is from progressive proof sheet showing only black sheet margins.

New York #554-569
Flags

1989

568PDa	Card, #558PD-561PD, 563PD, 564PD, 566PD-568PD (5)	—
569PDa	Card, #554PD-569PD (5)	—
554-569PP	Set of 24 sheets (1)	—
554-569PI	Set of 4 sheets (2)	—

On Nos. 554-569PP, there are six progressive proof sheets per issued sheet.

New York #570-571, Geneva #180-181, Vienna #95-96
Human Rights

1989

570PD	Strip of 3 + 3 labels (4)	—
571PD	Strip of 3 + 3 labels (4)	—
571PDa	Card, #570PD-571PD, #G180PD-G181PD, #V95PD-V96PD (4)	—
G180PD	3 singles or strip of 3 + 3 labels (4)	—
G181PD	Strip of 3 + 3 labels (4)	—
V95PD	Strip of 3 + 3 labels (4)	—
V96PD	3 singles or strip of 3 + 3 labels (4)	—
570PP	6 items (20)	—
	Cross gutter block (1)	—
	Horiz. pair with vert. gutter (2)	—
	Vert. pair with horiz. gutter (10)	—
571PP	6 items (20)	—
	Cross gutter block (1)	—
	Horiz. pair with vert. gutter (2)	—
	Vert. pair with horiz. gutter (10)	—
G180PP	6 items (20)	—
	Cross gutter block (1)	—
	Horiz. pair with vert. gutter (2)	—
	Vert. pair with horiz. gutter (10)	—
G181PP	6 items (20)	—
	Cross gutter block (1)	—
	Horiz. pair with vert. gutter (2)	—
	Vert. pair with horiz. gutter (10)	—
V95PP	6 items (48)	—
	Cross gutter block (1)	—
	Horiz. pair with vert. gutter (2)	—
	Vert. pair with horiz. gutter (10)	—
V96PP	6 items (48)	—
	Cross gutter block (1)	—
	Horiz. pair with vert. gutter (2)	—
	Vert. pair with horiz. gutter (10)	—
570PI	(12 pairs)	—
	Cross gutter block (1)	—

	Horiz. pair with vert. gutter (2)	—
571PI	Vert. pair with horiz. gutter (10)	—
	(12 pairs)	—
	Cross gutter block (1)	—
	Horiz. pair with vert. gutter (2)	—
	Vert. pair with horiz. gutter (10)	—
G180PI	(20 pairs)	—
	Cross gutter block (1)	—
	Horiz. pair with vert. gutter (2)	—
	Vert. pair with horiz. gutter (10)	—
G181PI	(20 pairs)	—
	Cross gutter block (1)	—
	Horiz. pair with vert. gutter (2)	—
	Vert. pair with horiz. gutter (10)	—
V95PI	(20 pairs)	—
	Cross gutter block (1)	—
	Horiz. pair with vert. gutter (2)	—
	Vert. pair with horiz. gutter (10)	—
V96PI	(20 pairs)	—
	Cross gutter block (1)	—
	Horiz. pair with vert. gutter (2)	—
	Vert. pair with horiz. gutter (10)	—

New York #572, Geneva #182, Vienna #97
International Trade Center

1990

572PDa	Card, #572PD, #G182PD, #V97PD with approval handstamp (5)	—
572TCa	Card, #572TC blue green ship, #G182TC red orange ship, #V97TC light pink building, with "not approved" handstamp (6)	—
572PP	9 items (50)	—
G182PP	7 items (50)	—
V97PP	8 items (50)	—
572PI	(50 pairs)	—
G182PI	(75 pairs)	—
V97PI	(50 pairs)	—

Geneva #183, Vienna #98
Definitives

1990

G183PD	(6)	—
V98PD	Proof on large sheet with approval or "not approved" handstamp, and set of 7 progressive proofs on large sheets (9)	—
G183PP	9 items (1)	—
V98PP	7 items (50)	—
G183PI	(50 pairs)	—
V98PI	(50 pairs)	—

The not approved proofs of No. V98PD are slightly lighter in color than the approved proofs.

New York #573-574, Geneva #184-185, Vienna #99-100, Souvenir Card #37
Fight AIDS Worldwide

1990

573PDa	Card, #573PD, #G184PD, #V99PD (4)	—
574PDa	Card, #574PD, #G185PD, #573TC white background, #G184TC white background, #V99TC white background, 10s essay of #V100 (4)	—
SC37PD	(4)	—
573PP	7 items (50)	—
574PP	6 items (50)	—
G184PP	7 items (50)	—
G185PP	7 items (50)	—
V99PP	7 items (50)	—
V100PP	6 items (50)	—
573PI	(50 pairs)	—
574PI	(50 pairs)	—
G184PI	(75 pairs)	—
G185PI	(75 pairs)	—
V99PI	(75 pairs)	—
V100PI	(75 pairs)	—

New York #575-576, Geneva #186-187, Vienna #101-102
Medicinal Plants

1990

576PDa	Card, #575PD-576PD, #G186PD-G187PD, #V101PD-V102PD (4)	—
G187PD	(4)	—
G186PP	6 items (50)	—
G187PP	6 items (50)	—
V101PP	6 items (50)	—
V102PP	6 items (50)	—
575PI	(50 pairs)	—
576PI	(50 pairs)	—
G186PI	(50 pairs)	—
G187PI	(50 pairs)	—
V101PI	(50 pairs)	—
V102PI	(50 pairs)	—

New York #577-579, Geneva #188-190, Vienna #103-105
United Nations, 45th Anniv.

1990

578PDa	Card, #577PD-578PD, #G188PD-G189PD, 6s essay of #V103, 8s essay of #V104 (4)	—
579PDa	Card, #579PD, #G190PD, #V105PD (4)	—
577PP	8 items (320)	—
	Horiz. pair with vert. gutter (40)	—
578PP	8 items (320)	—
	Horiz. pair with vert. gutter (40)	—
579PP	8 items (100)	—
G188PP	10 items (160)	—

	Horiz. pair with vert. gutter (20)	—
G189PP	8 items (320)	—
	Horiz. pair with vert. gutter (40)	—
G190PP	9 items (100)	—
V103PP	8 items (320)	—
	Horiz. pair with vert. gutter (40)	—
V104PP	8 items (320)	—
	Horiz. pair with vert. gutter (40)	—
V105PP	8 items (100)	—
577PI	(80 pairs)	—
	Horiz. pair with vert. gutter (10)	—
578PI	(80 pairs)	—
	Horiz. pair with vert. gutter (10)	—
579PI	(100 souvenir sheets)	—
G188PI	(260 pairs)	—
	Horiz. pair with vert. gutter (40)	—
G189PI	(260 pairs)	—
	Horiz. pair with vert. gutter (40)	—
G190PI	(100 souvenir sheets)	—
V103PI	(260 pairs)	—
	Horiz. pair with vert. gutter (40)	—
V104PI	(260 pairs)	—
	Horiz. pair with vert. gutter (40)	—
V105PI	(100 souvenir sheets)	—

New York #580-581, Geneva #191-192, Vienna #106-107, Souvenir Card #38
Crime Prevention

1990

581PDa	Card, #580PD-581PD, #G191PD-G192PD, #V106PD-V107PD, #SC38PD (5)	—
580PP	8 items (50)	—
581PP	8 items (50)	—
G191PP	8 items (50)	—
G192PP	8 items (50)	—
V106PP	8 items (100)	—
V107PP	8 items (100)	—
580PI	(50 pairs)	—
581PI	(50 pairs)	—
G191PI	(75 pairs)	—
G192PI	(75 pairs)	—
V106PI	(75 pairs)	—
V107PI	(75 pairs)	—

New York #582-583, Geneva #193-194, Vienna #108-109,
Human Rights

1990

582PDa	Strip of 3 + 3 labels (9)	—
583PDa	Strip of 3 + 3 labels with approval handstamp (4)	—
G193PDa	Strip of 3 + 3 labels (9)	—
G194PDa	Strip of 3 + 3 labels (9)	—
V108PDa	Strip of 3 + 3 labels (9)	—
V109PDa	Strip of 3 + 3 labels (9)	—
583TCa	Strip of 3 + 3 labels (chocolate panels) with "not approved" handstamp (5)	—
582PP	6 items (20)	—
	Cross gutter block (1)	—
	Horiz. pair with vert. gutter (2)	—
	Vert. pair with horiz. gutter (10)	—
583PP	6 items (20)	—
	Cross gutter block (1)	—
	Horiz. pair with vert. gutter (2)	—
	Vert. pair with horiz. gutter (10)	—
G193PP	6 items (20)	—
	Cross gutter block (1)	—
	Horiz. pair with vert. gutter (2)	—
	Vert. pair with horiz. gutter (10)	—
G194PP	8 items (20)	—
	Cross gutter block (1)	—
	Horiz. pair with vert. gutter (2)	—
	Vert. pair with horiz. gutter (10)	—
V108PP	6 items (20)	—
	Cross gutter block (1)	—
	Horiz. pair with vert. gutter (2)	—
	Vert. pair with horiz. gutter (10)	—
V109PP	6 items (20)	—
	Cross gutter block (1)	—
	Horiz. pair with vert. gutter (2)	—
	Vert. pair with horiz. gutter (10)	—
582PI	(20 pairs)	—
	Cross gutter block (1)	—
	Horiz. pair with vert. gutter (2)	—
	Vert. pair with horiz. gutter (10)	—
583PI	(20 pairs)	—
	Cross gutter block (1)	—
	Horiz. pair with vert. gutter (2)	—
	Vert. pair with horiz. gutter (10)	—
G193PI	(20 pairs)	—
	Cross gutter block (1)	—
	Horiz. pair with vert. gutter (2)	—
	Vert. pair with horiz. gutter (10)	—
G194PI	(20 pairs)	—
	Cross gutter block (1)	—
	Horiz. pair with vert. gutter (2)	—
	Vert. pair with horiz. gutter (10)	—
V108PI	(20 pairs)	—
	Cross gutter block (1)	—
	Horiz. pair with vert. gutter (2)	—
	Vert. pair with horiz. gutter (10)	—
V109PI	(20 pairs)	—
	Cross gutter block (1)	—
	Horiz. pair with vert. gutter (2)	—
	Vert. pair with horiz. gutter (10)	—

There is no appreciable difference between approved and not approved examples of Nos. 582PD, G193PD, G194PD, V108PD and V109PD.

New York #587a, Geneva #198a, Vienna #113a, Souvenir Card #39
Economic Council for Europe

1991

587aPDa	Card, #587aPD, #G198aPD, #V113aPD with printed perforations (2)	—
587aPDb	Card, #587aPDa, SC39PD (1)	—
SC39PD	(1)	—
587aPP	13 items (20 blocks)	—
G198aPP	13 items (20 blocks)	—
V113aPP	13 items (20 blocks)	—
587aPI	(40 blocks)	—
G198aPI	(40 blocks)	—
V113aPI	(40 blocks)	—

Second sets of blocks of Nos. 587aPP and G198aPP with 10 items, and No. V113aPP with 11 items (some items differing from the 13 item set) exist.

New York #588-589, Geneva #199-200, Vienna #114-115
Namibian Independence

1991

588PDa	Card, #588PD, #G199PD-G200PD, #V114PD-V115PD, 36c essay of #589 (8)	—
589PDa	Card, #588PD-589PD, #G199PD-G200PD, #V114PD-V115PD (1)	—
588PP	7 items (50)	—
589PP	7 items (50)	—
G199PP	8 items (50)	—
G200PP	8 items (50)	—
V114PP	6 items (50)	—
V115PP	6 items (50)	—
588PI	(100 pairs)	—
589PI	(100 pairs)	—
G199PI	(75 pairs)	—
G200PI	(75 pairs)	—
V114PI	(75 pairs)	—
V115PI	(75 pairs)	—

New York #590-592, Geneva #201-202, Vienna #116
Definitives

1991

590PD	With approval handstamp (4)	—
592PD	(4)	—
592PDa	Card, imperforate pane of 50 (1)	—
G201PD	(5)	—
G202PDa	Card, #G201PD-G202PD, #G213PD, #V116PD (4)	—
590TC	deep blue background (not approved) (5)	—
592TC	black (1)	—
590PP	8 items (80)	—
	Horiz. pair with vert. gutter (10)	—
591PP	4 items (150)	—
G201PP	8 items (50)	—
G202PP	7 items (50)	—
V116PP	7 items (50)	—
590PI	(90 pairs)	—
	Horiz. pair with vert. gutter (10)	—
591PI	(175 pairs)	—
592PI	(50 pairs)	—
G201PI	(75 pairs)	—
G202PI	(100 pairs)	—
V116PI	(75 pairs)	—

An essay of No. 592 with emblem in solid color exists.

New York #593-594, Geneva #203-204, Vienna #117-118, Souvenir Card #40
Rights of the Child

1991

593PDa	Card, #593PD, #G203PD-G204PD, #V117PD-V118PD, 90c essay of #594 (6)	—
594PDa	Card, #593PD-594PD, #G203PD-G204PD, #V117PD-V118PD (4)	—
594PDb	Card, #593PD-594PD (4)	—
SC40PD	(4)	—
593PP	9 items (50)	—
594PP	9 items (50)	—
G203PP	8 items (50)	—
G204PP	7 items (50)	—
V117PP	7 items (50)	—
V118PP	7 items (50)	—
SC40PP	15 items (1)	—
593PI	(75 pairs)	—
594PI	(75 pairs)	—
G203PI	(75 pairs)	—
G204PI	(75 pairs)	—
V117PI	(75 pairs)	—
V118PI	(75 pairs)	—

No. SC40PP may not be a complete set of progressive proofs. Five essays of No. SC40PD with the 90c essay of No. 594 exist; one is attached to No. 593PDa.

New York #595-596, Geneva #205-206, Vienna #119-120,
Banning of Chemical Weapons

1991

596PDa	Card, #595PD-596PD, #G205PD-G206PD, #V119PD-V120PD with approval handstamp (5)	—

596PDb   Card, #596PD, #G206PD, #V120PD, essays of #595, #G205, #V119 (each with gray panels taller than numerals) with "not approved" handstamp (4)   —

595PP	9 items (50)	—
596PP	9 items (50)	—
G205PP	9 items (100)	—
G206PP	9 items (100)	—
V119PP	8 items (50)	—
V120PP	8 items (50)	—
595PI	(125 pairs)	—
596PI	(125 pairs)	—
G205PI	(125 pairs)	—
G206PI	(125 pairs)	—
V119PI	(125 pairs)	—
V120PI	(125 pairs)	—

Second sets of six items of Nos. 595PP-596PP, G205PP-G206PP, and V119PP-V120PP exist. Some items differ from those found in the listed sets.

New York #597-598, Geneva #207-208, Vienna #121-122
UN Postal Administration, 40th Anniv.

1991

598PDa   Card, #597PD-598PD, #G207PD-G208PD, #V121PD-V122PD (4)   —
597TCa   Card, #597TC, #G207TC-G208TCD, #V121TC-V122TC (each with white background), 36c essay of #598 (6)   —

597PP	2 items (64)	—
	Cross gutter block (1)	—
	Horiz. pair with vert. gutter (8)	—
	Vert. pair with horiz. gutter (8)	—
598PP	2 items (64)	—
	Cross gutter block (1)	—
	Horiz. pair with vert. gutter (8)	—
	Vert. pair with horiz. gutter (8)	—
G207PP	2 items (64)	—
	Cross gutter block (1)	—
	Horiz. pair with vert. gutter (8)	—
	Vert. pair with horiz. gutter (8)	—
G208PP	2 items (64)	—
	Cross gutter block (1)	—
	Horiz. pair with vert. gutter (8)	—
	Vert. pair with horiz. gutter (8)	—
V121PP	2 items (64)	—
	Cross gutter block (1)	—
	Horiz. pair with vert. gutter (8)	—
	Vert. pair with horiz. gutter (8)	—
V122PP	2 items (64)	—
	Cross gutter block (1)	—
	Horiz. pair with vert. gutter (8)	—
	Vert. pair with horiz. gutter (8)	—
597PI	(120 pairs)	—
	Cross gutter block (3)	—
	Horiz. pair with vert. gutter (24)	—
	Vert. pair with horiz. gutter (24)	—
598PI	(120 pairs)	—
	Cross gutter block (3)	—
	Horiz. pair with vert. gutter (24)	—
	Vert. pair with horiz. gutter (24)	—
G207PI	(120 pairs)	—
	Cross gutter block (3)	—
	Horiz. pair with vert. gutter (24)	—
	Vert. pair with horiz. gutter (24)	—
G208PI	(120 pairs)	—
	Cross gutter block (3)	—
	Horiz. pair with vert. gutter (24)	—
	Vert. pair with horiz. gutter (24)	—
V121PI	(120 pairs)	—
	Cross gutter block (3)	—
	Horiz. pair with vert. gutter (24)	—
	Vert. pair with horiz. gutter (24)	—
V122PI	(120 pairs)	—
	Cross gutter block (3)	—
	Horiz. pair with vert. gutter (24)	—
	Vert. pair with horiz. gutter (24)	—

Four cross gutter blocks, 32 horizontal pairs with vertical gutters and 32 vertical pairs with horizontal gutters can be cut from four perforated sheets of Nos. 597PI-598PI, G207PI-G208PI, V119PI-V120PI. No. 598PI is difficult to distinguish from one item from No. 598PP.

New York #599-600, Geneva #209-210, Vienna #123-124,
Human Rights

1991

599PDa	Strip of 3 + 3 labels with approval handstamp (4)	—
600PDa	Strip of 3 + 3 labels with approval handstamp (4)	—
G209PDa	Strip of 3 + 3 labels with approval handstamp (4)	—
G210PDa	Strip of 3 + 3 labels with approval handstamp (4)	—
V123PDa	Strip of 3 + 3 labels with approval handstamp (4)	—
V124PDa	Strip of 3 + 3 labels with approval handstamp (4)	—
599TC	Strip of 3 (dark gray background) + 3 labels with "not approved" handstamp (5)	—
600TC	Strip of 3 (dark green background) + 3 labels with "not approved" handstamp (5)	—
G209TC	Strip of 3 (light brown in painting) + 3 labels with "not approved" handstamp (5)	—
G210TC	Strip of 3 (dark green background) + 3 labels with "not approved" handstamp (5)	—

V124TC	Strip of 3 (black background) + 3 labels with "not approved" handstamp (5)	—
599PP	6 items (20)	—
	Cross gutter block (1)	—
	Horiz. pair with vert. gutter (2)	—
	Vert. pair with horiz. gutter (10)	—
600PP	6 items (20)	—
	Cross gutter block (1)	—
	Horiz. pair with vert. gutter (2)	—
	Vert. pair with horiz. gutter (10)	—
G209PP	6 items (20)	—
	Cross gutter block (1)	—
	Horiz. pair with vert. gutter (2)	—
	Vert. pair with horiz. gutter (10)	—
G210PP	6 items (20)	—
	Cross gutter block (1)	—
	Horiz. pair with vert. gutter (2)	—
	Vert. pair with horiz. gutter (10)	—
V123PP	6 items (20)	—
	Cross gutter block (1)	—
	Horiz. pair with vert. gutter (2)	—
	Vert. pair with horiz. gutter (10)	—
V124PP	6 items (20)	—
	Cross gutter block (1)	—
	Horiz. pair with vert. gutter (2)	—
	Vert. pair with horiz. gutter (10)	—
599PI	(56 pairs)	—
	Cross gutter block (1)	—
	Horiz. pair with vert. gutter (2)	—
	Vert. pair with horiz. gutter (10)	—
600PI	(56 pairs)	—
	Cross gutter block (1)	—
	Horiz. pair with vert. gutter (2)	—
	Vert. pair with horiz. gutter (10)	—
G209PI	(56 pairs)	—
	Cross gutter block (1)	—
	Horiz. pair with vert. gutter (2)	—
	Vert. pair with horiz. gutter (10)	—
G210PI	(56 pairs)	—
	Cross gutter block (1)	—
	Horiz. pair with vert. gutter (2)	—
	Vert. pair with horiz. gutter (10)	—
V123PI	(56 pairs)	—
	Cross gutter block (1)	—
	Horiz. pair with vert. gutter (2)	—
	Vert. pair with horiz. gutter (10)	—
V124PI	(56 pairs)	—
	Cross gutter block (1)	—
	Horiz. pair with vert. gutter (2)	—
	Vert. pair with horiz. gutter (10)	—

New York #601-602, Geneva #211-212, Vienna #125-126
World Heritage

1992

602PDa	Card, #601PD-602PD (5)	—
G212PDa	Card, #G211PD-G212PD (5)	—
V126PDa	Card, #V125PD-V126PD (5)	—
601PP	6 items (50)	—
602PP	6 items (50)	—
G211PP	6 items (50)	—
G212PP	6 items (50)	—
V125PP	6 items (50)	—
V126PP	6 items (50)	—
601PI	(50 pairs)	—
602PI	(50 pairs)	—
G211PI	(50 pairs)	—
G212PI	(50 pairs)	—
V125PI	(50 pairs)	—
V126PI	(50 pairs)	—

Geneva #213
Definitive

1992

G213PP	6 items (50)	—
G213PI	(75 pairs)	—

See No. G202PDa.

New York #604a, Geneva #215a, Vienna #128a
Clean Oceans

1992

604aPDa	Card, imperforate pane of 6 #604aPD (2)	—
604aPDb	Card, as "a," with one pair removed (1)	—
G215aPDa	Card, imperforate pane of 6 #G215aPD (2)	—
G215aPDb	(Card, as "a," with one pair removed (1)	—
V128aPDa	Card, imperforate pane of 6 #V128aPD (2)	—
V128aPDb	Card, as "a," with one pair removed (1)	—
604aPP	8 items, vert. pair of pairs with narrow horiz. gutter (20)	—
	Cross gutter block (1)	—
	Horiz. pair of pairs with vert. gutter (4)	—
	Vert. pair of pairs with wide horiz. gutter (10)	—
G215aPP	8 items, vert. pair of pairs with narrow horiz. gutter (20)	—
	Cross gutter block (1)	—
	Horiz. pair of pairs with vert. gutter (4)	—
	Vert. pair of pairs with wide horiz. gutter (10)	—
V128aPP	8 items, vert. pair of pairs with narrow horiz. gutter (20)	—
	Cross gutter block (1)	—
	Horiz. pair of pairs with vert. gutter (4)	—

	Vert. pair of pairs with wide horiz. gutter (10)	—
604aPI	Vert. pair of pairs with narrow horiz. gutter (20)	—
	Cross gutter block (1)	—
	Horiz. pair of pairs with vert. gutter (4)	—
	Vert. pair of pairs with wide horiz. gutter (10)	—
G215aPI	Vert. pair of pairs with narrow horiz. gutter (20)	—
	Cross gutter block (1)	—
	Horiz. pair of pairs with vert. gutter (4)	—
	Vert. pair of pairs with wide horiz. gutter (10)	—
V128aPI	Vert. pair of pairs with narrow horiz. gutter (20)	—
	Cross gutter block (1)	—
	Horiz. pair of pairs with vert. gutter (4)	—
	Vert. pair of pairs with wide horiz. gutter (10)	—

New York #608a, Geneva #219a, Vienna #132a
Earth Summit

1992

608aPDa	Card, #608aPD, #G219aPD, #V132aPD (5)	—
608aPP	4 items (10)	—
G219aPP	4 items (10)	—
V132aPP	4 items (10)	—
608aPI	(20 blocks)	—
G219aPI	(20 blocks)	—
V132aPI	(20 blocks)	—

New York #609-610, Geneva #220-221, Vienna #133-134
Mission to Planet Earth

1992

610PDa	Card, #610aPD, G221aPD, #V134aPD (3)	—
SC41PD	(3)	—
610aPP	6 items (5)	—
G221aPP	6 items (5)	—
V134aPP	6 items (5)	—
610aPI	(10 pairs)	—
G221aPI	(10 pairs)	—
V134aPI	(10 pairs)	—

One item in No. G221aPP is a blank from a sheet showing marginal inscriptions only.

New York #611-612, Geneva #222-223, Vienna #135-136, Souvenir Card #42
Science and Technology for Development

1992

611PDa	Card, 2 #611PD, 2 #V136PD (4)	—
612PDa	Card, #611PD-612PD, #G222PD-G223PD, #V135PD-V136PD (4)	—
SC42PD	(18)	—
611PP	6 items (50)	—
612PP	6 items (50)	—
G222PP	6 items (50)	—
G223PP	6 items (50)	—
V135PP	6 items (50)	—
V136PP	6 items (50)	—
611PI	(100 pairs)	—
612PI	(100 pairs)	—
G222PI	(100 pairs)	—
G223PI	(100 pairs)	—
V135PI	(100 pairs)	—
V136PI	(100 pairs)	—

There is no appreciable difference between approved and not approved die proofs.

New York #613-615, Vienna #137-138
Definitives

1992

614PDa	Card, #614PD, #V137PD-V138PD (4)	—
615PDa	Card, #613PD, #615PD (3)	—
613PP	6 items (50)	—
614PP	6 items (50)	—
615PP	6 items (50)	—
V137PP	6 items (50)	—
V138PP	6 items (50)	—
613PI	(50 pairs)	—
614PI	(269 pairs)	—
	Cross gutter block (2)	—
	Horiz. pair with vert. gutter (36)	—
	Vert. pair with horiz. gutter (16)	—
615PI	(50 pairs)	—
V137PI	(269 pairs)	—
	Cross gutter block (2)	—
	Horiz. pair with vert. gutter (36)	—
	Vert. pair with horiz. gutter (16)	—
V138PI	(269 pairs)	—
	Cross gutter block (2)	—
	Horiz. pair with vert. gutter (36)	—
	Vert. pair with horiz. gutter (16)	—

Three "not approved" cards containing essays of Nos. 613 and 615 lacking year date and designer inscriptions exist.

New York #616-617, Geneva #224-225, Vienna #139-140
Human Rights

1992

616PDa	Strip of 3 + 3 labels (4)	—
617PDa	Strip of 3 + 3 labels (4)	—
G224PDa	Strip of 3 + 3 labels (4)	—
G225PDa	Strip of 3 + 3 labels (4)	—
V139PDa	Strip of 3 + 3 labels (4)	—
V140PDa	Strip of 3 + 3 labels (4)	—
G225TCa	Strip of 3 (dark brown background under chair) + 3 labels (not approved) (5)	—
616PP	6 items (20)	—
	Cross gutter block (1)	—
	Horiz. pair with vert. gutter (2)	—
	Vert. pair with horiz. gutter (10)	—
617PP	6 items (20)	—
	Cross gutter block (1)	—
	Horiz. pair with vert. gutter (2)	—
	Vert. pair with horiz. gutter (10)	—
G224PP	6 items (20)	—
	Cross gutter block (1)	—
	Horiz. pair with vert. gutter (2)	—
	Vert. pair with horiz. gutter (10)	—
G225PP	6 items (20)	—
	Cross gutter block (1)	—
	Horiz. pair with vert. gutter (2)	—
	Vert. pair with horiz. gutter (10)	—
V139PP	6 items (20)	—
	Cross gutter block (1)	—
	Horiz. pair with vert. gutter (2)	—
	Vert. pair with horiz. gutter (10)	—
V140PP	6 items (20)	—
	Cross gutter block (1)	—
	Horiz. pair with vert. gutter (2)	—
	Vert. pair with horiz. gutter (10)	—
616PI	(32 pairs)	—
	Cross gutter block (4)	—
	Horiz. pair with vert. gutter (8)	—
	Vert. pair with horiz. gutter (40)	—
617PI	(32 pairs)	—
	Cross gutter block (4)	—
	Horiz. pair with vert. gutter (8)	—
	Vert. pair with horiz. gutter (40)	—
G224PI	(32 pairs)	—
	Cross gutter block (4)	—
	Horiz. pair with vert. gutter (8)	—
	Vert. pair with horiz. gutter (40)	—
G225PI	(32 pairs)	—
	Cross gutter block (4)	—
	Horiz. pair with vert. gutter (8)	—
	Vert. pair with horiz. gutter (40)	—
V139PI	(32 pairs)	—
	Cross gutter block (4)	—
	Horiz. pair with vert. gutter (8)	—
	Vert. pair with horiz. gutter (40)	—
V140PI	(32 pairs)	—
	Cross gutter block (4)	—
	Horiz. pair with vert. gutter (8)	—
	Vert. pair with horiz. gutter (40)	—

Five "not approved" cards contain 4.50s essays of No. V139, and five "not approved" cards contain 9.50s essays of No. V140.

New York #618-619, Geneva #226-227, Vienna #141-142
Aging With Dignity

1993

618PDa	Card, #618PD, #G226PD-G227PD, #V141PD-V142PD, #619TC yellow flowers (not approved) (5)	—
619PDa	Card, #618PD-619PD, #V141PD-V142PD, #G226TC pink denomination, #G227TC yellow denomination, with approval handstamp (4)	—
619TCb	Card, #618TC-619TC, #G226TC-G227TC, #V141TC-V142TC, each with white denominations (5)	—
618PP	7 items (50)	—
619PP	7 items (50)	—
G226PP	7 items (50)	—
G227PP	7 items (50)	—
V141PP	7 items (50)	—
V142PP	7 items (50)	—
618PI	(50 pairs)	—
619PI	(50 pairs)	—
G226PI	(50 pairs)	—
G227PI	(50 pairs)	—
V141PI	(50 pairs)	—
V142PI	(50 pairs)	—

New York #623a, Geneva #231a, Vienna #146a
Endangered Species

1993

623aPDa	Card, imperforate pane of 4 blocks of #623aPD (3)	—
G231aPDa	Card, imperforate pane of 4 blocks of #G231aPD (4)	—
V146aPDa	Card, imperforate pane of 4 blocks of #V146aPD (3)	—
G231aTCa	Card, imperforate pane of 4 blocks of #G231aTC black (1)	—
G231aPP	6 items (4 blocks)	—
	Cross gutter block (1)	—
	Horiz. pair with vert. gutter (2)	—
	Vert. pair with horiz. gutter (4)	—
V146aPP	6 items (4 blocks)	—
	Cross gutter block (1)	—
	Horiz. pair with vert. gutter (2)	—
	Vert. pair with horiz. gutter (4)	—
623aPI	(20 blocks)	—
	Cross gutter block (8)	—

	Horiz. pair with vert. gutter (8)	—
	Vert. pair with horiz. gutter (16)	—
G231aPI	(44 blocks)	—
	Cross gutter block (10)	—
	Horiz. pair with vert. gutter (10)	—
	Vert. pair with horiz. gutter (20)	—
V146aPI	(20 blocks)	—
	Cross gutter block (8)	—
	Horiz. pair with vert. gutter (8)	—
	Horiz. pair with vert. gutter (16)	—

New York #624-625, Geneva #232-233, Vienna #147-148, Souvenir Card #43
Healthy Environment

1993

625PDa	Card, #624PD-625PD, #V147PD-V148PD, 90c essay of #G232, 1.10fr essay of #G233 (4)	—
SC43PD	(4)	—
624PP	6 items (50)	—
625PP	6 items (50)	—
G232PP	6 items (50)	—
G233PP	6 items (50)	—
V147PP	6 items (50)	—
V148PP	6 items (50)	—
624PI	(50 pairs)	—
625PI	(50 pairs)	—
G232PI	(50 pairs)	—
G233PI	(50 pairs)	—
V147PI	(50 pairs)	—
V148PI	(50 pairs)	—

New York #626, Vienna #149
Definitives

1993

626PD	(5)	—
V149PD	(5)	—
626PP	8 items (144)	—
	Cross gutter block (1)	—
	Horiz. pair with vert. gutter (18)	—
	Vert. pair with horiz. gutter (8)	—
V149PP	5 items (50)	—
626PI	(194 pairs)	—
	Cross gutter block (2)	—
	Horiz. pair with vert. gutter (36)	—
	Vert. pair with horiz. gutter (16)	—
V149PI	(50 pairs)	—

New York #627-628, Geneva #234-235, Vienna #150-151
Human Rights

1993

627PDa	Strip of 3 + 3 labels (4)	—
628PDa	Strip of 3 + 3 labels (4)	—
G234PDa	Strip of 3 + 3 labels (4)	—
G235PDa	Strip of 3 + 3 labels (4)	—
V150PDa	Strip of 3 + 3 labels (3)	—
V151PDa	Strip of 3 + 3 labels (4)	—
627PP	6 items (20)	—
	Cross gutter block (1)	—
	Horiz. pair with vert. gutter (2)	—
	Vert. pair with horiz. gutter (10)	—
628PP	6 items (20)	—
	Cross gutter block (1)	—
	Horiz. pair with vert. gutter (2)	—
	Vert. pair with horiz. gutter (10)	—
G234PP	6 items (20)	—
	Cross gutter block (1)	—
	Horiz. pair with vert. gutter (2)	—
	Vert. pair with horiz. gutter (10)	—
G235PP	6 items (20)	—
	Cross gutter block (1)	—
	Horiz. pair with vert. gutter (2)	—
	Vert. pair with horiz. gutter (10)	—
627PI	(20 pairs)	—
	Cross gutter block (1)	—
	Horiz. pair with vert. gutter (2)	—
	Vert. pair with horiz. gutter (10)	—
628PI	(20 pairs)	—
	Cross gutter block (1)	—
	Horiz. pair with vert. gutter (2)	—
	Vert. pair with horiz. gutter (10)	—
G234PI	(20 pairs)	—
	Cross gutter block (1)	—
	Horiz. pair with vert. gutter (2)	—
	Vert. pair with horiz. gutter (10)	—
G235PI	(20 pairs)	—
	Cross gutter block (1)	—
	Horiz. pair with vert. gutter (2)	—
	Vert. pair with horiz. gutter (10)	—
V150PI	(6 pairs)	—
V151PI	(6 pairs)	—

New York #632a, Geneva #239a, Vienna #155a, Souvenir Card #44
International Peace Day

1993

632aPD	(4)	—
G239aPD	(4)	—
V155aPD	(4)	—
SC44PD	(4)	—
632aPP	7 items (10 blocks)	—
G239aPP	7 items (10 blocks)	—
V155aPP	7 items (10 blocks)	—
632aPI	(40 blocks)	—
G239aPI	(40 blocks)	—
V155aPI	(40 blocks)	—

New York #636a, Geneva #243a, Vienna #159a
Environment & Climate

1993

636aPDa	Card, #636aPD, #V159aPD (4)	—
G243aPD	(4)	—
636aPP	8 items (6 strips)	—
	Horiz. pair of strips with vert. gutter (6)	—
G243aPP	8 items (6 strips)	—
	Horiz. pair of strips with vert. gutter (6)	—
V155aPP	8 items (6 strips)	—
	Horiz. pair of strips with vert. gutter (6)	—
636aPI	(18 strips)	—
	Horiz. pair of strips with vert. gutter (18)	—
G243aPI	(18 strips)	—
	Horiz. pair of strips with vert. gutter (18)	—
V159aPI	(18 strips)	—
	Horiz. pair of strips with vert. gutter (18)	—

New York #637-638, Geneva #244-245, Vienna #160-161, Souvenir Card #45
International Year of the Family

1994

638PDa	Card, #637PD-638PD, #G244PD-G245PD, #V160PD-V161PD (4)	—
SC45PD	(4)	—
637PP	11 items (50)	—
638PP	11 items (50)	—
G244PP	10 items (50)	—
G245PP	10 items (50)	—
V160PP	11 items (50)	—
V161PP	11 items (50)	—
637PI	(100 pairs)	—
638PI	(100 pairs)	—
G244PI	(100 pairs)	—
G245PI	(100 pairs)	—
V160PI	(100 pairs)	—
V161PI	(100 pairs)	—

New York #642a, Geneva #249a, Vienna #165a
Endangered Species

1994

642aPDa	Card, imperforate pane of 4 #642aPD (9)	—
G249aPDa	Card, imperforate pane of 4 #G249aPD (4)	—
V165aPDa	Card, imperforate pane of 4 #V165aPD (4)	—
642aPP	6 items (4 blocks)	—
	Cross gutter block (2)	—
	Horiz. pair with vert. gutter (2)	—
	Vert. pair with horiz. gutter (4)	—
G249aPP	6 items (4 blocks)	—
	Cross gutter block (2)	—
	Horiz. pair with vert. gutter (2)	—
	Vert. pair with horiz. gutter (4)	—
V165aPP	6 items (4 blocks)	—
	Cross gutter block (2)	—
	Horiz. pair with vert. gutter (2)	—
	Vert. pair with horiz. gutter (4)	—
642aPI	(16 blocks)	—
	Cross gutter block (8)	—
	Horiz. pair with vert. gutter (8)	—
	Vert. pair with horiz. gutter (16)	—
G249aPI	(16 blocks)	—
	Cross gutter block (8)	—
	Horiz. pair with vert. gutter (8)	—
	Vert. pair with horiz. gutter (16)	—
V165aPI	(16 blocks)	—
	Cross gutter block (8)	—
	Horiz. pair with vert. gutter (8)	—
	Vert. pair with horiz. gutter (16)	—

There is no appreciable difference between approved and not approved examples of No. 642aPD. Five cards with imperforate panes of 40c essays of No. G249a and five cards with imperforate panes of 5s essays of No. V165a exist.

New York #643, Geneva #250, Vienna #166
Protection for Refugees

1994

643PDa	Card, #643PD, #G250PD, #V166PD (4)	—
643PP	8 items (50)	—
G250PP	8 items (50)	—
V166PP	6 items (50)	—
643PI	(69 pairs)	—
	Horiz. pair with vert. gutter (8)	—
G250PI	(69 pairs)	—
	Horiz. pair with vert. gutter (8)	—
V166PI	(69 pairs)	—
	Horiz. pair with vert. gutter (8)	—

New York #644-646, Vienna #167-169
Definitives

1994

645PDa	Card, #644PD-645PD, #V167PD-V169PD (5)	—
646PD	(1)	—
644PP	6 items (50)	—
645PP	6 items (50)	—
V167PP	12 items (50)	—
V168PP	11 items (50)	—
V169PP	11 items (50)	—
644PI	(100 pairs)	—
645PI	(100 pairs)	—
646PI	(50 pairs)	—

V167PI	(100 pairs)	—
V168PI	(100 pairs)	—
V169PI	(100 pairs)	—

There is no appreciable difference between approved and not approved examples of No. 645PDa.

New York #650a, Geneva #254a, Vienna #173a
International Decade for Natural Disaster Reduction

1994

650aPDa	Card, #650aPD, #G254aPD, #V173aPD (5)	—
650aPP	6 items (16 blocks)	—
	Cross gutter block (1)	—
	Horiz. pair with vert. gutter (8)	—
	Vert. pair with horiz. gutter (2)	—
G254aPP	6 items (16 blocks)	—
	Cross gutter block (1)	—
	Horiz. pair with vert. gutter (8)	—
	Vert. pair with horiz. gutter (2)	—
V173aPP	6 items (16 blocks)	—
	Cross gutter block (1)	—
	Horiz. pair with vert. gutter (8)	—
	Vert. pair with horiz. gutter (2)	—
650aPI	(48 blocks)	—
	Cross gutter block (3)	—
	Horiz. pair with horiz. gutter (24)	—
	Vert. pair with horiz. gutter (6)	—
G254aPI	(48 blocks)	—
	Cross gutter block (3)	—
	Horiz. pair with horiz. gutter (24)	—
	Vert. pair with horiz. gutter (6)	—
V173aPI	(48 blocks)	—
	Cross gutter block (3)	—
	Horiz. pair with horiz. gutter (24)	—
	Vert. pair with horiz. gutter (6)	—

Geneva #255-257
Definitives

1994

G257PDa	Card, #G255PD-G257PD (5)	—
G255PP	10 items (144)	—
	Cross gutter block (1)	—
	Horiz. pair with vert. gutter (18)	—
	Vert. pair with horiz. gutter (8)	—
G256PP	10 items (144)	—
	Cross gutter block (1)	—
	Horiz. pair with vert. gutter (18)	—
	Vert. pair with horiz. gutter (8)	—
G257PP	11 items (144)	—
	Cross gutter block (1)	—
	Horiz. pair with vert. gutter (18)	—
	Vert. pair with horiz. gutter (8)	—
G255PI	(288 pairs)	—
	Cross gutter block (4)	—
	Horiz. pair with horiz. gutter (72)	—
	Vert. pair with horiz. gutter (32)	—
G256PI	(288 pairs)	—
	Cross gutter block (4)	—
	Horiz. pair with horiz. gutter (72)	—
	Vert. pair with horiz. gutter (32)	—
G257PI	(288 pairs)	—
	Cross gutter block (4)	—
	Horiz. pair with horiz. gutter (72)	—
	Vert. pair with horiz. gutter (32)	—

New York #651-652, Geneva #258-259, Vienna #174-175, Souvenir Card #46
Population and Development

1994

652PDa	Card, #651PD-652PD, #G258PD-G259PD, #V174PD-V175PD (4)	—
SC46PD	(4)	—
G258PP	6 items (40)	—
G259PP	6 items (40)	—
G259PPa	Horiz. se-tenant pair with vert. gutter, #G258PP-G259PP (10)	—
V174PP	6 items (40)	—
V175PP	6 items (40)	—
V175PPa	Horiz. se-tenant pair with vert. gutter, #V174PP-V175PP (10)	—
651PI	(50 pairs)	—
652PI	(50 pairs)	—
G258PI	(70 pairs)	—
G259PI	(70 pairs)	—
G259PIa	Horiz. se-tenant pair with vert. gutter, #G258PI-G259PI (10)	—
V174PI	(70 pairs)	—
V175PI	(70 pairs)	—
V175PIa	Horiz. se-tenant pair with vert. gutter, #V174PI-V175PI (10)	—

New York #653-654, Geneva #260-261, Vienna #176-177
UNCTAD, 30th Anniv.

1994

653PP	15 items (40)	—
654PP	15 items (40)	—
654PPa	Horiz. se-tenant pair with vert. gutter, #653PP-654PP (10)	—
G260PP	16 items (40)	—
G261PP	16 items (40)	—
G261PPa	Horiz. se-tenant pair with vert. gutter, #G260PP-G261PP (10)	—
V176PP	14 items (40)	—
V177PP	14 items (40)	—
V177PPa	Horiz. se-tenant pair with vert. gutter, #V176PP-V177PP (10)	—
653PI	(60 pairs)	—
654PI	(60 pairs)	—
654PIa	Horiz. se-tenant pair with vert. gutter, #653PI-654PI (30)	—

G260PI	(60 pairs)	—
G261PI	(60 pairs)	—
G261PIa	Horiz. se-tenant pair with vert. gutter, #G260PI-G261PI (30)	—
V176PI	(60 pairs)	—
V177PI	(60 pairs)	—
V177PIa	Horiz. se-tenant pair with vert. gutter, #V176PI-V177PI (30)	—

Two items from No. G260PP and one from No. V176PP are blank due to color arrangement on progressive proof sheet.

New York # 655, Geneva #262, Vienna #178
United Nations, 50th Anniv.

1995

655PD	(3)	—
G262PD	(3)	—
V178PD	(3)	—
655PP	8 items (50)	—
G262PP	8 items (50)	—
V178PP	8 items (50)	—
655PI	(100 pairs)	—
G262PI	(200 pairs)	—
V178PI	(200 pairs)	—

New York #656, Geneva #263, Vienna #179, Souvenir Card #47
World Summit for Social Development, Copenhagen

1995

656PDa	Card, #656PD, #G263PD, #V179PD (3)	—
SC47PD	Card, 4 #SC47PD (1)	—
656PP	12 items (25)	—
G263PP	8 items (25)	—
V179PP	8 items (25)	—
656PI	(24 pairs)	—
G263PI	(24 pairs)	—
V179PI	(24 pairs)	—

New York #660a, Geneva #267a, Vienna #183a
Endangered Species

1995

660aPDa	Card, imperforate pane of 4 blocks, #660aPD (5)	—
660aPDb	Card, broken imperforate pane of 4 blocks, #660aPD (1)	—
660aPDc	Card, 2 imperforate panes of 4 blocks, #660aPD (1)	—
G267aPDa	Card, imperforate pane of 4 blocks, #G267aPD (6)	—
G267aPDb	Card, 2 imperforate panes of 4 blocks, #G267aPD (1)	—
V183aPDa	Card, imperforate pane of 4 blocks, #V183aPD with "14. Okt. 1994" handstamp (approved) (3)	—
V183aTCa	Card, imperforate pane of 4 blocks, #V183aTC (violet blue sky on #181TC), not approved (3)	—
V183aTCb	Card, 2 imperforate pane of 4 blocks, #V183aTC, not approved (1)	—
660aPP	6 items (9 blocks)	—
	Cross gutter block (3)	—
	Horiz. pair with vert. gutter (4)	—
	Vert. pair with horiz. gutter (7)	—
G267aPP	6 items (12 blocks)	—
	Cross gutter block (3)	—
	Horiz. pair with vert. gutter (4)	—
	Vert. pair with horiz. gutter (6)	—
V183aPP	6 items (12 blocks)	—
	Cross gutter block (3)	—
	Horiz. pair with vert. gutter (4)	—
	Vert. pair with horiz. gutter (7)	—
660aPI	(11 blocks)	—
	Cross gutter block (3)	—
	Horiz. pair with vert. gutter (4)	—
	Vert. pair with horiz. gutter (7)	—
G267aPI	(16 blocks)	—
	Cross gutter block (3)	—
	Horiz. pair with vert. gutter (4)	—
	Vert. pair with horiz. gutter (6)	—
V183aPI	(11 blocks)	—
	Cross gutter block (3)	—
	Horiz. pair with vert. gutter (4)	—
	Vert. pair with horiz. gutter (7)	—

Three cross gutter blocks, four horizontal pairs with vertical gutters, seven vertical pairs with horizontal gutters and nine blocks with untrimmed margins can be cut from perforated sheets of Nos. V180PI-V183PI.

New York #661-662, Geneva #268-269, Vienna #184-185, Souvenir Card #48
International Youth Year

1995

662PDa	Card, #661PD-662PD, #G268PD-G269PD, #V184PD-V185PD (6)	—
SC48PD	(6)	—
661PP	5 items (160)	—
	Cross gutter block (5)	—
	Horiz. pair with vert. gutter (25)	—
	Vert. pair with horiz. gutter (44)	—
662PP	8 items (160)	—
	Cross gutter block (5)	—
	Horiz. pair with vert. gutter (25)	—
	Vert. pair with horiz. gutter (44)	—
G268PP	6 items (208)	—
	Cross gutter block (5)	—
	Horiz. pair with vert. gutter (25)	—
	Vert. pair with horiz. gutter (44)	—
G269PP	5 items (208)	—

	Cross gutter block (5)	—
	Horiz. pair with vert. gutter (25)	—
	Vert. pair with horiz. gutter (44)	—
V184PP	7 items (101)	—
	Cross gutter block (2)	—
	Horiz. pair with vert. gutter (11)	—
	Vert. pair with horiz. gutter (12)	—
V185PP	6 items (197)	—
	Cross gutter block (5)	—
	Horiz. pair with vert. gutter (25)	—
	Vert. pair with horiz. gutter (44)	—
661PI	(128 pairs)	—
	Cross gutter block (5)	—
	Horiz. pair with vert. gutter (25)	—
	Vert. pair with horiz. gutter (44)	—
662PI	(128 pairs)	—
	Cross gutter block (5)	—
	Horiz. pair with vert. gutter (25)	—
	Vert. pair with horiz. gutter (44)	—
G268PI	(128 pairs)	—
	Cross gutter block (5)	—
	Horiz. pair with vert. gutter (25)	—
	Vert. pair with horiz. gutter (44)	—
G269PI	(128 pairs)	—
	Cross gutter block (5)	—
	Horiz. pair with vert. gutter (25)	—
	Vert. pair with horiz. gutter (44)	—
V184PI	(128 pairs)	—
	Cross gutter block (5)	—
	Horiz. pair with vert. gutter (25)	—
	Vert. pair with horiz. gutter (44)	—
V185PI	(128 pairs)	—
	Cross gutter block (5)	—
	Horiz. pair with vert. gutter (25)	—
	Vert. pair with horiz. gutter (44)	—

New York #663-665, Geneva #270-272, Vienna #186-188
United Nations, 50th Anniv.

1995

664PDa	Card, # 664PD, #663TC maroon, #663TC dark blue, #663TC green, #664TC dark blue, #664TC green (3)	—
663PI	(80 pairs)	—
664PI	(80 pairs)	—
664PIa	Horiz. se-tenant pair with vert. gutter, #663PI-664PI (40)	—
665PI	(8 pairs of souvenir sheets)	—
G270PI	(80 pairs)	—
G271PI	(80 pairs)	—
G271PIa	Horiz. se-tenant pair with vert. gutter, #G270PI-G271PI (40)	—
G272PI	(8 pairs of souvenir sheets)	—
V186PI	(80 pairs)	—
V187PI	(80 pairs)	—
V187PIa	Horiz. se-tenant pair with vert. gutter, #V186PI-V187PI (40)	—
V188PI	(8 pairs of souvenir sheets)	—

Three cards with non-engraved essays of No. 665 in red violet exist.

New York #666-667, Geneva #273-274, Vienna #189-190
Fourth World Conference on Women

1995

666PP	10 items, perforated (275)	—
667PP	10 items, perforated (250)	—
G273PP	10 items, perforated (100)	—
G274PP	10 items, perforated (250)	—
V189PP	9 items, perforated (275)	—
V190PP	9 items, perforated (275)	—
666PI	(144 pairs)	—
667PI	(144 pairs)	—
G273PI	(108 pairs)	—
G274PI	(144 pairs)	—
V189PI	(132 pairs)	—
V190PI	(144 pairs)	—

On No. V189PP and V190PP, 125 sets have a red and multicolored item while the remaining 150 sets have a blue and multicolored item.

New York #668
UN Headquarters

1995

668PD	(5)	—
668PP	6 items (162)	—
	Horiz. pair with vert. gutter (9)	—
	Vert. pair with horiz. gutter (5)	—
668PI	(85 pairs)	—
	Horiz. pair with vert. gutter (9)	—
	Vert. pair with horiz. gutter (5)	—

New York #669-670, Geneva #275-276, Vienna #191-192
United Nations, 50th Anniversary

1995

669PD	(4)	—
G275PD	(4)	—
V191PD	(4)	—
669PP	6 items (6)	—
G275PP	8 items (6)	—
V191PP	7 items (6)	—
669PI	(2 full panes)	—
669PIa	(3 pairs of full panes)	—
670PI	(3 booklets)	—
G275PI	(2 full panes)	—
G275PIa	(3 pairs of full panes)	—
G276PI	(3 booklets)	—

V191PI	(2 full panes)	—
V191PIa	(4 pairs of full panes)	—
V192PI	(3 booklets)	—

New York #671, Geneva #277, Vienna #193, Souvenir Card #49
World Federation of United Nations Associations, 50th Anniv.

1996

671PDa	Card, #671PD, #G277PD, #V193PD (3)	—
SC49PD	(4)	—
671PP	6 items (150)	—
	Horiz. pair with vert. gutter (25)	—
G277PP	6 items (150)	—
	Horiz. pair with vert. gutter (25)	—
V193PP	6 items (305)	—
	Cross gutter block (5)	—
	Horiz. pair with vert. gutter (40)	—
	Vert. pair with horiz. gutter (30)	—
671PI	(155 pairs)	—
	Horiz. pair with vert. gutter (55)	—
G277PI	(155 pairs)	—
	Horiz. pair with vert. gutter (55)	—
V193PI	(264 pairs)	—
	Cross gutter block (11)	—
	Horiz. pair with vert. gutter (88)	—
	Vert. pair with horiz. gutter (63)	—

New York #672-673, Geneva #278-279, Vienna #194-195
Definitives

1996

673PDa	Card, #672PD-673PD, #G278PD-G279PD, #V194PD-V195PD with approval handstamp (4)	—
673PDb	Card, #673PD, #672TC gray in vignette, #G278TC-G279TC tan background in panel, essays of #V194PD-V195PD (larger frames) (not approved) (4)	—
673PDc	#673PDa and 673PDb stapled together (1)	—
672PP	8 items (144)	—
	Cross gutter block (1)	—
	Horiz. pair with vert. gutter (18)	—
	Vert. pair with horiz. gutter (8)	—
673PP	8 items (144)	—
	Cross gutter block (1)	—
	Horiz. pair with vert. gutter (18)	—
	Vert. pair with horiz. gutter (8)	—
G278PP	8 items (144)	—
	Cross gutter block (1)	—
	Horiz. pair with vert. gutter (18)	—
	Vert. pair with horiz. gutter (8)	—
G279PP	8 items (144)	—
	Cross gutter block (1)	—
	Horiz. pair with vert. gutter (18)	—
	Vert. pair with horiz. gutter (8)	—
V194PP	8 items (144)	—
	Cross gutter block (1)	—
	Horiz. pair with vert. gutter (18)	—
	Vert. pair with horiz. gutter (8)	—
V195PP	8 items (144)	—
	Cross gutter block (1)	—
	Horiz. pair with vert. gutter (18)	—
	Vert. pair with horiz. gutter (8)	—
672PI	(216 pairs)	—
	Cross gutter block (3)	—
	Horiz. pair with vert. gutter (54)	—
	Vert. pair with horiz. gutter (16)	—
673PI	(144 pairs)	—
	Cross gutter block (3)	—
	Horiz. pair with vert. gutter (54)	—
	Vert. pair with horiz. gutter (16)	—
G278PI	(216 pairs)	—
	Cross gutter block (3)	—
	Horiz. pair with vert. gutter (54)	—
	Vert. pair with horiz. gutter (24)	—
G279PI	(216 pairs)	—
	Cross gutter block (3)	—
	Horiz. pair with vert. gutter (54)	—
	Vert. pair with horiz. gutter (24)	—
V194PI	(216 pairs)	—
	Cross gutter block (3)	—
	Horiz. pair with vert. gutter (24)	—
	Vert. pair with horiz. gutter (36)	—
V195PI	(216 pairs)	—
	Cross gutter block (3)	—
	Horiz. pair with vert. gutter (24)	—
	Vert. pair with horiz. gutter (36)	—

New York #677a, Geneva #283a, Vienna #199a
Endangered Species

1996

677aPDa	Card, imperforate pane of 4 blocks, #677aPD (3)	—
677aPDb	Card, broken imperforate pane of 4 blocks, #677aPD (1)	—
G283aPDa	Card, imperforate pane of 4 blocks, #G283aPD (3)	—
G283aPDb	Card, broken imperforate pane of 4 blocks, #G283aPD (1)	—
V199aPDa	Card, imperforate pane of 4 blocks, #V199aPD (3)	—
V199aPDb	Card, broken imperforate pane of 4 blocks, #V199aPD (1)	—
677aPP	6 items (14 blocks)	—
	Cross gutter block (5)	—
	Horiz. pair with vert. gutter (6)	—
	Vert. pair with horiz. gutter (11)	—
G283aPP	6 items (14 blocks)	—
	Cross gutter block (5)	—
	Horiz. pair with vert. gutter (6)	—

	Vert. pair with horiz. gutter (11)	—
V199aPP	6 items (14 blocks)	—
	Cross gutter block (5)	—
	Horiz. pair with vert. gutter (6)	—
	Vert. pair with horiz. gutter (11)	—
677aPI	(25 blocks)	—
	Cross gutter block (11)	—
	Horiz. pair with vert. gutter (12)	—
	Vert. pair with horiz. gutter (23)	—
G283aPI	(25 blocks)	—
	Cross gutter block (11)	—
	Horiz. pair with vert. gutter (12)	—
	Vert. pair with horiz. gutter (23)	—
V199aPI	(25 blocks)	—
	Cross gutter block (11)	—
	Horiz. pair with vert. gutter (12)	—
	Vert. pair with horiz. gutter (23)	—

New York #682a, Geneva #288a, Vienna #204a
City Summit

1996

682aPDa	Card, imperforate pane of 5 strips, #682aPD (4)	—
G288aPDa	Card, imperforate pane of 5 strips, #G288aPD (4)	—
V204aPDa	Card, imperforate pane of 5 strips, #V204aPD (4)	—
682aPP	10 items (15 horiz. pairs of strips with vert. gutter)	—
G288aPP	10 items (24 horiz. pairs of strips with vert. gutter)	—
	Cross gutter block of strips (3)	—
V204aPP	10 items (15 horiz. pairs of strips with vert. gutter)	—
682aPI	(35 horiz. pairs of strips with vert. gutter)	—
G288aPI	(56 horiz. pairs of strips with vert. gutter)	—
	Cross gutter block of strips (7)	—
V204aPI	(35 horiz. pairs of strips with vert. gutter)	—

New York #683-685, Geneva #289-291, Vienna #205-207
Sport and the Environment

1996

684PDa	Card, #683PD-684PD (10)	—
685PD	(10)	—
G290PDa	Card, #G289PD-G290PD (10)	—
G291PD	(10)	—
V206PDa	Card, #V205PD-V206PD (10)	—
V207PD	(10)	—
683PP	8 items (88)	—
	Cross gutter block (2)	—
	Horiz. pair with vert. gutter (16)	—
	Vert. pair with horiz. gutter (11)	—
684PP	8 items (88)	—
	Cross gutter block (2)	—
	Horiz. pair with vert. gutter (11)	—
	Vert. pair with horiz. gutter (16)	—
685PP	12 items (25 souvenir sheets)	—
G289PP	8 items (88)	—
	Cross gutter block (2)	—
	Horiz. pair with vert. gutter (16)	—
	Vert. pair with horiz. gutter (11)	—
G290PP	8 items (88)	—
	Cross gutter block (2)	—
	Horiz. pair with vert. gutter (11)	—
	Vert. pair with horiz. gutter (16)	—
G291PP	10 items (25 souvenir sheets)	—
V205PP	8 items (88)	—
	Cross gutter block (2)	—
	Horiz. pair with vert. gutter (16)	—
	Vert. pair with horiz. gutter (11)	—
V206PP	8 items (88)	—
	Cross gutter block (2)	—
	Horiz. pair with vert. gutter (11)	—
	Vert. pair with horiz. gutter (16)	—
V207PP	11 items (25 souvenir sheets)	—
683PI	(44 pairs)	—
	Cross gutter block (2)	—
	Horiz. pair with vert. gutter (11)	—
	Vert. pair with horiz. gutter (16)	—
684PI	(44 pairs)	—
	Cross gutter block (2)	—
	Horiz. pair with vert. gutter (11)	—
	Vert. pair with horiz. gutter (16)	—
685PI	(75 souvenir sheets)	—
G289PI	(88 pairs)	—
	Cross gutter block (4)	—
	Horiz. pair with vert. gutter (32)	—
	Vert. pair with horiz. gutter (22)	—
G290PI	(88 pairs)	—
	Cross gutter block (4)	—
	Horiz. pair with vert. gutter (22)	—
	Vert. pair with horiz. gutter (32)	—
G291PI	(75 souvenir sheets)	—
V205PI	(132 pairs)	—
	Cross gutter block (6)	—
	Horiz. pair with vert. gutter (48)	—
	Vert. pair with horiz. gutter (33)	—
V206PI	(132 pairs)	—
	Cross gutter block (6)	—
	Horiz. pair with vert. gutter (33)	—
	Vert. pair with horiz. gutter (48)	—
V207PI	(75 souvenir sheets)	—

New York #686-687, Geneva #292-293, Vienna #208-209
Plea for Peace

1996

687PDa	Card, #686PD-687PD, #G292PD-G293PD, #V208PD-V209PD (4)	—
686PP	10 items (112)	—

	Cross gutter block (3)	—
	Horiz. pair with vert. gutter (14)	—
	Vert. pair with horiz. gutter (24)	—
687PP	10 items (112)	—
	Cross gutter block (3)	—
	Horiz. pair with vert. gutter (14)	—
	Vert. pair with horiz. gutter (24)	—
G292PP	10 items (112)	—
	Cross gutter block (3)	—
	Horiz. pair with vert. gutter (24)	—
	Vert. pair with horiz. gutter (14)	—
G293PP	10 items (112)	—
	Cross gutter block (2)	—
	Horiz. pair with vert. gutter (24)	—
	Vert. pair with horiz. gutter (14)	—
V208PP	10 items (112)	—
	Cross gutter block (3)	—
	Horiz. pair with vert. gutter (14)	—
	Vert. pair with horiz. gutter (24)	—
V209PP	10 items (112)	—
	Cross gutter block (3)	—
	Horiz. pair with vert. gutter (14)	—
	Vert. pair with horiz. gutter (24)	—
686PI	(104 pairs)	—
	Cross gutter block (3)	—
	Horiz. pair with vert. gutter (14)	—
	Vert. pair with horiz. gutter (24)	—
687PI	(104 pairs)	—
	Cross gutter block (3)	—
	Horiz. pair with vert. gutter (14)	—
	Vert. pair with horiz. gutter (24)	—
G292PI	(80 pairs)	—
	Cross gutter block (3)	—
	Horiz. pair with vert. gutter (24)	—
	Vert. pair with horiz. gutter (14)	—
G293PI	(80 pairs)	—
	Cross gutter block (3)	—
	Horiz. pair with vert. gutter (24)	—
	Vert. pair with horiz. gutter (14)	—
V208PI	(80 pairs)	—
	Cross gutter block (3)	—
	Horiz. pair with vert. gutter (14)	—
	Vert. pair with horiz. gutter (24)	—
V209PI	(80 pairs)	—
	Cross gutter block (3)	—
	Horiz. pair with vert. gutter (14)	—
	Vert. pair with horiz. gutter (24)	—

New York #688-689, Geneva #294-295, Vienna #210-211, Souvenir Card #50
UNICEF, 50th Anniv.

1996

689PDa	Imperforate pane, #689PD (4)	—
G294PDa	Imperforate pane, #G294PD (4)	—
G295PDa	Imperforate pane, #G295PD (6)	—
V210PDa	Imperforate pane, #V210PD (on photographic paper) (2)	—
V211PDa	Imperforate pane, #V211PD (4)	—
SC50PD	(1)	—
688PP	10 items (18)	—
	Cross gutter block (6)	—
	Horiz. pair with vert. gutter (12)	—
	Vert. pair with horiz. gutter (15)	—
689PP	11 items (18)	—
	Cross gutter block (6)	—
	Horiz. pair with vert. gutter (12)	—
	Vert. pair with horiz. gutter (15)	—
G294PP	9 items (18)	—
	Cross gutter block (6)	—
	Horiz. pair with vert. gutter (12)	—
	Vert. pair with horiz. gutter (15)	—
G295PP	9 items (18)	—
	Cross gutter block (6)	—
	Horiz. pair with vert. gutter (12)	—
	Vert. pair with horiz. gutter (15)	—
V210PP	9 items (18)	—
	Cross gutter block (6)	—
	Horiz. pair with vert. gutter (18)	—
	Vert. pair with horiz. gutter (14)	—
V211PP	9 items (18)	—
	Cross gutter block (6)	—
	Horiz. pair with vert. gutter (18)	—
	Vert. pair with horiz. gutter (14)	—
688PI	(12 pairs)	—
	Cross gutter block (18)	—
	Horiz. pair with vert. gutter (36)	—
	Vert. pair with horiz. gutter (45)	—
689PI	(12 pairs)	—
	Cross gutter block (18)	—
	Horiz. pair with vert. gutter (36)	—
	Vert. pair with horiz. gutter (45)	—
G294PI	(12 pairs)	—
	Cross gutter block (18)	—
	Horiz. pair with vert. gutter (36)	—
	Vert. pair with horiz. gutter (45)	—
G295PI	(12 pairs)	—
	Cross gutter block (18)	—
	Horiz. pair with vert. gutter (36)	—
	Vert. pair with horiz. gutter (45)	—
V210PI	(12 pairs)	—
	Cross gutter block (18)	—
	Horiz. pair with vert. gutter (36)	—
	Vert. pair with horiz. gutter (45)	—
V211PI	(12 pairs)	—
	Cross gutter block (18)	—
	Horiz. pair with vert. gutter (36)	—
	Vert. pair with horiz. gutter (45)	—

Two of the No. G295PDa items are on photographic paper. Four cards with imperforate panes of 32c Hansel & Gretel essays exist. Four cards with imperforate panes of 5.50s Yeh-Shen essays exist. Four essays of No. SC50 showing these two essay items exist.

New York #690-697
Flags

1997

690-697PP	Set of 20 sheets (1)	—
690-697PI	Set of 2 sheets (3)	—

On Nos. 690-697PP, there are ten progressive proof sheets per issued sheet.

New York #698-699, Geneva #296-297, Vienna #212-213
Definitives

1997

698PDa	Card, #698PD, #G296PD-G297PD, #V212PD-V213PD (1)	—
699PDa	Card, #698PD-699PD, #G296PD-G297PD, #V212PD-V213PD (4)	—
698PP	8 items (84)	—
	Cross gutter block (3)	—
	Horiz. pair with vert. gutter (18)	—
	Vert. pair with horiz. gutter (14)	—
699PP	8 items (84)	—
	Cross gutter block (3)	—
	Horiz. pair with vert. gutter (14)	—
	Vert. pair with horiz. gutter (18)	—
G296PP	8 items (84)	—
	Cross gutter block (3)	—
	Horiz. pair with vert. gutter (14)	—
	Vert. pair with horiz. gutter (18)	—
G297PP	8 items (84)	—
	Cross gutter block (3)	—
	Horiz. pair with vert. gutter (14)	—
	Vert. pair with horiz. gutter (18)	—
V212PP	10 items (84)	—
	Cross gutter block (3)	—
	Horiz. pair with vert. gutter (18)	—
	Vert. pair with horiz. gutter (14)	—
V213PP	10 items (84)	—
	Cross gutter block (3)	—
	Horiz. pair with vert. gutter (18)	—
	Vert. pair with horiz. gutter (14)	—
698PI	(60 pairs)	—
	Cross gutter block (3)	—
	Horiz. pair with vert. gutter (18)	—
	Vert. pair with horiz. gutter (14)	—
699PI	(60 pairs)	—
	Cross gutter block (3)	—
	Horiz. pair with vert. gutter (14)	—
	Vert. pair with horiz. gutter (18)	—
G296PI	(60 pairs)	—
	Cross gutter block (3)	—
	Horiz. pair with vert. gutter (14)	—
	Vert. pair with horiz. gutter (18)	—
G297PI	(60 pairs)	—
	Cross gutter block (3)	—
	Horiz. pair with vert. gutter (14)	—
	Vert. pair with horiz. gutter (18)	—
V212PI	(60 pairs)	—
	Cross gutter block (3)	—
	Horiz. pair with vert. gutter (18)	—
	Vert. pair with horiz. gutter (14)	—
V213PI	(60 pairs)	—
	Cross gutter block (3)	—
	Horiz. pair with vert. gutter (18)	—
	Vert. pair with horiz. gutter (14)	—

New York #703a, Geneva #301a, Vienna #217a
Endangered Species

1997

703aPDa	Card, imperforate pane of 4 blocks #703aPD, imperforate pane of 4 blocks of G301aPD (4)	—
V217aPDa	Card, imperforate pane of 4 blocks #V217aPD (4)	—
703aPP	6 items (4 blocks)	—
	Cross gutter block (2)	—
	Horiz. pair with vert. gutter (2)	—
	Vert. pair with horiz. gutter (4)	—
G301aPP	6 items (4 blocks)	—
	Cross gutter block (2)	—
	Horiz. pair with vert. gutter (2)	—
	Vert. pair with horiz. gutter (4)	—
V217aPP	6 items (4 blocks)	—
	Cross gutter block (2)	—
	Horiz. pair with vert. gutter (2)	—
	Vert. pair with horiz. gutter (4)	—
703aPI	(12 blocks)	—
	Cross gutter block (6)	—
	Horiz. pair with vert. gutter (6)	—
	Vert. pair with horiz. gutter (12)	—
G301aPI	(12 blocks)	—
	Cross gutter block (6)	—
	Horiz. pair with vert. gutter (6)	—
	Vert. pair with horiz. gutter (12)	—
V217aPI	(12 blocks)	—
	Cross gutter block (6)	—
	Horiz. pair with vert. gutter (6)	—
	Vert. pair with horiz. gutter (12)	—

New York #707a, 708, Geneva #305a, 306, Vienna #221a, 222
Earth Summit

1997

707aPP	6 items (6 blocks)	—
708PP	6 items (1 souvenir sheet)	—
708aPP	6 items (1 souvenir sheet)	—
G305aPP	6 items (6 blocks)	—
V221aPP	6 items (6 blocks)	—
707aPI	(15 blocks)	—
708PI	(6 souvenir sheets)	—
708aPI	(6 souvenir sheets)	—
G305aPI	(15 blocks)	—

G306PI	(6 souvenir sheets)	—
V221aPI	(15 blocks)	—
V222PI	(6 souvenir sheets)	—

New York #713a, Geneva #311a, Vienna #227a
Transportation

1997

713aPDa	Imperforate pane, #713aPD (9)	—
G311aPDa	Imperforate pane, #G311aPD (9)	—
V227aPDa	Imperforate pane, #V227aPD (9)	—
713aPP	9 items (6 strips)	—
	Cross gutter block of strips (1)	—
	Horiz. pair of strips with vert. gutter (6)	—
	Vert. pair of strips with horiz. gutter (1)	—
G311aPP	10 items (6 strips)	—
	Cross gutter block of strips (1)	—
	Horiz. pair of strips with vert. gutter (6)	—
	Vert. pair of strips with horiz. gutter (1)	—
V227aPP	9 items (6 strips)	—
	Cross gutter block of strips (1)	—
	Horiz. pair of strips with vert. gutter (6)	—
	Vert. pair of strips with horiz. gutter (1)	—
713aPI	(14 strips)	—
	Cross gutter block of strips (1)	—
	Horiz. pair of strips with vert. gutter (6)	—
	Vert. pair of strips with horiz. gutter (1)	—
G311aPI	(14 strips)	—
	Cross gutter block of strips (1)	—
	Horiz. pair of strips with vert. gutter (6)	—
	Vert. pair of strips with horiz. gutter (1)	—
V227aPI	(14 strips)	—
	Cross gutter block of strips (1)	—
	Horiz. pair of strips with vert. gutter (6)	—
	Vert. pair of strips with horiz. gutter (1)	—

New York #714-715, Geneva #312-313, Vienna #228-229, Souvenir Card #51
Philately

1997

715TCa	Card, #714TC-715TC, #G312TC-G313TC, #V228TC-V229TC, all with white denominations (4)	—
715TCb	Card, #714TC-715TC, #G312TC-G313TC, #V228TC-V229TC, all with light blue green backgrounds (1)	—
SC51PD	(4)	—
714PP	11 items (33)	—
	Horiz. pair with vert. gutter (6)	—
715PP	11 items (33)	—
	Horiz. pair with vert. gutter (6)	—
715PPa	Cross gutter block, 2 each #714PP-715PP (2)	—
715PPb	Vert. pair with horiz. gutter, #714PP-715PP (11)	—
G312PP	11 items (33)	—
	Horiz. pair with vert. gutter (6)	—
G313PP	11 items (33)	—
G313PPa	Cross gutter block, 2 each #G312PP-G313PP (2)	—
G313PPb	Vert. pair with horiz. gutter, #G312PP-G313PP (11)	—
V228PP	10 items (33)	—
	Horiz. pair with vert. gutter (6)	—
V229PP	10 items (33)	—
	Horiz. pair with vert. gutter (6)	—
V229PPa	Cross gutter block, 2 each #V228PP-V229PP (2)	—
V229PPb	Vert. pair with horiz. gutter, #V228PP-V229PP (11)	—
714PI	(48 pairs)	—
	Horiz. pair with vert. gutter (18)	—
715PI	(48 pairs)	—
	Horiz. pair with vert. gutter (18)	—
715PIa	Cross gutter block, 2 each #714PI-715PI (6)	—
715PIb	Vert. pair with horiz. gutter, #714PI-715PI (33)	—
G312PI	(48 pairs)	—
	Horiz. pair with vert. gutter (18)	—
G313PI	(48 pairs)	—
	Horiz. pair with vert. gutter (18)	—
G313PIa	Cross gutter block, 2 each #G312PI-G313PI (6)	—
G313PIb	Vert. pair with horiz. gutter, #G312PI-G313PI (33)	—
V228PI	(48 pairs)	—
	Horiz. pair with vert. gutter (18)	—
V229PI	(48 pairs)	—
	Horiz. pair with vert. gutter (18)	—
V229PIa	Cross gutter block, 2 each #V228PI-V229PI (6)	—
V229PIb	Vert. pair with horiz. gutter, #V228PI-V229PI (33)	—

On Nos. 714PP-715PP, G312PP-G313PP and V228PP-V229PP some progressive proof items are blank due to color arrangements on sheets.

New York #716-717, Geneva #314-315, Vienna #230-231
World Heritage

1997

717PDa	Stapled set of 6 layout sheets with #716PD-717PD, #G314PD-G315PD, #V230PD-V231PD affixed (3)	—
716PP	10 items (20)	—
717PP	10 items (20)	—
G314PP	10 items (20)	—
G315PP	10 items (20)	—
V230PP	10 items (20)	—
V231PP	10 items (20)	—
716PI	(30 pairs)	—
717PI	(30 pairs)	—
G314PI	(30 pairs)	—
G315PI	(30 pairs)	—
V230PI	(30 pairs)	—
V231PI	(30 pairs)	—

New York #719-726
Flags

1998

719-726PP	Set of 20 sheets (1)	—
719-726PI	Set of 2 sheets (3)	—

On Nos. 719-726PP, there are ten progressive proof sheets per issued sheet.

New York #727-729, Geneva #317, Vienna #233-234
Definitives

1998

727PDa	Card, #727PD, #G317TC black (1)	—
729PDa	Card, #727PD-729PD, #G317PD, #V233PD-V234PD (4)	—
727PP	10 items (84)	—
	Cross gutter block (3)	—
	Horiz. pair with vert. gutter (14)	—
	Vert. pair with horiz. gutter (18)	—
728PP	8 items (84)	—
	Cross gutter block (3)	—
	Horiz. pair with vert. gutter (14)	—
	Vert. pair with horiz. gutter (18)	—
729PP	9 items (84)	—
	Cross gutter block (3)	—
	Horiz. pair with vert. gutter (18)	—
	Vert. pair with horiz. gutter (14)	—
G317PP	10 items (84)	—
	Cross gutter block (3)	—
	Horiz. pair with vert. gutter (18)	—
	Vert. pair with horiz. gutter (14)	—
V233PP	8 items (84)	—
	Cross gutter block (3)	—
	Horiz. pair with vert. gutter (18)	—
	Vert. pair with horiz. gutter (14)	—
V234PP	10 items (84)	—
	Cross gutter block (3)	—
	Horiz. pair with vert. gutter (18)	—
	Vert. pair with horiz. gutter (14)	—
727PI	(60 pairs)	—
	Cross gutter block (3)	—
	Horiz. pair with vert. gutter (14)	—
	Vert. pair with horiz. gutter (18)	—
728PI	(60 pairs)	—
	Cross gutter block (3)	—
	Horiz. pair with vert. gutter (14)	—
	Vert. pair with horiz. gutter (18)	—
729PI	(60 pairs)	—
	Cross gutter block (3)	—
	Horiz. pair with vert. gutter (18)	—
	Vert. pair with horiz. gutter (14)	—
G317PI	(60 pairs)	—
	Cross gutter block (3)	—
	Horiz. pair with vert. gutter (18)	—
	Vert. pair with horiz. gutter (14)	—
V233PI	(60 pairs)	—
	Cross gutter block (3)	—
	Horiz. pair with vert. gutter (18)	—
	Vert. pair with horiz. gutter (14)	—
V234PI	(60 pairs)	—
	Cross gutter block (3)	—
	Horiz. pair with vert. gutter (18)	—
	Vert. pair with horiz. gutter (14)	—

New York #733a, Geneva #321a, Vienna #238a
Endangered Species

1998

733PDa	Card, imperforate pane of 4 blocks, #733aPD (1)	—
733PDb	Card, broken imperforate pane of 4 blocks, #733aPD (1)	—
G321PDa	Card, imperforate pane of 4 blocks, #G321aPD (1)	—
G321PDb	Card, broken imperforate pane of 4 blocks, #G321aPD (1)	—
V238PDa	Card, imperforate pane of 4 blocks, #V238aPD (1)	—
V238PDb	Card, broken imperforate pane of 4 blocks, #V238aPD (1)	—
733aPP	6 items (4 blocks)	—
	Cross gutter block (2)	—
	Horiz. pair with vert. gutter (2)	—
	Vert. pair with horiz. gutter (4)	—
G321aPP	4 items (4 blocks)	—
	Cross gutter block (2)	—
	Horiz. pair with vert. gutter (2)	—
	Vert. pair with horiz. gutter (4)	—
V238aPP	6 items (4 blocks)	—
	Cross gutter block (2)	—
	Horiz. pair with vert. gutter (2)	—
	Vert. pair with horiz. gutter (4)	—

733aPI	(12 blocks)	—
	Cross gutter block (2)	—
	Horiz. pair with vert. gutter (2)	—
	Vert. pair with horiz. gutter (4)	—
G321aPI	(12 blocks)	—
	Cross gutter block (2)	—
	Horiz. pair with vert. gutter (2)	—
	Vert. pair with horiz. gutter (4)	—
V238aPI	(12 blocks)	—
	Cross gutter block (2)	—
	Horiz. pair with vert. gutter (2)	—
	Vert. pair with horiz. gutter (4)	—

No. G321aPP is not a complete set, as there are no black only and cyan only items.

New York #734, Geneva #322, Vienna #239
International Year of the Ocean

1998

734PD	(not approved) (4)	—
G322PD	(4)	—
V239PD	(4)	—
734PP	6 items (6 panes)	—
G322PP	6 items (6 panes)	—
V239PP	6 items (6 panes)	—
734PI	(18 panes)	—
G322PI	(18 panes)	—
V239PI	(18 panes)	—

New York #735-736, Geneva #323-324, Vienna #240-241
Rain Forests

1998

735PDa	Card, imperforate pane of 20 #735PD (8)	—
736PDa	Card, #736PD, #G324PD, #V241PD (8)	—
G323PDa	Card, imperforate pane of 20 #G323PD (8)	—
V240PDa	Card, imperforate pane of 20 #V240PD (8)	—
735PP	6 items (see note)	—
G323PP	6 items (see note)	—
V240PP	6 items (see note)	—
735PI	(see note)	—
G323PI	(see note)	—
V240PI	(see note)	—

There are two types of Nos. 735PP and V240PP, one with cats lacking spots on the red item, the other with the cat with spots on the magenta item. There are 20 of each type.

There are two types of No. G323PP, one with orangutan with small dots in eyes on the cyan item, the other with large dots in eyes.

Similarly, there are two types of Nos. 735PI, G323PI and V240PI, one with a lighter background, the other with a bolder background. There are 20 pairs of each type.

New York #737-738, Geneva #325-326, Vienna #242-243, Souvenir Card #52
UN Peacekeeping Forces, 50th Anniv.

1998

737TC	Dark blue panel (on Cromalin paper) (5)	—
738TC	Dark blue panel (on Cromalin paper) (5)	—
G325TC	Dark blue panel (on Cromalin paper) (5)	—
G326TC	Dark blue panel (on Cromalin paper) (5)	—
V242TC	Dark blue panel (on Cromalin paper) (5)	—
V243TC	Dark blue panel (on Cromalin paper) (5)	—
SC52PD	(4)	—
737PP	10 items (20)	—
738PP	10 items (20)	—
G325PP	10 items (20)	—
G326PP	10 items (20)	—
V242PP	10 items (20)	—
V243PP	10 items (20)	—
737PI	(20 pairs)	—
738PI	(20 pairs)	—
G325PI	(20 pairs)	—
G326PI	(20 pairs)	—
V242PI	(20 pairs)	—
V243PI	(20 pairs)	—

New York #739-740, Geneva #327-328, Vienna #244-245, Souvenir Card #53
Universal Declaration of Human Rights, 50th Anniv.

1998

740PDa	Card, #739PD-740PD, #G327PD-G328PD, #V244PD-V245PD (4)	—
SC53PD	(4)	—
739PP	8 items (64)	—
	Cross gutter block (2)	—
	Horiz. pair with vert. gutter (8)	—
	Vert. pair with horiz. gutter (16)	—
740PP	8 items (64)	—
	Cross gutter block (2)	—
	Horiz. pair with vert. gutter (8)	—
	Vert. pair with horiz. gutter (16)	—
G327PP	8 items (64)	—
	Cross gutter block (2)	—
	Horiz. pair with vert. gutter (8)	—
	Vert. pair with horiz. gutter (16)	—
G328PP	8 items (64)	—
	Cross gutter block (2)	—
	Horiz. pair with vert. gutter (8)	—
	Vert. pair with horiz. gutter (16)	—
V244PP	8 items (64)	—

	Cross gutter block (2)	—
	Horiz. pair with vert. gutter (8)	—
	Vert. pair with horiz. gutter (16)	—
V245PP	8 items (64)	—
	Cross gutter block (2)	—
	Horiz. pair with vert. gutter (8)	—
	Vert. pair with horiz. gutter (16)	—
739PI	(52 pairs)	—
	Cross gutter block (2)	—
	Horiz. pair with vert. gutter (8)	—
	Vert. pair with horiz. gutter (16)	—
740PI	(52 pairs)	—
	Cross gutter block (2)	—
	Horiz. pair with vert. gutter (8)	—
	Vert. pair with horiz. gutter (16)	—
G327PI	(52 pairs)	—
	Cross gutter block (2)	—
	Horiz. pair with vert. gutter (8)	—
	Vert. pair with horiz. gutter (16)	—
G328PI	(52 pairs)	—
	Cross gutter block (2)	—
	Horiz. pair with vert. gutter (8)	—
	Vert. pair with horiz. gutter (16)	—
V244PI	(52 pairs)	—
	Cross gutter block (2)	—
	Horiz. pair with vert. gutter (8)	—
	Vert. pair with horiz. gutter (16)	—
V245PI	(52 pairs)	—
	Cross gutter block (2)	—
	Horiz. pair with vert. gutter (8)	—
	Vert. pair with horiz. gutter (16)	—

New York #741-743, Geneva #329-331, Vienna #246-248
Schönbrunn Palace

1998

742PDa	Card, blocks of 4, #741PD-742PD (3)	—
742PDb	Card, cut apart blocks of 4, #741PD-742PD (1)	—
G330PDa	Card, blocks of 4, #G329PD-G330PD (3)	—
G330PDb	Card, cut apart blocks of 4, #G329PD-G330PD (1)	—
V247PDa	Card, blocks of 4, #V246PD-V247PD (3)	—
V247PDb	Card, cut apart blocks of 4, #V246PD-V247PD (1)	—
742TCa	Card, block of 4 #742TC dark blue denomination (on photographic paper) (1)	—
743TCa	Card, strips of 3, #743aTC-743cTC bright red violet denomination (1)	—
743TCb	Card, blocks of 4, #743dTC-743fTC bright red violet denomination (on photographic paper) (1)	—
743TCc	Entire booklet (black & white, on photographic paper) (1)	—
G330TCa	Card, blocks of 4, #G329TC-G330TC bright red violet denominations (on photographic paper) (1)	—
G331TCa	Card, blocks of 4, #G331aTC-G331cTC bright red violet denomination (on photographic paper) (1)	—
G331TCb	Card, strips of 3, #G331dTC-G331fTC bright red violet denomination (1)	—
G331TCc	Entire booklet (black & white, on photographic paper) (1)	—
V247TCa	Card, block of 4 #V247TC bright green denomination (on photographic paper) (1)	—
V248TCa	Card, strips of 3, #V248aTC-V248cTC bright red violet denomination (on photographic paper) (1)	—
V248TCb	Card, blocks of 4, #V248dTC-V248fTC bright red violet denomination (on photographic paper) (1)	—
V248TCc	Entire booklet (black & white, on photographic paper) (1)	—
741PP	10 items (24)	—
742PP	10 items (24)	—
	Horiz. pair with vert. gutter (3)	—
742PPa	Cross gutter block, 2 #741PP-742PP (1)	—
742PPb	Vert. pair with horiz. gutter, #741PP-742PP (8)	—
G329PP	10 items (24)	—
G330PP	10 items (24)	—
	Horiz. pair with vert. gutter (3)	—
G330PPa	Cross gutter block, 2 #G329PP-G330PP (1)	—
G330PPb	Vert. pair with horiz. gutter, #G329PP-G330PP (8)	—
V246PP	10 items (24)	—
V247PP	10 items (24)	—
	Horiz. pair with vert. gutter (3)	—
V247PPa	Cross gutter block, 2 #V246PP-V247PP (1)	—
V247PPb	Vert. pair with horiz. gutter, #V246PP-V247PP (8)	—
741PI	(32 pairs)	—
	Vert. pair with horiz. gutter (3)	—
742PI	(32 pairs)	—
	Horiz. pair with vert. gutter (3)	—

742PIa	Cross gutter block, 2 #741PI-742PI (1)	—
742PIb	Vert. pair with horiz. gutter, #741PI-742PI (8)	—
G329PI	(32 pairs)	—
	Vert. pair with horiz. gutter (3)	—
G330PI	(32 pairs)	—
	Horiz. pair with vert. gutter (3)	—
G330PIa	Cross gutter block, 2 #G329PI-G330PI (1)	—
G330PIb	Vert. pair with horiz. gutter, #G329PI-G330PI (8)	—
V246PI	(32 pairs)	—
	Vert. pair with horiz. gutter (3)	—
V247PI	(32 pairs)	—
	Horiz. pair with vert. gutter (3)	—
V247PIa	Cross gutter block, 2 #V246PI-V247PI (1)	—
V247PIb	Vert. pair with horiz. gutter, #V246PI-V247PI (8)	—

Five cards with blocks of four essays with gold frames over vignette exist for each of the New York, Geneva and Vienna pairings.

New York #744-751
Flags

1999

744-751PP	Set of 20 sheets (1)	—
744-751PI	Set of 2 sheets (4)	—

On Nos. 744-751PP, there are ten progressive proof sheets per issued sheet.

New York #752-753, Geneva #332, Vienna #249
Definitives

1999

752PDa	Card, #752PD, #V249PD (3)	—
752PDb	Card, #752PD, #V249PD, #753TC lacking gray in pink frame boxes (1)	—
753PDa	Card, block of 4, #753PD (2)	—
753TC	Lacking gray in pink frame boxes (3)	—
G332TC	red (4)	—
G332TC	brown (4)	—
752PP	9 items (48)	—
	Cross gutter block (1)	—
	Horiz. pair with vert. gutter (6)	—
	Vert. pair with horiz. gutter (8)	—
753PP	10 items (20)	—
V249PP	9 items (48)	—
	Cross gutter block (1)	—
	Horiz. pair with vert. gutter (6)	—
	Vert. pair with horiz. gutter (8)	—
752PI	(24 pairs)	—
	Cross gutter block (3)	—
	Horiz. pair with vert. gutter (18)	—
	Vert. pair with horiz. gutter (24)	—
753PI	(20 pairs)	—
G332PI	(20 pairs)	—
V249PI	(72 pairs)	—
	Cross gutter block (3)	—
	Horiz. pair with vert. gutter (18)	—
	Vert. pair with horiz. gutter (24)	—

New York #754-756, Geneva #333-335, Vienna #250-252
World Heritage

1999

755PDa	Card, pairs of #754PD-755PD, #G333PD-G334PD, #V250PD-V251PD (1)	—
756PDa	Card, pairs of #756aPD-756fPD (1)	—
756PDb	Sheet, pairs of #754PD-755PD, #756aPD-756fPD, #G333PD-G334PD, #G335aPD-G335fPD, #V250PD-V251PD, #V252aPD-V252fPD (2)	—
756PDc	Cut-up section of #756PDb with pairs of stamps issued in sheets (2)	—
756PDd	Cut-up section of #756PDb with pairs of stamps issued in booklets (2)	—
754TC	Black and white image on layout sheet of photographic paper (2)	—
755TC	Black and white image on layout sheet of photographic paper (2)	—
G333TC	Black and white image on layout sheet of photographic paper (2)	—
G334TC	Black and white image on layout sheet of photographic paper (2)	—
V250TCa	Black and white image on layout sheet of photographic paper (2)	—
V250TCb	2 pairs of black and white images on layout sheet of photographic paper, affixed to card (1)	—
V251TCa	Black and white image on layout sheet of photographic paper (2)	—
V251TCb	2 pairs of black and white images on layout sheet of photographic paper, affixed to card (1)	—
754PP	6 items (32)	—
	Horiz. pair with vert. gutter (8)	—
755PP	6 items (32)	—
	Horiz. pair with vert. gutter (8)	—
755PPa	Cross gutter block, 2 #754PP-755PP (2)	—
755PPb	Vert. pair with horiz. gutter, #754PP-755PP (8)	—
G333PP	6 items (32)	—
	Horiz. pair with vert. gutter (8)	—
G334PP	6 items (32)	—

G334PPa	Horiz. pair with vert. gutter (8) Cross gutter block, 2 #G333PP-G334PP (2)	—
G334PPb	Vert. pair with horiz. gutter, #G333PP-G334PP (8)	—
V250PP	6 items (32)	—
V251PP	Horiz. pair with vert. gutter (8) 6 items (32)	—
V251PPa	Horiz. pair with vert. gutter (8) Cross gutter block, 2 #V250PP-V251PP (2)	—
V251PPb	Vert. pair with horiz. gutter, #V250PP-V251PP (8)	—
754PI	(52 pairs)	—
755PI	Horiz. pair with vert. gutter (16) (52 pairs)	—
755PIa	Horiz. pair with vert. gutter (16) Cross gutter block, 2 #754PI-755PI (4)	—
755PIb	Vert. pair with horiz. gutter, #754PI-755PI (16)	—
G333PI	(36 pairs)	—
G334PI	Horiz. pair with vert. gutter (8) (36 pairs)	—
G334PIa	Cross gutter block, 2 #G333PI-G334PI (2)	—
G334PIb	Vert. pair with horiz. gutter, #G333PI-G334PI (8)	—
V250PI	(36 pairs)	—
V251PI	Horiz. pair with vert. gutter (8) (36 pairs)	—
V251PIa	Horiz. pair with vert. gutter (8) Cross gutter block, 2 #V250PI-V251PI (2)	—
V251PIb	Vert. pair with horiz. gutter, #V250PI-V251PI (8)	—

New York #760a, Geneva #339a, Vienna #256a
Endangered Species

1999

760aPDa	Card, imperf pane of 4 blocks, #760aPD (2)	—
760aPDb	Card, 2 each #757PD-760PD (1)	—
G339aPDa	Card, 2 each #G336PD-G339PD (on Cromalin paper), broken pane of 80c essays of #G336-G339 (1)	—
V256aPDa	Card, imperf pane of 4 blocks, #V256aPD (3)	—
V256aPDb	Card, 2 each #V253PD-V256PD (1)	—
760aPP	6 items (4 blocks) Cross gutter block (2) Horiz. pair with vert. gutter (2) Vert. pair with horiz. gutter (4)	—
G339aPP	6 items (4 blocks) Cross gutter block (2) Horiz. pair with vert. gutter (2) Vert. pair with horiz. gutter (4)	—
V256aPP	6 items (4 blocks) Cross gutter block (2) Horiz. pair with vert. gutter (2) Vert. pair with horiz. gutter (4)	—
760aPI	(12 blocks) Cross gutter block (2) Horiz. pair with vert. gutter (2) Vert. pair with horiz. gutter (4)	—
G339aPI	(12 blocks) Cross gutter block (2) Horiz. pair with vert. gutter (2) Vert. pair with horiz. gutter (4)	—
V256aPI	(12 blocks) Cross gutter block (2) Horiz. pair with vert. gutter (2) Vert. pair with horiz. gutter (4)	—

Three cards exist containing imperforate panes of four blocks of the 80c essays.

New York #762a, 763, Geneva #341a, 342, Vienna #258a, 259
UNISPACE III

1999

762aPDa	Card, imperforate pane of 5 pairs, #762aPD (3)	—
763PD	With printed perforations on overlay (3)	—
763aPD	With printed perforations on overlay (2)	—
G341aPDa	Card, imperforate pane of 5 pairs, #G341aPD (4)	—
G342PD	With printed perforations on overlay (2)	—
G342aPD	With printed perforations on overlay (2)	—
V258aPDa	Card, imperforate pane of 5 pairs, #V258aPD (4)	—
V259PD	With printed perforations on overlay (2)	—
762PP	8 items (5 pairs)	—
762aPP	8 items (1 souvenir sheet)	—
763PP	9 items (1 pair)	—
763aPP	10 items (1 souvenir sheet)	—
762PI	(10 pairs)	—
763PI	(3 souvenir sheets)	—
763aPI	(4 souvenir sheets)	—
G341aPI	(10 pairs)	—
G342PI	(3 souvenir sheets)	—
V258aPI	(10 pairs)	—
V259PI	(3 souvenir sheets)	—

New York #767a, Geneva #346a, Vienna #263a, Souvenir Card #54
Universal Postal Union, 125th Anniv.

1999

767aPDa	Card, #767aPD, #G346aPD, #V263aPD with approval handstamp (4)	—
767aTCa	Card, #767aTC, #G346aTCD, #V263aTC (dark blue denominations, not approved) (4)	—
SC54PD	(4)	—
767aPP	8 items (6 blocks)	—
G346aPP	8 items (6 blocks)	—
V263aPP	8 items (6 blocks)	—
767aPI	(12 blocks)	—
G346aPI	(12 blocks)	—
V263aPI	(12 blocks)	—

New York #768-769, Geneva #347-348, Vienna #264-265
In Memoriam

1999

769PDa	Card, #768PD-769PD (4)	—
G348PDa	Card, #G347PD-G348PD (4)	—
V265PDa	Card, #V264PD-V265PD (4)	—
768PP	10 items (66) Cross gutter block (2) Horiz. pair with vert. gutter (12) Vert. pair with horiz. gutter (11)	—
769PP	10 items (66)	—
G347PP	10 items (66) Cross gutter block (2) Horiz. pair with vert. gutter (12) Vert. pair with horiz. gutter (11)	—
G348PP	10 items (24 souvenir sheets)	—
V264PP	10 items (66) Cross gutter block (2) Horiz. pair with vert. gutter (12) Vert. pair with horiz. gutter (11)	—
V265PP	10 items (24 souvenir sheets)	—
768PI	(52 pairs) Cross gutter block (2) Horiz. pair with vert. gutter (12) Vert. pair with horiz. gutter (11)	—
769PI	(24 souvenir sheets)	—
G347PI	(52 pairs) Cross gutter block (2) Horiz. pair with vert. gutter (12) Vert. pair with horiz. gutter (11)	—
G348PI	(24 souvenir sheets)	—
V264PI	(52 pairs) Cross gutter block (2) Horiz. pair with vert. gutter (12) Vert. pair with horiz. gutter (11)	—
V265PI	(24 souvenir sheets)	—

New York #770-771, Geneva #349-350, Vienna #266-267
Education

1999

771PDa	Card, #770PD-771PD, #G349PD-G350PD, #V266PD-V267PD with approval handstamp (4)	—
771PDb	Card, #770PD, #G350PD, #V266PD-V267PD, #771TC red denomination, #G349TC red violet denomination with "approved with corrections" handstamp (4)	—
770PP	9 items (20)	—
771PP	8 items (20)	—
G349PP	7 items (20)	—
G350PP	7 items (20)	—
V266PP	7 items (20)	—
V267PP	8 items (20)	—
770PI	(20 pairs)	—
771PI	(20 pairs)	—
G349PI	(30 pairs)	—
G350PI	(30 pairs)	—
V266PI	(30 pairs)	—
V267PI	(30 pairs)	—

New York #772, Geneva #351, Vienna #268
International Year of Thanksgiving

2000

772PDa	Card, #772PD, #G351PD, #V268PD (4)	—
772TCa	Card, #772TC, #G351TC, #V268TC, all with black background (4)	—
772PP	12 items (32) Horiz. pair with vert. gutter (4)	—
G351PP	12 items (32) Horiz. pair with vert. gutter (4)	—
V268PP	12 items (32) Horiz. pair with vert. gutter (4)	—
772PI	(36 pairs) Horiz. pair with vert. gutter (4)	—
G351PI	(36 pairs) Horiz. pair with vert. gutter (4)	—
V268PI	(36 pairs) Horiz. pair with vert. gutter (4)	—

New York #776a, Geneva #355a, Vienna #272a
Endangered Species

2000

776aPDa	Card, imperforate pane of 4 blocks, #776aPD (3)	—
776aPDb	Card, 3 each #773PD-776PD (1)	—
G355aPDa	Card, imperforate pane of 4 blocks, #G355aPD, imperforate pane of 4 blocks, #V272aPD (3)	—

G355aPDb	Card, 3 each #G352PD-G355PD, #V269PD-V272PD (1)	—
776aPP	6 items (4 blocks) Cross gutter block (2) Horiz. pair with vert. gutter (2) Vert. pair with horiz. gutter (4)	—
G355aPP	6 items (4 blocks) Cross gutter block (2) Horiz. pair with vert. gutter (2) Vert. pair with horiz. gutter (4)	—
V272aPP	6 items (4 blocks) Cross gutter block (2) Horiz. pair with vert. gutter (2) Vert. pair with horiz. gutter (4)	—
776aPI	(12 blocks) Cross gutter block (2) Horiz. pair with vert. gutter (2) Vert. pair with horiz. gutter (4)	—
G355aPI	(12 blocks) Cross gutter block (2) Horiz. pair with vert. gutter (2) Vert. pair with horiz. gutter (4)	—
V272aPI	(12 blocks) Cross gutter block (2) Horiz. pair with vert. gutter (2) Vert. pair with horiz. gutter (4)	—

New York #777-778, Geneva #356-357, Vienna #273-274
Our World 2000

2000

778PDa	Card, #777PD-778PD, #G356PD-G357PD, #V273PD-V274PD (4)	—
778PDb	Card, #777PD-778PD, #G356PD-G357PD, #V274PD, #V273TC black denomination, with "not approved" handstamp (2)	—
777PP	8 items (64) Cross gutter block (2) Horiz. pair with vert. gutter (16) Vert. pair with horiz. gutter (8)	—
778PP	8 items (64) Cross gutter block (2) Horiz. pair with vert. gutter (8) Vert. pair with horiz. gutter (16)	—
G356PP	8 items (64) Cross gutter block (2) Horiz. pair with vert. gutter (8) Vert. pair with horiz. gutter (16)	—
G357PP	8 items (64) Cross gutter block (2) Horiz. pair with vert. gutter (16) Vert. pair with horiz. gutter (8)	—
V273PP	8 items (64) Cross gutter block (2) Horiz. pair with vert. gutter (16) Vert. pair with horiz. gutter (8)	—
V274PP	8 items (64) Cross gutter block (2) Horiz. pair with vert. gutter (8) Vert. pair with horiz. gutter (16)	—
777PI	(52 pairs) Cross gutter block (2) Horiz. pair with vert. gutter (16) Vert. pair with horiz. gutter (8)	—
778PI	(52 pairs) Cross gutter block (2) Horiz. pair with vert. gutter (8) Vert. pair with horiz. gutter (16)	—
G356PI	(52 pairs) Cross gutter block (2) Horiz. pair with vert. gutter (16) Vert. pair with horiz. gutter (8)	—
G357PI	(52 pairs) Cross gutter block (2) Horiz. pair with vert. gutter (8) Vert. pair with horiz. gutter (16)	—
V273PI	(52 pairs) Cross gutter block (2) Horiz. pair with vert. gutter (16) Vert. pair with horiz. gutter (8)	—
V274PI	(52 pairs) Cross gutter block (2) Horiz. pair with vert. gutter (8) Vert. pair with horiz. gutter (16)	—

New York #779-781, Geneva #358-360, Vienna #275-277
United Nations, 55th Anniv.

2000

780TCa	Card, #779TC-780TC, #G358TC-G359TC, #V275TC-V276TC (all with white denominations with colored outlines (4)	—
781TCa	Card, #781TC, #G360TC, #V277TC (all with white denominations with colored outlines (4)	—
781TCb	Card, #779TC-781TC ultramarine & silver (2)	—
781TCc	Card, #779TC-781TC blue & silver (2)	—
781TCd	Card, #781TC, #G360TC silver backgrounds, white denominations with colored outlines (5)	—
G359TCa	Card, #G358TC-G359TC brown red & silver (2)	—
G360TCa	Card, #G358TC-G360TC carmine & silver (2)	—
G360TCb	Card, #G358TC-G360TC cerise & silver (2)	—
V277TCa	Card, #V275TC-V277TC green & silver (2)	—
V277TCb	Card, #V275TC-V277TC dark green & silver (2)	—
V277TCc	Silver background, white denominations with green outlines (5)	—

779PP	7 items (128)	—
	Cross gutter block (4)	—
	Horiz. pair with vert. gutter (16)	—
	Vert. pair with horiz. gutter (32)	—
780PP	7 items (128)	—
	Cross gutter block (4)	—
	Horiz. pair with vert. gutter (16)	—
	Vert. pair with horiz. gutter (32)	—
781PP	6 items (60 souvenir sheets)	—
G358PP	9 items (128)	—
	Cross gutter block (4)	—
	Horiz. pair with vert. gutter (16)	—
	Vert. pair with horiz. gutter (32)	—
G359PP	9 items (128)	—
	Cross gutter block (4)	—
	Horiz. pair with vert. gutter (16)	—
	Vert. pair with horiz. gutter (32)	—
G360PP	9 items (60 souvenir sheets)	—
V275PP	10 items (128)	—
	Cross gutter block (4)	—
	Horiz. pair with vert. gutter (16)	—
	Vert. pair with horiz. gutter (32)	—
V276PP	10 items (128)	—
	Cross gutter block (4)	—
	Horiz. pair with vert. gutter (16)	—
	Vert. pair with horiz. gutter (32)	—
V277PP	10 items (60 souvenir sheets)	—
779PI	(84 pairs)	—
	Cross gutter block (4)	—
	Horiz. pair with vert. gutter (16)	—
	Vert. pair with horiz. gutter (32)	—
780PI	(84 pairs)	—
	Cross gutter block (4)	—
	Horiz. pair with vert. gutter (16)	—
	Vert. pair with horiz. gutter (32)	—
781PI	(60 souvenir sheets)	—
G358PI	(84 pairs)	—
	Cross gutter block (4)	—
	Horiz. pair with vert. gutter (16)	—
	Vert. pair with horiz. gutter (32)	—
G359PI	(84 pairs)	—
	Cross gutter block (4)	—
	Horiz. pair with vert. gutter (16)	—
	Vert. pair with horiz. gutter (32)	—
V275PI	(84 pairs)	—
	Cross gutter block (4)	—
	Horiz. pair with vert. gutter (16)	—
	Vert. pair with horiz. gutter (32)	—
V276PI	(84 pairs)	—
	Cross gutter block (4)	—
	Horiz. pair with vert. gutter (16)	—
	Vert. pair with horiz. gutter (32)	—
781PI	(60 souvenir sheets)	—

One item in Nos. G358PP and G359PP is blank, coming from sheet with marginal inscriptions only.

New York #782
International Flag of Peace

2000

782PD	With approval handstamp (4)	—
782TC	Black and white photocopy of layout of pane of 20, with approval handstamp and signature (1)	—
782PP	9 items (96)	—
	Cross gutter block (2)	—
	Horiz. pair with vert. gutter (16)	—
	Vert. pair with horiz. gutter (8)	—
782PI	(96 pairs)	—
	Cross gutter block (6)	—
	Horiz. pair with vert. gutter (48)	—
	Vert. pair with horiz. gutter (24)	—

An essay with "age 12" after artist's name exists in five cards and a black and white layout of the pane of 20 on photographic paper.

New York #783, Geneva #361, Vienna #278
UN in the 21st Century

2000

783PDa	Card, #783PD, #G361PD, #V278PD with approval handstamp (4)	—
783TCa	Card, #783TC, #G361TC, #V278TC all with washed-out colors, with "not approved" handstamp (5)	—
783PP	8 items (1)	—
G361PP	8 items (1)	—
V278PP	8 items (1)	—
783PI	(2 sheets)	—
G361PI	(2 sheets)	—
V278PI	(2 sheets)	—

New York #784-786, Geneva #362-364, Vienna #279-281
World Heritage

2000

785PDa	Card, #784PD-785PD, #G362PD-G364PD, #V279PD-V280PD (4)	—
784TC	Black and white image of pane of 20 on layout sheet on photographic paper (1)	—
785TC	Black and white image of pane of 20 on layout sheet on photographic paper (1)	—
G362TC	Black and white image of pane of 20 on layout sheet on photographic paper (1)	—
G363TC	Black and white image of pane of 20 on layout sheet on photographic paper (1)	—
V279TC	Black and white image of pane of 20 on layout sheet on photographic paper (1)	—

V280TC	Black and white image of pane of 20 on layout sheet on photographic paper (1)	—
784PP	9 items (24)	—
785PP	9 items (24)	—
	Vert. pair with horiz. gutter (3)	—
785PPa	Cross gutter block, 2 #784PP-785PP (1)	—
785PPb	Horiz. pair with vert. gutter, #784PP-785PP (8)	—
786iPPa	9 items, Strip of #786gPP-786iPP, with vert. gutters between (4)	—
G362PP	9 items (24)	—
G363PP	9 items (24)	—
	Vert. pair with horiz. gutter (3)	—
G363PPa	Cross gutter block, 2 #G362PP-G363PP (1)	—
G363PPb	Horiz. pair with vert. gutter, #G362PP-G363PP (8)	—
V279PP	7 items (24)	—
	Vert. pair with horiz. gutter (3)	—
V280PP	7 items (24)	—
	Vert. pair with horiz. gutter (3)	—
V280PPa	Cross gutter block, 2 #V279PP-V280PP (1)	—
V280PPb	Horiz. pair with vert. gutter, #V279PP-V280PP (8)	—
784PI	(32 pairs)	—
	Vert. pair with horiz. gutter (3)	—
785PI	(32 pairs)	—
	Vert. pair with horiz. gutter (3)	—
785PIa	Cross gutter block, 2 #784PI-785PI (1)	—
785PIb	Horiz. pair with vert. gutter, #784PI-785PI (8)	—
786gPI	(5 booklet panes)	—
786hPI	(5 booklet panes)	—
786iPI	(5 booklet panes)	—
786iPIa	Strip of #786gPI-786iPI, with vert. gutters between (4)	—
786jPI	(5 booklet panes)	—
786kPI	(5 booklet panes)	—
786lPI	(5 booklet panes)	—
G362PI	(32 pairs)	—
	Vert. pair with horiz. gutter (3)	—
G363PI	(32 pairs)	—
	Vert. pair with horiz. gutter (3)	—
G363PIa	Cross gutter block, 2 #G362PI-G363PI (1)	—
G363PIb	Horiz. pair with vert. gutter, #G362PI-G363PI (8)	—
G364gPI	(5 booklet panes)	—
G364hPI	(5 booklet panes)	—
G364iPI	(5 booklet panes)	—
G364jPI	(5 booklet panes)	—
G364kPI	(5 booklet panes)	—
G364lPI	(5 booklet panes)	—
V279PI	(82 pairs)	—
	Vert. pair with horiz. gutter (3)	—
V280PI	(32 pairs)	—
	Vert. pair with horiz. gutter (3)	—
V280PIa	Cross gutter block, 2 #V279PI-V280PI (1)	—
V280PIb	Horiz. pair with vert. gutter, #V279PI-V280PI (8)	—
V281gPI	(5 booklet panes)	—
V281hPI	(5 booklet panes)	—
V281iPI	(5 booklet panes)	—
V281jPI	(5 booklet panes)	—
V281kPI	(5 booklet panes)	—
V281lPI	(5 booklet panes)	—

Some pairs of No. V279PI are defaced with blue marker.

New York #787-788, Geneva #365-366, Vienna #282-283, Souvenir Card #55
Respect for Refugees

2000

787PDa	Card, #787PD, #G365PD, #V282PD (4)	—
788PDa	Card, #788PD, #G366PD, #V283PD (4)	—
SC55PD	(4)	—
787PP	6 items (32)	—
	Horiz. pair with vert. gutter (4)	—
788PP	6 items (20 souvenir sheets)	—
G365PP	6 items (32)	—
	Cross gutter block (1)	—
	Horiz. pair with vert. gutter (6)	—
	Vert. pair with horiz. gutter (8)	—
G366PP	6 items (20 souvenir sheets)	—
V282PP	6 items (32)	—
	Horiz. pair with vert. gutter (4)	—
V283PP	6 items (20 souvenir sheets)	—
787PI	(36 pairs)	—
	Horiz. pair with vert. gutter (4)	—
788PI	(20 souvenir sheets)	—
G365PI	(44 pairs)	—
	Cross gutter block (1)	—
	Horiz. pair with vert. gutter (6)	—
	Vert. pair with horiz. gutter (8)	—
G366PI	(20 souvenir sheets)	—
V282PI	(36 pairs)	—
	Horiz. pair with vert. gutter (4)	—
V283PI	(20 souvenir sheets)	—

AIR POST STAMPS
New York #C1-C4
Plane and Gull, Swallows and UN Emblem

1951

C1PD	(1)	—
C2PD	(1)	—
C3PD	(1)	—
C4PD	(1)	—

C1PI	(25 pairs)	—
C2PI	(25 pairs)	—
C3PI	(25 pairs)	—
C4PI	(25 pairs)	—

New York #C5
Airplane Wing and Globe

1957

C5PD	(4)	—
C5TC	brown (not approved) (5)	—
C5TC	indigo (5)	—
C5PI	(40 pairs)	—
	Vert. pair with horiz. gutter (10)	—

New York #C6-C7
Airplane Wing and Globe; UN Flag and Plane

1959

C6PD	(1)	—
C6PDa	Card, #C6PD, 2 #C6TC in slightly different shades (2)	—
C6PDb	Card, 2 #C6PD, 2 #C7TC Prussian blue (1)	—
C7PD	(1)	—
C7PDa	Card, #C7PD, #C7TC Prussian blue, #C7TC dark blue (2)	—
C6TC	black (1)	—
C7TC	black (1)	—
C6PI	(115 pairs)	—
	Vert. pair with horiz. gutter (10)	—
C7PI	(90 pairs)	—
	Horiz. pair with vert. gutter (10)	—

New York #C8-C10
Definitives

1963

C10PDa	Card, #C8PD-C10PD (3)	—
C10PDb	Card, #C8PD, #C10PD, 3 #C9PD (3)	—
C8PP	3 items (80)	—
	Horiz. pair with vert. gutter (10)	—
C9PP	4 items (80)	—
	Vert. pair with horiz. gutter (10)	—
C10PP	4 items (80)	—
	Horiz. pair with vert. gutter (10)	—
C8PI	(80 pairs)	—
	Horiz. pair with vert. gutter (20)	—
C9PI	(80 pairs)	—
	Vert. pair with horiz. gutter (20)	—
C10PI	(80 pairs)	—
	Horiz. pair with vert. gutter (20)	—

New York #C11-C12
Definitives

1964

C11PDa	Card, #C11PD, #C12TC peach and brown background (disapproved) (2)	—
C12PD	(2)	—
C12PDa	Card, #C11PD-C12PD (4)	—
C11PI	(25 pairs)	—
C12PI	(25 pairs)	—

New York #C13
Jet and UN Emblem

1968

C13PD	(3)	—
C13PDa	Card, #C13PD, 2 #C13TC with slightly different shades (2)	—
C13PP	9 items, perforated, mounted on card (1)	—

New York #C14
Wings, Envelopes and UN Emblem

1969

| C14PD | (4) | — |
| C14PP | 6 items, perforated (50) | — |

New York #C15-C18
Definitives

1972

C15PD	(2)	—
C16PD	With approval handstamp (2)	—
C17PD	(2)	—
C18PD	(2)	—
C16TC	dark blue emblem (dated 16. Oct. 1971) (2)	—
C15PP	4 items (100)	—
C16PP	10 items (100)	—
C17PP	4 items (100)	—
C18PP	10 items (160)	—
	Horiz. pair with vert. gutter (20)	—
C16PI	(50 pairs)	—
C17PI	(50 pairs)	—

New York #C19-C21
Definitives

1974

C19PD	(3)	—
C20PD	(3)	—
C21PD	(3)	—
C19PP	8 items (50)	—
C21PP	5 items (50)	—
C19PI	(50 pairs)	—
C20PI	(50 pairs)	—
C21PI	(50 pairs)	—

Five cards with essays of No. C21 with incorrect Russian inscription exist.

New York #C22-C23
Definitives

1977

C22PD	With approval handstamp (4)	—
C22TC	Gray wings and envelope, with "not approved" handstamp (2)	—
C23PD	(1)	—
C23PDa	Card, #C23PD, #C22TC gray wings and envelope (3)	—
C22PP	6 items (50)	—
C22PI	(50 pairs)	—
C23PI	(50 pairs)	—

ENVELOPES
New York #U1
UN Emblem

1952

U1PD	(1)	—
U1TC	black (1)	—

New York #U2
UN Emblem

1958

U2PD	with manuscript approval (2)	—
U2TC	black, on card, with manuscript approval (1)	—

New York #U3
Stylized Globe and Weather Vane

1963

U3PD	(2)	—
U3PI	Indicia only on small piece of paper (1)	—

See No. UC6PI.

New York #U5
UN Headquarters

1973

U5PD	(41)	—
U5PP	6 items (5)	—
U5PI	Unfolded and uncut (2)	—

New York #U6
UN Headquarters

1975

U6PD	With approval handstamp (5)	—
U6PDa	Die cut and unfolded, without approval handstamp (4)	—

New York #U7
Bouquet of Ribbons

1985

U7PD	Indicia only, in folder (9)	—

Vienna #U1-U2
Donaupark

1995

VU1PD	On Cromalin paper (approved) (6)	—
VU1PDa	On AGFA paper (not approved) (5)	—
VU2PD	On Cromalin paper (approved) (6)	—
VU2PDa	On AGFA paper (not approved) (5)	—

New York #U10-U11
Cripticandina

1997

U10PD	On Cromalin paper (4)	—
U11PD	On Cromalin paper (4)	—

Vienna #U3
Landscape

1998

VU3PD	On Cromalin paper (4)	—

AIR POST ENVELOPES & AIR LETTER SHEETS
New York #UC1 Swallows and UN Emblem

1952

UC1PI	(32)	—
UC1PIa	On white paper (22)	—

New York #UC3
UN Flag and Plane Envelope

1959

UC3PD	(1)	—

New York #UC4
UN Flag and Plane Letter Sheet

1960

UC4PD	(1)	—

Two "not approved" essays exist with diagonal lines rather than bars around envelope.

New York #UC5 Plane and Gull

1961

UC5PD	With approval handstamp (1)	—
UC5aPD	With approval handstamp (3)	—

New York #UC6
UN Emblem

1963

UC6PDa	Sheet, #UC6PD, #U3PD, with approval handstamp (2)	—
UC6PI	(1)	—
UC6PIa	Sheet, #UC6PD (2 sizes), #U3PD (2 sizes) (6)	—
UC6PIb	As #UC6PIa with one #U3PI removed (1)	—

New York #UC7
UN Emblem and Stylized Plane

1968

UC7PD	With specimen perfin and approval handstamp (7)	—

New York #UC8
UN Emblem

1969

UC8PD	With specimen perfin at left (4)	—

Geneva #UC1
UN Emblem and Stylized Plane

1969

GUC1PD	With specimen perfin and approval handstamp (1)	—
GUC1TC	light blue (2)	—
GUC1TC	ultramarine (3)	—

New York #UC9
UN Emblem, "UN," Globe and Plane

1972

UC9PD	With approval handstamp (2)	—

New York #UC10
Birds in Flight

1973

UC10PDa	Small envelope, die cut and folded, with approval handstamp (1)	—
UC10PDb	Large envelope, partially folded, with approval handstamp (2)	—
UC10PPa	Uncut and unfolded, large and small envelopes (6 items)	—

Three sets of essays exist with blue UN inscriptions close.

New York #UC11
Globe and Jet

1975

UC11PD	With approval handstamp (5)	—
UC11PDa	Die cut and unfolded, without approval handstamp (1)	—

New York #UC12
UN Headquarters

1975

UC12PD	With approval handstamp (1)	—

New York #UC13
UN Emblem and Birds

1977

UC13PD	With approval handstamp (2)	—

Five "not approved" essays have design flaw at end of orange line.

New York #UC14, Vienna #UC1
Paper Airplane, Dove

1982

UC14PD	With approval handstamp (3)	—
UC14PDa	On thin card stock (1)	—
VUC1PD	With approval handstamp (3)	—
VUC1PDa	On thin card stock (1)	—

Vienna #UC3
Birds in Flight and UN Emblem

1987

VUC3PD	On plastic, with approval handstamp (4)	—

New York #UC16
UN Headquarters

1989

UC16PD	With approval handstamp (approved) (3)	—
UC16PDa	With approval handstamp (not approved) (10)	—

Vienna #UC5
Donaupark

1992

VUC5PD	On Cromalin paper (3)	—

New York #UC19
Winged Hand With Envelopes Surcharge

1995

UC19PD	On Cromalin paper (1)	—

New York #UC20
Cherry Blossoms

1997

UC20PD	(5)	—

POSTAL CARDS
New York #UX1
UN Headquarters

1952

UX1TC	olive brown, on white paper (1)	—
UX1PI	(4 pairs)	—

New York #UX2
UN Headquarters

1958

UX2PD	With approval handstamp (2)	—

New York #UX3
World Map

1963

UX3PD	(2)	—

New York #UX4
UN Emblem and Post Horn

1969

UX4PD	With approval handstamp on reverse (1)	—

Geneva #UX1-UX2
UN Emblem and Post Horn, Stylized Space View

1969

GUX1PD	With approval handstamp (3)	—
GUX1PI	(53 pairs)	—
GUX2PI	(52 pairs)	—

New York #UX5
"UN"

1973

UX5PD	(1)	—

Five "not approved" essays similar to #UX5 exist. Ten 7c essays exist, three with approval handstamp, the others lacking any handstamp.

New York #UX6
"UN"

1975

UX6PD	With specimen perfin and approval handstamp (4)	—

Five "not approved" essays have incorrect Russian inscription.

New York #UX7, Geneva #UX3-UX4
UN Emblem, UN Emblem in Rectangles, UN Emblem and Ribbons

1977

UX7PD	With specimen perfin at left (4)	—
GUX3PD	With specimen perfin (5)	—
GUX4PD	With specimen perfin at left (4)	—

New York #UX8, Vienna #UX1-UX2
"United Nations," Olive Branch, Bird Carrying Olive Branch

1982

UX8PD	(2)	—
VUX1PD	With approval handstamp on reverse (4)	—
VUX2PD	With approval handstamp on reverse (16)	—

Geneva #UX5-UX6, Vienna #UX3
Peace Dove, UN Emblem

1985

GUX5PD	(3)	—
GUX6PD	With approval handstamp on reverse (3)	—
VUX3PD	(3)	—

One example of No. GUX5PD has inked lines at left of card. One example of No. GUX6PD has inked lines around address lines.

New York #UX9-UX18
Views of UN Headquarters

1989

UX9PD	Message side (4)	—
UX9PDa	Picture side (4)	—
UX10PD	Message side (4)	—
UX10PDa	Picture side (4)	—
UX11PD	Message side (4)	—
UX11PDa	Picture side (4)	—
UX12PD	Message side (4)	—
UX12PDa	Picture side (4)	—
UX13PD	Message side (4)	—
UX13PDa	Picture side (4)	—
UX14PD	Message side (4)	—
UX14PDa	Picture side (4)	—
UX15PD	Message side (4)	—
UX15PDa	Picture side (4)	—
UX16PD	Message side (4)	—
UX16PDa	Picture side (4)	—
UX17PD	Message side (4)	—

UX17PDa	Picture side (4)	—
UX18PD	Message side (4)	—
UX18PDa	Picture side (4)	—

New York #UX19, Geneva #UX8, Vienna #UX5
UN Headquarters, Palais des Nations, Regschek Painting

1992
UX19PD	On Cromalin paper (4)	—
GUX8PD	On Cromalin paper (4)	—
VUX5PD	On Cromalin paper (4)	—
VUX5PDa	Sheet, #GUX8PD, #VUX5PD on Cromalin paper (1)	—
UX19TC	ultramarine (1)	—

Geneva #UX10, Vienna #UX6-UX7
Palais des Nations, Peoples of the World United, Donaupark

1993
GUX10PD	On Cromalin paper (4)	—
VUX6PD	On Cromalin paper (4)	—
VUX7PD	On Cromalin paper (4)	—

Vienna #UX12
The Gloriette

1999
VUX12TCa	Light blue text (4)	—

AIR POST POSTAL CARDS
New York #UXC1
UN Flag and Plane

1957
UXC1PD	With printer and approval handstamps (6)	—
UXC1PI	(30 pairs)	—

New York #UXC3
Airplane Wing and Globe

1959
UXC3PD	With approval handstamp (3)	—

Six essays of No. UXC3 lacking outlined letters on "Airmail" and "Poste Aerienne" exist.

New York #UXC4
Outer Space

1963
UXC4PD	(2)	—

New York #UXC6
Outer Space

1968
UXC6PD	With "Canceled" perfin (2)	—
UXC6PDa	Strip of 3 cards with 2 "Canceled" perfins (2)	—

New York #UXC7
UN Emblem and Stylized Planes

1969
UXC7PD	(1)	—
UXC7TC	black (2)	—

New York #UXC8
UN Emblem and Stylized Wing

1972
UXC8PDa	Folder with mounted #UXC8PD with approval handstamp, and #UXC8 (2)	—

New York #UXC9
UN Emblem and Stylized Planes

1972
UXC9PD	Folder with mounted #UXC9, with approval handstamp (2)	—

New York #UXC10-UXC11
Clouds; Pathways

1975
UXC10PD	With specimen perfin and approval handstamp (4)	—
UXC11PD	With specimen perfin and approval handstamp (4)	—
UXC10TC	With manuscript "Lighter as on sample," and approval handstamp (not approved) (5)	—

New York #UXC12
Flying Mailman

1982
UXC12PD	With approval handstamp on reverse (5)	—

U.N. TEMPORARY EXECUTIVE AUTHORITY, WEST NEW GUINEA

Located in the western half of New Guinea, southwest Pacific Ocean, the former Netherlands New Guinea became a territory under the administration of the United Nations Temporary Executive Authority on Oct. 1, 1962. The size was 151,789 sq. mi. and the population was estimated at 730,000 in 1958. The capital was Hollandia.

The territory came under Indonesian administration on May 1, 1963. For stamps issued by Indonesia see listings following Indonesia in Volume 3.

100 Cents = 1 Gulden

Catalogue values for all unused stamps in this country are for Never Hinged items.

First Printing (Hollandia)
Netherlands New Guinea Stamps of 1950-60
Overprinted

Overprint size: 17x3½mm. Top of "N" is slightly lower than the "U," and the base of the "T" is straight, or nearly so.

Photo.; Litho. (#4, 6, 8)

1962		**Unwmk.**	*Perf. 12½x12, 12½x13½*	
1	A4	1c vermilion & yellow, *Oct. 1*	.20	.20
2	A1	2c deep orange, *Oct. 1*	.25	.25
3	A4	5c chocolate & yellow, *Oct. 1*	.25	.25
4	A5	7c org red, bl & brn vio, *Nov. 1*	.25	.35
5	A4	10c aqua & red brown, *Oct. 1*	.25	.35
6	A5	12c green, bl & brn vio, *Nov. 1*	.25	.35
7	A4	15c deep yel & red brn, *Nov. 1*	.50	.50
8	A5	17c brown violet & blue, *Oct. 1*	.60	.75
9	A4	20c lt bl grn & red brn, *Nov. 1*	.60	.75
10	A6	25c red, *Oct. 1*	.35	.55
11	A6	30c deep blue, *Oct. 1*	.80	.80
12	A6	40c deep orange, *Oct. 1*	.80	.80
13	A6	45c dark olive, *Nov. 1*	1.40	1.60
14	A6	55c slate blue, *Nov. 1*	17.50	1.25
15	A6	80c dull gray violet, *Nov. 1*	5.75	5.75
16	A6	85c dark violet brown, *Nov. 1*	3.00	3.00
17	A6	1g plum, *Oct. 1*	9.75	3.00

Engr.

18	A3	2g reddish brown, *Oct. 1*	9.75	22.50
19	A3	5g green, *Oct. 1*	7.75	5.50
		Nos. 1-19 (19)	60.00	48.50

Overprinted locally and sold in West New Guinea. Stamps of the second printing were used to complete sets sold to collectors.

Second Printing (Haarlen, Netherlands)

Overprint size: 17x3½mm. Top of the "N" is slightly higher than the "U," and the base of the "T" is concave.

Photo.; Litho. (#4a, 6a, 8a)

1962		**Unwmk.**	*Perf. 12½x12, 12½x13½*	
1a	A4	1c vermilion & yellow	.20	.20
2a	A1	2c deep orange	.25	.20
3a	A4	5c chocolate & yellow	.25	.20
4a	A5	7c org red, bl & brn vio	.25	.20
5a	A4	10c aqua & red brown	.25	.20
6a	A5	12c green, bl & brn vio	.25	.20
7a	A4	15c deep yel & red brn	.50	.25
8a	A5	17c brown violet & blue	.60	.35
9a	A4	20c lt blue grn & red brn	.60	.35
10a	A6	25c red	.35	.30
11a	A6	30c deep blue	.80	.35
12a	A6	40c deep orange	.80	.35
13a	A6	45c dark olive	1.40	.75
14a	A6	55c slate blue	1.25	.55
15a	A6	80c dull gray violet	5.75	5.75
16a	A6	85c dark violet brown	3.00	3.00
17a	A6	1g plum	3.50	1.90

Engr.

18a	A3	2g reddish brown	9.75	13.00
19a	A3	5g green	6.00	3.50
		Nos. 1a-19a (19)	35.75	31.60

Overprinted in the Netherlands and sold by the UN in New York.

Third Printing

Overprint 14mm long.

Photo.; Litho. (#4b, 6b, 8b)

1963, Mar.		**Photo.**	**Unwmk.**	*Perf. 12½x12*
1b	A4	1c vermilion & yellow	4.25	2.00
3b	A4	5c chocolate & yellow	4.75	3.00
4b	A5	7c org red, bl & brn vio	20.00	20.00
5b	A4	10c aqua & red brown	4.75	3.00
6b	A5	12c green, bl & brn vio	30.00	30.00
7b	A4	15c deep yel & red brn	97.50	105.00
8b	A5	17c brown violet & blue	11.00	11.00
9b	A4	20c lt blue grn & red brn	6.25	3.75
		Nos. 1b-9b (8)	178.50	177.75

The third printing was applied in West New Guinea and it is doubtful whether it was regularly issued. Used values are for canceled to order stamps.

Fourth Printing

Overprint 19mm long.

Photogravure

1963, Mar.		**Unwmk.**	*Perf. 12½x12*	
1c	A4	1c vermilion & yellow	45.00	45.00
5c	A4	10c aqua & red brown	130.00	130.00

The fourth printing was applied in West New Guinea and it is doubtful whether it was regularly issued. Used values are for canceled to order stamps.

U.N. TRANSITIONAL AUTHORITY IN EAST TIMOR

A30

2000, Apr. 29   **Litho.**   **Perf. 12x11¾**
350 A30 Dom. red & multi   9.00   9.00
351 A30 Int. blue & multi   18.00   18.00

No. 350 sold for 10c and No. 351 sold for 50c on day of issue.

U.N. INTERIM ADMINISTRATION IN KOSOVO

These stamps were issued by the United Nations Interim Administration Mission in Kosovo and the Post & Telecommunications of Kosovo. Service was local for the first two months, with international use starting in mid-May 2000.
Starting with No. 6, stamps were not made available to collectors through the United Nations Postal Administration.

100 pfennigs = 1 mark
100 cents = €1 (2002)

Catalogue values for all unused stamps in this country are for Never Hinged items.

Peace in Kosovo — A1

Printed by La Poste, France. Panes of 40. Designed by Shyqri Nimani, Kosovo.
Designs: 20pf, Mosaic depicting Orpheus, c. 5th-6th cent., Podujeve. 30pf, Dardinian idol, Museum of Kosovo. 50pf, Silver coin of Damastion from 4th cent. B.C. 1m, Statue of Mother Teresa, Prizren. 2m, Map of Kosovo.

Perf. 13½x13, 13½x13¼ (30pf)
2000, Mar. 14   **Litho.**   **Unwmk.**
1 A1 20pf **multicolored**   1.00   1.00
   First day cover   1.50
2 A1 30pf **multicolored**   1.40   1.40
   First day cover   1.50
3 A1 50pf **multicolored**   2.25   2.25
   First day cover   1.75
4 A1 1m **multicolored**   4.50   4.50
   First day cover   4.00
5 A1 2m **multicolored**   9.00   9.00
   First day cover   7.00
   First day cover, #1-5   9.00
     Nos. 1-5 (5)   18.15   18.15

Peace in Kosovo — A2

Designs: 20pf, Bird. 30pf, Street musician. 50pf, Butterfly and pear. 1m, Children and stars. 2m, Globe and handprints.

2001, Nov. 12   **Litho.**   **Perf. 14**
6 A2 20pf **multicolored**   1.50   1.50
7 A2 30pf **multicolored**   2.00   2.00
8 A2 50pf **multicolored**   3.50   3.50
9 A2 1m **multicolored**   7.50   7.50
10 A2 2m **multicolored**   15.00   15.00
     Nos. 6-10 (5)   29.50   29.50

---

100 Cents = 1 Euro (€)
Peace in Kosovo Type of 2001 With Denominations in Euros Only
2002, May 2   **Litho.**   **Perf. 14**
11 A2 10c Like #6   1.75   1.75
12 A2 15c Like #7   2.50   2.50
13 A2 26c Like #8   3.75   3.75
14 A2 51c Like #9   7.50   7.50
15 A2 €1.02 Like #10   15.00   15.00
     Nos. 11-15 (5)   30.50   30.50

Christmas — A3

Designs: 50c, Candles and garland. €1, Stylized men.

2003, Dec. 20   **Litho.**   **Perf. 14**
16 A3 50c **multicolored**   17.50   16.00
17 A3 €1 **multicolored**   32.50   25.00

Return of Refugees — A4

Five Years of Peace — A5

2004, June 29   **Litho.**   **Perf. 13¼x13**
18 A4 €1 multicolored   20.00   20.00
19 A5 €2 multicolored   30.00   25.00

Musical Instruments — A6

2004, Aug. 31   **Litho.**   **Perf. 13¼x13**
20 A6 20c Flute   22.50   15.00
21 A6 30c Ocarina   32.50   20.00

Aprons — A7

Vests — A8

Designs: 20c, Apron from Prizren. 30c, Apron from Rugova. 50c, Three vests. €1, Two vests.

2004, Oct. 28   **Litho.**   **Perf. 13x13¼**
22 A7 20c **multicolored**   7.00   7.00
23 A7 30c **multicolored**   10.00   10.00
24 A8 50c **multicolored**   17.50   17.50
25 A8 €1 **multicolored**   35.00   35.00
     Nos. 22-25 (4)   69.50   69.50

Mirusha
Waterfall — A9

2004, Nov. 26   **Litho.**   *Perf. 13x13¼*
26 A9 €2 **multicolored**   17.50 17.50

House — A10

2004, Dec. 14   **Litho.**   *Perf. 13x13¼*
27 A10 50c **multicolored**   7.50 7.50

Flowers — A11

2005, June 29   **Litho.**   *Perf. 13½*
28 A11 15c Peony   3.50 3.50
29 A11 20c Poppies   4.50 4.50
30 A11 30c Gentian   7.00 7.00
     Nos. 28-30 (3)   15.00 15.00

A12

Handicrafts — A13

2005, July 20   *Perf. 13¼x13*
31 A12 20c shown   3.00 3.00
32 A12 30c Cradle   4.00 4.00
33 A13 50c shown   6.00 6.00
34 A12 €1 Necklace   12.00 12.00
     Nos. 31-34 (4)   25.00 25.00

Village — A14

Town — A15

City — A16

2005, Sept. 15   *Perf. 13x13½*
35 A14 20c **multicolored**   3.50 3.50
36 A15 50c **multicolored**   6.50 6.50
37 A16 €1 **multicolored**   12.50 12.50
     Nos. 35-37 (3)   22.50 22.50

Archaeological
Artifacts — A17

2005, Nov. 2   *Perf. 13½x13*
38 A17 20c shown   2.50 2.50
39 A17 30c Statue   3.50 3.50
40 A17 50c Sculpture   6.00 6.00
41 A17 €1 Helmet   13.00 13.00
     Nos. 38-41 (4)   25.00 25.00

Minerals
A18

2005, Dec. 10   *Perf. 13x13½*
42 A18 €2 **multicolored**   22.00 22.00

A19

Europa — A20

2006, July 20   *Perf. 13¼x13*
43 A19 50c **multicolored**   5.00 5.00
44 A20 €1 **multicolored**   10.00 10.00

Fauna
A21

2006, May 23   **Litho.**   *Perf. 13*
45 A21 15c Wolf   1.25 1.25
46 A21 20c Cow   1.75 1.75
47 A21 30c Pigeon   2.50 2.50
48 A21 50c Swan   3.50 3.50
49 A21 €1 Dog   6.50 6.50
a.   Souvenir sheet, #45-49, + label   17.00 17.00
     Nos. 45-49 (5)   15.50 15.50

Children
A22

Designs: 20c, Children in cradle. 30c, Children reading. 50c, Girls dancing. €1, Child in water.

2006, June 30   **Litho.**   *Perf. 13*
50 A22 20c **multicolored**   1.25 1.25
51 A22 30c **multicolored**   1.75 1.75
52 A22 50c **multicolored**   3.00 3.00
53 A22 €1 **multicolored**   6.00 6.00
a.   Souvenir sheet, #50-53   12.00 12.00
     Nos. 50-53 (4)   12.00 12.00

A23

A24

A25

Tourist
Attractions
A26

2006, Sept. 1   Litho.   Perf. 13
54   A23   20c   multicolored   1.25   1.25
55   A24   30c   multicolored   1.75   1.75
56   A25   50c   multicolored   3.00   3.00
57   A26   €1   multicolored   6.00   6.00
a.   Souvenir sheet, #54-57   12.00 12.00
      Nos. 50-53 (4)   12.00 12.00

Intl. Peace Day — A27

2006, Sept. 21   Litho.   Perf. 13
58   A27   €2   multicolored   10.00 10.00
      Min. Sheet of 4   40.00

Ancient Coins — A28

Various coins.

2006, Nov. 1   Litho.   Perf. 13
59   A28   20c   multicolored   1.25   1.25
60   A28   30c   multicolored   1.75   1.75
61   A28   50c   multicolored   3.00   3.00
62   A28   €1   multicolored   6.00   6.00
a.   Souvenir sheet, #59-62   12.00 12.00
      Nos. 59-62 (4)   12.00 12.00

Sculpture — A29

2006, Dec. 1   Litho.   Perf. 13
63   A29   €2   multicolored   7.50   7.50
a.   Miniature sheet, #45-57, 59-63, + 2 labels 60.00 60.00

Convention on the Rights
of Persons With
Disabilities — A30

Emblems of handicaps and: 20c, Children and butterfly. 50c,
Handicapped women. 70c, Map of Kosovo. €1, Stylized flower.

2007, Apr. 23   Litho.   Perf. 14x14¼
64   A30   20c   multicolored   1.25   1.25
65   A30   50c   multicolored   2.75   2.75
66   A30   70c   multicolored   4.00   4.00
67   A30   €1   multicolored   5.50   5.50
a.   Souvenir sheet, #64-67   12.50 12.50
      Nos. 64-67 (4)   13.50 13.50

Scouting,
Cent. — A31

Europa — A32

2007, May 12   Litho.   Perf. 13¼
68   A31   70c   multicolored   2.75   2.75
69   A32   €1   multicolored   4.00   4.00
a.   Souvenir sheet, #68-69   6.75   6.75

A33

A34

A35

International
Children's
Day — A36

2007, June 1   Litho.   Perf. 13¼
70   A33   20c   multicolored   1.25   1.25
71   A34   30c   multicolored   1.75   1.75
72   A35   70c   multicolored   3.50   3.50
73   A36   €1   multicolored   7.00   7.00
      Nos. 70-73 (4)   13.50 13.50

Native Costumes — A37

Designs: 20c, Serbian woman. 30c, Prizren Region woman.
50c, Sword dancer. 70c, Drenica Region woman. €1, Shepherd, Rugova.

2007, July 6   Litho.   Perf. 13½x13¼
74   A37   20c   multicolored   1.25   1.25
75   A37   30c   multicolored   1.75   1.75
76   A37   50c   multicolored   3.00   3.00
77   A37   70c   multicolored   5.00   5.00
78   A37   €1   multicolored   6.00   6.00
a.   Souvenir sheet, #74-78, + label   17.00 17.00
      Nos. 74-78 (5)   17.00 17.00

Masks — A38

Various masks.

2007, Sept. 11   Litho.   Perf. 13½x13¼
79   A38   15c   multicolored   .75   .75
80   A38   30c   multicolored   1.25   1.25
81   A38   50c   multicolored   2.25   2.25
82   A38   €1   multicolored   4.50   4.50
      Nos. 79-82 (4)   8.75   8.75

Sports — A39

Designs: 20c, Soccer ball, basketball, two people standing, person in wheelchair. 50c, Wrestlers. €1, Symbols of 24 sports.

2007, Oct. 2		**Litho.**	**Perf. 13¼x13½**	
83	A39	20c multicolored	1.00	1.00
84	A39	50c multicolored	2.50	2.50
85	A39	€1 multicolored	5.00	5.00
		Nos. 83-85 (3)	8.50	8.50

Architecture — A40

Designs: 30c, Stone bridge, Vushtrri. 50c, Hamam, Prizren. 70c, Tower. €1, Tower, diff.

2007, Nov. 6		**Litho.**	**Perf. 13¼**	
86	A40	30c multicolored	1.10	1.10
87	A40	50c multicolored	1.90	1.90
88	A40	70c multicolored	2.75	2.75
89	A40	€1 multicolored	3.75	3.75
		Nos. 86-89 (4)	9.50	9.50

Locomotives
A41

Designs: €1, Diesel locomotive. €2, Steam locomotive

2007, Dec. 7		**Litho.**	**Perf. 13¼**	
90	A41	€1 multicolored	3.50	3.50
91	A41	€2 multicolored	6.50	6.50

Skanderbeg (1405-68),
Albanian National
Hero — A42

2008, Jan. 17		**Litho.**	**Perf. 13¼**	
92	A42	€2 multicolored	6.25	6.25

Kosovo declared its independence from Serbia on Feb. 17, 2008, ending the United Nations Interim Administration. Stamps issued after Feb. 17, 2008, by the Republic of Kosovo will be listed under Kosovo in the *Scott Standard Postage Stamp Catalogue.*

INDEX TO ADVERTISERS – 2010 U.S. SPECIALIZED

2010

UNITED STATES SPECIALIZED

DEALER DIRECTORY

YELLOW PAGE LISTINGS

This section of your Scott Catalogue contains advertisements to help you conveniently find what you need, when you need it...!

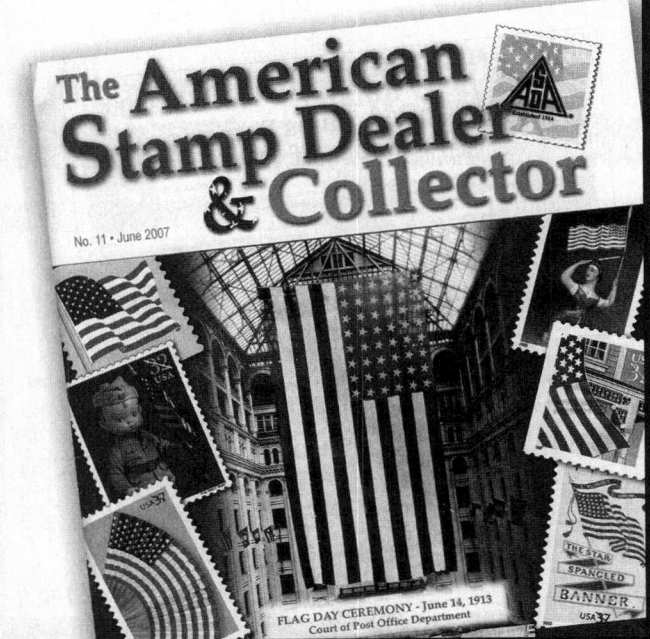
Accessories

BROOKLYN GALLERY COIN & STAMP, INC.
8725 4th Ave.
Brooklyn, NY 11209
PH: 718-745-5701
FAX: 718-745-2775
info@brooklyngallery.com
www.brooklyngallery.com

Appraisals

DAVID F. HULL STAMP CO
1420 Trafalgar Dr.
High Point, NC 27262-7472
PH: 336-885-1420
FAX: 925-401-1434
davehull@hullstamps.com
www.hullstamps.com

NATICK STAMPS & HOBBIES
411 E. Huntington Dr.
Suite 209
Arcadia, CA 91006
PH: 626-445-2185
natickco@att.net

PHILIP WEISS AUCTIONS
1 Neil Ct.
Oceanside, NY 11572
PH: 516-594-0731
FAX: 516-594-9414

Asia

MICHAEL ROGERS, INC.
415 S. Orlando Ave.
Winter Park, FL 32789-3683
PH: 407-644-2290
PH: 800-843-3751
FAX: 407-645-4434
Stamps@michaelrogersinc.com
www.michaelrogersinc.com

Auctions

DANIEL F. KELLEHER CO., INC.
20 Walnut St.
Suite 213
Wellesley, MA 02481
PH: 781-235-0990
FAX: 781-235-0945

JACQUES C. SCHIFF, JR., INC.
195 Main St.
Ridgefield Park, NJ 07660
PH: 201-641-5566
FAX: 201-641-5705

MICHAEL ROGERS, INC.
415 S. Orlando Ave.
Winter Park, FL 32789-3683
PH: 407-644-2290
PH: 800-843-3751
FAX: 407-645-4434
Stamps@michaelrogersinc.com
www.michaelrogersinc.com

Auctions

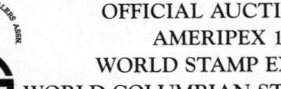

Auctions

PHILIP WEISS AUCTIONS
1 Neil Ct.
Oceanside, NY 11572
PH: 516-594-0731
FAX: 516-594-9414

R. MARESCH & SON LTD.
5th Floor - 6075 Yonge St.
Toronto, ON M2M 3W2
CANADA
PH: 416-363-7777
FAX: 416-363-6511
www.maresch.com

SAM HOUSTON PHILATELICS
PO Box 820087
Houston, TX 77282
PH: 281-493-6386
PH: 800-231-5926
FAX: 281-496-1445
shduck@aol.com
www.shpauctions.com

THE STAMP CENTER DUTCH COUNTRY AUCTIONS
4115 Concord Pike
Wilmington, DE 19803
PH: 302-478-8740
FAX: 302-478-8779
auctions@thestampcenter.com
www.thestampcenter.com

Auctions-Mail Bid

DALE ENTERPRISES, INC.
PO Box 539-C
Emmaus, PA 18049
PH: 610-433-3303
FAX: 610-965-6089
daleent@ptd.net
www.dalestamp.com

Auctions - Public

ALAN BLAIR STAMPS/ AUCTIONS
5405 Lakeside Ave.
Suite 1
Richmond, VA 23228
PH: 800-689-5602
FAX: 804-262-9307
alanblair@verizon.net
www.alanblairstamps.com

China

MICHAEL ROGERS, INC.
415 S. Orlando Ave.
Winter Park, FL 32789-3683
PH: 407-644-2290
PH: 800-843-3751
FAX: 407-645-4434
Stamps@michaelrogersinc.com
www.michaelrogersinc.com

Classics

GARY POSNER, INC.
1407 Ave. Z, PMB #535
Brooklyn, NY 11235
PH: 800-323-4279
CELL PH: 917-538-8133
FAX: 718-241-2801
garyposnerinc@aol.com
www.garyposnerinc.com
www.gemstamps.com

J. NALBANDIAN, INC.
PO Box 71
East Greenwich, RI 02818
PH: 401-885-5020
FAX: 401-885-3040
nalbandianj@earthlink.net
www.nalbandstamp.com

Confed. Stamps & Postal History

STANLEY M. PILLER & ASSOCIATES
(HOURS BY APPT. ONLY)
800 S. Broadway
Suite 201
Walnut Creek, CA 94596
PH: 925-938-8290
FAX: 925-938-8812
stmpdlr@aol.com
www.smpiller.com

SUN COAST STAMP CO.
8520 S. Tamiami Tr., Unit1
Sarasota, FL 34238
PH: 941-921-9761
PH: 800-927-3351
FAX: 941-921-1762
email@suncoaststamp.com

Covers-Zeppelins

HENRY GITNER PHILATELISTS, INC.
PO Box 3077-S
Middletown, NY 10940
PH: 845-343-5151
PH: 800-947-8267
FAX: 845-343-0068
hgitner@hgitner.com
www.hgitner.com

Ducks

MICHAEL JAFFE
PO Box 61484
Vancouver, WA 98666
PH: 360-695-6161
PH: 800-782-6770
FAX: 360-695-1616
mjaffe@brookmanstamps.com
www.brookmanstamps.com

SAM HOUSTON DUCK CO.
PO Box 820087
Houston, TX 77282
PH: 281-493-6386
PH: 800-231-5926
FAX: 281-496-1445
shduck@aol.com
www.shduck.com

TRENTON STAMP & COIN CO./COASTAL BEND DUCK STAMP CO.
Thomas DeLuca
Mail: PO Box 8574
Trenton, NJ 08650
Store: Forest Glen Plaza
1804 Route 33
Hamilton Square, NJ 08690
PH: 800-446-8664
PH: 609-584-8100
FAX: 609-587-8664
TOMD4TSC@aol.com

Egypt

KAMAL SHALABY
3, Aly Basha Fahmy St.
8th Floor, Gleem
Alexandria
EGYPT
PH/FAX: +203-5840254
Cell: +2-0105838213
alexstamplover@yahoo.com
www.stampsofegypt.com

Errors, Freaks & Oddities

J. NALBANDIAN, INC.
PO Box 71
East Greenwich, RI 02818
PH: 401-885-5020
FAX: 401-885-3040
nalbandianj@earthlink.net
www.nalbandstamp.com

SAM HOUSTON PHILATELICS
PO Box 820087
Houston, TX 77282
PH: 281-493-6386
PH: 800-231-5926
FAX: 281-496-1445
shduck@aol.com
www.shpauctions.com

Expertizing

STANLEY M. PILLER & ASSOCIATES
(HOURS BY APPT. ONLY)
800 S. Broadway
Suite 201
Walnut Creek, CA 94596
PH: 925-938-8290
FAX: 925-938-8812
stmpdlr@aol.com
www.smpiller.com

German Colonies

COLONIAL STAMP COMPANY
5757 Wilshire Blvd. PH #8
Los Angeles, CA 90036
PH: 323-933-9435
FAX: 323-939-9930
Toll Free in North America
PH: 877-272-6693
FAX: 877-272-6694
info@colonialstampcompany.com
www.colonialstampcompany.com

Hawaii Stamps & Postal History

STANLEY M. PILLER & ASSOCIATES
(HOURS BY APPT. ONLY)
800 S. Broadway
Suite 201
Walnut Creek, CA 94596
PH: 925-938-8290
FAX: 925-938-8812
stmpdlr@aol.com
www.smpiller.com

Japan

MICHAEL ROGERS, INC.
415 S. Orlando Ave.
Winter Park, FL 32789-3683
PH: 407-644-2290
PH: 800-843-3751
FAX: 407-645-4434
Stamps@michaelrogersinc.com
www.michaelrogersinc.com

Korea

MICHAEL ROGERS, INC.
415 S. Orlando Ave.
Winter Park, FL 32789-3683
PH: 407-644-2290
PH: 800-843-3751
FAX: 407-645-4434
Stamps@michaelrogersinc.com
www.michaelrogersinc.com

Manchukuo

MICHAEL ROGERS, INC.
415 S. Orlando Ave.
Winter Park, FL 32789-3683
PH: 407-644-2290
PH: 800-843-3751
FAX: 407-645-4434
Stamps@michaelrogersinc.com
www.michaelrogersinc.com

Middle East-Arab

MICHAEL ROGERS, INC.
415 S. Orlando Ave.
Winter Park, FL 32789-3683
PH: 407-644-2290
PH: 800-843-3751
FAX: 407-645-4434
Stamps@michaelrogersinc.com
www.michaelrogersinc.com

New Issues

**DAVIDSON'S STAMP
SERVICE**
PO Box 36355
Indianapolis, IN 46236-0355
PH: 317-826-2620
ed-davidson@earthlink.net
www.newstampissues.com

New Issues

NATICK STAMPS & HOBBIES
411 E. Huntington Dr.
Suite 209
Arcadia, CA 91006
PH: 626-445-2185
natickco@att.net

New Issues - Retail

BOMBAY PHILATELIC INC.
PO Box 90937
Raleigh, NC 27675
PH: 561-499-7990
FAX: 561-499-7553
sales@bombaystamps.com
www.bombaystamps.com

One of a Kind

DALE ENTERPRISES, INC.
PO Box 539-C
Emmaus, PA 18049
PH: 610-433-3303
FAX: 610-965-6089
daleent@ptd.net
www.dalestamp.com

Philatelic Literature

LEWIS KAUFMAN
PO Box 255
Kiamesha Lake, NY 12751
PH/FAX: 845-794-8013
PH/FAX: 800-491-5453
kerik1@aol.com

Postal History

**STANLEY M. PILLER &
ASSOCIATES**
(HOURS BY APPT. ONLY)
800 S. Broadway
Suite 201
Walnut Creek, CA 94596
PH: 925-938-8290
FAX: 925-938-8812
stmpdlr@aol.com
www.smpiller.com

Proofs & Essays

**HENRY GITNER
PHILATELISTS, INC.**
PO Box 3077-S
Middletown, NY 10940
PH: 845-343-5151
PH: 800-947-8267
FAX: 845-343-0068
hgitner@hgitner.com
www.hgitner.com

**STANLEY M. PILLER &
ASSOCIATES**
(HOURS BY APPT. ONLY)
800 S. Broadway
Suite 201
Walnut Creek, CA 94596
PH: 925-938-8290
FAX: 925-938-8812
stmpdlr@aol.com
www.smpiller.com

Souvenir Cards

AALLSTAMPS
38 N. Main St.
PO Box 249
Milltown, NJ 08850
PH: 732-247-1093
FAX: 732-247-1094
mail@aallstamps.com
www.aallstamps.com

STAMP STORES

California

**BROSIUS STAMP, COIN &
SUPPLIES**
2105 Main St.
Santa Monica, CA 90405
PH: 310-396-7480
FAX: 310-396-7455

**COLONIAL STAMP CO./
BRITISH EMPIRE
SPECIALIST**
5757 Wilshire Blvd. PH #8
(by appt.)
Los Angeles, CA 90036
PH: 323-933-9435
FAX: 323-939-9930
Toll Free in North America
PH: 877-272-6693
FAX: 877-272-6694
info@colonialstampcompany.com
www.colonialstampcompany.com

**FISCHER-WOLK
PHILATELICS**
22762 Aspan St.
Suite 211
Lake Forest, CA 92630
PH: 949-837-2932
fw@occoxmail.com

NATICK STAMPS & HOBBIES
411 E. Huntington Dr.
Suite 209
Arcadia, CA 91006
PH: 626-445-2185
natickco@att.net

Colorado

SHOWCASE STAMPS
3865 Wadsworth
Wheat Ridge, CO 80033
PH: 303-425-9252
kbeiner@colbi.net
www.showcasestamps.com

STAMP STORES

Connecticut

SILVER CITY COIN & STAMP
41 Colony St.
Meriden, CT 06451
PH: 203-235-7634
FAX: 203-237-4915

Florida

SUN COAST STAMP CO.
8520 S. Tamiami Tr., Unit1
Sarasota, FL 34238
PH: 941-921-9761
PH: 800-927-3351
FAX: 941-921-1762
email@suncoaststamp.com

Georgia

**STAMPS UNLIMITED OF
GEORGIA, INC.**
100 Peachtree St.
Suite 1460
Atlanta, GA 30303
PH: 404-688-9161
tonyroozen@yahoo.com

Illinois

**DR. ROBERT FRIEDMAN &
SONS**
2029 W. 75th St.
Woodridge, IL 60517
PH: 800-588-8100
FAX: 630-985-1588
drbobstamps@yahoo.com
www.drbobfriedmanstamps.com

SIDMORE STAMPS
145 E. Lincoln Hwy.
DeKalb, IL 60115
PH: 815-787-7000
sidmorestamps@verizon.net
www.sidmorestamps.net
Authorized APS Dealer

Indiana

KNIGHT STAMP & COIN CO.
237 Main St.
Hobart, IN 46342
PH: 219-942-4341
PH: 800-634-2646
knight@knightcoin.com
www.knightcoin.com

Massachusetts

KAPPY'S COINS & STAMPS
534 Washington St.
Norwood, MA 02062
PH: 781-762-5552
kappyscoins@aol.com

SUBURBAN STAMP INC.
176 Worthington St.
Springfield, MA 01103
PH: 413-785-5348
FAX: 413-746-3788
suburbanstamp@verizon.net

New Jersey

AALLSTAMPS
38 N. Main St.
PO Box 249
Milltown, NJ 08850
PH: 732-247-1093
FAX: 732-247-1094
mail@aallstamps.com
www.aallstamps.com

Stamp Shows

STAMP STORES

New Jersey

BERGEN STAMPS & COLLECTIBLES
306 Queen Anne Rd.
Teaneck, NJ 07666
PH: 201-836-8987

PHILLY STAMP & COIN CO., INC.
683 Haddon Ave.
Collingswood, NJ 08108
PH: 856-854-5333
FAX: 856-854-5377
phillysc@verizon.net
www.phillystampandcoin.com

TRENTON STAMP & COIN CO.
Thomas DeLuca
Store: Forest Glen Plaza
1804 Route 33
Hamilton Square, NJ 08690
Mail: PO Box 8574
Trenton, NJ 08650
PH: 800-446-8664
PH: 609-584-8100
FAX: 609-587-8664
TOMD4TSC@aol.com

New York

CHAMPION STAMP CO., INC.
432 W. 54th St.
New York, NY 10019
PH: 212-489-8130
FAX: 212-581-8130
championstamp@aol.com
www.championstamp.com

Ohio

HILLTOP STAMP SERVICE
Richard A. Peterson
PO Box 626
Wooster, OH 44691
PH: 330-262-8907
PH: 330-262-5378
hilltop@bright.net

THE LINK STAMP CO.
3461 E. Livingston Ave.
Columbus, OH 43227
PH/FAX: 614-237-4125
PH/FAX: 800-546-5726

Texas

SAM HOUSTON PHILATELICS
PO Box 820087
Houston, TX 77282
PH: 281-493-6386
PH: 800-231-5926
FAX: 281-496-1445
shduck@aol.com
www.shpauctions.com

Virginia

KENNEDY'S STAMPS & COINS, INC.
7059 Brookfield Plaza
Springfield, VA 22150
PH: 703-569-7300
FAX: 703-569-7644
j.w.kennedy@verizon.net

United States

USED   UNUSED

MOST GRADES & PRICE RANGES!

Here is your opportunity to have the older and scarcer stamps of our country at low, reasonable prices. Issues prior to the year 1950 worth anywhere from 25¢ up to several hundred dollars each.

JUST SEND 44¢ POSTAGE for complete price list. Compare for PROOF OF LOWEST PRICES before ordering, and find out what you have missed until you discovered us!!!

LOWELL S. DONALD CO.

P.O. BOX 728,
RUTLAND, VERMONT 05702

Virginia

LATHEROW & CO., INC.
5054 Lee Hwy.
Arlington, VA 22207
PH: 703-538-2727
PH: 800-647-4624
FAX: 703-538-5210
latherow@filatco.com

Supplies

A TO Z STAMPS & COINS
4950 E. Thomas Rd.
Phoenix, AZ 85018
PH: 480-844-9878
FAX: 602-759-1717
michael@azstampcoin.com
www.WorldwideStamps.com

Topicals-Columbus

MR. COLUMBUS
PO Box 1492
Fennville, MI 49408
PH: 269-543-4755
columbus@accn.org

United States

A TO Z STAMPS & COINS
4950 E. Thomas Rd.
Phoenix, AZ 85018
PH: 480-844-9878
FAX: 602-759-1717
michael@azstampcoin.com
www.WorldwideStamps.com

ACS STAMP COMPANY
10831 Chambers Way
Commerce City, CO 80022
PH: 303-841-8666
ACS@ACSStamp.com
www.acsstamp.com

BROOKMAN STAMP CO.
PO Box 90
Vancouver, WA 98666
PH: 360-695-1391
PH: 800-545-4871
FAX: 360-695-1616
larry@brookmanstamps.com
www.brookmanstamps.com

DALE ENTERPRISES, INC.
PO Box 539-C
Emmaus, PA 18049
PH: 610-433-3303
FAX: 610-965-6089
daleent@ptd.net
www.dalestamp.com

DAVID F. HULL STAMP CO
1420 Trafalgar Dr.
High Point, NC 27262-7472
PH: 336-885-1420
FAX: 925-401-1434
davehull@hullstamps.com
www.hullstamps.com

GARY POSNER, INC.
1407 Ave. Z, PMB #535
Brooklyn, NY 11235
PH: 800-323-4279
CELL PH: 917-538-8133
FAX: 718-241-2801
garyposnerinc@aol.com
www.garyposnerinc.com
www.gemstamps.com

United States

SUBURBAN STAMP INC.
176 Worthington St.
Springfield, MA 01103
PH: 413-785-5348
FAX: 413-746-3788
suburbanstamp@verizon.net

U.S.-Classics

DALE ENTERPRISES, INC.
PO Box 539-C
Emmaus, PA 18049
PH: 610-433-3303
FAX: 610-965-6089
daleent@ptd.net
www.dalestamp.com

J. NALBANDIAN, INC.
PO Box 71
East Greenwich, RI 02818
PH: 401-885-5020
FAX: 401-885-3040
nalbandianj@earthlink.net
www.nalbandstamp.com

STANLEY M. PILLER & ASSOCIATES
(HOURS BY APPT. ONLY)
800 S. Broadway
Suite 201
Walnut Creek, CA 94596
PH: 925-938-8290
FAX: 925-938-8812
stmpdlr@aol.com
www.smpiller.com

SUBURBAN STAMP INC.
176 Worthington St.
Springfield, MA 01103
PH: 413-785-5348
FAX: 413-746-3788
suburbanstamp@verizon.net

U.S.-Classics/Moderns

WULFF'S STAMPS
PO Box 661746
Sacramento, CA 95866
PH/FAX: 800-884-0656
PH/FAX: 916-489-0656
service@wulffstamps.com
www.wulffstamps.com

U.S.-Collections Wanted

DAVID F. HULL STAMP CO
1420 Trafalgar Dr.
High Point, NC 27262-7472
PH: 336-885-1420
FAX: 925-401-1434
davehull@hullstamps.com
www.hullstamps.com

DR. ROBERT FRIEDMAN & SONS
2029 W. 75th St.
Woodridge, IL 60517
PH: 800-588-8100
FAX: 630-985-1588
drbobstamps@yahoo.com
www.drbobfriedmanstamps.com

SUBURBAN STAMP INC.
176 Worthington St.
Springfield, MA 01103
PH: 413-785-5348
FAX: 413-746-3788
suburbanstamp@verizon.net

THE STAMP CENTER DUTCH COUNTRY AUCTIONS
4115 Concord Pike
Wilmington, DE 19803
PH: 302-478-8740
FAX: 302-478-8779
auctions@thestampcenter.com
www.thestampcenter.com

U.S.-Errors, Freaks & Oddities

GARY POSNER, INC.
1407 Ave. Z, PMB #535
Brooklyn, NY 11235
PH: 800-323-4279
CELL PH: 917-538-8133
FAX: 718-241-2801
garyposnerinc@aol.com
www. garyposnerinc.com
www.gemstamps.com

SUBURBAN STAMP INC.
176 Worthington St.
Springfield, MA 01103
PH: 413-785-5348
FAX: 413-746-3788
suburbanstamp@verizon.net

U.S.-Federal Ducks Stamps

SAM HOUSTON DUCK CO.
PO Box 820087
Houston, TX 77282
PH: 281-493-6386
PH: 800-231-5926
FAX: 281-496-1445
shduck@aol.com
www.shduck.com

U.S.-Plate Blocks

GARY POSNER, INC.
1407 Ave. Z, PMB #535
Brooklyn, NY 11235
PH: 800-323-4279
CELL PH: 917-538-8133
FAX: 718-241-2801
garyposnerinc@aol.com
www. garyposnerinc.com
www.gemstamps.com

U.S.-Postal History

SUN COAST STAMP CO.
8520 S. Tamiami Tr., Unit1
Sarasota, FL 34238
PH: 941-921-9761
PH: 800-927-3351
FAX: 941-921-1762
email@suncoaststamp.com

U.S.-Price Lists

DALE ENTERPRISES, INC.
PO Box 539-C
Emmaus, PA 18049
PH: 610-433-3303
FAX: 610-965-6089
daleent@ptd.net
www.dalestamp.com

U.S.-Proofs & Essays

J. NALBANDIAN, INC.
PO Box 71
East Greenwich, RI 02818
PH: 401-885-5020
FAX: 401-885-3040
nalbandianj@earthlink.net
www.nalbandstamp.com

SUBURBAN STAMP INC.
176 Worthington St.
Springfield, MA 01103
PH: 413-785-5348
FAX: 413-746-3788
suburbanstamp@verizon.net

U.S.-Rare Stamps

GARY POSNER, INC.
1407 Ave. Z, PMB #535
Brooklyn, NY 11235
PH: 800-323-4279
CELL PH: 917-538-8133
FAX: 718-241-2801
garyposnerinc@aol.com
www. garyposnerinc.com
www.gemstamps.com

U.S. Revenues

WULFF'S STAMPS
PO Box 661746
Sacramento, CA 95866
PH/FAX: 800-884-0656
PH/FAX: 916-489-0656
service@wulffstamps.com
www.wulffstamps.com

U.S.-Trust Territories

HENRY GITNER PHILATELISTS, INC.
PO Box 3077-S
Middletown, NY 10940
PH: 845-343-5151
PH: 800-947-8267
FAX: 845-343-0068
hgitner@hgitner.com
www.hgitner.com

Want Lists

CHARLES P. SCHWARTZ
PO Box 165
Mora, MN 55051
PH: 320-679-4705
charlesp@ecenet.com

Want Lists-U.S.

GARY POSNER, INC.
1407 Ave. Z, PMB #535
Brooklyn, NY 11235
PH: 800-323-4279
CELL PH: 917-538-8133
FAX: 718-241-2801
garyposnerinc@aol.com
www. garyposnerinc.com
www.gemstamps.com

Wanted-Collections

DALE ENTERPRISES, INC.
PO Box 539-C
Emmaus, PA 18049
PH: 610-433-3303
FAX: 610-965-6089
daleent@ptd.net
www.dalestamp.com

Wanted-Estates

DALE ENTERPRISES, INC.
PO Box 539-C
Emmaus, PA 18049
PH: 610-433-3303
FAX: 610-965-6089
daleent@ptd.net
www.dalestamp.com

Wanted-U.S.

GARY POSNER, INC.
1407 Ave. Z, PMB #535
Brooklyn, NY 11235
PH: 800-323-4279
CELL PH: 917-538-8133
FAX: 718-241-2801
garyposnerinc@aol.com
www. garyposnerinc.com
www.gemstamps.com

SUBURBAN STAMP INC.
176 Worthington St.
Springfield, MA 01103
PH: 413-785-5348
FAX: 413-746-3788
suburbanstamp@verizon.net

Wanted-U.S. Collections

BROOKMAN STAMP CO.
PO Box 90
Vancouver, WA 98666
PH: 360-695-1391
PH: 800-545-4871
FAX: 360-695-1616
larry@brookmanstamps.com
www.brookmanstamps.com

DAVID F. HULL STAMP CO
1420 Trafalgar Dr.
High Point, NC 27262-7472
PH: 336-885-1420
FAX: 925-401-1434
davehull@hullstamps.com
www.hullstamps.com

Wanted-Worldwide Collections

DANIEL F. KELLEHER CO., INC.
20 Walnut St.
Suite 213
Wellesley, MA 02481
PH: 781-235-0990
FAX: 781-235-0945

DR. ROBERT FRIEDMAN & SONS
2029 W. 75th St.
Woodridge, IL 60517
PH: 800-588-8100
FAX: 630-985-1588
drbobstamps@yahoo.com
www.drbobfriedmanstamps.com

SUBURBAN STAMP INC.
176 Worthington St.
Springfield, MA 01103
PH: 413-785-5348
FAX: 413-746-3788
suburbanstamp@verizon.net

THE STAMP CENTER DUTCH COUNTRY AUCTIONS
4115 Concord Pike
Wilmington, DE 19803
PH: 302-478-8740
FAX: 302-478-8779
auctions@thestampcenter.com
www.thestampcenter.com

Websites

A TO Z STAMPS & COINS
4950 E. Thomas Rd.
Phoenix, AZ 85018
PH: 480-844-9878
FAX: 602-759-1717
michael@azstampcoin.com
www.WorldwideStamps.com

ACS STAMP COMPANY
10831 Chambers Way
Commerce City, CO 80022
PH: 303-841-8666
ACS@ACSStamp.com
www.acsstamp.com

Websites

J. NALBANDIAN, INC.
PO Box 71
East Greenwich, RI 02818
PH: 401-885-5020
FAX: 401-885-3040
nalbandianj@earthlink.net
www.nalbandstamp.com

Wholesale-Dealers

GARY POSNER, INC.
1407 Ave. Z, PMB #535
Brooklyn, NY 11235
PH: 800-323-4279
CELL PH: 917-538-8133
FAX: 718-241-2801
garyposnerinc@aol.com
www. garyposnerinc.com
www.gemstamps.com

Worldwide

A TO Z STAMPS & COINS
4950 E. Thomas Rd.
Phoenix, AZ 85018
PH: 480-844-9878
FAX: 602-759-1717
michael@azstampcoin.com
www.WorldwideStamps.com